Small Business Sourcebook

ISSN 0883-3397

Small Business Sourcebook

The Entrepreneur's Resource

TWENTY-NINTH EDITION

Volume 5

General Small Business Topics
General Small Business Resources
(Includes State Sections)

(Entries 41281-53088)

Sonya D. Hill
Project Editor

GALE
CENGAGE Learning

Detroit • New York • San Francisco • New Haven, Conn • Waterville, Maine • London

GALE
CENGAGE Learning®

Small Business Sourcebook, 29th edition

Project Editor: Sonya D. Hill

Editorial Support Services: Charles Beaumont

Composition and Electronic Prepress: Gary Leach

Manufacturing: Rita Wimberley

For product information and technology assistance, contact us at
Gale Customer Support, 1-800-877-4253.
For permission to use material from this text or product,
submit all requests online at **www.cengage.com/permissions.**
Further permissions questions can be emailed to
permissionrequest@cengage.com

While every effort has been made to ensure the reliability of the information presented in this publication, Gale, a part of Cengage Learning, does not guarantee the accuracy of the data contained herein. Gale accepts no payment for listing; and inclusion in the publication of any organization, agency, institution, publication, service, or individual does not imply endorsement of the editors or publisher. Errors brought to the attention of the publisher and verified to the satisfaction of the publisher will be corrected in future editions.

EDITORIAL DATA PRIVACY POLICY. Does this publication contain information about you as an individual? If so, for more information about our data privacy policies, please see our Privacy Statement at www.gale.cengage.com.

Gale
27500 Drake Rd.
Farmington Hills, MI, 48331-3535

ISBN-13: 978-1-4144-6919-5 (set)
ISBN-10: 1-4144-6919-5 (set)
ISBN-13: 978-1-4144-6920-1 (vol. 1)
ISBN-10: 1-4144-6920-9 (vol. 1)
ISBN-13: 978-1-4144-6921-8 (vol. 2)
ISBN-10: 1-4144-6921-7 (vol. 2)
ISBN-13: 978-1-4144-6986-7 (vol. 3)
ISBN-10: 1-4144-6986-1 (vol . 3)
ISBN-13: 978-1-4144-6987-4 (vol . 4)
ISBN-10: 1-4144-6987-X (vol . 4)
ISBN-13: 978-1-4144-6988-1 (vol . 5)
ISBN-10: 1-4144-6988-8 (vol . 5)
ISBN-13: 978-1-4144-7694-0 (vol . 6)
ISBN-10: 1-4144-7694-9 (vol . 6)

ISSN 0883-3397

Printed in the United States of America
1 2 3 4 5   16 15 14 13 12

FD184

Contents

The appeal of small business ownership remains perpetually entrenched in American culture as one of the most viable avenues for achieving the American Dream. To many entrepreneurs going into business for themselves represents financial independence, an increased sense of identity and self-worth, and the fulfillment of personal goals. Small business owners strive to make their mark in today's competitive marketplace by establishing healthy businesses that can, over time, become legacies handed down from one generation to the next. Entrepreneurs from each generation tackle the obstacles and adversities of the current business and economic climate to test their business savvy and generate opportunities. Today's entrepreneurs face many of the problems of their predecessors, as well as some distinctly new challenges.

With the rightsizing, downsizing, and reorganization of corporate America, many individuals have decided to confront the risks of developing and operating their own businesses. Small business ownership is rapidly becoming a viable alternative to what is perceived as an equally unstable corporate environment. These entrepreneurs, many of whom have firsthand experience with the problems and inefficiencies inherent in today's large corporations, seek to improve upon an archaic business model and to capitalize on their own ingenuity and strengths. Led by their zeal, many would-be entrepreneurs let their desire, drive, and determination overshadow the need for business knowledge and skill. Ironically, aids in obtaining these components of entrepreneurial success are widely available, easily accessible, and often free of charge.

Small Business Sourcebook (*SBS*) is a six-volume annotated guide to more than 21,199 listings of live and print sources of information designed to facilitate the start-up, development, and growth of specific small businesses, as well as over 26,073 similar listings on general small business topics. An additional 8,679 state-specific listings and over 1,997 U.S. federal government agencies and offices specializing in small business issues, programs, and assistance are also included. *SBS* covers 340 specific small business profiles and 99 general small business topics.

Features of This Edition

This edition of *Small Business Sourcebook* has been revised and updated, incorporating thousand of changes to names, addresses, contacts, and descriptions of listings from the previous edition.

Contents and Arrangement

The geographical scope of *SBS* encompasses the United States and Canada, with expanded coverage for resources pertaining to international trade and for resources that have a U.S. or Canadian distributor or contact. Internet sites that are maintained outside of the U.S. and Canada are also included if they contain relevant information for North American small businesses. Resources that do not relate specifically to small businesses are generally not included.

The information presented in *SBS* is grouped within four sections: Specific Small Business Profiles, General Small Business Topics, State Listings, and Federal Government Assistance. Detailed outlines of these sections may be found in the Users' Guide following this Introduction. Also included is a Master Index to Volumes 1 through 6.

Specific Small Business Profiles This section includes the following types of resources: start-up information, associations and other organizations, educational programs, directories of educational programs, reference works, sources of supply, statistical sources, trade periodicals, videocassettes/audiocassettes, trade shows and conventions, consultants, franchises and business opportunities, computerized databases, computer systems/software, Internet databases, libraries, and research centers-all arranged by business type. Entries range from Accounting Service to Word Processing Service, and include such businesses as Airbag Replacement Service Centers, Computer Consulting, Damage Restoration Service, and Web Site Design.

General Small Business Topics This section offers such resources as associations, books, periodicals, articles, pamphlets, educational programs, directories of educational programs, videocassettes/audiocassettes, trade shows and conventions, consultants, computerized databases, Internet databases, software,libraries, and research centers, arranged alphabetically by business topic.

State Listings Entries include government, academic, and commercial agencies and organizations, as well as select coverage of relevant state-specific publications; listings are arranged alphabetically by state, territory, and Canadian province. Some examples include small business development consultants, educational programs, financing and loan programs, better business bureaus, and chambers of commerce.

Federal Government Assistance Listings specializing in small business issues, programs, assistance, and policyare arranged alphabetically by U.S. government agency or office; regional or branch offices are listed alphabetically by state.

Master Index All entries in Volumes 1 through 6 are arranged in one alphabetic index for convenience.

Entries in *SBS* include (as appropriate andavailable):

- Organization, institution, or product name
- Contact information, including contact name, address and phone, toll-free, and fax numbers
- Author/editor, date(s), and frequency
- Availability, including price
- Brief description of purpose, services, or content
- Company and/or personal E-mail addresses
- Web site addresses

SBS also features the following:

Guide to Publishers—An alphabetic listing of 2,425 companies, associations, institutions, and individuals that publish the periodicals, directories, guidebooks, and other publications noted in the Small Business Profiles and General Topics sections. Users are provided with full contact information, including address, phone, fax,and e-mail and URL when available. The Guide to Publishers facilitates contact with publishers and provides a one- stop resource for valuable information.

Method of Compilation

SBS was compiled by consulting small business experts and entrepreneurs, as well as a variety of resources, including direct contact with the associations, organizations, and agencies through telephone surveys, Internet research, or through materials provided by those listees; government resources; and data obtained from other relevant Gale directories. *SBS* was reviewed by a team of small business advisors, all of whom have numerous years of expertise in small business counseling and identification of small business information resources. The last and perhaps most important resource we utilize is direct contact with our readers, who provide valuable comments and suggestions to improve our publication. *SBS* relies on these comprehensive market contacts to provide today's entrepreneurs with relevant, current, and accurate informationon all aspects of small business.

Available in Electronic Formats

Licensing. Small Business Sourcebook is available for licensing. The complete database is provided in a fielded format and is deliverable on such media as disk or CD-ROM. For more information, contact Gale's Business Development Group at1-800-877-GALE, or visit our website at www.gale.com/bizdev.

Comments and Suggestions Welcome

Associations, agencies, business firms, publishers, and other organizations that provide assistance and information to the small business community are encouraged to submit material about their programs, activities, services, or products. Comments and suggestions from users of this directory are also welcomed and appreciated. Please contact:

Project Editor
Small Business Sourcebook
Gale, Cengage Learning
27500 Drake Rd.
Farmington Hills, MI 48331-3535
Phone: (248) 699-4253
Fax: (248) 699-8070
E-mail: BusinessProductsgale.com
URL: www.gale.com

Small Business Sourcebook (*SBS*) provides information in a variety of forms and presentations for comprehensive coverage and ease of use. The directory contains four parts within two volumes:

- Specific Small Business Profiles
- General Small Business Topics
- State Listings
- Federal Government Assistance

Information on specific businesses is arranged by type of business; the many general topics that are of interest to the owners, operators, or managers of all small businesses are grouped in a separate section for added convenience. Users should consult the various sections to benefit fully from the information *SBS* offers. For example, an entrepreneur with a talent or interest in the culinary arts could peruse a number of specific small business profiles, such as Restaurant, Catering, Cooking School, Specialty Food/Wine Shop, Bakery/Doughnut Shop, Healthy Restaurant, or Candy/Chocolate Store. Secondly, the General Small Business Topics section could be consulted for any applicable subjects, such as Service Industry, Retailing, Franchising, and other relevant topics. Then, the appropriate state within the State Listings section would offer area programs and offices providing information and support to small businesses, including venture capital firms and small business development consultants. Finally, the Federal Government Assistance section could supply relevant government offices, such as procurement contacts.

Features Included in Volumes 1 through 3

List of Small Business Profiles. This list provides an alphabetic outline of the small businesses profiled, with cross-references for related profiles and for alternate names by which businesses may be identified. The page number for each profile is indicated.

Standard Industrial Classification (SIC) Codes for Profiled Small Businesses. This section lists four-digit SIC codes and corresponding classification descriptions for the small businesses profiled in this edition. The SIC system, which organizes businesses by type, is a product of the Statistical Policy Division of the U.S. Office of Management and Budget. Statistical data produced by government, public, and private organizations is usually categorized according to SIC codes, thereby facilitating the collection, comparison, and analysis of data as well as providing a uniform method for presenting statistical information. Hence, knowing the SIC code for a particular small business increases access and the use of a variety of statistical data from many sources.

Guide to Publishers. This resource lists alphabetically the companies, associations, institutions, and individuals that publish the periodicals, directories, guidebooks, and other publications noted in the "Small Business Profiles" and "General Topics" sections. Users are provided with full contact information, including address, phone, fax, and e-mail and URL when available. The "Guide" facilitates contact with publishers and provides a one-stop resource for valuable information.

Glossary of Small Business Terms. This glossary defines nearly 400 small business terms, including financial, governmental, insurance, procurement, technical, and general business definitions. Cross-references and acronyms are also provided.

Small Business Profiles A-Z. A total of 340 small businesses is represented in volumes 1 through 3. Profiles are listed alphabetically by business name. Entries within each profile are arranged alphabetically by resource type, within up to 17 subheadings. These subheadings are detailed below:

- *Start-up Information*—Includes periodical articles, books, manuals, book excerpts, kits, and other sources of information. Entries offer title; publisher; address; phone, fax, toll-free numbers; company e-mail and URL addresses; and a description. Bibliographic data is provided for cited periodical articles whenever possible.

- *Associations and Other Oganizations*—Includes trade and professional associations whose members gather and disseminate information of interest to small business owners. Entries offer the association's name; address; phone, toll-free and fax numbers; company e-mail address; contact name; purpose and objective; a description of membership; telecommunication services; and a listing of its publications, including publishing frequency.

- *Educational Programs*—Includes university and college programs, schools, training opportunities, association seminars, correspondence courses, and other educational programs.Entries offer name of program or institution, sponsor name, address, phone, toll-free and fax numbers, e-mail and URL addresses; and description of program.

- *Directories of Educational Programs*—Includes directories and other publications that list educational programs. Entries offer name of publication; publisher name, address, and phone, toll-free and fax numbers; editor; frequency or date of publication; price; and description of contents, including directory arrangement and indexes.

- *Reference Works*—Includes handbooks, manuals, textbooks, guides, directories, dictionaries, encyclopedias, and other published reference materials. Entries offer name of publication; publisher name, address, and phone, toll-free and fax numbers; e-mail and URL addresses; and, when available, name of author or editor, publication year or frequency, and price. A brief description is often featured.

- *Sources of Supply*—Includes buyer's guides,directories, special issues of periodicals, and other publications that list sources of equipment, supplies, and services related to the operation of the profiled small business. Entries offer publication name; publisher name, address, and phone, toll-free and fax numbers; e-mail and URL addresses; and, when available, editor's name, frequency or publication year, and price. A brief description of the publication, including directory arrangement and indexes, is often provided.

- *Statistical Sources*—Includes books, reports, pamphlets, and other sources of statistical data of interest to an owner, operator or manager of the profiled small business, such as wage, salary, and compensation data; financial and operating ratios; prices and costs; demographics; and other statistical information. Entries offer publication/data source name; publisher (if applicable); address; phone, toll-free and fax numbers of data source; publication date or frequency; and price. A brief description of the publication/data source is often provided.

- *Trade Periodicals*—Includes trade journals, newsletters, magazines, and other serials that offer information about the management and operation of the profiled small business. Such periodicals often contain industry news; trends and developments; reviews; articles about new equipment and supplies;

and other information related to business operations. Entries offer publication name; publisher name, address, phone, toll-free and fax numbers, and e-mail and URL addresses; editor name; publication frequency; andprice. A brief description of the publication's content is also included, when known.

- *Videocassettes/Audiocassettes*—Includes videocassettes, audiocassettes, and other audiovisual media offering information on the profiled small business. Entries offer program title; distributor name, address, phone, toll-free and fax numbers, and e-mail and URL addresses; description of program; release date; price; and format(s).

- *Trade Shows and Conventions*—Includes tradeshows, exhibitions, expositions, conventions, and other industry meetings that provide prospective and existing business owners with the opportunity to meet and exchange information with their peers, review commercial exhibits, establish business or sales contacts, and attend educational programs. Entries offer event name; sponsor or management company name, address, phone, toll-free and fax numbers, and e-mail and URL addresses; a description of the event, including audience, frequency, principal exhibits, and dates and locations of event for as many years ahead as provided by the event's sponsor.

- *Consultants*—Includes consultants and consulting organizations that provide services specifically related to the profiled small business. Entries offer individual consultant or consulting organization name, address, and phone, toll-free and fax numbers; company and individual e-mail addresses; and a brief description of consulting services. (For e-mail and URL addresses, see the Small Business Development Consultants subheadings in the State Listings section in Volume 2.)

- *Franchises and Business Opportunities*—Includes companies granting franchise licenses for enterprises falling within the scope of the profiled small business, as well as other non-franchised business opportunities that operate within a given network or system. Entries offer franchise name, address, phone, toll-free and fax numbers, and e-mail and URL addresses, as well as a description of the franchise or business opportunity, which has been expanded whenever possible to include the number of existing franchises, the founding date of the franchise, franchise fees, equity capital requirements, royalty fees, any managerial assistance offered, and available training.

- *Computerized Databases*—Includes diskettes, magnetic tapes, CD-ROMs, online systems, and other computer-readable databases. Entries offer database name; producer name, address, phone, toll-free and fax numbers, e-mail and URL addresses; description; and available format(s), including vendor name.

(Many university and public libraries offer online information retrieval services that provide searches of databases, including those listed in this category.)

- *Computer Systems/Software*—Includes softwar-eand computerized business systems designed to assist in the operation of the profiled small business. Entries offer name of the software or system; publisher name, address, phone, toll-free and fax-numbers; price; and description.

- *Libraries*—Includes libraries and special collections that contain material especially applicable to the profiled small business. Entries offer library or collection name; parent organization (where applicable); address; phone, toll-free and fax numbers; e-mail and URL addresses; contact name and title; scope of collection; and description of holdings, subscriptions, and services.

- *Research Centers*—Includes university-related and independently operated research institutes and information centers that generate, through their research programs, data related to the operation of the profiled small business. Also listed are associations and other business-related organizations that conduct research programs. Entries offer name of organization; address; phone, toll-free and fax numbers; company web site address; contact name and personale-mail; a description of principal fields of research or services; publications, including title and frequency; and related conferences.

Features Included in Volumes 2 through 6

General Small Business Topics. This section offers chapters on different topics in the operation of any small business, for example, venture capital and other funding, or compensation. Chapters are listed alphabetically by small business topic; entries within each chapter are arranged alphabetically, within up to 14 subheadings, by resource type:

- *Associations and OtherOrganizations*—Includes trade and professional associations that gather and disseminate information of interest to small business owners. Entries offer the association's name; address; phone, toll-free and fax numbers; organization e-mail and URL addresses; contact name;purpose and objectives; a description of membership; telecommunication services; and a listing of its publications, including publishing frequency.

- *Educational Programs*—Includes university and college programs, schools, training opportunities, association seminars, correspondence courses, and other educational programs. Entries offer name of program or institution, sponsor name, address, phone, toll-free and fax numbers, e-mail and URL addresses, and description of program.

- *Directories of Educational Programs*—Includes directories and other publications that list educational programs. Entries offer name of publication; publisher name, address, phone, toll-free and fax numbers, and e-mail and URL addresses; editor; frequency or date of publication; price; and description of contents, including arrangement and indexes.

- *Reference Works*—Includes articles, handbooks, manuals, textbooks, guides, directories, dictionaries, encyclopedias, and other published reference materials. Entries offertitle of article, including bibliographic information; name of publication; publisher name, address, phone, toll-free and fax numbers, and e-mail and URL addresses; and, when available, name of author oreditor, publication year or frequency, and price. A brief descriptionis often featured.

- *Sources of Supply*—Includes buyer's guides,directories, special issues of periodicals, and other publications that list sources of equipment, supplies, and services. Entries offer publication name; publisher name, address, phone, toll-free and fax numbers, and e-mail and URL addresses; editor's name, frequency or publication year, price, and a brief description of the publication, when available.

- *Statistical Sources*—Includes books, reports, pamphlets, and other sources of statistical data of interest to an owner, operator, or manager of a small business, such as wage, salary, and compensation data; financial and operating ratios; prices and costs; demographics; and other statistical information. Entries offer publication/data source name; publisher (if applicable); address; phone, toll-free and fax numbers of data source; publication date or frequency; and price. A brief description is often provided.

- *Trade Periodicals*—Includes journals, newsletters, magazines, and other serials. Entries offer name of publication; publisher name, address, phone, toll-free and fax numbers, and e-mail and URL addresses; and name of editor, frequency, and price.A brief description of the periodical's content is included when known.

- *Videocassettes/Audiocassettes*—Includes videocassettes, audiocassettes, and other audiovisual media. Entries offer program title; distributor name, address, phone, toll-free and fax numbers, and e-mail and URL addresses; price; description of program; release date; and format(s).

- *Trade Shows and Conventions*—Includes tradeshows, exhibitions, expositions, seminars, and conventions. Entries offer event name; sponsor or management company name, address, phone, toll-free and fax numbers, and e-mail and URL addresses; frequency of event; and dates and locations of the event for as many years ahead as known.

- **Consultants**—Includes consultants and consulting organizations. Entries offer individual consultant or-consulting organization name, address, and phone, toll-free and fax numbers; company and individual e-mail addresses; and a brief description of consulting services. (See also Consultants in the State Listings section.)

- **Computerized Databases**—Includes diskettes, CD-ROMs, magnetic tape, online systems and other computer-readable databases. Entries offer database name; producer, address, phone, toll-free and fax numbers, and e-mail and URL addresses; description; and available format(s), including vendor name. (Many university and public libraries offer online information retrieval services that provide searches of databases, including those listed in this category.)

- **Computer Systems/Software**—Includes software and computerized business systems. Entries offer name of the software or system; publisher name, address, phone, toll-free and fax numbers, and e-mail and URL addresses; price; and description.

- **Libraries**—Includes libraries and special collections that contain material applicable to the small business topic. Entries offer library or collection name, parent organization (where applicable), address, phone and fax numbers, e-mail and URL addresses, scope of collection, and description of holdings and services.

- **Research Centers**— Includes university-related and independently operated research institutes and information centers that generate, through their research programs, data related to specific small business topics. Entries offer name of organization, address, phone, toll-free and fax numbers, e-mail and URL addresses, a description of principal fields of research or services, and related conferences.

State Listings. This section lists various sources of information and assistance available within given states, territories, and Canadian provinces; entries include governmental, academic, and commercial agencies, and are arranged alphabetically within up to 15 subheadings by resource type:

- **Small Business Development Center Lead Office**— Includes the lead small business development center (SBDC) for each state.

- **Small Business Development Centers**—Includes any additional small business development centers (SBDC) in the state, territory, or province. SBDCs provide support services to small businesses, including individual counseling, seminars, conferences, and learning center activities.

- **Small Business Assistance Programs**—Includes state small business development offices and other programs offering assistance to small businesses.

- **SCORE Offices**—Includes SCORE office(s) for each state. The Service Corps of Retired Executives Association (SCORE), a volunteer program sponsored by the Small Business Administration, offers counseling, workshops, and seminars across the U.S. for small business entrepreneurs.

- **Better Business Bureaus**—Includes various better business bureaus within each state. By becoming a member of the local Better Business Bureau, a small business owner can increase the prestige and credibility of his or her business within the community, as well as make valuable business contacts.

- **Chambers of Commerce**—Includes various chambers of commerce within each state. Chambers of Commerce are valuable sources of small business advice and information; often, local chambers sponsor SCORE counseling several times per month for a small fee, seminars, conferences, and other workshops to its members. Also, by becoming a member of the local Chamber of Commerce, a small business owner can increase the prestige and credibility of his or herbusiness within the community, as well as make valuable business contacts.

- **Minority Business Assistance Programs**—Includes minority business development centers and other sources of assistance for minority-owned business.

- **Financing and Loan Programs**—Includes venture capital firms, small business investment companies (SBIC), minority enterprise small business investment companies (MESBIC), and other programs that provide funding to qualified small businesses.

- **Procurement Assistance Programs**—Includes state services such as counseling, set-asides, and sheltered-market bidding, which are designed to aid small businesses in bidding on government contracts.

- **Incubators/Research and Technology Parks**— Includes small business incubators, which provide newly established small business owners with work sites, business services, training, and consultation; also includes research and technology parks, which sponsor research and facilitate commercialization of new technologies.

- **Educational Programs**—Includes university and college programs, as well as those sponsored by other organizations that offer degree, nondegree, certificate, and correspondence programs in entrepreneurship and in small business development.

- **Legislative Assistance**—Includes committees, subcommittees, and joint committees of each state's senate and house of representatives that are concerned with small business issues and regulations.

- *Consultants*—Includes consultants and consulting firms offering expertise in small business development.

- *Publications*—Includes publications related to small business operations within the profiled state.

- *Publishers*—Includes publishers operating in or for the small business arena within the profiled state.

Federal Government Assistance. This section lists federal government agencies and offices, many with additional listings for specific offices, as well as regional or district branches. Main agencies or offices are listed alphabetically; regional, branch, ordistrict offices are listed after each main office or agency.

Master Index. This index provides an alphabetic listing of all entries contained in Volumes 1 throgh 6. Citations are referenced by their entry numbers. Publication titles are rendered in italics.

The editors would like to extend sincere thanks to the following members of the Small Business Sourcebook advisory board for their expert guidance, recommendations, and suggestions for the ongoing development of this title:

Susan C. Awe
Assistant Director,
William J. Parish Memorial Business Library

Jill Clever
Business Technology Specialist,
Toledo-Lucas County Public Library

Jules Matsoff
District Manager,
Service Corps of Retired Executives (SCORE) Milwaukee
  Chapter

Ken MacKenzie
President,
Southeast Business Appraisal

The editors would also like to thank the individuals from associations and other organizations who provided information for the compilation of this directory.

List of General Small Business Topics

This section covers sources of assistance applicable to a variety of small businesses. Resources are arranged by topic and include associations, educational programs, directories of educational programs, reference works, sources of supply, statistical sources, periodicals, videocassettes/audiocassettes, trade shows and conventions, consultants, computerized databases, computer systems/software, Internet databases, libraries, and research centers.

ASSOCIATIONS AND OTHER ORGANIZATIONS

41281 ■ Independent Office Products and Furniture Dealers Association
301 N Fairfax St., Ste. 200
Alexandria, VA 22314
Free: 800-542-6672
Fax:(703)683-7552
Co. E-mail: cbates@nopanet.org
URL: http://www.iopfda.org
Contact: Carlene Wilson, Chair
Description: Represents and serves privately owned commercial dealers and their business partners in two divisions: National Office Products Alliance (NOPA); and Office Furniture Dealers Alliance (OFDA). Offers strategic information, government advocacy, business performance benchmarking, standards development, and management education services to members located throughout the United States and in key Canadian markets. **Publications:** *Office World News* (bimonthly).

41282 ■ International Association of Lighting Designers
Merchandise Mart, Ste. 9-104
Chicago, IL 60654
Ph:(312)527-3677
Fax:(312)527-3680
Co. E-mail: iald@iald.org
URL: http://www.iald.org
Contact: Marsha L. Turner CAE, Exec. VP
Description: Represents professionals, educators, students, and others working in the field of lighting design worldwide. Promotes the benefits of quality lighting design and emphasizes the potential impact of lighting on architectural design and environmental quality. Furthers professional standards of lighting designers and seeks to increase their function in the interior design industry. Sponsors national awards program, summer intern program for qualified college students interested in lighting design as a profession, and career development lectures and seminars. **Publications:** *e-Reflections* (monthly); *International Association of Lighting Designers—Membership Directory* (annual); *Why Hire an IALD Lighting Designer?* .

41283 ■ Planning and Visual Education Partnership
4651 Sheridan St., Ste. 470
Hollywood, FL 33021
Ph:(954)893-7225
Fax:(954)893-8375
Co. E-mail: pave@paveinfo.org
URL: http://www.paveinfo.org
Contact: Klein Merriman, Exec. Dir.
Description: Retail executives, visual merchandisers, store planners, architects, specifiers, students. Seeks to educate and motivate members and encourage interaction among their related fields. Holds annual design competition; offers an internship program; donates proceeds of shows toward financial aid for students. .

REFERENCE WORKS

41284 ■ "Bag It" in *Entrepreneur* (Vol. 36, May 2008, No. 5, pp. 48)
Pub: Entrepreneur Media, Inc.
Ed: Amanda C. Kooser. **Description:** Buyer's guide featuring bags and carrying cases for laptops is presented. Prices and attributes of the bags are provided.

41285 ■ *The Complete Startup Guide for the Black Entrepreneur*
Pub: Career Press Inc.
Ed: Bill Boudreaux. **Description:** President and founder of a consulting firm for home-based entrepreneurs share information to help minorities start their own companies. Tips to create a business plan, buy essential equipment, price products and services, pay the bills, and set up a work space are covered.

41286 ■ "CSE: Contractors Are Always Responsible" in *Contractor* (Vol. 56, November 2009, No. 11, pp. 34)
Pub: Penton Media, Inc.
Ed: Dave Yates. **Description:** Plumbing contractors should purchase a long snorkel hose, a tripod with manual-crank hoist, and a sump pump in order to prevent accidents associated with Confined Space Entry. Liability issues surrounding confined space entry prevention and accidents are discussed.

41287 ■ "The Dynamic DUO" in *Canadian Electronics* (Vol. 23, February 2008, No. 1, pp. 24)
Pub: CLB Media Inc.
Description: Citronics Corporation not only aims to proved a good working environment for its employees, it also values the opinions of its personnel. Citronics had its employees test different workbenches before finally purchasing thirty-five of Lista's Align adjustable height workstation, which combines flexibility with aesthetics. The design of the Alin workbench is described.

41288 ■ "The Easy Route" in *Entrepreneur* (Vol. 36, April 2008, No. 4, pp. 60)
Pub: Entrepreneur Media, Inc.
Ed: Amanda C. Kooser. **Description:** Buyer's guide of wireless office routers is presented. All products included in the list use the latest draft-n technology. Price and availability of the products are provided.

41289 ■ "Fabulous New Office Furniture: Ways to Revamp Your Workspace" in *Inc.* (Vol. 33, September 2011, No. 7, pp. 51)
Pub: Inc. Magazine
Ed: Nadine Heintz. **Description:** Various new looks to revamp any office space are highlighted including a table lamp by designer Peter Stathis for Joby.

41290 ■ "Firm Stays In the 'Family'; After Owner's Death, Employees Buy Company" in *Crain's Detroit Business* (Vol. 24, January 28, 2008)
Pub: Crain Communications Inc. - Detroit
Ed: Chad Halcom. **Description:** Sterling Office Systems Inc., distributor of photocopiers and other office machines was purchased from the owner's family after his demise. The new owners would like to hit $1.75 million in sales their first year.

41291 ■ "For Apple, It's Showtime Again" in *Barron's* (Vol. 90, August 30, 2010, No. 35, pp. 29)
Pub: Barron's Editorial & Corporate Headquarters
Ed: Eric J. Savitz. **Description:** Speculations on what Apple Inc. will unveil at its product launch event are presented. These products include a possible new iPhone Nano, a new update to its Apple TV, and possibly a deal with the Beatles to distribute their songs over iTunes.

41292 ■ "Formaspace Finds a Bigger Home" in *Austin Business JournalInc.* (Vol. 29, December 4, 2009, No. 39, pp. 1)
Pub: American City Business Journals
Ed: Kate Harrington. **Description:** Formaspace Technical Furniture has signed a lease for 56,700 square feet in Harris Ridge Business Center at Northeast Austin, Texas, which represents one of the area's largest leases for 2009. The new lease enables Formaspace to hire new employees, invest in new equipment, and take advantage of a taxing designation created for manufacturers.

41293 ■ "Handle with Care" in *Entrepreneur* (Vol. 35, November 2007, No. 11, pp. 24)
Pub: Entrepreneur Media Inc.
Ed: Jacquelyn Lynn. **Description:** Preventing equipment breakdown can be done by having a regular maintenance schedule. It is also recommended that companies use quality surge protectors or uninterruptible power supplies (UPSs) for electronic equipment that can be affected by power fluctuations and lightning. Other suggestions for preventive maintenance practices are outlined.

41294 ■ *How to Make Big Money*
Pub: Hyperion Books
Ed: Jeffrey J. Fox. **Released:** May 19, 2004. **Price:** $16.95. **Description:** Entrepreneur and consultant offers advice to help others create successful startups and prosper. Fox directs new business owners with a counterintuitive style and describes essential methods that beat the competition. Tips include: setting priorities, getting a personal driver, creating a contingency plan for employees, pricing to value, saving money, and getting an office outside of the home.

41295 ■ "How to Set Up an Effective Home Office" in *Women Entrepreneur* (August 22, 2008)
Pub: Entrepreneur Media Inc.
Ed: Laura Stack. **Description:** Checklist provides ways in which one can arrange their home office to provide the greatest efficiency which will allow maximum productivity and as a result the greater the chance of success.

41296 ■ "Intel Joins Movement to Turn Cube Farms Into Wide-Open Spaces" in *Sacramento Business Journal* (Vol. 28, May 27, 2011, No. 13, pp. 1)
Pub: Sacramento Business Journal
Ed: Melanie Turner. **Description:** Intel Corporation has remodeled its facility in Folsom, California. The

renovation has required some workers to give up their cubicles. Comments from executives are included.

41297 ■ "Island Co.: Isle Style" in *Entrepreneur* (Vol. 35, October 2007, No. 10, pp. 172)
Pub: Entrepreneur Media Inc.
Ed: Sara Wilson. **Description:** Island Co., producer of travel clothing and swimsuits was formed by Spencer Antle in 2002. Its office projects the Caribbean atmosphere, a strategy Antle used to promote the company's theme to its clients. Future plans for the company are also indicated.

41298 ■ "Mexican Companies to Rent Space in TechTown, Chinese Negotiating" in *Crain's Detroit Business* (Vol. 24, September 29, 2008, No. 39)
Pub: Crain Communications, Inc.
Ed: Tom Henderson. **Description:** Wayne State University's TechTown, the business incubator and research park, has signed an agreement with the Mexican government that will provide temporary office space to 25 Mexican companies looking to find customers or establish partnerships in Michigan. TechTown's executive director is negotiating with economic development officials from China. To accommodate foreign visitors the incubator is equipping offices with additional equipment and resources.

41299 ■ "Office Tech: A Pretty Little Vista" in *Canadian Business* (Vol. 80, January 29, 2007, No. 3, pp. 61)
Pub: Rogers Media
Ed: Andrew Wahl. **Description:** The features of the new version of Microsoft Windows Vista OS and Microsoft Office 2007 are described.

41300 ■ "Our Gadget of the Week" in *Barron's* (Vol. 88, March 24, 2008, No. 12, pp. 47)
Pub: Dow Jones & Company, Inc.
Ed: Tiernan Ray. **Description:** Review of the $299 Apple Time Capsule, which is a 500-megabyte hard disk drive and a Wi-Fi router, rolled into one device. The device allows users to create backup files without the need for sophisticated file management software.

41301 ■ "Our Gadget of the Week: Business Buddy" in *Barron's* (Vol. 88, July 7, 2008, No. 27, pp. 26)
Pub: Dow Jones & Co., Inc.
Ed: Jay Palmer. **Description:** Review and evaluation of the Lenovo X300 laptop computer which offers executives a variety of features despite its smaller size and weight. The laptop is about 0.73 inch thick, comes with a 64-gigabyte solid-state drive from Samsung, and weighs less than three pounds.

41302 ■ "Pick and Save" in *Entrepreneur* (Vol. 36, April 2008, No. 4, pp. 66)
Pub: Entrepreneur Media, Inc.
Ed: C.J. Prince. **Description:** Business owners can purchase the needed big equipment to offset this year's expected profit. They can also switch to annualized computing of quarterly income and estimated tax payments to pay less estimated taxes for the first half of the year. Other tips on tax planning are provided.

41303 ■ "Relationship "Farming" Tools" in *Agency Sales Magazine* (Vol. 39, August 2009, No. 8, pp. 46)
Pub: MANA
Ed: Terry L. Brock. **Description:** Manufacturer's representatives should spend time, money and effort in establishing and maintaining relationships; one tool to help is the new Fujitsu S1500 scanner. The scanner can accomplish critical tasks, quickly, easily and at low cost. Other suggestions to help build better business relationships are given.

41304 ■ "Shore Total Office Liquidates Massive Supply of Bank Furniture and Used Furniture" in *Internet Wire* (June 21, 2010)
Pub: Comtex
Description: Shore Total Office, located in San Diego, California, is liquidating quality bank furniture and used furniture to customers hoping to outfit their

facilities with stylish new furnishings. Shore Total Office is a leading supplier of high quality office furniture and designs.

41305 ■ "Simply Therapeutic" in *Women In Business* (Vol. 61, December 2009, No. 6, pp. 34)
Pub: American Business Women's Association
Ed: Maureen Sullivan. **Description:** Steps on minimizing office clutter are presented in an effort to also eliminate clutter from the office worker's mind. Allotting time for clutter reduction, setting realistic goals, file organization, labeling, and sticking to a clutter reduction system are suggested. Clutter reduction is expected to contribute to increased productivity in the workplace.

41306 ■ *The Small Business Owner's Manual: Everything You Need to Know to Start Up and Run Your Business*
Pub: Career Press, Incorporated
Ed: Joe Kennedy. **Released:** June 2005. **Price:** $19.99 (US), $26.95 (Canadian). **Description:** Comprehensive guide for starting a small business, focusing on twelve ways to obtain financing, business plans, selling and advertising products and services, hiring and firing employees, setting up a Web site, business law, accounting issues, insurance, equipment, computers, banks, financing, customer credit and collection, leasing, and more.

41307 ■ "Succeed With the Right Equipment" in *Pet Product News* (Vol. 64, November 2010, No. 11, pp. 42)
Pub: BowTie Inc.
Ed: Sandi Cain. **Description:** Grooming shop owners have been focusing on obtaining ergonomic, durable, and efficient products such as restraints, tables, and tubs. These products enhance the way grooming tasks are conducted. Ways pet supply manufacturers have responded to this trend are examined.

41308 ■ *Thank God It's Monday! How to Create a Workplace You and Your Customers Love*
Pub: FT Press
Ed: Roxanne Emmerich. **Released:** April 18, 2009. **Price:** $19.99. **Description:** Tips on creating a positive environment for both employees and customers.

41309 ■ "Touching the Future" in *Canadian Business* (Vol. 81, July 21, 2008, No. 11, pp. 41)
Pub: Rogers Media Ltd.
Ed: Matt McClearn. **Description:** Microsoft Corp. has launched a multi-touch product which is both a software and hardware technology called Microsoft Surface. The innovative product allows people to use it at the same time, however touch-based computers are reported to be around $100,000. Other features and benefits of the product are presented.

41310 ■ "Welcome to a New Kind of Cubicle Culture" in *Boston Business Journal* (Vol. 29, August 19, 2011, No. 15, pp. 1)
Pub: American City Business Journals Inc.
Ed: Alexander Jackson. **Description:** Beehive Baltimore offers a co-working space where independent freelancers and entrepreneurs can work. There are two other companies that provide the same service and the value of these services to these professional is that it provides them with an office that is both convenient and affordable aside from letting them network with peers.

41311 ■ "What Is In Your Company Library?" in *Modern Machine Shop* (Vol. 84, October 2011, No. 5, pp. 60)
Pub: Gardner Publications
Ed: Mike Lynch. **Description:** A good company library in any machine shop can help keep employees productive. Safety as well as information are critical to complete any task in a shop.

41312 ■ "A Whiteboard that Peels and Sticks" in *Inc.* (Volume 32, December 2010, No. 10, pp. 58)
Pub: Inc. Magazine
Ed: Issie Lapwosky. **Description:** Profile of an affordable adhesive whiteboard that can be restuck multiple times; the whiteboard was created by three

college friends. The students share insight in the contacts they used in order to promote the sale of their invention.

41313 ■ "Working on the Dock of the Bay" in *Canadian Business* (Vol. 83, July 20, 2010, No. 11-12, pp. 76)
Pub: Rogers Media Ltd.
Ed: Jacqueline Nelson. **Description:** A buyers guide of tools for employees working outdoors is presented. Information on price and availability are also presented.

VIDEOCASSETTES/ AUDIOCASSETTES

41314 ■ *Automating the Office*
Time-Life Video and Television
1450 Palmyra Ave.
Richmond, VA 23227-4420
Ph:(804)266-6330
Free: 800-950-7887
Fax:(757)427-7905
URL: http://www.timelife.com
Released: 1985. **Description:** A series of programs that clarify modern methods of automating workplaces for maximum efficency and productivity. **Availability:** VHS; 3/4U; Special order formats.

CONSULTANTS

41315 ■ AA Antivirus
1608 W Campbell Ave., Ste. 370
Campbell, CA 95008
Ph:(408)374-8000
Free: 800-478-1828
Fax:(408)374-2045
Co. E-mail: sales@aaantivirus.com
URL: http://www.aaantivirus.com
Contact: Julie Martens, Office Mgr
E-mail: roy@aaantivirus.com
Scope: Offers a range of local area networking and wide area networking solutions to small and medium-sized businesses. Assists business owners and administrators in planning, purchasing and installing networks. **Special Services:** Panda Security SaaS; Web Root Security SaaS; Kaspersky Anti virus; Trend Micro Anti virus; Mal Ware Bytes; Norman Anti virus; Red Condor Anti Spam SaaS; Borderware; Ironport; CyberRoam; Bloxx.

41316 ■ ABI Designs Inc.
8555 SW Apple Way, Ste. 120
Portland, OR 97225-1775
Ph:(503)292-0151
Fax:(503)292-0685
Co. E-mail: walkinthelight@hotmail.com
Contact: Adele E. Beck, President
Scope: Provides interior design services to architectural firms and individuals.

41317 ■ Advanced Network Consulting
12627 Gabbett Dr.
La Mirada, CA 90638
Ph:(562)903-3992
Free: 877-262-0999
Fax:(562)204-0655
Co. E-mail: info@ancsite.com
URL: http://www.ancsite.com
Contact: Christopher Staples, President
E-mail: chris@atsancsite.com
Scope: Provides LAN consulting as well as hardware and software services. Offers server-based solutions that include: Backup, antivirus LAN/WAN design, implementation and support, system administration and hardware warrantee contracts, and office automation for small businesses.

41318 ■ Agility Computer Network Services L.L.C.
1332 N Halsted St., Ste. 405
Chicago, IL 60642
Ph:(312)587-9894
Free: 877-244-5489

Fax:(312)587-9948
Co. E-mail: support@agilitynetworks.com
URL: http://www.agilitynetworks.com
Contact: Jeff Blada, Principle
E-mail: jblada@atsagilitynetworks.com
Scope: Provides networking and other related computer consulting services.

41319 ■ AIM Associates
100 Fair St.
Petaluma, CA 94952-2515
Ph:(707)763-3300
Fax:(707)763-6489
Co. E-mail: info@aimgreen.com
URL: http://www.aimgreen.com
Contact: George A. Beeler, Principle
E-mail: george@aimgreen.com
Scope: The firm has been providing green and high performance building consulting, integrated design team management, and full architectural and engineering services. Provides consulting to cities, school districts, AE firms, R&D facilities, other businesses, and individuals. The firm is also an architectural and project management firm that provides peer review, integrated design team management, and performance based design.

41320 ■ Anshen Allen
448 W Nationwide Blvd., Loft 100
Columbus, OH 43215
Ph:(415)882-9500
Fax:(415)882-9523
Co. E-mail: inquire@anshen.com
URL: http://www.anshen.com
Contact: Zigmund Rubel, Principal
E-mail: zr@anshen.com
Scope: Offers architectural consulting services from feasibility studies through construction administration. Also provides space planning and interior design services and facilities management utilizing CAD and database management. **Publications:** "Urban Land Green - Greening Health Care Facilties"; "Health Care Design Cost of Innovation"; "The Architecture of Medical Imaging"; "Health Facilities Management - Surolgy is Coming".

41321 ■ A.P. Designs
33 Merrall Dr., Ste. 1
Lawrence, NY 11559
Ph:(516)239-2931
Fax:(516)239-2932
Contact: Ann Pollack, President
Scope: Provides interior design business services. Industries served: All industries and individuals requiring interior design services.

41322 ■ Apple Electrical Services Inc.
11237 Somerset Ave.
PO Box 927
College Park, MD 20741
Ph:(301)345-9409
Fax:(301)345-9530
Co. E-mail: cissel2@aol.com
Contact: Carol Cissel, Principle
E-mail: cissel2@aol.com
Scope: Electrical lighting and design consultants specializing in interior and exterior lighting systems. Industries served: residential, commercial and industrial as well as government agencies.

41323 ■ Architectural Alliance
4300 Glumack Dr., Ste. LT 3191
Saint Paul, MN 55111-3003
Ph:(612)871-5703
Fax:(612)871-7212
Co. E-mail: pvesterholt@archalliance.com
URL: http://www.archalliance.com
Contact: Tom Hysell, Mgr
E-mail: thysell@archalliance.com
Scope: Offers architectural design, interior design, facility studies, programming, space planning, facilities master planning and renovation design services. Project types have included corporate offices, computer/data centers, retail facilities, college and university buildings, other educational facilities, airport facilities and public facilities (parks, city halls, police facilities, etc.). Industries served: public and private corporations/companies, school districts,

public colleges and universities, public (state and federal) agencies, commercial developers, municipalities and other institutions.

41324 ■ Array Healthcare Facilities Solutions
60 Madison Ave., Ste. 1001
New York, NY 10010
Ph:(610)270-0599
Free: 800-828-8199
Fax:(610)270-0995
Co. E-mail: info@arrayhfs.com
URL: http://www.arrayhfs.com
Contact: Udo H. Maron, Principal
E-mail: umaron@arrayhfs.com
Scope: Provides comprehensive architectural, facility master planning, interior design, project management, design/building and computer-aided facilities management services. Clients include nonprofit health care corporations, academic health centers, investor-owned enterprises, start-up entrepreneurs, management companies for long-term care units, physician groups and developers serving medical niche markets. Also serves government agencies. **Publications:** "Drawing a Meaning from a Mission," Oct, 2009; "Constructive Thinking," Sep, 2009; "A Patient Centered ED," Aug, 2009; "Multimedia Prototypes," May, 2009; "Keys to Success to a Hybrid Cath Lab," Mar, 2009; "Acuity Adaptable Rooms: Design Considerations Can Improve Patient Care," Feb, 2009; "Healthcare Spaces," Visual Reference Publications," Sep, 2008; "Healthcare Design," Sep, 2008; "Doctors Order: Translating University Hospitals' Healing Mission Into the Built Environment," Jul, 2008.

41325 ■ BBLM Architects
924 Cherry St., Ste. 1
Philadelphia, PA 19107-2411
Ph:(215)625-2500
Fax:(215)625-0275
Co. E-mail: ljs@bblm.com
Contact: Paul G. Shaffer, Principle
E-mail: ljs@bblm.com
Scope: Offers architecture, planning, and interior design consulting services, including color, furnishings, and lighting. Recent experience in health care design. Serves private institutions as well as government agencies.

41326 ■ Beck Powell & Parsons Inc.
26239 Royal Oak Rd.
Easton, MD 21601
Ph:(410)828-9220
Fax:(410)828-9661
Co. E-mail: main@beckpowell.com
URL: http://www.beckpowell.com
Contact: Mark H. Beck, Principal
E-mail: mb4833@aol.com
Scope: Architecture and interior design firm. Provides design services to governmental, corporate and institutional clients. **Publications:** "Active Solar Energy System Design Practice"; "Better Homes and Gardens"; "Solar Energy Analysis Guide"; "Solar Performance/Practice Guide"; "New Energy Conserving passive solar single family homes".

41327 ■ Bell Techlogics
8888 Keystone Crossing, Ste. 1700
Indianapolis, IN 46240
Ph:(317)704-6000
Free: 800-999-9813
Fax:(317)575-9401
Co. E-mail: bellservice@belltechlogix.com
URL: http://www.belltechlogix.com
Contact: Patrick Mallon, Vice President
Scope: Provides integrated technology and service solutions for organizations throughout the United States. Provides designing, implementing, and managing technology solutions that result in decreased costs, increased customer retention, improved service levels and operational efficiencies for small, mid-sized and Fortune 500 companies. Installs, configures, maintains and supports the local and wide area network technologies. Offers connectivity services that include secure Internet and Intranet communication solutions, virus scanning, and firewall protections. **Seminars:** Virtualization and Disaster Recovery, 2008.

41328 ■ Burt Hill, Inc.
101 E Diamond St.
Butler, PA 16001-5923
Ph:(724)285-4761
Fax:(724)285-6815
Co. E-mail: dianne.sinz@burthill.com
URL: http://www.burthill.com
Contact: Harry Gordon, Chairman of the Board
E-mail: john.brock@atsburthill.com
Scope: Offers architecture and engineering consulting services including space planning, facility evaluation, assessment of interior design, building infrastructure, landscape architecture and energy management. Industries served: healthcare, medical research, hospitality, high tech, education, corporate, housing, and manufacturing worldwide, with emphasis on the Eastern United States. **Publications:** "Metal Building Developer"; "Laboratory Design Construction and Renovation: Participants, Process, and Product," Board on Chemical Sciences and Technology, National Research Council, 1999; "Guidelines for planning and designing Biomedical Research Facilities," 1999; "Advances Technology Facilities Design," 1996; "Improving Collaboration: Architects and Engineers, Design and Construction," American Institute of Architects, 1996; "Fundamentals of Building Energy Dynamics; Energy Conservation and Management Strategies," MIT Press, 1996; "Teaching Space Utilization, Managing one of Higher Education's Most Significant Assets," 1996. **Seminars:** Advanced Technology Facilities Design and the Technology Intensive Workplace; Energy Conservation in Commercial Buildings Current Practice; Health care in the Baltics- Meeting the 21st Century; Architectural and Engineering Practice in the 21st Century; Class rooms of the Future; Class rooms of the Future; Campus-Wide Information Networks; Risk Allocation and Dispute Avoidance in Construction; Achieving Architectural and Engineering Collaboration in Building Design; Designing for Improved Occupant Comfort and Productivity; Construction Procurement; International Health Care; Campus-Wide Information Network.

41329 ■ Cambridge Seven Associates Inc.
1050 Massachusetts Ave.
Cambridge, MA 02138
Ph:(617)492-7000
Fax:(617)492-7007
Co. E-mail: marketing@c7a.com
URL: http://www.c7a.com
Contact: Charles Redmon, Principle
E-mail: simrich@atsc7a.com
Scope: Offers consulting in architecture, planning graphic, exhibit, habitat and interior design. Industries served: Colleges and universities, retail, corporations, museums, aquariums and government agencies. **Publications:** "On Strip, Hard Rock has a touch of interactivity," Oct, 2009; "Architectural follies surprise contest jurors," Sep, 2009; "Buck Center for Health and Fitness opens doors," Sep, 2009; "Die-hard fans hail The Hall at Patriot Place," Aug, 2009; "Mentors - Where are They When You Need Them," Aug, 2009; "Boston may soon have a history museum," Aug, 2009; "A New Lobby for the Charles Hotel," Aug, 2009; "New Balance Foundation Marine Mammal Center opening," Jul, 2009; "How Green is Your City," Metropolis, Sep, 2006; "Designing and Building for the Class of 2020," Sep, 2006; "Dumping Steel," The Boston Globe, Jun, 2006; "Healing Architecture," Architectural Record, Jun, 2005. **Seminars:** Where We Learn seminar.

41330 ■ Carmichael Associates
4255 Auburn St.
Wichita, KS 67220
Ph:(316)681-1535
Fax:(316)681-1548
Co. E-mail: joewmc@aol.com
Contact: Joe William Carmichael, President
E-mail: joewmc@aol.com
Scope: Architectural consultant active in legal assistance, library design, church design, health care projects, nursing homes, clinics, apartments, governmental buildings, renovations and remodeling work, residential and commercial, heavy truck maintenance and operations design, and small college buildings and planning.

41331 ■ Cassway/Albert Ltd.
1528 Walnut St., Ste. 1100
Philadelphia, PA 19102
Ph:(215)545-4900
Fax:(215)545-8222
Co. E-mail: cal@icdc.com
Contact: Elliot J. Rothschield, Principle
Scope: Consultants in architecture, landscape architecture, urban planning, interior design, and space planning.

41332 ■ C.E. Marquardt Lighting Design
13498 SE Wiese Rd.
Boring, OR 97009-8342
Ph:(503)658-5505
Contact: Craig E. Marquardt, Owner
Scope: Architectural lighting design firm offering services in both interior and exterior lighting. Services include custom control design, ceiling and skylight design, computer mock ups, scale models, and lighting art.

41333 ■ Champion Networks L.L.C.
1081 Mere Point Rd.
Brunswick, ME 04011
Ph:(207)725-8903
Fax:(207)721-0186
Contact: Trisha Z. Hunter, Controller
E-mail: thunter@atschampionnetworks.com
Scope: Firm specializes in network integration, total wide area network solutions, and network services.

41334 ■ Chicago-Edison Electrical & Lighting
189 Poplar Pl., Ste. 3
North Aurora, IL 60542
Ph:(630)264-6940
Fax:(630)264-6942
Contact: Larry C. Jeppesen, President
Scope: Lighting systems consultants. **Publications:** "An Efficient Solution: The right energy investments could pay big dividends," Barron's Magazine, Feb, 2002; "The Benefits of High Efficiency Lighting".

41335 ■ Chris Shaff Consulting
8641 Dasher Ave. NW
North Canton, OH 44720-4611
Ph:(330)494-1921
Contact: Grover Chris Shaff II, President
Scope: Specializes in business forms manufacturing and administration.

41336 ■ Cohn Consulting Corp.
2627 Sandy Plains Rd., Ste. 204
Marietta, GA 30066-4289
Ph:(770)321-5532
Fax:(770)321-4497
Co. E-mail: info@cohnconsultingcorp.com
URL: http://www.cohnconsultingcorp.com
Contact: Daniel S. Cohn, President
E-mail: dan@atscohnconsultingcorp.com
Scope: Firm provides a wide range of PC and LAN services. Specialized services includes Network administration, Backup and Disaster Recovery, Thin client computing, Internet services, Centralized fax solutions, Mainframe and midrange connectivity and Workgroup collaboration. **Publications:** "Total Network Solution Gets Title Insurance Agency Off To A Fast Start"; "Thin Client Solution Modernizes Psychological Practice". **Special Services:** Cohn Care™.

41337 ■ Cole & Goyette Architects & Planners Inc.
540 Franklin St.
Cambridge, MA 02139
Ph:(617)491-5662
Fax:(617)492-0856
Co. E-mail: colegoyette@earthlink.net
URL: http://www.colegoyette.com
Contact: Doris Cole, President
E-mail: colegoyette@earthlink.net
Scope: Offers services in architecture and planning, interior design and design review for educational, commercial, residential and governmental clients.

41338 ■ Computer Connections Inc.
1241-2 E Dixon Blvd., Ste. 2
PO Box 321
Shelby, NC 28150
Ph:(704)482-0057

Fax:(704)482-0950
Co. E-mail: ccsales@painlesspc.net
URL: http://www.painlesspc.net
Contact: Mike Houston, Mgr
E-mail: mikeh@atspainlesspc.net
Scope: Specializes in client or server networking environments. Offers service, upgrades, and repairs most IBM compatible computers. Networking services include: network design, implementation, and administration of novell and windows NT networks.

41339 ■ Crawley & Associates Inc.
121 Lincoln Ave.
Fair Lawn, NJ 07410
Ph:(973)636-7350
Free: 877-427-2953
Fax:(973)636-7360
Co. E-mail: sales@crawleyinc.com
URL: http://www.crawleyinc.com
Contact: Paul Crawley, President
E-mail: pcrawley@crawleyinc.com
Scope: Provides education technology management services for both public and private schools located in New Jersey; provides experienced guidance and direction. Services include: Design, budget development, hardware and software selection, implementation, project management and system monitoring. **Publications:** "Give Your Servers All the Attention," Oct, 2007; "The Importance of aTechnology Audit," Jun, 2007; "Eliminate Extended Warranties on Your-Workstation Purchases," May, 2007; "Beware of Hidden Cost When PurchasingWorkstations," Apr, 2007; "Top Five Overlooked Budget Items," Feb, 2007; "Technology Budgets: When to Say No," Jan, 2007. **Seminars:** Reducing Technology Costs.

41340 ■ Cutten Associates Lighting Design
PO Box 6926
Tahoe City, CA 96145-6926
Ph:(530)583-5002
Fax:(530)583-5525
Co. E-mail: medcut@yahoo.com
Contact: Merritt E. Cutten, President
E-mail: medcut@yahoo.com
Scope: Design consultant, offer expertise in lighting design and electrical engineering. Industries served construction residential, commercial, and industrial; also government agencies. **Seminars:** Lighting fundamentals course. **Special Services:** Auto CAD LT capability.

41341 ■ dEpagnier Furniture
14201 Notley Rd.
Silver Spring, MD 20904
Ph:(301)384-1663
Fax:(301)384-3201
Contact: Arnold D'Epagnier, Principle
Scope: Specializes in custom design and fabrication of furniture for corporate, residential or professional spaces. Performs architectural exterior and interior design consulting work with extensive knowledge in traditional cabinet making skills, solid woods and joinery. Design expertise in Greene and Greene genre of the American Arts and Crafts Movement. Offers advice on use, location and types of domestic woods in place of foreign exotic woods. Offers artistic high end functional quality built furniture. **Seminars:** Marquetry.

41342 ■ Design Collective Inc.
1701 E 12th St., Ste. 39
Cleveland, OH 44144
Ph:(614)464-2880
Fax:(614)464-1180
Co. E-mail: dcitn@aol.com
URL: http://www.dcollective.com
Contact: Robert B. Valentine, President
E-mail: rvalentine@dcollective.com
Scope: Firm offers expertise in interior design to clients in the commercial trade industry.

41343 ■ Dimension Data
2350 Corporate Park Dr., Ste. 425
Herndon, VA 20171
Ph:(571)203-4000

Fax:(571)203-4001
URL: http://www.dimensiondata.com
Contact: Connie de Lange, Mktg Mgr
Scope: A global technology company. Provides solutions and services that optimize and manage the performance of IT infrastructure to enable businesses to build competitive advantage.

41344 ■ Eaton Design Group Inc.
8115 Old Dominion Dr., Ste. 100
McLean, VA 22102
Ph:(703)790-8444
Free: 800-291-8444
Fax:(703)893-3256
Co. E-mail: eatondesgn@aol.com
Contact: Carl Blake, Principal
Scope: Nationally recognized McLean-based space planning and interior design firm.

41345 ■ E.F. Marburger Fine Flooring
9999 Allisonville Rd.
Fishers, IN 46038-2006
Ph:(317)841-7250
Fax:(317)841-7269
Co. E-mail: kshone@efmarburger.com
URL: http://www.efmarburger.com
Contact: Ron Marburger, President
E-mail: marburger@atsefmarburger.com
Scope: Offers counsel to architects, designers, interior decorators and institutions, on the proper type of carpeting to be used in commercial applications. Furnishes sound absorbing and sound loss transmission data on carpet wall coverings. Also offers counsel on acoustical absorption and sound transmission factors on other types of acoustical products. **Seminars:** Use of Glass in Your Kitchen and Bath Designs.

41346 ■ Engineered Lighting Products
10768 Lower Azusa Rd.
El Monte, CA 91731
Ph:(626)579-0943
Fax:(626)579-6803
Co. E-mail: contact@elplighting.com
URL: http://www.elplighting.com
Contact: Gary Thomas, Mgr
E-mail: gthomas@atsvidessence.tv
Scope: Firm offers lighting consulting for commercial, residential, and industrial projects. Provides design, specifications, and illumination calculations. Maintains a studio for mock-up design.

41347 ■ ePartners Inc.
12110 Sunset Hills Rd., Ste. 150
Reston, VA 20190
Ph:(703)817-1400
Free: 888-883-9797
Fax:(703)488-6799
Co. E-mail: info@epartnersolutions.com
URL: http://www.epartnersolutions.com
Contact: Bill Anderson, VP of Mktg
E-mail: sdharmasiri@atsepartnersolutions.com
Scope: A total solutions provider that designs, develops, implements, integrates, hosts, manages and supports comprehensive e-Business solutions.

41348 ■ Ergometrics Inc.
192 Monroe Ct.
Southampton, PA 18966-2722
Ph:(215)968-6943
Fax:(215)968-4250
Co. E-mail: ergodave@aol.com
Contact: David A. Rose, Director
E-mail: ergodave@aol.com
Scope: Provides occupational and forensic ergonomic services addressing work-site evaluations accident investigations, office ergonomics, tool, product and equipment evaluations, product liability, workplace accidents and occupational injuries. Specializes in heavy industrial, light industrial, service and office environments.

41349 ■ Error Analysis Inc.
5173 Waring Rd., Ste. 157
San Diego, CA 92120-2705
Ph:(619)464-4427

Fax:(619)464-4992
Co. E-mail: info@erroranalysis.com
URL: http://www.erroranalysis.com
Contact: Cynthia A. Larue, Principle
E-mail: clarue@atserroranalysis.com
Scope: Firm dedicated to research and consulting in the fields of human factors, safety and accident reconstruction. Provides consulting and expert witness services to attorneys, the insurance industry and businesses throughout the world. **Publications:** "Stairway falls: An ergonomics analysis of 80 cases," Professional Safety, 2009; "The practice of forensic human factors/ergonomics and related safety professions," Lawyers & Judges Publishing Company, 2009. **Seminars:** The role of a just culture, American Society of Safety Engineers, Costa Mesa, CA, Jan, 2009; Common trends in slip and falls, Las Vegas, NV, Sep, 2008; Safety; Risk Management; Premises and Product Liability.

41350 ■ Fowlie & Associates
630 Skyline Dr.
Ventura, CA 93003-1143
Ph:(805)644-0201
Fax:(805)644-9885
Co. E-mail: efowliearchitect@sbcglobal.net
Contact: Elmore I. Fowlie, Owner
E-mail: efowliearchitect@sbcglobal.net
Scope: Offers environmentally conscious architectural services, including interior design, urban planning, building program development, and site analysis. Industries served: Educational, industrial, residential, commercial, and municipal facilities.

41351 ■ FRCH Design Worldwide
311 Elm St., Ste. 600
Cincinnati, OH 45202-2774
Ph:(513)241-3000
Free: 800-434-3724
Fax:(513)241-5015
Co. E-mail: info@frch.com
URL: http://www.frch.com
Contact: Thomas Horwitz, Principle
E-mail: thorwitz@atsfrch.com
Scope: Offers interior design, architectural, graphic communications, graphic design, brand consulting and new media development services. **Seminars:** Futureshop: Inspiring Your Next Design.

41352 ■ Gary Steffy Lighting Design
2900 S State St., Ste. 12
Ann Arbor, MI 48104
Ph:(734)747-6630
Free: 800-537-1230
Fax:(734)747-6629
Co. E-mail: grs@gsld.net
URL: http://www.gsld.net
Contact: Gary R. Steffy, President
E-mail: grs@atsgsld.net
Scope: Lighting design consultants for interior and exterior lighting needs. Additional area of expertise is landscape lighting. Serves private industries as well as government agencies. **Publications:** "Architectural Lighting Design". **Seminars:** Office Lighting; Lighting for Electronic Offices; Lighting Design; Historic Lighting.

41353 ■ Glaser Associates Inc.
304 E 8th St.
Cincinnati, OH 45202-2231
Ph:(513)665-9555
Fax:(513)665-9857
Co. E-mail: shaber@glaserworks.com
URL: http://www.glaserworks.com
Contact: Jeff Raser, Principle
E-mail: jraser@atsglaserworks.com
Scope: Architectural consulting firm offers master planning, site and feasibility analysis, architectural and interior design, space planning, renovation and adaptive reuse. Industries served: museums, higher education and mixed-use developments.

41354 ■ GlobalNet Inc.
12000 Network Dr., Ste. 410
San Antonio, TX 78249
Ph:(832)778-9591

Fax:(210)579-1192
Co. E-mail: customercare@gbne.net
Contact: David F. Levy, President
Scope: Specializes in the installation, configuration, and technical support of local (LAN) and wide (WAN) Area Networks. Installs Multi-User and Multi-Platform systems (i.e. DOS, OS2, Windows NT, UNIX, NextStep, and Macintosh) which perform Accounting, client/server Database, Word Processing, Spreadsheet, and Computer Aide Design (CAD) tasks in a variety of industries.

41355 ■ Humanics ErgoSystems Inc.
PO Box 17388
Encino, CA 91416-7388
Ph:(818)345-3746
Fax:(818)705-3903
Co. E-mail: ergonomics@humanics-es.com
URL: http://www.humanics-es.com
Contact: Rani Lueder, Principle
E-mail: rani@humanics-es.com
Scope: Specializes in occupational ergonomics; ergonomic workplace evaluations; ergonomics research; ergonomic seminars and training; psychological and biomechanics testing (EMG, dynamic lumbar motion, strength assessment, nerve conduction); product evaluations; compliance with ergonomic standards; and expert witnessing. **Publications:** "The Future of Ergonomics in Children's Education," IEA 2009; "Ergonomics for Children; designing products and places for toddlers to teens," 2007; "Are Children just Little Adults? Child growth, development and age-related risk," Dec, 2003; "Rethinking Sitting," Oct, 2003; "Revisiting Ergonomics," May, 2003. **Seminars:** Teaching elder design, Las Vegas, Jul, 2008; Ergonomic considerations in seated work activities, University of California, Los Angeles, Jun, 2008; Rethinking back support: Sacral, lumbar or live backs, Dec, 2007; Adjunct Faculty, Human Factors and Design, 2006; Zen sitting and Western seating, 2005; Behavioral ergonomics, Oct, 2005; Sitting & seating in Zenmonasteries, Sep, 2005; Walking in their shoe.

41356 ■ Illuminated Concepts Inc.
23422 Peralta Dr., Ste. B
Laguna Hills, CA 92653
Ph:(949)455-9914
Fax:(949)951-3603
Co. E-mail: oclights@yahoo.com
URL: http://www.oclights.com
Contact: Chuck Evans, President
Scope: Provides extensive design and installation services for both interior and exterior lighting. Specialist in low voltage lighting and fiber optic systems.

41357 ■ IMC
399 Sackett Point Rd.
North Haven, CT 06473
Ph:(203)248-5324
Free: 800-840-9989
Fax:(203)248-5384
Co. E-mail: info@imcinternet.net
URL: http://www.imcinternet.net
Contact: Robert Caldarella, President
E-mail: bob@imcinternet.net
Scope: Specializes in the development of total office solutions for business which includes office networking, client/server technologies, Internet access and computer sales.

41358 ■ Integrated Security Technologies
520 Herndon Pky., Ste. C
Herndon, VA 20170
Ph:(703)464-4766
Free: 888-291-0120
Fax:(703)464-5836
Co. E-mail: info@ntllc.com
URL: http://www.ntllc.com
Contact: TaChung Chang, Vice President
E-mail: mmargolis@ntllc.com
Scope: Focuses on the application of information technologies to enhance the effectiveness of the business environment including collecting, organizing and storing information; designing, building and maintaining the appropriate architecture to make information available. to assess, design and implement solutions for security and Information Technology challenges.

Publications: "American University Wins High Marks for New Security System"; "All American Upgrade"; "IST named 77th on SDM's Top 100 System Integrators".

41359 ■ IRI Design Associates Inc.
122 E 42nd St.
New York, NY 10168-0002
Ph:(212)922-0632
Fax:(212)481-1856
Contact: Lisa Nikol, President
Scope: Full service interior architectural and design firm. Industries served: All.

41360 ■ Jacobs-Schneider Interior Design Inc.
1012 E 75th St.
Indianapolis, IN 46240-2843
Ph:(317)251-0312
Fax:(317)251-0339
Contact: Janie Jacobs, President
Scope: Interior design consulting firm.

41361 ■ Kajioka Design Associates
2614 Ross Rd.
Chevy Chase, MD 20815-3835
Ph:(301)565-3535
Fax:(301)565-3535
Contact: June J. Kajioka, Owner
Scope: Interior design consultant (licensed and certified in Maryland and Virginia) provides expertise in space planning, complete furnishings and installation of window treatments, floor and wall coverings, and in other areas.

41362 ■ KCS Computer Technology Inc.
9524 Franklin Ave.
Franklin Park, IL 60131
Ph:(847)288-9820
Fax:(847)288-9822
Co. E-mail: sales@kcstech.com
URL: http://www.kcstech.com
Contact: Kenneth Kollar, President
Scope: Offers a full line of business-class computers, servers, workstations, laptops, printers, and peripherals. Offers hardware, software, installation, configuration, maintenance and management. Specializes in software and computer reselling, Windows NT, Lantastic and Novell network installation and maintenance, custom programming, network communications fax/modem server installation and maintenance, Internet setup and training, custom html programming services, network and phone cabling, computer leasing, data conversion and data recovery and maintenance contracts.

41363 ■ KeyLAN Consulting Inc.
2399 Lenida Dr.
PO Box 333
North Gower, ON, Canada K0A 2T0
Ph:(613)489-2336
Fax:(613)489-4190
Co. E-mail: keylan@keylan.ca
URL: http://www.keylan.ca
Contact: James MacNabb, Principle
Scope: Specializes in all facets of local area networking, purchasing, installation, administration, training, automation, disaster planning, high security databases and security consulting.

41364 ■ Lam Partners Inc.
84 Sherman St.
Cambridge, MA 02140
Ph:(617)354-4502
Fax:(617)497-5038
Co. E-mail: info@lampartners.com
URL: http://www.lampartners.com
Contact: Keith Yancey Jr., Principle
E-mail: keithy@atslampartners.com
Scope: Architectural lighting consultants experienced in all phases of lighting design including artificial lighting, day lighting, lighting for urban design, and custom fixture design.

41365 ■ LAN Solutions
449 Hillway Dr.
Emerald Hills, CA 94062-3313
Ph:(650)261-1300

Fax:(650)361-8012
Co. E-mail: info@lansol.com
URL: http://www.lansol.com
Contact: Yung-I Chu, Principle
E-mail: yungi@atslansol.com
Scope: Offers Microsoft MCSE certified installation, service and consulting. Services include: network design and needs analysis, CD-Rom and FAX design and installation, network and Internet email design and installation, network troubleshooting and diagnostics, network performance optimization, system manager and user training and network cabling installation.

41366 ■ LBC Networks
675 King St. W, Ste. 210
Toronto, ON, Canada M5V 1M9
Ph:(416)727-9200
Free: 888-437-7741
Fax:(416)929-1173
Contact: Marcus Auguste, Principal
E-mail: marcusa@atslbcnetworks.com
Scope: Network consulting group that specializes in TCP/IP, Linux and other network technologies. Services include: Novell to NT migration, firewall and internet security, support, Linux, email solutions, virtual private networks, data wiring, network management, and web design.

41367 ■ Lighting Design Collaborative
27 W 24th St., Ste. 507
New York, NY 10010
Ph:(215)569-2115
Fax:(215)569-2580
Co. E-mail: info@ldc-pa.com
URL: http://www.lightingdesigncollaborative.com
Contact: Penelope Sarkioglu, Partner
Scope: Architectural lighting design firm offering expertise in commercial, interior and exterior, hotel/hospitality, retail, mixed-use, museum, healthcare, transportation, and educational projects. Serves private industries as well as government agencies.

41368 ■ Lino J. Agosti & Associates
1901 W Tudor Rd.
Anchorage, AK 99517-3114
Ph:(907)243-3556
Fax:(907)243-6709
Co. E-mail: tim.agosti@alaska.com
Contact: Lino Agosti, Principle
E-mail: tim.agosti@alaska.com
Scope: Offers food facility design, interior design and feasibility planning. Service offered: Concept development, design, feasibility.

41369 ■ The Luminations Group L.L.C.
9 Kilmer Dr.
Hillsborough, NJ 08844
Ph:(908)281-9027
Fax:(908)349-3270
Co. E-mail: info@luminationsgroup.com
URL: http://www.luminationsgroup.com
Contact: Terry Ramirez, Director
E-mail: michelle@atsluminationsgroup.com
Scope: Lighting consultants experienced with commercial, retail, institutional and residential projects.

41370 ■ M. Richler & Associates Ltd.
85 Skymark Dr., Ste. 2603
North York, ON, Canada M2H 3P2
Ph:(416)491-5264
Fax:(416)491-4557
Contact: Mitchell M. Richler, President
E-mail: mitchrichler@aol.com
Scope: A general management consulting firm specializing in acquisitions and mergers, costing and pricing, office layout design and management, production management and taxation, particularly for small businesses. Industries served: manufacturing, retail, wholesale, import/export, design services, and government agencies. **Seminars:** Keeping the Cottage in the Family; Maximizing Capital Gains Exemption; Minimizing Probate Fees; Plant Reorganization; Departmental Scheduling.

41371 ■ Major Electric Supply Inc.
558 W Main St.
Norwich, CT 06360
Ph:(401)724-7100

Free: 800-444-1660
Fax:(401)727-7563
Co. E-mail: showroom@majorelectricsupply.com
URL: http://www.majorelectricsupply.com
Contact: Jack Nugent, Mgr
E-mail: jacknugent@majorelectricsupply.com
Scope: Firm providing extensive lighting design services for commercial, residential, theatrical and landscape projects.

41372 ■ Marconi Designs
985 University Ave., Ste. 22
PO Box 320926
Los Gatos, CA 95032-0115
Ph:(408)807-8330
Fax:(408)841-7234
Co. E-mail: patricia@marconidesigns.com
URL: http://www.wahlichusa.com/design
Contact: Patricia A. Wahli, Owner
E-mail: patricia@marconidesigns.com
Scope: Provides interior design, space planning and facility design for commercial office buildings of any size. Renovation, remodel and reconfiguration of personnel workspaces and existing buildings the firms specialties. Tenant improvements for new and existing office space also handled. Industries served electronics, medical, banking industries and government agencies in California, statewide, with emphasis on San Francisco Bay Area.

41373 ■ Marshall Craft Associates Inc.
6112 York Rd.
Baltimore, MD 21212-2611
Ph:(410)532-3131
Fax:(410)532-9206
Co. E-mail: contact@marshallcraft.com
URL: http://www.marshallcraft.com
Contact: Linton S. Marshall, Principal
E-mail: lsm@atsmarshallcraft.com
Scope: Firm specializes in architecture, interior design, and planning. Offers professional services to health-care, academic, corporate and government clients.

41374 ■ Maxdeco Interior Design Inc.
160 Fresh Ponds Rd.
East Brunswick, NJ 08816-2408
Ph:(732)821-7850
Contact: Sarina Feldman, Owner
Scope: Interior design and decoration consultation and planning for commercial, institutional and residential clients. Serves private industries as well as government agencies in New Jersey, New York City and Philadelphia.

41375 ■ Michaels Associates Design Consultants Inc.
14809 N 73rd St.
Scottsdale, AZ 85260-3113
Ph:(480)998-7476
Fax:(480)998-9390
Co. E-mail: info@madeline.com
URL: http://www.madcinc.com
Contact: David Leroy Michaels, Vice President
E-mail: david@atsmadcinc.com
Scope: Twenty year specialization in all areas of library (public, academic, corporate and national) programming and planning, including needs assessments and interior and graphic design. Michaels Associates expertise also includes ADA audits, furniture and product design for offices, lighting and graphic design. **Publications:** "Forum III: Physical Spaces for the E-ssential Library," 2003; "Library facility Planning"; "Library Administration & Management"; "Enhance Security With Effective Interior Planning and Design"; "Designing for Technology in Todays Libraries". **Seminars:** Library Environments: Changing to Fit New Technologies and Services, Dowling College, Long Island, NY, Nov, 2004; Reconfiguration Strategies Library Space for the E-Library, Information Futures Institute, San Francisco, CA, Sep, 2004; Creative Learning Seminars; Library Interior Planning & Design; Accessible, Healthy, Imaginative Spaces: Old & New; Fresh Looks for Library Interiors; The Future is Now: Library Planning &Design for the 21st Century; ADA Furnishings Response for Today's Libraries; Lighting & Libraries; Library Planning Based on New Functional Space Guidelines; Crime Prevention through Environmental Design.

41376 ■ MindLabs.net
PO Box 171
Philadelphia, PA 19105-0171
Ph:(215)888-6220
Co. E-mail: email@mindlabs.net
URL: http://www.mindlabs.net
Contact: Mike Creech, Partner
E-mail: anne@atsmindlabs.net
Scope: Solutions include website design and development, website make over's, ongoing maintenance and support, website hosting and Internet marketing.

41377 ■ Mitchell B. Architectural Lighting Consultants
2256 Linden Ave.
Highland Park, IL 60035-2006
Ph:(847)433-0840
Fax:(847)433-0839
Co. E-mail: mitchell@mbklightingdesign.com
URL: http://www.mbklightingdesign.com
Contact: Mitchell B. Kohn, President
E-mail: mitchell@mbklightingdesign.com
Scope: Full service architectural lighting design firm provides interior lighting design for commercial projects. **Publications:** "Lighting Today's Office Environment," Professional Lighting Design Magazine, 2002; "Lighting Focus," 1998; "Lighting Considered," Apr, 1997; "Task Lighting for Offices," Apr, 1994; "Effective Lighting for Open Plan Offices," Facilities Magazine, Feb, 1992; "Task Lighting is a Key to Productivity," Consulting-Specifying Magazine, Nov, 1990; "Lighting Design and Vdts," Electrical Business Magazine, Mar, 1990; "Office Lighting for the 1990S," Commerce Magazine, Nov, 1989; "Lighting Offices Containing Vdts," Lighting Design and Application Magazine, Dec, 1988. **Seminars:** NEOCON, Chicago, 1999; Light Fair International, San Francisco, 1996; IIDACEU accredited seminars, 2004; IBD Chicago, Office Lighting Seminar, 1993.

41378 ■ MJS Lighting Consultants
3118 Richmond Ave., Ste. 100
Houston, TX 77098-3016
Ph:(713)850-1488
Fax:(713)521-4505
Co. E-mail: mjsmith@mjslight.com
URL: http://www.mjslight.com
Contact: Michael John Smith, Principle
E-mail: michael@atsmjslight.com
Scope: Full service architectural lighting design firm that provides expertise with interior, exterior, landscape, facade, roadway, and industrial illumination.

41379 ■ Networked Solutions Inc.
4280 Caparosa Cir.
Melbourne, FL 32940
Ph:(321)259-3242
Fax:(321)259-3846
Co. E-mail: info@ensusa.com
URL: http://www.ensusa.com
Contact: Sean Friese, Principle
E-mail: skf@atsensusa.com
Scope: Specializes in simultaneous Internet web and email access via LAN. Capabilities include: requirements analysis, computer system setup, network design and installation, software development, training and support. **Special Services:** SAAZ.

41380 ■ Notari Associates
175 W Ostend St., Ste. 100
Baltimore, MD 21230-3731
Ph:(410)752-0330
Fax:(410)685-6364
Co. E-mail: info@notariassociates.com
URL: http://www.notariassociates.com
Contact: Peter Notari, President
E-mail: pnotari@notariassociates.com
Scope: Architectural firm offering project management and interior design services.

41381 ■ Parachute Computer Services Inc.
11615 Angus Rd., Ste. 104L
PO Box 4492
Austin, TX 78765
Ph:(512)684-8250
Contact: Kristian Jones, Owner
Scope: Offers LAN/WAN services, on-site consultation, remote administration, and training.

41382 ■ Patrick B. Quigley & Associates Inc.
2340 Plz., Del Amo, Ste. 125
Torrance, CA 90501
Ph:(310)533-6064
Fax:(310)320-3482
Co. E-mail: lighting@pbqa.com
URL: http://www.pbqa.com
Contact: Patrick B. Quigley, Owner
E-mail: lighting@atspbqa.com
Scope: Firm offers full service architectural and landscape lighting design. Experienced with cruise vessels, hotels, theme parks, civic centers, libraries, office interiors, and residences.

41383 ■ Peckham Guyton Albers & Viets Inc.
200 N Broadway, Ste. 1000
Saint Louis, MO 63102-2754
Ph:(314)231-7318
Fax:(314)231-7433
Co. E-mail: mike.konzen@pgav.com
URL: http://www.pgav.com
Contact: Stephen N. Abend, Principle
E-mail: sabend@atsasaiarch.com
Scope: Provides programming, planning and urban design, architecture, engineering, interior design, space planning, graphics, landscape architecture, energy engineering, construction documents, feasibility studies, zoning and codes analysis, development analysis, computer aided design, computer based specifications, cost estimating, construction management and value engineering. Projects include the design of civic, criminal justice, educational, library, recreational, governmental/public, healthcare facilities and multi-family housing. Also experienced in historic preservation and restoration. Industries served: Governmental organizations, criminal justice, public administration, corporate administration, education and recreation. **Seminars:** Consensus Building in the Planning of Public Facilities; Juvenile Detention and Adult Detention Facilities.

41384 ■ Perceptive Technology Corp.
11309 Pk. Central Pl.
Dallas, TX 75230
Ph:(214)368-0900
Co. E-mail: vic@perceptive.net
Contact: Vic Summerour, President
E-mail: vic@perceptive.net
Scope: Services include: Business web site design and hosting, Internet connectivity, web server co location, Intranet design, LAN or WAN design and consulting.

41385 ■ Pinnix Design Inc.
2507 Goldcup Ln.
PO Box 8004
Reston, VA 20191-4219
Ph:(703)620-1167
Fax:(703)715-0811
Contact: Van L. Pinnix, President
E-mail: vlpinnix@sprynet.com
Scope: Architecture, bio-remediation, provides services in commercial interior design, space planning, architectural interior design, construction, specifications, procurement and installation management for commercial, institutional and industrial spaces. Serves private industries, particularly construction, as well as government agencies in the mid-Atlantic, northern and southeastern United States.

41386 ■ Plantkeeper Inc.
2211 N Beckley Ave.
PO Box 226142
Dallas, TX 75208-2114
Ph:(214)752-5750
Free: 800-340-4488
Fax:(214)651-0540
Co. E-mail: sales@plantkeeperinc.com
URL: http://www.plantkeeperinc.com
Contact: Burrell Galbreath, Mgr
E-mail: burrell@atsplantkeeperinc.com
Scope: Interior design consultants specializing in plants and containers. Serving architects, developing companies and other commercial accounts. Provides interior design and maintenance for bank, office buildings, hotels, malls and restaurants.

41387 ■ R & S Design Computer Services Inc.
10 W Front St.
Media, PA 19063-3306
Ph:(610)565-5523
Fax:(610)480-8398
Co. E-mail: info@rsdesign.com
URL: http://www.rsdesign.com
Contact: Amy Mensch, Principle
E-mail: amensch@atsrsdesign.com
Scope: Provides technology solutions. Offers the sale, installation and configuration of PC software for business and home use. Offers training for a wide variety of software applications, maintenance and repair of hardware and network systems.

41388 ■ RMJM Hillier
500 Alexander Pk.
Princeton, NJ 08543-6395
Ph:(609)452-8888
Free: 888-445-5437
Fax:(609)452-8332
Co. E-mail: princeton@rmjm.com
URL: http://www.hillier.com
Contact: Thomas K. Fridstein, Principle
E-mail: thomas.fridstein@atshillier.com
Scope: Provides services in architecture, planning, interior design, engineering, construction management, strategic facilities planning, real estate evaluation and graphic design. Industries served: public and private sector.

41389 ■ Robert J. Laughlin & Associates
255 Osceola Ct.
Winter Park, FL 32789
Ph:(407)740-0160
Fax:(407)629-0411
Co. E-mail: info@robertjlaughlin.com
URL: http://www.robertjlaughlin.com
Contact: Robert J. Laughlin, Owner
Scope: Full service architectural lighting design firm. **Publications:** "Architectural Records," May, 2005; "Florida Design," 2002; "House and Garden," Sep, 2000; "Sign Business," Nov, 1997.

41390 ■ Robert Newell Lighting Design
654 N Ave. W
Westfield, NJ 07090-1432
Ph:(908)654-9304
Fax:(908)654-9302
Co. E-mail: robert.newell@robertnewelllightingde-sign.com
URL: http://www.robertnewelllightingdesign.com
Contact: Robert Newell, Owner
E-mail: robert.newell@robertnewelllightingdesign.com
Scope: Full service architectural lighting design firm offers experience with commercial, corporate, educational, religious and residential environments.

41391 ■ Roeder Design
3878 Oak Lawn Ave., Ste. 220
Dallas, TX 75219
Ph:(214)528-2300
Fax:(214)521-2300
Co. E-mail: robert@roederdesign.com
URL: http://www.roederdesign.com
Contact: F. Levin, President
Scope: Lighting design consulting firm experienced with cruise ships, residences, hotels, casinos, office buildings, retail showrooms, and health-care facilities.

41392 ■ Rowland Design Inc.
701 E New York St.
Indianapolis, IN 46202
Ph:(317)636-3980
Fax:(317)263-2065
Co. E-mail: info@rowlanddesign.com
URL: http://www.rowlanddesign.com
Contact: Tricia Trick, Principle
E-mail: msargent@atsrowlanddesign.com
Scope: Architecture, interior design, environmental graphic design, club consulting, alternative workplace strategies, space planning, thematic entertainment, hospitality design, and museum/exhibit design.

41393 ■ RTKL Associates Inc.
901 S Bond St.
Baltimore, MD 21231-3339
Ph:(410)537-6000
Fax:(410)276-2136
Co. E-mail: baltimore-info@rtkl.com
URL: http://www.rtkl.com
Contact: Stephen Spinazzola, Vice President
E-mail: sspinazzola@atsrtkl.com
Scope: Provides architecture, engineering, planning and urban design, interior architecture and design, landscape architecture, and environmental graphic design services for clients in public and private sector. Engaged in office, retail, hospitality, mixed-use, health sciences, entertainment, transportation, residential, and planning projects worldwide. **Publications:** "Placemaking: The Critical Ingredients"; "Discovering the new urbanism"; "Showcasing success in Today's workplaces"; "Mixed-Use: The new Urban Warrior"; "What is a Brand-Rich Environment?"; "Waiting for Wi-Fi"; "The Unit Plan of the Future"; "The Keys to the District".

41394 ■ S & S Office Solutions Inc.
3480 Johnson Ferry Rd.
Roswell, GA 30075
Ph:(770)518-0868
Fax:(770)518-4483
Co. E-mail: info@ssos.com
URL: http://www.ssos.com
Contact: Annette Stone, President
Scope: Specialists in designing, installing, and consulting for LANs (Local Area Networks) and wiring systems for professional offices (MCSE). Offers total turn-key solution to networking challenge.

41395 ■ SBA Computers Inc.
620 E State St.
O'Fallon, IL 62269
Ph:(618)628-9590
Fax:(618)622-3717
Co. E-mail: info@sbacomputers.com
URL: http://www.sbaonsite.com
Contact: Jason Reese, Vice President
E-mail: jason@atssbacomputers.com
Scope: Provides web site and domain hosting. Offers domain registration services.

41396 ■ Schrager Lighting Design L.L.C.
412 Main St., Ste. H
Ridgefield, CT 06877
Ph:(203)438-1188
Fax:(203)438-2299
Co. E-mail: sspublic@schragerlightingdesign.com
URL: http://www.schragerlightingdesign.com
Contact: Sara Schrager, Principle
Scope: Provides consulting services in architectural lighting design, with experience in lighting museums, academic and religious institutions, historic preservation, public atriums, corporate interiors, exterior lighting for landscapes and hard capes, art collections, restaurants and fine homes and estates.

41397 ■ Scott M. Watson Inc.
15200 Shady Grove Rd., Ste. 350
Rockville, MD 20850
Ph:(301)869-8800
Fax:(301)869-8802
Co. E-mail: smwiald@aol.com
Contact: Mark Ketteran, Principle
E-mail: smwiald@starpower.net
Scope: Lighting design consultant for new and renovated commercial, institutional, and high-end residential projects. Particular expertise provided in lighting layouts, fixture specifications, control groupings, dimmer specifications, shop drawing review, punch-out and focus of installations. Custom fixtures and applications designed as needed. Serves architects, interior designers, and owners, as well as government agencies.

41398 ■ Simplified Technology Co.
PO Box 8281
Fremont, CA 94537
Ph:(510)794-5520
Free: 800-782-4435
Co. E-mail: sales200606@simplifiedtechnology.com
URL: http://www.simplifiedtechnology.com
Contact: Gregory Carvalho, President
E-mail: gregoryc@simplifiedtechnology.com
Scope: Specializes in providing system security, networking, custom software development and data availability. **Special Services:** MRO's Maximo and Datastream's Maintenance Package 2 (MP2).

41399 ■ Spacial Design
524 San Anselmo Ave., Ste. 146
San Anselmo, CA 94960
Ph:(415)457-3195
Fax:(415)457-1876
Co. E-mail: contactus@spacialdesign.com
URL: http://www.spacialdesign.com
Contact: Susan Lund, President
E-mail: susan@atsspacialdesign.com
Scope: Specializes in space planning for kitchens, closets and office. Works with individual homeowners and small businesses. Also advises clients on setting up systems and then designing spaces to accommodate those systems. **Seminars:** Kitchen Planning Seminar, Sonoma Valley Adult School, Oct, 2006; So. . .you'dlove a new kitchen?; Where do you begin?; What should you expect from the design and your budget?.

41400 ■ Symmes Maini & McKee Associates
1000 Massachusetts Ave.
Cambridge, MA 02138
Ph:(617)547-5400
Fax:800-648-4920
Co. E-mail: info@smma.com
URL: http://www.smma.com
Contact: Michael K. Powers, Chairman of the Board
E-mail: m_powers@atssmma.com
Scope: A full service architecture, master planning, urban design, and interior design firm serving healthcare, educational, financial, and commercial institutions with particular emphasis on hospitals, research laboratories, office buildings, and educational structures including athletic facilities.

41401 ■ Systems Alternatives International L.L.C.
1705 Indian Wood Cir., Ste. 100
Maumee, OH 43537
Ph:(419)891-1100
Fax:(419)891-1045
Co. E-mail: sales@sysalt.com
URL: http://www.sysalt.com
Contact: John W. Underwood, Principal
E-mail: dyoungman@sysalt.com
Scope: Provides a total solution with consulting and design, industry proven software and hardware, and training and support. Develops and delivers the highest standard in computerized systems and engineered solutions. Specializes in selling hardware and software. Provides innovative software and quality information technology services to the unique needs of the recycling and metals industries. **Special Services:** XSight; Version 4; CRES; CRIS.

41402 ■ T. Kondos Associates
333 W 39th St., Ste. 202
New York, NY 10018-1429
Ph:(212)736-5510
Fax:(212)594-6332
Co. E-mail: info@tkondos.com
URL: http://www.tkondos.com
Contact: Theo Kondos, Principle
E-mail: tkondos@atstkondos.com
Scope: Full service architectural lighting design firm. Expertise with product development, budgeting, production, and equipment specification.

41403 ■ Thomas R. Egan Consulting Inc.
1012 Ronda Ln.
Birmingham, AL 35214
Ph:(205)796-9541

Fax:(205)744-9404
Co. E-mail: tegan@treci.com
Contact: Thomas R. Egan, CEO
E-mail: tegan@treci.com
Scope: Provides consultation and design services, installation, and service/maintenance for several network platforms.

41404 ■ TLA-Lighting Consultants Inc.
7 Pond St.
Salem, MA 01970-4819
Ph:(978)745-6870
Fax:(978)741-4420
Co. E-mail: tmlattla@aol.com
Contact: Priscilla Lemons, Treasurer
E-mail: tmlattla@aol.com
Scope: Offers counsel on lighting installation design, lighting product design, lighting energy conservation studies and day lighting, optical systems design, system evaluation and testing, and product and market planning. Serves private industries as well as government agencies. **Seminars:** Reflector Design - Theory and Practice.

41405 ■ WNF Consulting Inc.
602 E Briles Rd.
PO Box 42118
Phoenix, AZ 85027-7886
Ph:(480)940-4808
Fax:(602)222-8616
Contact: Robert Murphy, President
E-mail: awoodwar@atswnf.com
Scope: Firm specializes in network analysis and design. Consulting engineers assist in understanding the characteristics of each network resource and segment, optimization of network hierarchy based on usage requirements, system performance and effective resource utilization, optimization of pooled server and application configurations, storage management methodology for day-to-day storage management and storage management methodology for automated storage management. **Special Services:** PX-EGuard™; Identity Management Service.

FRANCHISES AND BUSINESS OPPORTUNITIES

41406 ■ California Closet Company
1000 4th St., Ste. 800
San Rafael, CA 94901
Ph:(415)256-5500
Free: 800-241-3222
Fax:(415)256-8501
No. of Franchise Units: 77. **Founded:** 1978. **Franchised:** 1982. **Description:** Custom closet design, manufacture, and installation. **Equity Capital Needed:** $127,500-$377,000 total investment. **Franchise Fee:** $40,000. **Royalty Fee:** 6%. **Financial Assistance:** No. **Training:** Includes training at headquarters, franchisees location, mentor training with ongoing support.

LIBRARIES

41407 ■ Tech-U-Fit Corporation Library
400 Madison St., No. 210
Alexandria, VA 22314
Ph:(703)549-0512
Fax:(703)548-0780
Contact: John Molino
Scope: Engineering, psychology, human factors engineering, ergonomics. **Holdings:** 200 volumes.

RESEARCH CENTERS

41408 ■ New Jersey Institute of Technology–Center for Architecture and Building Science Research
335 Campbell Hall
323 Martin Luther King Blvd.
Newark, NJ 07102-1982
Ph:(973)596-3097
Fax:(973)596-8443
Co. E-mail: deane.evans@njit.edu
URL: http://www.cabsr.org
Contact: Deane M. Evans, Exec.Dir.
E-mail: deane.evans@njit.edu
Scope: The relationship between the built environment and the institutions, policies and trends that shape it, emphasizing building types and environments related to housing, education, health and aging, and developmental disabilities planning. The center also studies ways to optimize the use of available resources to create more effective and efficient environments to better serve users' needs, cost effective methods and approaches to translate research concepts into practice through programs, policies and actions devoted to improving new and existing facilities and related social conditions. programs, policies and actions devoted to improving new and existing facilities and related social conditions.

41409 ■ Rensselaer Polytechnic Institute–Lighting Research Center
School of Architecture
21 Union St.
Troy, NY 12180
Ph:(518)687-7100
Fax:(518)687-7120
Co. E-mail: ream@rpi.edu
URL: http://www.lrc.rpi.edu
Contact: Prof. Mark S. Rea PhD, Dir.
E-mail: ream@rpi.edu
Scope: Lighting systems, including studies in vision, visibility, daylighting, efficient lighting technologies, architecture, building systems interactions, control systems, design tools, glass science, lighting economics, technology transfer, vision, transportation lighting, light and health, and human responses to lighting, including productivity, mood, and perception of brightness and spaciousness. **Publications:** Delta Portfolios (periodically); Design books, evaluations; NLPIP Lighting Answers (periodically); NLPIP Specifier Reports (periodically). **Educational Activities:** Colloquia (biweekly); Industrial partners program; Roundtables, workshops, teleconferences, symposia, tours, demonstrations, and presentations; Utility Personnel Training Seminars.

41410 ■ University of Quebec at Montreal–Centre for Study of Biological Interactions Between Environment and Health–Centre de Recherche Interdisciplinaire sur la Biologie, la Santé, la Société et l'Environnement
Succursale Centre-ville
Case postale 8888
Montreal, QC, Canada H3C 3P8
Ph:(514)987-3000
Fax:(514)987-6183
Co. E-mail: saint-charles.johanne@uqam.ca
URL: http://www.cinbiose.uqam.ca
Contact: Johanne Saint-Charles, Dir.
E-mail: saint-charles.johanne@uqam.ca
Scope: Occupational health, ergonomics.

EDUCATIONAL PROGRAMS

41411 ■ Auditing Outsourced Operations
Seminar Information Service, Inc.
20 Executive Park, Ste. 120
Irvine, CA 92614
Ph:(949)261-9104
Free: 877-SEM-INFO
Fax:(949)261-1963
Co. E-mail: info@seminarinformation.com
URL: http://www.seminarinformation.com
Price: $1,850.00. **Description:** Explore the prime risk factors present in outsourcing arrangements. You will identify the key areas you must cover to ensure your audits protect your organization's interest, including audit procedures, maintaining and enforcing your right to audit with guaranteed access, and creating contracts that focus on delivery, ROI, and performance metrics. **Locations:** New York, NY; and Orlando, FL.

REFERENCE WORKS

41412 ■ "35-Year-Old Downtown Fabric Store Closes Doors" in *The Times and Democrat* **(September 29, 2009)**
Pub: The Times and Democrat
Description: Warren's Fashion Fabrics Inc., a 35-year-old retail fabric, decor and sewing store, officially closed its doors due, in part, to the changing tide of the industry in which fewer women sew and products from countries such as China are so cheap.

41413 ■ "Albany Molecular on Hiring Spree as Big Pharma Slashes Work Force" in *Business Review, Albany New York* **(December 28, 2007)**
Pub: American City Business Journals, Inc.
Ed: Barbara Pinckney. **Description:** Albany Molecular Research Inc. (AMRI) is an outsourcing company that provides work forces for pharmaceutical companies due to large numbers of downsizings in the year 2007. In 2008, AMRI plans to hire several workers.

41414 ■ "Auxis Introduces Services for Government Contracting" in *Entertainment Close-Up* **(December 22, 2010)**
Pub: Close-Up Media
Description: Profile of Auxis Inc., a management consulting and outsourcing company has launched a new service for companies involved in or bidding for government contracts. Details of the program are provided.

41415 ■ "Beaumont Outsources Purchasing as Route to Supply Cost Savings" in *Crain's Detroit Business* **(Vol. 25, June 1, 2009, No. 22)**
Pub: Crain Communications Inc. - Detroit
Ed: Jay Greene. **Description:** William Beaumont Hospitals in Royal Oak have begun outsourcing the purchasing of supplies in order to cut costs. So far,

Beaumont is the only hospital in southeast Michigan to outsource its purchasing department. Other hospitals employ their own purchasing supply workers.

41416 ■ "A Change Would Do You Good" in *Canadian Business* **(Vol. 80, November 19, 2007, No. 23, pp. 15)**
Pub: Rogers Media
Ed: Geoff Kirbyson. **Description:** Western Glove Works will be manufacturing clothing offshore, including Sheryl Crow's jeans collection, in countries such as China and the Philippines. The company decided to operate offshore after 86 years of existence due to the high price of manufacturing jeans in Canada. Western Glove's focus on producing celebrity-endorsed goods is discussed.

41417 ■ "ChemSW Software Development Services Available for Outsourcing" in *Information Today* **(Vol. 26, February 2009, No. 2, pp. 30)**
Pub: Information Today, Inc.
Description: ChemSW software development services include requirements analysis, specification development, design, development, testing, and system documentation as an IT outsourcing solution. The company can also develop software tracking systems for satellite stockrooms, provide asset management integration solutions and more.

41418 ■ "The China Syndrome" in *Canadian Business* **(Vol. 79, July 17, 2006, No. 14-15, pp. 25)**
Pub: Rogers Media
Ed: Peter Diekmeyer. **Description:** Contrasting pace of growth in China and India are presented. Reasons for the slow pace of growth of Canadian companies like CAE Inc. and Magna in India are also discussed.

41419 ■ "Closed Minds and Open Skies" in *Barron's* **(Vol. 88, March 10, 2008, No. 10, pp. 50)**
Pub: Dow Jones & Company, Inc.
Ed: Thomas Donlan. **Description:** American politicians have closed minds when it comes to fair trade. The American government must not interfere with the country's manufacturing industries or worry about outsourcing defense contracts to European aerospace company Airbus.

41420 ■ "Contract Design as a Firm Capability" in *Academy of Management Review* **(October 2007, pp. 1060)**
Pub: ScholarOne, Inc.
Ed: Nicholas Argyres, Kyle J. Mayer. **Description:** A firm's capabilities for designing detailed contracts and the role of managers, engineers, and lawyers in the design of such contracts is highlighted.

41421 ■ "Debt-Collection Agency to Lay Off 368 in Hampton Center" in *Virginian-Pilot* **(December 4, 2010)**
Pub: Virginian-Pilot
Ed: Tom Shean. **Description:** NCO Financial Systems Inc., provider of debt-collection and outsourcing services will permanently lay off 368 workers at its Hampton call center in 2011.

41422 ■ "Designing Events Updates Online Suite" in *Wireless News* **(October 25, 2009)**
Pub: Close-Up Media
Description: Designing Events, an outsourcing and consulting firm for conferences and meetings, announced the release of an update to its Designing Events Online suite of web-based management and marketing tools; features include enhanced versions of online registration and collaboration, content management, session development, social media and conference websites.

41423 ■ "Don't Try This Offshore" in *Harvard Business Review* **(Vol. 86, September 2008, No. 9, pp. 39)**
Pub: Harvard Business School Press
Ed: Description: Fictitious outsourcing scenario is presented, with contributors offering advice. The suggestions address the ease or complexity of offshoring business creativity, along with challenges and benefits.

41424 ■ "Fifth Third Grapples With Account Snafu" in *Business Courier* **(Vol. 24, December 7, 2008, No. 34, pp. 1)**
Pub: American City Business Journals, Inc.
Ed: Jon Newberry. **Description:** Fifth Third Bank's vendor committed an error which led to a badly damaged credit score for Brett and Karen Reloka. The couple reported the incident to the bank and are still waiting for action to be taken. A major outourced services vendor caused paid-off mortgages to be reported delinquent.

41425 ■ "Five Steps for Handling Independent Contractors" in *Hawaii Business* **(Vol. 53, January 2008, No. 7, pp. 49)**
Pub: Hawaii Business Publishing
Ed: Jason Ubay. **Description:** Small companies should be cautious in dealing with independent contractors. They must understand that they cannot dictate specific operational procedures, job duties, standards of conduct and performance standards to the contractors, and they cannot interfere with the evaluation and training of the contractors' employees. Tips on negotiating with independent contractors are given.

41426 ■ "The Future of Work" in *Black Enterprise* **(Vol. 41, August 2010, No. 1, pp. 65)**
Pub: Earl G. Graves Publishing Co. Inc.
Ed: Annya M. Lott. **Description:** Technology, globalization, and outsourcing will continue to shape the future of work. Social media is a means for small companies to market goods and services.

41427 ■ "Hire Power" in *Entrepreneur* **(Vol. 35, November 2007, No. 11, pp. 105)**
Pub: Entrepreneur Media Inc.
Ed: Mark Henricks. **Description:** Companies with big resources may hire human resource (HR) consultants to help with writing manuals, drafting policies and designing benefits for employees. HR consultants may also be hired to assist with specific functions or other strategic aspects.

41428 ■ *How to Start a Bankruptcy Forms Processing Service*
Pub: Graphico Publishing Company
Ed: Victoria Ring. **Released:** September 2004. **Price:** $39.00. **Description:** Due to the increase in bankruptcy filings, attorneys are outsourcing related jobs in order to reduce overhead.

41429 ■ "Importers Share Safety Liability" in *Feedstuffs* (Vol. 80, January 21, 2008, No. 3, pp. 19)
Pub: Miller Publishing Company, Inc.
Description: Pet food and toys containing lead paint are among products from China being recalled due to safety concerns. American Society for Quality's list of measures that outsourcing companies can take to help ensure safer products being imported to the U.S.

41430 ■ "Intel Forges New Strategy With Chinese Fabrication Plant" in *Globe & Mail* (March 26, 2007, pp. B6)
Pub: CTVglobemedia Publishing Inc.
Ed: Don Clark. **Description:** World's largest semiconductor manufacturing giant Intel Corp. is planning to construct a new chip fabrication plant in China. It will be investing an estimated $2.5 billion for this purpose.

41431 ■ "It's Time To Swim" in *Canadian Business* (Vol. 81, March 3, 2008, No. 3, pp. 37)
Pub: Rogers Media
Ed: Megan Harman. **Description:** Canadian manufacturers should consider Asian markets such as India and the United Arab Emirates as the U.S. economic downturn continues. Canada's shortage in skilled labor is also expected to negatively affect manufacturing industries. Ontario's plans to assist manufacturers are also presented.

41432 ■ "Knox County Schools Debate Outsourcing Janitorial Services" in (March 29, 2011)
Pub: Knoxville News Sentinel
Ed: Lola Alapo. **Description:** Custodial services of Knox County Schools in Tennessee may be outsourced in move to save money for the school district. Details of the proposed program are included.

41433 ■ "Local Manufacturers See Tax Proposal Hurting Global Operations" in *Crain's Cleveland Business* (Vol. 30, May 18, 2009, No. 20)
Pub: Crain Communications, Inc.
Ed: Dan Shingler. **Description:** New tax laws proposed by the Obama Administration could hinder the efforts of some Northeast Ohio industrial companies from expanding their overseas markets. The law is designed to prevent companies from moving jobs overseas.

41434 ■ "Lufthansa-Cathay Deal Reinforces Outsourcing" in *Globe & Mail* (March 30, 2007, pp. B9)
Pub: CTVglobemedia Publishing Inc.
Ed: Daniel Michaels. **Description:** Cathay Pacific Airways Ltd. signed a $300 million contract with Lufthansa Technik AG to outsource engine maintenance operations. The outsourcing of non-core operation is increasing in airline industry.

41435 ■ "May I Handle That For You?" in *Inc.* (March 2008, pp. 40, 42)
Pub: Gruner & Jahr USA Publishing
Ed: Taylor Mallory. **Description:** According to a recent survey, 53 percent of all companies outsource a portion of their human resources responsibilities. Ceridian, Administaff, Taleo, KnowledgeBank, and CheckPoint HR are among the companies profiled.

41436 ■ "Meet Rebecca. She's Here to Fire You" in *Inc.* (November 2007, pp. 25-26)
Pub: Gruner & Jahr USA Publishing
Ed: Max Chafkin. **Description:** Amid liability concerns as well as CEO guilt, more and more firms are using consulting companies to fire workers. These outsourced firms help small companies structure severance and document information in order to limit legal liability when firing an employee.

41437 ■ "New Work Order" in *Black Enterprise* (Vol. 38, March 2008, No. 8, pp. 60)
Pub: Earl G. Graves Publishing Co. Inc.
Description: Today's management challenges includes issues of more competition, globalization, outsourcing and technological advances. Suggestions to help create progressive leadership in small business that sustains a competitive edge are listed.

41438 ■ "Nobel Winners Provide Insight on Outsourcing, Contract Work" in *Workforce Management* (Vol. 88, November 16, 2009, No. 12, pp. 11)
Pub: Crain Communications, Inc.
Ed: Jeremy Smerd. **Description:** Insights into such workforce management issues as bonuses, employee contracts and outsourcing has been recognized by the Nobel Prize winners in economics whose research sheds a light on the way economic decisions are made outside markets.

41439 ■ *Outsourcing: Information Technology, Original Equipment Manufacturer, Leo, Oursourcing, Offshoring Research Network, Crowdsourcing*
Pub: General Books LLC
Released: May 1, 2010. **Price:** $14.14. **Description:** Chapters include information for outsourcing firms and how to maintain an outsourcing business.

41440 ■ "Overseas Overtures" in *Business Journal-Portland* (Vol. 24, October 26, 2007, No. 35, pp. 1)
Pub: American City Business Journals, Inc.
Ed: Robin J. Moody. **Description:** Oregon has a workforce shortage, specifically for the health care industry. Recruiting agencies, such as the International Recruiting Network Inc., answers the high demand for workforce by recruiting foreign employees. The difficulties recruiting companies experience with regards to foreign labor laws are investigated.

41441 ■ "Patently (Un)Clear" in *Business Strategy Review* (Vol. 21, Spring 2010, No. 1, pp. 28)
Pub: Wiley-Blackwell
Ed: Markus Reitzig, Stefan Wagner. **Description:** After developing a great product or process, it's important to protect it. The benefits of using internal patent lawyers versus outsourcing the task are examined.

41442 ■ "Prevent Disasters In Design Outsourcing" in *Harvard Business Review* (Vol. 86, September 2008, No. 9, pp. 30)
Pub: Harvard Business School Press
Ed: Jason Amaral; Geoffrey Parker. **Description:** Factors that could compromise the quality and success of product platform outsourcing are examined including misaligned objectives and inadequate version control.

41443 ■ "Rep Vs. Direct: Always an Interesting Story" in *Agency Sales Magazine* (Vol. 39, July 2009, No. 7, pp. 3)
Pub: MANA
Ed: Bryan C. Shirley. **Description:** Manufacturers benefit from outsourcing their field sales to professional sales representatives in the areas of multi-line selling and customer knowledge and relationship. Some misperceptions about sales reps include the belief that they are an additional 'channel' in sales.

41444 ■ "Research: Mind the Gap" in *Business Strategy Review* (Vol. 21, Summer 2010, No. 2, pp. 84)
Pub: Wiley-Blackwell
Description: Isabel Fernandez-Mateo's cumulative gender disadvantage in contract employment is presented.

41445 ■ "Stung by Recession, Hemmer Regroups with New Strategy" in *Business Courier* (Vol. 27, June 4, 2010, No. 5, pp. 1)
Pub: Business Courier
Ed: Lucy May. **Description:** Paul Hemmer Companies reduced its work force and outsourced operations such as marketing and architecture, in order for the commercial and construction firm to survive the recession. Hammer's total core revenue in 2009 dropped to less than $30 million forcing the closure of its Chicago office.

41446 ■ "Tata's Novi Unit Looks to Hire 200 Engineers" in *Crain's Detroit Business* (Vol. 26, January 18, 2010, No. 3, pp. 4)
Pub: Crain Communications, Inc.
Ed: Lindsay Chappell. **Description:** Indian conglomerate Tata Sons Ltd.'s Novi-based engineering subsidiary is expected to hire around 200 engineers in the next three months or so, in part due to a more sophisticated attitude about outsourcing vehicle engineering to other companies.

41447 ■ "To Offshore Or Not To Offshore?" in *Converting* (Vol. 25, October 1, 2007, No. 10, pp. 10)
Pub: Reed Business Information Inc.
Ed: Mark Spaulding. **Description:** Offshore manufacturing and the issue of buying raw materials from foreign suppliers by American companies is discussed. Results of a study conducted by Cap Gemini and Pro Logis regarding offshore manufacturing, especially to China, are presented.

41448 ■ "Two Local Firms Make Inc. List: Minority Business" in *Indianapolis Business Journal* (Vol. 31, August 30, 2010, No. 26, pp. 13A)
Pub: Indianapolis Business Journal Corporation
Description: Smart IT staffing agency and Entap Inc., an IT outsourcing firm were among the top ten fastest growing black-owned businesses in the U.S. by Inc. magazine.

41449 ■ "Uncovering Offshoring's Invisible Costs" in *HRMagazine* (Vol. 54, January 2009, No. 1, pp. 1)
Pub: Society for Human Resource Management
Ed: Rita Zeidner. **Description:** Nearly half of all offshore service work fails, often due to the invisible costs of communication and cultural friction according to researchers. The challenges of offshore services are discussed.

CONSULTANTS

41450 ■ C. Clint Bolte & Associates
809 Philadelphia Ave.
Chambersburg, PA 17201-1268
Ph:(717)263-5768
Fax:(717)263-8954
Co. E-mail: clint@clintbolte.com
URL: http://www.clintbolte.com
Contact: C. Clint Bolte, Principle
E-mail: cbolte3@comcast.net
Scope: Provides management consulting services to firms involved with the printing industry. Services include outsourcing studies, graphics supply chain management studies, company and equipment valuations, plant layout services, litigation support, fulfillment warehouse consulting and product development services. **Publications:** "UV Cost Savings Environmental Advantage"; "Possible Quebecor World Fall Out"; "80-20 Rule for Managing"; "Options Available in Starting Up a Mailing Operation"; "High Volume Print Buyers at Print 2009"; "Diversifying With Mailing & Fulfillment Services"; "New Business Model Needed for Magazine News stand Distribution"; "Purchasing Incentives Can Be Costly.."; "In-Plant New Product Opportunity for 2009: Tran promo Printing"; "Possible Quebecor World Fall Out"; "Offshore Print Evolution"; "Benefits of Third Party Lease Review"; "Unique Information Fulfillment Opportunities for In-Plant Printers"; "Tough Competition Forces New Strategic Realities for In-Plants"; "Direct Mail Industry Group Files Interpretive Ruling Requests with the Ssta"; "Interesting Opportunities Amid the Gray Clouds of 2007 Postal Rate Increases"; "Time to Break Through the Glass Ceiling," the Seybold Report, May, 2006; "Challenges and Opportunities Presented By Postal Rate Increases," the Seybold Report, May, 2006; "Packaging Roll Sheeting Comes of Age," the Seybold Report, May, 2006; "Diversifying with Mailing and Fulfillment Services," the Seybold Report, Jan, 2006. **Seminars:** How to compete with the majors.

FRANCHISES AND BUSINESS OPPORTUNITIES

41451 ■ Oxford Business Consulting Group, LLC
19 Beech Pl.
Huntington, NY 11743
Ph:(631)423-8570
Fax:(631)423-8580
Founded: 2000. **Description:** Outsourced franchise sales & development.

START-UP INFORMATION

41452 ■ *101 Businesses You Can Start with Less Than One Thousand Dollars: for Retirees*

Pub: Atlantic Publishing Company

Ed: Heather Lee Shepherd. **Released:** October 2007. **Price:** $21.95. **Description:** According to a study by the U.S. Department of Health and Human Resources, people starting their work careers will face the following situation when they retire at the age of 65: they will have annual incomes between $4,000 and $26,000. According to the Social Security Administration, today's retirees can count on corporate pensions and Social Security for 61 percent of their retirement income. The remainder must come from other sources. Therefore, if this holds true for the future, today's workers need to accumulate enough in personal savings to make up the 39 percent shortfall in retirement income. The solution for many will be to start a small part-time business.

ASSOCIATIONS AND OTHER ORGANIZATIONS

41453 ■ National Association of Part-Time and Temporary Employees
5800 Barton, Ste. 201
PO Box 3805
Shawnee, KS 66203
Ph:(913)962-7740
Co. E-mail: napte-champion@worldnet.att.net
URL: http://www.members.tripod.com/IAtnapte
Contact: Preston L. Conner, Pres.
Purpose: Promotes the economic and social interests of persons working on a part-time, contingent, or temporary basis through research, advocacy, and member services. Offers short-term portable health insurance. .

RESEARCH CENTERS

41454 ■ New Ways to Work
103 Morris St., Ste. A
Sebastopol, CA 95472
Ph:(707)824-4000
Fax:(707)824-4410
Co. E-mail: sgtrippe@newwaystowork.org
URL: http://www.nww.org
Contact: Steve Trippe, Pres./Exec.Dir.
E-mail: sgtrippe@newwaystowork.org
Scope: Flexible scheduling and staffing arrangements, including job sharing, flexible hours, telecommuting, extended leaves, and part-time temps and contract workers. Research on these issues focuses on youths, contingent workers, the legal profession, and other particular groups. **Publications:** Work Times (quarterly). **Educational Activities:** Programs, to educate employers and employees in work time options and policy issues; Workshops, to educate employers and employees in work time options and policy issues.

START-UP INFORMATION

41455 ■ *The Mousedriver Chronicles*
Pub: Perseus Books Group
Ed: John Lusk; Kyle Harrison. **Released:** 2003.
Price: $16.95. **Description:** Entrepreneurial voyage through the startup business of two ivy-league business school graduates and the lessons they learned while developing their idea of a computer mouse that looks like a golf driver into the marketplace. The book is an inspiration for those looking to turn an idea into a company.

41456 ■ *Partnership: Small Business Start-Up Kit*
Pub: Nova Publishing Company
Ed: Daniel Sitarz. **Released:** November 2005. **Price:** $29.95. **Description:** Guidebook detailing partnership law by state covering the formation and use of partnerships as a business form. Information on filing requirements, property laws, legal liability, standards, and the new Revised Uniform Partnership Act is covered.

41457 ■ *Structuring Your Business*
Pub: Adams Media Corporation
Ed: Michele Cagan. **Released:** 2004. **Price:** $19.95. **Description:** Accountant and author shares insight into starting a new company. The guide assists entrepreneurs through the process, whether it is a corporation, an LLC, a sole proprietorship, or a partnership. Tax codes, accounting practices and legislation affecting every business as well as tips on managing finances are among the topics covered.

41458 ■ *The Toilet Paper Entrepreneur: The Tell-It-Like-It-Is Guide to Cleaning Up In Business, Even If You Are At the End of Your Roll*
Pub: Obsidian Launch LLC
Ed: Mike Michalowicz. **Price:** $24.95. **Description:** The founder of three multimillion-dollar companies, including Obsidian Launch, a company that partners with first-time entrepreneurs to grow their concepts into industry leaders.

EDUCATIONAL PROGRAMS

41459 ■ AMA's Course on Mergers and Acquisitions
American Management Association
600 AMA Way
Saranac Lake, NY 12983-5534
Ph:(212)586-8100
Free: 877-566-9441
Fax:(518)891-0368
Co. E-mail: customerservice@amanet.org
URL: http://www.amaseminars.org
Price: $4,395.00 for non-members; $3,995.00 for AMA members; and $3,421.00 for General Services Administration (GSA) members. **Description:** Three-day seminar for executive managers; covers organizational, financial, planning, tax, and risk aspects of

mergers and acquisitions. **Locations:** Hilton Head Island, SC; Las Vegas, NV; La Jolla, CA; and San Francisco, CA.

REFERENCE WORKS

41460 ■ "3Par: Storing Up Value" in *Barron's* (Vol. 90, August 30, 2010, No. 35, pp. 30)
Pub: Barron's Editorial & Corporate Headquarters
Ed: Mark Veverka. **Description:** Dell and Hewlett Packard are both bidding for data storage company 3Par. The acquisition would help Dell and Hewlett Packard provide customers with a one-stop shop as customers move to a private cloud in the Internet.

41461 ■ "13D Filings" in *Barron's* (Vol. 88, March 10, 2008, No. 10, pp. M11)
Pub: Dow Jones & Company, Inc.
Description: Barington Capital and Clinton Group sent a letter to Dillard's demanding a list of the company's stockholders. Elliott Associates announced that it is prepared to take over Packeteer for $5.50 a share. Strongbow capital suggested a change in leadership in Duckwall-ALCO Stores.

41462 ■ "13D Filings: Investors Report to the SEC" in *Barron's* (Vol. 88, March 31, 2008, No. 13, pp. M10)
Pub: Dow Jones & Company, Inc.
Description: Obrem Capital Management wants Micrel to rescind Micrel's shareholder-rights plan and to boost its board to six members from five. Patricia L. Childress plans to nominate herself to the board of Sierra Bancorp, and Luther King Capital Management may consider a competing acquisition proposal for Industrial Distribution Group.

41463 ■ "$40M Fund Created for Big Energy Project" in *Austin Business JournalInc.* (Vol. 29, November 27, 2009, No. 38, pp. 1)
Pub: American City Business Journals
Ed: Christopher Calnan. **Description:** A group of Texas businessmen, called Republic Power Partners LP, is planning to raise $40 million in order to launch an alternative energy project. The 6,000-megawatt initiative would generate solar, biomass and wind power in West Texas and could cost as much as $10 billion.

41464 ■ "2008: Year of the Rat Race" in *Mergers & Acquisitions: The Dealmaker's Journal* (March 1, 2008)
Pub: SourceMedia, Inc.
Ed: Danelle Fugazy. **Description:** Although China still presents opportunities to Western investors, many are discovering that much more research needs to be done concerning doing business in that country before investing there becomes truly mainstream. According to one source, there are at least 300,000 small state-owned enterprises in China and millions of middle-market privately owned companies; the Chinese stock market can only handle about 50 to 70 IPOs a year and lists about 1,500 companies at a time.

41465 ■ "A Dog-Day Pooch" in *Canadian Business* (Vol. 79, September 11, 2006, No. 18, pp. 19)
Pub: Rogers Media
Ed: Andrew Wahl. **Description:** Acquisition deal of Hummingbird Ltd by Canadian software maker Open Text Corp., is discussed.

41466 ■ "A&E Networks" in *Brandweek* (Vol. 49, April 21, 2008, No. 16, pp. SR9)
Pub: VNU Business Media, Inc.
Ed: Anthony Crupi. **Description:** Provides contact information for sales and marketing personnel for the A&E Networks as well as a listing of the station's top programming and an analysis of the current season and the target audience for those programs running in the current season. A&E has reinvented itself as a premium entertainment brand over the last five years and with its $2.5 million per episode acquisition of The Sopranos, the station signaled that it was seriously about getting back into the scripted programming business. The acquisition also helped the network compete against other cable networks and led to a 20 percent increase in prime-time viewers.

41467 ■ "Abacast, Citadel Strike Radio Ad Deal" in *Business Journal Portland* (Vol. 27, December 31, 2010, No. 44, pp. 3)
Pub: Portland Business Journal
Ed: Erik Siemers. **Description:** Software firm Abacast Inc. has partnered with Citadel Media to aid the latter's advertising sales. Citadel provides radio networks and syndicated programs to 4,200 affiliate stations.

41468 ■ "Abaddon Acquires Pukaskwa Uranium Properties in NW Ontario" in *Canadian Corporate News* (May 16, 2007)
Pub: Comtex News Network Inc.
Ed: Description: Rubicon Minerals Corp. has entered into an Option Agreement with Consolidated Abaddon Resources Inc. for the acquisition of Pukaskwa uranium properties and plans to conduct an extensive exploration program to prove out the resource and geological potential of the area. Statistical data included.

41469 ■ "Achieve Tampa Bay Thrown a Lifeline in Proposed Merger" in *Tampa Bay Business Journal* (Vol. 30, January 22, 2010, No. 5, pp. 1)
Pub: American City Business Journals
Ed: Margie Manning. **Description:** Mental Health Care Inc. proposed a merger with Achieve Tampa Bay Inc. The former proposes to administer the latter's operations and take over its assets while paying its debts.

41470 ■ "Acquisition of a Uranium Exploration Project, Laguiche Basin, Opinaca Area, Quebec" in *Canadian Corporate News* (May 16, 2007)
Pub: Comtex News Network Inc.
Description: Dios Exploration Inc. negotiated an option agreement with Sirios Resources Inc. to explore the Opinaca Nord Property with a project that

comprises one main anomaly cluster for gold in association with arsenic and two detailed uranium anomaly clusters.

41471 ■ "AdvacePierre Heats Up" in
Business Courier (Vol. 27, October 29, 2010,
No. 26, pp. 1)
Pub: Business Courier
Ed: John Newberry. Description: Bill Toler, chief executive officer of AdvancePierre Foods, is aiming for more growth and more jobs. The company was formed after the merger of Pierre Foods with two Oklahoma-based food processing companies. Toler wants to expand production and is set to start adding employees in the next 6-12 months.

41472 ■ "Advertising May Take a Big Hit in
Southwest/AirTran Merger" in Baltimore
Business Journal (Vol. 28, October 1, 2010,
No. 21, pp. 1)
Pub: Baltimore Business Journal
Ed: Gary Haber. Description: Advertising on television stations and the publishing industry in Baltimore could drop as a result of the merger between rival discount airlines Southwest Airlines and AirTran Airways. Southwest is among the top advertisers in the U.S., spending $126 million in 2009. No local jobs are expected to be affected because neither airline uses a local advertising firm.

41473 ■ "Affordable Financing for
Acquisitions" in Franchising World (Vol. 42,
September 2010, No. 9, pp. 47)
Pub: International Franchise Association
Ed: Gene Cerrotti. Description: Acquisition pricing is reasonable and interest rates are low and quality franchised resale opportunities are priced 4.5 times EBITDA. Information about Small Business Administration loans is also included.

41474 ■ "Age-Old System of Bartering Is
Being Revolutionized by Phoenix Company,
Premier Barter" in Internet Wire (July 12,
2010)
Pub: Comtex
Description: Premier Barter is helping entrepreneurs rediscover the system of bartering as a method of exchanging goods and services without cash or credit.

41475 ■ "Aggenix Completes Merger with
German Giant" in Houston Business Journal
(Vol. 40, December 25, 2009, No. 33, pp. 2)
Pub: American City Business Journals
Ed: Mary Ann Azevedo. Description: Agennix Inc. has completed its transformation into a German company after Germany-based GPC Biotech merged into the former publicly traded Agennix AG. One quarter of Agennix's 60 employees will remain in Houston. Details on Agennix's drug trials are examined.

41476 ■ "AIC To Buy $350M of Real Estate"
in Austin Business JournalInc. (Vol. 28,
November 14, 2008, No. 35, pp. 1)
Pub: American City Business Journals
Ed: Kate Harrington. Description: Austin-based AIC Ventures LP is planning to buy $350 million worth of commercial real estate. The company's move will double its acquisitions. It is also planning to acquire 30 assets for its eight fun in 2009 from middle-market companies.

41477 ■ "Airline Mergers: United Next?" in
Crain's Chicago Business (Vol. 31, April 21,
2008, No. 16, pp. 12)
Pub: Crain Communications, Inc.
Description: Discusses a potential merger between United and Continental airlines; unions representing 48,900 pilots, mechanics, flight attendants, ticket agents and ramp workers at United have put the management on notice that they expect to be a factor in any merger discussions if the company wants their cooperation.

41478 ■ "Airlines Mount PR Push to Win
Public Support Against Big Oil" in
Advertising Age (Vol. 79, July 14, 2008, No. 7,
pp. 1)
Pub: Crain Communications, Inc.
Ed: Michael Bush. Description: Top airline executives from competing companies have banded together in a public relations plan in which they are sending e-mails to their frequent fliers asking for aid in lobbying legislators to put a restriction on oil speculation.

41479 ■ "Akerman Senterfitt Merger Deal
Close" in The Business Journal-Serving
Greater Tampa Bay (Vol. 28, July 18, 2008,
No. 30, pp. 1)
Pub: American City Business Journals, Inc.
Ed: Jeff Blumenthal. Description: Sources familiar to the negotiations of Akerman Senterfitt's planned merger with Wolf Block has disclosed that executive committees of both firms have approved the deal. They expect to create an 800-lawyer firm with a significant presence in the U.S. East Coast. Other views and information on the deal and its expected impact on law practice in Florida are presented.

41480 ■ "All About The Benjamins" in
Canadian Business (Vol. 81, September 29,
2008, No. 16, pp. 92)
Pub: Rogers Media Ltd.
Ed: David Baines. Description: Discusses real estate developer Royal Indian Raj International Corp., a company that planned to build a $3 billion "smart city" near the Bangalore airport; to this day nothing has ever been built. The company was incorporated in 1999 by Manoj C. Benjamin one investor, Bill Zack, has been sued by the developer for libel due to his website that calls the company a scam. Benjamin has had a previous case of fraud issued against him as well as a string of liabilities and lawsuits.

41481 ■ "All For One, None for All?" in
Canadian Business (Vol. 83, October 12,
2010, No. 17, pp. 60)
Pub: Rogers Media Ltd.
Ed: Michael McCullogh. Description: The effect of the growth of Canada's overseas provincial trade offices on Canadian trade is discussed. Economic development commissions in the country have devised a single 'Consider Canada' campaign to pitch foreign investors. It is hoped that large cities will gain from banding together rather than competing against one another.

41482 ■ "Altegrity Acquires John D. Cohen,
Inc." in (November 19, 2009, pp. 14)
Pub: Investment Weekly News
Description: John D. Cohen, Inc., a contract provider of national security policy guidance and counsel to the federal government, was acquired by Altegrity, Inc., a global screening and security solutions provider; the company will become part of US Investigations Services, LLC and operate under the auspices of Altegrity's new business, Altegrity Security Consulting.

41483 ■ "Aluminium maker Novelis Soars on
Indian Takeover Talk" in Globe & Mail
(January 27, 2007, pp. B5)
Pub: CTVglobemedia Publishing Inc.
Ed: Andy Hoffman. Description: The plans of India-based Kumar Mangalam Birla's Aditya Birla Group to bid for Atlanta-based rolled aluminium maker Novelis Inc. are discussed. The talks about the purchase have caused a rise in Novelis's share price.

41484 ■ "Amcon Distributing Co." in
Arkansas Business (Vol. 26, November 9,
2009, No. 45, pp. 13)
Pub: Journal Publishing Inc.
Description: Amcon Distributing Co., a consumer products company, has bought the convenience store distribution assets of Discount Distributors from its parent, Harps Food Stores Inc., significantly increasing its wholesale distribution presence in the northwest Arkansas market. The acquisition will be funded through Amcon's existing credit facilities.

41485 ■ "Analysts: More Mergers for the
Region's Hospitals" in Boston Business
Journal (Vol. 30, October 15, 2010, No. 36, pp.
1)
Pub: Boston Business Journal
Ed: Julie M. Donnelly. Description: A number of hospitals in Boston, Massachusetts are engaging in mergers and acquisitions. Caritas Christi Health Care is set to be purchased by Cerberus Capital Management. The U.S. healthcare reform law is seen to drive the development.

41486 ■ "And In This Briefcase" in Mergers
& Acquisitions: The Dealmaker's Journal
(March 1, 2008)
Pub: SourceMedia, Inc.
Description: ACG San Diego decided to address the impact the changes in the economy will have on potential private equity transactions as well as what criteria private equity firms are looking for when assessing a company. At the opening of the chapter's 2008 breakfast meeting, real-world case studies were utilized with the audiences' participation in order to assess pre-deal risk scenarios.

41487 ■ "Angel Investors Across State
Collaborate" in Austin Business Journal (Vol.
31, May 20, 2011, No. 11, pp. 1)
Pub: American City Business Journals Inc.
Ed: Christopher Calnan. Description: Texas' twelve angel investing groups are going to launch the umbrella organization Alliance of Texas Angel Networks (ATAN) to support more syndicated deals and boost investments in Texas. In 2010, these investing groups infused more than $24 million to startups in 61 deals.

41488 ■ "Angiotech to Buy Top Medical
Devices Company" in Globe & Mail (February
1, 2006, pp. B1)
Pub: CTVglobemedia Publishing Inc.
Ed: Leonard Zehr. Description: The details on Angiotech Pharmaceuticals Inc.'s acquisition of American Medical Instruments Holdings Inc. are presented.

41489 ■ "Arcelor Bid Wins Dofasco Board's
Blessing" in Globe & Mail (January 17, 2006,
pp. B1)
Pub: CTVglobemedia Publishing Inc.
Ed: Greg Keenan. Description: The details surrounding Arcelor SA's proposed acquisition of Dofasco Inc., for $5.5 billion, are presented.

41490 ■ "Area Small Businesses Enjoy
Benefits of Bartering Group" in News-Herald
(August 22, 2010)
Pub: The News-Herald
Ed: Brandon C. Baker. Description: ITEX is a publicly traded firm that spurs cashless, business-to-business transactions within its own marketplace. Details of the bartering of goods and services within the company are outlined.

41491 ■ "Around the World" in Entrepreneur
(Vol. 36, March 2008, No. 3, pp. 82)
Pub: Entrepreneur Media Inc.
Ed: Gail Dutton. Description: Joining a global consortium can improve a business greater access to services and expertise from other members around the world. The goal is to develop the company to be able to reach to a wider customer base; other details on the benefits of joining a consortium are discussed.

41492 ■ "As Capital Gains Tax Hike Looms,
Merger Activity Percolates" in Baltimore
Business Journal (Vol. 28, August 27, 2010,
No. 16, pp. 1)
Pub: Baltimore Business Journal
Ed: Scott Dance. Description: Concerns for higher capital gains taxes in 2011 have been provoking buyers and sellers to engage in mergers and acquisitions activity, which is expected to gain momentum before the end of 2010. Companies that had saved cash during the recession have been taking advantage of the buyer's market. Other trends in local and national mergers and acquisitions activity are presented.

41493 ■ "'The Asian Decade'" in Hawaii
Business (Vol. 53, January 2008, No. 7, pp.
19)
Pub: Hawaii Business Publishing
Ed: Cathy S. Cruz-George. Description: Chaney Brooks, a Hawaiian real estate company, has affiliated with commercial real estate network NAI Global. The NAI partnership will improve Hawaii's interna-

tional business, particularly its Asian investments. Hawaii's diverse workforce is evaluated, with regards to being an asset for international businesses.

41494 ■ "Astral Fine-Tunes Details of Standard Purchase" in *Globe & Mail* **(February 26, 2007, pp. B1)**
Pub: CTVglobemedia Publishing Inc.

Ed: Grant Robertson. **Description:** The proposed acquisition of Standard Radio Inc. by Astral Media Inc. for $1.2 billion is discussed.

41495 ■ "Astral Media Set to Broadcast Coast to Coast" in *Globe & Mail* **(February 24, 2007, pp. B5)**
Pub: CTVglobemedia Publishing Inc.

Ed: Grant Robertson. **Description:** The decision of Astral Media Inc. to acquire Standard Broadcasting Corp. Ltd. for $1.2 billion, with a view to increase its broadcast coverage, is discussed.

41496 ■ "ASU Explores Russian Partnership" in *The Business Journal - Serving Phoenix and the Valley of the Sun* **(Vol. 28, September 5, 2008)**
Pub: American City Business Journals, Inc.

Ed: Mike Sunnucks. **Description:** Arizona State University is planning to partner with Russia-based St. Petersburg State University (SPSU) regarding research, faculty and student exchange, and other joint efforts. SPSU is one of Russia's leading scientific and research institutions. Arizona State's partnerships with other foreign colleges are also mentioned.

41497 ■ "At 5-Year Mark, News 9 Makes Presence Felt in Competition for Ad Dollars" in *Business Review, Albany New York* **(October 5, 2007)**
Pub: American City Business Journals, Inc.

Ed: Barbara Pinckney. **Description:** The 24-hour news channel Capital News 9 can be watched live by viewers on their cell phones beginning late 2007 or early 2008 as part of a deal between Time Warner Cable and Sprint Nextel Corporation to bring Sprint's Pivot technology. News 9 marked its fifth year and plans to continue expanding coverage and provide better services to viewers.

41498 ■ "AT&T To Acquire Black Telecom Firm" in *Black Enterprise* **(Vol. 38, January 2008, No. 6, pp. 24)**
Pub: Earl G. Graves Publishing Co. Inc.

Ed: Alan Hughes. **Description:** Details of AT&T's acquisition of ChaseCom LP, a telecommunications company based in Houston, Texas, are covered.

41499 ■ "Atlific Adds Management of 4 Hotels to Its Portfolio in Fort McMurray" in *Canadian Corporate News* **(May 16, 2007)**
Pub: Comtex News Network Inc.

Description: Atlific Hotels & Resorts took over management for Merit Inn & Suites, The Merit Hotel, The Nomad Hotel and The Nomad Suites in Fort Mc-Murray. The company feels that they will be able to increase the hotels' abilities to promote their services through their vast network of sales personnel and marketing and e-commerce team.

41500 ■ "Attorney Guides Biotech Company in $6 Million Initial Public Offering" in *Miami Daily Business Review* **(March 26, 2008)**
Pub: ALM Media Inc.

Description: In order to raise capital to engage in a full-scale trial of MyoCell to receive clinical approval, Bioheart Inc., launched an initial public offering. Bioheart researches and develops cell therapies to treat heart damage.

41501 ■ "Aussie Rules" in *Canadian Business* **(Vol. 79, Winter 2006, No. 24, pp. 45)**
Pub: Rogers Media

Ed: Jeff Sanford. **Description:** The efforts of the Toronto-based private equity firm Onex, to acquire the Australian national airline, Qantas Airways Ltd., are described.

41502 ■ "Australian Firm Buys Off Sands Engineering Company for $1 Billion" in *Globe & Mail* **(February 8, 2007, pp. B3)**
Pub: CTVglobemedia Publishing Inc.

Ed: David Ebner. **Description:** Australia's Worley-Parson Ltd. acquires Colt Engineering Corp., a private petroleum company, for $1 billion. The acquisition will provide WorleyParson an opportunity to expand its operations in Australia.

41503 ■ "Auto Show Taps Moms" in *Marketing to Women* **(Vol. 21, April 2008, No. 4, pp. 3)**
Pub: EPM Communications, Inc.

Description: Teamed with Mother Proof, an online site which features automotive content aimed at moms, the Chicago Auto Show will present a full day of programming with the emphasis on mom.

41504 ■ "AV Concept Expands Into Green Energy Storage" in *Wireless News* **(January 25, 2010)**
Pub: Close-Up Media

Description: Electronics distributor and manufacturer AV Concept Holdings Limited announced a marketing partnership with Boston-Power, a provider of lithium-ion batteries, with a focus in the Chinese and Korean markets.

41505 ■ "Avnet Inc.'s Expansion Fueled By Mergers and Acquisitions" in *The Business Journal - Serving Phoenix and the Valley of the Sun* **(Vol. 28, September 12, 2008, No. 53, pp. 1)**
Pub: American City Business Journals, Inc.

Ed: Patrick O'Grady. **Description:** Avnet Inc. has grown and has nearly tripled its revenue in the past ten years through the company's acquisitions and consolidation. The company's revenue in 2008 is $17.9 billion. Other details about the company's growth are discussed.

41506 ■ "Baking Up Bigger Lance" in *Charlotte Business Journal* **(Vol. 25, December 3, 2010, No. 37, pp. 1)**
Pub: Charlotte Business Journal

Ed: Ken Elkins. **Description:** Events that led to the merger between Charlotte, North Carolina-based snack food manufacturer Lance Inc. and Pennsylvania-based pretzel maker Snyder's of Hanover Inc. are discussed. The merger is expected to help Lance in posting a 70 percent increase in revenue, which reached $900 million in 2009. How the merger would affect Snyder's of Hanover is also described.

41507 ■ "Baldwin Connelly Partnership Splits" in *Business Journal Serving Greater Tampa Bay* **(Vol. 30, November 19, 2010, No. 48, pp. 1)**
Pub: Tampa Bay Business Journal

Ed: Alexis Muellner. **Description:** The fast-growing insurance brokerage Baldwin Connelly is now breaking up after five years. Two different entrepreneurial visions have developed within the organization and founders Lowry Baldwin and John Connell will not take separate tracks. Staffing levels in the firm are expected to remain the same.

41508 ■ "The Bankrate Double Pay" in *Barron's* **(Vol. 88, March 24, 2008, No. 12, pp. 27)**
Pub: Dow Jones & Company, Inc.

Ed: Neil A. Martin. **Description:** Shares of Bankrate may rise as much as 25 percent from their level of $45.08 a share due to a strong cash flow and balance sheet. The company's Internet business remains strong despite weakness in the online advertising industry and is a potential takeover target.

41509 ■ "Banks Could Greet Tenants in One Year" in *Business Courier* **(Vol. 26, October 16, 2009, No. 25, pp. 1)**
Pub: American City Business Journals, Inc.

Ed: Lucy May. **Description:** The Banks project's initial phase is expected to start in 60 days, which may mean that the project's first tenant could move in by the end of 2010 or beginning of 2011. Carter, an Atlanta-based firm has partnered with Dawson

Company in this riverfront development. The first phase will include 80,000 square feet of retail and 300 apartments.

41510 ■ "Barbarians Set Bar Low With Lowly Canadian Telco" in *Globe & Mail* **(March 31, 2007, pp. B1)**
Pub: CTVglobemedia Publishing Inc.

Ed: Derek DeCloet. **Description:** The efforts of the private equity fund Kohlberg, Kravis, Roberts and Co. to acquire the Canadian telecommunications firm BCE are described.

41511 ■ "Bartering, Browsing, Borrowing to Save" in *Reading Eagle* **(July 20, 2010)**
Pub: Reading Eagle/Reading Times

Ed: Jessica Bakeman. **Description:** Various forms of bartering are outlined to help small companies as well as individuals.

41512 ■ "Bartering Makes a Return in Hard Times" in *Atlanta Journal-Constitution* **(October 2, 2010, pp. A15)**
Pub: Atlanta Journal-Constitution

Ed: Bill York. **Description:** The advantages of bartering are explored.

41513 ■ "Bartering Takes Businesses Back to Basics: Broker's Exchange Helps Members to Reach New Customers" in *Buffalo News* **(July 9, 2010)**
Pub: The Buffalo News

Ed: Dino Grandoni. **Description:** Bartering clubs can help small businesses reach new customers and to expand their business.

41514 ■ "Bartering Trades on Talents" in *Reading Eagle* **(June 20, 2010)**
Pub: Reading Eagle/Reading Times

Ed: Tony Lucia. **Description:** Bartering is not just a way of trading goods and services, it can be an essential tool for small business to survive in a bad economy.

41515 ■ "BASF Launches $4.9 Billion Bid for Rival Engelhard" in *Globe & Mail* **(January 4, 2006, pp. B7)**
Pub: CTVglobemedia Publishing Inc.

Ed: Mike Esterl; Steve Levine. **Description:** The plans of BASF AG, to acquire Engelhard Corp. for $4.9 billion, are presented.

41516 ■ "Battle of the Titans" in *Canadian Business* **(Vol. 81, March 17, 2008, No. 4, pp. 15)**
Pub: Rogers Media

Ed: Rachel Pulfer. **Description:** Regulatory authorities in Canada gave Thomson Corp and Reuters Group PLC the permission to go ahead with their merger. The merged companies could eclipse Bloomberg LP's market share of 33 percent. Authorities also required Thomson and Reuters to sell some of their databases to competitors.

41517 ■ "BCE Mulls Radical Changes With Industry Under Pressure" in *Globe & Mail* **(March 30, 2007, pp. B1)**
Pub: CTVglobemedia Publishing Inc.

Ed: Andrew Willis; Jacquie McNish; Catherine McLean. **Description:** An account on the expansion plans of BCE Inc., which plans to acquire TELUS Corp., is presented.

41518 ■ "Beat the Buck: Bartering Tips from In-The-Know Authors" in **(June 23, 2010)**
Pub: The Telegraph

Ed: Jill Moon. **Description:** The Art of Barter is a new book to help small businesses learn this art form in order to expand customer base and reserve cash flow.

41519 ■ "Because 10 Million Zumba Lovers Can't Be Wrong" in *Inc.* **(Volume 32, December 2010, No. 10, pp. 106)**
Pub: Inc. Magazine

Ed: Christine Lagorio. **Description:** Profile of partners, Alberto Perez, Alberto Perlman, and Alberto Aghion, founders of Zumba, a form of dance used for fitness.

41520 ■ "Being Big By Design" in *Canadian Business* (Vol. 82, April 27, 2009, No. 7, pp. 39)
Pub: Rogers Media
Ed: Andrew Wahl. **Description:** Gennum expects that its planned acquisition of Tundra Semiconductor will expand its market presence and leverage its research and development better than working alone. The proposed friendly acquisition could challenge Zarlink Semiconductor as the largest Canadian semiconductor firm in terms of revenue. The merger could expand Gennum's addressable market to about $2 billion.

41521 ■ "Beltway Monitor" in *Mergers & Acquisitions: The Dealmaker's Journal* (March 1, 2008)
Pub: SourceMedia, Inc.
Description: Discusses in detail The Foreign Investment and National Security Act of 2007 which was put into legislation due to the initially approved acquisition of certain U.S. ports by Dubai Ports World which set off a firestorm of controversy.

41522 ■ "Benefits of Bartering" in *Mail Tribune* (November 22, 2010)
Pub: Mail Tribune
Ed: Damian Mann. **Description:** Various people discuss the use of bartering for their small companies in order to improve business.

41523 ■ "Best Growth Stocks" in *Canadian Business* (Vol. 82, Summer 2009, No. 8, pp. 28)
Pub: Rogers Media
Ed: Calvin Leung. **Description:** Canadian stocks that are considered as the best growth stocks, and whose price-earnings ratio is less than their earnings growth rate, are suggested. Suggestions include pharmaceutical firm Paladin Labs, which was found to have 13 consecutive years of revenue growth. Paladin Labs acquires or licenses niche drugs and markets them in Canada.

41524 ■ "Beware this Chinese Export" in *Barron's* (Vol. 90, August 30, 2010, No. 35, pp. 21)
Pub: Barron's Editorial & Corporate Headquarters
Ed: Bill Alpert, Leslie P. Norton. **Description:** A look at 158 China reverse-merger stocks in the U.S. reveal that the median underperformed the index of U.S. listed Chinese companies by 75 percent in their first three years. These reverse merger stocks also lagged the Russell 2000 index of small cap stocks by 66 percent.

41525 ■ "Beyond Microsoft and Yahoo!: Some M&A Prospects" in *Barron's* (Vol. 88, March 17, 2008, No. 11, pp. 39)
Pub: Dow Jones & Company, Inc.
Ed: Eric J. Savitz. **Description:** Weak quarterly earnings report for Yahoo! could pressure the company's board to cut a deal with Microsoft. Electronic Arts is expected to win its hostile $26-a-share bid for Take-Two Interactive Software. Potential targets and buyers for mergers and acquisitions are mentioned.

41526 ■ "Beyond Zipcar: Collaborate Consumption" in *Harvard Business Review* (Vol. 88, October 2010, No. 10, pp. 30)
Pub: Harvard Business School Publishing
Ed: Rachel Botsman, Roo Rogers. **Description:** Description of the rise of collaborative consumption, the sharing or redistributing of products, rather than the purchasing thereof is discussed.

41527 ■ "Big Boys Drawn Back to Play in Oil Sands" in *Globe & Mail* (March 7, 2006, pp. B2)
Pub: CTVglobemedia Publishing Inc.
Ed: Deborah Yedlin. **Description:** The feasibility of companies such as Chevron Corp. in acquiring oil sands is discussed.

41528 ■ "Big Gains Brewing at Anheuser-Busch InBev" in *Barron's* (Vol. 90, August 30, 2010, No. 35, pp. 34)
Pub: Barron's Editorial & Corporate Headquarters
Ed: Christopher C. Williams. **Description:** Anheuser-Busch InBev is realizing cost synergies and it posted better than expected returns two years after the merger that formed the company. One analyst believes its American depositary receipt could be worth as much as 72 in a year.

41529 ■ *The Big Payback: The History of the Business of Hip-Hop*
Pub: New American Library/Penguin Group
Ed: Dan Charnas. **Price:** $24.95. **Description:** The complete history of hip-hop music is presented, by following the money and the relationship between artist and merchant. In its promise of economic security and creative control for black artist-entrepreneurs, it is the culmination of dreams of black nationalists and civil rights leaders.

41530 ■ "Big Spenders" in *Hawaii Business* (Vol. 53, November 2007, No. 5, pp. 28)
Pub: Hawaii Business Publishing
Ed: Cathy S. Cruz-George. **Description:** Blackstone Group announced its acquisition of Hilton Hotels Corp. valued at $26 billion in July 2007, one of the largest buyouts in the history of hotels. Blackstone now becomes the second most powerful landowners in Hawaii.

41531 ■ "Big Trouble at Sony Ericsson" in *Barron's* (Vol. 88, March 24, 2008, No. 12, pp. M9)
Pub: Dow Jones & Company, Inc.
Ed: Angelo Franchini. **Description:** Sony Ericsson is facing trouble as it warned that its sales and net income before taxes will fall by nearly half for the first quarter of 2008. The joint venture of Sony and Ericsson has a global mobile phone market share of nine percent as of 2007, fourth largest in the world.

41532 ■ "A Bigger Deal" in *Crain's Cleveland Business* (Vol. 28, November 12, 2007, No. 45, pp. 1)
Pub: Crain Communications, Inc.
Ed: Shawn A. Turner. **Description:** In an attempt to boost its revenue CBiz Inc., a provider of accounting and business services, is looking to balance its acquisitions of smaller companies with larger ones as part of its overall growth strategy.

41533 ■ "Biotechs Are Using Back Door to Go Public" in *Boston Business Journal* (Vol. 31, May 27, 2011, No. 18, pp. 1)
Pub: Boston Business Journal
Ed: Julie M. Donnelly. **Description:** Members of Massachusetts' biotechnology sector have been engaging in reverse mergers as an alternative to initial public offerings. Reverse mergers provide access to institutional investors and hedge funds.

41534 ■ "Black Diamond Holdings Corp. Receives SEC Approval" in *Canadian Corporate News* (May 16, 2007)
Pub: Comtex News Network Inc.
Description: Black Diamond Holdings, Corp., a British Columbia domiciled company and its two wholly owned subsidiaries are engaged in the bottling, importation, distribution, marketing, and brand creation of premium spirits and wines to worldwide consumers, announced that it has completed the SEC review process and has applied to list for trading in the United States on the OTC.BB.

41535 ■ "Blackstone Set to Sell Stake" in *Globe & Mail* (March 17, 2007, pp. B6)
Pub: CTVglobemedia Publishing Inc.
Ed: Tennille Tracy. **Description:** The plan of Blackstone Group to sell 10 percent of its stake to raise $4 billion and its proposal to go for initial public offering is discussed.

41536 ■ "Blackstone's Outlook Still Tough" in *Barron's* (Vol. 88, March 17, 2008, No. 11, pp. 19)
Pub: Dow Jones & Company, Inc.
Ed: Andrew Bary. **Description:** Earnings for the Blackstone Group may not recover soon since the company's specialty in big leveraged buyouts is floundering and may not recover until 2009. The company earns lucrative incentive fees on its funds but those fees went negative in the fourth quarter of 2007 and there could be more fee reversals in the future.

41537 ■ "BMW Makes Bet on Carbon Maker" in *Wall Street Journal Eastern Edition* (November 19 , 2011, pp. B3)
Pub: Dow Jones & Company Inc.
Ed: Christoph Rauwald. **Description:** Eight months ago, Volkswagen AG acquired a 10 percent holding in carbon-fiber maker SGL Carbon SE. Its rival BMW AG is catching up by acquiring 15.2 percent stake in SGL as it seeks alliances like the rest of the industry in order to share industrial costs of new product development.

41538 ■ "BofA Will Reach the Top with Countrywide Deal" in *Business North Carolina* (Vol. 28, March 2008, No. 3, pp. 36)
Pub: Business North Carolina
Description: Bank of America, headquartered in Charlotte, North Carolina, will add Countrywide to its let of credits. Countrywide is the largest U.S. mortgage lender. Statistical data included.

41539 ■ "Bonds v. Stocks: Who's Right About Recession?" in *Barron's* (Vol. 90, August 23, 2010, No. 34, pp. M3)
Pub: Barron's Editorial & Corporate Headquarters
Ed: Kopin Tan. **Description:** The future of treasury securities and stocks should the U.S. enter or avoid a recession are discussed. The back to school business climate and BHP Billiton's bid for Potash Corporation of Saskatchewan are also discussed.

41540 ■ "Boom and Bust in the Book Biz" in *Canadian Business* (Vol. 83, August 17, 2010, No. 13-14, pp. 16)
Pub: Rogers Media Ltd.
Ed: Jordan Timm. **Description:** Electronic book marketplace is booming with Amazon.com's e-book sales for the Kindle e-reader exceeding the hardcover sales. Kobo Inc. has registered early success with its Kobo e-reader and has partnered with Hong Kong telecom giant on an e-book store.

41541 ■ "Border Boletin: UA to Take Lie-Detector Kiosk to Poland" in *Arizona Daily Star* (September 14, 2010)
Pub: Arizona Daily Star
Ed: Brady McCombs. **Description:** University of Arizona's National Center for Border Security and Immigration Research will send a team to Warsaw, Poland to show border guards from 27 European Union countries the center's Avatar Kiosk. The Avatar technology is designed for use at border ports and airports to assist Customs officers detect individuals who are lying.

41542 ■ "Boston Scientific Makes Formal Offer for Guidant, Possibly Thwarting J&J" in *Globe & Mail* (January 9, 2006, pp. B6)
Pub: CTVglobemedia Publishing Inc.
Ed: Silvia Pagan Westphal; Thomas M. Burton; Dennis Berman. **Description:** The details on Boston Scientific Corp.'s $25 billion bid on Guidant Corp. are presented. The company makes the move to outbid Johnson & Johnson.

41543 ■ "Brazil's New King of Food" in *Barron's* (Vol. 89, July 13, 2009, No. 28, pp. 28)
Pub: Dow Jones & Co., Inc.
Ed: Kenneth Rapoza. **Description:** Perdigao and Sadia's merger has resulted in the creation of Brasil Foods and the shares of Brasil Foods provides a play on both Brazil's newly energized consumer economy and its role as a major commodities exporter. Brasil Foods shares could climb as much as 36 percent.

41544 ■ "Breadwinner Tries on Designer Jeans" in *Houston Business Journal* (Vol. 40, December 18, 2009, No. 32, pp. 1)
Pub: American City Business Journals
Ed: Allison Wollam. **Description:** Chuck Cain, the franchisee who introduced Panera Bread to Houston, Texas has partnered with tax accountant Jim Jacobsen to introduce custom-make Tattu Jeans. As more Tattu Jeans outlets are being planned, Cain is using entrepreneurial lessons learned from Panera Bread in the new venture. Both Panera Bread and Tattu Jeans were opened by Cain during economic downturns.

41545 ■ "Breaking Up" in *Canadian Business* (Vol. 80, March 12, 2007, No. 6, pp. 34)
Pub: Rogers Media
Ed: John Gray. **Description:** The need for business partners to draft a shareholder agreement in the beginning of their business to make it easier to break their relationship in case of disputes later is discussed.

41546 ■ "Brewed to Succeed; Mokarbia Perks Up Sales for King Coffee" in *Crain's Detroit Business* (Vol. 24, March 17, 2008, No. 11, pp. 3)
Pub: Crain Communications, Inc.
Ed: Brent Snavely. **Description:** Profile of King Coffee Tea Services, Royal Oak-based company, whose distributing deal with Mokarabia coffee has generated an increase in sales.

41547 ■ "Bridging the Talent Gap Through Partnership and Innovation" in *Canadian Business* (Vol. 81, October 27, 2008, No. 18, pp. 88)
Pub: Rogers Media Ltd.
Description: Research revealed that North America is short by more than 60,000 qualified networking professionals. Businesses, educators and communities are collaborating in order to address the shortfall.

41548 ■ "Briefly" in *Crain's Detroit Business* (Vol. 25, June 15, 2009, No. 24, pp. 18)
Pub: Crain Communications Inc. - Detroit
Ed: Tom Henderson, Jay Greene. **Description:** Details of the merger between PI= anning Alternatives Ltd. and Oakland Wealth Management are highlighted. The two investment advisory firms will have a combined staff of 12 and will maintain two offices.

41549 ■ "Bringing Big Guns" in *Business Courier* (Vol. 24, January 18, 2008, No. 41, pp. 1)
Pub: American City Business Journals, Inc.
Ed: Lucy May. **Description:** Chief executive officer of Nidland Co. John Hayden was assigend as Cincinnati USA Partnership chairman. Hayden will bring his expertise to help the partnership drive economic development in the Greater Cincinnati area. Details of the parntership's plans are suplied.

41550 ■ "Brookfield Eyes 'New World'" in *Globe & Mail* (February 6, 2007, pp. B1)
Pub: CTVglobemedia Publishing Inc.
Ed: Sinclair Stewart; Elizabeth Church. **Description:** The efforts of Brookfield Asset Management Inc. to acquire American paper company, Longview Fibre Co., and Australian construction company Multiplex Ltd. are discussed.

41551 ■ "Building His Dream" in *Business Courier* (Vol. 24, January 25, 2008, No. 42, pp. 1)
Pub: American City Business Journals, Inc.
Ed: Laura Baverman. **Description:** Technology entrepreneur Mahendra Vora plans to build a more than $100 million local IT headquarters for VTech Holdings Ltd by 2010. Acquisition of four $5 million companies within 2008 are part of the owner's plan to expand the office equipment company. Other plans for the IT company are discussed.

41552 ■ "Bumpy Ride Ahead for United" in *Crain's Chicago Business* (Vol. 31, May 5, 2008, No. 18, pp. 3)
Pub: Crain Communications, Inc.
Ed: John Pletz. **Description:** Continental Airlines Inc. walked away from merger talks with United Airlines last week. Now the choices facing United boil down to going it alone in an increasingly stormy airline business or a less-desirable merger with US Airways Group Inc. Analysts expect United to lose $977 million this year due, mainly, to the high price of fuel.

41553 ■ "The Business of Activism" in *Entrepreneur* (Vol. 37, September 2009, No. 9, pp. 43)
Pub: Entrepreneur Media, Inc.
Ed: Mary Catherine O'Connor. **Description:** San Francisco, California-based business incubator Virgance has been promoting sustainable projects by

partnering with businesses. The company has launched campaigns which include organizing homeowners in negotiating with solar installers. The company is also planning to expand its workforce.

41554 ■ "Business Diary" in *Crain's Detroit Business* (Vol. 26, January 11, 2010, No. 2, pp. 16)
Pub: Crain Communications, Inc.
Description: Listing of local businesses involved in acquisitions, contracts, expansions, new products and services as well as startups in the region.

41555 ■ "Businesses Band Together in Destin Bartering to Keep Heads Above Water" in *Destin Log* (July 24, 2010)
Pub: The Destin Log
Ed: Andrew Metz. **Description:** Profile of The Barter Company located in Destin, Florida, whose owner believes that bartering for goods and services can help small companies in a down economy.

41556 ■ "Canadian Satellite Investors Scoop Up Stratos" in *Globe & Mail* (March 20, 2007, pp. B4)
Pub: CTVglobemedia Publishing Inc.
Ed: Simon Avery. **Description:** The proposed acquisition of Stratos Global Corp. by CIP Canada Investment Inc. for $229 million is discussed.

41557 ■ "The Canadians Are Coming!" in *Canadian Business* (Vol. 80, October 22, 2007, No. 21, pp. 15)
Pub: Rogers Media
Ed: Rachel Pulfer. **Description:** Toronto-Dominion Bank declared its acquisition of the New Jersey-based Commerce Bancorp for C$8.5 billion. Royal Bank of Canada has scooped up Trinidad-based Financial Group for C$2.2 billion. Details of the foreign acquisitions, as well as the impact of high Canadian dollars on the mergers are discussed.

41558 ■ "Cancer Therapy Raises Debate Over Shared Technology" in *Crain's Detroit Business* (Vol. 24, March 10, 2008, No. 10, pp. 1)
Pub: Crain Communications, Inc.
Ed: Jay Greene. **Description:** Overview of a proposed collaborative approach among select hospitals that would allow the consortium to utilize proton-beam accelerators in order to treat cancer patients; this expensive new technology is possibly a better way to destroy cancers by using the proton beams to direct high dosages of radiation to destroy small tumors.

41559 ■ "Capital Position" in *Business Journal-Milwaukee* (Vol. 28, December 24, 2010, No. 12, pp. A1)
Pub: Milwaukee Business Journal
Ed: Rich Kirchen. **Description:** Canada-based BMO Financial Group has purchased Marshall and Isley Corporation (M and I), which dominated lending among Wisconsin businesses for decades. The sale of M and I will enable other banks to recruit M and I's customers but BMO Financial remains a stronger competitor since it possesses a more potent capital position.

41560 ■ "Capture New Markets" in *Pet Product News* (Vol. 64, December 2010, No. 12, pp. 12)
Pub: BowTie Inc.
Ed: Ethan Mizer. **Description:** Flea and tick treatments are among the product categories that can be offered in order to clinch new markets. With the help of manufacturers, pet store retailers are encouraged to educate themselves about these products considering that capturing markets involves variations in customer perceptions. Retailers would then be deemed as resources and sources for these products.

41561 ■ "Carveouts Back in Vogue" in *Mergers & Acquisitions: The Dealmaker's Journal* (March 1, 2008)
Pub: SourceMedia, Inc.
Ed: Ken MacFadyen. **Description:** Discusses ways in which companies look for hidden assets that they can exploit in worsening economic times; oftentimes

firms try to sell off assets or in other instances they will look to unlock value through public spinoffs or through internal reorganizations.

41562 ■ "Cash-Heavy Biovail on the Prowl for Deals" in *Globe & Mail* (March 24, 2006, pp. B1)
Pub: CTVglobemedia Publishing Inc.
Ed: Leonard Zehr. **Description:** Biovail Corp. posted 48 percent rise in profits for 2005. The business growth plans of the company through acquisitions are presented.

41563 ■ "Casinos See College as Job Jackpot" in *The Business Journal-Serving Metropolitan Kansas City* (Vol. 26, August 1, 2008, No. 47)
Pub: American City Business Journals, Inc.
Ed: Suzanna Stagemeyer. **Description:** Wyandotte County casino managers revealed plans to develop partnerships with Kansas City Kansas Community College. The planned partnership is expected to include curriculum development and degree programs that would help train employees for the planned casinos. Other views and information on the project are presented.

41564 ■ "CBC and Chrysler Strike Deal" in *Black Enterprise* (Vol. 37, December 2006, No. 5, pp. 36)
Pub: Earl G. Graves Publishing Co. Inc.
Ed: Kiara Ashanti. **Description:** Congressional Black Foundation and Chrysler Financial have partnered to provide financial education to students at historically black colleges and universities. The prime objective of the program is to reduce the number of college students that graduate with poor credit scores and high debt.

41565 ■ "CBC Eyes Partners for TV Downloads" in *Globe & Mail* (February 9, 2006, pp. B1)
Pub: CTVglobemedia Publishing Inc.
Ed: Grant Robertson. **Description:** The details on Canadian Broadcasting Corp.'s distribution agreement with Google Inc. and Apple Computer Inc. are presented.

41566 ■ "CE2 Carbon Capital and Dogwood Carbon Solutions Partner With Missouri Landowners" in *Nanotechnolgy Business Journal* (Jan. 25, 2010)
Pub: Investment Weekly News
Description: Dogwood Carbon Solutions, a developer of agriculture and forestry based conservation projects, has partnered with CE2 Carbon Capital, one of the largest investors and owners of U.S. carbon commodities and carbon emissions reduction projects, to develop high-quality carbon offsets from over 30,000 acres of privately-owned non-industrial forest in the Ozark mountain region of Arkansas and Missouri.

41567 ■ "Centrue Sets Down New Roots in St. Louis; Bank Looks to Expand in Exurbs of Chicago" in *Crain's Chicago Business* (May 5, 2008)
Pub: Crain Communications, Inc.
Ed: H. Lee Murphy. **Description:** Centrue Financial Corp. has moved its headquarters from Ottawa to suburban St. Louis in search of higher-growth markets. The banks acquisitions and expansion plans are also discussed.

41568 ■ "Centurion Signs Egypt Deal With Shell" in *Globe & Mail* (March 21, 2006, pp. B5)
Pub: CTVglobemedia Publishing Inc.
Ed: Dave Ebner. **Description:** Centurion Energy International Inc., a Calgary-based natural gas producer in Egypt, has signed contract with Royal Dutch Shell PLC to explore about 320,000 hectares of land in Egypt. Details of the agreement are presented.

41569 ■ "Cerner Works the Business Circuit" in *Business Journal-Serving Metropolitan Kansas City* (Vol. 26, October 5, 2007, No. 4, pp. 1)
Pub: American City Business Journals, Inc.
Ed: Rob Roberts. **Description:** Cerner Corporation is embracing the coming of the electronic medical

record exchange by creating a regional health information organization (RHIO) called the CareEntrust. The RHIO convinced health insurers to share claims data with patients and clinicians. At the Center Health Conference, held October 7 to 10, Cerner will demonstrate the software it developed for CareEntrust to the 40,000 healthcare and information technology professionals.

41570 ■ "Challenges Await Quad in Going Public" in Milwaukee Business Journal (Vol. 27, January 29, 2010, No. 18, pp. A1)
Pub: American City Business Journals
Ed: Rich Rovito. Description: Sussex, Wisconsin-based Quad/Graphics Inc.'s impending acquisition of rival Canadian World Color Press Inc. will transform it into a publicly held entity for the first time. Quad has operated as a private company for nearly 40 years and will need to adjust to changes, such as the way management shares information with Quad/Graphics' employees. Details of the merger are included.

41571 ■ "Champion Enterprises Buys UK Company" in Crain's Detroit Business (Vol. 24, March 17, 2008, No. 11, pp. 4)
Pub: Crain Communications, Inc.
Ed: Daniel Duggan. Description: With the acquisition of ModularUK Building Systems Ltd., a steel-frame modular manufacturer, Champion Enterprises has continued its expansion outside the United States.

41572 ■ The Changing Geography of Banking and Finance
Pub: Springer Publishing Company
Ed: Pietro Alessandrini, Michele Fratianni, Alberto Zazzaro. Released: May 1, 2009. Price: $139.00.
Description: The two contrasting trends that have emerged from the integration and consolidation processes of the banking industry in both Europe and the United States in the 1990s is examined.

41573 ■ "Channeling for Growth" in The Business Journal-Serving Greater Tampa Bay (Vol. 28, July 11, 2008, No. 29, pp. 1)
Pub: American City Business Journals, Inc.
Ed: Margie Manning. Description: HSN Inc., one of the largest employers in Tampa Bay, Florida, is expected to spend an additional $9.7 million annually as it plans to hire more accounting, internal audit, legal, treasury and tax personnel after its spin-off to a public company. Details on the company's sales growth are provided.

41574 ■ "Chelsea Community Hospital to Merge with St. Joseph Mercy Health" in Crain's Detroit Business (Vol. 24, March 24, 2008, No. 12)
Pub: Crain Communications, Inc.
Ed: Jay Greene. Description: Chelsea Community Hospital has signed a letter of intent to merge with St. Joseph Mercy Health System and will negotiate merger terms, including a plan to fund an unspecified amount of facility improvements and equipment purchases at Chelsea.

41575 ■ "Chemed's Vitas Aims to Acquire" in Business Courier (Vol. 27, July 9, 2010, No. 10, pp. 1)
Pub: Business Courier
Ed: James Ritchie. Description: Chemed Corporation's Vitas Healthcare Corporation is looking for smaller nonprofit hospices as it looks to become more streamlined in a tougher reimbursement environment. CFO David Williams syas they want to acquire these hospices as fast as they can integrate them.

41576 ■ "Chew On This: Soul Fans to 'Chew' Games' First Play" in Philadelphia Business Journal (Vol. 30, September 30, 2011, No. 33, pp. 3)
Pub: American City Business Journals Inc.
Ed: John George. Description: Arena football team Philadelphia Soul extended its marketing partnership with Just Born Inc. The team's fans will enter a contest where the winner will be allowed to select the team's first play during a home game.

41577 ■ "China Vs. the World: Whose Technology Is It?" in Harvard Business Review (Vol. 88, December 2010, No. 12, pp. 94)
Pub: Harvard Business School Publishing
Ed: Thomas M Hout, Pankaj Ghemawat. Description: Examination of the regulation the Chinese government is implementing that require foreign corporations wishing to do business in the country to give up their new technologies. These regulations avoid World Trade Organization technology transfer provisions and complicate the convergence of socialism and capitalism.

41578 ■ "China's ZTE in Hunt for Partners" in Globe & Mail (February 27, 2006, pp. B1)
Pub: CTVglobemedia Publishing Inc.
Ed: Gordon Pitts. Description: The business growth plans of ZTE Corp. in Canada, through partnership, are presented.

41579 ■ "CIBC Spends $1.1 Billion on Caribbean Expansion" in Globe & Mail (March 14, 2006, pp. B1)
Pub: CTVglobemedia Publishing Inc.
Ed: Sinclair Stewart. Description: Canadian Imperial Bank of Commerce (CIBC), the fifth-largest bank of Canada, is planning to spend $1.1billion to buy major share of Barbados-based First Caribbean International Bank. The details of the acquisition plan are presented.

41580 ■ "Citigroup Moves to Buy Japan's Nikko" in Globe & Mail (March 7, 2007, pp. B12)
Pub: CTVglobemedia Publishing Inc.
Ed: Jonathan Soble; Dan Wilchins. Description: Citigroup Inc. offered $10.8 billion to acquire troubled Nikko Cordial Corp., Japan's largest securities firm.

41581 ■ "City a Pawn in Airlines' Chess Game" in Business Courier (Vol. 24, January 18, 2008, No. 41, pp. 1)
Pub: American City Business Journals, Inc.
Ed: Lisa Biank Fasig. Description: Delta Air Lines is under negotitaions with Northwest Airlines and UAL Corp. for a proposed merger. The deal will have a negative impact on Cincinnati as a hub regardless whether it goes to UAL or Northwest. The impacts of the planned merger on Cincinnati's labor market and airport traffic are discussed.

41582 ■ "Clean-Tech Focus Sparks Growth" in Philadelphia Business Journal (Vol. 28, January 15, 2010, No. 48, pp. 1)
Pub: American City Business Journals
Ed: Peter Key. Description: Keystone Redevelopment Group and economic development organization Ben Franklin Technology Partners of Southeastern Pennsylvania have partnered in supporting the growth of new alternative energy and clean technology companies. Keystone has also been developing the Bridge Business Center.

41583 ■ "Closures Pop Cork on Wine Bar Sector Consolidation" in Houston Business Journal (Vol. 40, January 22, 2010, No. 37, pp. A2)
Pub: American City Business Journals
Ed: Allison Wollam. Description: Wine bar market in Houston, Texas is in the midst of a major shift and heads toward further consolidation due to the closure of pioneering wine bars that opened in the past decade. The Corkscrew owner, Andrew Adams, has blamed the creation of competitive establishments to the closure which helped wear out his concept.

41584 ■ "CMS Products and Avecto Team for Business Security Product Solutions" in Wireless News (November 11, 2009)
Pub: Close-Up Media
Description: CMS Products, a provider of data security, backup, content management and disaster recovery, has agreed on a strategic partnership with Avect, a provider in least privilege management. The partnership will allow the companies to bundle their products.

41585 ■ "Cold Stone in Licensing Agreement with Turin Chocolates" in Ice Cream Reporter (Vol. 22, December 20, 2008, No. 1, pp. 2)
Pub: Ice Cream Reporter
Description: Cold Stone Creamery and Turin Chocolatier are teaming up to offer a new line of chocolate truffles under the Cold Stone label. The treats will feature four the most popular Cold Stone flavors: Coffee Lovers Only, Chocolate Devotion, Our Strawberry Blonde, and Peanut Butter Cup Perfection.

41586 ■ "Colliers Shifts Its Brokerage Home" in Charlotte Business Journal (Vol. 25, November 5, 2010, No. 33, pp. 1)
Pub: Charlotte Business Journal
Ed: Will Boye. Description: Colliers International signed a long-term affiliate agreement with commercial real estate firm Clarus Properties, in a move that would allow Colliers to resume business in Charlotte, North Carolina. Colliers also hired well known brokers Brad Grow and Brent Royall.

41587 ■ "Colt Capital Corp. Acquires Two Uranium Properties From DIAGNOS" in Canadian Corporate News (May 16, 2007)
Pub: Comtex News Network Inc.
Description: DIAGNOS Inc., a leader in the use of artificial intelligence and advanced knowledge extraction techniques, announced an agreement with Colt Capital Corp., a Canadian mineral exploration company that will grant an exclusive option in two uranium properties.

41588 ■ "Comcast Networks" in Brandweek (Vol. 49, April 21, 2008, No. 16, pp. SR9)
Pub: VNU Business Media, Inc.
Ed: Anthony Crupi. Description: Provides contact information for sales and marketing personnel for the Comcast networks as well as a listing of the station's top programming and an analysis of the current season and the target audience for those programs running in the current season. Experts believe Comcast will continue to acquire more stations into their portfolio.

41589 ■ "Company Severs Ties with Chiquita, Starts Own Brand" in Business Journal-Serving Phoenix and the Valley of the Sun (October 5, 2007)
Pub: American City Business Journals, Inc.
Ed: Mike Sunnucks. Description: Melones International is ending a deal with Chiquita Brands International Inc. Melones will now distribute its produce in the U.S. under its own brand, called Plain Jane. Alejandro N. Canelos Jr., head of the firm, stated their relationship with Chiquita was good, but wants to promote the Plain Jane brand name.

41590 ■ "Competition At Last?" in Canadian Business (Vol. 81, July 22, 2008, No. 12-13, pp. 7)
Pub: Rogers Media Ltd.
Description: Competition Policy Review Panel's 'Compete to Win' report revealed that Canada is being 'hollowed-out' by foreign acquisitions. The panel investigated competition and foreign investment policies in Canada. Key information on the report, as well as views on the Investment Canada Act and the Competition Act, is presented.

41591 ■ "Competition Qualms Overblown: Inco" in Globe & Mail (February 15, 2006, pp. B1)
Pub: CTVglobemedia Publishing Inc.
Ed: Wendy Stueck. Description: Inco Ltd. plans the acquisition of Falconbridge Ltd., for $12.5 billion. The advantages of the acquisition for Inco Ltd. are presented.

41592 ■ "Construction Firms Support NAACP Plan" in Business Courier (Vol. 27, September 24, 2010, No. 21, pp. 1)
Pub: Business Courier
Ed: Lucy May. Description: Executives of Turner Construction Company and Messer Construction Company expressed their support for the Cincinnati National Association for the Advancement of Colored People Construction Partnership Agreement. The

agreement involves the setting of rules for the involvement of firms owned by African Americans in major projects in Cincinnati.

41593 ■ "Consulting Firm Goes Shopping" in *Crain's Chicago Business* **(Vol. 31, April 28, 2008, No. 17, pp. 45)**
Pub: Crain Communications, Inc.
Ed: Phuong Ly. **Description:** Clark & Wamberg LLC was created last year after the merger of Clark Inc. to a Dutch insurance conglomerate. Clark Inc. was a life insurance and benefits consultancy which had been on a downslide, returning just 5.6 percent a year to shareholders. In contrast Clark & Wamberg posted first-year revenue of $106.8 million, fueled by business from its executive compensation and health care clients.

41594 ■ "A Conversation With Steven Hilfinger, Foley & Lardner L.L.P." in *Crain's Detroit Business* **(Vol. 24, March 24, 2008, No. 12, pp. 1)**
Pub: Crain Communications, Inc.
Description: Interview with Steven Hilfinger who is a member of Foley & Lardner L.L.P.'s mergers and acquisitions practice and is co-chair of its automotive industry team. Hilfinger discusses such issues as the role a board of directors can play in the M&A process and the future of the auto market.

41595 ■ "CoolBrands" in *Canadian Business* **(Vol. 83, September 14, 2010, No. 15, pp. 25)**
Pub: Rogers Media Ltd.
Ed: Joe Castaldo. **Description:** CoolBrands International Inc.'s merger with Swisher International Inc., a US hygiene products and services company, has formally erased the last traces of the former ice cream company. CoolBrands began as a frozen yogurt stand in 1986 and flourished across the world. How the string of acquisitions and poor corporate governance led to its demise are cited.

41596 ■ "Copyright Clearance Center (CCC) Partnered with cSubs" in *Information Today* **(Vol. 28, November 2011, No. 10, pp. 14)**
Pub: Information Today, Inc.
Description: Copyright Clearance Center (CCC) partnered with cSubs to integrate CCC's point-of-content licensing solution RightsLink Basic directly into cSubs workflow. The partnership will allow cSubs' customers a user-friendly process for obtaining permissions. Csubs is a corporate subscription management service for books, newspapers, and econtent.

41597 ■ "Corporate Elite Show Resilience" in *The Business Journal-Serving Greater Tampa Bay* **(Vol. 28, August 1, 2008, No. 32, pp. 1)**
Pub: American City Business Journals, Inc.
Ed: Margie Manning; Alexis Muellner. **Description:** Stocks of the largest public companies in Tampa Bay, Florida, outperformed the S&P 500 index by 28 percent in the first half of 2008. The escalation is attributed to the growth orientation of the companies in the area and the lack of exposure to the real estate and financial services sectors.

41598 ■ "Corporate Training" in *Hawaii Business* **(Vol. 53, October 2007, No. 4, pp. 46)**
Pub: Hawaii Business Publishing
Ed: Cathy S. Cruz-George. **Description:** Kalani Pa, Mike Hann, and Li Si Yang are three of the fitness trainers who have worked with some of the participants at the Hawaii's Fittest CEO contest. Pa has trained Group Pacific Inc.'s Chip Doyle while Hann was Sharon Serene's trainer. Their insights on the profession of being a fitness trainer, and on working with executives are given.

41599 ■ "Corporex in Battle With Hedge Fund" in *Business Courier* **(Vol. 24, December 21, 2008, No. 36, pp. 1)**
Pub: American City Business Journals, Inc.
Ed: Jon Newberry. **Description:** Discusses a breach of contract complaint that was filed by Apollo Real Estate Advisors against Corporex Companies Inc. but Corporex said that the lawsuit was intended to counter an arbitration complaint filed by Corporex

against Apollo, which seeks $11 million in termination fees. The issue is in relation to the acquisition of Eagle Hospitality by Apollo earlier in 2007.

41600 ■ "Corporex Checks Into Hotel Niche" in *Business Courier* **(Vol. 24, October 12, 2008, No. 26, pp. 1)**
Pub: American City Business Journals, Inc.
Ed: Laura Baverman. **Description:** Corporex Companies Inc. is investing $900 million on select-service hotels ranging from $12 million to $20 million each, with eight hotels under construction and nine sites under contract.

41601 ■ "COSE Turns On To Electricity Market" in *Crain's Cleveland Business* **(Vol. 30, June 22, 2009, No. 24, pp. 4)**
Pub: Crain Communications, Inc.
Ed: Jay Miller. **Description:** Council of Smaller Enterprises is working to offer small businesses and their employees electricity at discount prices set at auction by the Public Utilities Commission of Ohio and even lower prices from the Northern Ohio Public Energy Council. Details of the program are offered.

41602 ■ "Crouching Tigers Spring to Life" in *Globe & Mail* **(April 14, 2007, pp. B1)**
Pub: CTVglobemedia Publishing Inc.
Ed: Grant Robertson. **Description:** The prospects of the acquisition of BCE Inc, by Canadian pension funds are discussed. The effect of the growth of these pension funds on the Canadian economy is described.

41603 ■ "CRTC Signals CHUM Deal Will Get Nod" in *Globe & Mail* **(May 2, 2007, pp. B3)**
Pub: CTVglobemedia Publishing Inc.
Ed: Grant Robertson. **Description:** The likely approval of Canadian Radio-Television and Telecommunications Commission to the proposed acquisition of CHUM Ltd. by CTVglobemedia Inc. is discussed.

41604 ■ "CTV's CHUM Proposal Gets Chilly Reception" in *Globe & Mail* **(May 1, 2007, pp. B1)**
Pub: CTVglobemedia Publishing Inc.
Ed: Grant Robertson. **Description:** The possible violation of broadcast regulations in case of acquisition of CHUM Ltd. by CTV Inc. for $1.4 billion is discussed.

41605 ■ "The CW" in *Brandweek* **(Vol. 49, April 21, 2008, No. 16, pp. SR8)**
Pub: VNU Business Media, Inc.
Ed: John Consoli. **Description:** Provides contact information for sales and marketing personnel for the CW network as well as a listing of the station's top programming and an analysis of the current season and the target audience for those programs running in the current season. Purchases of advertising feel that Warner Bros. and CBS made a mistake merging The WB and UPN into the new CW rather than folding UPN into the more-established WB; compared to last season ratings are down more than 20 percent across the board.

41606 ■ "Danaher to Acquire Tectronix" in *Canadian Electronics* **(Vol. 22, November-December 2007, No. 7, pp. 1)**
Pub: CLB Media Inc.
Description: Leading supplier of measurement, test and monitoring equipment Tektronix will be acquired by Danaher Corporation for $2.8 billion. Tektronix products are expected to complement Danaher's test equipment sector. The impacts of the deal on Tektronix shareholders and Danaher's operations are discussed.

41607 ■ "Dancing With Giants: Acquisition and Survival of the Family Firm" in *Family Business Review* **(Vol. 19, December 2006, No. 4, pp. 289)**
Pub: Family Firm Institute Inc.
Ed: Adam Steen, Lawrence S. Welch. **Description:** Responses of family firms to mergers and acquisitions are analyzed taking the example of the takeover of an Australian wine producer and family firm.

41608 ■ "David Maus Debuting New Dealership" in *Orlando Business Journal* **(Vol. 26, February 5, 2010, No. 36, pp. 1)**
Pub: American City Business Journals
Ed: Anjali Fluker. **Description:** Automotive dealers David Maus Automotive Group and Van Tuyl Automotive Investment Group will launch David Maus Chevrolet in Sanford, Florida in fall 2010. The 12-acre site of the Chevy dealership will be located adjacent to the David Maus Toyota dealership. The new store is expected to generate nearly 125 new jobs.

41609 ■ "Deal Braces Cramer for Growth Run" in *The Business Journal-Serving Metropolitan Kansas City* **(Vol. 26, July 4, 2008, No. 43, pp. 1)**
Pub: American City Business Journals, Inc.
Ed: James Dornbook. **Description:** Gardner, Kansas-based Cramer Products Inc. bought 100 percent of the stocks of Louisville, Kentucky-based Active Ankle Inc. from 26 private investors increasing its revenue by 20 percent. The latter is the second largest vendor of Cramer. Other details of the merger are presented.

41610 ■ "The Deal - Rhymes With Steal - Of A Lifetime" in *Barron's* **(Vol. 88, March 24, 2008, No. 12, pp. 24)**
Pub: Dow Jones & Company, Inc.
Ed: Andrew Bary. **Description:** JPMorgan Chase's impending acquisition of Bear Stearns for $2.50 a share is a huge steal for the former. JPMorgan is set to acquire a company with a potential annual earnings of $1 billion while the Federal Reserve funds Bear's illiquid assets by providing $30 billion in non-recourse loans.

41611 ■ "Dealer Gets a Lift with Acquisitions at Year's End" in *Crain's Detroit Business* **(Vol. 26, January 11, 2010, No. 2, pp. 3)**
Pub: Crain Communications, Inc.
Ed: Ryan Beene. **Description:** Alta Equipment Co., a forklift dealer, closed 2009 with a string of acquisitions expecting to double the firm's employee headcount and triple its annual revenue. Alta Lift Truck Services, Inc., as the company was known before the acquisitions, was founded in 1984 as Michigan's dealer for forklift manufacturer Yale Materials Handling Corp.

41612 ■ "Dealers Trying Not to Fold" in *Business First Columbus* **(Vol. 25, December 5, 2008, No. 15, pp. A1)**
Pub: American City Business Journals
Ed: Dan Eaton. **Description:** Increase in the number of automobile dealer closures in Ohio is seen to impact the state's economy. The trend of consolidation is forecasted to adversely affect employment and sales. Statistical data included.

41613 ■ "Death Spiral" in *Business Journal Serving Greater Tampa Bay* **(Vol. 30, October 29, 2010, No. 45, pp. 1)**
Pub: Tampa Bay Business Journal
Ed: Margie Manning. **Description:** Bay Cities Bank has started working on the loan portfolio of its acquisition, Progress Bank of Florida. Regulators closed Progress Bank in October 2010 after capital collapsed due to charge-offs and increases in the provision for future loan losses.

41614 ■ "Denver Will Put Up Fight for MillerCoors HQ" in *Business Journal-Milwaukee* **(Vol. 25, October 19, 2007, No. 3, pp. A1)**
Pub: American City Business Journals, Inc.
Ed: Rich Rovito. **Description:** A contention exists between Milwaukee and Denver over which city will become the new location of the Miller Brewing Company (Milwaukee) and Coors Brewing Company (Colorado) joint venture MillerCoors. Leaders of the breweries since the announcement of the merger, have contended frantically to prepare strategies to back up their own cities. The advantages and disadvantages of both cities are presented.

41615 ■ "Desmarais Makes Move into U.S." in *Globe & Mail* **(February 2, 2007, pp. B1)**
Pub: CTVglobemedia Publishing Inc.
Ed: Andrew Willis. **Description:** The decision of Desmarais family, which runs Great-West Lifeco Inc., to

acquire Putnam Investment Trust for $4.6 billion to enter the United States market, is discussed.

41616 ■ "Developer Banks On East Submarket, Slowdown Not a Hinderance" in *The Business Journal-Serving Greater Tampa Bay* **(August 1, 2008)**
Pub: American City Business Journals, Inc.
Ed: Janet Leiser. **Description:** CLW Industrial Group and Cobalt Industrial REIT II have teamed up to develop a 14-acre area in northeast Hillsborough County, Florida. The $15 million industrial park project includes the 175,000-square-foot New Tampa Commerce Center, scheduled for completion in the first quarter of 2009.

41617 ■ "A Different Breed of Deal Maker is Emerging" in *Globe & Mail* **(January 14, 2006, pp. B2)**
Pub: CTVglobemedia Publishing Inc.
Ed: Eric Reguly. **Description:** The managerial strategies of chief executive officers in business acquisitions of companies, such as Dofasco Inc., are presented.

41618 ■ "Digital Duplication" in *Crain's Cleveland Business* **(Vol. 28, October 1, 2007, No. 39, pp. 3)**
Pub: Crain Communications, Inc.
Ed: David Bennett. **Description:** Profile of the business plan of eBlueprint Holdings LLC, a reprographics company that found success by converting customers' paper blueprints to an electronic format; the company plans to expand into other geographic markets by acquiring solid reprographics companies and converting their computer systems so that customers' blueprints can be managed electronically.

41619 ■ "Doctors Buy In to Medical Timeshares" in *Houston Business Journal* **(Vol. 40, December 11, 2009, No. 31, pp. 1)**
Pub: American City Business Journals
Ed: Mary Ann Azevedo. **Description:** Memorial Hermann Hospital System has leased to doctors three examination rooms and medical office space in the Memorial Hermann Medical Plaza in line with its new timeshare concept. The concept was designed to bring primary care physicians to its Texas Medical Center campus.

41620 ■ "Don't Count Your Millions Yet" in *Business Courier* **(Vol. 24, January 11, 2008, No. 40, pp. 1)**
Pub: American City Business Journals, Inc.
Ed: Steve Watkins. **Description:** Merger and acquisition deals have been difficult to complete since 2007 largely due to a weaker economy and the credit crunch. Buyers have become more cautious because of the state of the economy and capital has become tougher to obtain because of the credit market crisis. The trends in mergers and acquisitions are analyzed further.

41621 ■ "Dow Champions Innovative Energy Solutions for Auto Industry at NAIAS" in *Business of Global Warming* **(January 25, 2010, pp. 7)**
Pub: Investment Weekly News
Description: This year's North American International Auto Show in Detroit will host the "Electric Avenue" exhibit sponsored by the Dow Chemical Company. The display will showcase the latest in innovative energy solutions from Dow as well as electric vehicles and the technology supporting them. This marks the first time a non-automotive manufacturer is part of the main floor of the show.

41622 ■ "Dow Jones Gives Apple-Loving Sales Professionals a Boost" in *Information Today* **(Vol. 26, February 2009, No. 2, pp. 30)**
Pub: Information Today, Inc.
Description: Dow Jones Sales Triggers for iPhone and iPod program helps sales professionals stay current to prospects and customers in their fields by providing real-time news on business changes, including management moves, mergers, and new investments. The application presents events that trigger best opportunities and allows users to look up companies and executives to retrieve information.

41623 ■ "Downtown Bank Got High Marks for Irwin Purchase, Is Looking For More" in *Business Courier* **(Vol. 27, September 3, 2010, No. 18, pp. 1)**
Pub: Business Courier
Ed: Steve Watkins. **Description:** First Financial Bancorp is looking to acquire more troubled banks following its purchase of Irwin Union Bank. The bank has reported a $383 million bargain purchase gain during the third quarter of 2009.

41624 ■ *Driving With No Brakes: How a Bunch of Hooligans Built the Best Travel Company in the World*
Pub: Grand Circle Corporation
Ed: Alan and Harriet Lewis. **Price:** $19.95. **Description:** Inspirational book about how two courageous leaders built a remarkable company that can thrive in change and succeed in an unpredictable world. Important lessons for any business leader trying to create value in the 21st Century are included.

41625 ■ "Drug-Maker Plans IPO" in *Business Courier* **(Vol. 24, November 23, 2008, No. 32, pp. 1)**
Pub: American City Business Journals, Inc.
Ed: James Ritchie; Steve Watkins. **Description:** Xanodyne Pharmaceuticals Inc. filed plans with the Securities and Exchange Commission on November 9, 2007 for an initial public offering. The company, with annual sales of $75 million, had lost $222 million since it was founded in 2001.

41626 ■ "DuPontas Pioneer Hi-Bred, Evogene to Develop Rust-Resistant Soybean Varieties" in *Farm Industry News* **(November 22, 2011)**
Pub: Penton Business Media Inc.
Ed: Karen McMahon. **Description:** DuPont and Evogene have signed a new contract to work together to develop resistance in soybeans to rust. Financial terms of the agreement were not disclosed.

41627 ■ "Earth Angels" in *Playthings* **(Vol. 106, September 1, 2008, No. 8, pp. 10)**
Pub: Reed Business Information
Ed: Karyn M. Peterson. **Description:** ImagiPlay toy company has partnered with Whole Foods Market to distribute the company's wooden playthings across the country. The company's Earth-friendly business model is outlined.

41628 ■ *The Economics of Integrity*
Pub: HarperStudio/HarperCollins
Ed: Anna Bernasek. **Released:** February 23, 2010. **Price:** $19.99. **Description:** Integrity is built over time and the importance of trust in starting and building business relationships is stressed.

41629 ■ "EDCO Doling Out Capital Along Border" in *Austin Business JournalInc.* **(Vol. 28, August 1, 2008, No. 20, pp. 1)**
Pub: American City Business Journals
Ed: Sandra Zaragoza. **Description:** Non-profit business incubator Economic Development Catalyst Organization Ventures is searching for promising startup companies. The company is targeting startups in green energy, technology and consumer markets. EDCO has partnered with consumer electronics repair company CherryFusion and technology firm MiniDonations.

41630 ■ "Elevated Status" in *Business Courier* **(Vol. 24, March 21, 2008, No. 50, pp. 1)**
Pub: American City Business Journals, Inc.
Ed: James Ritchie. **Description:** Overview of Tri-Health Inc.'s growth is presented. Currently, the company's revenue is estimated to be around $1 billion. Since 2004, the company was able to build patient towers, an outpatient facility in Lebanon, and was able to acquire the Group Health Associates physician practice. TriHealth recently hired 500 nurses in order to meet its needs.

41631 ■ "Embarq Sale Sets New Tone" in *The Business Journal-Serving Metropolitan Kansas City* **(Vol. 27, October 31, 2008, No. 8, pp. 1)**
Pub: American City Business Journals, Inc.
Ed: Suzsanna Stagemeyer. **Description:** CenturyTel Inc. has agreed to acquire Embarq Corp., a large

phone company based in Overland Park. The acquisition deal is valued at $11.6 billion. The potential impacts of the deal on Kansas City's economy are analyzed.

41632 ■ "Empire of the Sun" in *Canadian Business* **(Vol. 82, April 27, 2009, No. 7, pp. 42)**
Pub: Rogers Media
Ed: Jeff Sanford. **Description:** Suncor Energy Inc. and Petro-Canada announced on March 23, 2009 plans for a merger. The $19 billion merger will result in Suncor keeping their brand name and 60 percent of the company while Pe= tro-Canada will hold 40 percent. The new Suncor now has 7.5 billion barrels of proved and probable reserves of oil and could account for as much as 25 percent of North American production by 2025.

41633 ■ "Empty Office Blues" in *Business Journal Portland* **(Vol. 26, December 4, 2009, No. 39, pp. 1)**
Pub: American City Business Journals Inc.
Ed: Wendy Culverwell. **Description:** Portland's office vacancy rates could reach almost 15 percent by the end of 2010 due to job reductions and mergers.

41634 ■ "EnCana Gets Top Dollar for Gas Depot Division" in *Globe & Mail* **(March 7, 2006, pp. B6)**
Pub: CTVglobemedia Publishing Inc.
Ed: Dave Ebner. **Description:** The details on acquisition of natural gas storage assets of EnCana Corp. by Carlyle/Riverstone Global Energy and Power Fund II LP and Carlyle Group LP are presented.

41635 ■ "Endeca Gears Up for Likely IPO Bid" in *Boston Business Journal* **(Vol. 31, July 1, 2011, No. 23, pp. 1)**
Pub: Boston Business Journal
Ed: Kyle Alspach. **Description:** Endeca Inc. is readying itself for its plans to register as a public company. The search engine technology leader is enjoying continued growth with revenue up by 30 percent in 2010 while its expansion trend makes it an unlikely candidate for an acquisition.

41636 ■ "Entrepreneur Column" in *Entrepreneur* **(September 24, 2009)**
Pub: Entrepreneur Media, Inc.
Ed: Allen Moon. **Description:** In an attempt to compete with Google, Microsoft and Yahoo have entered a partnership to merge their search services; advice on the best ways to get noticed on this new search engine entitled Bing, is provided.

41637 ■ "eResearch Issues Initiating Report on Aldershot Resources Ltd." in *Canadian Corporate News* **(May 14, 2007)**
Pub: Comtex News Network Inc.
Description: Overview of Bob Weir and Michael Wood's Initiating Report on Aldershot Resources Ltd., a junior Canadian-based uranium exploration company with prospective projects in Canada, Zambia, Australia, and a base metals project in Chile.

41638 ■ "ESolar Partners With Penglai on Landmark Solar Thermal Agreement for China" in *Business of Global Warming* **(January 25, 2010, pp. 8)**
Pub: Investment Weekly News
Description: Penglai Electric, a privately-owned Chinese electrical power equipment manufacturer, and eSolar, a global provider of cost-effective and reliable solar power plants, announced a master licensing agreement in which eSolar will build at least 2 gigawatts of solar thermal power plants in China over the next 10 years.

41639 ■ "Ethnic Chambers Seek Combined Facility" in *Business Journal* **(Vol. 28, October 8, 2010, No. 18, pp. 1)**
Pub: Minneapolis Business Journal
Ed: Jim Hammerand. **Description:** Six ethnic business and commerce groups in St. Paul and Minneapolis, Minnesota, all members of the Minnesota Multi-Ethnic Chambers of Commerce Joint Council, are planning to move in together in order to save on

costs and to strengthen their organizations. The Council expects to transfer by September 2011. The project will cost about $290,000.

41640 ■ **"Executive Decision: Just What the Doctor Ordered" in** *Globe & Mail* **(February 11, 2006, pp. B3)**
Pub: CTVglobemedia Publishing Inc.
Ed: Leonard Zehr. **Description:** The leadership ability of chief executive William Hunter of Angiotech Pharmaceuticals Inc., who acquired American Medical Instruments Holdings Inc. for $785 million, is discussed.

41641 ■ **"Executive Decision: To Make Inroads Against RIM, Palm Steals Its Strategy" in** *Globe & Mail* **(March 25, 2006, pp. B3)**
Pub: CTVglobemedia Publishing Inc.
Ed: Simon Avery. **Description:** The Palm Inc., global leader in portable device manufacturing, is looking forward to improve its sales of Palm Treos, a wireless portable device that connects to internet and email. Palm is also planning to build partnerships, under the efficient management of Michael Moskowitz, general manager and vice-president of Palm Inc., with the other companies to increase the sales of its wireless devices.

41642 ■ **"Expanding Middleby's Food Processing Biz" in** *Crain's Chicago Business* **(Vol. 31, April 21, 2008, No. 16, pp. 6)**
Pub: Crain Communications, Inc.
Ed: David Sterrett. **Description:** Profile of the executive vice-president of the food processing company, Middleby Corp, whose business plan is to develop new products, begin looking for acquisitions and simplify operations in order to expand the firm.

41643 ■ **"Export Initiative Launched" in** *Philadelphia Business Journal* **(Vol. 28, December 11, 2009, No. 43, pp. 1)**
Pub: American City Business Journals
Ed: Athena D. Merritt. **Description:** The first initiative that came out of the partnership between the Export-Import Bank of the US, the city of Philadelphia, and the World Trade Center of Greater Philadelphia is presented. A series of export finance workshops have featured Ex-Im Bank resources that can provide Philadelphia businesses with working capital, insurance protection and buyer financing.

41644 ■ **"Exposed?" in** *Mergers & Acquisitions: The Dealmaker's Journal* **(March 1, 2008)**
Pub: SourceMedia, Inc.
Ed: Jerry Abejo. **Description:** State-run pension plans' contributions are declining due to a loss of tax revenue from plummeting home values.

41645 ■ *The Facebook Era: Tapping Online Social Networks to Build Better Products, Reach New Audiences, and Sell More Stuff*
Pub: Prentice Hall
Ed: Clara Shih. **Price:** $24.99. **Description:** The '90s were about the World Wide Web of information and the power of linking Web pages. Today it's about the World Wide Web of people and the power of the social graph. Online social networks are fundamentally changing the way we live, work, and interact. They offer businesses immense opportunities to transform customer relationships for profit: opportunities that touch virtually every business function, from sales and marketing to recruiting, collaboration to executive decision-making, product development to innovation.

41646 ■ **"Fair Exchange" in** *Food and Drink* **(Winter 2010, pp. 84)**
Pub: Schofield Media Group
Ed: Don Mardak. **Description:** Bartering can assist firms in the food and beverage industry to attract new customers, maximize resources, and reduce cash expenses.

41647 ■ *Family Limited Partnership Deskbook*
Pub: American Bar Association
Ed: David T. Lewis; Andrea C. Chomakos. **Released:** March 25, 2008. **Price:** $169.95. **Description:** Forming and funding a family limited partnership or limited

liability company is complicated. In-depth analysis of all facets of this business entity are examined using detailed guidance on the basic principles of drafting, forming, funding, and valuing an FLP or LLC and also covers tax concerns. Examples and extensive sample forms are included on a CD-ROM included with the book.

41648 ■ *Family Limited Partnerships Deskbook: Forming and Funding FLPs and Other Closely Held Business Entities*
Pub: American Bar Association
Ed: David T. Lewis. **Released:** March 2008. **Price:** $169.95. **Description:** Forming and funding a family limited partnership (FLP) or limited liability company (LLC) is common and complicated. This handbook offers in-depth analysis of issues facing these types of businesses. Guidance is given on the principles of drafting, forming, funding, and valuing an FLP or LLC as well as tax matters. Examples and sample forms are included on a CD-ROM.

41649 ■ **"FCC Adopts New Media Ownership Rules" in** *Black Enterprise* **(Vol. 38, March 2008, No. 8, pp. 26)**
Pub: Earl G. Graves Publishing Co. Inc.
Ed: Joyce Jones. **Description:** Federal Communications Commission approved a ruling that lifts a ban on newspaper and/or broadcast cross ownership. Because of declining sales in newspaper advertising and readership the ban will allow companies to share local news gathering costs across multiple media platforms.

41650 ■ **"Fertilizer for Growth" in** *Canadian Business* **(Vol. 83, September 14, 2010, No. 15, pp. 76)**
Pub: Rogers Media Ltd.
Ed: Bryan Borzykowski. **Description:** Australian-based BHP Billiton launches a C$38.5 billion hostile takeover bid for Saskatchewan-based Potash Corporation and some investors immediately bought Potash stock at C$130. However, Potash has resisted BHP's offer and announced a plan to try to stop the deal.

41651 ■ **"Fieldbrook Foods Acquired By Private Equity Firm" in** *Ice Cream Reporter* **(Vol. 23, October 20, 2010, No. 11, pp. 1)**
Pub: Ice Cream Reporter
Description: Fieldbrook Foods Corporation, manufacturer of frozen novelty and ice cream products was acquired by Chicago-based private equity firm Arbor Investments. Arbor partnered with Herman 'Bing' Graffunder, a long-term dairy industry partner, in its acquisition of Fieldbrook.

41652 ■ **"Fifth Third Spinoff" in** *Business Courier* **(Vol. 27, July 16, 2010, No. 11, pp. 1)**
Pub: Business Courier
Ed: Dan Monk, Steve Watkins. **Description:** Electronic-funds transfer company Fifth Third Solutions (FTPS), a spinoff of Fifth Third Bancorp, is seeking as much as 200,000 square feet of new office space in Ohio. The bank's sale of 51 percent ownership stake to Boston-based Advent International Corporation has paved the way for the growth of FTPS. How real estate brokers' plans have responded to FTPS' growth mode is discussed.

41653 ■ **"Film Giants Disney, Pixar Talk Marriage" in** *Globe & Mail* **(January 19, 2006, pp. B1)**
Pub: CTVglobemedia Publishing Inc.
Ed: Merissa Marr; Nick Wingfield. **Description:** The plans of Walt Disney Co. to acquire Pixar Animation Studios are presented.

41654 ■ **"Finalist: BlackEagle Partners L.L.C." in** *Crain's Detroit Business* **(Vol. 24, March 24, 2008, No. 12, pp. 12)**
Pub: Crain Communications, Inc.
Ed: Brent Snavely. **Description:** Overview of private-equity firm, BlackEagle Partners L.L.C., an upstart that acquired Rockford Products Corp. in order to improve the performance of the company who does business with several major tier-one automotive suppliers; Rockford manufactures highly engineered chassis and suspension components for automakers and the automotive aftermarket.

41655 ■ *Financing Growth: Strategies, Capital Structure, and M and A Transactions*
Pub: John Wiley & Sons, Inc.
Ed: Kenneth H. Marks, Larry E. Robbins, Gonzalo Fernandez, John P. Funkhouser, D.L. Williams. **Released:** September 1, 2009. **Price:** $95.00. **Description:** Guide for emerging growth and middle market companies includes information to help understand and apply the basics of corporate finance using empirical data and actual company cases to illustrate capital structures and financing approaches.

41656 ■ *Financing Your Small Business*
Pub: Barron's Educational Series, Incorporated
Ed: Robert Walter. **Released:** December 2003. **Description:** Tips for raising venture capital, dealing with bank officials, and initiating public offerings of stock shares for small business.

41657 ■ **"Finding Competitive Advantage in Adversity" in** *Harvard Business Review* **(Vol. 88, November 2010, No. 11, pp. 102)**
Pub: Harvard Business School Publishing
Ed: Bhaskar Chakravorti. **Description:** Four opportunities in adversity are identified and applied to business scenarios. These are matching unmet needs with unneeded resources, seeking collaboration from unlikely partners, developing small/appropriate solutions to large/complex issues, and focusing on the platform as well as the product.

41658 ■ **"Finding the Voice of the Marketplace" in** *Mergers & Acquisitions: The Dealmaker's Journal* **(March 1, 2008)**
Pub: SourceMedia, Inc.
Description: Companies oftentimes are unable to achieve their strategic goals through acquisition due, in part, to not understanding the target's market and its position in the marketplace.

41659 ■ **"First the Merger: Then, The Culture Clash. How To Fix the Little Things That Can Tear a Company Apart" in** *Inc.* **(January 2008)**
Pub: Gruner & Jahr USA Publishing
Ed: Elaine Appleton Grant. **Description:** Ways three CEOs handled the culture classes that followed after company mergers; companies profiled include Fuel Outdoor, an outdoor advertising company; Nelson, an interior design and architecture firm; and Beber Silverstein, an ad agency.

41660 ■ **"First U.S. :M-Press Tiger with Inline Screen Printing" in** *American Printer* **(Vol. 128, June 1, 2011, No. 6)**
Pub: Penton Media Inc.
Description: Graphic Tech located in California bought :M-Press Tiger, the first in North America with an inline screen printing unit.

41661 ■ **"Florida's Housing Gloom May Add To Woes of National City" in** *Crain's Cleveland Business* **(Vol. 28, October 29, 2007, No. 43, pp. 1)**
Pub: Crain Communications, Inc.
Ed: Shawn A. Turner. **Description:** Already suffering by bad loans in the troubled mortgage market, National City Corp. is attempting to diversify its geographic presence beyond the slow-growth industrial Midwest by acquiring two Florida firms. Analysts worry that the acquisitions may end up making National City vulnerable to a takeover if the housing slump continues and credit quality becomes more of an issue for the bank.

41662 ■ **"For Giving Us a Way To Say Yes To Solar: Lynn Jurich and Edward Fenster" in** *Inc.* **(Volume 32, December 2010, No. 10, pp. 110)**
Pub: Inc. Magazine
Description: Profile of entrepreneurs Lynn Jurich and Edward Fenster, cofounders of SunRun. The firm installs solar panels at little or no cost and homeowners sign 20-year contracts to buy power at a fixed price.

41663 ■ **"For Hospitals, a Dating Game" in** *Business Courier* **(Vol. 26, December 4, 2009, No. 32, pp. 1)**
Pub: American City Business Journals, Inc.
Ed: James Ritchie. **Description:** Drake Center, Fort Hamilton Hospital, and West Chester Medical Center are among the members of Cincinnati's Health Alli-

ance looking for potential buyers or partners. Meanwhile, Jewish Hospital, another member of the Alliance, will be bought by Mercy Health Partners by January 7, 2010.

41664 ■ "For Sale: Old Florida Panache" in *The Business Journal-Serving Greater Tampa Bay* **(Vol. 28, July 4, 2008, No. 28, pp. 1)**
Pub: American City Business Journals, Inc.
Ed: Jane Meinhardt. **Description:** Linger Lodge, owned by real estate investor and developer Martin Kaplan and Senator Michael Bennett, is now on the market for a sealed bid process facilitated by Levin & Associates. The business partners bought the riverfront property for about $3 million in 2005. Other details on the sale of the property are presented.

41665 ■ "Former Gov. Fletcher Starts Blue Ash Firm" in *Business Courier* **(Vol. 26, October 9, 2009, No. 24, pp. 1)**
Pub: American City Business Journals, Inc.
Ed: Lucy May. **Description:** Former Kentucky Governor Ernie Fletcher partnered with Belcan Corporation founder Ralph Anderson to purchase Blue Ash, Ohio-based Virtual Medical Network and form Alton Healthcare LLC. The company's goal is to increase practice revenues by adapting technology to reinvent clinical practices and deliver best possible care to more patients.

41666 ■ "Former Mayor Driving $500 Million Real Estate Equity Fund" in *The Business Journal - Serving Phoenix and the Valley of the Sun* **(Vol. 28, August 15, 2008, No. 50, pp. 1)**
Pub: American City Business Journals, Inc.
Ed: Jan Buchholz. **Description:** Paul John, the former mayor of Phoenix, is establishing a $500 million real estate asset management fund. The fund is dubbed Southwest Next Capital Management and has attracted three local partners, namely Joseph Meyer, Jay Michalowski, and James Mullany, who all have background in finance and construction.

41667 ■ "Fortis Snaps Up Terasen's Gas Utility Business" in *Globe & Mail* **(February 27, 2007, pp. B1)**
Pub: CTVglobemedia Publishing Inc.
Ed: Wendy Stueck. **Description:** The acquisition of Terasen Inc. from Kinder Morgan Inc. by Fortis Inc. is described.

41668 ■ "Fraser and Neave Acquires King's Creameries" in *Ice Cream Reporter* **(Vol. 23, November 20, 2010, No. 12, pp. 1)**
Pub: Ice Cream Reporter
Description: Fraser and Neave Ltd., a Singapore-based consumer products marketer, has entered a conditional agreement to acquire all outstanding shares of King's Creameries, the leading manufacturer and distributor of frozen desserts.

41669 ■ "Freeing the Wheels of Commerce" in *Hispanic Business* **(July-August 2007, pp. 50, 52, 54)**
Pub: Hispanic Business
Ed: Keith Rosenblum. **Description:** SecureOrigins, a border-based partnership with high-tech innovators is working to move goods faster, more efficiently, and securely.

41670 ■ "Fresh Direct's Crisis" in *Crain's New York Business* **(Vol. 24, January 14, 2008, No. 2, pp. 3)**
Pub: Crain Communications, Inc.
Ed: Lisa Fickenscher. **Description:** Freshdirect, an Internet grocery delivery service, finds itself under siege from federal immigration authorities, customers and labor organizations due to its employment practice of hiring illegals. At stake is the grocer's reputation as well as its ambitious growth plans, including an initial public offering of its stock.

41671 ■ "Friedland's Next Frontier: Drilling for Oil in Iraq" in *Globe & Mail* **(April 20, 2007, pp. B1)**
Pub: CTVglobemedia Publishing Inc.
Ed: Wendy Stueck. **Description:** The decision of the Canadian oil and gas company Ivanhoe Energy Inc. to partner with the Japanese oil and gas firm INPEX Corp. for the development of heavy oil fields in north central Iraq is discussed.

41672 ■ "Friends With Money" in *Canadian Business* **(Vol. 81, Summer 2008, No. 9, pp. 22)**
Pub: Rogers Media Ltd.
Description: Two of the most well connected managers in Canadian capital markets Rob Farquharson and Brian Gibson will launch Panoply Capital Asset Management in June. The investment management company aims to raise a billion dollars from institutions and high-net worth individuals.

41673 ■ "From Bikes to Building" in *Austin Business JournalInc.* **(Vol. 29, October 30, 2009, No. 34, pp. 1)**
Pub: American City Business Journals
Ed: Kate Harrington. **Description:** Tour de France champion Lance Armstrong, Bill Stapleton his long-time agent, and business manager Bart Knaggs have formed a privately held real estate investment company CSE Realty Parters in Austin, Texas. They see tremendous opportunity in the commercial real estate market in the area.

41674 ■ "From Lone Hero to a Culture of Leadership" in *Harvard Business Review* **(Vol. 88, November 2010, No. 11, pp. 146)**
Pub: Harvard Business School Publishing
Ed: Charles J. Palus, John B. McGuire. **Description:** Review of the book, 'Working Together: Why Great Partnerships Succeed', is given.

41675 ■ "From Malls to Steel Plants" in *Crain's Chicago Business* **(Vol. 31, April 28, 2008, No. 17, pp. 30)**
Pub: Crain Communications, Inc.
Ed: Samantha Stainburn. **Description:** Profile of the company Graycor Inc. which started out as a sandblasting and concrete-breaking firm but has grown into four businesses due to innovation and acquisitions. Graycor's businesses include: Graycor Industrial Constructors Inc., which builds and renovates power plants and steel mills; Graycor Construction Co., which erects stores, medical centers and office buildings; Graycor Blasting Co., which uses explosives and blasts tunnels for industrial cleaning, and Graycor International Inc., which provides construction services in Mexico.

41676 ■ "Futures Shock for the CME" in *Crain's Chicago Business* **(Vol. 31, November 10, 2008, No. 45, pp. 8)**
Pub: Crain Communications, Inc.
Ed: Ann Saphir. **Description:** Chicago-based CME Group Inc., the largest futures exchange operator in the U.S., is facing a potentially radically altered regulatory landscape as Congress weighs sweeping reform of financial oversight. The possible merger of the CFTC and the Securities and Exchange Commission are among CME's concerns. Other details of possible regulatory measures are provided.

41677 ■ "GeckoSystems Reduces Sensor Fusion Costs Due to Elder Care Robot Trials" in *Internet Wire* **(December 14, 2010)**
Pub: Comtex
Description: GeckoSystems International Corporation has been able to reduce the cost of its sensor fusion system while maintaining reliability and performance. The firm's ongoing first in-home elder care robot trials have sparked interest regarding its business model, technologies available for licensing, and joint domestic and international ventures.

41678 ■ "Getting in the Swing" in *Canadian Business* **(Vol. 80, February 26, 2007, No. 5, pp. 67)**
Pub: Rogers Media
Ed: Andrew Wahl. **Description:** The economic issues associated with the acquisition of Adams, Harkness and Hill Inc. by Canaccord Capital are presented. A large number of Canadian companies are entering into the United States.

41679 ■ "Giant Garages Could Rise Up Downtown" in *Business Courier* **(Vol. 27, October 22, 2010, No. 25, pp. 1)**
Pub: Business Courier
Ed: Dan Monk. **Description:** More than 2,500 new parking spaces could rise up to the eastern edge of downtown Cincinnati, Ohio as public and private

investors collect resources for new garage projects. These projects are expected to accommodate almost 1,500 monthly parkers who will lose access at Broadway Commons due to the construction of Harrah's casino.

41680 ■ "Give Me Liberty With DirecTV" in *Barron's* **(Vol. 89, July 13, 2009, No. 28, pp. M5)**
Pub: Dow Jones & Co., Inc.
Ed: Fleming Meeks. **Description:** Shares of Liberty Entertainment look cheap at $25.14 and the same goes for DirecTV at $23.19. A merger between the two companies was announced and the deal will likely close by September 2009. Barclays Capital has a target of $30 for Liberty Media and $32 for DirecTV.

41681 ■ "Glamis Reserves Get Boost With Western Silver Deal" in *Globe & Mail* **(February 25, 2006, pp. B3)**
Pub: CTVglobemedia Publishing Inc.
Ed: Wendy Stueck. **Description:** The details on Glamis Gold Ltd.'s proposed acquisition of Western Silver Corp., for $1.2 billion, are presented.

41682 ■ "Global Steel Makers Circle Stelco" in *Globe & Mail* **(April 19, 2007, pp. B3)**
Pub: CTVglobemedia Publishing Inc.
Ed: Greg Keenan. **Description:** The details of the take over bids offered to Stelco Inc. are presented. Due to these bids the shares of Stelco Inc rose up to 70 percent.

41683 ■ "GM-Chrysler Merger Could Cull Dealerships From Coast to Coast" in *Globe & Mail* **(February 20, 2007, pp. B17)**
Pub: CTVglobemedia Publishing Inc.
Ed: Greg Keenan. **Description:** General Motors Corp. is planning to acquire Chrysler Group. The challenges before the possible merger are presented.

41684 ■ "GM-Chrysler Merger: Just a Bigger Mess?" in *Globe & Mail* **(February 17, 2007, pp. B3)**
Pub: CTVglobemedia Publishing Inc.
Ed: Barrie McKenna; Greg Keenan. **Description:** The General Motors Corp. is negotiating talks to acquire DaimlerChrysler AG's Chrysler Group. The five reasons for the possible merger of the companies are presented.

41685 ■ "GM's Mortgage Unit Deal Brings in $9 Billion" in *Globe & Mail* **(March 24, 2006, pp. B3)**
Pub: CTVglobemedia Publishing Inc.
Ed: Shawn McCarthy. **Description:** General Motors Corp. sells General Motors Acceptance Corp.'s commercial real estate division to Kohlberg Kravis Roberts & Co. Five Mile Capital Partners LLC and Goldman Sachs Capital Partners. The reasons behind the deal are presented.

41686 ■ "Gold Handshake" in *Canadian Business* **(Vol. 79, September 11, 2006, No. 18, pp. 25)**
Pub: Rogers Media
Ed: John Gray. **Description:** Goldcorp Inc.'s company's planned takeover of Glamis Gold Ltd. is discussed. Implications of the merger on its investors are presented.

41687 ■ "Goldeye Completes Private Placement" in *Canadian Corporate News* **(May 16, 2007)**
Pub: Comtex News Network Inc.
Description: Goldeye, a Canadian mineral exploration company acquiring, exploring, and advancing properties in Chile and Canada, announced that it has completed a partially brokered private placement for gross proceeds of $1,232,660 which will be used to finance exploration on Goldeye's mineral properties in Chile and for administrative expenses, and working capital.

41688 ■ "Goldfingers" in *Canadian Business* **(Vol. 81, Summer 2008, No. 9, pp. 31)**
Pub: Rogers Media Ltd.
Ed: Sharda Prashad. **Description:** Large players in the mining industry are looking for junior mining companies in Canada to be acquired. The U.S. reces-

sion and subprime mortgage crisis have made it easier for giant miners to acquire small mining companies than to conduct the operations themselves. Junior miners are those that lack cash flow and expertise to build and operate mine

41689 ■ **"GoodNews.com and the Little Cupcake Shoppe Support Calgary Food Bank With Unique $1.00 Deal" in** *Marketwire Canada* **(March 9, 2011)**
Pub: Marketwire Canada
Description: Socially-conscious group-buying Website, GoodNews.com has partnered with The Little Cupcake Shoppe in Calgary, to raise funds for the Inter-Faith Food Bank. The fundraiser will feature a half dozen, pre-packaged assorted miniature cupcakes for $1.00. The entire amount is donated to the Calgary Food Bank.

41690 ■ **"Goodwill Haunts Local Companies; Bad Buyouts During Boom Times Producing Big Writedowns" in** *Crain's Chicago Business* **(Apr. 28, 2008)**
Pub: Crain Communications, Inc.
Ed: Ann Saphir. **Description:** Many companies are having to face the reality that they overpaid for acquisitions made in better economic times; investors often dismiss such one-time charges as mere accounting adjustments but writeoffs related to past acquisitions can signal future problems because they mean the expected profits that justified the purchase have not materialized. Writeoffs are particularly worrisome for firms with a lot of debt and whose banks require them to have enough assets to back up their borrowings.

41691 ■ **"Google, MySpace Deal Hits Snag" in** *Globe & Mail* **(February 7, 2007, pp. B11)**
Pub: CTVglobemedia Publishing Inc.
Ed: Julia Angwin; Kevin J. Delaney. **Description:** MySpace's intention to partner with eBay which is delaying the finalization of its $900 million online advertising deal signed with Google Inc. is discussed.

41692 ■ **"Great Stocks Cheap" in** *Canadian Business* **(Vol. 80, January 15, 2007, No. 2, pp. 31)**
Pub: Rogers Media
Ed: Calvin Leung. **Description:** The stock performance of top 10 international companies like Furgo, Moody's Investor Service, Adidas Group and Nestle is analyzed.

41693 ■ **"Green Acres" in** *Hawaii Business* **(Vol. 54, September 2008, No. 3, pp. 48)**
Pub: Hawaii Business Publishing
Ed: Jan Tenbruggencate. **Description:** Bill Cowern's Hawaiian Mahogany is a forestry business that processes low-value trees to be sold as wood chips, which can be burned to create biodiesel. Cowern is planning to obtain certification to market carbon credits and is also working with Green Energy Hawaii for the permit of a biomass-fueled power plant. Other details about Cowern's business are discussed.

41694 ■ **"Greenhouse Announces Merger With Custom Q, Inc." in** *Investment Weekly* **(January 30, 2010, pp. 338)**
Pub: Investment Weekly News
Description: In accordance with an Agreement and Plan of Share Exchange, GreenHouse Holdings, Inc., an innovative green solutions provider, has gone public via a reverse merger with Custom Q, Inc.

41695 ■ **"Grote Company Puts Final Wrap on Sandwich-Making Line" in** *Business First-Columbus* **(October 26, 2007, pp. A1)**
Pub: American City Business Journals, Inc.
Ed: Dan Eaton. **Description:** Grote Company acquired Oxfordshire, England-based Advanced Food Technology Ltd., giving the Ohio-based food cutting equipment company a manufacturing base in Europe. This is the company's second deal in four months. Details on Grote Company's plan to tap into the prepared fresh sandwich market are discussed.

41696 ■ **"Group-Buying Site Hones In on Hispanics" in** *Austin Business Journal* **(Vol. 31, July 1, 2011, No. 17, pp. 1)**
Pub: American City Business Journals Inc.
Ed: Vicky Garza. **Description:** Descuentl Libre is a new group-buying site from Austin, Texas that targets

the Hispanic market, offering discounts of practical items and family-friendly activities. The Hispanic market constitutes 17 percent of the U.S. population and spends $23 billion yearly online.

41697 ■ *Group Genius: The Creative Power of Collaboration*
Pub: Basic Books/Perseus Books Group
Ed: Keith Sawyer. **Released:** March 2008. **Price:** $16.95 paperback. **Description:** Organizations can foster creativity and innovation through discussion, argumentation and group activities.

41698 ■ *Growing Local Value: How to Build Business Partnerships That Strengthen Your Community*
Pub: Berrett-Koehler Publishers, Incorporated
Ed: Laury Hammel; Gun Denhart. **Released:** December 2006. **Price:** $15.00. **Description:** Advice and examples are provided for building socially responsible entrepreneurship.

41699 ■ **"Hain Celestial Acquires Greek Gods Yogurt" in** *Ice Cream Reporter* **(Vol. 23, July 20, 2010, No. 8, pp. 1)**
Pub: Ice Cream Reporter
Description: Hain Celestial Group acquired The Greek Gods LLC. Hain Celestial is a natural and organic products company and Greek Gods makes all natural, Greek-style yogurt and ice cream.

41700 ■ **"Hand-Held Heaven: Smallcakes Cupcakery" in** *Tulsa World* **(February 15, 2011)**
Pub: McClatchy Company
Description: Franchisee Carolyn Archer displays her products at Smallcakes Cupcakery, a Jenks shop that's the first to be co-branded with FreshBerry under the Beautiful Brands International banner. The shop's launch is part of a franchise deal between BBI and Jeff and Brandy Martin, co-owners of Smallcakes; twelve concepts have been developed and marketed already by Tulsa-based BBI.

41701 ■ *Happy About Joint Venturing: The 8 Critical Factors of Success*
Pub: Happy About
Ed: Valerie Orsoni-Vauthey. **Released:** June 2006. **Price:** $23.95. **Description:** An overview of joint venturing is presented.

41702 ■ **"The Harder Side of Sears" in** *Crain's Chicago Business* **(Vol. 31, March 31, 2008, No. 13, pp. 68)**
Pub: Crain Communications, Inc.
Ed: Steven R. Strahler. **Description:** Discusses the history of Sears Roebuck & Co. and its merger with Kmart Corp.

41703 ■ **"Harleysville Eyes Growth After Nationwide Deal" in** *Philadelphia Business Journal* **(Vol. 30, October 7, 2011, No. 34, pp. 1)**
Pub: American City Business Journals Inc.
Ed: Jeff Blumenthal. **Description:** Harleysville Group announced growth plans after the company was sold to Columbus, Ohio-based Nationwide Mutual Insurance Company for about $1.63 billion. Nationwide gained an independent agency platform in 32 states with the Harleysville deal.

41704 ■ **"Has Microsoft Found a Way to Get at Yahoo?" in** *Advertising Age* **(Vol. 79, July 7, 2008, No. 26, pp. 4)**
Pub: Crain Communications, Inc.
Ed: Abbey Klaassen. **Description:** Microsoft's attempt to acquire Yahoo's search business is discussed as is Yahoo's plans for the future at a time when the company's shares have fallen dangerously low.

41705 ■ **"HBC Sells Credit Card Division" in** *Globe & Mail* **(February 8, 2006, pp. B1)**
Pub: CTVglobemedia Publishing Inc.
Ed: Sinclair Stewart; Marina Strauss. **Description:** The details on General Electric Co.'s acquisition of Hudson's Bay Co.'s credit card division, for $370 million, are presented.

41706 ■ **"HBC Sets Friday as Deadline to Trump Zucker Takeover Bid" in** *Globe & Mail* **(January 18, 2006, pp. B1)**
Pub: CTVglobemedia Publishing Inc.
Ed: Marina Strauss. **Description:** The reasons behind Hudson's Bay Co.'s decision to seek alternative bids on the company are presented. Investor Jerry Zucker earlier offered $1.1 billion for the company.

41707 ■ **"Health Care of the Future" in** *Business Journal Serving Greater Tampa Bay* **(Vol. 30, November 19, 2010, No. 48, pp. 1)**
Pub: Tampa Bay Business Journal
Ed: Margie Manning. **Description:** Information about accountable care organizations (ACO), which are integrated care systems with doctors and hospitals working closely together to handle patient care, is provided. The Patient Protection and Affordable Care Act paved the way for ACOs as Medicare demonstration projects.

41708 ■ **"Health Care Leads Sectors Attracting Capital" in** *Hispanic Business* **(Vol. 30, March 2008, No. 3, pp. 14)**
Pub: Hispanic Business
Ed: Scott Williams. **Description:** Discusses the capital gains of Hispanic-owned companies and other Hispanic leaders in the investment and retail fields in the year 2007. Sectors like health care, media, food and technology saw a healthy flow of capital due to successful mergers, acquisitions and increased private equity investments.

41709 ■ **"HealthTronics Eager to Buy" in** *Austin Business JournalInc.* **(Vol. 28, September 12, 2008, No. 26, pp. 1)**
Pub: American City Business Journals
Ed: Laura Hipp. **Description:** HealthTronics Inc., an Austin, Texas urology equipment company has repeated its offer to buy Endocare Inc., an Irvine, California tumor technology firm for $26.9 million. The proposal has been revised to allow Endocare shareholders to choose between HealthTronics cash or shares. Endocare has not commented on the offer.

41710 ■ **"Healthy Fast Food Acquires Rights to U-Swirl Yogurt" in** *Ice Cream Reporter* **(Vol. 21, October 20, 2008, No. 11, pp. 5)**
Pub: Ice Cream Reporter
Description: Healthy Fast Food Inc. will acquire worldwide rights to U-Swirl Frozen Yogurt; the firm will use the new acquisition to create a yogurt superstore in a cafe setting concept for its operations.

41711 ■ **"The Heat Is On" in** *Crain's Chicago Business* **(Vol. 31, April 28, 2008, No. 17, pp. 4)**
Pub: Crain Communications, Inc.
Ed: Steve Daniels. **Description:** Discusses Nicor Inc., a natural-gas utility serving 2 million customers in Chicago's suburbs, and its potential acquirers; shares of the company have dropped 17 percent this year making Nicor the second-worst among 31 utilities in an index tracked by Standrd & Poor's. Statistical data included.

41712 ■ **"Heat's On, but Glacier Not Retreating" in** *Globe & Mail* **(January 26, 2006, pp. B3)**
Pub: CTVglobemedia Publishing Inc.
Ed: Grant Robertson. **Description:** The details on Glacier Ventures International Corp., which acquired Hollinger International Inc.'s assets, are presented.

41713 ■ **"His Way" in** *Inc.* **(February 2008, pp. 90-97)**
Pub: Gruner & Jahr USA Publishing
Ed: Stephanie Clifford. **Description:** Profile of Chris Reed, founder of a natural soda company, who undertook an initial public offering (IPO). Reed discusses the challenges he faced mediating with the Securities Exchange Commission regarding his firm's IPO.

41714 ■ **"Hispanic Business Group Leader Continues Push for Better Inclusion" in** *Crain's Cleveland Business* **(Vol. 30, June 22, 2009, No. 24)**
Pub: Crain Communications, Inc.
Ed: Jay Miller. **Description:** Hispanic Business Association is working to create more opportunities for

Hispanic business owners. The article discusses the Minority Business Accelerator 2.5 program of the Greater Cleveland Partnership that helps minority-owned small businesses.

41715 ■ "The Hollow Debate" in *Canadian Business* (Vol. 81, March 3, 2008, No. 3, pp. 26)
Pub: Rogers Media

Ed: Thomas Watson. **Description:** According to a report conducted by the Conference Board of Canada, the Canadian business community is not being hollowed out by acquisitions made by foreign companies. Findings further showed that local businesses are protected by dual shares and that the economy can benefit more from foreign acquisitions than local mergers. The need to relax foreign ownership restrictions and other recommendations are presented.

41716 ■ "Hong Kong's Boom in IPO" in *Barron's* (Vol. 89, July 13, 2009, No. 28, pp. M7)
Pub: Dow Jones & Co., Inc.

Ed: Nick Lord. **Description:** Hong Kong's IPO (initial public offering) market is booming with 13 Chinese IPOs already on the calendar for the year as July 2009. One of them is Bawang International which raised $214 million after generating $9 billion in order which makes it 42 times oversubscribed.

41717 ■ "Horizon Acquires Significant Working Interest in High Impact Prospect in Southeast Texas" in *Canadian Corporate News* (May 14, 2007)
Pub: Comtex News Network Inc.

Description: Horizon Industries Ltd., an emerging gas and oil exploration and production company, announced that it has entered into a Joint Venture agreement with Pan American Development Company, Inc. in which they will begin a drilling program in San Jacinto County, Texas.

41718 ■ "Hospital Fighting for Its Life; Board of St. Anthony Scrambles to Stem Losses" in *Crain's Chicago Business* (April 28, 2008)
Pub: Crain Communications, Inc.

Ed: Mike Colias. **Description:** Chicago's Catholic health chain was looking to sell the money-losing hospital St. Anthony Hospital on the West Side but with the financial picture improving and no merger offers in the works the investment bank hired to shop the hospital is hoping to operate the 111-year-old facility as an independent entity. St. Anthony serves as a "safety net" for the region since an increasing number of its patients are uninsured or on public aid, which pays far less than commercial insurers.

41719 ■ "How to Beat Jet Lag for $550,000" in *Globe & Mail* (January 3, 2006, pp. B1)
Pub: CTVglobemedia Publishing Inc.

Ed: Simon Avery. **Description:** The details on DreamWorks Animation SKG Inc., which developed videoconferencing software 'Halo' in association with Hewlett-Packard Co., are presented.

41720 ■ *How to Become a Great Boss: The Rules for Getting and Keeping the Best Employees*
Pub: Hyperion Special Markets

Ed: Jeffrey J. Fox. **Released:** May 15, 2002. **Price:** $16.95. **Description:** The book offers valuable advice to any manager or entrepreneur to improve leadership and management skills. Topics covered include: hiring, managing, firing, partnership and competition, self and organization, employee performance, attitude, and priorities.

41721 ■ "How to Conquer New Markets With Old Skills" in *Harvard Business Review* (Vol. 88, November 2010, No. 11, pp. 118)
Pub: Harvard Business School Publishing

Ed: Mauro F. Guillen, Esteban Garcia-Canal. **Description:** Exploration of business-networking factors that have helped lead to the success of Spain's multinational companies is provided. These include development of political skills, access to capabilities and resources, globalization partnerships, and speed of implementation.

41722 ■ "How I Did It: Jack Ma" in *Inc.* (January 2008, pp. 94-102)
Pub: Gruner & Jahr USA Publishing

Ed: Rebecca Fannin. **Description:** Profile of Jack Ma, who started as a guide and interpreter for Western tourists in Hangzhou. Ma used the Internet to build Alibaba.com, China's largest business-to-business site and one of the hottest IPOs in years.

41723 ■ "How to Play the Tech Mergers" in *Barron's* (Vol. 90, August 30, 2010, No. 35, pp. 18)
Pub: Barron's Editorial & Corporate Headquarters

Ed: Tiernan Ray. **Description:** The intense bidding by Hewlett-Packard and Dell for 3Par was foreseen in a previous Barron's cover story and 3Par's stock has nearly tripled since reported. Other possible acquisition targets in the tech industry include Brocade Communication Systems, NetApp, Xyratex, and Isilon Systems.

41724 ■ "How Yamana CEO First Struck Gold With Desert Sun" in *Globe & Mail* (February 27, 2006, pp. B3)
Pub: CTVglobemedia Publishing Inc.

Ed: Andrew Willis. **Description:** The role of chief executive officer Peter Marronne of Yamana Gold Inc. in the acquisition of Desert Sun Mining Corp. is discussed.

41725 ■ *I'm on LinkedIn - Now What? (Second Edition): A Guide to Getting the Most Out of LinkedIn*
Pub: Happy About

Ed: Diane Danielson. **Released:** January 7, 2009. **Price:** $19.95. **Description:** Designed to help get the most out of LinkedIn, the popular business networking site and follows the first edition and includes the latest and great approaches using LinkedIn. With over 32 million members there is a lot of potential to find and develop relationships to help in your business and personal life, but many professionals find themselves wondering what to do once they sign up. This book explains the different benefits of the system and recommends best practices (including LinkedIn Groups) so that you get the most out of LinkedIn.

41726 ■ "Imax in Play as It Explores Options" in *Globe & Mail* (March 10, 2006, pp. B3)
Pub: CTVglobemedia Publishing Inc.

Ed: Shirley Won. **Description:** Imax Corp. has put up itself for sale, and has also confirmed that it has received unsolicited offers for purchase.

41727 ■ "iMozi Integrates Esprida LiveControl for Advanced DVD Kiosk Hardware" in *Wireless News* (December 20, 2010)
Pub: Close-Up Media Inc.

Description: Provider of self-service entertainment technology, iMozi Canada has partnered with Esprida to make its automated DVD Kiosk solutions Esprida-enabled. Esprida develops remote device management solutions and will offer enhanced capabilities and to improve customer experience for users.

41728 ■ "The Impact of Acquisitions On the Productivity of Inventors at Semiconductor Firms" in *Academy of Management Journal* (October 2007)
Pub: Academy of Management

Ed: Rahul Kapoor, Kwanghui Lim. **Description:** Study examined the relation between knowledge-based and incentive-based outlook in explaining the impact of acquisitions on the productivity of inventors at acquired semiconductor firms. Results showed a definite relation between the two perspectives.

41729 ■ "In the Public Eye" in *Entrepreneur* (Vol. 35, November 2007, No. 11, pp. 75)
Pub: Entrepreneur Media Inc.

Ed: David Worrell. **Description:** The market for initial public offerings (IPOs) was booming in 2007 and strong fundamentals for companies that would like to go public are needed. The basics that companies should review before planning an IPO are outlined.

41730 ■ "Inco Takeover Faces Foreign Hurdles" in *Globe & Mail* (February 14, 2006, pp. B1)
Pub: CTVglobemedia Publishing Inc.

Ed: Paul Waldie. **Description:** The issues that impact Inco Ltd.'s acquisition of Falconbridge Ltd., for $12.5 billion, are presented. Inco Ltd. is awaiting foreign regulatory approval in the United States and Europe.

41731 ■ "Inco's Takeover Offer Extended Four Months" in *Globe & Mail* (February 22, 2006, pp. B1)
Pub: CTVglobemedia Publishing Inc.

Ed: Wendy Stueck. **Description:** United States and Europe competition authorities wanted more time to investigate Inco Ltd.'s takeover of Falconbridge Ltd. and compelling Inco to extend its $12.5 billion offer for the third time.

41732 ■ "Indian Buyer Gives Life to Algoma Expansion" in *Globe & Mail* (April 17, 2007, pp. B1)
Pub: CTVglobemedia Publishing Inc.

Ed: Greg Keenan. **Description:** The proposed capacity expansion of Algoma Steel Inc. after its acquisition by Essar Global Ltd. is discussed.

41733 ■ "Ingrian and Channel Management International Sign Distribution Agreement" in *Canadian Corporate News* (May 16, 2007)
Pub: Comtex News Network Inc.

Description: Channel Management International (CMI), a Canadian channel management and distribution company, and Ingrian Networks, Inc., the leading provider of data privacy solutions, announced a Canadian distribution agreement to resell Ingrian encryption solutions to the Canadian market.

41734 ■ "Inland Snaps Up Rival REITs" in *Crain's Chicago Business* (Vol. 31, November 17, 2008, No. 46, pp. 3)
Pub: Crain Communications, Inc.

Ed: Alby Gallun. **Description:** Discusses Inland American Real Estate Trust Inc., a real estate investment trust that is napping up depressed shares of publicly traded competitors, a possible first step toward taking over these companies; however, with hotel and retail properties accounting for approximately 70 percent of its portfolio, the company could soon face its own difficulties.

41735 ■ "Inmet Selling Nunavut Mining Properties" in *Globe & Mail* (February 15, 2006, pp. B6)
Pub: CTVglobemedia Publishing Inc.

Ed: Allan Robinson. **Description:** The details on Wolfden Resources Inc.'s acquisition of mining assets of Inmet Mining Corp. are presented.

41736 ■ "Innovative Growth" in *Small Business Opportunities* (March 2008)
Pub: Harris Publications Inc.

Ed: Peter Erickson. **Description:** Nine tips are outlined to help small companies and entrepreneurs to partner with larger companies.

41737 ■ *Instant Income*
Pub: McGraw-Hill Inc.

Ed: Janet Switzer. **Released:** February 2007. **Price:** $30.95 (CND). **Description:** Book covers small business advertising techniques, marketing, joint ventures, and sales.

41738 ■ "An Insurance Roll-Up In Danger of Unraveling" in *Barron's* (Vol. 88, March 17, 2008, No. 11, pp. 51)
Pub: Dow Jones & Company, Inc.

Ed: Bill Alpert. **Description:** Shares of National Financial Partners have fallen below their initial offering price as sputtering sales and management turnover leave many investors wondering. One of the company's star brokers is being sued for their "life settlement" contracts while another broker is being pursued by the IRS for unpaid taxes.

41739 ■ "International Nickel Ventures Corporation Reports Results for the First Quarter 2007" in *Canadian Corporate News* (May 16, 2007)
Pub: Comtex News Network Inc.

Description: Profile of International Nickel Ventures Corporation (INV) including its financial report for the first quarter of fiscal 2007, its partnership and possible acquisition of Teck Cominco Limited, and its plans for the future. Statistical data included.

41740 ■ **"Internet Translation Service Helps Burmese"** in *News-Sentinel* (May 10, 2011)
Pub: New-Sentinel

Ed: Ellie Bogue. **Description:** Catherine Kasper Place, Parkview Health Community Outreach, Allen County-Fort Wayne Department of Health and Advantage Health have partnered to help the Burmese Community in the area by providing an online service that links doctors' offices with translators in order to provide better healthcare.

41741 ■ **"Intrawest Puts Itself on Market"** in *Globe & Mail* (March 1, 2006, pp. B1)
Pub: CTVglobemedia Publishing Inc.

Ed: Elizabeth Church. **Description:** The reasons behind the decision of Intrawest Corp. to go for sale or seek partnerships are presented. The company appointed Goldman Sachs & Co. to meet the purpose.

41742 ■ **"Inventive Doctor New Venture Partner"** in *Houston Business Journal* (Vol. 40, January 29, 2010, No. 38, pp. A2)
Pub: American City Business Journals

Ed: Ford Gunter. **Description:** Dr. Billy Cohn, a surgeon from Houston, Texas has been named as venture partner for venture firm Sante Ventures LLC of Austin, Texas. Cohn will be responsible for seeing marketable developing technologies in the medical industry. The motivation for Cohn's naming as venture partner is his development of a minimally invasive therapy for end-stage renal disease.

41743 ■ **"Investment Bank Predicts Shakeup in Farm Equipment Industry"** in *Farm Industry News* (November 16, 2011)
Pub: Penton Business Media Inc.

Ed: Jodie Wehrspann. **Description:** Farming can expect to see more mergers and acquisitions in the agricultural equipment industry, as it appears to be in the early stages of growth over the next few years.

41744 ■ **"Investment Firms Unite: Coalition Fights New Tax Law"** in *Black Enterprise* (Vol. 38, December 2007, No. 5, pp. 52)
Pub: Earl G. Graves Publishing Co. Inc.

Ed: Joyce Jones. **Description:** Minorities working in private equity, real estate and investment management firms have united to form the Access to Capital Coalition to oppose legislation that they feel would adversely affect their ability to attract investments and executives. Details of the group are included.

41745 ■ **"ITT Places Its Bet With Defense Buy; Selling Equipment to Army Pays Off"** in *Crain's New York Business* (Vol. 24, January 7, 2008)
Pub: Crain Communications, Inc.

Description: ITT Corp.'s revenue has jumped by 20 percent in each of the past three years due to demand for the company's radio sets and night-vision goggles. The firm has acquired EDO Corp., which specializes in battlefield communications systems, in an attempt to expand its defense-industry division.

41746 ■ **"Jamieson Eyes $175 Million Trust IPO"** in *Globe & Mail* (March 7, 2006, pp. B1)
Pub: CTVglobemedia Publishing Inc.

Ed: Sinclair Stewart; Leonard Zehr. **Description:** The reasons behind $175 million initial public offering plans of Jamieson Laboratories Ltd. are presented.

41747 ■ **"Janet Froetscher, CEO, United Way of Metropolitan Chicago"** in *Crain's Chicago Business* (Vol. 31, May 5, 2008, No. 18, pp. 26)
Pub: Crain Communications, Inc.

Ed: Emily Stone. **Description:** Profile of Janet Froetscher who is the CEO of United Way of Metropolitan Chicago who organized the country's largest-ever merger of non-profits with 53 smaller suburban chapters consolidating with the Chicago one. The consolidation saves $4 million a year with departments such as finance, information technology and communications which allows that money be spent

funding job training, after-school programs and aid for 7,000 Hurricane Katrina evacuees living in the Chicago area.

41748 ■ **"Janson: Duke's Dynamo, Regional President Focuses on Economic Development"** in *Business Courier* (Vol. 27, July 9, 2010, No. 10, pp. 1)
Pub: Business Courier

Ed: Lucy May. **Description:** Duke Energy President Julie Janson is also chair of the Cincinnati USA Partnership for Economic Development and the co-chair of the Cincinnati Business Committee's Economic Development Task Force. Duke is launching a Site Readiness Pilot Program to help the region prepare for an economic recovery.

41749 ■ **"Jo-Ann Fabric and Craft Stores Joins ArtFire.com to Offer Free Online Craft Marketplace"** in *Internet Wire* (January 26, 2010)
Pub: Comtex News Network, Inc.

Description: Jo-Ann Fabric and Craft Stores has entered into a partnership with ArtFire.com which will provide sewers and crafters all the tools they need in order to make and sell their products from an online venue.

41750 ■ **"Joint Venture Plans Bronzeville Project"** in *Business Journal-Milwaukee* (Vol. 25, October 5, 2007, No. 1, pp. A1)
Pub: American City Business Journals, Inc.

Ed: Rich Kirchen. **Description:** Proposal for construction of an apartment building and possible expansion of Northtown Mall in Milwaukee, Wisconsin is being planned by developers in the city's Bronzeville area. The project for rehabilitating the existing mall and building of a 50-unit apartment would amount to about $12.5 million.

41751 ■ **"Juicy Feud; Deal Caps Years of Rancor in Wrigley Gum Dynasty"** in *Crain's Chicago Business* (Vol. 31, May 5, 2008, No. 18, pp. 1)
Pub: Crain Communications, Inc.

Ed: David Sterrett. **Description:** Discusses the sale of Wm. Wrigley Jr. Co. to Mars Inc. and Warren Buffett for $23 billion as well as the intra-family feuding which has existed for nearly a decade since William Wrigley Jr. took over as CEO of the company following his father's death.

41752 ■ **"KBA, Graphic Art System Partner on Cold Foil"** in *American Printer* (Vol. 128, June 1, 2011, No. 6)
Pub: Penton Media Inc.

Description: KBA North America has partnered with Graphic Art System to retrofit and equip presses with cold foil machines.

41753 ■ **"Keeping Railcars 'Busy At All Times' At TTX"** in *Crain's Chicago Business* (Vol. 31, April 28, 2008, No. 17, pp. 6)
Pub: Crain Communications, Inc.

Ed: Bob Tita. **Description:** Profile of the president of Chicago railcar pool operator TTX Co. and his business plan for the company which includes improving fleet management and car purchasing through better use of data on railroad demand.

41754 ■ **"Kerkorian Shakes Up Chrysler Race"** in *Globe & Mail* (April 6, 2007, pp. B1)
Pub: CTVglobemedia Publishing Inc.

Ed: Greg Keenan. **Description:** The bid of Kirk Kerkorian's Tracinda Corp. to acquire Daimler-Chrysler AG for $4.5 billion is discussed.

41755 ■ **"Kinross Holds Firm on Offer for Bema"** in *Globe & Mail* (January 20, 2007, pp. B5)
Pub: CTVglobemedia Publishing Inc.

Ed: Andy Hoffman. **Description:** The acquisition of Bema Gold Corp. by Kinross Gold Corp. is discussed.

41756 ■ **"Knight Sold as Industry Struggles"** in *Globe & Mail* (March 14, 2006, pp. D1)
Pub: CTVglobemedia Publishing Inc.

Ed: Christopher Rowland. **Description:** McClatchy Co. said that it would buy Knight Ridder Inc. for $4.5 billion, which is a newspaper giant in United States. The details of McClatchy acquisition plans for Knight Ridder news syndicate are analyzed.

41757 ■ **"Kodak Offers Cloud-Based Operating Option"** in *American Printer* (Vol. 128, June 1, 2011, No. 6)
Pub: Penton Media Inc.

Description: Kodak partnered with VMware to offer its first Virtual Operating Environment option for Kodak Unified Workflow Solutions. The new feature enables cost savings, increased efficiency and failover protection.

41758 ■ **"Kubicki Juggles Lineup at Vianda"** in *Business Courier* (Vol. 26, December 11, 2009, No. 33, pp. 1)
Pub: American City Business Journals, Inc.

Ed: Dan Monk. **Description:** Cincinnati real estate developer Chuck Kubicki replaced the management team of Vianda LLC and cancelled contracts with two vendors that caused a surge of customer complaints. Vianda is a direct-response marketing firm that sells and distributes dietary supplements for wellness and sexual performance.

41759 ■ **"Labatt to Swallow Lakeport"** in *Globe & Mail* (February 2, 2007, pp. B1)
Pub: CTVglobemedia Publishing Inc.

Ed: Keith McArthur. **Description:** The decision of Labatt Brewing Company Ltd. to acquire Lakeport Brewing Income Fund for $201.4 million is discussed.

41760 ■ **"Land Agent Taken Over"** in *Farmer's Weekly* (March 28, 2008, No. 320)
Pub: Reed Business Information

Description: Property business Smiths Gore will take over Cluttons' rural division, one of the oldest names in land agency. Cluttons said it had decided to sell its rural business as part of a strategic repositioning that would refocus the business on commercial, residential and overseas opportunities.

41761 ■ **"The Last Ingredient?"** in *Canadian Business* (Vol. 81, October 13, 2008, No. 17, pp. 88)
Pub: Rogers Media Ltd.

Ed: Rachel Pulfer. **Description:** Views and information on Cookie Jar Group's plan to acquire rights for Strawberry Shortcake and the Care Bears are discussed. The move would make Cookie Jar a major player in the global children's entertainment market. Cookie Jar chief executive, Michael Hirsh is believed to be securing funds for the planned $195 million acquisition.

41762 ■ **"Late to Minivan Party, VW Hitches Ride With Daimler"** in *Globe & Mail* (January 6, 2006, pp. B1)
Pub: CTVglobemedia Publishing Inc.

Ed: Greg Keenan. **Description:** DaimlerChrysler AG and Volkswagen AG plans to manufacture minivan. The details of joint venture are presented.

41763 ■ **"Lathrop Finds Partner In LA"** in *The Business Journal-Serving Metropolitan Kansas City* (Vol. 27, November 21, 2008, No. 11, pp. 1)
Pub: American City Business Journals, Inc.

Ed: Steve Vockrodt. **Description:** Kansas, Missouri-based Lathrop and Gage LLP is planning to merge with Spillane Shaeffer Aronoff Bandlow LLP. The merging of the business law firms will add entertainment clients to Lathrop's fold. Comments from executives are also presented.

41764 ■ **"Laugh or Cry?"** in *Barron's* (Vol. 88, March 24, 2008, No. 12, pp. 7)
Pub: Dow Jones & Company, Inc.

Ed: Alan Abelson. **Description:** Discusses the American economy which is just starting to feel the effect of the credit and housing crises. JPMorgan Chase purchased Bear Stearns for $2 a share, much lower than its share price of $60, while quasi-government entities Fannie Mae and Freddie Mac are starting to run into trouble.

41765 ■ **"Leadership Training"** in *Black Enterprise* (Vol. 37, January 2007, No. 6, pp. 56)
Pub: Earl G. Graves Publishing Co. Inc.

Ed: Sonia Alleyne. **Description:** Profile of Theopolis Holman, Group Vice-President of Duke Energy, who discusses how he prepared for the merger between Duke Energy and Cinergy. Holman oversees a division of 9,000 service contractors and employees.

41766 ■ **"Leapin' Lizards, Does SoBe Have Some Work To Do On Life Water" in** *Brandweek* **(Vol. 49, April 21, 2008, No. 16, pp. 32)**
Pub: VNU Business Media, Inc.
Ed: Amy Shea. **Description:** Discusses the competing marketing campaigns of both Vitaminwater, now owned by Coca-Cola, and SoBe Life Water which is owned by Pepsi; also looks at the repositioning of Life Water as a thirst-quencher, rather than a green product as well as the company's newest advertising campaign.

41767 ■ **"Lenders Capitalize on a Thinning Bulge Bracket" in** *Mergers & Acquisitions: The Dealmaker's Journal* **(March 1, 2008)**
Pub: SourceMedia, Inc.
Description: Regardless of what the economic markets look like, private equity firms will continue to invest capital and mid-market finance firms are becoming very attractive acquisition opportunities since not as much capital is needed to buy them.

41768 ■ **"Let the Big Fish Eat" in** *Canadian Business* **(Vol. 80, March 12, 2007, No. 6, pp. 4)**
Pub: Rogers Media
Ed: Joe Chidley. **Description:** The need for profitable Canadian banks to go for mergers to enjoy the benefits of globalization and compete with global banks is discussed.

41769 ■ *Let's Buy a Company: How to Accelerate Growth Through Acquisitions*
Pub: Career Press, Incorporated
Ed: H. Lee Rust. **Released:** January 2006. **Price:** $18.99 (US), $25.95 (Canadian). **Description:** Advice for negotiating terms and pricing as well as other aspects of mergers and acquisitions in small companies.

41770 ■ **"A Lifetime of Making Deals" in** *Crain's Detroit Business* **(Vol. 24, March 24, 2008, No. 12, pp. 11)**
Pub: Crain Communications, Inc.
Ed: Tom Henderson. **Description:** Profile of Walter "Bud" Aspatore who received Crain's Lifetime Achievement Award for mergers and acquisitions; Aspatore is chairman and co-founder of Amherst Partners L.L.C., an investment banking firm that does evaluations and financings, specializes in turnarounds and advises private and public companies on mergers and acquisitions.

41771 ■ **"Li'l Guy Rolls Up Into Bigger Company" in** *The Business Journal-Serving Metropolitan Kansas City* **(Vol. 26, September 12, 2008)**
Pub: American City Business Journals, Inc.
Ed: Suzanna Stagemeyer. **Description:** Li'l Guy Foods, a Mexican food company in Kansas City, Missouri, has merged with Tortilla King Inc. Li'l Guy's revenue in 2007 was $3.3 million, while a newspaper report said that Tortilla King's revenue in 2001 was $7.5 million. Growth opportunities for the combined companies and Li'l Guy's testing of the Wichita market are discussed.

41772 ■ **"A Limited Sphere of Influence" in** *Mergers & Acquisitions: The Dealmaker's Journal* **(March 1, 2008)**
Pub: SourceMedia, Inc.
Ed: Ken MacFadyen. **Description:** Changes to the interest rate has had little impact on the mergers and acquisitions market since the federal funds rate does not link directly to the liquidity available to the M&A market; lenders are looking at cash flows and are likely to remain cautious due to other factors impacting the market.

41773 ■ **"A Local Affair: Decisions for Tops Again Being Made at Amherst HQ" in** *Business First Buffalo* **(December 7, 2007, pp. 3)**
Pub: American City Business Journals, Inc.
Ed: James Fink. **Description:** Tops Market LLC merged with Morgan Stanley Private Equity and names its new CEO, Frank Curci. The company headquarters moved to its new location in Amherst, New York.

41774 ■ **"Local M&A Activity Sputters in 1Q" in** *Crain's Chicago Business* **(Vol. 31, April 21, 2008, No. 16, pp. 20)**
Pub: Crain Communications, Inc.
Ed: H. Lee Murphy. **Description:** Local mergers-and-acquisitions activity is down by 34 percent in the first quarter compared to the fourth quarter of last year due to the credit crisis making financing harder to obtain.

41775 ■ **"Local TV Hits Media Radar Screen" in** *Business Courier* **(Vol. 27, July 2, 2010, No. 9, pp. 1)**
Pub: Business Courier
Ed: Dan Monk. **Description:** Fort Wright, Kentucky-based broadcasting company Local TV LLC has acquired 18 television stations since its founding in 2007, potentially boosting its chances of becoming a media empire. In the last twelve months that ended in March 2010, Local TV LLC has posted total revenues of $415 million. How Local TV LLC has entered into cost-sharing deals with other stations is also discussed.

41776 ■ **"Looking For Financing?" in** *Hispanic Business* **(Vol. 30, July-August 2008, No. 7-8, pp. 16)**
Pub: Hispanic Business, Inc.
Ed: Frank Nelson. **Description:** Investment firms want to know about businesses that need funding for either expansion or acquisition; companies fitting this profile are interviewed and their perceptions are discussed. Investment firms need businesses to be realistic in their expectations and business plans which show spending of funds and expected benefits, long term goals, track record and strong management teams.

41777 ■ **"The Lost Opportunity for a Canadian Steel Giant" in** *Globe & Mail* **(April 23, 2007, pp. B1)**
Pub: CTVglobemedia Publishing Inc.
Ed: Greg Keenan. **Description:** The efforts of Algoma Steel Inc. to create a Canadian steel manufacturer that could survive the global trends of consolidation in the steel industry are described. The company's efforts to acquire Stelco Inc., Ivaco Inc. and Slater Steel Inc. are discussed.

41778 ■ **"Lundin Deal Leaves Nickel Market Thin" in** *Globe & Mail* **(April 5, 2007, pp. B4)**
Pub: CTVglobemedia Publishing Inc.
Ed: Andy Hoffman. **Description:** The likely acquisition of Rio Narcea Gold Mines Ltd. by Lundin Mining Corp. and the decreasing number of nickel mining companies on the list of Toronto Stock Exchange are discussed.

41779 ■ **"Magpower May Build Solar Panels Here" in** *Austin Business Journal* **(Vol. 31, May 13, 2011, No. 10, pp. A1)**
Pub: American City Business Journals Inc.
Ed: Christopher Calnan. **Description:** RRE Austin Solar LLC CEO Doven Mehta has revealed plans to partner with Portugal-based Magpower SA, only if Austin energy buys electricity from planned solar energy farm in Pflugerville. Austin Energy has received 100 bids from 35 companies to supply 200 megawatts of solar- and wind-generated electricity.

41780 ■ **"Making the Cut; Osprey Takes Undervalued Courses to the Leader Board" in** *Crain's Detroit Business* **(Vol. 24, April 7, 2008, No. 14)**
Pub: Crain Communications, Inc.
Ed: Jason Deegan. **Description:** Profile of Osprey Management Co., a diverse real estate company that continues to expand its golf portfolio through the company's recreation division; although many developers are getting out of the field due to Michigan's sluggish golf industry, Osprey has found success by purchasing properties in turmoil for more affordable prices.

41781 ■ **"M&T On the March?" in** *Baltimore Business Journal* **(Vol. 28, November 12, 2010, No. 27, pp. 1)**
Pub: Baltimore Business Journal
Ed: Gary Haber. **Description:** Information on the growth of M&T Bank, as well as its expansion plans are presented. M&T recently acquired Wilmington Trust and took over $500 million in deposits from the failed K Bank. Analysts believe that M&T would continue its expansion through Washington DC and Richmond, Virginia, especially after a bank executive acknowledged that the markets in those areas are attractive.

41782 ■ **"Manufacturers Become Part of Coalition" in** *Contractor* **(Vol. 56, July 2009, No. 7, pp. 40)**
Pub: Penton Media, Inc.
Description: Bradford White Water Heaters, Rheem Water Heating, Rinnai America Corp., and A.O. Smith Water Heaters have joined the Consortium for Energy Efficiency in the Coalition for Energy Star Water Heaters. The coalition seeks to increase the awareness of Energy Star water heaters.

41783 ■ **"Market Squeezes Some Lawyers" in** *Austin Business JournalInc.* **(Vol. 28, December 12, 2008, No. 39, pp. 1)**
Pub: American City Business Journals
Ed: Jean Kwon. **Description:** Austin, Texas-based lawyers have been adversely affected by the economic downturn. Fewer works for lawyers in mergers and acquisitions and other activities are being offered. Lawyers are refinancing debts and offering other services.

41784 ■ **"MBA Project Turns on Tastebuds" in** *The Business Journal - Serving Phoenix and the Valley of the Sun* **(Vol. 28, August 15, 2008, No. 50)**
Pub: American City Business Journals, Inc.
Ed: Angela Gonzales. **Description:** Amol Khade, Venkat Nallapati and Govind Arora, master of businesss administration graduates from Thunderbird School of Global Management, have opened an Indian restaurant, called The Daba, in Tempe, Arizona. The Indian name of the restaurant means 'a place for travelers to stop for rest and food'. Franchise plans for the restaurant are discussed.

41785 ■ **"McClatchy Believed Front-Runner in Knight Ridder Sale" in** *Globe & Mail* **(March 13, 2006, pp. B6)**
Pub: CTVglobemedia Publishing Inc.
Ed: Joseph T. Hallinan; Dennis K. Berman. **Description:** The details on proposed acquisition of Knight Ridder Inc. by McClatchy Co. are presented.

41786 ■ **"Meadowbrook CEO Sees 20 Percent Growth With New Acquisition" in** *Crain's Detroit Business* **(Vol. 24, March 10, 2008, No. 10, pp. 4)**
Pub: Crain Communications, Inc.
Ed: Jay Greene. **Description:** Discusses the major turnaround of Meadowbrook Insurance Group after Robert Cubbin became CEO and implemented a new business strategy.

41787 ■ **"Meadowbrook To Acquire ProCentury in $272.6 Million Deal" in** *Crain's Detroit Business* **(Vol. 24, February 25, 2008, No. 8, pp. 4)**
Pub: Crain Communications Inc. - Detroit
Description: Meadowbrook Insurance Group, based in Southfield, Michigan reports its proposed acquisition of ProCentury Corporation based in Columbus, Ohio. Meadowbrook provides risk-management to agencies, professional and trade associations and small-to-midsize businesses.

41788 ■ **"Measuring the Impact" in** *Mergers & Acquisitions: The Dealmaker's Journal* **(March 1, 2008)**
Pub: SourceMedia, Inc.
Ed: Ken MacFadyen. **Description:** Discusses a new study out of Europe which contends that the private equity market does not have as much impact on the overall economy as critics contend.

41789 ■ **"MEC, Churchill Downs Saddle Up in Racing Deal" in** *Globe & Mail* **(March 6, 2007, pp. B1)**
Pub: CTVglobemedia Publishing Inc.
Ed: Greg Keenan. **Description:** The formation of a company called TrackNet Media Group LLC by Magna Entertainment Corp. and Churchill Downs Inc.

for the broadcast of horse races on television is discussed. The efforts of the two companies to revive public interest in horse racing are described.

41790 ■ "Media Industry Collection Agency Completes Acquisition" in *Collections & Credit Risk* **(Vol. 15, December 1, 2010, No. 11, pp. 22)**
Pub: SourceMedia Inc.
Description: Media Receivable Management Inc. (MRM) will take over the collection operations at Borden, Jones & Mitchell, in Miami, Florida. MRM clients are basically magazine and electronic media publishers.

41791 ■ "Medicaid Insurers See Growth in Small Business Market" in *Boston Business Journal* **(Vol. 31, July 15, 2011, No. 25, pp. 1)**
Pub: Boston Business Journal
Ed: Julie M. Donnelly. **Description:** BMC HealthNet Plan announced plans to launch small business products to serve small businesses that are priced out of rising premium rates at large Massachusetts insurers. BMC joined competitors CeltiCare Health Plan and Neighborhood Health Plan in augmenting its core business.

41792 ■ "Medical Office Developers To Merge November 1" in *The Business Journal - Serving Phoenix and the Valley of the Sun* **(Vol. 29, September 26, 2008, No. 4, pp. 1)**
Pub: American City Business Journals, Inc.
Ed: Angela Gonzales. **Description:** Ensemble Real Estate Services LLC and DevMan Co. will merge effective November 1, 2008 and will call the firm Ensemble DevMan of Arizona after the merger. The two companies will combine their resources and expertise on planned projects that include the Phoenix Children's Hospital's Specialty Clinic and Banner Ironwood Medical Office Building.

41793 ■ "Melnyk Loses Round in Battle for Hemosol" in *Globe & Mail* **(January 24, 2007, pp. B3)**
Pub: CTVglobemedia Publishing Inc.
Ed: Leonard Zehr. **Description:** Biovail Corp. chairman Eugene Melnyk's loosing of the case against Catalyst Capital Group Inc. over the acquisition of Hemosol Corp. is discussed.

41794 ■ "Merger Brings New Force to Hispanic Marketing Industry" in *Hispanic Business* **(July-August 2007, pp. 60)**
Pub: Hispanic Business
Description: Merger between Latin Force LLC, a marketing strategy firm and Geoscape International Inc., a consumer intelligence and data analytics company is discussed.

41795 ■ "Merger Mania: Regional Snaps Up HVS" in *The Business Journal-Serving Greater Tampa Bay* **(Vol. 28, September 26, 2008, No. 40, pp. 1)**
Pub: American City Business Journals, Inc.
Ed: Alexis Muellner. **Description:** It was reported that Harper Van Scoik & Co. LLP has finalized a merger with Carr Riggs & Ingram LLC. The agreement, effective October 1, 2008, is a merger of HVS assets into CRI. Bill Carr, a managing partner, revealed that HVS' $5 million in revenue will take CRI from $78 million to $82 million in revenue.

41796 ■ *Mergers and Acquisitions from A to Z*
Pub: Amacom
Ed: Andrew J. Sherman, Milledge A. Hart. **Released:** January 2006. **Price:** $35.00. **Description:** Guide for the entire process of mergers and acquisitions, including taxes, accounting, laws, and projected financial gain.

41797 ■ "Mergers Mean Woe for Fliers; Airline Hookups Boost Fares, Diminish Service" in *Crain's Chicago Business* **(April 21, 2008)**
Pub: Crain Communications, Inc.
Ed: John Pletz. **Description:** Discusses the impact airline mergers will have on customer service, pricing and business travel, particularly at Chicago's O'Hare International Airport.

41798 ■ "Merrill Lynch in Talks to Buy BlackRock Stake" in *Globe & Mail* **(February 13, 2006, pp. B4)**
Pub: CTVglobemedia Publishing Inc.
Ed: Dennis K. Breman; Randall Smith. **Description:** Financial services firm Merrill Lynch and Co. Inc. is planning to acquire money managing company BlackRock Inc. for 8 million dollars. Sources report that this deal would create 1-trillion dollar huge fund management venture.

41799 ■ "Micro-Finance Agencies and SMEs" in *International Journal of Entrepreneurship and Small Business* **(Vol. 11, August 3, 2010)**
Pub: Publishers Communication Group
Ed: Patricia A. Rowe, Michael J. Christie, Frank Hoy. **Description:** Institutional preparedness of economic development agencies for developing small and medium-sized enterprises (SMEs) is discussed. The cases presented illustrate variations in the micro-finance lender agency-enterprise development of processes for sharing vision and interdependence.

41800 ■ "Microsoft's Big Gamble" in *Canadian Business* **(Vol. 81, March 3, 2008, No. 3, pp. 13)**
Pub: Rogers Media
Ed: Andrew Wahl. **Description:** Microsoft Corp. is taking a big risk in buying Yahoo, as it is expected to pay more than $31 a share to finalize the acquisition. The deal would be seven and a half times bigger than any other that Microsoft has entered before, an execution of such deal is also anticipated to become a challenge for Microsoft. Recommendations on how Microsoft should handle the integration of the two businesses are given.

41801 ■ "Milk Producers Target Moms" in *Marketing to Women* **(Vol. 21, January 2008, No. 1, pp. 3)**
Pub: EPM Communications, Inc.
Description: In an attempt to encourage moms to serve milk with meals, the American Dairy Association partners with the New York State Dietetic Association to promote milk via a new logo, website and contest.

41802 ■ "MindLeaders' Online Training Courses Come to ePath Learning" in *Information Today* **(Vol. 26, February 2009, No. 2, pp. 4)**
Pub: Information Today, Inc.
Description: MindLeaders has partnered with ePath Learning to provide clients with over 2,200 new online courses. ePath's integrated Learning Management Service (iLMS) allows organizations to create online training programs for employees.

41803 ■ "Minor-League Baseball's Sliders Plan Stock Offering" in *Crain's Detroit Business* **(Vol. 25, June 15, 2009, No. 24, pp. 3)**
Pub: Crain Communications Inc. - Detroit
Ed: Bill Shea. **Description:** New minor-league baseball team is raising funds to build a new stadium in Waterford Township, Michigan because banks are unwilling to provide loans for the project. Owners of the Midwest Sliders in Ypsilanti, Michigan are waiting for the federal Securities and Exchange Commission to approve a Regulation A public offering.

41804 ■ "Molson Coors Ends Ill-Fated Foray Into Brazil" in *Globe & Mail* **(January 17, 2006, pp. B1)**
Pub: CTVglobemedia Publishing Inc.
Ed: Andy Hoffman. **Description:** The details of loss incurred by Molson Coors Brewing Co., from the sale of Cervejarias Kaiser SA to Fomento Economico Mexicano S.A. de C.V., are presented.

41805 ■ "Molycorp Funds Wind Energy Technology Company" in *Manufacturing Close-Up* **(September 19, 2011)**
Pub: Close-Up Media
Description: Molycorp Inc., producer of rare earth oxides (REO) and a REO producer outside of China, announced it will invest in Boulder Wind Power, which has designed a rare earth magnet powered wind turbine generator. This new generator can produce

electricity as low as $0.04 per Kilowatt Hour. Boulder Wind Power's patented wind turbine technology allows for use of rare earth permanent magnets that do not require dysprosium, which is relatively scarce.

41806 ■ "MoneyGram In Pact With Payday Lender" in *American Banker* **(Vol. 173, March 7, 2008, No. 46, pp. 6)**
Pub: SourceMedia Inc.
Ed: William Launder. **Description:** Details of pact between MoneyGram International Inc. and Advance America Cash Advance Centers are examined.

41807 ■ "Montreal Exchange Buoyed by U.S. Takeover Moves" in *Globe & Mail* **(March 16, 2007, pp. B1)**
Pub: CTVglobemedia Publishing Inc.
Ed: Sinclair Stewart. **Description:** The rise in the share prices of Montreal Exchange due to the derivatives exchange's bid to acquire the Chicago Board of Trade is discussed. The trends pertaining to the consolidation of global stock markets are described.

41808 ■ "Montreal Port Head Lands CP Ships Deal" in *Globe & Mail* **(January 5, 2006, pp. B4)**
Pub: CTVglobemedia Publishing Inc.
Description: The opinions of president Dominic Taddeo, on the positive impact of TUI AG's acquisition of CP Ships Ltd. on operations at Port of Montreal, are presented.

41809 ■ "More Jobs Moving Out of City" in *Business Courier* **(Vol. 24, March 14, 2008, No. 49, pp. 1)**
Pub: American City Business Journals, Inc.
Ed: Steve Watkins; Laura Baverman. **Description:** UBS Financial Services Inc. is moving Gradison to Kenwood Town Place in Sycamore Township a year after UBS acquired Gradison. The township does not have a tax on earnings so the move will save Gradison's employees the 2.1 percent Cincinnati tax.

41810 ■ "More Questions Face Huntington" in *Business First-Columbus* **(December 7, 2007, pp. A3)**
Pub: American City Business Journals, Inc.
Ed: Adrian Burns. **Description:** Marty Adams' abrupt resignation has lead to speculation that he was dismissed by the bank in relation to the unexpected run-in with the subprime mortgage fiasco. Analysis predict Columbus-based Huntington Bancshares Inc. might be targeted for acquisition. Details on the company's revenues and shares of stock prices are presented.

41811 ■ "Move Marks KKR's Latest Push into Retail" in *Globe & Mail* **(March 13, 2007, pp. B17)**
Pub: CTVglobemedia Publishing Inc.
Ed: Heather Burke. **Description:** Investment giant Kohlberg Kravis Roberts and Co. has finalized a deal to acquire retail store chain Dollar General Corp. for an estimated 6.9 billion dollars. The company will be entering lucrative retail market by this acquisition.

41812 ■ "Muddy Portfolio Raises a Question: Just What Is National City Worth?" in *Crain's Detroit Business* **(Vol. 24, April 7, 2008, No. 14)**
Pub: Crain Communications, Inc.
Ed: Jay Miller. **Description:** National City Bank is looking at strategies to help it deal with its credit and loan problems which are reflected in its falling stock price. One possible solution is a merger with another bank, however most national banks are facing their own home-loan portfolio issues and may be unable to tackle another company's unresolved problems. Statistical data included.

41813 ■ "Nancy Hughes Anthony" in *Canadian Business* **(Vol. 81, October 13, 2008, No. 17, pp. 104)**
Pub: Rogers Media Ltd.
Ed: Andy Holloway. **Description:** Profile of Nancy Hughes Anthony, who believes her experience operating large enterprises as a public servant helped her earn positions that ultimately brought her to her current position as chief executive and president of

the Canadian Bankers Association. She also thinks there should be more public-private sector coordination within industries.

41814 ■ **"A Nasty Russian Tale"** in *Canadian Business* (Vol. 81, March 3, 2008, No. 3, pp. 85)
Pub: Rogers Media
Ed: Andrew Nikiforuk. **Description:** Billionaires Alex Shnaider and Michael Shtaif entered a partnership for an oil venture which ended in a slew of litigations. Cases of breach of contract, injurious falsehood and other related lawsuits were filed against Shnaider. Details of the lawsuits and the other parties involved in the disputes are presented.

41815 ■ **"Nat'l Instruments Connects with Lego"** in *Austin Business JournalInc.* (Vol. 28, August 22, 2008, No. 23, pp. 1)
Pub: American City Business Journals
Ed: Laura Hipp. **Description:** Austin-based National Instruments Corporation has teamed with Lego Group from Denmark to create a robot that can be built by children and can be used to perform tasks. Lego WeDo, their latest product, uses computer connection to power its movements. The educational benefits of the new product are discussed.

41816 ■ **"Navistar, Cat Talk Truck Deal"** in *Crain's Chicago Business* (Vol. 31, March 24, 2008, No. 12, pp. 1)
Pub: Crain Communications, Inc.
Ed: Bob Tita. **Description:** Caterpillar Inc. and Navistar International Corp. are negotiating a partnership in which Navistar would build Cat-branded trucks with engines supplied by the Peoria-based equipment manufacturer, Caterpillar.

41817 ■ **"Need Grub? Start Texting at Kroger"** in *Business Courier* (Vol. 24, December 21, 2008, No. 36, pp. 1)
Pub: American City Business Journals, Inc.
Ed: Laura Baverman. **Description:** Discusses the University of Cincinnati which is teaming up to release a technology platform called Macopay that would link a cell phone to a bank account and allow a person to make payments at participating retailers by sending a text message. Details with regard to the new service and its growth potential are discussed.

41818 ■ **"Nestle Acquires Waggin' Train Dog Treat Company"** in *Pet Product News* (Vol. 64, November 2010, No. 11, pp. 7)
Pub: BowTie Inc.
Description: Vevey, Switzerland-based Nestle has acquired South Carolina-based dog treat firm Waggin' Train LLC from private equity firm VMG Partners in September 2010. Waggin' Train LLC, which will be operated as a wholly owned subsidiary, is expected to fill a gap in Nestle's dog treat product portfolio.

41819 ■ **"NetSpend, Payday Firm in Pact"** in *American Banker* (Vol. 173, February 22, 2008, No. 7, pp. 7)
Pub: SourceMedia Inc.
Ed: Daniel Wolfe. **Description:** NetSpend Corporation of Austin, Texas is providing its prepaid cards to Advance America Cash Advance Centers Inc., a Spartanburg, South Carolina payday lender.

41820 ■ **"Neuromed Strikes Major Merck Deal"** in *Globe & Mail* (March 21, 2006, pp. B1)
Pub: CTVglobemedia Publishing Inc.
Ed: Leonard Zehr. **Description:** Neuromed Pharmaceuticals Ltd., a spin off of British Columbia University, has struck a drug research deal valued at up to $500 million (U.S) with giant Merck &Co. Inc., the biggest collaboration in Canada. Details of the deal are presented.

41821 ■ **"Never Boring: Ad Agencies' Big Changes"** in *Business Courier* (Vol. 24, February 8, 2008, No. 44, pp. 1)
Pub: American City Business Journals, Inc.
Ed: Dan Monk. **Description:** Many changes are occurring in Cincinnati's advertising industry, including new clients, acquisitions, and market leaders, and an increase in employment. Bridge Worldwide passed Northlich LLC as the city's largest advertising agency.

41822 ■ **"A New Alliance For Global Change"** in *Harvard Business Review* (Vol. 88, September 2010, No. 9, pp. 56)
Pub: Harvard Business School Publishing
Ed: Bill Drayton, Valeria Budinich. **Description:** Collaboration between social organizations and for-profit firms through the development of hybrid value chains to target complex global issues is promoted. While social organizations offer links to communities and consumers, firms provide financing and scale expertise.

41823 ■ **"The New Arsenal of Risk Management"** in *Harvard Business Review* (Vol. 86, September 2008, No. 9, pp. 92)
Pub: Harvard Business School Press
Ed: Kevin Bueler; Andrew Freeman; Ron Hulme. **Description:** Goldman Sachs Group Inc. is used to illustrate methods for successful risk management. The investment bank's business principles, partnerships, and oversight practices are discussed.

41824 ■ **"New Economy Initiative Gains Partners"** in *Crain's Detroit Business* (Vol. 25, June 1, 2009, No. 22, pp. M014)
Pub: Crain Communications Inc. - Detroit
Ed: Sherri Begin Welch. **Description:** New Economy Initiative is a $100 million philanthropic initiative that focuses on regional economic development. Recent grants awarded to Michigan companies are outlined.

41825 ■ **"A New Flavor for Second Street: Lamberts Chef Backs New Restaurant"** in *Austin Business JournalInc.* (Vol. 28, January 2, 2009)
Pub: American City Business Journals
Ed: Sandra Zaragoza. **Description:** Chef Larry McGuire has teamed up with the Icon Group to develop the La Condesa restaurant and the Malverde lounge in the Second Street district. The La Condesa restaurant will be a Mexico City-inspired restaurant, while the Malverde lounge atop the La Condesa will host DJs and live music.

41826 ■ **"New Life for Porsche's VW Dreams"** in *Barron's* (Vol. 89, July 6, 2009, No. 27, pp. 9)
Pub: Dow Jones & Co., Inc.
Ed: Vito J. Racanelli. **Description:** Porsche and Volkswagen moved closer to a merger after the Qatar Investment Authority offered to take a stake in Porsche. The QIA could take up to a 30 percent stake in Porsche and purchase all Volkswagen calls for up to $6 billion.

41827 ■ **"New York Firm Secures Sheffield, Amherst Centers for $26 Million"** in *Crain's Cleveland Business* (Vol. 28, December 3, 2007, No. 48)
Pub: Crain Communications, Inc.
Ed: Stan Bullard. **Description:** Silverman Realty Group completed a $26 million transaction which made it the new owner of the Sheffield Crossing and Amherst Marketplace shopping centers in Lorain County.

41828 ■ **"New Zealand Natural Co-Branding with Mrs. Fields"** in *Ice Cream Reporter* (Vol. 23, November 20, 2010, No. 12, pp. 2)
Pub: Ice Cream Reporter
Description: Mrs. Fields has partnered with a New Zealand firm to co-brand ice cream and cookies in Australian markets.

41829 ■ *The Nokia Revolution: The Story of an Extraordinary Company That Transformed an Industry*
Pub: AMACOM
Ed: Dan Steinbock. **Released:** May 31, 2001. **Description:** Profile of Nokia, the world's largest wireless communications company. Nokia started in 1865 in rural Finland and merged its rubber company and a cabling firm to form the corporation around 1965. The firm's corporate strategy in the mobile communications industry is highlighted.

41830 ■ **"Nonprofit NAIC Acquires Software Developer as For-Profit Arm"** in *Crain's Detroit Business* (Vol. 25, June 22, 2009, No. 25, pp. 10)
Pub: Crain Communications Inc. - Detroit
Ed: Sherri Begin Welch. **Description:** Details of National Association of Investors Corporation's acquisition of a Massachusetts investment software developer in order to offer more products to investment clubs and individual investors nationwide.

41831 ■ **"Nortel Romances Chinese Rival Huawei"** in *Globe & Mail* (February 2, 2006, pp. B1)
Pub: CTVglobemedia Publishing Inc.
Ed: Simon Avery. **Description:** The reasons behind Nortel Networks Corp.'s joint venture with Huawei Technologies Company Ltd. are presented.

41832 ■ **"Note to Leonard: Swim Fast"** in *Canadian Business* (Vol. 80, January 15, 2007, No. 2, pp. 29)
Pub: Rogers Media
Ed: Zena Olijnyk. **Description:** The decision of CanWest Entertainment Inc and Goldman Sachs Capital Partners to collectively acquire Toronto-based Alliance Atlantis Communications Inc. is discussed.

41833 ■ **"NovAtel Inc. Licensed to Sell Galileo Receivers"** in *Canadian Corporate News* (May 14, 2007)
Pub: Comtex News Network Inc.
Description: NovAtel Inc., a leading provider of precision Global Navigation Satellite System (GNSS) components and subsystems that afford its customers rapid integration of precise positioning technology, has received a license valid for ten years that allows NovAtel to sell receivers that track Galileo signals.

41834 ■ **"NStar Feels the Heat"** in *Cape Cod Times* (September 30, 2011)
Pub: Cape Cod Media Group
Ed: Patrick Cassidy. **Description:** Massachusetts energy officials wish to delay a merger between NStar and Northeast Utilities until it is clear how the partnership would meet the state's green energy goals. Governor Deval Patrick supports the proposed Nantucket Sound wind farm.

41835 ■ **"N.Y. Group Top Bidder for Last Duke Sites"** in *Crain's Cleveland Business* (Vol. 28, November 19, 2007, No. 46, pp. 1)
Pub: Crain Communications, Inc.
Ed: Stan Bullard. **Description:** Overview of the possible portfolio sale of Duke Realty Corp.'s last Northeast Ohio properties, 14 office buildings in Independence, Seven Hills and North Olmsted, believed to be purchased by a real estate investor group led by Nightingale Properties LLC of New York.

41836 ■ **"Nymex Dissidents Rattle Sabers"** in *Crain's Chicago Business* (Vol. 31, April 21, 2008, No. 16, pp. 2)
Pub: Crain Communications, Inc.
Ed: Ann Saphir. **Description:** Two groups of New York Mercantile Exchange members say they have more than enough votes to stop CME Group Inc.'s $10 billion deal to acquire the oil and metals exchange and they are threatening a proxy fight if the Chicago exchange doesn't raise its offer.

41837 ■ **"Oakland County Hopes Auto Suppliers Can Drive Medical Industry Growth"** in *Crain's Detroit Business* (March 10, 2008)
Pub: Crain Communications, Inc.
Ed: Chad Halcom. **Description:** Oakland County officials are hoping to create further economic development for the region by pairing health care companies and medical device makers with automotive suppliers in an attempt to discover additional crossover technology.

41838 ■ **"Ocean Choice in Running to Acquire Assets of FPI"** in *Globe & Mail* (March 15, 2007, pp. B9)
Pub: CTVglobemedia Publishing Inc.
Description: Ocean Choice International is bidding vigorously for acquiring assets St. Johns based of FPI Ltd. Complete details of these bids are discussed.

41839 ■ "Offer for Sears Canada 'Inadequate'" in *Globe & Mail* (February 10, 2006, pp. B4)

Pub: CTVglobemedia Publishing Inc.

Ed: Marina Strauss. **Description:** The financial feasibility of Sears Holdings Corp.'s proposed acquisition of Sears Canada Inc., for $835 million, is discussed.

41840 ■ "Oil Patch Expects Richer Shell Offer" in *Globe & Mail* (January 3, 2006, pp. B1)

Pub: CTVglobemedia Publishing Inc.

Ed: Andrew Willis; Patrick Brethour. **Description:** The concerns investors over the feasibility of Royal Dutch Shell PLC's acquisition of Shell Canada Ltd., for $7.6 billion, are presented. Shell Canada Ltd. reports rise in shares by ten percent.

41841 ■ "Old Friends Make Old Buildings Successful Restaurants" in *Crain's Detroit Business* (Vol. 24, February 4, 2008, No. 5, pp. 14)

Pub: Crain Communications Inc. - Detroit

Ed: Brent Snavely. **Description:** Profiles of Jon Carlson and Gregory Lobdell, founders of ten new restaurants in Ann Arbor, Royal Oak, and Traverse City, Michigan, and their plans to add four more in the near future.

41842 ■ "Olympus is Urged to Revise Board" in *Wall Street Journal Eastern Edition* (November 28, 2011, pp. B3)

Pub: Dow Jones & Company Inc.

Ed: Phred Dvorak. **Description:** Koji Miyata, once a director on the board of troubled Japanese photographic equipment company, is urging the company to reorganize its board, saying the present group should resign their board seats but keep their management positions. The company has come under scrutiny for its accounting practices and costly acquisitions.

41843 ■ "OMERS Joins Bid for U.K. Port Giant" in *Globe & Mail* (March 28, 2006, pp. B1)

Pub: CTVglobemedia Publishing Inc.

Ed: Paul Waldie. **Description:** The plans of Ontario Municipal Employees Retirement Board to partner with Goldman Sachs Group Inc., in order to acquire Associated British Ports PLC, are presented.

41844 ■ "On a Mission: Ginch Gonch Wants You to Get Rid of Your Tighty Whities" in *Canadian Business* (Vol. 81, September 29, 2008, No. 16)

Pub: Rogers Media Ltd.

Ed: Michelle Magnan. **Description:** New Equity Capital acquired underwear maker Ginch Gonch in July 2008; founder Jason Sutherland kept his position as creative director of the company and will retain his title as 'director of stitches and inches'. The company is known for its products, which are reminiscent of the days when people wore underwear covered in cowboys and stars as kids. The company also claims that Nelly, Justin Timberlake, and Hilary Duff have worn their products.

41845 ■ "Online Reverse Auctions: Common Myths Versus Evolving Reality" in *Business Horizons* (September-October 2007, pp. 373)

Pub: Elsevier Technology Publications

Ed: Tobias Schoenherr, Vincent A. Mabert. **Description:** Common misconceptions about online reverse auctions are examined based on the data obtained from 30 case study companies. Strategies for maintaining a good buyer-supplier relationship and implications for firms and supply managers are presented.

41846 ■ "Operation Fusion" in *Black Enterprise* (Vol. 38, November 2007, No. 4, pp. 30)

Pub: Earl G. Graves Publishing Co. Inc.

Ed: Tara C. Walker. **Description:** Entrepreneur Albert H. Frazier tells how he combined three separate acquisitions in order to create Goods Movement Inc.:-W&H Systems Inc., a systems integrator and material handler supplier and North American Conveyor

Inc. which fabricates and installs conveyor and sort equipment systems for the U.S. Postal Service and Total Transportation Services, a third-party logistics provider.

41847 ■ "The Oracle's Endgame; Wrigley Investment Isn't What Many Call a Classic Buffett Play" in *Crain's Chicago Business* (May 5, 2008)

Pub: Crain Communications, Inc.

Ed: Ann Saphir. **Description:** Discusses Warren Buffett's deal with Mars Inc. to buy Wm. Wrigley Jr. Co., a move which would make Mr. Buffett a minority shareholder in a privately held company, a departure from his typical investment strategy. Mr. Buffett's Berkshire Hathaway Inc. agreed to provide $4.4 billion to help finance the $23 billion deal to pay another $2.1 billion for an equity stake in the company once it became a subsidiary of Mars.

41848 ■ "Ottawa to Push for Gas Deal Between Petrocan, Gazpron" in *Globe & Mail* (February 13, 2006, pp. B1)

Pub: CTVglobemedia Publishing Inc.

Ed: Greame Smith. **Description:** Jim Flaherty, finance minister of Canada is negotiating a 1.3 billion dollar deal between state owned Petro-Canada and Russia's OAO Gazprom. This once again highlighted the country's increasing dependence on Russia for its energy requirements.

41849 ■ "Out of This World: Noah Samara and WorldSpace" in *Black Enterprise* (November 2007)

Pub: Earl G. Graves Publishing Co. Inc.

Ed: Anthony Calypso. **Description:** Profile of Noah Samara, CEO of WorldSpace Inc. who raised $1 billion to help create the technological architecture for satellite radio.

41850 ■ "Owner of IT Firm MK2 Tying Future to Software" in *Crain's Cleveland Business* (Vol. 30, June 15, 2009, No. 23, pp. 3)

Pub: Crain Communications, Inc.

Ed: Chuck Soder. **Description:** Donald Kasper, owner of MK2 Technologies LLC of Cleveland, Ohio discusses his recent acquisition of a portion of ProSource Solution. The move will help expand the two companies' custom software development plans.

41851 ■ "Parent Firm's Global Reach, Stricter Air Quality Rules Have Stock Smiling" in *Crain's Cleveland Business* (October 15, 2007)

Pub: Crain Communications, Inc.

Ed: David Bennett. **Description:** Since Stock Equipment Co., a firm that makes industrial pollution control equipment, was acquired by Schenck Process Group, a diversified global manufacturer based in Germany, the company's orders from abroad have been on the rise. The purchase has opened the doors to regions such as Eastern and Central Europe, Latin America and Australia.

41852 ■ "Partnering for Success" in *Art Business News* (Vol. 36, October 2009, No. 10, pp. 4)

Pub: Summit Business Media

Ed: Jennifer Dulin Wiley. **Description:** In such a volatile economy many savvy artists and gallery owners are turning to out-of-the-box partnerships for continued success; these partnerships are also pervading the Internet, especially with such social media networks as Facebook and Twitter where artists and businesses can develop a loyal following.

41853 ■ *The Partnership: The Making of Goldman Sachs*

Pub: Penguin Group USA Inc.

Ed: Charles D. Ellis. **Released:** 2009. **Price:** $37.95. **Description:** The history of Goldman Sachs is presented, along with a chronicle of Wall Street.

41854 ■ "Paterson Plots Comeback With Internet IPO" in *Globe & Mail* (February 20, 2006, pp. B1)

Pub: CTVglobemedia Publishing Inc.

Ed: Grant Robertson. **Description:** The initial public offering plans of chief executive officer Scott Paterson of JumpTV.com are presented.

41855 ■ "PC Connection Acquires Cloud Software Provider" in *New Hampshire Business Review* (Vol. 33, March 25, 2011, No. 6, pp. 8)

Pub: Business Publications Inc.

Description: Merrimack-based PC Connection Inc. acquired ValCom Technology, a provider of cloud-based IT service management software. Details of the deal are included.

41856 ■ "Peking Launches Trina Turk Bedding Collection" in *Home Textiles Today* (Vol. 31, May 24, 2011, No. 13, pp. 4)

Pub: Reed Business Information

Description: Peking Handicraft is launching designer Trina Turk's bedding collection of four beds that reflect her approach to contemporary fabric design using color and prints with strong graphic effects.

41857 ■ "Pepsi Co. Breaches the Walls of Coke Fortress McDonald's" in *Globe & Mail* (March 13, 2007, pp. B1)

Pub: CTVglobemedia Publishing Inc.

Ed: Keith McArthur. **Description:** Soft drinks giant Pepsi Co. has entered an agreement with fast food chain McDonald's for offering its products in outlets across Canada. Earlier Coca-Cola Co. used to offer its exclusive products in these outlets.

41858 ■ "Pioneers Get All The Perks" in *Canadian Business* (Vol. 81, March 3, 2008, No. 3, pp. 18)

Pub: Rogers Media

Description: Suncor Energy Inc. will face royalty payments from 25% to 30% of net profits as it signs a new deal with Alberta. Biovail Corp., meanwhile, is under a U.S. grand jury investigation for supposed improprieties in Cardizem LA heart drug launch. The Conference Board of Canada's proposal to impose taxes on greenhouse gas emissions and other developments in the business community are discussed.

41859 ■ "Please Pass the Mayo" in *Crain's Chicago Business* (Vol. 31, April 28, 2008, No. 17, pp. 32)

Pub: Crain Communications, Inc.

Ed: Samantha Stainburn. **Description:** Fort Dearborn Co. has come a long way since it started out as one-press print shop; the family-owned company was struggling to keep up with the technology of making consumer product labels for curvy bottles of products like V8 V-Fusion juice and in 2006 sold off to Genstar Capital LLC which has pushed for acquisitions; last year, Fort Derborn bought its biggest competitor, Renaissance Mark Inc., doubling its size and adding spirit and wine makers to its client roster.

41860 ■ "Polite Conversation" in *Mergers & Acquisitions: The Dealmaker's Journal* (March 1, 2008)

Pub: SourceMedia, Inc.

Description: In January, industry leaders and dealmakers met at Davos to discuss topics ranging from the possibility of a recession to what lies ahead in the deal market.

41861 ■ "Poor Economy Inspires Rich Alternatives In a Modern, and Tax-Free, Twist on Bartering" in *Houston Chronicle* (June 7, 2010)

Pub: Houston Chronicle Publishing Company

Ed: Michael Rubinkam. **Description:** Time banking helps individuals and firms receive goods or services by depositing time dollars into a bank reserved for receipt of goods and services.

41862 ■ "Porsche Raises VW Stake, Makes Bid for Firm" in *Globe & Mail* (March 26, 2007, pp. B5)

Pub: CTVglobemedia Publishing Inc.

Ed: Chad Thomas. Jeremy Van Logan. **Description:** Automobile giant Porsche AG has increased its stake in Volkswagen AG to $54 billion recently. The company is planning a merger by claiming 30% stake under German law.

41863 ■ **"Power Partnerships"** in *Business Courier* (Vol. 27, October 22, 2010, No. 25, pp. 1)
Pub: Business Courier
Ed: Lucy May. Description: The $400 million Harrah's casino and the $47 million redevelopment and expansion of Washington Park are project aimed at boosting the economy in downtown Cincinnati, Ohio. These projects will be done in cooperation with the National Association for the Advancement of Colored People. Insights into the role of minority-owned businesses in regional economic development are explored.

41864 ■ **"Powers Reels in Pinger"** in *Business Courier* (Vol. 24, December 21, 2008, No. 36, pp. 1)
Pub: American City Business Journals, Inc.
Ed: Lisa Biank Fasig. Description: Powers Agency has acquired Dan Pinger Public Relations Inc. after three years in planning. The new company is to be called 'Pinger PR at Powers'. Details of the deal and the new company are discussed.

41865 ■ **"Pre-Deal Trades More Common in Canada, Study Finds"** in *Globe & Mail* (March 23, 2007, pp. B5)
Pub: CTVglobemedia Publishing Inc.
Ed: John Kipphoff; Joe Schneider. Description: The results of the study conducted by Measuredmarkets Inc. to examine the impact of merger activity on insider trading of the companies are presented.

41866 ■ **"Precision Crop Control with Valley Irrigation/CropMetrics Partnership"** in *Farm Industry News* (January 6, 2011)
Pub: Penton Business Media Inc.
Description: Irrigation systems have become a precision farming tool since partnering with agronomic software systems to apply products across the field by prescription. Valley Irrigation and CropMetrics have partnered in order to variably control water, fertilizer and other crop management products through a center pivot irrigation system.

41867 ■ **"Preparing for Weed Control"** in *Farmer's Weekly* (March 28, 2008, No. 320)
Pub: Reed Business Information
Description: Profile of Richard Beachell who farms in a joint venture with his neighbor. Beachell discusses nitrogen applications, fungicides and the reduction of pesticides.

41868 ■ **"Private Equity Firm Links First Arizona Deal"** in *Business Journal-Serving Phoenix and the Valley of the Sun* (November 2, 2007)
Pub: American City Business Journals, Inc.
Ed: Chris Cassacchia. Description: Pacific Investment Partners and Your Source Financial launched a $10 million fund and signed their first deal. The two companies acquires a minority stake in Dreambrands Inc. for $3 million. Dreambrands is using the capital to market its personal lubricant product Carrageenana.

41869 ■ **"Private Equity Firms Focus on Failing Banks"** in *Baltimore Business Journal* (Vol. 28, July 16, 2010, No. 10, pp. 1)
Pub: Baltimore Business Journal
Ed: Gary Haber. Description: Four deals in which assets of failed banks were acquired by private equity firms have been approved by the Federal Deposit Insurance Corporation in the past couple of years. Bay Bank FSK, for example, purchased Bay National Bank's assets in July 2010. Forecasts on more private equity acquisitions in the community banking industry are given.

41870 ■ **"Procter & Gamble Boosts Bet on Exclusive Brands"** in *Business Courier* (Vol. 27, July 9, 2010, No. 10, pp. 1)
Pub: Business Courier
Ed: Jon Newberry. Description: Procter & Gamble is creating more special versions of its brands such as Pringles and Pampers exclusively for retail partners such as Tesco in the U.K. The greater push towards this direction is seen as a way to regain market share.

41871 ■ **"Profico Takes Itself Off the Market"** in *Globe & Mail* (March 14, 2006, pp. B1)
Pub: CTVglobemedia Publishing Inc.
Ed: Deborah Yedlin; Dave Ebner. Description: Profico Energy Management Ltd., Canada's largest junior energy explorer, has backed off its potential acquisition plans. The decreased prices of the natural gas are the main reasons that caused Profico to back off from the acquisition plan.

41872 ■ **"Prominent Hispanic Businessman Signs With Choice Hotels"** in *Hispanic Business* (Vol. 30, March 2008, No. 3, pp. 36)
Pub: Hispanic Business
Ed: Melinda Burns. Description: Chairman of the board of Lopez Food Inc., John C. Lopez signs the agreement with Choice Hotels International to build five new Cambria suites in the USA. This is his first hotel venture and also the first Hispanic franchisee to enter into business with Choice Hotels.

41873 ■ **"Proposed Law Would Stop REIS Bid for Annexation by Livonia"** in *Crain's Detroit Business* (Vol. 24, March 10, 2008, No. 10, pp. 2)
Pub: Crain Communications, Inc.
Ed: Chad Halcom. Description: REIS Northville L.L. C., a joint venture made up of Real Estate Interests Group Inc. and Schostak Bros. & Co., has proposed an $800 million project called Highwood at the former Northville Psychiatric Hospital site but has been stalled due to a disagreement with Northville Township on several terms including: the amount of retail at the site and the paying for cleanup of environmental and medical waste.

41874 ■ **"Proposed Triangle Redo in Motion"** in *Crain's Cleveland Business* (Vol. 28, October 15, 2007, No. 41, pp. 1)
Pub: Crain Communications, Inc.
Ed: Stan Bullard. Description: Zaremba Homes and MRN Ltd. are partnering to redevelop the so-called Triangle section of University Circle. The proposed project will include a total of 434 new rental and for-sale residential suites and as much as 227,000 square feet of retail and restaurant space.

41875 ■ **"PRWT Service Acquires Pharmaceutical Plant: Firm Wins Multimillion-Dollar Contract with Merck"** in *Black Enterprise* (March 2008)
Pub: Earl G. Graves Publishing Co. Inc.
Ed: Tamara E. Holmes. Description: PRWT Services Inc. expanded through its acquisition of a chemical manufacturing plant in New Jersey. The Whitehouse Station, part of Merck & Co. Inc. produces active pharmaceutical ingredients for antibiotics, making PRWT the first minority-owned company in the U.S. to manufacture active pharmaceutical ingredients.

41876 ■ **"Public Media Works to Launch DVD Kiosk Operations in Toronto, Canada"** in *Internet Wire* (November 15, 2010)
Pub: Comtex
Description: Public Media Works Inc. along with its EntertainmentXpress Inc., have partnered with Spot Venture Distribution Inc. and Signifi Solutions Inc., both headquartered in Toronto, Canada, to manage and expand the Spot DVD movie and game kiosk business in greater Toronto and other Canadian locations.

41877 ■ **"Public Opinion"** in *Entrepreneur* (Vol. 36, April 2008, No. 4, pp. 28)
Pub: Entrepreneur Media, Inc.
Ed: Aliza Sherman. Description: According to a 2007 report from Group and Organization Management, women in top positions can lead publicly traded companies to stock price and earnings growth. Some women business owners say that going public has provided them with the capital to grow. Details on the potential of women-managed publicly traded companies are discussed.

41878 ■ **"Pulp Friction: Spin Off Mills to Boost Wood Products"** in *Globe & Mail* (February 18, 2006, pp. B3)
Pub: CTVglobemedia Publishing Inc.
Ed: Peter Kennedy. Description: The reasons behind the decision of chief executive officer Jim Shepherd of Canfor Corp. to sell pulp mills are presented.

41879 ■ **"?Que Pasa? A Canadian-Cuban Credit Card Crisis"** in *Canadian Business* (Vol. 81, March 31, 2008, No. 5, pp. 10)
Pub: Rogers Media
Ed: Geoff Kirbyson. Description: Discusses the acquisition of CUETS Financial Ltd. by the Bank of America which means that CUETS-issued credit cards in Cuba are worthless since U.S. laws prohibit transactions from Cuba and other sanctioned countries. CUETS members are advised to take multiple payment methods to Cuba.

41880 ■ **"A Questionable Chemical Romance"** in *Barron's* (Vol. 88, July 14, 2008, No. 28, pp. 28)
Pub: Dow Jones & Co., Inc.
Ed: Andrew Bary. Description: Dow Chemical paid $78-a-share for the surprise takeover of Rohm & Haas. The acquisition is reducing Dow Chemical's financial flexibility at a time when chemical companies are being affected by high costs and a weak U.S. economy.

41881 ■ **"Ralcorp Investigated for Rejecting ConAgra Bid"** in *Saint Louis Business Journal* (Vol. 32, September 16, 2011, No. 3, pp. 1)
Pub: Saint Louis Business Journal
Ed: Evan Binns. Description: New York-based Levi & Korsinsky started investigating Ralcorp Holidngs Inc. after it rejected ConAgra Foods Inc.'s third and latest takeover bid of $5.17 billion. The investigation would determine whether Ralcorp's directors had acted on behalf of shareholders' best interest.

41882 ■ **"R&R Ice Cream"** in *Ice Cream Reporter* (Vol. 23, November 20, 2010, No. 12, pp. 8)
Pub: Ice Cream Reporter
Description: R&R Ice Cream, the United Kingdom's largest ice cream manufacturer, has completed a private offering of senior secured notes that has raised 298 million (pounds sterling) to fund expansion and acquisitions.

41883 ■ **"R&R Launches Upscale Spoony's and Low Fat Dragon's Den"** in *Ice Cream Reporter* (Vol. 23, August 20, 2010, No. 9, pp. 3)
Pub: Ice Cream Reporter
Description: European ice cream manufacturer R&R has acquired French ice cream maker Rolland and will position itself as an upscale challenger to brands like Ben & Jerry's.

41884 ■ **"RBC Holds Inside Card With HBC Credit Assets"** in *Globe & Mail* (January 25, 2006, pp. B1)
Pub: CTVglobemedia Publishing Inc.
Ed: Marina Strauss; Sinclair Stewart. Description: Hudson's Bay Co. (HBC) signed co-branding credit card agreement with Royal Bank of Canada are presented. The significance of the deal for HBC is discussed.

41885 ■ **"Rebels' Cause: Adult Stem Cell"** in *Austin Business Journal* (Vol. 31, June 3, 2011, No. 13, pp. 1)
Pub: American City Business Journals Inc.
Ed: Sandra Zaragoza. Description: MedRebels Foundation was launched in February 2011 with the goal of providing millions of dollars for research funding, education and advocacy for adult stem cell-focused medicine. The foundation, whose major contributor is SpineSmith LP, is a collaboration of other adult stem cell-related companies and nonprofit partners. It hopes to raise $200,000 by the end of 2011.

41886 ■ **"Recent Deals Signal an M&A Resurgence"** in *Austin Business JournalInc.* (Vol. 29, January 22, 2010, No. 46, pp. 1)
Pub: American City Business Journals
Ed: Jacob Dirr. Description: The acquisition of at least six Austin, Texas technology companies reflects the growing acquisition activity in the US. Corporations have bought 86 companies and spent $7.3 bil-

lion during the fourth quarter of 2009. Insights into the impact of the acquisition activity to Austin's entrepreneurial energy are also given.

41887 ■ "Redcorp Ventures Ltd.: Tulsequah Camp Construction Begins" in *Canadian Corporate News* **(May 16, 2007)**
Pub: Comtex News Network Inc.
Description: Redfern Reources Ltd., a subsidiary of Redcorp Ventures Ltd., announced that Modular Transportable Solutions LLC was selected to design and manufacture its prefabricated, modular construction camp, cookhouse, administration buildings, and mine dry at the Tulsequah Mine location in northwest British Columbia due to the virtually indestructible design of the units that withstand extreme weather conditions.

41888 ■ "Regal Venture Puts Imax Back in the Spotlight" in *Globe & Mail* **(March 13, 2007, pp. B5)**
Pub: CTVglobemedia Publishing Inc.
Ed: Shirley Won. **Description:** Imax Corp. has signed new contract with cinema hall operating giant Regal Entertainment Corp. for constructing two more giant screen theaters. Share prices of Imax Corp. have increased sharply after this announcement.

41889 ■ "Regent's Signal, Once Powerful, Fading From Local Scene" in *Business Courier* **(Vol. 27, June 4, 2010, No. 5, pp. 1)**
Pub: Business Courier
Ed: Dan Monk. **Description:** Los Angeles, California-based Oaktree Capital Management bought former Regent Communications Inc. from Chapter 11 bankruptcy and transformed it into Townsquare Media Inc., a privately held firm. Regent's corporate presence has faded fast in Cincinnati, Ohio as its operations wind down. Insights on Regent's failed business model are also given.

41890 ■ "Rehab Will Turn Hospital Into Incubator" in *The Business Journal-Serving Metropolitan Kansas City* **(Vol. 26, September 12, 2008)**
Pub: American City Business Journals, Inc.
Ed: Rob Roberts. **Description:** Independence Regional Health Center will be purchased by CEAH Realtors and be converted into the Independence Regional Entrepreneurial Center, a business incubator that will house startups and other tenants. Other details about the planned entrepreneurial center are provided.

41891 ■ "Research Note" in *International Journal of Globalisation and Small Business* **(Vol. 4, September 21, 2010, No. 1, pp. 92)**
Pub: Publishers Communication Group
Ed: Alexander Bode, Tobias B. Talmon I'Armee, Simon Alig. **Description:** The cluster concept has steadily increased its importance during the past years both from practitioners' and reearchers' points of view. Simultaneously, many corporate networks are established. Researchers from different areas (business management, economic social and geographical science) are trying to explain both phenomena.

41892 ■ "Research Reports" in *Barron's* **(Vol. 88, March 10, 2008, No. 10, pp. M13)**
Pub: Dow Jones & Company, Inc.
Description: Research reports on different company stocks by investment analysts are given. Shares of Cal Dive are rated Outperform by analysts, citing the shares' continued attractiveness and the company's acquisition of Horizon. Analysts recommend buying the shares of California Water Service Group.

41893 ■ "Research Reports: How Analysts Size Up Companies" in *Barron's* **(Vol. 88, March 31, 2008, No. 13, pp. M13)**
Pub: Dow Jones & Company, Inc.
Ed: Anita Peltonen. **Description:** Sirius Satellite's shares are ranked Outperform as it awaits approval from the Federal Communications Commission in its merger with XM. TiVo's shares are ranked Avoid as the company is in a sector that's being commoditized. Verizon Communications' rising dividend yield earns

it a Focus List ranking. The shares of Bear Stearns, Churchill Downs, Corning, and Deerfield Triarc Capital are also reviewed. Statistical data included.

41894 ■ "RIM Reinforces Claim as Top Dog by Expanding BlackBerry" in *Globe & Mail* **(March 11, 2006, pp. B3)**
Pub: CTVglobemedia Publishing Inc.
Ed: Simon Avery. **Description:** The plans of Research In Motion Ltd. to enhance the features of BlackBerry, through acquisition of Ascendent Systems, are presented.

41895 ■ "Rimfire Minerals Corporation: Jake Gold Project-Drilling Planned for 2007" in *Canadian Corporate News* **(May 16, 2007)**
Pub: Comtex News Network Inc.
Description: Rimfire Minerals Corporation and Island Arc Exploration Corporation formed a partnership to explore the Jake Property, a high-grade gold prospect with previously unrecognized potential to host economic gold mineralization, located 13 kilometers west of Clearwater, British Columbia

41896 ■ "Roll Your Own" in *Business North Carolina* **(Vol. 28, March 2008, No. 3, pp. 66)**
Pub: Business North Carolina
Ed: Amanda Parry. **Description:** Profile of U.S. Flue-Cured Tobacco Growers who process tobacco and make cigarettes. Details of the program are outlined.

41897 ■ "Roundtable - The Auto Sector Shifts Gears" in *Mergers & Acquisitions: The Dealmaker's Journal* **(March 1, 2008)**
Pub: SourceMedia, Inc.
Description: Industry professionals discuss the current state of the automotive sector as well as what they predict for the future of the industry; also provides information for investors about opportunities in the sector.

41898 ■ "Royal Dutch's Grip Firm on Shell" in *Globe & Mail* **(March 19, 2007, pp. B1)**
Pub: CTVglobemedia Publishing Inc.
Ed: David Ebner. **Description:** The proposed acquisition of Shell Canada Ltd. by Royal Dutch Shell PLC for $8.7 billion is discussed.

41899 ■ "Rumors Kill Algoma Takeover Talks" in *Globe & Mail* **(March 14, 2007, pp. B14)**
Pub: CTVglobemedia Publishing Inc.
Ed: Tara Perkins. **Description:** Canada-based steel manufacturing giant Salzgitter AG has dropped its acquisition negotiations with Algoma Steel Inc. The decision comes after the secret price quotation was leaked to competitors.

41900 ■ "Russia Eyes Nuclear Power Co-Operation With Canada" in *Globe & Mail* **(April 2, 2007, pp. B1)**
Pub: CTVglobemedia Publishing Inc.
Ed: Shawn McCarthy. **Description:** The plans of the Russian nuclear energy agency, Federal Atomic Energy Agency, to enter into a partnership with its Canadian counterpart Atomic Energy of Canada Ltd. for the generation of electric power are discussed.

41901 ■ "S3 Entertainment Group Partners with WFW International for Film Services in Michigan" in *Michigan Vue* **(July-August 2008)**
Pub: Entrepreneur Media Inc.
Description: William F. White (WFW), one of North America's largest production equipment providers has partnered with S3 Entertainment Group (S3EG), a Michigan-based full-service film production services company due to the new incentives package which currently offers the highest incentives in the United States, up to 42 percent. S3EG will actively store, lease, manage, distribute and sell WFW's equipment to the growing number of production teams that are filming in the state.

41902 ■ "Sabathia Deal Makes Dollars and Sense" in *The Business Journal-Milwaukee* **(Vol. 25, July 11, 2008, No. 42, pp. A1)**
Pub: American City Business Journals, Inc.
Ed: Mark Kass. **Description:** It was reported that the Milwaukee Brewers' acquisition of CC Sabathia will mean that the team will pick up an estimated $5 mil-

lion in salary that Sabathia is owed for the remainder of the season. Because of this, the team will not make a profit in 2008. The acquisition of Sabathia is expected to cause an increase in attendance and merchandise revenue over the remainder of the season.

41903 ■ "SABMiller Deal Hit by Tax Ruling" in *Wall Street Journal Eastern Edition* **(November 21 , 2011, pp. B9)**
Pub: Dow Jones & Company Inc.
Ed: David Fickling, Simon Zekaria. **Description:** SABMiller PLC, the giant brewer in the United Kingdom, is acquiring Australian beer icon Foster's Group Ltd. for US$9.9 billion, but will have to come up with another A$582 million following a tax ruling by the Australian Taxation Office in order that shareholders of Foster's don't lose.

41904 ■ "SAGE Publications Announced a Partnership with Which Medical Device" in *Information Today* **(Vol. 28, November 2011, No. 10, pp. 15)**
Pub: Information Today, Inc.
Description: SAGE Publications has partnered with Which Medical Device to offer insights, tutorials, and reviews of medical devices.

41905 ■ "St. Elizabeth Fights for Share at St. Lukes" in *Business Courier* **(Vol. 27, November 12, 2010, No. 28, pp. 1)**
Pub: Business Courier
Ed: James Ritchie. **Description:** Key information on how St. Elizabeth Healthcare helps partner St. Luke's Hospitals increase market share in the healthcare industry are presented. Some of St. Luke's hospitals, such as the St. Elizabeth Fort Thomas in Kentucky, are struggling with low occupancy rates, prompting St. Elizabeth to invest about $24 million to help St. Luke's increase its market share.

41906 ■ "Save the Date" in *Mergers & Acquisitions: The Dealmaker's Journal* **(March 1, 2008)**
Pub: SourceMedia, Inc.
Description: Listing of conferences and forums that deal with business and investing, particularly with mergers and acquisitions. Includes dates, locations and Internet addresses.

41907 ■ *The Savvy Gal's Guide to Online Networking (Or What Would Jane Austen Do?)*
Pub: Booklocker.com Inc.
Ed: Diane K. Danielson, Lindsey Pollak. **Released:** August 10, 2007. **Price:** $14.95. **Description:** It is a truth universally acknowledged that a woman in search of a fabulous career must be in want of networking opportunities. Or so Jane Austen would say if she were writing, or more likely, blogging today. So begins the must-read guide to networking in the 21st Century. Authors and networking experts share the nuts, bolts and savvy secrets that business-women need in order to use technology to build professional relationships.

41908 ■ "Scanning Dell's Shopping List" in *Barron's* **(Vol. 89, July 13, 2009, No. 28, pp. 24)**
Pub: Dow Jones & Co., Inc.
Ed: Mark Veverka. **Description:** It is believed that Dell will be looking for companies to acquire since they poached an experienced mergers-and-acquisitions executive. In addition Dell's CEO is reportedly telling people he plans to go shopping. Dell executives have also stated an interest in data storage.

41909 ■ "Scotiabank Tapped as Likely Buyer in Puerto Rico" in *Globe & Mail* **(January 30, 2007, pp. B3)**
Pub: CTVglobemedia Publishing Inc.
Ed: Andrew Willis. **Description:** Speculation over Bank of Nova Scotia's proposed acquisition of First BanCorp is discussed.

41910 ■ "Scripps' Dinner Bell" in *Business Courier* **(Vol. 24, October 19, 2008, No. 27, pp. 1)**
Pub: American City Business Journals, Inc.
Ed: Dan Monk. **Description:** Discusses the split of E.W. Scripps Co.'s Food Network into a separate

publicly traded company Scripps Networks Interactive could produce expansion into Asia and Europe.

41911 ■ "Sears' Lampert Solid in Game of Valuation Chicken" in *Globe & Mail* **(February 25, 2006, pp. B2)**
Pub: CTVglobemedia Publishing Inc.

Ed: Eric Reguly. **Description:** The feasibility of share value of Sears Canada Inc., following Sears Holdings Corp.'s acquisition, is discussed.

41912 ■ "Sears' Profit Result Puts Ball in Parent's Court" in *Globe & Mail* **(February 3, 2006, pp. B4)**
Pub: CTVglobemedia Publishing Inc.

Ed: Marina Strauss. **Description:** Sears Canada Inc. achieved $783.4 million in profits for fourth quarter 2005. The financial performance of the company paves way for the acquisition of Sears Holdings Corp.

41913 ■ *The Secret of Exiting Your Business Under Your Terms!*
Pub: Outskirts Press, Incorporated

Ed: Gene H. Irwin. **Released:** August 2005. **Price:** $29.95. **Description:** Topics include how to sell a business for the highest value, tax laws governing the sale of a business, finding the right buyer, mergers and acquisitions, negotiating the sale, and using a limited auction to increase future value of a business.

41914 ■ "A Security Risk?" in *Canadian Business* **(Vol. 80, October 22, 2007, No. 21, pp. 36)**
Pub: Rogers Media

Ed: Joe Castaldo. **Description:** Garda World Security Corporation declared a C$1.5 million loss in the second quarter of 2007. The company's securities have been falling since June and hit a 52-week low of $15.90 in September. Details of the physical and cash-handling firm's strategy to integrate its acquisitions are discussed.

41915 ■ "Sedo Keeps Trucking in Good Times and Bad" in *Crain's Chicago Business* **(Vol. 31, April 28, 2008, No. 17, pp. 35)**
Pub: Crain Communications, Inc.

Ed: Samantha Stainburn. **Description:** Discusses Seko Worldwide Inc., an Itasca-based freight forwarder, and its complicated road to growth and expansion on a global scale.

41916 ■ "Sense of Discovery" in *Business Journal Portland* **(Vol. 27, November 19, 2010, No. 38, pp. 1)**
Pub: Portland Business Journal

Ed: Erik Siemers. **Description:** Tigard, Oregon-based Exterro Inc. CEO Bobby Balachandran announced plans to go public without the help of an institutional investor. Balachandran believes Exterro could grow to a $100 million legal compliance software company in the span of three years. Insights on Exterro's growth as market leader in the $1 billion legal governance software market are also given.

41917 ■ "Shipbuilding & Defence" in *Canadian Sailings* **(July 7, 2008)**
Pub: Commonwealth Business Media

Ed: Sharon Hobson. **Description:** Overview of the Joint Support Ship Project whose initial budget was set at $2.1 billion for the acquisition of the ships required for the Canadian navy; another $800 million was allotted for 20 years of in-service support. Four teams of competitors bid for the contract and the Department of National Defence decided to fund two teams for the project definition phase of the competition.

41918 ■ "Shop Around" in *Houston Chronicle* **(December 7, 2010, pp. 3)**
Pub: Houston Chronicle

Ed: Tara Dooley. **Description:** Profile of Diana Candida and Maria Martinez who partnered to open Beatniks, a shop carrying vintage clothing, art from various artists, dance shoes, and jewelry.

41919 ■ "Sites Set" in *Entrepreneur* **(Vol. 35, November 2007, No. 11, pp. 112)**
Pub: Entrepreneur Media Inc.

Ed: Nichole L. Torres. **Description:** Marketing information online can be a good bui9sness if you know who to target. Partnering with other online companies to provide information services that cater to specific groups of people is also helpful.

41920 ■ "Six Tips To Maximize Networking Opportunities" in *Women Entrepreneur* **(November 3, 2008)**
Pub: Entrepreneur Media Inc.

Ed: Tamara Monosoff. **Description:** Networking events fall into the realm of business development as opposed to immediate sales opportunities. It is important to remember that these events provide a chance to build relationships that may someday help one's business. Tips to help make the most out of networking events are provided.

41921 ■ "Size Does Matter" in *International Journal of Globalisation and Small Business* **(Vol. 4, September 21, 2010, No. 1, pp. 61)**
Pub: Publishers Communication Group

Ed: Julia Cornnell, Ranjit Voola. **Description:** Examination of how members of an Australian-based manufacturing and engineering cluster share knowledge through networking as a means to improve competitive advantage.

41922 ■ "Small Firms Punch Ticket for Growth" in *Houston Business Journal* **(Vol. 40, January 29, 2010, No. 38, pp. 1)**
Pub: American City Business Journals

Ed: Allison Wollam. **Description:** Independent ticket agencies anticipate growth as American and Canadian authorities approved a merger between Ticketmaster and concert promoter Live Nation. Expansion of service offerings and acquisition of venues have also been done by independent ticket agencies in light of the merger. Details of the merger are included.

41923 ■ "SoBran Partners with U.S. Navy" in *Black Enterprise* **(Vol. 37, October 2006, No. 3, pp. 38)**
Pub: Earl G. Graves Publishing Co. Inc.

Ed: Glenn Townes. **Description:** SoBran Inc., partnered with Lockheed Martin and signed a three-Tear production service contract with the Naval Aviation Depot in Jacksonville, Florida. The $44 million contract will allow SoBran to transport and warehouse materials for Navy facilities.

41924 ■ "Software's Last Hurrah" in *Canadian Business* **(Vol. 81, December 24, 2007, No. 1, pp. 27)**
Pub: Rogers Media

Ed: Andrew Wahl. **Description:** Canada's software industry could be facing a challenge with IBM's acquisition of Cognos, which was the country's last major independent business intelligence company and was also IBM's largest acquisition ever. Next in line to Cognos in terms of prominence is Open Text Corporation, which could also be a possible candidate for acquisition, as analysts predict.

41925 ■ "Some Relief Possible Following Painful Week" in *Barron's* **(Vol. 88, July 14, 2008, No. 28, pp. M3)**
Pub: Dow Jones & Co., Inc.

Ed: Kopin Tan. **Description:** Dow Chemical is offering a 74 percent premium to acquire Rohm & Haas' coatings and electronics materials operations. Frontline amassed a 5.6 percent stake in rival Overseas Shipholding Group and a merger between the two would create a giant global fleet with pricing power. Highlights of the U.S. stock market during the week that ended in July 11, 2008 are discussed. Statistical data included.

41926 ■ "Sorrell Digs Deep to Snag TNS" in *Advertising Age* **(Vol. 79, July 14, 2008, No. 7, pp. 1)**
Pub: Crain Communications, Inc.

Ed: Michael Bush. **Description:** Martin Sorrell's strategic vision for expansion in order to become the largest ad-agency holding company in the world is discussed.

41927 ■ "South African Connections: Small Business Owners Work Toward Forming Strategic Alliances" in *Black Enterprise* **(March 2008)**
Pub: Earl G. Graves Publishing Co. Inc.

Ed: Aisha Sylvester. **Description:** National Minority Supplier Development Council Inc. is working to create business partnerships between African American businesses and black-owned South African companies within the country's pharmaceutical supply industry.

41928 ■ "Staples Advantage Receives NJPA National Contract for Janitorial Supplies" in *Professional Services Close-Up* **(April 22, 2011)**
Pub: Close-Up Media

Description: Staples Advantage, the business-to-business division of Staples Inc. was awarded a contract for janitorial supplies to members of the National Joint Powers Alliance (NJPA). NJPA is a member-owned buying cooperative serving public and private schools, state and local governments, and nonprofit organizations.

41929 ■ "The Start of a Beautiful Friendship: Partnering with Your Customers on R&D" in *Inc.* **(March 2008, pp. 37-38)**
Pub: Gruner & Jahr USA Publishing

Ed: Leigh Buchanan. **Description:** Joint research and development projects between customers and suppliers are a growing trend in the small business community; these ventures can help keep new product development costs lower. Four tips to maintain a good working relationship in these ventures are outlined.

41930 ■ "Startup Makes Attempt to 'Reform' Health Insurance" in *Austin Business JournalInc.* **(Vol. 29, January 15, 2010, No. 45, pp. 1)**
Pub: American City Business Journals

Ed: Sandra Zaragoza. **Description:** Health insurance provider ETMG LLC of Austin, Texas plans to act as a managing general agent and a third-party administrator that can facilitate customized plans for small businesses and sole proprietors. According to CEO Mark Adams, profitability is expected for ETMG, which have also clinched $1.5 million worth of investments. Entities that have agreed to do business with ETMG are presented.

41931 ■ "State Shock Prices Take Large Tumble" in *The Business Journal-Milwaukee* **(Vol. 25, September 12, 2008, No. 51, pp. A1)**
Pub: American City Business Journals, Inc.

Ed: Rich Rovito. **Description:** Weak economic times have caused the stocks of most publicly traded companies in Wisconsin to dip in 2008. Companies that appeared on the worst performing stocks list also experienced drops in share price to as much as 70 percent. Information about the companies that experienced increases in stock prices is also presented. Statistical data included.

41932 ■ "State of the Unions" in *Canadian Business* **(Vol. 81, December 8, 2008, No. 21, pp. 23)**
Pub: Rogers Media Ltd.

Ed: Sharda Prashad. **Description:** Companies planning on joint ventures should look for partners they can trust and respect and are also competent. Joint venture deals aim to bring existing products to a a new market or in acquiring a foreign product for an existing market.

41933 ■ "Stikemans' Ascent, Its Legacy, and Its Future" in *Globe & Mail* **(January 29, 2007, pp. B2)**
Pub: CTVglobemedia Publishing Inc.

Ed: Jacquie McNish. **Description:** Pierre Raymond, chairman of legal firm Stikeman Elliott LLP, talks about his strategies to handle competition, his challenges, and about Canada's present mergers and acquisition scenario. Stikeman achieved the first place in 2006 M&A legal rankings.

41934 ■ **"STMicroelectronics" in** *Canadian Electronics* **(Vol. 23, February 2008, No. 1, pp. 1)**
Pub: CLB Media Inc.

Description: STMicroelectronics, a semiconductor maker, revealed that it plans to acquire Genesis Microchip Inc. Genesis develops image and video processing systems. It was reported that the acquisition has been approved by Genesis' Board of Directors. It is expected that Genesis will enhance STMicroelectronics' technological capabilities.

41935 ■ **"Stockgroup Completes US $4.5 Million Financing" in** *Canadian Corporate News* **(May 16, 2007)**
Pub: Comtex News Network Inc.

Description: Stockgroup, a financial media company focused on collaborative technologies and user-generated content, will use the proceeds of the private placement for acquisitions and general working capital.

41936 ■ **"The Story Of Diane Greene" in** *Barron's* **(Vol. 88, July 14, 2008, No. 28, pp. 31)**
Pub: Dow Jones & Co., Inc.

Ed: Mark Veverka. **Description:** Discusses the ousting of Diane Greene as a chief executive of VMWare, a developer of virtualization software, after the firm went public; in this case Greene, a brilliant engineer, should not be negatively impacted by the decision because it is common for companies to bring in new executive leadership that is more operations oriented after the company goes public.

41937 ■ *Strategic Partnerships: An Entrepreneur's Guide to Joint Ventures and Alliances*
Pub: Kaplan Publishing

Ed: Robert Wallace. **Released:** September 2004. **Description:** Ways to develop and execute joint venture relationships with larger business entities for small company owners.

41938 ■ **"Subprime Hits Huntington" in** *Business First-Columbus* **(November 23, 2007, pp. A1)**
Pub: American City Business Journals, Inc.

Ed: Adrian Burns. **Description:** Huntington Bancshares Inc. picked up a $1.5 billion exposure to the country's subprime mortgage mess. It caused the bank to set aside $450 million to cover increases in loan losses. When Huntington acquired Sky Financial, it absorbed a 17-year relationship Sky had with Franklin Credit Corporation, which is a subprime lender and servicer.

41939 ■ **"Sudbury Waits With Future Up in the Air" in** *Globe & Mail* **(February 22, 2006, pp. B1)**
Pub: CTVglobemedia Publishing Inc.

Ed: Wendy Stueck. **Description:** The takeover of Falconbridge Ltd., by Inco Ltd Sudbury, is in the process with uncertainty. The transaction has been a long overdue.

41940 ■ **"Sullivan Led Bucyrus through Unforgettable Year" in** *Business Journal-Milwaukee* **(Vol. 28, December 17, 2010, No. 11, pp. A1)**
Pub: Milwaukee Business Journal

Ed: Rich Rovito. **Description:** Bucyrus International's president and CEO, Tim Sullivan, was chosen as Milwaukee, Wisconsin's Executive of the Year for 2010. Sullivan led Bucyrus through a year of dramatic change which started with the acquisition of the mining business of Terex Corporation and culminating with a deal to sell Caterpillar Inc.

41941 ■ **"Summit, Lions Gate are in Talks to Merge Studios" in** *Wall Street Journal Eastern Edition* **(November 29, 2011, pp. B2)**
Pub: Dow Jones & Company Inc.

Ed: Erica Orden, Michelle Kung. **Description:** Movie studio Summit Entertainment LLC is in talks with television producer Lions Gate Entertainment Corporation about a possible merger. Previous talks have taken place, but no deal was ever reached. Such a deal would create a large, independent studio able to compete in the market with the big Hollywood giants.

41942 ■ **"Sun Capital Partners Affiliate Acquires Timothy's Coffees" in** *Miami Daily Business Review* **(March 26, 2008)**
Pub: ALM Media Inc.

Description: An affiliate of Sun Capital Partners acquired Timothy's Coffees of the World. Timothy's operates and franchises 166 stores offering coffees, muffins, and Michel's Baguette products.

41943 ■ **"SunBank Plans Expansion Via Wall-Mart" in** *Business Journal-Serving Phoenix and the Valley of the Sun* **(Vol. 10, November 9, 2007)**
Pub: American City Business Journals, Inc.

Ed: Chris Casacchia. **Description:** SunBank plans to install 12 to 14 branches in Wal-Mart stores in Arizona and hire 100 bankers by the end of 2008. Wal-Mart also offers financial products at other stores through partnerships with other banks.

41944 ■ **"Sundt, DPR Score $470 Million Biotech Project" in** *The Business Journal - Serving Phoenix and the Valley of the Sun* **(Vol. 29, September 19, 2008, No. 3, pp. 1)**
Pub: American City Business Journals, Inc.

Ed: Jan Buchholz. **Description:** Sundt Inc. and DPR Construction Inc. were awarded the winning joint-venture contract to develop the second phase of the Arizona Biomedical Collaborative on the Phoenix Biomedical Campus. Both firms declined to comment, but an employee of the Arizona Board of Regents confirmed that the firms won the bidding. Views and information on the development project are presented.

41945 ■ **"Suppliers May Follow Fiat" in** *Crain's Detroit Business* **(Vol. 25, June 15, 2009, No. 24, pp. 1)**
Pub: Crain Communications Inc. - Detroit

Ed: Ryan Beene. **Description:** Italian suppliers to Fiat SpA are looking toward Detroit after the formation of Chrysler Group LLC, the Chrysler-Fiat partnership created from Chrysler's bankruptcy. The Italian American Alliance for Business and Technology is aware of two Italy-based powertrain component suppliers that are considering a move to Detroit.

41946 ■ **"Swedes Swoop In To Save Time4"** **in** *Advertising Age* **(Vol. 78, January 29, 2007, No. 5, pp. 4)**
Pub: Crain Communications, Inc.

Ed: Nat Ives. **Description:** Overview of Stockholm's Bonnier Group, a family-owned publisher that is looking to expand its U.S. presence; Bonnier recently acquired a number of Time Inc. magazines.

41947 ■ **"Sweet Spot" in** *Canadian Business* **(Vol. 79, November 20, 2006, No. 23, pp. 25)**
Pub: Rogers Media

Ed: John Gray. **Description:** The plans of Kinross Gold Corp., to acquire the stake of Bema Gold Corp., are discussed. Under the terms of the deal Kinross is offering Bema stockholders 0.441 of a Kinross share for each of Bema shares.

41948 ■ **"Swope: Breakup Won't Delay Job"** **in** *The Business Journal-Serving Metropolitan Kansas City* **(Vol. 26, August 22, 2008, No. 50, pp. 1)**
Pub: American City Business Journals, Inc.

Ed: Rob Roberts. **Description:** Swope Community Builders said that the Kansas City Redevelopment Project will not be delayed by the breakup of their partnership with Sherman Associates Inc. Swopes will be the sole master developer of the project.

41949 ■ **"Symbility Solutions Joins Motion Computing Partner Program" in** *Canadian Corporate News* **(May 14, 2007)**
Pub: Comtex News Network Inc.

Description: Symbility Solutions Inc., a wholly owned subsidiary of Automated Benefits Corp., announced an agreement with Alliance Partner of Motion Computing, a leader in wireless communications and mobile computing, in which both companies will invest in a sales and marketing strategy that focuses specifically on the insurance market.

41950 ■ **"Takeover Frenzy Stokes Steel Stocks" in** *Globe & Mail* **(February 7, 2006, pp. B1)**
Pub: CTVglobemedia Publishing Inc.

Description: The impact of merger speculations, on shares of steel companies such as Ipsco Inc., is discussed.

41951 ■ **"Taking Collections" in** *Investment Dealers' Digest* **(Vol. 75, October 9, 2009, No. 38, pp. 19)**
Pub: SourceMedia, Inc.

Ed: Aleksandrs Rozens. **Description:** Although the nation's debt-collection industry has grown with increased reliance by consumers on credit, valuations of these firms have lessened due to the economy which has hurt some of the success of these firms in obtaining the debt back from consumers who are experiencing trying economic times.

41952 ■ **"Taking on Intel" in** *Canadian Business* **(Vol. 79, October 23, 2006, No. 21, pp. 27)**
Pub: Rogers Media

Ed: Andrew Wahl. **Description:** The decision of ATI Technologies Inc., a Canadian computer peripherals company to acquire cash and stocks worth US$5.4-billion from American microprocessor maker Advanced Micro Devices Inc., is discussed.

41953 ■ **"Taking the Over-the-Counter Route to US" in** *Barron's* **(Vol. 88, July 7, 2008, No. 27, pp. 24)**
Pub: Dow Jones & Co., Inc.

Ed: Eric Uhlfelder. **Description:** Many multinational companies have left the New York Stock Exchange and allowed their shares to trade over-the-counter. The companies have taken advantage of a 2007 SEC rule allowing publicly listed foreign companies to change trading venues if less than 5 percent of global trading volume in the past 12 months occurred in the US.

41954 ■ **"Tampa Condo Conversion Sells for $14.8 Million Less" in** *The Business Journal-Serving Greater Tampa Bay* **(Vol. 28, September 5, 2008)**
Pub: American City Business Journals, Inc.

Ed: Janet Leiser. **Description:** Former apartment complex Village Oaks at Tampa, which was converted to condominiums, has been sold to Tennessee-based real estate investment trust Mid-America Apartment Communities Inc. for $21.2 million in August 2008. The amount was $14.2 million less than what developer Radco Management LLC paid for in 2005.

41955 ■ **"Tastee-Freez Celebrates 60th Anniversary" in** *Ice Cream Reporter* **(Vol. 23, July 20, 2010, No. 8, pp. 2)**
Pub: Ice Cream Reporter

Description: Tastee-Freez founders, Leo Moranz (inventor) and Harry Axene, an inventor partnered to market the soft-serve pump and freezer for serving frozen treats back in 1950.

41956 ■ **"Tasti D-Lite Has Franchise Agreement for Australia" in** *Ice Cream Reporter* **(Vol. 23, November 20, 2010, No. 12, pp. 3)**
Pub: Ice Cream Reporter

Description: Tasti D-Lite signed an international master franchise agreement with Friezer Australia Pty. Ltd. and will open 30 units throughout Australia over the next five years.

41957 ■ **"Tate & Lyle to Sell Redpath Division to American Sugar" in** *Globe & Mail* **(February 15, 2007, pp. B15)**
Pub: CTVglobemedia Publishing Inc.

Description: American Sugar Refining has agreed to acquire the Canadian sugar unit of Tate & Lyle PLC for $301.9 million. Tate & Lyle PLC has been selling off businesses and closing plants in order to focus on starches and Splenda.

41958 ■ "Teachers, U.S. Fund Providence Made Moves On BCE Buyout" in *Globe & Mail* **(April 10, 2007, pp. B17)**
Pub: CTVglobemedia Publishing Inc.
Ed: Boyd Erman; Sinclair Stewart; Jacquie McNish. **Description:** The Ontario Teachers Pension Plan, the largest shareholder of telecommunications firm BCE Inc., has called for a partnership with buyout firm Providence Equity Partners Inc. in order to acquire BCE Inc.

41959 ■ "Tech Deal Couples Homegrown Firms" in *The Business Journal-Serving Greater Tampa Bay* **(Vol. 28, July 4, 2008, No. 28, pp. 1)**
Pub: American City Business Journals, Inc.
Ed: Michael Hinman. **Description:** Tampa Bay, Florida-based Administrative Partners Inc. was acquired by Tribridge Inc. resulting in the strengthening of the delivery of Microsoft products to clients. Other details of the merger of the management consulting services companies are included.

41960 ■ "Tech's Payout Problem" in *Barron's* **(Vol. 90, September 13, 2010, No. 37, pp. 19)**
Pub: Barron's Editorial & Corporate Headquarters
Ed: Andrew Bary. **Description:** Big tech companies have the potential to be good dividend payers, but instead just hoard their cash for acquisitions and share buybacks. If these companies offered more dividends, they could boost their shares and attract more income-oriented investors.

41961 ■ "Tektronix Buys Arbor Networks for Security Business" in *eWeek* **(August 9, 2010)**
Pub: Ziff Davis Enterprise
Description: Tektronix Communications, provider of communications test and network intelligence solutions will acquire Arbor Networks. The deal will help Tektronix build a brand in security. Details of the transaction are included.

41962 ■ "TELUS Says No Thanks to Joining BCE Fray" in *Globe & Mail* **(April 24, 2007, pp. B1)**
Pub: CTVglobemedia Publishing Inc.
Ed: Eric Reguly; Catherine McLean. **Description:** The causes of the refusal of TELUS Corp. to try and acquire BCE Inc. are discussed. The prospects of the acquisition of TELUS Corp. by private equity funds are discussed, besides the availability of cash with private equity funds.

41963 ■ "Theme Park Sale has Vendor Upside" in *Tampa Bay Business Journal* **(Vol. 29, October 23, 2009, No. 44, pp. 1)**
Pub: American City Business Journals
Ed: Margie Manning. **Description:** Private equity firm The Blackstone Group has concluded its $2.7 billion purchase of Busch Entertainment Corporation. Aside from enhanced business opportunities in Florida's Tampa Bay area, new attractions might be built in the Busch Gardens and Adventure Island properties that will be acquired by Blackstone. Blackstone's other plans are also discussed.

41964 ■ "This Just In" in *Crain's Detroit Business* **(Vol. 25, June 1, 2009, No. 22, pp. 1)**
Pub: Crain Communications Inc. - Detroit
Description: Three veterans of the auto industry have partnered to create, Revitalizing Michigan, a nonprofit dedicated to help manufacturers improve their processes. The firm is seeking federal, state and private grants to fund the mission.

41965 ■ "Three Funds Look to Join CPP, Bypassing Teachers in BCE Hunt" in *Globe & Mail* **(April 23, 2007, pp. B1)**
Pub: CTVglobemedia Publishing Inc.
Ed: Sinclair Stewart. **Description:** The plans of the Ontario Municipal Employees Retirement Board, British Columbia Investment Management Corp. and the Alberta Investment Corp. to join the bidding consortium led by Canadian Pension Plan Investment Board, for the buyout of BCE Inc. are discussed. The efforts of the Ontario Teachers Pension Plan Board to form a bidding consortium for the same purpose are discussed.

41966 ■ "Tim Armstrong" in *Canadian Business* **(Vol. 81, July 21, 2008, No. 11, pp. 10)**
Pub: Rogers Media Ltd.
Ed: Calvin Leung. **Description:** Interview with Tim Armstrong who is the president of advertising and commerce department of Google Inc. for North America; the information technology company executive talked about the emerging trends and changes to YouTube made by the company since its acquisition in 2006.

41967 ■ "Timberland's CEO On Standing Up to 65,000 Angry Activists" in *Harvard Business Review* **(Vol. 88, September 2010, No. 9, pp. 39)**
Pub: Harvard Business School Publishing
Ed: Jeff Swartz. **Description:** Timberland Company avoided a potential boycott by taking a two-way approach. It addressed a supplier issue that posed a threat to the environment, and launched an email campaign to keep Greenpeace activists informed of the development of a new supplier agreement.

41968 ■ "Tiny Telecom Big Prize in Bell Aliant Bid Battle" in *Globe & Mail* **(April 4, 2007, pp. B1)**
Pub: CTVglobemedia Publishing Inc.
Ed: Catherine McLean. **Description:** The competition between Bell Aliant Regional Communications Income Fund of BCE Inc. and Bragg Communications Inc. to bid for acquiring Amtelecom Income Fund is discussed.

41969 ■ "TiVo, Domino's Team to Offer Pizza Ordering by DVR" in *Advertising Age* **(Vol. 79, November 17, 2008, No. 43, pp. 48)**
Pub: Crain Communications, Inc.
Ed: Brian Steinberg. **Description:** Domino's Pizza and TiVo are teaming up to make it possible for customers to order from the restaurant straight from their DVR. The companies see that this kind of interactive television and consumer experience will only serve to generate more sales as the customer can be exposed to a fuller range of menu selections and will not have to interrupt their viewing, while workers can spend more time making the product.

41970 ■ "To Help Maintain an Adequate Blood Supply During the Summer Months" in *Ice Cream Reporter* **(Vol. 21, August 20, 2008, No. 9, pp. 8)**
Pub: Ice Cream Reporter
Description: Friendly's and the American Red Cross have partnered to offer blood donors a coupon for one free carton of Friendly's ice cream in order to maintain an adequate supply during summer months.

41971 ■ "Toolmakers' New Tack" in *Crain's Detroit Business* **(Vol. 25, June 8, 2009,)**
Pub: Crain Communications Inc. - Detroit
Ed: Ryan Beene, Amy Lane. **Description:** MAG Industrial Automation Systems LLC and Dowding Machining Inc. have partnered to advance wind-turbine technology. The goal is to cut costs of wind energy to the same level as carbon-based fuel.

41972 ■ "Top 50 In Profits" in *Canadian Business* **(Vol. 81, Summer 2008, No. 9, pp. 116)**
Pub: Rogers Media Ltd.
Description: Royal Bank of Canada topped the Investor 500 by profits list despite the slower economic growth in Canada and the U.S. The bank was in the runner-up position in the 2007. RBC's growth strategy is through hefty acquisitions in the U.S.A. A table ranking the top 50 companies in Canada in terms of profits is presented.

41973 ■ "Top Law Firms Join Forces" in *Business Journal Portland* **(Vol. 27, December 3, 2010, No. 40, pp. 1)**
Pub: Portland Business Journal
Ed: Andy Giegerich. **Description:** Law Firms Powell PC and Roberts Kaplan LLP will forge a collaboration, whereby 17 Roberts Kaplan attorneys will join the Portland, Oregon-based office of Lane Powell. The partnership is expected to strengthen the law firms' grip on Portland's banking clients.

41974 ■ "Trading Down at the Supermarket" in *Barron's* **(Vol. 88, July 14, 2008, No. 28, pp. 36)**
Pub: Dow Jones & Co., Inc.
Ed: Alexander Eule. **Description:** Shares of Ralcorp Holdings are cheap at around $49.95 after slipping 20 percent prior to their acquisition of Post cereals from Kraft. Some analysts believe its shares could climb over 60 percent to $80 as value-seeking consumers buy more private label products.

41975 ■ "Transcontinental to Exchange Assets with Quad/Graphics" in *American Printer* **(Vol. 128, August 1, 2011, No. 8)**
Pub: Penton Media Inc.
Description: Transcontinental Inc. and Quad/Graphics Inc. entered into an agreement where Transcontinental will indirectly acquire all shares of Quad Graphics Canada Inc.

41976 ■ "Trust Buyouts Not My Fault, Flaherty Says" in *Globe & Mail* **(April 3, 2007, pp. B1)**
Pub: CTVglobemedia Publishing Inc.
Ed: Tara Perkins; Doug Saunders; Steven Chase. **Description:** The causes of the acquisition of Canadian firms by foreign investors are discussed by the Canadian Finance Minister Jim Flaherty.

41977 ■ "Trust Tax Under Fire as Drain on Revenue" in *Globe & Mail* **(April 9, 2007, pp. B1)**
Pub: CTVglobemedia Publishing Inc.
Ed: Steven Chase. **Description:** The economic aspects of the implementation of the trust levy by the Canadian government are discussed. The acquisition of Canadian income trusts by Canadian and international financial institutions is described.

41978 ■ "TSX Linkup Sets Stage for Battle" in *Globe & Mail* **(March 6, 2007, pp. B1)**
Pub: CTVglobemedia Publishing Inc.
Ed: Boyd Erman; Sinclair Stewart. **Description:** The strategic alliance between TSX Group Inc. and International Securities Exchange Holdings Inc. for the establishment of a derivatives exchange in Canada is discussed. The prospects of competition between the new exchange and the Montreal Exchange are discussed.

41979 ■ "Turner Broadcasting System" in *Brandweek* **(Vol. 49, April 21, 2008, No. 16, pp. SR13)**
Pub: VNU Business Media, Inc.
Ed: Anthony Crupi. **Description:** Provides contact information for sales and marketing personnel for the Turner Broadcasting System networks as well as a listing of the station's top programming and an analysis of the current season and the target audience for those programs running in the current season. Recent acquisitions are also discussed.

41980 ■ "TUSK Announces 2007 First Quarter Results" in *Canadian Corporate News* **(May 14, 2007)**
Pub: Comtex News Network Inc.
Description: TUSK Energy Corp. announced its financial and operating results for the first quarter ending March 31, 2007.

41981 ■ "Two Local Bakers Winners of TV's 'Cupcake Wars'" in *Toledo Blade* **(July 6, 2011)**
Pub: Toledo Times
Description: Winners of cable network Food Channel's Cupcake Wars, Lori Jacobs and Dana Iliev own Cake in a Cup in Toledo, Ohio. The partners shop features creative cupcakes with names such as Monkey Business, Pretty in Pink, and Tropical Getaway.

41982 ■ "Tying the Knot" in *Entrepreneur* **(Vol. 36, April 2008, No. 4, pp. 48)**
Pub: Entrepreneur Media, Inc.
Ed: Guy Kawasaki. **Description:** Tips to consider when forming business partnerships are presented.

41983 ■ "U-Swirl To Open in Salt Lake City Metro Market" in *Ice Cream Reporter* (Vol. 23, November 20, 2010, No. 12, pp. 4)
Pub: Ice Cream Reporter
Description: Healthy Fast Food Inc., parent company to U-SWIRL International Inc., the owner and franchisor of U-SWIRL Frozen Yogurt cafes signed a franchising area development agreement for the Salt Lake City metropolitan area with Regents Management and will open 5 cafes over a five year period.

41984 ■ "UBS Buys Out Canadian Partner" in *Globe & Mail* (January 20, 2006, pp. B1)
Pub: CTVglobemedia Publishing Inc.
Ed: Andrew Willis. **Description:** The details on UBS AG's acquisition of UBS Securities Canada Inc. are presented.

41985 ■ "UMKC, Hospital Drill Down on Deal" in *The Business Journal-Serving Metropolitan Kansas City* (Vol. 26, July 18, 2008, No. 45, pp. 1)
Pub: American City Business Journals, Inc.
Ed: Rob Roberts. **Description:** University of Missouri Kansas City and Children's Mercy Hospital are negotiating the hospital's potential acquisition of the university's School of Dentistry building. The deal would transfer the 240,000-square foot dental school building to Children's Mercy. Plans for a new dental school building for the UMKC are also presented.

41986 ■ "Under Fire, Sabia Triggers Battle for BCE" in *Globe & Mail* (April 14, 2007, pp. B1)
Pub: CTVglobemedia Publishing Inc.
Ed: Boyd Erman. **Description:** The announcement of negotiations for the sale of BCE Inc. by its chief executive officer Michael Sabia is discussed. The efforts of Ontario Teachers Pension Plan to submit its proposal for the sale are described.

41987 ■ "Underworld Acquires Yukon Gold Property" in *Canadian Corporate News* (May 16, 2007)
Pub: Comtex News Network Inc.
Description: Underworld Resources Inc., a well-structured junior exploration company, announced that it has secured an option to earn a 100 percent right, title, and interest in the 11,850 acre White and Black Fox gold Properties in Yukon Territory, Canada. The company will be exploring both vein hosted and sedimentary hosted gold targets.

41988 ■ "Unilever Acquiring Danish Operations of Diplom-Is Ice Cream" in *Ice Cream Reporter* (Vol. 23, August 20, 2010, No. 9, pp. 1)
Pub: Ice Cream Reporter
Description: Unilever will acquire Danish operations of the ice cream company Diplom-Is from Norwegian dairy group Tine.

41989 ■ "Unilever Acquiring EVGA's Ice Cream Brands in Greece" in *Ice Cream Reporter* (Vol. 23, October 20, 2010, No. 11, pp. 1)
Pub: Ice Cream Reporter
Description: Unilever will acquire the ice cream brands and distribution network of the Greek frozen dessert manufacturer EVGA.

41990 ■ "United Insurance To Grow St. Pete's Corporate Base" in *The Business Journal-Serving Greater Tampa Bay* (August 29, 2008)
Pub: American City Business Journals, Inc.
Ed: Margie Manning. **Description:** United Insurance Holdings LC is on its way to becoming a public company by agreeing in a reverse merger with FMG Acquisition Corp. The $104.3 million agreement will provide the company's St. Petersburg operations the opportunity to grow. The other impacts of the proposed reverse merger are examined.

41991 ■ "U.S. Buyer Rescues KCP From Trust Tax Burden" in *Globe & Mail* (April 3, 2007, pp. B1)
Pub: CTVglobemedia Publishing Inc.
Ed: Richard Blackwell. **Description:** The economic aspects of the buyout of KCP Income Fund by Caxton-Iseman Capital Inc. are discussed.

41992 ■ "U.S. Firm to Acquire Manufacturer GSW" in *Globe & Mail* (January 21, 2006, pp. B4)
Pub: CTVglobemedia Publishing Inc.
Ed: Gordon Pitts. **Description:** The details on A.O. Smith Corp.'s acquisition of GSW Inc. are presented.

41993 ■ "U.S. Savvy Helps Fuel TD's Fortunes" in *Globe & Mail* (February 23, 2007, pp. B1)
Pub: CTVglobemedia Publishing Inc.
Ed: Andrew Willis; Tavia Grant. **Description:** The rise in the revenues of Toronto-Dominion Bank due to its acquisition of American financial service providers and the rise in its domestic retail banking revenues are disussed.

41994 ■ "U.S. Widens Rocket Field" in *Wall Street Journal Eastern Edition* (October 17 , 2011, pp. B4)
Pub: Dow Jones & Company Inc.
Ed: Andy Pasztor. **Description:** An agreement has been reached between National Aeronautics and Space Administration, the Department of Defense and the Air Force that will assist small commercial space ventures in bidding for profitable contracts for government launching. The program will give those companies a chance to compete against larger corporations.

41995 ■ "Uniting Spring in OP Could Reduce Static" in *Business Journal-Serving Metropolitan Kansas City* (October 19, 2007)
Pub: American City Business Journals, Inc.
Ed: Jim Davis, Steve Vockrodt. **Description:** Sprint Nextel, the result of Sprint Corporation and Nextel Communications Inc. has been using Nextel's Reston office as corporate headquarters. The consolidation of Sprint Nextel's headquarters is expected to result in saving on cost of living and leases. The benefits of choosing Kansas City as the headquarters are evaluated.

41996 ■ "Universal Energy Group Releases March 31, 2007 Financial Statements" in *Canadian Corporate News* (May 14, 2007)
Pub: Comtex News Network Inc.
Description: Universal Energy Group Ltd., a company that sells electricity and natural gas to small to mid-size commercial and small industrial customers as well as residential customers, announced the release of its March 31, 2007 financial statements. Management's analysis and discussion of the company's financial condition and results of operations are listed. Statistical data included.

41997 ■ "Unwanted News for Hospitals" in *Business Courier* (Vol. 24, October 26, 2008, No. 28, pp. 1)
Pub: American City Business Journals, Inc.
Ed: Description: Christ and St. Luke Hospital might be sharing responsibility costs on the $207 million hospital being built by Health Alliance, the group they are parting with. Christ and St. Lu ke hospitals will be paying $60 million and $25 miilion for partial liability res pectively because the plans for the said project were already underway before they decided to withdraw. Christ Hospital is involved in a whistle-blower case that might cause $424 million in liability across the group.

41998 ■ "Uranerz Acquires Additional Uranium Property Adjoining Nichols Ranch" in *Canadian Corporate News* (May 14, 2007)
Pub: Comtex News Network Inc.
Description: Uranerz Energy Corporation announced the successful leasing of the fee mineral lands that appear to host the "nose" of the oxidation-rduction geochemical front and has the potential for increasing the known uranium mineralization at the Nichols Ranch project which lies west of and adjacent to Uranerz's Nichols Ranch ISR uranium project.

41999 ■ "US Airways Stock Up 5 Percent on Day Merger Try Ends" in *Charlotte Observer* (February 1, 2007)
Pub: Knight-Ridder/Tribune Business News
Ed: Steve Harrison. **Description:** US Airways stock rose 5 percent on the day Doug Parker, CEO, cancelled his offer to purchase Delta Air Lines.

42000 ■ "USAmeriBank Deals for Growth" in *The Business Journal-Serving Greater Tampa Bay* (Vol. 28, September 26, 2008, No. 40, pp. 1)
Pub: American City Business Journals, Inc.
Ed: Margie Manning. **Description:** It is believed that the pending $14.9 million purchase of Liberty Bank by USAmeriBank could be at the forefront of a trend. Executives of both companies expect the deal to close by the end of 2008. USAmeriBank will have $430 million in assets and five offices in Pinellas, Florida once the deal is completed.

42001 ■ "UT Deans Serious about Biz" in *Austin Business Journal* (Vol. 31, May 20, 2011, No. 11, pp. 1)
Pub: American City Business Journals Inc.
Ed: Sandra Zaragoza. **Description:** Dean Thomas Gilligan of the University of Texas, McCombs School of Business and engineering school Dean Gregory Fenves have partnered to develop a joint engineering and business degree. Their partnership has resulted in an undergraduate course on initiating startups.

42002 ■ "UV Suppliers Form Strategic Alliance" in *American Printer* (Vol. 128, June 1, 2011, No. 6)
Pub: Penton Media Inc.
Description: British ultra-violent curing systems developer Integration Technology Ltd. formed a strategic alliance with UV technology provider IST Metz GmbH of Germany in order to offer a complete line of UV solutions for the printing industry.

42003 ■ "Valener Announces that Gaz Metro has Achieved a Key Step in Acquiring CVPS" in *CNW Group* (September 30, 2011)
Pub: CNW Group
Description: Valener Inc., which owns about 29 percent of Gaz Metro Ltd. Partnership, announced that Gaz Metro welcomes the sale of Central Vermont Public Service Corporation (CVPS). Valener owns an indirect interest of 24.5 percent in the wind power projects jointly developed by Beaupre Eole General Partnership and Boralex Inc. on private lands in Quebec. Details of the deal are included.

42004 ■ "ValienteHernandez Acquired" in *The Business Journal-Serving Greater Tampa Bay* (Vol. 28, September 12, 2008, No. 38, pp. 1)
Pub: American City Business Journals, Inc.
Ed: Alexis Muellner. **Description:** Minnesota accounting firm LarsonAllen LLP has acquired Florida-based ValienteHernandez PA, creating a company with 35 employees to be based in ValienteHernandez's newly built office in Tampa Bay Area. Other details about the merger are provided.

42005 ■ "V&J Scores Partnership with Shaq" in *Business Journal-Milwaukee* (Vol. 25, October 12, 2007, No. 2, pp. A1)
Pub: American City Business Journals, Inc.
Ed: Rich Kirchen. **Description:** O'Neal Franchise Group has agreed to a partnership with V&J Foods of Milwaukee to handle Auntie Anne's shops in New York, South Africa, Michigan, and the Caribbean. V&J O'Neal Enterprises will open six Auntie Anne's soft pretzel shops in Detroit towards the end of 2007. Planned international ventures of the partnership are presented.

42006 ■ "VC-Heavy, Revenue-Light Sensicore Sold to GE Division" in *Crain's Detroit Business* (Vol. 24, April 14, 2008, No. 15, pp. 28)
Pub: Crain Communications, Inc.
Ed: Tom Henderson. **Description:** General Electric has acquired Sensicore Inc., which although one of Michigan's most successful companies in raising venture capital was unable to generate significant revenue from its handheld water-testing devices. GE is capable of penetrating a larger market than a private company and will be able to take the devices to the municipal marketplace.

42007 ■ **"Vicki Avril; Senior Vice-President of Tubular Division, Ipsco Inc."** in *Crain's Chicago Business* (Vol. 31, May 5, 2008, No. 18)

Pub: Crain Communications, Inc.

Ed: Miriam Gottfried. **Description:** Profile of Vicki Avril who is the senior vice-president of the tubular division at Ipsco Inc. where she supervises 2,800 employees and 13 mills throughout the United States and Canada.

42008 ■ **"Viewing Ironman As Gold, R.I. Firm Buys Its Parent"** in *The Business Journal-Serving Greater Tampa Bay* (Vol. 28, September 19, 2008)

Pub: American City Business Journals, Inc.

Ed: Pete Williams. **Description:** Providence Equity Partners purchased World Triathlon Corp., parent company of the Ironman Triathlon, for an undisclosed sum. The acquisition means that the World Triathlon Headquarters will move to Tampa, Florida, and allows Providence Equity Partners to stage or license rights to Ironman and half-Ironman distance events.

42009 ■ **"Vital Signs: The Big Picture"** in *Canadian Business* (Vol. 81, Summer 2008, No. 9, pp. 153)

Pub: Rogers Media Ltd.

Description: Results of the Investor 500 showing percentage of companies with positive returns, most actively traded companies over the past six months and market capitalization by industry are presented. Stock performance and revenues of publicly held corporations in Canada are also provided.

42010 ■ **"Vitamins to Spice Up Food"** in *Philadelphia Business Journal* (Vol. 28, October 2, 2009, No. 33, pp. 1)

Pub: American City Business Journals

Ed: John George. **Description:** VitaminSpice, a startup company established by Ed Bukstel, makes a line of spice and vitamin blends that come in seasoning form. The form of the blends could facilitate easier ingestion of vitamins into people's diets. A reverse merger that will allow a publicly-traded company status for VitaminSpice will be accomplished by early October 2009.

42011 ■ **"Vive La Resistance: Competing Logics and the Consolidation of U.S. Community Banking"** in *Academy of Management Journal* (August 2007)

Pub: Academy of Management

Ed: Christopher Marquis, Michael Lounsbury. **Description:** Ways in which competing logics facilitate resistance to institutional change is presented, highlighting on banking professionals' resistance to large, national banks acquisitions of smaller, local banks.

42012 ■ **"Wachovia Gears Up for Major Arizona Expansion"** in *Business Journal-Serving Phoenix and the Valley of the Sun* (Vol. 5, Oct. 5, 2007)

Pub: American City Business Journals, Inc.

Ed: Chris Casacchia. **Description:** Wachovia, America's fourth-largest bank is finalizing a deal to build its Arizona headquarters in downtown Phoenix. The bank plans to add an additional 100 employees by June 2008 and double its financial network to 30 offices in four years. Wachovia will also convert fifteen World Savings Bank branches it acquired in 2006 through Golden West Financial Corporation.

42013 ■ **"Walgreen Takes Up Doctoring"** in *Crain's Chicago Business* (Vol. 31, March 31, 2008, No. 13, pp. 18)

Pub: Crain Communications, Inc.

Ed: Mark Bruno. **Description:** Walgreen Co. has agreed to acquire two firms that provide on-site medical and pharmaceutical services to large companies. Walgreen feels that these facilities mark the future of health care for a number of large corporations.

42014 ■ **"Want Leverage? Multi-Unit Franchisees Deliver Substantial Savings"** in *Franchising World* (Vol. 42, October 2010, No. 10, pp. 39)

Pub: International Franchise Association

Ed: Aziz Hashim. **Description:** Many retail franchises selling the same product are able to buy in bulk. Volume-buying can save money for any franchise.

42015 ■ **"Water Treatment Play Zenon Goes to GE"** in *Globe & Mail* (March 15, 2006, pp. B1)

Pub: CTVglobemedia Publishing Inc.

Ed: Leonard Zehr. **Description:** General Electric Co. acquires Ontario-based company, Zenon Environmental Inc., a technology giant in purifying water in northern Canada.

42016 ■ **"Wayne, Oakland Counties Create Own 'Medical Corridor'"** in *Crain's Detroit Business* (Vol. 24, October 6, 2008, No. 40, pp. 8)

Pub: Crain Communications, Inc.

Ed: Jay Greene. **Description:** Woodward Medical Corridor that runs along Woodward Avenue and currently encompasses twelve hospitals and is rapidly growing with additional physician offices, advanced oncology centers and new hospitals. Beaumont Hospital is building a $160 million proton-beam therapy cancer center on its Royal Oak campus in a joint venture with Procure Treatment Centers of Bloomington Ind. That is expected to open in 2010 and will employ approximately 145 new workers.

42017 ■ **"The Wealth Portfolio"** in *Canadian Business* (Vol. 79, Winter 2006, No. 24, pp. 146)

Pub: Rogers Media

Ed: Jeff Sanford. **Description:** The trends pertaining to the pricing of shares of public enterprises, at the Montreal stock exchange, are described.

42018 ■ **"Web Biz Brulant Surfing for Acquisition Candidates"** in *Crain's Cleveland Business* (Vol. 28, December 3, 2007, No. 48, pp. 6)

Pub: Crain Communications, Inc.

Ed: Chuck Soder. **Description:** Brulant Inc., a provider of web development and marketing services, is looking to acquire other companies after growing for five years straight. The company is one of the largest technology firms in Northeast Ohio.

42019 ■ **"A Week of the Worst Kind of Selling"** in *Barron's* (Vol. 88, June 30, 2008, No. 26, pp. M3)

Pub: Dow Jones & Co., Inc.

Ed: Kopin Tan. **Description:** In the week that ended in June 27, 2008 the selloff in the U.S. stock market was brought on by mounting bank losses and the spread of economic slowdown on top of high oil prices. The 31 percent decrease in the share price of Ingersoll-Rand since October 2007 may have factored in most of its risks. The company has completed its acquisition of Trane to morph into a refrigeration-equipment company.

42020 ■ *The Weekly Corporate Growth Report*

Pub: NVST Inc.

Contact: Walter Jurek

Released: Weekly, Fifty times per year. **Publication Includes:** Current acquisition and merger transactions. **Entries Include:** Buyer and seller names and locations, annual sales and net income for each, seller's net worth and price-earnings ratio, and purchase price, including terms and various ratios. **Arrangement:** Classified by Standard Industrial Classification (SIC) code.

42021 ■ **"Wells Fargo Will Soon Lead Local Banks in Deposits"** in *Austin Business JournalInc.* (Vol. 28, December 5, 2008, No. 38, pp. A1)

Pub: American City Business Journals

Ed: Christopher Calnan. **Description:** Acquisition of Wachovia Corporation by Wells Fargo and Company will leave the latter as the top bank for deposits in Austin, Texas. The merged bank will have deposits of more than $ billion, more than the $3.9 billion deposits Bank of America maintains in the area.

42022 ■ **"Wendy's Speeds Up Tim's Spinout"** in *Globe & Mail* (January 11, 2006, pp. B1)

Pub: CTVglobemedia Publishing Inc.

Ed: Andrew Willis. **Description:** The reasons behind the decision of Wendy's International Inc. to bid Tim Hortons are presented.

42023 ■ **"What Players in the Midmarket Are Talking About"** in *Mergers & Acquisitions: The Dealmaker's Journal* (March 1, 2008)

Pub: SourceMedia, Inc.

Description: Sports Properties Acquisition Corp. went public at the end of January; according to the company's prospectus, it is not limiting its focus to just teams, it is also considering deals for stadium construction companies, sports leagues, facilities, sports-related advertising and licensing of products, in addition to other related segments.

42024 ■ **"What's In a Relationship? The Case of Commercial Lending"** in *Business Horizons* (Vol. 51, March-April 2008, No. 2, pp. 93)

Pub: Elsevier Advanced Technology Publications

Description: Academic literature on relationship lending and banking to small and medium enterprises is analyzed. This practice is best suited to some SME types but creates special challenges for bank managers. Relationship lending may also be better delivered by community banks.

42025 ■ **"When Anything (And Everything) Goes"** in *Globe & Mail* (January 12, 2007, pp. B4)

Pub: CTVglobemedia Publishing Inc.

Ed: Elizabeth Church. **Description:** The forecast on acquisition of different real estate firms is presented.

42026 ■ **"Where Are the Vultures?"** in *Mergers & Acquisitions: The Dealmaker's Journal* (March 1, 2008)

Pub: SourceMedia, Inc.

Ed: Ken MacFadyen. **Description:** Although the real estate market is distressed, not many acquisitions are being made by distress private equity investors; this is due, in part, to the difficulty in assessing real estate industry firms since it is a sector which is so localized.

42027 ■ **"Where Rubber Meets Road"** in *Canadian Business* (Vol. 80, March 12, 2007, No. 6, pp. 15)

Pub: Rogers Media

Ed: Michelle Magnan. **Description:** The partnership between Engineered Drilling Solutions Inc. and En-Cana Corp. to build road from rubber wastes and follow environment-friendly methods in work is discussed.

42028 ■ **"Who's Next?"** in *Boston Business Journal* (Vol. 27, November 16, 2007, No. 42, pp. 1)

Pub: American City Business Journals Inc.

Ed: Lisa van der Pool. **Description:** Boston, Massachusetts' burgeoning technology and biotech industries along with rising billing rates make it a unique legal market. Law firms cross the threshold either by merging with or acquiring a smaller law firm. Boston as a unique legal market is discussed.

42029 ■ **"Why Intel Should Dump Its Flash-Memory Business"** in *Barron's* (Vol. 88, March 10, 2008, No. 10, pp. 35)

Pub: Dow Jones & Company, Inc.

Ed: Eric J. Savitz. **Description:** Intel Corp. must sell its NAND flash-memory business as soon as it possibly can to the highest bidder to focus on its PC processor business and take advantage of other business opportunities. Apple should consider a buyback of 10 percent of the company's shares to lift its stock.

42030 ■ **"Why Nestle Should Sell Alcon"** in *Barron's* (Vol. 88, March 17, 2008, No. 11, pp. M12)

Pub: Dow Jones & Company, Inc.

Ed: Sean Walters. **Description:** Nestle should sell Alcon because Nestle can't afford to be complacent as its peers have made changes to their portfolios to boost competitiveness. Nestle's stake in Alcon and L'Oreal have been ignored by investors and Nestle could realize better value by strengthening its nutrition division through acquisitions.

42031 ■ *Wikinomics: How Mass Collaboration Changes Everything*
Pub: Penguin Group
Ed: Don Tapscott. **Released:** November 2006. **Price:** $25.95. **Description:** Guide to collaborate plans change beliefs about business hierarchies.

42032 ■ **"Wikinomics: The Sequel"** in *Business Strategy Review* **(Vol. 21, Summer 2010, No. 2, pp. 64)**
Pub: Wiley-Blackwell
Description: Ever-optimistic Don Tapscott and Anthony Williams, coauthors of Wikinomics and individually, of a number of other books that study the Internet and its relation to society, are now working on a new book, one for which they're using the Internet to determine its title.

42033 ■ **"Will Work for Equity"** in *Inc.* **(March 2008, pp. 50, 52)**
Pub: Gruner & Jahr USA Publishing
Ed: Ryan McCarthy. **Description:** Profile of Dave Graham and his information technology company; Graham built his business by taking equity in client firms rather than charging fees. Four tips to consider before signing a work-for-equity business deal are outlined.

42034 ■ **"Winner: Caparo Group Plc"** in *Crain's Detroit Business* **(Vol. 24, March 24, 2008, No. 12, pp. 12)**
Pub: Crain Communications, Inc.
Ed: Brent Snavely. **Description:** London-based Caparo Group plc saw its acquisition of Voestalpine Polynorm as an opportunity to gain a foothold in the North American automotive industry. Caparo was impressed with the company's breadth of manufacturing capabilities and quality systems as well as with the management team.

42035 ■ **"A Wireless Makes 8 Store-In-Store Kiosk Acquisitions"** in *Wireless News* **(October 16, 2010)**
Pub: Close-Up Media Inc.
Description: A Wireless, a retailer for Verizon Wireless has acquired eight of Verizon's retail kiosks that are positioned in home appliance and electronics stores.

42036 ■ **"Wirtz Partners With California Liquor Wholesaler To Expand Reach"** in *Chicago Tribune* **(December 17, 2008)**
Pub: McClatchy-Tribune Information Services
Ed: Mike Hughlett. **Description:** Young's Market Co. and Wirtz Beverage Group have tentatively agreed to a joint venture that will give both companies a larger reach in the wine and liquor distribution business.

42037 ■ **"With Algoma Steel Gone, Is Stelco Next?"** in *Globe & Mail* **(April 16, 2007, pp. B1)**
Pub: CTVglobemedia Publishing Inc.
Ed: Greg Keenan. **Description:** Speculation in Canadian steel industry over possible sale of Stelco Inc. too after the sale of Algoma Steel Inc. to Essar Global Ltd. is discussed.

42038 ■ *Working Together: Why Great Partnerships Succeed*
Pub: HarperBusiness
Ed: Michael D. Eisner with Aaron Cohen. **Price:** $25.99. **Description:** Michael D. Eisner, former CEO of the Walt Disney Company interviews corporate partners from various industries, including Bill and Melinda Gates and Warren Buffet and Charlie Munger. Why certain business partnerships succeed in the corporate world is discussed.

42039 ■ **"Wrigley's a Rich Meal for Mars"** in *Crain's Chicago Business* **(Vol. 31, May 5, 2008, No. 18, pp. 2)**
Pub: Crain Communications, Inc.
Ed: Steven R. Strahler. **Description:** Mars Inc. will have to manage wisely in order to make their acquisition of Wm. Wrigley Jr. Co. profitable due to the high selling price of Wrigley which far exceeds the industry norm. Statistical data included.

42040 ■ **"XM and Sirius Satellite Radio Face Up to Their Losses and Decide to Get Hitched"** in *Globe & Mail* **(February 20, 2007, pp. B17)**
Pub: CTVglobemedia Publishing Inc.
Ed: Grant Robertson. **Description:** XM Satellite Radio and Sirius Satellite Radio are planning to merge operations, after years of losses. The possible merger could create a $13 billion company.

42041 ■ **"Xstrata's Takeover Bid Comes Up Short in Shareholder's Eyes"** in *Globe & Mail* **(March 27, 2007, pp. B16)**
Pub: CTVglobemedia Publishing Inc.
Ed: Andy Hoffman. **Description:** The share holders of LionOre Mining International have expressed dissatisfaction over $4.6 billion take over by Xstrata PLC. Share holders are demanding more prices for share value.

42042 ■ **"The Yahoo Family Tree"** in *Conde Nast Portfolio* **(Vol. 2, June 2008, No. 6, pp. 34)**
Pub: Conde Nast Publications, Inc.
Ed: Blaise Zerega. **Description:** Yahoo, founded in 1994 by Stanford students Jerry Yang and David Filo, is still an Internet powerhouse. The company's history is also outlined as well as the reasons in which Microsoft desperately wants to acquire the firm.

42043 ■ **"Yahoo! - Microsoft Pact: Alive Again?"** in *Barron's* **(Vol. 89, July 27, 2009, No. 30, pp. 8)**
Pub: Dow Jones & Co., Inc.
Ed: Mark Veverka. **Description:** Yahoo! reported higher than expected earnings in the second quarter of 2009 under CEO Carol Bartz who has yet to articulate her long-term vision and strategy for turning around the company. The media reported that Yahoo! and Microsoft are discussing an advertising-search partnership which should benefit both companies.

42044 ■ **"Zucker Closes Deal on HBC With Sweeter Takeover Offer"** in *Globe & Mail* **(January 27, 2006, pp. B1)**
Pub: CTVglobemedia Publishing Inc.
Ed: Marina Strauss; Sinclair Stewart; Jacquie McNish. **Description:** Jerry Zucker, vice-president of InterTech Group Inc., has finalized a deal to buy retail store Hudson Bay Co, for 1.1 billion dollars. The shares will be purchased at a rate of 15.25 dollars per share in an all cash transaction. Complete details of the buyout are discussed.

42045 ■ **"Zucker's HBC Shakeup Imminent"** in *Globe & Mail* **(February 20, 2006, pp. B3)**
Pub: CTVglobemedia Publishing Inc.
Ed: Marina Strauss. **Description:** The plans of investor Jerry Zucker to revamp Hudson's Bay Co., upon its acquisition, are presented.

VIDEOCASSETTES/ AUDIOCASSETTES

42046 ■ *Fergi Builds a Business*
Phoenix Learning Group
2349 Chaffee Dr.
St. Louis, MO 63146-3306
Ph:(314)569-0211
Free: 800-221-1274
Fax:(314)569-2834
URL: http://www.phoenixlearninggroup.com
Released: 1990. **Price:** $400.00. **Description:** The process of forming and building a business is demonstrated. Included are dealing with success, failure, partnerships, corporations, capital and profits. **Availability:** VHS; EJ; 3/4U; Special order formats.

42047 ■ *Partnership Series*
Excellence in Training Corp.
c/o ICON Training
804 Roosevelt St.
Polk City, IA 50226

Free: 800-609-0479
Co. E-mail: info@icontraining.com
URL: http://www.icontraining.com
Released: 1990. **Price:** $895.00. **Description:** A four-part program designed to build more effective management. **Availability:** VHS; 3/4U; Special order formats.

42048 ■ *The Price: Update*
Commonwealth Films, Inc.
223 Commonwealth Ave.
Boston, MA 02116
Ph:(617)262-5634
Fax:(617)262-6948
Co. E-mail: info@commonwealthfilms.com
URL: http://www.commonwealthfilms.com
Released: 1989. **Price:** $395.00. **Description:** An updated version of the film on mergers, antitrust violations, and other big business dealings. **Availability:** VHS; 3/4U.

CONSULTANTS

42049 ■ AB Associates
7380 Sherman Rd.
PO Box 5190
Chesterland, OH 44026-2050
Ph:(330)672-1219
Fax:(330)672-0039
Co. E-mail: raggarwa@bsa3.kent.edu
Contact: Dr. Raj Aggarwal, Principle
Scope: Offers expertise in the areas of banking, capital budgeting, investing in emerging markets, international risk analysis, strategic planning and international accounting, management of foreign exchange and other accounting and financial policies. Additional services include acquisition and merger analysis, the valuation of a proposed purchase and development of appropriate post-merger managerial policies, and the implementation of computer-based receivable and inventory management policies.

42050 ■ Access Management Corp.
6135 Park S Dr.
PO Box 12059
Charlotte, NC 28220-2059
Ph:(704)554-9000
Fax:(704)554-0258
Contact: George A. Suter, President
E-mail: gasuter@webserve.net
Scope: Provides international management services specializing in trade financing (Worldwide Factoring) market development, licensing/technology transfer, and marketing. Experienced in merger/acquisition brokering, trade financing, letter of credit discounting and forfeiting, factoring, equipment financing, and debt recovery.

42051 ■ Agri-Personnel
5120 Old Bill Cook Rd.
Atlanta, GA 30349-0319
Ph:(404)768-5701
Fax:(404)768-5705
Contact: David J. Wicker, Owner
Scope: Agribusiness consultants active in executive/professional/technical recruitment and placement, and in mergers, acquisitions, and divestitures in various industries including dairy, feed, food, fertilizer, farm chemicals, poultry and egg, animal health, and pulp and paper.

42052 ■ AgriCapital Corp.
1410 Broadway, Ste. 1802
New York, NY 10018-5018
Ph:(212)944-9500
Fax:(212)944-9525
Co. E-mail: info@agricapital.com
URL: http://www.agricapital.com
Contact: David J. Repking Jr., Principle
E-mail: repking@atsagricapital.com
Scope: Provides investment banking services for agribusiness clients in the United States and abroad, including financial consulting, debt and equity placements and joint ventures, and mergers and acquisitions. Industries served: Agribusiness and food companies. **Publications:** "Seed world"; "Strategic Agribusiness Review," Dec, 2003; "Yield," Jun, 2003;

"Feed Management," May, 2002. **Seminars:** Thoughts on Private Equity and Agribusiness, Sep, 2009; Capital Markets and the Crop Input Sector, Oct, 2006; Views on the Crop Protection Industry, Sep, 2005; Mergers and Acquisitions in the US Food and Agribusiness Industry, Sep, 2002.

42053 ■ Air Comm Corp.
3300 Airport Rd.
Boulder, CO 80301
Ph:(303)440-4075
Free: 877-572-6800
Fax:(303)440-6355
Co. E-mail: info@aircommcorp.com
URL: http://www.aircommcorp.com
Contact: Keith Steiner, Principle
E-mail: ksteiner@atsaircommcorp.com
Scope: Aviation engineering consultants offering to clients design and FAA approval of aircraft accessories and aircraft modifications, as well as general business planning services, including acquisitions and mergers.

42054 ■ ALCO Capital Group Inc.
745 5th Ave., Ste. 1506
New York, NY 10151-1504
Ph:(212)751-9150
Free: 800-233-2526
Fax:(212)371-2768
Co. E-mail: alco745@aol.com
URL: http://www.alcocapital.com
Contact: Steve Goldstein, Principle
E-mail: alan.cohen@alcocapital.com
Scope: Consultants in financially troubled situations, specializing in Chapter 11 rehabilitations, Chapter 7 liquidation interface with the creditors committee, arrange for and provide funding for company rehabilitation; evaluation of company operations and procedures. Expertise includes investments, acquisitions, auctions, and liquidations.

42055 ■ AMC International Inc.
864 S Robertson Blvd., Ste. 207
PO Box 11292
Los Angeles, CA 90035
Ph:(310)652-5620
Fax:(310)652-6709
Co. E-mail: inquiry@amcusa.com
Contact: Abe Moradian, President
Scope: Offers day to day business management, business turn around, marketing strategies, development or refinement of corporate mission, and merger and acquisition evaluations. Industries served all.

42056 ■ American Appraisal Associates Inc.
411 E Wisconsin Ave., Ste. 1900
Milwaukee, WI 53202-4466
Ph:(414)271-7240
Free: 800-558-8650
Fax:(414)221-7065
Co. E-mail: moreinfo@american-appraisal.com
URL: http://www.american-appraisal.com
Contact: Kimberly R. Russo, CFO
E-mail: tbrown@atsamerican-appraisal.com
Scope: Performs valuations of business enterprises and their securities for tax-related purposes, estate, gift and income taxes, mergers and acquisitions including fairness opinions, and ESOPs. **Publications:** "Estimation of Hospital Real Property Values for Ad Valorem Tax Purposes"; "Developing Discount Rates in a Global Environment"; "Discount Rates for Foreign Investments"; "Getting a Grip on Foreign Discount Rates".

42057 ■ Aquinas Group L.L.P.
1733 Green Valley Rd., Ste. 100
Havertown, PA 19083-2520
Ph:(610)449-2290
Fax:(610)482-9157
Co. E-mail: rhrabner@theaquinasgroup.com
Contact: Charles P. Steckel, Director
E-mail: moir@theaquinasgroup.com
Scope: Offers business, financial and management consulting services. Activities include corporate planning and finance, production and marketing, management systems, organization development, merger and acquisition, startup and venture capital. Serves private industries as well as government agencies.

Investment banking services. **Seminars:** Productivity and Profit Improvement; Business Planning and Financing; Operational Auditing.

42058 ■ ARDITO Information & Research Inc.
1019 Sedwick Dr., Ste. G
Wilmington, DE 19803
Ph:(302)479-5373
Free: 800-836-9068
Fax:(302)479-5375
Co. E-mail: sardito@ardito.com
URL: http://www.ardito.com
Contact: Stephanie C. Ardito, President
E-mail: sardito@ardito.com
Scope: A full-service information and research firm. Provides information in areas of financial data, published research, demographic data, industry-specific publications, competitor data, marketing and sales trends, new product developments, government relations, bibliographies. Industries served are pharmaceutical, health, publishing, and environment, and business. **Publications:** "The Swine flu pandemic: Authoritative information versus community gossip," Searcher, Oct, 2009; "The Medical blogosphere: How social networking platforms are changing medical searching," Searcher, May, 2009; "Social Networking and Video Web Sites: MySpace and YouTube Meet the Copyright Cops," Searcher, May, 2007; "Copyright Clearance Center raises transactional fees," Information Today, Jul, 2004.

42059 ■ The Argus Group
5950 Canoga Ave., Ste. 515
Woodland Hills, CA 91367
Ph:(818)990-7200
Free: 800-339-9910
Fax:(818)990-7909
Co. E-mail: cbercy@aol.com
URL: http://www.arguslending.com
Contact: Patti Alley, Principle
E-mail: palley@atsarguslending.com
Scope: Provides asset based real estate loans.

42060 ■ Associated Management Systems Inc.
1000 Elwell Ct., Ste. 234
Palo Alto, CA 94303-4306
Ph:(650)852-9041
Fax:(650)967-9992
Co. E-mail: amsn@rcn.com
Contact: M. A. Quraishi, President
Scope: The firm's entrepreneurial and professional expertise includes corporate management, investment banking, finance, strategic planning, risk evaluation, due diligence studies and management audits. Also assists with mergers and acquisitions, and provides management for turnaround situations. Undertakes project packaging, plant relocations, capital restructuring and funding. Industries served: Agriculture, real estate, insurance, computers, communications, retail/wholesale, electronics/instruments, paper/printing, food processing, furniture/home products, travel, transportation, recreation, heavy industry, pharmaceuticals, and government agencies.

42061 ■ Associated Marketers
10 E Hartshorn Dr.
Short Hills, NJ 07078
Ph:(973)376-3835
Contact: Lauren K. Hagaman, President
Scope: Consulting services limited to area of mergers and acquisitions through a network of associates. Active in serving manufacturing, distributing and service businesses seeking new corporate homes, acquiring additional businesses, or divesting divisions or subsidiaries. Fields served include appliances, house wares, advertising, industrial, publishing, building materials, printing and graphic arts, banking, insurance, apparel and textiles, automotive, transportation, home furnishings, food and confectionery products, leisure products, mail order, natural resources, plastics, packaging, and service businesses and retailing.

42062 ■ Atlantic Management Company Inc.
875 Greenland Rd., Orchard Pk., Ste. A12
Portsmouth, NH 03801-7124
Ph:(603)436-8009

Fax:(603)427-0146
Co. E-mail: amc@atlantic-mgmt.com
URL: http://www.atlantic-mgmt.com
Contact: Theresa M. Murphy, Principle
E-mail: cpaterri@atscomcast.net
Scope: Offers business valuation services in connection with employee stock ownership plans, fairness opinions, management buyouts, mergers and acquisitions, divorce, stockholder disputes, estate planning and estate and gift tax. Additional ESOP advisory services include feasibility studies, equity allocations, and financing proposals. Serves private industries as well as government agencies. **Publications:** "Business Succession Strategies," 2006; "Selling a Company," 2006; "Case Study on Business Valuation and Industry Intelligence," 2006; "Lock, Stock, and Barrel: A Well Connected Hedge Firm Buys Bushmaster Firearms," Maine biz, May, 2006; "Tips for Lawyers When Working with Appraisers," New Hampshire Bar Review, Oct, 2005; "A Win All Around," Worcester Telegram and Gazette, Mar, 2005. **Seminars:** Current Techniques For Successful Business Transition, Keeley the Katerer Banquet Center, Sep, 2009; Maximizing the Value of Your ESOP in Challenging Times, Mar, 2009; Business Succession Planning & ESOPs - Creating a Buyer for the Closely-Held Company, Sep, 2008; Business Valuation II, Boston Tax Institute, Jun, 2008; Business Valuation I, Boston Tax Institute, Jun, 2008; Now That You've Built It, What Do You Want To Do With It?, May, 2008; Human Resource and Fiduciary Issues for New and Established ESOPs, Mar, 2008; Now That You've Built It, Feb, 2008; A Journey to Employee Ownership: The Future Is In Your Hands, Oct, 2007; Advanced Limited Liability Issues, Jun, 2007.

42063 ■ Bain & Company Inc.
131 Dartmouth St.
Boston, MA 02116-5134
Ph:(617)572-2000
Fax:(617)572-2427
Co. E-mail: corporate.inquiries@bain.com
URL: http://www.bain.com
Contact: Teresa Martin-Retortillo, Managering Director
E-mail: martin-retortillo@bain.com
Scope: Management consulting firm which focuses on helping clients improve their financial performance. Specifically, the firm operates in these areas: corporate and business unit strategy, manufacturing, mergers and acquisitions, value managed relationships, information technology, retailing, customer base management and retention, distribution and logistics, high technology, cost reduction, consumer marketing, change management and healthcare. Client base represents virtually all economic sectors manufacturing, wholesaling, retailing, transportation and services. **Publications:** "Individual philanthropy lags in India and China"; "Profit from the core: A return to growth in turbulent times," 2010; "Management Tools 2009: An Executive's Guide," 2009; "The Breakthrough Imperative: How the Best Managers Get Outstanding Results," Harper Collins Publishers, 2008; "Memo to the CEO: Lessons from Private Equity Any Company Can Use," Harvard Business Press, 2008; "Unstoppable: Finding Hidden Assets to Renew the Core and Fuel Profitable Growth," Harvard Business School Press, 2007; "Management Tools 2007: An Executive's Guide," 2007; "Growth in a slower-growth China"; "Falling profits signal radical changes for retail banks"; "Private equity firms sharpen their focus"; "Private equity's new landscape"; "The green edge: Why carbon competitiveness matter"; "After easy money: Managing in a new era"; "Managing IT to win in the recovery". **Seminars:** Internship intro seminar.

42064 ■ Biomedical Management Resources
PO Box 10977
Conway, AR 72034
Ph:(801)272-4668
Fax:(801)277-3290
Co. E-mail: SeniorManagement@BiomedicalManagement.com
URL: http://www.biomedicalmanagement.com
Contact: Ping Fong Jr., President
E-mail: pingfong@biomedicalmanagement.com
Scope: Provides business development, interim management, and executive search services. Assists

companies in strategic alliances, corporate partnering, business acquisition. Demonstrated success in identifying recruiting, and placing key managers in difficult to hire positions.

42065 ■ Business Brokers Hawaii L.L.C.
3230 Pikai Way
PO Box 1810
Kihei, HI 96753
Ph:(808)879-8833
Free: (866)239-1567
Fax:(808)879-5966
Co. E-mail: md@businessbrokershawaii.com
URL: http://www.business-brokers.com
Contact: Solana Poe, Principle
E-mail: solana@atsbusinessbrokershawaii.com
Scope: Offers buying or selling existing businesses, creation of new businesses, business evaluation and appraisal, assistance to clients on expansion and mergers, consultation with owners of businesses in trouble, and consultation on Unites States, Japan and Chinese commerce. **Seminars:** How to Start Your Own Business; How to Make a Sick Business Well Again; How to do Fiscal Forecasting and Cash Flow Projections.

42066 ■ The Business Place Ltd.
10 Kingsbridge Garden Cir., Ste. 506
Mississauga, ON, Canada L5R 3K6
Ph:(905)890-9245
Fax:(905)890-3229
Co. E-mail: gary.landa@thebusinessplace.com
URL: http://www.thebusinessplace.com
Contact: Gary R. Landa, President
E-mail: gary.landa@thebusinessplace.com
Scope: Assists in the buying and selling of businesses, arranging bank financing, venture capital loans/investments, mergers and acquisitions. **Publications:** "Did you find the right business for sale Part II," Feb, 2009; "Did you find the right business," Feb, 2009; "Buying a business what do you look for when looking at financial statements," Feb, 2009; "Business brokers how do you know if you found the right business broker," Feb, 2009; "Businesses how do you determine if you found the right one," Feb, 2009; "Start up businesses how do you value them when you are looking for equity," Feb, 2009; "Business locations time to move intone space, Feb, 2009; Business brokers are they helpful," Feb, 2009.

42067 ■ Business Team
1901 S Bascom Ave., Ste. 400
Campbell, CA 95008
Ph:(408)246-1102
Fax:(408)246-2219
Co. E-mail: sanjose@business-team.com
URL: http://www.business-team.com
Contact: William L. Kramer, Vice President
E-mail: mani@atsbusiness-team.com
Scope: Business consulting services offered to companies looking for buyers. Specializes in mergers and acquisitions, business brokerage, and valuations. **Seminars:** Business Valuation Enhancing the Value of Your Company.

42068 ■ The Change Agents
145 Columbia Ave.
Holland, MI 49423-2978
Ph:(616)392-5564
Contact: William G. Garlough, Managing Director
Scope: Provides consulting services related to mergers, acquisitions and divestitures. Services offered include: Assisting acquiring companies in establishing and managing effective acquisition programs; representing sellers in the sale of their companies, and bringing buyers and sellers together. Additional consulting services include: Advising on the structure of leveraged buy-outs; mediating sales between partners or in family succession; business valuations; due diligence examination of the marketing function; post-acquisition integration advice; and corporate strategy and planning.

42069 ■ Cole, Warren and Long Inc.
2 Penn Center Plz., Ste. 312
Philadelphia, PA 19102
Ph:(215)563-0701
Free: 800-394-8517
Fax:(215)563-2907
Co. E-mail: cwlserch@cwl-inc.com
URL: http://www.cwl-inc.com
Contact: Joan Bower, Principle
Scope: Offers management guidance to commercial, industrial, and government organizations specializing in the areas of organization studies, executive searches, acquisitions and mergers, compensation programs, audits, and improvement seminars. Conducts marketing, economic, and systems studies counsels on profit improvement, manpower control, operations, and systems integration.

42070 ■ Consortium House Co.
15 Bostan Rd.
PO Box 177
Malden on Hudson, NY 12453
Ph:(845)246-2336
Fax:(845)246-2338
Co. E-mail: eugenegs@aol.com
Contact: Gene Schwartz, President
E-mail: eugenegs@aol.com
Scope: Offers its services to book, periodical, multimedia, and electronic publishers. Specializes in web strategies and in education, training, professional and general trade markets. Advises in financial and business development, marketing, new product development, fulfillment and distribution, venture investment, mergers and acquisitions, literary and publishing properties, project management and operating systems troubleshooting. **Publications:** "From Eyeballs to I Balls: Reaching the Reader," Foreword Magazine, Jan, 2001; "Need to Know Guide to Books on Demand," Foreword Magazine, Jun, 2000; "Setting Industry-Wide Distribution Standards," Small Press, Jan, 1997. **Seminars:** Has presented Electronic Publishing; Print on Demand; Money and Publishing; Managing Profitability and Strategic and Business Plan Development.

42071 ■ The Consulting Firm Inc.
64 Sierra Ct., Ste. 1200
Old Bridge, NJ 08857-3050
Ph:(732)679-5520
Fax:(732)679-9451
Co. E-mail: efields128@aol.com
URL: http://www.edfields.com
Contact: Edward Fields, Principle
E-mail: efields128@aol.com
Scope: Offers acquisition and venture investment services including search, evaluation, negotiation, and financing. Also advises on product, profit center evaluation, and personnel benefits. Firm assists companies with serious business problems and those whose performance should be much better. Serves all industries. **Publications:** "The Essentials of Finance and Accounting for Non-Financial Managers," 2002.

42072 ■ CorDev Financial Inc.
Stanford Financial Sq.
2600 El Camino Real, Ste. 400
Palo Alto, CA 94306-1705
Ph:(650)493-9111
Fax:(650)493-9115
Co. E-mail: robert@cordevfinancial.com
URL: http://www.cordevfinancial.com
Contact: April K. Edner, Secretary
E-mail: robert@cordevfinancial.com
Scope: Specializes in corporate mergers and acquisitions for small to mid sized companies and CEO consulting.

42073 ■ Corporate Business Services of America Inc.
5 Palmer Dr.
PO Box 1352
Conway, AR 72032-9484
Ph:(501)329-2592
Contact: Gene Horton, President
Scope: Business management consulting firm specializes in profit engineering, management consulting, and business coaching. Industries served: Businesses with sales in the $500,000 to $25,000,000 range.

42074 ■ Corporate Growth Assistance Ltd.
1 Benvenuto Pl., Ste. 420
Toronto, ON, Canada M4V 2L1
Ph:(416)222-7772
Fax:(416)222-6091
Co. E-mail: millard@corporategrowth.ca
URL: http://www.corporategrowthassistance.com
Contact: Robert Macbean, Principle
E-mail: millard@corporategrowth.ca
Scope: Represents extensive experience in facilitating profitable growth and liquidity and will deliver: A broad network of contacts providing access to investment options, funding, and business development opportunities, the talent necessary to provide solid strategic and operating guidance, the experience to generate high rates of return while effectively managing challenging situations, hands on professionalism; A commitment to execution so as to maximize profit, market share and team building. Client involvement has included: Computerized car valuation database management for the insurance industry; dimensional art reproduction; dining and bedroom furniture manufacturing; employee and family assistance programs. **Seminars:** Expansion Equity And Management Engineering.

42075 ■ DeVries & Company Inc.
800 W 47th St.
Kansas City, MO 64112
Ph:(816)756-0055
Free: 877-428-7252
Fax:(816)756-0061
Contact: Rose Marie, Principle
Scope: Investment banking/financial consulting firm which helps companies solve financial problems and achieve growth and diversification goals. Helps established companies raise capital and assists new and developing companies secure venture capital and create public markets for their stocks. Provides confidential services to companies who want to sell or merge, aids companies in acquiring other companies, helps individuals and companies structure and negotiate leveraged buyouts, provides financial guidance, shapes business strategy and develops operating and financial strategies. Also performs business valuations for estate and gift tax and ESOPS. Renders fairness opinions and expert witness services.

42076 ■ Diego Chevere & Co.
Metro Parque 7, Ste. 301, Metro Office Pk.
PO Box 11930
Caparra Heights, PR 00920
Ph:(787)774-9595
Fax:(787)774-9566
Co. E-mail: dcco@coqui.net
Contact: Diego Chevere, Principal
Scope: Business consultants offering assistance with financial projections, strategic business planning, mergers, reorganizations, EDP system design and cash management. Serves private industries as well as government agencies. **Seminars:** EDP System Development; Loan Package Preparation.

42077 ■ Dorn & Associates Inc.
8506 Bass Lake Rd.
Minneapolis, MN 55428-5304
Ph:(763)533-7689
Fax:(763)533-1143
Contact: Chad L. Dorn, Vice President
E-mail: chad@dorn-associates.com
Scope: Services include accounting, marketing, employment partnership, new doctor agreements, personnel issues and human resources assessment, practice management, practice merger acquisition sale and liquidation, practice surveys and valuation, staff development and training.

42078 ■ Executive Consultants Inc.
78 Carlton Dr. NE
Atlanta, GA 30342-3202
Ph:(404)255-4801
Fax:(404)255-4801
Co. E-mail: spider42000@yahoo.com
Contact: Stuart Schwarzschild, President
Scope: Offers mergers and acquisition consulting, estate planning, pension planning, profit sharing advice, and insurance planning services.

42079 ■ Fowler, Anthony & Co.
20 Walnut St.
Wellesley, MA 02481
Ph:(781)237-4201
Fax:(781)237-7718
Co. E-mail: jquagliaroli@comcast.net
Contact: John A. Quagliaroli, President
E-mail: jquagliaroli@mediaone.net
Scope: Offers consulting services and direct investment into small businesses in mergers and acquisitions, capital financing and venture capital. Active with the following industries: Communications, computer related, consumer, distribution, electronic components and instrumentation, multimedia, on-line database/publishing, industrial products and equipment, food processing, multimedia, health care services, medical/health related and publishing.

42080 ■ Frankel and Topche P.C.
1700 Galloping Hill Rd.
Kenilworth, NJ 07033
Ph:(908)298-7700
Fax:(908)298-7701
Co. E-mail: info@frankelandtopche.com
URL: http://www.frankelandtopche.com
Contact: Aaron Saiewitz, Principle
E-mail: gtopche@atsfrankelandtopche.com
Scope: Offers financial consulting for closely held businesses. Assists in mergers and acquisitions, tax planning, strategic business planning, family succession planning, accounting, auditing, and obtaining financing. The firm serves small businesses in the service, retail, wholesale, and manufacturing industries. Specializes in real estate, lumber and building materials, and service businesses. **Seminars:** Annual Tax Seminar.

42081 ■ Haas Wheat & Partners L.P.
300 Crescent Ct., Ste. 1700
Dallas, TX 75201-1876
Ph:(214)871-8300
Fax:(214)871-8317
Co. E-mail: info@haaswheat.com
URL: http://www.haaswheat.com
Contact: Wyche H. Walton, Managing Director
E-mail: g.lichlyter@haaswheat.com
Scope: Business consulting firm offering expertise with mergers and acquisitions and financial investment in the United States.

42082 ■ Jacalyn E. S. Bennett & Co.
45 Water St.
Newburyport, MA 01950
Ph:(978)462-1966
Fax:(978)463-2062
Co. E-mail: sales@bennettcompany.com
URL: http://www.bennettcompany.com
Contact: Linda Wood, Mgr
E-mail: sales@bennettcompany.com
Scope: Developed a multitude of textile blends, including ecologically friendly fabrics, across all relevant fibers, in both knits and woven's, in silks, cottons and synthetics. Designed more than 60, 000 styles across all foundation, lingerie, sleepwear and related product categories.

42083 ■ James V. McTevia & Associates
1806 Old Okeechobee Rd.
West Palm Beach, FL 33409
Ph:(561)691-6270
Co. E-mail: jmctevia@mcteviallc.com
URL: http://www.mctevia.com
Contact: Sandra A. Dahlerup, Principle
E-mail: jmctevia@mcteviallc.com
Scope: Firm specializes in reorganization programs for businesses with serious financial problems. Services include debt restructuring, bankruptcy trustees, liquidations, management reorganization and acquisitions and mergers. Serves private industries as well as government agencies. **Publications:** "Survival in The Face of Change," Jun, 2006; "Tips for Picking An Outside Adviser," Sep, 2005; "Out-of-Court Problem Solving and Restructuring: Guide to a Successful Outcome," May, 2005; "Small Business: The Basics of Business Problem Solving," Mar, 2005; "Annual Business Check," Jan, 2005; "When Bad Things Happen To Good Family Businesses," Business Direct Weekly, Dec, 2001. **Seminars:** Alterna-

tive Methods of Financing for Underperforming Companies, Jun, 2009; Preventing or Structuring a Reorganization without Court Supervision, May, 2008; Business and Professions in Transition - Unlocking Your Business Potential, Jun, 2007; Professions in Transition, Oct, 2007; Preventing or Structuring a Reorganization without Court Supervision, Novi, Jun, 2006; Guiding the Customer in Preventing or Structuring a Reorganization Without Court Supervision, Atlanta, Jun, 2005.

42084 ■ James W. Davidson Company Inc.
23 Forest View Rd.
Wallingford, PA 19086
Ph:(610)566-1462
Co. E-mail: jwdmsd@comcast.net
Contact: James W. Davidson, President
E-mail: jwdmsd@comcast.net
Scope: Offers counsel to clients to improve business strategy, organization, controls, management effectiveness and profits. Provides planning, problem-analysis and implementation assistance. Also performs thorough, in-depth executive recruiting and acquisition and divestment search and analysis. Experienced with large and small manufacturing and service companies, including new ventures.

42085 ■ Jefferies Broadview
520 Madison Ave., 10th Fl.
New York, NY 10022
Ph:(212)284-2300
Fax:(212)284-8101
Co. E-mail: info@jefferiesbroadview.com
URL: http://www.jefferies.com
Contact: Andrew R. Whittaker, Managing Director
E-mail: rmcnamara@atsjefferies.com
Scope: A technology investment banking group, is an advisor in mergers and acquisitions to technology companies, private equity investors, media, health care technology and communications industries.

42086 ■ Johnson, Butler & Co.
7 Waterfront Plz., Ste. 400
Honolulu, HI 96813
Ph:(626)799-5200
Fax:(626)799-5274
Co. E-mail: info@johnsonbutler.com
URL: http://www.johnsonbutler.com
Contact: Richard F. Siefert, Principal
E-mail: rfs@johnsonbutler.com
Scope: Serves as a consultant and intermediary in merger-acquisition work, representing either buyer or seller. Performs acquisition searches for corporate buyers. Arranges corporate divestitures, management buyouts, joint ventures and financing. Other services include business valuations and strategic planning. Experienced in numerous industries including industrial product manufacturing, consumer goods manufacturing, distribution in all fields, hospitality industry services and life sciences.

42087 ■ KFA Services
4704 Pointes Dr., Ste. 103
Mukilteo, WA 98275-6074
Ph:(425)493-8020
Fax:(425)745-6860
Contact: Michael S. Katz, President
Scope: Offers consulting services in financial, accounting, and economic analysis including business valuations, financial projections and feasibility analysis, cost accounting, economic loss determination, mergers and acquisitions, and business policy and planning assistance. Also provides litigation support and construction claims analysis. Serves private industries as well as government agencies. **Seminars:** Economic Feasibility Analysis; The Use of Current Value Accounting for Measuring Port Profitability; Damages for Construction Delays: Analyzing Contractor Claims for Home Office Overhead Costs.

42088 ■ Kibel Green Inc.
1 Park Plz., Ste. 600
Irvine, CA 92614
Ph:(310)829-0255
Free: (866)875-0255

Fax:(310)453-6324
Co. E-mail: info@kginc.com
URL: http://www.kibelgreen.com
Contact: Tim Vadney, Managing Director
E-mail: tvadney@kginc.com
Scope: Provides services in turnaround and crisis management, value creation and investment banking. Serves manufacturing, service, technology, retail, distribution and real estate industries. **Publications:** "Shopping Center Owners Act Now or Lose Your Shirt," Apr, 2009; "Kibel Green Helps Save Media Company," Mar, 2009; "The Role of the Chief Restructuring Officer," Jan, 2009; "The Growth Paradox Effectively Resizing to Drive Profits," Dec, 2008. **Special Services:** The Kibel Green System™.

42089 ■ L.G. Kranick & Associates
1517 W Pierce St.
Milwaukee, WI 53204-1236
Ph:(414)671-3636
Fax:(414)671-4264
Contact: Thomas L. Kranick, President
Scope: Consulting services includes economic analysis of industry trends and long-range planning; market and product surveys and analysis; mergers and acquisitions; manufacturing methods and systems; organization structure and development; and interim management.

42090 ■ Lyons Solutions L.L.C.
15R Hartford Ave., Ste. 2A-D
Granby, CT 06035-0809
Ph:(203)642-4141
Co. E-mail: jlyons@lyonssolutions.com
URL: http://www.lyonssolutions.com
Contact: Kerry Horman, Principal
E-mail: kahorman@verizon.net
Scope: Strategic financial advisers to owners of health care, management consulting, marketing communications, technology and professional services firms. **Seminars:** How to Become More Attractive to a Buyer, 2007; The Nuts and Bolts of M&A Hardware for Buyers and Sellers, 2007; Mind Your M&A's: Track the Trends, Find the Funding and Seal the Deal, 2006; Run It Like You Are Going to Sell It!, 2006; M&A 2006: Who's Buying, What's Selling and Why, 2006; Mergers and Acquisitions, 2006.

42091 ■ M. Richler & Associates Ltd.
85 Skymark Dr., Ste. 2603
North York, ON, Canada M2H 3P2
Ph:(416)491-5264
Fax:(416)491-4557
Contact: Mitchell M. Richler, President
E-mail: mitchrichler@aol.com
Scope: A general management consulting firm specializing in acquisitions and mergers, costing and pricing, office layout design and management, production management and taxation, particularly for small businesses. Industries served: manufacturing, retail, wholesale, import/export, design services, and government agencies. **Seminars:** Keeping the Cottage in the Family; Maximizing Capital Gains Exemption; Minimizing Probate Fees; Plant Reorganization; Departmental Scheduling.

42092 ■ Mark Vanderstelt
9831 Gulfstream Ct.
Fishers, IN 46037
Ph:(317)576-9328
Fax:(317)576-9328
Scope: Consulting services include financial planning and analysis, inventory control, cash management, return on investment, budgeting, pricing, system design and analysis, mergers and acquisitions, feasibility studies, data processing, cost systems and controls, and performance measurement. Also performs operational and financial reviews.

42093 ■ Mertz Associates Inc.
1 Riverwood Pl., N17W24222 Riverwood Dr., Ste. 305
Waukesha, WI 53188-1132
Ph:(262)523-4200

Fax:(262)523-4202
Co. E-mail: mertz@mertz.com
URL: http://www.mertz.com
Contact: Laurance R. Newman, Principle
E-mail: d.marconnet@atsmertz.com
Scope: A merger and acquisition consulting firm representing either dedicated buyers or sellers of companies across the U.S. Clients range from small privately held companies to large public companies in all industries. **Publications:** "Why Successful Companies are Launching Acquisition Searches Now"; "On the Block"; "Selling Troubled Divisions and Companies"; "Don't Fear the D Word"; "M and A Multiples: A Key to Value Or a Distraction"; "Savvy CPA Levels the Playing Field"; "M and A Trends Strategic Focus Drives Success".

42094 ■ MRCworldwide
3020 Old Ranch Pky., 3rd Fl.
Seal Beach, CA 90740
Ph:(562)799-5510
Fax:(562)799-5594
Co. E-mail: jgollihugh@mrcworldwide.com
URL: http://www.mrcworldwide.com
Contact: Ted Johnston, Director
E-mail: tjohnston@atsmrcworldwide.com
Scope: Specializes in mergers and acquisitions, divestitures, strategic planning, executive leadership, product strategy, valuation, ESOPs, venture capital, and management development. Serves industries in graphic arts, printing, manufacturing, distribution, electronics, service, and high-technology and investment banking advisory services. **Seminars:** Executive Leadership; Integration; Strategic Planning; Valuation; Mergers and Acquisitions.

42095 ■ New Century Consultants
1600 2nd St.
Gulfport, MS 39501-2135
Ph:(228)864-3999
Fax:(228)868-4960
Co. E-mail: new-century@cwix.com
Contact: Stephen J. Bosarge, Principle
E-mail: new-century@cwix.com
Scope: Provides management consulting and strategies in public relations, communications, marketing, and advertising. Specializes in consulting services to the music, entertainment and casino industries. Recent experience with new business start-ups and new business acquisitions. Serves private industries as well as government agencies. Training, Executive Search. **Seminars:** Communicating With Power; Writing With Power; Communicating With Employees; Communicating With the Customer; Customer Service Communications; Creativity and Communications.

42096 ■ Nimark Group Inc.
238 Osborne Rd.
Harrison, NY 10528
Ph:(914)967-7600
Contact: Leonard Lipsky, President
Scope: Firm specializes in mergers, acquisitions, divestiture analysis and negotiation for middle market companies. Services include business valuations. Also provides expertise in crisis management. **Seminars:** How to Sell Your Business for the Most Profit.

42097 ■ The Rehmann Group
5800 Gratiot Rd., Ste. 201
PO Box 2025
Saginaw, MI 48638
Ph:(989)799-9580
Free: (866)799-9580
Fax:(989)799-0227
Co. E-mail: skelly@rehmann.com
URL: http://www.rehmann.com
Contact: James Carpp, Principle
E-mail: jcarpp@atsrehmann.com
Scope: Offers general business services that include profit enhancement consulting, investigative services (Kerby Bailey), assistance in preparation of a business plan, aid in obtaining financing, employee benefit plan analysis, systems counseling, incentive plans, cash management, marketing plans and research, as well as business valuations (litigation support) and mergers and acquisitions. Specializing

in services for health care, manufacturing and governmental units. **Publications:** "Manufacturing Monitor "; "Bwg Magazine"; "Bwd Magazine".

42098 ■ Robbinex Inc.
41 Stuart St.
Hamilton, ON, Canada L8L 1B5
Ph:(905)523-7510
Free: 888-762-2463
Fax:(905)523-4998
Co. E-mail: robbinex@robbinex.com
URL: http://www.robbinex.com
Contact: Virginia Selemidis, Mgr
E-mail: virginia@atsrobbinex.com
Scope: Business consultants specializing in the merger and acquisition area and financial planning for small to medium size companies. Other services include business financing, crisis management, acquisition search, business valuations, joint ventures and venture capital, resolution of partnership problems, implementation of franchise programs, and general assistance in site selection. **Seminars:** Creating Transitional Strategies; How to Start a Small Business; Growing Through Acquisition: How to Buy a Business; How to Successfully Manage Medium to Small Businesses; Expansion Through Acquisition; Growth Through Franchising; How to Borrow Money from a Bank; Syndicating Equity; Global Expansion: Are You Missing the Boat; Business succession planning: What's the hurry. **Special Services:** Robbinex^R.

42099 ■ Robert E. Wright Tax and Accounting
3533 Moncure Ave.
Falls Church, VA 22041-2017
Ph:(703)379-0592
Co. E-mail: rwrighttax@aol.com
Contact: Robert E. Wright, Owner
Scope: Business consultants specializing in tax and accounting services, including preparation of business and personal tax returns, quarterly reports, amended returns and special forms(1040s, 1120s, 990s, 941s, 1040Xs, 1099s, etc.). Additional services include the setup and maintenance of bookkeeping systems and the preparation of financial statements, articles of incorporation, corporate minutes and resolutions, articles of partnership, employment agreements, contracts, leases, deeds, promissory notes, etc., assistance with documentation and accounting services required for business licenses and permits, certificates of authority and tax-exempt status.

42100 ■ Sam Rosenbaum & Co.
419 Northfield Ave.
West Orange, NJ 07052-3091
Ph:(973)736-2323
Fax:(973)325-9080
Contact: Sam Rosenbaum, President
Scope: Specializes in mergers, acquisitions, and divestitures and also in marketing.

42101 ■ Samuel D. Begola Associates Inc.
37264 Agar Dr.
Sterling Heights, MI 48310-3601
Ph:(586)977-3335
Fax:(586)977-3335
Contact: Samuel D. Begola, President
Scope: A full service business valuation and financial management consulting firm. Part of the firm's function is to provide both manufacturing and service organizations with the kind of talent they need to get the job done. Provides business valuation for Employee Stock Option Plans ESOPs, buy and sell agreements, solvency opinions in leveraged buyouts, loan procurement and government loan assistance, merger and acquisitions, reorganizations, government sales contracts, minority business expertise, machine rate and quote systems, business plans, marketing, and administrative and turnaround management talent.

42102 ■ Siebrand-Wilton Associates Inc.
PO Box 369
Marlboro, NJ 07746-0369
Ph:(732)917-0239

Fax:(732)972-0214
Co. E-mail: clientsvcs@s-wa.com
URL: http://www.s-wa.com
Contact: John S. Sturges, President
E-mail: bencomp@s-wa.com
Scope: Assesses, plans and implements human resources aspects of mergers and acquisitions. Offers human resources consulting in compensation and benefit plan design, mergers and acquisitions (HR aspects), business ethics assessment and development, editing, writing and association management services, and contract professionals and interim executives. **Publications:** "Should Government or Business Try to Save Medicare," HR News; "Executive Temping," HR Horizons; "When is an Employee Truly an Employee," HR Magazine; "Examining Your Insurance Carrier," HR Magazine.

42103 ■ Stalley Associates Inc.
10635 James Cir. S
Minneapolis, MN 55431-4157
Ph:(952)888-0617
Fax:(952)888-5403
Co. E-mail: info@stalley.com
URL: http://www.stalley.com
Contact: Rodney E. Stalley, President
E-mail: rstalley@stalley.com
Scope: Advises management of companies in the areas of finance, administrative and general management, corporate objectives, policies and procedures, and management and organization audits. Firm has developed a particular expertise in advising management of young and growing companies. Advises in strategic planning, capital planning and financing strategies, securing private and public investment capital, establishing strategic alliances, management and staff organizational restructuring, working with board of directors, shareholders and serving as chief financial officer and chief operations officer on a contract basis. **Publications:** "Knowledge: The Key to Business Success"; "The Board of Directors: A Ceo's Source for Advice, Insight and Support"; "Controlling the Audit Expense".

42104 ■ Stockton Bates L.L.P.
1617 JFK Blvd., Ste. 1005
Philadelphia, PA 19103-1825
Ph:(215)241-7500
Fax:(215)567-3813
Co. E-mail: info@stocktonbates.com
URL: http://www.stocktonbates.com
Contact: Charlotte Brill, Mgr of Admin
E-mail: cbrill@atsstocktonbates.com
Scope: Business consultants whose wide-ranging services include operational audits, mergers and acquisitions expertise, litigation support, and computer hardware and software consulting. Industries served: manufacturing, construction, services, banking, retail and wholesale, and government agencies.

42105 ■ Throne & Co.
49 N Main St.
Stewartstown, PA 17363-4030
Ph:(717)993-3201
Co. E-mail: jthrone@throneco.com
Contact: James P. Throne, Partner
E-mail: jthrone@throneco.com
Scope: Business consultants, specializing in mergers and acquisitions with service specialization in leveraged buyouts, foreign investors, joint ventures, divestitures, marketing and licensing. Consulting also in negotiations, evaluations and structuring. **Seminars:** How to maximize the value of your business and exit on your own terms.

42106 ■ Value Creation Group Inc.
7820 Scotia Dr., Ste. 2000
Dallas, TX 75248-3115
Ph:(972)980-7407
Fax:(972)980-4619
Co. E-mail: john.antos@valuecreationgroup.com
URL: http://www.valuecreationgroup.com
Contact: Rick Balog, Principle
E-mail: john.antos@atsvaluecreationgroup.com
Scope: General business experts offering predictive strategic planning, Activity Based Costing ABC, Activity Based Management ABM, mergers and acquisitions, outsourcing, re engineering, process management, web enabling technology, bench marking,

installation of financial systems, executive search, training, teams, activity based budgeting, operational auditing, feature costing. Industries served financial services, food, health care, insurance, manufacturing, electronics, real estate, consumer products, nonprofit, telecommunication, oil, service, data processing, hotel and resort and government agencies. **Publications:** "Handbook of Process Management Based Predictive Accounting," Alcpa 2002; "Cost Management for Today's Manufacturing Environment and Activity Based Management for Service Environments, Government Entities and Nonprofit Organizations"; "Risks and Opportunities in International Finance and Treasury"; "Driving Value Using Activity Based Budgeting"; "Process Based Accounting Leveraging Processes to Predict Results"; "Handbook of Supply Chain Management"; "Economic Value Management Applications and Techniques"; "The Change Handbook": "Group Methods for Creating the Future"; "Why Value Management and Performance Measurement Through U.S. Binoculars," Journal of Strategic Performance Measurement; "Real Options, Intangibles Measurement and the Benefits of Human Capital Investment to Power the Organization," Journal of Strategic Performance Measurement. **Seminars:** Predictive Accounting; Performance measures; ABM for Manufacturing; ABM for Service Organizations; Finance and Accounting for Non-Financial Executives; Return on Investment/ Capital Expenditure Evaluation; Planning and Cost Control; The Next Step Intermediate Finance and Accounting for Non-financial Managers; Activity-Based Budgeting; Friendly Finance for Fund Raisers; Strategic Outsourcing.

42107 ■ Vencon Management Inc.
65 W 55th St.
New York, NY 10019
Ph:(212)581-8787

Fax:(208)955-5165
Co. E-mail: vencon@att.net
URL: http://www.venconinc.com
Contact: Yuming Shen, Principle
E-mail: vencon@worldnet.att.net
Scope: Venture capital firm and management consultants to corporations and entrepreneurs. Specializes in the areas of mergers and acquisitions evaluation and negotiation, and the preparation of marketing and business plans. Assists small or new businesses in expansion plans and financing. Also involved in new enterprise planning with industry and communities for rural economic analysis. Industries served: nanotechnology, photonics, optics, environment, semiconductor, electronics, chemicals, alternative energy, and health. **Seminars:** Heegaard Knot Diagrams, Sep, 2009; Issues in finite Approximation, Oct, 2009.

42108 ■ Wabash Equity Group
5460 W 84th St.
Indianapolis, IN 46268-1523
Ph:(317)579-6698
Fax:(317)228-1142
Co. E-mail: jjaquajr@msn.com
Contact: Donald K. Taylor, Partner
Scope: Business and financial consultants specializing in mergers and acquisitions for small companies and investments in small companies in central Indiana. Industries served: low tech manufacturing firms.

42109 ■ Wellbrock Inc.
27 Tall Timbers Rd.
Watchung, NJ 07069
Ph:(908)753-0590
Fax:(908)753-7197
Co. E-mail: rwellbro@optonline.net
Contact: Dr. Richard D. Wellbrock, President
E-mail: rwelbro@webspan.net
Scope: Business consultant for small businesses regarding mergers, acquisitions, real estate and venture capital.

42110 ■ White, Nelson & Company L.L.P.
2875 Michelle Dr., Ste. 300
Irvine, CA 92606
Ph:(714)978-1300
Fax:(714)978-7893
Co. E-mail: info@whitenelson.com
URL: http://www.whitenelson.com
Contact: David P. Doran, Partner
E-mail: ddoran@atswhitenelson.com
Scope: Computer technologies and international tax consultants. Mergers and acquisitions consultants for manufacturing and distribution organizations. **Publications:** "Financial Planning Guide"; "Small Business Guide"; "Tax Forms Library"; "IRSTax Publications Library".

RESEARCH CENTERS

42111 ■ Babson College–Arthur M. Blank Center for Entrepreneurship
231 Forest St.
Babson Park, MA 02457-0310
Ph:(781)233-5023
Fax:(781)239-4178
Co. E-mail: jstrimaitis@babson.edu
URL: http://www3.babson.edu/eship
Contact: Janet Strimaitis, Dir.
E-mail: jstrimaitis@babson.edu
Scope: Entrepreneurship and new and growing businesses, including studies in venture capital, starting and financing new value-creating ventures, family businesses, franchises, and harvesting enterprises through IPO's, merger or sale, and family succession. **Publications:** Babson Entrepreneurial Review; Frontiers of Entrepreneurship Research (annually). **Educational Activities:** Babson Entrepreneurship Research Conference (annually). **Awards:** Sponsors Global Academy of Distinguished Entrepreneurs, for outstanding entrepreneurship.

ASSOCIATIONS AND OTHER ORGANIZATIONS

42112 ■ American Society for Public Administration
1301 Pennsylvania Ave. NW, Ste. 840
Washington, DC 20004-1735
Ph:(202)393-7878
Fax:(202)638-4952
Co. E-mail: info@aspanet.org
URL: http://www.aspanet.org
Contact: Antoinette Samuel CAE, Exec. Dir.
Description: Promotes excellence in public service, including government, non-profit and private sectors, and academic community. **Publications:** *PA Times* (monthly); *Public Administration Review* (bimonthly).

42113 ■ National Academy of Public Administration
900 7th St. NW, Ste. 600
Washington, DC 20001
Ph:(202)347-3190
Fax:(202)393-0993
Co. E-mail: kmarcy@napawash.org
URL: http://www.napawash.org
Contact: Kristine M. Marcy, Pres./CEO
Description: Works to respond to specific requests from public agencies and non-governmental organizations. Promotes discourse on emerging trends in governance through standing panels and external funding. Assists federal agencies, congressional committees, state and local governments, civic organizations, and institutions overseas through problem solving, objective research, rigorous analysis, information sharing, development strategies for change, and connecting people and ideas. Promotes forward-looking ideas and of analyzing successes and failures of government reform. .

42114 ■ National Forum for Black Public Administrators
777 N Capitol St. NE, Ste. 807
Washington, DC 20002
Ph:(202)408-9300
Fax:(202)408-8558
Co. E-mail: jsaunders@nfbpa.org
URL: http://www.nfbpa.org
Contact: John E. Saunders III, Exec. Dir.
Description: Black city and county managers and assistant managers; chief administrative officers; agency directors; bureau and division heads; corporate executives; students. Works to promote, strengthen, and expand the role of blacks in public administration. Seeks to focus the influence of black administrators toward building and maintaining viable communities. Develops specialized training programs for managers and executives. Provides national public administrative leadership resource and skills bank. Works to further communication among black public, private, and academic institutions. Addresses issues that affect the administrative capacity of black managers. **Publications:** *Resource Guide* (annual)-;Membership Directory (semiannual).

42115 ■ Section for Women in Public Administration
1301 Pennsylvania Ave. NW, Ste. 840
Washington, DC 20004-1735
Ph:(202)393-7878
URL: http://www.swpanet.org
Contact: Barbara Lewkowitz, Vice Chair
Description: Established by the American Society for Public Administration to initiate action programs appropriate to the needs and concerns of women in public administration. Promotes equal educational and employment opportunities for women in public service, and full participation and recognition of women in all areas of government. Develops strategies for implementation of ASPA policies of interest to women in public administration; recommends qualified women to elective and appointive ASPA governmental leadership positions; acts as forum for communication among professional and laypeople interested in the professional development of women in public administration. .

42116 ■ Southern Public Administration Education Foundation
122 W High St.
Elizabethtown, PA 17022
Ph:(717)540-6126
Co. E-mail: paq@spaef.com
URL: http://www.spaef.com
Contact: Dr. T. Aaron Wachhaus, Ed.
Description: Represents researchers and scholars. Produces publications to educate scholars and practitioners. Publishes electronic journals. **Publications:** *Journal of Health and Human Resources Administration* (quarterly); *Public Administration Quarterly* (quarterly).

REFERENCE WORKS

42117 ■ "1914 Proved to Be Key Year for Chevy" in *Automotive News* (Vol. 86, October 31, 2011, No. 6488, pp. S18)
Pub: Crain Communications Inc.
Ed: Jamie Lareau. **Description:** Chevy Bow Tie emblem was born in 1914, creating the brand's image that has carried through to current days.

42118 ■ "Adidas' Brand Ambitions" in *Business Journal Portland* (Vol. 27, December 10, 2010, No. 41, pp. 1)
Pub: Portland Business Journal
Ed: Erik Siemers. **Description:** Adidas AG, the second-largest sporting goods brand in the world, hopes to increase global revenue by 50 percent by 2015. The German company, which reported $14.5 billion sales, plans to improve its U.S. market. The U.S. is Adidas' largest, but also the most underperforming market for the firm.

42119 ■ "Bill Kaneko" in *Hawaii Business* (Vol. 53, December 2007, No. 6, pp. 32)
Pub: Hawaii Business Publishing
Ed: David K. Choo. **Description:** Hawaii Institute for Public Affairs chief executive officer and president Bill Kaneko believes that the Hawaiian economy is boom-

ing, however, he also asserts that the economy is too focused on tourism and real estate. Kaneko has also realized the that the will of the people is strong while he was helping with the Hawaiian 2050 Sustainability Plan. The difficulties of making a sustainable Hawaii are discussed.

42120 ■ "Business Plan Refines Focus" in *Business Journal Portland* (Vol. 27, December 10, 2010, No. 41, pp. 1)
Pub: Portland Business Journal
Ed: Wendy Culverwell. **Description:** Organizers of the Oregon Business Plan's Leadership Summit 2010 seek the opinions of nearly 1,000 business, education, political, and civic leaders in an effort to address how to rehabilitate Oregon's economy. The opinion-seeking actions recognize the organizers' belief that the economic fate of the state depends on rural Oregon.

42121 ■ "Candidates Differ On State's Green Streak" in *Business Journal Portland* (Vol. 27, October 22, 2010, No. 34, pp. 1)
Pub: Portland Business Journal
Ed: Andy Giegerich. **Description:** The views of Oregon gubernatorial candidates Chris Dudley and John Kitzhaber on the state's economy and on environmental policies are presented. Both Dudley, who is a Republican, and his Democratic challenger believe that biomass could help drive the state's economy. Both candidates also pledged changes in Oregon's business energy tax credit (BETC) program.

42122 ■ "CBC Chief: Future is Now" in *Business Courier* (Vol. 27, August 13, 2010, No. 15, pp. 1)
Pub: Business Courier
Ed: Lucy May. **Description:** Tom Williams, chairman of the Cincinnati Business Committee (CBC), maintains that politicians and business leaders must cooperate to ensure the competitiveness of the city for the 21st Century. Under Williams' leadership, the CBC has put emphasis on initiatives related to government efficiency, economic development, and public education. Williams' views on a proposed inland port are given.

42123 ■ "City Consults Executives on Police Hire" in *Business Courier* (Vol. 27, August 27, 2010, No. 17, pp. 1)
Pub: Business Courier
Ed: Lucy May, Dan Monk. **Description:** The City of Cincinnati, Ohio has begun a selection process for the new police chief by consulting the city's business executives. The city charter amendment known as Issue 5 has removed civil service protection from the chief's post and enables City Manager Milton Dohoney to hire a chief from outside the department.

42124 ■ "City's Streetcar Utility Estimate Way Off Mark" in *Business Courier* (Vol27, November 19, 2010, No. 29. , pp. 1)
Pub: Business Courier
Ed: Dan Monk, Lucy May. **Description:** Duke Energy Corporation has released new estimates that show moving electric and gas lines alone for Cincinnati,

Ohio's proposed streetcar project could cost more than $20 million. However, the city has only estimated the relocation to cost $5 million in federal grant applications.

42125 ■ "Councilman May Revive Labor Bill" in *Baltimore Business Journal* (Vol. 28, August 13, 2010, No. 14, pp. 1)
Pub: Baltimore Business Journal

Ed: Daniel J. Sernovitz. Description: Baltimore, Maryland Councilman Bill Henry has started reviving controversial legislation that would force developers and contractors to give preference to union labor. The legislation requires contractors to give preference to city workers in order to lower Baltimore's unemployment rate.

42126 ■ "County Tract Pitched for Data Center" in *Baltimore Business Journal* (Vol. 28, July 23, 2010, No. 11, pp. 1)
Pub: Baltimore Business Journal

Ed: Scott Dance. Description: One hundred acres of land in Woodlawn, Maryland is set to be sold for use in the construction of a data center for the U.S. Social Security Administration. Baltimore County has submitted a bid for the $750M construction project.

42127 ■ "Dark Horse Murphy Means Business In Gubernatorial Race" in *Baltimore Business Journal* (Vol. 28, June 25, 2010, No. 7, pp. 1)
Pub: Baltimore Business Journal

Ed: Scott Dance. Description: Maryland gubernatorial candidate Brian Murphy has claimed better knowledge in helping small business owners than the other candidates, Governor Martin O'Malley and former Governor Robert Ehrlich. Murphy, who faces off against Ehrlich in the Republican primary, is banking on the benefit of his business background.

42128 ■ "Developers Give Big to Mayor's Bid" in *Boston Business Journal* (Vol. 29, August 26, 2011, No. 16, pp. 1)
Pub: American City Business Journals Inc.

Ed: Scott Dance. Description: Mayor Stephanie Rawlings-Blake received thousands of dollars in her political campaign from companies of real estate developers who are vying to build key development projects in Baltimore, Maryland. Rawlings-Blake created a major fundraising advantage over other mayoral candidates with the help of those contributions.

42129 ■ "Fed May Ban Amphibian Trade" in *Pet Product News* (Vol. 64, November 2010, No. 11, pp. 13)
Pub: BowTie Inc.

Description: U.S. Fish and Wildlife Service is seeking public input on a petition submitted by the conservation activist group Defenders of Wildlife. The petition involves possible classification of chytrid fungus-infected amphibians and amphibian eggs as 'injurious wildlife' under the Lacey Act. Interstate trading or importation of injurious wildlife into the U.S. is not allowed.

42130 ■ "Gov. Kasich to Put DOD On Short Leash" in *Business Courier* (Vol. 27, November 26, 2010, No. 30, pp. 1)
Pub: Business Courier

Ed: Dan Monk. Description: Ohio Governor-elect John Kasich proposed the privatization of the Ohio Department of Development in favor of a nonprofit corporation called JobsOhio. Kasich believes that the department has lost its focus by adding to its mission issues such as energy efficiency and tourism.

42131 ■ "Green Energy Exec Hits State Policy" in *Boston Business Journal* (Vol. 30, December 3, 2010, No. 45, pp. 1)
Pub: Boston Business Journal

Ed: Kyle Alspach. Description: American Superconductor Corporation President Dan McGahn believes that the state government of Massachusetts is not proactive enough to develop the state into a manufacturing hub for wind power technology. McGahn believes that while Governor Deval Patrick cam-

paigned for wind turbines in the state, his administration does not have the focus required to build the turbines in the state.

42132 ■ "Groundbreaking 2.0" in *Philadelphia Business Journal* (Vol. 30, September 23, 2011, No. 32, pp. 1)
Pub: American City Business Journals Inc.

Ed: Natalie Kostelni. Description: University Place Associates, the developer of 2.0 University Place in West Philadelphia, Pennsylvania, will break ground on a five-story, 97,000-square-foot office building in December 2011. The decision follows the Citizenship and Immigration Services signing of a 15-year lease as anchor tenant.

42133 ■ "Hotel Woes Reflect Area Struggle" in *Business Journal Serving Greater Tampa Bay* (Vol. 30, December 3, 2010, No. 50, pp. 1)
Pub: Tampa Bay Business Journal

Ed: Mark Holan. Description: Quality Inn and Suites in East Tampa, Florida has struggled against the sluggish economy but remained open to guests despite facing a foreclosure. The hotel project is the center of East Tampa's redevelopment plans and public officials defend the $650,000 investment in public amenities near the building.

42134 ■ "Janson: Duke's Dynamo, Regional President Focuses on Economic Development" in *Business Courier* (Vol. 27, July 9, 2010, No. 10, pp. 1)
Pub: Business Courier

Ed: Lucy May. Description: Duke Energy President Julie Janson is also chair of the Cincinnati USA Partnership for Economic Development and the co-chair of the Cincinnati Business Committee's Economic Development Task Force. Duke is launching a Site Readiness Pilot Program to help the region prepare for an economic recovery.

42135 ■ "Lawyers Lock Up Cops as Clients" in *Sacramento Business Journal* (Vol. 28, April 8, 2011, No. 6, pp. 1)
Pub: Sacramento Business Journal

Ed: Kathy Robertson. Description: Sacramento-based law firm Mastagni, Holstedt and Chiurazzi has grown its client base by specializing in law enforcement labor issues. The firm represents 80,000 public sector correctional officers in the US. The firm has been experiencing an increase in new business as public sector employers face huge budget deficits.

42136 ■ "Lotteries Scratch Their Way to Billions" in *Saint Louis Business Journal* (Vol. 31, August 19, 2011, No. 52, pp. 1)
Pub: Saint Louis Business Journal

Ed: Kelsey Volkmann. Description: Missouri Lottery reported $1 billion in sales in 2011. A six-fold increase in the lottery's advertising budget is seen to drive the revenue increase; a 4.5 percent rise in its scratch-off tickets and new sponsorships has also contributed to the development.

42137 ■ "Md. Tries to Recoup $73M from Actuary" in *Baltimore Business Journal* (Vol. 28, June 11, 2010, No. 5, pp. 1)
Pub: Baltimore Business Journal

Ed: Gary Haber. Description: Maryland State Retirement and Pension System has won nearly $73 million in administrative ruling against Milliman Inc. over pension loss miscalculations. However, Milliman filed two court cases seeking to reverse the decision and to recoup to the state any money a court orders.

42138 ■ "New Chief Walking the Talk" in *Business Courier* (Vol. 27, August 27, 2010, No. 17, pp. 1)
Pub: Business Courier

Ed: Lucy May. Description: National Brand & Tag Company president, Eric Haas, has vowed to put his various work experiences when he assumes the presidency of North Kentucky Chamber of Commerce. Haas wants to help the Chamber influence government policies that could help various businesses through the economic depression.

42139 ■ "Retailers, City Clash Over Wages" in *Baltimore Business Journal* (Vol. 28, July 9, 2010, No. 9, pp. 1)
Pub: Baltimore Business Journal

Ed: Daniel J. Sernovitz. Description: A bill pending before the City Council of Baltimore, Maryland would mandate the city's major retailers to pay their employees at least $10.57 per hour, $3 higher than was state law requires. Major retailers, as defined in the said bill by Councilwoman Mary Pat Clarke, have gross sales of at least $10 million. Reactions of the retailers affected are presented.

42140 ■ "Smart Businesses See Value, and Profit, in Promoting Women" in *Crain's Chicago Business* (Vol. 30, February 2007, No. 6, pp. 30)
Pub: Crain Communications, Inc.

Ed: Marc J. Lane. Description: Despite U.S. corporations making little progress in advancing women to leadership positions over the past ten years, enlightened corporate decision makers understand that gender diversity is good business as the highest percentages of women officers yielded, on average, a 34 percent higher total return to shareholders and a 35.1 percent higher return on equity than those firms with the lowest percentages of women officers, according to a 2004 Catalyst study of Fortune 500 companies.

42141 ■ "Staples Advantage Receives NJPA National Contract for Janitorial Supplies" in *Professional Services Close-Up* (April 22, 2011)
Pub: Close-Up Media

Description: Staples Advantage, the business-to-business division of Staples Inc. was awarded a contract for janitorial supplies to members of the National Joint Powers Alliance (NJPA). NJPA is a member-owned buying cooperative serving public and private schools, state and local governments, and nonprofit organizations.

42142 ■ "State Center Lease Deal High for Md." in *Baltimore Business Journal* (Vol. 28, August 6, 2010, No. 13, pp. 1)
Pub: Baltimore Business Journal

Ed: Daniel J. Sernovitz. Description: The proposed $1.5 billion State Center development project in Midtown Baltimore might cause the State of Maryland to pay the most expensive rental rates in the city. The state will have to pay an effective rental rate of $34 per square foot, including expenses, on the leasing. Other details of the redevelopment project are discussed.

42143 ■ "Study Puts Hub On Top of the Tech Heap" in *Boston Business Journal* (Vol. 30, November 26, 2010, No. 44, pp. 1)
Pub: Boston Business Journal

Ed: Galen Moore. Description: The Ewing Marion Kauffman Foundation ranked Massachusetts at the top in its evaluations of states' innovative industries, government leadership, and education. Meanwhile, research blog formDs.com also ranked Massachusetts number one in terms of venture-capital financings per capita.

42144 ■ "Swirling Debate" in *Business Courier* (Vol. 27, August 20, 2010, No. 16, pp. 1)
Pub: Business Courier

Ed: Lucy May. Description: The debate on whether to convert Greater Cincinnati Water Works into a public regional district is seen to impact the city's economic recovery. The utility's service area and customer base has significantly grown.

42145 ■ "Tourism Push Rising in Fall" in *Philadelphia Business Journal* (Vol. 30, August 26, 2011, No. 28, pp. 1)
Pub: American City Business Journals Inc.

Ed: Peter Van Allen. Description: Philadelphia is offering events for tourists this fall despite massive cuts for tourism promotion. Governor Tim Corbet slashed $5.5 million in funding for the state's tourism-promotion agencies which received $32 million in 2009. The agencies were forced to cooperate and fend for themselves using the hotel taxes that sustain them.

42146 ■ **"VA Seeking Bidders for Ft. Howard" in** *Baltimore Business Journal* **(Vol. 28, June 25, 2010, No. 7, pp. 1)**
Pub: Baltimore Business Journal
Ed: Daniel J. Sernovitz. **Description:** The Veterans Affairs Maryland Health Care Systems has requested proposals from developers to build a retirement community at Fort Howard in Baltimore County. The historic site, which has about 36 mostly vacant buildings, could become the home to hundreds of war veterans. Details of the proposed development are discussed.

42147 ■ **"Vision for Camden in Better Focus" in** *Philadelphia Business Journal* **(Vol. 30, September 30, 2011, No. 33, pp. 1)**
Pub: American City Business Journals Inc.
Ed: Natalie Kostelni. **Description:** More than $500 million worth of projects aimed at redeveloping the downtown and waterfront areas of Camden, New Jersey are being planned. These include the construction of residential, commercial, and education buildings.

42148 ■ **"Walker Seeks More Business Participation" in** *Business Journal-Milwaukee* **(Vol. 28, December 10, 2010, No. 10, pp. A1)**
Pub: Milwaukee Business Journal
Ed: Rich Kirchen. **Description:** Wisconsin governor Scott Walker is seeking the aid of Milwaukee business leaders to participate in resolving the challenges posed by the economic crisis. Walker is aiming to create 250,000 jobs. He is also planning to call a special session of the legislature to enact strategies to jumpstart the economy.

TRADE PERIODICALS

42149 ■ *American City and County*
Pub: Penton Media Inc.
Contact: Bill Wolpin, Editorial Dir.
E-mail: bill.wolpin@penton.com
Released: Monthly. **Price:** $67. **Description:** Municipal and county administration magazine.

42150 ■ *The American Review of Public Administration*
Pub: Sage Publications Inc.
Ed: John Clayton Thomas, Editor. **Released:** Quarterly. **Price:** $87 institutions single print; $13 single issue print; $485 institutions print & e-access; $437 institutions e-access; $475 institutions print; $60 print. **Description:** Academic journal covering public administration.

42151 ■ *Canadian Public Administration*
Pub: Institute of Public Administration of Canada
Contact: Frances Abele, Editorial Board
Released: Quarterly. **Price:** $323 institutions print plus online; $161 institutions print only; $275 institutions print only; $177 institutions print plus online. **Description:** Peer-reviewed journal printing refereed articles by administrative practitioners and academics for university teachers and public servants in federal, provincial, and municipal government (English and French).

42152 ■ *Demokratizatsiya*
Pub: Taylor & Francis Group Journals
Contact: Marshall Goldman, Exec. Ed.
Released: Quarterly. **Price:** $145 institutions print or online; $62 online only; $65 print and online; $175 institutions print and online. **Description:** Journal covering past and current political, economical, social, and legal changes and developments in the Soviet Union and its successor states.

42153 ■ *Governing Magazine*
Pub: Times Publishing Co.
Contact: Peter Harkness, Columnist
E-mail: pharkness@governing.com
Released: Monthly. **Price:** $19.95; $34.95 two years. **Description:** Magazine serving the public sector of federal, state and local government.

42154 ■ *Illinois Issues*
Pub: University of Illinois
Contact: Dana Heupel, Dir./Exec. Ed.
E-mail: heupel.dana@uis.edu
Released: 11/yr. **Price:** $39.95. **Description:** Magazine focusing on public affairs and state and local government.

42155 ■ *Journal of Policy Analysis and Management*
Pub: John Wiley & Sons Inc.
Contact: David Reingold, Editorial Board
Ed: Maureen Pirog, Editor. **Released:** Quarterly. **Price:** $385 U.S., Canada, and Mexico print only; $385 print only; $1,136 institutions print only; $1,176 institutions, Canada print only; $1,210 institutions, other countries print only; $1,250 institutions print with online; $1,290 institutions, Canada print with online; $1,324 institutions, other countries print with online. **Description:** Journal publishing articles on issues in public policy and public management.

42156 ■ *Missouri Municipal Review*
Pub: Missouri Municipal League
Contact: Katie Bradley, Ed./Advertising managing editorager
E-mail: kbradley@mocities.com
Released: Monthly, (Feb/March and Oct/Nov issues combined). **Price:** $25. **Description:** Magazine for local officials actively engaged in the procurement of products and services, policy-making, and local government administration.

42157 ■ *Municipal World*
Pub: Municipal World Inc.
Contact: Susan Gardner, Exec. Ed.
Released: Monthly. **Price:** $55 plus GST; $99 two years; $140.75 3 years; $7.95 single issue back issue; $80 other countries. **Description:** Magazine in the interest of good local government, covering municipal law, planning, technology, economic development and administration.

42158 ■ *PA Times*
Pub: American Society for Public Administration
Contact: Timothy Clark, Editorial Board
E-mail: tclark@qovexec.com
Released: Monthly. **Price:** $50 first class mail; $75 out of country. **Description:** Public administration newspaper (tabloid).

42159 ■ *Public Administration Abstracts*
Pub: EBSCO Publishing Inc.
Released: Quarterly. **Price:** $1,038 institutions print only; $261 print only; $285 institutions single print; $85 single print. **Description:** Journal containing abstracts on public administration.

42160 ■ *Public Administration Review*
Pub: American Society for Public Administration
Contact: Ladipo Adamolekun, Board of Ed.
Released: Bimonthly. **Price:** $354 institutions U.S., print premium online; $354 institutions European, print premium online; $354 institutions, other countries print premium online; $321 institutions U.S., print standard online; $321 institutions European, print standard online; $322 institutions, other countries print standard online; $306 institutions U.S., premium online only; $306 institutions European, premium online only; $306 institutions, other countries premium online only. **Description:** Public administration journal.

42161 ■ *Public Affairs Report*
Pub: Institute of Governmental Studies
Ed: Gerald C. Lubenow, Editor. **Released:** Bimonthly, 6/year. **Price:** Free. **Description:** Publishes essays on emerging governmental and public policy issues of significance to public officials and citizens in both California and the nation. Covers such subjects as pollution, politics, finance, transportation, health and housing policy, and California-Mexico trade relations. Recurring features include bibliographies.

42162 ■ *Public Management*
Pub: International City/County Management Association
Ed: Beth Payne, Editor, bpayne@icma.org. **Released:** 11/yr. **Price:** $46 nonmembers; $62 other countries. **Description:** Magazine for local government administrators.

42163 ■ *Tennessee Town & City*
Pub: Tennessee Municipal League
Contact: Margaret Mahery, Exec. Ed.
Released: Semimonthly. **Price:** $6 members; $15 nonmembers; $1 single issue. **Description:** Newspaper on politics and public management.

TRADE SHOWS AND CONVENTIONS

42164 ■ **Maryland Municipal League Convention**
Maryland Municipal League
1212 West St.
Annapolis, MD 21401
Ph:(410)268-5514
Free: 800-492-7121
Fax:(410)268-7004
Co. E-mail: mml@mdmunicipal.org
URL: http://www.mdmunicipal.org
Released: Annual. **Audience:** Municipal officials and other county and state officials. **Principal Exhibits:** Office equipment, public works equipment, insurance companies, consulting firms, recreation equipment, computers, engineering firms, police equipment, and code publishers. **Dates and Locations:** 2011 Jun 26-29, Ocean City, MD.

42165 ■ **New Jersey League of Municipalities Annual Conference**
New Jersey League of Municipalities
222 West State St.
Trenton, NJ 08608
Ph:(609)695-3481
Fax:(609)695-0151
Co. E-mail: league@njslom.com
URL: http://www.njslom.com
Released: Annual. **Audience:** Municipal officials. **Principal Exhibits:** Municipal products and services.

CONSULTANTS

42166 ■ **Institute of Public Administration**
411 Lafayette St., Ste. 303
New York, NY 10003
Ph:(212)992-9898
Free: 800-258-1102
Fax:(212)995-4876
Co. E-mail: p553@nyu.edu
URL: http://www.theipa.org
Contact: Yoshihiro Asano, Principle
Scope: A private nonprofit consulting, research and education organization experienced in management of governments and public enterprises. Firm's activities are directed toward the solution of emerging problems of government, organization, financial management and policies, and public enterprises in the United States and abroad. Programs are financed chiefly by contracts with local, state and federal governments, international aid agencies and foreign governments, public enterprises, and by foundation grants. Areas of concentration include personnel administration, structures and resources of local legislative bodies, training, structure and financing of public enterprises, public finance and fiscal reform, financial management and anti-corruption systems, sustainable urban development, urban and regional planning, organization and management, city/county charter revision, urban transportation, public sector ethics and citizenship, and management of government procurement systems. **Publications:** "Local Governance Approach to Social Reintegration and Economic Recovery in Post Conflict Countries: The Political Context for Programs of UNDP/UNCDF Assistance"; "Local Governance Approach to Social Reintegration and Economic Recovery in Post Conflict Countries: Programming Options for UNDP/UNCDF Assistance"; "Local Governance Approach to Social Reintegration and Economic Recovery in Post Conflict Countries: The View from Mozambique"; "Local Governance Approach to Social Reintegration and Economic Recovery in Post Conflict Countries: Towards a Definition and a Rationale"; "Local Governance Approach to Post Conflict Recovery: Perspective from Cambodia"; "The Sustainable Human Development Strategy: A Proposal for Post Conflict

Recovery Societies"; "Local Governance Approach to Post Conflict Recovery: Proceedings Report on the Workshop Organized by the Institute of Public Administration". **Seminars:** A Local Governance Approach to Post Conflict Recovery.

42167 ■ National Center for Public Policy Research
501 Capitol Ct. NE
Washington, DC 20002
Ph:(202)543-4110
Fax:(202)543-5975
Co. E-mail: info@nationalcenter.org
URL: http://www.nationalcenter.org
Contact: Amy Moritz Ridenour, Principal
E-mail: aridenour@atsnationalcenter.org
Scope: A communications and research nonprofit organization offering advice and information on international affairs and United States domestic affairs. Sponsors Project 21. Gives special emphasis an environmental and regulatory issues and civil rights issues. **Publications:** "National Policy Analysis"; "Legal Briefs"; "White Paper: National Policy Analysis 523"; "Shattered Dreams: One Hundred Stories of Government Abuse"; "Shattered Lives: 100 Victims of Government Health Care".

42168 ■ North Carolina Fair Share
3824 Barrett Dr., Ste. 312
PO Box 12543
Raleigh, NC 27609
Ph:(919)786-7474
Fax:(919)786-7475
Co. E-mail: ncfslrw@aol.com
URL: http://www.ncfairshare.org
Contact: Lynice Williams, Principle
Scope: Social services firm consults on community organizing and lobbying for health issues.

42169 ■ Practice Development Counsel
60 Sutton Pl. S
New York, NY 10022
Ph:(212)593-1549
Fax:(212)980-7940
Co. E-mail: pwhaserot@pdcounsel.com
URL: http://www.pdcounsel.com
Contact: Steven A. Lauer, Mgr
E-mail: stevelauer@atssprintmail.com
Scope: Specializes in business development, service quality, retention, organizational development work/ life excellence, and conflict resolution for professional firms. Provides coaching, client relationship management and quality service programs; strategic marketing planning/implementation; ancillary businesses/ diversification; market research, trend watching, bench marking; facilitation and planning for retreats and creative decision making; new business proposals and presentations; marketing communications and public relations; and business development training, coaching, and materials. Also offers speaker's services - engagements, publicity, etc. Industries served: law, accounting, and financial services, executive search, design, architecture, real estate, and management consultants worldwide. **Publications:** "The Rainmaking Machine: Marketing Planning, Strategy and Management For Law Firms"; "The Marketer's Handbook of Tips & Checklists"; "Venturesome Questions: The Law Firms Guide to Developing a New Business Venture"; "Navigating the Whitewater of Internal Politics"; "Changing Attitudes on Firm Flexibility"; "Transition Planning: A Looming Challenge"; "Don't You Think the Solution Is to Bring In a Good Rainmaker?"; "Aligning Firm Culture with the Needs of the Times"; "What New Partners Need to Know"; "Dangers of Lack of Diversity"; "Learn to Respect Emotion in Business"; "What New Partners Need to Know"; "Taking Responsibility: Implementing Personal Marketing Plans"; "How to Change Unwritten Rules"; "Mentoring and Networking Converge"; "Integrating a New Practice into the Firm"; "Using Conflict Resolution Skills for Marketing Success"; "Sports Team Models for Law Firm Management". **Seminars:** Managing Work Expectations; Effective Coaching Skills; Service Quality; End-Running the Resistance Professionals Have to Getting Client Input; Ancillary Business Activities; Marketing for Professional Firms; Marketing Ethics; Business Development Training; Trends in Professional Services Marketing; Client Relationship Management;

Collaborative Culture; Reaching Consensus; Conflict Resolution; Work life Balance; Generallional Issues; Preparing New Partners; Becoming the Employer of Choice; A Marketing Approach to Recruiting; Implementing Workplace Flexibility; The Business Case for Flexible Work Arrangements.

42170 ■ Praxis Media Inc.
48 Harbourview Ave.
South Norwalk, CT 06854
Ph:(203)866-6666
Fax:(203)853-8299
Co. E-mail: aldo@praxismediainc.com
Contact: Deborah Winegrad, Vice President
Scope: Media needs analysis and project planning specialists provide services in product introductions, communications planning, technology application, promotion and marketing communications. Also assists with focus groups, research, concept development, creative development, scripting and executive speech coaching/training. Industries served: Financial services, high-tech, travel and leisure, health and pharmaceutical and telecommunications.

42171 ■ Public Administration Service
7927 Jones Branch Dr., Ste. 100 S
McLean, VA 22102-3322
Ph:(703)734-8970
Fax:(703)734-4965
Contact: Ramesh Khatiwada, Treasurer
Scope: Performs a variety of consulting and research work in serving the special needs of governments and other public service institutions. Services range from technical studies of central management problems to analyses of public policy issues, and in development administration water sewerage management and systems, rural development, and small farmer organization privatization, and management. Devoted exclusively to improving the conduct of public activities. Consulting services in the United States include organization and management, data processing and automation plans, position classification and compensation plans, police and fire service studies, public works and utilities studies, and parks management studies.

42172 ■ Public Policy Communications
4163 Dingman Dr.
Sanibel, FL 33957
Ph:(941)395-6773
Fax:(941)395-6779
Contact: Robert Schaeffer, President
E-mail: bobschaeffer@earthlink.net
Scope: Provides strategic communications for progressive causes, candidates and socially-responsible businesses. These include public relations strategies, political campaign planning, organizational development and training. Substantial work in report writing, editing and design as well as production of a full range of media materials. Industries served: nonprofit, social change organizations, foundations, political campaigns, environmentally and consumer-oriented businesses, government agencies. **Publications:** "Winning Local and State Elections," Free Press MacMillan; "Giving the Media Your Message, and The News Media and the Big Lie". **Seminars:** Giving the Media Your Message; Effective Public Relations Practices; Winning Your Election; Understanding the Government Budget Process; How to Be an Effective Advocate; Strategic Planning for Non-Profits; How to Run a News Conference: Ten Key Steps, 1998.

42173 ■ Public Sector Consultants Inc.
600 W St. Joseph St., Ste. 10
Lansing, MI 48933-2267
Ph:(517)484-4954
Fax:(517)484-6549
Co. E-mail: psc@pscinc.com
URL: http://www.pscinc.com
Contact: Julie Metty Bennett, Vice President
E-mail: jmettybennett@atspscinc.com
Scope: Offers policy research expertise, specializing in opinion polling, public relations, conference planning, and legislative and economic analysis. Industries served: Associations, education, environment, health-care, and public finance. **Publications:** "Ingham Community Voices Final Evaluation Report," Nov, 2008; "First Class Schools Analysis," Aug, 2008;

"Opportunities for Achieving Efficiency in the Aging, Community Mental Health, Local Public Health, and Substance Abuse Coordinating Agency Networks," Aug, 2008; "Saginaw River Bay Area of Concern," Jun, 2008; "Portage Lake Water shed Forever Plan," May, 2008; "Smoke Free Workplaces," Apr, 2008; "Protecting and Restoring the Upper Looking Glass River," Feb, 2008; "Market Structures and the 21st Century Energy Plan," Sep, 2007; "The Growing Crisis of Aging Dams," Apr, 2007; "Financing Community Health Workers Why and How," Jan, 2007; "Hastings Area: Inter local Approaches to Growth Management," Jan, 2007; "Michigan's Part 201 Environmental Remediation Program Review," Jan, 2007.

42174 ■ Reed Royalty Public Affairs Inc.
30205 Hillside Terr.
San Juan Capistrano, CA 92675-1542
Ph:(949)240-2022
Fax:(949)240-0304
Co. E-mail: reed.royauy@home.com
Contact: Reed L. Royalty, President
E-mail: rroyalty@ocers.org
Scope: A governmental relations consultant who provides lobbying for changes in laws and government regulations, helps in obtaining licenses and permits, provides corporate training in governmental relations and assistance in winning government contracts. Services include crisis management, business association management and issue-specific community and media relations.

RESEARCH CENTERS

42175 ■ Boston College–Center on Wealth and Philanthropy
McGuinn Hall 515
140 Commonwealth Ave.
Chestnut Hill, MA 02467
Ph:(617)552-4070
Fax:(617)552-3903
Co. E-mail: paul.schervish@bc.edu
URL: http://www.bc.edu/research/cwp
Contact: Prof. Paul G. Schervish PhD, Dir.
E-mail: paul.schervish@bc.edu
Scope: Spirituality, wealth, philanthropy and other aspects of cultural life in an age of affluence. Projects explore the association among philanthropy, income, and wealth; the organizational and moral determinants of giving and volunteering; and the implications for fundraising and philanthropy. **Services:** Consulting. **Publications:** Newsletter (quarterly); Research reports. **Educational Activities:** Presentations; Research seminars.

42176 ■ California State University, Long Beach–Graduate Center for Public Policy and Administration
College of Health & Human Services, SSPA-228
1250 Bellflower Blvd.
Long Beach, CA 90840-5608
Ph:(562)985-4178
Fax:(562)985-4672
Co. E-mail: wbaber@csulb.edu
URL: http://www.csulb.edu/colleges/chhs/
   departments/public-policy-and-administration
Contact: Walter F. Baber PhD, Dir.
E-mail: wbaber@csulb.edu
Scope: Public policy and administrative problems, including transportation, port development, fiscal controls, contracting for services, management, organizational behavior, and productivity. Collects, compiles, and analyzes municipal data. Seeks to develop increased competency and perspective of administrative process of government. **Educational Activities:** Graduate education program, in public policy and administration; Graduate certificate programs, in public management analysis, public sector financial management, employer-employee relations and personnel management, transportation policy and planning, and urban executive management.

42177 ■ Carleton University–Carleton Research Unit on Innovation, Science, and Environment
Dunton Tower, Rm. 1001
School of Public Policy & Administration
1125 Colonel By Dr.
Ottawa, ON, Canada K1S 5B6

Ph:(613)520-2547
Fax:(613)520-2551
Co. E-mail: glen_toner@carleton.ca
URL: http://www2.carleton.ca/sppa/research/
research-centres/carleton-research-unit-
oninnovation-science-environment-cruise
Contact: Prof. Glen Toner, Dir.
E-mail: glen_toner@carleton.ca
Scope: Program evaluation and scientific and technical activities; science and technical indicators,
technology diffusion and standards; local level
industrial agglomeration or "clustering"; energy/
environment policies; and information technologies.
Services: Consulting. **Publications:** Journal (annually). **Educational Activities:** Conference (annually).

42178 ■ Carleton University–Centre for Policy and Program Assessment

Dunton Tower, 10th Fl.
School of Public Policy & Administration
1125 Colonel By Dr.
Ottawa, ON, Canada K1S 5B6
Ph:(613)520-2547
Fax:(613)520-2551
Co. E-mail: susan_phillips@carleton.ca
URL: http://www2.carleton.ca/sppa/research/
research-centres/centre-for-policy-and-prog ram-
assessment-cppa
Contact: Dr. Susan Phillips, Dir.
E-mail: susan_phillips@carleton.ca
Scope: Canadian and provincial government poli-
cies, urban policy, economic policy, and law. **Publica-
tions:** How Ottawa Spends. **Educational Activities:**
Conferences, short courses.

42179 ■ Citizens Budget Commission

2 Penn Plz., 5th Fl.
New York, NY 10121
Ph:(212)279-2605
Fax:(212)868-4745
Co. E-mail: info@cbcny.org
URL: http://www.cbcny.org
Contact: Corey Kunz, Dir. of Oper.
E-mail: info@cbcny.org
Scope: Management of New York City and New York
State's fiscal affairs and service delivery. Specific
studies include reviews of city and state expense
budgets, tax policy, public services, capital budget,
and state-city financial relationships. **Publications:**
Research Reports. **Awards:** Award for High Civic
Service to New York (annually); Prize for Public
Service Innovation (annually).

42180 ■ Cornell University–Program in International Studies in Planning

106 W Sibley Hall
Ithaca, NY 14853-3901
Ph:(607)255-4331
Fax:(607)255-1971
Co. E-mail: wwg2@cornell.edu
URL: http://www.aap.cornell.edu/crp/programs/grad/
mrp.cfm
Contact: Prof. William Goldsmith, Ch.
E-mail: wwg2@cornell.edu
Scope: Analysis of the regional and spatial dimensions of development issues with a focus—although
by no means exclusive—on the Third World, including political economy of regional and national development; planning and the global economy; critical
development theory; project planning and administration; political ecology and international environmental
planning; community economic development; gender
and development; infrastructure; and NGOs and
social movements. Areas of research include Latin
America, Caribbean, Africa, Europe, and Southeast
Asia. **Educational Activities:** Annual one-semester
lecture series; Courses abroad; Seminars, held
Fridays with visiting lecturers in the spring; Seminars;
Student travel grants.

42181 ■ Council on Foreign Relations

The Harold Pratt House
58 E 68th St.
New York, NY 10065
Ph:(212)434-9400

Fax:(212)434-9800
Co. E-mail: lgusts@cfr.org
URL: http://www.cfr.org
Contact: Lilita Gusts, Dir.
E-mail: lgusts@cfr.org
Scope: Long-range foreign policy problems, includ-
ing area, political, economic, and strategic studies.
Administers International Affairs, Military, State
Department, and Murrow press fellowship programs.
Publications: Annual Report; Foreign Affairs (bi-
monthly). **Educational Activities:** Seminars.

42182 ■ Florida State University–Florida Center for Public Management

227 N Bronough St., Ste. 4600
Tallahassee, FL 32301
Ph:(850)644-6460
Fax:(850)644-0152
Co. E-mail: cpm@admin.fsu.edu
URL: http://www.fcpm.fsu.edu
Contact: Ben Green, Dir.
E-mail: cpm@admin.fsu.edu
Scope: Studies state, county, and city government
management, planning, and budgeting. **Services:**
Conference planning. **Educational Activities:** Florida
Certified Public Manager Program; Florida Govern-
ment Technology Conference; Management consult-
ing and training.

42183 ■ George Washington University–Center for International Science and Technology Policy

Elliott School of International Affairs
1957 E St. NW, Ste. 403
Washington, DC 20052
Ph:(202)994-7292
Fax:(202)994-1639
Co. E-mail: vonortas@gwu.edu
URL: http://www.gwu.edu/lAtcistp
Contact: Prof. Nicholas S. Vonortas PhD, Dir.
E-mail: vonortas@gwu.edu
Scope: Interdisciplinary research and policy analysis.
Program includes such disciplines as public administration, political science, economics, international affairs, and environmental resources for application to
science and technology policy, international science
policy, technology transfer, research and development policy, risk analysis and management, regulatory process, institutional analysis, public perception
assessment, space policy, environmental quality,
economics of technology, networks and information
and telecommunications policy. **Educational Activities:** Seminar series, in science and technology
policy; Symposia.

42184 ■ Harvard University–A. Alfred Taubman Center for State and Local Government

John F. Kennedy School of Government
79 John F. Kennedy St.
Cambridge, MA 02138
Ph:(617)495-2199
Fax:(617)496-1722
Co. E-mail: edward_glaeser@ksg.harvard.edu
URL: http://www.hks.harvard.edu/centers/taubman
Contact: Edward L. Glaeser, Dir.
E-mail: edward_glaeser@ksg.harvard.edu
Scope: Politics, public management, and public
finance in state and local government, land use
policy, transportation, community development and
growth management, strategic uses of new technol-
ogy, education, and governance. **Publications:** An-
nual Report. **Educational Activities:** Forums and
conferences (periodically).

42185 ■ Murray State University–Bureau of Business and Economic Research

307 Business Bldg.
College of Business & Public Affairs
Murray, KY 42071
Ph:(270)809-4433
Fax:(270)809-3788
Co. E-mail: cbpa.bber@murraystate.edu
URL: http://www.murraystate.edu/qacd/cbpa/bber
Contact: Dr. Jim McCoy, Exec.Dir.
E-mail: cbpa.bber@murraystate.edu
Scope: Business development, economic planning,
economic impact analysis, socio-economic issues for
Western Kentucky and neighboring states. **Publica-

tions:** Business and Public Affairs Journal (periodi-
cally); Research reports; State of the Economy in
Western Kentucky (semiannually); Western Kentucky
Quarterly Economic Report (quarterly). **Educational
Activities:** Seminars (semiannually), for local civic
and educational organizations.

42186 ■ Ohio University–Institute for Local Government Administration and Rural Development

The Ridges, Bldg. 22
Voinovich School of Leadership & Public Affairs
1 Ohio University
Athens, OH 45701
Ph:(740)593-4388
Fax:(740)593-4398
Co. E-mail: gvsinfo@ohio.edu
URL: http://www.voinovichschool.ohio.edu
Contact: Mark L. Weinberg, Dir.
E-mail: gvsinfo@ohio.edu
Scope: Provides state and local officials in Ohio (with
primary focus in Southeast Ohio) with research and
technical assistance in economic development, public
policy and administration, and survey research and
geographic information systems, including aid in linking local and regional officials with state and national
resource persons. Partners with primary economic
development and capital access partners in the public
and private sector, providing sophisticated business
assistance for both start-up and existing businesses.
Services: Training programs and technical assistance, for local government and non-profits. **Publications:** Educational Access; Employment and Business Opportunities for Low Income Populations in SE
Ohio; Environmental Risk. **Educational Activities:**
Environmental remediation, including watershed planning, assessment, restoration and evaluation; Facilitation and evaluation; Public administration and policy
innovation and research; Survey analysis; Value-
added research; Business Assistance and Capital
Access (daily).

42187 ■ Oklahoma State University–Center for Local Government Technology

5202 N Richmond Hills Rd.
Stillwater, OK 74078-8088
Ph:(405)744-6049
Fax:(405)744-7268
Co. E-mail: clgt@okstate.edu
URL: http://clgt.okstate.edu
Contact: Dr. Michael Hughes, Dir.
E-mail: clgt@okstate.edu
Scope: Provides technical assistance and educa-
tional programs at state, county, and municipal
government levels relating to engineering, manage-
ment technology, and accounting, including county
officer training, computer applications in small city
and county government, vehicle fleet management,
tax procedures, productivity in local government, and
street, road, and bridge maintenance. **Publications:**
Manuals; Newsletters (quarterly); Project Journals;
Technical Fact Sheets; Workbooks. **Educational Activities:** Certification program, for county assessors
and deputies; Seminars; Workshops.

42188 ■ Public/Private Ventures

2000 Market St., Ste. 550
Philadelphia, PA 19103
Ph:(215)557-4400
Fax:(215)557-4469
Co. E-mail: publications@ppv.org
URL: http://www.ppv.org
Contact: Chelsea Farley, VP,Commun.
E-mail: publications@ppv.org
Scope: Mentoring, after-school programming, juve-
nile justice, youth development, prisoner reentry,
health, workforce development, program scaling and
replication. **Publications:** Annual reports; Case Stud-
ies; Executive Summaries; Policy briefs; Practitioner
Guides; Research Reports.

42189 ■ Queen's University at Kingston–Institute of Intergovernmental Relations

School of Policy Studies, Rm. 301
Kingston, ON, Canada K7L 3N6
Ph:(613)533-2080

Fax:(613)533-6868
Co. E-mail: ajuneau@queensu.ca
URL: http://www.queensu.ca/iigr/index.html
Contact: Andre Juneau, Dir.
E-mail: ajuneau@queensu.ca
Scope: Political, financial, and administrative intergovernmental relations and policymaking in federal systems, with particular emphasis on Canada, including self-generated projects and contract research. Specific research themes and projects include an examination of the Canadian federation, constitutional reform, the relationship between Quebec and its Confederation partners, the relationship between the structure of the Canadian federal system and the design and implementation of public policy (especially in the economic sphere), impact of the global economy on Canadian federalism, federalism and political theory, the structure of central institutions, the conduct of intergovernmental relations, and fiscal federalism and federal-provincial financial relations. **Publications:** Annual Reports; Bibliographies on Federalism; Canada: The State of the Federation (annually); Monographs; Reflections Series; Research Paper Series. **Educational Activities:** Institute's Advisory Council; Kenneth R. MacGregor Lectureship in Intergovernmental Relations; Seminars, on regionalism, economic policy, fiscal relations, interest groups, and other topics pertinent to Canadian federalism.

42190 ■ Rutgers University–National Center for Public Productivity

School of Public Affairs & Administration
111 Washington St.
Newark, NJ 07102
Ph:(973)353-5093
Fax:(973)353-5907
Co. E-mail: mholzer@pipeline.com
URL: http://ncpp.us
Contact: Dr. Marc Holzer, Exec.Dir.
E-mail: mholzer@pipeline.com
Scope: Applications of productivity improvement concepts and theoretical research in all functional areas focusing on productivity measurement, productivity dissemination, curriculum development, and labor-management relations. Seeks to improve productivity in the public sector. **Services:** Technical training and assistance. **Publications:** Newsletter (quarterly); Public Productivity and Management Review (quarterly).

42191 ■ Tennessee State University–Institute of Government

330-10th Ave. N, Ste. F-400
PO Box 140
Nashville, TN 37203-3401
Ph:(615)963-7241
Fax:(615)963-7245
Co. E-mail: arizzo@tnstate.edu
URL: http://www.tnstate.edu/interior.asp?mid=299
Contact: Ann Marie Rizzo PhD, Dir.
E-mail: arizzo@tnstate.edu
Scope: Public administration and public services. **Services:** Training and consultation programs for government and nonprofit organizations. **Publications:** The Public Servant (3/year).

42192 ■ University of California at Berkeley–Institute of Governmental Studies

109 Moses Hall, No. 2370
Berkeley, CA 94720-2370
Ph:(510)642-1473
Fax:(510)642-3020
Co. E-mail: gojack@berkeley.edu
URL: http://igs.berkeley.edu
Contact: Jack Citrin, Dir.
E-mail: gojack@berkeley.edu
Scope: American national, state, and local government and politics, public policy, public organization and administration, urban-metropolitan problems, federalism and intergovernmental relations, comparative methodology, and technology and government. **Publications:** Monographs; Public Affairs Report (quarterly); Research Reports. **Educational Activities:** Conferences; Lectures; Seminars, on government policies and social issues; Workshops.

42193 ■ University of Delaware–Institute for Public Administration

180 Graham Hall
College of Education & Public Policy
Newark, DE 19716-7380
Ph:(302)831-8971
Fax:(302)831-3488
Co. E-mail: jlewis@udel.edu
URL: http://www.ipa.udel.edu
Contact: Jerome R. Lewis PhD, Dir.
E-mail: jlewis@udel.edu
Scope: Integral unit of University of Delaware. Research, education, and public service program areas include civic education, conflict resolution, health care policy, land use planning, organizational development, school leadership, state and local management, water resources management, and women's leadership. **Publications:** Reports. **Educational Activities:** Policy forums; Training workshops, certificate programs.

42194 ■ University of Georgia–Carl Vinson Institute of Government

201 N Milledge Ave.
Athens, GA 30602-5482
Ph:(706)542-2736
Fax:(706)542-9301
Co. E-mail: jfrum@uga.edu
URL: http://www.cviog.uga.edu
Contact: Jennifer Frum PhD, Interim Dir.
E-mail: jfrum@uga.edu
Scope: Government, public administration, public finance, public personnel administration, science and technology policy, public law, and organizational development. **Services:** Technical and consultative advice and assistance, to state and local government officials. **Publications:** Books and reports (7/year); Project Reports; State and Local Government Review (3/year). **Educational Activities:** Short courses, for state and local government officials; Workshops.

42195 ■ University of Maryland at College Park–Institute for Governmental Service and Research

4321 Hartwick Rd., Ste. 208
College Park, MD 20742-3225
Ph:(301)405-4905
Fax:(301)314-9258
Co. E-mail: igsr@umd.edu
URL: http://www.igsr.umd.edu
Contact: Dr. Robin Parker Cox, Dir.
E-mail: igsr@umd.edu
Scope: Strategic planning, fiscal issues, land use and annexation, program evaluation, personnel management, and other related governmental areas. **Publications:** Compensation Survey of Maryland Local Governments (occasionally); Did You Know (occasionally); Handbook for Maryland Municipal Officials (annually); Home Rule Options in Maryland (5/year); Maryland Government Report (annually); Outreach Newsletter (5/year).

42196 ■ University of Minnesota, Duluth–Center for Community and Regional Research

329A Cina Hall
Department of Geography
1123 University Dr.
Duluth, MN 55812
Ph:(218)726-7331
Fax:(218)726-6540
Co. E-mail: okuhlke@d.umn.edu
URL: http://www.d.umn.edu/cla/CCRR/main/index.php
Contact: Olaf Kuhlke, Interim Dir.
E-mail: okuhlke@d.umn.edu
Scope: The primary focus of the Center is community-based education at UMD, providing faculty and students in the social and natural sciences and related fields the opportunity to work with local and regional community organizations. With this focus, students apply research skills and principles of social engagement and analysis, UMD faculty receive funding for projects in which they apply their expert knowledge and skills in a real-world local context, and local organizations, communities and agencies benefit through research on issues central to them.

42197 ■ University of North Florida–Center for Community Initiatives

Bldg. 51/2219
Department of Sociology & Anthropology
1 UNF Dr.
Jacksonville, FL 32224
Ph:(904)620-2463
Fax:(904)620-4415
Co. E-mail: jwill@unf.edu
URL: http://www.unf.edu/coas/cci
Contact: Jeffry A. Will PhD, Dir.
E-mail: jwill@unf.edu
Scope: Community, local, state and federal programs affecting community life in Northeast Florida.

42198 ■ University of South Dakota–Government Research Bureau

USD Farber House
414 E Clark St.
Vermillion, SD 57069
Ph:(605)677-5708
Fax:(605)677-6968
Co. E-mail: shane.nordyke@usd.edu
URL: http://www.usd.edu/arts-and-sciences/political-science/government-research-bureau
Contact: Shane Nordyke, Interim Dir.
E-mail: shane.nordyke@usd.edu
Scope: Governmental problems, including studies of state and local government, public administration, political party organization, political behavior, governmental finance, and miscellaneous governmental problems connected with South Dakota. Provides research training for students of the University. **Services:** Clearinghouse, for information on governmental administration; Consultation services, for governmental officials. **Publications:** Public Affairs (quarterly).

42199 ■ University of Utah–Center for Public Policy and Administration

260 S Central Campus Dr., Rm. 214
Salt Lake City, UT 84112-9154
Ph:(801)581-6781
Fax:(801)587-7861
Co. E-mail: robinson@cppa.utah.edu
URL: http://www.cppa.utah.edu
Contact: Jennifer Robinson PhD, Interim Dir.
E-mail: robinson@cppa.utah.edu
Scope: Local and state government finance, organization, and administration; public policy research on education, health, environment, transportation, resources, energy; Western regional policy issues and regional governance. **Services:** Consultation, to local, county, and state governments; Technical assistance; Training. **Publications:** Policy briefing papers (occasionally); Policy Perspectives (monthly). **Educational Activities:** Master Public Administration Alumni Conference; Policy Conference; Public administration educational programs; Utah Leadership Education and Development Program; Women's Conference. **Awards:** Dalmas Nelson Lectureship; Dalmas Nelson Student Award.

42200 ■ Virginia Commonwealth University–Center for Public Policy

L. Douglas Wilder School of Government & Public Affairs
PO Box 843061
Richmond, VA 23284-3061
Ph:(804)828-6837
Fax:(804)828-6838
Co. E-mail: clfunk@vcu.edu
URL: http://www.vcu.edu/cppweb/ppa
Contact: Carolyn L. Funk PhD, Dir.
E-mail: clfunk@vcu.edu
Scope: Public policy research, with special attention to health policy, urban and metropolitan development, and state and local government and politics.

ASSOCIATIONS AND OTHER ORGANIZATIONS

42201 ▪ Public Relations Society of America
33 Maiden Ln., 11th Fl.
New York, NY 10038-5150
Ph:(212)460-1400
Fax:(212)995-0757
Co. E-mail: william.murray@prsa.org
URL: http://www.prsa.org
Contact: William Murray, Pres./COO
Description: Professional society of public relations practitioners in business and industry, counseling firms, government, associations, hospitals, schools, and nonprofit organizations. Conducts professional development programs. Maintains a Professional Resource Center. Offers accreditation program. **Publications:** *Public Relations Tactics* (monthly).

REFERENCE WORKS

42202 ▪ "Airlines Mount PR Push to Win Public Support Against Big Oil" in *Advertising Age* (Vol. 79, July 14, 2008, No. 7, pp. 1)
Pub: Crain Communications, Inc.
Ed: Michael Bush. **Description:** Top airline executives from competing companies have banded together in a public relations plan in which they are sending e-mails to their frequent fliers asking for aid in lobbying legislators to put a restriction on oil speculation.

42203 ▪ "AllHipHop.com's Founders Thought a Weeklong Event Would Raise the Company'" in *Inc.* (February 2008, pp. 48-51)
Pub: Gruner & Jahr USA Publishing
Ed: Kermit Pattison. **Description:** Co-founders Greg Watkins and Chuck Creekmur, planned a weeklong festival to promote their company, AllHipHop.com; the event nearly ruined the firm. The online firm provides news about hip hop artists and the industry and is updated daily.

42204 ▪ "Back Talk With Terrie M. Williams" in *Black Enterprise* (Vol. 38, December 2007, No. 5, pp. 204)
Pub: Earl G. Graves Publishing Co. Inc.
Ed: Tennille M. Robinson. **Description:** Profile of Terrie M. Williams, president of a public relations agency as well as founder of a youth empowerment organization called Stay Strong Foundation. Williams reflects on her bouts with depression and how the disease impacts sufferers and talks about her book that will inspire others dealing with depression.

42205 ▪ "Banks Deposit Reassurance, Calm Customers" in *The Business Journal-Serving Greater Tampa Bay* (Vol. 28, August 22, 2008)
Pub: American City Business Journals, Inc.
Ed: Margie Manning. **Description:** Community banks in the Tampa Bay Area are training tellers and other customer care workers to help reassure customers that their deposits are safe. Other measures to reas-

sure depositors include joining a network that allows banks to share deposits. Additional information on moves community banks are making to reassure consumers is presented.

42206 ▪ "Banks Fret About Gist Of Bailout" in *The Business Journal-Serving Metropolitan Kansas City* (Vol. 27, September 26, 2008, No. 2)
Pub: American City Business Journals, Inc.
Ed: James Dornbrook. **Description:** Banks from the Kansas City area hope that the proposed $700 billion bailout will not send the wrong message. UMB Financial Corp. chairman says that he hopes that the bailout would benefit companies that were more risk restrained and punish those that took outsized risk. Other bank executives' perceptions on the planned bailout are given.

42207 ▪ "BBB Hires Marketing Firm to Attract More Businesses" in *Baltimore Business Journal* (Vol. 27, January 1, 2010, No. 35, pp. 1)
Pub: American City Business Journals
Ed: Julekha Dash. **Description:** Better Business Bureau (BBB) of Greater Maryland hired Bystry Carson & Associates Ltd. to assist in its rebranding efforts in order to entice more businesses. Bystry Carson will promote BBB's new mission at lectures, seminars, and networking events, as well as educate businesses about the agency through blogs and Twitter. BBB's services are also outlined.

42208 ▪ "BBB Reworks Logo, Grading System" in *Crain's Cleveland Business* (Vol. 28, October 8, 2007, No. 40, pp. 5)
Pub: Crain Communications, Inc.
Ed: John Booth. **Description:** During the next year, the Better Business Bureau will adopt a grading system that will establish performance minimums that will make it tougher for some types of businesses to become accredited; this nationwide rebranding effort is part of a campaign to sharpen the Better Business Bureau's image.

42209 ▪ "Better ROI Or Your Money Back, Says Buzz Agency" in *Advertising Age* (Vol. 79, July 14, 2008, No. 7, pp. 1)
Pub: Crain Communications, Inc.
Ed: Michael Bush. **Description:** Word-of-mouth marketing is discussed as well as the impact on the advertising industry. Although many firms specializing in this form of marketing have opened over the past few years, many marketers are reluctant to try this route.

42210 ▪ "Brand Imaging" in *Small Business Opportunities* (November 2010)
Pub: Harris Publications Inc.
Ed: Karen Harnesk. **Description:** Design and branding pro shares strategies and tips to help guide any small business' image development.

42211 ▪ "Branding Your Way" in *Canadian Business* (Vol. 80, February 12, 2007, No. 4, pp. 31)
Pub: Rogers Media
Ed: Erin Pooley. **Description:** The trend in involving consumers in brand marketing by seeking their views

through contests or inviting them to produce and submit commercials through Internet is discussed.

42212 ▪ "Building Confidence" in *Black Enterprise* (Vol. 38, January 2008, No. 6, pp. 50)
Pub: Earl G. Graves Publishing Co. Inc.
Ed: Marcia A. Reed-Woodard. **Description:** Patriot Management in Chicago offers courses at its Investment Management Training Academy for the institutional asset management and investment sector. Classes are designed to help build investor confidence amid the scandals that hit the financial, investment and asset management industry.

42213 ▪ "The Business Value of Social Networks" in *Agency Sales Magazine* (Vol. 39, July 2009, No. 7, pp. 44)
Pub: MANA
Ed: Daniel Burrus. **Description:** Personal and business uses of several Web 2.0 tools for salespeople are discussed. Leading questions which will guide salespeople in finding out if one particular tool will benefit them are presented.

42214 ▪ "Calming Customers" in *The Business Journal-Portland* (Vol. 25, August 29, 2008, No. 25, pp. 1)
Pub: American City Business Journals, Inc.
Ed: Kirsten Grind; Rob Smith. **Description:** Credit unions and banks in the Portland area are reaching out to clients in an effort to reassure them on the security of their money and the firms' financial stability. Roy Whitehead of Washington Federal Savings, for instance, wrote 41,000 customers of the bank to reassure them. The strategies of different banks and credit unions to answer their client's worries are discussed

42215 ▪ "Canon Focuses on New Moms" in *Marketing to Women* (Vol. 21, January 2008, No. 1, pp. 3)
Pub: EPM Communications, Inc.
Description: Canon launches a photo contest aimed at spotlighting baby's first pictures in an attempt to connect with new mothers.

42216 ▪ "Change Agent; What Peter Francese Says You Need to Know" in *Advertising Age* (Vol. 79, July 7, 2008, No. 26, pp. 13)
Pub: Crain Communications, Inc.
Ed: Peter Francese. **Description:** Advice for marketers on how to deal effectively with a changing consumer base is given.

42217 ▪ "The Changing Face of the U.S. Consumer" in *Advertising Age* (Vol. 79, July 7, 2008, No. 26, pp. 1)
Pub: Crain Communications, Inc.
Ed: Peter Francese. **Description:** It is essential for marketers to examine demographic shifts when looking at ways in which to market brands. The average head-of-households is aging and marketers must not continue to ignore them. Statistical data included.

42218 ■ "Creative Marketing: How to Cultivate a Network of Endless Referrals" in *Agency Sales Magazine* (Vol. 39, July 2009, No. 7, pp. 38)
Pub: MANA

Ed: Bob Burg. **Description:** Tips on how a salesperson can build a network of people that will bring them referrals are presented. Asking a person about their business and re-introducing one's self to an earlier acquaintance while remembering their names are some elements in the process of building this network.

42219 ■ "The Customer Is Right Even If He's Wrong" in *Contractor* (Vol. 57, February 2010, No. 2, pp. 12)
Pub: Penton Media, Inc.

Ed: Al Schwarz. **Description:** Mechanical contractors should note that customers will make a judgment based upon the impression that they form on their first meeting. Contractors can maintain a professional image by washing their trucks and having the personnel dress uniformly. Contractors have every right to demand that employees clean up and make a better impression on customers.

42220 ■ "Do the Math on Discounts" in *Entrepreneur* (Vol. 37, October 2009, No. 10, pp. 82)
Pub: Entrepreneur Media, Inc.

Ed: Jennifer Lawler. **Description:** Small business owners should consider all effects of discounts before implementing them. Some entrepreneurs do not discount prices for fear of damaging brands or their company's reputation.

42221 ■ "Down on the Boardwalk" in *Retail Merchandiser* (Vol. 51, September-October 2011, No. 5, pp. 56)
Pub: Phoenix Media Corporation

Ed: Eric Slack. **Description:** Classic board game, Monopoly, continues to be the most recognized game brand while staying fresh by entering new markets and gaming platforms for all walks of life. Monopoly is available in over 100 countries, translated into 43 languages and played by more than 1 billion people since its introduction, and the game is tailored to each geographic market it enters.

42222 ■ "Effective Use of Field Time" in *Agency Sales Magazine* (Vol. 39, July 2009, No. 7, pp. 40)
Pub: MANA

Description: Sales representatives need to consider the value of field visits to themselves and their customers ahead of time. Several anecdotes about field visits from the perspective of manufacturers and sale representatives are presented.

42223 ■ "Emotional Brand Attachment and Brand Personality" in *Journal of Marketing* (Vol. 75, July 2011, No. 4, pp. 35)
Pub: American Marketing Association

Ed: Lucia Malar, Harley Krohmer, Wayne D. Hoyer, Bettin Nyffeneger. **Description:** A study on whether the brand's personality should match the consumer's actual self or ideal self is presented. Actual self-congruence is found to have the most impact on emotional brand attachment.

42224 ■ "Empowered" in *Harvard Business Review* (Vol. 88, July-August 2010, No. 7-8, pp. 94)
Pub: Harvard Business School Publishing

Ed: Josh Bernoff, Ted Schadler. **Description:** HERO concept (highly empowered and resourceful operative) which builds a connection between employees, managers, and IT is outlined. The resultant additional experience and knowledge gained by employees improves customer relationship management.

42225 ■ *Facebook Marketing: Designing Your Next Marketing Campaign*
Pub: Que

Ed: Justin R. Levy. **Released:** May 1, 2010. **Price:** $24.99. **Description:** Detailed steps are given in order to develop, use, and create awareness for any

business. The book provides detailed instructions, along with case studies from known brands, for launching marketing campaigns on Facebook.

42226 ■ "For Baxter, A Lingering PR Problem; Ongoing Focus On Heparin Deaths Ups Heat On CEO" in *Crain's Chicago Business* (April 21, 2008)
Pub: Crain Communications, Inc.

Ed: Mike Colias. **Description:** Baxter International Inc.'s recall of the blood-thinning medication heparin has exposed the company to costly litigation and put the perils of overseas drug manufacturing in the spotlight. Wall Street investors predict that an indefinite halt in production of the drug should not hurt the company's bottom line since heparin represents a tiny sliver of the business. Since Baxter began recalling the drug in January its shares have continued to outpace most other medical stocks.

42227 ■ "FTC Takes Aim At Foreclosure 'Rescue' Firm" in *The Business Journal-Serving Greater Tampa Bay* (Vol. 28, September 19, 2008, No. 39)
Pub: American City Business Journals, Inc.

Ed: Michael Hinman. **Description:** United Home Savers LLP has been ordered to halt its mortgage foreclosure rescue services after the Federal Trade Commission accused it of deceptive advertising. The company is alleged to have charged customers $1,200 in exchange for unfulfilled promises to keep them in their homes.

42228 ■ "Good Questions and the Basics of Selling" in *Agency Sales Magazine* (Vol. 39, September-October 2009, No. 9, pp. 14)
Pub: MANA

Ed: Dave Kahle. **Description:** Six basic elements to enhance the job of a sales person in regards to his relationship to a customer are presented.

42229 ■ *Groundswell: Winning in a World Transformed by Social Technologies*
Pub: Harvard Business School Press

Ed: Charlene Li, Josh Bernoff. **Released:** 2008. **Price:** $29.95. **Description:** Corporate executives are struggling with a new trend: people using online social technologies (blogs, social networking sites, YouTube, podcasts) to discuss products and companies, write their own news, and find their own deals.

42230 ■ "Help Employees Give Away Some Of That Bonus" in *Harvard Business Review* (Vol. 86, July-August 2008, No. 8, pp. 1)
Pub: Harvard Business School Press

Ed: Michael I. Norton; Elizabeth W. Dunn. **Description:** Research indicates that how employees spend their bonuses is key to their resultant happiness, rather than simply receiving the bonus itself. Firms that offer donation options can thereby increase employee satisfaction.

42231 ■ "'Help Wanted' Meets 'Buy It Now': Why More Companies Are Integrating Marketing and Recruiting" in *Inc.* (November 2007, pp. 50-52)
Pub: Gruner & Jahr USA Publishing

Ed: Ryan McCarthy. **Description:** Five tips to merge marketing and recruiting together include: thinking every help wanted ad as a marketing opportunity, treating every job candidate as a potential customer, involving the youngest employees in the interview process, look for way to promote recruiting events, and to sponsor community-oriented events.

42232 ■ "Hopkins' Security, Reputation Face Challenges in Wake of Slaying" in *Baltimore Business Journal* (Vol. 28, August 6, 2010, No. 13)
Pub: Baltimore Business Journal

Ed: Gary Haber. **Description:** The slaying of Johns Hopkins University researcher Stephen Pitcairn has not tarnished the reputation of the elite school in Baltimore, Maryland among students. Maintaining Hopkins' reputation is important since it is Baltimore's largest employer with nearly 32,000 workers. Insights on the impact of the slaying among the Hopkins' community are also given.

42233 ■ "How to Boost Your Super Bowl ROI" in *Advertising Age* (Vol. 80, December 7, 2009, No. 41, pp. 3)
Pub: Crain's Communications

Ed: Abbey Klaassen. **Description:** Internet marketing is essential, even for the corporations that can afford to spend $3 million on a 30-second Super Bowl spot; last year, Super Bowl advertising reached an online viewership of 99.5 million while 98.7 million people watched the game on television validating the idea that public relations must go farther than a mere television ad campaign. Social media provides businesses with a longer shelf life for their ad campaigns. Advice is also given regarding ways in which to strategize a smart and well-thought plan for utilizing the online marketing options currently available.

42234 ■ "How Hard Could It Be? The Four Pillars of Organic Growth" in *Inc.* (January 2008, pp. 69-70)
Pub: Gruner & Jahr USA Publishing

Ed: Joel Spolsky. **Description:** Revenue, head count, public relations, and quality are the four most important aspects of any growing business.

42235 ■ "How to Ramp Up Marketing in a Downturn" in *Entrepreneur* (Vol. 37, July 2009, No. 7, pp. 55)
Pub: Entrepreneur Media, Inc.

Ed: Jeff Wuorio. **Description:** How businesses can save money while boosting their marketing efforts during a down economy is discussed. Using price-driven marketing, online social networks, and cause-driven marketing are among the suggested ways companies can attract more customers. Guarantees and warrantees, as well as contests, can also be used as marketing tools.

42236 ■ "How To Live To Be 100; John E. Green Co. Grows Through Diversification" in *Crain's Detroit Business* (February 18, 2008)
Pub: Crain Communications Inc. - Detroit

Ed: Chad Halcom. **Description:** Continuity, name recognition, and inventiveness are keys to continuing growth for Highland Park, Michigan's John E. Green Company, designer of pipe systems and mechanical contractor.

42237 ■ "How Two Flourishing Exporters Did It" in *Hispanic Business* (Vol. 30, July-August 2008, No. 7-8, pp. 46)
Pub: Hispanic Business, Inc.

Ed: Richard Kaplan. **Description:** Vigorous growth in export revenues posted by two Hispanic-owned export companies Compasa LLC and Ametza LLC is discussed; both firms have benefited from their closer locations to major Mexican markets, superior quality of their products, market knowledge and the relationships of trust developed with key business partners.

42238 ■ *If You Have to Cry, Go Outside: And Other Things Your Mother Never Told You*
Pub: HarperOne

Ed: Kelly Cutrone. **Released:** February 2, 2010. **Price:** $22.99. **Description:** Women's mentor advices on how to make it in one of the most competitive industries in the world, fashion. She has kicked people out of fashion shows, forced some of reality television's shiny start to fire their friends, and built her own company which is one of the most powerful public relations firms in the fashion business.

42239 ■ "In the Wake of Pet-Food Crisis, Iams Sales Plummet Nearly 17 Percent" in *Advertising Age* (Vol. 78, May 14, 2007, No. 18, pp. 3)
Pub: Crain Communications, Inc.

Ed: Jack Neff. **Description:** Although the massive U.S. pet-food recall impacted more than 100 brands, Procter & Gamble Co.'s Iams lost more sales and market share than any other industry player. According to Information Resources Inc. data, the brand's sales dropped 16.5 percent in the eight-week period ended April 22. Many analysts feel that the company could have handled the crisis in a better manner.

42240 ■ "Insurance: Marathon Effort" in *Canadian Business* (Vol. 80, January 29, 2007, No. 3, pp. 11)
Pub: Rogers Media

Ed: Jeff Sanford. **Description:** The efforts of the insurance firm ING Canada Inc. to manage its relations with its customers are described. The enhancement of the insurance services provided by the company is discussed.

42241 ■ *It's Not Who You Know - It's Who Knows You!: The Small Business Guide to Raising Your Profits by Raising Your Profile*
Pub: John Wiley & Sons, Inc.

Ed: David Avrin. **Released:** November 9, 2010. **Price:** $24.95. **Description:** When it comes to promoting a small business or a brand, it is essential to know how valuable high-profile attention can be. But for most small companies, the cost of hiring an outside firm to increase attention can be too expensive.

42242 ■ **"It's Time to Take Full Responsibility"** in *Harvard Business Review* (Vol. 88, October 2010, No. 10, pp. 42)
Pub: Harvard Business School Publishing

Ed: Rosabeth Moss Kanter. **Description:** A case for corporate responsibility is cited, focusing on long-term impact and the effects of public accountability.

42243 ■ **"Kraft Not Alone"** in *Crain's Chicago Business* (Vol. 30, February 2007, No. 6, pp. 8)
Pub: Crain Communications, Inc.

Description: Consumer watchdog group, The Center for Science in the Public Interest, has been putting pressure on food companies to be more truthful on their product labels. Listing of companies who have had misleading claims on their products is included.

42244 ■ **"Kuno Creative to Present B2B Social Media Campaign Webinar"** in *Entertainment Close-Up* (August 25, 2011)
Pub: Close-Up Media

Description: Kuno Creative, an inbound marketing agency, will host Three Steps of a Successful B2B Social Media Campaign. The firm is a provider of Website development, branding, marketing strategy, public relations, Internet marketing, and inbound marketing.

42245 ■ **"Leadership in Flight"** in *Women In Business* (Vol. 63, Fall 2011, No. 3, pp. 24)
Pub: American Business Women's Association

Ed: Leigh Elmore. **Description:** Flight attendants in major airlines are trained to keep passengers comfortable and to calmly deal with emergencies. They also have a significant role in brand image and customer loyalty as they interact with the customers directly. Examples of teamwork leadership for flight attendants are given.

42246 ■ **"Making Sense of Ambiguous Evidence"** in *Harvard Business Review* (Vol. 86, September 2008, No. 9, pp. 53)
Pub: Harvard Business School Press

Ed: Lisa Burrell. **Description:** Documentary filmmaker Errol Morris emphasizes the role of perception in portraying objective reality, and how investigation and analysis enhance the accuracy of that portrayal.

42247 ■ *Marketing in a Web 2.0 World - Using Social Media, Webinars, Blogs, and More to Boost Your Small Business on a Budget*
Pub: Atlantic Publishing Company

Ed: Peter VanRysdam. **Released:** June 1, 2010. **Price:** $24.95. **Description:** Web 2.0 technologies have leveled the playing field for small companies trying to boost their presence by giving them an equal voice against larger competitors. Advice is given to help target your audience using social networking hubs.

42248 ■ **"Massage the Message"** in *Canadian Business* (Vol. 79, Winter 2006, No. 24, pp. 137)
Pub: Rogers Media

Ed: Erin Pooley. **Description:** The methods adopted by Canadian billionaires to manage their public images are described.

42249 ■ **"McD's Warms Up For Olympics Performance"** in *Advertising Age* (Vol. 79, July 7, 2008, No. 26, pp. 8)
Pub: Crain Communications, Inc.

Ed: Description: Overview of McDonald's marketing plans for the company's sponsorship of the Olympics which includes a website, an alternate-reality game, names featured on U.S. athletes and on-the-ground activities.

42250 ■ *Media, Organizations and Identity*
Pub: Palgrave Macmillan

Ed: Lilie Chouliaraki, Mette Morsing. **Released:** January 19, 2010. **Price:** $90.00. **Description:** The mass media, press and television are a essential in the formation of corporate identity and the promotion of business image and reputation. This book offers a new perspective into the interrelationships between media and organizations over three dimensions: media as business, media in business and business in the media.

42251 ■ **"Menu Foods Seeks Answers in Death of Ten Pets"** in *Globe & Mail* (March 19, 2007, pp. B2)
Pub: CTVglobemedia Publishing Inc.

Ed: Thomas M. Burton. **Description:** The failure of Menu Foods Inc. to ascertain the cause of ten deaths of house pets, which were fed its food products, prompting the government to recall the products from the market, is discussed.

42252 ■ **"Microsoft Clicks Into High Speed"** in *Hispanic Business* (Vol. 30, July-August 2008, No. 7-8, pp. 54)
Pub: Hispanic Business, Inc.

Ed: Derek Reveron. **Description:** Microsoft's diversity hiring and vendor diversity program to capture more Hispanic consumer and business-to-business market is described. One of the main goals of these programs is to hire more Hispanic executives and managers who will help the company develop and market products and services that will appeal and benefit Hispanic consumers.

42253 ■ **"Network Like A Boy Scout"** in *Women Entrepreneur* (January 15, 2009)
Pub: Entrepreneur Media Inc.

Ed: Merrily Orsini. **Description:** Marketing for businesses that provide products or services that people only seek during emergencies or natural disasters such as hurricanes can be a challenge; tips for branding such businesses, networking and establishing a strong customer base that will refer your business to others are given.

42254 ■ *O'Dwyer's Directory of Public Relations Firms*
Pub: J.R. O'Dwyer Company Inc.
Contact: Fraser P. Seitel, Sen. Ed.
E-mail: yusake@aol.com

Released: Annual, Latest edition 2011. **Price:** $95, individuals. **Covers:** Over 1,600 public relations firms; international coverage. **Entries Include:** Firm name, address, phone, principal executives, branch and overseas offices, billings, date founded, and 7,750 clients are cross-indexed. **Arrangement:** Geographical by country. **Indexes:** Specialty (beauty and fashions, finance/investor, etc.), geographical, client.

42255 ■ **"Personal File: Laura Laing"** in *Canadian Business* (Vol. 80, April 23, 2007, No. 9, pp. 58)
Pub: Rogers Media

Description: A brief profile of Laura Laing, director of public relations at AdFarm, including her services, is presented.

42256 ■ **"Pet-Food Crisis a Boon to Organic Players"** in *Advertising Age* (Vol. 78, April 9, 2007, No. 15, pp. 3)
Pub: Crain Communications, Inc.

Ed: Jack Neff. **Description:** In the wake of the pet-food recall crisis, the natural-and-organic segment of the market is gaining recognition and sales; one such manufacturer, Blue Buffalo, has not only seen huge sale increases but also has witnessed a 50-60

percent increase in traffic to the brand's website which has led to the decision to move up the timetable for the brand's first national ad campaign.

42257 ■ **"Pet-Food Industry Too Slow"** in *Advertising Age* (Vol. 78, March 26, 2007, No. 13, pp. 29)
Pub: Crain Communications, Inc.

Ed: Description: Many crisis-communications experts believe that the pet-food industry mishandled the problem by waiting almost a month to recall the 60 million "wet-food" products after numerous consumer complaints. Experts site that the first 24 to 49 hours are the most important in dealing with a crisis of this nature.

42258 ■ **"Powers Reels in Pinger"** in *Business Courier* (Vol. 24, December 21, 2008, No. 36, pp. 1)
Pub: American City Business Journals, Inc.

Ed: Lisa Biank Fasig. **Description:** Powers Agency has acquired Dan Pinger Public Relations Inc. after three years in planning. The new company is to be called 'Pinger PR at Powers'. Details of the deal and the new company are discussed.

42259 ■ **"Promote Your Business Through New Media"** in *Business Week* (November 5, 2009)
Pub: McGraw-Hill Companies

Ed: Karen E. Klein. **Description:** Traditional public relations strategies are becoming more and more outdated due to the rapid shift in Internet marketing opportunities. Ideas for marketing your company online are presented.

42260 ■ *Public Relations Tactics—Member Services Directory—The Blue Book*
Pub: Public Relations Society of America
Contact: William Murray, President

Released: Annual, latest edition 2007. **Covers:** PRSA members—headquaters, staff contacts, and chapter, section, and district information. **Entries Include:** Name, professional affiliation and title, address, phone, membership rank. **Arrangement:** Alphabetical. **Indexes:** Geographical, organizational.

42261 ■ **"The Question: Who Do You Think Is the Most Genuine?"** in *Advertising Age* (Vol. 79, July 7, 2008, No. 26, pp. 4)
Pub: Crain Communications, Inc.

Ed: Ken Wheaton. **Description:** According to a survey conducted by Harris Interactive Reputation Quotient, Johnson & Johnson was deemed the most genuine brand. Google came in second followed by UPS.

42262 ■ **"Recalls Cause Consumers to Put More Stock in Online Reviews"** in *Crain's Cleveland Business* (Vol. 28, November 12, 2007, No. 45)
Pub: Crain Communications, Inc.

Ed: Jack Neff. **Description:** Due to the string of product recalls over the last year, consumers are looking at online product reviews to help them make purchasing decisions which could reshape marketing for a wide range of products.

42263 ■ **"Relationship "Farming" Tools"** in *Agency Sales Magazine* (Vol. 39, August 2009, No. 8, pp. 46)
Pub: MANA

Ed: Terry L. Brock. **Description:** Manufacturer's representatives should spend time, money and effort in establishing and maintaining relationships; one tool to help is the new Fujitsu S1500 scanner. The scanner can accomplish critical tasks, quickly, easily and at low cost. Other suggestions to help build better business relationships are given.

42264 ■ **"Report: McD's Pepsi Score Best With Young Hispanics"** in *Brandweek* (Vol. 49, April 21, 2008, No. 16, pp. 8)
Pub: VNU Business Media, Inc.

Ed: Della de Lafuente. **Description:** According to a new report, in order to reach Hispanic Gen Yers, marketing strategists need to understand this demographic's "bi-dentity," something which has proved an elusive task to many marketers. Another trend is the emergence of Latinas who have careers, as opposed to just jobs. There is an opportunity to tap this new, young and empowered female market with innovative messaging. Statistical data included.

42265 ■ "Reputation Warfare" in *Harvard Business Review* **(Vol. 88, December 2010, No. 12, pp. 70)**
Pub: Harvard Business School Publishing
Ed: Leslie Gaines-Ross. **Description:** Steps are presented for addressing attacks on corporate public image. These include responding promptly, avoiding disproportionate displays of force, empowering employees to present the firm's position, and stockpiling credentials to bolster credence.

42266 ■ "Restaurants Dish Up Meal Deals To Attract Customers" in *Crain's Detroit Business* **(Vol. 24, October 6, 2008, No. 40, pp. 1)**
Pub: Crain Communications, Inc.
Ed: Nathan Skid. **Description:** Restaurateurs are devising many creative and rewarding incentives to get customers to frequent their establishments during this economic crisis. Innovative ways in which even higher-end establishments are drawing in business are discussed.

42267 ■ "Rich Returns: Media Master" in *Entrepreneur* **(Vol. 35, October 2007, No. 10, pp. 42)**
Pub: Entrepreneur Media Inc.
Ed: Robert Kiyosaki. **Description:** Advertising is a powerful way of reaching clients, however, public relations is a less expensive method which is just as effective as advertising. Entrepreneurs must also be ready to try something new to be noticed by the public. Insights on how to master the use of media are given.

42268 ■ *Sarbanes-Oxley for Dummies, 2nd Ed.*
Pub: John Wiley and Sons, Inc.
Ed: Jill Gilbert Welytok. **Released:** February 2008. **Price:** $21.99. **Description:** Provides the latest Sarbanes-Oxley (SOX) legislation with procedures to safely and effectively reduce compliance costs. Topics include way to: establish SOX standards for IT professionals, minimize compliances costs for every aspect of a business, survive a Section 404 audit, avoid litigation under SOX, anticipate future rules and trends, create a post-SOX paper trail, increase a company's standing and reputation, work with SOX in a small business, meet new SOX standards, build a board that can't be bought, and to comply with all SOX management mandates.

42269 ■ "The Seat-Of-The-Pants School of Marketing" in *Brandweek* **(Vol. 49, April 21, 2008, No. 16, pp. 24)**
Pub: VNU Business Media, Inc.
Ed: David Vinjamuri. **Description:** Excerpt from the book "Accidental Branding: How Ordinary People Build Extraordinary Brands," by David Vinjamuri, discusses six shared principles for creating a brand that is unique and will be successful over the long-term.

42270 ■ "Shoestring-Budget Marketing" in *Women Entrepreneur* **(January 5, 2009)**
Pub: Entrepreneur Media Inc.
Ed: Maria Falconer. **Description:** Pay-per-click search engine advertising is the traditional type of e-marketing that may not only be too expensive for certain kinds of businesses but also may not attract the quality customer base a business looking to grow needs to find. Social networking websites have become a mandatory marketing tool for business owners who want to see growth in their sales; tips are provided for utilizing these networking websites in order to gain more visibility on the Internet which can, in turn, lead to the more sales.

42271 ■ "Sick of Trends? You Should Be" in *Brandweek* **(Vol. 49, April 21, 2008, No. 16, pp. 22)**
Pub: VNU Business Media, Inc.
Ed: Eric Zeitoun. **Description:** Eric Zeitoun, the president of Dragon Rouge, a global brand consultancy, discusses the importance of macrotrends as opposed to microtrends which he feels are often ir-

relevant, create confusion and cause marketers to lose site of the larger picture of their industry. Macrotrends, on the other hand, create a fundamental, societal shift that influences consumer attitudes over a long period of time.

42272 ■ "Smart Businesses See Value, and Profit, in Promoting Women" in *Crain's Chicago Business* **(Vol. 30, February 2007, No. 6, pp. 30)**
Pub: Crain Communications, Inc.
Ed: Marc J. Lane. **Description:** Despite U.S. corporations making little progress in advancing women to leadership positions over the past ten years, enlightened corporate decision makers understand that gender diversity is good business as the highest percentages of women officers yielded, on average, a 34 percent higher total return to shareholders and a 35.1 percent higher return on equity than those firms with the lowest percentages of women officers, according to a 2004 Catalyst study of Fortune 500 companies.

42273 ■ "Sound Check" in *Agency Sales Magazine* **(Vol. 39, August 2009, No. 8, pp. 14)**
Pub: MANA
Ed: Dave Kahle. **Description:** Most customers believe salespersons are unable to do well in terms of listening, which is one of the four fundamental competencies of a sales person. Listening is the primary tool to uncover deeper and more powerful needs and motivations of the customer. A guide on how to listen better and improve listening effectiveness is presented.

42274 ■ *Start Your Own Blogging Business, Second Edition*
Pub: Entrepreneur Press
Released: July 1, 2010. **Price:** $17.95. **Description:** Interviews with professional bloggers from some of the most popular blogs on the Internet will help anyone interested in starting their own blogging business.

42275 ■ "Stock Delisting Could Hamper First Mariner" in *Boston Business Journal* **(Vol. 29, July 29, 2011, No. 12, pp. 1)**
Pub: American City Business Journals Inc.
Ed: Gary Haber. **Description:** Possible delisting of First Mariner Bancorp from the Nasdaq stock exchange could adversely impact the bank's ability to attract institutional investors. Some institutions limit their investments to companies trading on the Nasdaq.

42276 ■ "The Sure Thing That Flopped" in *Harvard Business Review* **(Vol. 86, July-August 2008, No. 8, pp. 29)**
Pub: Harvard Business School Press
Ed: Gerald Zaltman; Lindsay Zaltman. **Description:** Fictitious brand extension scenario is presented, with contributors providing suggestions and advice. The company's struggles with expanding the brand may be alleviated by improving consumer research, focusing on emotional responses to products and services.

42277 ■ "Suspense Hangs Over Fledging Film Industry" in *Crain's Detroit Business* **(Vol. 26, January 18, 2010, No. 3, pp. 3)**
Pub: Crain Communications, Inc.
Ed: Bill Shea. **Description:** Overview of the film incentive package which has fostered a growth in the industry with 52 productions completed in 2009, bringing in $223.6 million in gross in-state production expenditures of which the state will refund $87.2 million. Opposition to the incentives has been growing among legislatures who believe that the initiatives cost more than they ultimately bring into the state. Experts believe that the initiatives will remain since they have already fostered economic growth and are good for the state's image.

42278 ■ "A Team Sport" in *Business Courier* **(Vol. 26, October 2, 2009, No. 23, pp. 1)**
Pub: American City Business Journals, Inc.
Ed: Lisa Biank Fasig. **Description:** Procter & Gamble (P&G) revised the way it works with marketing, design and public relations firms. Creative discussions will be managed by only two representatives,

the franchise leader and the brand agency leader in order for P&G to simplify operations as it grows larger and more global.

42279 ■ "The Tech 100" in *Canadian Business* **(Vol. 81, July 21, 2008, No. 11, pp. 48)**
Pub: Rogers Media Ltd.
Ed: Calvin Leung. **Description:** Absolute Software Corp. Day4 Energy Inc., Sandvine Corp., Norsat International Inc. and Call Genie Inc. are the five technology firms included in the annual ranking of top companies in Canada by market capitalization. The services and the one-year total return potential of the companies are presented.

42280 ■ "Timberland's CEO On Standing Up to 65,000 Angry Activists" in *Harvard Business Review* **(Vol. 88, September 2010, No. 9, pp. 39)**
Pub: Harvard Business School Publishing
Ed: Jeff Swartz. **Description:** Timberland Company avoided a potential boycott by taking a two-way approach. It addressed a supplier issue that posed a threat to the environment, and launched an email campaign to keep Greenpeace activists informed of the development of a new supplier agreement.

42281 ■ "Toss the Gum Before You Speak" in *Agency Sales Magazine* **(Vol. 39, July 2009, No. 7, pp. 34)**
Pub: MANA
Ed: Stephen D. Boyd. **Description:** When preparing to present to a prospective principal, a salesperson should anticipate the speaking situation and find out in advance the program events that occur around their speech. They should also practice their material in front of a friend or colleague.

42282 ■ "Traits that Makes Blogs Attractive to Book Publishers" in *Marketing to Women* **(Vol. 22, July 2009, No. 7, pp. 1)**
Pub: EPM Communications, Inc.
Description: Book publishers are finding a beneficial relationship between themselves and women bloggers on the Internet. A high visitor count, frequent updates and active readership are criteria for identifying the blogs with the most clout and therefore providing the greatest benefit to publishers.

42283 ■ "Tweaking On-Board Activities, Equipment Saves Fuel, Reduces CO2" in *Canadian Sailings* **(June 30, 2008)**
Pub: Commonwealth Business Media
Description: Optimizing ship activities and equipment uses less fuel and therefore reduces greenhouse gas emissions. Ways in which companies are implementing research and development techniques in order to monitor ship performance and analyze data in an attempt to become more efficient are examined.

42284 ■ "Utah Technology Council: Social Media Is Here to Stay; Embrace It" in *Wireless News* **(December 14, 2009)**
Pub: Close-Up Media
Description: Social media outlets such as Facebook and Twitter are blurring the lines between advertising, public relations, branding and marketing; businesses must stop thinking in terms of traditional marketing versus Internet marketing if they want to succeed in today's marketing climate.

42285 ■ "The Valuation of Players" in *Canadian Business* **(Vol. 80, October 22, 2007, No. 21, pp. 39)**
Pub: Rogers Media
Ed: Jeff Sanford. **Description:** Business professionals are supplementing their Masters in Business Administration degrees with CBV or chartered business valuator. CBVs are trained, not only in business tangibles, but also in business intangibles such as market position, reputation, intellectual property, and patent. Details of employment opportunities for chartered business valuators are discussed.

42286 ■ "Vanity Plates" in *Canadian Business* **(Vol. 82, April 27, 2009, No. 7, pp. 26)**
Pub: Rogers Media
Ed: Andy Holloway. **Description:** Politicians in the U.S. called for the review of firms that availed of the

bailout money but are under deals for naming rights of sports stadiums. Angus Reid's Corporate Reputation and Sponsorship Index found for example, that there is little correlation between sponsoring arenas on having a better brand image. It is suggested that firms who enter these deals build closer to people's homes.

42287 ■ "Voice: Rebuilding Trust" in Business Strategy Review (Vol. 21, Summer 2010, No. 2, pp. 79)
Pub: Wiley-Blackwell
Ed: David De Cremer. **Description:** The financial world's attempts to rebuild trust are charted. Three steps to jump-start that process are outlined.

42288 ■ "Wait for the Call" in Canadian Business (Vol. 80, April 9, 2007, No. 8, pp. 74)
Pub: Rogers Media
Ed: Andrew Wahl. **Description:** The effort of chief executive of BCE Inc. Michael Sabia to deal with rumors about the company's private equity deal with Kohlberg Kravis Roberts & Co. is discussed.

42289 ■ "'We Had to Won the Mistakes'" in Harvard Business Review (Vol. 88, July-August 2010, No. 7-8, pp. 108)
Pub: Harvard Business School Publishing
Ed: Adi Ignatius. **Description:** Interview with Howard Schultz, CEO of Starbucks, covers topics that include investment in retraining, the impact of competition, premium quality, authenticity, customer services, strategy development, work-and-life issues, and international presence.

42290 ■ "What School Did You Attend?" in Hawaii Business (Vol. 53, December 2007, No. 6, pp. 14)
Pub: Hawaii Business Publishing
Ed: Kelli Abe Trifonovitch. **Description:** Discusses the question "what school did you attend?" which is observed to be the most important inquiry in Hawaiian business discourse. The principle behind the question is based on establishing connections. The relation between the aforementioned inquiry and Hawaiian culture is explained.

42291 ■ When the Headline Is You: An Insider's Guide to Handling the Media
Pub: Jossey-Bass
Ed: Jeff Ansell, Jeff Lesson. **Price:** $29.95. **Description:** How-to guide for executives and other professionals whose high-visibility requires frequent interviews with the media. Tested techniques, tools, and insights for how to respond to all types of media in tough situation are provided. The books also reveals the lessons learned and the pitfalls to avoid by referencing actual news stores from around the world and provides exercises for readers who wish to sharpen their media-handling skills.

42292 ■ "Wise Guy: Get In Good" in Entrepreneur (Vol. 35, October 2007, No. 10, pp. 46)
Pub: Entrepreneur Media Inc.
Ed: Guy Kawasaki. **Description:** Good public relations are a requirement for business entrepreneurs, and it can be achieved through proper communication. Giving of and asking for favors are some of the ways to build relationships in the business world. Other tips on how to build good business relationships are provided.

42293 ■ "Women-Centric Events Can Captivate Consumers" in Crain's Cleveland Business (Vol. 28, November 12, 2007, No. 45, pp. 24)
Pub: Crain Communications, Inc.
Ed: Kimberly Bonvissuto. **Description:** Discusses innovative ways that companies are targeting the female consumer market including arranging networking and social events.

42294 ■ "You Have to Lead From Everywhere" in Harvard Business Review (Vol. 88, November 2010, No. 11, pp. 76)
Pub: Harvard Business School Publishing
Ed: Scott Berinato. **Description:** U.S. Coast Guard Admiral Thad W. Allen discusses effective leadership in successful crises management. Topics include

influence of media and public perspective, the applicability of military training to the business arena, and the responsibility of a leader to set morale.

42295 ■ "Your Big Give" in Small Business Opportunities (September 2008)
Pub: Entrepreneur Media Inc.
Ed: Michael Guld. **Description:** Cause related marketing is beneficial to businesses as well as the communities they inhabit; three small businesses that are elevating their standing in the community while at the same time increasing their customer base are profiled.

TRADE PERIODICALS

42296 ■ The Levison Letter
Pub: Ivan Levison & Associates
Ed: Ivan Levison, Editor, ivan@levison.com. **Released:** Monthly. **Price:** Free. **Description:** Offers tips for improving marketing.

VIDEOCASSETTES/ AUDIOCASSETTES

42297 ■ The Crisis Interview: A Media Relations Guide for Field Personnel
Gulf Publishing Co.
PO Box 2608
Houston, TX 77252
Ph:(713)529-4301
Free: 800-231-6275
Fax:(713)520-4433
Co. E-mail: customerservices@gulfpub.com
URL: http://www.gulfpub.com

Price: $495.00. **Description:** Offers media relations training for managers, supervisors, and field personnel. Dramatization shows a chemical company supervisor who is in the unaccustomed role of spokesperson as he arrives to oversee a cleanup of a chemical spill. Illustrates issues such as the community's right to know, how to take control of a situation, what is expected from a spokesperson, and how to end an interview on your own terms. Includes reference guide. **Availability:** VHS.

CONSULTANTS

42298 ■ Alan J. Zell
PO Box 69
Portland, OR 97207-0069
Ph:(503)241-1988
Fax:(503)241-1989
Co. E-mail: azell@aol.com
URL: http://www.sellingselling.com
Contact: Alan J. Zell, Owner
E-mail: azell@aol.com

Scope: An advisory service for those who sell their services, products or their organization's ideas, information, and skills through face-to-face and telephone conversations, printed materials, the media, electronic communications, schools, guilds, trade shows, and display presentations. Industries served: minority and woman-owned businesses; government and education; medicine, law, accounting, technology, manufacturers, distributors, and retailers; professional and trade associations; and nonprofit organizations. **Publications:** "Elements of Selling"; "An Unconventional Look at the Complex Subject of Selling"; "The Art Of Selling Art"; "Selling Situations"; "What Customers need to know"; "Turnover & Return on Investment"; "The Ultimate Business Oxymoron"; "Walkin The Aisles, Looking at the Booths, etc"; "Four Uses Of Internet". **Seminars:** Ambassador Of Selling; An Unconventional Look at the Complex Subject of Selling; Selling Change . . . Pain or Progress, Revolution or Evolution?; Giving GOOD SERVICE When Giving Good Service Is Not Good Enough; Two Sides Of A Trade Show; Selling For People Who Do Not Like To Sell; The Art Of Selling Art; Yes, Technically Trained People Can Learn To Sell; Beginning Business, How To Achieve Your Goals.

42299 ■ Bitner Goodman
701 W Cypress Creek Rd., Ste. 204
Fort Lauderdale, FL 33309-2045
Ph:(954)730-7730
Fax:(954)730-7130
Co. E-mail: gary@bitnergoodman.com
URL: http://www.bitnergoodman.com
Contact: Gary Bitner, President
Scope: A public relations, advertising and marketing consultancy. Serves industries including: travel, technology, telecommunications, financial services, consumer products, health-care, government, automotive, real estate and retail.

42300 ■ Burns Public Relations Services Inc.
1660 W 2nd St., Ste. 410
Cleveland, OH 44113-1454
Ph:(216)621-5950
Fax:(216)241-7300
Contact: Dargan J. Burns Sr., President
Scope: Full service public communicators and consultants. Specializations: marketing strategies, urban affairs, minority business enterprise; and Affirmative Action programming.

42301 ■ C. W. Hines and Associates Inc.
344 Churchill Cir., Sanctuary Bay
White Stone, VA 22578
Ph:(804)435-8844
Fax:(804)435-8855
Co. E-mail: turtlecwh@aol.com
URL: http://www.cwhinesassociates.org
Contact: William A. Hines Jr., Vice President
Scope: Management consultants with expertise in the following categories: advertising and public relations; health and human resources; management sciences; organizational development; computer sciences; financial management; behavioral sciences; environmental design; technology transfer; project management; facility management; program evaluation; and business therapy. Also included are complementary areas such as sampling procedures; job training; managerial effectiveness; corporate seminars; gender harassment; training for trainers and leadership and management skills development. **Publications:** "Money Muscle, 120 Exercises To Build Spiritual And Financial Strength," 2004; "Inside Track: Executives Coaching Executives"; "Money Muscle: 122 Exercises to Build Financial Strength"; "Nuts and Bolts of Work Force Diversity"; "Legal Issues, published in the Controllers Business Advisor"; "Identifying Racism: Specific Examples"; "BOSS Spelled Backwards is double SSOB! Or is it?"; "A No-Nonsense Guide to Being Stressed". **Seminars:** Career Development; Coaching and Counseling for Work Success; Communicating More Effectively in a Diverse Work Environment; Communications 600: Advanced Skills for Relationship Building; Customer Service: Building a Caring Culture.

42302 ■ Coyne Associates
4010 E Lake St.
Minneapolis, MN 55406-2201
Ph:(612)724-1188
Fax:(612)722-1379
Contact: Sandra Blanton, Principle
Scope: A marketing and public relations consulting firm that specializes in assisting architectural, engineering, and contractor/developer firms. Services include: marketing plains and audits, strategic planning, corporate identity, turnarounds, and sales training.

42303 ■ Devillier Communications Inc.
3315 Fessenden St., NW
Washington, DC 20008-2034
Ph:(202)362-4429
Fax:(202)966-5754
Co. E-mail: info@devillier.com
URL: http://www.devillier.com
Contact: Sylvia Landis, Accounting Manager
E-mail: slandis@atsdevillier.com
Scope: Firm marketing consultancy. Firm develops innovative solutions for a wide range of extra ordinary clients.

42304 ■ Donna Cornell Enterprises Inc.

68 N Plank Rd., Ste. 204
Newburgh, NY 12550-2122
Ph:(845)565-0088
Free: 888-769-3792
Fax:(845)565-0084
Co. E-mail: rc@cornellcareercenter.com
Contact: Donna Cornell, President
E-mail: rc@cornellcareercenter.com
Scope: Offers services in career consultant, professional search, job placement and national professional search. **Publications:** "The Power of the Woman Within"; "Juggling it All!"; "Journey: A Woman's Guide to Success"; "Shatter the Traditions".

42305 ■ Gary Ruben Inc., Marketing Communications Consultants

931 E 86th St., Ste. 206
Indianapolis, IN 46240-1860
Ph:(317)251-5330
Contact: Gary A. Ruben, President
Scope: A communications and marketing consulting firm whose services include: advertising agency selection, advertising agency performance review, advertising program structuring, creative assistance, advertising program measurement, public relations program structuring, advertising department personnel development, in house agency structuring, and executive counseling. Industries served include supermarket chains, franchise systems, and retail products and services.

42306 ■ Health Strategy Group Inc.

46 River Rd.
Chatham, NY 12037
Ph:(518)392-6770
Contact: John Fiorillo, Principle
Scope: Provides consulting services in the areas of strategic planning, feasibility studies, start-up businesses, organizational development, market research, customer service audits, new product development, marketing, public relations. **Publications:** "Online Consumer Surveys as a Methodology for Assessing the Quality of the United States Health Care System," 2004.

42307 ■ hightechbiz.com

4209 Santa Monica Blvd., Ste. 201
PO Box 189
Los Angeles, CA 90029-3027
Ph:(323)913-3355
Free: 877-648-4753
Fax:(323)913-3355
Contact: Jack Potter, Principal
Scope: A full service marketing agency specializing in integrated marketing solutions. Services include: marketing surveys; positioning surveys; strategic and tactical plans; implementation plans; management consulting; product brochures; product catalogs; product packaging; product data sheets; direct mail programs; media research; competitive research; complete creative; production and film; media placement; corporate identity; in-house creative; public relations.

42308 ■ Jeffrey Lant Associates Inc.

50 Follen St., Ste. 507
PO Box 38
Cambridge, MA 02138
Ph:(617)547-6372
Fax:(617)547-0061
Co. E-mail: drjlant@worldprofit.com
URL: http://www.jeffreylant.com
Contact: Sandy Hunter, Director of Information Technology
E-mail: sandi@atsworldprofit.com
Scope: Firm sets up businesses online, design websites and assists with marketing. **Publications:** "E-mail El Dorado," JLA Publications, 1998; "Web Wealth: How to Turn the World Wide Web Into a Cash Hose for Your Business. Whatever You're Selling," 1997; "Multi-Level Money," JLA Publications, 1994; "No More Cold Calls," JLA Publications, 1997; "Cash Copy"; "How to make at least $100000 a year"; "E-Money". **Seminars:** Business and personal development, including Establishing and Operating Your Successful Consulting Business; Successfully Promoting Your Small Business and Professional Practice; Succeeding in Your Mail Order Business; Successfully

Raising Money for Your Nonprofit Organization from Foundations, Corporations and Individuals; Money Making Marketing: Finding the People Who Need What You're Selling and Making Sure They Buy It; Getting Corporations, Foundations, and Individuals to Give You the Money Your Nonprofit Organization Needs.

42309 ■ Kelley Chunn & Associates

184 Dudley St., Ste. 106
PO Box 2348
Boston, MA 02119
Ph:(617)427-0997
Fax:(617)427-3997
Co. E-mail: kc4info@aol.com
URL: http://www.kelleychunn.com
Contact: Kelley C. Chunn, President
E-mail: kcprmail@aol.com
Scope: Consulting firm that specializes in multicultural and cause-related public relations and marketing. Services include: Cause-related marketing, strategic planning, community relations, corporate communications, guerrilla marketing, event planning and management, public affairs, media relations and training. **Publications:** "Education: Inner City Slickers," 2006. **Seminars:** Crisis communications; Guerrilla marketing; Ethnic marketing.

42310 ■ Marenghi Public Relations Inc.

23 Mayflower Rd.
Needham, MA 02492
Ph:(781)449-8591
Fax:(781)326-9370
Co. E-mail: catherine.marenghi@cognizant.com
Contact: Jessica Mularczyk, Accounting Manager
E-mail: jborgman@atsmarenghi.com
Scope: Full-service marketing and sales support agency serving high-tech and information businesses. Strategic counsel, value proposition analysis, positioning and messaging, sales tools, media and analyst relations, speaker placement, editorial services and media coaching.

42311 ■ Russ Fons Public Relations

7509 Turtle Dove Ct.
Las Vegas, NV 89129-6032
Ph:(702)658-7654
Free: 888-658-7654
Fax:(702)658-1349
Co. E-mail: russfons@cox.net
URL: http://www.russfons.com
Contact: Russ Fons, Owner
E-mail: russfons@cox.net
Scope: Offers corporate counseling and image development; media relations; marketing communications and product publicity; event management and special promotions; and graphic design and production. Industries served: All worldwide. Licensing and merchandising, literary services, Hispanic communications. Revenue Sharing/PI Advertising. **Publications:** "The Executive Crisis Manager, a planning guide to surviving corporate crisis".

42312 ■ S & S Public Relations Inc.

103 Carnegie Ctr., Ste. 203
Princeton, NJ 08540
Ph:(847)955-0700
Free: 800-287-2279
Fax:(847)955-7720
Co. E-mail: ssimon@sspr.com
URL: http://www.sspr.com
Contact: Tony Keller, Vice President
E-mail: tkeller@sspr.com
Scope: Offers a wide range of public relations consulting services particularly for franchisers, authors, consultants, and various products.

42313 ■ Shannon Staffing Inc.

5 W Ohio Ave.
PO Box 638
Mount Vernon, OH 43050
Ph:(740)622-2600
Fax:(740)622-9638
Co. E-mail: coshocton@shannonstaffing.com
URL: http://www.shannonmanagementgroup.com
E-mail: coshocton@shannonstaffing.com
Scope: Serving broad range of industries and public sector organizations and foundations. Specializing in human resources recruiting and outplacement coun-

seling on international scale for businesses of all sizes. Offers expertise in human resources policies and procedures, supervisor development, manager leadership style development, interview training, etc. Provides consulting to small business in human resources, advertising, marketing, sales, public relations and community relations. **Publications:** "Powells Rules for Picking People". **Seminars:** Time Management workshop.

42314 ■ Sol Abrams Public Relations Counsel & Marketing Consultants

331 Webster Dr.
New Milford, NJ 07646
Ph:(201)262-4111
Fax:(201)262-7669
Contact: Sol Abrams, Owner
E-mail: solbabrams@aol.com
Scope: Independent consulting provides publicity, public relations and marketing counsel and services to management of private and public enterprises. Also serves as public relations consultants to other public relations consulting firms, advertising agencies and marketing companies. Provides expert witness services involving public relations. Also lectures, trains, teaches, and conducts seminars in public relations and marketing. Industries served: Corporate management, businesses large and small including real estate, construction, entertainment, food, fashion, fundraising, automotive, aviation, franchising, government agencies, and nonprofit organizations. **Seminars:** How to Select a Public Relations Firm; Publicity and Promotion for Small Business Owner; Expose Yourself - Don't Be a Secret Agent -Increase Your Sales, Incomes, Images, Publicity, Profits and Prestige via Professional Public Relations.

42315 ■ Sparkworks Media

325 W Republican St.
Seattle, WA 98119-4008
Ph:(206)284-5500
Fax:(206)284-6611
Co. E-mail: info@sparkworksmedia.com
URL: http://www.sparkworksmedia.com
Contact: Victoria Clark, Mgr of Bus Devel
E-mail: michel@sparkworksmedia.com
Scope: Offers counsel on media and video production for medium and small businesses, governmental and educational institutions. Editing and other post production work as required. Distribution and marketing for products produced. Full service production firm for video and new media.

42316 ■ Steve Emerine Strategic Public Relations

4973 E Silver St.
PO Box 41824
Tucson, AZ 85717-1824
Ph:(520)323-1441
Fax:(520)881-4043
Co. E-mail: steveemerine@webtr.net
Contact: Steve Emerine, President
E-mail: steveemerine@webtr.net
Scope: Services offered in crisis management, environmental problems, litigation public relations, government relations, publicity, writing, editing and public information planning. **Seminars:** Crisis Public Relations; Media Relations; Environmental and Neighborhood Relations.

42317 ■ Tom Shillock Consulting

5545 SW Windsor Ct.
Portland, OR 97221-2150
Ph:(503)291-7928
Fax:(503)221-2052
Co. E-mail: tomsh@qwest.net
Contact: Tom Shillock, Principle
E-mail: tomsh@qwest.net
Scope: Offers consulting services in marketing and communications including public relations and advertising. Industries served: high technology.

42318 ■ Wayne Dean Public Relations

1064 Palmetto St.
Mobile, AL 36604-3041
Ph:(334)335-3601

Fax:(334)335-3601
Co. E-mail: revchief@fcbl.net
Contact: Bennett Wayne Dean Sr., President
Scope: Provides public relations consulting services to all industries, including government agencies,

religious organizations, and small businesses and organizations. Services include programming and budgeting, publicity (news releases, electronic spots, features), advertising, promotions, writing and editing, staff training, speeches and internal communica-

tion. Also does publicist work for entertainment industry. Operates internet vending of collectible and other items-goods and services. **Publications:** "The Swarming Bee Hive," 1984.

START-UP INFORMATION

42319 ■ **"Revel in Riches!" in** *Small Business Opportunities* **(May 2008)**
Pub: Harris Publications Inc.
Description: Profile of Proforma, a business-to-business franchise firm providing print and promotional products.

ASSOCIATIONS AND OTHER ORGANIZATIONS

42320 ■ **Advertising Club of New York**
235 Park Ave. S, 6th Fl.
New York, NY 10003-1450
Ph:(212)533-8080
Fax:(212)533-1929
Co. E-mail: gina@theadvertisingclub.org
URL: http://www.theadvertisingclub.org
Contact: Gina Grillo, Pres./CEO
Description: Professionals in advertising, publishing, marketing and business. Sponsors educational and public service activities, promotional and public relations projects and talks by celebrities and advertising persons. Conducts annual advertising and marketing course, which offers classes in copywriting, special graphics, verbal communication, advertising production, sale promotion, marketing and management. Sponsors competitions and charitable programs. **Publications:** *ACNY Membership Roster* (annual); *Auction Catalogue and Program* (annual).

42321 ■ **Advertising Council**
815 2nd Ave., 9th Fl.
New York, NY 10017
Ph:(212)922-1500
Free: 800-933-7727
Fax:(212)922-1676
Co. E-mail: info@adcouncil.org
URL: http://www.adcouncil.org
Contact: Peggy Conlon, Pres./CEO
Description: Founded and supported by American business, media, and advertising sectors to conduct public service advertising campaigns. Encourages advertising media to contribute time and space and advertising agencies to supply creative talent and facilities to further timely national causes. Specific campaigns include: Drug Abuse Prevention; AIDS Prevention; Teen-Alcoholism; Child Abuse; Crime Prevention; Forest Fire Prevention. **Publications:** *PSA Bulletin* (bimonthly).

42322 ■ **Advertising and Marketing International Network**
3587 Northshore Dr.
Wayzata, MN 55391
Ph:(952)457-1116
Fax:(952)471-7752
Co. E-mail: jsundby@aminworldwide.com
URL: http://www.aminworldwide.com
Contact: Janna Sperry Sundby, Membership Mgr.
Description: Comprised of cooperative worldwide network of non-competing independent advertising agencies organized to provide facilities and branch office services for affiliated agencies. .

42323 ■ **Advertising Research Foundation**
432 Park Ave. S, 6th Fl.
New York, NY 10016-8013
Ph:(212)751-5656
Co. E-mail: cassandra@thearf.org
URL: http://www.thearf.org
Contact: Robert L. Barocci, Pres./CEO
Description: Advertisers, advertising agencies, research organizations, associations, and the media are regular members of the foundation; colleges and universities are associate members. Objectives are to: further scientific practices and promote greater effectiveness of advertising and marketing by means of objective and impartial research; develop new research methods and techniques; analyze and evaluate existing methods and techniques, and define proper applications; establish research standards, criteria, and reporting methods. Compiles statistics and conducts research programs. **Publications:** *Journal of Advertising Research* (bimonthly).

42324 ■ **Advertising Women of New York**
25 W 45th St., Ste. 403
New York, NY 10036
Ph:(212)221-7969
Fax:(212)221-8296
Co. E-mail: awny@awny.org
URL: http://www.awny.org
Contact: Ms. Liz Schroeder MS, Exec. Dir.
Description: Women in advertising and related industries that provides a forum for professional growth, serves as catalyst for enhancement and advancement of women; promotes philanthropic endeavors. Conducts events of interest and benefit to members and non-members involved in the industry. Membership concentrated in the metropolitan New York area. .

42325 ■ **American Academy of Advertising**
24710 Shaker Blvd.
Beachwood, OH 44122
Ph:(786)393-3333
Free: (866)607-8512
Co. E-mail: director@aaasite.org
URL: http://www.aaasite.org
Contact: Patricia B. Rose, Exec. Dir.
Description: Serves as a professional organization for college and university teachers of advertising and for industry professionals who wish to contribute to the development of advertising education. **Publications:** *Journal of Advertising* (quarterly); *Journal of Interactive Advertising* (semiannual); *Proceedings of the Conference of the American Academy of Advertising* (annual); *Roster of Members* (annual).

42326 ■ **American Advertising Federation**
1101 Vermont Ave. NW, Ste. 500
Washington, DC 20005-6306
Ph:(202)898-0089
Free: 800-999-2231
Fax:(202)898-0159
Co. E-mail: aaf@aaf.org
URL: http://www.aaf.org
Contact: James Edmund Datri, Pres./CEO
Description: Works to advance the business of advertising as a vital and essential part of the American economy and culture through government and public relations; professional development and recognition; community service, social responsibility and high standards; and benefits and services to members. Operates Advertising Hall of Fame, Hall of Achievement, and National Student Advertising Competition. Maintains speakers' bureau. **Publications:** *Communicator* (monthly); *Newsline* (monthly).

42327 ■ **American Association of Advertising Agencies**
405 Lexington Ave., 18th Fl.
New York, NY 10174-1801
Ph:(212)682-2500
Fax:(212)682-8391
Co. E-mail: nhill@aaaa.org
URL: http://www.aaaa.org
Contact: Nancy Hill, Pres./CEO
Description: Fosters development of the advertising industry; assists member agencies to operate more efficiently and profitably. Sponsors member information and international services. Maintains 47 committees. Conducts government relations. **Publications:** *AAAA Publications Catalog* (periodic); *The Reporter* (bimonthly); *Roster of Members* (annual).

42328 ■ **American Lutheran Publicity Bureau**
PO Box 327
Delhi, NY 13753-0327
Ph:(607)746-7511
Fax:(607)746-7511
Co. E-mail: dkralpb@aol.com
URL: http://www.alpb.org
Contact: Pastor Frederick J. Schumacher, Exec. Dir.
Purpose: Organized by laymen and pastors of the Lutheran church to publicize its teachings, work, and activities in a movement towards Lutheran unity. Helps Lutherans to explain their faith to non-Lutherans and the unchurched and to discuss important issues in church and society. **Publications:** *For All the Saints: A Prayer Book For and By the Church*; *Forum Letter* (monthly); *Heaven on Earth: A Lutheran-Orthodox Odyssey*; *Lutheran Forum* (quarterly); *O Lord, Teach Me to Pray: A Catechetical Prayer Book for Personal Use*; *We Believe: A Prayer Book Based on the Augsburg Confession* .

42329 ■ **Association of Free Community Papers**
7445 Morgan Rd., Ste. 103
Liverpool, NY 13090
Free: 877-203-2327
Fax:(781)459-7770
Co. E-mail: afcp@afcp.org
URL: http://www.afcp.org
Contact: Loren Colburn, Exec. Dir.
Description: Represents publishers of nearly 3,000 free circulation papers and shopping/advertising guides. Offers national classified advertising placement service and national marketing for industry recognition. Conducts charitable programs. Sponsors competitions and compiles industry statistics. **Publications:** *Free Paper Ink* (monthly).

42330 ■ Association of Independent Commercial Producers
3 W 18th St., 5th Fl.
New York, NY 10011
Ph:(212)929-3000
Fax:(212)929-3359
Co. E-mail: mattm@aicp.com
URL: http://www.aicp.com
Contact: Matt Miller, Pres./CEO
Description: Represents the interests of companies that specialize in producing television commercials for advertisers and agencies, and the businesses that furnish supplies and services to this industry. Serves as a collective voice for the industry before government and business councils, and in union negotiations; disseminates information; works to develop industry standards and tools; provides professional development; and markets American production. **Publications:** *AICP National Newsletter* .

42331 ■ Association of National Advertisers
708 3rd Ave., 33rd Fl.
New York, NY 10017-4270
Ph:(212)697-5950
Fax:(212)687-7310
Co. E-mail: bliodice@ana.net
URL: http://www.ana.net
Contact: Robert D. Liodice, Pres./CEO
Description: Serves the needs of members by providing marketing and advertising industry leadership in traditional and e-marketing, legislative leadership, information resources, professional development and industry-wide networking. Maintains offices in New York City and Washington, DC. **Publications:** *The Advertiser* (bimonthly).

42332 ■ Eight Sheet Outdoor Advertising Association
PO Box 2680
Bremerton, WA 98310-0344
Ph:(360)377-9867
Free: 800-874-3387
Fax:(360)377-9870
Co. E-mail: dave@jacobsbillboards.com
URL: http://www.esoaa.com
Contact: David D. Jacobs, Exec. Dir.
Purpose: Promotes the use of 8-sheet poster panels in outdoor advertising. (8-sheet signs are smaller than the usual 24-sheet ones, and are most commonly composed of 1 or 3 sheets covering an area of 6 x 12 feet.) **Publications:** *Eight Sheet Outdoor Advertising Association-Sources: A Guide to Suppliers of Outdoor Materials and Services* (annual); *Rates and Allotments: 8 Sheet Poster Panels in the Top Population Ranked Markets* (annual).

42333 ■ Intermarket Agency Network
5307 S 92nd St.
Hales Corners, WI 53130
Ph:(414)425-8800
Fax:(414)425-0021
Co. E-mail: ekleban@juicecoms.com
URL: http://www.intermarketnetwork.com
Contact: Ed Ekleban, Pres.
Description: An active network of high-powered marketing/communications agencies in the United States, Canada, Central and South America, and Europe. .

42334 ■ International Advertising Association
275 Madison Ave., Ste. 2102
New York, NY 10016
Ph:(212)557-1133
Fax:(212)983-0455
Co. E-mail: membership@iaaglobal.org
URL: http://www.iaaglobal.org
Contact: Michael Lee, Exec. Dir.
Description: Global network of advertisers, advertising agencies, the media and related services, spanning 99 countries. Demonstrates to governments and consumers the benefits of advertising as the foundation of diverse, independent media. Protects and advances freedom of commercial speech and consumer choice, encourages greater practice and acceptance of advertising self-regulation, provides a forum to debate emerging professional marketing communications issues and their consequences in the fast-changing world environment, and takes the

lead in state-of-the-art professional development through education and training for the marketing communications industry of tomorrow. Conducts research on such topics as restrictions and taxes on advertising, advertising trade practices and related information, and advertising expenditures around the world. Sponsors IAA Education Program. Has compiled recommendations for international advertising standards and practices. **Publications:** *The Case for Advertising Self-Regulation*; *IAA Annual Report* (annual); *IAA Membership Directory* (annual).

42335 ■ International Communications Agency Network
PO Box 490
Rollinsville, CO 80474-0490
Ph:(303)258-9511
Fax:(303)484-4087
Co. E-mail: info@icomagencies.com
URL: http://www.icomagencies.com
Contact: Mr. Gary Burandt, Exec. Dir.
Description: Network of non-competing advertising agencies. Provides an interchange of management information, international facilities, and branch office service for partner agencies. Provides discounts on syndicated services and access to 1,000 computer databases. **Publications:** *Agency Client Lists* (monthly); *The Globe* (monthly); *Membership Roster* (annual).

42336 ■ Mailing and Fulfillment Service Association
1421 Prince St., Ste. 410
Alexandria, VA 22314-2806
Ph:(703)836-9200
Free: 800-333-6272
Fax:(703)548-8204
Co. E-mail: mfsa-mail@mfsanet.org
URL: http://www.mfsanet.org
Contact: Ken Garner, Pres./CEO
Description: Commercial direct mail producers, letter shops, mailing list houses, fulfillment operations, and advertising agencies. Conducts special interest group meetings. Offers specialized education; conducts research programs. **Publications:** *MFSA Wage Salary, and Fringe Benefit Survey* (semiannual); *Performance Profiles: The Financial Ratios for the Mailing Service Industry* (annual); *Postscripts* (monthly); *Who's Who: MASA's Buyers' Guide to Blue Ribbon Mailing Services* (annual).

42337 ■ Marketing and Advertising Global Network
1017 Perry Hwy., Ste. 5
Pittsburgh, PA 15237
Ph:(412)366-6850
Fax:(412)366-6840
Co. E-mail: mxdirector@verizon.net
URL: http://www.magnetglobal.org
Contact: Cheri D. Gmiter, Exec. Dir.
Description: Cooperative network of non-competing advertising, marketing, merchandising, and public relations agencies. Aims to bring about, through mutual cooperation, greater accomplishment and efficiency in the management of member advertising agencies. Other goals are: to raise standards of the advertising agency business through the exchange of information relative to agency management and all phases of advertising; to exchange information on all common problems, such as management, sales development, market studies, agency functions, and operations. Aims to inform the general public of current global marketing trends. **Publications:** *MAGNET Matters* (3/year); *This Week at MAGNET* (weekly).

42338 ■ National Advertising Review Board
70 W 36th St., 13th Fl.
New York, NY 10018
Ph:(212)705-0114
Co. E-mail: bhopewell@narc.bbb.org
URL: http://www.narbreview.org
Contact: Howard Bell, Chm.
Description: Individuals from industry and the public. Sponsored by the National Advertising Review Council for the purpose of sustaining high standards of truth and accuracy in national advertising. Aims to maintain a self-regulatory mechanism that responds constructively to public complaints about national

advertising and which significantly improves advertising performance and credibility. **Publications:** *NARB Panel Reports* .

42339 ■ National Association of Publishers' Representatives
1901 N Roselle Rd., Ste. 920
Schaumburg, IL 60195
Ph:(847)885-2410
Fax:(847)885-8393
Co. E-mail: mburnett@association-resources.com
URL: http://www.napronline.org
Contact: Matthew Burnett, Gen. Counsel
Description: Independent publishers' representatives selling advertising space for more than one publisher of consumer, industrial, direct response, and trade publications. **Publications:** *NAPR Newsletter* (monthly);Membership Directory (annual).

42340 ■ Outdoor Advertising Association of America
1850 M St. NW, Ste. 1040
Washington, DC 20036
Ph:(202)833-5566
Fax:(202)833-1522
Co. E-mail: kklein@oaaa.org
URL: http://www.oaaa.org
Contact: Ken Klein, Exec. VP for Government Relations
Description: Firms owning, erecting, and maintaining standardized poster panels and painted display advertising facilities. Aims to provide leadership, services, and standards to promote, protect and advance the outdoor advertising industry. .

42341 ■ Point-of-Purchase Advertising International
1600 Duke St., Ste. 610
Alexandria, VA 22314
Ph:(703)373-8800
Fax:(703)373-8801
URL: http://www.popai.com
Contact: Mr. Chris Young, Chm.
Description: Producers and suppliers of point-of-purchase advertising signs and displays and national and regional advertisers and retailers interested in use and effectiveness of signs, displays and other point-of-purchase media. Conducts student education programs; maintains speakers' bureau. **Publications:** *Marketing at Retail Global Journal of Research* (quarterly).

42342 ■ Promotional Products Association International
3125 Skyway Cir. N
Irving, TX 75038-3526
Ph:(972)252-0404
Free: 888-426-7724
Fax:(972)258-3004
Co. E-mail: membership@ppai.org
URL: http://www.ppai.org
Contact: Paul Bellantone CAE, Pres./CEO
Description: Suppliers and distributors of promotional products including incentives, imprinted ad specialties, premiums, and executive gifts. Promotes industry contacts in 60 countries. Holds executive development and sales training seminars. Conducts research and compiles statistics. Administers industry advertising and public relations program. Maintains speakers' bureau. Conducts trade shows, regional training, publishes educational resources. **Publications:** *PPB Newslink*; *Promotional Products Association International—Membership Directory and Reference Guide* (annual); *Promotional Products Business* (monthly); *Supplier Update* (biweekly).

42343 ■ Radio Advertising Bureau
1320 Greenway Dr., Ste. 500
Irving, TX 75038-2587
Ph:(212)681-7214
Free: 800-232-3131
Co. E-mail: jhaley@rab.com
URL: http://www.rab.com
Contact: Jeff Haley, Pres./CEO
Description: Includes radio stations, radio networks, station sales representatives, and allied industry services, such as producers, research firms, schools, and consultants. Calls on advertisers and agencies to promote the sale of radio time as an advertising

medium. Sponsors program to increase professionalism of radio salespeople, awarding Certified Radio Marketing Consultant designation to those who pass examination. Sponsors regional marketing conferences. Conducts extensive research program into all phases of radio sales. Issues reports on use of radio by national, regional, and local advertisers. Speaks before conventions and groups to explain benefits of radio advertising. Sponsors Radio Creative Fund. Compiles statistics. **Publications:** *Guide to Competitive Media* (biennial); *RAB Media Fact Book* (annual); *Radio Co-op Sources* (annual).

42344 ■ Scenic America
1250 Eye St. NW, Ste. 750
Washington, DC 20005
Ph:(202)638-0550
Fax:(202)638-3171
Co. E-mail: tracy@scenic.org
URL: http://www.scenic.org
Contact: Mary Tracy, Pres.
Description: Safeguards natural beauty and community character through billboard and sign control, appropriate siting of cellular towers and other utilities, promotion of scenic byways, context-sensitive highway design, and protection of scenic landscapes and cityscapes. Advocates for the preservation of scenic beauty, open space, and quality of life. Fights billboard proliferation and other forms of visual pollution; works for the conservation of scenic byways and for context-sensitive highway design. **Publications:** *Aesthetics, Community Character, and the Law; Fighting Billboard Blight: An Action for Citizens and Public Officials; Getting It Right In the Right-of-Way: Citizen Participation in Context-Sensitive Solutions; Gift of the Journey: America's Scenic Roadways; The Highway Beautification Act: A Broken Law; Looking at Change Before it Occurs; Power to the People: Strategies for Reducing the Visual Impact of Overhead Utilities; Signs, Signs: The Economic and Environment Benefits of Community Sign Control; Taming Wireless Telecommunications Towers; Tree Conservation Ordinances: Land Use Regulations Go Green; Trees Are Treasure: Sustaining the Community Forest; Viewpoints* (quarterly).

42345 ■ Television Bureau of Advertising
3 E 54th St., 10th Fl.
New York, NY 10022-3108
Ph:(212)486-1111
Fax:(212)935-5631
Co. E-mail: info@tvb.org
URL: http://www.tvb.org
Contact: Steve Lanzano, Pres./CEO
Description: Television stations, station sales representatives, and program producers/syndicates. Strives to increase advertiser dollars to U.S. spot television. Represents television stations to the advertising community. .

42346 ■ thinkLA
4223 Glencoe Ave., Ste. C-100
Marina del Rey, CA 90292
Ph:(310)823-7320
Fax:(310)823-7325
Co. E-mail: info@thinkla.org
URL: http://www.thinkla.org
Contact: Jerry McGee, Co-Pres.
Purpose: Assists heads of advertising agencies in the Western U.S. to operate their agencies more effectively and profitably. Offers assistance to agency management and staff. Provides a forum for discussion and exchange of information. Promotes members' interests. .

42347 ■ Traffic Audit Bureau for Media Measurement
271 Madison Ave., Ste. 1504
New York, NY 10016
Ph:(212)972-8075
Fax:(212)972-8928
Co. E-mail: inquiry@tabonline.com
URL: http://www.tabonline.com
Contact: Joseph C. Philport, Pres./CEO
Description: Advertisers, advertising agencies, operators of outdoor advertising plants, bus shelter advertising companies, and backlighted display and painted bulletin companies. Sets standard practices for the evaluation of circulation and visibility of outdoor advertising; issues statements on the circulation values of outdoor advertising plants. Encourages standardization of terminology and practices in the industry. Seeks to educate those involved in out-of-home media on ways of developing circulation data for advertising sites. Compiles statistics. **Publications:** *Building Accountability for Out of Home Media; TAB Eyes On Out of Home; TABBriefs; What You Should Know About the New TAB Audit* .

42348 ■ Transworld Advertising Agency Network
814 Watertown St.
Newton, MA 02465
Ph:(617)795-1706
Fax:(419)730-1706
Co. E-mail: peterg@taan.org
URL: http://www.taan.org
Contact: Peter Gerritsen, Pres.
Description: Independently owned advertising agencies that cooperate for exchange of management education and information, reciprocal service, and personal local contact. Allows members to seek aid of other members in campaign planning, creative services, merchandising, public relations, publicity, media, research, and test facilities. Conducts annual expertise audit. .

EDUCATIONAL PROGRAMS

42349 ■ Design and Page Layout Skills
Padgett-Thompson Seminars
Rockhurst University CEC
14502 W. 105th St.
Lenexa, KS 66215
Free: 800-349-1935
URL: http://www.findaseminar.com/tpd/Padgett-Thompson-Seminars.asp
Price: $249.00. **Description:** Workshop teaches participants to create publications, newsletters, brochures, fliers, and reports. **Locations:** Cities throughout the United States.

DIRECTORIES OF EDUCATIONAL PROGRAMS

42350 ■ CounselorConnect
Pub: Public Relations Society of America
Contact: Gale Spreter
E-mail: gale.spreter@prsa.org
Released: Latest edition 2007. **Covers:** Public relations firms and academy members. **Entries Include:** Name and contact information.

REFERENCE WORKS

42351 ■ *6 Steps to Free Publicity*
Pub: ReadHowYouWant.com, Ltd.
Ed: Marcia Yudkin. **Released:** July 9, 2010. **Price:** $15.99. **Description:** Six steps to help promote a small business are given. The history of the Internet and its use to help provide free publicity to small firms is outlined.

42352 ■ *49 Marketing Secrets (That Work) to Grow Sales*
Pub: Morgan James Publishing, LLC
Ed: Ronald Finklestein. **Released:** October 2007. **Price:** $19.95/ **Description:** This book was written to fill the void on marketing books and is tailored to the small business owner. The author helps the small business owner to understand marketing and who they can trust while doing business. The book includes information to help entrepreneurs discover winning marketing strategies, branding and corporate image, media strategies, networking tips, technology-based marketing ideas, event strategies, and sales strategies.

42353 ■ "1914 Proved to Be Key Year for Chevy" in *Automotive News* (Vol. 86, October 31, 2011, No. 6488, pp. S18)
Pub: Crain Communications Inc.
Ed: Jamie Lareau. **Description:** Chevy Bow Tie emblem was born in 1914, creating the brand's image that has carried through to current days.

42354 ■ "Airlines Mount PR Push to Win Public Support Against Big Oil" in *Advertising Age* (Vol. 79, July 14, 2008, No. 7, pp. 1)
Pub: Crain Communications, Inc.
Ed: Michael Bush. **Description:** Top airline executives from competing companies have banded together in a public relations plan in which they are sending e-mails to their frequent fliers asking for aid in lobbying legislators to put a restriction on oil speculation.

42355 ■ "AllHipHop.com's Founders Thought a Weeklong Event Would Raise the Company'" in *Inc.* (February 2008, pp. 48-51)
Pub: Gruner & Jahr USA Publishing
Ed: Kermit Pattison. **Description:** Co-founders Greg Watkins and Chuck Creekmur, planned a weeklong festival to promote their company, AllHipHop.com; the event nearly ruined the firm. The online firm provides news about hip hop artists and the industry and is updated daily.

42356 ■ "Alto Ventures Retains Investor Relations Professional" in *Canadian Corporate News* (May 16, 2007)
Pub: Comtex News Network Inc.
Description: Alto Ventures Ltd., a gold exploration and development company with a portfolio of eleven properties in the Canadian Shield, announced that it has engaged the consulting services of Mark Prosser in order to focus on increasing investor awareness and exposure to the investment community through the dissemination of corporate information to a network of North American and European institutions, retail brokerage firms, and private investors.

42357 ■ "Ampm Focus Has BP Working Overtime; New Convenience-Store Brand Comes to Chicago" in *Crain's Chicago Business* (April 28, 2008)
Pub: Crain Communications, Inc.
Ed: John T. Slania. **Description:** Britian's oil giant BP PLC is opening its ampm convenience stores in the Chicago market and has already begun converting most of its 78 Chicago-area gas stations to ampms. The company has also started to franchise the stores to independent operators. BP is promoting the brand with both traditional and unconventional marketing techniques such s real or simulated 3D snacks embedded in bus shelter ads and an in-store Guitar Hero contest featuring finalists from a recent contest at the House of Blues.

42358 ■ "AVT Featured on TD Waterhouse Market News Website and in Vending Times Magazine" in *Benzinga.com* (August 17, 2011)
Pub: Benzinga.com
Ed: Benzinga Staff. **Description:** AVT Inc. was featured online and in an article reporting the firm's plan to install automated vending machines in high-profile areas including malls, office buildings, stadiums and arenas.

42359 ■ "Banks Deposit Reassurance, Calm Customers" in *The Business Journal-Serving Greater Tampa Bay* (Vol. 28, August 22, 2008)
Pub: American City Business Journals, Inc.
Ed: Margie Manning. **Description:** Community banks in the Tampa Bay Area are training tellers and other customer care workers to help reassure customers that their deposits are safe. Other measures to reassure depositors include joining a network that allows banks to share deposits. Additional information on moves community banks are making to reassure consumers is presented.

42360 ■ "BBB Reworks Logo, Grading System" in *Crain's Cleveland Business* (Vol. 28, October 8, 2007, No. 40, pp. 5)
Pub: Crain Communications, Inc.
Ed: John Booth. **Description:** During the next year, the Better Business Bureau will adopt a grading system that will establish performance minimums that will make it tougher for some types of businesses to become accredited; this nationwide rebranding effort is part of a campaign to sharpen the Better Business Bureau's image.

42361 ■ **"Best Buy's CEO On Learning to Love Social Media" in** *Harvard Business Review* **(Vol. 88, December 2010, No. 12, pp. 43)**
Pub: Harvard Business School Publishing
Ed: Brian J. Dunn. **Description:** Effective utilization of online social networks to enhance brand identity, connect with consumers, and address bad publicity scenarios is examined.

42362 ■ **"Better ROI Or Your Money Back, Says Buzz Agency" in** *Advertising Age* **(Vol. 79, July 14, 2008, No. 7, pp. 1)**
Pub: Crain Communications, Inc.
Ed: Michael Bush. **Description:** Word-of-mouth marketing is discussed as well as the impact on the advertising industry. Although many firms specializing in this form of marketing have opened over the past few years, many marketers are reluctant to try this route.

42363 ■ *Beyond Buzz: The Next Generation of Word-of-Mouth Marketing*
Pub: AMACOM
Ed: Lois Kelly. **Released:** March 2007. **Price:** $24.95. **Description:** New marketing ideas to bring attention to any small business are showcased.

42364 ■ **"Brand Imaging" in** *Small Business Opportunities* **(November 2010)**
Pub: Harris Publications Inc.
Ed: Karen Harnesk. **Description:** Design and branding pro shares strategies and tips to help guide any small business' image development.

42365 ■ *Briefs for Building Better Brands: Tips, Parables and Insight into Market Leaders*
Pub: AGCD Brandspa Books
Ed: Allan Gorman. **Released:** September 2004. **Description:** In today's marketplace, a company needs to gain consumer trust in order to build a brand. By gaining trust, the brand gets sold by word-of-mouth publicity. The author calls this type of marketing: guerrilla marketing, and he believes it to be more effective than traditional advertising.

42366 ■ **"The Buck Stops Here" in** *Canadian Business* **(Vol. 81, November 10, 2008, No. 19, pp. 25)**
Pub: Rogers Media Ltd.
Ed: Sarka Halas. **Description:** Reputation strategist Leslie Gaines-Ross says that minimizing the damage followed by the identification of what went wrong are the first steps that companies need to take when trying to salvage their reputation. Gaines-Ross states that it is up to the CEO to ensure the company's speedy recovery and they need to be at the forefront of the process.

42367 ■ **"Building Confidence" in** *Black Enterprise* **(Vol. 38, January 2008, No. 6, pp. 50)**
Pub: Earl G. Graves Publishing Co. Inc.
Ed: Marcia A. Reed-Woodard. **Description:** Patriot Management in Chicago offers courses at its Investment Management Training Academy for the institutional asset management and investment sector. Classes are designed to help build investor confidence amid the scandals that hit the financial, investment and asset management industry.

42368 ■ **"Canon Focuses on New Moms" in** *Marketing to Women* **(Vol. 21, January 2008, No. 1, pp. 3)**
Pub: EPM Communications, Inc.
Description: Canon launches a photo contest aimed at spotlighting baby's first pictures in an attempt to connect with new mothers.

42369 ■ **"Change Agent; What Peter Francese Says You Need to Know" in** *Advertising Age* **(Vol. 79, July 7, 2008, No. 26, pp. 13)**
Pub: Crain Communications, Inc.
Ed: Peter Francese. **Description:** Advice for marketers on how to deal effectively with a changing consumer base is given.

42370 ■ **"City Slickers" in** *Canadian Business* **(Vol. 81, March 31, 2008, No. 5, pp. 36)**
Pub: Rogers Media
Ed: Joe Castaldo. **Description:** Richard Florida believes that the creative class drives the economy and the prosperity of countries depends on attracting and retaining these people. Florida has brought attention to developing livable and economically vibrant cities thanks in part to his promotional skills. However, he has also drawn critics who see his data on his theories as flimsy and inadequate.

42371 ■ **"Conversations Need to Yield Actions Measured in Dollars" in** *Advertising Age* **(Vol. 79, July 7, 2008, No. 26, pp. 18)**
Pub: Crain Communications, Inc.
Ed: Jonathan Salem Baskin. **Description:** New ways in which to market to consumers are discussed.

42372 ■ **"Dramatic Results: Making Opera (Yes, Opera) Seem Young and Hip" in** *Inc.* **(October 2007, pp. 61-62)**
Pub: Gruner & Jahr USA Publishing
Description: Profile of Peter Gelb, who turned New York's Metropolitan Opera into one of the most media-savvy organizations in the country, using a multifaceted marketing strategy through the media. Gelb used streaming audio and simulcasts on satellite radio and movie theaters to promote a message that opera is hip.

42373 ■ **"Easy Answers? Hall No" in** *Charlotte Business Journal* **(Vol. 25, December 17, 2010, No. 39, pp. 1)**
Pub: Charlotte Business Journal
Ed: Erik Spanberg. **Description:** Charlotte, North Carolina-based NASCAR Hall of Fame has been trying to recover from its shaky start, but still bullish on the future as officials intensify promotions. Sports museums and halls of fame are mainly dependent on families and always search for new exhibits and great appearances to boost attendance.

42374 ■ **"Economy Should Play Big Role When Presidential Spotlight Returns" in** *Business First-Columbus* **(November 9, 2007, pp. A1)**
Pub: American City Business Journals, Inc.
Ed: Jeff Bell. **Description:** Ohio leaders, including the president of Columbus Chamber, Ty Marsh, suggests that Ohio has benefited from past campaigns as candidates spend money on advertising along with the media exposure the state received. The significance of Ohio in determining the winner in the 2008 presidential elections is discussed.

42375 ■ **"Emotional Brand Attachment and Brand Personality" in** *Journal of Marketing* **(Vol. 75, July 2011, No. 4, pp. 35)**
Pub: American Marketing Association
Ed: Lucia Malar, Harley Krohmer, Wayne D. Hoyer, Bettin Nyffeneger. **Description:** A study on whether the brand's personality should match the consumer's actual self or ideal self is presented. Actual self-congruence is found to have the most impact on emotional brand attachment.

42376 ■ **"Empowered" in** *Harvard Business Review* **(Vol. 88, July-August 2010, No. 7-8, pp. 94)**
Pub: Harvard Business School Publishing
Ed: Josh Bernoff, Ted Schadler. **Description:** HERO concept (highly empowered and resourceful operative) which builds a connection between employees, managers, and IT is outlined. The resultant additional experience and knowledge gained by employees improves customer relationship management.

42377 ■ **"FTC Takes Aim At Foreclosure 'Rescue' Firm" in** *The Business Journal-Serving Greater Tampa Bay* **(Vol. 28, September 19, 2008, No. 39)**
Pub: American City Business Journals, Inc.
Ed: Michael Hinman. **Description:** United Home Savers LLP has been ordered to halt its mortgage foreclosure rescue services after the Federal Trade Commission accused it of deceptive advertising. The

company is alleged to have charged customers $1,200 in exchange for unfulfilled promises to keep them in their homes.

42378 ■ **"Fueling Business" in** *The Business Journal-Milwaukee* **(Vol. 25, July 25, 2008, No. 44, pp. A1)**
Pub: American City Business Journals, Inc.
Ed: David Doege. **Description:** Several businesses in Wisconsin's Milwaukee area are offering gas cards in order to attract customers. Examples of this include apartment manager Nancy Randle offering a $400 gas card to new tenants with a 1 year lease and dentist Perry Sukowatey giving a $25 gas card after examining patients. Other details on gas card promotions are discussed.

42379 ■ **"Get Personal" in** *Entrepreneur* **(Vol. 36, April 2008, No. 4)**
Pub: Entrepreneur Media, Inc.
Ed: Romanus Wolter. **Description:** Customers appreciate personal contact, and communicating with them can help business owners' customer relations. Some ways on how to keep a personal touch with customers and improve business dealings include blending technology with personal interaction and knowing what the customers want. Other tips are provided.

42380 ■ **"Get Real" in** *Entrepreneur* **(Vol. 36, April 2008, No. 4, pp. 86)**
Pub: Entrepreneur Media, Inc.
Ed: Kim T. Gordon. **Description:** Selling points of a product or service must show real benefits to women. Provide detailed information as women look at details more deeply before purchasing. Other tips on how to market products designed for women consumers are provided.

42381 ■ *Groundswell: Winning in a World Transformed by Social Technologies*
Pub: Harvard Business School Press
Ed: Charlene Li; Josh Bernoff. **Released:** April 21, 2008. **Price:** $29.95. **Description:** Individuals are using online social technologies such as blogs, social networking sites, YouTube, and podcasts to discuss products and companies, write their own news, and find their own deals. When consumers you've never met are rating your company's products in public forums with which you have no experience or influence, your company is vulnerable. This book teaches the tools and data necessary to turn this treat into an opportunity.

42382 ■ **"Half of Canadian Firms to Boost Marketing Budgets" in** *Globe & Mail* **(January 22, 2007, pp. B1)**
Pub: CTVglobemedia Publishing Inc.
Ed: Keith McArthur. **Description:** The advertising and marketing spending plans of different companies are presented.

42383 ■ **"'Help Wanted' Meets 'Buy It Now': Why More Companies Are Integrating Marketing and Recruiting" in** *Inc.* **(November 2007, pp. 50-52)**
Pub: Gruner & Jahr USA Publishing
Ed: Ryan McCarthy. **Description:** Five tips to merge marketing and recruiting together include: thinking every help wanted ad as a marketing opportunity, treating every job candidate as a potential customer, involving the youngest employees in the interview process, look for way to promote recruiting events, and to sponsor community-oriented events.

42384 ■ **"Hopkins' Security, Reputation Face Challenges in Wake of Slaying" in** *Baltimore Business Journal* **(Vol. 28, August 6, 2010, No. 13)**
Pub: Baltimore Business Journal
Ed: Gary Haber. **Description:** The slaying of Johns Hopkins University researcher Stephen Pitcairn has not tarnished the reputation of the elite school in Baltimore, Maryland among students. Maintaining Hopkins' reputation is important since it is Baltimore's largest employer with nearly 32,000 workers. Insights on the impact of the slaying among the Hopkins' community are also given.

42385 ■ **"How To Live To Be 100; John E. Green Co. Grows Through Diversification"** in *Crain's Detroit Business* (February 18, 2008)
Pub: Crain Communications Inc. - Detroit
Ed: Chad Halcom. **Description:** Continuity, name recognition, and inventiveness are keys to continuing growth for Highland Park, Michigan's John E. Green Company, designer of pipe systems and mechanical contractor.

42386 ■ *I Love You More Than My Dog*
Pub: Portfolio
Ed: Jeanne Bliss. **Price:** $22.95. **Description:** Ways to win passionate, loyal and vocal customers in order to build a small business is outlined.

42387 ■ *If You Have to Cry, Go Outside: And Other Things Your Mother Never Told You*
Pub: HarperOne
Ed: Kelly Cutrone. **Released:** February 2, 2010. **Price:** $22.99. **Description:** Women's mentor advices on how to make it in one of the most competitive industries in the world, fashion. She has kicked people out of fashion shows, forced some of reality television's shiny start to fire their friends, and built her own company which is one of the most powerful public relations firms in the fashion business.

42388 ■ **"The Impact of Incomplete Typeface Logos on Perceptions of the Firms"** in *Journal of Marketing* (Vol. 75, July 2011, No. 4, pp. 86)
Pub: American Marketing Association
Ed: Henrik Hagtvedt. **Description:** A study of the influence of incomplete typeface logos on consumer perceptions of the company is presented. The findings suggest that companies should avoid incomplete typeface logos if perceptions of trustworthiness are critical or if consumers are likely to have a prevention focus.

42389 ■ **"Increasing Building Work at Ryan Cos."** in *Crain's Chicago Business* (Vol. 34, May 23, 2011, No. 21, pp. 6)
Pub: Crain Communications Inc.
Ed: Eddie Baeb. **Description:** Profile of Tim Hennelly, who is working to make Ryan Company known as a pure builder rather than a developer-builder.

42390 ■ **"Industry Vet To Spread Glory's Word"** in *Business First-Columbus* (November 9, 2007, pp. A1)
Pub: American City Business Journals, Inc.
Ed: Dan Eaton. **Description:** Glory Foods, Inc. chose Jacqueline Neal as its new president in October 2007. Neal has eleven years experience in brand management and has worked with food industry leaders such as Mars Inc., Kraft Foods Inc., and Nabisco Holdings Corporation. Neil's plans for the company are presented.

42391 ■ *It's Not Who You Know - It's Who Knows You!: The Small Business Guide to Raising Your Profits by Raising Your Profile*
Pub: John Wiley & Sons, Inc.
Ed: David Avrin. **Released:** November 9, 2010. **Price:** $24.95. **Description:** When it comes to promoting a small business or a brand, it is essential to know how valuable high-profile attention can be. But for most small companies, the cost of hiring an outside firm to increase attention can be too expensive.

42392 ■ **"Kraft Not Alone"** in *Crain's Chicago Business* (Vol. 30, February 2007, No. 6, pp. 8)
Pub: Crain Communications, Inc.
Description: Consumer watchdog group, The Center for Science in the Public Interest, has been putting pressure on food companies to be more truthful on their product labels. Listing of companies who have had misleading claims on their products is included.

42393 ■ **"Kuno Creative to Present B2B Social Media Campaign Webinar"** in *Entertainment Close-Up* (August 25, 2011)
Pub: Close-Up Media
Description: Kuno Creative, an inbound marketing agency, will host Three Steps of a Successful B2B

Social Media Campaign. The firm is a provider of Website development, branding, marketing strategy, public relations, Internet marketing, and inbound marketing.

42394 ■ **"Leadership in Flight"** in *Women In Business* (Vol. 63, Fall 2011, No. 3, pp. 24)
Pub: American Business Women's Association
Ed: Leigh Elmore. **Description:** Flight attendants in major airlines are trained to keep passengers comfortable and to calmly deal with emergencies. They also have a significant role in brand image and customer loyalty as they interact with the customers directly. Examples of teamwork leadership for flight attendants are given.

42395 ■ **"Making Headlines"** in *Entrepreneur* (Vol. 36, April 2008, No. 4, pp. 126)
Pub: Entrepreneur Media, Inc.
Ed: John Janstch. **Description:** Tips on how to get journalists to notice your business and your new product offerings are presented. These include making a list of journalists that might be interested in the industry you are in and writing comments on their blogs.

42396 ■ **"Making Sense of Ambiguous Evidence"** in *Harvard Business Review* (Vol. 86, September 2008, No. 9, pp. 53)
Pub: Harvard Business School Press
Ed: Lisa Burrell. **Description:** Documentary filmmaker Errol Morris emphasizes the role of perception in portraying objective reality, and how investigation and analysis enhance the accuracy of that portrayal.

42397 ■ *Marketing in a Web 2.0 World - Using Social Media, Webinars, Blogs, and More to Boost Your Small Business on a Budget*
Pub: Atlantic Publishing Company
Ed: Peter VanRysdam. **Released:** June 1, 2010. **Price:** $24.95. **Description:** Web 2.0 technologies have leveled the playing field for small companies trying to boost their presence by giving them an equal voice against larger competitors. Advice is given to help target your audience using social networking hubs.

42398 ■ **"McD's Warms Up For Olympics Performance"** in *Advertising Age* (Vol. 79, July 7, 2008, No. 26, pp. 8)
Pub: Crain Communications, Inc.
Ed: **Description:** Overview of McDonald's marketing plans for the company's sponsorship of the Olympics which includes a website, an alternate-reality game, names featured on U.S. athletes and on-the-ground activities.

42399 ■ **"MEC, Churchill Downs Saddle Up in Racing Deal"** in *Globe & Mail* (March 6, 2007, pp. B1)
Pub: CTVglobemedia Publishing Inc.
Ed: Greg Keenan. **Description:** The formation of a company called TrackNet Media Group LLC by Magna Entertainment Corp. and Churchill Downs Inc. for the broadcast of horse races on television is discussed. The efforts of the two companies to revive public interest in horse racing are described.

42400 ■ *Media, Organizations and Identity*
Pub: Palgrave Macmillan
Ed: Lilie Chouliaraki, Mette Morsing. **Released:** January 19, 2010. **Price:** $90.00. **Description:** The mass media, press and television are a essential in the formation of corporate identity and the promotion of business image and reputation. This book offers a new perspective into the interrelationships between media and organizations over three dimensions: media as business, media in business and business in the media.

42401 ■ **"New Sony HD Ads Tout Digital"** in *Brandweek* (Vol. 49, April 21, 2008, No. 16, pp. 5)
Pub: VNU Business Media, Inc.
Description: Looking to promote Sony Electronics' digital imaging products, the company has launched another campaign effort known as HDNA, a play on the words high-definition and DNA; originally Sony focused the HDNA campaign on their televisions, the

new ads will include still and video cameras as well and marketing efforts will consist of advertising in print, Online, television spots and publicity at various venues across the country.

42402 ■ **"Next Generation Audi TT Hits Canadian Streets"** in *Canadian Corporate News* (May 16, 2007)
Pub: Comtex News Network Inc.
Description: Audi Canada prepares for the launch of the highly anticipated 2008 Audi TT, recipient of the 2007 World Car Design of the Year due to its contemporary look, powerful engine, and innovative technology, with a multiple touch-point marketing campaign.

42403 ■ **"Org to Moms: Eat Your Veggies"** in *Marketing to Women* (Vol. 21, April 2008, No. 4, pp. 3)
Pub: EPM Communications, Inc.
Description: In order to increase the purchase and consumption of fruit and vegetables to moms, the non profit Produce for Better Health Foundation is launching a series of initiatives.

42404 ■ *The Power of Social Networking: Using the Whuffie Factor to Build Your Business*
Pub: Crown Business Books
Ed: Tara Hunt. **Released:** May 4, 2010. **Price:** $15.00. **Description:** This book shows how any small business can harness its power by increasing whuffie, the store of social capital that is the currency of the digital world. Blogs and social networks such as Facebook and Twitter are used to help grow any small firm.

42405 ■ **"Psst...Spread the Word"** in *Boston Business Journal* (Vol. 27, November 23, 2007, No. 43, pp. 1)
Pub: American City Business Journals Inc.
Ed: Lisa van der Pool. **Description:** More and more Boston companies are using word-of-mouth marketing to boost sales, and spending on it rose to $981 million in 2006. It is projected that spending on word-of-mouth marketing will reach $1.4 billion in 2007, and marketing companies using this type of method are getting higher funding. Trends in word-of-mouth marketing are discussed.

42406 ■ **"Report: McD's Pepsi Score Best With Young Hispanics"** in *Brandweek* (Vol. 49, April 21, 2008, No. 16, pp. 8)
Pub: VNU Business Media, Inc.
Ed: Della de Lafuente. **Description:** According to a new report, in order to reach Hispanic Gen Yers, marketing strategists need to understand this demographic's "bi-dentity," something which has proved an elusive task to many marketers. Another trend is the emergence of Latinas who have careers, as opposed to just jobs. There is an opportunity to tap this new, young and empowered female market with innovative messaging. Statistical data included.

42407 ■ **"Restaurants Dish Up Meal Deals To Attract Customers"** in *Crain's Detroit Business* (Vol. 24, October 6, 2008, No. 40, pp. 1)
Pub: Crain Communications, Inc.
Ed: Nathan Skid. **Description:** Restaurateurs are devising many creative and rewarding incentives to get customers to frequent their establishments during this economic crisis. Innovative ways in which even higher-end establishments are drawing in business are discussed.

42408 ■ **"Rich Returns: Media Master"** in *Entrepreneur* (Vol. 35, October 2007, No. 10, pp. 42)
Pub: Entrepreneur Media Inc.
Ed: Robert Kiyosaki. **Description:** Advertising is a powerful way of reaching clients, however, public relations is a less expensive method which is just as effective as advertising. Entrepreneurs must also be ready to try something new to be noticed by the public. Insights on how to master the use of media are given.

42409 ■ "Roadside Attraction" in *Hawaii Business* (Vol. 53, January 2008, No. 7, pp. 39)

Pub: Hawaii Business Publishing

Ed: Jason Ubay. **Description:** Businesses beside the Kamehameha Highway find ways to survive in a rural community. Sunshine Arts Hawaii, for instance, uses a bright-colored and huge mural to attract tourists who drive along the highway. Other techniques employed by businesses in the aforementioned are des cribed.

42410 ■ "The Seat-Of-The-Pants School of Marketing" in *Brandweek* (Vol. 49, April 21, 2008, No. 16, pp. 24)

Pub: VNU Business Media, Inc.

Ed: David Vinjamuri. **Description:** Excerpt from the book "Accidental Branding: How Ordinary People Build Extraordinary Brands," by David Vinjamuri, discusses six shared principles for creating a brand that is unique and will be successful over the long-term.

42411 ■ "Shoestring-Budget Marketing" in *Women Entrepreneur* (January 5, 2009)

Pub: Entrepreneur Media Inc.

Ed: Maria Falconer. **Description:** Pay-per-click search engine advertising is the traditional type of e-marketing that may not only be too expensive for certain kinds of businesses but also may not attract the quality customer base a business looking to grow needs to find. Social networking websites have become a mandatory marketing tool for business owners who want to see growth in their sales; tips are provided for utilizing these networking websites in order to gain more visibility on the Internet which can, in turn, lead to the more sales.

42412 ■ "Show and Tell" in *Entrepreneur* (Vol. 36, May 2008, No. 5, pp. 54)

Pub: Entrepreneur Media, Inc.

Ed: Heather Clancy. **Description:** FreshStart Telephone uses recorded video testimonials of customers, by using Pure Digital Flip Video that downloads content directly to the computer, and uploads it in the company's website to promote their wireless phone service.

42413 ■ *The Small Business Bible: Everything You Need to Know to Succeed in Your Small Business*

Pub: John Wiley & Sons, Incorporated

Ed: Steven D. Strauss. **Released:** September 2008. **Price:** $19.95 (US), $28.99 (Canadian). **Description:** Comprehensive guide to starting and running a successful small business. Topics include bookkeeping and financial management, marketing, publicity, and advertising.

42414 ■ "Sponsorship, Booths Available for Spring Business Showcase" in *Bellingham Business Journal* (Vol. February 2010, pp. 3)

Pub: Sound Publishing Inc.

Description: Third Annual Spring Business Showcase still have space available for vendors and sponsors. The event gives local businesses the opportunity to increase their visibility and provides a means to increase sales and build relationships.

42415 ■ *Start Your Own Blogging Business, Second Edition*

Pub: Entrepreneur Press

Released: July 1, 2010. **Price:** $17.95. **Description:** Interviews with professional bloggers from some of the most popular blogs on the Internet will help anyone interested in starting their own blogging business.

42416 ■ *Start Your Own Fashion Accessories Business*

Pub: Entrepreneur Press

Released: March 1, 2009. **Price:** $17.95. **Description:** Entrepreneurs wishing to start a fashion accessories business will find important information for setting up a home workshop and office, exploring the market, managing finances, publicizing and advertising the business and more.

42417 ■ "Staying Power" in *Canadian Business* (Vol. 79, November 6, 2006, No. 22, pp. 73)

Pub: Rogers Media

Ed: John Gray. **Description:** The effects on brand image on customer choices are analyzed. The need of maintaining brand image is also emphasized.

42418 ■ "Stock Delisting Could Hamper First Mariner" in *Boston Business Journal* (Vol. 29, July 29, 2011, No. 12, pp. 1)

Pub: American City Business Journals Inc.

Ed: Gary Haber. **Description:** Possible delisting of First Mariner Bancorp from the Nasdaq stock exchange could adversely impact the bank's ability to attract institutional investors. Some institutions limit their investments to companies trading on the Nasdaq.

42419 ■ "Technology Protects Lottery" in *Arkansas Business* (Vol. 26, September 28, 2009, No. 39, pp. 1)

Pub: Journal Publishing Inc.

Ed: George Waldon. **Description:** Arkansas Lottery Commission was initially criticized for what was seen as a major breach in security protocol by revealing the exact location of 26 million lottery tickets during a publicity stunt in which the media was invited to the main distribution center; however, due to the high-tech security that has been implemented the tickets are worthless until their status is changed after passing through multiple security scans.

42420 ■ "Timberland's CEO On Standing Up to 65,000 Angry Activists" in *Harvard Business Review* (Vol. 88, September 2010, No. 9, pp. 39)

Pub: Harvard Business School Publishing

Ed: Jeff Swartz. **Description:** Timberland Company avoided a potential boycott by taking a two-way approach. It addressed a supplier issue that posed a threat to the environment, and launched an email campaign to keep Greenpeace activists informed of the development of a new supplier agreement.

42421 ■ "To Be Seen Is to Be Successful" in *Pet Product News* (Vol. 64, December 2010, No. 12, pp. 12)

Pub: BowTie Inc.

Ed: David Arvin. **Description:** Guidelines on how pet business retailers can boost customer visibility are described considering that complacency could hamper retailers' efforts to effectively market their businesses. To enhance customer base and stand out from competing businesses, being different, strategic, creative, and differentiated is emphasized.

42422 ■ "Too Much Information?" in *Black Enterprise* (Vol. 37, December 2006, No. 5, pp. 59)

Pub: Earl G. Graves Publishing Co. Inc.

Ed: James C. Johnson. **Description:** African American business owners often face the dilemma of whether or not to divulge their minority status when soliciting new customers and financial institutions. The quality of the products or services is always the key factor and race should never define one's business; however, it is appropriate to market oneself as a minority or women-owned business, especially if the company is in an industry where those clients are offered top-tier contracts.

42423 ■ *Twitterville: How Businesses Can Thrive in the New Global Neighborhoods*

Pub: Portfolio Hardcover

Ed: Shel Israel. **Price:** $23.95. **Description:** Twitter is the most rapidly adopted communication tool in history, going from zero to ten million users in just over two years. On Twitter, word can spread faster than wildfire. Companies no longer have the option of ignoring the conversation. Unlike other hot social media spaces, Twitterville is dominated by professionals, not students. And despite its size, it still feels like a small town. Twitter allows people to interact much the way they do face-to-face, honestly and authentically.

42424 ■ "UAlbany on the Hunt for New Brand" in *Business Review, Albany New York* (Vol. 34, October 5, 2007, No. 27, pp. 1)

Pub: American City Business Journals, Inc.

Ed: Richard A. D'Errico. **Description:** State University of New York at Albany is working on a new marketing and branding initiative to help communicate its message better. The initiative is for the school to better understand its target audiences and their perception of the university.

42425 ■ "Vanity Plates" in *Canadian Business* (Vol. 82, April 27, 2009, No. 7, pp. 26)

Pub: Rogers Media

Ed: Andy Holloway. **Description:** Politicians in the U.S. called for the review of firms that availed of the bailout money but are under deals for naming rights of sports stadiums. Angus Reid's Corporate Reputation and Sponsorship Index found for example, that there is little correlation between sponsoring arenas on having a better brand image. It is suggested that firms who enter these deals build closer to people's homes.

42426 ■ "'We Had to Won the Mistakes'" in *Harvard Business Review* (Vol. 88, July-August 2010, No. 7-8, pp. 108)

Pub: Harvard Business School Publishing

Ed: Adi Ignatius. **Description:** Interview with Howard Schultz, CEO of Starbucks, covers topics that include investment in retraining, the impact of competition, premium quality, authenticity, customer services, strategy development, work-and-life issues, and international presence.

42427 ■ "What You Look Like Online" in *Black Enterprise* (Vol. 37, January 2007, No. 6, pp. 56)

Pub: Earl G. Graves Publishing Co. Inc.

Ed: Marcia A. Reed-Woodard. **Description:** Of 100 executive recruiters 77 percent stated that they use search engines to check the backgrounds of potential job candidates, according to a survey conducted by ExecuNet. Of those surveyed 35 percent stated that they eliminate potential candidates based on information they find online so it is important to create a positive Web presence which highlights professional image qualities.

42428 ■ "What's In Your Toolbox" in *Women In Business* (Vol. 61, August-September 2009, No. 4, pp. 7)

Pub: American Business Women's Association

Ed: Mimi Kopulos. **Description:** Business owners are increasingly turning to using social networking websites, such as Facebook, LinkedIn and Twitter, to promote their companies. The number of adult social media users has increased from 8 percent in 2005 to 35 percent in 2009.

42429 ■ *When the Headline Is You: An Insider's Guide to Handling the Media*

Pub: Jossey-Bass

Ed: Jeff Ansell, Jeff Lesson. **Price:** $29.95. **Description:** How-to guide for executives and other professionals whose high-visibility requires frequent interviews with the media. Tested techniques, tools, and insights for how to respond to all types of media in tough situation are provided. The books also reveals the lessons learned and the pitfalls to avoid by referencing actual news stores from around the world and provides exercises for readers who wish to sharpen their media-handling skills.

42430 ■ "Women-Centric Events Can Captivate Consumers" in *Crain's Cleveland Business* (Vol. 28, November 12, 2007, No. 45, pp. 24)

Pub: Crain Communications, Inc.

Ed: Kimberly Bonvissuto. **Description:** Discusses innovative ways that companies are targeting the female consumer market including arranging networking and social events.

42431 ■ "You Have to Lead From Everywhere" in *Harvard Business Review* (Vol. 88, November 2010, No. 11, pp. 76)

Pub: Harvard Business School Publishing

Ed: Scott Berinato. **Description:** U.S. Coast Guard Admiral Thad W. Allen discusses effective leadership in successful crises management. Topics include influence of media and public perspective, the applicability of military training to the business arena, and the responsibility of a leader to set morale.

42432 ■ "Your Big Give" in *Small Business Opportunities* **(September 2008)**
Pub: Entrepreneur Media Inc.
Ed: Michael Guld. **Description:** Cause related marketing is beneficial to businesses as well as the communities they inhabit; three small businesses that are elevating their standing in the community while at the same time increasing their customer base are profiled.

TRADE PERIODICALS

42433 ■ *Accutips*
Pub: Accudata America
Released: Monthly. **Price:** Free. **Description:** Discusses promotion and marketing issues relevant to businesses.

42434 ■ *The Gauge*
Pub: Delahaye Medialink
Contact: Katharine Delahaye Paine, Publisher
E-mail: kpaine@delahaye.com
Ed: William Teunis Paarlberg, Editor, wpaarlberg@aol.com. **Released:** Bimonthly. **Price:** $75. **Description:** Provides information on and evaluates marketing communications activities of companies. Recurring features include interviews, news of research, and a calendar of events.

42435 ■ *The Publicity Hound*
Pub: Joan Stewart
Contact: Joan Stewart, Publisher
E-mail: jstewart@publicityhound.com
Released: Weekly. **Price:** Free internet service. **Description:** Provides techniques and strategies on self-promotion and inexpensive publicity. Recurring features include letters to the editor, interviews, news of research, book reviews, news of educational opportunities, notices of publications available, and columns titled Advice From Media People, Seasonal Story Ideas, Resource Page, Success Stories, and Media Insider Secrets. Does not report public relations agency staff changes.

VIDEOCASSETTES/ AUDIOCASSETTES

42436 ■ *Ad Campaigns That Work*
Instructional Video
2219 C St.
Lincoln, NE 68502
Ph:(402)475-6570
Free: 800-228-0164
Fax:(402)475-6500
Co. E-mail: feedback@insvideo.com
URL: http://www.insvideo.com
Price: $89.95. **Description:** Three successful ad agency executives furnish information on successful ad campaigns and why they were successful. Covers principles of successful advertising. **Availability:** VHS.

42437 ■ *Advertising the Small Business*
NETCHE (Nebraska Educational Television Council for Higher Education)
1800 N. 33rd St.
Lincoln, NE 68583
Ph:(402)472-3611
Free: 800-698-3426
Fax:(402)472-1785
Co. E-mail: netche@unl.edu
URL: http://www.netche.org
Released: 1981. **Price:** $100.00. **Description:** These two tapes, provide a step-by-step instructional course on how to best publicize a small business, from research/planning to managing/implementation. **Availability:** VHS; 3/4U.

42438 ■ *Advertising: The Hidden Language*
First Light Video Publishing
2321 Abbot Kinney Blvd., Top Fl.
Venice, CA 90291
Ph:(310)577-8581
Free: 800-262-8862

Fax:(310)574-0886
Co. E-mail: sales@firstlightvideo.com
URL: http://www.firstlightvideo.com
Description: Features Dr. Phillip Bell as he demostrates how successful ads grab the consumer and make them want to purchase the product. **Availability:** VHS.

42439 ■ *Advertising Tricks Without the Gimmicks*
Instructional Video
2219 C St.
Lincoln, NE 68502
Ph:(402)475-6570
Free: 800-228-0164
Fax:(402)475-6500
Co. E-mail: feedback@insvideo.com
URL: http://www.insvideo.com
Price: $79.00. **Description:** Offers an overview and practical hints on the basics of advertising. **Availability:** VHS.

42440 ■ *Promotion: Polishing the Apple*
RMI Media
1365 N. Winchester St.
Olathe, KS 66061-5880
Ph:(913)768-1696
Free: 800-745-5480
Fax:800-755-6910
Co. E-mail: actmedia@act.org
URL: http://www.actmedia.com
Released: 1991. **Price:** $89.95. **Description:** Presents promotional mixes developed by Apple Computers for the Apple IIc, the Macintosh, and the Macintosh Office to demonstrate successful uses of print and television advertising. **Availability:** VHS.

CONSULTANTS

42441 ■ *Alan J. Zell*
PO Box 69
Portland, OR 97207-0069
Ph:(503)241-1988
Fax:(503)241-1989
Co. E-mail: azell@aol.com
URL: http://www.sellingselling.com
Contact: Alan J. Zell, Owner
E-mail: azell@aol.com
Scope: An advisory service for those who sell their services, products or their organization's ideas, information, and skills through face-to-face and telephone conversations, printed materials, the media, electronic communications, schools, guilds, trade shows, and display presentations. Industries served: minority and woman-owned businesses; government and education; medicine, law, accounting, technology, manufacturers, distributors, and retailers; professional and trade associations; and nonprofit organizations. **Publications:** "Elements of Selling"; "An Unconventional Look at the Complex Subject of Selling"; "The Art Of Selling Art"; "Selling Situations"; "What Customers need to know"; "Turnover & Return on Investment"; "The Ultimate Business Oxymoron"; "Walkin The Aisles, Looking at the Booths, etc"; "Four Uses Of Internet". **Seminars:** Ambassador Of Selling; An Unconventional Look at the Complex Subject of Selling; Selling Change . . . Pain or Progress, Revolution or Evolution?; Giving GOOD SERVICE When Giving Good Service Is Not Good Enough; Two Sides Of A Trade Show; Selling For People Who Do Not Like To Sell; The Art Of Selling Art; Yes, Technically Trained People Can Learn To Sell; Beginning Business, How To Achieve Your Goals.

42442 ■ *COMsciences Inc.*
4712 Admiralty Way, Ste. 870
Marina del Rey, CA 90292
Ph:(310)823-5257
Fax:(323)937-0160
Co. E-mail: info@comsciences.com
URL: http://www.comsciences.com
Contact: Jack Torobin, CEO
E-mail: jtorobin@comsciences.com
Scope: Firm offers research services to support public relations, corporate advertising, impact of new communications media, communication entertainment, and internet/web development. Also provides

strategic management consulting on communications, marketing, opinion surveys, and organizational development and assessment. The company specializes in media campaigns and evaluation tools. Also conducts government sponsored and media sponsored surveys. Serves all industry sectors, especially.com, wireless telecommunications, interactive media, and consumer electronics. **Publications:** "Wanted: Radical Thinking," Pmg World Magazine, Mar, 2003. **Special Services:** iKIT[R]; imovio[R].

42443 ■ *Holcomb Gallagher Adams Advertising Inc.*
300 Marconi Blvd., Ste. 305
Columbus, OH 43215
Ph:(614)221-3343
Fax:(614)221-3367
Co. E-mail: sholcomb_1@earthlink.net
URL: http://www.hgainc.com
Contact: Rick Adams, Partner
E-mail: radams@atshgainc.com
Scope: Consults in strategic marketing planning, and new business, brand equity, creative strategy, and media strategy development. Industries served: Consumer goods and services, manufacturing, retail, business-to-business products and services, education, travel, and tourism.

42444 ■ *Russ Fons Public Relations*
7509 Turtle Dove Ct.
Las Vegas, NV 89129-6032
Ph:(702)658-7654
Free: 888-658-7654
Fax:(702)658-1349
Co. E-mail: russfons@cox.net
URL: http://www.russfons.com
Contact: Russ Fons, Owner
E-mail: russfons@cox.net
Scope: Offers corporate counseling and image development; media relations; marketing communications and product publicity; event management and special promotions; and graphic design and production. Industries served: All worldwide. Licensing and merchandising, literary services, Hispanic communications. Revenue Sharing/PI Advertising. **Publications:** "The Executive Crisis Manager, a planning guide to surviving corporate crisis".

42445 ■ *Sol Abrams Public Relations Counsel & Marketing Consultants*
331 Webster Dr.
New Milford, NJ 07646
Ph:(201)262-4111
Fax:(201)262-7669
Contact: Sol Abrams, Owner
E-mail: solbabrams@aol.com
Scope: Independent consulting provides publicity, public relations and marketing counsel and services to management of private and public enterprises. Also serves as public relations consultants to other public relations consulting firms, advertising agencies and marketing companies. Provides expert witness services involving public relations. Also lectures, trains, teaches, and conducts seminars in public relations and marketing. Industries served: Corporate management, businesses large and small including real estate, construction, entertainment, food, fashion, fundraising, automotive, aviation, franchising, government agencies, and nonprofit organizations. **Seminars:** How to Select a Public Relations Firm; Publicity and Promotion for Small Business Owner; Expose Yourself - Don't Be a Secret Agent -Increase Your Sales, Incomes, Images, Publicity, Profits and Prestige via Professional Public Relations.

42446 ■ *Steve Emerine Strategic Public Relations*
4973 E Silver St.
PO Box 41824
Tucson, AZ 85717-1824
Ph:(520)323-1441
Fax:(520)881-4043
Co. E-mail: steveemerine@webtr.net
Contact: Steve Emerine, President
E-mail: steveemerine@webtr.net
Scope: Services offered in crisis management, environmental problems, litigation public relations, government relations, publicity, writing, editing and

public information planning. **Seminars:** Crisis Public Relations; Media Relations; Environmental and Neighborhood Relations.

42447 ■ Westlife Consultants & Counsellors
4 Robert Speck Dr., Ste. 1500
Mississauga, ON, Canada L4Z 1S1
Ph:(905)867-0686
Fax:(416)799-5242
Co. E-mail: westlifeconsultant@hotmail.com
URL: http://www.westlifeconsultants.com
Contact: Tania Hussain, Treasurer
E-mail: tania.westlifeconsultant@atshotmail.com
Scope: Provides entrepreneurs and businesses with a highly commercial and global perspectives on the international business development ideas under consideration. **Publications:** "Innovative Management"; "Team Building and Leadership"; "Financial Planning"; "Estate Planning"; "Risk Management"; "Export/Import Trade Finance Mechanics"; "Marketing and Sales Management"; "What Your Banker Needs to Know"; "Building A Successful Financial Plan".

COMPUTERIZED DATABASES

42448 ■ *ABI/INFORM*
ProQuest LLC
789 E Eisenhower Pky.
PO Box 1346
Ann Arbor, MI 48106-1346
Ph:(734)761-4700
Free: 800-521-0600
Fax:(734)761-6450
Co. E-mail: info@proquest.com
URL: http://www.proquest.com
Description: Contains approximately 6 million full text or bibliographic citations to articles from more than 800 business and management publications worldwide. **Availability:** Online: Wolters Kluwer Health, ProQuest LLC, ProQuest LLC, Questel SA, STN International, Colorado Alliance of Research Libraries, Financial Times Ltd., LexisNexis Group, ProQuest LLC. **Type:** Full text; Bibliographic; Image.

42449 ■ *Advertiser & Agency Red Books Plus*
LexisNexis Group
9443 Springboro Pike
Dayton, OH 45342
Free: 888-285-3947
Co. E-mail: customer.support@lexisnexis.com
URL: http://www.lexisnexis.com
Contact: Greg Schraft, Gen. Sales
E-mail: gregory.schraft@lexisnexis.com
Released: Quarterly, Latest edition January, 2007.
Price: $2,195, individuals. **Description:** CD-ROM. Covers 15,750 of the world's top advertisers, their products and what media they use, as well as 13,900 U.S. and international ad agencies and nearly 100,000 key executives worldwide in management, creative, and media positions. **Entries Include:** For advertisers—Company name, job function/title, product/brand name, advertising expenditures by media. For personnel—Name and title.

42450 ■ *PR Newswire*
United Business Media LLC
350 Hudson St., Ste. 300
New York, NY 10014
Ph:(212)596-1500
Free: 800-776-8090
Fax:(212)793-9313
Co. E-mail: information@prnewswire.com
URL: http://www.prnewswire.com
Description: Contains the complete text of more than 1000 news releases issued by a variety of organizations and transmitted to the press by PR Newswire each day. Covers primarily business and financial news as well as sports, labor, entertainment, medicine, science, and general interest news. News releases include name and telephone number of issuing organization. Source organizations include some 20,000 corporations, public relations agencies, trade associations, labor unions, civic and cultural organizations, political parties, and government agencies. Note: on DIALOG, the database is contained in two separate files, one with current news May 1999

to date; the other with archive news from 1987 to April 1999. **Availability:** Online: ProQuest LLC, ProQuest LLC, Dow Jones & Company Inc., LexisNexis Group, LexisNexis Group, Track Data Corp., Bloomberg LP, Mzinga Inc. **Type:** Directory; Full text.

LIBRARIES

42451 ■ Burson-Marsteller Knowledge Center
230 Park Ave. S.
New York, NY 10003
Ph:(212)614-4000
Fax:(212)598-5320
Co. E-mail: tony.telloni@bm.com
URL: http://www.burson-marsteller.com/default.aspx
Contact: Tony Telloni, Mgr.
Scope: Advertising, public relations, marketing research. **Services:** Interlibrary loan; Library open to clients and librarians. **Holdings:** 1000 books. **Subscriptions:** 100 journals and other serials.

42452 ■ Campbell Mithun Library & Information Services
222 S. 9th St.
Minneapolis, MN 55402
Ph:(612)347-1508
Fax:(612)347-1041
Co. E-mail: psjolander@cmithun.com
Contact: Peggy Sjolander, Assoc.Dir.
Scope: Advertising, marketing. **Services:** Interlibrary loan; copying; Library open with permission. **Holdings:** 1000 books; 1000 volumes of client records; 500 files of pamphlets and clippings; 500 competitive advertising files. **Subscriptions:** 750 journals and other serials.

42453 ■ D'Arcy Masius Benton & Bowles Information Center
1 Memorial Dr.
St. Louis, MO 63102
Ph:(314)342-3925
Fax:(314)342-3584
URL: http://library.duke.edu/digitalcollections/rbmscl/dmbb/inv/
Contact: Rosanne Hadjri, Libn.
Scope: Advertising. **Services:** Library not open to the public. **Holdings:** 750 volumes; 375 VF drawers of pamphlets and clippings. **Subscriptions:** 750 journals and other serials.

42454 ■ Grey Worldwide Information Center
777 3rd Ave., 6th Fl.
New York, NY 10017
Ph:(212)546-2000
Fax:(212)546-2001
Co. E-mail: espross@grey.com
URL: http://www.grey.com/
Contact: Jim Heekin, Chm./CEO
Scope: Advertising, marketing, business, new business development. **Services:** Interlibrary loan. **Holdings:** 500 books; 200 directories. **Subscriptions:** 200 journals and other serials; 5 newspapers.

42455 ■ Ketchum Advertising–Library Services
1285 Avenue of the Americas, 4th Fl.
New York, NY 10019
Ph:(646)935-3900
Co. E-mail: kelley.skoloda@ketchum.com
URL: http://www.ketchum.com
Contact: Ray Kotcher, CEO
Scope: Advertising, marketing, general reference. **Services:** Interlibrary loan. **Holdings:** 1100 books; 40 VF drawers of marketing material; reference collection; Annual reports. **Subscriptions:** 450 journals and other serials.

42456 ■ Martin/Williams Advertising Inc. Library
60 S. 6th St., Ste. 2800
Minneapolis, MN 55402
Ph:(612)340-0800

Fax:(612)342-9700
URL: http://www.martinwilliams.com
Contact: Dru Frykberg, Libn.
Scope: Advertising, marketing, business. **Services:** Library open to agency employees and clients; open to the public with special permission. **Holdings:** Figures not available.

42457 ■ McCann-Erickson Advertising of Canada Ltd. Information Centre
10 Bay St., Ste. 1012
Toronto, ON, Canada M5J 2S3
Ph:(416)594-6400
Fax:(416)594-6272
Co. E-mail: contact@mccann.com
URL: http://www.mccann.com/
Contact: Valerie Walton, Info.Ctr.Mgr.
Scope: Advertising, marketing, business, industry. **Services:** Center not open to the public. **Holdings:** 1000 books. **Subscriptions:** 90 journals and other serials.

42458 ■ Reader's Digest–Marketing Information Center
260 Madison Ave.
New York, NY 10016
Ph:(212)850-7034
Fax:(212)683-8142
URL: http://www.readersdigest.com
Contact: Helen Fledderus, Cons.
Scope: Advertising, marketing, and media research. **Services:** Interlibrary loan. **Holdings:** 800 volumes; 23 lateral file drawers of commodity and industry data. **Subscriptions:** 74 journals and other serials.

RESEARCH CENTERS

42459 ■ Boston College–Center for Corporate Citizenship
Carroll School of Management
55 Lee Rd.
Chestnut Hill, MA 02467-3942
Ph:(617)552-4545
Fax:(617)552-8499
Co. E-mail: bradley.googins.1@bc.edu
URL: http://www.bcccc.net
Contact: Bradley K. Googins PhD, Exec.Dir.
E-mail: bradley.googins.1@bc.edu
Scope: Corporate community relations, public-private partnerships, corporate voluntarism, corporate citizenship, and corporate philanthropy. Projects include designing corporate social vision, best practice research, analyses of corporate images within local communities, impact of corporation's external affairs on employee behavior, and profiles of community relations professionals. **Services:** Contract research and consulting. **Publications:** Corporate Citizen magazine (annually); Research reports (periodically); Voice of Corporate Citizenship newsletter (monthly). **Educational Activities:** Conferences; Executive education, professional development courses in managing community involvement and corporate citizenship; Seminars and institutes.

42460 ■ Massachusetts College of Art–Design Research Unit
621 Huntington Ave.
Boston, MA 02115
Ph:(617)879-7793
Fax:(617)566-4034
Co. E-mail: rstreit@massart.edu
URL: http://babel.massart.edu/dru
Contact: Dan Wallis, Pres.
E-mail: rstreit@massart.edu
Scope: Design research and services, focusing on printed matter, including posters, letterheads, annual reports, brochures, identity systems, exhibition design, industrial design, illustration, and photography. **Services:** Provides design services to educational, research, charitable, and non-profit organizations. **Educational Activities:** Educational training in design, printing, and business.

ASSOCIATIONS AND OTHER ORGANIZATIONS

42461 ■ American Purchasing Society
PO Box 256
Aurora, IL 60506
Ph:(630)859-0250
Fax:(630)859-0270
Co. E-mail: propurch@propurch.com
URL: http://www.american-purchasing.com
Contact: Mr. Richard H. Hough, Exec. VP
Description: Seeks to certify qualified purchasing personnel. Maintains speakers' bureau and placement service. Conducts research programs; compiles statistics including salary surveys. Provides consulting service for purchasing, materials management, and marketing. Conducts seminars and online courses. **Publications:** *Annual Report of Purchasing Salaries and Employment Trends* (annual); *Benchmarking Purchasing* (annual); *Handbook of Buying and Purchasing Management*; *How To Get the Best Results from your Purchasing Department* (biennial).

42462 ■ National Purchasing Institute
PO Box 370192
Las Vegas, NV 89137-0192
Ph:(702)989-8095
Free: (866)877-7641
Fax:(702)967-0744
Co. E-mail: info@npiconnection.org
URL: http://www.npiconnection.org/home/index.asp
Contact: Craig Rowley, Exec. Dir.
Description: Purchasing agents, directors of purchasing and procurement, buyers, and others employed by governmental, educational, or other tax-supported agencies. Seeks to improve the field through development of simplified standards of specifications, improved communication, and promotion of uniform purchasing laws. Compiles statistics. **Publications:** *Annual Conference Program* (annual); *Membership Roster* (annual); *Public Purchasing Review* (bimonthly).

EDUCATIONAL PROGRAMS

42463 ■ Fundamentals of Purchasing (Canada)
Canadian Management Centre
150 York St., 5th Fl.
Toronto, ON, Canada M5H 3S5
Ph:(416)214-5678
Free: 877-262-2519
Fax:(416)214-6047
Co. E-mail: cmcinfo@cmctraining.org
URL: http://www.cmctraining.org
Price: $2,395.00 Canadian for non-members; $2,195.00 Canadian for CMC members. **Description:** Covers the steps involved in purchasing, negotiating, working with vendors and suppliers, cost and price analysis, and types of purchase contracts. **Locations:** Toronto, ON; and Mississauga, ON.

42464 ■ Fundamentals of Purchasing for the New Buyer
American Management Association
600 AMA Way
Saranac Lake, NY 12983-5534
Ph:(212)586-8100
Free: 877-566-9441
Fax:(518)891-0368
Co. E-mail: customerservice@amanet.org
URL: http://www.amaseminars.org
Price: $2,345.00 for non-members; $2,095.00 for AMA members; and $1,794.00 General Services Administration (GSA) members. **Description:** Covers the steps involved in purchasing, negotiating, working with vendors and suppliers, using e-procurement, and the materials management process. **Locations:** Cities throughout the United States.

42465 ■ How to Bargain & Negotiate with Vendors
Fred Pryor Seminars & CareerTrack
5700 Broadmoor St., Ste. 300
Mission, KS 66202
Free: 800-780-8476
Fax:(913)967-8849
Co. E-mail: customerservice@pryor.com
URL: http://www.pryor.com
Price: $179.00; $169.00 for groups of 5 or more. **Description:** Learn how to get lower prices, quicker delivery, higher quality and better service through negotiation. **Locations:** Cities throughout the United States.

REFERENCE WORKS

42466 ■ *Common Sense Purchasing: Hard Knock Lessons Learned from a Purchasing Pro*
Pub: Booksurge, LLC
Ed: Tom DePaoli. **Released:** February 2004. **Price:** $9.99. **Description:** Guide to purchasing and negotiating deals.

42467 ■ "Many Procter Products To Get Price Increase" in *Business Courier* (Vol. 24, November 16, 2008, No. 31, pp. 1)
Pub: American City Business Journals, Inc.
Ed: Lisa Biank Fasig. **Description:** Procter & Gamble Co. is increasing the prices of its products as a means to offset the rising costs of gas, plastics and raw materials. The price increase will be somewhere between 3 to 12 percent, depending on the product.

42468 ■ "New Beginnings for VIBE" in *Black Enterprise* (Vol. 37, November 2006, No. 4, pp. 34)
Pub: Earl G. Graves Publishing Co. Inc.
Ed: Mashaun D. Simon. **Description:** Danyel Smith replaced Mimi Valdes as editor-in-chief of VIBE magazine after the Wicks Group, private equity firm focused on selected segments of the media, communications, and information industries, purchased the magazine.

42469 ■ "Suiting Up; Yes, You're Smart, But Can You Look the Part" in *Crain's Chicago Business* (Vol. 30, February 2007, No. 6, pp. 39)
Pub: Crain Communications, Inc.
Ed: Kate Ryan. **Description:** For investment bankers, fashion is a must. Advice for men and women included.

TRADE PERIODICALS

42470 ■ *Business Consumer's Advisor*
Pub: Buyers Laboratory Inc.
Contact: Jane Lyons
Ed: Daria Hoffman, Editor. **Released:** Monthly. **Price:** $20. **Description:** Focuses on office equipment and supplies, offering purchasing advice and exploring methods of increasing office productivity through appropriate management of the equipment and its operators. Offers readers a chance to share their experiences, evaluate products and equipment, and gives results of Buyers Laboratory's testing.

42471 ■ *Caveat Emptor*
Pub: Ontario Public Buyers Association
Ed: C.B. Bott, Editor. **Released:** 4/year. **Price:** $99, individuals $99/year. **Description:** Contains information of interest to anyone who spends public funds. Recurring features include updates on OPBA's Internet Bid Document Advertising System and internal databank and articles dealing with new technology, management issues, and methodology related to the expenditure of public funds.

42472 ■ *Inside Supply Management*
Pub: Institute for Supply Management
Contact: Debbie Webber, Sen. VP & Treas.
E-mail: dwebber@ism.ws
Released: Monthly. **Description:** Trade magazine for purchasing and supply managers.

42473 ■ *The Journal of Supply Chain Management*
Pub: Institute for Supply Management
Contact: Craig R. Carter PhD, Co-Ed.-in-Ch.
E-mail: crcarter@unr.edu
Released: Quarterly. **Price:** $109 Americas print online; $103 print online; $68 rest of world print online; $279 institutions print online; $255 institutions print online; $201 institutions, other countries print online. **Description:** Academic journal covering purchasing and supply management.

42474 ■ *NAEP Bulletin*
Pub: National Association of Educational Procurement
Ed: Doreen Murner, Editor, dmurner@naeb.org. **Released:** Monthly, except May and April. **Price:** Included in membership. **Description:** Features information on institutional purchasing and news of the Association. Recurring features include a calendar of events, reports of meetings, news of educational opportunities, job listings, book reviews, notices of publications available, and columns titled Professional Perspective, Market Index, and Roamin' With Yeoman.

42475 ■ *NASPO Newsletter*
Pub: National Association of State Procurement Officials
Contact: Nicole Smith
Ed: Leslie Scott, Editor, lflynn@iglov.rom. **Released:** Quarterly, 2/year. **Price:** Included in membership. **Description:** Covers Association activities and purchasing innovations in state governments. Reports on developments in energy efficiency and recycling. Recurring features include news from the states, resources available, a calendar of events, and reports of state and federal legislation.

42476 ■ *Professional Purchasing*
Pub: American Purchasing Society
Contact: Harry E. Hough Ph.D.
Ed: Harry E. Hough, Ph.D., Editor, hehough@mgci.com. **Released:** Monthly. **Description:** Provides information on policies, procedures, methods, and prices of purchasing. Features price indexes. Recurring features include letters to the editor, news of research, reports of meetings, news of educational opportunities, job listings, book reviews, and notices of publications available.

42477 ■ *Progressive Purchasing*
Pub: Purchasing Management Association of Canada (PMAC)
Ed: A. Marshall, Editor, amarshall@pmac.ca. **Released:** Bimonthly. **Price:** Included in membership. **Description:** Presents news on the association's C.P.P. Accreditation program, new developments in purchasing, industry trends, and profiles of membership. Recurring features include a calendar of events, summary of national activities, and a column titled the National President's Message. Remarks: Also available in French.

42478 ■ *Purchasing b2b*
Pub: Rogers Media Publishing
Contact: Tim Dimopoulos, Exec. Publisher
E-mail: tim.dimopoulos@pb2b.rogers.com
Ed: Lisa Wichmann, Editor, lisa.wichmann@pb2b.rogers.com. **Released:** 10/yr. **Price:** $99 Canada plus applicable taxes; $160 two years plus applicable taxes; $170 U.S. **Description:** Magazine for purchasing professionals.

42479 ■ *Purchasing Magazine*
Pub: Reed Business Information
Contact: Paul Teague, Editor-in-Chief
E-mail: pteague@reedbusiness.com
Released: Monthly. **Description:** Magazine for buying professionals.

TRADE SHOWS AND CONVENTIONS

42480 ■ ISM Annual International Supply Management Conference
Institute for Supply Management
2055 E. Centennial Cir.
PO Box 22160
Tempe, AZ 85285-2160
Ph:(480)752-6276
Free: 800-888-6276
Fax:(480)752-7890
URL: http://www.ism.ws
Released: Annual. **Audience:** Purchasing professionals and general public. **Principal Exhibits:** Auctions, business service, capital equipment, computer hardware/software, consulting services, e-business services/software, logistics and transportation, MRO, office supply, procurement card services.

CONSULTANTS

42481 ■ Mark Vanderstelt
9831 Gulfstream Ct.
Fishers, IN 46037
Ph:(317)576-9328
Fax:(317)576-9328
Scope: Consulting services include financial planning and analysis, inventory control, cash management, return on investment, budgeting, pricing, system design and analysis, mergers and acquisitions, feasibility studies, data processing, cost systems and controls, and performance measurement. Also performs operational and financial reviews.

RESEARCH CENTERS

42482 ■ Arizona State University–CAPS Research
2055 E Centennial Cir.
PO Box 22160
Tempe, AZ 85285-2160
Ph:(480)752-2277
Fax:(480)491-7885
Co. E-mail: research@capsresearch.org
URL: http://www.capsresearch.org
Contact: Phillip Carter, Exec.Dir.
E-mail: research@capsresearch.org
Scope: World-class purchasing, performance benchmarks, supplier partnerships, total quality management, purchasing measurement, non-traditional purchasing, cycle-time reduction, total cost models, futures study, and minority business enterprise best practices. **Publications:** Critical Issue reports (quarterly); Practix (quarterly); Research reports (quarterly). **Educational Activities:** Executive Roundtable, Best Practices Forums/Workshops (10/year), for senior purchasing and supply management practitioners; Focus study research, benchmarking, critical issues reports, focused on executive participation in supply management research.

Remediation

TRADE SHOWS AND CONVENTIONS

42483 ■ **Society for Human Resource Management (SHRM) The HRM Marketplace Exposition**
Society for Human Resource Management
1800 Duke St.
Alexandria, VA 22314
Ph:(703)548-3440
Free: 800-283-SHRM
Fax:(703)535-6490
Co. E-mail: shrm@shrm.org
URL: http://www.shrm.org
Released: Annual. **Audience:** Human resource management and related professionals. **Principal Exhibits:** Human resource management products and services; including relocation human resource information systems, recruitment, executive search, temporary/contact personnel employee compensation and benefits, incentive program information, childcare/eldercare, and drug testing information.

CONSULTANTS

42484 ■ **Ambler Growth Strategy Consultants Inc.**
3432 Reading Ave.
Hammonton, NJ 08037-8008
Ph:(609)567-9669
Free: 888-253-6662
Fax:(609)567-3810
Co. E-mail: thegrowthstrategist@ambler.com
URL: http://www.thegrowthstrategist.com
Contact: Melissa Norcross, Chief Marketing Officer
E-mail: melissa@atsambler.com
Scope: Growth strategies, strategic assessments, CEO coaching. **Publications:** "A joint venture can deliver more than growth"; "Achieving competitive advantage"; "Achieving resilience for your business during difficult times"; "Achieving resilient growth during challenging times"; "Acquisitions: A growth strategy to consider"; "Attracting and retaining long-term corporate sponsors"; "Celebrate Selling: The Consultative Relationship Way"; "A Joint Venture Can Deliver More Than Growth"; "Achieving Competitive Advantage"; "Achieving Resilience for Your Business During Difficult Times"; "Balancing Revenue Growth with Growth of a Business"; "Capture Your Competitive Advantage"; "Ease Succession Planning"; "Games Employees Play"; "How to Spark Innovation in an Existing Company"; "Managers demands must change with growth"; "Motivating Generation employees"; "Knowing when to hire ratios provide answers"; "Better customer service can bring black ink". **Seminars:** Strategic Leadership; Managing Innovation; Breaking Through Classic Barriers to Growth; Energize Your Enterprise; Capture Your Competitive Advantage; Four Entrepreneurial Styles; Perservance and Resilience; Real-Time Strategic Planning/RO1.
Special Services: The Growth Strategist™.

42485 ■ **Effectiveness Resource Group Inc.**
2529 170th Pl. SE
PO Box 7149
Bellevue, WA 98008-5520
Ph:(206)949-4171
Fax:(425)957-9186
Co. E-mail: don@consultdon.com
URL: http://www.consultdon.com
Contact: Donald H. Swartz, President
E-mail: dhsergsri@aol.com
Scope: Provides problem solving help to client organizations in public and private sectors so they can release and mobilize the full potential of their personnel to achieve productive and satisfying results. Emphasis is on technical or human productivity improvement projects and systems, total human resource systems design and implementation, and a whole systems approach to organizational change design and implementation. Serves private industries as well as government agencies. Consults with both internal and external consultants via e-mail and phone. Also offers executive coaching. **Seminars:** Life/Work Goals Exploration; Influencing Change Thru Consultation; Designing and Leading Participative Meetings; Designing, Leading and Managing Change; Project Management and Leadership; Performance Management; Productive Management of Differences; Performance Correction.

42486 ■ **Goldore Consulting Inc.**
120-5 St. NW, Ste. 1
PO Box 590
Linden, AB, Canada T0M 1J0
Ph:(403)546-4208
Fax:(403)546-4208
Co. E-mail: goldore@leadershipessentials.com
Contact: Robert A. Orr, President
E-mail: orr@leadershipessentials.com
Scope: Provides consulting service in leadership and management skills. Industries served: primarily charities, non-profits; some businesses. **Seminars:** The Challenge Of Leadership.

42487 ■ **Harris Advertising**
G4162 Fenton Rd.
Flint, MI 48507-3637
Ph:(810)232-4120
Contact: Susan Kay Harris, President
Scope: Marketing and advertising firm provides advertisement services to private industries as well as government agencies.

42488 ■ **Norman E Joe and Associates**
700 - 6th Ave. SW, Ste. 100
Calgary, AB, Canada T2P 0T8
Ph:(952)595-8000
Fax:(952)595-0679
Co. E-mail: info@focustools.com
URL: http://www.focustools.com
E-mail: info@focustools.com
Scope: Consultants specializing in the development and implementation of problem-solving, decision-making and team processes for managers/supervisors and key people in a variety of organizations. Industries served: manufacturing, industrial, insurance/banking, healthcare and government. **Publica-**

tions: "What is the Decision Leader Review"; "Decision Focus Executive Learning". **Seminars:** How To Create Innovative Solutions On Demand, Jul, 2006; Essential tools to solve problems, make decisions and execute plans, faster and more effectively, Jul, 2006; Decision Focus; Creative Focus; The Focus; Team Focus. **Special Services:** Decision Focus 7.0^R.

42489 ■ **Organizational Improvement Associates L.L.C.**
40 Gilbert St.
Ridgefield, CT 06877
Ph:(203)417-4957
Fax:(203)244-5737
Co. E-mail: daveknibbe@oiaus.com
URL: http://www.oiaus.com
Contact: Valentina Espinosa-Shimizu, Principle
E-mail: daveknibbe@oiaus.com
Scope: Specializes in high-performance team development, executive coaching, employee development programs, performance management and reward systems and dispute mediation. Industries served: Consumer products, telecommunications, finance, health-care, amusement/leisure, hospitality/lodging, retail and pharmaceuticals.

42490 ■ **Performance Dynamics Group L.L.C.**
One Ridge Rd.
Green Brook, NJ 08812
Ph:(732)537-0381
Free: 888-720-7337
Co. E-mail: info@performance-dynamics.net
URL: http://www.performance-dynamics.net
Contact: Mark E. Green, President
E-mail: mark.green@atsperformance-dynamics.net
Scope: An organizational consulting group whose approach to learning and employee empowerment is designed to be both effective and efficient in achieving the specific knowledge and skill goals of a given program, in developing changes in thinking and behavior and also to foster and develop initiative, self confidence, creative problem-solving ability and interpersonal effectiveness of all participants. Brings improvement in areas of revenue growth, profitability, sales, marketing effectiveness, and employee and customer loyalty. **Seminars:** Accelerated Approach to Change; Commitment to Quality; Managing Cultural Diversity; The Corporate Energizer; The Power Pole Experience; Team Assessment; Self-Directed Work Teams.

42491 ■ **Sanford Consulting**
52 Perry Corners Rd., RR 1
PO Box 314A
Amenia, NY 12501
Ph:(845)373-8960
Fax:(845)373-8961
Co. E-mail: sanford@mohawk.com
Contact: Anne Sanford, President
E-mail: sanford@mohawk.com
Scope: Helps businesses find, sell, to, and keep customers. Provides management and marketing services, including problem analysis and solution design for new business development, market analysis and segmentation, departmental organization and administrative policies and procedures.

Industries served: small business, telecommunications, professional services, health care and nonprofits in the continental United States. **Seminars:** Trade show success; Finding customers; Business attitudes at not for profit and others.

42492 ■ The Walk The Talk Co.
1100 Parker Sq., Ste. 250
Flower Mound, TX 75028-7458
Ph:(972)899-8300
Free: 800-888-2811
Fax:(972)899-9291
Co. E-mail: info@walkthetalk.com
URL: http://www.walkthetalk.com
Contact: Doug Westmoreland, VP of Operations
E-mail: ericharvey@walkthetalk.com
Scope: Assists a wide variety of organizations in implementing proprietary performance management system developed by the firm which concentrates on individual responsibility and decision making instead of disciplinary penalties. Helps organizations develop and implement peer review, a proven system that helps solve employee problems in a remarkable way-through employees and an evaluation process software is used whereby feedback is compiled from a full-range of sources, including a self-evaluation, leadership development workshops and keynote presentations and publications. **Publications:** "Positive Discipline"; "Leadership Secrets of Santa Claus"; "Start Right-Stay Right"; "Walk Awhile in My Shoes"; "Listen Up, Leader!"; "Five Star Teamwork"; "Ethics4Everyone"; "Leadership Courage"; "The Manager's Communication Handbook"; "180 Ways to Walk the Recognition Talk"; "The Manager's Coaching Handbook"; "The Best Leadership Advice I Ever Got"; "Power Exchange". **Seminars:** Walk the Talk; Coaching for Continuous Improvement; Managing Employee Performance; Customized Management Development Forums; Keynote presentations; Leadership Development Workshops; Consulting Services and Publications; Customer service training; Ethics and Values training.

RESEARCH CENTERS

42493 ■ Institute for the Development of Emotional and Life Skills
4400 East West Hwy.
Bethesda, MD 20814
Ph:(301)986-1479
Fax:(301)680-3756
Co. E-mail: bguerney@nire.org
Contact: Dr. Bernard Guerney Jr., Pres.
E-mail: bguerney@nire.org
Scope: Applied studies of marriage and family intervention, parenting and parent education programs, filial therapy, therapeutic programs for parent and children, relationship enhancement programs, interpersonal relationships, communication and problem-solving skills, and premarital, marital, and family enrichment programs. **Educational Activities:** Training programs for professionals and the public.

42494 ■ Manchester College–Peace Studies Institute–Program in Conflict Resolution
604 E College Ave.
North Manchester, IN 46962-1276
Ph:(260)982-5343
Fax:(260)982-5043
Co. E-mail: klgraybrown@manchester.edu
URL: http://www.manchester.edu/academics/departments/peace_studies/index.shtml
Contact: Katy Gray Brown PhD, Dir.
E-mail: klgraybrown@manchester.edu
Scope: Peace, societal violence, social responsibility, socially-responsible investing. **Publications:** Bulletin of the Peace Studies Institute (annually); Connections Newsletter (quarterly). **Educational Activities:** Church as Peacemaker and the Ropchan Lecture series (5/year).

42495 ■ National Institute of Relationship Enhancement
4400 East-West Hwy., Ste. 28
Bethesda, MD 20814-4501
Ph:(301)986-1479
Fax:(301)680-3756
Co. E-mail: niremd@nire.org
URL: http://www.nire.org
Contact: Dr. Bernard Guerney Jr., Founder/Dir.
E-mail: niremd@nire.org
Scope: Interpersonal and conflict resolution skills for individuals and organization personnel, new methods for enhancing family and personnel relationships, and mental health education and interpersonal skills. **Educational Activities:** Practicum training; Workshops for training professionals, organizational personnel, and families.

Research and Development

START-UP INFORMATION

42496 ■ *Entrepreneurship: Frameworks and Empirical Investigations from Forthcoming Leaders of European Research*
Pub: Elsevier Science and Technology Books
Ed: Johan Wiklund; Dimo Dimov; Jerome A. Katz; Dean Shepherd. **Released:** July 2006. **Price:** $99.95. **Description:** Entrepreneurial research and theory cover the early growth of research-based startups and the role of learning in international entrepreneurship, focusing on Europe.

42497 ■ "Incubator Cooking Up Expansion Plans" in *Business First Columbus* (Vol. 25, December 5, 2008, No. 15, pp.)
Pub: American City Business Journals
Ed: Kevin Kemper. **Description:** United States-based Science and Technology Campus Corporation is planning to build additional office space in Columbus, Ohio. The site is designed to accommodate three large tenants. Comment from company executives are presented.

42498 ■ "Online Fortunes" in *Small Business Opportunities* (Fall 2008)
Pub: Entrepreneur Media Inc.
Description: Fifty hot, e-commerce enterprises for the aspiring entrepreneur to consider are featured; virtual assistants, marketing services, party planning, travel services, researching, web design and development, importing as well as creating an online store are among the businesses featured.

42499 ■ *Small Business Tool Kit*
Pub: Lessons Professional Publishing
Ed: Linda M. Magoon. **Released:** April 10, 2010. **Price:** $40.00. **Description:** When starting a business, new managers and entrepreneurs require many resources to get the company up and running successfully. This book covers a wide range of topics that are critical for any new business owner.

42500 ■ "Troy Patent Law Firm Launches Rent-Free Tech Incubator" in *Crain's Detroit Business* (Vol. 25, June 8, 2009, No. 23, pp. 4)
Pub: Crain Communications Inc. - Detroit
Ed: Tom Henderson. **Description:** Young Basile Hanlon MacFarlane & Helmholdt PC, a patent law firm located in Troy, Michigan has created a small, rent-free technology incubator on site. The incubator will be called North Woodward Tech Incubator and has room for four or five startups. The incubator is for the earliest or pre-seed stage for entrepreneurs who have not yet gotten significant investment capital.

42501 ■ "Wanted: Angels in the Country" in *Austin Business JournalInc.* (Vol. 28, July 18, 2008, No. 18, pp. 1)
Pub: American City Business Journals
Ed: Laura Hipp. **Description:** A proposal is being pushed forward by managers of Texas' Emerging Technology Fund to create an angel investors' network. The proposal is asking that tax credits for

those who invest in research and development projects be granted in order to boost the number of technology companies in the state.

REFERENCE WORKS

42502 ■ "The 100 Fastest-Growing Companies" in *Hispanic Business* (Vol. 30, July-August 2008, No. 7-8, pp. 22)
Pub: Hispanic Business, Inc.
Ed: Michael Bowker. **Description:** CEO's of the five fastest growing Hispanic-owned companies discuss the success of their companies; most of them attribute their success to proper investment and diversification, effective innovations and seeing growth opportunities where others see roadblocks.

42503 ■ "2011 U.S. Smart Grid – Saving Energy/Saving Money" in *Ecology,Environment & Conservation Business* (October 8, 2011, pp. 3)
Pub: HighBeam Research
Description: Highlights of the '2011 U.S. Smart Grid –Saving Energy/Saving Money Customers' Prospective Demand-Response assesses residential energy consumers' willingness to decrease their power consumption in order to mitigate power issues. Statistical details included.

42504 ■ "Abraxis Bets On Biotech Hub" in *Business Journal-Serving Phoenix and the Valley of the Sun* (Vol. 10, November 9, 2007, No. 28)
Pub: American City Business Journals, Inc.
Ed: Angela Gonzales. **Description:** Abraxis BioScience Inc. purchased a 200,000 square foot manufacturing facility in Phoenix, Arizona from Watson Pharmaceuticals Inc. The company has the technology to allow chemotherapy drugs to be injected directly into tumor cell membranes. A human protein, albumin is used to deliver the chemotherapy.

42505 ■ "Adapt or Die" in *Black Enterprise* (Vol. 38, August 2008, No. 12, pp. 127)
Pub: Earl G. Graves Publishing Co. Inc.
Ed: Oguntoyinbo Lekan. **Description:** Turbulence in the domestic auto industry is hitting auto suppliers hard and black suppliers, the majority of whom contract with the Big Three, are just beginning to establish relationships with import car manufacturers. The more savvy CEOs are adopting new technologies in order to weather the downturn in the economy and in the industry as a whole.

42506 ■ "Aggenix Completes Merger with German Giant" in *Houston Business Journal* (Vol. 40, December 25, 2009, No. 33, pp. 2)
Pub: American City Business Journals
Ed: Mary Ann Azevedo. **Description:** Agennix Inc. has completed its transformation into a German company after Germany-based GPC Biotech merged into the former publicly traded Agennix AG. One quarter of Agennix's 60 employees will remain in Houston. Details on Agennix's drug trials are examined.

42507 ■ "Alberta Star Begins Phase 2 Drilling On Its Eldorado & Contact Lake IOCG & Uranium Projects" in *Canadian Corporate News* (May 16, 2007)
Pub: Comtex News Network Inc.
Description: Profile of Alberta Star Development Corp., a Canadian mineral exploration company that identifies, acquires, and finances advanced stage exploration projects in Canada, and its current undertaking of its 2007 drill program in which the company intends to begin accelerating its uranium and poly-metallic exploration and drilling activities on all of its drill targets for 2007 now that it has been granted its permits.

42508 ■ "Angel Investments Tripled in 2009" in *Austin Business JournalInc.* (Vol. 29, January 8, 2010, No. 44, pp. 1)
Pub: American City Business Journals
Ed: Christopher Calnan. **Description:** Central Texas Angel Network (CTAN) has invested $3.5 million in 12 ventures, which include 10 in Austin, Texas in 2009 to triple the amount it invested during 2008. The largest recipient of CTAN's investments is life sciences, which attracted 20 percent of the capital, while software investments fell to 18 percent. The new screening process that helps startups secure CTAN capital is explored.

42509 ■ "Another Baby Step" in *Canadian Business* (Vol. 81, March 31, 2008, No. 5, pp. 32)
Pub: Rogers Media
Ed: Andrew Wahl. **Description:** Discusses the Canadian government's federal budget which makes it easier to tap into tax credits for corporate research and development. However, these steps do not really go far enough to boost industrial research levels in Canada. Making these incentives at least partially refundable could help during tough economic times.

42510 ■ "Apples, Decoded: WSU Scientist Unraveling the Fruit's Genetics" in *Puget Sound Business Journal* (Vol. 29, September 5, 2008, No. 20)
Pub: American City Business Journals
Ed: Clay Holtzman. **Description:** Washington State University researcher is working to map the apple's genome in order to gain information about how the fruit grows, looks and tastes. His work, funded by a research grant from the US Department of Agriculture and the Washington Apple Commission is crucial to improving the state's position as an apple-producing region.

42511 ■ "Ask Inc." in *Inc.* (October 2007, pp. 73-74)
Pub: Gruner & Jahr USA Publishing
Description: An online marketing research firm investigates the use of online communities such as MySpace and Second life in order to recruit individuals to answer surveys.

42512 ■ "Asterand Eyes Jump to Ann Arbor; TechTown Tenant" in *Crain's Detroit Business* (Vol. 25, June 22, 2009)
Pub: Crain Communications Inc. - Detroit
Ed: Tom Henderson. **Description:** Asterand PLC is considering a move to Ann Arbor from its current loca-

tion as anchor tenant at TechTown, an incubator and technology park associated with Wayne State University. The university believes the Ann Arbor location's rent is too expensive for the tissue bank company.

42513 ■ "ATI Now Ready to Pounce on Biotech" in *Austin Business JournalInc.* **(Vol. 28, August 22, 2008, No. 23, pp. 1)**
Pub: American City Business Journals

Ed: Laura Hipp. **Description:** Austin Technology Incubator has entered the biotechnology sector through a program of the University of Texas incubator. The company's bioscience program was set off by a grant from the City of Austin worth $125,000. The growth of Austin's biotechnology sector is examined.

42514 ■ "Attorney Guides Biotech Company in $6 Million Initial Public Offering" in *Miami Daily Business Review* **(March 26, 2008)**
Pub: ALM Media Inc.

Description: In order to raise capital to engage in a full-scale trial of MyoCell to receive clinical approval, Bioheart Inc., launched an initial public offering. Bioheart researches and develops cell therapies to treat heart damage.

42515 ■ "Auctions and Bidding: a Guide for Computer Scientists" in *ACM Computing Surveys* **(Vol. 43, Summer 2011, No. 2, pp. 10)**
Pub: Association for Computing Machinery

Ed: Simon Parsons, Juan A. Rodriguez-Aguilar, Mark Klein. **Description:** There are various actions: single dimensional, multi-dimensional, single-sided, double-sided, first-price, second-price, English, Dutch, Japanese, sealed-bid, and these have been extensively discussed and analyzed in economics literature. This literature is surveyed from a computer science perspective, primarily from the viewpoint of computer scientists who are interested in learning about auction theory, and to provide pointers into the economics literature for those who want a deeper technical understanding. In addition, since auctions are an increasingly important topic in computer science, the article also looks at work on auctions from the computer science literature. The aim is to identify what both bodies of work tell us about creating electronic auctions.

42516 ■ "Auxilium Drug's New Use: Putting Squeeze On Cellulite" in *Philadelphia Business Journal* **(Vol. 30, September 16, 2011, No. 31, pp. 1)**
Pub: American City Business Journals Inc.

Ed: John George. **Description:** Auxilium Pharmaceuticals and BioSpecifics Technologies are getting on with their plans of finding new uses for their drug Xiaflex, a possible treatment for cellulite. The two firms have dismissed their pending litigations and mapped out an amended licensing agreement for their search for the potential uses of the drug.

42517 ■ "Avoiding Invention Scams" in *Black Enterprise* **(Vol. 37, January 2007, No. 6, pp. 46)**
Pub: Earl G. Graves Publishing Co. Inc.

Ed: James C. Johnson. **Description:** Invention promotion firms provide inventors assistance in developing a prototype for product development. It is important to research these companies before making a commitment to work with them because there are a number of these firms that are not legitimate and have caused independent inventors to lose thousands of dollars by making false claims as to the market potential of the inventions.

42518 ■ "Banking on Cord Blood" in *Business Journal-Serving Phoenix & the Valley of the Sun* **(Vol. 31, September 10, 2010, No. 1, pp. 1)**
Pub: Phoenix Business Journal

Ed: Angela Gonzales. **Description:** Celebration Stem Cell Centre obtained contracts from Mercy Gilbert Medical Center and its two sister hospitals, St. Joseph Hospital and Medical Center in Phoenix, Arizona and Chandler Regional Medical Center. The contract will facilitate the donation of unused umbilical cord blood for research.

42519 ■ "Bar Hopping: Your Numbers At a Glance" in *Inc.* **(January 2008, pp. 44-45)**
Pub: Gruner & Jahr USA Publishing

Ed: Michael Fitzgerald. **Description:** Software that helps any company analyze data include Crystal Xcelsius, a program that takes data from Excel documents and turns them into animated gauges, charts and graphs; CashView, a Web-based application that tracks receivables and payables; iDashboards, a Web-based programs that produces animated gauges, maps, pie charts and graphs; Corda Human Capital Management, that transforms stats like head count, productivity, and attrition into graphs and dials; NetSuite, a Web-based application that tracks key indicators; and Cognos Now, that gauges, dials, and graphs data.

42520 ■ "Being Big By Design" in *Canadian Business* **(Vol. 82, April 27, 2009, No. 7, pp. 39)**
Pub: Rogers Media

Ed: Andrew Wahl. **Description:** Gennum expects that its planned acquisition of Tundra Semiconductor will expand its market presence and leverage its research and development better than working alone. The proposed friendly acquisition could challenge Zarlink Semiconductor as the largest Canadian semiconductor firm in terms of revenue. The merger could expand Gennum's addressable market to about $2 billion.

42521 ■ "Biotechnology Wants a Lead Role" in *Business North Carolina* **(Vol. 28, March 2008, No. 3, pp. 14)**
Pub: Business North Carolina

Description: According to experts, North Carolina is poised as a leader in the biotechnology sector. Highlights of a recent roundtable discussion sponsored by the North Carolina Biotechnology Center in Research Triangle Park are presented.

42522 ■ "Bloomberg Law Upgraded Its Online Legal Research Platform" in *Information Today* **(Vol. 28, September 2011, No. 8, pp. 28)**
Pub: Information Today, Inc.

Description: Bloomberg Law upgraded its online legal research platform for law practices. The new services includes a redesigned interface, improved search capabilities, and expanded collaboration and workflow features, while maintaining it comprehensive law resources such as mergers and acquisitions, antitrust, and securities.

42523 ■ "Border Boletin: UA to Take Lie-Detector Kiosk to Poland" in *Arizona Daily Star* **(September 14, 2010)**
Pub: Arizona Daily Star

Ed: Brady McCombs. **Description:** University of Arizona's National Center for Border Security and Immigration Research will send a team to Warsaw, Poland to show border guards from 27 European Union countries the center's Avatar Kiosk. The Avatar technology is designed for use at border ports and airports to assist Customs officers detect individuals who are lying.

42524 ■ "Born of Culture of Innovation" in *Canadian Business* **(Vol. 81, October 27, 2008, No. 18, pp. 98)**
Pub: Rogers Media Ltd.

Description: MaRS, an independent nonprofit organization, aims to better capture the relevant commercial potential of Ontario's research and to connect the worlds of science, business, and capital as well as to stimulate a culture of innovation. Profile of MaRS and its 'MaRS Innovation' program is included.

42525 ■ *Borrowing Brilliance: The Six Steps to Business Innovation by Building on the Ideas of Others*
Pub: Gotham

Ed: David Kord Murray. **Price:** $26.00. **Description:** The author builds the case that cherry-picking the ideas of others is a vital part of the research and development process for any small firm.

42526 ■ "Bridging the Worlds" in *Academy of Management Journal* **(Vol. 50, No. 5, October 2007, pp. 1043)**
Pub: Academy of Management

Ed: Lise Saari. **Description:** Need to transfer human resource research information published in journals to practitioners and organizations is investigated, along with suggestions on ways of achieving this goal.

42527 ■ "Business as Usual at RIM, Balsillie Says" in *Globe & Mail* **(March 6, 2007, pp. B1)**
Pub: CTVglobemedia Publishing Inc.

Ed: Simon Avery. **Description:** The continuation of normal business at Research In Motion Ltd., after the resignation of Jim Balsillie from the chairman's post, is described. The investigation of securities fraud at Research In Motion Ltd., and the continuation of Jim Balsillie as the co-chief executive officer of the company is discussed.

42528 ■ "California Company Suing City's Lupin Over its Generic Diabetes Drug" in *Baltimore Business Journal* **(Vol. 27, January 1, 2010)**
Pub: American City Business Journals

Ed: Gary Haber. **Description:** California-based Depomed Inc. is suing Baltimore, Maryland-based Lupin Pharmaceuticals Inc. and its parent company in India over the patents to a diabetes drug. Lupin allegedly infringed on Depomed's four patents for Glumetza when it filed for permission to sell its own version of the drug with the US Food and Drug Administration. Details on generic pharmaceutical manufacturer tactics are discussed.

42529 ■ "Can America Invent Its Way Back?" in *Business Week* **(September 22, 2008, No. 4100, pp. 52)**
Pub: McGraw-Hill Companies, Inc.

Description: Business leaders as well as economists agree that innovative new products, services and ways of doing business may be the only way in which America can survive the downward spiral of the economy; innovation economics may be the answer and may even provide enough growth to enable Americans to prosper in the years to come.

42530 ■ "Canadian Research Generates Innovation and Prosperity" in *Canadian Business* **(Vol. 81, October 27, 2008, No. 18, pp. 87)**
Pub: Rogers Media Ltd.

Description: Universities play a key role in helping Canadians achieve prosperity, competitiveness, and quality of life by conducting more than a third of Canada's research. Research in universities help train graduates to apply sophisticated knowledge to real problems.

42531 ■ "Cancer-Fighting Entrepreneurs" in *Austin Business Journal* **(Vol. 31, August 5, 2011, No. 22, pp. 1)**
Pub: American City Business Journals Inc.

Ed: Sandra Zaragoza. **Description:** Cancer Prevention and Research Institute of Texas has invested $10 million in recruiting known faculty to the University of Texas. The move is seen to bolster Austin's position as a major cancer research market. The institute has awarded grants to researchers Jonghwan Kim, Guangbin Dong and Kyle Miller.

42532 ■ "Cannabis Science Signs Exclusive and Non-Exclusive Agreement with Prescription Vending Machines" in *Benzinga.com* **(October 29, 2011)**
Pub: Benzinga.com

Ed: Benzinga Staff. **Description:** Cannabis Science Inc., a biotech company developing pharmaceutical cannabis products has partnered with Prescription Vending Machines Inc. and its principal Vincent Meddizadeh to provide industry specific consulting and advisory services to Cannabis Science.

42533 ■ "Caterpillar to Expand Research, Production in China" in *Chicago Tribune* **(August 27, 2008)**
Pub: McClatchy-Tribune Information Services

Ed: James P. Miller. **Description:** Caterpillar Inc., the Peoria-based heavy-equipment manufacturer, plans to establish a new research-and-development center at the site of its rapidly growing campus in Wuxi.

42534 ■ "Clean Wind Energy Tower Transitions from R&D Stage Company" in *Professional Services Close-Up* (September 30, 2011)
Pub: Close-Up Media

Description: Clean Wind Energy designed and is developing large downdraft towers that use benevolent, non-toxic natural elements to generate electricity and clean water. The firm is closing its internally staffed engineering office in Warrenton, Virginia and transitioning a development team to oversee and coordinate industry consultants and advisors to construct their first dual renewable energy tower.

42535 ■ "The CMO of Consequence" in *Business Strategy Review* (Vol. 21, Autumn 2010, No. 3, pp. 42)
Pub: Wiley-Blackwell

Ed: D. Eric Boyd, Rajesh K. Chandy, Marcus Cunha. **Description:** Do chief marketing officers matter? Some say that CMOs have limited effect on corporate performance and don't add significant value to the firm. The authors agree that the job in many firms is in great peril, but their research has uncovered why the contributions of some CMOs are invaluable.

42536 ■ "Commercial Water Efficiency Initiatives Announced" in *Contractor* (Vol. 56, November 2009, No. 11, pp. 5)
Pub: Penton Media, Inc.

Ed: Robert P. Mader. **Description:** Plumbing engineers John Koeller and Bill Gauley are developing a testing protocol for commercial toilets. The team said commercial toilets should have a higher level of flush performance than residential toilets for certification. The Environmental Protection Agency's WaterSense program wants to expand the program into the commercial/institutional sector.

42537 ■ "Congestion Relief" in *Canadian Business* (Vol. 80, February 12, 2007, No. 4, pp. 31)
Pub: Rogers Media

Ed: Andrea Jezovit. **Description:** The development of a satellite-based system for traffic management including paying for parking fees by Skymeter Corp. is discussed.

42538 ■ "Craig Muhlhauser" in *Canadian Business* (Vol. 81, September 15, 2008, No. 14-15, pp. 6)
Pub: Rogers Media Ltd.

Ed: Andrew Wahl. **Description:** Interview with Craig Muhlhauser who is the CEO of Celestica, a manufacturing company that provides services for the electronics sector; Muhlhauser discusses the company's restructuring program, which he feels was the secret to their surprising first-quarter results. Muhlhauser states that the company is operating with more forward visibility and that understanding the opportunities during the current economic situation presents the biggest challenge.

42539 ■ "A Curious Appeal (Market for Scientific Toys)" in *Playthings* (Vol. 106, October 1, 2008, No. 9, pp. 26)
Pub: Reed Business Information

Ed: Pamela Brill. **Description:** Science and nature toys are still popular with children. Kits allow kids to make candy, soap, grow miniature gardens, catch bugs and more. These hands-on kits have manufacturers watching trends to create more toys in this category.

42540 ■ "Dean Foods" in *Ice Cream Reporter* (Vol. 23, September 20, 2010, No. 10, pp. 8)
Pub: Ice Cream Reporter

Description: Dean Foods promoted Joseph Scalzo to President and Chief Operating Officer to oversee the firm's operational turnaround and near-term strategic initiatives as well as business units. Key functions will include worldwide supply chain and research and development.

42541 ■ "Defense Contractor May Expand Locally; BAE Systems Ramps Up Vehicle Prototypes" in *Crain's Detroit Business* (March 24, 2008)
Pub: Crain Communications, Inc.

Ed: Chad Halcom. **Description:** Profile of BAE Systems, a defense contractor, that has built a prototype in the highly competitive Joint Light Tactical Vehicle project; the company has also completed its prototype RG33L Mine Resistant Recovery Maintenance Vehicle and has plans for expansion.

42542 ■ "Describing the Entrepreneurial Profile" in *International Journal of Entrepreneurship and Small Business* (Vol. 11, November 1, 2010)
Pub: Publishers Communication Group

Ed: Serena Cubico, Elisa Bortolani, Giuseppe Favretto, Riccardo Sartori. **Description:** An illustration of metric characteristics and selected research applications of an instrument that can be used to define aptitude for an entrepreneurial profile (created in the 1990s) is examined. The entrepreneurial aptitude test (TAI) describes entrepreneurial potential with regard to eight factors.

42543 ■ "Dow AgroSciences Buys Wheat Breeding Firm in Pacific Northwest" in *Farm Industry News* (July 29, 2011)
Pub: Penton Business Media Inc.

Description: Dow AgroSciences purchased Northwest Plant Breeding Company, a cereals breeding station in Washington in 2011. The acquisition will help Dow expand its Hyland Seeds certified wheat seed program foundation in the Pacific Northwest. Financial terms of the deal were not disclosed.

42544 ■ "DuPontas Pioneer Hi-Bred, Evogene to Develop Rust-Resistant Soybean Varieties" in *Farm Industry News* (November 22, 2011)
Pub: Penton Business Media Inc.

Ed: Karen McMahon. **Description:** DuPont and Evogene have signed a new contract to work together to develop resistance in soybeans to rust. Financial terms of the agreement were not disclosed.

42545 ■ "East Coast Solar" in *Contractor* (Vol. 57, February 2010, No. 2, pp. 17)
Pub: Penton Media, Inc.

Ed: Dave Yates. **Description:** U.S. Department of Energy's Solar Decathlon lets 20 college student-led teams from around the world compete to design and build a solar-powered home. A mechanical contractor discusses his work as an advisor during the competition.

42546 ■ "Ed Otto, Director of Biotechnology at RCCC" in *Charlotte Observer* (February 8, 2007)
Pub: Knight-Ridder/Tribune Business News

Ed: Gail Smith-Arrants. **Description:** Profile of Ed Otto, director of biotechnology at Rowan-Cabarrus Community College. Before taking the position at RCCC, Otto directed the Food and Drug Administration office responsible for regulating cellular, tissue and gene therapies products.

42547 ■ "EMU, Spark Plan Business Incubator for Ypsilanti" in *Crain's Detroit Business* (Vol. 23, October 15, 2007, No. 42, pp. 3)
Pub: Crain Communications Inc. - Detroit

Ed: Chad Halcom. **Description:** Eastern Michigan University is seeking federal grants and other funding for a new business incubator program that would be in cooperation with Ann Arbor Spark. The site would become a part of a network of three Spark incubator programs with a focus on innovation in biotechnology and pharmaceuticals.

42548 ■ "Ending the Ebola Death Sentence" in *Canadian Business* (Vol. 83, August 17, 2010, No. 13-14, pp. 22)
Pub: Rogers Media Ltd.

Ed: Michael McCullough. **Description:** US Army Medical Research Institute of Infectious Diseases made a $140 million agreement with Tekmira Pharmaceuticals Corporation to develop both a drug delivery system and delivery technology for curing the Ebola virus. Tekmira's delivery technology, which has been shown to halt Ebola in laboratory animals, might be the key to finding a cure.

42549 ■ "Entrepreneurial Orientation and Firm Performance" in *Journal of Small Business and Entrepreneurship* (Vol. 23, Winter 2010, No. 1)
Pub: Canadian Council for Small Business and Entrepreneurship

Description: The article develops a theoretical model of the relationship between firm-level entrepreneurship and firm performance. This model is intended to further clarify the consequences of an 'entrepreneurial orientation', paying particular attention to the differential relationship that exists between the three sub-dimensions of entrepreneurial orientation and firm performance. Included in the theoretical model are other important variables (such as organizational structure and environmental characteristics) that may impact the EO-performance relationship. Propositions are developed regarding the various configurations of the sub-dimensions of EO and organizational structure that would be most appropriate in a given environmental context. Future research may also benefit from considering the important role that organizational strategy and life cycle stage play in this model. The implications of this model for both researchers and managers are discussed.

42550 ■ "The Executive Brain" in *Canadian Business* (Vol. 80, October 22, 2007, No. 21, pp. 41)
Pub: Rogers Media

Ed: Rachel Pulfer. **Description:** Studies by Jordan Petersen, Frank Schmidt, and John Hunter show that leaders have highly evolved capacities to think using the prefrontal cortex of the brain. Inspirational leadership ability is located in the parietal lobe. Other details of the research are discussed.

42551 ■ "Family Business Research" in *International Journal of Entrepreneurship and Small Business* (Vol. 12, December 3, 2010, No. 1)
Pub: Publishers Communication Group

Ed: A. Bakr Ibrahim, Jean B. McGuire. **Description:** Assessment of the growing field of family business and suggestions for an integrated framework. The paper addresses a number of key issues facing family business research.

42552 ■ "Feedback From Payers Will Be Vital For Future Developments" in *Farmer's Weekly* (March 28, 2008, No. 320)
Pub: Reed Business Information

Description: Potato Council staff will carry on working with levy payers to retain the same high caliber of marketing, research and other activities.

42553 ■ "Five New Scientists Bring Danforth Center $16 Million" in *Saint Louis Business Journal* (Vol. 32, October 7, 2011, No. 6, pp. 1)
Pub: Saint Louis Business Journal

Ed: E.B. Solomont. **Description:** Donald Danforth Plant Science Center's appointment of five new lead scientists has increased its federal funding by $16 million. Cornell University scientist Tom Brutnell is one of the five new appointees.

42554 ■ "Flu is a Booster for Firms Here" in *Philadelphia Business Journal* (Vol. 28, September 25, 2009, No. 32, pp. 1)
Pub: American City Business Journals

Ed: John George. **Description:** GlaxoSmithKline, AstraZeneca, CSL Biotherapies, and Sanofi Aventis were awarded contract by the US Government to supply swine flu vaccines. It is estimated that global sales of the vaccine could reach billions of dollars.

42555 ■ "Flue Vaccines are Going Green" in *Canadian Business* (Vol. 83, September 14, 2010, No. 15, pp. 24)
Pub: Rogers Media Ltd.

Ed: Angelia Chapman. **Description:** Quebec-based Medicago has found a solution to the bottleneck in the production of influenza vaccines by using plant-based processes instead of egg-based systems.

Medicago's US Department of Defense funded research has produced the technology that speeds up the production time for vaccines by almost two-thirds. Insights into Medicago's patented process are also given.

42556 ■ "Funding Drought Stalls Biotech Incubators" in *Saint Louis Business Journal* **(Vol. 31, July 29, 2011, No. 49, pp. 1)**
Pub: Saint Louis Business Journal
Ed: Angela Mueller. Description: Economic slow-down took its toll on cash-strapped startups that fill incubators such as the Bio-Research and Development Growth (BRDG) Park in Creve Coeur, Missouri and the Center for Emerging Technologies in Midtown St. Louis. BRDG put a hold on construction of of its two buildings.

42557 ■ "The Future of Work" in *Business Strategy Review* **(Vol. 21, Autumn 2010, No. 3, pp. 16)**
Pub: Blackwell Publishers Ltd.
Ed: Lynda Gratton. Description: Work is universal. But how, why, where and when we work has never been so open to individual interpretation. The certainties of the past have been replaced by ambiguity, questions and the steady hum of technology. Now, in a groundbreaking research project covering 21 global companies and more than 200 executives, the author is making sense of the future of work.

42558 ■ "Galvanizing the Scientific Community" in *Information Today* **(Vol. 26, February 2009, No. 2, pp. 20)**
Pub: Information Today, Inc.
Ed: Barbara Brynko. Description: Profile of John Haynes, newly appointed vice president of publishing for the American Institute of Physics; the Institute consists of ten organizations specializing in STM publishing as well as providing publishing services for over 170 science and engineering journals.

42559 ■ "Giving Biotech Startups a Hand" in *Philadelphia Business Journal* **(Vol. 28, January 8, 2010, No. 47, pp. 1)**
Pub: American City Business Journals
Ed: John George. Description: Elkins Park, Pennsylvania-based BioStrategy Partners is a virtual life sciences incubator that is seeking to improve the dull ranking of Philadelphia in the small business vitality index of life sciences. BioStrategy provides technology and business development services to startup life sciences companies and university-based research projects.

42560 ■ *Global Electronic Business Research: Opportunities and Directions*
Pub: Idea Group Publishing
Ed: Nabeel A.Y. Al-Qirim. Released: December 2005. Price: $ 74.95. Description: Importance electronic commerce research plays in small to medium-sized enterprises in various countries.

42561 ■ *Handbook of Quality Research in Entrepreneurship*
Pub: Edward Elgar Publishing, Incorporated
Ed: Neergaard. Released: March 2007. Price: $215.00. Description: Advice for researchers to make informed choices and to design more stringent and sophisticated studies in the field of entrepreneurship.

42562 ■ "The Hidden Advantages of Quiet Bosses" in *Harvard Business Review* **(Vol. 88, December 2010, No. 12, pp. 28)**
Pub: Harvard Business School Publishing
Ed: Adam M. Grant, Francesca Gino, David A. Hofmann. Description: Research on organizations behavior indicates that, while extroverts most often become managers, introvert managers paired with proactive employees make a highly efficient and effective combination.

42563 ■ "Hopkins' Security, Reputation Face Challenges in Wake of Slaying" in *Baltimore Business Journal* **(Vol. 28, August 6, 2010, No. 13)**
Pub: Baltimore Business Journal
Ed: Gary Haber. Description: The slaying of Johns Hopkins University researcher Stephen Pitcairn has not tarnished the reputation of the elite school in Baltimore, Maryland among students. Maintaining Hopkins' reputation is important since it is Baltimore's largest employer with nearly 32,000 workers. Insights on the impact of the slaying among the Hopkins' community are also given.

42564 ■ "Hopkins, UMd Worry Reduced NIH Budget Will Impact Research" in *Boston Business Journal* **(Vol. 29, August 19, 2011, No. 15, pp. 1)**
Pub: American City Business Journals Inc.
Ed: Scott Dance. Description: The budget for the National Institutes of Health (NIH) is slated to be cut by at least 7.9 percent to $2.5 billion in 2013. This will have a big negative effect on medical and bio-tech research in Maryland, especially Johns Hopkins University and University of Maryland, Baltimore which could face stiffer completion for grants from the NIH.

42565 ■ "How Green Is The Valley?" in *Barron's* **(Vol. 88, July 4, 2008, No. 28, pp. 13)**
Pub: Dow Jones & Co., Inc.
Description: San Jose, California has made a good start towards becoming a leader in alternative energy technology through the establishment of United Laboratories' own lab in the city. The certification process for photovoltaic cells will be dramatically shortened with this endeavor.

42566 ■ *How to Write a Business Plan*
Pub: Kogan Page, Limited
Ed: Brian Finch. Released: February 10, 2010. Price: $17.95. Description: Starting with the premise that there's only one chance to make a good impression, this book covers all the issues involved in producing a successful business plan, from profiling competitors to forecasting marketing development.

42567 ■ "Human Activity Analysis: a Review" in *ACM Computing Surveys* **(Vol. 43, Fall 2011, No. 3, pp. 16)**
Pub: Association for Computing Machinery
Ed: J.K. Aggarwal, M.S. Ryoo. Description: Human activity recognition is an important area of computer vision research and is studied in this report.

42568 ■ "Human Bone Breakthrough" in *Houston Business Journal* **(Vol. 40, January 8, 2010, No. 35, pp. 1)**
Pub: American City Business Journals
Ed: Casey Wooten. Description: Biotech startup company Osteosphere in Houston, Texas aims to market a technology in which laboratory-grown bone tissues can be processed to appear like a real human bone tissue. The technology was developed by a co-founder of the startup and it can be applied to bone disease and injury treatment. Osteophere's future plans, such as the search for possible investors, is also outlined.

42569 ■ "In Search of the Next Big Thing: It's Out There - Just Waiting For You To Find It" in *Inc.* **(Volume 32, December 2010, No. 10, pp. 34)**
Pub: Inc. Magazine
Ed: April Joyner. Description: Innovation is the future for small business. A new book, Inside Real Innovation: How the Right Approach Can Move Ideas from R&D to Market - And Get the Economy Moving helps to break down the process by which innovation occurs.

42570 ■ *Innovation Methodologies in Enterprise Research*
Pub: Edward Elgar Publishing, Incorporated
Ed: Hine. Released: December 2006. Price: $75.00. Description: The importance of qualitative, interpretist research in the field of enterprise research is discussed. The book stresses how enterprise research is a new method and permits a wide scope for new and innovative research studies.

42571 ■ "Innovation Station" in *Canadian Business* **(Vol. 80, October 8, 2007, No. 20, pp. 42)**
Pub: Rogers Media
Ed: Andrew Wahl. Description: Study and teaching of entrepreneurship at the University of Waterloo is discussed. Research projects in the university are expected to be influential in Canada's economic development. In spite of the success of these studies, financing is still a problem for the university, especially in technological innovations.

42572 ■ "The Innovator: Rob McEwen's Unique Vision of Philanthropy and Business" in *Canadian Business* **(Vol. 81, November 10, 2008, No. 19)**
Pub: Rogers Media Ltd.
Ed: Alex Mlynek. Description: Rob McEwen says that his donation to the Schulich School of Business is his first large donation. He went to the University Health Network and was told about their pan for regenerative medicine, helping him make the decision. McEwan wants to be involved in philanthropy in the areas of leadership and education.

42573 ■ *International Entrepreneurship*
Pub: Edward Elgar Publishing, Incorporated
Ed: Oviatt. Released: March 2007. Price: $295.00. Description: Universities are focusing research efforts on international entrepreneurship. The book features critical articles on the topic.

42574 ■ "The Interplay Between Theory and Method" in *Academy of Management Review* **(October 2007, pp. 1145)**
Pub: ScholarOne, Inc.
Ed: John Van Maanen, Jesper B. Sorensen, Terence R. Mitchell. Description: Discussion about the role of theory and method in particular organization and management studies, stressing the importance of balancing primacy of theory and evidence for better research results.

42575 ■ "Inventive Doctor New Venture Partner" in *Houston Business Journal* **(Vol. 40, January 29, 2010, No. 38, pp. A2)**
Pub: American City Business Journals
Ed: Ford Gunter. Description: Dr. Billy Cohn, a surgeon from Houston, Texas has been named as venture partner for venture firm Sante Ventures LLC of Austin, Texas. Cohn will be responsible for seeing marketable developing technologies in the medical industry. The motivation for Cohn's naming as venture partner is his development of a minimally invasive therapy for end-stage renal disease.

42576 ■ "Key FDA Approval Yanked for Avastin" in *Wall Street Journal Eastern Edition* **(November 19 , 2011, pp. B1)**
Pub: Dow Jones & Company Inc.
Ed: Thomas M. Burton, Jennifer Corbett Dooren. Description: Avastin, a drug manufactured by Genetech Inc. and used in the treatment of metastatic breast cancer in women, has had its approval by the US Food and Drug Administration withdrawn by the agency, which says there is no evidence the widely-used drug is successful in increasing the longevity of breast cancer patients.

42577 ■ "The Life Changers" in *Canadian Business* **(Vol. 81, October 27, 2008, No. 18, pp. 86)**
Pub: Rogers Media Ltd.
Description: The first season of 'The Life Changers' was produced in September 2007 to feature stories about research and development (R&D) efforts by universities in Atlantic Canada. The program addresses the need to inform the public about university R&D and its outcomes.

42578 ■ "Life Sciences Become State's Growth Powerhouse" in *Crain's Detroit Business* **(Vol. 25, June 1, 2009, No. 22, pp. M008)**
Pub: Crain Communications Inc. - Detroit
Ed: Amy Lane. Description: According to a study conducted by Anderson Economic Group, Michigan's University Research Corridor has helped grow the life sciences industry. Statistical details included.

42579 ■ "Li'l Guy Rolls Up Into Bigger Company" in *The Business Journal-Serving Metropolitan Kansas City* **(Vol. 26, September 12, 2008)**
Pub: American City Business Journals, Inc.
Ed: Suzanna Stagemeyer. Description: Li'l Guy Foods, a Mexican food company in Kansas City, Missouri, has merged with Tortilla King Inc. Li'l Guy's

revenue in 2007 was $3.3 million, while a newspaper report said that Tortilla King's revenue in 2001 was $7.5 million. Growth opportunities for the combined companies and Li'l Guy's testing of the Wichita market are discussed.

42580 ■ "Local Green Technology on Display" in *Crain's Detroit Business* **(Vol. 26, January 18, 2010, No. 3, pp. 1)**
Pub: Crain Communications, Inc.
Ed: Ryan Beene. **Description:** Detroit's 2010 North American International Auto Show put the newest, most innovative green technologies on display showing that the Southeast Michigan automobile industry is gaining traction with its burgeoning e-vehicle infrastructure. Think, a Norwegian electric city-car manufacturer is eyeing sites in Southeast Michigan in which to locate its corporate headquarters and technical center for its North American branch.

42581 ■ "Local Researchers Get Cash Infusion" in *Business Courier* **(Vol. 26, October 9, 2009, No. 24, pp. 1)**
Pub: American City Business Journals, Inc.
Ed: James Ritchie. **Description:** Cincinnati's Children's Hospital Medical Center and the University of Cincinnati researchers are set to receive at least $56 million from the stimulus bill. The cash infusion has reenergized research scientists and enhances Cincinnati's national clout as a major research center.

42582 ■ "Luster Lost" in *Saint Louis Business Journal* **(Vol. 32, September 16, 2011, No. 3, pp. 1)**
Pub: Saint Louis Business Journal
Ed: E.B. Solomont. **Description:** Express Cripts shares have plunged 22.71 percent since late July amid regulatory concerns, as the luster of the second-largest deal announced for 2011 wore off. Express Scripts has become the largest pharmacy benefit manager in the country after the $29 billion deal to take rival Medco Health Solutions.

42583 ■ "Making Waves" in *Business Journal Portland* **(Vol. 27, November 26, 2010, No. 39, pp. 1)**
Pub: Portland Business Journal
Ed: Erik Siemers. **Description:** Corvallis, Oregon-based Columbia Power Technologies LLC is about to close a $2 million Series A round of investment initiated by $750,000 from Oregon Angel Fund. The wave energy startup company was formed to commercialize the wave buoy technology developed by Oregon State University researchers.

42584 ■ *Marketing for Entrepreneurs*
Pub: FT Press
Ed: Jurgen Wolff. **Released:** December 9, 2010. **Price:** $24.99. **Description:** This text identifies marketing as the entire process of researching, creating, distributing and selling a product or service. It isn't about theory and metrics, rather it is a practical guide that starts with the basics of all marketing aspects.

42585 ■ "McD's Tries to Slake Consumer Thirst for Wider Choice of Drinks" in *Advertising Age* **(Vol. 79, June 9, 2008, No. 23, pp. 1)**
Pub: Crain Communications, Inc.
Ed: Natalie Zmuda; Emily Bryson York. **Description:** McDonald's is testing the sale of canned and bottled drinks in about 150 locations in an attempt to offer more options to consumers who are going elsewhere for their beverage choices.

42586 ■ "Meet UT's New Business Mind" in *Austin Business Journal* **(Vol. 31, May 13, 2011, No. 10, pp. A1)**
Pub: American City Business Journals Inc.
Ed: Sandra Zaragoza. **Description:** University of Texas (UT) chief commercialization officer, Dr. Richard Miller, has opened a satellite office in Silicon Valley, California in the hopes of luring Californian investors to the science and technology at UT. The satellite office is just one of Miller's efforts to reshape and widen the commercialization of UT-Austin. Insights into Miller's long-term view approach to commercialization are also covered.

42587 ■ *Memos to the Prime Minister: What Canada Could Be in the 21st Century*
Pub: John Wiley & Sons, Incorporated
Ed: Harvey Schacter. **Released:** April 11, 2003. **Price:** $16.95. **Description:** A look into the business future of Canada. Topics include business, healthcare, think tanks, policy groups, education, the arts, economy, and social issues.

42588 ■ "Methodological Fit in Management Field Research" in *Academy of Management Review* **(October 2007, pp. 1155)**
Pub: ScholarOne, Inc.
Ed: Amy C. Edmondson, Stacy E. McManus. **Description:** The importance of methodological fit in management field research is investigated in order to produce high quality results.

42589 ■ "MIR Growing With Help From Former Pfizer Workers" in *Crain's Detroit Business* **(Vol. 24, January 28, 2008, No. 4, pp. 33)**
Pub: Crain Communications Inc. - Detroit
Ed: Tom Henderson. **Description:** Molecular Imaging Research Inc. helps fund research at its parent firm, Molecular Therapeutics Inc. The company provides imaging services and other in vivo and in vitro services to help pharmaceutical companies test new compounds.

42590 ■ "Monsanto Acquires Targeted-Pest Control Technology Start-Up; Terms Not Disclosed" in *Benzinga.com* **(, 2011)**
Pub: Benzinga.com
Ed: Benzinga Staff. **Description:** Monsanto Company acquired Beelogics, a firm that researches and develops biological tools that control pests and diseases. Research includes a product that will help protect bee health.

42591 ■ "More Pain" in *Canadian Business* **(Vol. 81, December 24, 2007, No. 1, pp. 12)**
Pub: Rogers Media
Ed: Lauren McKeon. **Description:** Manufacturing sector in Canada is sinking with a forecast by as much as 23 percent for 2008, which can be offset as manufacturers say they plan to increase productivity by 25 percent. Details on the sector's competitiveness, workforce, importing of machinery from the U.S. and financial needs for research and development are examined.

42592 ■ "MPI Expansion Goes Back to Family Roots" in *Crain's Detroit Business* **(Vol. 25, June 1, 2009, No. 22, pp. M007)**
Pub: Crain Communications Inc. - Detroit
Ed: Sherri Begin Welch. **Description:** William Parfet, grandson of Upjohn Company founder, is expanding MPI Research's clinical and early clinical research operations into two buildings in Kalamazoo, land which was once part of his grandfather's farm.

42593 ■ "NASA Taps Younger Talent Pool to Supplement Aging Work Force" in *Crain's Cleveland Business* **(Vol. 30, June 22, 2009, No. 24, pp. 1)**
Pub: Crain Communications, Inc.
Ed: Chuck Soder. **Description:** NASA's Glenn Research Center has reversed the trend towards hiring older workers with more experience by recruiting for entry-level positions as part of a pilot program to attract younger talent.

42594 ■ "New Institutional Accounting and IFRS" in *Accounting and Business Research* **(Vol. 41, Summer 2011, No. 3, pp. 309)**
Pub: American Institute of CPAs
Ed: Peter Wysocki. **Description:** A new framework for institutional accounting research is presented. It has five fundamental components – efficient versus inefficient results, interdependencies, causation, level of analysis, and institutional structure. The use of the framework for evaluation accounting institutions such as the international financial reporting standards is discussed.

42595 ■ "Nine Sectors to Watch: Biotech" in *Canadian Business* **(Vol. 81, December 24, 2007, No. 1, pp. 48)**
Pub: Rogers Media
Ed: Calvin Leung. **Description:** Forecasts on the Canadian biotechnology sector for 2008 are presented. Details on the increase in the number of biotechnology companies and prediction on the government's plan for business incentives are discussed.

42596 ■ "The One Thing That's Holding Back Your Wellness Program" in *Employee Benefit News* **(Vol. 25, December 1, 2011, No. 15, pp. 8)**
Pub: SourceMedia Inc.
Ed: Kelley M. Butler. **Description:** A 13-year study shows that women who sat for more than six hours a day were 94 percent more likely to die during the study period. Most women sit at their desks an average of 7.7 hours while at work.

42597 ■ *Our Daily Meds: How the Pharmaceutical Companies Transformed Themselves into Slick Marketing Machines*
Pub: Farrar, Straus and Giroux
Ed: Melody Petersen. **Released:** 2009. **Price:** $26.00. **Description:** Petersen, using industry memos, transcripts of meetings, and other sources shows how some drug companies are more concerned with the bottom line than with helping patients. Some of these firms are actually inventing 'diseases' in order to sell marginal medicines.

42598 ■ "PA Tax Reforms See Some Progress" in *Philadelphia Business Journal* **(Vol. 28, October 16, 2009, No. 35, pp. 1)**
Pub: American City Business Journals
Ed: Athena D. Merritt. **Description:** It was reported that Pennsylvania's $27.8 billion budget arrived 101 days late, but business groups are encouraged that progress continues to be made on long-called-for tax reforms. The Research and Development Tax Credit, currently at $40 million, will drop to $20 million in 2009-2010.

42599 ■ "P&G vs. IRS: Split Decision" in *Business Courier* **(Vol. 27, July 16, 2010, No. 11, pp. 1)**
Pub: Business Courier
Ed: Jon Newberry. **Description:** Implications of a court ruling in a $435 million legal dispute between Procter & Gamble Company (P&G) and the Internal Revenue Service (IRS) are discussed. A $21 million win has been realized for P&G for its interpretation of research and development tax credits. However, the said case might involve more than $700 million in P&G tax deductions from 2001 through 2004 that the IRS had disallowed.

42600 ■ "Paralysis Foundation has Big Plans" in *Austin Business JournalInc.* **(Vol. 29, December 11, 2009, No. 40, pp. 1)**
Pub: American City Business Journals
Ed: Sandra Zaragoza. **Description:** Lone Star Paralysis Foundation revealed plans to launch a fundraising effort for the advancement of cures for spinal cord injuries via adult stem cells and also fund a new spinal injury rehabilitation center. Efforts to raise about $3 million will begin as soon as the adult stem cell research study by Dr. Wise Young receives Food and Drug Administration approval.

42601 ■ "Patently Absurd" in *Globe & Mail* **(January 28, 2006, pp. B4)**
Pub: CTVglobemedia Publishing Inc.
Ed: Barrie McKenna; Paul Waldie; Simon Avery. **Description:** An overview of facts about patent dispute between Research In Motion Ltd. and NTP Inc. is presented.

42602 ■ "Physics for Females" in *Occupational Outlook Quarterly* **(Vol. 55, Summer 2011, No. 2, pp. 22)**
Pub: U.S. Bureau of Labor Statistics
Description: Free resources to help females investigate careers in medical physics and health physics are available from the American Physical Society. The booklet is designed for girls in middle and high

school and describes the work of 15 women who use physics to solve medical mysteries, discover planets, research new materials, and more.

42603 ■ **"Positive Social Interactions and the Human Body at Work" in** *Academy of Management Review* **(January 2008, pp. 137)**
Pub: ScholarOne, Inc.

Ed: Emily D. Heaphy, Jane E. Dutton. **Description:** Research is recommended for the manner in which positive social interactions in organizational contexts can influence employees' health and physiological resourcefulness.

42604 ■ **"The Power of Innovation" in** *Canadian Business* **(Vol. 81, March 17, 2008, No. 4, pp. 57)**
Pub: Rogers Media

Ed: Andrew Wahl. **Description:** Canada ranks badly in terms innovation yardsticks that directly translate to economic growth such as business R&D as a percentage of GDP and R&D per capita. Canada's reliance on natural resources does not provide incentives to innovate unlike smaller countries with little natural resources. Canada could spur innovation through regulations that encourage industrial research.

42605 ■ **"Providing Expertise Required to Develop Microsystems" in** *Canadian Electronics* **(Vol. 23, February 2008, No. 1, pp. 6)**
Pub: CLB Media Inc.

Ed: Ian McWalter. **Description:** CMC Microsystems, formerly Canadian Microelectronics Corporation, is focused on empowering microelectronics and Microsystems research in Canada. Microsystems offers the basis for innovations in the fields of science, environment, technology, automotives, energy, aerospace and communications technology. CMC's strategy in developing Microsystems in Canada is described.

42606 ■ **"Putting 'Extra' in Extra-Silky Shampoo" in** *Crain's Chicago Business* **(Vol. 31, April 28, 2008, No. 17, pp. 37)**
Pub: Crain Communications, Inc.

Ed: Phuong Ly. **Description:** Profile of HallStar Co., a Chicago-based company which develops and manufactures specialty chemicals to upgrade existing products such as hair dye, lotion and deodorant. Hall-Star has seen its annual earnings rise more than 30 percent since 2002.

42607 ■ **"The Quest for the Smart Prosthetic" in** *Canadian Business* **(Vol. 83, October 12, 2010, No. 17, pp. 26)**
Pub: Rogers Media Ltd.

Ed: Jacqueline Nelson. **Description:** Information about a two-year research project led by Southern Methodist University (SMU) and funded by the Defense Advance Research Projects Agency (DARPA) is provided. The agency aims to create a 'smart prosthetic' which will improve the lives of military amputees. The planned prosthetic will use a sensor that can carry nerve signals through synthetic channels.

42608 ■ **"Race and Gender Diversity" in** *Business Horizons* **(November-December 2007, pp. 445)**
Pub: Elsevier Technology Publications

Ed: James C. Wimbush. **Description:** Research conducted on diversity building, employee recruitment, gender issues in management, and pay inequality from 2006 through present are discussed. Diversity conditions and attitudes toward it are slowly improving based on these findings.

42609 ■ **"R&D Will Remain a Key Priority" in** *Farmer's Weekly* **(March 28, 2008, No. 320)**
Pub: Reed Business Information

Description: Executives as well as the board of the new Horticultural Development Company (HDC) remain committed to the efficient delivery of research and development, a promotional drive and communications over the coming year.

42610 ■ **"Reading the Public Mind" in** *Harvard Business Review* **(Vol. 88, October 2010, No. 10, pp. 27)**
Pub: Harvard Business School Publishing

Ed: Andrew O'Connell. **Description:** Examination of the various methods for obtaining public opinion and consumer preferences is provided; an outline of the disadvantages and benefits of both are also given.

42611 ■ **"Real Estate Ambitions" in** *Black Enterprise* **(Vol. 37, January 2007, No. 6, pp. 101)**
Pub: Earl G. Graves Publishing Co. Inc.

Ed: Description: National Real Estate Investors Association is a nonprofit trade association for both advanced as well as novice real estate investors that offers information on builders to contractors to banks. When looking to become a real estate investor utilize this organization, talk to various investors like the president of your local chapter, let people know your aspirations, and see if you can find a partner who has experience in the field. Resources included.

42612 ■ **"Rebels' Cause: Adult Stem Cell" in** *Austin Business Journal* **(Vol. 31, June 3, 2011, No. 13, pp. 1)**
Pub: American City Business Journals Inc.

Ed: Sandra Zaragoza. **Description:** MedRebels Foundation was launched in February 2011 with the goal of providing millions of dollars for research funding, education and advocacy for adult stem cell-focused medicine. The foundation, whose major contributor is SpineSmith LP, is a collaboration of other adult stem cell-related companies and nonprofit partners. It hopes to raise $200,000 by the end of 2011.

42613 ■ **"Red One and The Rain Chronicles" in** *Michigan Vue* **(Vol. 13, July-August 2008, No. 4, pp. 30)**
Pub: Entrepreneur Media Inc.

Ed: Evan Cornish. **Description:** Troy-based film school the Motion Picture Institute (MPI) implemented the latest technology by shooting the second of their trilogy, "The Rain Chronicles", on the Red One camera. This is the first feature film in Michigan to utilize this exciting new camera, which includes proprietary software for rendering and color correction. Brian K. Johnson heads up the visual effects team as visual effects supervisor and lead CG artist. His company, Dream Conduit Studios, had to tackle the task of employing the new work flow through a post-production pipeline that would allow him to attack complex visual effects shots, many of which were shot with a moving camera, a technique rarely seen in films at this budgetary level where the camera is traditionally locked off.

42614 ■ **"Region to Be Named Innovation Hub" in** *Business Courier* **(Vol. 27, July 2, 2010, No. 9, pp. 1)**
Pub: Business Courier

Ed: Dan Monk. **Description:** The selection of Cincinnati's consumer-marketing cluster as a 'Hub of Innovation' by the Ohio Department of Development could boost Cincinnati's chances of receiving $100 million in grants from Ohio's Third Frontier program and other funding sources. Implications of the University of Cincinnati's designation as a Center of Excellence in Advanced Transportation and Aerospace are also discussed.

42615 ■ **"Region Ready to Dig Deeper into Tech Fund" in** *Business Courier* **(Vol. 26, October 30, 2009, No. 27, pp. 1)**
Pub: American City Business Journals, Inc.

Ed: James Ritchie. **Description:** Southwest Ohio region aims for a bigger share in the planned renewal of Ohio's Third Frontier technology funding program. Meanwhile, University of Cincinnati vice president Sarah Degen will be appointed to the program's advisory board if the renewal proceeds.

42616 ■ **"Renewable Energy Market Opportunities: Wind Testing" in** *PR Newswire* **(September 22, 2011)**
Pub: United Business Media

Description: Global wind energy test systems markets are discussed. Research conducted covers both non-destructive test equipment and condition monitoring equipment product segments.

42617 ■ **"A Research Firm With More Than One Foe" in** *Globe & Mail* **(February 24, 2006, pp. B1)**
Pub: CTVglobemedia Publishing Inc.

Ed: Shawn McCarthy. **Description:** The details of Biovail Corp.'s securities fraud case against Gradient Analytics Inc. are presented.

42618 ■ **"Research: Mind the Gap" in** *Business Strategy Review* **(Vol. 21, Summer 2010, No. 2, pp. 84)**
Pub: Blackwell Publishers Ltd.

Description: Gender disadvantage in contract employment is examined.

42619 ■ **"Research Note" in** *International Journal of Globalisation and Small Business* **(Vol. 4, September 21, 2010, No. 1, pp. 92)**
Pub: Publishers Communication Group

Ed: Alexander Bode, Tobias B. Talmon I'Armee, Simon Alig. **Description:** The cluster concept has steadily increased its importance during the past years both from practitioners' and reearchers' points of view. Simultaneously, many corporate networks are established. Researchers from different areas (business management, economic social and geographical science) are trying to explain both phenomena.

42620 ■ **"Research in Personnel and Human Resources Management, Vol. 28" in** *Human Resource Management* **(Vol. 49, July-August 2010, No. 4)**
Pub: John Wiley

Ed: Mukta Kulkarni. **Description:** An overview of the book, 'Research in Personnel and Human Resources Management', Vol. 28 is presented.

42621 ■ **"Research Reports: How Analysts Size Up Companies" in** *Barron's* **(Vol. 90, August 23, 2010, No. 34, pp. M13)**
Pub: Barron's Editorial & Corporate Headquarters

Description: Shares of Sirius XM Radio, Target and Deere and Company received an eBuyE rating, while shares of Research in Motion got an eNeutralE rating.

42622 ■ *Research Services Directory*
Pub: Grey House Publishing

Contact: Leslie MacKenzie, Publisher

Released: Annual, latest edition 9th, 2003/04. **Price:** $450, individuals softcover. **Covers:** More than 8,000 commercial laboratories, consultants, firms, data collection and analysis centers, individuals, and facilities in the private sector that conduct contractual or proprietary research in all areas of business, government, humanities, social science, and science and technology. **Entries Include:** Firm name, address, phone, fax, toll-free number, e-mail name of chief executive, name and title of contact, date founded, staff size and composition, rates charged, annual revenues, professional memberships, parent and/or affiliate organizations, description of research services and principal clients, affiliates, patents, licenses, special equipment. **Arrangement:** Alphabetical. **Indexes:** Research firm name, geographical, personal name, subject.

42623 ■ **"The Right Remedy: Entrepreneur's Success Is a Matter of Life and Death" in** *Black Enterprise* **(Vol. 38, February 2008, No. 7, pp. 46)**
Pub: Earl G. Graves Publishing Co. Inc.

Ed: Tamara E. Holmes. **Description:** Profile of Leah Brown, whose company conducts clinical trials to determine if specific drugs will relieve particular symptoms. Her company will also visit physician's offices to make certain doctors are following proper protocol for a clinical trial or will collect data from patients.

42624 ■ **"RIM Allegedly Caused 'Substantial Harm'" in** *Globe & Mail* **(January 18, 2006, pp. B6)**
Pub: CTVglobemedia Publishing Inc.

Ed: Simon Avery. **Description:** The details of dispute between Research In Motion Ltd. and NTP Inc. are presented.

42625 ■ "RIM Reinforces Claim as Top Dog by Expanding BlackBerry" in *Globe & Mail* **(March 11, 2006, pp. B3)**
Pub: CTVglobemedia Publishing Inc.
Ed: Simon Avery. **Description:** The plans of Research In Motion Ltd. to enhance the features of BlackBerry, through acquisition of Ascendent Systems, are presented.

42626 ■ "The Role for Canada's Research Universities" in *Canadian Business* **(Vol. 81, October 27, 2008, No. 18, pp. 84)**
Pub: Rogers Media Ltd.
Description: Great students tend to be the foundation of a great research-intensive university, enabling it to attract great teachers and researchers. Success is likely to attract the brightest graduate students to do research, leading to further success.

42627 ■ "Roswell Park Researcher Gets $1.5M From M&T" in *Business First Buffalo* **(October 19, 2007, pp. 1)**
Pub: American City Business Journals, Inc.
Ed: Annmarie Franczyk. **Description:** Roswell Park Cancer Institute researcher Dr. Thomas Tomasi has received the M&T Bank Endowed Chair in Cancer Research, wherein $1.5 million in research funds is included. The funding is an addition to Roswell Park's Leaders for Life endowment campaign which aims to raise $20 for research. Tomasi's plans and background are also given.

42628 ■ "RS Information Systems Signs Buyout Deal" in *Black Enterprise* **(February 2008)**
Pub: Earl G. Graves Publishing Co. Inc.
Ed: Alan Hughes. **Description:** Details of the RS Information Systems buyout by Wyle, a privately held provider of high-tech aerospace engineering, testing, and research services.

42629 ■ "Rumor Has It" in *Entrepreneur* **(Vol. 35, October 2007, No. 10, pp. 30)**
Pub: Entrepreneur Media Inc.
Ed: Chris Penttila. **Description:** Some entrepreneurs like Ren Moulton and Dan Scudder regard rumor sites and product blogs as great sources of market research. However, there are legal issues that must be studied before using these Internet sites in marketing and product development. The use and limitations of rumor sites and product blogs are provided.

42630 ■ "Scanning the Field" in *Business Courier* **(Vol. 26, January 8, 2010, No. 38, pp. 1)**
Pub: American City Business Journals, Inc.
Ed: Jon Newberry. **Description:** Anti-terror detection systems developer Valley Force Composite Technologies Inc. of Kentucky plans to enter the market with its high-resolution ODIN and Thor-LVX screening systems. These systems are expected to meet the increasing demand for airport security equipment.

42631 ■ *Science Lessons: What the Business of Biotech Taught Me About Management*
Pub: Harvard Business School Press
Ed: Gordon Binder, Philip Bashe. **Released:** 2009. **Price:** $29.95. **Description:** Former CFO of biotechnology startup Amgen and veteran of Ford Motor Company provides a universal guide to management based on some of the same scientific principles used to create new drugs.

42632 ■ "Scientific American Builds Novel Blog Network" in *Information Today* **(Vol. 28, September 2011, No. 8, pp. 12)**
Pub: Information Today, Inc.
Ed: Kurt Schiller. **Description:** Scientific American launched a new blog network that joins a diverse lineup of bloggers cover various scientific topics under one banner. The blog network includes 60 bloggers providing insights into the ever-changing world of science and technology.

42633 ■ "The Service Imperative" in *Business Horizons* **(Vol. 51, January-February 2008, No. 1, pp. 39)**
Pub: Elsevier Advanced Technology Publications
Ed: Mary Jo Bitner, Stephen W. Brown. **Description:** The importance of services is growing in developing countries like India and China, but little attention is given to service research, education and innovation. The 'service imperative' seeks to promote the advancement of services. The scope, objectives and philosophy of the service imperative platform are outlined.

42634 ■ "A Set-Theoretic Approach to Organizational Configurations" in *Academy of Management Review* **(October 2007, pp. 1180)**
Pub: ScholarOne, Inc.
Ed: Peer C. Fiss. **Description:** The author argues about the mismatch between theory and methods that have led to decline in research on organizational configurations. He suggests adoption of set-theoretic methods to overcome this mismatch.

42635 ■ "Shire Seeking New Digs for Headquarters" in *Philadelphia Business Journal* **(Vol. 30, September 2, 2011, No. 29, pp. 1)**
Pub: American City Business Journals Inc.
Ed: Natalie Kostelni. **Description:** Dublin, Ireland-based Shire PLC announced plans to relocate its North American headquarters from Chesterbrook Corporate Center in Wayne, Pennsylvania and currently evaluating their options. The specialty biopharmaceutical firm is also considering a move to New Jersey or Delaware.

42636 ■ "Slow but Steady into the Future" in *Barron's* **(Vol. 88, July 7, 2008, No. 27, pp. M)**
Pub: Dow Jones & Co., Inc.
Ed: Mark Veverka. **Description:** Investors are advised to maintain their watch on the shares of business software company NetSuite. The company's chief executive officer, Zach Nelson, claims that the company has a 10-year lead on its competitors with the development of software-as-a service.

42637 ■ "Some Women Warming Up to Economy's Prospects" in *Crain's Cleveland Business* **(Vol. 30, June 1, 2009, No. 21, pp. 9)**
Pub: Crain Communications, Inc.
Ed: Mark Dodosh. **Description:** According to a recent survey conducted by the Center for Women's Business Research and KeyBank focusing on the experience and opinions of women business owners, 48 percent of respondents believe the economy will improve over the next six months. Statistical data included.

42638 ■ "The Start of a Beautiful Friendship: Partnering with Your Customers on R&D" in *Inc.* **(March 2008, pp. 37-38)**
Pub: Gruner & Jahr USA Publishing
Ed: Leigh Buchanan. **Description:** Joint research and development projects between customers and suppliers are a growing trend in the small business community; these ventures can help keep new product development costs lower. Four tips to maintain a good working relationship in these ventures are outlined.

42639 ■ *Start and Run a Delicatessen: Small Business Starters Series*
Pub: How To Books
Ed: Deborah Penrith. **Released:** November 9, 2010. **Price:** $30.00. **Description:** Information for starting and running a successful delicatessen is provided. Insight is offered into selecting a location, researching the market, writing a business plan and more.

42640 ■ *Start-ups That Work: Surprise Research on What Makes or Breaks a New Company*
Pub: Penguin Group
Ed: Joel Kurtzman; Glenn Rifkin. **Released:** October 2005. **Price:** $25.95.

42641 ■ "Stronger Corn? Take It Off Steroids, Make It All Female" in *Farm Industry News* **(December 5, 2011)**
Pub: Penton Business Media Inc.
Ed: Brian Wallheimer. **Description:** Purdue University researcher found that higher improvements in corn crops, and possibly other crops, were yielded when steroids were discontinued.

42642 ■ "Study Puts Hub On Top of the Tech Heap" in *Boston Business Journal* **(Vol. 30, November 26, 2010, No. 44, pp. 1)**
Pub: Boston Business Journal
Ed: Galen Moore. **Description:** The Ewing Marion Kauffman Foundation ranked Massachusetts at the top in its evaluations of states' innovative industries, government leadership, and education. Meanwhile, research blog formDs.com also ranked Massachusetts number one in terms of venture-capital financings per capita.

42643 ■ "Surfing's Next Safari" in *Entrepreneur* **(Vol. 37, July 2009, No. 7, pp. 24)**
Pub: Entrepreneur Media, Inc.
Ed: Dennis Romero. **Description:** Profile of Firewire Surfboards, a San Diego-based maker of lightweight surfboards, aims to capture surfing enthusiasts' attention with its use of unusual and high-tech materials. Firewire's biggest challenge is the preference for old-school surfboards, but the company is determined to revolutionize how surfboards should be made. The company's various innovations and experiences are also discussed.

42644 ■ *Technological Entrepreneurship*
Pub: Edward Elgar Publishing, Incorporated
Ed: Donald Siegel. **Released:** October 2006. **Price:** $230.00. **Description:** Technological entrepreneurship at universities is discussed. The book covers four related topics: university licensing and patenting; science parks and incubators; university-based startups; and the role of academic science in entrepreneurship.

42645 ■ "Testing Firm to Add Jobs" in *Business Courier* **(Vol. 26, December 11, 2009, No. 33, pp. 1)**
Pub: American City Business Journals, Inc.
Ed: Dan Monk. **Description:** Cincinnati-based Q Laboratories announced plans to add dozens of jobs with the $1.6 million stimulus assisted expansion. The company hired Michael Lichtenberg & Sons Construction Co. to build a new 9,000 square foot laboratory building.

42646 ■ "Thinking Aloud" in *Business Strategy Review* **(Vol. 21, Summer 2010, No. 2, pp. 47)**
Pub: Wiley-Blackwell
Ed: Yiorgos Mylonadis. **Description:** In each issue we ask an academic to explain the big question on which their research hopes to shed light. Yiorgos Mylonadis looks at how people define and solve problems.

42647 ■ "Thinking Aloud: Julian Franks" in *Business Strategy Review* **(Vol. 21, Autumn 2010, No. 3, pp. 35)**
Pub: Wiley-Blackwell
Ed: Stuart Crainer. **Description:** Julian Franks is academic director of the Centre for Corporate Governance at London Business School and lead investigator for a (pounds sterling) 1.4 million grant for research into corporate governance.

42648 ■ "Top Worst Weeds in Corn" in *Farm Industry News* **(November 29, 2011)**
Pub: Penton Business Media Inc.
Ed: John Pocock. **Description:** Effective weed control for profitable crops is discussed with information from leading weed scientists from the University of Illinois Extension. It is important for farmers to know what their worst weed is in order to choose the best product, or mix of products, to control them.

42649 ■ "Twice the Innovation, Half the Tears" in *Business Courier* **(Vol. 24, March 7, 2008, No. 48, pp. 1)**
Pub: American City Business Journals, Inc.
Ed: Lisa Biank Fasig. **Description:** Procter & Gamble was able to develop a pant-style diaper called Pampers First Pants by creating a virtual, three-dimensional baby. The company was able to reduce the number of real mock-ups that it had to make by putting the diapers on the virtual baby first. Specifics about product designs were not revealed by the company.

42650 ■ "UA, BP Test Unmanned Aircraft" in *Alaska Business Monthly* **(Vol. 27, October 2011, No. 10, pp. 8)**
Pub: Alaska Business Publishing Company

Ed: Nancy Pounds. **Description:** University of Alaska Fairbanks Geophysical Institute and BP Exploration Alaska tested the oil-spill capabilities of an unmanned aircraft. The aircraft will be used to gather 3-D ariel data to aid in oil-spill cleanup.

42651 ■ "UC Lobbies for Big Chunk of New Funds" in *Business Courier* **(Vol. 24, February 22, 2008, No. 46, pp. 1)**
Pub: American City Business Journals, Inc.

Ed: Laura Baverman. **Description:** Discusses the University of Cincinnati (UC) which has requested $192 million funding from the Ohio Innovation Partnership. The program was launched by governor Stickland in an attempt to drive research and innovation in the studies of biotechnology, aeronautics, and other fields that reflects Ohio's strengths. Details of UC's grant proposals are supplied.

42652 ■ *Unique 3-in-1 Research & Development Directory*
Pub: Government Data Publications Inc.

Released: Annual. **Price:** $49.50, individuals. **Covers:** Firms that received research and development contracts from the federal government during preceding fiscal year. **Entries Include:** Awardees name, address, agency, description of work, dollar amount of contract, and other pertinent data. Additional contracts are listed in 'M R&D Contracts Monthly,' published in the same arrangement; $96 per year. **Arrangement:** First section alphabetical by name of firm; second section geographical by awarding agency; third section classified by nature of work. Similar information in each section.

42653 ■ *U.S. Source Book of R & D Spenders*
Pub: Schonfeld & Associates Inc.

Released: Annual. **Price:** $395, individuals book; $495, individuals book and disk. **Covers:** 5,700 public companies in the U.S. That spend money on research and development. **Entries Include:** Company name, address, phone, names and titles of key personnel, financial data, research and development budgets, fiscal year close, Standard Industrial Classification (SIC) code. **Arrangement:** Geographical by state, then classified by ZIP code. **Indexes:** Company name.

42654 ■ "USM Focuses on Turning Science Into New Companies, Cash" in *Boston Business Journal* **(Vol. 29, July 1, 2011, No. 8, pp. 1)**
Pub: American City Business Journals Inc.

Ed: Alexander Jackson. **Description:** University System of Maryland gears up to push for its plan for commercializing its scientific discoveries which by 2020 could create 325 companies and double the $1.4 billion the system's eleven schools garner in yearly research grants. It is talking with University of Utah and University Maryland, Baltimore to explore ways to make this plan a reality.

42655 ■ *Values and Opportunities in Social Entrepreneurship*
Pub: Palgrave Macmillan

Ed: Kai Hockerts. **Released:** November 1, 2009. **Price:** $90.00. **Description:** Social entrepreneurship has grown as a research field. This book discusses social entrepreneurship as well as the identification and exploitation of social venturing opportunities.

42656 ■ "Voices: Breaking the Corruption Habit" in *Business Strategy Review* **(Vol. 21, Autumn 2010, No. 3, pp. 67)**
Pub: Wiley-Blackwell

Ed: David De Cremer. **Description:** In times of crisis, it seems natural that people will work together for the common good. David De Cremer cautions that, on the contrary, both economic and social research prove otherwise. He proposes steps for organizations to take to prevent corrupt behaviors.

42657 ■ "Where the Future is Made" in *Indoor Comfort Marketing* **(Vol. 70, May 2011, No. 5, pp. 48)**
Pub: Industry Publications Inc.

Description: Research being performed at Brookhaven National Laboratory, located in Upton, New York, is discussed, focusing on new energy sources for our nation.

42658 ■ "Yes, No, and Somewhat Likely: Survey the World with Web Polls" in *Inc.* **(October 2007, pp. 58-59)**
Pub: Gruner & Jahr USA Publishing

Ed: Don Steinberg. **Description:** Online tools for surveying customers, employees and the general public include Zoomergan zPro and Zoomerang Sample, software designed to send surveys and allows viewing results; SurveyMonkey software creates, administers and allows viewing online surveys and results; Vizu software places a one-question poll on a particular Website; and Vovici EFM Feedback, a subscription service providing ongoing surveys to customers or employees.

TRADE PERIODICALS

42659 ■ *Dentaletter*
Pub: MPL Communications Inc.

Contact: John Hobez, Managing Editor
Ed: Dr. Brian Waters, Editor. **Released:** 11/year. **Price:** $119. **Description:** Publishes news of dental research. Also covers related web sites.

CONSULTANTS

42660 ■ Health Strategy Group Inc.
46 River Rd.
Chatham, NY 12037
Ph:(518)392-6770
Contact: John Fiorillo, Principle
Scope: Provides consulting services in the areas of strategic planning, feasibility studies, start-up businesses, organizational development, market research, customer service audits, new product development, marketing, public relations. **Publications:** "Online Consumer Surveys as a Methodology for Assessing the Quality of the United States Health Care System," 2004.

42661 ■ Hills Consulting Group Inc.
6 Partridge Ct.
Novato, CA 94945-1315
Ph:(415)898-3944
Contact: Michael R. Hills, President
Scope: Specializes in strategic planning; marketing surveys; market research; customer service audits; new product development; competitive analysis; and sales forecasting.

42662 ■ Kubba Consultants Inc.
1255 Montgomery Dr.
Deerfield, IL 60015
Ph:(847)729-0051
Fax:(847)729-8765
Co. E-mail: edkubba@aol.com
URL: http://www.kubbainc.com
Contact: Sam Sampat, Mgr
E-mail: edkubba@aol.com
Scope: Industrial and business-to-business marketing research and consulting. Services include new product research, new market evaluation, competitor analysis and customer value analysis.

42663 ■ Margiloff & Associates
621 Royalview St.
Duarte, CA 91010-1346
Ph:(626)303-1266
Fax:(626)303-0127
Co. E-mail: margiloff@compuserve.com
Contact: Irwin B. Margiloff, Principle
E-mail: margiloff@compuserve.com
Scope: Energy and water conservation studies, analysis of research and development, licensing, economics and project management. Projects involve development, training, utility review, cost analysis, manufacturing system improvement, process modeling and expert witness services. Clients include in the field of food, chemical, fermentation, energy, financial and legal services, government and general manufacturing fields.

42664 ■ Medical Imaging Consultants Inc.
1037 US Highway 46, Ste. G-2
Clifton, NJ 07013-2445
Ph:(973)574-8000
Free: 800-589-5685
Fax:(973)574-8001
Co. E-mail: info@micinfo.com
URL: http://www.micinfo.com
Contact: Dr. Philip A. Femano, President
E-mail: phil@micinfo.com
Scope: Provides professional support services for radiology management and comprehensive continuing education programs for radiologic technologists. Management services include resource-critical database logistics; customer registration in educational programs; educational program development and Category A accreditation; national agency notification (e.g., ASRT, SNM-TS) of CE credits earned; meeting planning; manpower assessment; market research; expert witness; think-tank probes and executive summaries of industry issues. **Seminars:** Sectional Anatomy and Imaging Strategies; CT Cross-Trainer; CT Registry Review Program; MR Cross Trainer; MRI Registry Review Program; Digital Mammography Essentials for Technologists; Radiology Trends for Technologists.

42665 ■ Miller, Hellwig Associates
150 W End Ave.
New York, NY 10023-5713
Ph:(212)799-0471
Fax:(212)877-0186
Co. E-mail: millerhelwig@earthlink.net
Contact: Ernest C. Miller, President
Scope: Consulting services in the areas of start-up businesses; small business management; employee surveys and communication; performance appraisals; executive searches; team building; personnel policies and procedures; market research. Also involved in improving cross-cultural and multi-cultural relationships, particularly with Japanese clients. **Seminars:** Objectives and standards/recruiting for boards of directors.

42666 ■ New Commons
545 Pawtucket Ave., Studio 106A
PO Box 116
Pawtucket, RI 02860
Ph:(401)351-7110
Fax:(401)351-7158
Co. E-mail: info@newcommons.com
URL: http://www.newcommons.com
Contact: Robert Leaver, Principal
E-mail: rleaver@atsnewcommons.com
Scope: Builder of agile human networks to champion innovation and mobilize change; to pursue business opportunities; to custom design agile organizations and communities, to foster civic engagement. Clients include organizations on-profits, corporations, government agencies, educational institutions; networks-Trade/professional groups, IT services collaborations, service-sharing collectives; and communities- municipalities, states and statewide agencies, regional collaborations. **Publications:** "Plexus Imperative," Sep, 2005; "Creating 21st Century Capable Innovation Systems," Aug, 2004; "Call to Action: Building Providences Creative and Innovative Economy"; "Getting Results from Meetings"; "The Entrepreneur as Artist," Commonwealth Publications; "Leader and Agent of Change," Commonwealth Publications; "Achieving our Providence: Lessons of City-Building," Commonwealth Publications. **Seminars:** Introduction to Social Computing (Web 2.0), Jan, 2009; Every Company Counts, Jun, 2009; Facilitating for Results; Story-Making and Story-Telling.

42667 ■ Plans and Solutions Inc.
7823 Mistic View Ct.
PO Box 8905
Derwood, MD 20855
Ph:(301)947-8150

Fax:(240)525-5601
Co. E-mail: info@plansandsolutions.com
URL: http://www.plansandsolutions.com
Contact: Kenneth D. Weiss, President
E-mail: kw@plansandsolutions.com
Scope: Market research and competitive analysis; marketing and promotion planning, and executing promotion plans. Specializes in registration and problem solving services that include food canning establishment and process registration, registration under the terrorism act, assistance in case of detention of shipments, and on-site inspection of processing plants and records. Most clients are minority-owned businesses in the USA and companies overseas that want to begin or increase exports to the United States and Canada. **Publications:** "Building an Import/Export Business," John Wiley & Sons, 2002; "How to Conquer the U.S. Market "; "Going Global (Getting Started in International Trade)". **Seminars:** U.S. Import Regulations on Food Products.

42668 ■ Via Nova Consulting
1228 Winburn Dr.
Atlanta, GA 30344
Ph:(404)761-7484
Fax:(404)762-7123
Scope: Consulting services in the areas of strategic planning; privatization; executive searches; market research; customer service audits; new product development; competitive intelligence; and Total Quality Management (TQM).

FRANCHISES AND BUSINESS OPPORTUNITIES

42669 ■ Supperworks
481 North Service Rd. W, Unit A39
Oakville, ON, Canada L6M 2V6
Ph:(905)849-1550
Fax:(905)481-0785
Co. E-mail: mohan@supperworks.com
URL: http://www.supperworks.com
No. of Franchise Units: 15. **No. of Company-Owned Units:** 1. **Founded:** 2005. **Franchised:** 2006. **Description:** Meal preparation. **Equity Capital Needed:** $350,000; $150,000 start-up capital required. **Franchise Fee:** $40,000. **Training:** Includes 3 weeks training.

LIBRARIES

42670 ■ Allen County Public Library Business and Technology Department
900 Library Plaza
Fort Wayne, IN 46801-2270
Ph:(260)421-1200

Fax:(260)421-1386
Co. E-mail: ask@acpl.info
URL: http://www.acpl.lib.in.us
Contact: David K. Sedestrom, Treas.
Scope: Business, economics, investments, sciences, medicine, agriculture, automobiles, home economics, management, manufacturing, engineering, law. **Services:** Interlibrary loan; copying. **Holdings:** 80,000 books; 22,000 bound periodical volumes. **Subscriptions:** 1500 journals and other serials; 45 newspapers.

42671 ■ Honeywell–Federal Manufacturing and Technologies–Technical Information Center (2000)
2000 E. 95th St.
PO Box 419159
Kansas City, MO 64141-6159
Ph:(816)997-2000
Free: 800-225-8829
Fax:(816)997-4094
Co. E-mail: customer_inquiry@kcp.com
URL: http://www51.honeywell.com/aero/kcp
Contact: Luis Perez, TIC POC
Scope: Materials, processing, computers, manufacturing. **Services:** Interlibrary loan; Center not open to the public. **Holdings:** 6000 books; military and federal specifications and standards; technical reports; vendor catalogs. **Subscriptions:** 300 journals and other serials.

RESEARCH CENTERS

42672 ■ Midwest Research Institute
425 Volker Blvd.
Kansas City, MO 64110-2241
Ph:(816)753-7600
Fax:(816)753-8420
Co. E-mail: info@mriresearch.org
URL: http://www.mriglobal.org/Pages/Default.aspx
Contact: Michael F. Helmstetter PhD, Pres./CEO
E-mail: info@mriresearch.org
Scope: Conducts research, development, and engineering activities in the major areas of health, chemistry, the environment, national security and defense, agriculture and food safety, and technology. Specific interests in the health area are pharmaceutical development and regulatory support, vaccine development, preclinical toxicology, metabolism studies, integrated clinical and preclinical drug development support, phytochemicals and designer foods, pesticide product registration support, chemistry support for toxicology, biotechnology, immunoassay development, DNA assay development, proteomics, high through-put automated assay systems, nanotechnology, food safety, seed technology, antibody production, biosensor development, electromagnetic field effects, neurobehavioral toxicology, reversal theory, and health risk behavior. In the field of

chemistry, MRI focuses on analytical chemistry methods, including method development, improvement, validation, and application for programs involving immunoanalytical chemistry, exposure assessment, biological monitoring, industrial hygiene, environmental monitoring, chemical surety, site remediation, demilitarization, atmospheric chemistry, and product analysis of foods, consumer and commercial products, drinking water, and other materials. Environmental programs address environmental measurements, emission inventory development, emission factor development, modeling, water quality, waste minimization, pollution prevention, environmental control strategy development, process analysis and industry profiling, nonpoint source pollution, ambient air toxics, indoor air quality, industrial hygiene, multimedia environmental sampling and analysis, environmental impact assessment, facility assessment, environmental audits, waste processing and characterization, waste combustion, solar soil detoxification, risk analysis, regulatory support, policy analysis, cooling tower performance testing, permitting assistance, and tank and pipeline management. Technology areas include thermo electrics, microclimate conditioning systems, industrial systems evaluation, safety engineering, engineering design, prototype development, bench-scale testing, technology testing, dental biomaterial formulation, dental polymer development, pipeline coating technology, deicing chemical evaluation, traffic engineering, economic impact assessment, financial and business analysis, economic development, strategic planning, international programs, instructional material development, training program design and presentation, technology transfer, etc. **Services:** Science Pioneers program, that provides science related activities, written materials, and services to students and teachers in the 36 school districts of Greater Kansas City. **Publications:** Innovations; Midwest Research Institute Annual Report. **Educational Activities:** Science Pioneers; Workshops, seminars.

42673 ■ National Conference on the Advancement of Research
Georgia Tech Savannah
210 Technology Cir.
Savannah, GA 31407
Ph:(912)966-6765
Co. E-mail: kristy.reeves@gtsav.gatech.edu
URL: http://www.ncar.org
Contact: Kristy Reeves
E-mail: kristy.reeves@gtsav.gatech.edu

Scope: Advancement of research and development at every level of society. **Educational Activities:** Annual conference, to discuss policy issues relating to research; Forums, for members on problems in the field; International conferences and seminars, for academic, industry, government and research associated organizations.

START-UP INFORMATION

42674 ■ *55 Surefire Food-Related Businesses: You Can Start for Under $5000*
Pub: Entrepreneur Press
Ed: Cheryl Kimball. **Released:** March 1, 2009. **Price:** $17.95. **Description:** Advice is given to start 55 various food-related companies and goes beyond restaurant or catering services. Home-based, retail and mail order ventures are covered, as well as food safety and standards.

42675 ■ *Cute Little Store: Between the Entrepreneurial Dream and Business Reality*
Pub: Outskirts Press, Incorporated
Ed: Adeena Mignogna. **Released:** May 2006. **Price:** $11.95. **Description:** Challenges of starting and growing a retail business are profiled.

42676 ■ *Design and Launch Your Online Boutique in a Week*
Pub: Entrepreneur Press
Ed: Melissa Campanelli. **Released:** June 26, 2008. **Price:** $17.95. **Description:** Tips for starting an online boutique in a short amount of time are given. The books shows how to build the online boutique with designer goods or your own product, ways to create eye-catching content, online tools to handle payments and accept orders, marketing and advertising techniques, and customer service.

42677 ■ *EBay Income: How ANYONE of Any Age, Location, and/or Background Can Build a Highly Profitable Online Business with eBay (Revised 2nd Edition)*
Pub: Atlantic Publishing Company
Released: December 1, 2010. **Price:** $24.95. **Description:** A complete overview of eBay is given and guides any small company through the entire process of creating the auction and auction strategies, photography, writing copy, text and formatting, multiple sales, programming tricks, PayPal, accounting, creating marketing, merchandising, managing email lists, advertising plans, taxes and sales tax, best time to list items and for how long, sniping programs, international customers, opening a storefront, electronic commerce, buy-it now pricing, keywords, Google marketing and eBay secrets.

42678 ■ *How to Open and Operate a Financially Successful Bookstore on Amazon and Other Web Sites: With Companion CD-ROM*
Pub: Atlantic Publishing Company
Released: December 1, 2010. **Price:** $39.95. **Description:** This book was written for every used book aficionado and bookstore owner who currently wants to take advantage of the massive collection of online resources available to start and run your own online bookstore business.

42679 ■ *How to Start a Home-Based Online Retail Business*
Pub: Globe Pequot Press
Ed: Jeremy Shepherd. **Released:** February 2007. **Price:** $18.95. **Description:** Information for starting an online retail, home-based business is shared.

42680 ■ *How to Use the Internet to Advertise, Promote, and Market Your Business or Web Site: With Little or No Money*
Pub: Atlantic Publishing Company
Released: December 1, 2010. **Price:** $24.95. **Description:** Information is given to help build, promote, and make money from your Website or brick and mortar store using the Internet, with minimal costs.

42681 ■ *In Fashion: From Runway to Retail, Everything You Need to Know to Break Into the Fashion Industry*
Pub: Crown Business Books
Ed: Annemarie Iverson. **Released:** August 10, 2010. **Price:** $16.99. **Description:** Whether your dream is to photograph models, outfit celebrities, design fashions, this book provides details into every aspect for working in the fashion industry.

42682 ■ *Mommy Millionaire: How I Turned My Kitchen Table Idea Into a Million Dollars and How You Can, Too!*
Pub: St. Martin's Press LLC
Ed: Kim Lavine. **Released:** February 19, 2008. **Price:** $14.95. **Description:** Advice, secrets and lessons for making a million dollars from a mom who turned her kitchen into a successful business; tools cover developing and patenting an idea, cold calling, trade shows, QVC, big retailers, manufacturing, and raising venture capital.

42683 ■ *Scrapbooking for Profit: Cashing in on Retail, Home-Based and Internet Opportunities*
Pub: Allworth Press
Ed: Rebecca Pittman. **Released:** June 2005. **Price:** $19.95 (US), $22.95 (Canadian). **Description:** Eleven strategies for starting a scrapbooking business, including brick-and-mortar stores, home-based businesses, and online retail and wholesale outlets.

42684 ■ *Small Business Desk Reference*
Pub: Penguin Books (USA) Incorporated
Ed: Gene Marks. **Released:** December 2004. **Description:** Comprehensive guide for starting or running a successful small business, focusing on buying a business or franchise, writing a business plan, financial management, accounting, legal issues, human resources management, operations, marketing, sales, customer service, taxes, insurance, and ethics. Information for launching a restaurant, property management firm, retail outlet, consulting firm, and service business is included.

42685 ■ *The Specialty Shop: How to Create Your Own Unique and Profitable Retail Business*
Pub: AMACOM
Ed: Dorothy Finell. **Released:** February 27, 2007. **Price:** $21.95. **Description:** Advise to start retail businesses, including bakeries, gift shops, toy stores, book shops, tea houses, clothing boutiques, and other unique stores.

42686 ■ *Starting a Yahoo! Business for Dummies*
Pub: John Wiley & Sons, Incorporated
Ed: Rob Snell. **Released:** June 2006. **Price:** $24.99. **Description:** Rob Snell offers advice for turning online browsers into buyers, increase online traffic, and build an online store from scratch.

ASSOCIATIONS AND OTHER ORGANIZATIONS

42687 ■ **Electronic Retailing Association**
2000 N 14th St., Ste. 300
Arlington, VA 22201
Ph:(703)841-1751
Free: 800-987-6462
Fax:(703)841-8290
Co. E-mail: info@retailing.org
URL: http://www.retailing.org
Contact: Julie Coons, Pres./CEO
Description: Serves companies that use the power of electronic media to sell goods and services to the public. Its global membership includes television, radio and Internet retailers, along with expert backend suppliers. **Publications:** *E-News Weekly* (weekly); *Marketing, Meetings and Membership* (monthly); *Retailing.org* (bimonthly); *Retailing.org Daily* (daily).

42688 ■ **National Association for Retail Marketing Services**
2417 Post Rd.
Stevens Point, WI 54481
Ph:(715)342-0948
Fax:(715)342-1943
Co. E-mail: admin@narms.com
URL: http://www.narms.com
Contact: Mary Jo Bastuba, Chair
Description: Individuals and businesses providing retail merchandising services. Seeks to advance the retail merchandising industries. Represents members' collective interests; facilitates communication and cooperation among members. .

42689 ■ **National Retail Federation**
325 7th St. NW, Ste. 1100
Washington, DC 20004
Ph:(202)783-7971
Free: 800-673-4692
Fax:(202)737-2849
Co. E-mail: shaym@nrf.com
URL: http://www.nrf.com
Contact: Matt Shay, Pres./CEO
Description: Represents state retail associations, several dozen national retail associations, as well as large and small corporate members representing the breadth and diversity of the retail industry's establishment and employees. Conducts informational and educational conferences related to all phases of retailing including financial planning and cash management, taxation, economic forecasting, expense planning, shortage control, credit, electronic data processing, telecommunications, merchandise management, buying, traffic, security, supply, materials

handling, store planning and construction, personnel administration, recruitment and training, and advertising and display. **Publications:** *NRF Foundation Focus* (quarterly); *NRF Update; STORES Magazine* (monthly); *Washington Retail Report* (weekly).

42690 ■ Planning and Visual Education Partnership
4651 Sheridan St., Ste. 470
Hollywood, FL 33021
Ph:(954)893-7225
Fax:(954)893-8375
Co. E-mail: pave@paveinfo.org
URL: http://www.paveinfo.org
Contact: Klein Merriman, Exec. Dir.

Description: Retail executives, visual merchandisers, store planners, architects, specifiers, students. Seeks to educate and motivate members and encourage interaction among their related fields. Holds annual design competition; offers an internship program; donates proceeds of shows toward financial aid for students. .

DIRECTORIES OF EDUCATIONAL PROGRAMS

42691 ■ *Directory of Private Accredited Career Schools and Colleges of Technology*
Pub: Accrediting Commission of Career Schools and Colleges of Technology
Contact: Michale S. McComis, Exec. Dir.

Released: On web page. **Price:** Free. **Description:** Covers 3900 accredited post-secondary programs that provide training programs in business, trade, and technical fields, including various small business endeavors. Entries offer school name, address, phone, description of courses, job placement assistance, and requirements for admission. Arrangement is alphabetical.

REFERENCE WORKS

42692 ■ "13D Filings" in *Barron's* (Vol. 88, March 10, 2008, No. 10, pp. M11)
Pub: Dow Jones & Company, Inc.

Description: Barington Capital and Clinton Group sent a letter to Dillard's demanding a list of the company's stockholders. Elliott Associates announced that it is prepared to take over Packeteer for $5.50 a share. Strongbow capital suggested a change in leadership in Duckwall-ALCO Stores.

42693 ■ "$50 Million Project for West Chester" in *Business Courier* (Vol. 24, December 14, 2008, No. 35, pp. 1)
Pub: American City Business Journals, Inc.

Ed: Laura Baverman. **Description:** Commercial developer Scott Street Partners is planning to invest $50 million for the development of a site south of the Streets of West Chester retail center. The 31-acre project will generate 1,200 jobs, and will bring in offices, restaurants and a hotel. The development plans and the features of the site are discussed as well.

42694 ■ "The ABCs of a Good Show" in *Playthings* (Vol. 106, October 1, 2008, No. 9, pp. 18)
Pub: Reed Business Information

Ed: Karyn M. Peterson. **Description:** ABC Kids Expo 2008 made a strong showing with products for babies, kids and new/expecting parents. The new Naturally Kids section promoting eco-friendly products was the highlight of the show.

42695 ■ "Add Aquatics to Boost Business" in *Pet Product News* (Vol. 64, December 2010, No. 12, pp. 20)
Pub: BowTie Inc.

Ed: David Lass. **Description:** Pet stores are encouraged to add aquatics departments to increase profitability through repeat sales. This goal can be realized by sourcing, displaying, and maintaining high quality live fish. Other tips regarding the challenges associated with setting up an aquatics department are presented.

42696 ■ "Amid Recession, Companies Still Value Supplier Diversity Programs" in *Hispanic Business* (July-August 2009, pp. 34)
Pub: Hispanic Business

Ed: Joshua Molina. **Description:** The decline of traditionally strong industries, from automotive manufacturing to construction, has shaken today's economy and has forced small businesses, especially suppliers and minority-owned firms, turn to diversity programs in order to make changes.

42697 ■ "Apparel Apparatchic at Kmart" in *Barron's* (Vol. 88, March 17, 2008, No. 11, pp. 16)
Pub: Dow Jones & Company, Inc.

Description: Kmart began a nationwide search for women to represent the company in a national advertising campaign. Contestants need to upload their photos to Kmart's website and winners will be chosen by a panel of celebrity judges. The contest aims to reverse preconceived negative notions about the store's quality and service.

42698 ■ "Aquatic Medications Engender Good Health" in *Pet Product News* (Vol. 64, November 2010, No. 11, pp. 47)
Pub: BowTie Inc.

Ed: Madelaine Heleine. **Description:** Pet supply manufacturers and retailers have been exerting consumer education and preparedness efforts to help aquarium hobbyists in tackling ornamental fish disease problems. Aquarium hobbyists have been also assisted in choosing products that facilitate aquarium maintenance before disease attacks their pet fish.

42699 ■ "Are You Looking for an Environmentally Friendly Dry Cleaner?" in *Inc.* (Vol. 30, December 2008, No. 12, pp. 34)
Pub: Mansueto Ventures LLC

Ed: Shivani Vora. **Description:** Greenopia rates the greenness of 52 various kinds of businesses, including restaurants, nail salons, dry cleaners, and clothing stores. The guidebooks are sold through various retailers including Barnes & Noble and Amazon.com.

42700 ■ "Attention, Shoppers Take a Deep Breath: Why It Pays to Help Customers Relax" in *Inc.* (Vol. 33, November 2011, No. 9, pp. 26)
Pub: Inc. Magazine

Ed: J.J. McCorvey. **Description:** According to a current study, along with festive music and decorations for holiday shoppers, some merchants are considering back messages and pedicures to keep customers happy.

42701 ■ "Austin to Make it Easier for Stores to Just Pop In" in *Austin Business Journal* (Vol. 31, August 19, 2011, No. 24, pp. A1)
Pub: American City Business Journals Inc.

Ed: Vicky Garza. **Description:** Temporary retail stores may soon become common in Austin as City Council has urged the city manager to look into the possibility of amending the city codes to permit businesses to temporarily fill the vacant spaces downtown.

42702 ■ *Avon: Building the World's Premier Company for Women*
Pub: John Wiley & Sons, Incorporated

Ed: Laura Klepacki. **Released:** May 2006. **Price:** $21.99. **Description:** Profile of Avon, the world's largest direct sales company. Avon representatives number four million in over 140 countries.

42703 ■ "Bangles, BMWs Elbow Out Delis and Discount Shops" in *Crain's New York Business* (Vol. 24, January 14, 2008, No. 2, pp. 35)
Pub: Crain Communications, Inc.

Ed: Wendy Davis. **Description:** Lured by a growing number of affluent residents and high-earning professionals, a number of upscale retailers have opened locations downtown which is driving up rents and forcing out longtime independent merchants.

42704 ■ "Banks Could Greet Tenants in One Year" in *Business Courier* (Vol. 26, October 16, 2009, No. 25, pp. 1)
Pub: American City Business Journals, Inc.

Ed: Lucy May. **Description:** The Banks project's initial phase is expected to start in 60 days, which may mean that the project's first tenant could move in by the end of 2010 or beginning of 2011. Carter, an Atlanta-based firm has partnered with Dawson Company in this riverfront development. The first phase will include 80,000 square feet of retail and 300 apartments.

42705 ■ "Banks, Retailers Squabble Over Fees" in *Baltimore Business Journal* (Vol. 28, June 18, 2010, No. 6, pp. 1)
Pub: Baltimore Business Journal

Ed: Gary Haber. **Description:** How an amendment to the financial regulatory reform bill would affect the bankers' and retailers' conflict over interchange fees is discussed. Interchange fees are paid for by retailers every time consumers make purchases through debit cards. Industry estimates indicate that approximately $50 million in such fees are paid by retailers.

42706 ■ "Bedding a Leader in Kohl's Q1 Gains" in *Home Textiles Today* (Vol. 31, May 24, 2011, No. 13, pp. 1)
Pub: Reed Business Information

Description: Kohl's credited home furnishings, particularly bedding, as the leading source of its first-quarter sales and profit gains in 2011. Statistical data included.

42707 ■ "Beer Sales 'Foament' a Dispute" in *Philadelphia Business Journal* (Vol. 28, October 9, 2009, No. 34, pp. 1)
Pub: American City Business Journals

Ed: Peter van Allen. **Description:** Malt Beverages Distributors Association of Pennsylvania filed a case against the Liquor Control Board (LCB) at the Pennsylvania Supreme Court in order to further restrict store sales. The dispute stems from the supermarket chains circumventing the liquor law with the blessings of LCB.

42708 ■ "Best Buy's CEO On Learning to Love Social Media" in *Harvard Business Review* (Vol. 88, December 2010, No. 12, pp. 43)
Pub: Harvard Business School Publishing

Ed: Brian J. Dunn. **Description:** Effective utilization of online social networks to enhance brand identity, connect with consumers, and address bad publicity scenarios is examined.

42709 ■ "Better Than New" in *Bellingham Business Journal* (Vol. February 2010, pp. 16)
Pub: Sound Publishing Inc.

Ed: Ashley Mitchell. **Description:** Profile of family owned Better Than New clothing store that sells overstock items from department stores and clothing manufacturers. The stores location makes it easy to miss and its only advertising is a large sign posted outside. This is the sixth store owned by the couple, Keijeo and Sirba Halmekanqas.

42710 ■ "Betting on the Glitz" in *Canadian Business* (Vol. 79, October 9, 2006, No. 20, pp. 104)
Pub: Rogers Media

Ed: Zena Olijnyk. **Description:** Holt, Renfrew & Comany's expansion plans to cash on the booming demand for high end retail luxury markets are discussed.

42711 ■ *Big-Box Swindle: The True Cost of Mega-Retailers and the Fight for America's Independent Businesses*
Pub: Beacon Press

Ed: Stacy Mitchell. **Released:** October 2007. **Price:** $15.00. **Description:** Examination of the economic, environmental, and social damage done by big-box retailers like Wal-Mart, Costco, and Home Depot. Labor policies of these retailers, particularly those enforced by Wal-Mart, are discussed at length.

42712 ■ *The Big Payback: The History of the Business of Hip-Hop*

Pub: New American Library/Penguin Group

Ed: Dan Charnas. **Price:** $24.95. **Description:** The complete history of hip-hop music is presented, by following the money and the relationship between artist and merchant. In its promise of economic security and creative control for black artist-entrepreneurs, it is the culmination of dreams of black nationalists and civil rights leaders.

42713 ■ "Birdcage Optimization" in *Pet Product News* (Vol. 64, November 2010, No. 11, pp. 54)

Pub: BowTie Inc.

Description: Manufacturers have been emphasizing size, security, quality construction, stylish design, and quick cleaning when guiding consumers on making birdcage options. Selecting a birdcage is gaining importance considering that cage purchases have become the highest expense associated with owning a bird. Other avian habitat trends are also examined.

42714 ■ "Blues at the Toy Fair: Industry Reeling From Recalls, Lower Sales Volumes" in *Crain's New York Business* (February 18, 2008)

Pub: Crain Communications Inc.

Ed: Elisabeth Cordova. **Description:** Over 1,500 toy developers and vendors will attend the American International Toy Fair, expected to be low-key due to recent recalls of toys not meeting American safety standards. Toy retailers and manufacturers, as well as the Chinese government, are promoting product testing to prevent toxic metals in toys.

42715 ■ "Bond Hill Cinema Site To See New Life" in *Business Courier* (Vol. 27, October 29, 2010, No. 26, pp. 1)

Pub: Business Courier

Ed: Dan Monk. **Description:** Avondale, Ohio's Corinthian Baptist Church will redevelop the 30-acre former Showcase Cinema property to a mixed-use site that could feature a college, senior home, and retail. Corinthian Baptist, which is one of the largest African-American churches in the region, is also planning to relocate the church.

42716 ■ "Boom and Bust in the Book Biz" in *Canadian Business* (Vol. 83, August 17, 2010, No. 13-14, pp. 16)

Pub: Rogers Media Ltd.

Ed: Jordan Timm. **Description:** Electronic book marketplace is booming with Amazon.com's e-book sales for the Kindle e-reader exceeding the hardcover sales. Kobo Inc. has registered early success with its Kobo e-reader and has partnered with Hong Kong telecom giant on an e-book store.

42717 ■ "Boots Treat Street Rolls Out Trolley Dash App on Androis and iPhone OS" in *Entertainment Close-Up* (October 24, 2011)

Pub: Close-Up Media

Description: Shoppers using Boots Treat Street can now download the Trolley Dash app game, available from the Apple Store and the Android Market, and enjoy the pastel colored street featuring favorite retailers such as eBay, New Look and Play.com collecting prizes while avoiding hazards.

42718 ■ "The Bottom Line" in *Retail Merchandiser* (Vol. 51, July-August 2011, No. 4, pp. 60)

Pub: Phoenix Media Corporation

Description: Hanky Panky believes that comfort and style don't have to be mutually exclusive when designing their line of intimate apparel for women. The lingerie retailer was launched in 1977.

42719 ■ *Building Buzz to Beat the Big Boys*

Pub: Greenwood Publishing Group Inc.

Ed: Steve O'Leary. **Released:** March 2008. **Price:** $39.95. **Description:** Marketing methods to help small retailers compete against big box stores are examined. It is important for local stores to create a strong customer base.

42720 ■ "Building Your Business: A Strong Web Presence Is a Must" in *Black Enterprise* (Vol. 38, December 2007, No. 5, pp. 74)

Pub: Earl G. Graves Publishing Co. Inc.

Ed: Tennille M. Robinson. **Description:** Building a strong presence on the Internet is crucial to any growing business. Websites can provide information or sell merchandise, but the site must also make sure the customer knows how to use and navigate around within the site. Common mistakes to avoid when designing a small business Website are outlined.

42721 ■ "Burritos New Bag for Shopping Developer" in *Houston Business Journal* (Vol. 40, December 4, 2009, No. 30, pp. 4A)

Pub: American City Business Journals

Ed: Allison Wollam. **Description:** Houston, Texas-based Rob Johnson is the newest franchisee for Bullritos and plans to open eight area locations to market the quick-casual burrito concept. The former shopping center developer was looking for a new business sector after selling off his shopping center holdings.

42722 ■ "The Business Case for Mobile Content Acceleration" in *Streaming Media* (November 2011, pp. 78)

Pub: Information Today Inc.

Ed: Dan Rayburn. **Description:** Last holiday season, eBay became a mobile commerce (m-commerce) giant when sales rose by 134 percent, as most online retailers offered customers the ability to purchase items using their mobile devices.

42723 ■ "Buy Local to Land Great Deals" in *Inside Business* (Vol. 13, September-October 2011, No. 5, pp. SS8)

Pub: Great Lakes Publishing Company

Description: Buy Lakewood! Loyalty Program offers residents great bargains for shopping at local retailers. Residents sign up online and the city mails them a letter of appreciations along with a key card. Showing the key card at any participating businesses listed on the Website will provide discounts.

42724 ■ "Buying Chanel (All Of It)" in *Conde Nast Portfolio* (Vol. 2, June 2008, No. 6, pp. 34)

Pub: Conde Nast Publications, Inc.

Ed: Willow Duttge. **Description:** Overview of the luxury company Chanel and an estimated guess as to what the company is worth.

42725 ■ "Buying In" in *Harvard Business Review* (Vol. 86, September 2008, No. 9, pp. 36)

Pub: Harvard Business School Press

Ed: Andrew O'Connell. **Description:** Review of the book entitled, "Buying In: The Secret Dialogue between What We Buy and Who We Are" which offers tips that those in the field of marketing will find useful.

42726 ■ "Buying Power of Hispanics Growing" in *Austin Business JournalInc.* (Vol. 29, November 27, 2009, No. 38, pp. 1)

Pub: American City Business Journals

Ed: Sandra Zaragoza. **Description:** Hispanic Marketing Symposium presented a report stating that the buying power of Hispanics of Austin, Texas has grown by 54 percent in last five years to $9.4 billion in 2009. Details on the projected growth of the Hispanic market in the are is covered.

42727 ■ "Can Avenue be Fashionable Again? Livernois Merchants, City Want Revival" in *Crain's Detroit Business* (March 10, 2008)

Pub: Crain Communications, Inc.

Ed: Nancy Kaffer. **Description:** Once a busy retail district, the Avenue of Fashion, a Livernois Avenue strip between Six Mile and Eight Mile roads, is facing a community business effort being backed by city support whose aim is to restore the area to its former glory.

42728 ■ "Capture New Markets" in *Pet Product News* (Vol. 64, December 2010, No. 12, pp. 12)

Pub: BowTie Inc.

Ed: Ethan Mizer. **Description:** Flea and tick treatments are among the product categories that can be offered in order to clinch new markets. With the help

of manufacturers, pet store retailers are encouraged to educate themselves about these products considering that capturing markets involves variations in customer perceptions. Retailers would then be deemed as resources and sources for these products.

42729 ■ "Casey's Buys Second Marion Convenience Store" in *Gazette* (December 14, 2010)

Pub: Gazette

Ed: Dave DeWitte. **Description:** Casey's General Stores Inc. has acquired a Short Stop convenience store on Marion's west side in Iowa. The new store includes a car and truck wash.

42730 ■ *Cheap: The High Cost of Discount Culture*

Pub: Penguin Group USA Inc.

Ed: Ellen Ruppel Shell. **Released:** July 2, 2009. **Price:** $25.95. **Description:** The American drive toward bargain-hunting and low-price goods has hidden costs in lower wages for workers and reduced quality of goods for consumers.

42731 ■ "Christ Hospital to Expand" in *Business Courier* (Vol. 27, June 25, 2010, No. 8, pp. 3)

Pub: Business Courier

Ed: Dan Monk, James Ritchie. **Description:** Christ Hospital intends to invest more than $300 million and generate 200 jobs in an expansion of its Mount Auburn campus in Cincinnati, Ohio. About $22 million in retail activity can be created by the hospital expansion, which will also include a replacement garage and new surgery facilities.

42732 ■ "Clothier Delays Opening" in *The Business Journal-Serving Metropolitan Kansas City* (Vol. 27, November 14, 2008, No. 10, pp. 1)

Pub: American City Business Journals, Inc.

Ed: Suzanna Stagemeyer. **Description:** Jos A. Bank Clothiers Inc. has delayed the opening of its store at the Kansas City Power and Light District in Missouri for the first quarter of 2009. The company is still waiting for other tenants to open shop in the district. Comments from officials concerning the retail sector are also presented.

42733 ■ "Come Together" in *Pet Product News* (Vol. 64, December 2010, No. 12, pp. 28)

Pub: BowTie Inc.

Ed: Lizett Bond. **Description:** Pet supply retailers have posted improved sales and improved customer service by bundling their offerings. Bundling pertains to grouping related items such as collars and leashes into a single unit for marketing purposes. Aside from providing convenience and enhanced product information to customers, bundling has facilitated more efficient purchases.

42734 ■ "Commercial Builders Take It on the Chin" in *Crain's Chicago Business* (Vol. 31, April 28, 2008, No. 17, pp. 16)

Pub: Crain Communications, Inc.

Ed: Alby Gallun. **Description:** Although the health care development sector has seen growth, the rest of Chicago's local commercial building industry has seen steep declines in the first quarter of this year. According to McGraw-Hill Construction, Chicago-area non-residential construction starts totaled $731 million in the quarter, a 60 percent drop from the year-earlier period. Volume in the retail, office and hotel markets fell by nearly 70 percent.

42735 ■ *Consumer Behavior*

Pub: Prentice Hall Business Publishing

Ed: Leon Schiffman, Leslile Kanuk. **Released:** August 7, 2009. **Price:** $180.00. **Description:** Consumer behavior is central to the planning, development and implementation of marketing strategies.

42736 ■ "Convenience Store Expanding" in *Clovis News Journal* (November 9, 2010)

Pub: Freedom Communications Inc.

Description: Allsup's convenience store on North Prince Street in Clovis, New Mexico will expand its facilities. The current building is being demolished to make way for the new construction.

42737 ■ **"Convenience Store Owners Will Request New Zoning Once More" in** *Daily Republic* **(November 1, 2010)**
Pub: McClatchy Tribune Information Services
Ed: Tom Lawrence. **Description:** Zoning change has been requested for a proposed convenience store in Mitchell, South Dakota. Details are included.

42738 ■ **"A Counter Offer" in** *Inc.* **(February 2008, pp.)**
Pub: Gruner & Jahr USA Publishing
Ed: Elaine Appleton Grant. **Description:** Online retailer offering a line of kitchen and home products has upgraded its Website in order to make the business more attractive to possible buyers of the company. The firm is asking $9.9 million and reported gross revenue of $12.7 in 2007. The owner suggests that a buyer add product lines geared towards more rooms of the home than currently offer on the retail site.

42739 ■ **"Crowdsourcing their Way into One Big Mess" in** *Brandweek* **(Vol. 51, October 25, 2010, No. 38, pp. 26)**
Pub: Nielsen Business Media, Inc.
Ed: Gregg S. Lipman. **Description:** The Gap, was counting on crowdsourcing to provide feedback for its new logo, but it did not prove positive for the retailer. However, a massive outcry of negative opinion, via crowdsourcing, may not always equal valid, constructive criticism.

42740 ■ **"A Curious Appeal (Market for Scientific Toys)" in** *Playthings* **(Vol. 106, October 1, 2008, No. 9, pp. 26)**
Pub: Reed Business Information
Ed: Pamela Brill. **Description:** Science and nature toys are still popular with children. Kits allow kids to make candy, soap, grow miniature gardens, catch bugs and more. These hands-on kits have manufacturers watching trends to create more toys in this category.

42741 ■ **"Cyber Thanksgiving Online Shopping a Growing Tradition" in** *Marketing Weekly News* **(December 12, 2009, pp. 137)**
Pub: Investment Weekly News
Description: According to e-commerce analysts, Thanksgiving day is becoming increasingly important to retailers in terms of online sales. Internet marketers are realizing that consumers are already searching for Black Friday sales and if they find deals on the products they are looking for, they are highly likely to make their purchase on Thanksgiving day instead of waiting.

42742 ■ **"Deltona to Get First Movie Theater, Shopping Center" in** *Orlando Business Journal* **(Vol. 26, December 4, 2009, No. 26, pp. 1)**
Pub: American City Business Journals
Ed: Anjali Fluker. **Description:** Epic Theaters Inc. revealed plans to build a new 900,000 square foot retail center anchored by a 12-screen movie theater in the city of Deltona in Volusia County, Florida by 2010. The project, dubbed Deltona Village, would provide the city with its first movie theater and shopping center.

42743 ■ **"Despite Hot Toys, Holiday Sales Predicted To Be Ho-Ho-Hum" in** *Drug Store News* **(Vol. 29, November 12, 2007, No. 14, pp. 78)**
Pub: Drug Store News
Ed: Doug Desjardins. **Description:** Summer toy recalls have retailers worried about holiday sales in 2007. Mattel was heavily impacted from the recall of millions of toys manufactured in China.

42744 ■ **"Developer Backs Out of Major Bastrop Project" in** *Austin Business JournalInc.* **(Vol. 28, December 19, 2008, No. 40, pp. 1)**
Pub: American City Business Journals
Ed: Kate Harrington. **Description:** Weingarten Realty Investors, a Houston, Texas-based real estate company, has backed out of its contract on more than 1 million square feet of retail space at the County Road 304 and State Highway 71 corner in Bastrop,

Texas, according to landowner Tom Brundage. Analysts say that the Bastrop area is not ready for big retail projects.

42745 ■ *Directory of Department Stores*
Pub: Chain Store Guide
Released: Annual, Latest edition 2011. **Price:** $395, individuals directory; $445, individuals online lite; $1,075, individuals online pro. **Covers:** 6,000 department store companies, 1,600 shoe store companies, jewelry store companies, 95 optical store companies, and 70 leather and luggage store companies in the United States and Canada, with annual sales of $160 billion. **Entries Include:** Company name; physical and mailing addresses; phone and fax numbers, company e-mail and web addresses; listing type; total sales; industry sales; total selling square footage; store prototype sizes; total units; units by trade name; trading areas; projected openings and remodeling; self-distributing indicator; distribution center locations; resident buyers' name and location; leased departments area, name, and location; mail order catalog indicator; Internet order processing indicator; private label softlines, hardlines, and credit card indicators; furniture styles and price lines; average number of checkouts; year founded; public company indicator; parent company name and location; subsidiaries' names and locations; regional and divisional office locations; key personnel with titles; store locations, with address, phone number, and manager name (department stores only); 3,000 personnel email addresses. **Arrangement:** Geographical. **Indexes:** Alphabetical, product lines, exclusions.

42746 ■ **"Discount Shopping: Holiday Shopping Meets Social Media" in** *Employee Benefit News* **(Vol. 25, December 1, 2011, No. 15)**
Pub: SourceMedia Inc.
Ed: Rob J. Thurston. **Description:** Offering employees access to discount shopping using social media sites for Christmas bonuses, could be the gift that keeps on giving.

42747 ■ **"Dollar General Selects GSI Commerce to Launch Its eCommerce Business" in** *Benzinga.com* **(October 29, 2011)**
Pub: Benzinga.com
Ed: Benzinga Staff. **Description:** Dollar General Corporation chose GSI Commerce, a leading provider of ecommerce and interactive marketing solutions, to launch its online initiative. GSI Commerce is an eBay Inc. company.

42748 ■ **"Dollar Tree Store To Open Mid-July in Shelby Mall" in** *La Crosse Tribune* **(June 20, 2010)**
Pub: La Crosse Tribune
Ed: Steve Cahalan. **Description:** Dollar Tree Inc. plans to open a new store in the location formerly occupied by Family Dollar.

42749 ■ **"Dots Sings To New Tune With Its Radio Station" in** *Crain's Cleveland Business* **(Vol. 30, June 15, 2009, No. 23, pp. 7)**
Pub: Crain Communications, Inc.
Description: Dots LLC, a women's clothing retailer, has launched an online radio station on its Website. The station plays the in-store music to customers while they are shopping online.

42750 ■ **"Down by the Bay" in** *Canadian Business* **(Vol. 81, December 8, 2008, No. 21, pp. 15)**
Pub: Rogers Media Ltd.
Ed: Calvin Leung. **Description:** Hudsons Bay Company chief executive Jeffrey Sherman believes that his vast experience in retail will help him find the company's customer base. Sales are estimated to increase 3.6 percent in 2009 after posting average annual retail sales increases of 5 percent between 2006 and 2008.

42751 ■ **"Downtown Detroit Needs More Retail" in** *Crain's Detroit Business* **(Vol. 24, March 10, 2008, No. 10, pp. 9)**
Pub: Crain Communications, Inc.
Ed: Robin Boyle; James Bieri. **Description:** Although Detroit is doing well with event-driven traffic, the city remains far off the site selection rosters of major national retailers as well as smaller retail outlets.

42752 ■ **"Downtown Retail Site Sold to ATCO" in** *Austin Business JournalInc.* **(Vol. 29, November 20, 2009, No. 37, pp. 1)**
Pub: American City Business Journals
Ed: Kate Harrington. **Description:** New York-based real estate company ATCO Advisory Services purchased a 13,700 square foot retail space in Austin, Texas from 360 Condominiums. The selection of the retail space, named the Shops at 360 has been attributed to the local tenant mix and its location in downtown Austin. Meanwhile, ATCO may continue investing in the area in the near future.

42753 ■ **"Eastland Future Unclear: Local Merchants Say They're OK Amid Closings of 4 More Stores" in** *Charlotte Observer* **(February 8, 2007)**
Pub: Knight-Ridder/Tribune Business News
Ed: Nichole Monroe Bell. **Description:** Retailers in the Eastland Mall that market goods to shoppers looking for the urban, hip-hop look are most successful.

42754 ■ **"eBay Introduces Open Commerce Ecosystem" in** *Entertainment Close-Up* **(October 24, 2011)**
Pub: Close-Up Media
Description: eBay's new X.commerce is an open commerce ecosystem that will arm developers and merchants with the technology tools required to keep pace with the ever-changing industry. X.commerce brings together the technology assets and developer communities of eBay, PayPal, Magento and partners to expand on eBays vision for enabling commerce.

42755 ■ **"eBay and Jonathan Adler Team to Launch 'The eBay Inspiration Shop'" in** *Entertainment Close-Up* **(October 25, 2011)**
Pub: Close-Up Media
Description: Designer Jonathan Adler partnered with eBay to create a collection of new must-have merchandise for the fall season. Top trendsetters, including actors, designers, bloggers, stylists, editors, photographers, models and musicians helped curate the items being featured in the windows by sharing their shopping wish lists with users.

42756 ■ **"Eckerd Sales Spell Relief for Coutu" in** *Globe & Mail* **(January 18, 2006, pp. B4)**
Pub: CTVglobemedia Publishing Inc.
Ed: Bertrand Marotte. **Description:** The details on Eckerd Corp., which posted rise in sales by 2.7 percent in December 2005, are presented. Eckerd Corp. is a unit of Jean Coutu Group (PJC) Inc.

42757 ■ *The Essential Online Solution: The 5-Step Formula for Small Business Success*
Pub: John Wiley & Sons, Incorporated
Ed: Rick Segel; Barbara Callan-Bogia. **Released:** October 2006. **Price:** $22.95. **Description:** Strategies to help any small business increase its online presence and compete with big retail chains. Tips for success Web design are included.

42758 ■ **"Ethnic Businesses Ending Vacancies" in** *Business First-Columbus* **(Vol. 26, August 20, 2010, No. 51, pp. 1)**
Pub: Business First
Ed: Carrie Ghose. **Description:** The Morse Road commercial corridor in Columbus, Ohio has several immigrant-owned businesses that were recognized as instrumental in preventing widespread vacancies when the Northland Mall closed in 2002. The ethnic stores have created a diverse destination that attracted traffic and more businesses.

42759 ■ *Ethnic Solidarity for Economic Survival: Korean Greengrocers in New York City*
Pub: Russell Sage Foundation Publications
Ed: Pyong Gap Min. **Released:** August 2008. **Price:** $32.50. **Description:** Investigations into the entrepreneurial traditions of Korean immigrant families in New York City running ethnic businesses, particularly small grocery stores and produce markets. Social, cultural and economic issues facing these retailers are discussed.

42760 ■ "Executives Exit at Wal-Mart in China" in *Wall Street Journal Eastern Edition* (October 17 , 2011, pp. B3)
Pub: Dow Jones & Company Inc.
Ed: Laurie Burkitt. **Description:** Woes for Wal-Mart Inc.'s subsidiary in China are adding up as Wal-Mart China president and chief executive Ed Chan stepped down, as well as the company's senior vice president for human resources, Clara Wong. The company has been charged by regulators with mislabeling pork products, the result which has forced stores to close. Sales in China have been slow at the retail stores.

42761 ■ "Experts Strive to Educate on Proper Pet Diets" in *Pet Product News* (Vol. 64, November 2010, No. 11, pp. 40)
Pub: BowTie Inc.
Ed: John Hustace Walker. **Description:** Pet supply manufacturers have been bundling small mammal food and treats with educational sources to help retailers avoid customer misinformation. This action has been motivated by the customer's quest to seek proper nutritional advice for their small mammal pets.

42762 ■ "Familiar Fun" in *Crain's Cleveland Business* (Vol. 28, October 22, 2007, No. 42, pp. 3)
Pub: Crain Communications Inc.
Ed: John Booth. **Description:** Marketing for the 2007 holiday season has toy retailers focusing on American-made products because of recent recalls of toys produced in China that do not meet U.S. safety standards.

42763 ■ "Feldman Pushing Past 'Pain' of Cost Overruns, Delays at Colonie Center" in *Business Review, Albany New York* (November 9, 2007)
Pub: American City Business Journals, Inc.
Ed: Michael DeMasi. **Description:** Details of major improvements at Colonie Center are presented. The total cost for these projects increased by $15 million, and the construction of the nearly ten-story theater in the mall is experiencing delays. According to Larry Feldman, chairman of Feldman Mall Properties, which owns a minority stake in the mall, the cost over-runs have pushed the company's renovation costs to around $85 million.

42764 ■ "Fifty Percent of Global Online Retail Visits Were to Amazon, eBay and Alibaba in June 2011" in *Benzinga.com* (October 29, 2011)
Pub: Benzinga.com
Ed: Benzinga Staff. **Description:** Current statistics and future forecasts through the year 2015 for Amazon, eBay and Alibaba are explored.

42765 ■ "Filling the Gap" in *Canadian Business* (Vol. 80, March 12, 2007, No. 6, pp. 62)
Pub: Rogers Media
Ed: Andrew Wahl. **Description:** The chief executive officer of GAP, Bruce Poon Tip, shares his experience and efforts in the growth of the company to a leading position in Canada.

42766 ■ "The Final Piece; Lowe's to Fill Last Big Parcel Near Great Lakes Crossing" in *Crain's Detroit Business* (March 10, 2008)
Pub: Crain Communications, Inc.
Ed: Daniel Duggan. **Description:** Silverman Development Co. is developing a Lowe's home-improvement store on the last major retail parcel near the intersection of I-75 and Joslyn Road, an area which was once desolate but is now home to several restaurants and other retail facilities.

42767 ■ "Financo Panel Lauds Product, Online Marketing" in *Home Textiles Today* (Vol. 31, January 25, 2010, No. 3, pp. 1)
Pub: Reed Business Information, Inc.
Ed: James Mammarella. **Description:** Overview of the Financo Annual Merchandising Industry Chief Executives Event during which there was much discussion on the merits of e-commerce, online marketing as well as the traditional methods of brand recognition and retailing.

42768 ■ "Finishing Touches: the Fashion Statement is in the Detail" in *Black Enterprise* (Vol. 37, January 2007, No. 6, pp. 106)
Pub: Earl G. Graves Publishing Co. Inc.
Ed: Sonia Alleyne. **Description:** Men are discovering the importance of dressing for success. Paying attention to the details such as shoes, socks, cuffs, and collars are just as important as finding the right suit.

42769 ■ "Fire Destroys Surplus Store, Sets Off Live Rounds Near Jacksonville NAS" in *Florida Times-Union* (December 5, 2010)
Pub: Florida Times-Union
Ed: John Leacock. **Description:** Fire which caused numerous explosions at a military surplus store near Jacksonville Naval Air Station is under investigation. Heat and flames ignited lighter fluid and set off live rounds of ammunition sold in the store.

42770 ■ "Five Reasons Why the Gap Fell Out of Fashion" in *Globe & Mail* (January 27, 2007, pp. B4)
Pub: CTVglobemedia Publishing Inc.
Ed: Keith McArthur. **Description:** The five major market trends that have caused the decline of fashion clothing retailer Gap Inc.'s sales are discussed. The shift in brand, workplace fashion culture, competition, demographics, and consumer preferences have lead to the Gap's brand identity.

42771 ■ "Fledgling Brands May Take the Fall With Steve & Barry's" in *Advertising Age* (Vol. 79, July 7, 2008, No. 26, pp. 6)
Pub: Crain Communications, Inc.
Ed: Natalie Zmuda. **Description:** Steve & Barry's, a retailer that holds licensing deals with a number of designers and celebrities, may have to declare bankruptcy; this leaves the fate of the retailer's hundreds of licensing deals and exclusive celebrity lines in question.

42772 ■ "Food Fight" in *Canadian Business* (Vol. 79, November 6, 2006, No. 22, pp. 18)
Pub: Rogers Media
Ed: Zena Olijnyk. **Description:** The war between Canadian grocers and Wal-Mart due to its plans for opening new stores is analyzed.

42773 ■ "Food as Nature Intended" in *Pet Product News* (Vol. 64, November 2010, No. 11, pp. 30)
Pub: BowTie Inc.
Ed: Nikki Moustaki. **Description:** Dog owners have been extending their health-consciousness to their pets by seeking natural products that will address their pets' raw food diet. Retailers response to this trend are outlined.

42774 ■ "For $150 Million Mall, Failure to Launch" in *Business Courier* (Vol. 24, January 25, 2008, No. 42, pp. 1)
Pub: American City Business Journals, Inc.
Ed: Lisa Biank Fasig. **Description:** Blue Ash-based Bear Creek Capital and Chattanooga, Tennessee-based CBL & Associates Properties had abandoned their plan to build a mixed-use project in South Lebanon. The construction of the proposed $475 million open-air mall was cancelled when real estate developer CBL failed to secure retailers.

42775 ■ "Forget Your Pants, Calvin Klein Wants Into Your Bedroom" in *Globe & Mail* (March 31, 2007, pp. B4)
Pub: CTVglobemedia Publishing Inc.
Ed: Barrie McKenna. **Description:** The plans of Phillips-Van Heusen Corp. to open more Calvin Klein stores for selling the new ranges of clothing, personal care products, luggage and mattresses are discussed.

42776 ■ "Free Your Mind" in *Entrepreneur* (Vol. 37, October 2009, No. 10, pp. 24)
Pub: Entrepreneur Media, Inc.
Ed: Joe Robinson. **Description:** Writer Chris Anderson believes that firms in the digital age should allow products and services to initially be sold for free.

These companies could then charge for premium versions of these products and services after the free versions have gained attention.

42777 ■ "From Craft Biz To Wholesale Giant" in *Women Entrepreneur* (January 19, 2009)
Pub: Entrepreneur Media Inc.
Ed: Maria Falconer. **Description:** Advice is given on how to turn a small craft business into a full-time venture; tips to help one transition from a part-time designer to a full-time wholesaler and brand are also included.

42778 ■ "Furniture Chain Moving to Harford" in *Baltimore Business Journal* (Vol. 27, January 22, 2010, No. 38, pp. 1)
Pub: American City Business Journals
Ed: David J. Sernovitz. **Description:** Manchester, Connecticut-based Bob's Discount Furniture signed a lease for 672,000 square feet of space in Harford County, Maryland. The site will become the discount furniture retailer's distribution center in mid-Atlantic US. As many as 200 jobs could be generated when the center opens.

42779 ■ "Gables Unveils Plan for Downtown Tower" in *Austin Business JournalInc.* (Vol. 28, August 8, 2008, No. 21, pp. A1)
Pub: American City Business Journals
Ed: Jean Kwon. **Description:** Gables Residential plans to develop a residential tower with 220 units and 15,000 square feet of retail and commercial spaces in the Warehouse District in Ohio. The development is expected to start in late 2009 and be completed in 18 to 24 months.

42780 ■ "Gateway Delays Start" in *The Business Journal-Serving Metropolitan Kansas City* (Vol. 27, October 31, 2008, No. 8, pp. 1)
Pub: American City Business Journals, Inc.
Ed: Rob Roberts. **Description:** Economic problems caused, in part, by the Wall Street crisis has resulted in the setback of a proposed mixed-use redevelopment project, The Gateway. The $307 million project, which includes the Kansas Aquarium, will be delayed due to financing problems. Details of the project are given.

42781 ■ "Get Real" in *Entrepreneur* (Vol. 36, April 2008, No. 4, pp. 86)
Pub: Entrepreneur Media, Inc.
Ed: Kim T. Gordon. **Description:** Selling points of a product or service must show real benefits to women. Provide detailed information as women look at details more deeply before purchasing. Other tips on how to market products designed for women consumers are provided.

42782 ■ "Give It Your All, and Don't Worry About the Rest" in *Inc.* (Vol. 33, November 2011, No. 9, pp. 37)
Pub: Inc. Magazine
Ed: Norm Brodsky. **Description:** In the early stage of a service company, the owners sell themselves to the customers.

42783 ■ "GM's Decision to Boot Dealer Prompts Sale" in *Baltimore Business Journal* (Vol. 27, November 6, 2009, No. 26, pp. 1)
Pub: American City Business Journals
Ed: Daniel J. Sernovitz. **Description:** General Motors Corporation's (GM) decision to strip Baltimore's Anderson Automotive Group Inc. of its GM franchise has prompted the owner, Bruce Mortimer, to close the automotive dealership and sell the land to a developer. The new project could make way for new homes, a shopping center and supermarket.

42784 ■ "Going Green, Going Slowly" in *Playthings* (Vol. 106, September 1, 2008, No. 8, pp. 17)
Pub: Reed Business Information
Ed: Nancy Zwiers. **Description:** Sustainability and greener materials for both product and packaging in the toy industry has become important for protecting our environment. However, in a recent survey nearly 60 percent of responders stated environmental issues did not play a part in purchasing a toy or game for their children.

42785 ■ "Good Price, Best Brands" in *Retail Merchandiser* **(Vol. 51, July-August 2011, No. 4, pp. 58)**
Pub: Phoenix Media Corporation
Description: Flemington Department Store has been a family-owned and operated retailer for over 50 years. Customer service is key to the store's success.

42786 ■ "Good Things Happen When We Buy Local" in *Crain's Detroit Business* **(Vol. 24, October 6, 2008, No. 40, pp. 7)**
Pub: Crain Communications, Inc.
Description: Michigan is facing incredibly difficult economic times. One way in which each one of us can help the state and the businesses located here is by purchasing our goods and services from local vendors. The state Agriculture Department projected that if Michigan households earmarked $10 per week in their grocery purchases to made-in-Michigan products, this would generate $30 million a week in economic impact.

42787 ■ "Grand Letdown" in *The Business Journal-Milwaukee* **(Vol. 25, September 12, 2008, No. 51, pp. A1)**
Pub: American City Business Journals, Inc.
Ed: Rich Kirchen. **Description:** Overview of retail trade in Milwaukee, Wisconsin is presented. It has been observed that vacancies in storefronts both east and west of the Milwaukee River have increased, and the Shops of Grand Avenue has yet to attract new retailers or shoppers. The completion of the Marquette Interchange is also discussed.

42788 ■ "Green and Clean" in *Retail Merchandiser* **(Vol. 51, July-August 2011, No. 4, pp. 56)**
Pub: Phoenix Media Corporation
Description: Green Valley Grocery partnered with Paragon Solutions consulting firm to make their stores environmentally green.

42789 ■ "Green Counting" in *Canadian Business* **(Vol. 81, October 13, 2008, No. 17, pp. 27)**
Pub: Rogers Media Ltd.
Ed: Joe Castaldo. **Description:** Procter and Gamble research revealed that only 10 percent of North American consumers are willing to accept trade-offs for a greener product. Three out of four North American consumers will not accept a higher price or a decrease in a product's performance for an environmental benefit. Details on green marketing are also discussed.

42790 ■ "Group-Buying Site Hones In on Hispanics" in *Austin Business Journal* **(Vol. 31, July 1, 2011, No. 17, pp. 1)**
Pub: American City Business Journals Inc.
Ed: Vicky Garza. **Description:** Descuentl Libre is a new group-buying site from Austin, Texas that targets the Hispanic market, offering discounts of practical items and family-friendly activities. The Hispanic market constitutes 17 percent of the U.S. population and spends $23 billion yearly online.

42791 ■ "H&M Offers a Dress for Less" in *Canadian Business* **(Vol. 83, September 14, 2010, No. 15, pp. 20)**
Pub: Rogers Media Ltd.
Ed: Laura Cameron. **Description:** Swedish clothing company H&M has implemented loss leader strategy by pricing some dresses at extremely low prices. The economy has forced retailers to keep prices down despite the increasing cost of manufacturing, partly due to Chinese labor becoming more expensive. How the trend will affect apparel companies is discussed.

42792 ■ "The Harder Side of Sears" in *Crain's Chicago Business* **(Vol. 31, March 31, 2008, No. 13, pp. 68)**
Pub: Crain Communications, Inc.
Ed: Steven R. Strahler. **Description:** Discusses the history of Sears Roebuck & Co. and its merger with Kmart Corp.

42793 ■ "Hartco Income Fund Announces the Completion of the CompuSmart Strategic Review" in *Canadian Corporate News* **(May 14, 2007)**
Pub: Comtex News Network Inc.
Description: Hartco Income Fund announced that it has completed the process of exploring strategic options for CompuSmart and found that it should implement a plan to sell select stores and assets while consolidating remaining CompuSmart locations over the next sixty days.

42794 ■ "HBC Enlists IBM to Help Dress Up Its On-Line Shopping" in *Globe & Mail* **(February 7, 2006, pp. B3)**
Pub: CTVglobemedia Publishing Inc.
Ed: Simon Avery. **Description:** The details of management contract between Hudson's Bay Co. and International Business Machines Corp. are presented.

42795 ■ "HBC Sets Friday as Deadline to Trump Zucker Takeover Bid" in *Globe & Mail* **(January 18, 2006, pp. B1)**
Pub: CTVglobemedia Publishing Inc.
Ed: Marina Strauss. **Description:** The reasons behind Hudson's Bay Co.'s decision to seek alternative bids on the company are presented. Investor Jerry Zucker earlier offered $1.1 billion for the company.

42796 ■ "Health Care Leads Sectors Attracting Capital" in *Hispanic Business* **(Vol. 30, March 2008, No. 3, pp. 14)**
Pub: Hispanic Business
Ed: Scott Williams. **Description:** Discusses the capital gains of Hispanic-owned companies and other Hispanic leaders in the investment and retail fields in the year 2007. Sectors like health care, media, food and technology saw a healthy flow of capital due to successful mergers, acquisitions and increased private equity investments.

42797 ■ "High Anxiety" in *Canadian Business* **(Vol. 80, November 19, 2007, No. 23, pp. 11)**
Pub: Rogers Media
Ed: Zena Olijnyk. **Description:** Value of Canadian dollar continues to rise, and consumers are asking for lower prices of goods. Retailers, on the other hand, are facing concerns over losing sales. The impacts of the rising Canadian dollar on the business sector and consumer behavior are examined.

42798 ■ "High Growth Reported for the Natural Supermarket Pet Department Close-Up" in *Canadian Corporate News* **(October 20, 2008)**
Pub: Comtex News Network Inc.
Description: Leading natural supermarket chains have been outperforming mainstream grocers by carrying natural and organic pet products. Statistical data included.

42799 ■ "Hispantelligence Report" in *Hispanic Business* **(January-February 2009, pp. 10)**
Pub: Hispanic Business
Description: U.S. Hispanic purchasing power is expected to reach $958 billion in 2009 and projected to reach $1.25 trillion by 2015, a rate of more than two times the overall national rate. Statistical data included.

42800 ■ "Ho, Ho, Ho!" in *Retail Merchandiser* **(Vol. 51, September-October 2011, No. 5, pp. 10)**
Pub: Phoenix Media Corporation
Ed: Ted Vaughan. **Description:** Despite consumer caution and economic woes, retail leaders are expecting a high volume holiday selling season for 2011 Christmas. Statistical data covering holiday sales expectations is included.

42801 ■ "Holiday Sales Look Uncertain for Microsoft and PC Sellers" in *Puget Sound Business Journal* **(Vol. 29, November 28, 2008, No. 32)**
Pub: American City Business Journals
Ed: Todd Bishop. **Description:** Personal computer makers face uncertain holiday sales for 2008 as a result of the weak U.S. economy and a shift toward low-cost computers. Personal computer shipments for the fourth quarter 2008 are forecast to drop 1 percent compared to the same quarter 2007.

42802 ■ "Home Depot Eyes Wholesale Spinoff" in *Globe & Mail* **(February 13, 2007, pp. B13)**
Pub: CTVglobemedia Publishing Inc.
Description: Home Depot Inc. is planning to sell or spinoff its professional supply business to focus on retail stores. The weakening sales and profits are the main driving force behind the company's decision.

42803 ■ "Home Helps Push Macy's to First-Quarter Profit" in *Home Textiles Today* **(Vol. 31, May 24, 2011, No. 13, pp. 2)**
Pub: Reed Business Information
Description: Macy's Inc. reported home goods as one of the three strong performing categories for first quarter 2011. Home goods sales, both big and small ticket items, have improved significantly for the retailer.

42804 ■ "Home Improvement Marketers Target Women With New Products, New Campaigns and Plenty of Pink" in *Marketing to Women* **(March 2008)**
Pub: EPM Communications, Inc.
Description: From creating tools that fit a woman's ergonomics to designs that fit a woman's fashion sense, home improvement is finding new ways in which to market to women.

42805 ■ "Home Shows Signs of Life at Target" in *Home Textiles Today* **(Vol. 31, May 24, 2011, No. 13, pp. 1)**
Pub: Reed Business Information
Description: Retailer, Target, is experience a boost in sales for apparel and products for the home.

42806 ■ "Home Sits Out Q1 Surge at JCP" in *Home Textiles Today* **(Vol. 31, May 24, 2011, No. 13, pp. 1)**
Pub: Reed Business Information
Ed: James Mammarella. **Description:** JCPenney chairman and CEO, Mike Ullman, reported sales gains for first quarter 2011 in all products except home goods.

42807 ■ "Hometown Value" in *Retail Merchandiser* **(Vol. 51, July-August 2011, No. 4, pp. 50)**
Pub: Phoenix Media Corporation
Ed: Todd Vowell. **Description:** Profile of family-owned Vowell's Marketplace located in Noxapater, Mississippi. The 10-store chain caters to its Southern roots and is run by the third generation of the Vowell family.

42808 ■ "Hot Kicks, Cool Price" in *Black Enterprise* **(Vol. 37, December 2006, No. 5, pp. 34)**
Pub: Earl G. Graves Publishing Co. Inc.
Ed: Topher Sanders. **Description:** Stephon Marbury of the New York Nicks introduced a new basketball shoe, the Starbury One, costing $14.98. The shoes are an addition to the Starbury clothing line and although the privately owned company would not disclose figures; stores sold out of a month's worth of inventory in merely three days.

42809 ■ "How Growers Buy" in *Farm Industry News* **(Vol. 42, January 1, 2009, No. 1)**
Pub: Penton Media, Inc.
Ed: Karen McMahon. **Description:** According to a survey regarding the buying habits among large commercial growers, most prefer to purchase from local retailers, customer service is important concerning their decision on who to buy products from, and price and convenience seem to be more important then brand.

42810 ■ *How to Market and Sell Your Art, Music, Photographs, and Handmade Crafts Online*
Pub: Atlantic Publishing Group, Inc.
Ed: Lee Rowley. **Released:** May 2008. **Price:** $24.95. **Description:** The book provides all the basics for starting and running an online store selling arts,

crafts, photography or music. There are more than 300 Websites listed to help anyone market and promote their arts and/or crafts online.

42811 ■ *How Walmart is Destroying America (And the World): And What You Can Do About It*
Pub: Ten Speed Press
Ed: Bill Quinn. **Released:** April 2005. **Price:** $10.95. **Description:** Wal-Mart employs 1.5 million employees and operates more than 3,500 stores, making it the largest private employer globally. Wal-Mart's impact on mom-and-pop business is discussed.

42812 ■ "Hy-Vee Plans Expansion, Convenience Store in Cedar Rapids" in *Gazette* (November 26, 2010)
Pub: Gazette
Ed: George Ford. **Description:** Hy-Vee Inc. is awaiting approval to expand its supermarket in Cedar Rapids, Iowa. Hy-Vee is a food and drug store chain will construct a convenience store and gas station on the site.

42813 ■ "Hyde Park Hungry for Expansion at Cap" in *Business First-Columbus* (October 12, 2007, pp. A1)
Pub: American City Business Journals, Inc.
Ed: Dan Eaton. **Description:** The Cap, an area developed for the retail and restaurant industry, is experiencing major changes such as Hyde Park Restaurant System's planned expansion, and the expected departure of other tenants. The expansion of Hyde Park will lead to the relocation of Schakolad Chocolate Factory.

42814 ■ "An Ill Wind: Icelandic Bank Failures Chill Atlantic Canada" in *Canadian Business* (Vol. 81, November 10, 2008, No. 19, pp. 10)
Pub: Rogers Media Ltd.
Ed: Charles Mandel. **Description:** Bank failures in Iceland have put a stop to flights ferrying Icelanders to Newfoundland to purchase Christmas gifts, thereby threatening Newfoundland's tourism industry. The credit of Newfoundland's fisheries is also being squeezed since most of Atlantic Canadian seafood processors hold lines of credit from Icelandic banks.

42815 ■ "Inland Snaps Up Rival REITs" in *Crain's Chicago Business* (Vol. 31, November 17, 2008, No. 46, pp. 3)
Pub: Crain Communications, Inc.
Ed: Alby Gallun. **Description:** Discusses Inland American Real Estate Trust Inc., a real estate investment trust that is napping up depressed shares of publicly traded competitors, a possible first step toward taking over these companies; however, with hotel and retail properties accounting for approximately 70 percent of its portfolio, the company could soon face its own difficulties.

42816 ■ "Inside Out" in *Playthings* (Vol. 107, January 1, 2009, No. 1, pp. 3)
Pub: Reed Business Information
Description: Mattel signed on as the global master toy licensee for Cartoon Network's The Secret Saturdays while Toy Island signed a deal for wooden toys based on several leading Nick Jr. properties.

42817 ■ "It's All in the Details" in *Canadian Business* (Vol. 80, December 25, 2006, No. 1, pp. 11)
Pub: Rogers Media
Description: The failure of several Canadian clothing retailers to disclose their labor practices is discussed.

42818 ■ "Izod, Loft Outlets Coming To Tanger" in *New Hampshire Business Review* (Vol. 33, March 25, 2011, No. 6, pp. 30)
Pub: Business Publications Inc.
Description: Izod and Lots stores will open at the Tanger Outlet Center in Tilton, New Hampshire. Both stores will feature fashions and accessories.

42819 ■ "Keeping Customers Satisfied" in *Pet Product News* (Vol. 64, December 2010, No. 12, pp. 10)
Pub: BowTie Inc.
Ed: Devon McPhee. **Description:** Windsor, California-based Debbie's Pet Boutique, recipient of Pet Product News International's Outstanding Customer Service Award, has been dedicated to combining topnotch grooming services with a robust retail selection. These features might gain return customers for Debbie's Pet Boutique.

42820 ■ "Kent Officials Seek Further KSU, City Unity" in *Crain's Cleveland Business* (Vol. 28, December 3, 2007, No. 48, pp. 3)
Pub: Crain Communications, Inc.
Ed: Jay Miller. **Description:** Kent State University and Portage County are searching for a developer who will use a three-acre parcel to bring new life to the city's sagging downtown and create an area that will better link the town and the Kent State campus. The project will include a hotel and conference center as well as retail and restaurant space.

42821 ■ "Killings Remind Convenience Store Workers of Job's Potential Risks" in *Waterloo Courier* (November 19, 2010)
Pub: Gazette
Ed: Tina Hinz. **Description:** Potential risks for convenience store workers is stressed citing shootings in area shops; safety plans are important for these stores.

42822 ■ *The Leadership Challenge*
Pub: Jossey-Bass Publishers
Ed: James M. Kouzes, Barry Z. Posner. **Released:** June 30, 1995. **Price:** $22.00. **Description:** According to research by the authors, people can make extraordinary things happen by liberating the leader within everyone around them. This handbook gives practical tips to aspire leaders in retail, manufacturing, government, community, church and school settings.

42823 ■ "Leaning Tower" in *Business Courier* (Vol. 27, June 4, 2010, No. 5, pp. 1)
Pub: Business Courier
Ed: Jon Newberry. **Description:** New York-based developer Armand Lasky, owner of Tower Place Mall in downtown Cincinnati, Ohio has sued Birmingham, Alabama-based Regions Bank to prevent the bank's foreclosure on the property. Regions Bank claims Lasky was in default on an $18 million loan agreement. Details on the mall's leasing plan is also discussed.

42824 ■ "Leasing Midway; Look for Higher Parking Fees, More Retail Under Private Airport Operator" in *Crain's Chicago Business* (May 5, 2008)
Pub: Crain Communications, Inc.
Ed: Paul Merrion. **Description:** According to experts, bids for the first privatization of a major U.S. airport could run as high as $3.5 billion. Information-gathering and negotiations will soon get under way with some or all of the six major international investor groups that recently expressed interest in running Midway.

42825 ■ "Let Emerging Market Customers Be Your Teachers" in *Harvard Business Review* (Vol. 88, December 2010, No. 12, pp. 115)
Pub: Harvard Business School Publishing
Ed: Guillermo D'Andrea, David Marcotte, Gwen Dixon Morrison. **Description:** Examination of effective strategies for emerging markets is presented. These include helping educate customers as well as selling to them, adapting to customers' habits, and focusing brands appropriately. Magazine Luiza, a chain store in Brazil, is used to illustrate these points.

42826 ■ "Let's Go Team: When a Retail Professional Leads by Example, Everyone Benefits" in *Black Enterprise* (Vol. 41, November 2010, No. 4)
Pub: Earl G. Graves Publishing Co. Inc.
Ed: Aisha I. Jefferson. **Description:** Profile of Derek Jenkins, senior vice president of Target Stores Northeast Region is presented. Jenkins oversees the management of 450 retail stores with nearly 75,000 workers. He shares insight into managing by making sure every interaction with his team counts.

42827 ■ "Life After Cod" in *Globe & Mail* (March 18, 2006, pp. B1)
Pub: CTVglobemedia Publishing Inc.
Ed: Gordon Pitts. **Description:** Canadian fishing industry is under threat because of Chinese process-ing competition, high energy costs, rise of powerful retailers and the rise of Canadian dollar value. Fishing industry of Canada is analyzed.

42828 ■ "Loblaw's Apparel Guru No Average Joe" in *Globe & Mail* (March 13, 2006, pp. B1)
Pub: CTVglobemedia Publishing Inc.
Ed: Marina Strauss. **Description:** The details on Loblaw Companies Ltd., which unveiled Joe Fresh Style line of clothing, are presented.

42829 ■ "Local Firms Will Feel Impact Of Wall St. Woes" in *The Business Journal-Milwaukee* (Vol. 25, September 19, 2008, No. 52, pp. A1)
Pub: American City Business Journals, Inc.
Ed: Rich Kirchen. **Description:** Wall Street's crisis is expected to affect businesses in Wisconsin, in terms of decreased demand for services and products and increased financing costs. Businesses in Milwaukee area may face higher interest rates and tougher loan standards. The potential impacts of the Wall Street crisis on local businesses are examined further.

42830 ■ "A Look Ahead Into 2007" in *Canadian Business* (Vol. 80, December 25, 2006, No. 1, pp. 40)
Pub: Rogers Media
Description: The 2007 forecasts for various industrial sectors like telecom, information technology, manufacturing, retail, financial and energy among others is discussed.

42831 ■ "Look Who's Eating Loblaw's Lunch" in *Canadian Business* (Vol. 80, February 26, 2007, No. 5, pp. 44)
Pub: Rogers Media
Ed: Zena Olijnyk. **Description:** Loblaw Cos. Ltd. and Shoppers Drug Mart Corp. of Canada are finding increased competition from the global retail giant Wal-Mart Inc. The financial performance of the companies is analyzed.

42832 ■ "Looking For Good Buys" in *Black Enterprise* (Vol. 38, November 2007, No. 4, pp. 39)
Pub: Earl G. Graves Publishing Co. Inc.
Ed: Steve Garmhausen. **Description:** Lower interest rates mean consumers generally have more money to spend, which could spur economic growth in the retail sector of the U.S.

42833 ■ "Looking for a Sales Tax Extension" in *Milwaukee Business Journal* (Vol. 27, January 29, 2010, No. 18, pp. A1)
Pub: American City Business Journals
Ed: Mark Kass. **Description:** Milwaukee, Wisconsin-area business executives believe the extension of the Miller Park 0.1 percent sales tax could help fund a new basketball arena to replace the 21-year-old Bradley Center in downtown Milwaukee. However, any sales tax expansion that includes the new basketball arena would need approval by Wisconsin's legislature.

42834 ■ "Loyalty Cards Score Points" in *Crain's Cleveland Business* (Vol. 30, June 8, 2009, No. 22, pp. 1)
Pub: Crain Communications, Inc.
Ed: Chuck Soder. **Description:** Northeast Ohio retailers are promoting loyalty and rewards programs in order to attract and maintain loyal customers.

42835 ■ "Luxe Men Are In Style" in *Brandweek* (Vol. 49, April 21, 2008, No. 16, pp. 12)
Pub: VNU Business Media, Inc.
Description: According to a recent survey by Unity Marketing, among 1,300 luxury shoppers found that men spent an average of $2,401 on fashion items over a three-month period which is nearly $1,000 more than women. Men also spring for more luxury items such as vehicles and memberships to exclusive clubs.

42836 ■ "Luxury Still Sells Well" in *Puget Sound Business Journal* (Vol. 29, September 5, 2008, No. 20, pp. 1)
Pub: American City Business Journals
Ed: Jeanne Lang Jones. **Description:** High fashion retailers are planning to open stores in the Puget

Sound area despite the economic slowdown, citing high incomes in the area despite the weak U.S. dollar.

42837 ■ "Macy's Seeks Balance in All Things Ad-Related" in *Crain's Chicago Business* **(Vol. 31, March 31, 2008, No. 13, pp. 19)**
Pub: Crain Communications, Inc.

Ed: Natalie Zmuda. **Description:** Macy's Inc. is seeking to balance its national television campaign with locally tailored promotions and products.

42838 ■ "Major Golf Retail Show in the Rough for 2010" in *Orlando Business Journal* **(Vol. 26, January 15, 2010, No. 33, pp. 1)**
Pub: American City Business Journals

Ed: Anjali Fluker. **Description:** The 57th Annual PGA Merchandise Show in Orlando, Florida is projected to attract 39,000 attendees in 2010, compared with 41,000 in 2009. According to the Orange County Convention Center, economic benefits that could be obtained from the 2010 edition of the golf retail show might reach only $77 million, compared with $78 million generated last year.

42839 ■ "Major Renovation Planned for Southridge" in *Business Journal-Milwaukee* **(Vol. 28, November 12, 2010, No. 6, pp. A1)**
Pub: Milwaukee Business Journal

Ed: Stacy Vogel Davis. **Description:** Simon Property Group plans to invest more than $20 million in upgrading and renovating Southridge Mall in Milwaukee County, Wisconsin. The project, which is partially financed by a $10 million grant from the Village of Greendale, could boost the property's value by $52.5 million.

42840 ■ "Many Retailers Soften Return Policies" in *Austin Business JournalInc.* **(Vol. 28, December 26, 2008, No. 41, pp. 1)**
Pub: American City Business Journals

Ed: Jean Kwon. **Description:** National Retail Federation reported the percentage of retailers saying their holiday return policy in 2008 will slacken compared to last season has increased from 3.4 percent to 11 percent. An increasing percentage of retailers are also getting stingier, as 17.1 percent revealed that their return policies will be stricter.

42841 ■ "Marathon Money" in *Hawaii Business* **(Vol. 53, December 2007, No. 6, pp. 127)**
Pub: Hawaii Business Publishing

Ed: Jolyn Okimoto Rosa. **Description:** Discusses the effects of the Honolulu Marathon on small businesses' sales. The Running Room, for instance, experience growth in sales starting from the training season up to the end of the race, as a surge of Hawaiian residents and tourists come into the store for items such as running shoes and blister kits. The marathon's impact on Hawaii's tourism is examined as well.

42842 ■ "Market for Retail Space Flat, but Recovery Still Uncertain" in *Sacramento Business Journal* **(Vol. 28, August 26, 2011, No. 26, pp. 1)**
Pub: Sacramento Business Journal

Ed: Kelly Johnson. **Description:** The retail market in the Sacramento, California region remains challenged with the stock market volatility being the latest of its hurdles. The overall vacancy was 13.1 percent as of mid-2011, but retail real estate professionals express hopes that the worst is behind. A list and description of the region's winners and losers in retail vacancies is provided.

42843 ■ "Market Share" in *Business Journal-Milwaukee* **(Vol. 28, December 3, 2010, No. 9, pp. A1)**
Pub: Milwaukee Business Journal

Ed: Stacy Vogel Davis. **Description:** Roundy's Supermarkets' market share has decreased with the expansion of low-price grocery chains in Milwaukee, Wisconsin. Wal-Mart stores Inc., Aldi Inc., and Target Corporation have all opened new stores in the area.

42844 ■ "Marketers Push for Mobile Tuesday as the New Black Friday" in *Advertising Age* **(Vol. 79, December 1, 2008, No. 44, pp. 21)**
Pub: Crain Communications, Inc.

Ed: Natalie Zmuda. **Description:** Marketers are using an innovative approach in an attempt to stimulate business on the Tuesday following Thanksgiving by utilizing consumer's cell phones to alert them of sales or present them with coupons for this typically slow retail business day; with this campaign both advertisers and retailers are hoping to start Mobile Tuesday, another profitable shopping day in line with Black Friday and Cyber Monday.

42845 ■ "Marketing: 'Twill Be the Season" in *Entrepreneur* **(Vol. 35, October 2007, No. 10, pp. 108)**
Pub: Entrepreneur Media Inc.

Ed: Kim T. Gordon. **Description:** Entrepreneurs should plan ahead in order to promote products for the holiday season, since it is peak sales time. They can unify their business theme, use customer incentives, advertise early using TV or radio, and reorganize the company Website. Other ways to market for the holiday season are provided.

42846 ■ "Mars Advertising's Orbit Grows as Other Ad Segments Fall" in *Crain's Detroit Business* **(Vol. 25, June 1, 2009, No. 22, pp. 10)**
Pub: Crain Communications Inc. - Detroit

Ed: Bill Shea. **Description:** An electrical fire burned at Mars Advertising's headquarters in Southfield, Michigan. The company talks about its plans for regrouping and rebuilding. The family firm specializes in in-store marketing that targets consumers already in the buying mode.

42847 ■ "Martha Stewart Launches Macys Line" in *Marketing to Women* **(Vol. 21, March 2008, No. 3, pp. 5)**
Pub: EPM Communications, Inc.

Description: Martha Stewart launches an exclusive line of home decor called Wedgwood as part of her relationship with Macy's stores.

42848 ■ "Maternity Wear Goes Green" in *Marketing to Women* **(Vol. 21, March 2008, No. 3, pp. 3)**
Pub: EPM Communications, Inc.

Description: Mother's Work Inc. has launched a series of environmentally-friendly products made from such sustainable fibers as organic cotton and bamboo.

42849 ■ "Mattel's Got a Monster Holiday Hit, But Will Franchise Have Staying Power?" in *Advertising Age* **(Vol. 81, December 6, 2010, No. 43)**
Pub: Crain Communications, Inc.

Ed: Beth Snyder Bulik. **Description:** Monster High transmedia play expands beyond dolls to merchandise, apparel and entertainment.

42850 ■ "Men May Wear the Pants in the Family, But Women Retain the Power of the Purse" in *Marketing to Women* **(Vol. 22, August 2009, No. 8)**
Pub: EPM Communications, Inc.

Description: Nearly 8 in 10 women say that their opinion holds the most sway in the families' financial decisions. Significant factors that influence women's $100 or more purchases include Online reviews, the opinion of spouse or significant other and expert recommendations. Statistical data included.

42851 ■ "Midtown Tampa Bay Taking Shape" in *The Business Journal-Serving Greater Tampa Bay* **(Vol. 28, September 12, 2008, No. 38, pp. 1)**
Pub: American City Business Journals, Inc.

Ed: Janet Leiser. **Description:** Midtown Tampa Bay's 610,000 square foot shopping and entertainment center is being planned in Florida and is to replace the Tampa Bay One project proposed years earlier. The retail center is to be developed by Bromley Cos. and Opus South Corp. and is expected to have five buildings. Other details about the plan are discussed.

42852 ■ "Midwest Test" in *Crain's Cleveland Business* **(Vol. 28, November 26, 2007, No. 47, pp. 1)**
Pub: Crain Communications, Inc.

Ed: John Booth. **Description:** Provides an overview of the experimental Wal-Mart Supercenter in Elyria which researches consumer preferences with department layouts, new merchandise and even exterior architecture. Store manager Bob Butler said, "We're trying to get out of that box-store look."

42853 ■ "Millennials: The Great White Hope for Wine Industry" in *Advertising Age* **(Vol. 81, December 6, 2010, No. 43, pp. 2)**
Pub: Crain Communications, Inc.

Ed: E.J. Shultz. **Description:** Generation offers category of most growth potential in 30 years and 7-Eleven and vintner are taking notice.

42854 ■ *Million Dollar Website: Simple Steps to Help You Compete with the Big Boys-Even on a Small Business Budget*
Pub: Prentice Hall Press

Ed: Lori Culwell. **Released:** May 9, 2010. **Price:** $19.95. **Description:** Resource for any small business owner wishing to build a successful Website in order to compete with big box stores.

42855 ■ "Minimizing Import Risks" in *Canadian Sailings* **(July 7, 2008)**
Pub: Commonwealth Business Media

Ed: Jack Kohane. **Description:** New food and product safety laws may be enacted by Canada's Parliament; importers, retailers and manufacturers could face huge fines if the new laws are passed.

42856 ■ "Modern Bride Unveiled Exclusively at JCPenney" in *Benzinga.com* **(February 3, 2011)**
Pub: Benzinga.com

Ed: Benzinga Staff. **Description:** JCPenney created its new Modern Bride concept in its bridal find jewelry departments. The new shopping experience is a collaboration between the retailer and Conde Nast catering to the bridal customer.

42857 ■ *The Mom and Pop Store: How the Unsung Heroes of the American Economy Are Surviving and Thriving*
Pub: Walker & Company

Ed: Robert Spector. **Released:** September 1, 2009. **Price:** $26.00. **Description:** The history of small independent retail enterprises and how mom and pop stores in the U.S. continue to thrive through customer service and renewed community support for local businesses.

42858 ■ "Moms Are Still Shopping" in *Marketing to Women* **(Vol. 21, February 2008, No. 2, pp. 1)**
Pub: EPM Communications, Inc.

Description: According to a monthly poll by Parenting Magazine, although the economic signs worsen many moms are still shopping. Statistical data included.

42859 ■ "More Details Emerge on Maersk Plan" in *Charlotte Business Journal* **(Vol. 25, August 13, 2010, No. 21, pp. 1)**
Pub: Charlotte Business Journal

Ed: Will Boye. **Description:** Children Klen Properties has announced the details of its redevelopment plan for a property in Charlotte, North Carolina. The plan includes office and retail space and residential units. The construction of a hotel has also been proposed.

42860 ■ "More Leading Retailers Using Omniture Conversion Solutions to Boost Sales and Ecommerce Performance" in *Internet Wire* **(Sept. 22,2009)**
Pub: Comtex News Network, Inc.

Description: Many retailers are utilizing Omniture conversion solutions to improve the performance of their ecommerce businesses; recent enhancements to Omniture Merchandising and Omniture Recommendations help clients drive increased conversion to their Internet ventures.

42861 ■ "More SouthPark Shopping" in *Charlotte Business Journal* (Vol. 25, July 16, 2010, No. 17, pp. 1)
Pub: Charlotte Business Journal

Ed: Will Boye. **Description:** Charlotte, North Carolina-based Bissel Companies has announced plans to expand its retail presence at the Siskey and Sharon properties in SouthPark. Bissel Companies has requested a rezoning to a mixed-use development classification so that it can utilize the entire ground floor of the Siskey building for restaurant and retail uses.

42862 ■ "Move Marks KKR's Latest Push into Retail" in *Globe & Mail* (March 13, 2007, pp. B17)
Pub: CTVglobemedia Publishing Inc.

Ed: Heather Burke. **Description:** Investment giant Kohlberg Kravis Roberts and Co. has finalized a deal to acquire retail store chain Dollar General Corp. for an estimated 6.9 billion dollars. The company will be entering lucrative retail market by this acquisition.

42863 ■ "A Muddle at Marks & Spencer" in *Barron's* (Vol. 88, July 7, 2008, No. 27, pp. M7)
Pub: Dow Jones & Co., Inc.

Ed: Molly Neal. **Description:** British retail outfit Marks & Spencer is encountering turbulent financial conditions but remains confident in spending 900 million pounds sterling. The company has not made a profit forecast for the first half of 2008 and is suffering from a shrinking cash flow.

42864 ■ "Murdock Carrousel Sold" in *Charlotte Observer* (January 31, 2007)
Pub: Knight-Ridder/Tribune Business News

Ed: Bob Fliss. **Description:** Details on the sale of the Murdock Carrousel shopping center are highlighted. The deal was reported at $281 million.

42865 ■ "Must Work for Food" in *Pet Product News* (Vol. 64, November 2010, No. 11, pp. 24)
Pub: BowTie Inc.

Ed: Wendy Bedwell-Wilson. **Description:** Pet supply retailers can benefit from stocking foods and treats that address obesity, which according to the American Veterinary Medical Association, has become the most prevalent nutritional disorder in dogs. With the rise in dog obesity, products like work-for-their food toys have been sought by dog owners.

42866 ■ "National Cattlemen's Beef Association" in *Retail Merchandiser* (Vol. 51, September-October 2011, No. 5, pp. 77)
Pub: Phoenix Media Corporation

Description: National Cattlemen's Beef Association offers a wide range of tools and information to keep its members informed regarding the state of the beef industry. Their Website provides tools to help cattle producers improve operations.

42867 ■ "Neighbors Rally for Dollar Store" in *Chattanooga Times/Free Press* (August 4, 2010)
Pub: Chattanooga Times/Free Press

Description: Neighbors are rallying to keep the Family Dollar Store in their city open. The proposed new store would expand the grocery portion of its retail discount shop.

42868 ■ "New Dollar Store Opens in Shoppes at Richland" in *Aiken Standard* (October 15, 2010)
Pub: Aiken Standard

Ed: Haley Hughes. **Description:** Information regarding the opening of Froogle's Dollar Store is given. The store opened in Richland area of South Carolina.

42869 ■ "New Family Dollar Store Now Open in Hermon" in *Bangor Daily News* (August 12, 2010)
Pub: Bangor Daily News

Ed: Dawn Gagnon. **Description:** A new Family Dollar Store opened its doors at the newly expanded Hermon Shopping Center in Bangor, Maine.

42870 ■ "A New Mix of Tenants Settles In" in *Crain's New York Business* (Vol. 24, January 14, 2008, No. 2, pp. 26)
Pub: Crain Communications, Inc.

Ed: Andrew Marks. **Description:** More and more nonfinancial firms are relocating downtown due to the new retailers and restaurants that are reshaping the look and feel of lower Manhattan.

42871 ■ "New York Firm Secures Sheffield, Amherst Centers for $26 Million" in *Crain's Cleveland Business* (Vol. 28, December 3, 2007, No. 48)
Pub: Crain Communications, Inc.

Ed: Stan Bullard. **Description:** Silverman Realty Group completed a $26 million transaction which made it the new owner of the Sheffield Crossing and Amherst Marketplace shopping centers in Lorain County.

42872 ■ "Nine Sectors to Watch: Retail" in *Canadian Business* (Vol. 81, December 24, 2007, No. 1, pp. 56)
Pub: Rogers Media

Ed: Zena Olijnyk. **Description:** Canadian consumers are expected to spend more in 2008 as the Canadian dollar hit par with the U.S. greenback after the slowdown in the U.S. economy. Forecasts on retail sales growth are presented.

42873 ■ "No Frills - And No Dodge" in *Crain's Detroit Business* (Vol. 24, September 22, 2008, No. 38, pp. 3)
Pub: Crain Communications, Inc.

Ed: Bradford Wernie. **Description:** Chrysler LLC is in the middle of a business plan known as Project Genesis, a five-year strategy in which the company will reduce the dealer count by combining its Jeep, Chrysler and Dodge brands under one rooftop wherever possible. Not every dealer will be able to arrange this deal because of the investment required to expand stores in which have low-overhead; many of these stores feel that low-overhead structures are more likely to survive difficult times than the larger stores in which the Genesis consolidation plan intends to implement.

42874 ■ "Nordstrom Points for Richmond Heights" in *Saint Louis Business Journal* (Vol. 31, August 5, 2011, No. 50, pp. 1)
Pub: Saint Louis Business Journal

Ed: E.B. Solomont. **Description:** Nordstrom is set to upgrade its offerings for its second full-line store in St. Louis, Missouri. The new store is expected to benefit nearby shops.

42875 ■ "Offer for Sears Canada 'Inadequate'" in *Globe & Mail* (February 10, 2006, pp. B4)
Pub: CTVglobemedia Publishing Inc.

Ed: Marina Strauss. **Description:** The financial feasibility of Sears Holdings Corp.'s proposed acquisition of Sears Canada Inc., for $835 million, is discussed.

42876 ■ *On the Make: Clerks and the Quest for Capital in Nineteenth-Century America*
Pub: NYU Press

Ed: Brian Luskey. **Released:** January 1, 2010. **Price:** $48.00. **Description:** Through exploration into the diaries, newspapers, credit reports, census data, advice literature and fiction, the book presents the origins of the white collar culture, the antebellum clerk.

42877 ■ "Online All the Time" in *Retail Merchandiser* (Vol. 51, July-August 2011, No. 4, pp. 18)
Pub: Phoenix Media Corporation

Description: Ecommerce sales are rising at a steady pace and for cross-channel retailers it is boosting sales in the weak economy. Online sales are expected to reach $188 billion in 2011, boasting a 13.7 rate of growth.

42878 ■ "Online Security Crackdown: Scanning Service Oversees Site Security at David's Bridal" in (Vol. 84, July 2008, No. 7, pp. 46)
Pub: Chain Store Age

Ed: Samantha Murphy. **Description:** Online retailers are beefing up security on their Websites. Cyber

thieves use retail systems in order to gain entry to consumer data. David's Bridal operates over 275 bridal showrooms in the U.S. and has a one-stop wedding resource for new brides planning weddings.

42879 ■ "Options Abound in Winter Wares" in *Pet Product News* (Vol. 64, November 2010, No. 11, pp. 1)
Pub: BowTie Inc.

Ed: Maggie M. Shein. **Description:** Pet supply manufacturers emphasize creating top-notch construction and functional design in creating winter clothing for pets. Meanwhile, retailers and pet owners seek human-inspired style, quality, and versatility for pets' winter clothing. How retailers generate successful sales of pets' winter clothing outside of traditional brand marketing is also examined.

42880 ■ *Over the Counter*
Pub: The Mercier Press, Ltd.

Ed: Keogh. **Released:** January 1, 2009. **Price:** $54.95. **Description:** An overview of the changing landscape of Cork, Ireland's retail stores is presented.

42881 ■ "Peacocks Launches Its First Wedding Dress" in *Benzinga.com* (July 1, 2011)
Pub: Benzinga.com

Ed: Benzinga Staff. **Description:** Peacocks, a leading fashion retailer in the United Kingdom launched its first wedding dress available for sale in August 2011.

42882 ■ "Penney's Buys Wal-Mart Site" in *Crain's Chicago Business* (Vol. 31, March 31, 2008, No. 13, pp. 13)
Pub: Crain Communications, Inc.

Ed: Eddie Baeb. **Description:** J.C. Penny Co. bought the closed Wal-Mart location in Crystal Lake and plans to open a store next year in its push to become more prominent in non-mall locations; Penney plans to expand and renovate the store.

42883 ■ "Penny Chief Shops For Shares" in *Barron's* (Vol. 88, July 7, 2008, No. 27, pp. 29)
Pub: Dow Jones & Co., Inc.

Ed: Teresa Rivas. **Description:** Myron Ullman III, chairman and chief executive officer of J.C. Penney, purchased $1 million worth of shares of the company. He now owns 393,140 shares of the company and an additional 1,282 on his 401(k) plan.

42884 ■ "People; E-Commerce, Online Games, Mobile Apps" in *Advertising Age* (Vol. 80, October 19, 2009, No. 35, pp. 14)
Pub: Crain's Communications

Ed: Nat Ives. **Description:** Profile of People Magazine and the ways in which the publisher is moving its magazine forward by exploring new concepts in a time of declining newsstand sales and advertising pages; among the strategies are e-commerce such as the brand People Style Watch in which consumers are able highlight clothing and jewelry and then connect to retailers' sites and a channel on Taxi TV, the network of video-touch screens in New Your City taxis.

42885 ■ "People; E-Commerce, Online Games, Mobile Apps: This Isn't Your Mom's People" in *Advertising Age* (Vol. 80, October 19, 2009, No. 35)
Pub: Crain's Communications

Ed: Nat Ives. **Description:** Profile of People Magazine and the ways in which the publisher is moving its magazine forward by exploring new concepts in a time of declining newsstand sales and advertising pages; among the strategies are e-commerce such as the brand People Style Watch in which consumers are able highlight clothing and jewelry and then connect to retailers' sites and a channel on Taxi TV, the network of video-touch screens in New Your City taxis.

42886 ■ "Perfecting Customer Services" in *Pet Product News* (Vol. 64, November 2010, No. 11, pp. 18)
Pub: BowTie Inc.

Description: Pet supply retailers are encouraged to emphasize customer experience and sales representatives' knowledge of the store's product offerings to foster repeat business. Employee protocols could be implemented to improve customer interaction. Other guidelines on developing a pet supply retail environment that advances repeat business are presented.

42887 ■ "PGA Tour: Course Management" in Retail Merchandiser (Vol. 51, September-October 2011, No. 5, pp. 38)
Pub: Phoenix Media Corporation

Ed: Eric Slack. Description: PGA Tour must reach new customers and solidify relationships with its traditional base in order to continue its success. The PGA brand equity has translated into one of the largest retail licensing operations worldwide.

42888 ■ "Phillips Edison Launches $1.8B Retail REIT" in Business Courier (Vol. 27, October 15, 2010, No. 24, pp. 1)
Pub: Business Courier

Ed: Dan Monk. Description: Retail center operator Phillips Edison & Company is organizing a real estate investment trust (REIT) to raise $1.8 billion to finance the planned purchase of 150 grocery-centered shopping centers around the U.S. The offering would be Phillips largest. Phillips Edison employesss 174 workers and operates 250 shopping centers nationwide.

42889 ■ "Pink Label: Victoria's Sales Secret" in Advertising Age (Vol. 79, July 7, 2008, No. 26, pp. 4)
Pub: Crain Communications, Inc.

Ed: Natalie Zmuda. Description: Victoria Secret's Pink label accounted for roughly 17 percent of the retailer's total sales last year. The company is launching a Collegiate Collection which will be promoted by a campus tour program.

42890 ■ "Plans for $160M Condo Resort in Wisconsin Dells Moves Forward" in Commercial Property News (March 18, 2008)
Pub: Nielsen Company

Description: Plans for the Grand Cambrian Resort in the Wisconsin Dells is discussed. The luxury condominium resort will include condos, townhomes, and condo-hotel style residences, two water parts, meeting space and indoor entertainment space, as well as a spa, four restaurants and retail offerings.

42891 ■ "Point, Click, Buy" in Barron's (Vol. 90, September 6, 2010, No. 36, pp. 11)
Pub: Barron's Editorial & Corporate Headquarters

Ed: Vito J. Racanelli. Description: Non-travel online retail sales from January to July 2010 increased nine percent which indicates that online shopping for the coming holidays will be good. Online sales are outpacing traditional shopping, but pricing is still critical.

42892 ■ "Pop N Go Launching Into Dollar Store Market" in Internet Wire (July 14, 2009)
Pub: Comtex News Network, Inc.

Description: Pop N Go, Inc. announced that it will test the company's flagship popcorn vending machine in the rapidly growing dollar store distribution channel.

42893 ■ "Population Growing Faster Than Retail, Service Sector" in Crain's New York Business (Vol. 24, January 14, 2008, No. 2, pp. 30)
Pub: Crain Communications, Inc.

Ed: Andrew Marks. Description: Downtown Manhattan is seeing more residential development; however, as more families call the area home the need for more retail and services is becoming evident.

42894 ■ "'Pre-Sale' for Planned Could Mich Tower" in Crain's Chicago Business (Vol. 31, March 24, 2008, No. 12, pp. 14)
Pub: Crain Communications, Inc.

Ed: Eddie Baeb. Description: Condominium developer William Warman is planning to build a mixed-use tower at 300 North Michigan Avenue which would include a hotel, retail space, apartments and a parking garage. Mr. Warman is looking for investors to buy part or all of the space in order to make it easier to land financing.

42895 ■ "Prepaid Cards and State Unclaimed Property Laws" in Franchise Law Journal (Vol. 27, Summer 2007, No. 1, pp. 23)
Pub: American Bar Association

Ed: Phillip W. Bohl, Kathryn J. Bergstrom, Kevin J. Moran. Description: Unredeemed value of electronic prepaid stored-value credit cards for retail purchases is known as breakage. Laws governing unclaimed property as it relates to these gift cards is covered.

42896 ■ "Procter & Gamble Boosts Bet on Exclusive Brands" in Business Courier (Vol. 27, July 9, 2010, No. 10, pp. 1)
Pub: Business Courier

Ed: Jon Newberry. Description: Procter & Gamble is creating more special versions of its brands such as Pringles and Pampers exclusively for retail partners such as Tesco in the U.K. The greater push towards this direction is seen as a way to regain market share.

42897 ■ "Profit Strong Rona to Maintain Acquisition Strategy" in Globe & Mail (February 22, 2007, pp. B14)
Pub: CTVglobemedia Publishing Inc.

Description: Canada-based Rona Inc., home improvement retailer that reported record annual profit in 2006, will continue its strategy of acquisitions. The company has reported profits of $190.6 million in 2006.

42898 ■ "Promotions Create a Path to Better Profit" in Pet Product News (Vol. 64, December 2010, No. 12, pp. 1)
Pub: BowTie Inc.

Ed: Joan Hustace Walker. Description: Pet store retailers can boost small mammal sales by launching creative marketing and promotions such as social networking and adoption days.

42899 ■ "Proposed Triangle Redo in Motion" in Crain's Cleveland Business (Vol. 28, October 15, 2007, No. 41, pp. 1)
Pub: Crain Communications, Inc.

Ed: Stan Bullard. Description: Zaremba Homes and MRN Ltd. are partnering to redevelop the so-called Triangle section of University Circle. The proposed project will include a total of 434 new rental and for-sale residential suites and as much as 227,000 square feet of retail and restaurant space.

42900 ■ "Pssst! Buzz About Target" in Barron's (Vol. 89, July 27, 2009, No. 30, pp. 15)
Pub: Dow Jones & Co., Inc.

Ed: Katherine Cheng. Description: Target rebutted the rumor that they will disassociate themselves from a line of clothing inspired by the television show 'Gossip Girl'. Target's spokesman says that the retailer intends to remain closely identified with the show. Target's sales should benefit from the hotly anticipated clothing line.

42901 ■ "Q&A: David Labistour" in Canadian Business (Vol. 81, March 17, 2008, No. 4, pp. 10)
Pub: Rogers Media

Ed: Lauren McKeon. Description: David Labistour says that the difference between being a co-op retailer and a corporate-owned retailer in the case of Mountain Equipment Co-op (MEC) is that the company is owned by their customers and not by shareholders. Labistour also says that MEC works with their factories to ensure that these maintain ethical standards in the manufacturing process.

42902 ■ QuickBooks X for Dummies
Pub: John Wiley & Sons, Incorporated

Ed: Stephen L. Nelson. Released: November 2006. Price: $21.99. Description: Key features of QuickBooks software for small business are introduced. Invoicing and credit memos, recoding sales receipts, accounting, budgeting, taxes, payroll, financial reports, job estimating, billing, tracking, data backup, are among the features.

42903 ■ "Recovery on Tap for 2010?" in Orlando Business Journal (Vol. 26, January 1, 2010, No. 31, pp. 1)
Pub: American City Business Journals

Ed: Melanie Stawicki Azam, Richard Bilbao, Christopher Boyd, Anjali Fluker. Description: Economic forecasts for Central Florida's leading business sectors in 2010 are presented. These sectors include housing, film and TV, sports business, law, restaurants, aviation, tourism and hospitality, banking and finance, commercial real estate, retail, health care, insurance, higher education, and manufacturing. According to some local executives, Central Florida's economy will slowly recover in 2010.

42904 ■ "Rent Check" in Boston Business Journal (Vol. 31, July 29, 2011, No. 27, pp. 1)
Pub: Boston Business Journal

Ed: Lisa van der Pool. Description: Merchants at Newbury Street in Boston, Massachusetts are concerned with the annual increase of already inflated rents that prevent many small businesses from expanding.

42905 ■ "Report: McD's Pepsi Score Best With Young Hispanics" in Brandweek (Vol. 49, April 21, 2008, No. 16, pp. 8)
Pub: VNU Business Media, Inc.

Ed: Della de Lafuente. Description: According to a new report, in order to reach Hispanic Gen Yers, marketing strategists need to understand this demographic's "bi-dentity," something which has proved an elusive task to many marketers. Another trend is the emergence of Latinas who have careers, as opposed to just jobs. There is an opportunity to tap this new, young and empowered female market with innovative messaging. Statistical data included.

42906 ■ "Research Reports: How Analysts Size Up Companies" in Barron's (Vol. 90, August 23, 2010, No. 34, pp. M13)
Pub: Barron's Editorial & Corporate Headquarters

Description: Shares of Sirius XM Radio, Target and Deere and Company received an eBuyE rating, while shares of Research in Motion got an eNeutralE rating.

42907 ■ "Rest Easy, Retailers" in Pet Product News (Vol. 64, December 2010, No. 12, pp. S1)
Pub: BowTie Inc.

Ed: Wendy Bedwell-Wilson. Description: Pointers on how retailers can market all-natural beds and bedding products for pets are provided. The demand for these pet beds and bedding products has been increasing as customers become aware of the benefits of natural rest and relaxation products.

42908 ■ "Retail in Austin Strong, Will Continue to Be" in Austin Business JournalInc. (Vol. 29, January 22, 2010, No. 46, pp. 1)
Pub: American City Business Journals

Ed: Jacob Dirr. Description: Retail sector in Austin, Texas has outpaced the national average in value, mid-tier, high-end and drugs retail sectors, according to a report by Pitney Bowes. The national consulting firm's report has projected growth in every sector until the end of fiscal 2012. Data regarding other sectors is also included.

42909 ■ "Retail Briefs - Dollar Store Opens in Long Leaf Mall" in Star-News (November 5, 2010)
Pub: Star-News Media

Ed: Judy Royal. Description: Dollar Delight$ opened a new shop in Long Leaf Mall in Wilmington, North Carolina. The store will carry gift bags, balloons, party supplies, greeting cards, school supplies, health and beauty products, hardware, baby items, toys, Christmas goods, crafts, housewares and jewelry in its inventory.

42910 ■ "Retail Center Pitched" in Business Courier (Vol. 27, June 18, 2010, No. 7, pp. 1)
Pub: Business Courier

Ed: Dan Monk. Description: Jeffrey R. Anderson Real Estate Inc.'s plan for a retail center in Butler County, Ohio could have three department stores in the 1.1 million-square-foot property. An outdoor sports retailer is also part of the plans.

42911 ■ "Retail Center Planned for Canton Site" in Boston Business Journal (Vol. 29, May 20, 2011, No. 2, pp. 1)
Pub: American City Business Journals Inc.

Ed: Daniel J. Sernovitz. Description: A real estate development team is planning to build a shopping center at Canton Crossing in Baltimore, Maryland and is near closing the deal with ExxonMobil Corporation who owns the waterfront site.

42912 ■ **"Retail Franchises to Start Now" in** *Entrepreneur* **(Vol. 37, August 2009, No. 8, pp. 88)**
Pub: Entrepreneur Media, Inc.
Ed: Tracy Stapp. **Description:** Listing of retail franchises is presented and is categorized based on their products sold. The total cost of the franchise and the website are also included as well as additional statistical data.

42913 ■ **"Retail: Loblaw Goes for Broke" in** *Canadian Business* **(Vol. 80, January 29, 2007, No. 3, pp. 7)**
Pub: Rogers Media
Ed: Zena Oiljnyk. **Description:** The efforts of Loblaw Companies Limited to reduce its operational expenses are described. The company's decision to reduce the number of employees at its national and regional offices, besides closing some of its facilities, is discussed.

42914 ■ *The Retail Revolution: How Wal-Mart Created a Brave New World of Business*
Pub: Metropolitan Books
Ed: Nelson Lichtenstein. **Released:** July 21, 2009. **Price:** $25.00. **Description:** Comprehensive discussion on how Wal-Mart changed retailing, and its place in the changing global economy.

42915 ■ **"Retail Slump Deflates Local Development" in** *Business Courier* **(Vol. 24, February 29, 2008, No. 47, pp. 1)**
Pub: American City Business Journals, Inc.
Ed: Lisa Biank Fasig. **Description:** 2007 sales of the retail industry are the slowest since the year 2003, driving retail stores to reconsider their expansion plans for 2008. A number of retail projects have been delayed, cancelled or altered, including Newport Pavilion, Rivers Crossing, Wal-Mart Supercenters, Legacy Place and Millworks. The impacts of retail slowdown on development projects are analyzed further.

42916 ■ **"Retail Woes: The Shoe Doesn't Fit for Gerald Loftin's Stock Picks" in** *Black Enterprise* **(Vol. 38, July 2008, No. 12, pp. 40)**
Pub: Earl G. Graves Publishing Co. Inc.
Ed: Steve Garmhausen. **Description:** Each of the three stocks that Gerald Loftin picked in May 2007 have lost money; DSW, the designer shoe retailer, fell by 63.7 percent; paint and coatings retailer Sherwin-Williams Co. fell by 7.2 percent; and Verizon Communications Inc. fell by 1.4 percent. Statistical data included.

42917 ■ **"Retailers, City Clash Over Wages" in** *Baltimore Business Journal* **(Vol. 28, July 9, 2010, No. 9, pp. 1)**
Pub: Baltimore Business Journal
Ed: Daniel J. Sernovitz. **Description:** A bill pending before the City Council of Baltimore, Maryland would mandate the city's major retailers to pay their employees at least $10.57 per hour, $3 higher than was state law requires. Major retailers, as defined in the said bill by Councilwoman Mary Pat Clarke, have gross sales of at least $10 million. Reactions of the retailers affected are presented.

42918 ■ **"Retailers Dig In For Holiday Shopping Push" in** *Business Review, Albany New York* **(Vol. 34, November 30, 2007, No. 35, pp. 1)**
Pub: American City Business Journals, Inc.
Ed: Michael DeMasi. **Description:** Tough economic conditions have led to lower consumer spending and retailers in Albany, New York and nationwide experienced mix results during the Black Friday weekend. Local retailers enjoyed higher sales in 2007 compared to 2006 and the National Retail Federation projects that retail sales will climb by four percent. Holiday retail trade forecasts are discussed.

42919 ■ **"Retailers Pull Out All Stops to Combat Poor Projections" in** *Austin Business JournalInc.* **(Vol. 28, November 21, 2008, No. 36, pp. 1)**
Pub: American City Business Journals
Ed: Jean Kwon. **Description:** Report from Wachovia Economics Group reports that holiday sales for 2008

are expected to decline by 2 percent and local retailers are planning to boost holiday sales through marketing efforts, which include giving freebies to early shoppers. Details on marketing strategies of several retailers are provided.

42920 ■ **"Retailers Report 'Shrinkage' of Inventory on the Rise" in** *Arkansas Business* **(Vol. 26, September 28, 2009, No. 39, pp. 17)**
Pub: Journal Publishing Inc.
Ed: Mark Friedman. **Description:** According to a National Retail Security Survey report released last June, retailers across the country have lost about $36.5 billion in shrinkage, most of it at the hands of employees and shoplifters alike. Statistical data included.

42921 ■ **"Retailers Tap into War-Room Creativity of Employees" in** *Globe & Mail* **(March 12, 2007, pp. B1)**
Pub: CTVglobemedia Publishing Inc.
Ed: Marina Strauss. **Description:** The methods adopted by Canadian Tire Corporation Ltd. to utilize the creative abilities of its employees for innovation during new product development are discussed.

42922 ■ **"Retailers, Your Will, and More" in** *Agency Sales Magazine* **(Vol. 39, July 2009, No. 7, pp. 46)**
Pub: MANA
Ed: Melvin H. Daskal. **Description:** IRS audit guide for small retail businesses is presented. Tips on how to make a will with multiple beneficiaries are discussed together with medical expenses that can not be deducted.

42923 ■ **"The Return of the Infomercial" in** *Canadian Business* **(Vol. 83, September 14, 2010, No. 15, pp. 19)**
Pub: Rogers Media Ltd.
Ed: James Cowan. **Description:** Infomercials or direct response ads have helped some products succeed in the marketplace. The success of infomercials is due to the cheap advertising rates, expansion into retail stores and the products' oddball appeal. Insights into the popularity of infomercial products on the Internet and on television are given.

42924 ■ **"Riding High" in** *Small Business Opportunities* **(November 2008)**
Pub: Entrepreneur Media Inc.
Ed: Stan Roberts. **Description:** Profile of David Sanborn who found a way to turn his passion for biking into a moneymaking opportunity by opening his own bicycle shops; Sanborn's goal is to become the largest independent bike retailer in the United States.

42925 ■ **"The Rise of Pompei" in** *Retail Merchandiser* **(Vol. 51, September-October 2011, No. 5, pp. 13)**
Pub: Phoenix Media Corporation
Description: Soho creative consulting group follows its C3 philosophy to create an invigorated brand experience that transforms customers from consumers to empowered buyers. Pompei AD is a leading creative consultancy that specializes in design and branding for retail, museum, hospitality, and other sectors.

42926 ■ **"The Role of Human and Financial Capital in the Profitability and Growth of Women-Owned Small Firms" in** *Journal of Small Business Management*
Pub: Blackwell Publishing, Inc.
Ed: Susan Coleman. **Description:** Examines the relationship between the human and financial capital in both men and women-owned businesses and firm performance in the service and retail sectors.

42927 ■ **"Ross Stores Reports Spectacular First Quarter" in** *Home Textiles Today* **(Vol. 31, May 24, 2011, No. 13, pp. 2)**
Pub: Reed Business Information
Ed: James Mammarella. **Description:** Retailer Ross Stores reported strong sales and profit gains for first quarter 2011, with their home department helping to lead the way.

42928 ■ **"Rough Q1 Begs Question: Is the Crocs Craze Over?" in** *Brandweek* **(Vol. 49, April 21, 2008, No. 16, pp. 16)**
Pub: VNU Business Media, Inc.
Ed: Eric Newman. **Description:** Crocs, a rubber shoemaker, announced last week that it missed its expected first quarter revenues by 15 percent. The popular rubber sandals are suffering in sales due to a number of factors including a tougher economic environment, less expensive, knock-off brands, the cold weather delay of the spring season and fading consumer interest in plastic shoes.

42929 ■ **"Roundtable: Functional Foods and Treats" in** *Pet Product News* **(Vol. 64, December 2010, No. 12, pp. S1)**
Pub: BowTie Inc.
Description: Executives and business owners from the pet supplies industries deliberate on the role of functional foods in the retail sector. Functional foods pertain to foods with specified health benefits. Insight into marketing functional foods and convincing pet owners to make the transition to these products is examined.

42930 ■ **"Rule of the Masses: Reinventing Fashion Via Crowdsourcing" in** *WWD* **(Vol. 200, July 26, 2010, No. 17, pp. 1)**
Pub: Conde Nast Publications Inc.
Ed: Cate T. Corcoran. **Description:** Large apparel brands and retailers are crowdsourcing as a way to increase customer loyalty and to build their businesses.

42931 ■ **"Sears' Profit Result Puts Ball in Parent's Court" in** *Globe & Mail* **(February 3, 2006, pp. B4)**
Pub: CTVglobemedia Publishing Inc.
Ed: Marina Strauss. **Description:** Sears Canada Inc. achieved $783.4 million in profits for fourth quarter 2005. The financial performance of the company paves way for the acquisition of Sears Holdings Corp.

42932 ■ **"Secrets To Trade Show Success" in** *Women Entrepreneur* **(September 12, 2008)**
Pub: Entrepreneur Media Inc.
Ed: Lesley Spencer Pyle. **Description:** Trade shows require an enormous amount of work, but they are an investment that can pay off handsomely because they allow a business to get their product or service in front of their target market. Advice regarding trade shows is given including selecting the correct venue, researching the affair and following up on leads obtained at the event.

42933 ■ *Selling Online: Canada's Bestselling Guide to Becoming a Successful E-Commerce Merchant*
Pub: John Wiley and Sons Canada Ltd.
Ed: Jim Carroll; Rick Broadhead. **Released:** September 6, 2002. **Description:** Helps individuals build online retail enterprises; this updated version includes current tools, information and success strategies, how to launch an online storefront, security, marketing strategies, and mistakes to avoid.

42934 ■ **"Sheets Makers Optimistic Amid Price, Delivery Issues" in** *Home Textiles Today* **(Vol. 31, May 24, 2011, No. 13, pp. 8)**
Pub: Reed Business Information
Ed: Jill Rowen. **Description:** Retail sales of sheets and pillowcases dropped 4.7 percent in volume in 2009. Retailers pulled back inventory significantly in 2010. Statistical data included.

42935 ■ **"Shopped Out; Retailing Gloom" in** *The Economist* **(Vol. 390, January 3, 2009, No. 8612, pp. 26)**
Pub: The Economist Newspaper Inc.
Description: Economic volatility in the retail sector is having an impact on a number of countries around the globe. Europe is experiencing hard economic times as well and unless businesses have a strong business plan banks feel unable to lend the money necessary to tide the retailers over. The falling pound has increased the cost of imported goods and small to midsize retail chains may not be able to weather such an unforgiving economic climate.

42936 ■ "Shoppers Targets an Upscale Move" in *Globe & Mail* **(January 19, 2007, pp. B4)**
Pub: CTVglobemedia Publishing Inc.
Ed: Marina Strauss. **Description:** Shoppers Drug Mart Corp.'s plan to boost sales of cosmetics and take up global sourcing to offer new products is discussed.

42937 ■ "Shoppes of Kenwood Files Chap. 11" in *Business Courier* **(Vol. 26, December 18, 2009, No. 34, pp. 1)**
Pub: American City Business Journals, Inc.
Ed: Jon Newberry. **Description:** Shoppes of Kenwood filed for Chapter 11 reorganization in US Bankruptcy Court just as the property was scheduled to be offered at a sheriff's auction. Details of the filing are included.

42938 ■ "Shopping Around for New Ideas" in *Canadian Business* **(Vol. 79, July 17, 2006, No. 14-15, pp. 76)**
Pub: Rogers Media
Description: Pensions should be a win-win situation for both the employer and the employee. The perspective of both parties concerning pension plans is explored as well as the need to amend laws in order to make sure that one class of merchant does not suffer at the cost of another.

42939 ■ "Silver Springs Creamery Opens Retail" in *Bellingham Business Journal* **(Vol. March 2010, pp. 3)**
Pub: Sound Publishing Inc.
Description: Eric Sundstrom, owner of Silver Springs Creamery, announced the opening of its on-site retail store that will sell the farm's goat and cow cheese, yogurt, ice cream and flesh milk.

42940 ■ "Six Sears Board Members to Resign in April" in *Globe & Mail* **(March 1, 2006, pp. B1)**
Pub: CTVglobemedia Publishing Inc.
Ed: Marina Strauss. **Description:** The reasons behind the departure of six board members of Sears Canada Inc. are presented.

42941 ■ "The Sky's the Limit" in *Retail Merchandiser* **(Vol. 51, July-August 2011, No. 4, pp. 64)**
Pub: Phoenix Media Corporation
Ed: John Capizzi. **Description:** Mars Retail Group (MRG) is the licensing division handling M&M's Brand Candies. Since taking over the brand they have expanded from 12 licensees to 50 licensees with new offerings.

42942 ■ "Small Business Sales" in *Small Business Economic Trends* **(January, pp. 7)**
Pub: National Federation of Independent Business
Description: Graph from a survey of small businesses in the U.S. is given, representing sales from January 1986 to December 2007. Actual sales (prior three months) and expected sales (next three months) were compared in the graph. Tables of actual sales changes and sales expectations from January 2002 to December 2007 are also given.

42943 ■ "Small Fish, Big Box Stores" in *Hawaii Business* **(Vol. 53, November 2007, No. 5, pp. 55)**
Pub: Hawaii Business Publishing
Ed: Jolyn Okimoto Rosa. **Description:** Ohana Seafoods can be found at big-box stores such as Costco, Marukai and Don Quijote. Owner Jeffrey Yee spends his weekend at a farmers market to have direct contact with his customers and get feedback right away. Ohana offers ready-to cook fish products, sauces and fish.

42944 ■ "Smarts Drive Sales" in *Pet Product News* **(Vol. 64, December 2010, No. 12, pp. 1)**
Pub: BowTie Inc.
Ed: Karen Shugart. **Description:** Retailers could make smart decisions by deciding how to best attract customers into their stores or resolving whether to nurture in-store or buy herps (reptiles) from suppliers.

Paying attention to these smart decisions could help boost customer interest in herps and address customer demands.

42945 ■ "Smoke Signals: Johnny Drake On What To Expect In a Fine Cigar" in *Black Enterprise* **(Vol. 38, December 2007, No. 5, pp. 195)**
Pub: Earl G. Graves Publishing Co. Inc.
Ed: Alan Hughes. **Description:** Profile of Johnny Drake, co-owner of the retail tobacco company Renaissance Cigar Emporium. According to the Retail Tobacco Dealers of America, 320 million handmade cigars are sold in the U.S. annually.

42946 ■ "Some Atlantic Beach Leaders Leery About Convenience Store Safety Measure" in *Florida Times-Union* **(November 3, 2010)**
Pub: Florida Times-Union
Ed: Drew Dixon. **Description:** Jacksonville, Florida authorities are proposing a new ordinance that would require convenience stores to upgrade safety measures to protect store workers and customers from robbery and other crimes.

42947 ■ "Staples Advantage Receives NJPA National Contract for Janitorial Supplies" in *Professional Services Close-Up* **(April 22, 2011)**
Pub: Close-Up Media
Description: Staples Advantage, the business-to-business division of Staples Inc. was awarded a contract for janitorial supplies to members of the National Joint Powers Alliance (NJPA). NJPA is a member-owned buying cooperative serving public and private schools, state and local governments, and nonprofit organizations.

42948 ■ "The State of the Stores" in *Playthings* **(Vol. 106, November 1, 2008, No. 10, pp. 8)**
Pub: Reed Business Information
Ed: Dana French. **Description:** Investigation into the top twenty-five toy and game retailers shows that video games and related handheld and console systems as well as computer games were number one with America's children in 2007.

42949 ■ "Staying Power" in *Canadian Business* **(Vol. 79, November 6, 2006, No. 22, pp. 73)**
Pub: Rogers Media
Ed: John Gray. **Description:** The effects on brand image on customer choices are analyzed. The need of maintaining brand image is also emphasized.

42950 ■ "Steady Spending in Retail" in *Business Week* **(September 22, 2008, No. 4100, pp. 13)**
Pub: McGraw-Hill Companies, Inc.
Ed: Tara Kalwarski. **Description:** Retail jobs have begun to decline on the national level despite the two percent growth in the industry over the last year; much of the growth has been attributed to the sales of higher-priced oil products.

42951 ■ "Storm Takes Toll On Area Businesses" in *The Business Journal - Serving Phoenix and the Valley of the Sun* **(Vol. 28, September 5, 2008, No. 52, pp. 1)**
Pub: American City Business Journals, Inc.
Ed: Chris Casacchia. **Description:** Many small businesses in Phoenix, Arizona have lost sales and goods from storms and power outages. Retailers were forced to dispose of spoiled products. Details of damages inflicted by the storm are also presented.

42952 ■ "Studies Mixed on State's 2008 Retail Outlook" in *Crain's Detroit Business* **(Vol. 24, March 24, 2008, No. 12, pp. 28)**
Pub: Crain Communications, Inc.
Ed: Nancy Kaffer. **Description:** Marcus and Millichap Real Estate Investment Services and the Michigan Retailers Association have released two separate studies concerning Michigan retailers in 2008. According to its report, MRA is forecasting modest retail growth later this year; however, the study conducted

by national commercial real estate brokers Marcus and Millichap predicts increasing vacancy rates, flat employment and decreasing sales for Detroit-area retailers.

42953 ■ "Study: New Moms Build A Lot of Brand Buzz" in *Brandweek* **(Vol. 49, April 21, 2008, No. 16, pp. 7)**
Pub: VNU Business Media, Inc.
Description: According to a new survey which sampled 1,721 pregnant women and new moms, this demographic is having 109 word-of-mouth conversations per week concerning products, services and brands. Two-thirds of these conversations directly involve brand recommendations. The Internet is driving these word-of-mouth, or W-O-M, conversations among this segment, beating out magazines, television and other forms of media.

42954 ■ "Suited for Success" in *Retail Merchandiser* **(Vol. 51, July-August 2011, No. 4, pp. 6)**
Pub: Phoenix Media Corporation
Description: MyBestFit is a size-matching body scanner that helps consumers find the perfect size clothing for themselves, giving brick and mortar retailers an edge on ecommerce competitors.

42955 ■ "SunBank Plans Expansion Via Wall-Mart" in *Business Journal-Serving Phoenix and the Valley of the Sun* **(Vol. 10, November 9, 2007)**
Pub: American City Business Journals, Inc.
Ed: Chris Casacchia. **Description:** SunBank plans to install 12 to 14 branches in Wal-Mart stores in Arizona and hire 100 bankers by the end of 2008. Wal-Mart also offers financial products at other stores through partnerships with other banks.

42956 ■ "Sunbrella Engages Consumers Via Social Media" in *Home Textiles Today* **(Vol. 31, May 24, 2011, No. 13, pp. 4)**
Pub: Reed Business Information
Description: Performance fabric brand Sunbrella is marketing to social media, such as Facebook and Twitter, in order to boost consumer interest and retailer support.

42957 ■ "The Sure Thing That Flopped" in *Harvard Business Review* **(Vol. 86, July-August 2008, No. 8, pp. 29)**
Pub: Harvard Business School Press
Ed: Gerald Zaltman; Lindsay Zaltman. **Description:** Fictitious brand extension scenario is presented, with contributors providing suggestions and advice. The company's struggles with expanding the brand may be alleviated by improving consumer research, focusing on emotional responses to products and services.

42958 ■ "Surplus Store Rebuilding Again" in *Spokesman-Review* **(November 17, 2010)**
Pub: Spokesman Review
Ed: Chelsea Bannach. **Description:** Retail business owner, David Arnold Sr., is rebuilding his Army Surplus store in Spokane, Washington after a truck crashed into the building.

42959 ■ "Survey Says Commercial Real Estate Headed for Turbulence" in *Commercial Property News* **(March 17, 2008)**
Pub: Nielsen Company
Description: Commercial real estate sector is declining due to the sluggish U.S. economy. According to a recent survey, national office, retail and hospitality markets are also on the decline.

42960 ■ "Survival Guide: There Can Be an Upside to Managing a Downturn" in *Canadian Business* **(Vol. 81, November 10, 2008, No. 19, pp. 54)**
Pub: Rogers Media Ltd.
Ed: Sharda Prashad. **Description:** Canada-based Foxy is already limiting its exposure to retailers who could be a credit problem in case of recession. Retirement Life Communities is entering into fixed-rate and fixed-term loans for them to have sufficient financing to grow. Business owners need to realize that customers want more for less.

42961 ■ "Sustaining Health" in *Pet Product News* (Vol. 64, November 2010, No. 11, pp. 28)
Pub: BowTie Inc.
Ed: Angela Pham. **Description:** How pet supply retailers have responded to dog owners' interest in health supplements and their ingredients is discussed. Dog owners are showing interest in the ingredients inside the supplements and are reading labels. Retailers must now prove the beneficial effects of these ingredients in order to make the sale.

42962 ■ "Sustaining Supply" in *Crain's Cleveland Business* (Vol. 28, November 19, 2007, No. 46, pp. 3)
Pub: Crain Communications, Inc.
Ed: David Bennett. **Description:** Local firms are playing key roles in preparing Wal-Mart suppliers to develop sustainable, or ecologically conscious, packaging. New products such as the innovative "eco-bottle" - a collapsed container made of recyclable plastic that will expand to its traditional size and shape once water is added and would transform to such items as window cleaner when the water mixes with the container's dry contents - are being designed by firms such as Nottingham Spirk.

42963 ■ "Take 'Em Out of the Ball Game" in *Canadian Business* (Vol. 79, November 20, 2006, No. 23, pp. 19)
Pub: Rogers Media
Ed: Andy Holloway. **Description:** Strategies adopted by retailers to retain profitable customers are discussed.

42964 ■ "Tapping the 'Well' in Wellness" in *Pet Product News* (Vol. 64, November 2010, No. 11, pp. 1)
Pub: BowTie Inc.
Ed: Wendy-Bedwell Wilson. **Description:** Healthy food and treats are among the leading wellness products being sought by customers from specialty retailers to keep their pets healthy. With this demand for pet wellness products, retailers suggest making sure that staff know key ingredients to emphasize to customers. Other insights into this trend and ways to engage customers are discussed.

42965 ■ "Target Gets Exclusive with Ben & Jerry's" in *Ice Cream Reporter* (Vol. 23, July 20, 2010, No. 8, pp. 1)
Pub: Ice Cream Reporter
Description: Target Corporation will launch two new Ben & Jerry's ice cream flavors at its retail stores in 49 states. The new ice cream flavors will be available in mini cups and pints and are called Berry Voluntary and Brownie Chew Gooder.

42966 ■ "Tax-Free Zones Need Shows; Out-of-State Shoppers Are Key To Success" in *Crain's Detroit Business* (Vol. 24, January 28, 2008, No. 4)
Pub: Crain Communications Inc. - Detroit
Ed: Daniel Duggan. **Description:** Sales tax-free zones are being considered by Michigan's legislators in order to promote the state as a conference destination.

42967 ■ "Teachable Moments: Worth Every Penny" in *Pet Product News* (Vol. 64, December 2010, No. 12, pp. 34)
Pub: BowTie Inc.
Ed: Cheryl Reeves. **Description:** Pet bird retailers can attain both outreach to customers and enhanced profitability by staging educational events such as the annual Parrot Palooza event of Burlington, New Jersey-based Bird Paradise. Aside from attracting a global audience, Parrot Palooza features seminars, workshops, classes, and bird-related contests.

42968 ■ "The Trouble With $150,000 Wine" in *Barron's* (Vol. 88, July 7, 2008, No. 27, pp. 33)
Pub: Dow Jones & Co., Inc.
Ed: Orley Ashenfelter. **Description:** Review of the book, "The Billionaire's Vinegar: The Mystery of the World's Most Expensive Bottle of Wine," which discusses vintners along with the marketing and distribution of wine as well as the winemaking industry as a whole.

42969 ■ "Things Really Clicking for Macy's Online" in *Business Courier* (Vol. 24, November 30, 2008, No. 33, pp. 1)
Pub: American City Business Journals, Inc.
Ed: Lisa Biank Fasig. **Description:** Retailer Macy's online division Macys.com are projecting sales at $1billion in 2007, compared to $620 million in 2006. Macy's new online features and products and the growth of online retail sector are also discussed.

42970 ■ "Three Trails Blazes Tax Credit Deal" in *The Business Journal-Serving Metropolitan Kansas City* (Vol. 27, November 7, 2008, No. 9)
Pub: American City Business Journals, Inc.
Ed: Rob Roberts. **Description:** Three Trails Redevelopment LLC plans to redevelop the Bannister Mall area. The Missouri Development Finance Board is expected to approve $30 million in tax credits for the project. A verbal agreement on the terms and conditions has already been reached according to the agency's executive director.

42971 ■ "To Be Seen Is to Be Successful" in *Pet Product News* (Vol. 64, December 2010, No. 12, pp. 12)
Pub: BowTie Inc.
Ed: David Arvin. **Description:** Guidelines on how pet business retailers can boost customer visibility are described considering that complacency could hamper retailers' efforts to effectively market their businesses. To enhance customer base and stand out from competing businesses, being different, strategic, creative, and differentiated is emphasized.

42972 ■ "Too Much too Soon" in *Barron's* (Vol. 89, July 27, 2009, No. 30, pp. 33)
Pub: Dow Jones & Co., Inc.
Ed: Leslie P. Norton. **Description:** Shares of hhgregg have risen 85 percent in the year leading up to July 2009 and analysts believe the stock could hit 25. However, their 113 outlets are concentrated in states where unemployment is above 10 percent and expanding into areas already overstored. Competition is also rife and credit availability is still tight.

42973 ■ "Tough Climate for Nurseries" in *Crain's Cleveland Business* (Vol. 30, June 29, 2009, No. 25, pp. 1)
Pub: Crain Communications, Inc.
Ed: Stan Bullard. **Description:** After 81 years in the business, Sunnybrook Farms & Nursery is closing its doors. The owner sites the bad economy along with cold weather the reason for lack of sales. Other nursery owners discuss the bad economy and weather conditions and how they are affecting their business.

42974 ■ "Tough-Love Boss at BMO Demands Retail Turnaround" in *Globe & Mail* (March 2, 2007, pp. B13)
Pub: CTVglobemedia Publishing Inc.
Ed: Andrew Willis. **Description:** William Downe, the newly appointed chief executive of Bank of Montreal (BMO), discusses strategies to improve the number of retail customers. The BMO reported $292 million profits in the first quarter of 2007.

42975 ■ "Tower City Hopes Restrictions on Minors Boost Retail Center" in *Crain's Cleveland Business* (Vol. 28, November 5, 2007, No. 44)
Pub: Crain Communications, Inc.
Ed: John Booth. **Description:** Tower City Center, a shopping mall in downtown Cleveland, hopes to generate more business with their new rules restricting the access of unaccompanied minors after 2:30 p.m.

42976 ■ "Toy Story: U.S.-Made a Hot Seller" in *Crain's Detroit Business* (Vol. 23, December 17, 2007, No. 51, pp. 3)
Pub: Crain Communications Inc. - Detroit
Ed: Chad Halcom. **Description:** American Plastic Toys, located in Walled Lake, Michigan reports all its toys are made in the U.S. and have passed all U.S. safety standards. Revenue for American Plastic Toys

reached nearly $33 million in 2005, and the company expects to exceed that because of recent toy safety recalls of products produced in China.

42977 ■ "Tradeshow Attendance Incentives Add Up" in *Pet Product News* (Vol. 64, December 2010, No. 12, pp. 14)
Pub: BowTie Inc.
Ed: Mark E. Battersby. **Description:** Pointers on how pet specialty retailers can claim business travel tax and income tax deductions for expenses paid or incurred in participation at tradeshows, conventions, and meetings are presented. Incentives in form of these deductions could allow pet specialty retailers to gain business benefits, aside from the education and enjoyment involved with the travel.

42978 ■ *Treasure Hunt*
Pub: Penguin Group Incorporated
Ed: Michael J. Silverstein; John Butman. **Released:** May 4, 2006. **Description:** Explanation of people's spending habits and how to capitalize on retail sales.

42979 ■ "Turmoil Means Changes For Retailers" in *The Business Journal-Serving Metropolitan Kansas City* (Vol. 27, October 10, 2008, No. 4)
Pub: American City Business Journals, Inc.
Ed: Suzanna Stagemeyer. **Description:** Impacts of the financial crisis on Kansas Metropolitan Area retailers are varied. Rob Dalzell, for instance, found it difficult to secure a loan for his new self-serve yogurt store Yummo. The trends in retailing in the area are examined further as well as ways in which local businesses are changing in an attempt to stay solvent during the economic downturn.

42980 ■ "Turning Trust Into Success" in *Retail Merchandiser* (Vol. 51, July-August 2011, No. 4, pp. 52)
Pub: Phoenix Media Corporation
Ed: Karen Kondilis. **Description:** Shopko Stores employs tenured and trustworthy pharmacists and believes it is the core to their success.

42981 ■ "The Twittering Class" in *Entrepreneur* (Vol. 37, September 2009, No. 9, pp. 40)
Pub: Entrepreneur Media, Inc.
Ed: Mikal E. Belicove. **Description:** Advice on how entrepreneurs can use online social networks to promote their businesses is presented. Facebook offers applications and advertising solutions to promote Websites, products and services. Twitter, on the other hand, provides instant messaging, which can be done through computer or cell phone.

42982 ■ "U.S. Retailer Eyes 'Tween' Market" in *Globe & Mail* (January 30, 2007, pp. B1)
Pub: CTVglobemedia Publishing Inc.
Ed: Marina Strauss. **Description:** The decision of Tween Brands Inc. (Too Incorporated) to open 100 new stores in Canada as part of its expansion is discussed. The company's focus on targeting girls for its products is detailed.

42983 ■ "U.S. Savvy Helps Fuel TD's Fortunes" in *Globe & Mail* (February 23, 2007, pp. B1)
Pub: CTVglobemedia Publishing Inc.
Ed: Andrew Willis; Tavia Grant. **Description:** The rise in the revenues of Toronto-Dominion Bank due to its acquisition of American financial service providers and the rise in its domestic retail banking revenues are disussed.

42984 ■ *Up the Loyalty Ladder*
Pub: HarperCollins Publishers Inc.
Ed: Murray Rephel; Neil Raphel. **Released:** September 1996. **Description:** Marketing consultants share insight into growing any retail business and gain customer loyalty.

42985 ■ "Uptick in Clicks: Nordstrom's Online Sales Surging" in *Puget Sound Business Journal* (Vol. 29, August 22, 2008, No. 18, pp. 1)
Pub: American City Business Journals
Ed: Gregg Lamm. **Description:** Nordstrom Inc.'s online division grew its sales by 15 percent in the second quarter of 2008, compared to 2007's 4.3

percent in overall decline. The company expects their online net sales to reach $700 million in 2008 capturing eight percent of overall sales.

42986 ■ "US Cavalry Store" in *Retail Merchandiser* **(Vol. 51, September-October 2011, No. 5, pp. 70)**
Pub: Phoenix Media Corporation
Description: US Cavalry Store serves enlisted military members. The store has launched a newly upgraded Website and has expanded its distribution center.

42987 ■ "VeriFone Announces Global Security Solutions Business" in *Marketing Weekly News* **(October 3, 2009)**
Pub: Investment Weekly News
Description: Focused on delivering innovative security solutions, VeriFone Holdings, Inc. announced the formation of its Global Security Solutions Business Unit, including VeriShield Protect, an end-to-end encryption to protect cardholder data throughout the merchant and processor systems. The business will focus on consulting, sales and implementation of these new products in order to help retailers and processors protect customer data.

42988 ■ "Wal-Mart Doesn't Sell Council" in *The Business Journal-Serving Metropolitan Kansas City* **(Vol. 26, July 4, 2008, No. 43, pp. 1)**
Pub: American City Business Journals, Inc.
Ed: Steve Vockrodt. **Description:** Wal-Mart Stores Inc. announced that it will move the location of its annual convention from Kansas City, Missouri to Orlando, Florida. The change of venue came after Rick Hughes, Kansas City Convention and Visitors Association president rejected Wal-Mart's proposal to subsidize a new hotel in the downtown area that is needed for the event.

42989 ■ "'Wal-Mart Effect' Feeds Grocer Price Wars" in *Globe & Mail* **(March 15, 2007, pp. B14)**
Pub: CTVglobemedia Publishing Inc.
Ed: Marina Strauss. **Description:** The decrease in profit reports by Canadian grocery giants amidst high expansion plans by Wal-Mart Stores Inc. are discussed. This industry is witnessing the most severe pricing competitions in recent times.

42990 ■ "Wal-Mart Expansion Plans Hit Roadblock" in *Crain's Chicago Business* **(Vol. 31, March 24, 2008, No. 12, pp. 2)**
Pub: Crain Communications, Inc.
Ed: Monee Fields-White. **Description:** Wal-Mart Stores Inc.'s expansion plans in Chicago have suffered a series of setbacks due to a shifting political landscape in which may require the company to pay higher wages. Wal-Mart claims that its hourly pay and benefits are fair; however, the labor force does not agree.

42991 ■ "Wal-Mart Proposed for Timmerman Plaza" in *Business Journal-Milwaukee* **(Vol. 28, December 31, 2010, No. 14, pp. A1)**
Pub: Milwaukee Business Journal
Ed: Sean Ryan. **Description:** Dickson, Tennessee-based Gatlin Development Company Inc. owner Franklin C. Gatlin III revealed plans for a new Wal-Mart store in Timmerman Plaza in Milwaukee, Wisconsin. Wal-Mart plans to open up approximately 18 new stores in southeast Wisconsin in 2012 and the Timmerman project is the first of four that Gatlin will submit for city approval.

42992 ■ "Wal-Mart Relaunches Private Brand, Reimagines Stores Layout" in *Marketing to Women* **(Vol. 22, July 2009, No. 7, pp. 5)**
Pub: EPM Communications, Inc.
Description: Wal-Mart is focusing its strategies by centering on new store layouts that they believe will match their new branding of "fast, friendly, and clean" and enable mothers to "just get on with what they need to do."

42993 ■ "Wal-Mart Sharpens Focus on Roxbury" in *Boston Business Journal* **(Vol. 31, July 8, 2011, No. 24, pp. 1)**
Pub: Boston Business Journal
Ed: Mary Moore. **Description:** Wal-Mart Stores is boosting its search for a possible location in the Rox-

bury section of Boston, Massachusetts. The search is focused on underserved communities in terms of jobs and access to reasonably-priced merchandise. The extent Boston's African American community has clashed with Mayor Thomas M. Memino over the accommodations of the retailer in Roxbury is discussed.

42994 ■ "Wal-Mart Takes Expansion Up a Notch" in *Globe & Mail* **(March 21, 2007, pp. B8)**
Pub: CTVglobemedia Publishing Inc.
Ed: Shirley Won. **Description:** Retail giant Wal-Mart Canada Corp. is planning to invest $500 million for expanding its business in Ontario region. It will open 21 new outlets by the end of 2007.

42995 ■ "Walmart, Target Moving to Convenience Store Near You" in *Hardware Retailing* **(Vol. 199, November 2010, No. 5, pp. 60)**
Pub: North American Retail Hardware Association
Description: Walmart has plans to move into small convenience stores in Chicago, Detroit, San Francisco, and Los Angeles.

42996 ■ "Want Leverage? Multi-Unit Franchisees Deliver Substantial Savings" in *Franchising World* **(Vol. 42, October 2010, No. 10, pp. 39)**
Pub: International Franchise Association
Ed: Aziz Hashim. **Description:** Many retail franchises selling the same product are able to buy in bulk. Volume-buying can save money for any franchise.

42997 ■ "Wary Investors Turn to a Different Market for Strong Returns" in *Boston Business Journal* **(Vol. 29, September 2, 2011, No. 17, pp. 1)**
Pub: American City Business Journals Inc.
Ed: Daniel J. Sernovitz. **Description:** Maryland-based investors have been choosing to put their money in the supermarket business. Retail property sales have increased during the second quarter of 2011.

42998 ■ "Wattles Plugs Back Into State" in *Business Journal Portland* **(Vol. 27, November 19, 2010, No. 38, pp. 1)**
Pub: Portland Business Journal
Ed: Wendy Culverwell. **Description:** Denver, Colorado-based Ultimate Electronics Inc.'s first store in Oregon was opened in Portland and the 46th store in the chain of electronic superstores is expected to employ 70-80 workers. The venture is the latest for Mark Wattles, one of Oregon's most successful entrepreneurs, who acquired Ultimate from bankruptcy.

42999 ■ "Waugh Chapel to Expand" in *Baltimore Business Journal* **(Vol. 28, August 27, 2010, No. 16, pp. 1)**
Pub: Baltimore Business Journal
Ed: Daniel J. Sernovitz. **Description:** Developer Greenberg Gibbons Corporation has broken ground on a $275 million, 1.2 million-square-foot addition to its Village at the Waugh Chapel mixed-use complex. Aside from creating 2,600 permanent jobs, the addition, named Village South, is expected to lure Target and Wegmans Food Markets to Crofton, Maryland. Funding for this project is discussed.

43000 ■ "Weaving a Stronger Fabric: Organizing a Global Sweat-Free Apparel Production Agreement" in *WorkingUSA* **(Vol. 11, June 2008, No. 2)**
Pub: Blackwell Publishers Ltd.
Ed: Eric Dirnbach. **Description:** Tens of millions of workers working under terrible sweatshop conditions in the global apparel industry. Workers are employed at apparel contractors and have been largely unsuccessful in organizing and improving their working conditions. The major apparel manufacturers and retailers have the most power in this industry, and they have adopted corporate social responsibility programs as a false solution to the sweatshop problem. The major North American apparel unions dealt with similar sweatshop conditions a century ago by organizing the contractors and brands into joint association contracts that significantly raised stan-

dards. Taking inspiration from their example, workers and their anti-sweatshop allies need to work together to coordinate a global organizing effort that builds worker power and establishes a global production agreement that negotiates with both contractors and the brands for improved wages, benefits, and working conditions.

43001 ■ "Web Sight: Do You See What I See?" in *Entrepreneur* **(Vol. 35, October 2007, No. 10, pp. 58)**
Pub: Entrepreneur Media Inc.
Ed: Heather Clancy. **Description:** Owners of Trunkt, a boutique in New York that showcases independent designs, have created a new style of Website called Trunkt.org. The Website allows buyers to select the products they want to see and designers can choose anytime which of their items will be displayed on the site. An explanation of the strategy that helped bring Trunkt closer to its clients is presented.

43002 ■ "Website for Women 50+ Launches" in *Marketing to Women* **(Vol. 21, April 2008, No. 4, pp. 5)**
Pub: EPM Communications, Inc.
Description: Vibrantnation.com is an online community targeting women over age 50; members can share recommendations on a variety of topics such as vacation spots, retailers and financial issues.

43003 ■ "Wedding Present Shopping – What to Get the Couple Who Have Everything" in *Benzinga.com* **(April 19, 2011)**
Pub: Benzinga.com
Ed: Benzinga Staff. **Description:** Tips for purchasing the perfect wedding gift are outlined.

43004 ■ "Well-Heeled Startup" in *Business Journal Portland* **(Vol. 27, November 12, 2010, No. 37, pp. 1)**
Pub: Portland Business Journal
Ed: Erik Siemers. **Description:** Oh! Shoes LLC expects to receive about $1.5 million in funding from angel investors, while marketing a new line of high heel shoes that are comfortable, healthy, and attractive. The new line of shoes will use the technology of athletic footwear while having the look of an Italian designer. Oh! Shoes hopes to generate $35 million in sales by 2014.

43005 ■ "Welsh Meat Sales on the Rise" in *Farmer's Weekly* **(March 28, 2008, No. 320)**
Pub: Reed Business Information
Description: Due, in part, to marketing efforts, retail sales of Welsh lamb and beef rose significantly in the first two months of 2008.

43006 ■ "What Dead Zone?" in *Entrepreneur* **(Vol. 37, October 2009, No. 10, pp. 128)**
Pub: Entrepreneur Media, Inc.
Ed: Jason Daley. **Description:** Joe Purifico, Halloween Adventure franchises co-owner and chief executive officer, discusses the Halloween superstore phenomenon. Malls allow seasonal leasing for Halloween stores due to the high number of customers these stores attract.

43007 ■ "What the Future Holds for Consumers" in *Black Enterprise* **(Vol. 41, August 2010, No. 1, pp. 47)**
Pub: Earl G. Graves Publishing Co. Inc.
Ed: Sheiresa Ngo. **Description:** The way people purchase goods and service has changed with technology. With an increased focus on security (as well as privacy and fairness) the U.S. Congress began regulating the credit card industry with the Fair Credit Reporting Act of 1970 and the Credit Card Accountability, Responsibility, and Disclosure (CARD) Act of 2009.

43008 ■ "What Slump? Davis Likely to Fill Borders Gap Quickly" in *Sacramento Business Journal* **(Vol. 28, July 29, 2011, No. 22, pp. 1)**
Pub: Sacramento Business Journal
Ed: Kelly Johnson. **Description:** The nationwide shutdown of Borders bookstores worry most cities, but not Davis, California, which is experiencing a relatively low retail vacancy rate of 6.3 percent.

43009 ■ "When Virtue Is A Vice" in *Harvard Business Review* (Vol. 86, July-August 2008, No. 8, pp. 22)
Pub: Harvard Business School Press
Ed: Anat Keinan; Ran Kivetz. **Description:** Negative consequences of habitually denying self-indulgence, from work and life balance to consumer shopping behaviors are discussed.

43010 ■ "White Cat Media Tells You Where to Get a Bargain. Now It's Shopping for $1.5 Million" in *Inc.* (March 2008, pp. 48)
Pub: Gruner & Jahr USA Publishing
Ed: Athena Schindelheim. **Description:** Profile of White Cat Media which runs two shopping Websites: SheFinds.com for fashion and beauty items, and MomFinds.com for mothers. The New York City firm reported revenues for 2007 at $400,000 and is looking for funding capital in the amount of $1.7 million.

43011 ■ "Will mCommerce Make Black Friday Green?" in *Retail Merchandiser* (Vol. 51, September-October 2011, No. 5, pp. 8)
Pub: Phoenix Media Corporation
Ed: Scott Miller. **Description:** Retailers speculate the possibilities of mobile commerce and are implementing strategies at their stores. Consumers using mobile devices accounted for only 0.1 percent of visits to retail Websites on Black Friday 2009 and rose to 5.6 percent in 2010; numbers are expected to rise for 2011.

43012 ■ "Williams-Sonoma Beats Expectations in Q1" in *Home Textiles Today* (Vol. 31, May 24, 2011, No. 13, pp. 2)
Pub: Reed Business Information
Description: Both retail nameplates, Williams-Sonoma and Pottery Barn reported gains in 2011's first quarter, accredited to the way shoppers responded to new opening price point programs for several of its brands.

43013 ■ "The Wine Spectator" in *Business Courier* (Vol. 27, November 26, 2010, No. 30, pp. 1)
Pub: Business Courier
Ed: Dan Monk. **Description:** Vintner Select, a wine distributor, will introduce an internationally known portfolio of more than 50 German and Austrian wines. The company now distributes about 900 different wine labels from 220 producers in 10 countries to smaller, independent retailers in Indiana, Kentucky and Ohio.

43014 ■ "A Wireless Makes 8 Store-In-Store Kiosk Acquisitions" in *Wireless News* (October 16, 2010)
Pub: Close-Up Media Inc.
Description: A Wireless, a retailer for Verizon Wireless has acquired eight of Verizon's retail kiosks that are positioned in home appliance and electronics stores.

43015 ■ "WNY Casing In On Loonie's Climb" in *Business First Buffalo* (November 23, 2007, pp. 1)
Pub: American City Business Journals, Inc.
Ed: Scott Thomas. **Description:** Economy of Western New York has rebounded since the 9/11 recession and the rise of the Canadian dollar, which has contributed to the areas economic growth. Canadian shoppers are frequenting markets in the area due to the parity of the U.S. and Canadian dollar. Details of the cross-border shopping and its impact in WNY are discussed.

43016 ■ "Woes Portend Consumer Shift" in *The Business Journal-Serving Metropolitan Kansas City* (Vol. 27, September 26, 2008, No. 2, pp. 1)
Pub: American City Business Journals, Inc.
Ed: Suzanna Stagemeyer. **Description:** Black Bamboo owner Tim Butt believes that prolonged tightening in the credit market will result in consumer spending becoming more cash-driven that credit card driven. The financial crisis has already constricted spending among consumers. Forecasts for the US economy are provided.

43017 ■ "Women: Send Me An Angel" in *Entrepreneur* (Vol. 35, October 2007, No. 10, pp. 38)
Pub: Entrepreneur Media Inc.
Ed: Aliza Sherman. **Description:** Golden Seeds has invested in Enter Artemis Woman LLC when the latter decided to put its products into Wal-Mart. Golden Seeds was formed by angel investors who aim to help women build their own businesses. Tips on how to approach angel investors and getting angel funding are given.

43018 ■ "Worldwide Food Services (EREI) Tests Mini Dollar Store Program" in *Internet Wire* (August 6, 2009)
Pub: Comtex News Network, Inc.
Description: Mini Dollar Stores and Eagle View LLC, wholly-owned subsidiaries of Worldwide Food Services, Inc., recently met with government officials and purchasing agents to lay out a test program which would distribute Mini Dollar Store items into VA hospital gift shops.

43019 ■ "Young Adult, Childless May Help Fuel Post-Recession Rebound" in *Pet Product News* (Vol. 64, November 2010, No. 11, pp. 4)
Pub: BowTie Inc.
Description: Pet industry retailers and marketers are encouraged to tap into the young adult and childless couple sectors to boost consumer traffic and sales to pre-recession levels. Among young adult owners, pet ownership increased from 40 percent in 2003 to 49 percent in 2009. Meanwhile, the childless couple sector represented 63 percent of all dog/cat owners in 2009.

43020 ■ "Zebra's Changing Stripes" in *Crain's Chicago Business* (Vol. 31, November 17, 2008, No. 46, pp. 4)
Pub: Crain Communications, Inc.
Ed: John Pletz. **Description:** Zebra Technologies Corp., the world's largest manufacturer of bar-code printers is profiled; the company's stock has plunged with shares declining 40 percent in the past three months grinding the firm's growth to a halt. Zebra's plans to regain revenue growth are also discussed.

43021 ■ "Zeon Solutions Teams with Endeca for SaaS Version of Endeca InFront" in *Entertainment Close-Up* (October 25, 2011)
Pub: Close-Up Media
Description: Zeon Solutions, an enterprise e-commerce and Website development firm announced a special licensing partnership with Endeca Technologies. Endeca is an information management software company that provides small and mid-size retailers with high-performance Customer Experience Management technology.

43022 ■ "Zucker Closes Deal on HBC With Sweeter Takeover Offer" in *Globe & Mail* (January 27, 2006, pp. B1)
Pub: CTVglobemedia Publishing Inc.
Ed: Marina Strauss; Sinclair Stewart; Jacquie McNish. **Description:** Jerry Zucker, vice-president of InterTech Group Inc., has finalized a deal to buy retail store Hudson Bay Co, for 1.1 billion dollars. The shares will be purchased at a rate of 15.25 dollars per share in an all cash transaction. Complete details of the buyout are discussed.

STATISTICAL SOURCES

43023 ■ *RMA Annual Statement Studies*
Pub: Robert Morris Associates (RMA)
Released: Annual. **Price:** $175.00 2006-07 edition, $105.00. **Description:** Contains composite balance sheets and income statements for more than 360 industries, including the accounting, auditing, and bookkeeping industries. Also contains five years of comparative historical data for discerning trends. Includes 16 commonly used ratios, computed for most of the size groupings for nearly every industry.

43024 ■ *Value Retailing in the 1990s: Off-Pricers, Factory Outlets, and Closeout*
Pub: John Wiley & Sons, Inc.
Released: 1994. **Price:** $425.00 (Print on Demand).
Description: Published by Packaged StoresCloseout Stores Facts. Examines off-price stores and manufac-

turers' outlets, covering market size and growth, competition, industry trends, and consumers. Also includes profiles of value retailers and regional outlet mall developers.

TRADE PERIODICALS

43025 ■ *Barnard's Retail Trend Report*
Pub: Barnard Enterprises Inc.
Contact: Kurt Barnard, Publisher & Chief Editor
E-mail: kbarnard@retailtrends.com
Released: Bimonthly. **Price:** $179; $199, other countries; $45, single issue. **Description:** Forecasts predictions, analyzes, explains, and identifies trends and events affecting retail operations. Recurring features include market statistics and news of research.

43026 ■ *Loeb Retail Letter*
Pub: Loeb Associates Inc.
Contact: Phyllis Loeb
Ed: Walter F. Loeb, Editor, loeb@idt.net. **Released:** 11/year. **Price:** $300, U.S.; $325, Canada; $350, elsewhere. **Description:** Publishes articles on the retail industry. Recurring features include news of research.

43027 ■ *NSSRA Newsletter*
Pub: National Ski & Snowboard Retailers Association
Contact: Thomas B. Doyle, President
E-mail: tdoyle@nssra.com
Released: Quarterly. **Price:** Included in membership. **Description:** Informs ski and snowboard retail stores on critical industry issues such as guidelines and litigation exposure and marketing.

43028 ■ *Retail Info Systems News*
Pub: Edgell Communications Inc.
Released: Monthly. **Description:** RIS News serves the retail market targeting the technology buying team.

43029 ■ *Retailing Today*
Pub: Lebhar-Friedman Inc.
Ed: Tim Craig, Editor. **Released:** Biweekly. **Price:** $229, U.S.; $350, elsewhere. **Description:** Provides up-to-date information on what is happening in the retail industry and how current economic conditions affect retailing. Summarizes actions, acquisitions, and policies of major retail chains across the U.S. Discusses problems facing retail operations, i.e., shoplifting and retaining customer loyalty.

43030 ■ *Western-English Industry Report*
Pub: Western English Retailers Association
Contact: Susan Leach, Exec. Editor
Released: Bimonthly. **Price:** $29. **Description:** Disseminates information on trends, markets, business techniques, and issues on the nation's retailers of Western and English apparel, tack, and equipment.

VIDEOCASSETTES/ AUDIOCASSETTES

43031 ■ *Beware the Naked Man Who Offers You His Shirt*
PBS Home Video
Catalog Fulfillment Center
PO Box 751089
Charlotte, NC 28275-1089
Ph:800-531-4727
Free: 800-645-4PBS
Co. E-mail: info@pbs.org
URL: http://www.pbs.org
Released: 1990. **Price:** $395.00. **Description:** The author of "Swim With the Sharks Without Being Eaten Alive" offers insights and advice on increasing sales productivity. **Availability:** VHS; 3/4U.

43032 ■ *Shoplifting Prevented*
American Media, Inc.
4621 121st St.
Urbandale, IA 50323-2311
Ph:(515)224-0919
Free: 888-776-8268

Fax:(515)327-2555
Co. E-mail: custsvc@ammedia.com
URL: http://www.ammedia.com
Released: 1988. **Price:** $450.00. **Description:** Employees are shown some simple things they can do to keep their store from getting ripped off. **Availability:** VHS; 3/4U.

TRADE SHOWS AND CONVENTIONS

43033 ■ EuroShop - Global Retail Trade Fair
Messe Dusseldorf North America MDNA
150 N. Michigan Ave., Ste. 2920
Chicago, IL 60601
Ph:(312)781-5180
Fax:(312)781-5188
Co. E-mail: info@mdna.com
URL: http://www.mdna.com
Released: Triennial. **Principal Exhibits:** International trade fair for retail information, communications and security technology.

CONSULTANTS

43034 ■ G.G.W. and Associates
1213 Hampton Dr.
Jackson, MI 49203
Ph:(517)782-2255
Fax:(517)784-1256
Contact: Gerard G. Wood, President
Scope: Consultants to retail businesses with services that include profit and loss strategy, business planning short or long term, marketing strategies, market survey analysis, advertising budget, merchandise control systems and effective internal security and employee communications programs. Serves private industries as well as government agencies. **Seminars:** Retraining for the 90's; How to Start and Manage a Small Business.

43035 ■ Gordian Concepts & Solutions
16 Blueberry Ln.
Lincoln, MA 01773
Ph:(617)259-8341
Co. E-mail: gordian@usa1.com
Contact: Stephen R. Low, President
Scope: Engineering and management consultancy offering general, financial, and valuation services, civil and tax litigation support. Assists clients in entering new businesses, planning new products and services, and evaluating feasibility. Targets industrial concerns engaged in manufacturing, assembly, warehousing, energy production, process systems and biotechnology, steel, paper, and electronics. Serves businesses such as retailing, financial services, health care, satellite broadcasting and cable television, outdoor advertising and professional practices. **Publications:** "Establishing Rural Cellular Company Values," Cellular Business.

43036 ■ Kurt Salmon Associates Inc.
1355 Peachtree St. NE, Ste. 900
Atlanta, GA 30309-3257
Ph:(404)892-0321
Fax:(404)872-7271
Co. E-mail: services@kurtsalmon.com
URL: http://www.kurtsalmon.com
Contact: William B. Pace, Director
E-mail: whbeck@atskurtsalmon.com
Scope: Offers retail consulting services for retailers and consumer products makers in strategic planning, product development and sourcing, merchandising and planning, supply chain services, store operations services, customer experience, information technology and private equity. Health care consulting services include strategy setting; facility development; operational planning and information technology. **Publications:** "Europe's 2009 Global Sourcing Reference"; "The Three Stages of Retail PLM Adoption"; "Optimizing Your Outsourced Sourcing Strategy"; "Using Strategic Sourcing to Cut Costs"; "Supply Chain Effectiveness"; "Managing the Assortment Lifecycle"; "Managing a Supply Chain of Proprietary Products"; "Creating a Successful Product Development Operation". **Seminars:** Leading the Surf Industry; Time to Talk Turnaround.

43037 ■ Lougheed Resource Group Inc.
17608 Deer Isle Cir.
Winter Garden, FL 34787
Ph:(407)654-1212
Fax:(407)654-5419
Co. E-mail: info@lrgconstruction.com
URL: http://www.lrgconstruction.com
Contact: Karen Lougheed, Owner
E-mail: karen@lrgmanagement.com
Scope: Construction consultants specializing in project strategies, scope preparation, contract negotiation, project management, document and code evaluation, peer reviews, scheduling/estimates, dispute resolution, and forensic analysis expert testimony.

43038 ■ Stan Knipe & Associates
3176 Silver Sands Cir.
Virginia Beach, VA 23451-1185
Ph:(757)496-5475
Fax:(757)560-7631
Co. E-mail: sknipe3566@aol.com
Contact: Stan W. Knipe, President
Scope: Specializes in retail management, strategic and organizational planning and operations, and consumer repair service. **Seminars:** Leadership and management development.

FRANCHISES AND BUSINESS OPPORTUNITIES

43039 ■ Aarons Sales & Lease Ownership
Aaron Rents, Inc.
309 E Paces Ferry Rd.
Atlanta, GA 30305
Ph:(678)402-3778
Free: 800-551-6015
Fax:(678)402-3540
No. of Franchise Units: 632. **No. of Company-Owned Units:** 1,143. **Founded:** 1955. **Franchised:** 1992. **Description:** Furniture, electronics, computer, and appliance leasing and sales. **Equity Capital Needed:** $233,870-$607,580. **Franchise Fee:** $15,000-$50,000. **Royalty Fee:** 6%. **Financial Assistance:** Limited third-party financing available. **Training:** Provides 3 days at headquarters, less than 30 days at franchisees location and 1 week at regional locations with ongoing support.

43040 ■ Adam & Eve Stores
AEFC, Inc.
302 Meadowland Dr.
Hillsborough, NC 27278
Free: 800-217-7423
Fax:(919)644-1704
Co. E-mail: franchising@adameve.com
URL: http://www.adameve.com/stores
No. of Company-Owned Units: 33. **Founded:** 1970. **Franchised:** 2004. **Description:** The adult industry is now offering retail store franchise opportunities. With over 30 years experience and over 4,000,000 customers nationwide, you benefit from the Adam & Eve brand name recognized around the country. **Equity Capital Needed:** $192,000-$345,000; cash $50,000. **Franchise Fee:** $30,000. **Financial Assistance:** No. **Training:** Training and support program will show you everything from planning 'open buys' to buying, working with vendors, merchandise inventory control, and the merchandising and display products in your store. Onsite training prior to opening.

43041 ■ Beehive Co-op LLC
66 Farrington Rd.
Croton-on-Hudson, NY 10520
Ph:(678)429-1418
Fax:(404)929-6695
No. of Franchise Units: 1. **No. of Company-Owned Units:** 1. **Founded:** 2004. **Franchised:** 2007. **Description:** Retail cooperative for local designers. **Equity Capital Needed:** $71,800-$130,750. **Franchise Fee:** $25,000. **Royalty Fee:** 4%. **Financial Assistance:** No. **Training:** 2 days at headquarters, 3 days at franchisee's location and ongoing support.

43042 ■ Brilliant Sky Toys & Books
TT & B, Inc.
5100 Marsh Rd., Ste. D-2
Okemos, MI 48823
Ph:(517)381-1655
Fax:(517)381-1622
No. of Franchise Units: 14. **No. of Company-Owned Units:** 1. **Founded:** 2002. **Franchised:** 2007. **Description:** Retail, toys, games, and books. **Equity Capital Needed:** $100,000 liquid investment. **Franchise Fee:** $35,000. **Financial Assistance:** No. **Training:** Yes.

43043 ■ Buck or Two Plus!
11B Director Court
Vaughan, ON, Canada L4L 4S5
Ph:(905)265-3168
Free: 800-890-8633
Fax:(905)265-3162
Co. E-mail: fburt@extremeretail.ca
URL: http://www.buckortwo.com
No. of Franchise Units: 65. **No. of Company-Owned Units:** 1. **Founded:** 1990. **Franchised:** 2004. **Description:** Buck or Two is a Canada-wide chain of specialty retail stores offering everyday quality basics with an ever changing mix of seasonable and extreme value products, as well as special deals. **Equity Capital Needed:** $275,000-$600,000. **Franchise Fee:** $25,000. **Training:** Includes 10 days training.

43044 ■ DirectBuy
8450 Broadway
Merrillville, IN 46410
Ph:(219)641-6480
Free: 800-827-6400
Fax:(219)756-2859
Co. E-mail: franchising@directbuy.com
URL: http://www.directbuyfranchising.com
No. of Franchise Units: 19. **No. of Company-Owned Units:** 13. **Founded:** 1971. **Franchised:** 1972. **Description:** DirectBuy is an international leader in providing the best alternative to conventional retail buying. Members of DirectBuy are able to avoid traditional markups and purchase from an unprecedented selection of quality merchandise, direct from manufacturers, at unparalleled prices. **Equity Capital Needed:** $500,000-$1,000,000. **Franchise Fee:** $75,000. **Training:** Provides 9 weeks training, field sales and service support.

43045 ■ Discount Sport Nutrition
Discount Sport Nutrition Franchising, L.P.
1920 Abrams Pky., Ste. 422
Dallas, TX 75214
Ph:(972)489-7925
Fax:(214)292-8619
Co. E-mail: franchising@sportsupplements.com
URL: http://www.sportsupplements.com
No. of Franchise Units: 6. **Founded:** 1996. **Franchised:** 2000. **Description:** Nutritional sport supplements retail store. **Equity Capital Needed:** $92,774-$185,344. **Franchise Fee:** $25,000. **Financial Assistance:** Yes. **Training:** 3 phase initial hands on training program located at current stores, as well as your location. Provides assistance with site location, leases, layout design, suppliers, advertising, marketing, and ongoing assistance.

43046 ■ Dollar Chest Franchising Corporation Inc.
3535 St. Charles Boul., St. 305
Kirkland, QC, Canada H9H 5B9
Ph:(514)693-9776
Fax:(514)693-9775
Co. E-mail: info@dollarchest.com
URL: http://www.dollarchest.com
No. of Franchise Units: 5. **No. of Company-Owned Units:** 1. **Founded:** 2006. **Franchised:** 2006. **Description:** Value dollar stores, offering consumers cleaning supplies, disposables, health and beauty, plastic wares, household, home decors, kitchen, and accessories, picture frames, hardware, electronics, lighting, stationary, candies, snacks, beverages, party supplies, novelties, gifts, pet supplies, outdoor products, foods and all basic home and household accessories, all at a unique price of one dollar. **Equity**

Capital Needed: $170,000-$203,000. Franchise Fee: $25,000. Training: Provides complete training and full range of online support.

43047 ■ EmbroidMe
1959 Upper Water St., Ste. 1713
Halifax, NS, Canada B3J 3N2
Ph:(416)238-6934
Free: (866)933-6337
Fax:(866)497-3533
Co. E-mail: franchise@embroidme.ca
URL: http://www.embroidme.com
No. of Franchise Units: 18. **Founded:** 2003 Canada; 2000 U.S. **Franchised:** 2000. **Description:** Full service promotional products, screen printing and corporate apparel franchise. Showrooms feature a large selection of casual apparel of various sizes, colours and styles. **Equity Capital Needed:** $195,000-$245,000. **Franchise Fee:** $49,500. **Training:** Includes 2 weeks training at headquarters and 2 weeks onsite.

43048 ■ Eola Wine Company Franchising
Eola Wine Company
500 E Central Ave.
Orlando, FL 32801
Ph:(813)935-5087
Fax:(813)425-5799
No. of Company-Owned Units: 1. **Founded:** 2004. **Franchised:** 2007. **Description:** Wine company. **Equity Capital Needed:** $338,000-$460,000. **Franchise Fee:** $50,000. **Financial Assistance:** No. **Training:** Yes.

43049 ■ Furla
Furla Licensing (USA), Inc.
389 Fifth Ave., Ste. 700
New York, NY 10016
Ph:(212)213-1177
Fax:(212)685-5910
Co. E-mail: bruce@furlausa.com
URL: http://www.furlausa.com
No. of Franchise Units: 18. **No. of Company-Owned Units:** 15. **Founded:** 1927. **Franchised:** 1998. **Description:** Furla sells women's handbags, shoes, belts, small leather goods, watches, jewelry and accessories. All products are exclusively designed by our own cadre of designers and primarily manufactured in Italy. Furla products are updated classic in styling and targeted towards the upscale modern woman with prices ranging between $180-$350 for handbags and shoes. Our brand is known worldwide through over 200 exclusive shops. **Equity Capital Needed:** $284,000-$480,000. **Franchise Fee:** $25,000. **Financial Assistance:** No direct financing, but very competitive invoice terms, generous product buyback program and a merchandise credit rebate for qualifying new stores. **Training:** 1 week training program at New York City office and in our corporate stores. Provides initial store set-up and opening training and ongoing training as requested.

43050 ■ Giant Tiger/Tigre Geant
Giant Tiger Stores Limited
2480 Walkley Rd.
Ottawa, ON, Canada K1G 6A9
Ph:(613)521-8222
Fax:(613)260-6398
Co. E-mail: careers@giantiger.com
URL: http://www.gianttiger.com
No. of Franchise Units: 203. **No. of Company-Owned Units:** 1. **Founded:** 1961. **Franchised:** 1964. **Description:** Franchise involves retailing services. **Financial Assistance:** Yes. **Training:** Training, site selection, lease negotiations and advisory council are provided.

43051 ■ Great Canadian Dollar Store (1993) Ltd.
2957 Jutland Rd., Ste. 101
Victoria, BC, Canada V8T 5J9
Ph:(250)388-0123
Free: 877-388-0123
Fax:(250)388-9763
Co. E-mail: franchise@dollarstores.com
URL: http://www.dollarstores.com
No. of Franchise Units: 120. **Founded:** 1993. **Franchised:** 1993. **Description:** Offers an excellent opportunity to market a wide range of exciting merchan-

dise. **Equity Capital Needed:** $150,000-$400,000. **Franchise Fee:** $19,880. **Training:** Offers training and ongoing support.

43052 ■ Hempire Sales Ltd.
1462 10th Ave.
PO Box 359
Fernie, BC, Canada V0B 1M0
Ph:(250)423-3970
Co. E-mail: marsha@hempirecanada.com
URL: http://www.hempirecanada.com
No. of Franchise Units: 4. **No. of Company-Owned Units:** 1. **Founded:** 1998. **Franchised:** 2006. **Description:** Unique retail store specializing in the sale of hemp and hemp related products. Offers a wide variety of environmentally friendly products, as well as smoking supplies. **Equity Capital Needed:** $80,000-$100,000; $40,000-$50,000 start-up capital required. **Franchise Fee:** $20,000. **Training:** Provides 1-2 weeks training; initial onsite and ongoing support.

43053 ■ Marcello's Market & Deli Inc.
2450 Lancaster Rd., Unit 41
Ottawa, ON, Canada K1B 5N3
Ph:(613)260-3773
Fax:(613)738-2699
Co. E-mail: fkachi@marcellos.ca
URL: http://www.marcellos.ca
No. of Franchise Units: 14. **No. of Company-Owned Units:** 5. **Founded:** 1998. **Franchised:** 1998. **Description:** European style market and deli take-out restaurant. **Equity Capital Needed:** $350,000-$1,000,000; $150,000-$400,000 start-up capital required. **Franchise Fee:** None. **Training:** Provides 2 weeks training.

43054 ■ Max Muscle
210 W Taft Ave.
Orange, CA 92865
Ph:(714)456-0700
Free: (866)MAX-MUSC
Fax:(714)456-0725
No. of Franchise Units: 151. **No. of Company-Owned Units:** 1. **Founded:** 1991. **Franchised:** 2001. **Description:** The franchise deals mainly with retailing. **Equity Capital Needed:** $50,000-$75,000. **Franchise Fee:** $35,000. **Financial Assistance:** Yes. **Training:** Yes.

43055 ■ Nicholby's Franchise Systems Inc.
3791 Victoria Park Ave., Unit 6
Toronto, ON, Canada M1W 3K6
Ph:(416)492-6424
Fax:(416)492-4852
Co. E-mail: rob@nicholbys.com
No. of Franchise Units: 25. **No. of Company-Owned Units:** 2. **Founded:** 1980. **Description:** Retail stores operating in hospitals, hotels, highways and office buildings. **Equity Capital Needed:** $27,000-$66,000. **Franchise Fee:** $9,900. **Training:** Offers 3-4 weeks training and ongoing support.

43056 ■ Nutrition House Canada Inc.
80 West Beaver Creek Rd., Unit 12
Richmond Hill, ON, Canada L4B 1H3
Ph:(905)707-7633
Free: 888-466-3085
Fax:(905)707-5102
Co. E-mail: wayneparent@nutritionhouse.com
URL: http://www.nutritionhouse.com
No. of Franchise Units: 52. **No. of Company-Owned Units:** 10. **Founded:** 1979. **Franchised:** 1993. **Description:** Retail "Lifesyle" stores featuring proprietary and national brands of vitamins, supplements, body care, weight loss, sports nutrition and health related products. Stores feature a "Sante Fe" design and are located in major malls and Big Box "Lifestyle" centres across Canada. **Equity Capital Needed:** $50-$75,000. **Franchise Fee:** $25,000. **Training:** Includes 3 weeks training.

43057 ■ Panda Franchises Ltd.
259 Labelle Blvd. Suite 201
Rosemere, QC, Canada J7A 2H3
Ph:(450)818-9741

Fax:(450)622-2939
Co. E-mail: Linda.g@pandashoes.com
URL: http://www.pandashoes.com
No. of Franchise Units: 31. **No. of Company-Owned Units:** 1. **Founded:** 1972. **Franchised:** 1974. **Description:** Children's shoes. **Equity Capital Needed:** $200,000-$350,000. **Franchise Fee:** $25,000. **Training:** Complete training to franchisees and staff, buying, selling, administration, merchandising, advertising, etc.

43058 ■ Party Central
True Value Specialty Company, LLC
203 Jandus Rd.
Cary, IL 60013-2861
Free: 800-833-3004
No. of Franchise Units: 475. **Founded:** 1910. **Franchised:** 1985. **Description:** Rental store. **Equity Capital Needed:** $250,000-$325,000. **Franchise Fee:** $1,500. **Training:** Yes.

43059 ■ Personal Edge
Centre Du Rasoir
10200 Cote de Liesse
Lachine, QC, Canada H8T 1A3
Ph:(514)636-4512
Fax:(514)636-8356
Co. E-mail: jean-claude@cdrem.com
URL: http://www.personaledge.com
No. of Franchise Units: 64. **Founded:** 1959. **Franchised:** 1980. **Description:** Our stores, located in major shopping malls, feature one of Canada's largest selection of electric shavers and other personal grooming products, as well as small household appliances and specialty gifts from leading manufacturers. We have a unique mix of quality brand name products and onsite repair services. **Equity Capital Needed:** $50,000-$80,000. **Franchise Fee:** No franchise fee for new store. **Training:** Includes 6 weeks training.

43060 ■ Planet Clean
1609 Derwent Way
Delta, BC, Canada V3M 6K8
Ph:(604)540-5300
Free: 877-877-5877
Fax:(604)540-5302
Co. E-mail: info@janitors-warehouse.ca
URL: http://www.planetclean.com
No. of Franchise Units: 4. **No. of Company-Owned Units:** 12. **Founded:** 1982. **Franchised:** 2006. **Description:** Retail of commercial cleaning supplies, equipment and training needs. Planet Clean brings you the highest quality, most innovative and environmentally considerate products. **Equity Capital Needed:** $15,000/$50,000. **Franchise Fee:** $25,000. **Training:** Yes.

43061 ■ Port City Java
PCJ Franchising Co., LLC
2101 Market St.
Wilmington, NC 28403
Ph:(910)796-6646
Fax:(910)796-6611
No. of Franchise Units: 28. **No. of Company-Owned Units:** 12. **Founded:** 1995. **Franchised:** 2003. **Description:** Gourmet coffee cafe with wireless web. **Equity Capital Needed:** $210,300-$413,900 total investment; $300,000 liquid capital; $500,000 net worth. **Franchise Fee:** $20,000. **Financial Assistance:** Third party financing available. **Training:** Offers 18 days at headquarters and 14 days at franchisee's location with ongoing support. ort.

43062 ■ Printwear Xpress
Printwear Xpress Franchise Corp.
1819 Wazee St.
Denver, CO 80202
Ph:(303)771-7100
Free: 888-241-0337
Fax:(303)771-7133
Co. E-mail: info@printwearxpress.com
URL: http://www.printwearxpress.com
No. of Company-Owned Units: 1. **Founded:** 2007. **Franchised:** 2007. **Description:** Printwear Xpress (PWX)combines shopping experience, technology & customer service to deliver a highly competitive business model. PWX stores are modern, attractive & well merchandised to help customers select the right

product for their needs. Production is showcased to illustrate the capabilities of the business & customer service is second to none. PWX stores are located in neighborhood strip centers & don't require an anchor tenant. **Equity Capital Needed:** $148,200-$169,600. **Franchise Fee:** $29,900. **Royalty Fee:** 5%. **Financial Assistance:** Third party financing available. **Training:** Offers 1 week classroom in Denver and 1 week onsite during opening, as well as vendor training.

43063 ■ Saxbys Coffee Worldwide, LLC
Proven Record, Inc.
730 E Elm St.
Conshohocken, PA 19428
Ph:(610)574-3250
Free: 888-672-9297
Fax:(610)397-1672
Co. E-mail: brianwhittaker@saxbyscoffee.com
URL: http://www.saxbyscoffee.com
No. of Franchise Units: 30. **Founded:** 2002. **Franchised:** 2003. **Description:** Coffee retail store, specializing in gourmet espresso drinks, smoothies, and tea. An affordable initial investment, a rewarding career, a simple business to own and operate, and an easy restaurant to staff. **Equity Capital Needed:** $50,000 cash, $200,000 equity. **Franchise Fee:** $30,000. **Financial Assistance:** No. **Training:** 5 day owner training before opening the store and a 5 day owner and employee training upon opening the store.

43064 ■ Sports Experts 2000 Inc.
The Forzani Group, Ltd.
4855 Louis-B Mayer St.
Laval, QC, Canada H7P 6C8
Ph:(450)680-2051
Fax:(450)687-0502
Co. E-mail: mstcharles@forzanigroup.com
URL: http://www.forzanigroup.com
No. of Franchise Units: 228. **No. of Company-Owned Units:** 260. **Founded:** 1967. **Franchised:**

1967. **Description:** Retailer and wholesaler of sporting goods clothing, footwear and equipment. **Equity Capital Needed:** Varies. **Franchise Fee:** Banner specific. **Training:** Yes.

43065 ■ Tastings - A Wine Experience
201 N Illinois St., Ste. 1632
Indianapolis, IN 46204
Free: 877-425-0071
Co. E-mail: info@awineexperience.com
No. of Franchise Units: 12. **Founded:** 2005. **Franchised:** 2006. **Description:** Wine tasting store. **Franchise Fee:** $50,000. **Training:** Yes. Yes.

43066 ■ Theater Xtreme
140 Bradford Dr.
West Berlin, NJ 08091
Ph:(302)455-1334
Fax:(302)455-1612
No. of Franchise Units: 6. **No. of Company-Owned Units:** 5. **Founded:** 2003. **Franchised:** 2004. **Description:** Home theaters and furnishings. **Equity Capital Needed:** $400,000-$700,000. **Franchise Fee:** $40,000. **Royalty Fee:** 4%. **Financial Assistance:** Third party financing available. **Training:** Offers 2 weeks at headquarters, onsite and ongoing electronic training. ing.

43067 ■ Vintage Stock
202 E 32nd St.
Joplin, MO 64804
Ph:(417)623-1550
Fax:(417)782-0024
No. of Company-Owned Units: 13. **Founded:** 1980. **Franchised:** 2005. **Description:** DVDs, videogames, music and sports cards. **Equity Capital Needed:** $337,700-$585,400. **Franchise Fee:** $30,000. **Royalty Fee:** 5%. **Financial Assistance:** No. **Training:** Offers 1 week of training at headquarters, 2-3 weeks onsite and ongoing support.

43068 ■ Watch It! Inc.
10544B-82 Ave.
Edmonton, AB, Canada T6E 2A4
Ph:(780)435-2824
Free: 877-404-2824
Fax:(780)434-5039
Co. E-mail: partner@watchit.ca
URL: http://www.watchit.ca
No. of Franchise Units: 17. **No. of Company-Owned Units:** 6. **Founded:** 1999. **Franchised:** 2004. **Description:** Watch It! Is a cool and funky retail boutique that offers a wide selection of premium brand name watches, sunglasses and accessories. With its trademarked names, a consistent look and feel across stores, low start-up costs and operating procedures that are polished and efficient, purchasing a Watch It franchise is a sensible investment. **Equity Capital Needed:** $200,000-$350,000. **Franchise Fee:** $33,000. **Training:** Yes.

COMPUTER SYSTEMS/ SOFTWARE

43069 ■ Business Controller
MicroBiz
17075 Newhope St., Ste. A
Fountain Valley, CA 92708
Ph:800-726-3282
Fax:(201)785-1568
Co. E-mail: info@microbiz.com
URL: http://www.microbiz.com
Price: Contact MicroBiz for pricing. **Description:** This new version of the Business Controller Plus for Windows is a true 32 bit program that runs in Windows or NT. The software does inventory, invoicing, customer tracking, accounts receivable, reordering, purchasing and much more. It also includes a Query module that allows you to design your own reports and it's Internet Ready!

START-UP INFORMATION

43070 ■ *How to Start and Run Your Own Corporation: S-Corporations For Small Business Owners*
Pub: HCM Publishing
Ed: Peter I. Hupalo. **Released:** March 6, 2003. **Price:** $22.95. **Description:** Basics of corporate business structure are explained. Topics include discovering the best business structure for your company; how to decided between an S-Corporation and LLC; choosing the state in which to incorporate, how to form a corporation, an LLC, a sole proprietorship, or a partnership. Tax codes, accounting practices and legislation affecting every business as well as tips on managing finances are among the topics covered.

43071 ■ *Structuring Your Business*
Pub: Adams Media Corporation
Ed: Michele Cagan. **Released:** 2004. **Price:** $19.95. **Description:** Accountant and author shares insight into starting a new company. The guide assists entrepreneurs through the process, whether it is a corporation, an LLC, a sole proprietorship, or a partnership. Tax codes, accounting practices and legislation affecting every business as well as tips on managing finances are among the topics covered.

REFERENCE WORKS

43072 ■ "All Indicators in Michigan Innovation Index Drop in 4Q" in *Crain's Detroit Business* (Vol. 25, June 22, 2009, No. 25, pp. 9)
Pub: Crain Communications Inc. - Detroit
Ed: Ryan Beene. **Description:** Economic indicators that rate Michigan's innovation fell in the fourth quarter of 2008. The index of trademark applications, SBA loans, venture capital funding, new incorporations and other indicators traced dropped 12.6 points.

43073 ■ "Angel Investments Tripled in 2009" in *Austin Business JournalInc.* (Vol. 29, January 8, 2010, No. 44, pp. 1)
Pub: American City Business Journals
Ed: Christopher Calnan. **Description:** Central Texas Angel Network (CTAN) has invested $3.5 million in 12 ventures, which include 10 in Austin, Texas in 2009 to triple the amount it invested during 2008. The largest recipient of CTAN's investments is life sciences, which attracted 20 percent of the capital, while software investments fell to 18 percent. The new screening process that helps startups secure CTAN capital is explored.

43074 ■ "Attend To Your Corporate Housekeeping" in *Women Entrepreneur* (December 4, 2008)
Pub: Entrepreneur Media Inc.
Ed: Nina Kaufman. **Description:** Business owners can lose all the benefits and privileges of the corporate form if they do not follow proper corporate formalities such as holding an annual meeting, electing officers and directors and adopting or passing corporate resolutions. Creditors are able to take from one's personal assets if such formalities have not been followed.

43075 ■ *Breaking Free: How to Work at Home with the Perfect Small Business Opportunity*
Pub: Lulu.com
Ed: Brian Armstrong. **Released:** June 2007. **Price:** $24.95. **Description:** Three ways to smooth the transition from working for someone else to starting your own business are outlined. Seven exercises to help discover the type of business you should start, how to incorporate, get important tax benefits, and start accepting payments immediately are examined.

43076 ■ *Choosing the Right Legal Form of Business: The Complete Guide to Becoming a Sole Proprietor, Partnership, LLC, or Corporation*
Pub: Atlantic Publishing Company
Ed: Pat Mitchell. **Released:** January 1, 2009. **Price:** $24.95. **Description:** According to the U.S. Small Business Administration, nearly 250,000 new businesses start up annually; currently there are over nine million small companies in the nation. The importance of choosing the proper legal form of business is stressed.

43077 ■ "A Conversation with Mark Lange" in *Crain's Detroit Business* (Vol. 26, January 18, 2010, No. 3, pp. 9)
Pub: Crain Communications, Inc.
Ed: Nancy Kaffer. **Description:** Second-stage companies have different needs from other kinds of startups since they often are moving very fast and dealing with several complex problems at the same time.

43078 ■ *Entrepreneurial Finance*
Pub: Pearson Education, Limited
Ed: Philip J. Adelman; Alan M. Marks. **Released:** July 2006. **Price:** $87.35. **Description:** Financial aspects of running a small business are covered; topics include sole proprietorships, partnerships, limited liability companies, and private corporations.

43079 ■ *Fast-Track Business Start-Up Kit: California*
Pub: DP Group, Incorporated
Ed: Carolyn Usinger. **Released:** September 2006. **Price:** $29.00. **Description:** Step-by-step guide for starting and running a business in California, including information on sole proprietors, partnerships, limited liability companies, S and C corporations, as well as details concerning business entities, sales taxes, environmental issues, human resources, and more.

43080 ■ *Getting Rich In Your Underwear: How To Start and Run a Profitable Home-Based Business*
Pub: HCM Publishing
Ed: Peter I. Hupalo. **Released:** April 1, 2005. **Price:** $17.95. **Description:** Book offers insight into starting a home-based business. Entrepreneurs will learn about business models and the home business; distribution and fulfillment of product or service; marketing and sales; how to overcome the fear of starting a business; personal success characteristics; naming a business; zoning and insurance; intellectual capital; copyrights, trademarks, and patents; limited liability companies and S-corporations; business expenses and accounting; taxes; fifteen basic steps for starting a home-based business, state resources for starting a home company; and seven home-based business ideas.

43081 ■ *How to Form Your Own Corporation without a Lawyer for Under $75.00*
Pub: Dearborn Trade Publishing Inc.
Ed: Ted Nicholas; Sean P. Melvin. **Price:** $19.95.

43082 ■ *Incorporate Your Business: A 50 State Legal Guide to Forming a Corporation*
Pub: Nolo
Ed: Anthony Mancuso. **Released:** January 2004. **Description:** Legal guide to incorporating a business in the U.S., covering all 50 states.

43083 ■ *Own Your Own Corporation: Why the Rich Own Their Own Companies and Everyone Else Works for Them*
Pub: Business Plus
Ed: Garrett Sutton; Robert T. Kiyosaki; Ann Blackman. **Released:** June 2008. **Price:** $17.99 paperback. **Description:** Part of the Rich Dad Advisor's Series, this edition shows how individuals can incorporate themselves and their businesses to save thousands of dollars in taxes and protect against financial disaster.

43084 ■ *Simplified Incorporation Kit*
Pub: Nova Publishing Company
Ed: Daniel Sitarz. **Released:** March 2007. **Price:** $19.95. **Description:** Kit includes all the forms, instructions, and information necessary for incorporating any small business in any state (CD-ROM included).

43085 ■ "Test Your Structural Integrity" in *Entrepreneur* (Vol. 37, August 2009, No. 8, pp. 60)
Pub: Entrepreneur Media, Inc.
Ed: Jennifer Lawler. **Description:** Tax considerations can be important when choosing a business structure. For example, profits are taxed to the corporation in a C corp while profits are taxed only once at an S corp or a limited liability company. Meeting a tax professional should be done prior to switching to a different structure.

43086 ■ "To Be or Not To Be an S Corporation" in *Modern Machine Shop* (Vol. 84, September 2011, No. 4, pp. 38)
Pub: Gardner Publications
Ed: Irving L. Blackman. **Description:** The definitions of both C corporations and S corporations are defined to help any machine shop discover which best suits the owner's business plan.

TRADE PERIODICALS

43087 ■ *Taxes—The Tax Magazine*
Pub: CCH Inc.
Released: Monthly. **Price:** $349. **Description:** Magazine on tax laws and regulations.

COMPUTERIZED DATABASES

43088 ■ *Federal Income Taxation of S Corporations*
Thomson Reuters
395 Hudson St., 4th Fl.
New York, NY 10014
Ph:(212)367-6300
Free: 800-431-9025
Co. E-mail: ria@thomson.com
URL: http://ria.thomsonreuters.com
Description: Contains the full text of the fourth edition of *Federal Income Taxation of S Corporations.* Covers income tax issues spanning the entire life of an S corporation, from election to operation to termination. Provides authoritative interpretations and insights into rules and regulations controlling S corporations. Includes guidance on daily operation and long-term maintenance of the S corporation. **Availability:** Online: Thomson Reuters, Thomson Reuters. **Type:** Full text.

LIBRARIES

43089 ■ Cornell University–Johnson Graduate School of Management Library
101 Sage Hall
Ithaca, NY 14853
Ph:(607)255-3389
Fax:(607)255-8633
Co. E-mail: akh8@cornell.edu
URL: http://www.library.cornell.edu/johnson
Contact: Angela Horne, Dir.
Scope: Business administration and management science, finance, investment, accounting, marketing, managerial economics, operations management and quantitative analysis. **Services:** Interlibrary loan. **Holdings:** 164,000 volumes; 1096 non-book materials; 860,000 microfiche; 2800 microfilm; 450 CD-ROMs. **Subscriptions:** 1300 journals and other serials; 23 newspapers.

RESEARCH CENTERS

43090 ■ Jackson State University–Bureau of Business and Economic Research
1230 Raymond Rd., Box 500
Jackson, MS 39204
Ph:(601)979-2795
Fax:(601)914-0833
Co. E-mail: lurlene.irvin@jsums.edu
URL: http://www.jsums.edu/business/bber
Contact: Lurlene Irvin PhD, Dir.
E-mail: lurlene.irvin@jsums.edu
Scope: Small business, including applied and theoretical studies which contribute to the development of Mississippi business economy. **Services:** Consulting for local business. **Publications:** Annual Demographic Databook (annually); Economic Indicators (monthly); Reports. **Educational Activities:** College of Business Annual Research Symposiums; Seminars in areas of finance, marketing, management, accounting, and secretarial education, for business personnel and entrepreneurs in the Jackson area. **Awards:** Research Awards, for faculty.

43091 ■ St. Francis Xavier University–Coady International Institute
PO Box 5000
Antigonish, NS, Canada B2G 2W5
Ph:(902)867-3960
Free: (866)-820-7835
Fax:(902)867-3907
Co. E-mail: coady@stfx.ca
URL: http://www.coady.stfx.ca
Contact: Gordon Cunningham, Interim Dir.
E-mail: coady@stfx.ca
Scope: International development, community development, adult education, health education, gender and development, advocacy, microenterprise, microcredit, peacebuilding, evaluation. **Publications:** Annual report; Coady Connection (biennially); Newsletters.

43092 ■ University of Maryland at College Park–Dingman Center for Entrepreneurship
2518 Van Munching Hall
Robert H. Smith School of Business
College Park, MD 20742
Ph:(301)405-9545
Fax:(301)314-7971
Co. E-mail: aepstein@rhsmith.umd.edu
URL: http://www.rhsmith.umd.edu/dingman
Contact: Asher Epstein, Mng.Dir.
E-mail: aepstein@rhsmith.umd.edu
Scope: Entrepreneurship, new venture creation, technology commercialization, and venture capital. **Services:** Assistance, to emerging growth firms through mentor program; Business Plan Reviews. **Publications:** Newsletters for the entrepreneurial community and for volunteers (monthly). **Educational Activities:** Dingman Day Lunches; Dingman Jumpstart (biennially), three week program aimed at getting students comfortable with start-up culture within the center's experiential learning environment and bringing their business ideas to life; Industry forums; Networking breakfasts; Seminars; Speaker events, in entrepreneurship and entrepreneurship concentration in MBA curriculum; Venture Capital Forums. **Awards:** Pitch Dingman (monthly), includes $2,500 in start-up funds to any 5- to 8-minute power point presentation directed towards an investor audience.

START-UP INFORMATION

43093 ■ Design and Launch Your Online Boutique in a Week
Pub: Entrepreneur Press
Ed: Melissa Campanelli. **Released:** June 26, 2008. **Price:** $17.95. **Description:** Tips for starting an online boutique in a short amount of time are given. The books shows how to build the online boutique with designer goods or your own product, ways to create eye-catching content, online tools to handle payments and accept orders, marketing and advertising techniques, and customer service.

43094 ■ "Five Low-Cost Home Based Startups" in Women Entrepreneur (December 16, 2008)
Pub: Entrepreneur Media Inc.
Ed: Lesley Spencer Pyle. **Description:** During tough economic times, small businesses have an advantage over large companies because they can adjust to economic conditions more easily and without having to go through corporate red tape that can slow the implementation process. A budding entrepreneur may find success by taking inventory of his or her skills, experience, expertise and passions and utilizing those qualities to start a business. Five low-cost home-based startups are profiled. These include starting an online store, a virtual assistant service, web designer, sales representative and a home staging counselor.

43095 ■ "Follow the Numbers: It's the Best Way To Spot Problems Before They Become Life-Threatening" in Inc. (January 2008, pp. 63-64)
Pub: Gruner & Jahr USA Publishing
Ed: Norm Brodsky. **Description:** It is important for any small business to track monthly sales and gross margins by hand for the first year or two. When writing the numbers, be sure to break them out by product category or service type and by customer.

43096 ■ Mommy Millionaire: How I Turned My Kitchen Table Idea Into a Million Dollars and How You Can, Too!
Pub: St. Martin's Press LLC
Ed: Kim Lavine. **Released:** February 19, 2008. **Price:** $14.95. **Description:** Advice, secrets and lessons for making a million dollars from a mom who turned her kitchen into a successful business; tools cover developing and patenting an idea, cold calling, trade shows, QVC, big retailers, manufacturing, and raising venture capital.

ASSOCIATIONS AND OTHER ORGANIZATIONS

43097 ■ Canadian Professional Sales Association–L'association Canadienne des Professionnels de la Vente
655 Bay St., Ste. 400
Toronto, ON, Canada M5G 2K4
Ph:(416)408-2685
Free: 888-267-CPSA
Fax:(416)408-2684
URL: http://www.cpsa.com
Contact: Harvey Copeman, Pres./CEO
Description: Professional salespeople. Promotes professional advancement of members. Represents members' interests before government agencies, industrial organizations, and the public. Conducts continuing professional education programs. **Publications:** Contact (quarterly).

43098 ■ Direct Selling Association
1667 K St. NW, Ste. 1100
Washington, DC 20006
Ph:(202)452-8866
Fax:(202)452-9010
Co. E-mail: info@dsa.org
URL: http://www.dsa.org
Contact: Mr. Neil H. Offen, Pres.
Description: Manufacturers and distributors selling consumer products through person-to-person sales, by appointment, and through home-party plans. Products include food, gifts, house wares, dietary supplements, cosmetics, apparel, jewelry, decorative accessories, reference books, and telecommunications products and services. Offers specialized education; conducts research programs; compiles statistics. Maintains hall of fame. Sponsors Direct Selling Education Foundation. **Publications:** State Status Sheet (weekly).

43099 ■ Direct Selling Education Foundation
1667 K St. NW, Ste. 1100
Washington, DC 20006-1660
Ph:(202)452-8866
Fax:(202)452-9015
Co. E-mail: info@dsef.org
URL: http://www.dsef.org
Contact: Charles L. Orr, Exec. Dir.
Description: Serves the public interest with education, information, and research, thereby enhancing acceptance and public awareness of direct selling in the global marketplace. **Publications:** DSEF: A Foundation That Works; Moral Suasion .

43100 ■ Marketing Agencies Association Worldwide
89 Woodland Cir.
Minneapolis, MN 55424
Ph:(952)922-0130
Fax:(760)437-4141
Co. E-mail: keith.mccracken@maaw.org
URL: http://www.maaw.org
Contact: Mr. Keith McCracken, Exec. Dir.
Description: Represents the interests of CEOs, presidents, managing directors and principals of top marketing services agencies. Provides opportunity for marketing professionals to meet with peers, raise company profile on both a national and a global platform, and influence the future of industry. Fosters networking through conferences. .

43101 ■ Professional Society for Sales and Marketing Training
113 McHenry Rd., No. 141
Buffalo Grove, IL 60089
Ph:(973)882-3931
Free: 800-219-0096
Co. E-mail: smtpowerofe@gmail.com
URL: http://www.smt.org
Contact: Teresa Hiatt, Pres.
Description: Directors of training. Seeks to improve sales, marketing and customer relations through training. Conducts educational conferences and sales training clinics. .

43102 ■ World Federation of Direct Selling Associations
1667 K St. NW, Ste. 1100
Washington, DC 20006
Ph:(202)452-8866
Fax:(202)452-9010
Co. E-mail: info@wfdsa.org
URL: http://www.wfdsa.org
Description: Organized for the purpose of promoting the common business interests of its members. Exchanges information among members. Fosters highest standards of direct selling practices, consumer protection and ethics in the marketplace, by adoption and promotion of the Codes of Conduct for Direct Selling. Improves communications through sponsorship of World Congress of direct selling. Encourages personal relationships and cooperation among people in direct selling. Promotes education internationally through programs and funding, relying on the United States Direct Selling Education Foundation (USDSEF) to help it towards this objective. **Publications:** World Federation News (bimonthly).

EDUCATIONAL PROGRAMS

43103 ■ Advanced Sales Management
American Management Association
600 AMA Way
Saranac Lake, NY 12983-5534
Ph:(212)586-8100
Free: 877-566-9441
Fax:(518)891-0368
Co. E-mail: customerservice@amanet.org
URL: http://www.amaseminars.org
Price: $2,545.00 for non-members; $2,295.00 for AMA members; and $1,965.00 for General Services Administration (GSA) members. **Description:** Covers increasing productivity and efficiency through team building, adapting to a changing environment, and decision, and problem solving techniques. **Locations:** Chicago, IL; San Francisco, CA; Hilton Head Island, SC; and New York, NY.

43104 ■ Cracking New Accounts: High Pay-Off Prospecting (Onsite)
Seminar Information Service, Inc.
20 Executive Park, Ste. 120
Irvine, CA 92614
Ph:(949)261-9104
Free: 877-SEM-INFO
Fax:(949)261-1963
Co. E-mail: info@seminarinformation.com
URL: http://www.seminarinformation.com
Price: $595.00 per person; $580.00 each for three to five attendees; $365.00 each for six to 10 attendees; $335.00 each for 11+ attendees. **Description:** Cov-

ers building relationships, winning against competition and maximizing your sales and profit potentials in today's crowded marketplace, including 50 power prospecting techniques and why 85% or more of all sales calls are wasted and how to gain access to anybody at any time. **Locations:** Cities throughout the United States.

43105 ■ The Distinct Advantage (Onsite)
Seminar Information Service, Inc.
20 Executive Park, Ste. 120
Irvine, CA 92614
Ph:(949)261-9104
Free: 877-SEM-INFO
Fax:(949)261-1963
Co. E-mail: info@seminarinformation.com
URL: http://www.seminarinformation.com
Price: $1,499.00. **Description:** Provides valuable, innovative, measurable skills that can be put into immediate practice and can dramatically impact the chances of closing a sale-and ultimately the organization's bottom line. **Locations:** Cleveland, OH.

43106 ■ Fundamental Selling Techniques for the New or Prospective Salesperson Level I
Seminar Information Service, Inc.
20 Executive Park, Ste. 120
Irvine, CA 92614
Ph:(949)261-9104
Free: 877-SEM-INFO
Fax:(949)261-1963
Co. E-mail: info@seminarinformation.com
URL: http://www.seminarinformation.com
Price: $1,995.00; $1,795.00 for AMA members. **Description:** Gain the skills and confidence to sell your product or service successfully, including listening and prospecting skills. **Locations:** Cities throughout the United States.

43107 ■ Mastering the Complex Sale (Onsite)
Seminar Information Service, Inc.
20 Executive Park, Ste. 120
Irvine, CA 92614
Ph:(949)261-9104
Free: 877-SEM-INFO
Fax:(949)261-1963
Co. E-mail: info@seminarinformation.com
URL: http://www.seminarinformation.com
Price: $1,595.00. **Description:** Seminar that combines the best university level learning with the best of street-smart selling into a proven system for success in the high-stakes sale. **Locations:** Boston, MA; Santa Clara, CA; Houston, TX; Minneapolis, MN; and Chicago, IL.

43108 ■ Principles of Professional Selling
American Management Association
600 AMA Way
Saranac Lake, NY 12983-5534
Ph:(212)586-8100
Free: 877-566-9441
Fax:(518)891-0368
Co. E-mail: customerservice@amanet.org
URL: http://www.amaseminars.org
Price: $2,345.00 for non-members; $2,095.00 for AMA members; and $1,794.00 for General Services Administration (GSA) members. **Description:** Three-day seminar for seasoned sales professionals; covers consultative selling, planning the sales process, building relationships with customers, the sales process, utilizing technology, listening skills, telephone techniques, and time management. **Locations:** New York, NY; Chicago, IL; Washington, DC; Atlanta, GA; Morristown, NJ; and San Francisco, CA.

43109 ■ Prospecting Strategies to Build a Qualified Pipeline (Onsite)
Seminar Information Service, Inc.
20 Executive Park, Ste. 120
Irvine, CA 92614
Ph:(949)261-9104
Free: 877-SEM-INFO
Fax:(949)261-1963
Co. E-mail: info@seminarinformation.com
URL: http://www.seminarinformation.com
Price: $1,995.00. **Description:** Learn a proactive approach to successful prospecting by first perfecting your lead qualification followed by practicing your

prospecting skills through role-plays, applying your new insights to determine what has value to your qualified customer. **Locations:** San Francisco, CA.

43110 ■ Retail Automobile Sales (Onsite)
Seminar Information Service, Inc.
20 Executive Park, Ste. 120
Irvine, CA 92614
Ph:(949)261-9104
Free: 877-SEM-INFO
Fax:(949)261-1963
Co. E-mail: info@seminarinformation.com
URL: http://www.seminarinformation.com
Price: $395.00. **Description:** Main areas covered are overcoming objections, advanced inter-personal communications skills, and things to do to avoid job burn-out, stay enthusiastic and motivated, and how to positively influence the emotional states of those around them. **Locations:** Portland, OR; and Phoenix, AZ.

43111 ■ Selling to Major Accounts: A Strategic Approach
American Management Association
600 AMA Way
Saranac Lake, NY 12983-5534
Ph:(212)586-8100
Free: 877-566-9441
Fax:(518)891-0368
Co. E-mail: customerservice@amanet.org
URL: http://www.amaseminars.org
Price: $2,345.00 for non-members; $2,095.00 for AMA members; and $1,794.00 for General Services Administration (GSA) members. **Description:** Covers strategies for developing successful relationships with major accounts. **Locations:** Chicago, IL; Las Vegas, NV; San Francisco, CA; Atlanta, GA; and New York, NY.

43112 ■ Strategic Sales Negotiations
American Management Association
600 AMA Way
Saranac Lake, NY 12983-5534
Ph:(212)586-8100
Free: 877-566-9441
Fax:(518)891-0368
Co. E-mail: customerservice@amanet.org
URL: http://www.amaseminars.org
Price: $2,095.00 for non-members; $1,895.00 for AMA members; and $1,623.00 for General Services Administration (GSA) members. **Description:** Covers the tools, techniques, and negotiation tactics for effectively influencing a buyer's perception of cost, benefits, and value. **Locations:** Chicago, IL; and San Francisco, CA.

43113 ■ Successful Sales Skills (Onsite)
Seminar Information Service, Inc.
20 Executive Park, Ste. 120
Irvine, CA 92614
Ph:(949)261-9104
Free: 877-SEM-INFO
Fax:(949)261-1963
Co. E-mail: info@seminarinformation.com
URL: http://www.seminarinformation.com
Price: $370.00. **Description:** Learn how to enhance their ability to deal with buying objections, and refine their skills in closing sales and negotiating win-win agreements leading to long-term relationships with customers. **Locations:** Waukesha, WI; and Palatine, IL.

43114 ■ Successful Telephone Selling Techniques
600 AMA Way
Saranac Lake, NY 12983-5534
Ph:(212)586-8100
Free: 877-566-9441
Fax:(518)891-0368
Co. E-mail: customerservice@amanet.org
URL: http://www.amaseminars.org
Price: $1,995.00 for non-members; $1,795.00 for AMA members; and $1,537.00 for General Services Administration (GSA) members. **Description:** Gain the strategies, techniques and take-away tools you need to move every customer toward a buying decision. **Locations:** Atlanta, GA; Arlington, VA; and New York, NY.

43115 ■ Territory and Time Management for Salespeople
American Management Association
600 AMA Way
Saranac Lake, NY 12983-5534
Ph:(212)586-8100
Free: 877-566-9441
Fax:(518)891-0368
Co. E-mail: customerservice@amanet.org
URL: http://www.amaseminars.org
Price: $2,095.00 for non-members; $1,895.00 for AMA members; and $1,623.00 for General Services Administration (GSA) members. **Description:** Two-day seminar covers setting goals, attitude, organizational skills, developing a territory strategy, and increasing productivity. **Locations:** New York, NY; San Francisco, CA; Arlington, VA; Washington, DC; and Chicago, IL.

43116 ■ Track Selling System Workshop
Seminar Information Service, Inc.
20 Executive Park, Ste. 120
Irvine, CA 92614
Ph:(949)261-9104
Free: 877-SEM-INFO
Fax:(949)261-1963
Co. E-mail: info@seminarinformation.com
URL: http://www.seminarinformation.com
Price: $1,895.00 per person; $1,845.00 each for 2 attending the same program, $1795.00 each for three attending the same program. **Description:** Teaches salespeople to be customer oriented rather than product-centered, how to translate product/service features into customer benefits, using role playing extensively, and orients and motivates participants towards sales as a profession, and introduces a consultative selling process and a guaranteed method of closing. **Locations:** Seattle, WA.

REFERENCE WORKS

43117 ■ "$1M Home Sales Spike" in *Business Courier* (Vol. 27, December 3, 2010, No. 31, pp. 1)
Pub: Business Courier

Ed: Tom Demeropolis. **Description:** Cincinnati Area Board of Realtors reported the increase of sales of multi-million dollar Tri-State homes in 2010, particularly in Indian Hill where sales surged nearly 60 percent. Sales of homes of $1 million and above are up 21 percent through November in Hamilton County with 58 homes sales.

43118 ■ *The 4 Routes to Entrepreneurial Success*
Pub: Berrett-Koehler Publishers

Ed: John B. Miner. **Price:** $18.95. **Description:** After researching one hundred successful entrepreneurs, the author discovered there are basically four personality types of entrepreneurs: the personal achiever, the super salesperson, the real manager, and the expert idea generator.

43119 ■ *31 Days to Greeting Card Marketing Mastery*
Pub: Desktop Wings Inc.

Ed: Bruce Brown. **Released:** February 19, 2010. **Price:** $17.95. **Description:** The use of simple greeting cards for marketing and increasing sales is explained.

43120 ■ *49 Marketing Secrets (That Work) to Grow Sales*
Pub: Morgan James Publishing, LLC

Ed: Ronald Finklestein. **Released:** October 2007. **Price:** $19.95/ **Description:** This book was written to fill the void on marketing books and is tailored to the small business owner. The author helps the small business owner to understand marketing and who they can trust while doing business. The book includes information to help entrepreneurs discover winning marketing strategies, branding and corporate image, media strategies, networking tips, technology-based marketing ideas, event strategies, and sales strategies.

43121 ■ "2009 Real Estate in Review: Median Prices Drop, Sales Up" in *Bellingham Business Journal* **(Vol. February 2010, pp. 15)**
Pub: Sound Publishing Inc.
Ed: Isaac Bonnell. **Description:** Bellingham and Whatcom County, Washington saw a rise in home sales in 2008. Single family home sales were up 3.3 percent in Bellingham and 0.5 percent for the entire county. Statistical data included.

43122 ■ "2010 Book of Lists" in *Austin Business JournalInc.* **(Vol. 29, December 25, 2009, No. 42, pp. 1)**
Pub: American City Business Journals
Description: Rankings of companies and organizations within the business services, finance, healthcare, hospitality and travel, insurance, marketing and media, professional services, real estate, education and technology industries in Austin, Texas are presented. Rankings are based on sales, business size, and other statistics.

43123 ■ "2010 Book of Lists" in *Tampa Bay Business Journal* **(Vol. 30, December 22, 2009, No. 53, pp. 1)**
Pub: American City Business Journals
Description: Rankings of companies and organizations within the human resources, banking and finance, business services, healthcare, real estate, technology, hospitality and travel, and education industries in the Greater Tampa Bay area are presented. Rankings are based on sales, business size, and more.

43124 ■ "A&E Networks" in *Brandweek* **(Vol. 49, April 21, 2008, No. 16, pp. SR9)**
Pub: VNU Business Media, Inc.
Ed: Anthony Crupi. **Description:** Provides contact information for sales and marketing personnel for the A&E Networks as well as a listing of the station's top programming and an analysis of the current season and the target audience for those programs running in the current season. A&E has reinvented itself as a premium entertainment brand over the last five years and with its $2.5 million per episode acquisition of The Sopranos, the station signaled that it was serious about getting back into the scripted programming business. The acquisition also helped the network compete against other cable networks and led to a 20 percent increase in prime-time viewers.

43125 ■ "ABC" in *Brandweek* **(Vol. 49, April 21, 2008, No. 16, pp. SR6)**
Pub: VNU Business Media, Inc.
Ed: John Consoli. **Description:** Provides contact information for sales and marketing personnel for the ABC network as well as a listing of the station's top programming and an analysis of the current season and the target audience for those programs running in the current season.

43126 ■ *The Accidental Entrepreneur: The 50 Things I Wish Someone Had Told Me About Starting a Business*
Pub: AMACOM
Ed: Susan Urquhart-Brown. **Released:** March 2008. **Price:** $17.95. **Description:** Advice is offered to any would-be entrepreneur, including eight questions to ask before launching a new business, ten traits of a successful entrepreneur, how to obtain licenses and selling permits, best way to create a business plan, ten ways to get referrals, six secrets of marketing, investment and financial information, ways to avoid burnout, and the seven biggest pitfalls to avoid.

43127 ■ "Active Sales" in *Green Industry Pro* **(Vol. 23, September 2011)**
Pub: Cygnus Business Media
Ed: Gregg Wartgow. **Description:** Craig den Hartog, owner of Emerald Magic Lawn Care located in Holtsville, New York, describes the various marketing tactics he has developed to increase sales in the current economic environment. Statistical data included.

43128 ■ "Add Aquatics to Boost Business" in *Pet Product News* **(Vol. 64, December 2010, No. 12, pp. 20)**
Pub: BowTie Inc.
Ed: David Lass. **Description:** Pet stores are encouraged to add aquatics departments to increase profitability through repeat sales. This goal can be realized by sourcing, displaying, and maintaining high quality live fish. Other tips regarding the challenges associated with setting up an aquatics department are presented.

43129 ■ *Advanced Selling for Dummies*
Pub: John Wiley and Sons, Inc.
Ed: Ralph R. Roberts; Joe Kraynak (As told to). **Released:** September 2007. **Price:** $21.99. **Description:** This book explores topics such as: visualizing success (includes exercises), investing and reinvesting in your own success, harnessing media and multimedia outlets, calculating risks that stretch your limits, creating lasting relationships, finding balance to avoid burnout and more. This guide is for salespeople who have already read 'Selling for Dummies' and now want forward-thinking, advanced strategies for recharging and reenergizing their careers and their lives. Blogging, Internet leads and virtual assistants are also discussed.

43130 ■ *Advancing Research on Minority Entrepreneurship*
Pub: SAGE Publications, Inc.
Ed: James H. Johnson Jr.; Timothy Bates; William E. Jackson III; James H. Johnson; William E. Jackson. **Released:** September 2007. **Price:** $34.00. **Description:** Although minorities are more likely to engage in start-up businesses than others, minority entrepreneurs are less likely to get their enterprises off the ground or succeed in growing their businesses. The higher failure rates, lower sales and profits and less employment are among topics discussed.

43131 ■ *Alpha Dogs: How Your Small Business Can Become a Leader of the Pack*
Pub: HarperInformation
Ed: Donna Fenn. **Released:** May 2007. **Price:** $14.95. **Description:** Ways for an entrepreneur to outsmart competitors in the marketplace, to generate higher sales, and earn lasting customer and employee loyalty.

43132 ■ "Angels for the Jobless; Church Volunteer Groups Give Career Guidance" in *Crain's Detroit Business* **(Vol. 24, March 31, 2008, No. 13)**
Pub: Crain Communications, Inc.
Ed: Sherri Begin. **Description:** St. Andrew Catholic Church, located in Rochester, offers the St. Andrew Career Mentoring Ministry, a program that brings in professionals who volunteer to aid those seeking jobs or, in numerous cases, new careers.

43133 ■ "Art of the Online Deal" in *Farm Industry News* **(March 25, 2011)**
Pub: Penton Business Media Inc.
Description: Farmers share advice for shopping online for machinery; photos, clean equipment, the price, equipment details, and online sources topped their list.

43134 ■ "Ask Inc" in *Inc.* **(February 2008, pp. 52)**
Pub: Gruner & Jahr USA Publishing
Ed: James Dyson. **Description:** Owner of a consulting firm seeks advice to help his sales staff become more successful.

43135 ■ "avVaa World Health Care Products Rolls Out Internet Marketing Program" in *Health and Beauty Close-Up* **(September 18, 2009)**
Pub: Close-Up Media
Description: avVaa World Health Care Products, Inc., a biotechnology company, manufacturer and distributor of nationally branded therapeutic, natural health care and skin products, has signed an agreement with Online Performance Marketing to launch of an Internet marketing campaign in order to broaden its presence online. The impact of advertising on the Internet to generate an increase in sales is explored.

43136 ■ "Back to Business for Bishop Museum" in *Hawaii Business* **(Vol. 54, August 2008, No. 2, pp. 53)**
Pub: Hawaii Business Publishing
Ed: Shara Enay. **Description:** Bishop Museum, ranked 224 in Hawaii Business' top 250 companies for 2008, had $29.5 million in gross sales for 2007, up 52.8 percent from the $19.3 million gross sales in 2006. The company has cut 24 positions in a restructuring effort for the museum's sustainability. Grants, artifacts and plans for sustainable operations are discussed.

43137 ■ *Baseline Selling*
Pub: AuthorHouse
Ed: Dave Kurlan. **Released:** November 2005. **Price:** $18.49. **Description:** Training manual for sales people that provides methods for "baseline selling." This practice involves a process similar to baseball, where a deal is worked from one base to the next until the deal is closed. First base is the appointment, second means the prospect wants what you are selling, third base shows two parties are qualified to do business together, home base is presenting a winning solution and making the sale.

43138 ■ "BayTSP, NTT Data Corp. Enter Into Reseller Pact to Market Online IP Monitoring" in *Professional Services Close-Up* **(Sept. 11, 2009)**
Pub: Close-Up Media
Description: Due to incredible interest from distributors and content owners across Asia, NTT Data Corp. will resell BayTSP's online intellectual property monitoring, enforcement, business intelligence and monetization services in Japan.

43139 ■ *Be the Elephant: Build a Bigger, Better Business*
Pub: Workman Publishing Company
Ed: Steve Kaplan. **Price:** $19.95. **Description:** Entrepreneur and author sets out an accessible, no-frills plan for business owners, managers, and other industrialists to grow their businesses into elephants: big and strong but also smart. Advice is given on fostering a growth mind-set, assessing risk, and creating unique selling propositions.

43140 ■ *Behind the Cloud*
Pub: Jossey-Bass
Ed: Marc Benioff, Carlye Adler. **Released:** 2010. **Price:** $27.95. **Description:** Salesforce.com is the world's most successful business-to-business cloud-computing company that sells an online service that helps businesses manage sales, customer service, and marketing functions.

43141 ■ "Being all a-Twitter" in *Canadian Business* **(Vol. 81, December 8, 2008, No. 21, pp. 22)**
Pub: Rogers Media Ltd.
Ed: Andrew Wahl. **Description:** Marketing experts suggest that advertising strategies have to change along with new online social media. Companies are advised to find ways to incorporate social software because workers and customers are expected to continue its use.

43142 ■ "Best Value Stocks" in *Canadian Business* **(Vol. 82, Summer 2009, No. 8, pp. 30)**
Pub: Rogers Media
Ed: Calvin Leung. **Description:** Canadian companies that are believed to have the best value stocks are suggested. Suggestions include publishing firm Glacier Media, which has reported a four-fold growth in sales in the last three years. While publishers like Glacier Media face challenges such as declining circulation, the firm's industry diversification is expected to help it weather the economic downturn.

43143 ■ "The Best and Worst Economic Times" in *Agency Sales Magazine* **(Vol. 39, December 2009, No. 11, pp. 22)**
Pub: MANA
Ed: Mark Young. **Description:** U.S. gross domestic product grew 3.5 percent and the stock market has improved but manufacturers are cutting commissions or dropping sales representatives. Despite these challenges, it can a good time for salespeople because clients need them more than ever. Salesmen should find new ways to do business for their clients during this current challenging environment.

43144 ■ "Better Business: Get Ready (Marketing Strategies for Better Sales Performance)" in *Entrepreneur* **(Vol. 35, October 2007, No. 10)**
Pub: Entrepreneur Media Inc.
Ed: Gwen Moran. **Description:** Good sales practice increases sales performance and revenue. Sales consultant Paul S. Goldner believes that salespeople should research prospective clients before negotiating with them, while another consultant, Chet Holmes thinks that companies should support their salespeople and set sales performance standards. Other proven effective marketing strategies are presented.

43145 ■ "Better Made's Better Idea: Diversify Despite Rising Costs" in *Crain's Detroit Business* **(Vol. 24, September 22, 2008, No. 38, pp. 18)**
Pub: Crain Communications, Inc.
Ed: Nathan Skid. **Description:** Better Made Snack Foods Inc. is planning to expand its product lines and market reach as well as boost manufacturing capability during a time in which the company is being buffeted by rising commodity and fuel costs. The company feels that diversification is the key to maintain sales and growth.

43146 ■ "Big Trouble at Sony Ericsson" in *Barron's* **(Vol. 88, March 24, 2008, No. 12, pp. M9)**
Pub: Dow Jones & Company, Inc.
Ed: Angelo Franchini. **Description:** Sony Ericsson is facing trouble as it warned that its sales and net income before taxes will fall by nearly half for the first quarter of 2008. The joint venture of Sony and Ericsson has a global mobile phone market share of nine percent as of 2007, fourth largest in the world.

43147 ■ "BMW Revs Up for a Rebound" in *Barron's* **(Vol. 89, July 13, 2009, No. 28, pp. M7)**
Pub: Dow Jones & Co., Inc.
Ed: Jonathan Buck. **Description:** Investors may like BMW's stocks because the company has maintained its balance sheet strength and has an impressive production line of new models that should boost sales in the next few years. The company's sales are also gaining traction, although their vehicle delivery was down 1.7 percent year on year on June 2009, this was still the best monthly sales figure for 2009.

43148 ■ "Book of Lists 2010" in *Philadelphia Business Journal* **(Vol. 28, December 25, 2009, No. 45, pp. 1)**
Pub: American City Business Journals
Description: Rankings of companies and organizations within the banking, biotechnology, economic development, healthcare, hospitality, law and accounting, marketing and media, real estate, and technology industries in the Philadelphia, Pennsylvania area are presented. Rankings are based on sales, business size, and more.

43149 ■ "Boom and Bust in the Book Biz" in *Canadian Business* **(Vol. 83, August 17, 2010, No. 13-14, pp. 16)**
Pub: Rogers Media Ltd.
Ed: Jordan Timm. **Description:** Electronic book marketplace is booming with Amazon.com's e-book sales for the Kindle e-reader exceeding the hardcover sales. Kobo Inc. has registered early success with its Kobo e-reader and has partnered with Hong Kong telecom giant on an e-book store.

43150 ■ "Boosting Worried Customers' Confidence" in *Gallup Management Journal* **(November 8, 2011)**
Pub: Gallup
Ed: Jessica Tyler, Patrick Whiston. **Description:** While customers fear a double-dip recession and US economic confidence is low, leading edge firms have found a timely and creative way to win customers: they are improving their wellbeing.

43151 ■ "Boosting Your Merchant Management Services With Wireless Technology" in *Franchising World* **(Vol. 42, August 2010, No. 8, pp. 27)**
Pub: International Franchise Association
Ed: Michael S. Slominski. **Description:** Franchises should have the capability to accept credit cards

away from their businesses. This technology will increase sales.

43152 ■ "Bottoms Up!" in *Entrepreneur* **(Vol. 36, April 2008, No. 4, pp. 128)**
Pub: Entrepreneur Media, Inc.
Ed: Amanda C. Kooser. **Description:** Jill Bernheimer launched her online alcohol business Domaine547 in 2007, and encountered challenges as legal issues over the licensing and launching of the business took about seven months to finish. Domain547 features blog and forum areas. Marketing strategy that connects to the social community is one of the ways to reach out to customers.

43153 ■ "Brite-Strike Tactical Launches New Internet Marketing Initiatives" in *Internet Wire* **(September 15, 2009)**
Pub: Comtex News Network, Inc.
Description: Brite-Strike Tactical Illumination Products, Inc. has enlisted the expertise of Internet marketing guru Thomas J. McCarthy to help revamp the company's Internet campaign. An outline of the Internet marketing strategy is provided.

43154 ■ "Building Your Business: A Strong Web Presence Is a Must" in *Black Enterprise* **(Vol. 38, December 2007, No. 5, pp. 74)**
Pub: Earl G. Graves Publishing Co. Inc.
Ed: Tennille M. Robinson. **Description:** Building a strong presence on the Internet is crucial to any growing business. Websites can provide information or sell merchandise, but the site must also make sure the customer knows how to use and navigate around within the site. Common mistakes to avoid when designing a small business Website are outlined.

43155 ■ *Business Black Belt: Develop the Strength, Flexibility and Agility to Run Your Company*
Pub: Career Press, Inc.
Ed: Burke Franklin. **Released:** November 1, 2010. **Price:** $15.99. **Description:** Manual offering insights that will enable anyone to become successful in small business. Seventy short chapters included topics such as attitude, management, marketing, selling, employees, money, MBAs, lawyers, consultants, and investors.

43156 ■ "The Business Case for Mobile Content Acceleration" in *Streaming Media* **(November 2011, pp. 78)**
Pub: Information Today Inc.
Ed: Dan Rayburn. **Description:** Last holiday season, eBay became a mobile commerce (m-commerce) giant when sales rose by 134 percent, as most online retailers offered customers the ability to purchase items using their mobile devices.

43157 ■ "Business Forecast: Stormy and Successful" in *Women In Business* **(Vol. 62, June 2010, No. 2, pp. 12)**
Pub: American Business Women's Association
Ed: Kathleen Leighton. **Description:** Stormy Simon, vice president of customer service at Overstock.com is a self-made career woman who started out as a temporary employee in the company in 2001. She was not able to attend college because she had two sons to care for after her divorce. Simon got involved in advertising and media buying and shares her love for business.

43158 ■ "The Business Value of Social Networks" in *Agency Sales Magazine* **(Vol. 39, July 2009, No. 7, pp. 44)**
Pub: MANA
Ed: Daniel Burrus. **Description:** Personal and business uses of several Web 2.0 tools for salespeople are discussed. Leading questions which will guide salespeople in finding out if one particular tool will benefit them are presented.

43159 ■ *Business Warrior: Strategy for Entrepreneurs*
Pub: Clearbridge Publishing
Ed: Sun Tzu. **Released:** September 2006. **Price:** $19.95. **Description:** Advice to help entrepreneurs understand competitive strategies in order to succeed, focusing on sales, marketing, and personnel management.

43160 ■ *Buying In: The Secret Dialogue Between What We Buy and Who We Are*
Pub: Random House
Ed: Rob Walker. **Released:** 2008. **Price:** $25.00. **Description:** The book offers a look at the state of advertising today and shows why even those who feel like they see through marketing feel attached to specific brands as a way to both project and foster their identities.

43161 ■ *Buying and Selling a Business*
Pub: Entrepreneur Press
Ed: Ira Nottonson. **Released:** April 2008. **Price:** $32.95. **Description:** Tips for negotiating sales are presented. Attorney, Ira Nottonson presents both sides of negotiations by presenting the both buyer's and seller's perspectives. Critical steps in the sale process, including presentation, negotiation and documentations are discussed. The book teaches how to gain the upper hand, minimize financial risk and be a winner regardless of side.

43162 ■ "Calling All Recruiters: Agent HR Puts Staffing Agents In Charge" in *Black Enterprise* **(Vol. 38, December 2007, No. 5, pp. 72)**
Pub: Earl G. Graves Publishing Co. Inc.
Ed: Chana Garcia. **Description:** Recruiting and staffing agencies are seeing a drop in services due to slow economic growth. AgentHR partners with full-service recruiters who have three to five year's experience-specialists soliciting their own clients, provide staffing services, and manage their own accounts, thus combining the roles of recruiter and salesperson.

43163 ■ "Can You Hear Them Now?" in *Hawaii Business* **(Vol. 54, August 2008, No. 2, pp. 48)**
Pub: Hawaii Business Publishing
Ed: Jason Ubay. **Description:** Coral Wireless LLC (dba Mobi PCS) is ranked 237 in Hawaii Business' list of the state's top 250 companies for 2008. The company is a local wireless phone provider, which has expanded its market to Oahu, Maui and the Big Island since opening in 2006, offering 13 phones and unlimited texts and calls. Details on the company's sales are provided.

43164 ■ "Cash in Your Attic: Is Your Junk Someone Else's Treasure?" in *Black Enterprise* **(Vol. 37, November 2006, No. 4, pp. 156)**
Pub: Earl G. Graves Publishing Co. Inc.
Ed: Angela P. Moore-Thorpe. **Description:** Selling items accumulated over the years or purchased at auctions or garage sales can be a lucrative way to make extra cash. Advice and resources on auctions, collecting, and consignment shops included.

43165 ■ "CBS" in *Brandweek* **(Vol. 49, April 21, 2008, No. 16, pp. SR6)**
Pub: VNU Business Media, Inc.
Ed: John Consoli. **Description:** Provides contact information for sales and marketing personnel for the CBS network as well as a listing of the station's top programming and an analysis of the current season and the target audience for those programs running in the current season.

43166 ■ "CBS Television Distribution" in *Brandweek* **(Vol. 49, April 21, 2008, No. 16, pp. SR13)**
Pub: VNU Business Media, Inc.
Ed: Marc Berman. **Description:** Provides contact information for sales and marketing personnel for CBS Television Distribution as well as a listing of the station's top programming and an analysis of the current season and the target audience for those programs running in the current season. Due to the unprecedented, decade-plus advantage of first-run leaders such as Wheel of Fortune, Oprah, Judge Judy and Entertainment Tonight, CBS is poised to remain a leader among the syndicates.

43167 ■ "Channeling for Growth" in *The Business Journal-Serving Greater Tampa Bay* **(Vol. 28, July 11, 2008, No. 29, pp. 1)**
Pub: American City Business Journals, Inc.
Ed: Margie Manning. **Description:** HSN Inc., one of the largest employers in Tampa Bay, Florida, is expected to spend an additional $9.7 million annually

as it plans to hire more accounting, internal audit, legal, treasury and tax personnel after its spin-off to a public company. Details on the company's sales growth are provided.

43168 ■ "Characteristics of Great Salespeople" in *Agency Sales Magazine* **(Vol. 39, November 2009, No. 10, pp. 40)**
Pub: MANA
Ed: Paul Pease. **Description:** Tips for managers in order to maximize the performance of their sales personnel are presented through several vignettes. Using performance based commission that rewards success, having business systems that support sales activity, and having an organizational culture that embraces sales as a competitive edge are some suggestions.

43169 ■ "Charged Up for Sales" in *Charlotte Business Journal* **(Vol. 25, October 15, 2010, No. 30, pp. 1)**
Pub: Charlotte Business Journal
Ed: Susan Stabley. **Description:** Li-Ion Motors Corporation is set to expand its production lines of electric cars in Sacramento, California. The plan is seen to create up to 600 jobs. The company's total investment is seen to reach $500 million.

43170 ■ "Cheap Thrills: Where to Look When You're Craving a Low-Price Wine" in *Chicago Tribune* **(January 12, 2009)**
Pub: McClatchy-Tribune Information Services
Ed: Bill Daley. **Description:** Wines priced $15 and above are being hit the hardest by the economic downturn while cheaper wines, specifically those priced between $3 and $6, are seeing a growth in sales.

43171 ■ "Click Here to Book" in *Caterer & Hotelkeeper* **(October 28, 2011, No. 288)**
Pub: Reed Reference Publishing
Ed: Ross Bentley. **Description:** Customers expectations are determined by the quality of a Website when booking hotel rooms.

43172 ■ *Clued In*
Pub: Financial Times/Prentice Hall
Ed: Lewis Carbone. **Released:** May 24, 2004. **Price:** $34.99. **Description:** Tips for providing excellent customer service that keeps clients coming back are shared. Brand management and Experience Value Management are defined.

43173 ■ "Comcast Networks" in *Brandweek* **(Vol. 49, April 21, 2008, No. 16, pp. SR9)**
Pub: VNU Business Media, Inc.
Ed: Anthony Crupi. **Description:** Provides contact information for sales and marketing personnel for the Comcast networks as well as a listing of the station's top programming and an analysis of the current season and the target audience for those programs running in the current season. Experts believe Comcast will continue to acquire more stations into their portfolio.

43174 ■ "Come Together" in *Pet Product News* **(Vol. 64, December 2010, No. 12, pp. 28)**
Pub: BowTie Inc.
Ed: Lizett Bond. **Description:** Pet supply retailers have posted improved sales and improved customer service by bundling their offerings. Bundling pertains to grouping related items such as collars and leashes into a single unit for marketing purposes. Aside from providing convenience and enhanced product information to customers, bundling has facilitated more efficient purchases.

43175 ■ *The Complete Guide to Google Adwords: Secrets, Techniques, and Strategies You Can Learn to Make Millions*
Pub: Atlantic Publishing Company
Released: December 1, 2010. **Price:** $24.95. **Description:** Google AdWords, when it launched in 2002 signaled a fundamental shift in what the Internet was for so many individuals and companies. Learning and understanding how Google AdWords operates and how it can be optimized for maximum exposure, boosting click through rates, conversions, placement, and selection of the right keywords, can be the key to a successful online business.

43176 ■ "Condo Markdown" in *Boston Business Journal* **(Vol. 27, November 30, 2007, No. 44, pp. 1)**
Pub: American City Business Journals Inc.
Ed: Michelle Hillman. **Description:** Boston real estate market is softening, and condominium developers such as Beacon Communities LLC are sending out various incentives like markdowns and unit upgrades. Developers have also held auctions and even offered brand new cars to lure buyers. Other perks being offered by various Boston developers are discussed.

43177 ■ *Consumer Behavior*
Pub: Prentice Hall Business Publishing
Ed: Leon Schiffman, Leslile Kanuk. **Released:** August 7, 2009. **Price:** $180.00. **Description:** Consumer behavior is central to the planning, development and implementation of marketing strategies.

43178 ■ *Content Rich: Writing Your Way to Wealth on the Web*
Pub: 124 S Mercedes Rd.
Ed: Jon Wuebben. **Released:** April 2008. **Price:** $19.95. **Description:** A definitive search engine optimization (SEO) copywriting guide for search engine rankings and sales conversion. It includes topics not covered in other books on the subject and targets the small to medium sized business looking for ways to maximize online marketing activities as well as designers and Web developers seeking to incorporate more SEO techniques into design and content.

43179 ■ "Contractors Debate Maximizing Green Opportunities, Education" in *Contractor* **(Vol. 56, November 2009, No. 11, pp. 3)**
Pub: Penton Media, Inc.
Ed: Robert P. Mader. **Description:** Attendees at the Mechanical Service Co ntractors Association convention were urged to get involved with their local U.S. Green Building Council chapter by one presenter. Another presenter says that one green opportunity for contractors is the commissioning of new buildings.

43180 ■ "Contractors Fret Over Credit, People, Government" in *Contractor* **(Vol. 57, February 2010, No. 2, pp. 7)**
Pub: Penton Media, Inc.
Ed: Robert P. Mader. **Description:** Telephone interviews with 22 plumbing and HVAC contractors reveal that only two had sales increases for 2009 and that overall, contractors were down anywhere from seven to 25 percent. In the repair/service market, the residential sector was holding its own but the commercial portion was lagging behind.

43181 ■ "Contracts" in *Agency Sales Magazine* **(Vol. 39, September-October 2009, No. 9, pp. 7)**
Pub: MANA
Description: One session at the MANAfest conference provided suggestions to sales representatives when negotiating a contract with their principals. New sales representatives need to stand their ground and to negotiate a fair and balanced contract with every principal that they sign on with.

43182 ■ "Coping With a Shrinking Planet" in *Agency Sales Magazine* **(Vol. 39, December 2009, No. 11, pp. 46)**
Pub: MANA
Ed: Mark Young. **Description:** China and India are forcing big changes in the world and are posing a huge threat to U.S. manufacturers and their sales representatives. Reps may want to consider expanding into these territories. Helping sell American products out of the country presents an opportunity for economic expansion.

43183 ■ "Counting on Cornhole: Popular Bean Bag Game Brings Crowds to Bars" in *Boston Business Journal* **(Vol. 29, July 15, 2011, No. 10, pp. 1)**
Pub: American City Business Journals Inc.
Ed: Alexander Jackson. **Description:** Cornhole game is being used by bars to spur business as the games hikes beer and food sales on slow weekdays. The

game is played with two cornhole boards facing each other and is played with one or two people on one team who try to place a bag on the board.

43184 ■ "Courier 250 Companies Hope to Rebound From 2009" in *Business Courier* **(Vol. 27, July 16, 2010, No. 11, pp. 1)**
Pub: Business Courier
Ed: Dan Monk, Jon Newberry. **Description:** Private companies that are featured in the Courier 250 publication have lost almost $4 billion in revenue, while combined sales dropped by 11 percent to 32 billion in 2009. Courier 250 is a guide to public companies, large nonprofits, private firms, and other related entities in Ohio's Cincinnati region.

43185 ■ "Covington's Business Owners Get Bridge Relief" in *Business Courier* **(Vol. 27, October 29, 2010, No. 26, pp. 1)**
Pub: Business Courier
Ed: Dan Monk. **Description:** Engineers of Brent Spence Bridge have developed a new 'second chance' exit that preserves highway access to Covington, Kentucky's main business districts. It is believed that the planned ramp off Interstate 75 represents a compromise between highway planners, who wish to maintain continuous traffic for interstate users.

43186 ■ *Craft Inc: Turn Your Creative Hobby into a Business*
Pub: Chronicle Books LLC
Ed: Meg Mateo Ilasco. **Released:** September 2007. **Price:** $16.95. **Description:** Guide to help any crafter turn their hobby into a successful business. The book covers all aspects including pricing, sales and marketing, trade shows, as well as interviews with successful craft artisans Jonathan Adler, Lotta Jansdotter, Denyse Schmidt and Jill Bliss.

43187 ■ "Creative Marketing: How to Cultivate a Network of Endless Referrals" in *Agency Sales Magazine* **(Vol. 39, July 2009, No. 7, pp. 38)**
Pub: MANA
Ed: Bob Burg. **Description:** Tips on how a salesperson can build a network of people that will bring them referrals are presented. Asking a person about their business and re-introducing one's self to an earlier acquaintance while remembering their names are some elements in the process of building this network.

43188 ■ *Crossing the Chasm: Marketing and Selling Disruptive Products to Mainstream Customers*
Pub: HarperInformation
Ed: Geoffrey A. Moore. **Released:** September 2002. **Price:** $17.95. **Description:** A guide for marketing in high-technology industries, focusing on the Internet.

43189 ■ "The CW" in *Brandweek* **(Vol. 49, April 21, 2008, No. 16, pp. SR8)**
Pub: VNU Business Media, Inc.
Ed: John Consoli. **Description:** Provides contact information for sales and marketing personnel for the CW network as well as a listing of the station's top programming and an analysis of the current season and the target audience for those programs running in the current season. Purchases of advertising feel that Warner Bros. and CBS made a mistake merging The WB and UPN into the new CW rather than folding UPN into the more-established WB; compared to last season ratings are down more than 20 percent across the board.

43190 ■ "Cyber Thanksgiving Online Shopping a Growing Tradition" in *Marketing Weekly News* **(December 12, 2009, pp. 137)**
Pub: Investment Weekly News
Description: According to e-commerce analysts, Thanksgiving day is becoming increasingly important to retailers in terms of online sales. Internet marketers are realizing that consumers are already searching for Black Friday sales and if they find deals on the products they are looking for, they are highly likely to make their purchase on Thanksgiving day instead of waiting.

43191 ■ "Dealers Fight To Steer Course" in *The Business Journal-Serving Metropolitan Kansas City* (Vol. 27, November 7, 2008, No. 9, pp. 1)
Pub: American City Business Journals, Inc.

Ed: Steve Vockrodt. **Description:** One local automobile dealer says that their sales are down by 30 to 40 percent and that car financing is now in the low 60 percentile from 85 to 88 percent. The National Automobile Dealers Association says that 700 dealerships are likely to be lost for 2008.

43192 ■ "Dealers Trying Not to Fold" in *Business First Columbus* (Vol. 25, December 5, 2008, No. 15, pp. A1)
Pub: American City Business Journals

Ed: Dan Eaton. **Description:** Increase in the number of automobile dealer closures in Ohio is seen to impact the state's economy. The trend of consolidation is forecasted to adversely affect employment and sales. Statistical data included.

43193 ■ "Dear Customer: Managing E-Mail Campaigns" in *Inc.* (March 2008, pp. 58-59)
Pub: Gruner & Jahr USA Publishing

Ed: Ryan Underwood. **Description:** Internet services that help firms manage their online business including email marketing, to manage subscriber lists, comply with spam regulations, monitor bouncebacks, and track potential customers are profiled. Constant Contact, MobileStorm Stun, Campaign Monitor, Pop Commerce, Emma, and StrongMail E-mail Server are among software and services highlighted.

43194 ■ *Design and Launch Your Online Boutique in a Week*
Pub: Entrepreneur Press

Ed: Melissa Campanelli. **Released:** June 2008. **Price:** $17.95. **Description:** Guide to start an online boutique includes information on business planning, Website design and funding.

43195 ■ "Deskside Story: As the Latest Buzzword Suggests, PR Firms Are Happy To Drop By" in *Inc.* (December 2007, pp. 70, 73)
Pub: Gruner & Jahr USA Publishing

Ed: Nitasha Tiku. **Description:** Setting up a meeting between a company's CEO and a journalist is known as deskside and is becoming popular again whereby a publicist offers clients deskside visits, briefings and alerts to help promote public relations for a company.

43196 ■ "Discovery Networks" in *Brandweek* (Vol. 49, April 21, 2008, No. 16, pp. SR9)
Pub: VNU Business Media, Inc.

Ed: Anthony Crupi. **Description:** Provides contact information for sales and marketing personnel for the Discovery networks as well as a listing of the station's top programming and an analysis of the current season and the target audience for those programs running in the current season. The networks flagship station returned to the top 10 in 2007, averaging 1.28 million viewers.

43197 ■ "Disney-ABC Domestic Television Distribution" in *Brandweek* (Vol. 49, April 21, 2008, No. 16, pp. SR13)
Pub: VNU Business Media, Inc.

Ed: Marc Berman. **Description:** Provides contact information for sales and marketing personnel for Disney-ABC Domestic Television Distribution as well as a listing of the station's top programming and an analysis of the current season and the target audience for those programs running in the current season.

43198 ■ "Do You Really Know Who Your Best Salespeople Are?" in *Harvard Business Review* (Vol. 88, December 2010, No. 12, pp. 34)
Pub: Harvard Business School Publishing

Ed: Lynette Ryals, Iain Davies. **Description:** Eight salesperson performance types are identified and charted using statistics of their effectiveness in given scenarios.

43199 ■ "Don't Cry For Me?" in *Canadian Business* (Vol. 83, July 20, 2010, No. 11-12, pp. 47)
Pub: Rogers Media Ltd.

Ed: Joe Castaldo. **Description:** Canada's theaters are faced with low ticket sales, donations and endowments. The industry is producing popular works as a response to the situation.

43200 ■ "The Don't Do Lists" in *Inc.* (Vol. 33, October 2011, No. 8, pp. 65)
Pub: Inc. Magazine

Ed: Jennifer Alsever, Adam Bluestein. **Description:** Ten business leaders and experts share their don't do lists, the things that should be avoided when going on sales calls, planning business lunches, motivating employees and more are presented.

43201 ■ "Dow Jones Gives Apple-Loving Sales Professionals a Boost" in *Information Today* (Vol. 26, February 2009, No. 2, pp. 30)
Pub: Information Today, Inc.

Description: Dow Jones Sales Triggers for iPhone and iPod program helps sales professionals stay current to prospects and customers in their fields by providing real-time news on business changes, including management moves, mergers, and new investments. The application presents events that trigger best opportunities and allows users to look up companies and executives to retrieve information.

43202 ■ "Down by the Bay" in *Canadian Business* (Vol. 81, December 8, 2008, No. 21, pp. 15)
Pub: Rogers Media Ltd.

Ed: Calvin Leung. **Description:** Hudsons Bay Company chief executive Jeffrey Sherman believes that his vast experience in retail will help him find the company's customer base. Sales are estimated to increase 3.6 percent in 2009 after posting average annual retail sales increases of 5 percent between 2006 and 2008.

43203 ■ "Dozens 'Come Alive' in Downtown Chicago" in *Green Industry Pro* (July 2011)
Pub: Cygnus Business Media

Ed: Gregg Wartgow. **Description:** Highlights from the Come Alive Outside training event held in Chicago, Illinois July 14-15, 2011 are shared. Nearly 80 people representing 38 landscape companies attended the event that helps contractors review their services and find ways to sell them in new and various ways.

43204 ■ "Dream Big! When the Going Gets Tough, Reps Work Harder and Smarter" in *Agency Sales Magazine* (Vol. 39, July 2009, No. 7, pp. 22)
Pub: MANA

Ed: John Chapin. **Description:** Sales representatives should use the tough economy as a warning and motivation to work harder and smarter. Reps should improve their selling by reading books, listening to tapes and CDs. They should also keep a good attitude and build relationships.

43205 ■ "Drug-Maker Plans IPO" in *Business Courier* (Vol. 24, November 23, 2008, No. 32, pp. 1)
Pub: American City Business Journals, Inc.

Ed: James Ritchie; Steve Watkins. **Description:** Xanodyne Pharmaceuticals Inc. filed plans with the Securities and Exchange Commission on November 9, 2007 for an initial public offering. The company, with annual sales of $75 million, had lost $222 million since it was founded in 2001.

43206 ■ *EBay Business Start-up Kit: 100s of Live Links to All the Information and Tools You Need*
Pub: NOLO

Ed: Richard Stim. **Released:** July 2008. **Price:** $24.99. **Description:** Interactive kit that connects user directly to EBay is presented.

43207 ■ *eBay Business the Smart Way*
Pub: AMACOM

Ed: Joseph T. Sinclair. **Released:** June 6, 2007. **Price:** $17.95. **Description:** eBay commands ninety percent of all online auction business. Computer and

software expert and online entrepreneur shares information to help online sellers get started and move merchandise on eBay. Tips include the best ways to build credibility, find products to sell, manage inventory, create a storefront Website, and more.

43208 ■ *EBay Income: How ANYONE of Any Age, Location, and/or Background Can Build a Highly Profitable Online Business with eBay (Revised 2nd Edition)*
Pub: Atlantic Publishing Company

Released: December 1, 2010. **Price:** $24.95. **Description:** A complete overview of eBay is given and guides any small company through the entire process of creating the auction and auction strategies, photography, writing copy, text and formatting, multiple sales, programming tricks, PayPal, accounting, creating marketing, merchandising, managing email lists, advertising plans, taxes and sales tax, best time to list items and for how long, sniping programs, international customers, opening a storefront, electronic commerce, buy-it now pricing, keywords, Google marketing and eBay secrets.

43209 ■ *Ebay the Smart Way: Selling, Burying, and Profiting on the Web's Number One Auction Site*
Pub: AMACOM

Ed: Joseph T. Sinclair. **Released:** May 2007. **Price:** $17.95. **Description:** Resource to help individuals sell, buy and profit using the Internet auction site Ebay.

43210 ■ "Economic Crises Calls For Better Marketing Plans" in *Entrepreneur* (October 1, 2008)
Pub: Entrepreneur Media Inc.

Ed: Tim Berry. **Description:** Revising one's business plan is essential, especially during times of economic crisis; sales and marketing plans should be reviewed, analyzed and changed in an attempt to survive the economic downturn.

43211 ■ "Economic Trends for Small Business" in *Small Business Economic Trends* (April 2008, pp. 1)
Pub: National Federation of Independent Business

Ed: William C. Dunkelberg, Holly Wade. **Description:** Summary of economic trends for small businesses in the U.S. is presented. Economic indicators such as capital spending, inventories and sales, inflation, and profits are given. Analysis of credit markets is also provided.

43212 ■ "Effective Use of Field Time" in *Agency Sales Magazine* (Vol. 39, July 2009, No. 7, pp. 40)
Pub: MANA

Description: Sales representatives need to consider the value of field visits to themselves and their customers ahead of time. Several anecdotes about field visits from the perspective of manufacturers and sale representatives are presented.

43213 ■ *Electronic Commerce*
Pub: Course Technology

Ed: Gary Schneider, Bryant Chrzan, Charles McCormick. **Released:** May 1, 2010. **Price:** $117.95. **Description:** E-commerce can open the door to more opportunities than ever before for small business. Packed with real-world examples and cases, the book delivers comprehensive coverage of emerging online technologies and trends and their influence on the electronic marketplace. It details how the landscape of online commerce is evolving, reflecting changes in the economy and how business and society are responding to those changes. Balancing technological issues with the strategic business aspects of successful e-commerce, the new edition includes expanded coverage of international issues, social networking, mobile commerce, Web 2.0 technologies, and updates on spam, phishing, and identity theft.

43214 ■ "Emack & Bolio" in *Ice Cream Reporter* (Vol. 23, October 20, 2010, No. 11, pp. 8)
Pub: Ice Cream Reporter

Description: Emack & Bolio's is engaging in scent marketing using various odors to help boost sales by attracting consumers with scents appropriate to their products.

43215 ■ *Exceptional Selling: How the Best Connect and Win in High Stakes Sales*
Pub: John Wiley & Sons, Incorporated

Ed: Jeff Thull. **Released:** August 18, 2006. **Price:** $24.95. **Description:** New approach to B2B selling, called diagnostic selling to help sales professionals achieve.

43216 ■ *The Facebook Era: Tapping Online Social Networks to Build Better Products, Reach New Audiences, and Sell More Stuff*
Pub: Prentice Hall

Ed: Clara Shih. **Price:** $24.99. **Description:** The '90s were about the World Wide Web of information and the power of linking Web pages. Today it's about the World Wide Web of people and the power of the social graph. Online social networks are fundamentally changing the way we live, work, and interact. They offer businesses immense opportunities to transform customer relationships for profit: opportunities that touch virtually every business function, from sales and marketing to recruiting, collaboration to executive decision-making, product development to innovation.

43217 ■ *"Feet on the Street: Reps Are Ready to Hit the Ground Running"* in *Agency Sales Magazine* (Vol. 39, July 2009, No. 7, pp. 12)
Pub: MANA

Ed: Jack Foster. **Description:** One of the major benefits to manufacturers in working with sales representatives is the concept of synergistic selling where the rep shows his mettle. The rep of today is a solution provider that anticipates and meets the customer's needs.

43218 ■ *"First: Package Deal"* in *Entrepreneur* (Vol. 35, October 2007, No. 10, pp. 114)
Pub: Entrepreneur Media Inc.

Ed: Nichole L. Torres. **Description:** Unique packaging of Me! Bath's products proved to be an effective marketing strategy for the company, which has over $3 million dollar sales yearly. Their ice cream-looking bath products have become popular and are much appreciated by vendors. Details of how packaging can affect sales are presented.

43219 ■ *"Five Distinct Divisions, One Collective Focus"* in *Green Industry Pro* (Vol. 23, October 2011)
Pub: Cygnus Business Media

Ed: Gregg Wartgow. **Description:** Profile of ACLS Inc., an amalgamation of All Commercial Landscape Service (commercial maintenance), All Custom Landscape Service (design/build), Fresno Tree Service, Certified Water Consulting (irrigation), and Tractor Service (disking and flailing services on everything from one-acre lots to hundreds of acres of open land). The firm discusses its rebranding effort in order to increase sales.

43220 ■ *"For Gilead, Growth Beyond AIDS"* in *Barron's* (Vol. 88, June 30, 2008, No. 26, pp. 18)
Pub: Dow Jones & Co., Inc.

Ed: Jay Palmer. **Description:** First-quarter 2008 revenue for Gilead Sciences grew by 22 percent and an earnings gain of 19 percent thanks to their HIV-treatment drugs that comprised over two-thirds of the company's sales in 2007. An analyst has a 12-month target from June, 2008 of 65 per share. The factors behind the company's prospects are also discussed.

43221 ■ *"Formaspace Finds a Bigger Home"* in *Austin Business JournalInc.* (Vol. 29, December 4, 2009, No. 39, pp. 1)
Pub: American City Business Journals

Ed: Kate Harrington. **Description:** Formaspace Technical Furniture has signed a lease for 56,700 square feet in Harris Ridge Business Center at Northeast Austin, Texas, which represents one of the area's largest leases for 2009. The new lease enables Formaspace to hire new employees, invest in new equipment, and take advantage of a taxing designation created for manufacturers.

43222 ■ *"Formula for Success: Dispelling the Age-Old Myths"* in *Agency Sales Magazine* (Vol. 39, July 2009, No. 7, pp. 26)
Pub: MANA

Ed: Douglas Smith. **Description:** Common misperceptions about selling and salespeople include the idea that anyone can be successful in selling if they work hard enough and that successful salespeople are born that way. In fact, top performers take risks and they invest in themselves.

43223 ■ *"Fox"* in *Brandweek* (Vol. 49, April 21, 2008, No. 16, pp. SR3)
Pub: VNU Business Media, Inc.

Ed: John Consoli. **Description:** Provides contact information for sales and marketing personnel for the Fox network as well as a listing of the station's top programming and an analysis of the current season and the target audience for those programs running in the current season. In terms of upfront advertising dollars, it looks as if Fox will be competing against NBC for third place due to its success at courting the 18-49-year-old male demographic.

43224 ■ *"Fox Cable Entertainment Networks"* in *Brandweek* (Vol. 49, April 21, 2008, No. 16, pp. SR10)
Pub: VNU Business Media, Inc.

Ed: Anthony Crupi. **Description:** Provides contact information for sales and marketing personnel for the Fox Cable Entertainment networks as well as a listing of the station's top programming and an analysis of the current season and the target audience for those programs running in the current season.

43225 ■ *"Funds "Friend" Facebook"* in *Barron's* (Vol. 89, July 27, 2009, No. 30, pp. 30)
Pub: Dow Jones & Co., Inc.

Ed: Leslie P. Norton. **Description:** Mutual-fund companies are the latest entrants to the "social media" space and several companies have already set up Facebook and Twitter pages. The use of this technology pose special challenges for compliance and regulators especially since the Financial Industry Regulatory Authority reminds companies that advertising, sales and literature are governed by regulations.

43226 ■ *"Funny Business"* in *Canadian Business* (Vol. 82, April 27, 2009, No. 7, pp. 27)
Pub: Rogers Media

Ed: Rachel Pulfer. **Description:** Companies are advised to use humor in marketing to drive more revenue. IBM Canada, for example, commissioned Second City Communications for a marketing campaign that involved humor. While IBM Canada declined to give sales or traffic figures, firm executives rank the marketing campaign as an overall success.

43227 ■ *"Gain the 'Come Alive Outside' Selling Edge"* in *Green Industry Pro* (July 2011)
Pub: Cygnus Business Media

Ed: Jim Paluch. **Description:** Marketing the 'Come Alive Outside' slogan can help landscapers to increase their market share by identifying and applying these elements to each customer as well as their workers.

43228 ■ *"Games Gone Wild: City's Newest Public Company Aims for the Sky"* in *Business Courier* (Vol. 27, September 24, 2010, No. 21, pp. 1)
Pub: Business Courier

Ed: Dan Monk. **Description:** Video game company Zoo Entertainment Inc., which is based in Norwood near Cincinnati, Ohio aims to build a strong company and to position itself for future growth. The company reported $27.6 million in revenue for the first half of 2010 and analysts project $100 million in sales for 2011.

43229 ■ *"Get Back To Business Planning Fundamentals"* in *Entrepreneur* (October 24, 2008)
Pub: Entrepreneur Media Inc.

Ed: Tim Berry. **Description:** During a recession it is important to know what adjustment to make to your business plan. Some fundamentals to remember

include: watching things more closely by tracking progress on cash, sales, new projects, customer satisfaction, ad spending and expenses; looking for built-in indicators such as what drives sales or expenses; watching what drives cash flow; and do not make mistakes such as laying off experienced employees too soon.

43230 ■ *"Get Personal"* in *Entrepreneur* (Vol. 36, April 2008, No. 4)
Pub: Entrepreneur Media, Inc.

Ed: Romanus Wolter. **Description:** Customers appreciate personal contact, and communicating with them can help business owners' customer relations. Some ways on how to keep a personal touch with customers and improve business dealings include blending technology with personal interaction and knowing what the customers want. Other tips are provided.

43231 ■ *"Get Sold On eBay"* in *Entrepreneur* (Vol. 36, March 2008, No. 3, pp. 94)
Pub: Entrepreneur Media Inc.

Ed: Marcia Layton Turner. **Description:** Entrepreneurs are increasingly using eBay to sell products. Some tips to start selling products through eBay include: starting with used items, developing a niche to sell specific products, and researching product pricing. Other tips with regard to starting an eBay business are covered.

43232 ■ *Getting Clients and Keeping Clients for Your Service Business*
Pub: Atlantic Publishing Company

Ed: Anne M. Miller; Gail Brett Levine. **Released:** August 28, 2008. **Price:** $24.95 paperback. **Description:** Tips are offered to help any small service business identify customers, brand and grow the business, as well as development of logos, brochures and Websites.

43233 ■ *"Getting a Grip on the Saddle: Chasms or Cycles?"* in *Journal of Marketing* (Vol. 75, July 2011, No. 4, pp. 21)
Pub: American Marketing Association

Ed: Deepa Chandrasekaran, Gerald J. Tellis. **Description:** A study of the saddle's generality across products and countries is presented. The saddle is fairly pervasive based on empirical analysis of historical sales data from ten products across 19 countries. The results indicate chasms and technological cycles for information/entertainment products while business cycles and technological cycles affect kitchen/laundry products.

43234 ■ *Getting More: How to Negotiate to Achieve Your Goals in the Real World*
Pub: Crown Business Books

Ed: Stuart Diamond. **Released:** December 28, 2010. **Price:** $26.00. **Description:** When negotiating, people fail to meet their goals due to focusing on power and the 'win-win' instead of on relationships and perceptions, thus not finding enough things to trade. They think others should be rational when they are dealing with emotions and they get distracted from the real goal.

43235 ■ *Getting Rich In Your Underwear: How To Start and Run a Profitable Home-Based Business*
Pub: HCM Publishing

Ed: Peter I. Hupalo. **Released:** April 1, 2005. **Price:** $17.95. **Description:** Book offers insight into starting a home-based business. Entrepreneurs will learn about business models and the home business; distribution and fulfillment of product or service; marketing and sales; how to overcome the fear of starting a business; personal success characteristics; naming a business; zoning and insurance; intellectual capital; copyrights, trademarks, and patents; limited liability companies and S-corporations; business expenses and accounting; taxes; fifteen basic steps for starting a home-based business; state resources for starting a home company; and seven home-based business ideas.

43236 ■ *"Give It Your All, and Don't Worry About the Rest"* in *Inc.* (Vol. 33, November 2011, No. 9, pp. 37)
Pub: Inc. Magazine

Ed: Norm Brodsky. **Description:** In the early stage of a service company, the owners sell themselves to the customers.

43237 ■ The Golden 120 Seconds of Every Sales Call: A Fresh Innovative Look at the Sales Process
Pub: NorlightsPress.com
Ed: Peter G. Dennis. **Released:** October 28, 2009. **Price:** $15.95. **Description:** Salespeople who want to find their personal style, gain confidence, and avoid deal-killing mistakes must read this book. It will show both new and experienced sales professionals how to use key fundamentals with every call, every selling interaction, and every opportunity to make something happen. Anyone who sells for a living has experienced the magic moments that can make or break a sale. Advice is given to help recognize, and learn to cultivate, this vital part of the sales process.

43238 ■ "Good Questions and the Basics of Selling" in Agency Sales Magazine (Vol. 39, September-October 2009, No. 9, pp. 14)
Pub: MANA
Ed: Dave Kahle. **Description:** Six basic elements to enhance the job of a sales person in regards to his relationship to a customer are presented.

43239 ■ "Graceful Landing" in Entrepreneur (Vol. 37, November 2009, No. 11, pp. 59)
Pub: Entrepreneur Media, Inc.
Ed: Mikal E. Belicove. **Description:** Successful marketers regularly use Website landing pages to capture qualified leads and make sales. It is believed that an effective landing page devoted to a single product or service offering can significantly boost leads and conversion rates. Organizations can create a top-notch landing page by anticipating customer expectations and focusing on a clear call to action.

43240 ■ "Harness the Internet to Boost Equipment Sales" in Indoor Comfort Marketing (Vol. 70, July 2011, No. 7, pp. 24)
Pub: Industry Publications Inc.
Ed: Richard Rutigliano. **Description:** Advice is given to increase HVAC/R equipment sales using the Internet.

43241 ■ "Hawaii Business 2008 SB Success Awards" in Hawaii Business (Vol. 53, February 2008, No. 8, pp. 43)
Pub: Hawaii Business Publishing
Description: Winners in the Hawaii Business 2008 SB Success Awards are presented; the awards give recognition for Hawaii small businesses with less than 100 employees and are based on four criteria, namely: unique service or product; rapid expansion or sales growth; longevity; and competency in overcoming challenges.

43242 ■ Heads in Beds
Pub: Prentice Hall PTR
Ed: Ivo Raza. **Released:** May 28, 2004. **Description:** Advice is given to help build brands, generate sales and grow profits through marketing for any hospitality or tourism business.

43243 ■ "Heavy Duty: The Case Against Packing Lightly" in Crain's Chicago Business (Vol. 31, April 21, 2008, No. 16, pp. 29)
Pub: Crain Communications, Inc.
Ed: Sarah A. Klein. **Description:** Penelope Biggs, a Northern Trust executive who manages sales teams in North America, Europe and Asia gives advice on traveling abroad for business including time management skills, handling time-zone hops and avoiding jet-lag.

43244 ■ "Help Customers Choose Full Service Over Discount" in Indoor Comfort Marketing (Vol. 70, September 2011, No. 9, pp. 10)
Pub: Industry Publications Inc.
Ed: Richard Rutigliano. **Description:** Marketing strategies for HVAC/R firms to use in 2011 and 2012 heating seasons are outlined, focusing on oil heat.

43245 ■ "Helping Customers Fight Pet Waste" in Pet Product News (Vol. 64, November 2010, No. 11, pp. 52)
Pub: BowTie Inc.
Ed: Sandy Robins. **Description:** Pet cleaning products manufacturers have been enjoying high sales figures by paying attention to changing pet ownership

trends and environmental awareness. Meanwhile, the inclusion of user-friendly features in these products has also been boosted by the social role of pets and the media attention to pet waste. How manufacturers have been responding to this demand is explored.

43246 ■ High Trust Selling: Make More Money, in Less Time, with Less Stress
Pub: Nelson Business
Ed: Todd Duncan. **Released:** April 2007. **Price:** $14.99. **Description:** Laws governing salesmanship are divided into two sections. The first deals with attitudes, aptitudes, and abilities required for successful selling; the second with communication, courtship, camaraderie and commitments between salespeople and their clients.

43247 ■ A History of Small Business in America
Pub: University of North Carolina Press
Ed: Mansel G. Blackford. **Released:** May 2003. **Price:** $22.95. **Description:** History of American small business from the colonial era to present, showing how it has played a role in the nation's economic, political, and cultural development across manufacturing, sales, services and farming.

43248 ■ "Ho, Ho, Ho!" in Retail Merchandiser (Vol. 51, September-October 2011, No. 5, pp. 10)
Pub: Phoenix Media Corporation
Ed: Ted Vaughan. **Description:** Despite consumer caution and economic woes, retail leaders are expecting a high volume holiday selling season for 2011 Christmas. Statistical data covering holiday sales expectations is included.

43249 ■ "Hoover's Mobile, MobileSP Now Available" in Information Today (Vol. 26, February 2009, No. 2, pp. 29)
Pub: Information Today, Inc.
Description: Hoover's Inc. introduced its Hoover's Mobile for iPhone, BlackBerry and Windows Mobile smartphones along with Hoover's MobileSP for BlackBerry and Windows Mobile. Both products allow users to access customer, prospect, and partner information; analyze competitors; prepare for meetings; and find new opportunities. In addition, MobileSP adds one-click calling to executives, GPS-enabled location searches, advanced search and list building, and a custom call queue and a 'save to contacts' capabilities.

43250 ■ "How to Dominate in Residential Maintenance" in Green Industry Pro (Vol. 23, October 2011)
Pub: Cygnus Business Media
Ed: Gregg Wartgow. **Description:** Lawn care services were ranked among the most expendable consumer expenditures, according to the National Retail Federation data accumulated in early 2011. This makes it critical for any landscape firm to target sales efforts toward higher-income households and higher-value homes.

43251 ■ "How Good Advice 'Online' Can Attract Customers" in Indoor Comfort Marketing (Vol. 70, August 2011, No. 8, pp. 20)
Pub: Industry Publications Inc.
Ed: Richard Rutigilano. **Description:** Online marketing tips for heating and cooling small businesses are explained.

43252 ■ "How to Keep Your Sales from Running Out of Gas" in Agency Sales Magazine (Vol. 39, July 2009, No. 7, pp. 30)
Pub: MANA
Ed: John Graham. **Description:** Salespeople can let the good times deceive them into thinking that success will go on forever. Salespeople and businesses should see prospecting as a strategy for creating a continuing flow of business.

43253 ■ How to Make Money with Social Media: Using New and Emerging Media to Grow Your Business
Pub: FT Press
Ed: Jamie Turner, Reshma Shah. **Released:** October 1, 2010. **Price:** $24.99. **Description:** Marketers, executives, entrepreneurs are shown more effective

ways to utilize Internet social media to make money. This guide brings together both practical strategies and proven execution techniques for driving maximum value from social media marketing.

43254 ■ How to Market and Sell Your Art, Music, Photographs, and Handmade Crafts Online
Pub: Atlantic Publishing Group, Inc.
Ed: Lee Rowley. **Released:** May 2008. **Price:** $24.95. **Description:** The book provides all the basics for starting and running an online store selling arts, crafts, photography or music. There are more than 300 Websites listed to help anyone market and promote their arts and/or crafts online.

43255 ■ How to Open and Operate a Financially Successful Bookstore on Amazon and Other Web Sites: With Companion CD-ROM
Pub: Atlantic Publishing Company
Released: December 1, 2010. **Price:** $39.95. **Description:** This book was written for every used book aficionado and bookstore owner who currently wants to take advantage of the massive collection of online resources available to start and run your own online bookstore business.

43256 ■ "How to Plan and Execute Effective Sales Meetings" in Agency Sales Magazine (Vol. 39, August 2009, No. 8, pp. 8)
Pub: MANA
Ed: Jack Foster. **Description:** Basic guide to successful representative-manufacturer sales meetings based on effective planning is presented. The representative and the manufacturer will reap the benefits of a productive meeting only when they both focus on what's going to transpire before, during and after the event. Insights from industry players are also presented.

43257 ■ "How a Unique Culture Proposition Became a USP" in Business Strategy Review (Vol. 21, Spring 2010, No. 1, pp. 52)
Pub: Wiley-Blackwell
Ed: Adam Kingl. **Description:** How can you transform the way you do things into a compelling sales proposition? Zurich Insurance has created a Unique Culture Proposition which may be its Unique Selling Point.

43258 ■ "The Human Approach" in Entrepreneur (Vol. 37, September 2009, No. 9, pp. 30)
Pub: Entrepreneur Media, Inc.
Description: Focusing on customer's needs is seen to result in better sales performance. Understanding customer needs is a question of emotional and social intelligence. Such sales competencies are seen as learned capabilities.

43259 ■ "Hyundai's Hitting Its Stride" in Barron's (Vol. 89, July 20, 2009, No. 29, pp. M7)
Pub: Dow Jones & Co., Inc.
Ed: Assif Shameen. **Description:** Hyundai Motors has kept growing by producing better products, enabling it to increase its sales and market share despite the weaker automotive market. The shares of Hyundai and Kia are poised to rise due to their improved finances.

43260 ■ "I Hear You're Interested In a..." in Inc. (January 2008, pp. 40-43)
Pub: Gruner & Jahr USA Publishing
Ed: Leah Hoffmann. **Description:** Four tips to help any small business generate sales leads online are examined.

43261 ■ "An Ice Boost in Revenue; Wings Score With Expanded Corporate Sales" in Crain's Detroit Business (Vol. 25, June 1, 2009, No. 22)
Pub: Crain Communications Inc. - Detroit
Ed: Bill Shea. **Description:** Stanley Cup finals always boost business for the Detroit area, even during a recession. The Red Wings corporate office

reported corporate sponsorship revenue luxury suite rentals, Legends Club seats and advertising were up 40 percent this year over 2008.

43262 ■ **"If the Opportunity is There, Move Boldly" in** *Indoor Comfort Marketing* **(Vol. 70, March 2011, No. 3, pp.)**
Pub: Industry Publications Inc.

Ed: Rich Rutigliano. **Description:** Suggestions are offered to help improve air conditioning sales.

43263 ■ **"Indulgent Parsimony: an Enduring Marketing Approach" in** *Strategy and Leadership* **(Vol. 39, March-April 2011, No. 2, pp. 36)**
Pub: Emerald Group Publishing Inc.

Ed: Kenneth Alan Grossberg. **Description:** Indulgent parsimony (IP), a marketing strategy employed on consumers that are affected by recession, is found to be a relevant and appropriate approach that can help encourage buying. IP involves the selling of cheaper goods and services that allow consumers experience comfort and relief from stress.

43264 ■ *Influence: The Psychology of Persuasion*
Pub: HarperCollins Publishers

Ed: Robert B. Cialdini. **Released:** June 2, 2009. **Price:** $17.99. **Description:** Whether you are the consumer or the salesperson, this book will help you understand the psychological foundations of marketing.

43265 ■ **"Info Junkie" in** *Crain's Chicago Business* **(Vol. 34, October 24, 2011, No. 42, pp. 35)**
Pub: Crain Communications Inc.

Ed: Christina Le Beau. **Description:** Greg Colando, president of Flor Inc., an eco-friendly carpet company located I Chicago discusses his marketing program to increase sales.

43266 ■ *Instant Cashflow: Hundreds of Proven Strategies to Win Customers, Boost Margins and Take More Money Home*
Pub: McGraw-Hill Companies

Ed: Bradley J. Sugars. **Released:** December 2005. **Price:** $17.95 (US), $22.95 (Canadian). **Description:** Nearly 300 proven marketing and sales strategies are shared by the author, a self-made millionaire. Advice on creating the proper mindset, generating new leads, boosting the conversion rate of leads to sales, maximizing the value of the average sale, and measuring results is included.

43267 ■ *Instant Income*
Pub: McGraw-Hill Inc.

Ed: Janet Switzer. **Released:** February 2007. **Price:** $30.95 (CND). **Description:** Book covers small business advertising techniques, marketing, joint ventures, and sales.

43268 ■ **"Insuraprise Growing Fast" in** *Austin Business Journal* **(Vol. 31, April 22, 2011, No. 7, pp. 1)**
Pub: American City Business Journals Inc.

Ed: Sandra Zaragoza. **Description:** Austin, Texas-based Insuraprise Inc. is finalizing the purchase of a 24,000-square-foot office at 12116 Jekel Circle. The firm, with 23 salespeople and sales that are growing nearly 300 percent over the past 18 months, will now have room to grow. Insuraprise plans to hire 35 new salespersons for its call center.

43269 ■ **"Internet Marketing 2.0: Closing the Online Chat Gap" in** *Agent's Sales Journal* **(November 2009, pp. 14)**
Pub: Summit Business Media

Ed: Jeff Denenholz. **Description:** Advice regarding the implementation of an Internet marketing strategy for insurance agencies includes how and why to incorporate a chat feature in which a sales agent can communicate in real-time with potential or existing customers. It is important to understand if appropriate response mechanisms are in place to convert leads into actual sales.

43270 ■ **"Is the Generation Gap Gone?" in** *Agency Sales Magazine* **(Vol. 39, November 2009, No. 10, pp. 3)**
Pub: MANA

Ed: Bryan C. Shirley. **Description:** Four generations are working side-by-side in the workplace for the first time in history and this is a big opportunity to get different perspectives and views on life. In the sales representatives business, there is a need to better understand the upcoming generations and understand their specific abilities to their risk/reward business.

43271 ■ *Island of Profit in a Sea of Red Ink Why 40 Percent of Your Business Is Unprofitable and How to Fix It*
Pub: Portfolio

Ed: Jonathan L.S. Byrnes. **Released:** October 14, 2010. **Price:** $27.95. **Description:** Top companies from around the world turn to Jonathan Byrnes to figure out where to find profit for their companies. He shows which parts of a business are worth expanding, and which are just a drain on resources. He has found that roughly 40 percent of any new client's business is unprofitable, and that profit increases of thirty percent or more are within reach.

43272 ■ **"It's Not About You" in** *Entrepreneur* **(Vol. 35, November 2007, No. 11, pp. 102)**
Pub: Entrepreneur Media Inc.

Ed: Barry Farber. **Description:** Companies should focus on the customers' need and show them that they care about them. Listening to and learning about your customers can make selling easier; tips on how to stay focused on the customers' needs are outlined.

43273 ■ **"Jay Berkowitz to Present Making Social Media Money Seminar at Affiliate Summit West" in** *Entertainment Close-Up* **(January 15, 2010)**
Pub: Close-Up Media

Description: Highlights of Jay Berkowitz's conference, "Making Social Media Make Money" include ways in which to develop Internet marketing strategies that will maximize Website traffic and convert that traffic to sales.

43274 ■ **"Keeping Tabs" in** *Entrepreneur* **(Vol. 36, February 2008, No. 2, pp. 38)**
Pub: Entrepreneur Media Inc.

Ed: Robert Kiyosaki. **Description:** Measuring and reporting the number of customers being served by a business can help in the company's growth. Details on this idea are discussed.

43275 ■ **"Keys to Overcome Fear of Follow-Up" in** *Agency Sales Magazine* **(Vol. 39, December 2009, No. 11, pp. 26)**
Pub: MANA

Ed: Judy Garmaise. **Description:** In order to be more successful at making follow-up calls, salespeople should not take rejection personally and never assume that they are going to annoy prospects if they follow-up. Those that follow-up with prospects stand out among others since few salespeople do this.

43276 ■ *Knock Your Socks Off Selling*
Pub: Amacom

Ed: Jeffrey Gitomer. **Released:** May 1999. **Price:** $17.95. **Description:** Tips for salespeople to succeed in a competitive sales environment.

43277 ■ **"Last Founder Standing" in** *Conde Nast Portfolio* **(Vol. 2, June 2008, No. 6, pp. 124)**
Pub: Conde Nast Publications, Inc.

Ed: Kevin Maney. **Description:** Interview with Amazon CEO Jeff Bezos in which he discusses the economy, the company's new distribution center and the hiring of employees for it, e-books, and the overall vision for the future of the firm.

43278 ■ **"Let Emerging Market Customers Be Your Teachers" in** *Harvard Business Review* **(Vol. 88, December 2010, No. 12, pp. 115)**
Pub: Harvard Business School Publishing

Ed: Guillermo D'Andrea, David Marcotte, Gwen Dixon Morrison. **Description:** Examination of effective strategies for emerging markets is presented. These include helping educate customers as well as selling to them, adapting to customers' habits, and focusing brands appropriately. Magazine Luiza, a chain store in Brazil, is used to illustrate these points.

43279 ■ **"Let's Go Team: When a Retail Professional Leads by Example, Everyone Benefits" in** *Black Enterprise* **(Vol. 41, November 2010, No. 4)**
Pub: Earl G. Graves Publishing Co. Inc.

Ed: Aisha I. Jefferson. **Description:** Profile of Derek Jenkins, senior vice president of Target Stores Northeast Region is presented. Jenkins oversees the management of 450 retail stores with nearly 75,000 workers. He shares insight into managing by making sure every interaction with his team counts.

43280 ■ **"Lifetime Networks" in** *Brandweek* **(Vol. 49, April 21, 2008, No. 16, pp. SR10)**
Pub: VNU Business Media, Inc.

Ed: Anthony Crupi. **Description:** Provides contact information for sales and marketing personnel for the ABC network as well as a listing of the station's top programming and an analysis of the current season and the target audience for those programs running in the current season. Lifetime will still produce its original signature movies but will now focus its emphasis more clearly on series development in order to appeal to a younger, hipper female demographic.

43281 ■ **"Lombard Leaves Starbucks" in** *Black Enterprise* **(Vol. 38, July 2008, No. 12, pp. 28)**
Pub: Earl G. Graves Publishing Co. Inc.

Ed: Tamara E. Holmes. **Description:** Ken Lombard stepped down from his position as head of Starbuck's entertainment division; the company is restructuring its entertainment unit in an attempt to revitalize sales and reduce costs.

43282 ■ **"Loseley Dairy Ice Cream" in** *Ice Cream Reporter* **(Vol. 23, November 20, 2010, No. 12, pp. 8)**
Pub: Ice Cream Reporter

Description: Neil Burchell has been named managing director of Loseley Dairy Ice Cream, one of the UK's largest independent producers. Burchell, with over 30 years experience in the food industry, was recently managing director of Rachel's, the leading organic dairy foods company in the UK, where he is credited with driving a sixfold increase in sales.

43283 ■ **"A Love of Likes" in** *Boston Business Journal* **(Vol. 31, July 8, 2011, No. 24, pp. 1)**
Pub: Boston Business Journal

Ed: Lisa van der Pool. **Description:** An increasing number of companies in Boston, Massachusetts have been keen on getting Facebook 'likes' from people. Business owners realize that Facebook 'likes' could generate sales and based on some studies, equate to specific dollar values.

43284 ■ **"Loyalty Cards Score Points" in** *Crain's Cleveland Business* **(Vol. 30, June 8, 2009, No. 22, pp. 1)**
Pub: Crain Communications, Inc.

Ed: Chuck Soder. **Description:** Northeast Ohio retailers are promoting loyalty and rewards programs in order to attract and maintain loyal customers.

43285 ■ *Lucrative List Building*
Pub: Morgan James Publishing, LLC

Ed: Glen Hopkins. **Released:** July 2006. **Price:** $13.95. **Description:** List building guaranteed to double profits is outlined.

43286 ■ **"Make Relationships Count: CRM Software That Works" in** *Black Enterprise* **(Vol. 38, February 2008, No. 7, pp. 60)**
Pub: Earl G. Graves Publishing Co. Inc.

Ed: Fiona Haley. **Description:** Customer relationship management (CRM) software can help any small business keep track of clients. Descriptions of the latest CRM software offered are profiled, including Salesforce.com, Microsoft Dynamics, and Saga Software.

43287 ■ "MANAfest Provides Reps with Tools for the Future" in *Agency Sales Magazine* (Vol. 39, September-October 2009, No. 9, pp. 36)

Pub: MANA

Ed: Jack Foster. **Description:** Former Harley Davidson director of communications Ken Schmidt was the keynote speaker at the MANAfest conference; he discussed how the company delivered itself from bankruptcy. Selling Power magazine publisher Gerhard Gschwandtner also made a presentation; he believes that there will be opportunities for sales people involved in relationship selling.

43288 ■ "Marathon Money" in *Hawaii Business* (Vol. 53, December 2007, No. 6, pp. 127)

Pub: Hawaii Business Publishing

Ed: Jolyn Okimoto Rosa. **Description:** Discusses the effects of the Honolulu Marathon on small businesses' sales. The Running Room, for instance, experience growth in sales starting from the training season up to the end of the race, as a surge of Hawaiian residents and tourists come into the store for items such as running shoes and blister kits. The marathon's impact on Hawaii's tourism is examined as well.

43289 ■ "Marketing in the Digital World: Here's How to Craft a Smart Online Strategy" in *Black Enterprise* (Vol. 40, July 2010, No. 12, pp. 47)

Pub: Earl G. Graves Publishing Co. Inc.

Ed: Sonya A. Donaldson. **Description:** Social media is an integral part of any small business plan in addressing marketing, sales, and branding strategies.

43290 ■ *Marketing for Entrepreneurs*

Pub: FT Press

Ed: Jurgen Wolff. **Released:** December 9, 2010. **Price:** $24.99. **Description:** This text identifies marketing as the entire process of researching, creating, distributing and selling a product or service. It isn't about theory and metrics, rather it is a practical guide that starts with the basics of all marketing aspects.

43291 ■ "Marketing: 'Twill Be the Season" in *Entrepreneur* (Vol. 35, October 2007, No. 10, pp. 108)

Pub: Entrepreneur Media Inc.

Ed: Kim T. Gordon. **Description:** Entrepreneurs should plan ahead in order to promote products for the holiday season, since it is peak sales time. They can unify their business theme, use customer incentives, advertise early using TV or radio, and reorganize the company Website. Other ways to market for the holiday season are provided.

43292 ■ *Marketing Without Money for Small and Midsize Businesses: 300 FREE and Cheap Ways to Increase Your Sales*

Pub: Halle House Publishing

Ed: Nicholas E. Bade. **Released:** July 2005. **Price:** $16.95. **Description:** Three hundred practical low-cost or no-cost strategies to increase sales, focusing on free advertising, free marketing assistance, and free referrals to the Internet.

43293 ■ *Mastering the Complex Sales: How to Compete and Win When the Stakes Are High!*

Pub: John Wiley & Sons, Incorporated

Ed: Jeff Thull. **Released:** May 2003. **Price:** $24.95. **Description:** Guide to compete for and win in complex selling, the business-to-business transactions involving multiple decisions by multiple people from multiple perspectives.

43294 ■ *Masters of Sales: Secrets from Top Sales Professionals That Will Transform You Into a World Class Salesman*

Pub: Entrepreneur Press

Ed: Ivan R. Misner; Don Morgan. **Released:** August 15, 2007. **Price:** $19.95. **Description:** Eighty successful salespeople share insight into selling.

43295 ■ *Maximum Marketing, Minimum Dollars: The Top 50 Ways to Grow Your Small Business*

Pub: Kaplan Books

Ed: Kim Gordon. **Released:** April 2006. **Price:** $24.00. **Description:** Marketing tips to increase sales are presented. Small business owners will learn to maximize marketing with 50 innovative and affordable methods, including online marketing.

43296 ■ "Mini Melts" in *Ice Cream Reporter* (Vol. 23, August 20, 2010, No. 9, pp. 8)

Pub: Ice Cream Reporter

Description: Mini Melts appointed David S. Tade to position of director of sales USA in order to cultivate existing distributors and add new partners to its distribution network.

43297 ■ "More Ad Shops Link Payment to Results" in *Boston Business Journal* (Vol. 30, November 12, 2010, No. 42, pp. 1)

Pub: Boston Business Journal

Ed: Lisa van der Pool. **Description:** A growing number of advertising firms are proposing a 'value-based' payment scheme where they are paid a base fee plus a bonus if certain sales goals or other targets are met. The proposed shift in payment scheme is seen as reminiscent of the dot-com boom about ten years ago. Advertising firms are traditionally paid by the hour.

43298 ■ "More Leading Retailers Using Omniture Conversion Solutions to Boost Sales and Ecommerce Performance" in *Internet Wire* (Sept. 22,2009)

Pub: Comtex News Network, Inc.

Description: Many retailers are utilizing Omniture conversion solutions to improve the performance of their ecommerce businesses; recent enhancements to Omniture Merchandising and Omniture Recommendations help clients drive increased conversion to their Internet ventures.

43299 ■ "More Sales Leads, Please: Or, What Happened When Frontline Selling Started Practicing What It Preaches" in *Inc.* (November 2007)

Pub: Gruner & Jahr USA Publishing

Description: Frontline Selling located in Oakland, New Jersey helps train sales teams to generate and convert sales leads. The consulting firm doubled their marketing budget to increase their own sales.

43300 ■ *More Than a Pink Cadillac*

Pub: McGraw-Hill

Ed: Jim Underwood. **Released:** 2002. **Price:** $23.95. **Description:** Profile of Mary Kay Ash who turned her $5,000 investment into a billion-dollar corporation. Ash's nine principles that form the foundation of her company's global success are outlined. Stories from her sales force leaders share ideas for motivating employees, impressing customers and building a successful company. The book emphasizes the leadership skills required to drive performance in any successful enterprise.

43301 ■ "MTV Networks" in *Brandweek* (Vol. 49, April 21, 2008, No. 16, pp. SR10)

Pub: VNU Business Media, Inc.

Ed: Anthony Crupi. **Description:** Provides contact information for sales and marketing personnel for the MTV networks as well as a listing of the station's top programming and an analysis of the current season and the target audience for those programs running in the current season. MTV networks include MTV, VH1, Nickelodeon and Comedy Central.

43302 ■ "NBC" in *Brandweek* (Vol. 49, April 21, 2008, No. 16, pp. SR6)

Pub: VNU Business Media, Inc.

Ed: John Consoli. **Description:** Provides contact information for sales and marketing personnel for the NBC network as well as a listing of the station's top programming and an analysis of the current season and the target audience for those programs running in the current season. NBC also devised a new strategy of announcing its prime-time schedule 52 weeks in advance which was a hit for advertisers who felt this gave them a better opportunity to plan

for product placement. Even with the station's creative sales programs, they could face a challenge from Fox in terms of upfront advertisement purchases.

43303 ■ "NBC Universal Cable" in *Brandweek* (Vol. 49, April 21, 2008, No. 16, pp. SR11)

Pub: VNU Business Media, Inc.

Ed: Anthony Crupi. **Description:** Provides contact information for sales and marketing personnel for the NBC Universal Cable networks as well as a listing of the station's top programming and an analysis of the current season and the target audience for those programs running in the current season. The network's stations include USA, Sci Fi and Bravo. Ad revenue for the network grew 30 percent in the first quarter.

43304 ■ "NBC Universal Domestic Television Distribution" in *Brandweek* (Vol. 49, April 21, 2008, No. 16, pp. SR13)

Pub: VNU Business Media, Inc.

Ed: Marc Berman. **Description:** Provides contact information for sales and marketing personnel for NBC Universal Domestic Television Distribution as well as a listing of the station's top programming and an analysis of the current season and the target audience for those programs running in the current season.

43305 ■ "Network Marketing Strategies for Marketing Professionals" in *Black Enterprise* (Vol. 38, October 2007, No. 3, pp. 70)

Pub: Earl G. Graves Publishing Co. Inc.

Description: Network marketing programs are redefining the sales business and leveraging opportunities in the ever-expanding global, highly networked, and ultra-specialized marketplace.

43306 ■ "A New Challenge Facing Reps: The Generation Gap!" in *Agency Sales Magazine* (Vol. 39, November 2009, No. 10, pp. 9)

Pub: MANA

Ed: Roger Ralston. **Description:** Different generations in the workplace is one of the many drivers of change that reps are facing today. Pre-boomers and boomers historically put work first while Gen-Xers and Millennials think lifestyle before work. A sales rep should listen and learn, while providing a strong sense of flexibility in this environment.

43307 ■ "The Next Dimension" in *Entrepreneur* (Vol. 35, November 2007, No. 11, pp. 62)

Pub: Entrepreneur Media Inc.

Ed: Heather Clancy. **Description:** Entrepreneurs can make use of virtual worlds like Second Life to promote their products or services. Details and cautions on the use of virtual worlds are discussed.

43308 ■ "North American Pet Health Insurance Market Poised for Growth" in *Pet Product News* (Vol. 64, December 2010, No. 12, pp. 4)

Pub: BowTie Inc.

Ed: David Lummis. **Description:** The pet health insurance market is expected to further grow after posting about $350 million in sales in 2009, a gain of more than $40 million. Pet insurance firms have offered strategies such as product humanization in response to this growth forecast. Meanwhile, pet insurance shoppers have been provided more by insurance firms with wider choices.

43309 ■ "Norvax University Health Insurance Sales Training and Online Marketing Conference" in *Internet Wire* (January 27, 2010)

Pub: Comtex News Network, Inc.

Description: Overview of the Norvax University Marketing and Sales Success Conference Tour which includes insurance sales training seminars, proven and innovative online marketing techniques and a host of additional information and networking opportunities.

43310 ■ "Not All Contracts a Good Fit for Fashion Reps" in *Agency Sales Magazine* **(Vol. 39, September-October 2009, No. 9, pp. 10)**
Pub: MANA
Ed: Jack Foster. **Description:** Difficult situations regarding the relationship between sales representatives and their principals in the fashion industry are presented and suggestions on how to create contracts that seek to prevent potential problems are provided. Sales reps should make sure that manufacturer has a viable business that is well thought-out and adequately financed.

43311 ■ "A Novel Approach to the Market" in *Agency Sales Magazine* **(Vol. 39, December 2009, No. 11, pp. 10)**
Pub: MANA
Ed: Jack Foster. **Description:** R/B Sales created a "merchandising specialist" position that travels their territory and works with distributor counter sales teams. This puts them ahead of their competition as it increases their visibility, appeal and mix of products in their area.

43312 ■ "Nowspeed and OneSource to Conduct Webinar" in *Internet Wire* **(December 14, 2009)**
Pub: Comtex News Network, Inc.
Description: OneSource, a leading provider of global business information, and Nowspeed, an Internet marketing agency, will conduct a webinar titled "How to Develop Social Media Content That Gets Results" in order to provide marketers insight into how to develop and optimize effective social media content to get consumer results that translate into purchases and lead generation.

43313 ■ "On Beyond Powerpoint: Presentations Get a Wake-Up Call" in *Inc.* **(November 2007, pp. 58-59)**
Pub: Gruner & Jahr USA Publishing
Ed: Michael Fitzgerald. **Description:** New software that allows business presentations to be shared online are profiled, including ProfCast, audio podcasts for sales, marketing, and training; SmartDraw2008, software that creates professional graphics; Dimdim, an open-Web conferencing tool; Empressr, a hosted Web service for creating, managing, and sharing multimedia presentations; Zentation, a free tool that allows users to watch slides and a videos of presenter; Spresent, a Web-based presentation tool for remote offices or conference calls.

43314 ■ "On the Go: a Busy Executive Is Always Well-Equipped for Travel" in *Black Enterprise* **(Vol. 40, July 2010, No. 12, pp. 106)**
Pub: Earl G. Graves Publishing Co. Inc.
Ed: Sonia Alleyne. **Description:** Successful sales executive, Henry Watkins, shares tips on business travel.

43315 ■ "The One Thing You Must Get Right When Building a Brand" in *Harvard Business Review* **(Vol. 88, December 2010, No. 12, pp. 80)**
Pub: Harvard Business School Publishing
Ed: Patrick Barwise, Sean Meehan. **Description:** Four uses for new media include: communicating a clearly defined customer promise, creating trust via delivering on the promise, regularly improving on the promise, and innovating past what is familiar.

43316 ■ "Online All the Time" in *Retail Merchandiser* **(Vol. 51, July-August 2011, No. 4, pp. 18)**
Pub: Phoenix Media Corporation
Description: Ecommerce sales are rising at a steady pace and for cross-channel retailers it is boosting sales in the weak economy. Online sales are expected to reach $188 billion in 2011, boasting a 13.7 rate of growth.

43317 ■ "Online Book Sales Surpass Bookstores" in *Information Today* **(Vol. 28, September 2011, No. 8, pp. 11)**
Pub: Information Today, Inc.
Ed: Cindy Martine. **Description:** Online book sales outpaced bookstore purchases in the United States,

signaling a shift in the US book industry. Statistical data included.

43318 ■ "Options Abound in Winter Wares" in *Pet Product News* **(Vol. 64, November 2010, No. 11, pp. 1)**
Pub: BowTie Inc.
Ed: Maggie M. Shein. **Description:** Pet supply manufacturers emphasize creating top-notch construction and functional design in creating winter clothing for pets. Meanwhile, retailers and pet owners seek human-inspired style, quality, and versatility for pets' winter clothing. How retailers generate successful sales of pets' winter clothing outside of traditional brand marketing is also examined.

43319 ■ *Our Daily Meds: How the Pharmaceutical Companies Transformed Themselves into Slick Marketing Machines*
Pub: Farrar, Straus and Giroux
Ed: Melody Petersen. **Released:** 2009. **Price:** $26.00. **Description:** Petersen, using industry memos, transcripts of meetings, and other sources shows how some drug companies are more concerned with the bottom line than with helping patients. Some of these firms are actually inventing 'diseases' in order to sell marginal medicines.

43320 ■ "Paid to Persuade: Careers in Sales" in *Occupational Outlook Quarterly* **(Vol. 55, Summer 2011, No. 2, pp. 24)**
Pub: U.S. Bureau of Labor Statistics
Ed: Ilka Maria Torpey. **Description:** Sales workers are paid to persuade others to buy goods and services. There were over 13 million wage and salary sales workers in the US in 2010. Wages in sales careers can vary and some become lucrative, lifelong career positions. Seven sales occupations with annual wages higher than $33,000 are profiled.

43321 ■ "P&G to Mine E-Commerce Potential" in *Business Courier* **(Vol. 26, September 18, 2009, No. 21, pp. 1)**
Pub: American City Business Journals, Inc.
Ed: Lisa Biank Fasig. **Description:** Procter & Gamble (P&G) is looking to turn the hits to the company's Websites into increased sales. The program will include a shop now option to track all emerging sales.

43322 ■ "Pay or Play: Do Nice (Sales) Guys Finish Last?" in *Agency Sales Magazine* **(Vol. 39, August 2009, No. 8, pp. 8)**
Pub: MANA
Ed: Julia M. Rahn. **Description:** How positive interpersonal relationships among salespersons, program coordinators, and other business-related professions will pay in terms of business success is presented. Business people should know the ideal customers, promise only what they can do, refer out when needed, and follow through with any stated promise. Further insight into these ideas is presented.

43323 ■ "Perfecting Customer Services" in *Pet Product News* **(Vol. 64, November 2010, No. 11, pp. 18)**
Pub: BowTie Inc.
Description: Pet supply retailers are encouraged to emphasize customer experience and sales representatives' knowledge of the store's product offerings to foster repeat business. Employee protocols could be implemented to improve customer interaction. Other guidelines on developing a pet supply retail environment that advances repeat business are presented.

43324 ■ *Playing Bigger Than You Are: How to Sell Big Accounts Even If You're David in a World of Goliaths*
Pub: John Wiley & Sons, Inc.
Ed: William T. Brooks, William P.G. Brooks. **Released:** November 1, 2009. **Price:** $18.99. **Description:** Small and mid-size companies are shown how to compete with larger firms and sell big accounts.

43325 ■ "Point, Click, Buy" in *Barron's* **(Vol. 90, September 6, 2010, No. 36, pp. 11)**
Pub: Barron's Editorial & Corporate Headquarters
Ed: Vito J. Racanelli. **Description:** Non-travel online retail sales from January to July 2010 increased nine percent which indicates that online shopping for the coming holidays will be good. Online sales are outpacing traditional shopping, but pricing is still critical.

43326 ■ "Power Up" in *Entrepreneur* **(Vol. 35, November 2007, No. 11, pp. 140)**
Pub: Entrepreneur Media Inc.
Ed: Amanda C. Kooser. **Description:** PowerSeller is a status in the Internet company eBay, wherein sellers average at least $1,000 in sales per month for three consecutive months. There are five tiers in the PowerSeller status, which ranges from Bronze to Titanium. Launching startups at eBay can help entrepreneurs pick up a wide customer base, but getting and maintaining PowerSeller status is a challenge.

43327 ■ *Prepare to Be a Teen Millionaire*
Pub: Health Communications, Inc.
Ed: Robyn Collins; Kimberly Spinks Burleson. **Released:** April 1, 2008. **Price:** $16.95. **Description:** Business reference for any teenager wishing to become a successful entrepreneur; advice is given from successful teenage millionaires. Topics covered include: choosing a business name, type, and location; use of the Internet; legal issues; branding, sales, and marketing; funding and financial management; return on investment; retirement; development of a sound business plan; and certification for minority or women-owned companies.

43328 ■ "Private Label Manufacturers Association" in *Ice Cream Reporter* **(Vol. 23, July 20, 2010, No. 8, pp. 7)**
Pub: Ice Cream Reporter
Description: Branded frozen dessert manufacturers sold more frozen desserts in terms of sales volume and revenue and market share in 2009. Statistical details included.

43329 ■ "Promotions Create a Path to Better Profit" in *Pet Product News* **(Vol. 64, December 2010, No. 12, pp. 1)**
Pub: BowTie Inc.
Ed: Joan Hustace Walker. **Description:** Pet store retailers can boost small mammal sales by launching creative marketing and promotions such as social networking and adoption days.

43330 ■ "Pssst! Buzz About Target" in *Barron's* **(Vol. 89, July 27, 2009, No. 30, pp. 15)**
Pub: Dow Jones & Co., Inc.
Ed: Katherine Cheng. **Description:** Target rebutted the rumor that they will disassociate themselves from a line of clothing inspired by the television show 'Gossip Girl'. Target's spokesman says that the retailer intends to remain closely identified with the show. Target's sales should benefit from the hotly anticipated clothing line.

43331 ■ "Psst...Spread the Word" in *Boston Business Journal* **(Vol. 27, November 23, 2007, No. 43, pp. 1)**
Pub: American City Business Journals Inc.
Ed: Lisa van der Pool. **Description:** More and more Boston companies are using word-of-mouth marketing to boost sales, and spending on it rose to $981 million in 2006. It is projected that spending on word-of-mouth marketing will reach $1.4 billion in 2007, and marketing companies using this type of method are getting higher funding. Trends in word-of-mouth marketing are discussed.

43332 ■ "Real Estate Wheeling and Dealing Picks Up" in *Business Journal Portland* **(Vol. 27, October 29, 2010, No. 35, pp. 1)**
Pub: Portland Business Journal
Ed: Wendy Culverwell. **Description:** LoopNet has listed 33 prominent commercial properties for sale in Portland, Oregon's real estate market. However, reasons for the sales rush are not totally clear, but speculations point to the end of the Bush tax cuts in 2010 that prompted real estate investors to close the deals and avoid the increase in capital gains taxes.

43333 ■ "Recovery a Ruse?" in *Baltimore Business Journal* **(Vol. 28, August 6, 2010, No. 13, pp. 1)**
Pub: Baltimore Business Journal
Ed: Scott Dance. **Description:** Baltimore, Maryland-area businesses have remained cautious as their optimism faded along with the latest indicators on

economic recovery. Economists believe they might be justified with their concern since sales were better, but there is no security that they will stay that way.

43334 ■ "Rediscovering the Land of Opportunity" in Green Industry Pro (July 2011)
Pub: Cygnus Business Media
Ed: Gregg Wartgow. Description: Landscape contractors need to discover new strategies that will generate leads and convert those leads into sales.

43335 ■ "Refreshing" in Canadian Business (Vol. 79, September 11, 2006, No. 18, pp. 22)
Pub: Rogers Media
Ed: Joe Castaldo. Description: Turnaround strategies and initiatives adopted by Canadian Beverage Corp. to boost its declining sales are presented.

43336 ■ "Reinventing Your Rep Training Program" in Agency Sales Magazine (Vol. 39, August 2009, No. 8, pp. 40)
Pub: MANA
Description: Tips on how to encourage manufacturer's representatives to attend scheduled training sessions are given. Manufacturers should learn the value of keeping the training program up-to-date and communicate with the sales team to know what needs to be revamped. Problems faced by representatives with inside sales staff should also be addressed by the manufacturer.

43337 ■ "Renewed Vision" in Hawaii Business (Vol. 54, August 2008, No. 2, pp. 49)
Pub: Hawaii Business Publishing
Ed: Jason Ubay. Description: Saint Francis Healthcare System of Hawaii, ranked 81 in Hawaii's top 250 companies for 2008, has been rebranding to focus on senior community healthcare and sold some of its operations, which explains the decline in gross sales from $219.5M in 2006 to $122.7M in 2007. The system's senior services and home hospice service expansion are provided.

43338 ■ "Rep Contracts: Simple, Clear, Fair" in Agency Sales Magazine (Vol. 39, September-October 2009, No. 9, pp. 3)
Pub: MANA
Ed: Bryan C. Shirley. Description: Things that a manufacturer and a sales representative needs to strive for when creating an Agreement for Representation includes an agreement that is simple and complete, one that covers all the needs of both parties and is fair, equitable, and balanced. Sales representatives need to make more sales calls and find new opportunities during this recession.

43339 ■ "Rep Vs. Direct: Always an Interesting Story" in Agency Sales Magazine (Vol. 39, July 2009, No. 7, pp. 3)
Pub: MANA
Ed: Bryan C. Shirley. Description: Manufacturers benefit from outsourcing their field sales to professional sales representatives in the areas of multi-line selling and customer knowledge and relationship. Some misperceptions about sales reps include the belief that they are an additional 'channel' in sales.

43340 ■ "Reps Continue to Move to International Trade" in Agency Sales Magazine (Vol. 39, September-October 2009, No. 9, pp. 24)
Pub: MANA
Ed: Jack Foster. Description: Sales representatives should get involved and look into international trade if they want to be successful in the future. The weak U.S. dollar, labor costs, and the low cost of transportation are factors that drive the trend towards international trade.

43341 ■ "Reps Have Needs Too!" in Agency Sales Magazine (Vol. 39, December 2009, No. 11, pp. 16)
Pub: MANA
Ed: Bill Heyden. Description: There is common information that a sales representatives needs to know prior to choosing a manufacturer to represent. Both parties must keep promises made to customers and prospects. Reps also need the support from the manufacturers and to clear matters regarding their commission. Interviewing tips for representatives to get this vital information are presented.

43342 ■ "Reps Vs. Factory Direct Sales Force...Which Way to Go?" in Agency Sales Magazine (Vol. 39, September-October 2009, No. 9, pp. 28)
Pub: MANA
Ed: Eric P. Johnson. Description: Hiring independent manufacturers' sales representative is a cost-effective alternative to a direct sales force. Sales reps have predictable sales costs that go up and down with sales, stronger local relationships and better market intelligence.

43343 ■ "Revisiting Rep Coping Strategies" in Agency Sales Magazine (Vol. 39, December 2009, No. 11, pp. 32)
Pub: MANA
Ed: Jack Foster. Description: Independent manufacturers representatives should become a well-rounded and complete businessman with continued education. The new type of representative is a problem solver and the resource for answering questions. Employing the concept of synergistic selling is also important to salespeople.

43344 ■ "Right From the Start" in Small Business Opportunities (July 2010)
Pub: Harris Publications Inc.
Ed: Ed Krug. Description: Ed Krug from Pitch Blue provides sales support services by partnering with small and mid-sized companies to set and reach new revenue targets.

43345 ■ "The Rise of Pompei" in Retail Merchandiser (Vol. 51, September-October 2011, No. 5, pp. 13)
Pub: Phoenix Media Corporation
Description: Soho creative consulting group follows its C3 philosophy to create an invigorated brand experience that transforms customers from consumers to empowered buyers. Pompei AD is a leading creative consultancy that specializes in design and branding for retail, museum, hospitality, and other sectors.

43346 ■ "Sales and the Absolute Power of Information" in Agency Sales Magazine (Vol. 39, July 2009, No. 7, pp. 16)
Pub: MANA
Ed: Dave Kahle. Description: Having good information can help a sales representative deliver effective sales performance. A process for collecting information about customers, prospects, and competitors is discussed.

43347 ■ Sales Bible
Pub: Collins Publications
Ed: Jeffery Gitomer. Released: May 6, 2008. Price: $29.95. Description: An expert in sales provides the definitive sales reference.

43348 ■ "Sales Communications in a Mobile World" in Business Communication Quarterly (December 2007, pp. 492)
Pub: Sage Publications USA
Ed: Daniel T. Norris. Description: Salespeople can take advantage of the latest mobile technologies while maintaining a personal touch with clients and customers through innovation, formality in interactions, client interactions, and protection and security of mobile data.

43349 ■ "Sales Force Expertise: A Competitive Advantage" in Agency Sales Magazine (Vol. 39, November 2009, No. 10, pp. 10)
Pub: MANA
Ed: Ken Valla. Description: Maintaining an expert sales force is a competitive advantage that sales leaders can count on. The skills that the sales force need to have include "consultative selling" or the ability to understand and link to a customer's business priorities, conducting a process conversation, and asking discovery questions.

43350 ■ "Sales Gave W&S Record '07" in Business Courier (Vol. 24, March 14, 2008, No. 49, pp. 1)
Pub: American City Business Journals, Inc.
Ed: Jon Newberry. Description: Western & Southern Financial Group was able to achieve a record $365 million in net income thanks in large part to the double-digit increases in profits by its W&S Agency Group field offices and non-insurance businesses. The sale of their Integrated Investment Services Subsidiary and shares in several Marriot hotels also added to the record profit.

43351 ■ Salesforce.com Secrets of Success: Best Practices for Growth and Profitability
Pub: Prentice Hall Business Publishing
Ed: David Taber. Released: May 15, 2009. Price: $34.99. Description: Guide for using Salesforce. com; it provides insight into navigating through user groups, management, sales, marketing and IT departments in order to achieve the best results.

43352 ■ "Say Goodbye to Voicemail" in Agency Sales Magazine (Vol. 39, November 2009, No. 10, pp. 3)
Pub: MANA
Description: Salespeople should think twice before leaving a voicemail. The emerging modern etiquette is to send a text message or to e-mail the customer or client. Communication suggestions for both salespeople and their principals are presented.

43353 ■ "Scripps Networks" in Brandweek (Vol. 49, April 21, 2008, No. 16, pp. SR12)
Pub: VNU Business Media, Inc.
Ed: Anthony Crupi. Description: Provides contact information for sales and marketing personnel for the Scripps networks as well as a listing of the station's top programming and an analysis of the current season and the target audience for those programs running in the current season. Scripps networks include HGTV and the Food Network. HGTV boasts on of the industry's best commercial-retention averages, keeping nearly 97 percent of its viewers during advertising breaks.

43354 ■ "The Secret Strategy for Meaningful Sales Meetings" in Agency Sales Magazine (Vol. 39, December 2009, No. 11, pp. 40)
Pub: MANA
Ed: Dave Kahle. Description: Sales meetings can be made more meaningful by focusing on the end results that the meeting seeks to achieve. Describing the changed behavior that is sought from the sales force and working backwards from there also help make a sales meeting more meaningful.

43355 ■ "Sell: Going Zen" in Entrepreneur (Vol. 35, October 2007, No. 10, pp. 106)
Pub: Entrepreneur Media Inc.
Ed: Barry Farber. Description: Principles of Zen can actually be used to improve selling skills. Some of the Zen values such as being prepared, keeping silent, and practicing open-mindedness are applicable in the marketing world. Details on what salespeople can learn from Zen are provided.

43356 ■ Sell More of Anything to Anyone: Sales Tips for Individuals, Business Owners and Sales Professionals
Pub: Allen & Unwin
Ed: Andrew Griffiths. Released: May 10, 2010. Price: $16.95. Description: Tips are shared to help anyone improve sales skills while providing strong customer service.

43357 ■ Selling the Invisible: A Field Guide to Modern Marketing
Pub: Business Plus
Ed: Harry Beckwith. Price: $22.95. Description: Tips for marketing and selling intangibles such as health care, entertainment, tourism, legal services, and more are provided.

43358 ■ Selling Online: Canada's Bestselling Guide to Becoming a Successful E-Commerce Merchant
Pub: John Wiley and Sons Canada Ltd.
Ed: Jim Carroll; Rick Broadhead. Released: September 6, 2002. Description: Helps individuals build online retail enterprises; this updated version includes

current tools, information and success strategies, how to launch an online storefront, security, marketing strategies, and mistakes to avoid.

43359 ■ **"Selling With Strengths; Talent Trumps Training" in** *Gallup Management Journal* **(March 24, 2011)**
Pub: Gallup
Description: What are the strengths of salespeople, and how can organizations develop them? What do great sales managers do differently? The authors of, 'Strengths Based Selling' answer these questions and others, including: why money is overrated as a motivator.

43360 ■ *Selling to Zebras: How to Close 90 Percent of the Business You Pursue Faster, More Easily and More Profitably*
Pub: Greenleaf Book Group Press
Ed: Jeff Koser, Chad Koser. **Released:** October 1, 2008. **Price:** $19.95. **Description:** Authors argue that the key to closing more sales is to spend more time researching and meeting with clients.

43361 ■ **"Shoestring-Budget Marketing" in** *Women Entrepreneur* **(January 5, 2009)**
Pub: Entrepreneur Media Inc.
Ed: Maria Falconer. **Description:** Pay-per-click search engine advertising is the traditional type of e-marketing that may not only be too expensive for certain kinds of businesses but also may not attract the quality customer base a business looking to grow needs to find. Social networking websites have become a mandatory marketing tool for business owners who want to see growth in their sales; tips are provided for utilizing these networking websites in order to gain more visibility on the Internet which can, in turn, lead to the more sales.

43362 ■ **"Should You Invest in the Long Tail?" in** *Harvard Business Review* **(Vol. 86, July-August 2008, No. 8, pp. 88)**
Pub: Harvard Business School Press
Ed: Anita Elberse. **Description:** Relevance of the long tail, or the sustainability of sales after a given product's launch is examined. It is posited that niche sales are not as sustainable as those for products with broader appeal.

43363 ■ **"Single Most Important Problem" in** *Small Business Economic Trends* **(July 2010, pp. 18)**
Pub: National Federation of Independent Business
Description: A table showing the single most important problem among small businesses surveyed in the U.S. for June 2010 is presented. Poor sales was selected by 30 percent of firms as the single most important problem, followed by taxes and government requirements and red tape. Graphs comparing selected single most important problem from January 1986 to June 2010 are also given.

43364 ■ *Six SIGMA for Small Business*
Pub: Entrepreneur Press
Ed: Greg Brue. **Released:** October 2005. **Price:** $19.95 (US), $26.95 (Canadian). **Description:** Jack Welch's Six SIGMA approach to business covers accounting, finance, sales and marketing, buying a business, human resource development, and new product development.

43365 ■ **"Six Tips To Maximize Networking Opportunities" in** *Women Entrepreneur* **(November 3, 2008)**
Pub: Entrepreneur Media Inc.
Ed: Tamara Monosoff. **Description:** Networking events fall into the realm of business development as opposed to immediate sales opportunities. It is important to remember that these events provide a chance to build relationships that may someday help one's business. Tips to help make the most out of networking events are provided.

43366 ■ **"Skinner's No Drive-Thru CEO" in** *Crain's Chicago Business* **(Vol. 31, April 28, 2008, No. 17, pp. 1)**
Pub: Crain Communications, Inc.
Ed: David Sterrett. **Description:** Profile of James Skinner who was named CEO for McDonald's Corp. in November 2004 and has proved to be a success-

ful leader despite the number of investors who doubted him when he came to the position. Mr. Skinner has overseen three years of unprecedented sales growth and launched the biggest menu expansion in 30 years.

43367 ■ **"The Small 300" in** *Canadian Business* **(Vol. 81, Summer 2008, No. 9, pp. 137)**
Pub: Rogers Media Ltd.
Description: Small cap-companies are ranked based on market capitalization and stock performance. Calgary-based Grande Cache Coal Corp. topped the roster with 1,000 percent of return resulting from strong sales. A table showing the 2008 rankings of the companies is presented.

43368 ■ **"Small Budget, Big Impact" in** *Small Business Opportunities* **(Summer 2010)**
Pub: Harris Publications Inc.
Ed: Hilary J.M. Topper. **Description:** Ways to use social media to get in from of a target audience for small businesses are examined.

43369 ■ *Small Business Desk Reference*
Pub: Penguin Books (USA) Incorporated
Ed: Gene Marks. **Released:** December 2004. **Description:** Comprehensive guide for starting or running a successful small business, focusing on buying a business or franchise, writing a business plan, financial management, accounting, legal issues, human resources management, operations, marketing, sales, customer service, taxes, insurance, and ethics. Information for launching a restaurant, property management firm, retail outlet, consulting firm, and service business is included.

43370 ■ *The Small Business Owner's Manual: Everything You Need to Know to Start Up and Run Your Business*
Pub: Career Press, Incorporated
Ed: Joe Kennedy. **Released:** June 2005. **Price:** $19.99 (US), $26.95 (Canadian). **Description:** Comprehensive guide for starting a small business, focusing on twelve ways to obtain financing, business plans, selling and advertising products and services, hiring and firing employees, setting up a Web site, business law, accounting issues, insurance, equipment, computers, banks, financing, customer credit and collection, leasing, and more.

43371 ■ **"Small Business Prices" in** *Small Business Economic Trends* **(January 2008, pp. 8)**
Pub: National Federation of Independent Business
Description: Graph from a survey of small businesses in the U.S. is given representing business prices from January 1986 to December 2007. Actual prices (last three months) and planned prices (next three months) were compared in the graph. Tables of actual price changes and price plans from January 2002 to December 2007 are also supplied.

43372 ■ **"Small Business Sales" in** *Small Business Economic Trends* **(March 2008, pp. 7)**
Pub: National Federation of Independent Business
Ed: William C. Dunkelberg, Holly Wade. **Description:** Two tables and a graph that present sales figures for small businesses in the U.S. are given. Statistics for sales changes and sales expectations are provided. The figures in the graph include data from 1986 to 2008.

43373 ■ **"Smart Car Sales Take Big Hit in Recession" in** *Business Journal-Milwaukee* **(Vol. 28, December 10, 2010, No. 10, pp. A1)**
Pub: Milwaukee Business Journal
Ed: Stacey Vogel Davis. **Description:** Sales of smart cars in Milwaukee declined in 2010. Smart Center Milwaukee sold only 52 new cars through October 2010. Increased competition is seen as a reason for the decline in sales.

43374 ■ **"Smarts Drive Sales" in** *Pet Product News* **(Vol. 64, December 2010, No. 12, pp. 1)**
Pub: BowTie Inc.
Ed: Karen Shugart. **Description:** Retailers could make smart decisions by deciding how to best attract customers into their stores or resolving whether to

nurture in-store or buy herps (reptiles) from suppliers. Paying attention to these smart decisions could help boost customer interest in herps and address customer demands.

43375 ■ *The Social Media Bible: Tactics, Tools, and Strategies for Business Success*
Pub: John Wiley & Sons, Inc.
Ed: Lon Safko, David Brake. **Released:** June 17, 2009. **Price:** $29.95. **Description:** Information is given to build or transform a business into social media, where customers, employees, and prospects connect, collaborate, and champion products and services in order to increase sales and to beat the competition.

43376 ■ **"Solar Hot Water Sales Are Hot, Hot, Hot" in** *Contractor* **(Vol. 56, December 2009, No. 12, pp. 22)**
Pub: Penton Media, Inc.
Ed: Dave Yates. **Description:** Plumbing contractors in the United States can benefit from the increased sales of solar thermal water systems. Licensed plumbers have the base knowledge on the risks associated from heating and storing water. Safety issues associated with solar water heaters are also included.

43377 ■ **"Sony Pictures Television" in** *Brandweek* **(Vol. 49, April 21, 2008, No. 16, pp. SR13)**
Pub: VNU Business Media, Inc.
Ed: Marc Berman. **Description:** Provides contact information for sales and marketing personnel for Sony Pictures Television Distribution as well as a listing of the station's top programming and an analysis of the current season and the target audience for those programs running in the current season.

43378 ■ **"Sound Check" in** *Agency Sales Magazine* **(Vol. 39, August 2009, No. 8, pp. 14)**
Pub: MANA
Ed: Dave Kahle. **Description:** Most customers believe salespersons are unable to do well in terms of listening, which is one of the four fundamental competencies of a sales person. Listening is the primary tool to uncover deeper and more powerful needs and motivations of the customer. A guide on how to listen better and improve listening effectiveness is presented.

43379 ■ **"Spillover Effects" in** *Crain's Detroit Business* **(Vol. 24, October 6, 2008, No. 40, pp. 29)**
Pub: Crain Communications, Inc.
Description: Earlier this year, the Detroit Regional Chamber estimated that the Detroit Tiger's baseball team's 81 home games would have a $277 million positive economic impact on the region. Due to the poor performance of the team, fewer fans are spending money on tickets, which translates into fewer dollars coming into the region. Lower viewership on television has also been a result of the Tiger's losing season.

43380 ■ **"Sponsorship, Booths Available for Spring Business Showcase" in** *Bellingham Business Journal* **(Vol. February 2010, pp. 3)**
Pub: Sound Publishing Inc.
Description: Third Annual Spring Business Showcase still have space available for vendors and sponsors. The event gives local businesses the opportunity to increase their visibility and provides a means to increase sales and build relationships.

43381 ■ **"Stop Trying to Delight Your Customers" in** *Harvard Business Review* **(Vol. 88, July-August 2010, No. 7-8, pp. 116)**
Pub: Harvard Business School Publishing
Ed: Matthew Dixon, Karen Freeman, Nicholas Toman. **Description:** Importance of resolving issues for customers is key to increasing their loyalty, rather than by exceeding customer expectations. Areas to address include decreasing customer need for follow-up calls, switching service channels, and the potential for negative emotional response.

43382 ■ *Streetwise Small Business Book of Lists: Hundreds of Lists to Help You Reduce Costs, Increase Revenues, and Boost Your Profits!*

Pub: Adams Media Corporation

Ed: Gene Marks. **Released:** September 2006. **Price:** $25.95. **Description:** Strategies to help small business owners locate services, increase sales, and lower expenses.

43383 ■ **"Suited for Success"** in *Retail Merchandiser* (Vol. 51, July-August 2011, No. 4, pp. 6)

Pub: Phoenix Media Corporation

Description: MyBestFit is a size-matching body scanner that helps consumers find the perfect size clothing for themselves, giving brick and mortar retailers an edge on ecommerce competitors.

43384 ■ **"Summary. Economic Trends for Small Business"** in *Small Business Economic Trends* (February 2008, pp. 1)

Pub: National Federation of Independent Business

Ed: William C. Dunkelberg, Holly Wade. **Description:** Summary of economic trends for small businesses in the U.S. is provided. Economic indicators such as capital spending, inventories and sales, inflation, and profits are given. Analysis of credit markets is also provided.

43385 ■ **"Super Success"** in *Small Business Opportunities* (November 2008)

Pub: Entrepreneur Media Inc.

Description: Profile of PromoWorks LLC, a company founded by Michael Kent, that distributes samples of food at grocery stores for clients like Kraft Foods, Inc. and Kellogg Co. and also handles the logistics, provides the employees and tracks the products' sales.

43386 ■ **"Suppliers Look to Rack Up Big Sales to Distributors"** in *The Business Journal-Serving Metropolitan Kansas City* (August 15, 2008)

Pub: American City Business Journals, Inc.

Ed: James Dornbrook. **Description:** Suppliers of shelving units, conveyor systems and other equipment used in distribution facilities are expecting new business opportunities along with the planned intermodal projects in the Kansas City area. Suppliers have already observed that small distributors have started to relocate to the city because of the intermodal projects. Demand for shelves and lifts have also increased.

43387 ■ **"Sustaining Health"** in *Pet Product News* (Vol. 64, November 2010, No. 11, pp. 28)

Pub: BowTie Inc.

Ed: Angela Pham. **Description:** How pet supply retailers have responded to dog owners' interest in health supplements and their ingredients is discussed. Dog owners are showing interest in the ingredients inside the supplements and are reading labels. Retailers must now prove the beneficial effects of these ingredients in order to make the sale.

43388 ■ **"Sweet Harmony"** in *Canadian Business* (Vol. 82, April 27, 2009, No. 7, pp. 6)

Pub: Rogers Media

Description: Canada will harmonize its 5 percent federal goods and services tax wit the 8 percent provincial sales tax effective July 1, 2010. Meanwhile, provinces like Ontario and Quebec have switched the sales taxes that are charged in new investments into a value-added tax. The conversion has led to an 11 percent increase in investments in Quebec and the three other provinces that made the conversion.

43389 ■ **"Sweet Tea; Neil Golden"** in *Advertising Age* (Vol. 79, November 17, 2008, No. 43, pp. 4)

Pub: Crain Communications, Inc.

Ed: Emily Bryson York. **Description:** McDonald's launch of iced coffee and sweat tea, which were promoted via price cuts over the summer, helped to boost sales at the fast-food chain.

43390 ■ **"Take Out the Garbage"** in *Entrepreneur* (Vol. 37, August 2009, No. 8, pp. 26)

Pub: Entrepreneur Media, Inc.

Ed: Michael Port. **Description:** Canned 1-2-3 sales tactics should be ditched since consumers express their values with the products and services they buy. Sales people should instead work their call list and become a masterful permission marketer, make relevant sales offers proportionate to the trust they have earned, and build credibility with the people they are meant to serve.

43391 ■ **"Taking a Chance"** in *Baltimore Business Journal* (Vol. 28, July 16, 2010, No. 10, pp. 1)

Pub: Baltimore Business Journal

Ed: Scott Dance. **Description:** North Avenue in Baltimore, Maryland is considered a rough neighborhood due to the dangers of prostitution and drug dealing. However, some entrepreneurs have taken the risk of building their businesses on North Avenue as revitalization efforts grow. One of the challenges for businesses in rough neighborhoods is bringing customers to their stores or offices.

43392 ■ **"Tap Into Food Truck Trend to Rev Up Sales, Build Buzz"** in *Nation's Restaurant News* (Vol. 45, February 7, 2011, No. 3, pp. 18)

Pub: Penton Media Inc.

Ed: Brian Sacks. **Description:** Food truck trend is growing, particularly in New York City, Philadelphia, Washington DC, and Los Angeles, California. Man entrepreneurs are using a mobile food component to market their food before opening a restaurant.

43393 ■ **"Teachable Moments: Worth Every Penny"** in *Pet Product News* (Vol. 64, December 2010, No. 12, pp. 34)

Pub: BowTie Inc.

Ed: Cheryl Reeves. **Description:** Pet bird retailers can attain both outreach to customers and enhanced profitability by staging educational events such as the annual Parrot Palooza event of Burlington, New Jersey-based Bird Paradise. Aside from attracting a global audience, Parrot Palooza features seminars, workshops, classes, and bird-related contests.

43394 ■ **"Technically Speaking"** in *Black Enterprise* (Vol. 38, February 2008, No. 7, pp. 64)

Pub: Earl G. Graves Publishing Co. Inc.

Ed: Sonia Alleyne. **Description:** Marketing manager for Texas Instruments discusses the Strategic Marketing of Technology Products course offered at the California Institute of Technology. The course helps turn products into profits.

43395 ■ **"Telemundo"** in *Brandweek* (Vol. 49, April 21, 2008, No. 16, pp. SR8)

Pub: VNU Business Media, Inc.

Ed: John Consoli. **Description:** Provides contact information for sales and marketing personnel for the Telemundo network as well as a listing of the station's top programming and an analysis of the current season and the target audience for those programs running in the current season.

43396 ■ **"Tell Us What You Really Think Collecting Customer Feedback"** in *Inc.* (Vol. 30, December 2008, No. 12, pp. 52)

Pub: Mansueto Ventures LLC

Ed: Ryan Underwood. **Description:** According to a recent survey, nearly 77 percent of online shoppers review consumer-generated reviews of products before making a purchase.

43397 ■ **"That's the Spirit"** in *Entrepreneur* (Vol. 36, March 2008, No. 3, pp. 78)

Pub: Entrepreneur Media Inc.

Ed: Barry Farber. **Description:** Tips on how to maintain confidence and deal with challenges when it is difficult to sell a product.

43398 ■ **"The Simon Cowell of Sales"** in *Inc.* (March 2008, pp. 81-82)

Pub: Gruner & Jahr USA Publishing

Ed: Norm Brodsky. **Description:** Successful selling tips to help anyone trying to close a deal are examined.

43399 ■ **"Thomas Industrial Network Unveils Custom SPEC"** in *Entertainment Close-Up* (March 3, 2011)

Pub: Close-Up Media

Description: Thomas Industrial Network assists custom manufacturers and industrial service providers a complete online program called Custom SPEC which includes Website development and Internet exposure.

43400 ■ *Titanium EBay: A Tactical Guide to Becoming a Millionaire PowerSeller*

Pub: Penguin Group Incorporated

Ed: Skip McGrath. **Released:** June 2006. **Price:** $24.95. **Description:** Advice is given to help anyone selling items on eBay to become a Power Seller, an award presented based on monthly gross merchandise sales.

43401 ■ **"Title Creep: The Chief Revenue Officer"** in *Inc.* (March 2008, pp. 28)

Pub: Gruner & Jahr USA Publishing

Ed: The title, Chief Revenue Officer, is growing. The marketing function of the CRO is to oversee sales, new product development, and pricing.

43402 ■ **"TiVo, Domino's Team to Offer Pizza Ordering by DVR"** in *Advertising Age* (Vol. 79, November 17, 2008, No. 43, pp. 48)

Pub: Crain Communications, Inc.

Ed: Brian Steinberg. **Description:** Domino's Pizza and TiVo are teaming up to make it possible for customers to order from the restaurant straight from their DVR. The companies see that this kind of interactive television and consumer experience will only serve to generate more sales as the customer can be exposed to a fuller range of menu selections and will not have to interrupt their viewing, while workers can spend more time making the product.

43403 ■ **"Tofutti Brands"** in *Ice Cream Reporter* (Vol. 23, September 20, 2010, No. 10, pp. 6)

Pub: Ice Cream Reporter

Description: Tofutti Brands announced net sales at $4.5 million for second quarter 2010.

43404 ■ **"Toss the Gum Before You Speak"** in *Agency Sales Magazine* (Vol. 39, July 2009, No. 7, pp. 34)

Pub: MANA

Ed: Stephen D. Boyd. **Description:** When preparing to present to a prospective principal, a salesperson should anticipate the speaking situation and find out in advance the program events that occur around their speech. They should also practice their material in front of a friend or colleague.

43405 ■ **"Training: an Investment in Performance Improvement"** in *Franchising World* (Vol. 42, September 2010, No. 9, pp. 22)

Pub: International Franchise Association

Ed: Catherine Monson. **Description:** Advantages of training provided by franchisors that are available to franchisees and their employees is discussed.

43406 ■ *Treasure Hunt*

Pub: Penguin Group Incorporated

Ed: Michael J. Silverstein; John Butman. **Released:** May 4, 2006. **Description:** Explanation of people's spending habits and how to capitalize on retail sales.

43407 ■ **"Tripped by Trump?"** in *The Business Journal-Serving Greater Tampa Bay* (Vol. 28, July 25, 2008, No. 31, pp. 1)

Pub: American City Business Journals, Inc.

Ed: Michael Hinman. **Description:** Jean Shahnasarian, a buyer of the Trump Tower Tampa, filed cases against Donald Trump, The Trump Organization Inc., and Trump Tower Tampa for giving misleading information about Trump's involvement in the project. She wants a return of her $278,000 deposit and does not want to take part in the sale of the project.

43408 ■ **"Turner Broadcasting System"** in *Brandweek* (Vol. 49, April 21, 2008, No. 16, pp. SR13)

Pub: VNU Business Media, Inc.

Ed: Anthony Crupi. **Description:** Provides contact information for sales and marketing personnel for the Turner Broadcasting System networks as well as a listing of the station's top programming and an analysis of the current season and the target audience for those programs running in the current season. Recent acquisitions are also discussed.

43409 ■ "Twentieth Television" in *Brandweek* **(Vol. 49, April 21, 2008, No. 16, pp. SR16)**
Pub: VNU Business Media, Inc.
Ed: Marc Berman. **Description:** Provides contact information for sales and marketing personnel for Twentieth Television as well as a listing of the station's top programming and an analysis of the current season and the target audience for those programs running in the current season.

43410 ■ "Two Ways to Find New Customers" in *Inc.* **(Vol. 31, January-February 2009, No. 1, pp. 41)**
Pub: Mansueto Ventures LLC
Description: Latest software programs that help sales staff connect to new leads are profiled. Salesconx provides online leads while Demandbase reports users on a particular Website.

43411 ■ *The Ultimate Guide to Electronic Marketing for Small Business: Low-Cost/High Return Tools and Techniques That Really Work*
Pub: John Wiley & Sons, Incorporated
Ed: Tom Antion. **Released:** June 2005. **Price:** $19.95 (US), $25.99 (Canadian). **Description:** Online marketing techniques for small business to grow and increase sales.

43412 ■ *The Ultimate Sales Machine: Turbocharge Your Business With Relentless Focus on 12 Key Strategies*
Pub: Penguin Group
Ed: Chet Holmes. **Released:** June 21, 2007. **Price:** $24.95. **Description:** Offers insight and step-by-step instructions to build a strong sales force.

43413 ■ *The Ultimate Small Business Marketing Toolkit: All the Tips, Forms, and Strategies You'll Ever Need!*
Pub: McGraw-Hill Inc.
Ed: Beth Goldstein. **Released:** July 2007. **Price:** $27.95. **Description:** An all-in-one sales and marketing resource for entrepreneurs to grow a business.

43414 ■ *Understanding Exporting in the Small and Micro Enterprise*
Pub: Nova Science Publishers, Inc.
Ed: Densil A. Williams. **Released:** April 1, 2009. **Price:** $79.00. **Description:** An examination into the reasons why some small and micro locally-owned businesses choose to sell a portion of their goods abroad while others facing similar market conditions remain focused on the domestic market.

43415 ■ "Understanding Persuasive Online Sales Messages from eBay Auctions" in *Business Communication Quarterly* **(December 2007, pp. 482)**
Pub: Sage Publications USA
Ed: Barbara Jo White, Daniel Clapper, Rita Noel, Jenny Fortier, Pierre Grabolosa. **Description:** eBay product listings were studied to determine the requirements of persuasive sales writing. Potential sellers should use the proper keywords and make an authentic description with authentic photographs of the item being auctioned.

43416 ■ "Univision" in *Brandweek* **(Vol. 49, April 21, 2008, No. 16, pp. SR8)**
Pub: VNU Business Media, Inc.
Ed: John Consoli. **Description:** Provides contact information for sales and marketing personnel for the Univision network as well as a listing of the station's top programming and an analysis of the current season and the target audience for those programs running in the current season. Univision is the No. 1 network on Friday nights in the 18-34 demographic, beating all English-language networks.

43417 ■ "Unleashing the Power of Marketing" in *Harvard Business Review* **(Vol. 88, October 2010, No. 10, pp. 90)**
Pub: Harvard Business School Publishing
Ed: Beth Comstock, Ranjay Gulati, Stephen Liguori. **Description:** Chronicle of the development of General Electric's marketing framework that focused on

three key factors: Principles, people and process. GE determined that successful marketing fulfills four functions: instigating, innovating, implementing, and integrating.

43418 ■ *Up the Loyalty Ladder*
Pub: HarperCollins Publishers Inc.
Ed: Murray Rephel; Neil Raphel. **Released:** September 1996. **Description:** Marketing consultants share insight into growing any retail business and gain customer loyalty.

43419 ■ "Use Social Media to Enhance Brand, Business" in *Contractor* **(Vol. 56, December 2009, No. 12, pp. 14)**
Pub: Penton Media, Inc.
Ed: Elton Rivas. **Description:** Advice on how plumbing contractors should use online social networks to increase sales is presented including such issues as clearly defining goals and target audience. An additional advantage to this medium is that advertisements can easily be shared with other users.

43420 ■ *Use What You've Got*
Pub: Portfolio Publishing
Ed: Barbara Corcoran, Bruce Littlefield. **Released:** 2003. **Price:** $24.95. **Description:** Founder and chairman of New York's premier real estate company, the Corcoran Group, shares her successes in the real estate industry. The book offers tips and pointers to salespeople, entrepreneurs and business people alike. Corcoran explains how she went from waiting tables and borrowed $1,000 from a boyfriend to build her real estate company into the industry's powerhouse.

43421 ■ *Values Sell: Transforming Purpose into Profit through Creative Sales and Distribution Strategies*
Pub: Berrett-Koehler Publishers, Incorporated
Ed: Nadine A. Thompson; Angela E. Soper. **Released:** March 28, 2007. **Price:** $16.95. **Description:** Sales and distribution are the lifeblood of any business, socially responsible businesses are no different.

43422 ■ "VC Boosts WorkForce; Livonia Software Company to Add Sales, Marketing Staff" in *Crain's Detroit Business* **(March 24, 2008)**
Pub: Crain Communications, Inc.
Ed: Tom Henderson. **Description:** WorkForce Software Inc., a company that provides software to manage payroll processes and oversee compliance with state and federal regulations and with union rules, plans to use an investment of $5.5 million in venture capital to hire more sales and marketing staff.

43423 ■ "Warner Bros. Domestic Television Distribution" in *Brandweek* **(Vol. 49, April 21, 2008, No. 16, pp. SR16)**
Pub: VNU Business Media, Inc.
Ed: Marc Berman. **Description:** Provides contact information for sales and marketing personnel for Warner Bros. Domestic Television Distribution as well as a listing of the station's top programming and an analysis of the current season and the target audience for those programs running in the current season.

43424 ■ "Web-Based Marketing Excites, Challenges Small Business Use" in *Colorado Springs Business Journal* **(January 20, 2010)**
Pub: Dolan Media Co.
Ed: Becky Hurley. **Description:** Business-to-business and consumer-direct firms alike are using the fast-changing Web technologies to increase sales, leads and track consumer behavior but once a company commits to an Online marketing plan, experts believe, they must be prepared to consistently tweak and overhaul content and distribution vehicles in order to keep up.

43425 ■ "What Are You Doing Differently?" in *Agency Sales Magazine* **(Vol. 39, December 2009, No. 11, pp. 3)**
Pub: MANA
Ed: Bryan C. Shirley. **Description:** Strategies that sales representatives can do to plan for a good year include professional development, networking with

other reps, and making more sales calls and seeing more people. The end of the year is the perfect time for reps to write or re-write their mission statement and to conduct line profitability.

43426 ■ "When Are Sales Representatives Also Franchisees?" in *Franchise Law Journal* **(Vol. 27, Winter 2008, No. 3, pp. 151)**
Pub: American Bar Association
Ed: John R.F. Baer, David A. Beyer, Scott P. Weber. **Description:** Review of the traditional definitions of sales representatives along with information on how these distribution models could fit into various legal tests for a franchise.

43427 ■ "When Success Isn't Enough" in *Entrepreneur* **(Vol. 35, November 2007, No. 11, pp. 78)**
Pub: Entrepreneur Media Inc.
Ed: Chris Penttila. **Description:** Companies that achieve success can often times continue to push for more growth. Details on planning expansion and boosting sales of several companies are explored.

43428 ■ *Who's Your Gladys?: How to Turn Even the Most Difficult Customer into Your Biggest Fan*
Pub: AMACOM
Ed: Marilyn Suttle, Lori Jo Vest. **Released:** September 9, 2009. **Price:** $22.95. **Description:** Every customer oriented business has a hard-to-satisfy client. This book shows how to serve customers who require a higher degree of skill to manage.

43429 ■ "Why You Need a New-Media 'Ringmaster'" in *Harvard Business Review* **(Vol. 88, December 2010, No. 12, pp. 78)**
Pub: Harvard Business School Publishing
Ed: Patrick Spenner. **Description:** The concept of ringmaster is applied to brand marketing. This concept includes integrative thinking, lean collaboration skills, and high-speed decision cycles.

43430 ■ "Will mCommerce Make Black Friday Green?" in *Retail Merchandiser* **(Vol. 51, September-October 2011, No. 5, pp. 8)**
Pub: Phoenix Media Corporation
Ed: Scott Miller. **Description:** Retailers speculate the possibilities of mobile commerce and are implementing strategies at their stores. Consumers using mobile devices accounted for only 0.1 percent of visits to retail Websites on Black Friday 2009 and rose to 5.6 percent in 2010; numbers are expected to rise for 2011.

43431 ■ "William Barr III; President, Co-Founder, Universal Windows Direct, 33" in *Crain's Cleveland Business* **(November 19, 2007)**
Pub: Crain Communications, Inc.
Ed: David Bennett. **Description:** Profile of William Barr III, the president and co-founder of Universal Windows Direct, a manufacturer of vinyl windows and siding, whose successful salesmanship and leadership has propelled his company forward.

43432 ■ "With New Listings, Business Brokers See Hope" in *Business Courier* **(Vol. 27, September 3, 2010, No. 18, pp. 1)**
Pub: Business Courier
Ed: Lucy May. **Description:** Business brokers in Cincinnati, Ohio are expecting better prices in view of the strengthening economy.

43433 ■ "Women Clicking to Earn Virtual Dollars" in *Sales and Marketing Management* **(November 11, 2009)**
Pub: Nielsen Business Media, Inc.
Ed: Stacy Straczynski. **Description:** According to a new report from Internet marketing firm Q Interactive, women are increasingly playing social media games where they are able to click on an ad or sign up for a promotion to earn virtual currency. Research is showing that this kind of marketing may be a potent tool, especially for e-commerce and online stores.

43434 ■ "Women Workers Spend Lunchtime on Fridays Shopping Online" in *Marketing to Women* **(Vol. 23, November 2010, No. 11, pp. 8)**

Pub: EPM Communications, Inc.

Description: Forty percent of women shop online during work hours, particularly on Fridays. The largest number of women make these purchases during their lunch break. Demographics are included.

43435 ■ "YoCream" in *Ice Cream Reporter* **(Vol. 23, September 20, 2010, No. 10, pp. 6)**

Pub: Ice Cream Reporter

Description: YoCream reported a sales increase for third quarter 2010 at 15.6 percent and net income increasing 25 percent to $2,141,000 for that quarter.

43436 ■ "You Can't Beat Habit" in *Entrepreneur* **(Vol. 37, July 2009, No. 7, pp. 61)**

Pub: Entrepreneur Media, Inc.

Ed: Neale Martin. **Description:** Customers are changing their spending behavior because of the financial meltdown, and this poses an opportunity for businesses to change their marketing practices in order to regain customers. Being flexible is one way to reestablish purchase behavior, along with paying attention to customer feedback.

43437 ■ "Young Adult, Childless May Help Fuel Post-Recession Rebound" in *Pet Product News* **(Vol. 64, November 2010, No. 11, pp. 4)**

Pub: BowTie Inc.

Description: Pet industry retailers and marketers are encouraged to tap into the young adult and childless couple sectors to boost consumer traffic and sales to pre-recession levels. Among young adult owners, pet ownership increased from 40 percent in 2003 to 49 percent in 2009. Meanwhile, the childless couple sector represented 63 percent of all dog/cat owners in 2009.

43438 ■ "Your Booming Business: How You Can Align Sales and Marketing for Dynamic Growth" in *Small Business Opportunities* **(Spring 2008)**

Pub: Harris Publications Inc.

Ed: Voss W. Graham. **Description:** Voss Graham, founder and CEO of Inneractive Consulting Group Inc., works with companies to develop and hire successful sales teams. A checklist from the American Bankers Association to help write a business plan is included.

43439 ■ "Your Turn in the Spotlight" in *Inc.* **(Volume 32, December 2010, No. 10, pp. 57)**

Pub: Inc. Magazine

Ed: John Brandon. **Description:** Examples of three video blogs created by entrepreneurs to promote their businesses and products are used to show successful strategies. Wine Library TV promotes a family's wine business; SHAMA.TV offers marketing tips and company news; and Will It Blend? promotes sales of a household blender.

43440 ■ "Zebra's Changing Stripes" in *Crain's Chicago Business* **(Vol. 31, November 17, 2008, No. 46, pp. 4)**

Pub: Crain Communications, Inc.

Ed: John Pletz. **Description:** Zebra Technologies Corp., the world's largest manufacturer of bar-code printers is profiled; the company's stock has plunged with shares declining 40 percent in the past three months grinding the firm's growth to a halt. Zebra's plans to regain revenue growth are also discussed.

TRADE PERIODICALS

43441 ■ *Counterman*
Pub: Babcox

Ed: Mark Phillips, Editor, mphillips@babcox.com. **Released:** Monthly. **Description:** Magazine devoted to improving the effectiveness of professional automotive parts counter-sales personnel.

43442 ■ *The Selling Advantage*
Pub: Progressive Business Publications

Ed: Phil Ahr, Editor. **Released:** Semimonthly. **Price:** $94.56, individuals. **Description:** Explores new strategies and proven techniques to improve sales performance. Recurring features include book reviews and a column titled Tale of the Sale.

43443 ■ *Selling Power*
Pub: Personal Selling Power Inc.
Contact: Joanne Yankey
E-mail: joanneyankey@sellingpower.com

Released: 10/yr. **Price:** $27 U.S.; $56 Canada (includes GST); $76 other countries; $155 U.S., 3 years; $50 Canada 3-years (includes GST); $19 digital edition. **Description:** Magazine presenting motivational and sales skills and techniques for sales and marketing executives.

43444 ■ *Selling to Seniors*
Pub: CD Publications

Ed: Jean Van Ryzin, Editor. **Released:** Monthly. **Price:** $294, individuals. **Description:** Suggests effective ways to reach the "over 50" market by emphasizing successful marketing strategies. Recurring features include interviews, case studies, and demographic data. Remarks: Incorporates the former Maturity Market Perspectives and Mature Market Report. Editor: Allison Patterson

43445 ■ *Targets*
Pub: Salesforce Training & Consulting Inc.

Ed: Lorraine Jeffrey, Editor, lorraine@salesforcetraining.com. **Released:** Quarterly. **Price:** Free. **Description:** Provides sales professionals with information on developments and improvements within the marketing, sales, and advertising industries. Recurring features include columns titled Publishers Podium, Guest Column, Hints-Tips-Ideas, and Sales Manager's Corner.

43446 ■ *What's Working in Sales Management*
Pub: Progressive Business Publications

Ed: Steve Trimble, Editor. **Released:** 22x/Year. **Price:** $264, individuals. **Description:** Acts as a time-saving resource for busy sales managers. Recurring features include interviews, news of research, a calendar of events, and news of educational opportunities.

VIDEOCASSETTES/ AUDIOCASSETTES

43447 ■ *Achieve Success by Prospecting with Phillip Wexler*
Instructional Video
2219 C St.
Lincoln, NE 68502
Ph:(402)475-6570
Free: 800-228-0164
Fax:(402)475-6500
Co. E-mail: feedback@insvideo.com
URL: http://www.insvideo.com

Price: $95.00. **Description:** Phillip Wexler offers prospecting training program for sales people. Only available in the U.S. **Availability:** VHS.

43448 ■ *American Business Sales Series*
Instructional Video
2219 C St.
Lincoln, NE 68502
Ph:(402)475-6570
Free: 800-228-0164
Fax:(402)475-6500
Co. E-mail: feedback@insvideo.com
URL: http://www.insvideo.com

Description: Business education series aimed at improving phone-selling skills. **Availability:** VHS.

43449 ■ *Ask for the Order. . .and Get It!*
Dartnell Corp.
2222 Sedwick Drive, Ste. 101
Durham, NC 27713
Free: 800-233-8720

Fax:800-508-2592
Co. E-mail: customerservice@dartnellcorp.com
URL: http://www.dartnellcorp.com
Released: 1972. **Description:** Hammers home a key principle of salesmanship—to get an order you must ask for it; from the "Tough-Minded Salesmanship" series. **Availability:** VHS; 3/4U; Special order formats.

43450 ■ *Ask for the Order...and Get It! (Revised)*
Excellence in Training Corp.
c/o ICON Training
804 Roosevelt St.
Polk City, IA 50226
Free: 800-609-0479
Co. E-mail: info@icontraining.com
URL: http://www.icontraining.com

Released: 1991. **Price:** $469.00. **Description:** An updated look at the timeless issues of selling. **Availability:** VHS; 3/4U; Special order formats.

43451 ■ *Bakery Merchandising 101*
International Dairy-Deli-Bakery Association (IDDBA)
636 Science Dr.
PO Box 5528
Madison, WI 53705-0528
Ph:(608)310-5000
Fax:(608)238-6330
Co. E-mail: iddba@iddba.org
URL: http://www.iddba.org

Price: $50.00. **Description:** Discusses ways for successful promotion and product appeal to help increase bakery sales. **Availability:** VHS.

43452 ■ *Bakery Merchandising Certificate Program*
International Dairy-Deli-Bakery Association (IDDBA)
636 Science Dr.
PO Box 5528
Madison, WI 53705-0528
Ph:(608)310-5000
Fax:(608)238-6330
Co. E-mail: iddba@iddba.org
URL: http://www.iddba.org

Price: $160.00. **Description:** Examines the benefits of suggestive selling, sampling, displays, and event merchandising. **Availability:** VHS.

43453 ■ *Beware the Naked Man Who Offers You His Shirt*
PBS Home Video
Catalog Fulfillment Center
PO Box 751089
Charlotte, NC 28275-1089
Ph:800-531-4727
Free: 800-645-4PBS
Co. E-mail: info@pbs.org
URL: http://www.pbs.org

Released: 1990. **Price:** $395.00. **Description:** The author of "Swim With the Sharks Without Being Eaten Alive" offers insights and advice on increasing sales productivity. **Availability:** VHS; 3/4U.

43454 ■ *Business Library Series: Sales and Motivation*
Instructional Video
2219 C St.
Lincoln, NE 68502
Ph:(402)475-6570
Free: 800-228-0164
Fax:(402)475-6500
Co. E-mail: feedback@insvideo.com
URL: http://www.insvideo.com

Price: $19.95. **Description:** Offers humorous look at the fundamental elements of executing a sale. Emphasizes planning and determination as the essence of everyday success. **Availability:** VHS.

43455 ■ *Clean, Fresh & Friendly*
International Dairy-Deli-Bakery Association (IDDBA)
636 Science Dr.
PO Box 5528
Madison, WI 53705-0528
Ph:(608)310-5000

Fax:(608)238-6330
Co. E-mail: iddba@iddba.org
URL: http://www.iddba.org
Price: $160.00. **Description:** Deli customer service training video. **Availability:** VHS.

43456 ■ *The Cold Call*
Video Arts, Inc.
c/o Aim Learning Group
8238-40 Lehigh
Morton Grove, IL 60053-2615
Free: 877-444-2230
Fax:(416)252-2155
Co. E-mail: service@aimlearninggroup.com
URL: http://www.aimlearninggroup.com
Released: 1976. **Price:** $695.00. **Description:** This program demonstrates the specific skills and disciplines of telephone selling, and the dangers of ignoring them. **Availability:** VHS; 8mm; 3/4U; Special order formats.

43457 ■ *The Competitive Edge*
Film Library/National Safety Council California Chapter
4553 Glencoe Ave., Ste. 150
Marina Del Rey, CA 90292
Ph:(310)827-9781
Free: 800-421-9585
Fax:(310)827-9861
Co. E-mail: California@nsc.org
URL: http://www.nsc.org/nsc_near_you/FindYourLocalChapter/Pages/California.aspx
Released: 1989. **Description:** This program emphasizes finding out your customer's most immediate concern, and selling to that concern. **Availability:** VHS; 3/4U.

43458 ■ *Customer-Responsive Selling*
Excellence in Training Corp.
c/o ICON Training
804 Roosevelt St.
Polk City, IA 50226
Free: 800-609-0479
Co. E-mail: info@icontraining.com
URL: http://www.icontraining.com
Price: $995.00. **Description:** A comprehensive program for increasing sales, customer satisfaction, and the corporate image. Workshop materials are available. **Availability:** VHS; 3/4U; Special order formats.

43459 ■ *Customer Service 101*
International Dairy-Deli-Bakery Association (IDDBA)
636 Science Dr.
PO Box 5528
Madison, WI 53705-0528
Ph:(608)310-5000
Fax:(608)238-6330
Co. E-mail: iddba@iddba.org
URL: http://www.iddba.org
Price: $50.00. **Description:** Teaches how to build repeat business, increase sales, and maximize productivity. **Availability:** VHS.

43460 ■ *Dealing with Difficult Prospects*
American Management Association
1601 Broadway
New York, NY 10087-7327
Ph:877-566-9441
Free: 800-262-9699
Fax:(518)891-0368
Co. E-mail: customerservice@amanet.org
URL: http://www.amanet.org
Price: $495.00. **Description:** Contains information and techniques on how to sell successfully, even to the most difficult prospect. **Availability:** VHS.

43461 ■ *The Effective Manager*
Nightingale-Conant Corp.
6245 W. Howard St.
Niles, IL 60714
Ph:(847)647-0300
Free: 800-560-6081
URL: http://www.nightingale.com
Price: $95.00. **Description:** A series of award-winning programs designed to promote effective management and help increase sales. Audio tapes and booklets are included, and the series can be purchased individually or as a set. **Availability:** VHS.

43462 ■ *Explode Those Sales Myths*
Dartnell Corp.
2222 Sedwick Drive, Ste. 101
Durham, NC 27713
Free: 800-233-8720
Fax:800-508-2592
Co. E-mail: customerservice@dartnellcorp.com
URL: http://www.dartnellcorp.com
Released: 1976. **Description:** Designed to explode misleading old tales and beliefs that negatively affect salesmanship. **Availability:** VHS; 3/4U; Special order formats.

43463 ■ *Five Steps to Successful Selling*
Cambridge Educational
c/o Films Media Group
132 West 31st Street, 17th Floor
Ste. 124
New York, NY 10001
Free: 800-257-5126
Fax:(609)671-0266
Co. E-mail: custserve@films.com
URL: http://www.cambridgeol.com
Released: 1990. **Price:** $54.95. **Description:** Zig Ziglar condenses his years of selling experience down to this presentation on sales techniques. **Availability:** VHS.

43464 ■ *Follow-Up: Proven Methods & Strategies That Will Covert Your Contacts into Closings*
Tapeworm Video Distributors
25876 The Old Road 141
Stevenson Ranch, CA 91381
Ph:(661)257-4904
Fax:(661)257-4820
Co. E-mail: sales@tapeworm.com
URL: http://www.tapeworm.com
Price: $29.95. **Description:** Sales education training program that offers tips on how to become a successful multiple call salesperson, including skills that will help with follow through and follow-up until the sale is final. **Availability:** VHS.

43465 ■ *Friendly Persuasion: The Art of Converting Objections into Sales*
American Media, Inc.
4621 121st St.
Urbandale, IA 50323-2311
Ph:(515)224-0919
Free: 888-776-8268
Fax:(515)327-2555
Co. E-mail: custsvc@ammedia.com
URL: http://www.ammedia.com
Released: 1985. **Description:** Salesman Joe Batten outlines the objection-into-sales theories that profit salesman best in any area. **Availability:** VHS; 3/4U.

43466 ■ *Handling Objections*
American Management Association
1601 Broadway
New York, NY 10087-7327
Ph:877-566-9441
Free: 800-262-9699
Fax:(518)891-0368
Co. E-mail: customerservice@amanet.org
URL: http://www.amanet.org
Price: $695.00. **Description:** Presents a three step process on the secrets of successful selling. **Availability:** VHS.

43467 ■ *A Happy Beginning*
Resources for Education & Management, Inc.
1804 Montreal Ct., Ste. A
Tucker, GA 30084
Released: 1971. **Description:** An examination of closing the sale, asking for the order, and answering the customer's objections. How to become a confident sale closer. **Availability:** VHS; 3/4U.

43468 ■ *How to Close the Sale*
Dartnell Corp.
2222 Sedwick Drive, Ste. 101
Durham, NC 27713
Free: 800-233-8720

Fax:800-508-2592
Co. E-mail: customerservice@dartnellcorp.com
URL: http://www.dartnellcorp.com
Released: 1981. **Description:** This program shows salespeople how to ask for the order, and how to get it. **Availability:** VHS; 3/4U; Special order formats.

43469 ■ *How to Find New Customers*
Instructional Video
2219 C St.
Lincoln, NE 68502
Ph:(402)475-6570
Free: 800-228-0164
Fax:(402)475-6500
Co. E-mail: feedback@insvideo.com
URL: http://www.insvideo.com
Price: $39.95. **Description:** Top sales professionals furnish advice on how to be successful in sales. Includes Leroy Leale, sales rep. from Shearson Lehman Bros.; Jim Kilcoyne, account executive for SARNS/3M; and Elaine Bailey, sales rep. for Connect Software. **Availability:** VHS.

43470 ■ *How to Raise Your Batting Average in Selling*
Dartnell Corp.
2222 Sedwick Drive, Ste. 101
Durham, NC 27713
Free: 800-233-8720
Fax:800-508-2592
Co. E-mail: customerservice@dartnellcorp.com
URL: http://www.dartnellcorp.com
Released: 1968. **Description:** Dr. Peale shows how any salesman can operate at peak efficiency that will eventually help improve sales average. **Availability:** VHS; 3/4U; Special order formats.

43471 ■ *How to Take the Butt Out of a Sales Rebuttal*
Dartnell Corp.
2222 Sedwick Drive, Ste. 101
Durham, NC 27713
Free: 800-233-8720
Fax:800-508-2592
Co. E-mail: customerservice@dartnellcorp.com
URL: http://www.dartnellcorp.com
Released: 1967. **Description:** A look at how to cope with the difficult problem of rebutting a customer's objection-without being objectionable. **Availability:** VHS; 3/4U; Special order formats.

43472 ■ *Knowing the Prospect*
Resources for Education & Management, Inc.
1804 Montreal Ct., Ste. A
Tucker, GA 30084
Released: 1971. **Description:** Shows the relationship of product or service benefits to the sales prospect's personal goals, and illustrates the value of knowing a prospect's needs. Ignores the fast-talking sales pitch. **Availability:** VHS; 3/4U.

43473 ■ *Making It Live*
Resources for Education & Management, Inc.
1804 Montreal Ct., Ste. A
Tucker, GA 30084
Released: 1971. **Description:** This tape demonstrates a key to sales success-knowing your product or service and telling your story with enthusiasm and conviction. **Availability:** VHS; 3/4U.

43474 ■ *The Making of a Salesman*
Exec-U-Service Associates
4326 US Highway 1
Princeton, NJ 08540
Released: 1984. **Description:** Provides basic material to enhance a sales training program. All programs are available individually. **Availability:** VHS; 3/4U; Special order formats.

43475 ■ *Manage Your Time to Build Your Territory*
Dartnell Corp.
2222 Sedwick Drive, Ste. 101
Durham, NC 27713
Free: 800-233-8720

Fax:800-508-2592
Co. E-mail: customerservice@dartnellcorp.com
URL: http://www.dartnellcorp.com
Released: 1974. **Description:** An examination of time thieves that rob salespeople of both hours and sales volume. From the "Tough-Minded Salesmanship" series. **Availability:** VHS; 3/4U; Special order formats.

43476 ■ *Managing Sales Stress*
American Management Association
1601 Broadway
New York, NY 10087-7327
Ph:877-566-9441
Free: 800-262-9699
Fax:(518)891-0368
Co. E-mail: customerservice@amanet.org
URL: http://www.amanet.org
Price: $495.00. **Description:** Outlines techniques on handling stress from day-to-day sales. **Availability:** VHS.

43477 ■ *Million Dollar Sales Strategy*
Nightingale-Conant Corp.
6245 W. Howard St.
Niles, IL 60714
Ph:(847)647-0300
Free: 800-560-6081
URL: http://www.nightingale.com
Price: $39.95. **Description:** Jim Cathcart and Dr. Tony Alessandra share tips on time management, prospecting, closing, and successful customer relations. **Availability:** VHS.

43478 ■ *Negotiating Profitable Sales*
Video Arts, Inc.
c/o Aim Learning Group
8238-40 Lehigh
Morton Grove, IL 60053-2615
Free: 877-444-2230
Fax:(416)252-2155
Co. E-mail: service@aimlearninggroup.com
URL: http://www.aimlearninggroup.com
Released: 197?. **Price:** $695.00. **Description:** The first program in this two-part series exposes and analyzes the most-frequent and costly errors of untrained negotiators and shows a salesman being briefed by his superiors. The second program shows the prepared salesman actually negotiating with the buyer. The programs are available individually. Also available as a seminar kit. **Availability:** VHS; 8mm; 3/4U; Special order formats.

43479 ■ *The New Selling with Service*
RMI Media
1365 N. Winchester St.
Olathe, KS 66061-5880
Ph:(913)768-1696
Free: 800-745-5480
Fax:800-755-6910
Co. E-mail: actmedia@act.org
URL: http://www.actmedia.com
Released: 1993. **Price:** $89.95. **Description:** Philip Wexler explains how to implement a marketing philosophy to maintain and increase customers. **Availability:** VHS.

43480 ■ *Non-Verbal Communication*
Resources for Education & Management, Inc.
1804 Montreal Ct., Ste. A
Tucker, GA 30084
Released: 1979. **Description:** Helps the sales trainee become more aware of the non-verbal messages others send and become more conscious of his own. **Availability:** 3/4U; Special order formats.

43481 ■ *Overcoming Objections*
Film Library/National Safety Council California Chapter
4553 Glencoe Ave., Ste. 150
Marina Del Rey, CA 90292
Ph:(310)827-9781
Free: 800-421-9585

Fax:(310)827-9861
Co. E-mail: California@nsc.org
URL: http://www.nsc.org/nsc_near_you/FindYourLocalChapter/Pages/California.aspx
Released: 198?. **Description:** This film emphasizes the importance of understanding the customer's point of view. **Availability:** VHS; 3/4U.

43482 ■ *Path to Profit*
International Dairy-Deli-Bakery Association (IDDBA)
636 Science Dr.
PO Box 5528
Madison, WI 53705-0528
Ph:(608)310-5000
Fax:(608)238-6330
Co. E-mail: iddba@iddba.org
URL: http://www.iddba.org
Price: $160.00. **Description:** Analyzes strategies for increasing bakery impulse sales and bottom-line profitability. Discusses how to control shrink and effectively schedule labor. **Availability:** VHS.

43483 ■ *The Perfect Sale*
Skillsoft
107 Northeastern Blvd.
Nashua, NH 03062
Free: 877-545-5763
Co. E-mail: info@netg.com
URL: http://www.skillsoft.com/
Released: 1984. **Description:** This program emphasizes the art of selling from approach to close. **Availability:** VHS; 3/4U.

43484 ■ *Prescription for Complaints*
Video Arts, Inc.
c/o Aim Learning Group
8238-40 Lehigh
Morton Grove, IL 60053-2615
Free: 877-444-2230
Fax:(416)252-2155
Co. E-mail: service@aimlearninggroup.com
URL: http://www.aimlearninggroup.com
Released: 1975. **Price:** $695.00. **Description:** This program shows a six-step, objective method for dealing with customer complaints. **Availability:** VHS; 8mm; 3/4U; Special order formats.

43485 ■ *Presenting the Story*
Resources for Education & Management, Inc.
1804 Montreal Ct., Ste. A
Tucker, GA 30084
Released: 1971. **Description:** How a salesman can best communicate benefits to a customer. Emphasis is on preparation of the story and practice. **Availability:** VHS; 3/4U.

43486 ■ *The Real Estate Success Series*
Council of Real Estate Brokerage Managers
430 N. Michigan Ave.
Chicago, IL 60611
Free: 800-621-8738
Fax:(312)329-8882
Co. E-mail: info@crb.com
URL: http://www.crb.com
Released: 1981. **Description:** This training series, designed to increase skills and profitability through proven training techniques, concentrates on building sales skills step-by-step. **Availability:** VHS; 3/4U.

43487 ■ *Real Selling: How to Increase Sales in Growing Companies*
Excellence in Training Corp.
c/o ICON Training
804 Roosevelt St.
Polk City, IA 50226
Free: 800-609-0479
Co. E-mail: info@icontraining.com
URL: http://www.icontraining.com
Released: 1990. **Price:** $495.00. **Description:** A five-part sales training program that shows how to make more sales, more effectively. Workbooks are included. **Availability:** VHS; 3/4U; Special order formats.

43488 ■ *The Sales Film*
American Media, Inc.
4621 121st St.
Urbandale, IA 50323-2311
Ph:(515)224-0919
Free: 888-776-8268

Fax:(515)327-2555
Co. E-mail: custsvc@ammedia.com
URL: http://www.ammedia.com
Released: 1982. **Description:** Fundamental sales techniques are covered for new, as well as seasoned salespeople. This program includes in-field and industrial sales practices, with methods that bring results. **Availability:** VHS; 3/4U.

43489 ■ *The Sales Professionals: Building Your Clients' Confidence*
Video Arts, Inc.
c/o Aim Learning Group
8238-40 Lehigh
Morton Grove, IL 60053-2615
Free: 877-444-2230
Fax:(416)252-2155
Co. E-mail: service@aimlearninggroup.com
URL: http://www.aimlearninggroup.com
Released: 1991. **Price:** $790.00. **Description:** The need for long-term client trust is emphasized in this video, which focuses on how to be a consultant, problem solver, and partner. **Availability:** VHS; 8mm; 3/4U; Special order formats.

43490 ■ *Self-Motivation in Selling*
Learning Communications LLC
5520 Trabuco Rd.
Irvine, CA 92620
Free: 800-622-3610
Fax:(949)727-4323
Co. E-mail: sales@learncom.com
URL: http://www.learncomhr.com
Released: 1979. **Description:** A look at how to avoid sales slumps and maintain peak performances. Four untitled programs cover frustrations and turndowns, seeking feedback, how to keep personal problems from affecting performance, and how sales managers can keep their people motivated. **Availability:** VHS; 3/4U.

43491 ■ *Sell It to Me!*
Encyclopedia Britannica
331 N. LaSalle St.
Chicago, IL 60654
Ph:(312)347-7159
Free: 800-323-1229
Fax:(312)294-2104
URL: http://www.britannica.com
Released: 1994. **Price:** $870.00. **Description:** Presents foundation skills in a series of situations will help sales people improve their salesmanship. Includes a leader's guide and briefcase book let. **Availability:** VHS.

43492 ■ *Selling in the '90s*
Nightingale-Conant Corp.
6245 W. Howard St.
Niles, IL 60714
Ph:(847)647-0300
Free: 800-560-6081
URL: http://www.nightingale.com
Released: 1990. **Price:** $95.00. **Description:** Sales guru Larry Wilson offers this guide to maintaining a competitive edge in sales. Included is a look at what consumers really want, the keys to partnership selling, and how to deliver a product through dreams and solutions. Two audio cassettes and two workbooks are included. **Availability:** VHS.

43493 ■ *Selling Skills: Have I Got a Deal for You!*
Cambridge Educational
c/o Films Media Group
132 West 31st Street, 17th Floor
Ste. 124
New York, NY 10001
Free: 800-257-5126
Fax:(609)671-0266
Co. E-mail: custserve@films.com
URL: http://www.cambridgeol.com
Released: 1991. **Price:** $79.00. **Description:** For maximum effectiveness, learn to match sales style with the product being sold. Real-life dramatic skits bring different sales techniques to life. **Availability:** VHS.

43494 ■ Selling: The Power of Confidence
Film Library/National Safety Council California
  Chapter
4553 Glencoe Ave., Ste. 150
Marina Del Rey, CA 90292
Ph:(310)827-9781
Free: 800-421-9585
Fax:(310)827-9861
Co. E-mail: California@nsc.org
URL: http://www.nsc.org/nsc_near_you/FindYourLo-
  calChapter/Pages/California.aspx
Released: 1989. **Description:** Pride makes for the
most successful sales staff, and this program explains
how to achieve it. **Availability:** VHS; 3/4U.

43495 ■ Service That Sells
International Dairy-Deli-Bakery Association (IDDBA)
636 Science Dr.
PO Box 5528
Madison, WI 53705-0528
Ph:(608)310-5000
Fax:(608)238-6330
Co. E-mail: iddba@iddba.org
URL: http://www.iddba.org
Price: $160.00. **Description:** Bakery customer
service training video. **Availability:** VHS.

**43496 ■ Sharpen Your Sales Presentation:
Make It a Winner**
Dartnell Corp.
2222 Sedwick Drive, Ste. 101
Durham, NC 27713
Free: 800-233-8720
Fax:800-508-2592
Co. E-mail: customerservice@dartnellcorp.com
URL: http://www.dartnellcorp.com
Released: 1981. **Description:** Gaining attention,
arousing interest, key benefit selling, the demonstra-
tion, and closing on cue are among the sales tech-
niques outlined and defined by Joe Batten. **Avail-
ability:** VHS; 3/4U; Special order formats.

**43497 ■ So You Want to Be a Success at
Selling?**
Video Arts, Inc.
c/o Aim Learning Group
8238-40 Lehigh
Morton Grove, IL 60053-2615
Free: 877-444-2230
Fax:(416)252-2155
Co. E-mail: service@aimlearninggroup.com
URL: http://www.aimlearninggroup.com
Released: 1982. **Price:** $790.00. **Description:** Four
videos that describe the fundamental skills of selling,
from the initial research to the close. Part 1 focuses
on the preparation, including client research and
product knowledge. Part 2 looks at the skills and
techniques of sales presentation. Part 3 shows how
to deal with problem clients. Part 4 demonstrates the
tactics for successfully closing a sale. Also available
as a complete seminar kit. **Availability:** VHS; 8mm;
3/4U; Special order formats.

43498 ■ Suggestive Selling 101
International Dairy-Deli-Bakery Association (IDDBA)
636 Science Dr.
PO Box 5528
Madison, WI 53705-0528
Ph:(608)310-5000
Fax:(608)238-6330
Co. E-mail: iddba@iddba.org
URL: http://www.iddba.org
Price: $50.00. **Description:** Teaches how to under-
stand and encourage impulse sales, increase sales,
and close sales using product samples. **Availability:**
VHS.

43499 ■ Time Is Money!
Aspen Publishers
7201 McKinney Circ.
Frederick, MD 21704
Ph:(301)698-7100
Free: 800-234-1660

Fax:800-901-9075
URL: http://www.aspenpublishers.com
Released: 197?. **Description:** Helps solve salespeople's time problems by teaching them good habits,
and provides them with timesaving techniques so
they'll spend their time more profitably. **Availability:**
VHS; 3/4U.

43500 ■ Time and Territory Management
American Management Association
1601 Broadway
New York, NY 10087-7327
Ph:877-566-9441
Free: 800-262-9699
Fax:(518)891-0368
Co. E-mail: customerservice@amanet.org
URL: http://www.amanet.org
Price: $495.00. **Description:** Instructs salespeople
to take full advantage of prime selling time and how
to turn downtime into productive time. **Availability:**
VHS.

**43501 ■ Tony Alessandra, Ph.D.: On
Collaborative Selling**
Instructional Video
2219 C St.
Lincoln, NE 68502
Ph:(402)475-6570
Free: 800-228-0164
Fax:(402)475-6500
Co. E-mail: feedback@insvideo.com
URL: http://www.insvideo.com
Price: $95.00. **Description:** Part of the Tony Alessan-
dra, Ph.D. Series. Offers advice on how to change
from persuading, telling, and selling to problem-
solving, asking, and helping. Also discusses how to
develop your competitive advantage statement,
explore customer needs, assure customer satisfac-
tion, and how to question, listen, create, and select
options. **Availability:** VHS.

43502 ■ The Unorganized Salesperson
Video Arts, Inc.
c/o Aim Learning Group
8238-40 Lehigh
Morton Grove, IL 60053-2615
Free: 877-444-2230
Fax:(416)252-2155
Co. E-mail: service@aimlearninggroup.com
URL: http://www.aimlearninggroup.com
Released: 199?. **Price:** $790.00. **Description:**
These two videos show how to organize one's time
and skills to be more effective in selling. **Availability:**
VHS; 8mm; 3/4U; Special order formats.

43503 ■ What Is Salesmanship?
Resources for Education & Management, Inc.
1804 Montreal Ct., Ste. A
Tucker, GA 30084
Released: 1971. **Description:** This tape introduces
the idea that selling can be broken down into identifi-
able steps, each of which can improve selling success. **Availability:** VHS; 3/4U.

**43504 ■ When You're Turned Down—Turn
On!**
Dartnell Corp.
2222 Sedwick Drive, Ste. 101
Durham, NC 27713
Free: 800-233-8720
Fax:800-508-2592
Co. E-mail: customerservice@dartnellcorp.com
URL: http://www.dartnellcorp.com
Released: 1977. **Description:** Examines the ques-
tion: When is a turndown a true rejection and when is
it just a disguised objection?; from the "Tough—
Minded Salesmanship" series. **Availability:** VHS;
3/4U; Special order formats.

**43505 ■ Zig Ziglar: 5 Steps to Successful
Selling**
Nightingale-Conant Corp.
6245 W. Howard St.
Niles, IL 60714
Ph:(847)647-0300

Free: 800-560-6081
URL: http://www.nightingale.com
Price: $54.95. **Description:** Ziglar examines the
personality traits that are shared by the nation's top
salespersons, and offers a program to develop these
traits. **Availability:** VHS.

**43506 ■ Zig Ziglar: Selling, a Great Way to
Reach the Top**
Nightingale-Conant Corp.
6245 W. Howard St.
Niles, IL 60714
Ph:(847)647-0300
Free: 800-560-6081
URL: http://www.nightingale.com
Released: 1987. **Price:** $49.95. **Description:** Ziglar
offers this guide to developing winning sales skills,
including relating to the client, presenting a product
and closing the deal. **Availability:** VHS.

CONSULTANTS

**43507 ■ The Beveridge Consulting Group
Inc.**
113 N Grant St.
Barrington, IL 60010
Ph:(847)381-7797
Free: 800-227-4332
Fax:(847)381-7301
URL: http://www.4thgenerationsystems.com
Contact: Dirk Beveridge, President
E-mail: dirk@4thgenerationsystems.com
Scope: Sales, marketing and management consult-
ants. Special emphasis on the development of profes-
sional, sophisticated selling skills as well as modern
sales management systems. **Publications:** "Sales
Management: Why the Best are Better," Walsworth,
1992; "The Superman Syndrome"; "Sustaining Re-
source Selling Skills". **Seminars:** BOSS-The Manda-
tory Business Operating System Standards; Sales
Management Why The Best Are Better; Proactive
Customer Focused Sales; Marketing In The Age Of
Technology; Marketing - The Perception of Difference; Why Successful Businesses Don't Stay;
Everyone is Part of the Sales Promise.

43508 ■ Bran Management Services Inc.
2106 High Ridge Rd.
Louisville, KY 40207-1128
Ph:(502)896-1632
Contact: Robert C. Braverman, CEO
Scope: Offers management consulting services to
companies in manufacturing, distribution and services
to help them cope with growth and change. Helps
small businesses create and identify product strategies. Services include developing international business opportunities; turnaround management; sales
and marketing development; business planning;
acquisitions and mergers.

43509 ■ Coyne Associates
4010 E Lake St.
Minneapolis, MN 55406-2201
Ph:(612)724-1188
Fax:(612)722-1379
Contact: Sandra Blanton, Principle
Scope: A marketing and public relations consulting
firm that specializes in assisting architectural,
engineering, and contractor/developer firms. Services
include: marketing plains and audits, strategic planning, corporate identity, turnarounds, and sales training.

43510 ■ Harding & Co.
511 Harvard Ave.
Swarthmore, PA 19081
Ph:(973)763-9284
Fax:(973)763-9347
Co. E-mail: fharding@hardingco.com
URL: http://www.hardingco.com
Contact: Gary Pines, Principle
E-mail: gpines@atshardingco.com
Scope: Firm specializes in sales management, client
development and employee training. **Publications:**
"Cross-Selling Success: A Rainmakers Guide to
Professional Account Development," Aug, 2002; "Rain

Making: The Professional's Guide to Attracting New Clients"; "Creating Rainmakers: The Managers Guide to Training Professionals to Attract New Clients".

43511 ■ High Probability Selling
103 Chesley Dr., Ste. 200
Media, PA 19063
Ph:(610)566-1535
Free: 800-394-7762
Fax:(610)891-2711
Co. E-mail: contact_us@highprobsell.com
URL: http://www.highprobsell.com
Contact: Jacques Werth, President
Scope: Consultancy transforms sales training into a model of integrity which eliminates sales resistance and establishes relationships of trust and respect, sales management and target marketing. Industries served: All. **Publications:** "Features vs. Benefits"; "Training the 'D Team'"; "Top 6 Pitfalls of Leaving Voice Mail Messages"; "Building Rapport: Don't"; "The One-Call Close"; "Getting Real About Sales Training"; "Top 10 Reasons Sales Managers Fail"; "Top 10 Reasons Salespeople Fail"; "A Clearly Defined Sales Process Yields Big Results"; "Being "Right" vs. Being Rich"; "Poison Words: The Top 6 Words that Sabotage Sales"; "Overcoming Question Reluctance"; "Top Producers- How They Get There". **Seminars:** High Probability Selling; High Probability Prospecting and The Power of Experiential Learning; HPS Telecourse: Training in the Basic Process; Overcoming Skepticism and Distrust; How to Turn Cold-Calls into Warm Calls.

43512 ■ James J. Prihoda & Associates
400 Island Way, Ste. 707
Clearwater Beach, FL 33767
Ph:(727)446-4082
Contact: James J. Prihoda, President
Scope: Specializes in marketing and sales.

43513 ■ Keiei Senryaku Corp.
19191 S Vermont Ave., Ste. 530
Torrance, CA 90502-1049
Ph:(310)366-3331
Free: 800-951-8780
Fax:(310)366-3330
Co. E-mail: takenakaes@earthlink.net
Contact: Kurt Miyamoto, President
Scope: Offers consulting services in the areas of strategic planning; feasibility studies; profit enhancement; organizational development; start-up businesses; mergers and acquisitions; joint ventures; divestitures; executive searches; sales management; and competitive analysis.

43514 ■ Marketing Resource Group
31 Valley Forge Way
Foxboro, MA 02035
Ph:(508)543-8452
Fax:(508)842-7252
Contact: Candace la Chapelle, Vice President
E-mail: candacemrg@aol.com
Scope: Customized sales skills and field training systems for sales people, sales managers, executives and non-selling staff. Curriculum can be developed and branded for in-house program to be used with future trainees and new hires. Offers pre-screening of sales candidates and strategic consulting. **Seminars:** Basic Sales Skills; Consultative Selling; Relationship Selling; Networking to Maximize Your Business; Six Critical Steps for Every Sales Call; Selling Skills for the Non-Sales Professional; Effective Sales Management; Maximizing Revenue.

43515 ■ Max Sacks International
A0608, Free Town, Ste. 58 Donsanhuan South Rd.
Beijing 100022, People's Republic of China
Ph:(206)706-4119
Free: 800-488-4629
Fax:(206)706-5359
Co. E-mail: info@maxsacks.com
URL: http://www.maxsacks.com
Contact: Roy E. Chitwood, President
Scope: Offers sales and sales management training and consulting. Industries served: all. **Publications:** "Ultimate Success -7 Secrets to Spiritually-based Leadership"; "Don't repeat seven deadly sins of customer service"; "Creating a true business partnership with customers"; "The logistics of merging sales

and marketing"; "Toughest job in management: The sales manager"; "Time to erase the lack of respect felt by the sales profession"; "Civility plays a huge role in salesperson's success," 2007. **Seminars:** Track Selling System, 2006; The Guaranteed Close A Scientific Selling Procedure; World Class Selling; Sales Management Clinic and Coaching; Telemarketing; World Class Customer Service; Track Selling Graduate Program. **Special Services:** The Track Selling System™; Online Track Selling™; World-Class Selling™; The Guaranteed Close: A Scientific Selling Procedure™; The Seven Steps To Closing More Sales™; World Class Customer Service™; Track Selling Graduate Program™.

43516 ■ Porter Henry & Co. Inc.
455 E 86th St.
New York, NY 10016-0941
Ph:(212)953-5544
Fax:(212)953-5899
Co. E-mail: sales@porterhenry.com
URL: http://www.porterhenry.com
Contact: Warren Kurzrock, CEO
E-mail: sales@porterhenry.com
Scope: Consulting and custom-designed training in sales and sales management. Work includes sales force studies and needs analyses, systems design, and visual sales presentations. Have 25 validated sales and sales management training programs. **Publications:** "The Sales Strategist-6 Breakthrough Strategies to Win New Business". **Seminars:** AccountAbility; ManageAbility; SalesAbility: Totaling 25 off- the-shelf programs. Mobliesales/motivation, 1999. Infield reinforcement selling skills and motivational program for sales people.

43517 ■ The Tactix Group
1619 N 102 St.
Omaha, NE 68114
Ph:(402)393-3800
Fax:(402)393-5151
Co. E-mail: info@thetactixgroup.com
URL: http://www.thetactixgroup.com
Contact: Douglas R. Little, President
E-mail: dlittle@tactixinc.com
Scope: Offers integrated marketing system design and implementation, for customer relationship management. Serves manufacturing, distributing, high-tech, banking, and executive benefit industries. **Special Services:** Saleslogix (Client Server) Sales Automation Software.

43518 ■ Westlife Consultants & Counsellors
4 Robert Speck Dr., Ste. 1500
Mississauga, ON, Canada L4Z 1S1
Ph:(905)867-0686
Fax:(416)799-5242
Co. E-mail: westlifeconsultant@hotmail.com
URL: http://www.westlifeconsultants.com
Contact: Tania Hussain, Treasurer
E-mail: tania.westlifeconsultant@atshotmail.com
Scope: Provides entrepreneurs and businesses with a highly commercial and global perspectives on the international business development ideas under consideration. **Publications:** "Innovative Management"; "Team Building and Leadership"; "Financial Planning"; "Estate Planning"; "Risk Management"; "Export/Import Trade Finance Mechanics"; "Marketing and Sales Management"; "What Your Banker Needs to Know"; "Building A Successful Financial Plan".

43519 ■ William Blades L.L.C.
1240 Red Tail Way
Cheyenne, WY 82009
Ph:(307)287-3671
Co. E-mail: wblades@aol.com
URL: http://www.williamblades.com
Contact: William H. Blades, President
E-mail: wblades@aol.com
Scope: A business consulting firm with expertise in marketing and sales. Presents seminars, workshops and keynotes on the following topics: re-energizing the organization; professional selling and marketing; corporate culture; proactive leadership; world-class customer service; creativity; great teamwork. **Publications:** "Selling-The Mother of All Enterprise"; "Leadership Defined"; "Why Do We Make Change So Hard"; "10 Crucial Steps for Sales Management Success"; "In Sales, it's all About Accountability"; "Conver-

sations Of Success"; "Celebrate Selling"; "Vision: Help Your Mind"; "Leadership Defined"; "Managing to Improve: 10 Areas of Emphasis for Workplace Leaders"; "Creativity: Let the Juices Flow in the Workplace"; "Get Bill Blades Philosophy on Boot Camps"; "Great Leadership Grows From a Mixed Bag"; "Self Improvement - The Million Dollar Equation". **Seminars:** Sales Leadership Culture Creativity; Sales and Management; Coaching for Executives and Sales Managers; Sales and Marketing Action Plans.

43520 ■ William E. Kuhn & Associates
234 Cook St.
Denver, CO 80206-5305
Ph:(303)322-8233
Fax:(303)331-9032
Co. E-mail: billkuhn1@cs.com
Contact: William E. Kuhn, Owner
E-mail: billkuhn1@cs.com
Scope: Firm specializes in strategic planning; profit enhancement; small business management; mergers and acquisitions; joint ventures; divestitures; human resources management; performance appraisals; team building; sales management; appraisals and valuations. **Publications:** "Creating a High-Performance Dealership," Office SOLUTIONS & Office DEALER, Jul-Aug, 2006.

FRANCHISES AND BUSINESS OPPORTUNITIES

43521 ■ DEI Franchise Systems
PO Box 20169
Cincinnati, OH 45230
Ph:(212)581-7390
Free: 800-224-2140
Fax:(212)245-7897
Co. E-mail: franchise@dei-sales.com
URL: http://www.dei-sales.com
No. of Franchise Units: 32. **No. of Company-Owned Units:** 1. **Founded:** 1979. **Franchised:** 2003. **Description:** Sales training industry. **Equity Capital Needed:** $60,000-$75,000. **Franchise Fee:** $50,000. **Royalty Fee:** 7%. **Financial Assistance:** No. **Training:** Offers 2 weeks home-based training and 2 weeks at headquarters with ongoing support.

43522 ■ DEI Sales Training Systems
DEI Franchise Systems, Inc.
250 W 57th St., Ste. 2217
New York, NY 10107
Ph:(212)581-7390
Free: 800-224-2140
Fax:(212)245-7897
No. of Franchise Units: 31. **Founded:** 1979. **Franchised:** 2003. **Description:** Selling and delivering of sales training programs. **Equity Capital Needed:** $99,400-$153,700. **Franchise Fee:** $50,000. **Royalty Fee:** 7%. **Financial Assistance:** Limited in-house financial assistance. **Training:** Provides 2 weeks at headquarters and ongoing support.

43523 ■ Sandler Training (Canada)
3625 McGill St.
Vancouver, BC, Canada V5K 1J3
Ph:(604)254-4341
Free: 800-669-3537
Fax:(604)251-8060
Co. E-mail: rtaylor@sandler.com
URL: http://www.sandler.com
No. of Franchise Units: 16. **Founded:** 1967. **Franchised:** 1983. **Description:** Sales and sales management training. Provides ongoing incremental reinforced sales and management training for individuals and companies. **Equity Capital Needed:** $80,000. **Franchise Fee:** $68,000. **Training:** Provides personal coaching, ongoing reinforced training and coaching support with excellent products and programs.

LIBRARIES

43524 ■ Canadian Professional Sales Association–Sales Resource Centre
310 Front St. W., Ste. 800
Toronto, ON, Canada M5J 3B5
Ph:(416)408-2685

Free: 888-267-2772
Fax:(416)408-2684
Co. E-mail: asksrc@cpsa.com
URL: http://www.cpsa.com
Contact: Anna Fredericks, Mgr.

Scope: Sales - management, negotiation, selling skills, training, marketing, presentations, meetings, conventions, industry directories, speakers bureau. **Services:** Interlibrary loan; copying; Library open to the public by permission only. **Holdings:** 2500 books; 400 audiocassettes; 400 videotapes. **Subscriptions:** 8 journals and other serials.

43525 ■ Point-of-Purchase Advertising International Information Center
1600 Duke St., Ste. 400
Alexandria, VA 22314
Ph:(703)373-8809
Fax:(703)373-8801
Co. E-mail: info@popai.com
URL: http://www.popai.com
Contact: Dietra Brandon, Exec.Adm.
Scope: Point-of-purchase research information, slide and videotape presentation. **Holdings:** 162 volumes; reports; surveys; 10 research publications; 10 reference guides; 200 audio seminars. **Subscriptions:** 90 journals and other serials; 10 newspapers.

43526 ■ University of Akron–Fisher Institute of Professional Selling–Sales Education Learning Library (Colle)
College of Business Administration
259 S. Broadway
Akron, OH 44325-4805
Ph:(330)972-6303
URL: http://www.uakron.edu
Scope: Selling and sales management. **Services:** Library open to students. **Holdings:** Books; audiotapes; CDs; videos.

RESEARCH CENTERS

43527 ■ University of Akron–Fisher Institute for Professional Selling
259 S Broadway St.
Akron, OH 44325
Ph:(330)972-5447
Fax:(330)972-5798
Co. E-mail: linda@uakron.edu
URL: http://www.uakron.edu/cba/cba-home/dept-cent-inst/fisher/
Contact: Dr. Linda Orr, Interim Dir.
E-mail: linda@uakron.edu

Scope: Professional selling techniques and sales management. **Services:** Consulting; Corporate training. **Educational Activities:** Continuing education courses, and management development courses for sales executives; Seminars.

Scientific and Technical Research/Development

START-UP INFORMATION

43528 ■ *Entrepreneurship: Frameworks and Empirical Investigations from Forthcoming Leaders of European Research*
Pub: Elsevier Science and Technology Books
Ed: Johan Wiklund; Dimo Dimov; Jerome A. Katz; Dean Shepherd. **Released:** July 2006. **Price:** $99.95. **Description:** Entrepreneurial research and theory cover the early growth of research-based startups and the role of learning in international entrepreneurship, focusing on Europe.

43529 ■ "Incubator Cooking Up Expansion Plans" in *Business First Columbus* (Vol. 25, December 5, 2008, No. 15, pp.)
Pub: American City Business Journals
Ed: Kevin Kemper. **Description:** United States-based Science and Technology Campus Corporation is planning to build additional office space in Columbus, Ohio. The site is designed to accommodate three large tenants. Comment from company executives are presented.

43530 ■ "Troy Patent Law Firm Launches Rent-Free Tech Incubator" in *Crain's Detroit Business* (Vol. 25, June 8, 2009, No. 23, pp. 4)
Pub: Crain Communications Inc. - Detroit
Ed: Tom Henderson. **Description:** Young Basile Hanlon MacFarlane & Helmholdt PC, a patent law firm located in Troy, Michigan has created a small, rent-free technology incubator on site. The incubator will be called North Woodward Tech Incubator and has room for four or five startups. The incubator is for the earliest or pre-seed stage for entrepreneurs who have not yet gotten significant investment capital.

43531 ■ "The Ultimate Cure" in *Conde Nast Portfolio* (Vol. 2, June 2008, No. 6, pp. 110)
Pub: Conde Nast Publications, Inc.
Ed: David Ewing Duncan. **Description:** Small upstarts as well as pharmaceutical giants are developing drugs for the neurotechnology industry; these firms are attempting to adapt groundbreaking research into the basic workings of the brain to new drugs for ailments ranging from multiple sclerosis to dementia to insomnia.

43532 ■ "Wanted: Angels in the Country" in *Austin Business JournalInc.* (Vol. 28, July 18, 2008, No. 18, pp. 1)
Pub: American City Business Journals
Ed: Laura Hipp. **Description:** A proposal is being pushed forward by managers of Texas' Emerging Technology Fund to create an angel investors' network. The proposal is asking that tax credits for those who invest in research and development projects be granted in order to boost the number of technology companies in the state.

ASSOCIATIONS AND OTHER ORGANIZATIONS

43533 ■ **Federation of American Scientists**
1725 DeSales St. NW, 6th Fl.
Washington, DC 20036
Ph:(202)546-3300

Fax:(202)675-1010
Co. E-mail: fas@fas.org
URL: http://www.fas.org
Contact: Charles D. Ferguson, Pres.
Description: Natural and social scientists, engineers, and individuals concerned with problems of science and society. Aims to "act on public issues where the opinions of scientists are relevant, those which affect science or in which the experience or perspective of scientists is a needed guide." Functions through testimony to Congress and government agencies, public statements, and articles. Maintains the Federation of American Scientists Fund, a research and education arm of the association. **Publications:** *FAS Public Interest Report* (bimonthly).

REFERENCE WORKS

43534 ■ "13D Filings: Investors Report to the SEC" in *Barron's* (Vol. 88, July 4, 2008, No. 28, pp. M10)
Pub: Dow Jones & Co., Inc.
Description: Robino Stortini Holdings will seek control of Investors Capital Holdings either alone or with members of the company's management. Discovery Group I will withhold its votes at the nomination of directors for TESSCO Technologies while JMB Capital Partners Master Fund plans to nominate a slate of candidates to the board of Maguire Properties.

43535 ■ "100-BU. Beans" in *Farm Industry News* (Vol. 42, January 1, 2009, No. 1)
Pub: Penton Media, Inc.
Ed: Lynn Grooms. **Description:** Demand for soybeans has increased and growers are seeing an increase in yields as well due to breeders that are using molecular-assisted selection; other aspects of the soybean market are presented.

43536 ■ "2011 U.S. Smart Grid – Saving Energy/Saving Money" in *Ecology,Environment & Conservation Business* (October 8, 2011, pp. 3)
Pub: HighBeam Research
Description: Highlights of the '2011 U.S. Smart Grid –Saving Energy/Saving Money Customers' Prospective Demand-Response assesses residential energy consumers' willingness to decrease their power consumption in order to mitigate power issues. Statistical details included.

43537 ■ "Abaddon Acquires Pukaskwa Uranium Properties in NW Ontario" in *Canadian Corporate News* (May 16, 2007)
Pub: Comtex News Network Inc.
Ed: Description: Rubicon Minerals Corp. has entered into an Option Agreement with Consolidated Abaddon Resources Inc. for the acquisition of Pukaskwa uranium properties and plans to conduct an extensive exploration program to prove out the resource and geological potential of the area. Statistical data included.

43538 ■ "Abraxis Bets On Biotech Hub" in *Business Journal-Serving Phoenix and the Valley of the Sun* (Vol. 10, November 9, 2007, No. 28)
Pub: American City Business Journals, Inc.
Ed: Angela Gonzales. **Description:** Abraxis BioScience Inc. purchased a 200,000 square foot manufacturing facility in Phoenix, Arizona from Watson Pharmaceuticals Inc. The company has the technology to allow chemotherapy drugs to be injected directly into tumor cell membranes. A human protein, albumin is used to deliver the chemotherapy.

43539 ■ "Aggenix Completes Merger with German Giant" in *Houston Business Journal* (Vol. 40, December 25, 2009, No. 33, pp. 2)
Pub: American City Business Journals
Ed: Mary Ann Azevedo. **Description:** Agennix Inc. has completed its transformation into a German company after Germany-based GPC Biotech merged into the former publicly traded Agennix AG. One quarter of Agennix's 60 employees will remain in Houston. Details on Agennix's drug trials are examined.

43540 ■ "Angel Investments Tripled in 2009" in *Austin Business JournalInc.* (Vol. 29, January 8, 2010, No. 44, pp. 1)
Pub: American City Business Journals
Ed: Christopher Calnan. **Description:** Central Texas Angel Network (CTAN) has invested $3.5 million in 12 ventures, which include 10 in Austin, Texas in 2009 to triple the amount it invested during 2008. The largest recipient of CTAN's investments is life sciences, which attracted 20 percent of the capital, while software investments fell to 18 percent. The new screening process that helps startups secure CTAN capital is explored.

43541 ■ "Angiotech to Buy Top Medical Devices Company" in *Globe & Mail* (February 1, 2006, pp. B1)
Pub: CTVglobemedia Publishing Inc.
Ed: Leonard Zehr. **Description:** The details on Angiotech Pharmaceuticals Inc.'s acquisition of American Medical Instruments Holdings Inc. are presented.

43542 ■ "Apples, Decoded: WSU Scientist Unraveling the Fruit's Genetics" in *Puget Sound Business Journal* (Vol. 29, September 5, 2008, No. 20)
Pub: American City Business Journals
Ed: Clay Holtzman. **Description:** Washington State University researcher is working to map the apple's genome in order to gain information about how the fruit grows, looks and tastes. His work, funded by a research grant from the US Department of Agriculture and the Washington Apple Commission is crucial to improving the state's position as an apple-producing region.

43543 ■ "Ardesta Venture-Capital Fund Folds" in *Crain's Detroit Business* (Vol. 24, September 22, 2008, No. 38, pp. 24)
Pub: Crain Communications, Inc.
Ed: Tom Henderson. **Description:** Due to the downturn in the local economy, Ann Arbor-based Ardesta LLC, a venture-capital firm specializing in micro- and

nanotechnology research, has pulled the plug on its planned fund of $100 million and said no to an investment of up to $15 million from the state.

43544 ■ "Asterand Eyes Jump to Ann Arbor; TechTown Tenant" in *Crain's Detroit Business* (Vol. 25, June 22, 2009)
Pub: Crain Communications Inc. - Detroit
Ed: Tom Henderson. **Description:** Asterand PLC is considering a move to Ann Arbor from its current location as anchor tenant at TechTown, an incubator and technology park associated with Wayne State University. The university believes the Ann Arbor location's rent is too expensive for the tissue bank company.

43545 ■ "ASU Explores Russian Partnership" in *The Business Journal - Serving Phoenix and the Valley of the Sun* (Vol. 28, September 5, 2008)
Pub: American City Business Journals, Inc.
Ed: Mike Sunnucks. **Description:** Arizona State University is planning to partner with Russia-based St. Petersburg State University (SPSU) regarding research, faculty and student exchange, and other joint efforts. SPSU is one of Russia's leading scientific and research institutions. Arizona State's partnerships with other foreign colleges are also mentioned.

43546 ■ "ATI Now Ready to Pounce on Biotech" in *Austin Business JournalInc.* (Vol. 28, August 22, 2008, No. 23, pp. 1)
Pub: American City Business Journals
Ed: Laura Hipp. **Description:** Austin Technology Incubator has entered the biotechnology sector through a program of the University of Texas incubator. The company's bioscience program was set off by a grant from the City of Austin worth $125,000. The growth of Austin's biotechnology sector is examined.

43547 ■ "Atlantis-Resistant Figures on the Up" in *Farmer's Weekly* (March 28, 2008, No. 320)
Pub: Reed Business Information
Description: Researches are studying the number of cases in which blackgrass became resistant to Atlantis to determine if the resistance is due mainly to the ALS target-site mechanism or enhanced metabolism.

43548 ■ "Attorney Guides Biotech Company in $6 Million Initial Public Offering" in *Miami Daily Business Review* (March 26, 2008)
Pub: ALM Media Inc.
Description: In order to raise capital to engage in a full-scale trial of MyoCell to receive clinical approval, Bioheart Inc., launched an initial public offering. Bioheart researches and develops cell therapies to treat heart damage.

43549 ■ "Auctions and Bidding: a Guide for Computer Scientists" in *ACM Computing Surveys* (Vol. 43, Summer 2011, No. 2, pp. 10)
Pub: Association for Computing Machinery
Ed: Simon Parsons, Juan A. Rodriguez-Aguilar, Mark Klein. **Description:** There are various actions: single dimensional, multi-dimensional, single-sided, double-sided, first-price, second-price, English, Dutch, Japanese, sealed-bid, and these have been extensively discussed and analyzed in economics literature. This literature is surveyed from a computer science perspective, primarily from the viewpoint of computer scientists who are interested in learning about auction theory, and to provide pointers into the economics literature for those who want a deeper technical understanding. In addition, since auctions are an increasingly important topic in computer science, the article also looks at work on auctions from the computer science literature. The aim is to identify what both bodies of work tell us about creating electronic auctions.

43550 ■ "Banking on Cord Blood" in *Business Journal-Serving Phoenix & the Valley of the Sun* (Vol. 31, September 10, 2010, No. 1, pp. 1)
Pub: Phoenix Business Journal
Ed: Angela Gonzales. **Description:** Celebration Stem Cell Centre obtained contracts from Mercy Gilbert Medical Center and its two sister hospitals, St.

Joseph Hospital and Medical Center in Phoenix, Arizona and Chandler Regional Medical Center. The contract will facilitate the donation of unused umbilical cord blood for research.

43551 ■ "Being Big By Design" in *Canadian Business* (Vol. 82, April 27, 2009, No. 7, pp. 39)
Pub: Rogers Media
Ed: Andrew Wahl. **Description:** Gennum expects that its planned acquisition of Tundra Semiconductor will expand its market presence and leverage its research and development better than working alone. The proposed friendly acquisition could challenge Zarlink Semiconductor as the largest Canadian semiconductor firm in terms of revenue. The merger could expand Gennum's addressable market to about $2 billion.

43552 ■ "Biotechnology Wants a Lead Role" in *Business North Carolina* (Vol. 28, March 2008, No. 3, pp. 14)
Pub: Business North Carolina
Description: According to experts, North Carolina is poised as a leader in the biotechnology sector. Highlights of a recent roundtable discussion sponsored by the North Carolina Biotechnology Center in Research Triangle Park are presented.

43553 ■ "Blood Bank" in *Canadian Business* (Vol. 80, February 12, 2007, No. 4, pp. 36)
Pub: Rogers Media
Ed: Erin Pooley. **Description:** The plan of Insception Biosciences to popularize stem cell banks, which can store stem cells, is discussed.

43554 ■ "Bloomberg Law Upgraded Its Online Legal Research Platform" in *Information Today* (Vol. 28, September 2011, No. 8, pp. 28)
Pub: Information Today, Inc.
Description: Bloomberg Law upgraded its online legal research platform for law practices. The new services includes a redesigned interface, improved search capabilities, and expanded collaboration and workflow features, while maintaining it comprehensive law resources such as mergers and acquisitions, antitrust, and securities.

43555 ■ "Border Boletin: UA to Take Lie-Detector Kiosk to Poland" in *Arizona Daily Star* (September 14, 2010)
Pub: Arizona Daily Star
Ed: Brady McCombs. **Description:** University of Arizona's National Center for Border Security and Immigration Research will send a team to Warsaw, Poland to show border guards from 27 European Union countries the center's Avatar Kiosk. The Avatar technology is designed for use at border ports and airports to assist Customs officers detect individuals who are lying.

43556 ■ "Born of Culture of Innovation" in *Canadian Business* (Vol. 81, October 27, 2008, No. 18, pp. 98)
Pub: Rogers Media Ltd.
Description: MaRS, an independent nonprofit organization, aims to better capture the relevant commercial potential of Ontario's research and to connect the worlds of science, business, and capital as well as to stimulate a culture of innovation. Profile of MaRS and its 'MaRS Innovation' program is included.

43557 ■ *Borrowing Brilliance: The Six Steps to Business Innovation by Building on the Ideas of Others*
Pub: Gotham
Ed: David Kord Murray. **Price:** $26.00. **Description:** The author builds the case that cherry-picking the ideas of others is a vital part of the research and development process for any small firm.

43558 ■ "Bridging the Worlds" in *Academy of Management Journal* (Vol. 50, No. 5, October 2007, pp. 1043)
Pub: Academy of Management
Ed: Lise Saari. **Description:** Need to transfer human resource research information published in journals to practitioners and organizations is investigated, along with suggestions on ways of achieving this goal.

43559 ■ "Bristol-Myers Close to Settling Lawsuit" in *Globe & Mail* (January 23, 2006, pp. B6)
Pub: CTVglobemedia Publishing Inc.
Ed: Barbara Martinez. **Description:** The details of shareholder case against Bristol-Myers Squibb Co. are presented. The dispute is over the company's claim on the efficiency of Vanlev drug.

43560 ■ "California Company Suing City's Lupin Over its Generic Diabetes Drug" in *Baltimore Business Journal* (Vol. 27, January 1, 2010)
Pub: American City Business Journals
Ed: Gary Haber. **Description:** California-based Depomed Inc. is suing Baltimore, Maryland-based Lupin Pharmaceuticals Inc. and its parent company in India over the patents to a diabetes drug. Lupin allegedly infringed on Depomed's four patents for Glumetza when it filed for permission to sell its own version of the drug with the US Food and Drug Administration. Details on generic pharmaceutical manufacturer tactics are discussed.

43561 ■ "Can America Invent Its Way Back?" in *Business Week* (September 22, 2008, No. 4100, pp. 52)
Pub: McGraw-Hill Companies, Inc.
Description: Business leaders as well as economists agree that innovative new products, services and ways of doing business may be the only way in which America can survive the downward spiral of the economy; innovation economics may be the answer and may even provide enough growth to enable Americans to prosper in the years to come.

43562 ■ "Canadian Research Generates Innovation and Prosperity" in *Canadian Business* (Vol. 81, October 27, 2008, No. 18, pp. 87)
Pub: Rogers Media Ltd.
Description: Universities play a key role in helping Canadians achieve prosperity, competitiveness, and quality of life by conducting more than a third of Canada's research. Research in universities help train graduates to apply sophisticated knowledge to real problems.

43563 ■ "Cancer Care's Quantum Leap" in *Hawaii Business* (Vol. 53, October 2007, No. 4, pp. 17)
Pub: Hawaii Business Publishing
Ed: Cathy S. Cruz-George. **Description:** Tomo-Therapy is an innovative device for cancer treatment that gives high-intensity radiation to more accurate parts of the body compared to conventional treatments. Hawaii has one of the 70 TomoTherapy machines in the nation, and it is expected to help advance cancer care in the area. Details on how the machine works are provided.

43564 ■ "Cancer-Fighting Entrepreneurs" in *Austin Business Journal* (Vol. 31, August 5, 2011, No. 22, pp. 1)
Pub: American City Business Journals Inc.
Ed: Sandra Zaragoza. **Description:** Cancer Prevention and Research Institute of Texas has invested $10 million in recruiting known faculty to the University of Texas. The move is seen to bolster Austin's position as a major cancer research market. The institute has awarded grants to researchers Jonghwan Kim, Guangbin Dong and Kyle Miller.

43565 ■ "Cancer Therapy Raises Debate Over Shared Technology" in *Crain's Detroit Business* (Vol. 24, March 10, 2008, No. 10, pp. 1)
Pub: Crain Communications, Inc.
Ed: Jay Greene. **Description:** Overview of a proposed collaborative approach among select hospitals that would allow the consortium to utilize proton-beam accelerators in order to treat cancer patients; this expensive new technology is possibly a better way to destroy cancers by using the proton beams to direct high dosages of radiation to destroy small tumors.

43566 ■ "Cannabis Science Signs Exclusive and Non-Exclusive Agreement with Prescription Vending Machines" in *Benzinga.com* **(October 29, 2011)**
Pub: Benzinga.com

Ed: Benzinga Staff. **Description:** Cannabis Science Inc., a biotech company developing pharmaceutical cannabis products has partnered with Prescription Vending Machines Inc. and its principal Vincent Meddizadeh to provide industry specific consulting and advisory services to Cannabis Science.

43567 ■ "Caterpillar to Expand Research, Production in China" in *Chicago Tribune* **(August 27, 2008)**
Pub: McClatchy-Tribune Information Services

Ed: James P. Miller. **Description:** Caterpillar Inc., the Peoria-based heavy-equipment manufacturer, plans to establish a new research-and-development center at the site of its rapidly growing campus in Wuxi.

43568 ■ "Chicago Botanic Garden Builds Green Research Facility" in *Contractor* **(Vol. 56, December 2009, No. 12, pp. 5)**
Pub: Penton Media, Inc.

Ed: Candace Roulo. **Description:** Chicago Botanic Garden has built a laboratory and research facility in Illinois. The facility is set to receive a United States Green Building Council LEED Gold certification. The building features a solar photovoltaic array, radiant flooring and water-conserving plumbing products.

43569 ■ "Chief Boo Boo Officer" in *Marketing to Women* **(Vol. 21, February 2008, No. 2, pp. 1)**
Pub: EPM Communications, Inc.

Ed: Ellen Neuborne. **Description:** Pharmaceutical companies are reaching out to women through innovative marketing techniques.

43570 ■ "Clean Wind Energy Tower Transitions from R&D Stage Company" in *Professional Services Close-Up* **(September 30, 2011)**
Pub: Close-Up Media

Description: Clean Wind Energy designed and is developing large downdraft towers that use benevolent, non-toxic natural elements to generate electricity and clean water. The firm is closing its internally staffed engineering office in Warrenton, Virginia and transitioning a development team to oversee and coordinate industry consultants and advisors to construct their first dual renewable energy tower.

43571 ■ "Cleaner and Greener" in *Canadian Business* **(Vol. 80, February 12, 2007, No. 4, pp. 45)**
Pub: Rogers Media

Ed: Zena Olijnyk. **Description:** Canadian research and government investments in clean coal technology is discussed.

43572 ■ "A Click In the Right Direction: Website Teaches Youth Financial Literacy" in *Black Enterprise* **(Vol. 38, December 2007, No. 5)**
Pub: Earl G. Graves Publishing Co. Inc.

Ed: Nicole Norfleet. **Description:** Profile of Donald Lee Robinson who launched SkillsThatClick, a Website that teaches young individuals ages 12 to 15 about money management. Robinson shares how he used his Navy career as a model for designing the site.

43573 ■ "The CMO of Consequence" in *Business Strategy Review* **(Vol. 21, Autumn 2010, No. 3, pp. 42)**
Pub: Wiley-Blackwell

Ed: D. Eric Boyd, Rajesh K. Chandy, Marcus Cunha. **Description:** Do chief marketing officers matter? Some say that CMOs have limited effect on corporate performance and don't add significant value to the firm. The authors agree that the job in many firms is in great peril, but their research has uncovered why the contributions of some CMOs are invaluable.

43574 ■ "The Code-Cracker" in *Business Courier* **(Vol. 24, January 11, 2008, No. 40, pp. 1)**
Pub: American City Business Journals, Inc.

Ed: James Ritchie. **Description:** Michael Kennedy, a professor in the chemistry and biochemistry department at the Miami University, is a part of the Protein Structure Initiative, a project that is aimed at forming a catalog of three-dimensional protein structures. The initiative is a project of the Northeast Structural Genomics consortium, of which the Miami University is a member. The impacts of the research on drug development are discussed.

43575 ■ "Colt Capital Corp. Acquires Two Uranium Properties From DIAGNOS" in *Canadian Corporate News* **(May 16, 2007)**
Pub: Comtex News Network Inc.

Description: DIAGNOS Inc., a leader in the use of artificial intelligence and advanced knowledge extraction techniques, announced an agreement with Colt Capital Corp., a Canadian mineral exploration company that will grant an exclusive option in two uranium properties.

43576 ■ "Connectors for Space, Mil/Aero and Medical Applications" in *Canadian Electronics* **(Vol. 23, June-July 2008, No. 4, pp. 13)**
Pub: Action Communication Inc.

Ed: Gilles Parguey. **Description:** Product information on electrical connectors for use in space, military, aeronautics, and medical applications is provided. These connectors are built to withstand the extreme conditions offered by the harsh working environments in those applications.

43577 ■ "Cost Remains Top Factor In Considering Green Technology" in *Canadian Sailings* **(June 30, 2008)**
Pub: Commonwealth Business Media

Ed: Julie Gedeon. **Description:** Improving its environmental performance remains a priority in the shipping industry; however, testing new technologies can prove difficult due to the harsh conditions that ships endure as well as installation which usually requires a dry dock.

43578 ■ "Craig Muhlhauser" in *Canadian Business* **(Vol. 81, September 15, 2008, No. 14-15, pp. 6)**
Pub: Rogers Media Ltd.

Ed: Andrew Wahl. **Description:** Interview with Craig Muhlhauser who is the CEO of Celestica, a manufacturing company that provides services for the electronics sector; Muhlhauser discusses the company's restructuring program, which he feels was the secret to their surprising first-quarter results. Muhlhauser states that the company is operating with more forward visibility and that understanding the opportunities during the current economic situation presents the biggest challenge.

43579 ■ "A Curious Appeal (Market for Scientific Toys)" in *Playthings* **(Vol. 106, October 1, 2008, No. 9, pp. 26)**
Pub: Reed Business Information

Ed: Pamela Brill. **Description:** Science and nature toys are still popular with children. Kits allow kids to make candy, soap, grow miniature gardens, catch bugs and more. These hands-on kits have manufacturers watching trends to create more toys in this category.

43580 ■ "Dean Foods" in *Ice Cream Reporter* **(Vol. 23, September 20, 2010, No. 10, pp. 8)**
Pub: Ice Cream Reporter

Description: Dean Foods promoted Joseph Scalzo to President and Chief Operating Officer to oversee the firm's operational turnaround and near-term strategic initiatives as well as business units. Key functions will include worldwide supply chain and research and development.

43581 ■ "Deere to Open Technology Center in Germany" in *Chicago Tribune* **(September 3, 2008)**
Pub: McClatchy-Tribune Information Services

Ed: James P. Miller. **Description:** Deere & Co. plans to open a technology and innovation center in Germany; details of the company's expansion plans are discussed.

43582 ■ "Defense Contractor May Expand Locally; BAE Systems Ramps Up Vehicle Prototypes" in *Crain's Detroit Business* **(March 24, 2008)**
Pub: Crain Communications, Inc.

Ed: Chad Halcom. **Description:** Profile of BAE Systems, a defense contractor, that has built a prototype in the highly competitive Joint Light Tactical Vehicle project; the company has also completed its prototype RG33L Mine Resistant Recovery Maintenance Vehicle and has plans for expansion.

43583 ■ "A Different Kind of Waiting List" in *Canadian Business* **(Vol. 80, April 9, 2007, No. 8, pp. 17)**
Pub: Rogers Media

Ed: Erin Pooley. **Description:** The adverse impact on drug companies' profitability due to regulatory delays in approving drugs is discussed.

43584 ■ "The Doctor Is In" in *Canadian Business* **(Vol. 80, February 12, 2007, No. 4, pp. 38)**
Pub: Rogers Media

Ed: Erin Pooley. **Description:** The research at McMaster University to make a pill having imaging devices to takes pictures of any possible cancerous cells in the human body is discussed.

43585 ■ "Dow AgroSciences Buys Wheat Breeding Firm in Pacific Northwest" in *Farm Industry News* **(July 29, 2011)**
Pub: Penton Business Media Inc.

Description: Dow AgroSciences purchased Northwest Plant Breeding Company, a cereals breeding station in Washington in 2011. The acquisition will help Dow expand its Hyland Seeds certified wheat seed program foundation in the Pacific Northwest. Financial terms of the deal were not disclosed.

43586 ■ "Drug Trial Halt at YM Sets Stage for Selloff" in *Globe & Mail* **(January 31, 2007, pp. B3)**
Pub: CTVglobemedia Publishing Inc.

Ed: Leonard Zehr. **Description:** The decision of YM Biosciences Inc. to stop its trial of cancer drug tesmilifene and stocks following government concern over the safety of the drug is discussed.

43587 ■ "DuPontas Pioneer Hi-Bred, Evogene to Develop Rust-Resistant Soybean Varieties" in *Farm Industry News* **(November 22, 2011)**
Pub: Penton Business Media Inc.

Ed: Karen McMahon. **Description:** DuPont and Evogene have signed a new contract to work together to develop resistance in soybeans to rust. Financial terms of the agreement were not disclosed.

43588 ■ "Eco-Preneuring" in *Small Business Opportunities* **(July 2008)**
Pub: Entrepreneur Media Inc.

Ed: Mary C. Pearl. **Description:** Profile of Wildlife Trust, a rapidly growing global organization dedicated to innovative conservation science linking health and ecology. With partners in nearly twenty countries, Wildlife Trust draws on global strengths in order to respond to well-defined local needs. In the Dominican Republic, they are working with the community and local biologists in order to restore fishing and create jobs in the field of ecotourism.

43589 ■ "Ed Otto, Director of Biotechnology at RCCC" in *Charlotte Observer* **(February 8, 2007)**
Pub: Knight-Ridder/Tribune Business News

Ed: Gail Smith-Arrants. **Description:** Profile of Ed Otto, director of biotechnology at Rowan-Cabarrus Community College. Before taking the position at RCCC, Otto directed the Food and Drug Administration office responsible for regulating cellular, tissue and gene therapies products.

43590 ■ "Electronic Design and a Greener Environment" in *Canadian Electronics* **(Vol. 23, June-July 2008, No. 4, pp. 6)**
Pub: Action Communication Inc.

Ed: Nicholas Deeble. **Description:** Companies seeking to minimize their environmental impact are using

Design methodologies of Cadence Design Systems Ltd. The company's Low Power Format and Low Power Design Flow help reduce carbon dioxide emissions.

43591 ■ "EMU, Spark Plan Business Incubator for Ypsilanti" in *Crain's Detroit Business* **(Vol. 23, October 15, 2007, No. 42, pp. 3)**
Pub: Crain Communications Inc. - Detroit

Ed: Chad Halcom. **Description:** Eastern Michigan University is seeking federal grants and other funding for a new business incubator program that would be in cooperation with Ann Arbor Spark. The site would become a part of a network of three Spark incubator programs with a focus on innovation in biotechnology and pharmaceuticals.

43592 ■ "Ending the Ebola Death Sentence" in *Canadian Business* **(Vol. 83, August 17, 2010, No. 13-14, pp. 22)**
Pub: Rogers Media Ltd.

Ed: Michael McCullough. **Description:** US Army Medical Research Institute of Infectious Diseases made a $140 million agreement with Tekmira Pharmaceuticals Corporation to develop both a drug delivery system and delivery technology for curing the Ebola virus. Tekmira's delivery technology, which has been shown to halt Ebola in laboratory animals, might be the key to finding a cure.

43593 ■ "Entrepreneurial Orientation and Firm Performance" in *Journal of Small Business and Entrepreneurship* **(Vol. 23, Winter 2010, No. 1)**
Pub: Canadian Council for Small Business and Entrepreneurship

Description: The article develops a theoretical model of the relationship between firm-level entrepreneurship and firm performance. This model is intended to further clarify the consequences of an 'entrepreneurial orientation', paying particular attention to the differential relationship that exists between the three sub-dimensions of entrepreneurial orientation and firm performance. Included in the theoretical model are other important variables (such as organizational structure and environmental characteristics) that may impact the EO-performance relationship. Propositions are developed regarding the various configurations of the sub-dimensions of EO and organizational structure that would be most appropriate in a given environmental context. Future research may also benefit from considering the important role that organizational strategy and life cycle stage play in this model. The implications of this model for both researchers and managers are discussed.

43594 ■ "eResearch Issues Initiating Report on Aldershot Resources Ltd." in *Canadian Corporate News* **(May 14, 2007)**
Pub: Comtex News Network Inc.

Description: Overview of Bob Weir and Michael Wood's Initiating Report on Aldershot Resources Ltd., a junior Canadian-based uranium exploration company with prospective projects in Canada, Zambia, Australia, and a base metals project in Chile.

43595 ■ "The Executive Brain" in *Canadian Business* **(Vol. 80, October 22, 2007, No. 21, pp. 41)**
Pub: Rogers Media

Ed: Rachel Pulfer. **Description:** Studies by Jordan Petersen, Frank Schmidt, and John Hunter show that leaders have highly evolved capacities to think using the prefrontal cortex of the brain. Inspirational leadership ability is located in the parietal lobe. Other details of the research are discussed.

43596 ■ "Executive Decision: Just What the Doctor Ordered" in *Globe & Mail* **(February 11, 2006, pp. B3)**
Pub: CTVglobemedia Publishing Inc.

Ed: Leonard Zehr. **Description:** The leadership ability of chief executive William Hunter of Angiotech Pharmaceuticals Inc., who acquired American Medical Instruments Holdings Inc. for $785 million, is discussed.

43597 ■ "Family Business Research" in *International Journal of Entrepreneurship and Small Business* **(Vol. 12, December 3, 2010, No. 1)**
Pub: Publishers Communication Group

Ed: A. Bakr Ibrahim, Jean B. McGuire. **Description:** Assessment of the growing field of family business and suggestions for an integrated framework. The paper addresses a number of key issues facing family business research.

43598 ■ "Fast-Release Calcium Could Help Control Club Root" in *Farmer's Weekly* **(March 28, 2008, No. 320)**
Pub: Reed Business Information

Description: According to initial observations from a new HGCA club root research study, applications of fertilizers that rapidly release calcium may help improve performance of both susceptible and resistant oilseed rape varieties.

43599 ■ "Federal Fund Valuable Tool For Small-Biz Innovators" in *Crain's Detroit Business* **(Vol. 24, September 29, 2008, No. 39, pp. 42)**
Pub: Crain Communications, Inc.

Ed: Nancy Kaffer. **Description:** Grants from the Small Business Innovation Research Program, or SBIR grants, are federal funds that are set aside for 11 federal agencies to allocate to tech-oriented small-business owners. Firms such as Biotechnology Business Consultants help these companies apply for SBIR grants.

43600 ■ *Federal Research in Progress (FEDRIP)*
Pub: Office of Product Management

Released: Monthly. **Price:** $450 single user subscription; $625 1 network; $950 2-5 networks; $1,400 6-10 networks. **Database Covers:** more than 150,000 federally-funded research projects currently in progress in the physical sciences, engineering, health, agriculture, and life sciences areas. **Database Includes:** Project title, starting date, principal investigator, performing and sponsoring organization, detailed abstract, description of the research, objective, and findings (when available).

43601 ■ "FinOvation 2009" in *Farm Industry News* **(Vol. 42, January 1, 2009, No. 1)**
Pub: Penton Media, Inc.

Ed: Karen McMahon; David Hest; Mark Moore. **Description:** New and innovative products and technologies are presented.

43602 ■ "First Venture Reports Proprietary Yeasts Further Reduce Ethyl Carbamate in Sake" in *Canadian Corporate News* **(May 16, 2007)**
Pub: Comtex News Network Inc.

Description: First Ventures Technologies Corp., a biotechnology company that develops and commercializes advanced yeast products, confirmed that two of their proprietary yeasts used in the making of sake have yielded reductions in ethyl carbamate compared to previous sake brewing trials.

43603 ■ "Five New Scientists Bring Danforth Center $16 Million" in *Saint Louis Business Journal* **(Vol. 32, October 7, 2011, No. 6, pp. 1)**
Pub: Saint Louis Business Journal

Ed: E.B. Solomont. **Description:** Donald Danforth Plant Science Center's appointment of five new lead scientists has increased its federal funding by $16 million. Cornell University scientist Tom Brutnell is one of the five new appointees.

43604 ■ "Flu is a Booster for Firms Here" in *Philadelphia Business Journal* **(Vol. 28, September 25, 2009, No. 32, pp. 1)**
Pub: American City Business Journals

Ed: John George. **Description:** GlaxoSmithKline, AstraZeneca, CSL Biotherapies, and Sanofi Aventis were awarded contract by the US Government to supply swine flu vaccines. It is estimated that global sales of the vaccine could reach billions of dollars.

43605 ■ "Flue Vaccines are Going Green" in *Canadian Business* **(Vol. 83, September 14, 2010, No. 15, pp. 24)**
Pub: Rogers Media Ltd.

Ed: Angelia Chapman. **Description:** Quebec-based Medicago has found a solution to the bottleneck in the production of influenza vaccines by using plant-based processes instead of egg-based systems. Medicago's US Department of Defense funded research has produced the technology that speeds up the production time for vaccines by almost two-thirds. Insights into Medicago's patented process are also given.

43606 ■ "For Gilead, Growth Beyond AIDS" in *Barron's* **(Vol. 88, June 30, 2008, No. 26, pp. 18)**
Pub: Dow Jones & Co., Inc.

Ed: Jay Palmer. **Description:** First-quarter 2008 revenue for Gilead Sciences grew by 22 percent and an earnings gain of 19 percent thanks to their HIV-treatment drugs that comprised over two-thirds of the company's sales in 2007. An analyst has a 12-month target from June, 2008 of 65 per share. The factors behind the company's prospects are also discussed.

43607 ■ "From OTC Sellers to Surgeons, Healthcare Marketers Target Women to Achieve Growth" in *Marketing to Women* **(February 2008)**
Pub: EPM Communications, Inc.

Description: Healthcare companies are targeting women with ad campaigns, new product development and new technology in order to reach and develop brand loyalty.

43608 ■ "FSU's OGZEB Is Test Bed for Sustainable Technology" in *Contractor* **(Vol. 56, October 2009, No. 10, pp. 1)**
Pub: Penton Media, Inc.

Ed: Candace Roulo. **Description:** Florida State University was one of 14 off-grid zero emissions buildings (OGZEB) in the U.S. ; it was built to research sustainable and alternative energy systems. The building produces electricity from 30 photovoltaic panels and it also has three AET water heating solar panels on the roof.

43609 ■ "Funding Drought Stalls Biotech Incubators" in *Saint Louis Business Journal* **(Vol. 31, July 29, 2011, No. 49, pp. 1)**
Pub: Saint Louis Business Journal

Ed: Angela Mueller. **Description:** Economic slowdown took its toll on cash-strapped startups that fill incubators such as the Bio-Research and Development Growth (BRDG) Park in Creve Coeur, Missouri and the Center for Emerging Technologies in Midtown St. Louis. BRDG put a hold on construction of of its two buildings.

43610 ■ "The Future of Work" in *Business Strategy Review* **(Vol. 21, Autumn 2010, No. 3, pp. 16)**
Pub: Blackwell Publishers Ltd.

Ed: Lynda Gratton. **Description:** Work is universal. But how, why, where and when we work has never been so open to individual interpretation. The certainties of the past have been replaced by ambiguity, questions and the steady hum of technology. Now, in a groundbreaking research project covering 21 global companies and more than 200 executives, the author is making sense of the future of work.

43611 ■ "Galvanizing the Scientific Community" in *Information Today* **(Vol. 26, February 2009, No. 2, pp. 20)**
Pub: Information Today, Inc.

Ed: Barbara Brynko. **Description:** Profile of John Haynes, newly appointed vice president of publishing for the American Institute of Physics; the Institute consists of ten organizations specializing in STM publishing as well as providing publishing services for over 170 science and engineering journals.

43612 ■ "Giving Biotech Startups a Hand" in *Philadelphia Business Journal* **(Vol. 28, January 8, 2010, No. 47, pp. 1)**
Pub: American City Business Journals

Ed: John George. **Description:** Elkins Park, Pennsylvania-based BioStrategy Partners is a virtual life sciences incubator that is seeking to improve the dull ranking of Philadelphia in the small business vitality index of life sciences. BioStrategy provides technology and business development services to startup life sciences companies and university-based research projects.

43613 ■ "Good for Business: Houston is a Hot Spot for Economic Growth" in *Black Enterprise* **(Vol. 37, October 2006, No. 3, pp. 216)**
Pub: Earl G. Graves Publishing Co. Inc.

Ed: Jeanette Valentine. **Description:** Fast-growing sectors in the biotechnology and healthcare industries are among the driving forces of Houston's economic growth. More than 76,000 small businesses in the area employ about one in four area workers, according to the Small Business Administration. Housing and business costs are 26 and 11 percent below the national average, respectively, garnering the attention of corporate giants.

43614 ■ "Growing Field" in *Crain's Detroit Business* **(Vol. 26, January 11, 2010, No. 2, pp. 3)**
Pub: Crain Communications, Inc.

Description: Detroit's TechTown was awarded a combination loan and grant of $4.1 million from the U.S. Department of Housing and Urban Development to build a 15,000-square-foot stem cell center, a collection of laboratories that will be available to both for-profit companies and university researchers.

43615 ■ "Henry Ford Health Leases Lab Space at TechTown" in *Crain's Detroit Business* **(Vol. 24, March 31, 2008, No. 13, pp. 5)**
Pub: Crain Communications, Inc.

Ed: Tom Henderson. **Description:** Henry Ford Health System has signed a seven-year lease at TechTown, the high-tech incubator and research park affiliated with Wayne State University, to take over 14,000 square feet of space for four research groups and laboratories. Construction has already begun and Henry Ford officials hope to take occupancy as early as June 1.

43616 ■ "High Energy: Gaurdie Banister Joins Aera As President and CEO" in *Black Enterprise* **(Vol. 38, July 2008, No. 12, pp. 30)**
Pub: Earl G. Graves Publishing Co. Inc.

Ed: Brenda Porter. **Description:** Gaurdie Banister Jr. has been appointed president and CEO of Aera Energy L.L.C., becoming one of the first African Americans in the nation to run a major energy corporation. His plans for the firm include utilizing new, sophisticated technologies in order to unlock the 3-1/2 billion barrels of resources the company has on their books in a safe and environmentally friendly way. He also hopes to increase production and maintain cost leadership.

43617 ■ "The Hired Guns" in *Business Courier* **(Vol. 26, November 13, 2009, No. 29, pp. 1)**
Pub: American City Business Journals, Inc.

Ed: Lisa Biank Fasig. **Description:** YourForce has nearly 6,000 retired scientists and researchers who work together in helping Procter & Gamble (P&G) and other companies in addressing various project needs. Operating as an online innovation community, YourEncore is a result of P&G's Connect + Develop program.

43618 ■ "Hopkins' Security, Reputation Face Challenges in Wake of Slaying" in *Baltimore Business Journal* **(Vol. 28, August 6, 2010, No. 13)**
Pub: Baltimore Business Journal

Ed: Gary Haber. **Description:** The slaying of Johns Hopkins University researcher Stephen Pitcairn has not tarnished the reputation of the elite school in Baltimore, Maryland among students. Maintaining Hopkins' reputation is important since it is Baltimore's largest employer with nearly 32,000 workers. Insights on the impact of the slaying among the Hopkins' community are also given.

43619 ■ "Hopkins, UMd Worry Reduced NIH Budget Will Impact Research" in *Boston Business Journal* **(Vol. 29, August 19, 2011, No. 15, pp. 1)**
Pub: American City Business Journals Inc.

Ed: Scott Dance. **Description:** The budget for the National Institutes of Health (NIH) is slated to be cut by at least 7.9 percent to $2.5 billion in 2013. This will have a big negative effect on medical and biotech research in Maryland, especially Johns Hopkins University and University of Maryland, Baltimore which could face stiffer completion for grants from the NIH.

43620 ■ "Hospitals See Major Shift To Outpatient Care" in *The Business Journal-Milwaukee* **(Vol. 25, September 12, 2008, No. 51, pp. A1)**
Pub: American City Business Journals, Inc.

Ed: Corrinne Hess. **Description:** Statistics show that the revenue of Wisconsin hospitals from outpatient medical care is about to surpass revenue from hospital patients who stay overnight. This revenue increase is attributed to new technology and less-invasive surgery. Trends show that the shift toward outpatient care actually started in the late 1980s and early 1990s.

43621 ■ "How Green Is The Valley?" in *Barron's* **(Vol. 88, July 4, 2008, No. 28, pp. 13)**
Pub: Dow Jones & Co., Inc.

Description: San Jose, California has made a good start towards becoming a leader in alternative energy technology through the establishment of United Laboratories' own lab in the city. The certification process for photovoltaic cells will be dramatically shortened with this endeavor.

43622 ■ "How Pixar Fosters Collective Creativity" in *Harvard Business Review* **(Vol. 86, September 2008, No. 9, pp. 64)**
Pub: Harvard Business School Press

Ed: Ed Catmull. **Description:** Pixar Animation Studios illustrates peer-culture methods for fostering product development. These include allowing any employee to communicate with any other employee, providing a safe environment for new ideas, and watching the academic community closely for innovations.

43623 ■ "Human Activity Analysis: a Review" in *ACM Computing Surveys* **(Vol. 43, Fall 2011, No. 3, pp. 16)**
Pub: Association for Computing Machinery

Ed: J.K. Aggarwal, M.S. Ryoo. **Description:** Human activity recognition is an important area of computer vision research and is studied in this report.

43624 ■ "Human Bone Breakthrough" in *Houston Business Journal* **(Vol. 40, January 8, 2010, No. 35, pp. 1)**
Pub: American City Business Journals

Ed: Casey Wooten. **Description:** Biotech startup company Osteosphere in Houston, Texas aims to market a technology in which laboratory-grown bone tissues can be processed to appear like a real human bone tissue. The technology was developed by a co-founder of the startup and it can be applied to bone disease and injury treatment. Osteophere's future plans, such as the search for possible investors, is also outlined.

43625 ■ "Ian Delaney" in *Canadian Business* **(Vol. 81, Summer 2008, No. 9, pp. 168)**
Pub: Rogers Media Ltd.

Ed: Joe Castaldo. **Description:** Interview with Ian Delaney who is the executive chairman of chemical company Sherritt International Corp.; Delaney previously worked as chief executive for a holding company owned by Peter Munk. Details of his beliefs, profession and family life are discussed.

43626 ■ "IMRA's Ultrafast Lasers Bring Precision, profits; Ann Arbor Company Eyes Expansion" in *Crain's Detroit Business* **(March 10, 2008)**
Pub: Crain Communications, Inc.

Ed: Tom Henderson. **Description:** IMRA America Inc. plans to expand its headquarters and has applied for permits to build a fourth building that will

house research and development facilities and allow the company more room for manufacturing; the company plans to add about 20 more employees that would include research scientists, manufacturing and assembly workers, engineers and salespeople. The growth is due mainly to a new technology of ultrafast fiber lasers that reduce side effects for those getting eye surgeries and help manufacturers of computer chips to reduce their size and cost.

43627 ■ "In Search of the Next Big Thing: It's Out There - Just Waiting For You To Find It" in *Inc.* **(Volume 32, December 2010, No. 10, pp. 34)**
Pub: Inc. Magazine

Ed: April Joyner. **Description:** Innovation is the future for small business. A new book, Inside Real Innovation: How the Right Approach Can Move Ideas from R&D to Market - And Get the Economy Moving helps to break down the process by which innovation occurs.

43628 ■ "The Innovator: Rob McEwen's Unique Vision of Philanthropy and Business" in *Canadian Business* **(Vol. 81, November 10, 2008, No. 19)**
Pub: Rogers Media Ltd.

Ed: Alex Mlynek. **Description:** Rob McEwen says that his donation to the Schulich School of Business is his first large donation. He went to the University Health Network and was told about their pan for regenerative medicine, helping him make the decision. McEwan wants to be involved in philanthropy in the areas of leadership and education.

43629 ■ *International Research Centers Directory*
Pub: Gale

Released: Annual, Latest edition 27th; November, 2011. **Price:** $916, individuals. **Covers:** Over 9,500 research and development facilities maintained outside the United States by governments, universities, or independent organizations, and concerned with all areas of physical, social, and life sciences, technology, business, military science, public policy, and the humanities. **Entries Include:** Facility name, address, phone, fax, telex, e-mail, URLs, name of parent agency or other affiliation, date established, number of staff, type of activity and fields of research, special research facilities, publications, educational activities, services, and library holdings. **Arrangement:** Subject. **Indexes:** Master, subject, personal name and country.

43630 ■ "Inventive Doctor New Venture Partner" in *Houston Business Journal* **(Vol. 40, January 29, 2010, No. 38, pp. A2)**
Pub: American City Business Journals

Ed: Ford Gunter. **Description:** Dr. Billy Cohn, a surgeon from Houston, Texas has been named as venture partner for venture firm Sante Ventures LLC of Austin, Texas. Cohn will be responsible for seeing marketable developing technologies in the medical industry. The motivation for Cohn's naming as venture partner is his development of a minimally invasive therapy for end-stage renal disease.

43631 ■ "Iron Man Forges New Path" in *Canadian Business* **(Vol. 80, February 12, 2007, No. 4, pp. 41)**
Pub: Rogers Media

Ed: Rachel Pulfer. **Description:** The research of Donald Sadoway of Massachusetts Institute of Technology in making iron in an environmentally friendly method using electrolysis is discussed.

43632 ■ "Is Your Employees' BMI Your Business?" in *Canadian Business* **(Vol. 83, September 14, 2010, No. 15, pp. 98)**
Pub: Rogers Media Ltd.

Ed: Jacqueline Nelson. **Description:** Canada's Public Health Agency's research shows that there is a solid business case for companies to promote active living to their employees. However, employers must toe the line between being helpful and being invasive. Insights into the issues faces by companies when introducing health programs are discussed.

43633 ■ "Key FDA Approval Yanked for Avastin" in *Wall Street Journal Eastern Edition* (November 19 , 2011, pp. B1)
Pub: Dow Jones & Company Inc.
Ed: Thomas M. Burton, Jennifer Corbett Dooren. Description: Avastin, a drug manufactured by Genetech Inc. and used in the treatment of metastatic breast cancer in women, has had its approval by the US Food and Drug Administration withdrawn by the agency, which says there is no evidence the widely-used drug is successful in increasing the longevity of breast cancer patients.

43634 ■ "Lack of Support Drives Scientists Away from Valley" in *The Business Journal - Serving Phoenix and the Valley of the Sun* (Vol. 28, August 1, 2008, No. 48, pp. 1)
Pub: American City Business Journals, Inc.
Ed: Angela Gonzales. Description: Lack of support for scientists has caused scientists like Dietrich Stephan to depart from the city. Stephan is expected to relocate to California where he has found funding for his company Navigenics. Other views and information on the rising rate of the departure of scientists are presented.

43635 ■ "Lawrence: Larger than Life Sciences" in *Business Journal-Serving Metropolitan Kansas City* (Vol. 26, November 2, 2007, No. 8, pp. 1)
Pub: American City Business Journals, Inc.
Ed: Rob Roberts. Description: Greater Kansas City Community Foundation has more than $1 billion to spend on life sciences initiatives and chairwoman Sandra Lawrence will unveil a multimillion-dollar master plan for Children's Mercy Hospitals and Clinics. Details regarding Lawrence's dedication to the foundation are discussed.

43636 ■ "Letting the Sunshine In" in *Barron's* (Vol. 89, July 6, 2009, No. 27, pp. 11)
Pub: Dow Jones & Co., Inc.
Ed: Katherine Cheng. Description: Solar energy industry leaders believe the industry needs aid from the US government regarding the funding of its research efforts and lowering solar energy costs. The climate change bill passed by the US House of Representatives signifies the US government's desire to significantly reduce carbon dioxide emissions.

43637 ■ "The Life Changers" in *Canadian Business* (Vol. 81, October 27, 2008, No. 18, pp. 86)
Pub: Rogers Media Ltd.
Description: The first season of 'The Life Changers' was produced in September 2007 to feature stories about research and development (R&D) efforts by universities in Atlantic Canada. The program addresses the need to inform the public about university R&D and its outcomes.

43638 ■ "Life Sciences Become State's Growth Powerhouse" in *Crain's Detroit Business* (Vol. 25, June 1, 2009, No. 22, pp. M008)
Pub: Crain Communications Inc. - Detroit
Ed: Amy Lane. Description: According to a study conducted by Anderson Economic Group, Michigan's University Research Corridor has helped grow the life sciences industry. Statistical details included.

43639 ■ "Lifebank Grants Stock Options" in *Canadian Corporate News* (May 16, 2007)
Pub: Comtex News Network Inc.
Description: Lifebank, a biomedical service company that provides processing cryogenic storage of umbilical cord blood stem cells, announced that, under its stock option plan, it has granted incentive stock options to directors, officers, and consultants of the company.

43640 ■ "The Little Insect" in *Canadian Electronics* (Vol. 23, June-July 2008, No. 4, pp. 6)
Pub: Action Communication Inc.
Ed: Tim Gouldson. Description: Electronics designers should not be underestimated because they can manufacture technologies vital to saving lives and bringing peace. They have designed robots and other electronic equipment that are as small as insects.

43641 ■ "Local Researchers Get Cash Infusion" in *Business Courier* (Vol. 26, October 9, 2009, No. 24, pp. 1)
Pub: American City Business Journals, Inc.
Ed: James Ritchie. Description: Cincinnati's Children's Hospital Medical Center and the University of Cincinnati researchers are set to receive at least $56 million from the stimulus bill. The cash infusion has reenergized research scientists and enhances Cincinnati's national clout as a major research center.

43642 ■ "Major Tech Employers Pulling Out" in *Sacramento Business Journal* (Vol. 25, August 1, 2008, No. 22, pp. 1)
Pub: American City Business Journals, Inc.
Ed: Celia Lamb. Description: Biotechnology company Affymetrix Inc. is planning to close its West Sacramento, California plant and lay off 110 employees. The company said it will expand a corporate restructuring plan. Affymetrix also plans to lease out or sell its building at Riverside Parkway.

43643 ■ "Making Waves" in *Business Journal Portland* (Vol. 27, November 26, 2010, No. 39, pp. 1)
Pub: Portland Business Journal
Ed: Erik Siemers. Description: Corvallis, Oregon-based Columbia Power Technologies LLC is about to close a $2 million Series A round of investment initiated by $750,000 from Oregon Angel Fund. The wave energy startup company was formed to commercialize the wave buoy technology developed by Oregon State University researchers.

43644 ■ "mChip: Claros Diagnostics" in *Inc.* (Vol. 33, November 2011, No. 9, pp. 42)
Pub: Inc. Magazine
Ed: Christine Lagorio. Description: Harvard University researchers have developed a device called the mChip that produces accurate blood tests in about 10 minutes. Plans to apply for FDA approval for the mChip in the US should happen in 2012.

43645 ■ "Meet UT's New Business Mind" in *Austin Business Journal* (Vol. 31, May 13, 2011, No. 10, pp. A1)
Pub: American City Business Journals Inc.
Ed: Sandra Zaragoza. Description: University of Texas (UT) chief commercialization officer, Dr. Richard Miller, has opened a satellite office in Silicon Valley, California in the hopes of luring Californian investors to the science and technology at UT. The satellite office is just one of Miller's efforts to reshape and widen the commercialization of UT-Austin. Insights into Miller's long-term view approach to commercialization are also covered.

43646 ■ "Mexican Companies to Rent Space in TechTown, Chinese Negotiating" in *Crain's Detroit Business* (Vol. 24, September 29, 2008, No. 39)
Pub: Crain Communications, Inc.
Ed: Tom Henderson. Description: Wayne State University's TechTown, the business incubator and research park, has signed an agreement with the Mexican government that will provide temporary office space to 25 Mexican companies looking to find customers or establish partnerships in Michigan. TechTown's executive director is negotiating with economic development officials from China. To accommodate foreign visitors the incubator is equipping offices with additional equipment and resources.

43647 ■ "MIR Growing With Help From Former Pfizer Workers" in *Crain's Detroit Business* (Vol. 24, January 28, 2008, No. 4, pp. 33)
Pub: Crain Communications Inc. - Detroit
Ed: Tom Henderson. Description: Molecular Imaging Research Inc. helps fund research at its parent firm, Molecular Therapeutics Inc. The company provides imaging services and other in vivo and in vitro services to help pharmaceutical companies test new compounds.

43648 ■ "Monsanto Acquires Targeted-Pest Control Technology Start-Up; Terms Not Disclosed" in *Benzinga.com* (, 2011)
Pub: Benzinga.com
Ed: Benzinga Staff. Description: Monsanto Company acquired Beelogics, a firm that researches and develops biological tools that control pests and diseases. Research includes a product that will help protect bee health.

43649 ■ "More Pain" in *Canadian Business* (Vol. 81, December 24, 2007, No. 1, pp. 12)
Pub: Rogers Media
Ed: Lauren McKeon. Description: Manufacturing sector in Canada is sinking with a forecast by as much as 23 percent for 2008, which can be offset as manufacturers say they plan to increase productivity by 25 percent. Details on the sector's competitiveness, workforce, importing of machinery from the U.S. and financial needs for research and development are examined.

43650 ■ "Mosaid Grants First Wireless Parent License To Matsushita" in *Canadian Electronics* (Vol. 23, June-July 2008, No. 5, pp. 1)
Pub: Action Communication Inc.
Description: Matsushita Electric Industrial Co. Ltd. has been granted a six-and-a-half-year license by Mosaid Technologies Inc. to manufacture the latter's products. The patent portfolio license agreement covers Mosaid's Wi-Fi, Wi-Max, CDMA-enabled notebook computers and other products.

43651 ■ "MPI Expansion Goes Back to Family Roots" in *Crain's Detroit Business* (Vol. 25, June 1, 2009, No. 22, pp. M007)
Pub: Crain Communications Inc. - Detroit
Ed: Sherri Begin Welch. Description: William Parfet, grandson of Upjohn Company founder, is expanding MPI Research's clinical and early clinical research operations into two buildings in Kalamazoo, land which was once part of his grandfather's farm.

43652 ■ "Nanoready?" in *Entrepreneur* (Vol. 36, May 2008, No. 5, pp. 20)
Pub: Entrepreneur Media, Inc.
Ed: Andrea Cooper. Description: Experts predict that the medicine and energy sectors are among those that will see nanotechnology innovations in the coming years, and that nanotechnology will produce significant commercial value in new products. Some entrepreneurs are investing in nanotech and are partnering with universities. Details on nanotech funding concerns are discussed.

43653 ■ "NASA Taps Younger Talent Pool to Supplement Aging Work Force" in *Crain's Cleveland Business* (Vol. 30, June 22, 2009, No. 24, pp. 1)
Pub: Crain Communications, Inc.
Ed: Chuck Soder. Description: NASA's Glenn Research Center has reversed the trend towards hiring older workers with more experience by recruiting for entry-level positions as part of a pilot program to attract younger talent.

43654 ■ "Neuromed Strikes Major Merck Deal" in *Globe & Mail* (March 21, 2006, pp. B1)
Pub: CTVglobemedia Publishing Inc.
Ed: Leonard Zehr. Description: Neuromed Pharmaceuticals Ltd., a spin off of British Columbia University, has struck a drug research deal valued at up to $500 million (U.S) with giant Merck &Co. Inc., the biggest collaboration in Canada. Details of the deal are presented.

43655 ■ "New Drug Could Revitalize Amgen" in *Barron's* (Vol. 88, July 7, 2008, No. 27, pp. 23)
Pub: Dow Jones & Co., Inc.
Ed: Johanna Bennett. Description: Shares of the biotechnology company Amgen could receive a boost from the release of the anti-osteoporosis drug denosumab. The shares, priced at $48.84 each, are trading at 11 times expected earnings for 2008 and could also be boosted by cost cutting measures.

43656 ■ "New Institutional Accounting and IFRS" in *Accounting and Business Research* (Vol. 41, Summer 2011, No. 3, pp. 309)
Pub: American Institute of CPAs
Ed: Peter Wysocki. Description: A new framework for institutional accounting research is presented. It has five fundamental components – efficient versus

inefficient results, interdependencies, causation, level of analysis, and institutional structure. The use of the framework for evaluation accounting institutions such as the international financial reporting standards is discussed.

43657 ■ "New Life for Old Chemistries" in *Farm Industry News* **(Vol. 42, January 1, 2009, No. 1)**
Pub: Penton Media, Inc.
Ed: Mark Moore. Description: To expand the uses of familiar crop protection products, chemical companies are utilizing biotechnology research and development tools; many off-patent products are being rejuvenated with small changes to make the product even better than it was when originally conceived.

43658 ■ "The Next Big Thing" in *Farm Industry News* **(Vol. 42, January 1, 2009, No. 1)**
Pub: Penton Media, Inc.
Ed: David Hest. Description: Communication technology that allows farmers to detect equipment location, travel speed and real-time fuel and sprayer/combine tank levels will pay off with better machine use efficiency, improved maintenance and reduced downtime. These telemetry systems will be widely available in the next few years.

43659 ■ "Nine Sectors to Watch: Biotech" in *Canadian Business* **(Vol. 81, December 24, 2007, No. 1, pp. 48)**
Pub: Rogers Media
Ed: Calvin Leung. Description: Forecasts on the Canadian biotechnology sector for 2008 are presented. Details on the increase in the number of biotechnology companies and prediction on the government's plan for business incentives are discussed.

43660 ■ "No Lines, No Waiting" in *The Business Journal-Serving Greater Tampa Bay* **(Vol. 28, August 15, 2008, No. 34, pp. 1)**
Pub: American City Business Journals, Inc.
Ed: Jane Meinhardt. Description: Voda LLC, which was founded to commercialize developments by David Fries, develops outdoor sensor networks used for environmental monitoring by markets like research, the security industry, and the government. Fries already licensed 12 technologies for clients for about $130,000 per technology. Other information on Voda LLC is presented.

43661 ■ "No-Shed Dogs Lead the Way to Big Growth" in *Business Courier* **(Vol. 26, January 8, 2010, No. 38, pp. 1)**
Pub: American City Business Journals, Inc.
Ed: Lucy May. Description: Ed Lukacevic of Grant County, Kentucky is developing Dinovite, a dietary supplement that minimizes shedding and scratching in dogs. Statistical data included.

43662 ■ "OccuLogix Shares Plummet 65 Percent" in *Globe & Mail* **(February 4, 2006, pp. B5)**
Pub: CTVglobemedia Publishing Inc.
Ed: Leonard Zehr. Description: The shares of OccuLogix drop by 65% in Canada. The decline in share price is attributed to failure of blood filtering system.

43663 ■ "The One Thing That's Holding Back Your Wellness Program" in *Employee Benefit News* **(Vol. 25, December 1, 2011, No. 15, pp. 8)**
Pub: SourceMedia Inc.
Ed: Kelley M. Butler. Description: A 13-year study shows that women who sat for more than six hours a day were 94 percent more likely to die during the study period. Most women sit at their desks an average of 7.7 hours while at work.

43664 ■ "OPEC Exposed" in *Hawaii Business* **(Vol. 54, September 2008, No. 3, pp. 2)**
Pub: Hawaii Business Publishing
Ed: Serena Lim. Description: Organization of the Petroleum Exporting Countries (OPEC) has said that their effort in developing an alternative energy source has driven prices up. The biofuel sector is criticizing the statement, saying that a research study found

that biofuels push petroleum prices down by 15 percent. Details on the effect of rising petroleum prices are discussed.

43665 ■ "Optimal Awarded US $256 Thousand Contract to Conduct LiDAR Survey for a Major Electric Utility in the Southwest" in *Canadian Corporate News*
Pub: Comtex News Network Inc.
Description: Optimal Geomatics, a company specializing in the science and technology of analyzing, gathering, interpreting, distributing, and using geographic information, was awarded a new contract from a long-standing electric utility customer in the Southwest to conduct a LiDAR survey for a part of the utility's overhead transmission line system.

43666 ■ *Our Daily Meds: How the Pharmaceutical Companies Transformed Themselves into Slick Marketing Machines*
Pub: Farrar, Straus and Giroux
Ed: Melody Petersen. Released: 2009. Price: $26.00. Description: Petersen, using industry memos, transcripts of meetings, and other sources shows how some drug companies are more concerned with the bottom line than with helping patients. Some of these firms are actually inventing 'diseases' in order to sell marginal medicines.

43667 ■ "PA Tax Reforms See Some Progress" in *Philadelphia Business Journal* **(Vol. 28, October 16, 2009, No. 35, pp. 1)**
Pub: American City Business Journals
Ed: Athena D. Merritt. Description: It was reported that Pennsylvania's $27.8 billion budget arrived 101 days late, but business groups are encouraged that progress continues to be made on long-called-for tax reforms. The Research and Development Tax Credit, currently at $40 million, will drop to $20 million in 2009-2010.

43668 ■ "P&G vs. IRS: Split Decision" in *Business Courier* **(Vol. 27, July 16, 2010, No. 11, pp. 1)**
Pub: Business Courier
Ed: Jon Newberry. Description: Implications of a court ruling in a $435 million legal dispute between Procter & Gamble Company (P&G) and the Internal Revenue Service (IRS) are discussed. A $21 million win has been realized for P&G for its interpretation of research and development tax credits. However, the said case might involve more than $700 million in P&G tax deductions from 2001 through 2004 that the IRS had disallowed.

43669 ■ "Paralysis Foundation has Big Plans" in *Austin Business JournalInc.* **(Vol. 29, December 11, 2009, No. 40, pp. 1)**
Pub: American City Business Journals
Ed: Sandra Zaragoza. Description: Lone Star Paralysis Foundation revealed plans to launch a fundraising effort for the advancement of cures for spinal cord injuries via adult stem cells and also fund a new spinal injury rehabilitation center. Efforts to raise about $3 million will begin as soon as the adult stem cell research study by Dr. Wise Young receives Food and Drug Administration approval.

43670 ■ "Past Promises Haunt Project" in *The Business Journal-Portland* **(Vol. 25, August 1, 2008, No. 21, pp. 1)**
Pub: American City Business Journals, Inc.
Ed: Aliza Earnshaw. Description: Oregon University System and Oregon Health and Science University will face the state Legislature to defend their request for a $250 million in state bonds to fund a life-sciences collaborative research building. The project is meant to help grow the Oregon bioscience industry. Comments from industry observers and legislators are also presented.

43671 ■ "Physics for Females" in *Occupational Outlook Quarterly* **(Vol. 55, Summer 2011, No. 2, pp. 22)**
Pub: U.S. Bureau of Labor Statistics
Description: Free resources to help females investigate careers in medical physics and health physics are available from the American Physical Society. The booklet is designed for girls in middle and high

school and describes the work of 15 women who use physics to solve medical mysteries, discover planets, research new materials, and more.

43672 ■ "The Power of Innovation" in *Canadian Business* **(Vol. 81, March 17, 2008, No. 4, pp. 57)**
Pub: Rogers Media
Ed: Andrew Wahl. Description: Canada ranks badly in terms innovation yardsticks that directly translate to economic growth such as business R&D as a percentage of GDP and R&D per capita. Canada's reliance on natural resources does not provide incentives to innovate unlike smaller countries with little natural resources. Canada could spur innovation through regulations that encourage industrial research.

43673 ■ "The Price Is Right: What You Can Learn From the Wine Industry" in *Advertising Age* **(Vol. 88, February 11, 2008, No. 6, pp. 14)**
Pub: Crain Communications, Inc.
Ed: Lenore Skenazy. Description: In California a wine study was conducted in which participants' brains were hooked up to an MRI so researchers could watch what was happening in both the taste centers as well as the pleasure centers; the participants were given three different wines but were told that the samples were from a variety of wines that differed radically in price; surprisingly, the differences did not affect the taste centers of the brain, however, when the participants were told that a sample was more expensive, the pleasure centers were greatly affected.

43674 ■ "Providing Expertise Required to Develop Microsystems" in *Canadian Electronics* **(Vol. 23, February 2008, No. 1, pp. 6)**
Pub: CLB Media Inc.
Ed: Ian McWalter. Description: CMC Microsystems, formerly Canadian Microelectronics Corporation, is focused on empowering microelectronics and Microsystems research in Canada. Microsystems offers the basis for innovations in the fields of science, environment, technology, automotives, energy, aerospace and communications technology. CMC's strategy in developing Microsystems in Canada is described.

43675 ■ "Putting 'Extra' in Extra-Silky Shampoo" in *Crain's Chicago Business* **(Vol. 31, April 28, 2008, No. 17, pp. 37)**
Pub: Crain Communications, Inc.
Ed: Phuong Ly. Description: Profile of HallStar Co., a Chicago-based company which develops and manufactures specialty chemicals to upgrade existing products such as hair dye, lotion and deodorant. HallStar has seen its annual earnings rise more than 30 percent since 2002.

43676 ■ "The Quest for the Smart Prosthetic" in *Canadian Business* **(Vol. 83, October 12, 2010, No. 17, pp. 26)**
Pub: Rogers Media Ltd.
Ed: Jacqueline Nelson. Description: Information about a two-year research project led by Southern Methodist University (SMU) and funded by the Defense Advance Research Projects Agency (DARPA) is provided. The agency aims to create a 'smart prosthetic' which will improve the lives of military amputees. The planned prosthetic will use a sensor that can carry nerve signals through synthetic channels.

43677 ■ "A Questionable Chemical Romance" in *Barron's* **(Vol. 88, July 14, 2008, No. 28, pp. 28)**
Pub: Dow Jones & Co., Inc.
Ed: Andrew Bary. Description: Dow Chemical paid $78-a-share for the surprise takeover of Rohm & Haas. The acquisition is reducing Dow Chemical's financial flexibility at a time when chemical companies are being affected by high costs and a weak U.S. economy.

43678 ■ **"Radiant Commences In-Lab Testing for US Air Mobility Command"** in *Canadian Corporate News* (May 16, 2007)
Pub: Comtex News Network Inc.
Description: The Boeing Company will be conducting in-lab infrared material testing for the Radiant Energy Corporation, developer and marketer of InfraTek, the environmentally friendly, patented infrared pre-flight aircraft deicing system.

43679 ■ **"Reading the Public Mind"** in *Harvard Business Review* (Vol. 88, October 2010, No. 10, pp. 27)
Pub: Harvard Business School Publishing
Ed: Andrew O'Connell. **Description:** Examination of the various methods for obtaining public opinion and consumer preferences is provided; an outline of the disadvantages and benefits of both are also given.

43680 ■ **"Rebels' Cause: Adult Stem Cell"** in *Austin Business Journal* (Vol. 31, June 3, 2011, No. 13, pp. 1)
Pub: American City Business Journals Inc.
Ed: Sandra Zaragoza. **Description:** MedRebels Foundation was launched in February 2011 with the goal of providing millions of dollars for research funding, education and advocacy for adult stem cell-focused medicine. The foundation, whose major contributor is SpineSmith LP, is a collaboration of other adult stem cell-related companies and nonprofit partners. It hopes to raise $200,000 by the end of 2011.

43681 ■ **"Region to Be Named Innovation Hub"** in *Business Courier* (Vol. 27, July 2, 2010, No. 9, pp. 1)
Pub: Business Courier
Ed: Dan Monk. **Description:** The selection of Cincinnati's consumer-marketing cluster as a 'Hub of Innovation' by the Ohio Department of Development could boost Cincinnati's chances of receiving $100 million in grants from Ohio's Third Frontier program and other funding sources. Implications of the University of Cincinnati's designation as a Center of Excellence in Advanced Transportation and Aerospace are also discussed.

43682 ■ **"Region Ready to Dig Deeper into Tech Fund"** in *Business Courier* (Vol. 26, October 30, 2009, No. 27, pp. 1)
Pub: American City Business Journals, Inc.
Ed: James Ritchie. **Description:** Southwest Ohio region aims for a bigger share in the planned renewal of Ohio's Third Frontier technology funding program. Meanwhile, University of Cincinnati vice president Sarah Degen will be appointed to the program's advisory board if the renewal proceeds.

43683 ■ **"Rehab Will Turn Hospital Into Incubator"** in *The Business Journal-Serving Metropolitan Kansas City* (Vol. 26, September 12, 2008)
Pub: American City Business Journals, Inc.
Ed: Rob Roberts. **Description:** Independence Regional Health Center will be purchased by CEAH Realtors and be converted into the Independence Regional Entrepreneurial Center, a business incubator that will house startups and other tenants. Other details about the planned entrepreneurial center are provided.

43684 ■ **"Renewable Energy Market Opportunities: Wind Testing"** in *PR Newswire* (September 22, 2011)
Pub: United Business Media
Description: Global wind energy test systems markets are discussed. Research conducted covers both non-destructive test equipment and condition monitoring equipment product segments.

43685 ■ *Research Centers Directory*
Pub: Gale
Released: Annual, Latest edition 41st; October, 2011. **Price:** $1,071, individuals paperback. **Covers:** About 14,800 university, government, and other nonprofit research organizations established on a permanent basis to carry on continuing research programs in all areas of study; includes research institutes, laboratories, experiment stations, research parks, technology

transfer centers, and other facilities and activities; coverage includes Canada. **Entries Include:** Unit name, name of parent institution, address, phone, fax, name of director, e-mail addresses, URLs, year founded, governance, staff, educational activities, public services, sources of support, annual volume of research, principal fields of research, publications, special library facilities, special research facilities. **Arrangement:** Classified by broad subjects, then alphabetical by unit name. **Indexes:** Alphabetical (includes centers, institutions, and keywords), subject, geographical, personal name.

43686 ■ **"Research Note"** in *International Journal of Globalisation and Small Business* (Vol. 4, September 21, 2010, No. 1, pp. 92)
Pub: Publishers Communication Group
Ed: Alexander Bode, Tobias B. Talmon l'Armee, Simon Alig. **Description:** The cluster concept has steadily increased its importance during the past years both from practitioners' and reearchers' points of view. Simultaneously, many corporate networks are established. Researchers from different areas (business management, economic social and geographical science) are trying to explain both phenomena.

43687 ■ **"Research Reports"** in *Barron's* (Vol. 88, March 24, 2008, No. 12, pp. M10)
Pub: Dow Jones & Company, Inc.
Description: Investors are recommending purchasing shares of Ampco Pittsburgh due to an expected surge in earnings. Deteriorating credit quality presents problems for the shares of BankAtlantic Bancorp, whose price targets have been lowered from $7 to $5 each. Shares of Helicos Biosciences are expected to move sideways from their $6 level. Statistical data included.

43688 ■ **"Research Reports: How Analysts Size Up Companies"** in *Barron's* (Vol. 90, August 23, 2010, No. 34, pp. M13)
Pub: Barron's Editorial & Corporate Headquarters
Description: Shares of Sirius XM Radio, Target and Deere and Company received an eBuyE rating, while shares of Research in Motion got an eNeutralE rating.

43689 ■ **"The Right Remedy: Entrepreneur's Success Is a Matter of Life and Death"** in *Black Enterprise* (Vol. 38, February 2008, No. 7, pp. 46)
Pub: Earl G. Graves Publishing Co. Inc.
Ed: Tamara E. Holmes. **Description:** Profile of Leah Brown, whose company conducts clinical trials to determine if specific drugs will relieve particular symptoms. Her company will also visit physician's offices to make certain doctors are following proper protocol for a clinical trial or will collect data from patients.

43690 ■ **"Rimfire Minerals Corporation: Jake Gold Project-Drilling Planned for 2007"** in *Canadian Corporate News* (May 16, 2007)
Pub: Comtex News Network Inc.
Description: Rimfire Minerals Corporation and Island Arc Exploration Corporation formed a partnership to explore the Jake Property, a high-grade gold prospect with previously unrecognized potential to host economic gold mineralization, located 13 kilometers west of Clearwater, British Columbia

43691 ■ **"Rising in the East; Research and Development"** in *The Economist* (Vol. 390, January 3, 2009, No. 8612, pp. 47)
Pub: The Economist Newspaper Inc.
Description: Impressive growth of the technological research and development in Asian countries is discussed. Statistical data included.

43692 ■ **"The Role for Canada's Research Universities"** in *Canadian Business* (Vol. 81, October 27, 2008, No. 18, pp. 84)
Pub: Rogers Media Ltd.
Description: Great students tend to be the foundation of a great research-intensive university, enabling it to attract great teachers and researchers. Success is likely to attract the brightest graduate students to do research, leading to further success.

43693 ■ **"Roswell Park Researcher Gets $1.5M From M&T"** in *Business First Buffalo* (October 19, 2007, pp. 1)
Pub: American City Business Journals, Inc.
Ed: Annmarie Franczyk. **Description:** Roswell Park Cancer Institute researcher Dr. Thomas Tomasi has received the M&T Bank Endowed Chair in Cancer Research, wherein $1.5 million in research funds is included. The funding is an addition to Roswell Park's Leaders for Life endowment campaign which aims to raise $20 for research. Tomasi's plans and background are also given.

43694 ■ **"RS Information Systems Signs Buyout Deal"** in *Black Enterprise* (February 2008)
Pub: Earl G. Graves Publishing Co. Inc.
Ed: Alan Hughes. **Description:** Details of the RS Information Systems buyout by Wyle, a privately held provider of high-tech aerospace engineering, testing, and research services.

43695 ■ **"Rumor Has It"** in *Entrepreneur* (Vol. 35, October 2007, No. 10, pp. 30)
Pub: Entrepreneur Media Inc.
Ed: Chris Penttila. **Description:** Some entrepreneurs like Ren Moulton and Dan Scudder regard rumor sites and product blogs as great sources of market research. However, there are legal issues that must be studied before using these Internet sites in marketing and product development. The use and limitations of rumor sites and product blogs are provided.

43696 ■ **"Safer Ammonium-Nitrate-Based Fertilizer"** in *Farm Industry News* (Vol. 42, January 1, 2009, No. 1)
Pub: Penton Media, Inc.
Description: Honeywell has patented a new technology which it will use to develop a highly effective, safer ammonium-nitrate-based fertilizer that has a significantly lower potential for explosion.

43697 ■ **"Saudi Overtures"** in *The Business Journal-Portland* (Vol. 25, August 15, 2008, No. 23, pp. 1)
Pub: American City Business Journals, Inc.
Ed: Aliza Earnshaw. **Description:** Saudi Arabia's huge revenue from oil is creating opportunities for Oregon companies as the country develops new cities, industrial zones, and tourism centers. Oregon exported only $46.8 million worth of goods to Saudi Arabia in 2007 but the kingdom is interested in green building materials and methods, renewable energy and water quality control, and nanotechnology all of which Oregon has expertise in.

43698 ■ **"Scanning the Field"** in *Business Courier* (Vol. 26, January 8, 2010, No. 38, pp. 1)
Pub: American City Business Journals, Inc.
Ed: Jon Newberry. **Description:** Anti-terror detection systems developer Valley Force Composite Technologies Inc. of Kentucky plans to enter the market with its high-resolution ODIN and Thor-LVX screening systems. These systems are expected to meet the increasing demand for airport security equipment.

43699 ■ *Science Lessons: What the Business of Biotech Taught Me About Management*
Pub: Harvard Business School Press
Ed: Gordon Binder, Philip Bashe. **Released:** 2009. **Price:** $29.95. **Description:** Former CFO of biotechnology startup Amgen and veteran of Ford Motor Company provides a universal guide to management based on some of the same scientific principles used to create new drugs.

43700 ■ *Science et Technologie au Quebec*
Pub: Quebec Dans Le Monde
Released: Biennial, Latest edition 2011-2012. **Price:** $52.95, individuals. **Covers:** over 1,150 scientific associations, periodicals, research and development facilities, and research centers in Quebec. **Entries Include:** Organization name, address, phone, fax, toll-free phone, description of services. **Arrangement:** Alphabetical. **Indexes:** Subject.

43701 ■ "Scientific American Builds Novel Blog Network" in *Information Today* (Vol. 28, September 2011, No. 8, pp. 12)
Pub: Information Today, Inc.
Ed: Kurt Schiller. Description: Scientific American launched a new blog network that joins a diverse lineup of bloggers cover various scientific topics under one banner. The blog network includes 60 bloggers providing insights into the ever-changing world of science and technology.

43702 ■ "Selling Michigan; R&D Pushed as Reason For Chinese To Locate In State" in *Crain's Detroit Business* (Vol. 24, January 14, 2008)
Pub: Crain Communications Inc. - Detroit
Ed: Marti Benedetti. Description: Southeast Michigan Economic Development organizations are working to develop relationships with Chinese manufacturers so they will locate their automotive research and development operations in the state.

43703 ■ "The Service Imperative" in *Business Horizons* (Vol. 51, January-February 2008, No. 1, pp. 39)
Pub: Elsevier Advanced Technology Publications
Ed: Mary Jo Bitner, Stephen W. Brown. Description: The importance of services is growing in developing countries like India and China, but little attention is given to service research, education and innovation. The 'service imperative' seeks to promote the advancement of services. The scope, objectives and philosophy of the service imperative platform are outlined.

43704 ■ "Shipbuilding & Defence" in *Canadian Sailings* (July 7, 2008)
Pub: Commonwealth Business Media
Ed: Sharon Hobson. Description: Overview of the Joint Support Ship Project whose initial budget was set at $2.1 billion for the acquisition of the ships required for the Canadian navy; another $800 million was allotted for 20 years of in-service support. Four teams of competitors bid for the contract and the Department of National Defence decided to fund two teams for the project definition phase of the competition.

43705 ■ "Shire Seeking New Digs for Headquarters" in *Philadelphia Business Journal* (Vol. 30, September 2, 2011, No. 29, pp. 1)
Pub: American City Business Journals Inc.
Ed: Natalie Kostelni. Description: Dublin, Ireland-based Shire PLC announced plans to relocate its North American headquarters from Chesterbrook Corporate Center in Wayne, Pennsylvania and currently evaluating their options. The specialty biopharmaceutical firm is also considering a move to New Jersey or Delaware.

43706 ■ "Slick Science" in *Canadian Business* (Vol. 81, September 15, 2008, No. 14-15, pp. 55)
Pub: Rogers Media Ltd.
Ed: Andrew Nikiforuk. Description: N-Solv Corp's John Nenniger has discovered a better alternative to steam-assisted gravity drainage methods for extracting bitumen. Nenniger's technique also relies on gravity but replaces steam with propane, which leaves behind impurities like asphaltenes and heavy metals that are too dirty to burn.

43707 ■ "Slow but Steady into the Future" in *Barron's* (Vol. 88, July 7, 2008, No. 27, pp. M)
Pub: Dow Jones & Co., Inc.
Ed: Mark Veverka. Description: Investors are advised to maintain their watch on the shares of business software company NetSuite. The company's chief executive officer, Zach Nelson, claims that the company has a 10-year lead on its competitors with the development of software-as-a service.

43708 ■ "Smart Medicine" in *Canadian Business* (Vol. 80, February 26, 2007, No. 5, pp. 73)
Pub: Rogers Media
Ed: Zena Olijnyk. Description: The stock price stability and future earnings prospects of Canadian biotechnology firm YM Biosciences are analyzed.

43709 ■ "Some Relief Possible Following Painful Week" in *Barron's* (Vol. 88, July 14, 2008, No. 28, pp. M3)
Pub: Dow Jones & Co., Inc.
Ed: Kopin Tan. Description: Dow Chemical is offering a 74 percent premium to acquire Rohm & Haas' coatings and electronics materials operations. Frontline amassed a 5.6 percent stake in rival Overseas Shipholding Group and a merger between the two would create a giant global fleet with pricing power. Highlights of the U.S. stock market during the week that ended in July 11, 2008 are discussed. Statistical data included.

43710 ■ "Sophia Siskel; CEO, Chicago Botanic Garden" in *Crain's Chicago Business* (Vol. 31, May 5, 2008, No. 18, pp. 36)
Pub: Crain Communications, Inc.
Ed: John Rosenthal. Description: Profile of Sophia Siskel who is the CEO of the Chicago Botanic Garden and is overseeing the $100 million expansion which will put the Botanic Garden at the forefront of plant conservation science; Ms. Siskel is also an efficient marketer and researcher.

43711 ■ "Southwestern Resources Project Update" in *Canadian Corporate News* (May 14, 2007)
Pub: Comtex News Network Inc.
Description: Southwestern Resources Corp. provides a quarterly update on its various exploration projects in both Peru and China.

43712 ■ "STAR TEC Incubator's Latest Resident Shows Promise" in *The Business Journal-Serving Greater Tampa Bay* (August 8, 2008)
Pub: American City Business Journals, Inc.
Ed: Jane Meinhardt. Description: Field Forensics Inc., a resident of the STAR Technology Enterprise Center, has grown after being admitted into the business accelerator. The producer of defense and security devices and equipment has doubled 2007 sales as of 2008.

43713 ■ "The Start of a Beautiful Friendship: Partnering with Your Customers on R&D" in *Inc.* (March 2008, pp. 37-38)
Pub: Gruner & Jahr USA Publishing
Ed: Leigh Buchanan. Description: Joint research and development projects between customers and suppliers are a growing trend in the small business community; these ventures can help keep new product development costs lower. Four tips to maintain a good working relationship in these ventures are outlined.

43714 ■ "The Stem Cell Revolution" in *Canadian Business* (Vol. 79, November 20, 2006, No. 23, pp. 31)
Pub: Rogers Media
Ed: Erin Pooley. Description: The commercial prospects and the future of stem cell therapeutics are presented. The use of stem cell therapy to heal the chronic conditions of patients is also discussed.

43715 ■ "Stronger Corn? Take It Off Steroids, Make It All Female" in *Farm Industry News* (December 5, 2011)
Pub: Penton Business Media Inc.
Ed: Brian Wallheimer. Description: Purdue University researcher found that higher improvements in corn crops, and possibly other crops, were yielded when steroids were discontinued.

43716 ■ "Study Puts Hub On Top of the Tech Heap" in *Boston Business Journal* (Vol. 30, November 26, 2010, No. 44, pp. 1)
Pub: Boston Business Journal
Ed: Galen Moore. Description: The Ewing Marion Kauffman Foundation ranked Massachusetts at the top in its evaluations of states' innovative industries, government leadership, and education. Meanwhile, research blog formDs.com also ranked Massachusetts number one in terms of venture-capital financings per capita.

43717 ■ "Sundt, DPR Score $470 Million Biotech Project" in *The Business Journal - Serving Phoenix and the Valley of the Sun* (Vol. 29, September 19, 2008, No. 3, pp. 1)
Pub: American City Business Journals, Inc.
Ed: Jan Buchholz. Description: Sundt Inc. and DPR Construction Inc. were awarded the winning joint-venture contract to develop the second phase of the Arizona Biomedical Collaborative on the Phoenix Biomedical Campus. Both firms declined to comment, but an employee of the Arizona Board of Regents confirmed that the firms won the bidding. Views and information on the development project are presented.

43718 ■ "Superior Completes Second Vertical Hole Through Morin Kimberlite and Intersects 141 Metres of Crater Facies Material at the Ville Marie Project" in
Pub: Comtex News Network Inc.
Description: Superior Diamonds Inc., a junior Canadian exploration company that primarily searches for diamonds in the highly prospective and under-explored regions of the Canadian Shield, announced completion of a second vertical hole through the western side of Superior's Morin kimberlite pipe to try to determine the type and thickness of the kimberlite material.

43719 ■ "Tabular Dreams" in *Canadian Business* (Vol. 80, February 12, 2007, No. 4, pp. 36)
Pub: Rogers Media
Ed: Christina Campbell. Description: The research of Raymor Industries in developing carbon nanotubes by bonding carbon atoms using high technology is discussed.

43720 ■ "The Tech 100" in *Canadian Business* (Vol. 81, July 21, 2008, No. 11, pp. 48)
Pub: Rogers Media Ltd.
Ed: Calvin Leung. Description: Absolute Software Corp. Day4 Energy Inc., Sandvine Corp., Norsat International Inc. and Call Genie Inc. are the five technology firms included in the annual ranking of top companies in Canada by market capitalization. The services and the one-year total return potential of the companies are presented.

43721 ■ "Tech Coaltion Warns Takeover Spree is Nigh" in *Globe & Mail* (February 6, 2007, pp. B1)
Pub: CTVglobemedia Publishing Inc.
Ed: Steven Chase. Description: The declaration by an alliance of technology-rich companies, that the huge credits that these companies have to endure due to research and development activities may lead to company takeovers, is discussed.

43722 ■ *Technological Entrepreneurship*
Pub: Edward Elgar Publishing, Incorporated
Ed: Donald Siegel. Released: October 2006. Price: $230.00. Description: Technological entrepreneurship at universities is discussed. The book covers four related topics: university licensing and patenting; science parks and incubators; university-based startups; and the role of academic science in entrepreneurship.

43723 ■ "Testing Firm to Add Jobs" in *Business Courier* (Vol. 26, December 11, 2009, No. 33, pp. 1)
Pub: American City Business Journals, Inc.
Ed: Dan Monk. Description: Cincinnati-based Q Laboratories announced plans to add dozens of jobs with the $1.6 million stimulus assisted expansion. The company hired Michael Lichtenberg & Sons Construction Co. to build a new 9,000 square foot laboratory building.

43724 ■ "Thinking Aloud" in *Business Strategy Review* (Vol. 21, Summer 2010, No. 2, pp. 47)
Pub: Wiley-Blackwell
Ed: Yiorgos Mylonadis. Description: In each issue we ask an academic to explain the big question on which their research hopes to shed light. Yiorgos Mylonadis looks at how people define and solve problems.

43725 ■ "Thinking Aloud: Julian Franks" in *Business Strategy Review* **(Vol. 21, Autumn 2010, No. 3, pp. 35)**
Pub: Wiley-Blackwell
Ed: Stuart Crainer. **Description:** Julian Franks is academic director of the Centre for Corporate Governance at London Business School and lead investigator for a (pounds sterling) 1.4 million grant for research into corporate governance.

43726 ■ "To Build for the Future, Reach Beyond the Skies" in *Canadian Business* **(Vol. 83, June 15, 2010, No. 10, pp. 11)**
Pub: Rogers Media Ltd.
Ed: Richard Branson. **Description:** Richard Branson says that tackling an engineering challenge or a scientific venture is a real adventure for an entrepreneur. Branson discusses Virgin's foray into the aviation business and states that at Virgin, they build for the future.

43727 ■ "Top 50 in the Capital Market" in *Canadian Business* **(Vol. 81, Summer 2008, No. 9, pp. 117)**
Pub: Rogers Media Ltd.
Description: Research in Motion Ltd. topped the list of companies in Canada in terms of market capitalization. The company's share prices surge to 119.8 percent in the year ended April 4. A table showing the top 50 Canadian companies in terms of market capitalization is presented.

43728 ■ "Top Worst Weeds in Corn" in *Farm Industry News* **(November 29, 2011)**
Pub: Penton Business Media Inc.
Ed: John Pocock. **Description:** Effective weed control for profitable crops is discussed with information from leading weed scientists from the University of Illinois Extension. It is important for farmers to know what their worst weed is in order to choose the best product, or mix of products, to control them.

43729 ■ "Tweaking On-Board Activities, Equipment Saves Fuel, Reduces CO2" in *Canadian Sailings* **(June 30, 2008)**
Pub: Commonwealth Business Media
Description: Optimizing ship activities and equipment uses less fuel and therefore reduces greenhouse gas emissions. Ways in which companies are implementing research and development techniques in order to monitor ship performance and analyze data in an attempt to become more efficient are examined.

43730 ■ "UA, BP Test Unmanned Aircraft" in *Alaska Business Monthly* **(Vol. 27, October 2011, No. 10, pp. 8)**
Pub: Alaska Business Publishing Company
Ed: Nancy Pounds. **Description:** University of Alaska Fairbanks Geophysical Institute and BP Exploration Alaska tested the oil-spill capabilities of an unmanned aircraft. The aircraft will be used to gather 3-D ariel data to aid in oil-spill cleanup.

43731 ■ "UC Lobbies for Big Chunk of New Funds" in *Business Courier* **(Vol. 24, February 22, 2008, No. 46, pp. 1)**
Pub: American City Business Journals, Inc.
Ed: Laura Baverman. **Description:** Discusses the University of Cincinnati (UC) which has requested $192 million funding from the Ohio Innovation Partnership. The program was launched by governor Stickland in an attempt to drive research and innovation in the studies of biotechnology, aeronautics, and other fields that reflects Ohio's strengths. Details of UC's grant proposals are supplied.

43732 ■ "USM Focuses on Turning Science Into New Companies, Cash" in *Boston Business Journal* **(Vol. 29, July 1, 2011, No. 8, pp. 1)**
Pub: American City Business Journals Inc.
Ed: Alexander Jackson. **Description:** University System of Maryland gears up to push for its plan for commercializing its scientific discoveries which by 2020 could create 325 companies and double the $1.4 billion the system's eleven schools garner in

yearly research grants. It is talking with University of Utah and University Maryland, Baltimore to explore ways to make this plan a reality.

43733 ■ *Values and Opportunities in Social Entrepreneurship*
Pub: Palgrave Macmillan
Ed: Kai Hockerts. **Released:** November 1, 2009. **Price:** $90.00. **Description:** Social entrepreneurship has grown as a research field. This book discusses social entrepreneurship as well as the identification and exploitation of social venturing opportunities.

43734 ■ "Voices: Breaking the Corruption Habit" in *Business Strategy Review* **(Vol. 21, Autumn 2010, No. 3, pp. 67)**
Pub: Wiley-Blackwell
Ed: David De Cremer. **Description:** In times of crisis, it seems natural that people will work together for the common good. David De Cremer cautions that, on the contrary, both economic and social research prove otherwise. He proposes steps for organizations to take to prevent corrupt behaviors.

43735 ■ "Water Distiller" in *Canadian Business* **(Vol. 81, September 29, 2008, No. 16, pp. 52)**
Pub: Rogers Media Ltd.
Ed: Matthew McClearn. **Description:** Les Fairn's invention of a water distiller called a Solarsphere was recognized in the Great Canadian Invention Competition. Fairn's invention resembles a buoy that uses the sun's energy to vaporize dirty water then leaves the impurities behind in a sump. The invention has an application for producing potable water in impoverished countries.

43736 ■ "The Way to the Market's Heart?" in *Canadian Business* **(Vol. 80, March 26, 2007, No. 7, pp. 74)**
Pub: Rogers Media
Ed: Erin Pooley. **Description:** The financial and stock performance of Canadian biotechnology companies Medicure Inc. and Angiotech Pharmaceuticals Inc. are analyzed.

43737 ■ "Where the Future is Made" in *Indoor Comfort Marketing* **(Vol. 70, May 2011, No. 5, pp. 48)**
Pub: Industry Publications Inc.
Description: Research being performed at Brookhaven National Laboratory, located in Upton, New York, is discussed, focusing on new energy sources for our nation.

43738 ■ "Where the Money Is" in *Conde Nast Portfolio* **(Vol. 2, June 2008, No. 6, pp. 113)**
Pub: Conde Nast Publications, Inc.
Description: Revenue generated from treatments for common brain disorders that are currently on the market are listed.

43739 ■ "Whistling in the Dark" in *Canadian Business* **(Vol. 79, September 25, 2006, No. 19, pp. 17)**
Pub: Rogers Media
Ed: Jack Mintz. **Description:** Increasing subsidies for research projects in Canada is discussed.

43740 ■ "Young-Kee Kim; Deputy Director, Fermi National Accelerator Laboratory" in *Crain's Chicago Business* **(Vol. 31, May 5, 2008, No. 18)**
Pub: Crain Communications, Inc.
Ed: Phuong Ly. **Description:** Profile of Young-Kee Kim who is the deputy director of Fermilab, a physics lab where scientists study the smallest particles in the universe; Ms. Kim was a researcher at Fermilab before becoming deputy director two years ago; Fermilab is currently home to the most powerful particle accelerator in the world and is struggling to compete with other countries despite cuts in federal funding.

TRADE PERIODICALS

43741 ■ *Alloy Digest*
Pub: ASM International
Released: Bimonthly. **Price:** $749 nonmembers; $328 members. **Description:** Engineering research journal.

43742 ■ *The Anatomical Record*
Pub: John Wiley & Sons Inc.
Contact: David H. Bernanke, Board of Reviewers
Ed: Kurt H. Albertine, PhD, Editor, kurt.albertine@hsc.utah.edu. **Released:** Monthly. **Price:** $7,310 institutions print; $7,478 institutions, Canada print; $7,562 institutions, other countries print. **Description:** Research journal.

43743 ■ *Applied Engineering in Agriculture*
Pub: American Society of Agricultural and Biological Engineers
Contact: Donna M. Hull, Dir. of Publication
Released: Bimonthly. **Price:** $79 members; $157 nonmembers; $29 nonmembers outside U.S.; $20 members outside United States. **Description:** Peer-reviewed journal focused on practical applications of current research related to engineering for agricultural, food and biological systems.

43744 ■ *Biochemistry and Cell Biology*
Pub: National Research Council Canada, NRC Research Press
Released: Bimonthly. **Price:** $845 institutions print; $710 institutions electronic; $1,060 institutions print & electronic; $89 institutions satellite; $200 electronic; $270 print & electronic; $102 airmail. **Description:** Scholarly journal on biochemistry research (English and French).

43745 ■ *Biopolymers*
Pub: John Wiley & Sons Inc.
Contact: Robert Kaptein, Advisory Board
Released: Semimonthly. **Price:** $10,840 institutions print or online; $10,840 institutions, Canada and Mexico print only; $10,840 institutions, other countries print only. **Description:** Journal containing original research papers on the structure, properties, interactions and assemblies of biomolecules. Deals with organic and physical chemistry; experimental and theoretical research. Subjects include broad aspects of biospectroscopy. Also covers static and dynamic aspects of structure.

43746 ■ *Bioscience Technology*
Pub: Advantage Business Media
Released: Monthly. **Description:** Journal covering life science research and biotechnology products.

43747 ■ *BioTechniques*
Pub: Eaton Publishing
Contact: Colleen Smith, Managing Editor
E-mail: colleen.smith@informausa.com
Released: Monthly. **Description:** Research journal.

43748 ■ *Biotechnology Advances*
Pub: Elsevier Science B.V.
Contact: M. Moo-Young, Editor-in-Chief
E-mail: mooyoung@cape.uwaterloo.ca
Ed: E.A. Bayer, Editor, ed.bayer@weizmann.ac.il.
Released: 6/yr. **Price:** $2,129 institutions except Europe, Japan and Iran; $1,905 institutions European countries and Iran; $252,600 institutions Japan; $24,900; $162; $216. **Description:** Journal covering research, reviews and patent abstracts on biotechnology.

43749 ■ *Biotechnology & Bioengineering*
Pub: John Wiley & Sons Inc.
Contact: Lee R. Lynd, Advisory Board
E-mail: lee.h.lynd@dartmouth.edu
Released: 18/yr. **Price:** $800 print only; $800 Canada print only; $968 other countries print only; $8,489 institutions print only; $8,741 institutions, Canada print only; $8,867 institutions, other countries print only. **Description:** Journal providing an international forum for original research on all aspects of biochemical and microbial technology, including products, process development and design, and equipment.

43750 ■ *Birth Defects Research Part B*
Pub: John Wiley & Sons Inc.
Contact: Philippe Shubick, Editor-in-Chief
Released: Bimonthly. **Description:** Journal publishing research on the detection, classification, and evaluation of risk associated with exposure to environmental agents which may induce teratogenesis, carcinogenesis, or mutagenesis.

43751 ■ Brain, Behavior, and Immunity
Pub: Elsevier Science B.V.
Contact: Kelly W. Kelley, Editor-in-Chief
Released: 8/yr. **Price:** $1,114 institutions for all countries except Europe, Japan and Iran; $431 for all countries except Europe, Japan and Iran; $175 students for all countries except Europe, Japan and Iran. **Description:** Journal publishing research data on the interactions between the nervous system and the immune system at the molecular, cellular, and organismic levels.

43752 ■ Canadian Journal of Chemistry
Pub: National Research Council Canada, NRC Research Press
Ed: Dr. Derek G. Leaist, Editor. **Released:** Monthly. **Price:** $1,510 institutions print only; $1,375 institutions electronic; $2,060 institutions print & electronic; $190 institutions satellite; $400 electronic; $540 print & electronic. **Description:** Journal on research in chemistry (English and French).

43753 ■ Cell Motility and the Cytoskeleton
Pub: John Wiley & Sons Inc.
Released: Monthly. **Price:** $5,910 institutions print; $6,078 institutions, Canada and Mexico print; $6,162 institutions, other countries print. **Description:** Science research journal.

43754 ■ Cereal Chemistry
Pub: American Association of Cereal Chemists
Released: Bimonthly. **Price:** $117 single issue U.S.; $128 single issue elsewhere; $667 print; $712 elsewhere print; $124 single issue back issue; $135 elsewhere back issue. **Description:** Journal focusing on cereal chemistry and research on raw materials, processes and products in the cereals area.

43755 ■ Chemical Engineering Research and Design ChERD
Pub: Mosby
Contact: Dr. Eva Sorensen, Editor-in-Chief
E-mail: e.sorensen@ucl.ac.uk
Released: Monthly. **Price:** $1,830 institutions, other countries; $223,000 institutions Japan; $1,418 institutions European countries and Iran. **Description:** Journal publishing papers on all aspects of experimental work, development and theory in chemical engineering.

43756 ■ Chemical and Petroleum Engineering
Pub: Springer-Verlag New York Inc.
Contact: L.N. Anokhina, Assoc. Ed.
Released: Monthly. **Price:** $4,604 institutions print or online; $5,524.80 institutions print & enchanced access. **Description:** Research Journal. A translation of Khimicheskoe: Neftyanoe Mashinostroenie.

43757 ■ Communication Outlook
Pub: Artificial Language Laboratory
Contact: Deanna Hoopingarner, Assoc. Ed.
Ed: Rebecca Ann Baird, Editor. **Released:** Quarterly. **Price:** $18 North and South America; $24 other countries; $5 single issue. **Description:** Magazine reporting on the newest developments in the application of technology for neurologically impaired persons.

43758 ■ Computer Animation & Virtual Worlds
Pub: John Wiley & Sons Inc.
Contact: Nadia Magnenat Thalmann, Editor-in-Chief
E-mail: thalmann@miralab.unige.ch
Released: 6/yr. **Price:** $1,316 other countries print only; $1,747 institutions, other countries print only; $1,126 institutions, other countries print only; $891 institutions print only. **Description:** Journal featuring research papers, film case studies, and critiques of the latest uses of computer animation.

43759 ■ Computing in Science and Engineering
Pub: Institute of Electrical and Electronics Engineers Inc.
Contact: Isabel Beichl, Editor-in-Chief
E-mail: isabel.beichl@nist.org
Released: Quarterly. **Price:** $47 members; $78 nonmembers; $625 institutions. **Description:** Peer-reviewed journal focusing on physics, medicine, astronomy and other hard sciences.

43760 ■ Corrosion
Pub: NACE International
Contact: Dr. J.B. Lumsden, Tech. Ed.
Released: Monthly. **Price:** $85 members online access only; $150 nonmembers online access only; $280 libraries online access only; $105 members print and online access; international; $60 students member -printed and online access; $210 nonmembers U.S. non-member-printed and online access; $275 other countries non-member-printed and online access; $390 U.S. library-printed and online access; $430 other countries library-printed and online access. **Description:** Journal on corrosion science and engineering research.

43761 ■ Diesel & Gas Turbine Worldwide
Pub: Diesel & Gas Turbine Publications
Contact: Brent Haight, Editor & Publisher
Released: Monthly, (Jan /Feb., July/Aug. issues combined). **Price:** $65; Free to qualified subscribers. **Description:** International magazine covering the design, application, and operation of diesel, natural gas, and gas turbine engine systems.

43762 ■ DISCOVERY
Pub: Office of Research and Creative Activity
Ed: Annette Trinity-Stevens, Editor, annettet@montana.edu. **Released:** Monthly, during the academic year. **Price:** Free. **Description:** Features news of University research in agriculture, engineering, life sciences, and the humanities.

43763 ■ DNA and Cell Biology
Pub: Mary Ann Liebert Incorporated Publishers
Contact: Jo Handelsman, Editor-in-Chief
Released: Monthly. **Price:** $749 print and online; $895 other countries print and online; $689 online only; $3,724 institutions print and online; $4,029 institutions, other countries print and online; $2,962 institutions print only; $3,408 institutions, other countries print only; $3,103 institutions online only. **Description:** Medical journal providing research findings in cell biology.

43764 ■ Earth and Mineral Sciences
Pub: Pennsylvania State University
Contact: Colleen L. Swetland, Asst. Dir. of Alumni Relations
E-mail: swetland@ems.psu.edu
Released: Semiannual. **Description:** Magazine covering research on mineral engineering, earth sciences, and materials science and engineering.

43765 ■ Electric Power Components and Systems
Pub: Taylor & Francis Group Journals
Contact: Dr. Ion Boldea, Assoc. Ed.
Released: 14/yr. **Price:** $2,731 institutions print & online; $2,595 institutions online; $1,208; $1,647 institutions print & online; $1,565 institutions online; $727. **Description:** Journal publishing original theoretical and applied research in electromechanics, electric machines, and power systems.

43766 ■ Electrical Engineering in Japan
Pub: John Wiley & Sons Inc.
Contact: Toshiro Matsumura, Assoc. Ed.
Ed: Hironori Hirata, Editor. **Released:** 16/yr. **Price:** $9,849 institutions print only; $10,073 institutions, Canada and Mexico print only; $10,185 institutions, other countries print only; $10,835 institutions print with online; $11,059 institutions, Canada and Mexico print with online; $11,171 institutions, other countries print with online. **Description:** Journal publishing original research results in power generation, transmission and conversion, electrical machinery, and related subjects. Translated from Japanese.

43767 ■ Engineering Design and Automation
Pub: John Wiley & Sons Inc.
Released: Quarterly. **Description:** Journal of new research on the design and analysis of production systems, artificial intelligence, and neural networks.

43768 ■ Environmental Toxicology and Chemistry
Pub: Society of Environmental Toxicology & Chemistry
Contact: Dr. C.H. Ward, Editor-in-Chief
Released: Monthly. **Price:** $1,512 institutions print & online; $1,286 institutions online only; $1,548 institutions, Canada and Mexico print & online; $1,590 institutions, other countries print & online; $1,286 institutions, other countries online. **Description:** Official journal of the Society of Environmental Toxicology and Chemistry; contains research in environmental chemistry and toxicology and hazard/risk assessment.

43769 ■ Experimental Heat Transfer
Pub: Taylor & Francis Group Journals
Contact: Melany L. Hunt, Editorial Advisory Board
E-mail: hunt@caltech.edu
Ed: Ishwar K. Puri, Editor, ikpuri@vt.edu. **Released:** Quarterly. **Price:** $435 institutions print & online; $413 institutions online only; $207; $722 institutions print & online; $686 institutions online only; $344. **Description:** Forum for original research on heat and mass transfer and in related fluid flows.

43770 ■ Gear Technology
Pub: Randall Publishing Inc.
Contact: Michael Goldstein, Pres., Publisher, Ed.-in-Ch.
Released: Bimonthly. **Price:** $15 single issue back issue; $70 other countries; $115 other countries two years. **Description:** Magazine featuring design, testing, processing, and new technology for gears and gear manufacturing products, and equipment.

43771 ■ Geomicrobiology Journal
Pub: Taylor & Francis Group Journals
Released: 8/yr. **Price:** $437 print only; $1,348 institutions online only; $1,418 institutions print & online; $853 institutions print & online; $810 institutions online only; $262 print only. **Description:** Journal publishing research and review articles on microbial transformations of materials that comprise the earth's crust.

43772 ■ Human Mutation
Pub: John Wiley & Sons Inc.
Contact: Dr. Haig H. Kazazian Jr., Founding Co-Ed.
Released: Monthly. **Price:** $1,588 institutions print only; $1,756 institutions, Canada and Mexico print only; $1,840 institutions, other countries print only. **Description:** Journal containing information about mutation research and genetic disorders.

43773 ■ IBM Journal of Research and Development
Pub: IBM Corp.
Contact: John J. Ritsko, Editor-in-Chief
E-mail: ritsko@us.ibm.com
Released: Bimonthly. **Price:** $995 libraries online. **Description:** Technical journal focusing on professional scientific research and engineering developments.

43774 ■ International Journal of Adaptive Control and Signal Processing
Pub: John Wiley & Sons Inc.
Contact: Brian D.O. Anderson, Ed.-at-Large
Ed: Angelo Alessandri, Editor. **Released:** 12/yr. **Price:** $2,128 other countries print only; $2,837 institutions, other countries print only; $1,830 institutions, other countries print only; $1,447 institutions print only. **Description:** Journal covering research in industrial control systems. Also features numerical aspects of algorithms and expert systems.

43775 ■ International Journal on Artificial Intelligence Tools
Pub: World Scientific Publishing
Contact: Dr. N.G. Bourbakis, Editor-in-Chief
Released: Bimonthly. **Price:** $898 institutions electronic print; $862 institutions electronic only; $47 postage; $719 institutions electronic print; $690 institutions electronic only; $36 postage. **Description:** Journal covering design, development, and testing of AI tools.

43776 ■ International Journal of Computer Integrated Manufacturing
Pub: Taylor & Francis Group Journals
Contact: Prof. Stephen Newman, Editor-in-Chief
E-mail: ijcimeditor@bath.ac.uk
Released: 12/yr. **Price:** $2,590 institutions online only; $2,726 institutions print and online; $1,862 institutions online only; $1,650 print and online. De-

scription: Journal containing information of new knowledge, research and applications used in specific manufacturing situations.

43777 ■ *International Journal of Computer Simulation*
Pub: University of Wisconsin-Eau Claire
Ed: Vijay K. Madisetti, Editor. **Released:** Quarterly. **Description:** Journal covering research and development, product development, and tutorials in computer simulation.

43778 ■ *International Journal of Energy Research*
Pub: John Wiley & Sons Inc.
Contact: Prof. J.T. McMullan, Honorary Ed.
Released: 15/yr. **Price:** $4,738 other countries print only; $6,286 institutions, other countries print only; $4,056 institutions, other countries print only; $3,208 institutions print only. **Description:** Journal providing information on energy research and development.

43779 ■ *International Journal of Hyperthermia*
Pub: Informa Healthcare
Released: 8/yr. **Price:** $1,755 institutions; $3,065 institutions; $2,455 institutions. **Description:** Peer-reviewed journal containing information on research and clinical papers on hyperthermia.

43780 ■ *International Journal of Intelligent Systems*
Pub: John Wiley & Sons Inc.
Contact: John R. Anderson, Editorial Board
Ed: Ronald R. Yager, Editor. **Released:** Monthly. **Price:** $220 U.S., Canada, and Mexico print only; $304 other countries print only; $3,083 institutions print only; $3,251 institutions, Canada and Mexico print only; $3,335 institutions, other countries print only. **Description:** Journal featuring peer-reviewed work on the systematic development of theory used in the construction of intelligent systems. Covers areas such as man-computer interactions and the use of language, neural networks, and machine learning; includes book reviews.

43781 ■ *Journal of the American Oil Chemists' Society*
Pub: AOCS Press
Contact: Richard W. Hartel, Editor-in-Chief
E-mail: rwhartel@wisc.edu
Released: Monthly. **Price:** $155 members; $619. **Description:** Technical journal devoted to fundamental and practical research in the field of fats, oils, oleochemicals, proteins, surfactants, and detergents.

43782 ■ *Journal of Andrology*
Pub: American Society of Andrology
Contact: Arthur Burnett, Editor-in-Chief
Released: Bimonthly. **Price:** $390 institutions print only; $420 institutions, other countries print only; $510 institutions print and online; $380 print and online; $540 institutions, other countries print and online; $410 other countries print and online; $450 institutions online only; $320 online only. **Description:** Journal covering clinical and laboratory research in the structure and function of the male reproductive system and male gametes.

43783 ■ *Journal of Biochemical and Molecular Toxicology*
Pub: John Wiley & Sons Inc.
Released: Bimonthly. **Price:** $988 institutions print only; $1,072 institutions, Canada and Mexico print only; $1,114 institutions, other countries print only; $1,088 institutions print with online; $1,172 institutions, Canada and Mexico print with online; $1,214 institutions, other countries print with online. **Description:** Journal featuring research papers, rapid communications, and mini-reviews focusing on the molecular mechanisms of action and detoxication of exogenous and endogenous chemical toxic agents. The scope includes effects on organisms at all stages of development.

43784 ■ *Journal of Bioenergetics and Biomembranes*
Pub: Springer Netherlands
Released: Bimonthly. **Price:** $1,061 institutions print or online; $1,273.20 institutions print & enchanced access. **Description:** Journal focusing on biological membranes research.

43785 ■ *Journal of Biological Rhythms*
Pub: Sage Publications Inc.
Contact: Timothy J. Bartness, Advisory Board
Released: Bimonthly. **Price:** $1,060 institutions combined (print & e-access); $1,166 institutions combined plus backfile; $954 institutions e-access; $1,060 institutions e-access plus backfile; $1,054 institutions e-access (content through 1998); $1,039 institutions print only; $218 print only; $190 institutions single print; $47 single print. **Description:** Journal focusing on experimental biological research.

43786 ■ *Journal of Cellular Biochemistry*
Pub: John Wiley & Sons Inc.
Contact: C. Fred Fox, Exec. Ed.
E-mail: fredfox@microbio.ucla.edu
Released: 18/yr. **Price:** $10,121 institutions print only; $10,337 institutions, Canada print only; $10,463 institutions, other countries print only. **Description:** Research journal.

43787 ■ *Journal of Chemical Ecology*
Pub: Springer Netherlands
Contact: Jeff Aldrich, Assoc. Ed.
Released: Monthly. **Price:** $2,171 institutions print & online; $2,605.20 institutions print & enchanced access. **Description:** Scientific research journal.

43788 ■ *Journal of Chemical Technology and Biotechnology*
Pub: John Wiley & Sons Inc.
Contact: Jack Melling, Editor-in-Chief
E-mail: jmelling@ptd.net
Released: Monthly. **Price:** $1,645 institutions, other countries print only; $1,300 institutions print only; $2,548 institutions, other countries print only; $1,810 institutions, other countries print with online; $1,430 institutions print with online; $2,803 institutions, other countries print with online. **Description:** Journal on scientific discoveries and inventions in the disciplines of biotechnology and chemical technology.

43789 ■ *Journal of Clinical Microbiology*
Pub: ASM Journals
Contact: Gary V. Doern, Editor-in-Chief
Released: Monthly. **Price:** $131 members print; $176 members print & online; $173 members Canada, print; $218 members Canada, print & online. **Description:** Journal publishing primary research in microbiological aspects of human and animal infections and infestations, with particular emphasis on their etiologic agents, diagnosis, and epidemiology.

43790 ■ *Journal of Communications Technology and Electronics*
Pub: John Wiley & Sons Inc.
Contact: Vladislav I. Pustovoit, Dep. Ed.-in-Ch.
Released: Monthly. **Price:** $4,012 U.S. and Canada; $4,613; $4,613 other countries. **Description:** Journal of research in communications and electronics engineering from the Russian Academy of Sciences.

43791 ■ *Journal of Environmental Engineering*
Pub: American Society of Civil Engineers
Ed: Raymond A. Ferrara, PhD, Editor. **Released:** Monthly. **Price:** $1,151 institutions print & online; $1,211 institutions, other countries print & online; $1,036 institutions print; $1,096 institutions, other countries print; $978 U.S. and other countries online; $288 members print & online; $348 members international; print & online; $259 members print; $319 members international; print; $245 U.S. and other countries online only. **Description:** Peer-reviewed journal on the practice and status of research in environmental engineering science, systems engineering, and sanitation.

43792 ■ *Journal of Investigative Surgery*
Pub: Taylor & Francis Group Journals
Contact: Eugen Faist, Assoc. Ed.
Released: 6/yr. **Price:** $494 print only; $1,084 institutions online only; $1,141 institutions print & online; $690 institutions print & online; $655 institutions online only; $300 print only. **Description:** Biomedical research journal dealing with scientific articles for the advancement of surgery, to the ultimate benefit of patient care and rehabilitation.

43793 ■ *Journal of Labelled Compounds and Radiopharmaceuticals*
Pub: John Wiley & Sons Inc.
Ed: B. Langstrom, Editor, bengt.langstrom@ge.com.
Released: 14/yr. **Price:** $3,312 institutions, other countries print only; $5,133 institutions, other countries print only; $2,619 institutions print only; $3,644 institutions, other countries print with online; $2,881 institutions print with online; $5,647 institutions, other countries print with online. **Description:** Journal providing original scientific manuscripts on recent research and development in labelled compound preparation, analytical control, self radiolysis, quality control handling and storage.

43794 ■ *Journal of Materials in Civil Engineering*
Pub: American Society of Civil Engineers
Contact: Antonio Nanni PhD, Editor-in-Chief
Released: Monthly. **Price:** $939 institutions print & online; $999 institutions, other countries print & online; $826 institutions print; $886 institutions, other countries print; $751 U.S. and other countries online; $235 members print & online; $295 members international; print & online; $188 members print; $267 members international; print; $188 U.S. and other countries online only. **Description:** Journal on current topics of materials in civil engineering.

43795 ■ *Journal of Morphology*
Pub: John Wiley & Sons Inc.
Ed: Matthias J. Starck, Editor, starck@uni-muenchen. de. **Released:** Monthly. **Price:** $6,393 institutions print only; $6,561 institutions, Canada print only; $6,645 institutions, other countries print only. **Description:** Medical research journal.

43796 ■ *Journal of Natural History*
Pub: Taylor & Francis Group Journals
Contact: P.J. Hayward, Editorial Advisory Board
Ed: A. Polaszek, Editor. **Released:** Semimonthly. **Price:** $8,881 institutions online only; $9,349 institutions print and online; $5,639 institutions print and online; $5,357 institutions online only. **Description:** Journal publishing papers on research, reviews, opinions and correspondence in systematics and evolutionary and interactive biology, taxonomic works in entomology and zoology, cladistics, experimental taxonomy, parasitology, ecology, behaviour and the interaction of organisms with their environment.

43797 ■ *Journal of Neurochemistry*
Pub: John Wiley & Sons Inc.
Contact: Anthony J. Turner, Editor-in-Chief
E-mail: a.j.turner@leeds.ac.uk
Released: Bimonthly. **Price:** $978 print and online; $930 online only; $4,805 institutions print & online; $4,369 institutions print, online; $19 members online only. **Description:** Journal providing coverage of significant advances in neurochemistry and molecular and cellular biology.

43798 ■ *Journal of Pharmaceutical Sciences*
Pub: American Pharmacists Association
Contact: Bradley D. Anderson, Assoc. Ed.
Ed: Dr. Ronald T. Borchardt, Editor. **Released:** Monthly. **Price:** $325 print; $382 other countries print; $1,399 institutions print only; $1,456 institutions, other countries print only; $1,539 institutions print and online; $1,596 institutions, other countries print and online. **Description:** Professional journal publishing research articles in the pharmaceutical sciences.

43799 ■ *Journal of Polymer Science*
Pub: John Wiley & Sons Inc.
Ed: Craig J. Hawker, Editor, hawker@mrl.ucsb.edu.
Released: 48/yr. **Price:** $22,399 institutions print only; $22,735 institutions, Canada print only; $22,903 institutions, other countries print only; $24,640 institutions print with online; $24,976 institutions, Canada print with online; $25,144 institutions, other countries print with online. **Description:** Journal publishing results of fundamental research in all areas of high polymer chemistry and physics. Three monthly editions: Polymer Chemistry, Polymer Physics, and Polymer Letters.

43800 ■ Journal of Pressure Vessel Technology
Pub: American Society of Mechanical Engineers
Ed: G.E. Otto Widera, Editor, geo.widera@marquette.edu. **Released:** Quarterly. **Price:** $60 members USA; print & online; $107 members international; print & online; $51 members internet only; $509 nonmembers U.S.; print & online; $556 nonmembers international; print & online. **Description:** Peer-reviewed journal focusing on pressure vessel research.

43801 ■ Journal of Turbomachinery
Pub: American Society of Mechanical Engineers
Ed: David C. Wisler, Editor, davewisler@mac.com. **Released:** Quarterly. **Price:** $50 members print and online; $88 members international; print and online; $43 members internet only; $391 nonmembers U.S.; print and online; $429 nonmembers international; print and online. **Description:** Peer-reviewed journal featuring scholarly research on turbomachinery technology.

43802 ■ Machine Design
Pub: Penton Media Inc.
Contact: Steve Mraz, Sen. Ed.
E-mail: steve.mraz@penton.com
Released: 22/yr. **Price:** $144 Canada; $126 Canada 2 years; $157.50 other countries print only; $265 other countries 2 years, print only; $108 students print only; $162 students 2 years, print only. **Description:** Magazine on design engineering function.

43803 ■ Microbiology Abstracts Section A
Pub: Cambridge Scientific Abstracts
Released: Monthly, except December. **Description:** Scientific journal covering research and applications in agricultural, chemical, pharmaceutical industries.

43804 ■ Microscopy Research and Technique
Pub: John Wiley & Sons Inc.
Contact: George Ruben, Editor-in-Chief
E-mail: george.c.ruben@dartmouth.edu
Released: Monthly. **Price:** $8,289 institutions print; $8,457 institutions, Canada and Mexico print; $8,541 institutions, other countries print. **Description:** Journal covering the application of and research on advanced microscopy.

43805 ■ Molecular Physics
Pub: Taylor & Francis Group Journals
Released: Semimonthly. **Price:** $7,956 institutions online only; $8,375 institutions print and online; $1,402. **Description:** Journal containing information on research papers on chemical physics.

43806 ■ Neurobiology of Learning and Memory
Pub: Elsevier Science B.V.
Contact: D.L. Alkon, Editorial Board
Released: 8/yr. **Price:** $1,533 institutions for all countries except Europe, Japan and Iran; $677 for all countries except Europe, Japan and Iran; $339 students for all countries except Europe, Japan and Iran. **Description:** Journal publishing information on current neural-oriented behavioral research. Emphasizes the areas of neural plasticity and the mechanisms of learning and memory.

43807 ■ Numerical Heat Transfer, Part A: Applications
Pub: Taylor & Francis Group Journals
Contact: W.J. Minkowycz, Editor-in-Chief
E-mail: wjm@uic.edu
Released: 24/yr. **Price:** $7,951 institutions print and online; $2,956; $7,553 institutions online only. **Description:** Journal publishing research in the field of heat and mass transfer, and fluid flow.

43808 ■ Particulate Science and Technology
Pub: Taylor & Francis Group Journals
Contact: Dr. Malay K. Mazumder, Editor-in-Chief
Released: Quarterly. **Price:** $444 print only; $1,062 institutions online only; $1,124 print and online. **Description:** Journal publishing original research and review material dealing with particulate science and technology.

43809 ■ The Plant Cell
Pub: American Society of Plant Biologists
Contact: Nancy A. Winchester, Publications Dir.
E-mail: nancyw@aspb.org
Released: Monthly. **Price:** $185 members print; $120 students print; $375 nonmembers. **Description:** Academic research journal reporting major advances in plant cellular and molecular biology.

43810 ■ Progress in Photovoltaics
Pub: John Wiley & Sons Inc.
Contact: Ryne P. Raffaelle, Managing Editor
Released: 8/yr. **Price:** $671 other countries print only; $1,945 institutions, other countries print only; $1,255 institutions, other countries print only; $992 institutions print only. **Description:** Journal focusing on practical implementation and research in the field of photovoltaics.

43811 ■ The Quarterly Review of Biology
Pub: University of Chicago Press
Contact: Daniel E. Dykhuizen, Editor-in-Chief
Ed: John J. Wiens, Editor. **Released:** Quarterly. **Price:** $54 print and electronic; $45 electronic only; $46 print only; $27 students electronic only; $97 two years print and electronic; $49 students electronic only, two years; $138 print and electronic, three years. **Description:** Journal reviewing recent research and newly published books and software dealing with the life sciences.

43812 ■ R & D Magazine
Pub: Advantage Business Media
Contact: Martha Walz, Editor-in-Chief
E-mail: martha.walz@advantagemedia.com
Released: Monthly. **Description:** Magazine serving research scientists, engineers, and technical managers. Reports significant advances, problems, and trends that affect the performance, funding, and administration of applied research and development.

43813 ■ Random Structures & Algorithms
Pub: John Wiley & Sons Inc.
Contact: Joel Spencer, Ed. Emeritus
Released: 8/yr. **Price:** $1,478 institutions print; $1,590 institutions, Canada and Mexico print; $1,730 institutions, other countries print; $1,627 institutions print with online; $1,739 institutions, Canada and Mexico print with online; $1,879 institutions, other countries print with online. **Description:** Journal describing research on random structures and applications of probabilistic techniques to problem solving in mathematics, computer science and operations research.

43814 ■ Rapid Communications in Mass Spectrometry
Pub: John Wiley & Sons Inc.
Contact: Prof. Kermit K. Murray, Internet Resources Ed.
E-mail: kermit.murray@chem.lsu.edu
Released: Semimonthly. **Price:** $4,602 institutions, other countries print; $3,639 institutions print; $7,132 institutions, other countries print; $5,063 institutions, other countries print with online; $4,004 institutions print with online; $7,846 institutions, other countries print with online. **Description:** Journal containing information on research ideas and results on all aspects of the science of gas-phase ions.

43815 ■ Reviews in Medical Virology
Pub: John Wiley & Sons Inc.
Contact: Prof. Paul Griffiths, Editor-in-Chief
E-mail: pgriffiths@medsch.ucl.ac.uk
Ed: Dr. Brian W.J. Mahy, Editor, bmx1@cdc.gov. **Released:** Bimonthly. **Price:** $453 print only; $811 other countries print only; $1,297 institutions, other countries print only; $837 institutions, other countries print only; $662 institutions print only; $921 institutions, other countries print with online; $729 institutions print with online; $1,427 institutions, other countries print with online. **Description:** Journal focusing on current research and new information on all viruses of medical importance.

43816 ■ Rubber Chemistry and Technology
Pub: Rubber Division
Released: 5/yr. **Price:** $550 institutions print only; $450 nonmembers print only; $350 members print only; $450 other countries member; print only; $650 institutions, other countries print only. **Description:** Journal on developments in the technology of rubber.

43817 ■ Sensor Technology
Pub: Technical Insights/M John Wiley & Sons Inc.
Ed: Leo O'Connor, Editor. **Released:** Monthly. **Price:** $650, U.S. and Canada year; $710, elsewhere year. **Description:** Informs readers of the latest scientific and technological developments in the field of sensors. Focuses on process and machine control, including robotics; also covers environmental and medical uses. Recurring features include a calendar of events, news of research, book reviews, and columns titled Key Patents and Keep an Eye On.

43818 ■ Software Process
Pub: John Wiley & Sons Inc.
Contact: Prof. Darren Dalcher, Editor-in-Chief
E-mail: d.dalcher@mdx.ac.uk
Released: 7/yr. **Price:** $209 print; $363 other countries print; $727 institutions, other countries print; $469 institutions, other countries print; $370 institutions print. **Description:** Journal for those involved in the software development process. Features experience reports, research papers, and critical discussion.

43819 ■ Strategic S&T
Pub: EPRI
Ed: Gail McCarthy, Editor. **Released:** 3/year. **Description:** Profiles research projects, results, and activities of the SS&T program. Recurring features include news of research, reports of meetings, and listing of SS&T reports with ordering information.

43820 ■ Systems and Computers in Japan
Pub: John Wiley & Sons Inc.
Contact: Hiroyuki Morikawa, Editorial Board
Ed: Shoji Shinoda, Editor. **Released:** 14/yr. **Description:** Translation journal reports on Japanese developments in computer architecture, large system design, advanced digital circuitry, data transmission, interface devices, data processing, programming techniques, automata, formal languages, and biomedical applications of computers.

43821 ■ Yeast
Pub: John Wiley & Sons Inc.
Contact: S.G. Oliver, Founding Ed.
Released: 16/yr. **Price:** $2,322 other countries print only; $3,372 institutions, other countries print only; $2,176 institutions, other countries print only; $1,721 institutions print only; $2,394 institutions, other countries print with online; $1,894 institutions print with online; $3,710 institutions, other countries print with online. **Description:** Journal containing information on current yeast research and pertinent reviews.

43822 ■ Zoo Biology
Pub: John Wiley & Sons Inc.
Contact: Patrick Thomas, Reviews Ed.
Released: Bimonthly. **Price:** $300 U.S., Canada, and Mexico print only; $342 other countries print only; $2,214 institutions print only; $2,298 institutions, Canada print only; $2,340 institutions, other countries print only. **Description:** Journal featuring research on wild animals in captive settings.

VIDEOCASSETTES/ AUDIOCASSETTES

43823 ■ The Science of Energy
Human Relations Media
41 Kensico Dr.
Mount Kisco, NY 10549
Ph:(914)244-0486
Free: 800-431-2050
Fax:(914)244-0485
Co. E-mail: orders@hrmvideo.com
URL: http://www.hrmvideo.com
Released: 1994. **Price:** $189. **Description:** Introduces students to biology and physics, touching on the scientific history of energy from Galileo to Einstein, thermodynamics, the sun as the Earth's energy source, photosynthesis and respiration. Complete with teacher's resource book. **Availability:** VHS.

43824 ■ Science on Ice: Research in Antarctica
Encyclopedia Britannica
331 N. LaSalle St.
Chicago, IL 60654

Ph:(312)347-7159
Free: 800-323-1229
Fax:(312)294-2104
URL: http://www.britannica.com
Released: 1988. **Price:** $59.00. **Description:** Illustrates the advantages of researching in the Antarctica and provides information on some of the current research taking place in the region. **Availability:** VHS; 3/4U; SVS.

43825 ■ *Technical Studies*
Home Vision Cinema
c/o Image Entertainment
20525 Nordhoff St., Ste. 200
Chatsworth, CA 91311
Co. E-mail: inquiries@image-entertainment.com
URL: http://www.homevision.com
Released: 1981. **Description:** This series is designed to illustrate the practical application of concepts in materials and engineering science. **Availability:** VHS; 3/4U.

TRADE SHOWS AND CONVENTIONS

43826 ■ American Technical Education Association National Conference on Technical Education
American Technical Education Association
c/o North Dakota State College of Science
800 N. 6th St.
Wahpeton, ND 58076-0002
Ph:(701)671-2301
Fax:(701)671-2260
URL: http://www.ateaonline.org
Released: Annual. **Audience:** Technical educators and administrators of post-secondary technical education. **Principal Exhibits:** Supplies and services related to post secondary technical education.

43827 ■ Estuarine Research Federation Conference
Estuarine Research Federation
PO Box 510
University of Southwest Louisiana
Dept. of Biology
Port Republic, MD 20676
Ph:(410)326-7467
Fax:(410)326-7466
Co. E-mail: info@erf.org
URL: http://www.erf.org
Released: Biennial. **Principal Exhibits:** Exhibits for persons actively engaged in biological, hydrographic, or related investigations of estuarine problems.

CONSULTANTS

43828 ■ Bio-Technical Resources L.P.
1035 S 7th St.
Manitowoc, WI 54220-5301
Ph:(920)684-5518
Fax:(920)684-5519
Co. E-mail: info@biotechresources.com
URL: http://www.biotechresources.com
Contact: Tom Jerrell, President
E-mail: jerrell@atsbiotechresources.com
Scope: Services include strain improvement, process development and metabolic engineering. Solutions are also offered for the development of biotechnology products and processes through contract services in research and development, bio process scale-up, pilot scale manufacturing, technology and economic assessments. Target audience: pharmaceutical, biotechnology, chemical and food and feed industries. Client base may be global leaders as well as small companies and startups. **Publications:** "A Novel Fungus for the Production of Efficient Cellulases and Hemi-Cellulases," Jun, 2009; "Linoleic Acid Isomerase from Propionibacterium acnes: Purification, Characterization, Molecular Cloning, and Heterologous Expression," 2007; "Purification and Characterization of a Membrane-Bound Linoleic Acid Isomerase from Clostridium sporogenes," 2007; "Metabolic Engineering of Sesquiterpene Metabolism in Yeast," 2007; "Purification and Characterization of a Membrane-Bound Linoleic Acid Isomerase from

Clostridium sporogenes," 2007; "Reduction of Background Interference in the Spectrophotometric Assay of Mevalonate Kinase," 2006; "A Soluble Form of Phosphatase in Saccharomyces cerevisiae Capable of Converting Farnesyl Diphosphate to E, E-Farnesol," 2006; "Ascorbate Biosynthesis: A Diversity of Pathways," BIOS Scientific Publishers, 2004; "The Biotechnology of Ascorbic Acid Manufacture," BIOS Scientific Publishers, 2004; "Detection of Farnesyl Diphosphate Accumulation in YeastERG9 Mutants," 2003; "Reverse Two-Hybrid System: Detecting Critical Interaction Domains and Screening for Inhibitors," Eaton Publishing, 2000. **Seminars:** Metabolic Engineering for Industrial Production of Glucosamine and N-Acetylglucosamine, Aug, 2003; Metabolic Engineering of E. coli for the Industrial Production of Glucosamine, Apr, 2003.

43829 ■ BioChem Technology Inc.
3620 Horizon Dr., Ste. 200
King of Prussia, PA 19406-2110
Ph:(610)768-9360
Fax:(610)768-9363
Co. E-mail: sales@biochemtech.com
URL: http://www.biochemtech.com
Contact: Allan Myers, Principle
E-mail: charlesxu@atsbiochemtech.com
Scope: A process consultation firm specializing in the monitoring, optimization and control of wastewater treatment processes. The technological optimization services include assessment of treatment capacities, facility re-rating, optimization services, debottlenecking services, flow dynamics/mixing pattern analysis. **Publications:** "A Novel Approach for Monitoring and Control of Denitrification in a Biological Nutrient Removal Facility," Oct, 1999; "A Unique Approach for Assessing the Capacity of a Biological Nutrient Removal Facility," Oct, 1999; "Enhancing Competitiveness of an Operations Staff: Five Years Experience with a BNR Wastewater Treatment Facility," Oct, 1998; "Optimization of Nitrification Process By On-Line Monitoring of Nitrification Time," Jun, 1997; "Monitoring and Control of the Nitrification Process Marine Park Water Reclamation Facility, City of Vancouver, WA," Oct, 1997; "Operational Improvements in a Biological Nutrient Removal Facility Using an Innovative Biological Activity Meter," May, 1996; "Operator Education and an Innovative Monitoring Technology Improve Performance of a Biological Nutrient Removal Facility," Oct, 1996; "Performance Enhancement of a BNR Wastewater Treatment Facility Utilizing a Microcosm Reactor Equipped With a Biological Activity Meter," Oct, 1996; "Optimization of Biological Denitrification Through Biological Activity Monitoring: System Development," Jun, 1995. **Seminars:** A Five Year Case Study of a Feed Forward Nitrogen Reduction Process Control System, Jun, 2009; Alternate DO Control Based on On-line Ammonia Measurement, Jun, 2009.

43830 ■ Education Development Center Inc.
55 Chapel St.
Newton, MA 02458-1060
Ph:(617)969-7100
Free: 800-225-4276
Fax:(617)969-5979
Co. E-mail: comment@edc.org
URL: http://www.edc.org
Contact: Luther Luedtke, President
E-mail: rrotner@atsedc.org
Scope: Services include research, training, educational materials and strategy, with activities ranging from seed projects to large-scale national and international initiatives. Specialize in program and fiscal management. Serves to design, deliver and evaluate innovative programs to address some of the world's most urgent challenges in education, health, and economic opportunity. Renders services to U.S. and foreign government agencies, private foundations, healthcare sectors, educational institutions, nonprofit organizations, universities, and corporations. **Publications:** "A Call to Action: HIV/AIDS, Health, Safety, and the Youth Employment Summit"; "A Case Against "Binge" as the Term of Choice: How to Get College Students to Personalize Messages about Dangerous Drinking"; "A Description of Foundation Skills Interventions for Struggling Middle-Grade Readers in Four Urban Northeast and Islands Region School Districts"; "A Guide to Facilitating Cases in

Education"; "A Look at Social, Emotional, and Behavioral Screening Tools for Head Start and Early Head Start"; "A Multifaceted Social Norms Approach to Reduce High-Risk Drinking: Lessons from Hobart and William Smith Colleges"; "The New Media Literacy Handbook"; "Helping Children Outgrow War"; "Worms, Shadows, and Whirlpools: Science in the Early Childhood Classroom"; "Teacher Leadership in Mathematics and Science Casebook and Facilitator's Guide"; "Teachers' Professional Development and the Elementary Mathematics Classroom: Bringing Understandings to Light". **Seminars:** Designed to Introduce the Materials; To Guide Schools Through the Issues.

43831 ■ Flett Research Ltd.
440 DeSalaberry Ave.
Winnipeg, MB, Canada R2L 0Y7
Ph:(204)667-2505
Fax:(204)667-2505
Co. E-mail: flett@flettresearch.ca
URL: http://www.flettresearch.ca
Contact: Dawn Gilbert, Principle
E-mail: flett@flettresearch.ca
Scope: Provides environmental audits and assessments. Offers contract research and consultation on environmental topics, specializing in limnology, with emphasis in microbiology, bio-geochemistry and radio-chemistry. Performs dating of sediments via Pb-210 and CS-137 methods, to determine sediment accumulation rates in lakes. One of a handful of labs in the world able to carry out total mercury and methyl mercury analyses at the sub-nanogram and L concentration in water.

43832 ■ Innovative Scientific Analysis & Computing
6168 Flagstaff Rd.
PO Box 1636
Boulder, CO 80302
Ph:(303)440-7673
Fax:(303)545-6674
Co. E-mail: ros5e@isaac.com
URL: http://www.ros5e.com
Contact: Herrn C. Rose, Principle
E-mail: ros5e@isaac.com
Scope: Engineering services includes mathematical analysis specializing in optimal estimation, scientific programming, and database design and development, data encryption and security.

43833 ■ Mankind Research Foundation Inc.
1315 Apple Ave.
Silver Spring, MD 20910-3614
Ph:(301)587-8686
Fax:(301)585-8959
Contact: Carl Schleicher, CEO
Scope: Firm provide an organization for scientific development and application of technology that could have positive impact on the health, education, and welfare of mankind. Provide solution to seek and apply futuristic solutions to current problems. Provides services in the areas of advanced sciences, biotechnical, bionic, biocybernetic, biomedical, holistic health, bioimmunology, solar energy, accelerated learning, and sensory aids for handicapped. Current specific activities involve research in AIDS, drug abuse, affordable housing, food for the hungry, and literacy and remedial education.

43834 ■ Midwest Research Institute
425 Volker Blvd.
Kansas City, MO 64110-2241
Ph:(816)753-7600
Fax:(816)753-8420
Co. E-mail: info@mriresearch.org
URL: http://www.mriresearch.org
Contact: Dr. William Hall, Chairman of the Board
E-mail: jshular@atsmriresearch.org
Scope: Independent not-for-profit research institute offering scientific services in the areas of national defense, health sciences, agriculture and food safety, engineering, energy, and infrastructure. Services include biomedical electronics, remote sensing, automation and control electromagnetic radiation, environmental sampling and analysis programs for industry and government, program management, engineering studies, exposure and risk assessment, waste management strategies, contaminant identifica-

tion, pollution prevention, and waste minimization. Expertise in highway safety/accident analysis, chemometrics/pattern recognition/neural networks, statistical support, process and product engineering.

43835 ■ Technology Management Group Co.
PO Box 3260
New Haven, CT 06515-0360
Ph:(203)387-1430
Fax:(203)387-1470
Co. E-mail: info@commtechsoftware.com
URL: http://www.ratafia.net
Contact: Manny Ratafia, President
E-mail: manny@commtechsoftware.com
Scope: Consulting services include analysis of market opportunities; product introductions; new ventures; acquisitions analysis; licensing, joint ventures, and OEM arrangements. Emphasis on polymers, medical devices, biotechnology, pharmaceuticals, and chemicals. **Special Services:** CommTechPowerSearch[R].

COMPUTERIZED DATABASES

43836 ■ *BooksInPrint.com Professional*
R.R. Bowker LLC
630 Central Ave.
New Providence, NJ 07974
Ph:(908)268-1090
Free: 888-269-5372
Fax:(908)665-3528
Co. E-mail: customerservice@bowker.com
URL: http://www.bowker.com
Description: Contains bibliographic descriptions and ordering information for more than 5 million books currently in print or declared out of print (from July 1979 to date), active and inactive audios and videos, and soon-to-be-published titles from some 200,000 publishers. Also contains more than 700,000 full-text reviews, more than 200,000 book jacket images, author biographies, and 140,000 tables of contents. Coverage includes scholarly, popular, adult, juvenile, reprint, and other books on all subjects published by U.S. publishers or exclusively distributed in the United States and available to the trade or general public for single- or multiple-copy purchases. Such items as government publications, Bibles, free books, and subscription-only titles are excluded. Also provides the complete text of reviews from *Library Journal*, *Publisher's Weekly*, and *School Library Journal*. Corresponds to *Books in Print*, *Books Out of Print*, *Forthcoming Books*, *Books in Print Supplement*, *Scientific and Technical Books in Print*, *Medical and Health Care Books in Print*, *Children's Books in Print*, *Paperbound Books in Print*, and *Law Books in Print*. Subject classification scheme utilizes more than 72,000 Library of Congress subject headings as well as Sears headings. **Availability:** Online: R.R. Bowker LLC, Colorado Alliance of Research Libraries, ProQuest LLC; CD-ROM: R.R. Bowker LLC. **Type:** Bibliographic.

RESEARCH CENTERS

43837 ■ American Defense Institute
1055 N Fairfax St., Ste. 200
Alexandria, VA 22314
Ph:(703)519-7000
Fax:(703)519-8627
Co. E-mail: ebm1@americandefinst.org
URL: http://www.ojc.org/adi/
Contact: Eugene McDaniel, Pres.
E-mail: ebm1@americandefinst.org
Scope: Defense and national security policy issues, focusing on the privileges and obligations of citizenship in a free society and America's strength and freedom in the 21st century. Special projects include a military voter program which encourages service

personnel to register and vote. **Services:** National speakers' bureau. **Publications:** ADI Briefs; ADI Newsletter; ADI Security Review. **Educational Activities:** National Security Leadership Seminar (annually), in Washington; POW awareness campaign. **Awards:** Outstanding Leadership Award, for individual citizens committed to America's national defense.

43838 ■ New Mexico State University–Arts and Sciences Research Center
PO Box 30001, MSCRC
Las Cruces, NM 88003
Ph:(575)646-7441
Fax:(575)646-4188
Co. E-mail: rczernia@nmsu.edu
URL: http://artsci.nmsu.edu/Research/
Contact: Dr. Robert J. Czerniak, Dir.
E-mail: rczernia@nmsu.edu
Scope: Administers research activities in the arts and physical, natural, and behavioral sciences. Also serves as coordinating center for faculty research in the College.

43839 ■ Polytechnic University–Institute for Technology and Enterprise
New York Information Technology Center
55 Broad St., Ste. 13B
New York, NY 10004
Ph:(212)547-7030
Fax:(212)547-7029
Co. E-mail: horwitch@poly.edu
URL: http://www.ite.poly.edu
Contact: Prof. Mel Horwitch, Dir.
E-mail: horwitch@poly.edu
Scope: High-level education, including the integration of new technologies, particularly the Internet and intranets, and multimedia, with business strategy as they affect management. **Educational Activities:** Round Tables (periodically); Workshops (periodically).

43840 ■ San Diego State University–Mount Laguna Observatory
Department of Astronomy
5500 Campanile Dr.
San Diego, CA 92182-1221
Ph:(619)594-6182
Fax:(619)594-1413
Co. E-mail: etzel@sciences.sdsu.edu
URL: http://mintaka.sdsu.edu
Contact: Prof. Paul B. Etzel PhD, Dir.
E-mail: etzel@sciences.sdsu.edu
Scope: Astronomy. **Publications:** MLOA Newsletter (3/year). **Educational Activities:** Planetarium shows, lectures, and telescope viewing (semiannually), on campus, for general public; Summer Star Party, for the public viewing Friday and Saturday nights in the summer.

43841 ■ State University of New York at Binghamton–Institute for Materials Research
Vestal Pky. E
Binghamton, NY 13902-6000
Ph:(607)777-4623
Fax:(607)777-4623
Co. E-mail: stanwhit@binghamton.edu
URL: http://materials.binghamton.edu
Contact: Prof. M. Stanley Whittingham, Dir.
E-mail: stanwhit@binghamton.edu
Scope: Preparation and physical and chemical properties of novel inorganic oxide materials using, in particular, soft chemistry approaches. Current research focuses on finding new synthetic routes to prepare metastable compounds that cannot be prepared by traditional techniques and the understanding and exploitation of ionic motion in solids and its use in electrochromic devices and batteries. **Publications:** Papers, books, and reviews.

43842 ■ Syracuse University–Center for Technology and Information Policy
419 Crouse-Hinds Hall
Maxwell School of Citizenship & Public Affairs
900 S Crouse Ave.
Syracuse, NY 13244-2130
Ph:(315)443-1890
Fax:(315)443-1075
Co. E-mail: sibretsc@maxwell.syr.edu
URL: http://ctip.maxwell.syr.edu
Contact: Stuart Bretschneider PhD, Dir.
E-mail: sibretsc@maxwell.syr.edu
Scope: Nexus of technology, information, and public policy, particularly computer-based technological forecasting and assessment, management of scientific and technical information flows in organizations, technological innovation studies, and Pacific Rim science policy. **Publications:** TIPP Working Paper series. **Educational Activities:** Seminars.

43843 ■ University of Delaware–Center for Molecular and Engineering Thermodynamics
Colburn Laboratory
Department of Chemical Engineering
150 Academy St.
Newark, DE 19716
Ph:(302)831-4500
Fax:(302)831-4466
Co. E-mail: furst@udel.edu
URL: http://www.che.udel.edu/cmet
Contact: Prof. Eric M. Furst PhD, Dir.
E-mail: furst@udel.edu
Scope: Chemical engineering, including molecular thermodynamics and its applications in environmental problems, purification of pharmaceuticals and biological materials, and new separations technologies. Theoretical research areas also include ab-initio quantum mechanics calculations, Monte Carlo and molecular dynamics simulation and statistical mechanics, development of new applied thermodynamics methods for equations of state and activity coefficients models, and the description of surfactant and micellar solutions.

43844 ■ University of Toronto–Institute for the History and Philosophy of Science and Technology
Victoria College, Rm. 316
91 Charles St. W
Toronto, ON, Canada M5S 1K7
Ph:(416)978-5397
Fax:(416)978-3003
Co. E-mail: anjan.chakravartty@utoronto.ca
URL: http://www.hps.utoronto.ca
Contact: Prof. Anjan Chakravartty, Dir.
E-mail: anjan.chakravartty@utoronto.ca
Scope: History and philosophy of science and technology, particularly the history of biology, including classification, invertebrate morphology, Darwinism, and ecology; history of chemistry, including the eighteenth and nineteenth centuries; history of mathematics, including foundation of analysis, eighteenth and nineteenth century mechanics, Joseph Lagrange, Nicolas Sadi Carnot, and Jean Le Rond d'Alembert; history of medicine, including history of social medicine/public health,; medicine and national socialism; history of microbiology; history of physics, including Kepler, Descartes, seventeenth through nineteenth century electromagnetism; history of technology, including medieval and Renaissance, eighteenth century French technology and war; medieval and Renaissance science; Science Revolution; the Enlightenment; Victorian science; Romanticism; Canadian science, including Arctic exploration; and philosophy of science, including probability, statistics, experimental science, language, early modern natural philosophy, and foundations of Newtonian dynamics; exact sciences in antiquity. **Educational Activities:** Colloquia and public lectures (biweekly), historic-scientific experiments, open to the University of Toronto community and public.

START-UP INFORMATION

43845 ■ **"Firefighter Wins ABC's American Inventor"** in *Hispanic Business* (September 2007, pp. 94)
Pub: Hispanic Business
Description: Greg Chavez, firefighter, won ABC televisions American Inventor award of $1 million for his Guardian Angel invention. The device makes Christmas trees safer.

43846 ■ **"Options Abound in Winter Wares"** in *Pet Product News* (Vol. 64, November 2010, No. 11, pp. 1)
Pub: BowTie Inc.
Ed: Maggie M. Shein. **Description:** Pet supply manufacturers emphasize creating top-notch construction and functional design in creating winter clothing for pets. Meanwhile, retailers and pet owners seek human-inspired style, quality, and versatility for pets' winter clothing. How retailers generate successful sales of pets' winter clothing outside of traditional brand marketing is also examined.

REFERENCE WORKS

43847 ■ **"Austin to Make it Easier for Stores to Just Pop In"** in *Austin Business Journal* (Vol. 31, August 19, 2011, No. 24, pp. A1)
Pub: American City Business Journals Inc.
Ed: Vicky Garza. **Description:** Temporary retail stores may soon become common in Austin as City Council has urged the city manager to look into the possibility of amending the city codes to permit businesses to temporarily fill the vacant spaces downtown.

43848 ■ **"Discount Shopping: Holiday Shopping Meets Social Media"** in *Employee Benefit News* (Vol. 25, December 1, 2011, No. 15)
Pub: SourceMedia Inc.
Ed: Rob J. Thurston. **Description:** Offering employees access to discount shopping using social media sites for Christmas bonuses, could be the gift that keeps on giving.

43849 ■ **"Early Spring Halts Drilling Season"** in *Globe & Mail* (March 14, 2007, pp. B14)
Pub: CTVglobemedia Publishing Inc.
Ed: Norval Scott. **Description:** Decreased petroleum productivity in Canadian oil drilling rigs due to early spring season in western regions is discussed.

43850 ■ **"eBay and Jonathan Adler Team to Launch 'The eBay Inspiration Shop'"** in *Entertainment Close-Up* (October 25, 2011)
Pub: Close-Up Media
Description: Designer Jonathan Adler partnered with eBay to create a collection of new must-have merchandise for the fall season. Top trendsetters, including actors, designers, bloggers, stylists, editors, photographers, models and musicians helped curate the items being featured in the windows by sharing their shopping wish lists with users.

43851 ■ **"Farming Season Starts in December"** in *Farm Industry News* (November 29, 2011)
Pub: Penton Business Media Inc.
Ed: Kent Lock. **Description:** One farmer suggests the season starts in December because one third of his seed and fertilizer for the following year has already been bought and paid for and his cropping mix changes little from one year to another.

43852 ■ **"Freak Weather Dampens Intrawest Forecast"** in *Globe & Mail* (February 8, 2006, pp. B3)
Pub: CTVglobemedia Publishing Inc.
Ed: Peter Kennedy. **Description:** Intrawest Corp. dropped its earnings forecast by 7 percent. The impact of weather on earnings is discussed.

43853 ■ **"Ghouls, Goblins, and Harry Potter: Cashing In On Halloween"** in *Inc.* (Vol. 33, October 2011, No. 8, pp. 24)
Pub: Inc. Magazine
Ed: Darren Dahl. **Description:** Costume Craze, an online costume retailer reports $13.2 million in sales last year. Originally the family business started out as a software company called StaticAdvantage, but switched gears.

43854 ■ **"Help Customers Choose Full Service Over Discount"** in *Indoor Comfort Marketing* (Vol. 70, September 2011, No. 9, pp. 10)
Pub: Industry Publications Inc.
Ed: Richard Rutigliano. **Description:** Marketing strategies for HVAC/R firms to use in 2011 and 2012 heating seasons are outlined, focusing on oil heat.

43855 ■ **"Ho, Ho, Ho!"** in *Retail Merchandiser* (Vol. 51, September-October 2011, No. 5, pp. 10)
Pub: Phoenix Media Corporation
Ed: Ted Vaughan. **Description:** Despite consumer caution and economic woes, retail leaders are expecting a high volume holiday selling season for 2011 Christmas. Statistical data covering holiday sales expectations is included.

43856 ■ **"Marketing: 'Twill Be the Season"** in *Entrepreneur* (Vol. 35, October 2007, No. 10, pp. 108)
Pub: Entrepreneur Media Inc.
Ed: Kim T. Gordon. **Description:** Entrepreneurs should plan ahead in order to promote products for the holiday season, since it is peak sales time. They can unify their business theme, use customer incentives, advertise early using TV or radio, and reorganize the company Website. Other ways to market for the holiday season are provided.

43857 ■ **"Mattel's Got a Monster Holiday Hit, But Will Franchise Have Staying Power?"** in *Advertising Age* (Vol. 81, December 6, 2010, No. 43)
Pub: Crain Communications, Inc.
Ed: Beth Snyder Bulik. **Description:** Monster High transmedia play expands beyond dolls to merchandise, apparel and entertainment.

43858 ■ **"Oilheating Delivery Issues"** in *Indoor Comfort Marketing* (Vol. 70, September 2011, No. 9, pp. 14)
Pub: Industry Publications Inc.
Ed: John Levey. **Description:** Tools and techniques for delivery heating oil to customers this season are discussed.

43859 ■ **"Playfair Receives Drill Permit for Risby, Yukon Tungsten Deposit"** in *Canadian Corporate News* (May 16, 2007)
Pub: Comtex News Network Inc.
Description: Playfair Mining announced that it has received a 5 year Class III land use permit from the Mineral Resources Branch, Yukon which will allow the company to carry out a drill program during the upcoming drill season on the company-owned Risby, Yukon tungsten deposit. Statistical data included.

43860 ■ **"Point, Click, Buy"** in *Barron's* (Vol. 90, September 6, 2010, No. 36, pp. 11)
Pub: Barron's Editorial & Corporate Headquarters
Ed: Vito J. Racanelli. **Description:** Non-travel online retail sales from January to July 2010 increased nine percent which indicates that online shopping for the coming holidays will be good. Online sales are outpacing traditional shopping, but pricing is still critical.

43861 ■ **"Sabathia Deal Makes Dollars and Sense"** in *The Business Journal-Milwaukee* (Vol. 25, July 11, 2008, No. 42, pp. A1)
Pub: American City Business Journals, Inc.
Ed: Mark Kass. **Description:** It was reported that the Milwaukee Brewers' acquisition of CC Sabathia will mean that the team will pick up an estimated $5 million in salary that Sabathia is owed for the remainder of the season. Because of this, the team will not make a profit in 2008. The acquisition of Sabathia is expected to cause an increase in attendance and merchandise revenue over the remainder of the season.

43862 ■ **"Scream Therapy: A Chain of New York City Beauty Stores Perfect Halloween Pop-Ups"** in *Inc.* (Vol. 33, October 2011, No. 8, pp. 99)
Pub: Inc. Magazine
Ed: Amy Barrett. **Description:** Ricky's Halloween stores will open 30 temporary stores for about two months, 28 of which are permanent beauty supply shops the rest of the year.

43863 ■ **"Seasonal Franchises"** in *Franchising World* (Vol. 42, August 2010, No. 8, pp. 50)
Pub: International Franchise Association
Ed: Jennifer Lemcke. **Description:** Seasonal franchises, such as tax businesses can be slow during the summer months. Restaurants are slow during the months of January and February. The various challenges faced by seasonal franchises are examined.

43864 ■ **"Strathmore Receives Permit to Drill oca Honda Project in New Mexico"** in *Canadian Corporate News* (May 14, 2007)
Pub: Comtex News Network Inc.
Description: New Mexico's Mining and Minerals Division approved a permit to allow Strathmore Minerals

Corp. to conduct drilling at its Roca Honda Project located in McKinley County, New Mexico.

43865 ■ **"Uranerz Acquires Additional Uranium Property Adjoining Nichols Ranch"** in *Canadian Corporate News* **(May 14, 2007)**
Pub: Comtex News Network Inc.

Description: Uranerz Energy Corporation announced the successful leasing of the fee mineral lands that appear to host the "nose" of the oxidation-rduction geochemical front and has the potential for increasing the known uranium mineralization at the Nichols Ranch project which lies west of and adjacent to Uranerz's Nichols Ranch ISR uranium project.

43866 ■ **"What Dead Zone?"** in *Entrepreneur* **(Vol. 37, October 2009, No. 10, pp. 128)**
Pub: Entrepreneur Media, Inc.
Ed: Jason Daley. **Description:** Joe Purifico, Halloween Adventure franchises co-owner and chief executive officer, discusses the Halloween superstore phenomenon. Malls allow seasonal leasing for Halloween stores due to the high number of customers these stores attract.

43867 ■ **"Why Oil Fell, and How It May Rise"** in *Globe & Mail* **(January 18, 2007, pp. B2)**
Pub: CTVglobemedia Publishing Inc.
Ed: Eric Reguly. **Description:** The causes of the decline in oil prices in Canada are discussed, along with prospects of an increase in the same.

43868 ■ **"Will mCommerce Make Black Friday Green?"** in *Retail Merchandiser* **(Vol. 51, September-October 2011, No. 5, pp. 8)**
Pub: Phoenix Media Corporation

Ed: Scott Miller. **Description:** Retailers speculate the possibilities of mobile commerce and are implementing strategies at their stores. Consumers using mobile devices accounted for only 0.1 percent of visits to retail Websites on Black Friday 2009 and rose to 5.6 percent in 2010; numbers are expected to rise for 2011.

REFERENCE WORKS

43869 ■ "Avoiding Invention Scams" in *Black Enterprise* (Vol. 37, January 2007, No. 6, pp. 46)
Pub: Earl G. Graves Publishing Co. Inc.

Ed: James C. Johnson. **Description:** Invention promotion firms provide inventors assistance in developing a prototype for product development. It is important to research these companies before making a commitment to work with them because there are a number of these firms that are not legitimate and have caused independent inventors to lose thousands of dollars by making false claims as to the market potential of the inventions.

43870 ■ *Behind the Cloud*
Pub: Jossey-Bass

Ed: Marc Benioff, Carlye Adler. **Released:** 2010. **Price:** $27.95. **Description:** Salesforce.com is the world's most successful business-to-business cloud-computing company that sells an online service that helps businesses manage sales, customer service, and marketing functions.

43871 ■ "Benchmark Makes Granduca Entrance" in *Houston Business Journal* (Vol. 40, January 8, 2010, No. 35, pp. 2)
Pub: American City Business Journals

Ed: Jennifer Dawson. **Description:** Houston, Texas-based Interfin Company, owner of the Hotel Granduca, has tapped the services of Benchmark Hospitality International to manage the property. The hiring of Benchmark is part of Interfin's efforts to develop Granduca hotels in other markets. Statistical data included.

43872 ■ *It's Not Who You Know - It's Who Knows You!: The Small Business Guide to Raising Your Profits by Raising Your Profile*
Pub: John Wiley & Sons, Inc.

Ed: David Avrin. **Released:** November 9, 2010. **Price:** $24.95. **Description:** When it comes to promoting a small business or a brand, it is essential to know how valuable high-profile attention can be. But for most small companies, the cost of hiring an outside firm to increase attention can be too expensive.

43873 ■ "Legal Aid: Sample Legal Documents can Lower Your Attorney Fees" in *Black Enterprise* (Vol. 37, October 2006, No. 3, pp. 210)
Pub: Earl G. Graves Publishing Co. Inc.

Ed: Tamara E. Holmes. **Description:** FreeLegalForms.net provides thousands of free legal forms. These forms are not a substitute for consultation with an attorney but the sample documents can help save you time and money.

43874 ■ "Online Self-Publishing Services" in *Black Enterprise* (Vol. 37, November 2006, No. 4, pp. 90)
Pub: Earl G. Graves Publishing Co. Inc.

Description: Profiles of five online self-publishing services.

CONSULTANTS

43875 ■ **Expense Control Systems Inc.**
117 E Butler Ave.
Ambler, PA 19002
Ph:(215)643-4610

Fax:(215)643-4614
Contact: John F. Frustaci Sr., President
Scope: Telecommunications consulting service specializing in voice and data network analyses, equipment evaluations and accounting services. It serves all industries nationwide.

43876 ■ **Service 800**
1668 Central Ave.
PO Box 634
Deerfield, IL 60015-0634
Ph:(847)940-9333
Fax:(847)940-9808
Contact: Steve Friedlander, President
E-mail: steve@telephoneservice.com
Scope: Telecommunications consultants and brokers of broadband and local telecom services.

RESEARCH CENTERS

43877 ■ **Indiana Small Business Development Center**
1 N Capitol Ave., Ste. 900
Indianapolis, IN 46204
Ph:(317)234-2082
Free: 888—472-3244
Fax:(317)232-8872
Co. E-mail: leadcenter@isbdc.org
URL: http://www.isbdc.org
Contact: Jeff Heinzmann, Dir.
E-mail: leadcenter@isbdc.org
Scope: Small business development. **Services:** Management consulting, business evaluation, and assistance with identification, of business and management problems. **Educational Activities:** Conferences and workshops, for small business owners and those starting new businesses; co-sponsors are universities, professionals, I.E., attorneys, and CPAs; Specialized training and individual consultation, in business management, marketing, and finance; Workshops and forums.

Selling a Business

START-UP INFORMATION

43878 ■ *Legal Guide for Starting and Running a Small Business*
Pub: NOLO
Ed: Fred Steingold. **Released:** April 2008. **Price:** $34.99. **Description:** Information for starting a new business focusing on choosing a business structure, taxes, employees and independent contractors, trademark and service marks, licensing and permits, leasing and improvement of commercial space, buying and selling a business, and more.

REFERENCE WORKS

43879 ■ "ACE Aims High With Spinoff of Repair Unit" in *Globe & Mail* (January 31, 2007, pp. B15)
Pub: CTVglobemedia Publishing Inc.
Ed: Brent Jang. **Description:** The decision of ACE Aviation Holdings Inc. to sell its aircraft maintenance division and add workforce at its El Salvador plant is discussed.

43880 ■ "Algoma Resolves Hedge Fund Fight" in *Globe & Mail* (March 8, 2006, pp. B1)
Pub: CTVglobemedia Publishing Inc.
Ed: Greg Keenan. **Description:** Algoma Steel Inc. has ended a dispute with Paulson and Co., a New York hedge fund, by offering to pay $200 million special dividend, appointing new directors, and continue to go for a sale.

43881 ■ *American Bar Association Legal Guide for Small Business: Everything You Need to Know About Small Business*
Pub: Random House Information Group
Ed: American Bar Association. **Released:** June 10, 2010. **Description:** The American Bar Association provides insight into financial, health and family issues affecting small business, including start up issues, employment laws, financing a business, and selling a business.

43882 ■ "Apartment Tower in River North Fetches More Than $90 Million" in *Crain's Chicago Business* (Vol. 34, October 24, 2011, No. 42, pp. 17)
Pub: Crain Communications Inc.
Ed: Alby Gallun. **Description:** Apartment tower in River North was sold for over $90 million to a Texas pension fund adviser. Details are included.

43883 ■ "Ask Inc." in *Inc.* (November 2007, pp. 70)
Pub: Gruner & Jahr USA Publishing
Description: Advice is given for any entrepreneur considering the sale of a company.

43884 ■ "Attention, Please" in *Entrepreneur* (Vol. 36, April 2008, No. 4, pp. 52)
Pub: Entrepreneur Media, Inc.
Ed: Andrea Cooper. **Description:** Gurbaksh Chahal created his own company ClickAgents at the age of 16, and sold it two years later for $40 million to Val-

ueClick. He then founded BlueLithium, an online advertising network on behavioral targeting, which Yahoo! Inc. bought in 2007 for $300 million. Chahal, now 25, talks about his next plans and describes how BlueLithium caught Yahoo's attention.

43885 ■ "Auxilium Drug's New Use: Putting Squeeze On Cellulite" in *Philadelphia Business Journal* (Vol. 30, September 16, 2011, No. 31, pp. 1)
Pub: American City Business Journals Inc.
Ed: John George. **Description:** Auxilium Pharmaceuticals and BioSpecifics Technologies are getting on with their plans of finding new uses for their drug Xiaflex, a possible treatment for cellulite. The two firms have dismissed their pending litigations and mapped out an amended licensing agreement for their search for the potential uses of the drug.

43886 ■ "Big Sell-Off At Sunwest" in *The Business Journal-Portland* (Vol. 25, July 25, 2008, No. 20, pp. 1)
Pub: American City Business Journals, Inc.
Ed: Robin J. Moody. **Description:** Oregon's largest operator of assisted living facilities Sunwest Management Inc. is expected to sell 132 of its properties. The planned sale, which is believed to be worth more than $1 billion, will help Sunwest pay creditors and investors. Other views and information on the planned sale, as well as on Sunwest's services which include adult day care, are presented.

43887 ■ "Black On Black Business: Moorehead Buys Hank Aaron's Toyota Dealership" in *Black Enterprise* (Vol. 38, February 2008, No. 7, pp. 28)
Pub: Earl G. Graves Publishing Co. Inc.
Ed: Brenda Porter. **Description:** In a move to expand his automotive business, Thomas A. Moorehead, CEO of BMW/MINI of Sterling, Georgia bought Hank Aaron's Toyota automobile dealership in McDonough, Georgia. Moorehead stated that he will call the new store Toyota of McDonough.

43888 ■ "BofA May Part With U.S. Trust" in *Boston Business Journal* (Vol. 31, May 20, 2011, No. 17, pp. 1)
Pub: Boston Business Journal
Ed: Tim McLaughlin. **Description:** Bank of America Corporation is willing to sell its U.S. Trust private banking division to improve its capital ratio. The unit remains to be the corporation's core asset and posted $696 million revenue in the first quarter 2010 in contract with Merrill Lynch Global Wealth Management's $3.5 billion. Analysts say that U.S. Trust would fetch more than $3 billion.

43889 ■ *Building a Dream: A Canadian Guide to Starting Your Own Business*
Pub: McGraw-Hill Ryerson Ltd.
Ed: Walter S. Good. **Released:** 2005. **Description:** Topics covered include evaluating business potential, new business ideas, starting or buying a business, franchise opportunities, business organization, protecting an idea, arranging financing, and developing a business plan.

43890 ■ "Business For Sale: Your Cold Calling?" in *Inc.* (December 2007, pp. 34)
Pub: Gruner & Jahr USA Publishing
Ed: Elaine Appleton Grant. **Description:** Profile of a recreational outfitting company in northern New England with an asking price of $6.185 million, with gross revenue of $9.4 million in 2007.

43891 ■ *Buying and Selling a Business*
Pub: Entrepreneur Press
Ed: Ira Nottonson. **Released:** April 2008. **Price:** $32.95. **Description:** Tips for negotiating sales are presented. Attorney, Ira Nottonson presents both sides of negotiations by presenting the both buyer's and seller's perspectives. Critical steps in the sale process, including presentation, negotiation and documentations are discussed. The book teaches how to gain the upper hand, minimize financial risk and be a winner regardless of side.

43892 ■ "Calista Sells Rural Newspapers" in *Alaska Business Monthly* (Vol. 27, October 2011, No. 10, pp. 8)
Pub: Alaska Business Publishing Company
Ed: Nancy Pounds. **Description:** Calista sold its six newspapers, a magazine, shoppers and its printing house. Details of the sales are given.

43893 ■ "CanWest Plotting Buyback of Newspaper Income Trust" in *Globe & Mail* (February 7, 2007, pp. B1)
Pub: CTVglobemedia Publishing Inc.
Ed: Sinclair Stewart; Boyd Erman; Grant Robertson. **Description:** The CanWest Global Communications Corp.'s decision to sell its media assets in Australia and New Zealand in order to finance its plans of repurchasing its newspaper income trust CanWest MediaWorks Income Fund is discussed.

43894 ■ "Carveouts Back in Vogue" in *Mergers & Acquisitions: The Dealmaker's Journal* (March 1, 2008)
Pub: SourceMedia, Inc.
Ed: Ken MacFadyen. **Description:** Discusses ways in which companies look for hidden assets that they can exploit in worsening economic times; oftentimes firms try to sell off assets or in other instances they will look to unlock value through public spinoffs or through internal reorganizations.

43895 ■ "Coca-Cola Bottler Up for Sale: CEO J. Bruce Llewellyn Seeks Retirement" in *Black Enterprise* (Vol. 37, December 2006, No. 5, pp. 31)
Pub: Earl G. Graves Publishing Co. Inc.
Ed: Marcia A. Wade. **Description:** J. Bruce Llewellyn of Brucephil Inc., the parent company of the Philadelphia Coca-Cola Bottling Co. has agreed to sell its remaining shares to Coca-Cola Co., which previously owned 31 percent of Philly Coke. Analysts believe that Coca-Cola will eventually sell its shares to another bottler.

43896 ■ *The Complete Guide to Buying a Business*
Pub: NOLO
Ed: Fred S. Steingold. **Released:** November 2007. **Price:** $24.99. **Description:** Key steps in buying a

business are highlighted, focusing on legal issues, tax considerations, approaches for valuing a business, financing, structuring the deal, along with forms and documents for taking ownership are included.

43897 ■ *The Complete Guide to Selling a Business*
Pub: NOLO

Ed: Fred S. Steingold. **Released:** November 2007. **Price:** $34.99. **Description:** When selling a business it is critical that a sales agreement covers all key concerns from price and payment terms to liability protection and restrictions on future competition.

43898 ■ "A Counter Offer" in *Inc.* (February 2008, pp.)
Pub: Gruner & Jahr USA Publishing

Ed: Elaine Appleton Grant. **Description:** Online retailer offering a line of kitchen and home products has upgraded its Website in order to make the business more attractive to possible buyers of the company. The firm is asking $9.9 million and reported gross revenue of $12.7 in 2007. The owner suggests that a buyer add product lines geared towards more rooms of the home than currently offer on the retail site.

43899 ■ "Cyberwise" in *Black Enterprise* (Vol. 41, September 2010, No. 2, pp. 49)
Pub: Earl G. Graves Publishing Co. Inc.

Ed: Marcia Wade Talbert. **Description:** Advice is given to assist in selling an online store called theupscalegaragesale.com. A listing of business brokers specializing in the sale of Internet businesses is included.

43900 ■ "Defer Tax with Installment Sale Election" in *Business Owner* (Vol. 35, September-October 2011, No. 5, pp. 12)
Pub: DL Perkins Company

Description: It is critical to consult with a tax professional before selling any high-value asset in order to minimize taxes.

43901 ■ "For Hospitals, a Dating Game" in *Business Courier* (Vol. 26, December 4, 2009, No. 32, pp. 1)
Pub: American City Business Journals, Inc.

Ed: James Ritchie. **Description:** Drake Center, Fort Hamilton Hospital, and West Chester Medical Center are among the members of Cincinnati's Health Alliance looking for potential buyers or partners. Meanwhile, Jewish Hospital, another member of the Alliance, will be bought by Mercy Health Partners by January 7, 2010.

43902 ■ "For the Seasoned Buyer" in *Inc.* (Vol. 30, November 2008, No. 11, pp. 32)
Pub: Mansueto Ventures LLC

Ed: Darren Dahl. **Description:** Dominick Fimiano shares his plans to sell his ten-year-old business that manufactures and sells frozen pizza dough and crusts as well as a variety of topped pizzas. Products are purchased by schools, hospitals, bowling alleys and amusement parks. The business sale includes the buyer's taking on Fimiano's son the firm's most senior employee.

43903 ■ "Fred Weber CEO Tom Dunne: Sales Talks Confidential" in *Saint Louis Business Journal* (Vol. 32, September 23, 2011, No. 4, pp. 1)
Pub: Saint Louis Business Journal

Ed: Evan Binns. **Description:** Fred Weber Inc. CEO Tom Dunne Sr. signed a letter of confidentiality as part of an inquiry made by interested party to the construction company. However, Dunne denied the company is in a fire sale and has been continuing to bid for work and has not stopped securing projects.

43904 ■ "A Graceful (and Lucrative) Exit" in *Black Enterprise* (Vol. 38, November 2007, No. 4, pp. 108)
Pub: Earl G. Graves Publishing Co. Inc.

Ed: Tamara E. Holmes. **Description:** BlueKey Business Brokerage helps clients buy, grow or sell a business. Four key points are examined in order to successfully exit a business.

43905 ■ "Harleysville Eyes Growth After Nationwide Deal" in *Philadelphia Business Journal* (Vol. 30, October 7, 2011, No. 34, pp. 1)
Pub: American City Business Journals Inc.

Ed: Jeff Blumenthal. **Description:** Harleysville Group announced growth plans after the company was sold to Columbus, Ohio-based Nationwide Mutual Insurance Company for about $1.63 billion. Nationwide gained an independent agency platform in 32 states with the Harleysville deal.

43906 ■ "Hartco Income Fund Announces the Completion of the CompuSmart Strategic Review" in *Canadian Corporate News* (May 14, 2007)
Pub: Comtex News Network Inc.

Description: Hartco Income Fund announced that it has completed the process of exploring strategic options for CompuSmart and found that it should implement a plan to sell select stores and assets while consolidating remaining CompuSmart locations over the next sixty days.

43907 ■ "Health Alliance Could Sell Group" in *Business Courier* (Vol. 27, June 18, 2010, No. 7, pp. 1)
Pub: Business Courier

Ed: James Ritchie. **Description:** Health Alliance could sell the 31-doctor Greater Cincinnati Associated Physicians Group. The group has seen several members withdraw ever since the group filed a complaint asking to be released from services to Health Alliance.

43908 ■ "Hospital Fighting for Its Life; Board of St. Anthony Scrambles to Stem Losses" in *Crain's Chicago Business* (April 28, 2008)
Pub: Crain Communications, Inc.

Ed: Mike Colias. **Description:** Chicago's Catholic health chain was looking to sell the money-losing hospital St. Anthony Hospital on the West Side but with the financial picture improving and no merger offers in the works the investment bank hired to shop the hospital is hoping to operate the 111-year-old facility as an independent entity. St. Anthony serves as a "safety net" for the region since an increasing number of its patients are uninsured or on public aid, which pays far less than commercial insurers.

43909 ■ *How to Buy and/or Sell a Small Business for Maximum Profit: A Step-by-Step Guide*
Pub: Atlantic Publishing Company

Ed: Rene V. Richards. **Released:** January 2006. **Price:** $24.95. **Description:** Suggestions, insights and techniques for buying and selling small businesses, includes advice on when to buy or sell, how to market the business, explanation of legal and financial documents involved in the sale and closing of a deal.

43910 ■ "How I Did It: Laurel Touby Mediabistro" in *Inc.* (March 2008, pp. 124-126)
Pub: Gruner & Jahr USA Publishing

Ed: Eric Schine. **Description:** Profile of Laurel Touby and her business plan; Touby started Mediabistro as a series of parties that turned into an influential job listing and training Website for journalists. Last year she sold it for $23 million.

43911 ■ "Imax in Play as It Explores Options" in *Globe & Mail* (March 10, 2006, pp. B3)
Pub: CTVglobemedia Publishing Inc.

Ed: Shirley Won. **Description:** Imax Corp. has put up itself for sale, and has also confirmed that it has received unsolicited offers for purchase.

43912 ■ "Inmet Selling Nunavut Mining Properties" in *Globe & Mail* (February 15, 2006, pp. B6)
Pub: CTVglobemedia Publishing Inc.

Ed: Allan Robinson. **Description:** The details on Wolfden Resources Inc.'s acquisition of mining assets of Inmet Mining Corp. are presented.

43913 ■ "Intel to Buy McAfee Security Business for 768B" in *eWeek* (August 19, 2010)
Pub: Ziff Davis Enterprise

Description: Intel will acquire security giant McAfee for approximately $7.68 billion, whereby McAfee would become a wholly owned subsidiary of Intel and would report to Intel's Software and Services Group.

43914 ■ "Intrawest Puts Itself on Market" in *Globe & Mail* (March 1, 2006, pp. B1)
Pub: CTVglobemedia Publishing Inc.

Ed: Elizabeth Church. **Description:** The reasons behind the decision of Intrawest Corp. to go for sale or seek partnerships are presented. The company appointed Goldman Sachs & Co. to meet the purpose.

43915 ■ "Kerry Steel to Sell Inventory, Close Business After 30 Years" in *Crain's Detroit Business* (Vol. 24, March 17, 2008, No. 11, pp. 26)
Pub: Crain Communications, Inc.

Ed: Brent Snavely. **Description:** Kerry Steel Inc. has confirmed that it is selling all of its inventory and equipment and is going out of business; the company, which was once one of the largest steel service centers in the Midwest, has sustained financial losses and is in violation of its loan agreements.

43916 ■ "Legacy Hotels Looks for a Buyer" in *Globe & Mail* (March 2, 2007, pp. B3)
Pub: CTVglobemedia Publishing Inc.

Ed: Elizabeth Church. **Description:** Legacy Hotels Real Estate Investment Trust, which has a portfolio of 25 properties, plans to sell its businesses. The shares of the real estate investment trust climbed $13.21, as the sales news was delivered.

43917 ■ "Major Tech Employers Pulling Out" in *Sacramento Business Journal* (Vol. 25, August 1, 2008, No. 22, pp. 1)
Pub: American City Business Journals, Inc.

Ed: Celia Lamb. **Description:** Biotechnology company Affymetrix Inc. is planning to close its West Sacramento, California plant and lay off 110 employees. The company said it will expand a corporate restructuring plan. Affymetrix also plans to lease out or sell its building at Riverside Parkway.

43918 ■ "McIntosh Family Sells Car Dealership" in *Black Enterprise* (Vol. 38, December 2007, No. 5)
Pub: Earl G. Graves Publishing Co. Inc.

Ed: Brenda Porter. **Description:** Seattle's McIntosh family sold its Kirkland Chrysler Jeep dealership to private equity firm Cerberus Capital Management. Details of the deal are given.

43919 ■ *Mergers and Acquisitions from A to Z*
Pub: Amacom

Ed: Andrew J. Sherman, Milledge A. Hart. **Released:** January 2006. **Price:** $35.00. **Description:** Guide for the entire process of mergers and acquisitions, including taxes, accounting, laws, and projected financial gain.

43920 ■ "Milton Touts ACE Unit to Would-Be Buyers" in *Globe & Mail* (February 10, 2007, pp. B6)
Pub: CTVglobemedia Publishing Inc.

Ed: Brent Jang. **Description:** The decision of Air Canada chairman Robert Milton to sell Air Canada Technical Services unit is presented. ACE Aviation Holdings Inc. is the parent company of Air Canada.

43921 ■ "Murdock Carrousel Sold" in *Charlotte Observer* (January 31, 2007)
Pub: Knight-Ridder/Tribune Business News

Ed: Bob Fliss. **Description:** Details on the sale of the Murdock Carrousel shopping center are highlighted. The deal was reported at $281 million.

43922 ■ "My Day" in *Business Strategy Review* (Vol. 21, Autumn 2010, No. 3, pp. 77)
Pub: Wiley-Blackwell

Ed: Julie Meyer. **Description:** Julie Meyer shot to prominence as cofounder of the entrepreneurial network, First Tuesday. The firm was sold for $50 million in 2000.

43923 ■ "NexCen Brands Sells Chains and Will Liquidate" in *Ice Cream Reporter* **(Vol. 23, August 20, 2010, No. 9, pp. 1)**
Pub: Ice Cream Reporter
Description: NexCen Brands is closing the sale of its franchise businesses, which include the frozen dessert chains MaggieMoo's and Marbel Slab Creamery, to Global Franchise Group.

43924 ■ "The Next Chapter" in *Business Courier* **(Vol. 26, November 20, 2009, No. 30, pp. 1)**
Pub: American City Business Journals, Inc.
Ed: Lucy May. **Description:** Eric Browne and Mel Gravely purchased controlling interest in TriVersity Construction Group from CM-GC CEO Schuyler Murdoch and MBJ Consultants President Monroe Barnes. One third of the company was still owned by Cincinnati-based Messer and TriVersity and will continue to be a certified minority business enterprise.

43925 ■ "Nursing Home Group Put on the Block" in *Globe & Mail* **(February 23, 2006, pp. B1)**
Pub: CTVglobemedia Publishing Inc.
Ed: Elizabeth Church. **Description:** The reasons behind the decision of Exetendicare Inc. to go for sale are presented.

43926 ■ "On the Cutting Edge" in *Inc.* **(November 2007, pp. 28)**
Pub: Gruner & Jahr USA Publishing
Ed: Elaine Appleton Grant. **Description:** Information is provided about a Nashville-area glass and glazing company that is on the market for $8.2 million. The owner started the company from the back of his truck in 2990 with $2,200. The firm has $9 million worth of contracts signed through 2008. Statistical data included.

43927 ■ "P/Kaufmann Sells Bennettsville" in *Home Textiles Today* **(Vol. 31, May 24, 2011, No. 13, pp. 6)**
Pub: Reed Business Information
Description: Decorative Screen Printers purchased the printing and finishing facility of P/Kaufmann in Bennettsville, South Carolina. However, the firm will continue its focus on its core business, a vat printing facility for home furnishings fabrics.

43928 ■ "Pocket Change?" in *Inc.* **(Vol. 30, December 2008, No. 12, pp. 28)**
Pub: Mansueto Ventures LLC
Ed: Ryan McCarthy. **Description:** Owner of a chain of nine retail billiard showrooms grew his business by starting to deliver pool tables for Sears. The company, consisting of seven retail locations and two warehouses, is now for sale. Details are included.

43929 ■ "Points of Light Sells MissionFish to eBay" in *Non-Profit Times* **(Vol. 25, May 15, 2011, No. 7, pp. May 15, 2011)**
Pub: NPT Publishing Group Inc.
Description: eBay purchased MissionFish, a subsidiary of Points of Light Institute for $4.5 million. MissionFish allows eBay sellers to give proceeds from sales to their favorite nonprofit organization and helps nonprofits raise funds by selling on eBay.

43930 ■ "Portland's Hilton For Sale" in *Business Journal Portland* **(Vol. 27, October 22, 2010, No. 34, pp. 1)**
Pub: Portland Business Journal
Ed: Wendy Culverwell. **Description:** Hilton Portland & Executive Tower, Portland's biggest hotel, is being sold by Cornerstone Real Estate Advisers LLC. Cornerstone hopes to close the deal for the 782-room complex by the end of 2010. Cornerstone contracted Jones Lang LaSalle to manage the sale, but terms to the deal are not available.

43931 ■ "Potash Sale Must Be Blocked" in *Canadian Business* **(Vol. 83, October 12, 2010, No. 17, pp. 24)**
Pub: Rogers Media Ltd.
Ed: Kasey Coholan. **Description:** Chief executive officers (CEOs) and corporate leaders in Canada are concerned about the possible sale of Potash Corporation to foreign buyers. A Compas Inc. poll recently

asked CEOs whether the Canadian Government should step in to block the sale of the country's largest fertilizer firm.

43932 ■ "Roy MacDowell Jr." in *Boston Business Journal* **(Vol. 31, June 10, 2011, No. 20, pp. 1)**
Pub: Boston Business Journal
Ed: Craig M. Douglas. **Description:** Real estate developer Roy MacDowell is selling his Boston, Massachusetts estate. The asking price for the property is $21.8 million. MacDowell recently suffered setbacks in his finances.

43933 ■ "RS Information Systems Signs Buyout Deal" in *Black Enterprise* **(February 2008)**
Pub: Earl G. Graves Publishing Co. Inc.
Ed: Alan Hughes. **Description:** Details of the RS Information Systems buyout by Wyle, a privately held provider of high-tech aerospace engineering, testing, and research services.

43934 ■ "Sale of Solo Cup Plant Pending" in *Boston Business Journal* **(Vol. 29, June 17, 2011, No. 6, pp. 1)**
Pub: American City Business Journals Inc.
Ed: Daniel J. Sernovitz. **Description:** Baltimore developers Vanguard Equities Inc. and Greenberg Gibbons Commercial have contracted to buy the Solo Cup Company facility in Owing Mills and are now considering several plans for the property. Sale should be completed by September 2011 but no proposed sale terms are disclosed.

43935 ■ *The Secret of Exiting Your Business Under Your Terms!*
Pub: Outskirts Press, Incorporated
Ed: Gene H. Irwin. **Released:** August 2005. **Price:** $29.95. **Description:** Topics include how to sell a business for the highest value, tax laws governing the sale of a business, finding the right buyer, mergers and acquisitions, negotiating the sale, and using a limited auction to increase future value of a business.

43936 ■ *Sell Your Business Your Way: Getting Out, Getting Rich, and Getting on with Your Life*
Pub: American Management Association
Ed: Rick Rickertsen; Robert Gunther. **Released:** 2006. **Price:** $27.95.

43937 ■ "Selling Your Company" in *Inc.* **(March 2008, pp. 78)**
Pub: Gruner & Jahr USA Publishing
Ed: Myra Goodman. **Description:** Owner of a safety consulting company seeks advice for selling the firm.

43938 ■ "Serial Starter" in *Entrepreneur* **(Vol. 36, April 2008, No. 4, pp. 17)**
Pub: Entrepreneur Media, Inc.
Ed: Andrea Cooper. **Description:** Some entrepreneurs are engaged in serial entrepreneurship as they feel that they are no longer satisfied with their business and they decide to sell it. Others start out new businesses because they believe they can try out and be successful in different kinds of businesses. Details on how to identify and handle new entrepreneurial opportunities are discussed.

43939 ■ "Sign, Sign, Everywhere a Sign: How I Did It: Richard Schaps" in *Inc.* **(October 2007, pp. 128)**
Pub: Gruner & Jahr USA Publishing
Ed: Stephanie Clifford. **Description:** Richard Schaps shares the story of selling his outdoor-advertising firm, Van Wagner for $170 million and sharing the wealth with his employees. Schaps then started another outdoor-sign company.

43940 ■ "Silverdome Bidders Bring New Proposals" in *Crain's Detroit Business* **(Vol. 24, March 17, 2008, No. 11, pp. 23)**
Pub: Crain Communications, Inc.
Ed: Daniel Duggan. **Description:** Discusses the seven plans which have been proposed as part of the third round of bidding for the Pontiac Silverdome; proposals range from Global Baseball Inc., a baseball league that would pit a team from every country

against one another, to an Indian casino, a musical "hall of fame", a convention center, a horse track, a hotel and an indoor water park.

43941 ■ "S.M. Whitney Co. (1868-2010)" in *Canadian Business* **(Vol. 83, October 12, 2010, No. 17, pp. 27)**
Pub: Rogers Media Ltd.
Ed: Angelina Chapin. **Description:** A history of S.M. Whitney Company is presented. The cotton company was opened in 1868. The cotton is sold to textile manufacturers after crops have been picked, ginned and baled. The company closed down in 2010 after chief executive officer Barry Whitney decided to sell his last bale of cotton.

43942 ■ "Souled Out" in *Canadian Business* **(Vol. 81, March 3, 2008, No. 3, pp. 35)**
Pub: Rogers Media
Ed: Calvin Leung. **Description:** According to a survey of over 100 entrepreneurs, 78 percent responded that selling their business was emotionally draining for them. Greig Clark, for example, says that one of the toughest times of his life was selling College Pro Painters, after putting 18 years into that business. The economic impacts of selling out are also examined.

43943 ■ "Speedway Explored Sale" in *Business Courier* **(Vol. 24, October 12, 2008, No. 26, pp. 1)**
Pub: American City Business Journals, Inc.
Ed: Jon Newberry. **Description:** Court records revealed that Kentucky Speedway discussed a possible sale of its Gallatin County track to International Speedway Corp. (ISC) before it sued NASCAR and ISC in 2005 for monopolizing bigtime racing. Kentucky Speedway chairman Jerry Carroll explained in a sworn statement that ISC was only interested in the sale if it can buy the track for a cheap price. The court proceedings and the sale allegations are discussed.

43944 ■ *Stop Working: Start a Business, Globalize It, and Generate Enough Cash Flow to Get Out of the Rat Race*
Pub: Eye Contact Media
Ed: Rohan Hall. **Released:** November 2004. **Price:** $15.99. **Description:** Advice is given to small companies to compete in the global marketplace by entrepreneur using the same strategy for his own business.

43945 ■ "Suitors Circling Chrysler as Sale Likely" in *Globe & Mail* **(February 19, 2007, pp. B1)**
Pub: CTVglobemedia Publishing Inc.
Ed: Jason Singer. **Description:** DaimlerChrysler AG is planning to sell or spin-off the Chrysler Group, as a cost cutting strategy. Chrysler reported a 40 percent drop in fourth quarter profit because of the $1.5 billion operating loss.

43946 ■ "Sullivan Led Bucyrus through Unforgettable Year" in *Business Journal-Milwaukee* **(Vol. 28, December 17, 2010, No. 11, pp. A1)**
Pub: Milwaukee Business Journal
Ed: Rich Rovito. **Description:** Bucyrus International's president and CEO, Tim Sullivan, was chosen as Milwaukee, Wisconsin's Executive of the Year for 2010. Sullivan led Bucyrus through a year of dramatic change which started with the acquisition of the mining business of Terex Corporation and culminating with a deal to sell Caterpillar Inc.

43947 ■ "Sunwest Vies To Stave Off Bankruptcy" in *The Business Journal-Portland* **(Vol. 25, August 15, 2008, No. 23, pp. 1)**
Pub: American City Business Journals, Inc.
Ed: Robin J. Moody. **Description:** Sunwest Management Inc. is teetering on the edge of bankruptcy as creditors start foreclosure on nine of their properties. This could potentially displace residents of the assisted living operator. Sunwest is trying to sell smaller packages of properties to get a $100 million bridge loan to maintain operations.

43948 ■ "Symantic Completes Acquisition of VeriSign's Security Business" in *Internet Wire* **(August 9, 2010)**
Pub: Comtex

Description: Symantec Corporation acquired Veri-Sign's identity and authentication business, which includes Secure Sockets Layer (SSL) and Code Signing Certificate Services, the Managed Public Key Infrastructure (MPKI) Services, the VeriSign Trust Seal, the VeriSign Identity Protection (VIP) Authentication Service and the VIP Fraud Protection Service (FDS). The agreement also included a majority stake in VeriSign Japan.

43949 ■ "Tampa Condo Conversion Sells for $14.8 Million Less" in *The Business Journal-Serving Greater Tampa Bay* **(Vol. 28, September 5, 2008)**
Pub: American City Business Journals, Inc.

Ed: Janet Leiser. **Description:** Former apartment complex Village Oaks at Tampa, which was converted to condominiums, has been sold to Tennessee-based real estate investment trust Mid-America Apartment Communities Inc. for $21.2 million in August 2008. The amount was $14.2 million less than what developer Radco Management LLC paid for in 2005.

43950 ■ "Tektronix Buys Arbor Networks for Security Business" in *eWeek* **(August 9, 2010)**
Pub: Ziff Davis Enterprise

Description: Tektronix Communications, provider of communications test and network intelligence solutions will acquire Arbor Networks. The deal will help Tektronix build a brand in security. Details of the transaction are included.

43951 ■ "To Sell or Not To Sell" in *Inc.* **(December 2007, pp. 80)**
Pub: Gruner & Jahr USA Publishing

Ed: Patrick J. Sauer. **Description:** Owner of a private equity discusses the challenges he faces when deciding to sell his family's business.

43952 ■ "Today's Business Sale Climate" in *Business Owner* **(Vol. 35, September-October 2011, No. 5, pp. 10)**
Pub: DL Perkins Company

Description: Despite the weak economy, there is a surplus of individuals wanting to purchase a small business. The Small Business Administration loan guarantees program helps with its loans for purchase/sale of business assistance.

43953 ■ *Ultimate Guide to Buying or Selling Your Business*
Pub: Entrepreneur Press

Ed: Ira N. Nottonson. **Released:** September 2004. **Price:** $24.95 (US), $35.95 (Canadian). **Description:** Proven strategies to evaluate, negotiate, and buy or sell a small business. Franchise and family business succession planning is included.

43954 ■ "The VC Shakeout" in *Harvard Business Review* **(Vol. 88, July-August 2010, No. 7-8, pp. 21)**
Pub: Harvard Business School Publishing

Ed: Joseph Ghalbouni, Dominque Rouzies. **Description:** Authors argue that in order to be successful, venture capital needs to focus less on how to sell a newly acquired investment and more on ways to grow a good company.

43955 ■ "Welcome Back" in *Canadian Business* **(Vol. 82, April 27, 2009, No. 7, pp. 25)**
Pub: Rogers Media

Ed: Sarka Halas. **Description:** Some Canadian companies such as Gennum Corporation have taken advantage of corporate sale-leasebacks to raise money at a time when credit is hard to acquire. Corporate sale-leasebacks allow companies to sell their property assets while remaining as tenants of the building. Sale-leasebacks allow firms to increase capital while avoiding the disruptions that may result with moving.

43956 ■ "With New Listings, Business Brokers See Hope" in *Business Courier* **(Vol. 27, September 3, 2010, No. 18, pp. 1)**
Pub: Business Courier

Ed: Lucy May. **Description:** Business brokers in Cincinnati, Ohio are expecting better prices in view of the strengthening economy.

43957 ■ "Wrap It Up" in *Entrepreneur* **(Vol. 36, April 2008, No. 4, pp. 84)**
Pub: Entrepreneur Media, Inc.

Ed: Barry Farber. **Description:** Tips on how to manage and get through the closing of a business sale are presented. Focus on what solutions you can bring and not on emotional attachments that can show your eagerness for the sale. Having a track of positive accomplishments can also help.

43958 ■ "Your Turn in the Spotlight" in *Inc.* **(March 2008, pp. 30)**
Pub: Gruner & Jahr USA Publishing

Ed: Elaine Appleton Grant. **Description:** Profile of a Tennessee business that produces events and concerts. The company offers a complete package of services handling staging, lighting, video, musical instrument rentals, and audio support. The founder has decided to sell the business and details of the asking price, price rationale, the pros and cons of buying the firm and its bottom line are examined.

VIDEOCASSETTES/AUDIOCASSETTES

43959 ■ *Selling a Business*
American Institute of Small Business (AISB)
23075 Highway 7, Ste. 200
Shorewood, MN 55331
Ph:(952)545-7001
Free: 800-328-2906
Fax:(952)545-7020
Co. E-mail: judy@aisb.biz
URL: http://www.pfa.com/AISB.htm
Released: 1994. **Price:** $59.95. **Description:** Includes interviews with consultants and attorneys. **Availability:** VHS.

CONSULTANTS

43960 ■ The Blaine Group Inc.
8665 Wilshire Blvd., Ste. 301
Beverly Hills, CA 90211-2975
Ph:(310)360-1499
Fax:(310)360-1498
Co. E-mail: devon@blainegroupinc.com
URL: http://www.blainegroupinc.com
Contact: Devon Blaine, President
E-mail: devon@atsblainegroupinc.com
Scope: The firm provides a variety of special communications services to its clients. These include managing crisis situations conceiving, coordinating seminars and press conferences, event and party planning, developing master plans and collateral materials, proposal, article, letter and speech writing, conducting surveys and publishing newsletters and brochures. **Publications:** "They Don't Want You to Know About".

43961 ■ Business Brokers Hawaii L.L.C.
3230 Pikai Way
PO Box 1810
Kihei, HI 96753
Ph:(808)879-8833
Free: (866)239-1567
Fax:(808)879-5966
Co. E-mail: md@businessbrokershawaii.com
URL: http://www.business-brokers.com
Contact: Solana Poe, Principle
E-mail: solana@atsbusinessbrokershawaii.com
Scope: Offers buying or selling existing businesses, creation of new businesses, business evaluation and appraisal, assistance to clients on expansion and mergers, consultation with owners of businesses in trouble, and consultation on Unites States, Japan and Chinese commerce. **Seminars:** How to Start Your Own Business; How to Make a Sick Business Well Again; How to do Fiscal Forecasting and Cash Flow Projections.

43962 ■ Business Team
1901 S Bascom Ave., Ste. 400
Campbell, CA 95008
Ph:(408)246-1102
Fax:(408)246-2219
Co. E-mail: sanjose@business-team.com
URL: http://www.business-team.com
Contact: William L. Kramer, Vice President
E-mail: mani@atsbusiness-team.com
Scope: Business consulting services offered to companies looking for buyers. Specializes in mergers and acquisitions, business brokerage, and valuations. **Seminars:** Business Valuation Enhancing the Value of Your Company.

43963 ■ The Change Agents
145 Columbia Ave.
Holland, MI 49423-2978
Ph:(616)392-5564
Contact: William G. Garlough, Managing Director
Scope: Provides consulting services related to mergers, acquisitions and divestitures. Services offered include: Assisting acquiring companies in establishing and managing effective acquisition programs; representing sellers in the sale of their companies, and bringing buyers and sellers together. Additional consulting services include: Advising on the structure of leveraged buy-outs; mediating sales between partners or in family succession; business valuations; due diligence examination of the marketing function; post-acquisition integration advice; and corporate strategy and planning.

43964 ■ Corporate Business Services of America Inc.
5 Palmer Dr.
PO Box 1352
Conway, AR 72032-9484
Ph:(501)329-2592
Contact: Gene Horton, President
Scope: Business management consulting firm specializes in profit engineering, management consulting, and business coaching. Industries served: Businesses with sales in the $500,000 to $25,000,000 range.

43965 ■ DeVries & Company Inc.
800 W 47th St.
Kansas City, MO 64112
Ph:(816)756-0055
Free: 877-428-7252
Fax:(816)756-0061
Contact: Rose Marie, Principle
Scope: Investment banking/financial consulting firm which helps companies solve financial problems and achieve growth and diversification goals. Helps established companies raise capital and assists new and developing companies secure venture capital and create public markets for their stocks. Provides confidential services to companies who want to sell or merge, aids companies in acquiring other companies, helps individuals and companies structure and negotiate leveraged buyouts, provides financial guidance, shapes business strategy and develops operating and financial strategies. Also performs business valuations for estate and gift tax and ESOPS. Renders fairness opinions and expert witness services.

43966 ■ Equity Partners of America Ltd.
1450 W Long Lake Rd., Ste. 340
Troy, MI 48098-6351
Ph:(248)952-0300
Fax:(248)952-0314
Co. E-mail: equitypartners@email.msn.com
Contact: Albert A. Koch, Managing Director
Scope: Private investment bank specializing in debt and equity capital procurement; buying and selling businesses; shareholder value enhancement strategies; and litigation and alternative dispute resolution assistance; including expert witness assistance. Serves manufacturing, distribution and service industries. **Seminars:** Preparation of a business plan; Use of financial statements in damage claims; Determining the value of a business; When to sell a family business.

43967 ■ Hampton Group
7172 Regional St., Ste. 290
Dublin, CA 94568
Ph:(925)830-3447
Free: 800-820-6424
Fax:(925)831-8194
Co. E-mail: dataforpeter@hotmail.com
Contact: Peter Siegel, Owner
E-mail: dataforpeter@hotmail.com
Scope: Consults on the buying and selling of small and medium-sized businesses.

43968 ■ James W. Davidson Company Inc.
23 Forest View Rd.
Wallingford, PA 19086
Ph:(610)566-1462
Co. E-mail: jwdmsd@comcast.net
Contact: James W. Davidson, President
E-mail: jwdmsd@comcast.net
Scope: Offers counsel to clients to improve business strategy, organization, controls, management effectiveness and profits. Provides planning, problem-analysis and implementation assistance. Also performs thorough, in-depth executive recruiting and acquisition and divestment search and analysis. Experienced with large and small manufacturing and service companies, including new ventures.

43969 ■ Management Services & Development Ltd.
103 Carmalt Ave.
Punxsutawney, PA 15767-2502

Ph:(814)938-8170
Free: 800-633-0688
Fax:(814)938-8177
Co. E-mail: rdm@mergermentor.com
URL: http://www.mergermentor.com
Contact: Richard D. Mowrey, President
E-mail: rdm@mergermentor.com
Scope: Specializes in valuation and financial services for acquisition or sale of businesses. Performs appraisals and facilitates the actual transfer of business ownership. Also specializes in the sale of privately owned manufacturing businesses. Professional intermediaries who handle all phases of the project including initial analysis, planning, valuating, qualifying of prospective buyers, negotiations and execution of the transaction. Industries served: Businesses, manufacturing firms and government agencies. Serves United States and Canada. **Publications:** "Business Owner's Journal". **Seminars:** Exit Planning; How to Determine the Value of Your Business; How to Maximize the Value of Your Business; Success without Stress. **Special Services:** XL Template for Assessment Business Valuation Process.

43970 ■ Mertz Associates Inc.
1 Riverwood Pl., N17W24222 Riverwood Dr., Ste. 305
Waukesha, WI 53188-1132
Ph:(262)523-4200

Fax:(262)523-4202
Co. E-mail: mertz@mertz.com
URL: http://www.mertz.com
Contact: Laurance R. Newman, Principle
E-mail: d.marconnet@atsmertz.com
Scope: A merger and acquisition consulting firm representing either dedicated buyers or sellers of companies across the U.S. Clients range from small privately held companies to large public companies in all industries. **Publications:** "Why Successful Companies are Launching Acquisition Searches Now"; "On the Block"; "Selling Troubled Divisions and Companies"; "Don't Fear the D Word"; "M and A Multiples: A Key to Value Or a Distraction"; "Savvy CPA Levels the Playing Field"; "M and A Trends Strategic Focus Drives Success".

FRANCHISES AND BUSINESS OPPORTUNITIES

43971 ■ Upside Group Franchise Consulting Corp.
11445 E Via Linda, Ste. 2-495
Scottsdale, AZ 85259
Free: 888-445-2882
Fax:(480)664-1627
Founded: 2000. **Description:** Full franchise consulting/sales development. **Training:** Yes.

REFERENCE WORKS

43972 ■ "On Target" in *Canadian Business*
(Vol. 81, July 22, 2008, No. 12-13, pp. 45)
Pub: Rogers Media Ltd.

Ed: Calvin Leung. **Description:** Companies such as LavalifePRIME, a dating website devoted to singles 45 and older, discuss the value of marketing and services aimed at Canada's older consumers. One-third of Canada's 33 million people are 50-plus, controlling 77 percent of the countries wealth.

43973 ■ "A Second Chance to Make a Living" in *The Business Journal-Milwaukee*
(Vol. 25, September 19, 2008, No. 52, pp. A1)

Pub: American City Business Journals, Inc.
Description: Unemployed workers and baby boomers are driving interest in purchasing small businesses. BizBuySell general manager Mike Handelsman reveals that the supply of small businesses for sale is decreasing due to the increased demand. The trends in the small business market are analyzed.

LIBRARIES

43974 ■ Virginia Commonwealth University–Virginia Center on Aging–Information Resources Center (730 E)
730 E. Broad St.
Theatre Row Building
Richmond, VA 23219

Ph:(804)828-1525
Fax:(804)828-7905
Co. E-mail: eansello@vcu.edu
URL: http://www.vcu.edu/vcoa
Contact: Dr. Edward F. Ansello, Dir.

Scope: Gerontology, mental health, sociology and the politics of aging, geriatrics, family relationships, long-term care, lifelong learning. **Services:** Library open to the public with restrictions. Audiovisual materials available to Virginia residents only. **Holdings:** 1500 books; 4 archives; 120 AV items. **Subscriptions:** 6 journals and other serials.

Service Industry

START-UP INFORMATION

43975 ■ **"Business Start-Up a Learning Experience for Young Bellingham Entrepreneur"** in *Bellingham Herald* (July 18, 2010)
Pub: Bellingham Herald
Ed: Dave Gallagher. **Description:** Profile of 21-year-old entrepreneur, Chase Larabee, who developed an online program that helps airport fixed-based operators handle refueling, hotel and transportation reservations and other requests from private airplane pilots.

43976 ■ **"Fast-Forward Fortune"** in *Small Business Opportunities* (July 2010)
Pub: Harris Publications Inc.
Description: Profile of Steve Dalbec and his home-based Home Video Studio where he earns income by offering a wide variety of video services to clients from duplicating CDs, video to DVD transfer, sports videos and more. Dalbec believes this is the perfect home-based business.

43977 ■ **"Fixing Up the Area: Leo Piatz Opens General Repair Business"** in *The Dickinson Press* (November 16, 2010)
Pub: Dickinson Press
Ed: Ashley Martin. **Description:** Profile of Leo Piatz, owner of Leo's Repair in Dickinson, North Dakota; Piatz provides welding and fabricating services to farmers and ranchers in the area.

43978 ■ *Foreclosure Cleanout Business: High Profits – Low Start Up Cost*
Pub: James R. Tolliver
Ed: James Tolliver. **Released:** October 11, 2011. **Price:** $17.99. **Description:** Foreclosure cleanout business is booming. This manual teaches how to start a foreclosure firm, who to contact, what to charge, services provided and more.

43979 ■ *Getting Rich In Your Underwear: How To Start and Run a Profitable Home-Based Business*
Pub: HCM Publishing
Ed: Peter I. Hupalo. **Released:** April 1, 2005. **Price:** $17.95. **Description:** Book offers insight into starting a home-based business. Entrepreneurs will learn about business models and the home business; distribution and fulfillment of product or service; marketing and sales; how to overcome the fear of starting a business; personal success characteristics; naming a business; zoning and insurance; intellectual capital; copyrights, trademarks, and patents; limited liability companies and S-corporations; business expenses and accounting; taxes; fifteen basic steps for starting a home-based business, state resources for starting a home company; and seven home-based business ideas.

43980 ■ *How to Make Money While You Look for a Job*
Pub: Booklocker.com, Incorporated
Ed: Donna Boyette. **Released:** March 2005. **Price:** $11.95. **Description:** Six steps to make money while searching for employment are outlined, from setting up a home-based office to selling a service.

43981 ■ **"Online Fortunes"** in *Small Business Opportunities* (Fall 2008)
Pub: Entrepreneur Media Inc.
Description: Fifty hot, e-commerce enterprises for the aspiring entrepreneur to consider are featured; virtual assistants, marketing services, party planning, travel services, researching, web design and development, importing as well as creating an online store are among the businesses featured.

43982 ■ *Small Business Desk Reference*
Pub: Penguin Books (USA) Incorporated
Ed: Gene Marks. **Released:** December 2004. **Description:** Comprehensive guide for starting or running a successful small business, focusing on buying a business or franchise, writing a business plan, financial management, accounting, legal issues, human resources management, operations, marketing, sales, customer service, taxes, insurance, and ethics. Information for launching a restaurant, property management firm, retail outlet, consulting firm, and service business is included.

43983 ■ *Start Your Own Net Services Business*
Pub: Entrepreneur Press
Released: February 1, 2009. **Price:** $17.95. **Description:** Web design, search engine marketing, new-media online, and blogging, are currently the four most popular web services available. This book provides information to start a net service business.

43984 ■ *Your Million-Dollar Idea: From Concept to Marketplace (Without a Business Degree)*
Pub: Adams Media Corporation
Ed: Sandy Abrams. **Released:** March 1, 2010. **Price:** $14.95. **Description:** Self-taught entrepreneur provides a 12-step plan to make a new product or service a profitable reality.

ASSOCIATIONS AND OTHER ORGANIZATIONS

43985 ■ **Coalition of Service Industries**
1090 Vermont Ave. NW, Ste. 420
Washington, DC 20005
Ph:(202)289-7460
Fax:(202)379-9864
Co. E-mail: gololobov@uscsi.org
URL: http://www.uscsi.org
Contact: J. Robert Vastine, Pres.
Description: Increases attention to measurement of productivity in services and revises national economic indicators to account for services. Represents US service sector in multilateral trade negotiations. Works with interested groups internationally. .

REFERENCE WORKS

43986 ■ **"2010 Book of Lists"** in *Austin Business JournalInc.* (Vol. 29, December 25, 2009, No. 42, pp. 1)
Pub: American City Business Journals
Description: Rankings of companies and organizations within the business services, finance, health-

care, hospitality and travel, insurance, marketing and media, professional services, real estate, education and technology industries in Austin, Texas are presented. Rankings are based on sales, business size, and other statistics.

43987 ■ **"2010 Book of Lists"** in *Business Courier* (Vol. 26, December 26, 2009, No. 36, pp. 1)
Pub: American City Business Journals, Inc.
Description: Rankings of companies and organizations within the business services, education, finance, health care, hospitality and tourism, real estate, and technology industries in the Cincinnati, Ohio-Northern Kentucky area are presented. Rankings are based on sales, business size, or other statistics.

43988 ■ **"2010 Book of Lists"** in *Tampa Bay Business Journal* (Vol. 30, December 22, 2009, No. 53, pp. 1)
Pub: American City Business Journals
Description: Rankings of companies and organizations within the human resources, banking and finance, business services, healthcare, real estate, technology, hospitality and travel, and education industries in the Greater Tampa Bay area are presented. Rankings are based on sales, business size, and more.

43989 ■ **"ABM Janitorial Services Receives Service Excellence Award from Jones Lang LaSalle"** in *Investment Weekly News* (July 16, 2011, pp. 75)
Pub: News RX
Description: ABM Janitorial Services was awarded the 2010 Jones Lang LaSalle Distinction award in the category of Service Excellence. LaSalle is a leading financial and professional services firm that specializes in real estate services and investment management. The program recognizes supplier partners who play a vital role in LaSalle's aim to provide the highest quality of services, value and innovation to clients.

43990 ■ **"ACE Agrees to Pay Out $266 Million to Investors"** in *Globe & Mail* (February 17, 2006, pp. B1)
Pub: CTVglobemedia Publishing Inc.
Ed: Brent Jang. **Description:** Canada-based commercial aviation firm ACE Aviation Holdings has agreed to pay 266 million dollars to its investors after filing a bankruptcy one year ago. Complete details of this pay off are discussed.

43991 ■ *Achieving Planned Innovation: A Proven System for Creating Successful New Products and Services*
Pub: Simon and Schuster
Ed: Frank R. Bacon. **Released:** August 2007. **Price:** $16.95. **Description:** Planned innovation is a disciplined and practical step-by-step sequence of procedures for reaching the intended destination point: successful products. This easy-to-read book explains the system along with an action-oriented program for continuous success in new-product innovations. Five steps outlined include: a disciplined reasoning process; lasting market orientation; proper selection

criteria that reflect both strategic and tactical business objectives and goals along with dynamic matching of resources to present and future opportunities, and positive and negative requirements before making major expenditures; and proper organizational staffing. The author explains what to do and evaluating the potential of any new product or service, ranging from ventures in retail distribution to the manufacture of goods as diverse as bicycles, motorcycles, aerospace communication and navigation equipment, small business computers, food packaging, and medical products.

43992 ■ "Actiontec and Verizon Team Up for a Smarter Home" in *Ecology,Environment & Conservation Business* **(November 5, 2011, pp. 3)**
Pub: HighBeam Research
Description: Verizon is implementing Actiontec Electronics' SG200 Service Gateway as a basic component of its Home Monitoring and Control service. This new smart home service allows customers to remotely check their homes, control locks and appliances, view home-energy use and more using a smartphone, PC, or FiOS TV.

43993 ■ "Active Sales" in *Green Industry Pro* **(Vol. 23, September 2011)**
Pub: Cygnus Business Media
Ed: Gregg Wartgow. **Description:** Craig den Hartog, owner of Emerald Magic Lawn Care located in Holtsville, New York, describes the various marketing tactics he has developed to increase sales in the current economic environment. Statistical data included.

43994 ■ "Age-Old System of Bartering Is Being Revolutionized by Phoenix Company, Premier Barter" in *Internet Wire* **(July 12, 2010)**
Pub: Comtex
Description: Premier Barter is helping entrepreneurs rediscover the system of bartering as a method of exchanging goods and services without cash or credit.

43995 ■ "Air Canada to Slash 600 Non-Union Jobs" in *Globe & Mail* **(February 11, 2006, pp. B3)**
Pub: CTVglobemedia Publishing Inc.
Ed: Brent Jang. **Description:** The reasons behind workforce reduction by ACE Aviation Holdings Inc. at Air Canada are presented.

43996 ■ "Air Canada, WestJet Fill More Seats" in *Globe & Mail* **(January 6, 2006, pp. B3)**
Pub: CTVglobemedia Publishing Inc.
Ed: Brent Jang. **Description:** The reasons behind the increase in passenger for Air Canada and West-Jet Airlines Ltd. are presented.

43997 ■ "Air Canada's Flight Plan for 777s Excludes India" in *Globe & Mail* **(March 28, 2007, pp. B5)**
Pub: CTVglobemedia Publishing Inc.
Ed: Brent Jang. **Description:** The decision of Air Canada to exclude India and to fly its Boeing 777s due to poor economic returns is discussed.

43998 ■ "Airline Mergers: United Next?" in *Crain's Chicago Business* **(Vol. 31, April 21, 2008, No. 16, pp. 12)**
Pub: Crain Communications, Inc.
Description: Discusses a potential merger between United and Continental airlines; unions representing 48,900 pilots, mechanics, flight attendants, ticket agents and ramp workers at United have put the management on notice that they expect to be a factor in any merger discussions if the company wants their cooperation.

43999 ■ "Airlines Mount PR Push to Win Public Support Against Big Oil" in *Advertising Age* **(Vol. 79, July 14, 2008, No. 7, pp. 1)**
Pub: Crain Communications, Inc.
Ed: Michael Bush. **Description:** Top airline executives from competing companies have banded together in a public relations plan in which they are sending e-mails to their frequent fliers asking for aid in lobbying legislators to put a restriction on oil speculation.

44000 ■ "All Bundled Up" in *Entrepreneur* **(Vol. 35, November 2007, No. 11, pp. 104)**
Pub: Entrepreneur Media Inc.
Ed: Kim T. Gordon. **Description:** Bundling is a marketing strategy that combines a variety of features to present products and services as a whole. Tips on how to handle bundling are outlined.

44001 ■ "All the Trimmings" in *Green Industry Pro* **(Vol. 23, March 2011, No. 3, pp. 29)**
Pub: Cygnus Business Media
Ed: Gregg Wartgow. **Description:** When choosing lawn mowing equipment, it is advised to purchase commercial-grade 21-inch walk mowers rather than less expensive consumer-grade mowers. John Deere is reentering the commercial 21-inch walk behind mower market after a five-year hiatus.

44002 ■ "Ann Alexander; Senior Attorney, Natural Resources Defense Council" in *Crain's Chicago Business* **(Vol. 31, May 5, 2008, No. 18)**
Pub: Crain Communications, Inc.
Ed: Emily Stone. **Description:** Profile of Ann Alexander who is the senior attorney at the Natural Resources Defense Council and is known for her dedication to the environment and a career spent battling oil companies, steelmakers and the government to change federal regulations. One recent project aims to improve the Bush administration's fuel economy standards for SUVs. Past battles include her work to prevent permits from slipping through the cracks such as the proposal by London-based BP PLC to dump 54 percent more ammonia and 35 percent more suspended solids from its Whiting, Indiana refinery into Lake Michigan-the source of drinking water for Chicago and its surrounding communities.

44003 ■ "Anybody Out There?" in *Canadian Business* **(Vol. 81, July 21 2008, No. 11, pp. 31)**
Pub: Rogers Media Ltd.
Ed: Andrew Wahl. **Description:** Virtual offices or shared office services provide solutions to companies that can no longer accommodate additional workspaces. The alternative working arrangement allows the company to have a kind of distributed work system. The disadvantages of employing virtual offices are presented.

44004 ■ "App Time: Smartphone Applications Aren't Just for Fun and Games Anymore" in *Inc.* **(Volume 32, December 2010, No. 10, pp. 116)**
Pub: Inc. Magazine
Ed: Jason Del Rey. **Description:** Smart phone technology can help any small business market their products and services.

44005 ■ "Astral Media Set to Broadcast Coast to Coast" in *Globe & Mail* **(February 24, 2007, pp. B5)**
Pub: CTVglobemedia Publishing Inc.
Ed: Grant Robertson. **Description:** The decision of Astral Media Inc. to acquire Standard Broadcasting Corp. Ltd. for $1.2 billion, with a view to increase its broadcast coverage, is discussed.

44006 ■ "AT&T Wins Networking Deal from GM Worth $1 Billion" in *Globe & Mail* **(February 22, 2007, pp. B14)**
Pub: CTVglobemedia Publishing Inc.
Description: AT&T Inc., the largest telephone company in the United States, won a $1 billion contract from General Motors Corp. to provide communications services to integrate the automaker's networks.

44007 ■ "Aussie Rules" in *Canadian Business* **(Vol. 79, Winter 2006, No. 24, pp. 45)**
Pub: Rogers Media
Ed: Jeff Sanford. **Description:** The efforts of the Toronto-based private equity firm Onex to acquire the Australian national airline, Qantas Airways Ltd., are described.

44008 ■ "Auxis Introduces Services for Government Contracting" in *Entertainment Close-Up* **(December 22, 2010)**
Pub: Close-Up Media
Description: Profile of Auxis Inc., a management consulting and outsourcing company has launched a new service for companies involved in or bidding for government contracts. Details of the program are provided.

44009 ■ "A Banking Play Without Banking Plagues" in *Barron's* **(Vol. 88, March 31, 2008, No. 13, pp. 26)**
Pub: Dow Jones & Company, Inc.
Ed: Jack Willoughby. **Description:** Fiserv's shares have been dragged down by about 20 percent which presents an appealing entry point since the shares could rise by 30 percent or more by 2009. The company enables banks to post and open new checks and keeps track of loans which are not discretionary processes of banks.

44010 ■ "Bankruptcies" in *Crain's Detroit Business* **(Vol. 24, March 24, 2008, No. 12, pp. 6)**
Pub: Crain Communications, Inc.
Description: Current list of business that filed for Chapter 7 or 11 protection in U.S. Bankruptcy Court in Detroit include a construction company, a medical care company, a physical therapy firm and a communications firm.

44011 ■ "Banks Fall Short in Online Services for Savvy Traders" in *Barron's* **(Vol. 88, March 17, 2008, No. 11, pp. 35)**
Pub: Dow Jones & Company, Inc.
Ed: Theresa W. Carey. **Description:** Banc of America Investment Services, WellsTrade, and ShareBuilder are at the bottom of the list of online brokerages because they offer less trading technologies and product range. Financial shoppers miss out on a lot of customized tools and analytics when using these services.

44012 ■ "Barbarians Set Bar Low With Lowly Canadian Telco" in *Globe & Mail* **(March 31, 2007, pp. B1)**
Pub: CTVglobemedia Publishing Inc.
Ed: Derek DeCloet. **Description:** The efforts of the private equity fund Kohlberg, Kravis, Roberts and Co. to acquire the Canadian telecommunications firm BCE are described.

44013 ■ "Bartering Trades on Talents" in *Reading Eagle* **(June 20, 2010)**
Pub: Reading Eagle/Reading Times
Ed: Tony Lucia. **Description:** Bartering is not just a way of trading goods and services, it can be an essential tool for small business to survive in a bad economy.

44014 ■ "BCE's Aliant Trust Spinoff Valued at About $8.5 Billion" in *Globe & Mail* **(March 8, 2006, pp. B1)**
Pub: CTVglobemedia Publishing Inc.
Ed: Catherine McLean. **Description:** The details pertaining to the spinoff of Aliant Inc.'s landline business into an income trust by BCE Inc. are presented. The trust is valued at $8.5 billion.

44015 ■ "Be Innovative In Other Ways" in *Green Industry Pro* **(Vol. 23, March 2011, No. 3, pp. 4)**
Pub: Cygnus Business Media
Ed: Rod Dickens. **Description:** Emphasis is put on the importance of putting the customer first in order to successfully market any product or service. Six marketing ideas are presented to promote a landscaping business.

44016 ■ "Beam My Data Up" in *Canadian Business* **(Vol. 80, February 12, 2007, No. 4, pp. 42)**
Pub: Rogers Media
Ed: Marlene Rego. **Description:** Innovations in the field of teleportation since its invention by Gilles Brassard in 1992 is discussed.

44017 ■ *Behind the Cloud*
Pub: Jossey-Bass
Ed: Marc Benioff, Carlye Adler. **Released:** 2010. **Price:** $27.95. **Description:** Salesforce.com is the world's most successful business-to-business cloud-computing company that sells an online service that helps businesses manage sales, customer service, and marketing functions.

44018 ■ "The Bell Tolls for Thee" in *Canadian Business* (Vol. 81, March 3, 2008, No. 3, pp. 36)
Pub: Rogers Media
Ed: Andrew Wahl. **Description:** Bell Canada has formed the Canadian Coalition for Tomorrow's IT Skills to solve the shortage of technology talent in the country. Canada's total workforce has only around 4%, or 600,000 people employed in information technology-related fields. The aims of the Bell-led coalition, which is supported by different industry associations and 30 corporations, are investigated.

44019 ■ "Benchmark Makes Granduca Entrance" in *Houston Business Journal* (Vol. 40, January 8, 2010, No. 35, pp. 2)
Pub: American City Business Journals
Ed: Jennifer Dawson. **Description:** Houston, Texas-based Interfin Company, owner of the Hotel Granduca, has tapped the services of Benchmark Hospitality International to manage the property. The hiring of Benchmark is part of Interfin's efforts to develop Granduca hotels in other markets. Statistical data included.

44020 ■ "Bernier Open to Telecom Changes" in *Globe & Mail* (March 22, 2006, pp. B1)
Pub: CTVglobemedia Publishing Inc.
Ed: Simon Tuck. **Description:** Federal Industry Minister Maxime Bernier of Canada says that he is open to scrapping restrictions on foreign ownership in telecommunications. His views on telecom industry are detailed.

44021 ■ *Beyond Booked Solid: Your Business, Your Life, Your Way-It's All Inside*
Pub: John Wiley and Sons, Inc.
Ed: Michael Port. **Released:** April 2008. **Price:** $24.95. **Description:** Professional service providers and small business owners will discover tactics and strategies for growing and expanding their companies while allowing them to find time to relax and enjoy their lives. Owners will learn to attract new clients and grow profits.

44022 ■ "Big Sell-Off At Sunwest" in *The Business Journal-Portland* (Vol. 25, July 25, 2008, No. 20, pp. 1)
Pub: American City Business Journals, Inc.
Ed: Robin J. Moody. **Description:** Oregon's largest operator of assisted living facilities Sunwest Management Inc. is expected to sell 132 of its properties. The planned sale, which is believed to be worth more than $1 billion, will help Sunwest pay creditors and investors. Other views and information on the planned sale, as well as on Sunwest's services which include adult day care, are presented.

44023 ■ "Big Trouble at Sony Ericsson" in *Barron's* (Vol. 88, March 24, 2008, No. 12, pp. M9)
Pub: Dow Jones & Company, Inc.
Ed: Angelo Franchini. **Description:** Sony Ericsson is facing trouble as it warned that its sales and net income before taxes will fall by nearly half for the first quarter of 2008. The joint venture of Sony and Ericsson has a global mobile phone market share of nine percent as of 2007, fourth largest in the world.

44024 ■ "Bill Lee's Auto Repair Business Chugs Along Despite Life's Obstacles" in *Bradenton Herald* (August 22, 2010)
Pub: Bradenton Herald
Ed: Grace Gagliano. **Description:** Profile of Bill Lee's Professional Automotive Services located in Bradenton, Florida. The auto repair business was opened 26 years ago and provides repair for an assortment of fleet vehicles, including truck repair.

44025 ■ "Black Gold" in *Canadian Business* (Vol. 79, August 14, 2006, No. 16-17, pp. 57)
Pub: Rogers Media
Ed: Erin Pooley. **Description:** A list of the top ten jobs in the petroleum industry in Canada along with pay and nature of jobs, is presented.

44026 ■ "Blockbuster Launches Internet Movie Downloads to Compete Against Netflix, Others" in *Chicago Tribune* (December 3, 2008)
Pub: McClatchy-Tribune Information Services
Ed: Eric Benderoff. **Description:** Blockbuster Inc., the DVD rental giant, has launched a new service that delivers movies to their customer's homes via the Internet in an attempt to compete against Netflix and other competitors.

44027 ■ "Blood Bank" in *Canadian Business* (Vol. 80, February 12, 2007, No. 4, pp. 36)
Pub: Rogers Media
Ed: Erin Pooley. **Description:** The plan of Insception Biosciences to popularize stem cell banks, which can store stem cells, is discussed.

44028 ■ "Bombardier Wins Chinese Rail Deal" in *Globe & Mail* (March 20, 2006, pp. B1)
Pub: CTVglobemedia Publishing Inc.
Ed: Geoffrey York. **Description:** Bombardier Inc. has won a $68 million (U.S) contract to provide railway cars for rapid transit-link between Beijing and its international airport for 2008 Olympics in China. Details of the contract are presented.

44029 ■ "Bookkeeping Service Opens First Sacramento Franchise" in *Sacramento Bee* (April 13, 2011)
Pub: Sacramento Bee
Ed: Mark Glover. **Description:** Franchise bookkeeping service called BookKeeping Express opened its new office in Roseville, California; its first shop in the area.

44030 ■ "Bountiful Barrels: Where to Find $140 Trillion" in *Barron's* (Vol. 88, July 14, 2008, No. 28, pp. 40)
Pub: Dow Jones & Co., Inc.
Ed: Andrew Bary. **Description:** Surge in oil prices has caused a large transfer of wealth to oil-producing countries thereby reshaping the global economy. Oil reserves of oil exporting countries are now valued at $140 trillion. Economist Stephen Jen believes that this wealth will be transformed into paper assets as these countries invest in global stocks and bonds.

44031 ■ "Brief: Janitorial Company Must Pay Back Wages" in *Buffalo News* (September 24, 2011)
Pub: The Buffalo News
Ed: Jonathan D. Epstein. **Description:** Knights Facilities Management, located in Michigan, provides grounds maintenance and janitorial services at the Ralph Wilson Stadium in Buffalo, New York. The US Department of Labor ordered the firm to pay $22,000 in back wages and damages to 26 employees for overtime and minimum wage compensation. Details of the company's violation of the Fair Labor Standards Act are included.

44032 ■ *Building Buzz to Beat the Big Boys*
Pub: Greenwood Publishing Group, Inc.
Ed: Steve O'Leary; Kim Sheehan. **Released:** March 30, 2008. **Price:** $39.95. **Description:** Seventy to eighty percent of small retail stores fail within the first five years of opening due to competition from big-box retailers and online stores. Service providers and small retailers should capitalize on the fact that they are local and can connect on a personal level with customers in a way the big stores cannot. Word of mouth marketing methods are very critical to any small retail or service company. This book is designed to help any small business compete against large competitors.

44033 ■ "Bumpy Ride Ahead for United" in *Crain's Chicago Business* (Vol. 31, May 5, 2008, No. 18, pp. 3)
Pub: Crain Communications, Inc.
Ed: John Pletz. **Description:** Continental Airlines Inc. walked away from merger talks with United Airlines last week. Now the choices facing United boil

down to going it alone in an increasingly stormy airline business or a less-desirable merger with US Airways Group Inc. Analysts expect United to lose $977 million this year due, mainly, to the high price of fuel.

44034 ■ "Burton Group Answers Industry Need for Practical Data Center Advice" in *Canadian Corporate News* (May 14, 2007)
Pub: Comtex News Network Inc.
Description: Burton Group, an IT research firm focused on in-depth technical analysis of enterprise IT infrastructures, launched a new service providing practical advice for IT professionals facing critical data center decisions which due to technological advances can be more efficient while reducing costs.

44035 ■ "Businesses Band Together in Destin Bartering to Keep Heads Above Water" in *Destin Log* (July 24, 2010)
Pub: The Destin Log
Ed: Andrew Metz. **Description:** Profile of The Barter Company located in Destin, Florida, whose owner believes that bartering for goods and services can help small companies in a down economy.

44036 ■ "Butane Heated Pressure Washer Offers Diverse Cleaning Options" in *Product News Network* (March 8, 2011)
Pub: Product News Network
Description: Profile of the Super Max (TM) 6000B power sprayer the can clean with cold or heated water and wet steam. Daimer Industries, provider of janitorial supplies, announced the availability of the machine that offers a variety of cleaning options for a range of applications.

44037 ■ "Call of Prepaid Heard by More" in *Chicago Tribune* (November 26, 2008)
Pub: McClatchy-Tribune Information Services
Ed: Wailin Wong. **Description:** Due to the economic downturn, more consumers are switching to no-contract, prepaid cell phone service. Customers find that the cost savings, flexibility and lack of contract are appealing in such uncertain times.

44038 ■ "Can You Hear Them Now?" in *Hawaii Business* (Vol. 54, August 2008, No. 2, pp. 48)
Pub: Hawaii Business Publishing
Ed: Jason Ubay. **Description:** Coral Wireless LLC (dba Mobi PCS) is ranked 237 in Hawaii Business' list of the state's top 250 companies for 2008. The company is a local wireless phone provider, which has expanded its market to Oahu, Maui and the Big Island since opening in 2006, offering 13 phones and unlimited texts and calls. Details on the company's sales are provided.

44039 ■ "The Case of the Deflated IPO" in *Boston Business Journal* (Vol. 29, June 24, 2011, No. 7, pp. 1)
Pub: American City Business Journals Inc.
Ed: Scott Dance. **Description:** IPO market is on the rebound from the recession but for some companies in Maryland, the time is not yet ripe to go public. One of the companies that chooses to wait for better timing is SafeNet Inc. and it is eyeing some possible acquisitions while doing so.

44040 ■ "The Caterer and Hotelkeeper Interview Patrick Harbour and Nathan Jones" in *Caterer & Hotelkeeper* (October 28, 2011, No. 288)
Pub: Reed Reference Publishing
Description: Profiles of Patrick Harbour and Nathan Jones who quit their jobs to start their own catering business. The partners discuss their business strategy when launching their boutique catering firm and ways they are adapting to the slow economy in order to remain successful.

44041 ■ "Cell Phone the Ticket on American Airlines" in *Chicago Tribune* (November 14, 2008)
Pub: McClatchy-Tribune Information Services
Ed: Julie Johnsson. **Description:** American Airlines is testing a new mobile boarding pass at O'Hare International Airport. Travelers on American can board flights and get through security checkpoints by

flashing a bar code on their phones. Passengers must have an Internet-enabled mobile device and an active e-mail address in order to utilize this service.

44042 ■ "Certification Experts Germanischer Lloyd Wind Energy Assist NaiKun's Offshore Wind Project" in *Canadian Corporate News* **(May 14, 2007)**
Pub: Comtex News Network Inc.
Description: Germanischer Lloyd Wind Energy (GL Wind) will examine, inspect, and provide quality management services for the engineering, design, and construction of the offshore wind project planned by NaiKun Wind Development Inc. in northwest British Columbia.

44043 ■ "Certified Technicians can Increase Bottom Line" in *Contractor* **(Vol. 56, September 2009, No. 9, pp. 37)**
Pub: Penton Media, Inc.
Ed: Ray Isaac. **Description:** Certified technicians increase the value of HVAC firms, a survey by Service Round Table has reported. The increased value has been attributed to fewer callbacks, less warranty work and greater ability to educate consumers. Meanwhile, consumers are willing to pay more for the services of certified technicians.

44044 ■ "Check Provider Says It Plans to Close Call Center in Charlotte" in *Charlotte Observer* **(February 6, 2007)**
Pub: Knight-Ridder/Tribune Business News
Ed: Rick Rothacker. **Description:** Clarke American Checks Inc. is closing its call center located in Charlotte, North Carolina. Clarke provides checks and other services to financial institutions and customers.

44045 ■ "City a Pawn in Airlines' Chess Game" in *Business Courier* **(Vol. 24, January 18, 2008, No. 41, pp. 1)**
Pub: American City Business Journals, Inc.
Ed: Lisa Biank Fasig. **Description:** Delta Air Lines is under negotitaions with Northwest Airlines and UAL Corp. for a proposed merger. The deal will have a negative impact on Cincinnati as a hub regardless whether it goes to UAL or Northwest. The impacts of the planned merger on Cincinnati's labor market and airport traffic are discussed.

44046 ■ "City Seeks More Minorities" in *Austin Business JournalInc.* **(Vol. 28, November 7, 2008, No. 34, pp. A1)**
Pub: American City Business Journals
Ed: Jean Kwon. **Description:** Austin, Texas is planning to increase the participation of minority- and women-owned businesses in government contracts. Contractors are required to show 'good faith' to comply with the specified goals. The city is planning to effect the changes in the construction and professional services sector.

44047 ■ "Columbia's JPB Raising $175M to Acquire Companies, Real Estate" in *Boston Business Journal* **(Vol. 29, May 27, 2011, No. 3, pp. 1)**
Pub: American City Business Journals Inc.
Ed: Gary Haber. **Description:** JPB Enterprises is preparing to raise $175 million in its goal of acquiring companies and real estate that are major names in America. The $75 million will be raised for a buyout fund that will target wide range of industries while the $100 million will be used for land investment projects in the Florida Panhandle. Baltimore firms are expected to benefit from this deal.

44048 ■ "Compelling Opportunities" in *Barron's* **(Vol. 88, March 10, 2008, No. 10, pp. 39)**
Pub: Dow Jones & Company, Inc.
Ed: Neil A. Martin. **Description:** Michael L. Reynal, portfolio manager of Principal International Emerging Markets Fund, is bullish on the growth prospects of stocks in emerging markets. He is investing big on energy, steel, and transportation companies.

44049 ■ "Complete Discovery Source, Inc. (CDS) Receives Minority Owned Business Certification" in *Internet Wire* **(December 14, 2010)**
Pub: Comtex
Description: Complete Discovery Source Inc. (CDS) was granted Minority-Owned Business Enterprise

status by the New York State Department of Economic Development. The certification provides CDS, an end-to-end eDiscovery services provider, with access to contracting opportunities with 130 government agencies throughout New York state.

44050 ■ The Complete Startup Guide for the Black Entrepreneur
Pub: Career Press Inc.
Ed: Bill Boudreaux. **Description:** President and founder of a consulting firm for home-based entrepreneurs share information to help minorities start their own companies. Tips to create a business plan, buy essential equipment, price products and services, pay the bills, and set up a work space are covered.

44051 ■ The Concierge Manual: A Step-by-Step Guide to Starting Your Own Concierge Service or Lifestyle Management Company
Pub: New Road Publishing
Ed: Katharine C. Giovanni. **Released:** September 9, 2010. **Price:** $23.00. **Description:** Answering some of the biggest questions about the logistics of running a concierge business, this guide provides all the tools necessary to create a successful concierge, lifestyle management, errand service, or personal assistant company.

44052 ■ "Conquering Your Fear of Fees" in *Entrepreneur* **(Vol. 37, October 2009, No. 10, pp. 86)**
Pub: Entrepreneur Media, Inc.
Ed: Rosalind Resnick. **Description:** Entrepreneurs should study money management charges carefully before investing. They should understand how different forms of investments work and how much money managers and mutual funds charge for their services.

44053 ■ "CoolBrands" in *Canadian Business* **(Vol. 83, September 14, 2010, No. 15, pp. 25)**
Pub: Rogers Media Ltd.
Ed: Joe Castaldo. **Description:** CoolBrands International Inc.'s merger with Swisher International Inc., a US hygiene products and services company, has formally erased the last traces of the former ice cream company. CoolBrands began as a frozen yogurt stand in 1986 and flourished across the world. How the string of acquisitions and poor corporate governance led to its demise are cited.

44054 ■ "Count Out The Consumer" in *Barron's* **(Vol. 88, July 7, 2008, No. 27, pp. 10)**
Pub: Dow Jones & Co., Inc.
Description: American consumers are not expected to give the US economy its much-needed boost as the rising food and energy prices are taking their toll. US consumers have cut spending on utilities and food and are increasing their use of credit cards.

44055 ■ "CPI Corporation Acquires Assets of Bella Pictures" in *Benzinga.com* **(January 28, 2011)**
Pub: Benzinga.com
Ed: Benzinga Staff. **Description:** CPI Corporation acquired assets of Bella Pictures Inc., a leading provider of branded wedding photography services. Details of the acquisition are explained.

44056 ■ "CPR-CN Deal to Ease Vancouver Logjam" in *Globe & Mail* **(January 27, 2006, pp. B4)**
Pub: CTVglobemedia Publishing Inc.
Ed: Brent Jang. **Description:** In a bid to lessen West coast port grid lock Canadian Pacific Railway Ltd and Canadian National Railway Co. has agreed to share tracks in the Vancouver region. This will allow the trains to operate more efficiently from the Vancouver Port.

44057 ■ "CPR Signals a Switch in Strategy to Narrow Competitive Gap With CN" in *Globe & Mail* **(January 20, 2006, pp. B3)**
Pub: CTVglobemedia Publishing Inc.
Ed: Brent Jang. **Description:** The reasons behind the restructuring efforts of Canadian Pacific Railway Ltd. are presented.

44058 ■ "Customer Retention is Proportionate to Employee Retention" in *Green Industry Pro* **(Vol. 23, September 2011)**
Pub: Cygnus Business Media
Description: Presented in a question-answer format, information is provided to help retain customers as well as keeping workers happy.

44059 ■ "Customized Before Custom Was Cool" in *Green Industry Pro* **(July 2011)**
Pub: Cygnus Business Media
Ed: Gregg Wartgow. **Description:** Profile of Turf Care Enterprises and owner Kevin Vogeler, who discusses his desire to use more natural programs using little or no chemicals in 1986. At that time, that sector represented 20 percent of his business, today it shares 80 percent.

44060 ■ "The Data Drivers" in *Canadian Business* **(Vol. 81, September 15, 2008, No. 14-15, pp. 1)**
Pub: Rogers Media Ltd.
Ed: Andrew Wahl. **Description:** Canadian regulators hope that an auction of telecommunications companies will inject more competition into the industry; however, newcomers may not be able to rely on lower prices in order to gain market share from the three major telecommunications companies that already have a stronghold on the market. Analysts feel that providing additional data service is the key to surviving market disruptions.

44061 ■ "Data Firm Growth 'Opportunistic'" in *Tampa Bay Business Journal* **(Vol. 30, January 29, 2010, No. 6, pp. 1)**
Pub: American City Business Journals
Ed: Michael Hinman. **Description:** E Solutions Corporation is experiencing growth amid the economic downturn, with its Park Tower data center occupancy in Tampa Florida expanding from 14,000 square feet to 20,000 square feet. Details on the increased operations fueled by demand for information storage and management services offered by the company are discussed.

44062 ■ "Daycare Dollars" in *Small Business Opportunities* **(Winter 2009)**
Pub: Entrepreneur Media Inc.
Description: Profile of Maui Playcare, a franchise that provides parents drop-in daycare for their children without having to purchase a membership, make reservations or pay costly dues; the company is expanding beyond its Hawaiian roots onto the mainland and is expected to have between 40 and 50 locations signed by the end of 2010.

44063 ■ "Dear Customer: Managing E-Mail Campaigns" in *Inc.* **(March 2008, pp. 58-59)**
Pub: Gruner & Jahr USA Publishing
Ed: Ryan Underwood. **Description:** Internet services that help firms manage their online business including email marketing, to manage subscriber lists, comply with spam regulations, monitor bouncebacks, and track potential customers are profiled. Constant Contact, MobileStorm Stun, Campaign Monitor, Pop Commerce, Emma, and StrongMail E-mail Server are among software and services highlighted.

44064 ■ "Debt-Collection Agency to Lay Off 368 in Hampton Center" in *Virginian-Pilot* **(December 4, 2010)**
Pub: Virginian-Pilot
Ed: Tom Shean. **Description:** NCO Financial Systems Inc., provider of debt-collection and outsourcing services will permanently lay off 368 workers at its Hampton call center in 2011.

44065 ■ "Deep in the Heart of Drought" in *Green Industry Pro* **(Vol. 23, October 2011)**
Pub: Cygnus Business Media
Ed: Gregg Wartgow. **Description:** Challenges faced by landscape contractors during the recent drought in Texas are explored. Despite these challenges, opportunity for contractors providing irrigation services has risen.

44066 ■ *Delivering Knock Your Socks Off Service, 4th Edition*
Pub: American Management Association
Ed: Performance Research Associates. **Released:** 2006.

44067 ■ "Descartes Launches Ocean Shipment Management Suite" in *Canadian Corporate News* (May 16, 2007)
Pub: Comtex News Network Inc.
Description: Descartes Systems Group, a global on-demand software-as-a-service (SaaS) logistics solutions provider, launched the latest release of its Descartes Ocean Shipment Management Suite. The release integrates customs compliance services with Descartes' Rate Builder solution, a central database for global shipment and rate information, and Descartes Global Logistics Network (GLN) messaging capabilities.

44068 ■ "Do the Right Thing" in *Contractor* (Vol. 56, December 2009, No. 12, pp. 16)
Pub: Penton Media, Inc.
Ed: Robert P. Mader. **Description:** Applewood Plumbing, Heating and Electric has won Contractor magazine's 2009 Contractor of the Year Award. The company was ranked eighth among more than 300 service companies in the United States. A brief history of the company is also provided.

44069 ■ "Dollar General Selects GSI Commerce to Launch Its eCommerce Business" in *Benzinga.com* (October 29, 2011)
Pub: Benzinga.com
Ed: Benzinga Staff. **Description:** Dollar General Corporation chose GSI Commerce, a leading provider of ecommerce and interactive marketing solutions, to launch its online initiative. GSI Commerce is an eBay Inc. company.

44070 ■ "Don't' Hang Up On FairPoint" in *Barron's* (Vol. 88, July 7, 2008, No. 27, pp. M5)
Pub: Dow Jones & Co., Inc.
Ed: Fleming Meeks. **Description:** Shares of Fair-Point Communications, priced at $6.63 each, are undervalued and should be worth over $12 each. The company increased its size by more than five times by acquiring Verizon's local telephone operations in Vermont, New Hampshire, and Maine, but must switch customers in those areas into their system by the end of September 2007.

44071 ■ "Don't' Hate the Cable Guy" in *Saint Louis Business Journal* (Vol. 31, August 5, 2011, No. 50, pp. 1)
Pub: Saint Louis Business Journal
Ed: Angela Mueller. **Description:** Charter Communications named John Birrer as senior vice president of customer experience. The company experienced problems with its customer services.

44072 ■ "Dozens 'Come Alive' in Downtown Chicago" in *Green Industry Pro* (July 2011)
Pub: Cygnus Business Media
Ed: Gregg Wartgow. **Description:** Highlights from the Come Alive Outside training event held in Chicago, Illinois July 14-15, 2011 are shared. Nearly 80 people representing 38 landscape companies attended the event that helps contractors review their services and find ways to sell them in new and various ways.

44073 ■ "Drilling Deep and Flying High" in *Barron's* (Vol. 88, June 30, 2008, No. 26, pp. 34)
Pub: Dow Jones & Co., Inc.
Ed: Kenneth Rapoza. **Description:** Shares of Petrobras could rise another 25 percent if the three deep-water wells that the company has found proves as lucrative as some expect. Petrobras will become an oil giant if the reserves are proven.

44074 ■ "DST Turns to Banks for Credit" in *The Business Journal-Serving Metropolitan Kansas City* (Vol. 27, October 3, 2008, No. 3, pp. 1)
Pub: American City Business Journals, Inc.
Ed: Rob Roberts. **Description:** Kansas City, Missouri-based DST Systems Inc., a company that provides sophisticated information processing,

computer software services and business solutions, has secured a new five-year, $120 million credit facility from Enterprise Bank and Bank of the West. The deal is seen to reflect that the region and community-banking model remain stable. Comments from executives are also provided.

44075 ■ "eBay Inc. Completes Acquisition of Zong" in *Benzinga.com* (October 29, 2011)
Pub: Benzinga.com
Ed: Benzinga Staff. **Description:** eBay Inc. acquired Zong, a provider of payments through mobile carrier billing. Terms of the agreement are outlined.

44076 ■ "eBay and Jonathan Adler Team to Launch 'The eBay Inspiration Shop'" in *Entertainment Close-Up* (October 25, 2011)
Pub: Close-Up Media
Description: Designer Jonathan Adler partnered with eBay to create a collection of new must-have merchandise for the fall season. Top trendsetters, including actors, designers, bloggers, stylists, editors, photographers, models and musicians helped curate the items being featured in the windows by sharing their shopping wish lists with users.

44077 ■ "Embarq Sale Sets New Tone" in *The Business Journal-Serving Metropolitan Kansas City* (Vol. 27, October 31, 2008, No. 8, pp. 1)
Pub: American City Business Journals, Inc.
Ed: Suzsanna Stagemeyer. **Description:** CenturyTel Inc. has agreed to acquire Embarq Corp., a large phone company based in Overland Park. The acquisition deal is valued at $11.6 billion. The potential impacts of the deal on Kansas City's economy are analyzed.

44078 ■ "EnCana Gets Top Dollar for Gas Depot Division" in *Globe & Mail* (March 7, 2006, pp. B6)
Pub: CTVglobemedia Publishing Inc.
Ed: Dave Ebner. **Description:** The details on acquisition of natural gas storage assets of EnCana Corp. by Carlyle/Riverstone Global Energy and Power Fund II LP and Carlyle Group LP are presented.

44079 ■ "EnCana Surpasses All Canadian Profit Records" in *Globe & Mail* (February 16, 2007, pp. B5)
Pub: CTVglobemedia Publishing Inc.
Ed: David Ebner. **Description:** Canada-based energy giant EnCana Corp. has reported $5.65 billion profits for the fiscal year 2006. The company has outpaced expectations by this impressive figure.

44080 ■ "Energy, MLPs: Pipeline to Profits" in *Barron's* (Vol. 89, July 27, 2009, No. 30, pp. 9)
Pub: Dow Jones & Co., Inc.
Ed: Dimitra DeFotis. **Description:** Energy master limited partnership stocks are range-bound in the next few months from July 2009 but there are there are some opportunities that remain. These include Energy Transfer Equity, Enterprise GP holdings, NuStar GP Holdings, and Plains All American Pipeline.

44081 ■ "Energy Sparks Job Growth" in *The Business Journal-Serving Greater Tampa Bay* (Vol. 28, August 8, 2008, No. 33, pp. 1)
Pub: American City Business Journals, Inc.
Ed: Margie Manning. **Description:** Energy infrastructure projects in Tampa Bay, Florida, are increasing the demand for labor in the area. Energy projects requiring an increase in labor include TECO Energy Inc.'s plan for a natural gas pipeline in the area and the installation of energy management system in Bank of America's branches in the area.

44082 ■ "Everett Dowling" in *Hawaii Business* (Vol. 54, August 2008, No. 2, pp. 32)
Pub: Hawaii Business Publishing
Ed: Jason Ubay. **Description:** Real estate developer Everett Dowling, president of Dowling Company Inc., talks about the company's sustainable management and services. The company's office has been retrofitted to earn a Leadership in Energy and Environmental

Design (LEED) certification. Dowling believes that real estate development can be part of the sustainable solution.

44083 ■ *Exceptional Service, Exceptional Profit: The Secrets of Building a Five-Star Customer Service Organization*
Pub: AMACOM
Ed: Leonard Inghilleri, Micah Solomon. **Released:** April 1, 2010. **Price:** $21.95. **Description:** Team of insiders share exclusive knowledge of the loyalty-building techniques pioneered by the world's most successful service leaders, including brick-and-mortar stars such as The Ritz-Carlton and Lexus and online success stories such as Netflix and CD Baby.

44084 ■ "Exxon Braving the Danger Zones" in *Globe & Mail* (March 8, 2007, pp. B1)
Pub: CTVglobemedia Publishing Inc.
Ed: Shawn McCarthy. **Description:** The plans of Exxon Mobil Corp. to increase its revenues through the expansion of its operations in Asia, Africa, and the Middle East are discussed.

44085 ■ "Facebook, Adobe, Kenshoo, Outright and Cignex Datamatics Sign On to X.commerce" in *Entertainment Close-Up* (October 24, 2011)
Pub: Close-Up Media
Description: Facebook, Adobe, Kenshoo, Outright and Cignex Datamatics have all partnered with X.commerce's ecosystem, where developers build and merchants can come to shop for new technologies and services.

44086 ■ "Fairfax Announces Acquisition of William Ashley" in *Benzinga.com* (August 16, 2011)
Pub: Benzinga.com
Ed: Benzinga Staff. **Description:** Fairfax Financial Holdings Limited acquired the family-owned William Ashley China company, leader within the dinnerware and wedding registry industries and was the first company in North America to introduce a computerized wedding registry system.

44087 ■ "Family Throne" in *Hawaii Business* (Vol. 53, March 2008, No. 9, pp. 51)
Pub: Hawaii Business Publishing
Ed: Cathy S. Cruz-George. **Description:** Jeanette and George Grace inherited Paradise Lua Inc., a portable toilet company founded by George's father. The toilets are rented by Aloha Stadium during football season and St. Patrick's Day block party among others. The company has 2,500 toilets and 20 pumping trucks and had earnings of $1.3 million in 2007.

44088 ■ "A Few Points of Contention" in *Barron's* (Vol. 88, July 14, 2008, No. 28, pp. 3)
Pub: Dow Jones & Co., Inc.
Ed: Michael Santoli. **Description:** Headline inflation tends to revert to the lower core inflation, which excludes food and energy in its calculation over long periods. Prominent private equity figures believe that regulators should allow more than the de facto 10 percent to 25 percent limit of commercial banks to hasten the refunding of the financial sector.

44089 ■ "Fifth Third Spinoff" in *Business Courier* (Vol. 27, July 16, 2010, No. 11, pp. 1)
Pub: Business Courier
Ed: Dan Monk, Steve Watkins. **Description:** Electronic-funds transfer company Fifth Third Solutions (FTPS), a spinoff of Fifth Third Bancorp, is seeking as much as 200,000 square feet of new office space in Ohio. The bank's sale of 51 percent ownership stake to Boston-based Advent International Corporation has paved the way for the growth of FTPS. How real estate brokers' plans have responded to FTPS' growth mode is discussed.

44090 ■ "Finding a Way to Continue Growing" in *Green Industry Pro* (Vol. 23, March 2011, No. 3, pp. 31)
Pub: Cygnus Business Media
Description: Profile of Brett Lemcke, VP of R.M. Landscape located in Rochester, New York. Lemcke tells how his Landscape Industry Certified credentials helped him to grow his business and beat out his competition.

44091 ■ **"Five Distinct Divisions, One Collective Focus"** in *Green Industry Pro* (Vol. 23, October 2011)

Pub: Cygnus Business Media

Ed: Gregg Wartgow. **Description:** Profile of ACLS Inc., an amalgamation of All Commercial Landscape Service (commercial maintenance), All Custom Landscape Service (design/build), Fresno Tree Service, Certified Water Consulting (irrigation), and Tractor Service (disking and flailing services on everything from one-acre lots to hundreds of acres of open land). The firm discusses its rebranding effort in order to increase sales.

44092 ■ **"Fix-It Career: Jobs in Repair"** in *Occupational Outlook Quarterly* (Vol. 54, Fall 2010, No. 3, pp. 26)

Pub: U.S. Bureau of Labor Statistics

Ed: Elka Maria Torpey. **Description:** Auto mechanics and HVAC technician occupations require repair skills. Advantages for individuals with proper skills are outlined.

44093 ■ **"Flat or Slight Decline Seen for Nortel 2007 Revenue"** in *Globe & Mail* (March 17, 2007, pp. B3)

Pub: CTVglobemedia Publishing Inc.

Ed: Catherine McLean. **Description:** The forecast about Nortel Network Corp's decrease in the 2007 revenue and its restructuring to reduce costs is discussed.

44094 ■ **"Flight of Capital?"** in *Canadian Business* (Vol. 80, February 26, 2007, No. 5, pp. 76)

Pub: Rogers Media

Description: The economic reasons, which forced Air Canada to pullback its direct daily service from Toronto to New Delhi, India, are presented. The views of Michael Treacy, United States' entrepreneur, on the economic conditions of Canada are also presented.

44095 ■ **"Flights of Fancy"** in *Crain's Chicago Business* (Vol. 31, April 21, 2008, No. 16, pp. 27)

Pub: Crain Communications, Inc.

Ed: Sarah A. Klein. **Description:** Due to the competition for business travelers, who account for 30 percent of airline revenue, airlines are offering a number of luxury amenities, especially on long-haul routes.

44096 ■ **"Flying High Down Under"** in *Entrepreneur* (Vol. 37, August 2009, No. 8, pp. 16)

Pub: Entrepreneur Media, Inc.

Ed: Dan Oko. **Description:** V Australia offers direct flights from Los Angeles International Airport to Brisbane, Melbourne, and Sydney in Australia. Their Boeing 777-300ER aircrafts has a fully stocked sit-down bar in the business class, touch screens with audio and video on demand and passengers get to perk up with Bulgari toiletries kits.

44097 ■ **"Flying the Unfriendly Skies"** in *Crain's Chicago Business* (Vol. 31, April 21, 2008, No. 16, pp. 26)

Pub: Crain Communications, Inc.

Ed: Sarah A. Klein. **Description:** Due to the number of Chicago companies and entrepreneurs who are traveling overseas more frequently in order to strengthen ties with customers, companies and oftentimes even business partners, the number of flights leaving O'Hare International Airport for destinations abroad has surged; In 2007, international passengers departing O'Hare totaled 5.7 million, up from 2.4 million in 1990.

44098 ■ **"The Fort"** in *Hawaii Business* (Vol. 53, November 2007, No. 5, pp. 19)

Pub: Hawaii Business Publishing

Ed: Jason Ubay. **Description:** DRFortress' flagship data center The Fort located at Honolulu's Airport Industrial Park provides companies a place to store their servers in an ultra-secure environment. Anything stored in here that requires power has a back up and

in case of an outage generators can supply power up to 80 hrs. The Fort caters to major carriers and Internet service providers.

44099 ■ **"Fortis Snaps Up Terasen's Gas Utility Business"** in *Globe & Mail* (February 27, 2007, pp. B1)

Pub: CTVglobemedia Publishing Inc.

Ed: Wendy Stueck. **Description:** The acquisition of Terasen Inc. from Kinder Morgan Inc. by Fortis Inc. is described.

44100 ■ **"Forward Motion"** in *Green Industry Pro* (July 2011)

Pub: Cygnus Business Media

Ed: Gregg Wartgow. **Description:** Several landscape contractors have joined this publication's Working Smarter Training Challenge over the last year. This process is helping them develop ways to improve work processes, boost morale, drive out waste, reduce costs, improve customer service, and be more competitive.

44101 ■ **"Free Your Mind"** in *Entrepreneur* (Vol. 37, October 2009, No. 10, pp. 24)

Pub: Entrepreneur Media, Inc.

Ed: Joe Robinson. **Description:** Writer Chris Anderson believes that firms in the digital age should allow products and services to initially be sold for free. These companies could then charge for premium versions of these products and services after the free versions have gained attention.

44102 ■ **"Friedland's Next Frontier: Drilling for Oil in Iraq"** in *Globe & Mail* (April 20, 2007, pp. B1)

Pub: CTVglobemedia Publishing Inc.

Ed: Wendy Stueck. **Description:** The decision of the Canadian oil and gas company Ivanhoe Energy Inc. to partner with the Japanese oil and gas firm INPEX Corp. for the development of heavy oil fields in north central Iraq is discussed.

44103 ■ **"Fuel for Thought; Canadian Business Leaders on Energy Policy"** in *Canadian Business* (Vol. 81, September 15, 2008, No. 14-15, pp. 12)

Pub: Rogers Media Ltd.

Ed: Joe Castaldo. **Description:** Most Canadian business leaders worry about the unreliability of the oil supply but feel that Canada is in a better position to benefit from the energy supply crisis than other countries. Many respondents also highlighted the need to invest in renewable energy sources.

44104 ■ **"The Future of Work"** in *Black Enterprise* (Vol. 41, August 2010, No. 1, pp. 65)

Pub: Earl G. Graves Publishing Co. Inc.

Ed: Annya M. Lott. **Description:** Technology, globalization, and outsourcing will continue to shape the future of work. Social media is a means for small companies to market goods and services.

44105 ■ **"Gain the 'Come Alive Outside' Selling Edge"** in *Green Industry Pro* (July 2011)

Pub: Cygnus Business Media

Ed: Jim Paluch. **Description:** Marketing the 'Come Alive Outside' slogan can help landscapers to increase their market share by identifying and applying these elements to each customer as well as their workers.

44106 ■ **"Get Paid and Get Moving"** in *Entrepreneur* (Vol. 37, October 2009, No. 10, pp. 38)

Pub: Entrepreneur Media, Inc.

Description: GoPayments application from Intuit allows mobile telephones to process payments like credit card terminals. The application costs $19.95 a month and can be used on the Internet browsers of mobile telephones.

44107 ■ **Getting Clients and Keeping Clients for Your Service Business**

Pub: Atlantic Publishing Company

Ed: Anne M. Miller; Gail Brett Levine. **Released:** August 28, 2008. **Price:** $24.95 paperback. **Description:** Tips are offered to help any small service busi-

ness identify customers, brand and grow the business, as well as development of logos, brochures and Websites.

44108 ■ **"Getting In On the Ground Floor"** in *Entrepreneur* (Vol. 37, September 2009, No. 9, pp. 90)

Pub: Entrepreneur Media, Inc.

Description: Franchise businesses in the United States are listed. Franchise services are mentioned. Statistical data and contact information included.

44109 ■ **"The GHG Quandary: Whose Problem Is It Anyway?"** in *Canadian Business* (Vol. 81, September 15, 2008, No. 14-15, pp. 72)

Pub: Rogers Media Ltd.

Ed: Matthew McClearn. **Description:** Nongovernmental organizations were able to revoke the permit for Imperial Oil Ltd's Kearl oilsands project on the grounds of its expected greenhouse gas emission but the court's ruling was rendered irrelevant by bureaucratic paper-shuffling shortly after. The idea of an environmental impact assessment as a guide to identify the consequences of a project is also discussed.

44110 ■ **"Give It Your All, and Don't Worry About the Rest"** in *Inc.* (Vol. 33, November 2011, No. 9, pp. 37)

Pub: Inc. Magazine

Ed: Norm Brodsky. **Description:** In the early stage of a service company, the owners sell themselves to the customers.

44111 ■ **"Give This Pooch a Home"** in *Advertising Age* (Vol. 78, August 13, 2007, No. 32, pp. 4)

Pub: Crain Communications, Inc.

Ed: Kimberly D. Williams. **Description:** Overview of FlexPetz, a pet-sharing program that targets customers that live in metropolitan areas and travel frequently, who want to have a dog but cannot care for one on a full time basis.

44112 ■ **"Giving Biotech Startups a Hand"** in *Philadelphia Business Journal* (Vol. 28, January 8, 2010, No. 47, pp. 1)

Pub: American City Business Journals

Ed: John George. **Description:** Elkins Park, Pennsylvania-based BioStrategy Partners is a virtual life sciences incubator that is seeking to improve the dull ranking of Philadelphia in the small business vitality index of life sciences. BioStrategy provides technology and business development services to startup life sciences companies and university-based research projects.

44113 ■ **"Global Pain: Alberta's Gain"** in *Canadian Business* (Vol. 79, August 14, 2006, No. 16-17, pp. 60)

Pub: Rogers Media

Ed: Jeff Sanford. **Description:** Political problems and conflicts in oil-rich countries like Iran, Venezuela, and Russia among others, which have benefited the petroleum industry in Alberta, is discussed.

44114 ■ **"Good Going, Partners: Energy-Asset Firms Do Their Parents Proud"** in *Barron's* (Vol. 89, July 27, 2009, No. 30, pp. M8)

Pub: Dow Jones & Co., Inc.

Ed: Shirley A. Lazo. **Description:** Four master limited partnerships boosted their dividends. Sunoco Logistics raised theirs by 11.2 percent, El Paso Pipeline by 12 percent, Holly Energy upped their dividends by a penny, and Western Gas hiked their dividend to 31 cents per unit.

44115 ■ **"Good Things Happen When We Buy Local"** in *Crain's Detroit Business* (Vol. 24, October 6, 2008, No. 40, pp. 7)

Pub: Crain Communications, Inc.

Description: Michigan is facing incredibly difficult economic times. One way in which each one of us can help the state and the businesses located here is by purchasing our goods and services from local vendors. The state Agriculture Department projected that if Michigan households earmarked $10 per week in their grocery purchases to made-in-Michigan products, this would generate $30 million a week in economic impact.

44116 ■ "Grace Puma; Senior Vice-President of Strategic Sourcing, United Airlines" in *Crain's Chicago Business* **(May 5, 2008)**
Pub: Crain Communications, Inc.

Ed: John Rosenthal. **Description:** Profile of Grace Puma who is the senior vice-president of strategic sourcing at United Airlines and is responsible for cutting costs at the company in a number of ways including scheduling safety inspections at the same time as routine maintenance, thereby reducing the downtime of each aircraft by five days as well as replacing a third of her staff with outside talent.

44117 ■ "Grave Concerns" in *Canadian Business* **(Vol. 81, July 21 2008, No. 11, pp. 25)**
Pub: Rogers Media Ltd.

Ed: Andrew Nikiforuk. **Description:** Air pollution control regulations to reduce greenhouse gasses have been implemented by the Canadian government. The federal government is planning to construct a carbon funeral industry that will store the global warming gases, however the expenditure for the project will be shifted to the taxpayers. Details of the Bruce Peachy's initiative on how to reduce GHGs are presented.

44118 ■ "Green Assets Powering Boralex Shares" in *Globe & Mail* **(March 30, 2007, pp. B10)**
Pub: CTVglobemedia Publishing Inc.

Ed: Richard Blackwell. **Description:** The impact of econ-friendly power plant portfolio on the stock performance of Kingsey Falls-based Boralex Inc. is analyzed.

44119 ■ "The Green Industry Jobs Gap" in *Green Industry Pro* **(Vol. 23, October 2011)**
Pub: Cygnus Business Media

Ed: Gregg Wartgow. **Description:** According to the U.S. Bureau of Labor Statistics, the landscaping industry employs over 829,000 workers. According to another private study, the industry would employ more if they were able to find more people interested in performing the required work.

44120 ■ "Greg Stringham" in *Canadian Business* **(Vol. 81, March 3, 2008, No. 3, pp. 8)**
Pub: Rogers Media

Ed: Michelle Magnan. **Description:** Canadian Association of Petroleum Producers' Greg Stringham thinks that the new royalty plan will result in companies pulling out their investments for Alberta's conventional oil and gas sector. Stringham adds that Alberta is losing its competitive advantage and companies must study their cost profiles to retrieve that advantage. The effects of the royalty system on Alberta's economy are examined further.

44121 ■ "Groomers Eye Profit Growth Through Services" in *Pet Product News* **(Vol. 64, December 2010, No. 12, pp. 26)**
Pub: BowTie Inc.

Ed: Kathleen M. Mangan. **Description:** Pet groomers can successfully offer add-on services by taking into account insider customer knowledge, store image, and financial analysis in the decision-making process. Many pet groomers have decided to add services such as spa treatments and training due to a slump in the bathing and grooming business. How some pet groomers gained profitability through add-on services is explored.

44122 ■ "Growing Subscriber Base Fuels Roger's Rosy Outlook for 2007" in *Globe & Mail* **(February 16, 2007, pp. B3)**
Pub: CTVglobemedia Publishing Inc.

Ed: Catherine McLean. **Description:** Canada-based Rogers Communications Inc. has projected increased profits for the 2007 fiscal year. The company has increased its market share by 14 percent with fourth quarter revenues of $176 million.

44123 ■ "Have Tag, Will Travel" in *Inc.* **(Vol. 33, November 2011, No. 9, pp. 48)**
Pub: Inc. Magazine

Ed: Abram Brown. **Description:** Truleytag and Boomerangit are provide services to protect luggage while traveling. Turlytag provides brightly colored ID tags and stickers that attach to any item and feature words Return Me along with the company's contact information. Boomerangit's ID tags and labels feature the words Return for Reward along with their information.

44124 ■ "Hawaii Business 2008 SB Success Awards" in *Hawaii Business* **(Vol. 53, February 2008, No. 8, pp. 43)**
Pub: Hawaii Business Publishing

Description: Winners in the Hawaii Business 2008 SB Success Awards are presented; the awards give recognition for Hawaii small businesses with less than 100 employees and are based on four criteria, namely: unique service or product; rapid expansion or sales growth; longevity; and competency in overcoming challenges.

44125 ■ "Headwinds From the New Sod Slow Aer Lingus" in *Barron's* **(Vol. 88, March 10, 2008, No. 10, pp. M6)**
Pub: Dow Jones & Company, Inc.

Ed: Sean Walters; Arindam Nag. **Description:** Aer Lingus faces a drop in its share prices with a falling US market, higher jet fuel prices, and lower long-haul passenger load factors. British media companies Johnston Press and Yell Group are suffering from weaker ad revenue and heavier debt payments due to the credit crunch.

44126 ■ "The Heat Is On" in *Crain's Chicago Business* **(Vol. 31, April 28, 2008, No. 17, pp. 4)**
Pub: Crain Communications, Inc.

Ed: Steve Daniels. **Description:** Discusses Nicor Inc., a natural-gas utility serving 2 million customers in Chicago's suburbs, and its potential acquirers; shares of the company have dropped 17 percent this year making Nicor the second-worst among 31 utilities in an index tracked by Standrd & Poor's. Statistical data included.

44127 ■ "Hey, You Can't Do That" in *Green Industry Pro* **(Vol. 23, September 2011)**
Pub: Cygnus Business Media

Ed: Rod Dickens. **Description:** Manufacturers of landscape equipment are making better use of energy resources, such as the use of fuel-injection systems instead of carburetors, lightweight materials, better lubricants, advanced battery technology, and innovative engine designs.

44128 ■ "H.I.G. Capital Announces Acquisition of Next Generation Vending" in *Benzinga.com* **(October 29, 2011)**
Pub: Benzinga.com

Ed: Benzinga Staff. **Description:** H.I.G. Capital LLC, a leader in global private investments, acquired Next Generation Vending and Food Service Inc.. Next Generation is a provider of vending services for corporate and institutional clients in Northeastern United States.

44129 ■ "Higher Freight Rates Keep CPR Rolling in Profit" in *Globe & Mail* **(February 1, 2006, pp. B3)**
Pub: CTVglobemedia Publishing Inc.

Ed: Brent Jang. **Description:** Canadian Pacific Railway Ltd. posted $135.4 million in revenues for fourth quarter 2005. The company's earnings projections for 2006 and workforce reduction plans are presented.

44130 ■ "Hispanic Business 100 Fastest-Growing Companies" in *Hispanic Business* **(July-August 2009, pp. 16-18)**
Pub: Hispanic Business

Ed: Joshua Molina. **Description:** Despite the recession, the 100 fastest growing companies profiled are able to maintain their competitive edge; federal contracts are key to their success. Service companies are at the top of the list and Texas and Florida are the states in which the top are located

44131 ■ *A History of Small Business in America*
Pub: University of North Carolina Press

Ed: Mansel G. Blackford. **Released:** May 2003. **Price:** $22.95. **Description:** History of American small business from the colonial era to present, showing how it has played a role in the nation's economic, political, and cultural development across manufacturing, sales, services and farming.

44132 ■ "Hot For All The Wrong Reasons" in *Canadian Business* **(Vol. 81, March 31, 2008, No. 5, pp. 19)**
Pub: Rogers Media

Ed: Andrea Jezovit. **Description:** Soaring platinum prices are due to South Africa's platinum mining industry's safety issues and power supply disruptions that exacerbate the metal's supply problems. South Africa supplies 80 percent of the world's platinum. South Africa's power utility has said that it cannot guarantee the industry's power needs until 2013.

44133 ■ "Hotel Tax Eyed For Waukesha" in *The Business Journal-Milwaukee* **(Vol. 25, August 29, 2008, No. 49, pp. A1)**
Pub: American City Business Journals, Inc.

Ed: Rich Kirchen. **Description:** Midwest Airlines Center chairman Frank Gimbel wants Waukesha County to help in the funding of the $200-million expansion of the convention center through a hotel room tax. The Waukesha hotel industry is expected to oppose the new room tax. Other views and information on the planned new room tax in Waukesha are presented.

44134 ■ "How Dell Will Dial for Dollars" in *Austin Business JournalInc.* **(Vol. 29, December 4, 2009, No. 39, pp. 1)**
Pub: American City Business Journals

Ed: Christopher Calnan. **Description:** Dell Inc. revealed plans to launch a Mini3i smartphone in China which could enable revenue sharing by bundling with wireless service subscription. Dell's smartphone plan is similar to the netbook business, which Dell sold with service provided by AT&T Inc.

44135 ■ "How to Dominate in Residential Maintenance" in *Green Industry Pro* **(Vol. 23, October 2011)**
Pub: Cygnus Business Media

Ed: Gregg Wartgow. **Description:** Lawn care services were ranked among the most expendable consumer expenditures, according to the National Retail Federation data accumulated in early 2011. This makes it critical for any landscape firm to target sales efforts toward higher-income households and higher-value homes.

44136 ■ "How Growers Buy" in *Farm Industry News* **(Vol. 42, January 1, 2009, No. 1)**
Pub: Penton Media, Inc.

Ed: Karen McMahon. **Description:** According to a survey regarding the buying habits among large commercial growers, most prefer to purchase from local retailers, customer service is important concerning their decision on who to buy products from, and price and convenience seem to be more important then brand.

44137 ■ "How Our Picks Beat The Bear" in *Barron's* **(Vol. 88, July 14, 2008, No. 28, pp. 18)**
Pub: Dow Jones & Co., Inc.

Ed: Andrew Bary. **Description:** Performance of the stocks that Barron's covered in the first half of 2008 is discussed; some of the worst picks and most rewarding pans have been in the financial sector while the best plays were in the energy, materials, and the transportation sectors.

44138 ■ "How to Plug in to the Wireless Revolution" in *Globe & Mail* **(March 11, 2006, pp. B3)**
Pub: CTVglobemedia Publishing Inc.

Ed: Catherine McLean. **Description:** The plans of president David Dobbin of Toronto Hydro Telecom Inc., to establish WiFi service, are presented.

44139 ■ "How To Turn Your Efforts Into Results" in *Green Industry Pro* (Vol. 23, September 2011)
Pub: Cygnus Business Media
Ed: Bob Coulter. **Description:** Working Smarter Training Challenge teaches that leaders are able to carry out solutions directly into their organization, develop skills and drive business results in key areas by creating a culture of energized workers who are able to take ownership of their performance as well as the performance of the company as a whole.

44140 ■ "Huberman Failing to Keep CTA on Track" in *Crain's Chicago Business* (Vol. 31, April 21, 2008, No. 16, pp. 22)
Pub: Crain Communications, Inc.
Description: Discusses the deplorable service of CTA, the Chicago Transit Authority, as well as CTA President Ron Huberman who, up until last week had riders hoping he had the management skills necessary to fix the system's problems; Tuesday's event left hundreds of riders trapped for hours and thousands standing on train platforms along the Blue Line waiting for trains that never came.

44141 ■ "In Surging Oil Industry, Good Fortune Comes In Stages" in *Barron's* (Vol. 88, July 7, 2008, No. 27, pp. 12)
Pub: Dow Jones & Co., Inc.
Ed: Sandra Ward. **Description:** Shares of US land oil and gas driller Helmerich and Payne, priced at $69 each, are estimated to be at peak levels. The shares are trading at 17 times 2008 earnings and could be in for some profit taking.

44142 ■ "Industrial Evolution" in *Entrepreneur* (Vol. 35, November 2007, No. 11, pp. 142)
Pub: Entrepreneur Media Inc.
Ed: Nichole L. Torres. **Description:** Businesses often target specific customer bases, but it is possible that your business does not fit a particular industry as your services may also be needed in other fields. Details with regard to expanding businesses into other industries are discussed.

44143 ■ "Ingrian and Channel Management International Sign Distribution Agreement" in *Canadian Corporate News* (May 16, 2007)
Pub: Comtex News Network Inc.
Description: Channel Management International (CMI), a Canadian channel management and distribution company, and Ingrian Networks, Inc., the leading provider of data privacy solutions, announced a Canadian distribution agreement to resell Ingrian encryption solutions to the Canadian market.

44144 ■ "Intel to Buy McAfee Security Business for 768B" in *eWeek* (August 19, 2010)
Pub: Ziff Davis Enterprise
Description: Intel will acquire security giant McAfee for approximately $7.68 billion, whereby McAfee would become a wholly owned subsidiary of Intel and would report to Intel's Software and Services Group.

44145 ■ *International Handbook of Women and Small Business Entrepreneurship*
Pub: Edward Elgar Publishing, Incorporated
Ed: Sandra L. Fielden, Marilyn Davidson. **Released:** December 2006. **Price:** $50.00. **Description:** The number of women entrepreneurs is growing at a faster rate than male counterparts worldwide. Insight into the phenomenon is targeted to scholars and students of women in management and entrepreneurship as well as policymakers and small business service providers.

44146 ■ "It's Back to Business for the Ravens" in *Boston Business Journal* (Vol. 29, July 29, 2011, No. 12, pp. 1)
Pub: American City Business Journals, Inc.
Ed: Scott Dance. **Description:** The Baltimore Ravens football team has been marketing open sponsorship packages following the end of the National Football League lockout. Team officials are working to get corporate logos and slogans on radio and television commercials and online advertisements.

44147 ■ "Jack Be Nimble" in *Business Courier* (Vol. 24, October 26, 2008, No. 28, pp. 1)
Pub: American City Business Journals, Inc.
Ed: Laura Baverman. **Description:** Cincinnati Bell is losing around 47,000 phone lines a year due to the advent of wireless technology and increased competition from cable companies.

44148 ■ "Jacksonville-based Interline Expanding in Janitorial-Sanitation Market" in *Florida Times-Union* (May 10, 2011)
Pub: Florida Times-Union
Ed: Mark Basch. **Description:** Interline Brands Inc., located in Jacksonville, Florida, aims to grow its business with two recent acquisitions of firms that distribute janitorial and sanitation products. Interline markets and distributes maintenance, repair and operations products.

44149 ■ "Janitorial Equipment and Supplies US Market" in *PR Newswire* (October 24, 2011)
Pub: PR Newswire
Description: United States demand for janitorial equipment and supplies (excluding chemical products) is predicted to rise 2.4 percent per year to $7.6 billion in 2013. New product development will lead to increased sales of higher-value goods in the industry.

44150 ■ "Juiced on Energy" in *Barron's* (Vol. 88, July 14, 2008, No. 28, pp. 33)
Pub: Dow Jones & Co., Inc.
Ed: Leslie P. Norton. **Description:** Brad Evans and his team at Heartland Value Plus were able to outperform their peers by significantly undercommitting to financials and overexposing themselves with energy stocks. Brad Evans believes that there is a lot of value left in energy stocks such as natural gas.

44151 ■ "Just Be Nice" in *Canadian Business* (Vol. 79, October 9, 2006, No. 20, pp. 141)
Pub: Rogers Media
Ed: Joe Castaldo. **Description:** The customer relationship management strategies on customer retention and satisfaction adopted by WestJet are discussed.

44152 ■ "Just Hang Up" in *Barron's* (Vol. 88, March 10, 2008, No. 10, pp. 45)
Pub: Dow Jones & Company, Inc.
Ed: Tiernan Ray. **Description:** Sprint's shares are expected to continue falling while the company attempts to attract subscribers by cutting prices, cutting earnings in the process. The company faces tougher competition from better-financed AT&T and Verizon Communications.

44153 ■ "Keeping Railcars 'Busy At All Times' At TTX" in *Crain's Chicago Business* (Vol. 31, April 28, 2008, No. 17, pp. 6)
Pub: Crain Communications, Inc.
Ed: Bob Tita. **Description:** Profile of the president of Chicago railcar pool operator TTX Co. and his business plan for the company which includes improving fleet management and car purchasing through better use of data on railroad demand.

44154 ■ "Kenyans Embrace Moving Money By Text Message" in *Chicago Tribune* (October 7, 2008)
Pub: McClatchy-Tribune Information Services
Ed: Laurie Goering. **Description:** Cell phone banking services are becoming more common, especially for foreign residents; customers are able to establish a virtual cell phone bank account through companies such as M-Pesa which allows their customers to pay bills, withdraw cash, pay merchants or text money to relatives.

44155 ■ "Kerry Steel to Sell Inventory, Close Business After 30 Years" in *Crain's Detroit Business* (Vol. 24, March 17, 2008, No. 11, pp. 26)
Pub: Crain Communications, Inc.
Ed: Brent Snavely. **Description:** Kerry Steel Inc. has confirmed that it is selling all of its inventory and equipment and is going out of business; the company,

which was once one of the largest steel service centers in the Midwest, has sustained financial losses and is in violation of its loan agreements.

44156 ■ "The King of Kincardine" in *Canadian Business* (Vol. 79, October 9, 2006, No. 20, pp. 101)
Pub: Rogers Media
Ed: Paul Webster. **Description:** Motives of Duncan Hawthorne, president and chief executive officer of Bruce Power Ltd., behind investing in nuclear power plant in Ontario, Canada through private financing are discussed.

44157 ■ "Know It All Finds Applicants are Stretching the Truth" in *Philadelphia Business Journal* (Vol. 28, September 11, 2009, No. 30, pp. 1)
Pub: American City Business Journals
Ed: Athena D. Merritt. **Description:** Know It All Background Research Services has reported that discrepancies in background checks reached 19.8 percent in 2009. Reports show that 42 percent of the discrepancies involve lying about previous employment, and 37 percent involve education information. Marc Bourne, the company's vice president, believes that employers have cause to be concerned.

44158 ■ "Knox County Schools Debate Outsourcing Janitorial Services" in (March 29, 2011)
Pub: Knoxville News Sentinel
Ed: Lola Alapo. **Description:** Custodial services of Knox County Schools in Tennessee may be outsourced in move to save money for the school district. Details of the proposed program are included.

44159 ■ "Labor of Love" in *Green Industry Pro* (Vol. 23, March 2011, No. 3, pp. 14)
Pub: Cygnus Business Media
Ed: Gregg Wartgow. **Description:** Profile of CLS Landscape Management in Chino, California and its owner who started the company when he was 21 years old. Kevin Davis built his landscape firm into a $20 million a year business without using any dedicated salesperson.

44160 ■ "Leasing Midway; Look for Higher Parking Fees, More Retail Under Private Airport Operator" in *Crain's Chicago Business* (May 5, 2008)
Pub: Crain Communications, Inc.
Ed: Paul Merrion. **Description:** According to experts, bids for the first privatization of a major U.S. airport could run as high as $3.5 billion. Information-gathering and negotiations will soon get under way with some or all of the six major international investor groups that recently expressed interest in running Midway.

44161 ■ "Lifebank Grants Stock Options" in *Canadian Corporate News* (May 16, 2007)
Pub: Comtex News Network Inc.
Description: Lifebank, a biomedical service company that provides processing cryogenic storage of umbilical cord blood stem cells, announced that, under its stock option plan, it has granted incentive stock options to directors, officers, and consultants of the company.

44162 ■ "Live and Learn: Lionel Hurtubise" in *Canadian Business* (Vol. 80, January 29, 2007, No. 3, pp. 64)
Pub: Rogers Media
Ed: Andy Holloway. **Description:** The views of Lionel Hurtubise, the chairman of SR Telecom, PolarSat, and STP, on his life and the growth of the Canadian telecommunications industry are presented.

44163 ■ "Local Firms Will Feel Impact Of Wall St. Woes" in *The Business Journal-Milwaukee* (Vol. 25, September 19, 2008, No. 52, pp. A1)
Pub: American City Business Journals, Inc.
Ed: Rich Kirchen. **Description:** Wall Street's crisis is expected to affect businesses in Wisconsin, in terms of decreased demand for services and products and increased financing costs. Businesses in Milwaukee

area may face higher interest rates and tougher loan standards. The potential impacts of the Wall Street crisis on local businesses are examined further.

44164 ■ "Local Hotels Brace for Downturn" in *Crain's Chicago Business* (Vol. 31, March 31, 2008, No. 13, pp. 3)
Pub: Crain Communications, Inc.

Ed: Bob Tita. **Description:** Chicago hotels are seeing a noticeable drop in business-related guests so far this year due to a slumping national economy, tighter corporate expense budgets and higher airfares.

44165 ■ "Locally Based Stocks Escape Worst of Market's Turmoil" in *Crain's Detroit Business* (Vol. 24, September 22, 2008, No. 38, pp. 4)
Pub: Crain Communications, Inc.

Ed: Daniel Duggan. **Description:** Locally-based companies did not take as big a hit as might be expected with the shock to the financial markets last week; this is due mainly to the fact that the region does not have heavy exposure to energy or capital markets.

44166 ■ "A Look Ahead Into 2007" in *Canadian Business* (Vol. 80, December 25, 2006, No. 1, pp. 40)
Pub: Rogers Media

Description: The 2007 forecasts for various industrial sectors like telecom, information technology, manufacturing, retail, financial and energy among others is discussed.

44167 ■ "Losses Threaten Comp Care's Future Viability" in *The Business Journal-Serving Greater Tampa Bay* (Vol. 28, August 15, 2008, No. 34)
Pub: American City Business Journals, Inc.

Ed: Margie Manning. **Description:** Comprehensive Care Corp. expressed that it may have to cease or drastically curtail its operations if it won't be able to raise additional funding in the next two or three months. The firm, which provides managed behavioral health care services, is also believed to be exploring a sale. Other views and information on Comprehensive Care's finances and plans are presented.

44168 ■ *Low-Budget Online Marketing for Small Business*
Pub: International Self-Counsel Press, Limited

Ed: Holly Berkley. **Released:** July 2005. **Price:** $14.95. **Description:** Low-cost, effective online marketing tips for small companies selling products or services over the Internet.

44169 ■ "Lower Prices No Shoo-In as Telcos Near Deregulation" in *Globe & Mail* (March 28, 2007, pp. B1)
Pub: CTVglobemedia Publishing Inc.

Ed: Catherine McLean. **Description:** The fall in market share and low quality of service among other issues that may disallow telecommunication industries in Canada from setting their phone rates is discussed.

44170 ■ "Madeleine Paquin" in *Canadian Business* (Vol. 81, March 3, 2008, No. 3, pp. 92)
Pub: Rogers Media

Ed: Regan Ray. **Description:** Madeleine Paquin, chief executive officer and president of Logistec Corp., talks about how she balanced her career and her life as a mother to two girls. Paquin thinks that working mothers need to focus on some things instead of trying to do everything. Her career in the marine cargo handling industry is also discussed.

44171 ■ "Making Visitors Out Of Listeners" in *Hawaii Business* (Vol. 54, July 2008, No. 1, pp. 18)
Pub: Hawaii Business Publishing

Ed: Casey Chin. **Description:** Japanese workers are subscribing to the Official Hawaii Podcast in iTunes, which offers a free 20-minute, Japanese-language

audio content on different topics, such as dining reviews and music from local artists. The concept is a way to attract Japanese travelers to come to Hawaii.

44172 ■ *Marketing for Entrepreneurs*
Pub: FT Press

Ed: Jurgen Wolff. **Released:** December 9, 2010. **Price:** $24.99. **Description:** This text identifies marketing as the entire process of researching, creating, distributing and selling a product or service. It isn't about theory and metrics, rather it is a practical guide that starts with the basics of all marketing aspects.

44173 ■ "Maryland Senate Gets Read to Talk Taxes" in *Boston Business Journal* (Vol. 29, July 1, 2011, No. 8, pp. 1)
Pub: American City Business Journals Inc.

Ed: Scott Dance. **Description:** Maryland Senate Budget and Taxation Committee will meet July 26, 2011 to discuss some of business community's concerns including sales tax expansion to cover services, a restructuring of the corporate income tax brackets and an answer to questions regarding transportation funding project.

44174 ■ "May I Handle That For You?" in *Inc.* (March 2008, pp. 40, 42)
Pub: Gruner & Jahr USA Publishing

Ed: Taylor Mallory. **Description:** According to a recent survey, 53 percent of all companies outsource a portion of their human resources responsibilities. Ceridian, Administaff, Taleo, KnowledgeBank, and CheckPoint HR are among the companies profiled.

44175 ■ "mChip: Claros Diagnostics" in *Inc.* (Vol. 33, November 2011, No. 9, pp. 42)
Pub: Inc. Magazine

Ed: Christine Lagorio. **Description:** Harvard University researchers have developed a device called the mChip that produces accurate blood tests in about 10 minutes. Plans to apply for FDA approval for the mChip in the US should happen in 2012.

44176 ■ "Mergers Mean Woe for Fliers; Airline Hookups Boost Fares, Diminish Service" in *Crain's Chicago Business* (April 21, 2008)
Pub: Crain Communications, Inc.

Ed: John Pletz. **Description:** Discusses the impact airline mergers will have on customer service, pricing and business travel, particularly at Chicago's O'Hare International Airport.

44177 ■ "Microsoft Clicks Into High Speed" in *Hispanic Business* (Vol. 30, July-August 2008, No. 7-8, pp. 54)
Pub: Hispanic Business, Inc.

Ed: Derek Reveron. **Description:** Microsoft's diversity hiring and vendor diversity program to capture more Hispanic consumer and business-to-business market is described. One of the main goals of these programs is to hire more Hispanic executives and managers who will help the company develop and market products and services that will appeal and benefit Hispanic consumers.

44178 ■ "Midwest Looks 'Back to the Future" in *The Business Journal-Milwaukee* (Vol. 25, July 18, 2008, No. 43, pp. A1)
Pub: American City Business Journals, Inc.

Ed: Rich Rovito. **Description:** Midwest Air Group Inc. announced plans to reduce their work force by 40 percent or 1,200 employees after an earlier announcement of a drastic fleet reduction. These steps are being taken by the company in an effort to avoid filing bankruptcy since this would cost the airline millions of dollars in legal and other professional fees.

44179 ■ "Midwest Seeks Concessions From Creditors" in *The Business Journal-Milwaukee* (Vol. 25, July 25, 2008, No. 44, pp. A1)
Pub: American City Business Journals, Inc.

Ed: Rich Rovito. **Description:** Midwest Airlines Inc. is turning to creditors and lease holders for the financial aspect of its restructuring, which involves going back to serving popular business destinations. Chief executive officer Timothy believes that the

company can survive in a niche market as long as it provides quality service. He discusses Midwest's restructuring plan.

44180 ■ "Milton Touts ACE Unit to Would-Be Buyers" in *Globe & Mail* (February 10, 2007, pp. B6)
Pub: CTVglobemedia Publishing Inc.

Ed: Brent Jang. **Description:** The decision of Air Canada chairman Robert Milton to sell Air Canada Technical Services unit is presented. ACE Aviation Holdings Inc. is the parent company of Air Canada.

44181 ■ "A Mixed-Bag Quarter" in *Barron's* (Vol. 88, July 7, 2008, No. 27, pp. 19)
Pub: Dow Jones & Co., Inc.

Ed: Shirley A. Lazo. **Description:** Seven component companies of the Dow Jones Industrial Average increased their dividend payouts in the second quarter of 2008 despite the weak performance of the index. Five companies in the Dow Jones Transportation index and three in the Dow Jones Utilities also increased their dividends.

44182 ■ "Mobile: Juanes Fans Sing for Sprint" in *Advertising Age* (Vol. 79, November 3, 2008, No. 41, pp. 22)
Pub: Crain Communications, Inc.

Ed: Laurel Wentz. **Description:** Marketers are appealing to the Hispanic market since they are more prone to use their cell phones to respond to contests, download videos, ringtones, or other data activity. Sprint recently sponsored a contest inviting people to sing like Colombian megastar Juanes; the participants filmed and sent their videos using their cell phones rather than laptops or camcorders illustrating the Hispanic overindex on mobile-phone technology. The contest generated hundreds of thousands of dollars in additional fee revenue, as monthly downloads increased 63 percent.

44183 ■ "Monopoly Money Madness" in *Canadian Business* (Vol. 81, March 17, 2008, No. 4, pp. 9)
Pub: Rogers Media

Description: Enbridge was given permission by the Ontario Energy Board to collect $22 million it spent on an out-of-court settlement for charging unfair fees from 1994 to 2002. Customers are essentially being gouged twice in this scenario. The monopoly of Enbridge should end and the consumers should not have to pay for the system's faults.

44184 ■ "Monsanto Acquires Targeted-Pest Control Technology Start-Up; Terms Not Disclosed" in *Benzinga.com* (, 2011)
Pub: Benzinga.com

Ed: Benzinga Staff. **Description:** Monsanto Company acquired Beelogics, a firm that researches and develops biological tools that control pests and diseases. Research includes a product that will help protect bee health.

44185 ■ "Montgomery & Barnes: a Service-Disabled, Veteran-Owned Small Business" in *Underground Construction* (Vol. 65, October 2010, No. 10)
Pub: Oildom Publishing Company of Texas Inc.

Description: Gary Montgomery, chairman of Montgomery and Barnes announced that President Wendell (Buddy) Barnes is now majority owner, thus making the Houston-based civil engineering and consulting services firm, eligible to quality as a Service-Disabled Veteran-Owned Small Business (SDVOSB).

44186 ■ "The Moral Legitimacy of NGOs as Partners of Corporations" in *Business Ethics Quarterly* (Vol. 21, October 2011, No. 4, pp. 579)
Pub: Society for Business Ethics

Ed: Dorothea Baur, Guido Palazzo. **Description:** Partnerships between companies and NGOs have received considerable attention in CSR in the past years. However, the role of NGO legitimacy in such partnerships has thus far been neglected. The article argues that NGOs assume a status as special stakeholders of corporations which act on behalf of the common good. This role requires a particular focus on their moral legitimacy. An introduction to the conceptual framework analyzing the moral legitimacy of NGOs along three dimensions, building on the theory of deliberative democracy.

44187 ■ "More Callers Are Cutting Their Landlines" in *Chicago Tribune* **(December 30, 2008)**
Pub: McClatchy-Tribune Information Services
Ed: Eric Benderoff. **Description:** Despite sporadic outages for cell phone users, the trend for consumers to cut out the expense of a landline does not appear to be slowing; experts believe that the recession will further increase the number of consumers who decide to go completely wireless.

44188 ■ "Most Popular Tools? The Survey Says" in *Contractor* **(Vol. 57, February 2010, No. 2, pp. 1)**
Pub: Penton Media, Inc.
Ed: Robert P. Mader. **Description:** According to a survey of individuals in the field, mechanical contractors are purchasing more of their tools at home centers and they are also increasingly working in the service, repair, and retrofit markets. The survey also found that the reciprocating saw is the most used corded power tool. Additional purchasing habits of mechanical contractors are listed.

44189 ■ "My Favorite Tool for Managing Expenses" in *Inc.* **(Volume 32, December 2010, No. 10, pp. 60)**
Pub: Inc. Magazine
Ed: J.J. McCorvey. **Description:** Web-based service called Expensify is outlined. The service allows companies to log expenses while away from the office using the service's iPhone application.

44190 ■ "A Nasty Russian Tale" in *Canadian Business* **(Vol. 81, March 3, 2008, No. 3, pp. 85)**
Pub: Rogers Media
Ed: Andrew Nikiforuk. **Description:** Billionaires Alex Shnaider and Michael Shtaif entered a partnership for an oil venture which ended in a slew of litigations. Cases of breach of contract, injurious falsehood and other related lawsuits were filed against Shnaider. Details of the lawsuits and the other parties involved in the disputes are presented.

44191 ■ "Network Like A Boy Scout" in *Women Entrepreneur* **(January 15, 2009)**
Pub: Entrepreneur Media Inc.
Ed: Merrily Orsini. **Description:** Marketing for businesses that provide products or services that people only seek during emergencies or natural disasters such as hurricanes can be a challenge; tips for branding such businesses, networking and establishing a strong customer base that will refer your business to others are given.

44192 ■ "New Boss at Nortel Mines GE for New Executives" in *Globe & Mail* **(February 6, 2006, pp. B1)**
Pub: CTVglobemedia Publishing Inc.
Ed: Catherine McLean. **Description:** Chief executive officer Mike Zafirovski of Nortel Networks Corp. appoints executives Dennis Carey, Joel Hackney and Don McKenn of GE Electric Co. The managerial abilities of Mike are discussed.

44193 ■ "The New Face of Detroit" in *Inc.* **(Vol. 33, October 2011, No. 8, pp. 6)**
Pub: Inc. Magazine
Ed: Elizabeth Sile. **Description:** Basketball legend Magic Johnson has joined Detroit Venture Partners and Detroit will be one of the firm's three inaugural cities to host fellows from Venture for America, a new organization that places recent college graduates in start-up companies.

44194 ■ "New Sprint Phone Whets Appetite for Applications" in *The Business Journal-Serving Metropolitan Kansas City* **(Vol. 26, July 25, 2008)**
Pub: American City Business Journals, Inc.
Ed: Suzanna Stagemeyer. **Description:** Firms supporting the applications of the new Samsung Instinct, which was introduced by Sprint Nextel Corp. in June 2008, have reported usage rates increase for their products. Handmark, whose mobile services Pocket

Express comes loaded with Instinct, has redirected employees to meet the rising demand for the services. Other views and information on Instinct, are presented.

44195 ■ "New Tax Sends Biz Scrambling; Service Levy Will Affect 16,000 Businesses" in *Crain's Detroit Business* **(October 8, 2007)**
Pub: Crain Communications Inc. - Detroit
Ed: Amy Lane. **Description:** Legislation that imposes a tax on services in Michigan has business leaders upset. The new law exerts a 6 percent tax on 57 categories of services that affects 16,000 businesses in the state.

44196 ■ "A New Way to Tell When to Fold" in *Barron's* **(Vol. 88, July 7, 2008, No. 27, pp. 27)**
Pub: Dow Jones & Co., Inc.
Ed: Theresa W. Carey. **Description:** Overview of the Online trading company SmartStops, a firm that aims to tell investors when to sell the shares of a particular company. The company's Web site categorizes stocks as moving up, down, or sideways, and calculates exit points for individual stocks based on an overall market trend.

44197 ■ *Niche and Grow Rich*
Pub: Entrepreneur Press
Ed: Jennifer Basye Sander; Peter Sander. **Released:** 2003. **Description:** Consultants share insight to entrepreneurs wishing to find a profitable niche market. Authors write that good niche businesses are easy to start and easy to defend from competitors. They also report that finding a successful niche can attract and maintain good customers who are willing to pay more for unique goods and services.

44198 ■ "Niche Markets, Green Will Be Okay in 2010" in *Contractor* **(Vol. 57, January 2010, No. 1, pp. 1)**
Pub: Penton Media, Inc.
Ed: Robert P. Mader . **Description:** Mechanical contractors will see most of their work stemming from niche markets, such as green work, as well as service work in 2010. It is said that things will turn around for the industry in 2012 and 2013 and one forecast believes that anything outside of the institutional or more public sector work could be down 15 to 30 percent.

44199 ■ "Nighttime Shuttle to Connect Detroit, Ferndale, Royal Oak" in *Crain's Detroit Business* **(Vol. 24, October 6, 2008, No. 40, pp. 24)**
Pub: Crain Communications, Inc.
Ed: Nancy Kaffer. **Description:** With hopes of bridging the social gap between the cities and suburbs, Chris Ramos has launched The Night Move, a new shuttle service that will ferry passengers between Royal Oak, Ferndale and downtown Detroit. The cost for a round trip ticket is $12.

44200 ■ "Nortel Makes Customers Stars in New Campaign" in *Brandweek* **(Vol. 49, April 21, 2008, No. 16, pp. 8)**
Pub: VNU Business Media, Inc.
Ed: Mike Beirne. **Description:** Nortel has launched a new television advertising campaign in which the business-to-business communications technology provider cast senior executives in 30-second TV case studies that show how Nortel's technology helped their businesses innovate.

44201 ■ "Nortel Outlook Shows Recovery Won't Come Quickly" in *Globe & Mail* **(March 20, 2007, pp. B4)**
Pub: CTVglobemedia Publishing Inc.
Ed: Catherine McLean. **Description:** The forecast about the unlikely recovery of Nortel Networks Corp. from decrease in its share prices is discussed.

44202 ■ "Nothing Plus Nothing" in *Entrepreneur* **(Vol. 37, October 2009, No. 10, pp. 25)**
Pub: Entrepreneur Media, Inc.
Ed: Joe Robinson. **Description:** Jason Fried and David Heinemeier Hansson of Web application firm 37signals believe that free Web services will never

become profitable in the long term. They believe that Web service providers should charge a fair price on such services.

44203 ■ "NovAtel Inc. Licensed to Sell Galileo Receivers" in *Canadian Corporate News* **(May 14, 2007)**
Pub: Comtex News Network Inc.
Description: NovAtel Inc., a leading provider of precision Global Navigation Satellite System (GNSS) components and subsystems that afford its customers rapid integration of precise positioning technology, has received a license valid for ten years that allows NovAtel to sell receivers that track Galileo signals.

44204 ■ "Nuclear Plans May Stall on Uranium Shortage" in *Globe & Mail* **(March 22, 2007, pp. B4)**
Pub: CTVglobemedia Publishing Inc.
Ed: Shawn McCarthy. **Description:** The poor investments in uranium production and enrichment despite growing demand for it for nuclear energy is discussed.

44205 ■ "Oce Business Services: Discovery Made Easy" in *Information Today* **(Vol. 26, February 2009, No. 2, pp. 31)**
Pub: Information Today, Inc.
Ed: Barbara Brynko. **Description:** Oce Business Services provides document process management and electronic discovery through its CaseData repertoire of legal management solutions.

44206 ■ "OK, Bring in the Lawyers" in *Crain's Chicago Business* **(Vol. 31, November 17, 2008, No. 46, pp. 26)**
Pub: Crain Communications, Inc.
Ed: Daniel Rome Levine. **Description:** Bankruptcy attorneys are finding the economic and credit crisis a benefit for their businesses due to the high number of business owners and mortgage holders that are need of their services. One Chicago firm is handling ten times the number of cases they did the previous year and of that about 80 percent of their new clients are related to the real estate sector.

44207 ■ "The Old Railway is on a Roll" in *Globe & Mail* **(January 26, 2006, pp. B1)**
Pub: CTVglobemedia Publishing Inc.
Description: The reasons behind 5 percent rise in shares for Canadian National Railway Co. are presented.

44208 ■ "Omniplex on the Case" in *Black Enterprise* **(Vol. 37, December 2006, No. 5, pp. 38)**
Pub: Earl G. Graves Publishing Co. Inc.
Ed: Glenn Townes. **Description:** Office of Personnel Management in Washington D.C. recently awarded a service contract to Omniplex World Services Corp. Virginia-based, The Chantilly, will perform security investigations and background checks on current and prospective federal employees and military personnel and contractors.

44209 ■ "On Policy: Where Talk is Cheap" in *Canadian Business* **(Vol. 80, January 29, 2007, No. 3, pp. 19)**
Pub: Rogers Media
Ed: Jack Mintz. **Description:** The comparative analysis of the telecommunications policy of Canada and the United States of America is presented. The methods of improving Canada's telecommunications policy are discussed.

44210 ■ "On Target" in *Canadian Business* **(Vol. 81, July 22, 2008, No. 12-13, pp. 45)**
Pub: Rogers Media Ltd.
Ed: Calvin Leung. **Description:** Companies such as LavalifePRIME, a dating website devoted to singles 45 and older, discuss the value of marketing and services aimed at Canada's older consumers. One-third of Canada's 33 million people are 50-plus, controlling 77 percent of the countries wealth.

44211 ■ "Open Skies: Opportunity, Challenge for Airlines" in *Crain's Chicago Business* **(April 21, 2008)**
Pub: Crain Communications, Inc.
Ed: Paul Merrion. **Description:** Discusses the new aviation agreement between Europe and the United States known as Open Skies; the pact creates op-

portunities for U.S. carriers to fly to new destinations in Europe from more U.S. cities; it also allows carriers to fly between European cities, something they have not been able to do until now.

44212 ■ "Open the Telecom Market" in
Canadian Business (Vol. 80, April 23, 2007, No. 9, pp. 80)
Pub: Rogers Media

Description: The effects of federal telecommunication law on foreign investments in telecommunication industry are presented.

44213 ■ "Optima Public Relations Gains Partners" in *Alaska Business Monthly* (Vol. 27, October 2011, No. 10, pp. 10)
Pub: Alaska Business Publishing Company

Ed: Nancy Pounds. **Description:** OPrima Public Relations has partnered with Gogerty Marriott of Seattle and Seattle Design Group.

44214 ■ "Optimal Awarded US $256 Thousand Contract to Conduct LiDAR Survey for a Major Electric Utility in the Southwest" in *Canadian Corporate News*
Pub: Comtex News Network Inc.

Description: Optimal Geomatics, a company specializing in the science and technology of analyzing, gathering, interpreting, distributing, and using geographic information, was awarded a new contract from a long-standing electric utility customer in the Southwest to conduct a LiDAR survey for a part of the utility's overhead transmission line system.

44215 ■ "Ordering Pizza Hut From Your Facebook Page?" in *Advertising Age* (Vol. 79, November 10, 2008, No. 42, pp. 50)
Pub: Crain Communications, Inc.

Ed: Emily Bryson York. **Description:** Fast-food chains are experimenting with delivery/takeout services via social networks such as Facebook and iPhone applications. This also allows the chains to build valuable databases of their customers.

44216 ■ "OSHA Proposes Historic Safety Penalty on BP" in *Workforce Management* (Vol. 88, November 16, 2009, No. 12, pp. 8)
Pub: Crain Communications, Inc.

Ed: Mark Schoeff Jr. **Description:** Labor Secretary Hilda Solis has warned that she aims to toughen the enforcement of workplace laws; OSHA, the Occupational Safety and Health Administration, an agency within the Department of Labor, is penalizing BP Products North America Inc. for their failure to improve workplace safety.

44217 ■ "Our Gadget of the Week: Easy as a Snap" in *Barron's* (Vol. 90, September 13, 2010, No. 37, pp. 35)
Pub: Barron's Editorial & Corporate Headquarters

Ed: Jay Palmer. **Description:** SanMyPhotos.com offers a service whereby people can receive an empty box they can fill with photos then send back to the company to be stored digitally. The photos are returned to the customer with a disc containing the digital photographs. The service costs $150 for one box and $300 for three boxes.

44218 ■ "Owning the Right Risks" in *Harvard Business Review* (Vol. 86, September 2008, No. 9, pp. 102)
Pub: Harvard Business School Press

Ed: Kevin Bueler; Andrew Freeman; Ron Hulme. **Description:** TXU Corp. is used to illustrate methods for successful risk management. The electric utility's practices include determining which risks are natural, embedding risk in all processes and decisions, and organizing corporate governance around risk.

44219 ■ "Panel to Call for Reduced Restraints on Telecom Sector" in *Globe & Mail* (March 17, 2006, pp. B1)
Pub: CTVglobemedia Publishing Inc.

Ed: Simon Tuck. **Description:** A federal panel called to adopt a more market-friendly approach to the lucrative telecommunications sector in Canada. Details of the report are presented.

44220 ■ "Panel Calls for 'Fundamental' Change to Telecom Regulation" in *Globe & Mail* (March 23, 2006, pp. B1)
Pub: CTVglobemedia Publishing Inc.

Ed: Catherine McLean. **Description:** A federal panel review at Ottawa called for a shakeup of regulations and policies that govern telecommunications companies to contend with sweeping technological changes. Details of the panel review are presented.

44221 ■ "Patients to Elect to Cut Care" in *The Business Journal-Serving Metropolitan Kansas City* (Vol. 27, November 21, 2008, No. 11, pp. 1)
Pub: American City Business Journals, Inc.

Ed: Rob Roberts. **Description:** Patients in Kansas City, Missouri are cutting down on health care services due to the economic crisis. A decline in diagnostic procedures has been observed at Northland Cardiology. Elective reconstructive procedures have also been reduced by 25 percent. Additional information and statistics regarding the healthcare sector is included.

44222 ■ "PDAs Are Great - As Long As You Can Find Them" in *Crain's Chicago Business* (Vol. 31, May 5, 2008, No. 18, pp. 41)
Pub: Crain Communications, Inc.

Ed: Jennifer Olvera. **Description:** Discusses a new service from Global Lost & Found Inc. in which after paying a one-time fee, customers receive a label with an identification number and a toll free phone number so if they lose a gadget such as a cell phone, PDA or laptop the finder can return the device and are rewarded with a gift card.

44223 ■ "PDX Bucks National Trend" in *The Business Journal-Portland* (Vol. 25, August 1, 2008, No. 21, pp. 1)
Pub: American City Business Journals, Inc.

Ed: Erik Siemers. **Description:** Portland International Airport could face problems as air carriers are planning to reduce capacity at the airport. The airport is showing signs of growth despite the slowdown in the airline industry. Other airlines that are planning to reduce seating capacity at the airport are also presented.

44224 ■ "The Phone-Service Test" in *Canadian Business* (Vol. 79, October 9, 2006, No. 20, pp. 137)
Pub: Rogers Media

Ed: Rachel Pulfer. **Description:** Suggestions to improve the customer services provided by airlines through call centers are discussed.

44225 ■ "Pioneering Strategies for Entrepreneurial Success" in *Business Horizons* (Vol. 51, January-February 2008, No. 1, pp. 21)
Pub: Elsevier Advanced Technology Publications

Ed: Candida G. Brush. **Description:** Entrepreneurs are known for new products, services, processes, markets and industries. In order to achieve success, they have to develop a clear vision, creatively manage finances, and use social skills to persuade others to commit to the venture. Pioneering strategies and their implementation are examined.

44226 ■ "Pioneers Get All The Perks" in *Canadian Business* (Vol. 81, March 3, 2008, No. 3, pp. 18)
Pub: Rogers Media

Description: Suncor Energy Inc. will face royalty payments from 25%to 30% of net profits as it signs a new deal with Alberta. Biovail Corp., meanwhile, is under a U.S. grand jury investigation for supposed improprieties in Cardizem LA heart drug launch. The Conference Board of Canada's proposal to impose taxes on greenhouse gas emissions and other developments in the business community are discussed.

44227 ■ "Plans for Coal-Fired Electricity Could Go Up in Smoke" in *Globe & Mail* (March 5, 2007, pp. B7)
Pub: CTVglobemedia Publishing Inc.

Ed: Steve James. **Description:** The coal-fired power project initiated by Texas-based utility company TXU

Corp. is receiving legal challenges from green groups. The possible disasters caused by the coal-fired plant are presented.

44228 ■ "Poisoning Relationships: Perceived Unfairness in Channels of Distribution" in *Journal of Marketing* (Vol. 75, May 2011, No. 3, pp. 99)
Pub: American Marketing Association

Ed: Stephen A. Samaha, Robert W. Palmatier, Rajiv P. Dant. **Description:** The effects of perceived unfairness on the relationships among members of distribution channels are examined. Perceived unfairness is found to directly damage relationships, aggravate the negative effects of conflict and opportunism, and undermine the benefits of the contract.

44229 ■ "Poor Economy Inspires Rich Alternatives In a Modern, and Tax-Free, Twist on Bartering" in *Houston Chronicle* (June 7, 2010)
Pub: Houston Chronicle Publishing Company

Ed: Michael Rubinkam. **Description:** Time banking helps individuals and firms receive goods or services by depositing time dollars into a bank reserved for receipt of goods and services.

44230 ■ "Population Growing Faster Than Retail, Service Sector" in *Crain's New York Business* (Vol. 24, January 14, 2008, No. 2, pp. 30)
Pub: Crain Communications, Inc.

Ed: Andrew Marks. **Description:** Downtown Manhattan is seeing more residential development; however, as more families call the area home the need for more retail and services is becoming evident.

44231 ■ "Post-Prison Center Idea Rankles OTR" in *Business Courier* (Vol. 26, November 27, 2009, No. 31, pp. 1)
Pub: American City Business Journals, Inc.

Ed: Lucy May. **Description:** Cincinnati officials and community leaders oppose Firetree Ltd.'s plan to launch a residential program for federal offenders near the School for the Creative and Performing Arts in Over-the-Rhine. Firetree, a Pennsylvania-based reentry center services firm, proposed a five-year contract with the Federal Bureau of Prisons based on a letter to Cincinnati Police Chief Thomas Streicher.

44232 ■ "Powder River Reports First Quarter Revenues Over 5 Million" in *Canadian Corporate News* (May 16, 2007)
Pub: Comtex News Network Inc.

Description: Financial report for Powder River Basin Gas Corp., a revenue generating producer, marketer, and acquirer of crude oil and natural gas properties. Statistical data included.

44233 ■ "The Power Brokers" in *Crain's Chicago Business* (Vol. 31, April 28, 2008, No. 17, pp. 41)
Pub: Crain Communications, Inc.

Ed: Samantha Stainburn. **Description:** Profile of BlueStar Energy Services Inc., one of the first suppliers to cash in on the deregulation f the electricity market by the Illinois Legislature; last year BlueStar's revenue was $171.1 million, up from $600,000 in 2002, the year the company was founded.

44234 ■ "The Price of Profitability" in *Green Industry Pro* (Vol. 23, March 2011, No. 3, pp. 18)
Pub: Cygnus Business Media

Ed: Tony Bass. **Description:** Profit Builder Process is used to help landscaping companies be more competitive. Landscape contractors report pricing among their largest challenges and although the economy is improving, homeowners are paying closer attention to quality and service.

44235 ■ "Pride Lands Janitorial Work at New Terminal" in *Sacramento Business Journal* (Vol. 28, June 10, 2011, No. 15, pp. 1)
Pub: Sacramento Business Journal

Ed: Kelly Johnson. **Description:** Pride Industries Inc. won the five-year $9.4 million contract to clean the Sacramento International Airport's new Terminal B, which will open in fall 2011. The nonprofit organization posts a revenue of $191 million for 2011 and currently employs more than 2,400 people with disabilities. The contract is expected to provide savings of over $3 million a year to the airport.

44236 ■ "Prime-Time Exposure" in *Inc.* **(March 2008, pp. 66, 68)**
Pub: Gruner & Jahr USA Publishing
Ed: Adam Bluestein. **Description:** Product placement in television shows has increase sales for many companies. Tips for placing products or services into TV shows are explained: consider hiring an agency, target efforts, dream up a plot point, be ready to go on short notice, and work the niches.

44237 ■ *Professional Services Marketing: How the Best Firms Build Premier Brands*
Pub: John Wiley & Sons, Inc.
Ed: Mike Schultz, John Doerr. **Released:** July 27, 2009. **Price:** $27.95. **Description:** Research based on best practices and processes for the professional services industry is presented. The book covers five key areas: creating a custom marketing and growth strategy, establishing a brand, implementing a marketing communications program, developing a lead strategy, and winning new clients.

44238 ■ "Put Power in Your Direct Mail Campaigns" in *Contractor* **(Vol. 56, September 2009, No. 9, pp. 64)**
Pub: Penton Media, Inc.
Ed: Matt Michel. **Description:** Advice on how members of the United States plumbing industry should manage direct mail marketing campaigns are offered. Determining the purpose of a campaign is recommended. Focusing on a single message, product or service is also encouraged.

44239 ■ "Put Your Heating Cap On..." in *Indoor Comfort Marketing* **(Vol. 70, September 2011, No. 9, pp. 26)**
Pub: Industry Publications Inc.
Ed: George Carey. **Description:** Tools and techniques for HVAC/R technicians servicing boilers are outlined.

44240 ■ "Putting the Service-Profit Chain to Work" in *Harvard Business Review* **(Vol. 86, July-August 2008, No. 8, pp. 118)**
Pub: Harvard Business School Press
Ed: James L. Heskett; Thomas O. Jones; Gary W. Loveman; W. Earl Sasser Jr.; Leonard A. Schlesinger. **Description:** Advice is given on how to foster profitability in service businesses. Topics include the link between employee satisfaction and customer satisfaction, internal service quality, external service value, and revenue growth.

44241 ■ "Q&A" in *Canadian Business* **(Vol. 81, July 22, 2008, No. 12-13, pp. 8)**
Pub: Rogers Media Ltd.
Ed: Michelle Magnan. **Description:** Interview with Scott Saxberg who discusses Crescent Point Energy Trust's discovery of resources in Saskatchewan and believes that this is a once-in-a-lifetime type of event. Crescent Point holds 75 percent of its resources in Saskatchewan; this new finding being considered the second-largest pool discovered since the 1950s. Saxberg's other views as well as information on Crescent Point's services are presented.

44242 ■ "Quicksilver Resources Receives Favorable Judgement" in *Canadian Corporate News* **(May 16, 2007)**
Pub: Comtex News Network Inc.
Description: The 236th Judicial District Court of Texas ruled in favor of Quicksilver Resources Inc., a crude oil and natural gas exploration and production company, in the litigation between Quicksilver and CMS Marketing Services and Trading Company regarding the sale and purchase of 10,000 million British thermal units of natural gas per day at a minimum price of $2.47 per MMbtu, with the condition that the parties share any upside equally. The Court has rescinded the contract, rendering it void.

44243 ■ "Race-Week Schedule Filling Up With Galas, Nonprofit Fundraisers" in *Boston Business Journal* **(Vol. 29, July 22, 2011, No. 11, pp. 1)**
Pub: American City Business Journals Inc.
Ed: Alexander Jackson. **Description:** Baltimore, Maryland-based businesses and nonprofit groups

have been planning their own events to coincide with the Baltimore Grand Prix during the Labor Day weekend. They also plan to partner with others in hopes of drumming up new business, raising money or to peddle their brands.

44244 ■ "Ready for the Worst? How to Disaster-Proof Your Business" in *Inc.* **(Vol. 33, September 2011, No. 7, pp. 38)**
Pub: Inc. Magazine
Ed: J.J. McCorvey, Dave Smith. **Description:** Twelve products to and services designed to help small businesses run smoothly in the event of a disaster are outlined.

44245 ■ "Recipe for Disaster?" in *Sacramento Business Journal* **(Vol. 25, July 4, 2008, No. 18, pp. 1)**
Pub: American City Business Journals, Inc.
Ed: Mark Anderson. **Description:** Restaurateurs are challenged with balancing rising operating costs and what customers are willing to pay for their services. Flour prices in 2008 have increased by 46 percent from April 2007. Other views on the situation, as well as trends, forecasts and statistics on sales, outlook on economic conditions, consumer price index, and the typical split of restaurant revenue, are presented.

44246 ■ "Red Tape Ties Detroit Housing Rehab Plan" in *Crain's Detroit Business* **(Vol. 24, September 22, 2008, No. 38, pp. 1)**
Pub: Crain Communications, Inc.
Ed: Ryan Beene. **Description:** Venture-capital firm Wilherst Oxford LLC is a Florida-based company that has purchased 300 inner-city homes which were in foreclosure in Detroit. Wilherst Oxford is asking the city to forgive the existing tax and utility liens so the firm can utilize the money for home improvements. The city, however, is reluctant but has stated that they are willing to negotiate.

44247 ■ "Rediscovering the Land of Opportunity" in *Green Industry Pro* **(July 2011)**
Pub: Cygnus Business Media
Ed: Gregg Wartgow. **Description:** Landscape contractors need to discover new strategies that will generate leads and convert those leads into sales.

44248 ■ "Renren Partners With Recruit to Launch Social Wedding Services" in *Benzinga.com* **(June 7, 2011)**
Pub: Benzinga.com
Ed: Benzinga Staff. **Description:** Renren Inc. and Recruit Company Ltd. partnered to build a wedding social media catering to engaged couples and newlyweds in China. The platform will integrate online wedding related social content and offline media such as magazine and wedding exhibitions.

44249 ■ "Renren Partnership With Recruit to Launch Social Wedding Services" in *Benzinga.com* **(June 7, 2011)**
Pub: Benzinga.com
Ed: Benzinga Staff. **Description:** Renren Inc., the leading real name social networking Internet platform in China has partnered with Recruit Company Limited, Japan's largest human resource and classified media group to form a joint venture to build a wedding social media catering to the needs of engaged couples and newlyweds in China.

44250 ■ "Reports of Banks' Revival were Greatly Exaggerated" in *Barron's* **(Vol. 88, July 7, 2008, No. 27, pp. L14)**
Pub: Dow Jones & Co., Inc.
Ed: Jack Willoughby. **Description:** Performance of mutual funds improved for the second quarter of 2008 compared to the previous quarter, registering an average gain of 0.13 percent; funds focusing on natural resources rose the highest, their value rising by an average of 24.50 percent.

44251 ■ "Research Reports" in *Barron's* **(Vol. 88, March 10, 2008, No. 10, pp. M13)**
Pub: Dow Jones & Company, Inc.
Description: Research reports on different company stocks by investment analysts are given. Shares of Cal Dive are rated Outperform by analysts, citing the

shares' continued attractiveness and the company's acquisition of Horizon. Analysts recommend buying the shares of California Water Service Group.

44252 ■ "Research Reports: How Analysts Size Up Companies" in *Barron's* **(Vol. 88, March 31, 2008, No. 13, pp. M13)**
Pub: Dow Jones & Company, Inc.
Ed: Anita Peltonen. **Description:** Sirius Satellite's shares are ranked Outperform as it awaits approval from the Federal Communications Commission in its merger with XM. TiVo's shares are ranked Avoid as the company is in a sector that's being commoditized. Verizon Communications' rising dividend yield earns it a Focus List ranking. The shares of Bear Stearns, Churchill Downs, Corning, and Deerfield Triarc Capital are also reviewed. Statistical data included.

44253 ■ "'Resume Mining' Services Can Save Time, Money" in *HR Specialist* **(Vol. 8, September 2010, No. 9, pp. 7)**
Pub: Capitol Information Group Inc.
Description: Low-cost resume mining services can help human resource departments save time and money by searching online resume databases for candidates matching specific job qualifications.

44254 ■ "Retail Woes: The Shoe Doesn't Fit for Gerald Loftin's Stock Picks" in *Black Enterprise* **(Vol. 38, July 2008, No. 12, pp. 40)**
Pub: Earl G. Graves Publishing Co. Inc.
Ed: Steve Garmhausen. **Description:** Each of the three stocks that Gerald Loftin picked in May 2007 have lost money; DSW, the designer shoe retailer, fell by 63.7 percent; paint and coatings retailer Sherwin-Williams Co. fell by 7.2 percent; and Verizon Communications Inc. fell by 1.4 percent. Statistical data included.

44255 ■ *Riches in Niches: How to Make It Big in a Small Market*
Pub: Career Press, Inc.
Ed: Susan Friedmann. **Released:** May 10, 2007. **Price:** $21.99. **Description:** The multiple factors that separate the experts from the service professionals who may actually have betters skills, but are never heard about, are discussed. The seven secrets every entrepreneur should know are listed.

44256 ■ "Right From the Start" in *Small Business Opportunities* **(July 2010)**
Pub: Harris Publications Inc.
Ed: Ed Krug. **Description:** Ed Krug from Pitch Blue provides sales support services by partnering with small and mid-sized companies to set and reach new revenue targets.

44257 ■ "Ring Ka-Ching" in *Canadian Business* **(Vol. 79, November 6, 2006, No. 22, pp. 106)**
Pub: Rogers Media
Description: A brief profile of Jajah including its web activated telephone services is presented.

44258 ■ "The Role of Human and Financial Capital in the Profitability and Growth of Women-Owned Small Firms" in *Journal of Small Business Management*
Pub: Blackwell Publishing, Inc.
Ed: Susan Coleman. **Description:** Examines the relationship between the human and financial capital in both men and women-owned businesses and firm performance in the service and retail sectors.

44259 ■ "Russia Eyes Nuclear Power Co-Operation With Canada" in *Globe & Mail* **(April 2, 2007, pp. B1)**
Pub: CTVglobemedia Publishing Inc.
Ed: Shawn McCarthy. **Description:** The plans of the Russian nuclear energy agency, Federal Atomic Energy Agency, to enter into a partnership with its Canadian counterpart Atomic Energy of Canada Ltd. for the generation of electric power are discussed.

44260 ■ "The Rypple Effect; Performance Management" in *The Economist* **(Vol. 390, January 3, 2009, No. 8612, pp. 48)**
Pub: The Economist Newspaper Inc.
Description: New companies such as Rypple, a new, web-based service, claim that they can satisfy the Net Generation's need for frequent assessments while easing the burden this creates for management.

44261 ■ **"S2C Global Installs Its First Mass Production Aquaduct Unit in North America"** in *Canadian Corporate News* (May 16, 2007)
Pub: Comtex News Network Inc.
Description: S2C Global Systems, a leader of distributing 5-gallon bottled water units to the consumer, has announced the installation of its first mass production Aquaduct in Surrey, British Columbia.

44262 ■ **"S3 Entertainment Group Partners with WFW International for Film Services in Michigan"** in *Michigan Vue* (July-August 2008)
Pub: Entrepreneur Media Inc.
Description: William F. White (WFW), one of North America's largest production equipment providers has partnered with S3 Entertainment Group (S3EG), a Michigan-based full-service film production services company due to the new incentives package which currently offers the highest incentives in the United States, up to 42 percent. S3EG will actively store, lease, manage, distribute and sell WFW's equipment to the growing number of production teams that are filming in the state.

44263 ■ **"St. Luke's Gets Shot in the Arm From Outpatient Services"** in *Saint Louis Business Journal* (Vol. 31, August 19, 2011, No. 52, pp. 1)
Pub: Saint Louis Business Journal
Ed: Angela Mueller, E.B. Solomont. **Description:** St. Louis, Missouri-based St. Luke's Hospital benefited from investing in outpatient services as contained in its latest bond offering. Fitch Ratings gave the bond issuance an A+ rating.

44264 ■ **"Screening for the Best Stock Screens"** in *Barron's* (Vol. 90, September 13, 2010, No. 37, pp. 36)
Pub: Barron's Editorial & Corporate Headquarters
Ed: Mike Hogan. **Description:** Pros and cons of the new and revised stock screening tools from Zack, Finviz.com, and GuruFocus are discussed. FinVix.com is more capable for screening through stocks and the service is free.

44265 ■ **"Sean Durfy"** in *Canadian Business* (Vol. 80, April 23, 2007, No. 9, pp. 14)
Pub: Rogers Media
Ed: Michelle Magnan. **Description:** Sean Durfy, president of WestJet Airlines Ltd., feels that marketing is essential factor for growth of airline industry.

44266 ■ **"Secrets To Trade Show Success"** in *Women Entrepreneur* (September 12, 2008)
Pub: Entrepreneur Media Inc.
Ed: Lesley Spencer Pyle. **Description:** Trade shows require an enormous amount of work, but they are an investment that can pay off handsomely because they allow a business to get their product or service in front of their target market. Advice regarding trade shows is given including selecting the correct venue, researching the affair and following up on leads obtained at the event.

44267 ■ **"Self-Employment in the United States"** in *Montly Labor Review* (Vol. 133, September 2010, No. 9, pp. 17)
Pub: Bureau of Labor Statistics
Description: Self employment in 2009 in the U.S. continued to be more common among men, Whites, Asians, and older workers and in the agriculture, construction, and services industries.

44268 ■ *Selling the Invisible: A Field Guide to Modern Marketing*
Pub: Business Plus
Ed: Harry Beckwith. **Price:** $22.95. **Description:** Tips for marketing and selling intangibles such as health care, entertainment, tourism, legal services, and more are provided.

44269 ■ **"The Service Imperative"** in *Business Horizons* (Vol. 51, January-February 2008, No. 1, pp. 39)
Pub: Elsevier Advanced Technology Publications
Ed: Mary Jo Bitner, Stephen W. Brown. **Description:** The importance of services is growing in developing countries like India and China, but little attention is given to service research, education and innovation. The 'service imperative' seeks to promote the advancement of services. The scope, objectives and philosophy of the service imperative platform are outlined.

44270 ■ *Services in Canada*
Pub: Routledge Inc.
Ed: W.R. Frisbee. **Released:** March 29, 1990. **Price:** $215.00. **Description:** Profiles of the services industry in Canada.

44271 ■ **"Shaw, Telus Take Up Battle Positions"** in *Globe & Mail* (January 1, 2006, pp. B1)
Pub: CTVglobemedia Publishing Inc.
Ed: Catherine McKLean. **Description:** The competition between Shaw Communications Inc. and Telus Corp. over voice over Internet protocol offer for customers is presented.

44272 ■ **"Ship Shape"** in *Hawaii Business* (Vol. 53, January 2008, No. 7, pp. 46)
Pub: Hawaii Business Publishing
Ed: David K. Choo. **Description:** Ship Maintenance LLC is in charge of repairing and maintaning the U.S. Navy ships at Pearl Harbor's Middle Noch, having renewed a five-year contract with the navy. Cleaning a ship is a difficult process, which involves degreasing and removal of sensitive items such as guns and missiles. The awards given to Ship Maintenance are also discussed.

44273 ■ **"Shipping 2.0"** in *Entrepreneur* (Vol. 36, April 2008, No. 4, pp. 54)
Pub: Entrepreneur Media, Inc.
Ed: Heather Clancy. **Description:** Doggypads.com contacted with Web 2.0 service provider Shipwire to handle its warehouse concerns. The service works by paying a rent to Shipwire and they will store the client's items. The client's customers can continue to order from the client's website and Shipwire will take care of delivery. Doggypads was able to save up on costs by using Shipwire.

44274 ■ **"Show and Tell"** in *Entrepreneur* (Vol. 36, May 2008, No. 5, pp. 54)
Pub: Entrepreneur Media, Inc.
Ed: Heather Clancy. **Description:** FreshStart Telephone uses recorded video testimonials of customers, by using Pure Digital Flip Video that downloads content directly to the computer, and uploads it in the company's website to promote their wireless phone service.

44275 ■ **"A Simple Old Reg that Needs Dusting Off"** in *Barron's* (Vol. 88, June 30, 2008, No. 26, pp. 35)
Pub: Dow Jones & Co., Inc.
Ed: Gene Epstein. **Description:** Senator Joe Lieberman has a point when he accused speculators of inflating the prices of food and fuel futures but introducing legislation to address speculation has an alternative. The senator's committee should instead demand that the Commodity Futures Trading Commission enforce position limits on the maximum number of contracts in a given market per speculative entity.

44276 ■ **"The Skype's the Limit"** in *Canadian Business* (Vol. 80, February 12, 2007, No. 4, pp. 70)
Pub: Rogers Media
Ed: Gerry Blackwell. **Description:** The increase in the market share of Skype Technologies S.A.'s Internet phone service to 171 million users is discussed.

44277 ■ **"Slow but Steady into the Future"** in *Barron's* (Vol. 88, July 7, 2008, No. 27, pp. M)
Pub: Dow Jones & Co., Inc.
Ed: Mark Veverka. **Description:** Investors are advised to maintain their watch on the shares of business software company NetSuite. The company's chief executive officer, Zach Nelson, claims that the company has a 10-year lead on its competitors with the development of software-as-a service.

44278 ■ **"Small Business Unsure of Impact of New Tax Law"** in *Crain's Detroit Business* (Vol. 23, October 15, 2007, No. 42, pp. 13)
Pub: Crain Communications Inc. - Detroit
Ed: Sheena Harrison. **Description:** Small business owners in Michigan are concerned with issues surrounding the proposed increases in state taxes geared at small business, which includes a 6 percent service tax.

44279 ■ **"Small Firms Punch Ticket for Growth"** in *Houston Business Journal* (Vol. 40, January 29, 2010, No. 38, pp. 1)
Pub: American City Business Journals
Ed: Allison Wollam. **Description:** Independent ticket agencies anticipate growth as American and Canadian authorities approved a merger between Ticketmaster and concert promoter Live Nation. Expansion of service offerings and acquisition of venues have also been done by independent ticket agencies in light of the merger. Details of the merger are included.

44280 ■ **"SoBran Partners with U.S. Navy"** in *Black Enterprise* (Vol. 37, October 2006, No. 3, pp. 38)
Pub: Earl G. Graves Publishing Co. Inc.
Ed: Glenn Townes. **Description:** SoBran Inc., partnered with Lockheed Martin and signed a three-Tear production service contract with the Naval Aviation Depot in Jacksonville, Florida. The $44 million contract will allow SoBran to transport and warehouse materials for Navy facilities.

44281 ■ *The Social Media Bible: Tactics, Tools, and Strategies for Business Success*
Pub: John Wiley & Sons, Inc.
Ed: Lon Safko, David Brake. **Released:** June 17, 2009. **Price:** $29.95. **Description:** Information is given to build or transform a business into social media, where customers, employees, and prospects connect, collaborate, and champion products and services in order to increase sales and to beat the competition.

44282 ■ **"A Socko Payout Menu: Rural Phone Carrier Plots to Supercharge Its Shares"** in *Barron's* (Vol. 88, June 30, 2008, No. 26, pp. M5)
Pub: Dow Jones & Co., Inc.
Ed: Shirley A. Lazo. **Description:** CenturyTel boosted its quarterly common payout to 70 cents from 6.75 cents per share die to its strong cash flows and solid balance sheet. Eastman Kodak's plan for a buyback will be partially funded by its $581 million tax refund. CME Group will buyback stocks through 2009 worth $1.1 billion.

44283 ■ **"Sprint Tries to Wring Out Positives"** in *The Business Journal-Serving Metropolitan Kansas City* (Vol. 26, August 8, 2008, No. 48)
Pub: American City Business Journals, Inc.
Ed: Suzanna Stagemeyer. **Description:** Sprint Nextel Corp. reported that 901,000 subscribers left the company in the quarter ending June 30, 2008; fewer than the nearly 1.1 million it lost in the previous quarter. Customer turnover also dropped to just less than 2 percent, compared to 2.45 percent in the first quarter of 2008.

44284 ■ **"Staffing Firms are Picking Up the Pieces, Seeing Signs of Life"** in *Milwaukee Business Journal* (Vol. 27, February 5, 2010, No. 19)
Pub: American City Business Journals
Ed: Rich Rovito. **Description:** Milwaukee, Wisconsin-based staffing firms are seeing signs of economic rebound as many businesses turned to temporary employees to fill the demands for goods and services. Economic observers believe the growth in temporary staffing is one of the early indicators of economic recovery.

44285 ■ **"Staples Advantage Receives NJPA National Contract for Janitorial Supplies"** in *Professional Services Close-Up* (April 22, 2011)
Pub: Close-Up Media
Description: Staples Advantage, the business-to-business division of Staples Inc. was awarded a contract for janitorial supplies to members of the

National Joint Powers Alliance (NJPA). NJPA is a member-owned buying cooperative serving public and private schools, state and local governments, and nonprofit organizations.

44286 ■ "Still in the Jet Set" in *Barron's* **(Vol. 89, July 13, 2009, No. 28, pp. 13)**
Pub: Dow Jones & Co., Inc.
Ed: Brad Davis. **Description:** Coastal Jet Service will be offering coast-to-coast flights and a one way ride on their Cessna Citation X will cost $4,600 plus tax. The service is a compromise between a corporate jet and a first-class seat on a commercial flight and the jets fly out of Westchester County, New York and land in Burbank, California.

44287 ■ "Stockerts Open Repair Business" in *Dickinson Press* **(July 13, 2010)**
Pub: Dickinson Press
Ed: Ashley Martin. **Description:** Ed Stockert is opening his new appliance repair firm in Dickinson, North Dakota with his wife Anna.

44288 ■ "Stoneham Drilling Trust Announces Cash Distribution for May 2007" in *Canadian Corporate News* **(May 16, 2007)**
Pub: Comtex News Network Inc.
Description: Stoneham Drilling Trust, an income trust that provides contract drilling services to natural gas and oil exploration and production companies operating in western Canada, announced that its cash distribution for the period from May 1, 2007 to May 31, 2007 will be $0.15 per trust unit ($1.80 per annum).

44289 ■ "Study: New Moms Build A Lot of Brand Buzz" in *Brandweek* **(Vol. 49, April 21, 2008, No. 16, pp. 7)**
Pub: VNU Business Media, Inc.
Description: According to a new survey which sampled 1,721 pregnant women and new moms, this demographic is having 109 word-of-mouth conversations per week concerning products, services and brands. Two-thirds of these conversations directly involve brand recommendations. The Internet is driving these word-of-mouth, or W-O-M, conversations among this segment, beating out magazines, television and other forms of media.

44290 ■ "Suits Keep Flying in Wireless Service Marketing Wars" in *Globe & Mail* **(March 22, 2007, pp. B3)**
Pub: CTVglobemedia Publishing Inc.
Ed: Catherine McLean. **Description:** The suit filed by Telus Corp. against BCE Mobile Communications Inc. over the latter's alleged misleading advertisement in the press is discussed.

44291 ■ "The Sure Thing That Flopped" in *Harvard Business Review* **(Vol. 86, July-August 2008, No. 8, pp. 29)**
Pub: Harvard Business School Press
Ed: Gerald Zaltman; Lindsay Zaltman. **Description:** Fictitious brand extension scenario is presented, with contributors providing suggestions and advice. The company's struggles with expanding the brand may be alleviated by improving consumer research, focusing on emotional responses to products and services.

44292 ■ "Survey Distorts Cost of Capitals" in *Canadian Business* **(Vol. 83, October 12, 2010, No. 17, pp. 22)**
Pub: Rogers Media Ltd.
Ed: Matthew McClearn. **Description:** Swiss bank UBS publishes a study comparing the costs of goods and services in megalopolises every three years. The study ranked Toronto and Montreal outside the Top 30 in 2009, but the two cities jumped to eighth and ninth in a recent update. This change can be contributed to the conversion of prices into Euros before making comparisons.

44293 ■ "Sweet Harmony" in *Canadian Business* **(Vol. 82, April 27, 2009, No. 7, pp. 6)**
Pub: Rogers Media
Description: Canada will harmonize its 5 percent federal goods and services tax wit the 8 percent provincial sales tax effective July 1, 2010. Meanwhile, provinces like Ontario and Quebec have switched the sales taxes that are charged in new investments into

a value-added tax. The conversion has led to an 11 percent increase in investments in Quebec and the three other provinces that made the conversion.

44294 ■ "Take This Job and Love It" in *Green Industry Pro* **(Vol. 23, October 2011)**
Pub: Cygnus Business Media
Ed: Gregg Wartgow. **Description:** Details of the lawsuit filed by the Professional Landcare Network (PLANET) against the U.S. Department of Labor are explained. Challenges faced by landscape firms because of employment costs are outlined. Statistical data included.

44295 ■ "Teachers, U.S. Fund Providence Made Moves On BCE Buyout" in *Globe & Mail* **(April 10, 2007, pp. B17)**
Pub: CTVglobemedia Publishing Inc.
Ed: Boyd Erman; Sinclair Stewart; Jacquie McNish. **Description:** The Ontario Teachers Pension Plan, the largest shareholder of telecommunications firm BCE Inc., has called for a partnership with buyout firm Providence Equity Partners Inc. in order to acquire BCE Inc.

44296 ■ "A Team Sport" in *Business Courier* **(Vol. 26, October 2, 2009, No. 23, pp. 1)**
Pub: American City Business Journals, Inc.
Ed: Lisa Biank Fasig. **Description:** Procter & Gamble (P&G) revised the way it works with marketing, design and public relations firms. Creative discussions will be managed by only two representatives, the franchise leader and the brand agency leader in order for P&G to simplify operations as it grows larger and more global.

44297 ■ "Telesat's New Rocket Man" in *Canadian Business* **(Vol. 80, January 29, 2007, No. 3, pp. 21)**
Pub: Rogers Media
Ed: Andrew Wahl. **Description:** The plans of Dan Goldberg, the chief executive officer of Telesat Canada, for the enhancement of the company's services are discussed.

44298 ■ "TELUS Drawing More Power From Its Wireless Operations" in *Globe & Mail* **(February 17, 2007, pp. B3)**
Pub: CTVglobemedia Publishing Inc.
Ed: Catherine McLean. **Description:** TELUS Corp., the fast-growing wireless business company, posted tripled profits in the fourth quarter of 2006. The revenues of the company increased 8 percent in the same period.

44299 ■ "Thomas Industrial Network Unveils Custom SPEC" in *Entertainment Close-Up* **(March 3, 2011)**
Pub: Close-Up Media
Description: Thomas Industrial Network assists custom manufacturers and industrial service providers a complete online program called Custom SPEC which includes Website development and Internet exposure.

44300 ■ "Time to Fight Back" in *Green Industry Pro* **(Vol. 23, March 2011, No. 3, pp. 8)**
Pub: Cygnus Business Media
Ed: Rod Dickens. **Description:** Lawn care operators in the United States must learn from Canada that a shift to socialism will impact their industry in a negative way. Government regulation over the application of control products regarding environmental health in Canada has been a death sentence for small lawn care businesses.

44301 ■ "Time for State Tax Restructure?" in *Crain's Detroit Business* **(Vol. 26, January 18, 2010, No. 3, pp. 3)**
Pub: Crain Communications, Inc.
Ed: Amy Lane. **Description:** Business Leaders for Michigan, a statewide CEO group, launched a proposal to cut the Michigan Business Tax by about $1.1 billion and replace the revenue by taxing services. Statistical data included.

44302 ■ "Tiny Telecom Big Prize in Bell Aliant Bid Battle" in *Globe & Mail* **(April 4, 2007, pp. B1)**
Pub: CTVglobemedia Publishing Inc.
Ed: Catherine McLean. **Description:** The competition between Bell Aliant Regional Communications Income Fund of BCE Inc. and Bragg Communications Inc. to bid for acquiring Amtelecom Income Fund is discussed.

44303 ■ "To JM On Its 75th Anniversary" in *Journal of Marketing* **(Vol. 75, July 2011, No. 4, pp. 129)**
Pub: American Marketing Association
Ed: Ruth M. Bolton. **Description:** How the Journal of Marketing influenced the marketing science and practice is presented. The Marketing Science Institute's 50th anniversary coincides with the journal's 75th anniversary and both have collaborated to tackle important marketing issues identified in MSI's priorities. The mind-set of managers worldwide was also influenced by ideas in the journal's articles.

44304 ■ "To Keep Freight Rolling, Springfield Must Grease the Hub" in *Crain's Chicago Business* **(Vol. 31, April 21, 2008, No. 16, pp. 22)**
Pub: Crain Communications, Inc.
Ed: Paul O'Connor. **Description:** Discusses the importance of upgrading Chicago's continental-hub freight rail system which is integral to moving international products as well as domestic ones. Global tonnage is expected to double by 2020 and unless more money is designated to upgrade the infrastructure the local and national economy will suffer.

44305 ■ "Top 50 By 1-Year Return" in *Canadian Business* **(Vol. 81, Summer 2008, No. 9, pp. 121)**
Pub: Rogers Media Ltd.
Description: Table showing the top 50 Canadian companies ranked in terms of one-year return is presented. Toronto, Canada-based Timminco Ltd. topped the roster with a 1,294.2 percent in one-year return. However, the share prices of the company were affected by the recent controversy in its silicon purification process.

44306 ■ "Top 100 Consolidate Gains" in *Hispanic Business* **(Vol. 30, July-August 2008, No. 7-8, pp. 30)**
Pub: Hispanic Business, Inc.
Ed: Richard Kaplan. **Description:** Data developed by HispanTelligence on the increase in revenue posted by the top 100 fastest-growing U.S. Hispanic firms over the last five years is reported. Despite the economic downturn, the service sector, IT and health suppliers showed an increase in revenue whereas construction companies showed a marginal slump in revenue growth.

44307 ■ *Trade-Off: The Ever-Present Tension Between Quality and Conscience*
Pub: Crown Business Books
Ed: Kevin Maney. **Released:** August 17, 2010. **Price:** $15.00. **Description:** The tension between fidelity (the quality of a consumer's experience) and convenience (the ease of getting and paying for a product) are shown to be the forces that determine the success or failure of new products and services in the marketplace.

44308 ■ "Traffic Slows at O'Hare; As Airlines Cut Flights, City Tries to Push Expansion Forward" in *Crain's Chicago Business* **(April 28, 2008)**
Pub: Crain Communications, Inc.
Ed: Paul Merrion; John Pletz. **Description:** O'Hare International Airport is seeing a decline in passenger traffic just as the city of Chicago presses cash-strapped airlines to fund the second phase of the airport's expansion which would include the extension of one runway, the relocation of two others and the construction of a new western terminal.

44309 ■ "A Train of Our Own" in *Canadian Business* **(Vol. 79, July 17, 2006, No. 14-15, pp. 71)**
Pub: Rogers Media
Ed: Victor Dwyer. **Description:** The luxuries and pleasure of traveling in private rail road cars are discussed.

44310 ■ "TransCanada Builds on Proud Olympic History by Joining Vancouver 2010" in *Canadian Corporate News* (May 14, 2007)
Pub: Comtex News Network Inc.
Description: TransCanada is the official supplier in the Natural Gas Pipeline Operator category for the Vancouver 2010 Olympic and Paralympic Winter Games.

44311 ■ "Transportation: Laidlaw's Chief Driver" in *Canadian Business* (Vol. 80, January 29, 2007, No. 3, pp. 14)
Pub: Rogers Media
Ed: Michelle Magnan. **Description:** The role of Kevin Benson in the restructuring and growth of the bankrupt transportation company Laidlaw Inc. is described. The increase in the revenues of the restructures company is discussed.

44312 ■ "Travel Leery" in *Crain's Chicago Business* (Vol. 31, March 31, 2008, No. 13, pp. 3)
Pub: Crain Communications, Inc.
Description: Due to the rise in airline prices and a possible recession, many companies are starting to change their travel policies and limit travel spending.

44313 ■ "The Traveler's Traveler" in *Entrepreneur* (Vol. 37, September 2009, No. 9, pp. 22)
Pub: Entrepreneur Media, Inc.
Ed: Kim Orr. **Description:** Business travel columnist Joe Sharkey says technology may someday replace business travel. Airlines are realizing that a part of the business travel market has disappeared. Sharkey also says airlines can never get those customers back.

44314 ■ "Trend: Tutors to Help You Pump Up the Staff" in *Business Week* (September 22, 2008, No. 4100, pp. 45)
Pub: McGraw-Hill Companies, Inc.
Ed: Reena Janaj. **Description:** High-level managers are turning to innovation coaches in an attempt to obtain advice on how to better sell new concepts within their companies. Individuals as well as consulting firms are now offering this service.

44315 ■ "Turbulent Skies" in *The Business Journal-Portland* (Vol. 25, August 29, 2008, No. 25, pp. 1)
Pub: American City Business Journals, Inc.
Ed: Erik Siemers. **Description:** Small airlines are struggling to keep their commercial services amid the troubled commercial airline sector. Small communities, for example, were expected to pony up about $650,000 in revenue guarantees each in order to convince SkyWest Airlines to offer two direct flights to Portland daily beginning October 12, 2008. The trends in the commercial airline industry are analyzed.

44316 ■ "The Turkey Has Landed" in *Canadian Business* (Vol. 79, November 20, 2006, No. 23, pp. 38)
Pub: Rogers Media
Ed: Erik Heinrich. **Description:** The design and construction of Toronto Pearson International Airport to handle domestic, international and transborder flights in one facility is discussed.

44317 ■ "TV Revenue Slide Hits CanWest Profit" in *Globe & Mail* (January 13, 2006, pp. B3)
Pub: CTVglobemedia Publishing Inc.
Ed: Grant Robertson. **Description:** CanWest Global Communications Corp. posted drop in profits by 14 percent for first quarter 2006. The downward trend in profits is attributed to low television revenues.

44318 ■ "U Overhauling Its Janitorial Program, but Custodians Taking Exception" in *Saint Paul Pioneer Press* (August 20, 2011)
Pub: McClatchy-Tribune Regional News
Ed: Mila Koumpilova. **Description:** University of Minnesota developed a new team cleaning approach for its campus. The new custodian program will save $3.1 million annually while providing a cleaner campus. The union representing the custodians questions both claims.

44319 ■ "U.S. Savvy Helps Fuel TD's Fortunes" in *Globe & Mail* (February 23, 2007, pp. B1)
Pub: CTVglobemedia Publishing Inc.
Ed: Andrew Willis; Tavia Grant. **Description:** The rise in the revenues of Toronto-Dominion Bank due to its acquisition of American financial service providers and the rise in its domestic retail banking revenues are disussed.

44320 ■ "United's Next Hurdle: Costly Repairs" in *Crain's Chicago Business* (Vol. 31, April 14, 2008, No. 15, pp. 1)
Pub: Crain Communications, Inc.
Ed: John Pletz. **Description:** Discusses the recent crackdown by aviation regulators concerning airline safety at United Airlines as well as other carriers. Maintenance costs at United for the upkeep on the company's older planes is severely affecting its bottom line which is already sagging under heavy fuel costs. .

44321 ■ "Utilities Report Lower Customer Growth Rate, Power Use" in *The Business Journal - Serving Phoenix and the Valley of the Sun* (Vol. 28, August 8, 2008, No. 49, pp. 1)
Pub: American City Business Journals, Inc.
Ed: Patrick O'Grady. **Description:** Arizona Public Service Co. and Salt River Project are experiencing sharp decrease in customer growth rates due to less movement of people to the Valley. Arizona Public Service Co. expects a further decline of just 1 percent customer growth by the end of 2008 while Salt River Project expects this to grow between 1 to 2 percent for the two years ahead of 2008.

44322 ■ "VC-Heavy, Revenue-Light Sensicore Sold to GE Division" in *Crain's Detroit Business* (Vol. 24, April 14, 2008, No. 15, pp. 28)
Pub: Crain Communications, Inc.
Ed: Tom Henderson. **Description:** General Electric has acquired Sensicore Inc., which although one of Michigan's most successful companies in raising venture capital was unable to generate significant revenue from its handheld water-testing devices. GE is capable of penetrating a larger market than a private company and will be able to take the devices to the municipal marketplace.

44323 ■ "Ventura Police Install Electronic Kiosk to Access Services" in *Ventura County Star* (October 28, 2010)
Pub: Ventura County Star
Description: Ventura Police Department installed a kiosk in the front lobby of its building in order to provide services to the public. The kiosk allows access to the Department's Website; to retrieve a collision report, file an abandoned vehicle report, receive a permit for an oversized vehicle, or filing a citizen's complaint; information can be obtained about alarms, programs and permits; users can pay a parking ticket and review calls for services on an interactive map.

44324 ■ "Virgin Mobile has Big Plans for Year Two" in *Globe & Mail* (March 6, 2006, pp. B5)
Pub: CTVglobemedia Publishing Inc.
Ed: Catherine McLean. **Description:** The business growth plans of Virgin Mobile Canada are presented.

44325 ■ "Vista-Based NCV Bought by Canteen Vending" in *North County Times* (October 18, 2011)
Ed: Pat Maio. **Description:** Details of North Carolina-based Canteen Vending Services' acquisition of NCV Refreshment Services, are given.

44326 ■ "Wall Street Is No Friend to Radical Innovation" in *Harvard Business Review* (Vol. 88, July-August 2010, No. 7-8, pp. 28)
Pub: Harvard Business School Publishing
Ed: Julia Kirby. **Description:** Research indicates that investors are skittish about backing a business that proposes significant changes to its product or service status quo.

44327 ■ "War Veteran Hit Payoff with Repair Business" in *Tulsa World* (July 28, 2010)
Pub: Tulsa World
Ed: Tim Stanley. **Description:** Profile of Sam Melton, Korean War veteran and retired Air Force staff sergeant, launched appliance repair stores in the Tulsa, Oklahoma area 50 years ago.

44328 ■ "Warning Lights Flashing for Air Canada: Carty's Back" in *Globe & Mail* (February 22, 2006, pp. B1)
Pub: CTVglobemedia Publishing Inc.
Ed: Brent Jang. **Description:** Air Canada's rival, Donald Carty, former chief executive officer at American Airlines and new chairman of Toronto based Regco Holdings Inc., launches Porter Airlines Inc. out of Toronto City Center Airport this fall.

44329 ■ "Waste Not" in *Entrepreneur* (Vol. 36, April 2008, No. 4, pp. 21)
Pub: Entrepreneur Media, Inc.
Ed: JJ Ramberg. **Description:** RecycleBank is a company that provides homes with carts in which recyclables are thrown. An identification chip measures the amount of recyclables and converts them into points, which can be redeemed in stores, such as Starbucks and Whole Foods. RecycleBank earns revenue from cities that save landfill waste spending with the use of the program.

44330 ■ "Water Treatment Play Zenon Goes to GE" in *Globe & Mail* (March 15, 2006, pp. B1)
Pub: CTVglobemedia Publishing Inc.
Ed: Leonard Zehr. **Description:** General Electric Co. acquires Ontario-based company, Zenon Environmental Inc., a technology giant in purifying water in northern Canada.

44331 ■ "Way More Than Mowing" in *Green Industry Pro* (Vol. 23, September 2011)
Pub: Cygnus Business Media
Ed: Rod Dickens. **Description:** Shipp Shape Lawn Services located in Sylvester, Georgia now offers aeration, fertilizing and weed control, mulching, yard renovation, flowerbed maintenance, landscaping, as well as irrigation repairs and installation in order to diversify the business and stay competitive.

44332 ■ "Web Translation Made Simple" in *Inc.* (Vol. 33, October 2011, No. 8, pp. 44)
Pub: Inc. Magazine
Ed: Adam Baer. **Description:** Smartling is a Web-based service that translates sites into more than 50 foreign languages. The software will begin translation right after setting up the account.

44333 ■ "Website Backup Made Simple" in *Inc.* (Vol. 33, September 2011, No. 7, pp. 52)
Pub: Inc. Magazine
Ed: John Brandon. **Description:** Tools to back up content on a Website are profiled. Vaultpress works only with sites that run on the WordPress publishing platform and CodeGuard works with a variety of publishing platforms and hosting services.

44334 ■ "Welcome to a New Kind of Cubicle Culture" in *Boston Business Journal* (Vol. 29, August 19, 2011, No. 15, pp. 1)
Pub: American City Business Journals Inc.
Ed: Alexander Jackson. **Description:** Beehive Baltimore offers a co-working space where independent freelancers and entrepreneurs can work. There are two other companies that provide the same service and the value of these services to these professional is that it provides them with an office that is both convenient and affordable aside from letting them network with peers.

44335 ■ "WestJet Gears Up for Domestic Dogfight" in *Globe & Mail* (May 1, 2007, pp. B6)
Pub: CTVglobemedia Publishing Inc.
Ed: Brent Jang. **Description:** The effort of WestJet Airlines Ltd. to compete with Air Canada for greater market share of passengers is discussed.

44336 ▪ "WestJet Ponders Growth Plan Following Record Profit" in *Globe & Mail* (February 15, 2007, pp. B15)
Pub: CTVglobemedia Publishing Inc.
Ed: Brent Jang. **Description:** The Calgary-based WestJet Airlines Ltd., which reported a record $114.7 million profit last year, is planning to expand its operations by 2010. The airline is planning new services and carriers.

44337 ▪ "What Will Green Power Cost? Surcharge, Spending Cap Considered" in *Crain's Detroit Business* (Vol. 24, March 10, 2008, No. 10, pp. 1)
Pub: Crain Communications, Inc.
Ed: Amy Lane. **Description:** Due to a proposed mandate, which states that 10 percent of power will have to come from renewable sources by 2015 in the state of Michigan, concern is being raised about the higher electricity prices this legislation will undoubtedly cause to business and residential customers.

44338 ▪ "Why Change?" in *Canadian Business* (Vol. 80, October 8, 2007, No. 20, pp. 9)
Pub: Rogers Media
Ed: Joe Chidley. **Description:** The need for economic change in Canada is discussed. Despite the country's economic growth and low unemployment rate, economic reform is needed in order to maximize its economic potential in the future. Other reasons for the need to further develop its economy, such as the rise of manufacturing and service industries in Asia and the emergence of regional trade pacts in South America are also tackled.

44339 ▪ "Why-Max?" in *Canadian Business* (Vol. 81, July 22, 2008, No. 12-13, pp. 19)
Pub: Rogers Media Ltd.
Ed: Andrew Wahl. **Description:** Nascent technology known as LTE (Long Term Evolution) is expected to challenge Intel's WiMax wireless technology as the wireless broadband standard. LTE , which is believed to be at least two years behind WiMax in development, is likely to be supported by wireless and mobile-phone carriers. Views and information on WiMax and LTE are presented.

44340 ▪ "Wild-Goose Chaser" in *Entrepreneur* (Vol. 37, September 2009, No. 9, pp. 96)
Pub: Entrepreneur Media, Inc.
Ed: Jason Daley. **Description:** Geese Police owner David Marcks says he discovered that trained collies could chase geese off golf courses, which started his business. He gives new franchises two dogs to start their business. The company has fared well even during the economic crisis.

44341 ▪ "Will Work for Equity" in *Inc.* (March 2008, pp. 50, 52)
Pub: Gruner & Jahr USA Publishing
Ed: Ryan McCarthy. **Description:** Profile of Dave Graham and his information technology company; Graham built his business by taking equity in client firms rather than charging fees. Four tips to consider before signing a work-for-equity business deal are outlined.

44342 ▪ "Women as 21st Century Leaders" in *Women In Business* (Vol. 63, Summer 2011, No. 2, pp. 26)
Pub: American Business Women's Association
Ed: Leigh Elmore. **Description:** American Business Women's Association and Park University have partnered to provide a leadership training program to attendees of the 2011 National Women's Leadership Conference. The courses will incorporate introduction to concepts, development of critical thinking skills and direct application through exercises. Comments from executives are also included.

44343 ▪ "Women Losing IT Ground" in *Marketing to Women* (Vol. 21, February 2008, No. 2, pp. 6)
Pub: EPM Communications, Inc.
Description: According to a study conducted by The National Center for Women & Information Technology, women in technology are losing ground. Statistical data included.

44344 ▪ "Work Smarter" in *Entrepreneur* (Vol. 36, April 2008, No. 4, pp. 70)
Pub: Entrepreneur Media, Inc.
Ed: Amanda C. Kooser. **Description:** Online applications that address a business' particular needs are presented. These web applications offer email services, collaboration services of sharing and editing documents and presentations, and tie-ups with online social networking sites. Details on various web applications are provided.

44345 ▪ "XM Mulls Betting the Bank in Competitive Game of Subscriber Growth" in *Globe & Mail* (March 18, 2006, pp. B3)
Pub: CTVglobemedia Publishing Inc.
Ed: Grant Robertson. **Description:** Canadian Satellite Radio Inc., XM Canada, president and Chief Operating Officer Stephen Tapp feel that establishing a profile in satellite radio to attract subscribers is a very big challenge. His views on the Canadian radio market are detailed.

44346 ▪ "Xtium Has Its Head in the Clouds" in *Philadelphia Business Journal* (Vol. 30, September 23, 2011, No. 32, pp. 1)
Pub: American City Business Journals Inc.
Ed: Peter Key. **Description:** Philadelphia-based cloud computing firm Xtium LLC received an $11.5 million first-round investment from Boston-Massachusetts-based OpenView Venture Partners. Catering to midsize businesses and unit of bigger firms, Xtium offers disaster-recovery, hosting, and managed-information-technology-infrastructure services.

44347 ▪ "Yammer Gets Serious" in *Inc.* (Volume 32, December 2010, No. 10, pp. 58)
Pub: Inc. Magazine
Ed: Eric Markowitz. **Description:** Yammer, an internal social network for companies, allows coworkers to share ideas and documents in real-time. Details of this service are included.

44348 ▪ "You Won't Go Broke Filling Up On These Stocks" in *Barron's* (Vol. 88, July 14, 2008, No. 28, pp. 38)
Pub: Dow Jones & Co., Inc.
Ed: Assif Shameen. **Description:** Due to high economic growth, pro-business policies and a consumption boom, the Middle East is a good place to look for equities. The best ways in which to gain exposure to this market include investing in the real estate industry and telecommunications markets as well as large banks that serve corporations and consumers.

44349 ▪ "Young Giants" in *Canadian Business* (Vol. 79, August 14, 2006, No. 16-17, pp. 47)
Pub: Rogers Media
Ed: Brad Purdy. **Description:** New generations of young chiefs of oil and gas companies in Canada, are featured.

44350 ▪ "Your Next Big Customer" in *Business Owner* (Vol. 35, November-December 2011, No. 6, pp. 7)
Pub: DL Perkins Company
Description: Learn how to sell goods and services to the Federal Government. The Office of Government Contracting is the agency responsible for coordinating government purchases.

44351 ▪ "You're a What? Wind Turbine Service Technician" in *Occupational Outlook Quarterly* (Vol. 54, Fall 2010, No. 3, pp. 34)
Pub: U.S. Bureau of Labor Statistics
Ed: Drew Liming. **Description:** Profile of Brandon Johnson, former member of the Air Force, found a career as a wind turbine service technician.

44352 ▪ "Zeon Solutions Teams with Endeca for SaaS Version of Endeca InFront" in *Entertainment Close-Up* (October 25, 2011)
Pub: Close-Up Media
Description: Zeon Solutions, an enterprise e-commerce and Website development firm announced a special licensing partnership with Endeca Technologies. Endeca is an information management software company that provides small and mid-size retailers with high-performance Customer Experience Management technology.

FRANCHISES AND BUSINESS OPPORTUNITIES

44353 ▪ ACFN - The ATM Franchise Business
ACFN Franchised, Inc.
111 Saint John St., 6th Fl.
San Jose, CA 95113
Free: 888-794-2236
Fax:888-708-8600
Co. E-mail: franchising@acfn.info.com
URL: http://www.acfnfranchised.com
No. of Franchise Units: 180. **No. of Company-Owned Units:** 1. **Founded:** 1996. **Franchised:** 2003. **Description:** The ATM FRANCHISE business. Develop & operate your own private network of ATM machines in hotels and Other travel & entertainment based businesses. Potential to earn significant long term residual income. Proven business plan with impressive list of corporate clients. Prior experience not necessary. **Equity Capital Needed:** $15,000-$50,000. **Franchise Fee:** $25,000. **Financial Assistance:** Yes. **Training:** 1 week at corporate office in California and ongoing support in all aspects of operating your ATM network.

44354 ▪ Advanced Maintenance
2820 Kerr Ave.
Wilmington, NC 28405
Ph:(910)200-8018
Free: 888-452-9206
Fax:(910)251-0095
No. of Franchise Units: 6. **No. of Company-Owned Units:** 3. **Founded:** 2000. **Franchised:** 2005. **Description:** Onsite fleet vehicle services. **Equity Capital Needed:** $117,900-$175,450. **Franchise Fee:** $35,000, Franchise fee discount for Honorable Discharge Veterans. **Financial Assistance:** No. **Training:** Yes.

44355 ▪ ChemDry Canada Ltd.
8472 Harvard Pl.
Chilliwack, BC, Canada V2P 7Z5
Free: 888-243-6379
Fax:(604)795-7-71
Co. E-mail: franchisesales@chemdry.ca
URL: http://www.franchisedirectory.ca
No. of Franchise Units: 77. **Description:** Carpet and upholstery cleaning service. **Equity Capital Needed:** $20,000-$60,000 total investment; $20,000 startup capital required. **Franchise Fee:** $815/month. **Financial Assistance:** Yes. **Managerial Assistance:** Manuals and computer software provided. **Training:** Provides training and ongoing support by technical and commercial support staff who make oneon-one visits, and run scheduled Business Development Events and Seminars, an annual convention and a regular program of specialist courses.

44356 ▪ College Hunks Hauling Junk
4836 W Gandy Blvd.
Tampa, FL 33611
Free: 800-586-5872
Fax:(301)881-5865
No. of Franchise Units: 92. **No. of Company-Owned Units:** 16. **Founded:** 2003. **Franchised:** 2007. **Description:** Junk removal service. **Equity Capital Needed:** $92,000-$114,000. **Franchise Fee:** $35,000. **Royalty Fee:** 7%. **Financial Assistance:** Third party financing available. **Training:** Provides 7-10 days training at headquarters, 3 days onsite and ongoing support.

44357 ▪ DoodyCalls
114 4th St. SE, No. A
Charlottesville, VA 22902
Free: 800-366-3922
Fax:(703)995-0601
No. of Franchise Units: 49. **No. of Company-Owned Units:** 8. **Founded:** 2000. **Franchised:** 2004. **Description:** Pet waste removal service. **Equity Capital Needed:** $42,230-$59,030. **Franchise Fee:** $34,500. **Royalty Fee:** 9%. **Financial Assistance:** Assistance with franchise fee. **Training:** Offers 30 hours training at headquarters and ongoing training as needed.

44358 ■ ease e-waste
3016 S Halladay St., Ste. F
Santa Ana, CA 92705
Free: (866)548-8100
Fax:(775)871-5259
No. of Franchise Units: 1. **No. of Company-Owned Units:** 2. **Founded:** 2003. **Franchised:** 2005. **Description:** Electronic waste collection and recycling services. **Equity Capital Needed:** $134,800-$224,100. **Franchise Fee:** $50,000. **Royalty Fee:** 5%. **Financial Assistance:** None. **Training:** Provides 1 week training at headquarters, 1 week onsite and ongoing support.

44359 ■ Flamingo A Friend
FAF Franchising Inc.
110 Crosscut Rd.
Alabaster, AL 35007
Ph:(205)621-7400
No. of Franchise Units: 8. **Founded:** 1994. **Franchised:** 1998. **Description:** Special occasion yard decorations. **Equity Capital Needed:** $5,000 down; balance paid end of 12 months. **Franchise Fee:** $2,500 and up. **Financial Assistance:** Yes. **Training:** YES.

44360 ■ 4Refuel
9440 202 St., Ste. 215
Langley, BC, Canada V1M 4A6
Free: 888-456-8896
Fax:(905)257-2580
Co. E-mail: jvaleriote@4refuel.com
URL: http://www.4refuel.com
No. of Franchise Units: 59. **No. of Company-Owned Units:** 6. **Founded:** 1995. **Franchised:** 1995. **Description:** 4Refuel has evolved from being a product provider to being a complete service and solutions provider (diesel fuel, environmentally friendly, timely and safe delivery, information/data collection and reporting.) We reinvented our company and are ready to grow into new markets and attract thousands of new clients because no one else in the world does what we do. **Equity Capital Needed:** $100,000-$150,000. **Franchise Fee:** $75,000+.

44361 ■ The Franchise Co., Inc.
5397 Eglinton Ave. W, Ste. 108
Etobicoke, ON, Canada M9C 5K6
Ph:(416)620-4700
Fax:(416)620-9955
Co. E-mail: info@thefranchisecompany.com
URL: http://www.thefranchisecompany.com
No. of Franchise Units: 1,800. **Founded:** 1992. **Description:** Focus is on home and business services with six distinct systems as California Closets, Certa ProPainters, Stained Glass Overlay, Paul Davis Restoration (US), College Pro Painters, Action Window Cleaners and Nutri-Lawn. **Equity Capital Needed:** Varies.

44362 ■ Ident-A-Kid
Ident-A-Kid Franchising Corp.
2810 Scherer Dr., Ste. 100
St. Petersburg, FL 33716
Free: 800-890-1000
Fax:(727)576-8258
Co. E-mail: franchise@ident-a-kid.com
URL: http://www.Ident-A-Kid.com
No. of Franchise Units: 254. **Founded:** 1986. **Franchised:** 2000. **Description:** Provides laminated child ID cards that contain photograph, fingerprints, and physical description. Program is marketed through public and private schools. **Equity Capital Needed:** $24,900 total investment, including equipment, software, supplies, marketing, materials, etc. **Franchise Fee:** $24,900. **Financial Assistance:** Yes. **Training:** Provides 2 day training session at the distributor's residence. Training includes: The identification process, equipment operation, computer and marketing techniques.

44363 ■ InfantHouse.com
6101 Long Prarie, Ste. 744-115
Flower Mound, TX 75028
Free: (866)463-2685
Fax:(972)691-8807
No. of Company-Owned Units: 1. **Founded:** 2005. **Franchised:** 2007. **Description:** Baby proofing. **Equity Capital Needed:** $23,500-$26,000. **Franchise**

Fee: $7,000. **Royalty Fee:** 7%. **Financial Assistance:** No. **Training:** 1 week training at headquarters and ongoing support.

44364 ■ Jon'Ric International Spas
PO Box 1856
Deland, FL 32721
Ph:(386)804-7698
Free: 888-609-0123
Fax:(407)358-5421
No. of Franchise Units: 52. **No. of Company-Owned Units:** 2. **Founded:** 1983. **Franchised:** 2003. **Description:** Medical, dental and day spas. **Equity Capital Needed:** $95,000-$350,000. **Franchise Fee:** $29,500. **Financial Assistance:** Yes. **Training:** Yes.

44365 ■ Mr. Appliance
1010 N University Parks Dr.
Waco, TX 76707
Free: 800-290-1422
Fax:(254)745-2590
Co. E-mail: steven.cox@dwyergroup.com
URL: http://www.mrappliancefranchise.com
No. of Franchise Units: 10. **Founded:** 1996. **Franchised:** 1996. **Description:** Home and commercial appliance repair and maintenance. **Equity Capital Needed:** $24,000 investment required; $30,000 start-up capital required. **Franchise Fee:** $24,000, per 100,000 population. **Training:** Initial, onsite, intranet and ongoing support.

44366 ■ On Track Power Window Repair
On Track Franchising, LLC
4616 Popular Level Rd.
Louisville, KY 40213
Ph:(502)777-0114
Fax:(502)962-6250
Co. E-mail: john@ontrackrepair.com
URL: http://www.OnTrackRepair.com
No. of Company-Owned Units: 1. **Founded:** 2002. **Franchised:** 2007. **Description:** Power window repair. This is virtually an untapped multi-billion dollar market. There is a continuous supply of window systems to repair. **Equity Capital Needed:** $64,200-$77,900. **Franchise Fee:** $32,000. **Royalty Fee:** 7%. **Financial Assistance:** Yes. **Managerial Assistance:** Business management skills, manuals and toll free support. **Training:** Provides 2 weeks hands on training and in depth technical instruction as it relates to power and manual window, door locks, mirrors, latches and door handles.

44367 ■ 1-800-Radiator
4401 Park Rd.
Benicia, CA 94510
Ph:(707)580-5318
Free: (866)780-9392
Fax:(707)747-7401
Co. E-mail: kellyg@1800radiator.com
URL: http://www.1800radiator.com
No. of Franchise Units: 230. **No. of Company-Owned Units:** 5. **Founded:** 1983. **Franchised:** 2003. **Description:** Each franchise operation is typically comprised of a 2,000 to 3,000 square foot warehouse stocked with approximately 1,200 radiators. You and your staff of 1 to 3 people will make field sales calls, take phone orders, manage inventory, dispatch drivers and deliver products within 3 hours of orders being taken. You will typically be open 9 hours per day, 5 1/2 days per week. Your ability to call on new prospective customers and service them to high levels will be the key to your success. **Equity Capital Needed:** $172,000. **Franchise Fee:** $45,000. **Royalty Fee:** 8%.

44368 ■ Pet Butler
HomeTask
1800 SW 152nd St., Ste. 100
Seattle, WA 98166
Ph:(206)763-6800
Free: 800-PET-BUTLER
Fax:(206)763-6883
No. of Franchise Units: 36. **Founded:** 1988. **Franchised:** 2005. **Description:** Pet waste cleanup, removal & more. **Equity Capital Needed:** $17,000-$29,000. **Franchise Fee:** $15,000. **Financial Assistance:** Yes. **Training:** Yes.

44369 ■ Pirtek USA
501 Haverty Ct.
Rockledge, FL 32955
Ph:(321)504-4422
Fax:(321)504-4433
No. of Franchise Units: 289. **Founded:** 1980. **Description:** Offers industrial services. **Equity Capital Needed:** $125,000 minimum. **Franchise Fee:** $48,000. **Financial Assistance:** No. **Training:** Yes.

44370 ■ Play N Trade Franchise Inc.
131 Calle Iglesia, Ste. 200
San Clemente, CA 92672
Free: 888-768-4263
No. of Franchise Units: 146. **No. of Company-Owned Units:** 1. **Founded:** 2001. **Franchised:** 2003. **Description:** New & used video games. **Equity Capital Needed:** $144,500-$276,000. **Franchise Fee:** $30,000. **Royalty Fee:** 5%. **Financial Assistance:** Limited third party financing available. **Training:** Training available at headquarters, at franchisee's location and ongoing including distance learning.

44371 ■ Precision Door Service
Precision Holdings of Brevard, Inc.
2395 S Washington Ave., Ste. 5
Titusville, FL 32780
Ph:(321)225-3500
Free: 800-985-1430
Fax:(321)225-3511
Co. E-mail: edresser@precisiondoor.net
URL: http://www.precisiondoor.net
No. of Franchise Units: 68. **Founded:** 1997. **Franchised:** 1999. **Description:** Garage door repair and installation service. **Equity Capital Needed:** $200,000. **Franchise Fee:** $10,000-$200,000. **Financial Assistance:** No. **Training:** Complete training and ongoing support.

44372 ■ Receil it Professional Ceiling Restoration
175-B Liberty St.
Copiague, NY 11726
Ph:(631)842-0099
Free: 800-234-5464
Fax:(631)980-7668
No. of Franchise Units: 2. **No. of Company-Owned Units:** 1. **Founded:** 1992. **Franchised:** 2002. **Description:** Restoration or cleaning of drop ceilings. **Equity Capital Needed:** $38,900-$55,000. **Franchise Fee:** $17,500. **Financial Assistance:** Limited in-house financing available. **Training:** Provides 6 days training at headquarters, 2 days at franchisee's location, and ongoing support.

44373 ■ Servicemaster of Canada Limited
5462 Timberlea Blvd.
Mississauga, ON, Canada L4W 2T7
Ph:(905)670-0000
Free: 800-263-5928
Fax:(905)670-0077
Co. E-mail: thould@smclean.com
URL: http://www.servicemaster.com
No. of Franchise Units: 180. **Founded:** 1948. **Franchised:** 1950. **Description:** Offers a variety of services including disaster restoration, commercial carpet and upholstery cleaning, residential carpet and upholstery cleaning, contract janitorial services. **Equity Capital Needed:** $25,000-$100,000. **Franchise Fee:** $24,000-$67,000. **Financial Assistance:** Financing available OAC. **Training:** Offers 2 weeks at ServiceMaster Academy then ongoing support out of Canadian Head Office.

44374 ■ Squeegee Squad
Jack & Joes Franchising Inc.
8862 Zealand Ave. N., Ste. A
Minneapolis, MN 55445
Ph:(763)780-0492

Fax:(763)780-7372

No. of Franchise Units: 23. **No. of Company-Owned Units:** 1. **Founded:** 1999. **Franchised:** 2006. **Description:** Residential & new construction window cleaning. **Equity Capital Needed:** $25,300-$70,110. **Franchise Fee:** $14,900. **Financial Assistance:** No. **Training:** Yes.

44375 ■ Suspended In Time, Inc.
122 S Mountainway Dr.
Orem, UT 84058
Ph:(801)227-0075
Free: (866)756-0059

Fax:(801)221-1003
Co. E-mail: info@suspendedintime.com
URL: http://www.suspendedintime.com
No. of Franchise Units: 47. **Founded:** 1997. **Description:** With the remarkable discovery of Suspended in Time's technology in floral preservation over the last 10 years, we are expanding our business opportunities. This is not a Freeze Dry Method. We offer an excellent dealership package with low start-up fees. This preservation process only takes an average of 3-5 days to complete. **Equity Capital Needed:** $4,886. **Financial Assistance:** No. **Training:** Training provided at the corporate location 3, 10 hour days, which includes lunch - large discount on room accommodations and ongoing support as long as needed.

44376 ■ Worldwide Wireless
Worldwide Wireless Franchise Services LLC
1000 Eagle Ridge Dr.
Schererville, IN 46375
Ph:(219)864-9991
Free: 877-FIN-DWWW
Fax:(219)864-9992
URL: http://www.worldwidewirelessinc.com

Founded: 1999. **Franchised:** 2006. **Description:** Exclusive Sprint dealership. **Equity Capital Needed:** $75,000-$150,000. **Franchise Fee:** $30,000. **Financial Assistance:** Yes. **Training:** Yes.

Site Selection

START-UP INFORMATION

44377 ■ *The Canadian Small Business Survival Guide: How to Start and Operate Your Own Successful Business*
Pub: Dundurn Group
Ed: Benj Gallander. FRQ June 2002. **Price:** $26.99. **Description:** Ideas for starting and running a successful small business. Topics include selecting a business, financing, government assistance, locations, franchises, and marketing ideas.

44378 ■ *The Complete Idiot's Guide to Starting and Running a Thrift Store*
Pub: Alpha Publishing House
Ed: Ravel Buckley, Carol Costa. **Released:** January 5, 2010. **Price:** $18.95. **Description:** Thrift stores saw a 35 percent increase in sales during the falling economy in 2008. Despite the low startup costs, launching and running a thrift store is complicated. Two experts cover the entire process, including setting up a store on a nonprofit basis, choosing a location, funding, donations for saleable items, recruiting and managing staff, sorting items, pricing, and recycling donations.

44379 ■ "Geo-Marketing: Site Selection by the Numbers" in *Franchising World* (Vol. 42, September 2010, No. 9, pp.)
Pub: International Franchise Association
Ed: Kellen Vaughan. **Description:** Site location is critical when starting a new franchise. Information to help franchisees choose the right location is included.

44380 ■ "Head West, Young Startup?" in *Boston Business Journal* (Vol. 30, October 22, 2010, No. 39, pp. 1)
Pub: Boston Business Journal
Ed: Galen Moore. **Description:** Startup companies Lark Technologies, Baydin and E la Cart Inc. are planning to leave Boston, Massachusetts for Silicon Valley. Lark has developed a vibrating wrist strap that syncs with a mobile phone's alarm clock.

44381 ■ "Where to be an Entrepreneur: Ten Startup-Friendly Cities" in *Entrepreneur* (Vol. 37, August 2009, No. 8, pp. 49)
Pub: Entrepreneur Media, Inc.
Ed: Jason Daley. **Description:** Ten U.S. cities that embody the entrepreneurial spirit are presented. These cities are ideal for startup companies and profiles of businesses that are making it in these cities are discussed.

44382 ■ *Working for Yourself: An Entrepreneur's Guide to the Basics*
Pub: Kogan Page, Limited
Ed: Jonathan Reuvid. **Released:** September 2006. **Description:** Guide for starting a new business venture, focusing on raising financing, legal and tax issues, marketing, information technology, and site location.

REFERENCE WORKS

44383 ■ "Aeronautics Seeking New HQ Site" in *The Business Journal-Milwaukee* (Vol. 25, September 5, 2008, No. 50, pp. 1)
Pub: American City Business Journals, Inc.
Ed: Rich Kirchen. **Description:** Milwaukee, Wisconsin-based Aeronautics Corp. of America is

planning to move its headquarters to a new site. The company has started to search for a new site. It also plans to consolidate its operations under one roof.

44384 ■ "Aircraft Maker May Land Here" in *Austin Business Journal* (Vol. 31, April 15, 2011, No. 6, pp. 1)
Pub: American City Business Journals Inc.
Ed: Jacob Dirr. **Description:** Icon Aircraft Inc. is planning to build a manufacturing facility in Austin, Texas. The company needs 100,000 square feet of space in a new or renovated plant. Executive comments are included.

44385 ■ "Allen Tate Expanding to Research Triangle Park: Firm Expects Raleigh Market to Grow Faster" in *Charlotte Observer* (January 31, 2007)
Pub: Knight-Ridder/Tribune Business News
Ed: Doug Smith; Dudley Price. **Description:** Allen Tate Realtors expanded its operations to the Research Triangle area. The firm is predicting a strong market and growth in Charlotte, North Carolina.

44386 ■ "AMC Scouts Downtown for New HQ" in *Business Journal-Serving Metropolitan Kansas City* (Vol. 26, October 19, 2007, No. 6, pp. 1)
Pub: American City Business Journals, Inc.
Ed: Jim Davis. **Description:** AMC Entertainment Inc. is seeking a new 100,000 square foot office in downtown Kansas City. The new headquarters is expected to bring additional employment and revenue to the city. AMC's stay on Main Street since 2002 is discussed.

44387 ■ "Another California Firm On Way" in *Austin Business Journal* (Vol. 31, May 6, 2011, No. 9, pp. 1)
Pub: American City Business Journals Inc.
Ed: Christopher Calnan. **Description:** Main Street Hub Inc. is planning to build a facility in Austin, Texas. The company helps businesses manage their online reputations. Main Street has selected Aquila Commercial LLC as its real estate broker.

44388 ■ "Aquila HQ Hits the Market" in *The Business Journal-Serving Metropolitan Kansas City* (Vol. 26, July 25, 2008, No. 46, pp. 1)
Pub: American City Business Journals, Inc.
Ed: Rob Roberts. **Description:** Commercial real estate experts believe that Aquila Inc.'s former headquarters will be hard to rent out. The historic value of the building, being Kansas City's first skyscraper, is not expected to add value to the price of the rent. Other views and information on the building, as well as on Aquila, are presented.

44389 ■ "'The Asian Decade'" in *Hawaii Business* (Vol. 53, January 2008, No. 7, pp. 19)
Pub: Hawaii Business Publishing
Ed: Cathy S. Cruz-George. **Description:** Chaney Brooks, a Hawaiian real estate company, has affiliated with commercial real estate network NAI Global.

The NAI partnership will improve Hawaii's international business, particularly its Asian investments. Hawaii's diverse workforce is evaluated, with regards to being an asset for international businesses.

44390 ■ "Asterand Eyes Jump to Ann Arbor; TechTown Tenant" in *Crain's Detroit Business* (Vol. 25, June 22, 2009)
Pub: Crain Communications Inc. - Detroit
Ed: Tom Henderson. **Description:** Asterand PLC is considering a move to Ann Arbor from its current location as anchor tenant at TechTown, an incubator and technology park associated with Wayne State University. The university believes the Ann Arbor location's rent is too expensive for the tissue bank company.

44391 ■ "Austin Ponders Annexing F1 Racetrack" in *Austin Business Journal* (Vol. 31, July 8, 2011, No. 18, pp. 1)
Pub: American City Business Journals Inc.
Ed: Vicky Garza. **Description:** City planners in Austin, Texas are studying the feasibility of annexing the land under and around the Circuit of the Americas Formula One Racetrack being constructed east of the city. The annexation could generate at least $13 million in financial gain over 25 years from property taxes alone.

44392 ■ "BancVue to Expand" in *Austin Business JournalInc.* (Vol. 29, November 27, 2009, No. 38, pp. 1)
Pub: American City Business Journals
Ed: Kate Harrington. **Description:** Significant growth of BancVue in the past six years has prompted the company to look for a site that could increase its office space from 25,000 square feet to 65,000 square feet. BancVue offers bank and credit union software solutions and is planning to lease or buy a property in Austin, Texas.

44393 ■ "Bank Bullish on Austin" in *Austin Business JournalInc.* (Vol. 29, November 13, 2009, No. 36, pp. A1)
Pub: American City Business Journals
Ed: Kate Harrington. **Description:** American Bank's presence in Austin, Texas has been boosted by new management and a new 20,000 square foot building. This community bank intends to focus on building relationship with commercial banking customers. American Bank also plans to extend investment banking, treasury management, and commercial lending services.

44394 ■ "Before Signing a Lease" in *Business Owner* (Vol. 35, September-October 2011, No. 5, pp. 14)
Pub: DL Perkins Company
Description: The following terms are essential to investigate before renewing or negotiating a lease for a small business: Term, Neighbors, Actual Usable Space, Gross or Net, Tenant Improvements, Renewal Option, Purchase Option, Cancelation Option, Sublease or Assignment, Security Deposit, Code Restrictions and Zoning, Parking, Relief and Lease Agreement.

44395 ■ "Betting On Slots" in *Baltimore Business Journal* (Vol. 28, November 19, 2010, No. 28, pp. 1)

Pub: Baltimore Business Journal

Ed: Rachel Bernstein. **Description:** Penn National Gaming Company's Hollywood Casino in Perryville, Maryland has been betting on the slot machines to lure slot players to the region to boost the town's growth. The success of Maryland's first casino is expected to lead to the development of land in the area.

44396 ■ "Biz Assesses 'Textgate' Fallout; Conventions, Smaller Deals Affected" in *Crain's Detroit Business* (Vol. 24, March 31, 2008)

Pub: Crain Communications, Inc.

Ed: Tom Henderson. **Description:** Businesspeople who were trying to measure the amount of economic damage is likely to be caused due to Mayor Kwame Kilpatrick's indictment on eight charges and found that: automotive and other large global deals are less likely to be affected than location decisions by smaller companies and convention site decisions. Also being affected are negotiations in which Mexican startup companies were planning a partnership with the TechTown incubator to pursue opportunities in the auto sector; those plans are being put on hold while they look at other sites.

44397 ■ "Boeing's Next Flight May Well Be to the South" in *Puget Sound Business Journal* (Vol. 29, November 21, 2008, No. 31, pp.)

Pub: American City Business Journals

Ed: Steve Wilhelm. **Description:** Southern states in the U.S. are luring Boeing Company to locate a new plant in their region which is experiencing a growing industrial base while offering permissive labor laws as selling points.

44398 ■ "Bond Hill Cinema Site To See New Life" in *Business Courier* (Vol. 27, October 29, 2010, No. 26, pp. 1)

Pub: Business Courier

Ed: Dan Monk. **Description:** Avondale, Ohio's Corinthian Baptist Church will redevelop the 30-acre former Showcase Cinema property to a mixed-use site that could feature a college, senior home, and retail. Corinthian Baptist, which is one of the largest African-American churches in the region, is also planning to relocate the church.

44399 ■ "A Bright Spot: Industrial Space in Demand Again" in *Sacramento Business Journal* (Vol. 28, October 21, 2011, No. 34, pp. 1)

Pub: Sacramento Business Journal

Ed: Michael Shaw. **Description:** Sacramento, California's industrial sites have been eyed by potential tenants who are actively seeking space larger than 50,000 square feet.

44400 ■ "Brokerages Seek a Foothold in Local Real Estate Market" in *Charlotte Business Journal* (Vol. 25, October 15, 2010, No. 30, pp. 1)

Pub: Charlotte Business Journal

Ed: Will Boye. **Description:** Charlotte, North Carolina has become an attractive destination for out-of-town brokerage firms. Colliers International has signed an affiliate deal with Anthony and Company to set up shop in Charlotte. Grubb and Ellis Company, on the other hand, is planning to open an office in the city.

44401 ■ "Business Plan Refines Focus" in *Business Journal Portland* (Vol. 27, December 10, 2010, No. 41, pp. 1)

Pub: Portland Business Journal

Ed: Wendy Culverwell. **Description:** Organizers of the Oregon Business Plan's Leadership Summit 2010 seek the opinions of nearly 1,000 business, education, political, and civic leaders in an effort to address how to rehabilitate Oregon's economy. The opinion-seeking actions recognize the organizers' belief that the economic fate of the state depends on rural Oregon.

44402 ■ "Challenges, Responses and Available Resources" in *Journal of Small Business and Entrepreneurship* (Vol. 23, Winter 2010, No. 1)

Pub: Canadian Council for Small Business and Entrepreneurship

Ed: Lynne Siemens. **Description:** Rural communities and their residents are exploring the potential of small business and entrepreneurship to address the economic changes they are facing. While these rural areas present many opportunities, business people in these areas face challenges which they must navigate to operate successfully.

44403 ■ "Chinese Solar Panel Manufacturer Scopes Out Austin" in *Austin Business JournalInc.* (Vol. 29, October 30, 2009, No. 34, pp. 1)

Pub: American City Business Journals

Ed: Jacob Dirr. **Description:** China's Yingli Green Energy Holding Company Ltd. is looking for a site in order to construct a $20 million photovoltaic panel plant. Both Austin and San Antonio are vying to house the manufacturing hub. The project could create about 300 jobs and give Austin a chance to become a player in the solar energy market. Other solar companies are also considering Central Texas as an option to set up shop.

44404 ■ "Chuy's Gears Up to Serve Atlants, Other Untapped Cities" in *Austin Business Journal* (Vol. 31, June 17, 2011, No. 15, pp. 1)

Pub: American City Business Journals Inc.

Ed: Cody Lyon. **Description:** Chuy's Holdings Inc. plans to expand into the Southeastern United States, particularly in Atlanta, Georgia. The restaurant, which secured $67.5 million in debt financing in May 2011, added 20 stores in five years and plans to open eight locations in 2011.

44405 ■ "Cities Work to Attract Small Biz" in *Crain's Detroit Business* (Vol. 25, June 8, 2009, No. 23, pp. 20)

Pub: Crain Communications Inc. - Detroit

Ed: Nancy Kaffer. **Description:** Royal Oak and other metropolitan cities are trying to attract small companies to their towns.

44406 ■ "City Wooing Red Roof Inn for Return of Corporate HQ" in *Business First-Columbus* (October 19, 2007, pp. A1)

Pub: American City Business Journals, Inc.

Ed: **Description:** Department of Development of Columbus, Ohio offered Red Roof Inns Inc. a four-year, 40 percent jobs growth initiative to entice the company to move its corporate headquarters into the city from Dallas, Texas. The Watermark Island office building off Dublin Road and Grandview Avenue will be the headquarters of the company if it accepts the offer.

44407 ■ "City's Streetcar Utility Estimate Way Off Mark" in *Business Courier* (Vol27, November 19, 2010, No. 29. , pp. 1)

Pub: Business Courier

Ed: Dan Monk, Lucy May. **Description:** Duke Energy Corporation has released new estimates that show moving electric and gas lines alone for Cincinnati, Ohio's proposed streetcar project could cost more than $20 million. However, the city has only estimated the relocation to cost $5 million in federal grant applications.

44408 ■ "Conversation: Historian Geoffrey Jones On Why Knowledge Stays Put" in *Harvard Business Review* (Vol. 86, July-August 2008, No. 8)

Pub: Harvard Business School Press

Ed: Gardiner Morse. **Description:** Geoffrey Jones, Harvard Business School's professor of business history, discusses factors that cause knowledge to concentrate in particular regions, rather than disperse, such as the location of wealth.

44409 ■ "Coors Execs Listen to Milwaukee Pitch" in *Business Journal-Milwaukee* (Vol. 25, November 2, 2007, No. 5, pp. A1)

Pub: American City Business Journals, Inc.

Ed: Rich Rovito. **Description:** Coors Brewing Company officials met with Wisconsin Governor Jim Doyle and Milwaukee Mayor Tom Barnett about putting the MillerCoors corporate headquarters in Milwaukee. The city is competing with Denver, Colorado for the headquarters of the joint venture.

44410 ■ "Could This Be Your Next Office Building?" in *Austin Business Journal* (Vol. 31, May 13, 2011, No. 10, pp. A1)

Pub: American City Business Journals Inc.

Ed: Cody Lyon. **Description:** Falcon Containers moved to a 51-acre site in Far East Austin, Texas and started construction of a 2,500-square-foot headquarters made from eight 40-foot shipping containers. Falcon's CEO Stephen Shang plans to use his headquarters building as a showroom to attract upscale, urban hipsters. Insights on the construction's environmental and social impact are shared.

44411 ■ "Could UNCC Be Home to Future Med School Here?" in *Charlotte Business Journal* (Vol. 25, July 23, 2010, No. 18, pp. 1)

Pub: Charlotte Business Journal

Ed: Jennifer Thomas. **Description:** University of North Carolina, Charlotte chancellor Phil Dubois is proposing that a medical school be established at the campus. The idea began in 2007 and Dubois' plan is for students to spend all four years in Charlotte and train at the Carolinas Medical Center.

44412 ■ "Cupcake Maker Grabs Outpost" in *Crain's New York Business* (Vol. 27, August 15, 2011, No. 33, pp. 16)

Pub: Crain Communications Inc.

Ed: Jermaine Taylor. **Description:** Family-owned miniature cupcake maker, Baked by Melissa, singed a ten-year lease, expanding their stores to five. The business was started three years ago by advertising executive Melissa Bushell.

44413 ■ "Deal Made for Pontiac Home of Film Studio" in *Crain's Detroit Business* (Vol. 25, June 1, 2009, No. 22, pp. 3)

Pub: Crain Communications Inc. - Detroit

Ed: Daniel Duggan. **Description:** Details of the $75 million movie production and training facility in Pontiac, Michigan are revealed.

44414 ■ "Delta Looks at Downtown Departure" in *Business Courier* (Vol. 27, October 1, 2010, No. 22, pp. 1)

Pub: Business Courier

Ed: Dan Monk. **Description:** Delta Air Lines Inc. has been looking for a smaller office for its reservations center in downtown Cincinnati, Ohio. Delta has informed the city of its plan to seek proposals on office space alternatives in advance of the 2011 lease expiration. Insights on the current employment status at the reservations center are also given.

44415 ■ "Denver Will Put Up Fight for MillerCoors HQ" in *Business Journal-Milwaukee* (Vol. 25, October 19, 2007, No. 3, pp. A1)

Pub: American City Business Journals, Inc.

Ed: Rich Rovito. **Description:** A contention exists between Milwaukee and Denver over which city will become the new location of the Miller Brewing Company (Milwaukee) and Coors Brewing Company (Colorado) joint venture MillerCoors. Leaders of the breweries since the announcement of the merger, have contended frantically to prepare strategies to back up their own cities. The advantages and disadvantages of both cities are presented.

44416 ■ "Downtown Detroit Needs More Retail" in *Crain's Detroit Business* (Vol. 24, March 10, 2008, No. 10, pp. 9)

Pub: Crain Communications, Inc.

Ed: Robin Boyle; James Bieri. **Description:** Although Detroit is doing well with event-driven traffic, the city remains far off the site selection rosters of major national retailers as well as smaller retail outlets.

44417 ■ "Downtown Retail Site Sold to ATCO" in *Austin Business JournalInc.* (Vol. 29, November 20, 2009, No. 37, pp. 1)

Pub: American City Business Journals

Ed: Kate Harrington. **Description:** New York-based real estate company ATCO Advisory Services purchased a 13,700 square foot retail space in Austin,

Texas from 360 Condominiums. The selection of the retail space, named the Shops at 360 has been attributed to the local tenant mix and its location in downtown Austin. Meanwhile, ATCO may continue investing in the area in the near future.

44418 ■ "Drawn to York County: Less-Expensive Homes, Good Schools Attract Charlotteans" in *Charlotte Observer* **(February 4, 2007)**
Pub: Knight-Ridder/Tribune Business News
Ed: Taylor Bright. **Description:** York County, North Carolina offers low-priced homes and good schools, making it attractive to workers and small business.

44419 ■ *The Emerging Digital Economy: Entrepreneurship, Clusters, and Policy*
Pub: Springer
Ed: Borje Johansson; Charlie Karlsson; Roger Stough. **Released:** August 2006. **Price:** $119.00. **Description:** The new economy, or digital economy, and its impact on the way industries and firms choose to locate and cluster geographically.

44420 ■ "Exiting Stage Left" in *Baltimore Business Journal* **(Vol. 28, June 18, 2010, No. 6, pp. 1)**
Pub: Baltimore Business Journal
Ed: Scott Dance. **Description:** Film professionals including crew members and actors have been leaving Maryland to find work in other states such as Michigan, Louisiana, and Georgia where bigger budgets and film production incentives are given. Other consequences of this trend in local TV and film production are discussed.

44421 ■ "Feds, Not City, Will Pick GSA Office Site" in *Business Journal-Serving Metropolitan Kansas City* **(Vol. 26, November 30, 2007, No. 12)**
Pub: American City Business Journals, Inc.
Ed: Jim Davis. **Description:** Mark Funkhouser wants the federal government to decide the location of the General Services Administration building site. The act of the Mayor enraged the executive director of Kansas City Port Authority, Vincent Gauthier. Details of the GSAs building location plans are discussed.

44422 ■ "Fifth Third Spinoff" in *Business Courier* **(Vol. 27, July 16, 2010, No. 11, pp. 1)**
Pub: Business Courier
Ed: Dan Monk, Steve Watkins. **Description:** Electronic-funds transfer company Fifth Third Solutions (FTPS), a spinoff of Fifth Third Bancorp, is seeking as much as 200,000 square feet of new office space in Ohio. The bank's sale of 51 percent ownership stake to Boston-based Advent International Corporation has paved the way for the growth of FTPS. How real estate brokers' plans have responded to FTPS' growth mode is discussed.

44423 ■ "Formaspace Finds a Bigger Home" in *Austin Business JournalInc.* **(Vol. 29, December 4, 2009, No. 39, pp. 1)**
Pub: American City Business Journals
Ed: Kate Harrington. **Description:** Formaspace Technical Furniture has signed a lease for 56,700 square feet in Harris Ridge Business Center at Northeast Austin, Texas, which represents one of the area's largest leases for 2009. The new lease enables Formaspace to hire new employees, invest in new equipment, and take advantage of a taxing designation created for manufacturers.

44424 ■ "Franchises with an Eye on Chicago" in *Crain's Chicago Business* **(Vol. 34, March 14, 2011, No. 11, pp. 20)**
Pub: Crain Communications Inc.
Description: Profiles of franchise companies seeking franchisees for the Chicago area include: Extreme Pita, a sandwich shop; Hand and Stone, offering massage, facial and waxing service; Molly Maid, home-cleaning service; Primrose Schools, private accredited schools for children 6 months to 6 hears and after-school programs; Protect Painters, residential and light-commercial painting contractor; and Wingstop, a restaurant offering chicken wings in nine flavors, fries and side dishes.

44425 ■ "Furniture Chain Moving to Harford" in *Baltimore Business Journal* **(Vol. 27, January 22, 2010, No. 38, pp. 1)**
Pub: American City Business Journals
Ed: David J. Sernovitz. **Description:** Manchester, Connecticut-based Bob's Discount Furniture signed a lease for 672,000 square feet of space in Harford County, Maryland. The site will become the discount furniture retailer's distribution center in mid-Atlantic US. As many as 200 jobs could be generated when the center opens.

44426 ■ "Game Changer" in *Canadian Business* **(Vol. 83, June 15, 2010, No. 10, pp. 52)**
Pub: Rogers Media Ltd.
Ed: Jordan Timm. **Description:** Ubisoft chose Ontario to be the site for its new development studio and it has appointed Jade Raymond as its managing director. Raymond was born in Montreal in 1975 and studied computer science at McGill. Raymond is said to possess the understanding of the game industry's technical, art, and business components.

44427 ■ *Getting Rich In Your Underwear: How To Start and Run a Profitable Home-Based Business*
Pub: HCM Publishing
Ed: Peter I. Hupalo. **Released:** April 1, 2005. **Price:** $17.95. **Description:** Book offers insight into starting a home-based business. Entrepreneurs will learn about business models and the home business; distribution and fulfillment of product or service; marketing and sales; how to overcome the fear of starting a business; personal success characteristics; naming a business; zoning and insurance; intellectual capital; copyrights, trademarks, and patents; limited liability companies and S-corporations; business expenses and accounting; taxes; fifteen basic steps for starting a home-based business, state resources for starting a home company; and seven home-based business ideas.

44428 ■ "Good for Business: Houston is a Hot Spot for Economic Growth" in *Black Enterprise* **(Vol. 37, October 2006, No. 3, pp. 216)**
Pub: Earl G. Graves Publishing Co. Inc.
Ed: Jeanette Valentine. **Description:** Fast-growing sectors in the biotechnology and healthcare industries are among the driving forces of Houston's economic growth. More than 76,000 small businesses in the area employ about one in four area workers, according to the Small Business Administration. Housing and business costs are 26 and 11 percent below the national average, respectively, garnering the attention of corporate giants.

44429 ■ "Green Firm Scouts Sites in Tri-State" in *Business Courier* **(Vol. 27, July 23, 2010, No. 12, pp. 1)**
Pub: Business Courier
Ed: Dan Monk. **Description:** CresaPartners is searching for a manufacturing facility in Cincinnati, Ohio. The company is set to tour about ten sites in the area.

44430 ■ "Hispanic Business 100 Fastest-Growing Companies" in *Hispanic Business* **(July-August 2009, pp. 16-18)**
Pub: Hispanic Business
Ed: Joshua Molina. **Description:** Despite the recession, the 100 fastest growing companies profiled are able to maintain their competitive edge; federal contracts are key to their success. Service companies are at the top of the list and Texas and Florida are the states in which the top are located

44431 ■ "Hispanic Businesses Try to Drum Up Cash to Battle Crime Spree" in *Baltimore Business Journal* **(Vol. 28, September 3, 2010, No. 17)**
Pub: Baltimore Business Journal
Ed: Scott Dance. **Description:** Hispanic businesses in Baltimore, Maryland have been raising funds to pay off-duty police officers to patrol a few blocks of Broadway in Fells Point to help curb crime. Efforts to

make the area a Latin Town have failed owing to muggings, prostitution and drug dealing. Comments from small business owners are also given.

44432 ■ "Horizon Acquires Significant Working Interest in High Impact Prospect in Southeast Texas" in *Canadian Corporate News* **(May 14, 2007)**
Pub: Comtex News Network Inc.
Description: Horizon Industries Ltd., an emerging gas and oil exploration and production company, announced that it has entered into a Joint Venture agreement with Pan American Development Company, Inc. in which they will begin a drilling program in San Jacinto County, Texas.

44433 ■ *How to Start and Run Your Own Corporation: S-Corporations For Small Business Owners*
Pub: HCM Publishing
Ed: Peter I. Hupalo. **Released:** March 6, 2003. **Price:** $22.95. **Description:** Basics of corporate business structure are explained. Topics include discovering the best business structure for your company; how to decided between an S-Corporation and LLC; choosing the state in which to incorporate, how to form a corporation, angel investing, special issues for one-person corporations, the role of bylaws and corporate minutes, board of directors, taxes, workers' compensation issues, retirement plans, and more.

44434 ■ "In Addition, Pinkberry Reports It Is Opening a New Shop in Sunnyvale, CA" in *Ice Cream Reporter* **(Vol. 23, October 20, 2010)**
Pub: Ice Cream Reporter
Description: Pinkberry opened a new shop in Sunnyvale, California, its fourth opening in the South Bay and its 101st location worldwide.

44435 ■ "Incentives In Play for Astronautics" in *Business Journal-Milwaukee* **(Vol. 28, November 5, 2010, No. 5, pp. A1)**
Pub: Milwaukee Business Journal
Ed: Sean Ryan. **Description:** Astronautics Corporation was offered incentives by local government officials in Milwaukee, Wisconsin and by Brewery Project LLC to move into a building in The Brewery in the city. The company's officials remain indecisive over the offers and incentives.

44436 ■ "Insitu Looks to Oregon" in *Business Journal Portland* **(Vol. 27, October 29, 2010, No. 35, pp. 1)**
Pub: Portland Business Journal
Ed: Erik Siemers. **Description:** Bingen, Washington-based Insitu Inc. announced that it has narrowed the search for a new corporate campus into five locations within the Columbia Gorge region. However, state economic development officials are curious whether the company will land in Oregon or Washington. Insights on economic impact of Insitu's decision are also given.

44437 ■ "Insuraprise Growing Fast" in *Austin Business Journal* **(Vol. 31, April 22, 2011, No. 7, pp. 1)**
Pub: American City Business Journals Inc.
Ed: Sandra Zaragoza. **Description:** Austin, Texas-based Insuraprise Inc. is finalizing the purchase of a 24,000-square-foot office at 12116 Jekel Circle. The firm, with 23 salespeople and sales that are growing nearly 300 percent over the past 18 months, will now have room to grow. Insuraprise plans to hire 35 new salespersons for its call center.

44438 ■ "It's Not Perfect; But Illinois a Good Home for Business" in *Crain's Chicago Business* **(Vol. 34, October 24, 2011, No. 42, pp. 18)**
Pub: Crain Communications Inc.
Description: Focusing on all factors that encompass Illinois' business environment, findings show that Illinois is a good place to start and grow a business. The study focused on corporate income tax rates and the fact that talent, access to capital and customers along with transportation connections are among the important factors the state has for small businesses.

44439 ■ **"Kellog Pores Over KC Sites"** in *Business Journal-Serving Metropolitan Kansas City* (Vol. 26, November 23, 2007, No. 11, pp. 1)

Pub: American City Business Journals, Inc.

Ed: Jim Davis. **Description:** Kellog Company is searching Kansas City for a parcel about 1.3 million square feet to build its product distribution center. According to brokers, a selection might come by end of November 2007. Some of the potential sites are detailed.

44440 ■ **"Kodiak Bucks Bear Market"** in *Austin Business JournalInc.* (Vol. 29, December 18, 2009, No. 41, pp. 1)

Pub: American City Business Journals

Ed: Kate Harrington. **Description:** Austin, Texas-based Kodiak Assembly Solutions LLC, a company that installs components into printed circuit boards for product or evaluation tool kit prototyping purposes, will expand despite the recession. It will relocate from a 28,000 square foot space to a 42,000 square foot space in North Austin. The firm will also increase its workforce by 20 employees.

44441 ■ **"KXAN Seeks Larger Studio, Office Space"** in *Austin Business Journal* (Vol. 31, May 27, 2011, No. 12, pp. A1)

Pub: American City Business Journals Inc.

Ed: Cody Lyon. **Description:** Austin NBC affiliate KXAN Television is opting to sell its property north of downtown and relocate to another site. The station is now inspecting possible sites to house its broadcasting facility and employees totaling as many as 200 people. Estimated cost of the construction of the studios and offices is $13 million plus another million in moving the equipment.

44442 ■ **"Law Firm Jones Day Coming to Boston"** in *Boston Business Journal* (Vol. 30, November 19, 2010, No. 43, pp. 1)

Pub: Boston Business Journal

Ed: Lisa van der Pool. **Description:** Jones Day is set to open an office in Boston, Massachusetts. The company will be the largest law firm to enter Boston since 2007. The firm will open with at least three partners.

44443 ■ **"Local Green Technology on Display"** in *Crain's Detroit Business* (Vol. 26, January 18, 2010, No. 3, pp. 1)

Pub: Crain Communications, Inc.

Ed: Ryan Beene. **Description:** Detroit's 2010 North American International Auto Show put the newest, most innovative green technologies on display showing that the Southeast Michigan automobile industry is gaining traction with its burgeoning e-vehicle infrastructure. Think, a Norwegian electric city-car manufacturer is eyeing sites in Southeast Michigan in which to locate its corporate headquarters and technical center for its North American branch.

44444 ■ **"Luxury Still Sells Well"** in *Puget Sound Business Journal* (Vol. 29, September 5, 2008, No. 20, pp. 1)

Pub: American City Business Journals

Ed: Jeanne Lang Jones. **Description:** High fashion retailers are planning to open stores in the Puget Sound area despite the economic slowdown, citing high incomes in the area despite the weak U.S. dollar.

44445 ■ **"Magpower May Build Solar Panels Here"** in *Austin Business Journal* (Vol. 31, May 13, 2011, No. 10, pp. A1)

Pub: American City Business Journals Inc.

Ed: Christopher Calnan. **Description:** RRE Austin Solar LLC CEO Doven Mehta has revealed plans to partner with Portugal-based Magpower SA, only if Austin energy buys electricity from planned solar energy farm in Pflugerville. Austin Energy has received 100 bids from 35 companies to supply 200 megawatts of solar- and wind-generated electricity.

44446 ■ **"Mandel Site Favored For UWM Hall"** in *The Business Journal-Milwaukee* (Vol. 25, September 19, 2008, No. 52, pp. A1)

Pub: American City Business Journals, Inc.

Description: University of Wisconsin-Milwaukee student residence hall's leading location is a site pushed by Mandel Group Inc. Real estate sources say that the developer's proposal offers the best opportunity for business development and the least conflict with nearby neighborhoods. Plans for the Mandel site are presented.

44447 ■ **"M&T On the March?"** in *Baltimore Business Journal* (Vol. 28, November 12, 2010, No. 27, pp. 1)

Pub: Baltimore Business Journal

Ed: Gary Haber. **Description:** Information on the growth of M&T Bank, as well as its expansion plans are presented. M&T recently acquired Wilmington Trust and took over $500 million in deposits from the failed K Bank. Analysts believe that M&T would continue its expansion through Washington DC and Richmond, Virginia, especially after a bank executive acknowledged that the markets in those areas are attractive.

44448 ■ **"Mapping Out a Career"** in *Occupational Outlook Quarterly* (Vol. 54, Fall 2010, No. 3, pp. 12)

Pub: U.S. Bureau of Labor Statistics

Ed: Audrey Watson. **Description:** Geographic distribution of occupations is studied, along with lifestyle considerations when choosing a career.

44449 ■ **"Mayor Unveils Business Plan"** in *Boston Business Journal* (Vol. 29, September 16, 2011, No. 19, pp. 1)

Pub: American City Business Journals Inc.

Ed: Gary Haber. **Description:** Mayor Stephanie Rawlings-Blake of Baltimore, Maryland unveiled her plan to push the economy forward. Her key objectives include giving more support for the city's technology companies and refocusing the Baltimore Development Corporation on job creation and retention.

44450 ■ **"Meet UT's New Business Mind"** in *Austin Business Journal* (Vol. 31, May 13, 2011, No. 10, pp. A1)

Pub: American City Business Journals Inc.

Ed: Sandra Zaragoza. **Description:** University of Texas (UT) chief commercialization officer, Dr. Richard Miller, has opened a satellite office in Silicon Valley, California in the hopes of luring Californian investors to the science and technology at UT. The satellite office is just one of Miller's efforts to reshape and widen the commercialization of UT-Austin. Insights into Miller's long-term view approach to commercialization are also covered.

44451 ■ **"Mission: Poach California"** in *Business Journal Portland* (Vol. 26, December 11, 2009, No. 40, pp. 1)

Pub: American City Business Journals Inc.

Ed: Andy Giegerich. **Description:** Leaders of Greenlight Greater Portland, a privately funded economic development organization, will visit California five times in 2010 in an attempt to lure California businesses to expand or relocate in Oregon.

44452 ■ **"More Offices Planned For Percheron Square"** in *The Business Journal-Milwaukee* (Vol. 25, August 22, 2008, No. 48, pp. A1)

Pub: American City Business Journals, Inc.

Ed: Pete Millard. **Description:** More office projects are under way at Percheron Square. Ryan Cos. US Inc., for example, plans to build over 200,000 square feet of office space at the area. Details of new office projects in Wisconsin are presented.

44453 ■ **"Move South Could Bring Big Benefits"** in *Business Journal-Portland* (Vol. 24, November 9, 2007, No. 36, pp. 1)

Pub: American City Business Journals, Inc.

Ed: Matthew Kish. **Description:** Freightliner LLC has announced that it would move around one-tenth of its jobs to Fort Mill, South Carolina, but stated that immediate plans for headquarters relocation have not been made. The relocation of its headquarters is expected to earn $100 million in economic incentives. The benefits of moving to the area, aside from the economic incentives, are discussed.

44454 ■ **"Moving On: What's It Worth?"** in *Entrepreneur* (Vol. 36, February 2008, No. 2, pp. 32)

Pub: Entrepreneur Media Inc.

Ed: Jacquelyn Lynn. **Description:** An area's cost of living should be considered by business owners when relocating, as it can affect operating costs and salary expenses, among other issues. Details on how to decide on business relocation with regard to cost of living concerns are examined.

44455 ■ **"N.E.'s Largest Solar Site Set for Scituate Landfill"** in *Boston Business Journal* (Vol. 30, December 17, 2010, No. 47, pp. 1)

Pub: Boston Business Journal

Ed: Kyle Alspach. **Description:** A closed 12-acre landfill in Scituate, Massachusetts is the proposed site for a 2.4-megawatt solar power plant. The town government will buy the power at a discounted rate, saving it $200,000 annually.

44456 ■ **"New Kittinger Showroom Twice the Size of the Last One"** in *Business First Buffalo* (December 7, 2007, pp. 4)

Pub: American City Business Journals, Inc.

Ed: Tracey Drury. **Description:** Kittinger Furniture Company, an upscale furniture maker, has opened a 6,000 square foot retail outlet at the Transit Road, New York. The company's moved to attract suburban and affluent customers for its high-end furniture products.

44457 ■ **"Nordstrom Points for Richmond Heights"** in *Saint Louis Business Journal* (Vol. 31, August 5, 2011, No. 50, pp. 1)

Pub: Saint Louis Business Journal

Ed: E.B. Solomont. **Description:** Nordstrom is set to upgrade its offerings for its second full-line store in St. Louis, Missouri. The new store is expected to benefit nearby shops.

44458 ■ **"Novi Eyed for $11 Million, 100-Bed Medilodge"** in *Crain's Detroit Business* (Vol. 25, June 1, 2009, No. 22, pp. M032)

Pub: Crain Communications Inc. - Detroit

Description: Novi, Michigan is one of the cities being considered for construction of a new 110-bed skilled nursing facility. Details of the project are included.

44459 ■ **"Ohio Business Incentives Lag Offerings By Other States"** in *Crain's Cleveland Business* (Vol. 30, May 18, 2009, No. 20, pp. 1)

Pub: Crain Communications, Inc.

Ed: Jay Miller. **Description:** Incentives designed to attract business and promote business expansion in Ohio has not done their job. According to a new study, despite tax changes made four years ago, the state's ability to attract new business has gone unchanged.

44460 ■ **"Ohio's Reputation Lags Its Business Ranking"** in *Business Courier* (Vol. 24, November 23, 2008, No. 32, pp. 1)

Pub: American City Business Journals, Inc.

Ed: Jon Newberry. **Description:** Site Selection magazine's annual ranking of the top states for new business facilities has ranked Ohio and Kentucky in seventh and eight place respectively, but an opinion survey of real estate executives had placed Ohio much lower at 14. The survey asked 6,000 executives if Ohio's conditions were best for new building projects.

44461 ■ **"Old Ford Plant to Sign New Tenants"** in *Business Courier* (Vol. 27, August 13, 2010, No. 15, pp. 1)

Pub: Business Courier

Ed: Dan Monk. **Description:** Ohio Realty Advisors LLC, a company handling the marketing of the 1.9 million-square-foot former Ford Batavia plant is on the brink of landing one distribution and three manufacturing firms as tenants. These tenants are slated to occupy about 20 percent of the facility and generate as many as 250 jobs in Ohio.

44462 ■ "Organic Chain Scouting Tri-State Sites, Including Kenwood" in *Business Courier* **(Vol. 27, December 3, 2010, No. 31, pp. 1)**
Pub: Business Courier

Ed: Tom Demeropolis. **Description:** Asheville, North Carolina-based Earth Fare has been planning to add a total of six stores in 2011, including the potential opening of more than one store in the Greater Cincinnati area market. Earth Fare has not named specific locations but Kenwood area was reportedly being considered for its first location. Insights on growing trends toward health food stores are also given.

44463 ■ "PNC Begins Search for New Local HQ" in *Baltimore Business Journal* **(Vol. 28, June 4, 2010, No. 4, pp. 1)**
Pub: Baltimore Business Journal

Ed: Daniel J. Sernovitz. **Description:** PNC Financial Services Group Inc. is searching for a new headquarters building in Greater Baltimore, Maryland. The company is seeking about 150,000 square feet for its regional operations. However, PNC could also end up moving out of Baltimore for space in the surrounding suburbs.

44464 ■ "Portland Wooing Under Armour to West Coast Facility" in *Baltimore Business Journal* **(Vol. 27, January 29, 2010, No. 39, pp. 1)**
Pub: American City Business Journals

Ed: Andy Giegerich. **Description:** Baltimore, Maryland sports apparel maker, Under Armour, is planning a west coast expansion with Portland, Oregon among the sites considered to house its apparel and footwear design center. Portland officials counting on the concentration of nearly 10,000 activewear workers in the city will help lure the company to the city.

44465 ■ *Prepare to Be a Teen Millionaire*
Pub: Health Communications, Inc.

Ed: Robyn Collins; Kimberly Spinks Burleson. **Released:** April 1, 2008. **Price:** $16.95. **Description:** Business reference for any teenager wishing to become a successful entrepreneur; advice is given from successful teenage millionaires. Topics covered include: choosing a business name, type, and location; use of the Internet; legal issues; branding, sales, and marketing; funding and financial management; return on investment; retirement; development of a sound business plan; and certification for minority or women-owned companies.

44466 ■ "Priced-Out Tenants Flocking to Class B" in *Boston Business Journal* **(Vol. 27, October 19, 2007, No. 38, pp. 1)**
Pub: American City Business Journals Inc.

Ed: Michelle Hillman. **Description:** Tenants who usually rent top-tier office buildings are migrating to buildings that are not as expensive. The shift from Class A to Class B buildings is influenced by the high rental cost of the flashy office towers.

44467 ■ "Restaurateurs Follow High-End Apartments Into Kendall Square" in *Boston Business Journal* **(Vol. 31, July 22, 2011, No. 26, pp. 3)**
Pub: Boston Business Journal

Ed: Lisa van der Pool. **Description:** Kendall Square in Cambridge, Massachusetts is attracting restaurants, 16 of which have opened since 2009. The influx of restaurants is being driven by lower commercial rents.

44468 ■ "River Plan in Disarray" in *Business Journal Portland* **(Vol. 26, December 4, 2009, No. 39, pp. 1)**
Pub: American City Business Journals Inc.

Ed: Andy Giegerich. **Description:** Portland's proposed rules on a waterfront development plan for the Willamette River calls for fees intended for river bank preservation, a move that could drive industrial manufacturers away. The manufacturers, under the Working Waterfront Coalition, claim that the proposals could increase riverfront building costs by 15 percent.

44469 ■ "Roseville Investing Big in Downtown" in *Sacramento Business Journal* **(Vol. 28, September 2, 2011, No. 27, pp. 1)**
Pub: Sacramento Business Journal

Ed: Michael Shaw. **Description:** The city of Roseville, California is planning to invest in downtown development projects. The plan includes a new town square, a venue for a farmers market and an interactive water fountain.

44470 ■ "Roundy' Pushing Chicago Expansion" in *Milwaukee Business Journal* **(Vol. 27, February 12, 2010, No. 20, pp. A1)**
Pub: American City Business Journals

Ed: Rich Kirchen. **Description:** Roundy Supermarkets Inc. is expanding in Chicago, Illinois as the Milwaukee-based company is set to open one store in downtown Chicago and another in the Arlington suburb. The store openings have been pushed back to spring and early summer in 2010 due to the economic downturn.

44471 ■ "Running the Numbers" in *Entrepreneur* **(Vol. 37, July 2009, No. 7, pp. 87)**
Pub: Entrepreneur Media, Inc.

Ed: Carol Tice. **Description:** Ways in which entrepreneurs can assess if they are ready to be a multi-unit franchisee are presented. Choosing the right locations, knowing how much assistance they can get from the franchisor, and financing are the key considerations when planning additional franchise units. Examples of success in multi-unit operations and multi-unit terms are also presented.

44472 ■ "The Secret's Out About Kansas City" in *Women In Business* **(Vol. 61, August-September 2009, No. 4, pp. 26)**
Pub: American Business Women's Association

Ed: Leigh Elmore. **Description:** Missouri's Kansas City offers various attractions, such as public fountains, the 18th and Vine Historic Districts for jazz enthusiasts, and the Crossroads Arts District with a variety of art galleries. Details on other cultural attractions and neighborhoods in the city are presented.

44473 ■ "Shire Seeking New Digs for Headquarters" in *Philadelphia Business Journal* **(Vol. 30, September 2, 2011, No. 29, pp. 1)**
Pub: American City Business Journals Inc.

Ed: Natalie Kostelni. **Description:** Dublin, Ireland-based Shire PLC announced plans to relocate its North American headquarters from Chesterbrook Corporate Center in Wayne, Pennsylvania and currently evaluating their options. The specialty biopharmaceutical firm is also considering a move to New Jersey or Delaware.

44474 ■ "The Silvery Moon Moves to Larger Space" in *Bellingham Business Journal* **(Vol. March 2010, pp. 5)**
Pub: Sound Publishing Inc.

Description: Jewelry store, the Silvery Moon, moved to a larger location in order to expand its business. The new location was chosen because it offers the firm more visibility. The store offers find silver and gold pieces and specializes in Pacific Northwest native jewelry.

44475 ■ "Sobering Consequences" in *The Business Journal-Milwaukee* **(Vol. 25, July 11, 2008, No. 42, pp. A1)**
Pub: American City Business Journals, Inc.

Ed: Rich Rovito. **Description:** Milwaukee Mayor Tom Barrett and Wisconsin Governor Jim Doyle met with MillerCoors management in an effort to convince the company to locate its corporate headquarters in the city. The company is expected to announce its decision by mid-July 2008. It was revealed that the decision-making process is focusing on determining an optimal location for the headquarters.

44476 ■ "Solo, But Not Alone" in *Entrepreneur* **(Vol. 37, October 2009, No. 10, pp. 99)**
Pub: Entrepreneur Media, Inc.

Ed: David Port. **Description:** Co-working spaces are emerging in different US cities, allowing entrepreneurs and other independent workers to co-exist.

These work spaces, which can be availed for about $500 a month or $25 a day, also afford networking opportunities.

44477 ■ "Soured Relationship Plays Out in Courts" in *The Business Journal-Serving Greater Tampa Bay* **(Vol. 28, September 19, 2008, No. 39)**
Pub: American City Business Journals, Inc.

Ed: Janet Leiser. **Description:** Heirs of developer Julian Hawthorne Lifset won a court battle to end a 50-year lease with Specialty Restaurants Corp. in Rocky Point. The decision opens the Tampa Bay prime waterfront property for new development.

44478 ■ "South Park Draws Brewers, Vintners" in *Puget Sound Business Journal* **(Vol. 29, August 29, 2008, No. 19, pp. 1)**
Pub: American City Business Journals

Ed: Heidi Dietrich. **Description:** Craft breweries and wineries are moving into Seattle, Washington's South Park neighborhood due to the area's low rents, convenience, and ample equipment space. These industries bring a more upscale flavor to the heavily industrial area and the tastings and festivals draw people from throughout the Seattle region.

44479 ■ "Southwestern Resources Project Update" in *Canadian Corporate News* **(May 14, 2007)**
Pub: Comtex News Network Inc.

Description: Southwestern Resoures Corp. provides a quarterly update on its various exploration projects in both Peru and China.

44480 ■ *Start and Run a Delicatessen: Small Business Starters Series*
Pub: How To Books

Ed: Deborah Penrith. **Released:** November 9, 2010. **Price:** $30.00. **Description:** Information for starting and running a successful delicatessen is provided. Insight is offered into selecting a location, researching the market, writing a business plan and more.

44481 ■ "State Center Lease Deal High for Md." in *Baltimore Business Journal* **(Vol. 28, August 6, 2010, No. 13, pp. 1)**
Pub: Baltimore Business Journal

Ed: Daniel J. Sernovitz. **Description:** The proposed $1.5 billion State Center development project in Midtown Baltimore might cause the State of Maryland to pay the most expensive rental rates in the city. The state will have to pay an effective rental rate of $34 per square foot, including expenses, on the leasing. Other details of the redevelopment project are discussed.

44482 ■ "State Film Business Tops $1.3 Billion" in *The Business Journal-Portland* **(Vol. 25, August 22, 2008, No. 24, pp. 1)**
Pub: American City Business Journals, Inc.

Ed: Andy Giegerich. **Description:** Oregon's film industry has generated $1.39 billion in direct and indirect economic impact in 2007, a 55 percent rise from 2005 levels. The growth of the industry is attributed to tax incentives issued in 2007, which attracted film production companies from other states.

44483 ■ "Still on the Block" in *Entrepreneur* **(Vol. 35, November 2007, No. 11, pp. 22)**
Pub: Entrepreneur Media Inc.

Ed: Laura Tiffany. **Description:** Neighborhoods where business enterprises are located sometimes go into decline, particularly in low-income communities with high crime rates. Some entrepreneurs share stories about getting involved to help revive the community and keep their businesses thriving.

44484 ■ "Stimulus 'Loser' Won't Build Plant in Mass." in *Boston Business Journal* **(Vol. 30, November 5, 2010, No. 41, pp. 1)**
Pub: Boston Business Journal

Ed: Kyle Alspach. **Description:** Boston-Power Inc. no longer plans to build an electric vehicle battery plant in Massachusetts after it failed to obtain stimulus funds from the federal government. The company is instead looking to build a lithium-ion battery plant in China and possibly Europe.

44485 ■ "Suppliers May Follow Fiat" in *Crain's Detroit Business* **(Vol. 25, June 15, 2009, No. 24, pp. 1)**
Pub: Crain Communications Inc. - Detroit

Ed: Ryan Beene. **Description:** Italian suppliers to Fiat SpA are looking toward Detroit after the formation of Chrysler Group LLC, the Chrysler-Fiat partnership created from Chrysler's bankruptcy. The Italian American Alliance for Business and Technology is aware of two Italy-based powertrain component suppliers that are considering a move to Detroit.

44486 ■ "Taking a Chance" in *Baltimore Business Journal* **(Vol. 28, July 16, 2010, No. 10, pp. 1)**
Pub: Baltimore Business Journal

Ed: Scott Dance. **Description:** North Avenue in Baltimore, Maryland is considered a rough neighborhood due to the dangers of prostitution and drug dealing. However, some entrepreneurs have taken the risk of building their businesses on North Avenue as revitalization efforts grow. One of the challenges for businesses in rough neighborhoods is bringing customers to their stores or offices.

44487 ■ "Taylor Tests Land Grant Program" in *Austin Business Journal* **(Vol. 31, June 3, 2011, No. 13, pp. 1)**
Pub: American City Business Journals Inc.

Ed: Vicky Garza. **Description:** Taylor Economic Development Corporation implemented a land grant program called Build On Our Lot to lure businesses to Taylor City, Austin, Texas. They are targeting small businesses, especially those in the renewable energy, advanced manufacturing, technical services and food products. Program details are included.

44488 ■ "UC May Expand into Old Ford Plant" in *Business Courier* **(Vol. 26, December 25, 2009, No. 35, pp. 1)**
Pub: American City Business Journals, Inc.

Ed: Dan Monk. **Description:** Developer Stuart Lichter is planning to acquire University of Cincinnati (UC) as a tenant at a two-story office building on a 132-acre site where a vacant Ford transmission plant is located. Details of the transaction are outlined.

44489 ■ "U.S. Playing Card Might Shuffle HQ" in *Business Courier* **(Vol. 24, March 21, 2008, No. 50, pp. 1)**
Pub: American City Business Journals, Inc.

Ed: Jon Newberry. **Description:** United States Playing Card Co. is considering the possibility of relocating. It is expected that the company will finalize its decision by June 2008. According to Phil Dolci, the company's president, the firm is looking at certain locations in Ohio, Kentucky, and Indiana. He also revealed that the plan to relocate was prompted by the desire to improve the company's manufacturing facilities.

44490 ■ "Uniting Spring in OP Could Reduce Static" in *Business Journal-Serving Metropolitan Kansas City* **(October 19, 2007)**
Pub: American City Business Journals, Inc.

Ed: Jim Davis, Steve Vockrodt. **Description:** Sprint Nextel, the result of Sprint Corporation and Nextel Communications Inc. has been using Nextel's Reston office as corporate headquarters. The consolidation of Sprint Nextel's headquarters is expected to result in saving on cost of living and leases. The benefits of choosing Kansas City as the headquarters are evaluated.

44491 ■ "Wal-Mart Sharpens Focus on Roxbury" in *Boston Business Journal* **(Vol. 31, July 8, 2011, No. 24, pp. 1)**
Pub: Boston Business Journal

Ed: Mary Moore. **Description:** Wal-Mart Stores is boosting its search for a possible location in the Roxbury section of Boston, Massachusetts. The search is focused on underserved communities in terms of jobs and access to reasonably-priced merchandise. The extent Boston's African American community has clashed with Mayor Thomas M. Memino over the accommodations of the retailer in Roxbury is discussed.

44492 ■ "Water Company Eyeing Region for a New Plant" in *Charlotte Business Journal* **(Vol. 25, December 10, 2010, No. 38, pp. 1)**
Pub: Charlotte Business Journal

Ed: Ken Elkins. **Description:** California-based Niagara Bottling Company is hoping to find a site in Charlotte, North Carolina where it can build a water bottling plant that would employ 70 workers. The investment is expected to cost about $25 million to $40 million.

44493 ■ "Wattles Plugs Back Into State" in *Business Journal Portland* **(Vol. 27, November 19, 2010, No. 38, pp. 1)**
Pub: Portland Business Journal

Ed: Wendy Culverwell. **Description:** Denver, Colorado-based Ultimate Electronics Inc.'s first store in Oregon was opened in Portland and the 46th store in the chain of electronic superstores is expected to employ 70-80 workers. The venture is the latest for Mark Wattles, one of Oregon's most successful entrepreneurs, who acquired Ultimate from bankruptcy.

44494 ■ "Welcome: From the Chamber of Commerce" in *Inside Business* **(Vol. 13, September-October 2011, No. 5, pp. SS5)**
Pub: Great Lakes Publishing Company

Ed: Diane Helbig. **Description:** Diane Helbig, Chairperson for the Lakewood Chamber of Commerce in Ohio touts the areas as the best place to start and run a small company. Two colleges, real estate, and culture are among the reasons cited.

44495 ■ "Welcome to the Neighborhood" in *Hawaii Business* **(Vol. 53, October 2007, No. 4, pp. 48)**
Pub: Hawaii Business Publishing

Ed: Jolyn Okimoto Rosa. **Description:** Finance Factors is planning to build branches in Manoa and Liliha, as part of its strategy to position itself in high-yield areas. The company chose Manoa and Liliha due to thee sites' rich deposits. Its strategy with regards to the branches' location and to the building design is discussed.

44496 ■ "Who's Next?" in *Boston Business Journal* **(Vol. 27, November 16, 2007, No. 42, pp. 1)**
Pub: American City Business Journals Inc.

Ed: Lisa van der Pool. **Description:** Boston, Massachusetts' burgeoning technology and biotech industries along with rising billing rates make it a unique legal market. Law firms cross the threshold either by merging with or acquiring a smaller law firm. Boston as a unique legal market is discussed.

44497 ■ *Who's Your City? How the Creative Economy is Making Where to Live the Most Important Decision of Your Life*
Pub: Basic Books

Ed: Richard Florida. **Released:** 2009. **Price:** $26.95. **Description:** Richard Florida disagrees with the notion that under globalization, a leveling has taken away the economic advantages of any place in particular. Florida believes that globalization has also created higher-level economic activities such as innovation, design, finance, and media to cluster in a smaller number of locations.

TRADE PERIODICALS

44498 ■ *Business Facilities*
Pub: Group C Communications Inc.
Contact: Judy Nowell, Advertising Production Coord.
E-mail: jnowell@groupc.com
Released: Monthly. **Description:** Professional magazine focusing on corporate expansion, commercial/industrial real estate, and economic development.

44499 ■ *Expansion Management*
Pub: Penton Media Inc.
Contact: Ron Lowy, Publisher
E-mail: ron.lowy@penton.com

Ed: Josh Cable, Editor, josh.cable@penton.com. **Released:** 6/yr. **Price:** $50 Canada; $68 institutions international. **Description:** Magazine assisting

executives and managers worldwide in planning and overseeing their companies' facilities development and other expansion and relocation activities.

44500 ■ *Site Selection Magazine*
Pub: Conway Data Inc.
Contact: Julie Clarke, Circulation Mgr
E-mail: julie.clarke@sitesselection.com
Released: Bimonthly. **Price:** $95; $135 other countries; $160 two years; $246 two years and other countries. **Description:** Magazine on real estate and site selectors.

44501 ■ *Urban Land Magazine*
Pub: Urban Land Institute
Released: 11/yr. **Description:** Professional magazine for land use and development practitioners.

CONSULTANTS

44502 ■ Architectural Research Consultants Inc.
220 Gold Ave. SW, Ste. A
PO Box 1158
Albuquerque, NM 87102
Ph:(505)842-1254
Fax:(505)766-9269
Co. E-mail: jppetronis@arcplanning.com
URL: http://www.arcplanning.com/
Contact: Jennifer Abbott, Editor
E-mail: jabbott@atsarcplanning.com
Scope: Performs feasibility studies; site selection; site development plans; zoning and utilization studies; geographic information management; community planning; preservation planning; cultural resource management; determination of the demand for services and establishing operating parameters for service delivery systems. Develops comprehensive statement of facility and organization requirements based on functional and environmental needs; assessment of the physical and functional suitability of existing facilities; and plans and development of guidelines for future endeavors and master planning. Special expertise in education facilities; hospitals; and recreational facilities. Other services include identification and documentation of information resources; preparation and assistance in preparation of proposals and specialized management consulting. Serves private industries as well as government agencies. **Publications:** "Post-Occupancy Evaluation and edited Facility Programming"; "Programming the Built Environment"; "Building Evaluation"; "Pueblo Style and Regional Architecture"; "Design Intervention: Toward A More Humane Architecture"; "Professional Practice in Facility Programming"; "Design Review: Challenging Urban Aesthetic Control"; "New Directions in Urban Public Housing"; "Directions in Person-Environment Research and Practice"; "Universal Design Handbook"; "Assessing Building Performance"; "Designing for Designers".

44503 ■ LSA Associates Inc.
20 Executive Pk., Ste. 200
Irvine, CA 92614
Ph:(949)553-0666
Fax:(949)553-8076
Co. E-mail: irvine@lsa-assoc.com
URL: http://www.lsa-assoc.com
Contact: Art Homrighausen, Mgr
E-mail: art.homrighausen@atslsa-assoc.com
Scope: Provides environmental planning and assessment services to public and private clients. Offers professional services in environmental assessment, community planning, natural resources analysis, transportation, cultural resources, noise and air quality analysis and GIS.

44504 ■ Pomeroy Appraisal Associates Inc.
Pomeroy Pl., 225 W Jefferson St.
Syracuse, NY 13202-2334
Ph:(315)422-7106
Fax:(315)476-1011
Co. E-mail: info@pomeroyappraisal.com
URL: http://www.pomeroyappraisal.com
Contact: Chadik J. Stropp, Principle
E-mail: cstropp@atspomeroyappraisal.com
Scope: Advises clients on commercial and industrial properties, site analysis, real estate tax problems, land development and all types of real estate valuation problems and projects.

44505 ■ Space Management Programs Inc.
55 W Wacker Dr., Ste. 600
Chicago, IL 60601-1609
Ph:(312)263-0700
Fax:(312)263-1228

Contact: Michael J. Cohen, President
E-mail: mcohen@ghk.net
Scope: A facilities and technology consulting firm experienced in all aspects of design and corporate relocation. Available for site evaluation, strategic plan-ning through the writing of briefs, or architectural programs through space planning, design and construction documents.

START-UP INFORMATION

44506 ■ **"Big Bucks In Pet-ty Cash"** in *Small Business Opportunities* (Fall 2008)
Pub: Entrepreneur Media Inc.
Description: Twenty-five ways in which to start a business that caters to pets by either creating a product or a service that pet owners desire are profiled.

44507 ■ **"Bottoms Up!"** in *Entrepreneur* (Vol. 36, April 2008, No. 4, pp. 128)
Pub: Entrepreneur Media, Inc.
Ed: Amanda C. Kooser. **Description:** Jill Bernheimer launched her online alcohol business Domaine547 in 2007, and encountered challenges as legal issues over the licensing and launching of the business took about seven months to finish. Domain547 features blog and forum areas. Marketing strategy that connects to the social community is one of the ways to reach out to customers.

44508 ■ **"Business Diary"** in *Crain's Detroit Business* (Vol. 24, October 6, 2008, No. 40, pp. 23)
Pub: Crain Communications, Inc.
Description: Detailed listing of acquisitions, expansions, new products, new services, business contracts and startups from the Detroit area is provided.

44509 ■ **"A Class Act"** in *Hawaii Business* (Vol. 53, March 2008, No. 9, pp. 25)
Pub: Hawaii Business Publishing
Ed: Cathy S. Cruz-George. **Description:** UBoost is a startup company that offers online content for the educational magazine 'Weekly Reader'. The website features quizzes and allows users to accumulate points and redeem rewards afterward. Other details about the company are discussed.

44510 ■ **"Confessions Of Serial Entrepreneurs"** in *Entrepreneur* (January 8, 2009)
Pub: Entrepreneur Media Inc.
Ed: Jennifer Wang. **Description:** Serial entrepreneurs are those individuals that are able to start business after business. These individuals enjoy the process of starting a company then handing off the finished product and starting over with a new endeavor. Several serial entrepreneurs are profiled.

44511 ■ **"Find the Upside to a Down Economy"** in *Women Entrepreneur* (September 30, 2008)
Pub: Entrepreneur Media Inc.
Ed: Tamara Monosoff. **Description:** Starting a new business in this economic crisis may not be as daunting of a pursuit as one might think. Aspiring entrepreneurs may find success by looking for opportunities in unusual places and relying on what they do best.

44512 ■ **"Five Low-Cost Home Based Startups"** in *Women Entrepreneur* (December 16, 2008)
Pub: Entrepreneur Media Inc.
Ed: Lesley Spencer Pyle. **Description:** During tough economic times, small businesses have an advantage over large companies because they can adjust to economic conditions more easily and without having to go through corporate red tape that can slow the implementation process. A budding entrepreneur may find success by taking inventory of his or her skills, experience, expertise and passions and utilizing those qualities to start a business. Five low-cost home-based startups are profiled. These include starting an online store, a virtual assistant service, web designer, sales representative and a home staging counselor.

44513 ■ **"Friends With Money"** in *Entrepreneur* (Vol. 37, August 2009, No. 8, pp. 74)
Pub: Entrepreneur Media, Inc.
Ed: Asheesh Advani. **Description:** Providing a strong introduction to an investor will maximize a startup's chances of getting a second meeting. Startups should also pick an achievable fund raising goal and to keep track of their labor-adjusted net capital when fund raising.

44514 ■ **"Fun And Easy Gold Mines"** in *Small Business Opportunities* (Fall 2008)
Pub: Entrepreneur Media Inc.
Description: Twenty-five businesses that cater to the booming children's market are profiled; day care services, party planning, special events videomaking, tutoring, personalized children's toys and products and other services geared toward the kids market are included.

44515 ■ **"Getting Others To Take Your Startup Seriously"** in *Women Entrepreneur* (August 1, 2008)
Pub: Entrepreneur Media Inc.
Ed: Tamara Monosoff. **Description:** Writing a serious business plan is essential if you want others to take your startup endeavor seriously. As friends, family and acquaintances see you taking positive steps toward your goal they will begin to lend their support and may even help get the business off the ground.

44516 ■ **"Home Grown"** in *Hawaii Business* (Vol. 53, November 2007, No. 5, pp. 51)
Pub: Hawaii Business Publishing
Ed: Jolyn Okimoto Rosa. **Description:** Discusses a program that focuses on Native Hawaiian entrepreneurs and offers business training at the Kapiolani Community College; upon completion of the program, participants may apply for a loan provided by the Office of Hawaiian Affairs (OHA) to help them start their business. OHA plans to present the restructured loan program in November 2007, with aims of shortening the loan process.

44517 ■ **"Home Work"** in *Black Enterprise* (Vol. 37, October 2006, No. 3, pp. 78)
Pub: Earl G. Graves Publishing Co. Inc.
Ed: James C. Johnson. **Description:** Information on starting a resume-writing service is profiled.

44518 ■ **"I Have A Business Idea. What Now?"** in *Women Entrepreneur* (October 15, 2008)
Pub: Entrepreneur Media Inc.
Ed: Cheryl Isaac. **Description:** Four pre-planning steps to take before launching a new business are discussed in detail.

44519 ■ **"Is Entrepreneurship Right For You?"** in *Women Entrepreneur* (July 25, 2008)
Pub: Entrepreneur Media Inc.
Ed: Bonnie Price. **Description:** Assessing the marketplace, evaluating your skills and sizing up your passions are three necessary elements to examine before starting a business.

44520 ■ **"The New Orleans Saints"** in *Entrepreneur* (Vol. 37, August 2009, No. 8, pp. 40)
Pub: Entrepreneur Media, Inc.
Ed: Jason Meyers. **Description:** Idea Village is a nonprofit group that fosters entrepreneurship in New Orleans, Louisiana. Entrepreneurship is indeed growing in the city during a time when the city is still recovering from the damage of hurricane Katrina.

44521 ■ **"Online Fortunes"** in *Small Business Opportunities* (Fall 2008)
Pub: Entrepreneur Media Inc.
Description: Fifty hot, e-commerce enterprises for the aspiring entrepreneur to consider are featured; virtual assistants, marketing services, party planning, travel services, researching, web design and development, importing as well as creating an online store are among the businesses featured.

44522 ■ **"The Perfect Formula to Build Your Brand"** in *Entrepreneur* (Vol. 37, July 2009, No. 7, pp. 70)
Pub: Entrepreneur Media, Inc.
Ed: Susan J. Linder. **Description:** Combining a product with expertise and a promise is the formula in building a brand for startups. The product will not sell itself, so one must consider what makes the product truly unique. Meanwhile, establishing trust and a foundation for a brand can be achieved by making a promise to the consumer and fulfilling it.

44523 ■ **"Recession-Proof Your Startup"** in *Crain's Chicago Business* (Vol. 31, November 10, 2008, No. 45, pp. 24)
Pub: Crain Communications, Inc.
Description: Detailed information concerning ways in which to start a business during an economic crisis is provided. Ways in which to find financing, the importance of a solid business plan, customer service, problem-solving and finding the right niche for the region are also discussed.

44524 ■ **"Rehab Will Turn Hospital Into Incubator"** in *The Business Journal-Serving Metropolitan Kansas City* (Vol. 26, September 12, 2008)
Pub: American City Business Journals, Inc.
Ed: Rob Roberts. **Description:** Independence Regional Health Center will be purchased by CEAH Realtors and be converted into the Independence Regional Entrepreneurial Center, a business incubator that will house startups and other tenants. Other details about the planned entrepreneurial center are provided.

44525 ■ "Serial Starter" in _Entrepreneur_ (Vol. 36, April 2008, No. 4, pp. 17)
Pub: Entrepreneur Media, Inc.
Ed: Andrea Cooper. **Description:** Some entrepreneurs are engaged in serial entrepreneurship as they feel that they are no longer satisfied with their business and they decide to sell it. Others start out new businesses because they believe they can try out and be successful in different kinds of businesses. Details on how to identify and handle new entrepreneurial opportunities are discussed.

44526 ■ "Should You Go Into Business With Your Spouse?" in _Women Entrepreneur_ (September 1, 2008)
Pub: Entrepreneur Media Inc.
Ed: Tamara Monosoff. **Description:** Things to consider before starting a business with one's spouse are discussed. Compatible work ethics, clear expectations of one another, long-term goals for the company and the status of the relationship are among the things to consider before starting a business endeavor with a spouse.

44527 ■ "So You Want to Start a Business?" in _Women Entrepreneur_ (August 5, 2008)
Pub: Entrepreneur Media Inc.
Ed: Cynthia McKay. **Description:** Advice for taking an idea and turning it into a legitimate business is given.

44528 ■ "Spread Your Wings" in _Canadian Business_ (Vol. 81, March 17, 2008, No. 4, pp. 31)
Pub: Rogers Media
Ed: Megan Harman. **Description:** Financing from angel investors is one avenue that should be explored by startups. Angel investors are typically affluent individuals who invest their own money. Angel investors usually want at least 10 times their initial investment within eight years but they benefit the businesses through their help in decision-making and the industry expertise they provide.

44529 ■ "Take the Plunge" in _Small Business Opportunities_ (July 2008)
Pub: Entrepreneur Media Inc.
Description: Resources are provided for starting a new business venture for under $500 as well as fifteen different suggestions for different kinds of businesses that can be created with minimal expense.

44530 ■ "Three Weeks To Startup" in _Entrepreneur_ (December 19, 2008)
Pub: Entrepreneur Media Inc.
Ed: Tim Berry; Sabrina Parsons. **Description:** Breakdown for realistically starting a business in three weeks is provided in detail.

44531 ■ "Time for a Leap Of Faith?" in _Women Entrepreneur_ (November 18, 2008)
Pub: Entrepreneur Media Inc.
Ed: Cynthia McKay. **Description:** Starting a new business, despite the downturn in the economy, can prove to be a successful endeavor if one has the time, energy and most importantly a good idea.

44532 ■ "UM-Dearborn to Launch Program for Entrepreneurs" in _Crain's Detroit Business_ (Vol. 24, April 14, 2008, No. 15, pp. 7)
Pub: Crain Communications, Inc.
Ed: Chad Halcom. **Description:** Starting this fall the University of Michigan-Dearborn will begin its Product Realization and Technology Commercialization Program for entrepreneurs and innovators with lab-tested, high-technology products. Ultimately, 20 businesses will each work with the university in creating a customer base, commercializing a new high-tech product or process and connecting with venture capitalists who may invest in the new companies.

44533 ■ "Victoria Colligan; Co-Founder, Ladies Who Launch Inc., 38" in _Crain's Cleveland Business_ (Vol. 28, November 19, 2007, No. 46)
Pub: Crain Communications, Inc.
Ed: Jay Miller. **Description:** Profile of Victoria Colligan who is the co-founder of Ladies Who Launch Inc., an organization with franchises in nearly 50 cit-

ies; the company offers women entrepreneurs workshops and a newsletter to help women balance their businesses with other aspects of their lives. Ms. Colligan found that women were learning about being business owners differently than men and she felt that there was a need to create opportunities for networking for women launching businesses that had more of a lifestyle purpose.

44534 ■ "What Are You Afraid Of?" in _Entrepreneur_ (Vol. 37, July 2009, No. 7, pp. 79)
Pub: Entrepreneur Media, Inc.
Ed: Lindsay Holloway. **Description:** According to a survey of entrepreneurs in the US, failure, economic uncertainty, not having enough personal time, being their own boss, and staying afloat are the biggest fears when starting a business. Advice on how to deal with these fears is also given.

44535 ■ "Where to be an Entrepreneur: Ten Startup-Friendly Cities" in _Entrepreneur_ (Vol. 37, August 2009, No. 8, pp. 49)
Pub: Entrepreneur Media, Inc.
Ed: Jason Daley. **Description:** Ten U.S. cities that embody the entrepreneurial spirit are presented. These cities are ideal for startup companies and profiles of businesses that are making it in these cities are discussed.

44536 ■ "Your Startup may be Worth Less than You Think" in _Entrepreneur_ (Vol. 37, October 2009, No. 10, pp. 96)
Pub: Entrepreneur Media, Inc.
Ed: Asheesh Advani. **Description:** Valuations of startups at the idea stage are dropping due to the effects of the recession. This drop is due to the decreasing availability of investment capital, the reduction in portfolio values of investors, and the increase in early stage startups.

ASSOCIATIONS AND OTHER ORGANIZATIONS

44537 ■ Action for Enterprise
2009 N 14th St., Ste. 301
Arlington, VA 22201
Ph:(703)243-9172
Fax:(703)243-9123
Co. E-mail: info@actionforenterprise.org
URL: http://www.actionforenterprise.org
Contact: Frank Lusby, Exec. Dir./Founder
Description: Seeks to design and implement small enterprise development programs, based on a comprehensive analysis of business sectors and the interrelationships of enterprises that function with them. Initiates efforts to develop sustainable business development service providers at the local level.
.

44538 ■ Association of Small Business Development Centers
8990 Burke Lake Rd., 2nd Fl.
Burke, VA 22015
Ph:(703)764-9850
Fax:(703)764-1234
Co. E-mail: tee.rowe@asbdc-us.org
URL: http://www.asbdc-us.org
Contact: C. Edward Rowe III, Pres./CEO
Description: Local centers providing advice for those planning to establish a small business. Aims to facilitate information exchange among members and to represent their interests before the federal government. Informs the Small Business Administration on issues of interest to the small business community. **Publications:** _Business Plan Workbook for Special Use Permits_ .

44539 ■ BEST Employers Association
2505 McCabe Way
Irvine, CA 92614
Free: (866)706-2225
URL: http://www.beassoc.org
Description: Provides small independent businesses with managerial, economic, financial and sales information helpful for business improvement. Orga-

nizes and sponsors healthcare alliances for small employers. (The acronym BEST stands for Beneficial Employees Security Trust). .

44540 ■ British-American Business Council
52 Vanderbilt Ave., 20th Fl.
New York, NY 10017
Ph:(212)661-5660
Fax:(212)661-1886
Co. E-mail: info@babinc.org
URL: http://www.babc.org
Contact: Robin Hayes, Chm.
Description: British and American businesses. Strives to provide a forum in which members can exchange information and ideas. Hosts various programs and activities.

44541 ■ Canadian Association of Family Enterprise–Association Canadienne des Entreprises Familiales
465 Morden Rd., Ste. 112
Oakville, ON, Canada L6K 3W6
Free: (866)849-0099
Fax:(905)337-0572
Co. E-mail: office@cafenational.org
URL: http://www.cafecanada.ca
Contact: Allen S. Taylor, Chm.
Description: Family-owned businesses. Seeks to "encourage, educate, and inform members in disciplines unique to the family business." Fosters increased understanding of the importance of family-owned enterprises in the national economy among government agencies and the public. Gathers and disseminates information of interest to members. Conducts educational and lobbying activities. Provides technical support and advisory services to small businesses in areas including succession planning, taxation, family law, and arbitration and mediation. Maintains network of Family Councils, which serve as a forum for discussion of family and business matters. **Publications:** _Family Business Magazine_ (quarterly); _Family Enterpriser_ (quarterly); _International Magazine for Family Businesses_ (bimonthly).

44542 ■ Canadian Federation of Independent Business–Federation Canadienne de l'Entreprise Independante
4141 Yonge St., Ste. 401
Toronto, ON, Canada M2P 2A6
Ph:(416)222-8022
Fax:(416)222-6103
Co. E-mail: cfib@cfib.ca
URL: http://www.cfib-fcei.ca/english/index.html
Contact: Catherine Swift, Chair/Pres./CEO
Description: Independent businesses. Promotes economic well-being of members and seeks to maintain a healthy domestic business climate. Represents members' interests before government agencies, labor and industrial organizations, and the public. **Publications:** _Mandate_ (quarterly); _Quarterly Business Barometer_ (3/year).

44543 ■ Employers of America
310 Meadow Ln.
Mason City, IA 50401
Ph:(641)424-3187
Free: 800-728-3187
Fax:(641)424-3187
Co. E-mail: employer@employerhelp.org
URL: http://www.employerhelp.org
Contact: Mr. Jim Collison, Pres.
Description: Assists employers, managers, and supervisors in keeping their businesses profitable by maintaining the best possible workplace policies and practices, and to deal safely, effectively, and profitably with employees. Publishes e-Letter to help members achieve more with their employees. **Publications:** _Empowered @ Work_ (monthly).

44544 ■ Entrepreneurs' Organization
500 Montgomery St., Ste. 500
Alexandria, VA 22314
Ph:(703)519-6700

Fax:(703)519-1864
Co. E-mail: info@eonetwork.org
URL: http://www.eonetwork.org
Contact: Michael Caito, Chm.
Description: Entrepreneurs under the age of 50 who have either founded, co-founded, are a controlling shareholder of, or own a firm with annual gross revenues exceeding $1,000,000 (membership is by invitation only). Engages leading entrepreneurs to learn and grow. Serves as a focal point for networking and development of members through small group learning sessions, regular local chapter social and learning events, and global conference-based education programs. **Publications:** *Octane* (quarterly); *Overdrive* (monthly).

44545 ■ The Entrepreneurship Institute
3592 Corporate Dr., Ste. 101
Columbus, OH 43231
Ph:(614)895-1153
Free: 800-736-3592
Co. E-mail: janz@tei.net
URL: http://www.tei.net
Contact: Dr. Jan W. Zupnick, Pres.
Description: Provides encouragement and assistance to entrepreneurs who operate companies with revenue in excess of $1 million. Unites financial, legal, and community resources to help foster the success of companies. Promotes sharing of information and interaction between members. Operates President's forums and projects which are designed to improve communication between businesses, develop one-to-one business relationships between small and mid-size businesses and local resources, provide networking, and stimulate the growth of existing companies. **Publications:** *The President's Forum* (monthly).

44546 ■ National Association for Business Organizations
5432 Price Ave.
Baltimore, MD 21215
Ph:(410)367-5309
Co. E-mail: nahbb@msn.com
URL: http://www.ameribizs.com/global
Contact: Rudolph Lewis, Pres.
Description: Business organizations that develop and support small businesses that have the capability to provide their products or services on a national level. Promotes small business in a free market system; represents the interests of small businesses to government and community organizations on small business affairs; monitors and reviews laws that affect small businesses; promotes a business code of ethics. Supplies members with marketing and management assistance; encourages joint marketing services between members. Operates a Home Based Business Television Network that provides an affordable audio/visual media for small and home based businesses. .

44547 ■ National Association for the Self-Employed
PO Box 241
Annapolis Junction, MD 20701-0241
Free: 800-232-6273
URL: http://www.nase.org
Contact: Kristie Arslan, Pres.
Description: Self-employed and small independent businesspersons. Acts as an advocate at the state and federal levels for self-employed people. Provides discounts on products and services important to self-employed and small business owners. **Publications:** *Self-Employed America* (bimonthly); *Washington Watch* (weekly).

44548 ■ National Business Association
PO Box 700728
Dallas, TX 75370
Ph:(972)458-0900
Free: 800-456-0440
Fax:(972)960-9149
Co. E-mail: info@nationalbusiness.org
URL: http://www.nationalbusiness.org
Contact: Raj Nisankarao, Pres.
Description: Employed owners of small businesses. Promotes and assists the growth and development of small businesses. Aids members in obtaining government small business and education loans; makes

available insurance policies and software in conjunction with the U.S. Small Business Administration. Maintains career, educational institution, and scholarship information program for members and their dependents. Offers over 100 benefits, services and programs in the areas of Business, Health, Lifestyle and Education. **Publications:** *Biz Corner* (weekly); *NBA boss* (bimonthly).

44549 ■ National Business Incubation Association
20 E Circle Dr., No. 37198
Athens, OH 45701-3571
Ph:(740)593-4331
Fax:(740)593-1996
Co. E-mail: info@nbia.org
URL: http://www.nbia.org
Contact: Mr. David Monkman, Pres./CEO
Description: Incubator developers and managers; corporate joint venture partners, venture capital investors; economic development professionals. (Incubators are business assistance programs providing business consulting services and financing assistance to start-up and fledgling companies.) Helps newly formed businesses to succeed. Educates businesses and investors on incubator benefits; offers specialized training in incubator formation and management. Conducts research and referral services; compiles statistics; maintains speakers' bureau; publishes information relevant to business incubation and growing companies. **Publications:** *NBIA Insights* (monthly); *NBIA Memberabilia* (biweekly); *NBIA Review* (bimonthly).

44550 ■ National Small Business Association
1156 15th St. NW, Ste. 1100
Washington, DC 20005
Ph:(202)293-8830
Free: 800-345-6728
Fax:(202)872-8543
Co. E-mail: membership@nsba.biz
URL: http://www.nsba.biz
Contact: Todd McCracken, Pres./CEO
Description: Small businesses including manufacturing, wholesale, retail, service, and other firms. Works to advocate at the federal level on behalf of smaller businesses. **Publications:** *Advocate* (bimonthly).

44551 ■ Support Services Alliance
PO Box 130
Schoharie, NY 12157
Ph:(518)295-7966
Free: 800-836-4772
Fax:(518)295-7951
Co. E-mail: info@ssamembers.com
URL: http://www.ssamembers.com
Contact: Edward Van Buren, Dir., Membership Services
Description: Represents small businesses (less than 50 employees), the self-employed, and associations of such individuals. Provides services and programs such as group purchasing discounts, health coverage, legislative advocacy, and business and financial support services. **Publications:** *Capital Crier*; *SmallBiz Growth* (monthly).

REFERENCE WORKS

44552 ■ "The 100 Fastest-Growing Companies" in *Hispanic Business* (Vol. 30, July-August 2008, No. 7-8, pp. 22)
Pub: Hispanic Business, Inc.
Ed: Michael Bowker. **Description:** CEO's of the five fastest growing Hispanic-owned companies discuss the success of their companies; most of them attribute their success to proper investment and diversification, effective innovations and seeing growth opportunities where others see roadblocks.

44553 ■ "Analyzing the Analytics" in *Entrepreneur* (Vol. 37, October 2009, No. 10, pp. 42)
Pub: Entrepreneur Media, Inc.
Ed: Mikal E. Belicove. **Description:** Startups can maximize Web analytics by using them to monitor traffic sources and identify obstacles to converting

them into targeted behaviors . Startups should set trackable Web site goals and continuously track traffic and conversion rates.

44554 ■ "Athletes Face Wins and Losses After Pro Sport" in *The Business Journal - Serving Phoenix and the Valley of the Sun* (Vol. 29, September 19, 2008, No. 3, pp. 1)
Pub: American City Business Journals, Inc.
Ed: Chris Casacchia. **Description:** Professional athletes like hockey star Jeremy Roenick start businesses, while others like Joel Adamson work to boost local communities. Former athletes were found to be particularly interested with real estate businesses. Other views and information on former athletes and their life after sports are presented.

44555 ■ "Bailout May Force Cutbacks, Job Losses" in *The Business Journal - Serving Phoenix and the Valley of the Sun* (Vol. 29, September 26, 2008, No. 4, pp. 1)
Pub: American City Business Journals, Inc.
Ed: Mike Sunnucks. **Description:** Economists say the proposed $700 billion bank bailout could affect Arizona businesses as banks could be forced to reduce the amount and number of loans it has thereby forcing businesses to shrink capital expenditures and then jobs. However, the plan could also stimulate the economy by taking bad loans off banks balance sheets according to another economist.

44556 ■ "Bangles, BMWs Elbow Out Delis and Discount Shops" in *Crain's New York Business* (Vol. 24, January 14, 2008, No. 2, pp. 35)
Pub: Crain Communications, Inc.
Ed: Wendy Davis. **Description:** Lured by a growing number of affluent residents and high-earning professionals, a number of upscale retailers have opened locations downtown which is driving up rents and forcing out longtime independent merchants.

44557 ■ "'Biggest Loser' Adds Bit of Muscle to Local Economy" in *Crain's Detroit Business* (Vol. 26, January 4, 2010, No. 1, pp. 1)
Pub: Crain Communications, Inc.
Ed: Chad Halcom. **Description:** NBC's weight-loss reality show, "The Biggest Loser" has helped the local economy and generated a new crop of local startup businesses due to past contestants that were from the Detroit area.

44558 ■ "Book Smart" in *Hawaii Business* (Vol. 53, December 2007, No. 6, pp. 39)
Pub: Hawaii Business Publishing
Ed: David K. Choo. **Description:** Different parts of a biography entry in the Black Book are examined in relation to their usage in starting a conversation with an executive. The second part, which is the educational background, is considered the most significant of all, due to the amount of information given. The importance of making connections in Hawaii is discussed.

44559 ■ "Breaking the Mold" in *Entrepreneur* (Vol. 37, September 2009, No. 9, pp. 87)
Pub: Entrepreneur Media, Inc.
Ed: Tracy Stapp. **Description:** Profiles of top franchise businesses in the United States are presented. Hey Buddy! Pet Supply Vending Co. offers pet supply vending machines. Home Health Mates, on the other hand, provides professional medical care at home.

44560 ■ "Bryan Berg" in *Hawaii Business* (Vol. 53, March 2008, No. 9, pp. 28)
Pub: Hawaii Business Publishing
Ed: David K. Choo. **Description:** Bryan Berg, senior vice president at Target Corp.'s Region 1, shares his thoughts about entering the Hawaiian market and Target representatives bringing malasadas when visiting a business in the state. Berg finds the state's aloha spirit interesting and feels that it is important to be respectful of the Hawaiian culture and traditions in doing their business there.

44561 ■ "Business Diary" in *Crain's Detroit Business* (Vol. 26, January 11, 2010, No. 2, pp. 16)
Pub: Crain Communications, Inc.
Description: Listing of local businesses involved in acquisitions, contracts, expansions, new products and services as well as startups in the region.

44562 ■ "The Business End of Staying in Business" in *Contractor* (Vol. 56, September 2009, No. 9, pp. 51)
Pub: Penton Media, Inc.
Ed: Al Schwartz. **Description:** Advice on how to manage a new plumbing business in the United States are offered. The transition from being a workman to an employer is seen as one that accompanies a steep learning curve. The importance of managing cash flow is also highlighted.

44563 ■ "Can America Invent Its Way Back?" in *Business Week* (September 22, 2008, No. 4100, pp. 52)
Pub: McGraw-Hill Companies, Inc.
Description: Business leaders as well as economists agree that innovative new products, services and ways of doing business may be the only way in which America can survive the downward spiral of the economy; innovation economics may be the answer and may even provide enough growth to enable Americans to prosper in the years to come.

44564 ■ "Capital Ideas: Regions to Lansing: Focus on Taxes, Reform, Keeping Talent" in *Crain's Detroit Business* (Vol. 24, October 6, 2008)
Pub: Crain Communications, Inc.
Ed: Amy Lane. **Description:** Michigan must make bold and dramatic changes in public policy regarding business legislation. The tax structure, unemployment issues and attracting and retaining talent are among the issues the state must confront, especially in this tough economic climate.

44565 ■ "Celebrate Success. Embrace Innovation" in *Black Enterprise* (Vol. 37, February 2007, No. 7, pp. 145)
Pub: Earl G. Graves Publishing Co. Inc.
Description: 2007 Women of Power Summit provides networking opportunities, empowerment sessions, and nightly entertainment. More than 500 executive women of color are expected to attend this inspiring summit in Phoenix, February 7-10.

44566 ■ "City Sets Yamhill Makeover" in *The Business Journal-Portland* (Vol. 25, July 4, 2008, No. 17, pp. 1)
Pub: American City Business Journals, Inc.
Ed: Andy Giegerich. **Description:** City government is scheduled to redevelop Peterson's property on Yamhill Street in Portland. The redevelopment is seen as a way to better developing commercial properties in the area. Problems associated with the project, which include cost and developer selection, are also discussed.

44567 ■ "Conversation: Historian Geoffrey Jones On Why Knowledge Stays Put" in *Harvard Business Review* (Vol. 86, July-August 2008, No. 8)
Pub: Harvard Business School Press
Ed: Gardiner Morse. **Description:** Geoffrey Jones, Harvard Business School's professor of business history, discusses factors that cause knowledge to concentrate in particular regions, rather than disperse, such as the location of wealth.

44568 ■ "A Conversation with Mark Lange" in *Crain's Detroit Business* (Vol. 26, January 18, 2010, No. 3, pp. 9)
Pub: Crain Communications, Inc.
Ed: Nancy Kaffer. **Description:** Second-stage companies have different needs from other kinds of startups since they often are moving very fast and dealing with several complex problems at the same time.

44569 ■ "Deep Thoughts: Getting Employees to Think Better Requires a Bit of Creative Thinking Itself" in *Canadian Business* (March 17, 2008)
Pub: Rogers Media
Ed: Lauren McKeon. **Description:** Discusses the reason a company needs to make their employees understand that ideas are the stuff of life. For employees to be more creative, they need to cultivate spark moments, play with possibilities, and venture into the unknown.

44570 ■ *Directory of Venture Capital and Private Equity Firms*
Pub: Grey House Publishing
Released: Latest edition 2011. **Price:** $685, individuals Softcover; $450, libraries softcover. **Covers:** 2,300 domestic and international venture capital and private equity firms. **Entries Include:** Firm name, address, phone, fax, e-mail, URL, description of services, names and titles of key personnel.

44571 ■ "The Early Bird Gets the Worm" in *Black Enterprise* (Vol. 37, January 2007, No. 6, pp. 111)
Pub: Earl G. Graves Publishing Co. Inc.
Ed: Tykisha N. Lundy. **Description:** General Motors hosts the Black Enterprise Conference And Expo: Where Deals Are Made at Walt Disney World's Swan and Dolphin Resort, May 9-12. The conference will offer great information to entrepreneurs.

44572 ■ "Federal Fund Valuable Tool For Small-Biz Innovators" in *Crain's Detroit Business* (Vol. 24, September 29, 2008, No. 39, pp. 42)
Pub: Crain Communications, Inc.
Ed: Nancy Kaffer. **Description:** Grants from the Small Business Innovation Research Program, or SBIR grants, are federal funds that are set aside for 11 federal agencies to allocate to tech-oriented small-business owners. Firms such as Biotechnology Business Consultants help these companies apply for SBIR grants.

44573 ■ "Five More Great Books on Entrepreneurship" in *Entrepreneur* (Vol. 37, July 2009, No. 7, pp. 19)
Pub: Entrepreneur Media, Inc.
Description: 800-CEO-Read founder, Jack Covert, and president, Todd Sattersten, share five books that would have been included in the book, 'The 100 Business Books of All Time' if space was not an issue. 'You Need to Be a Little Crazy,' 'Oh, the Places You'll Go!,' 'Founders at Work,' 'The Innovator's Dilemma,' and 'Purple Cow' are highly recommended for entrepreneurs.

44574 ■ "Five Steps to an Effective Business Call" in *Hawaii Business* (Vol. 53, October 2007, No. 4, pp. 64)
Pub: Hawaii Business Publishing
Ed: Matthew K. Ing. **Description:** University of Hawaii professor Libda Patrylak believes that communication skills are integral to business success, which is why businesses should know how to properly handle phone conversations. Presented are five ways of achieving effective business phone calls, such as setting rules for employees to follow with regards to answering calls and providing undivided attention to the other speaker.

44575 ■ "Five Steps to an Effective Meeting" in *Hawaii Business* (Vol. 53, March 2008, No. 9, pp. 55)
Pub: Hawaii Business Publishing
Ed: Jason Ubay. **Description:** Identifying goals and writing them down can help in knowing what needs get done. Engaging everyone is a way to get cooperation in reaching the goals set. Other tips on how to have an effective meeting are discussed.

44576 ■ "Five Steps for Handling Independent Contractors" in *Hawaii Business* (Vol. 53, January 2008, No. 7, pp. 49)
Pub: Hawaii Business Publishing
Ed: Jason Ubay. **Description:** Small companies should be cautious in dealing with independent contractors. They must understand that they cannot dictate specific operational procedures, job duties, standards of conduct and performance standards to the contractors, and they cannot interfere with the evaluation and training of the contractors' employees. Tips on negotiating with independent contractors are given.

44577 ■ "Five Steps to Killer Business Ideas" in *Hawaii Business* (Vol. 53, December 2007, No. 6, pp. 135)
Pub: Hawaii Business Publishing
Ed: Jason Ubay. **Description:** Five ways to formulating good business concepts are presented. The importance of keeping an open mind and analyzing the market is discussed.

44578 ■ "From Craft Biz To Wholesale Giant" in *Women Entrepreneur* (January 19, 2009)
Pub: Entrepreneur Media Inc.
Ed: Maria Falconer. **Description:** Advice is given on how to turn a small craft business into a full-time venture; tips to help one transition from a part-time designer to a full-time wholesaler and brand are also included.

44579 ■ "From War Zone to Franchise Zone" in *Entrepreneur* (Vol. 37, August 2009, No. 8, pp. 104)
Pub: Entrepreneur Media, Inc.
Ed: Jason Daley. **Description:** Ross Paterson says that he realized that the material he used in the Growth Coach franchise could give the people of Afghanistan the systematic model they need. Paterson says that the Afghans are very business-oriented people but that they work in a different system than Americans.

44580 ■ "George Cohon" in *Canadian Business* (Vol. 79, November 20, 2006, No. 23, pp. 70)
Pub: Rogers Media
Ed: Zena Olijnyk. **Description:** George Cohon, the founder of McDonald's in Canada and Russia, speaks about the Canadian market and the experience of starting McDonald's in Canada.

44581 ■ "Going to Bat" in *Canadian Business* (Vol. 80, February 26, 2007, No. 5, pp. S7)
Pub: Rogers Media
Description: Various strategies to make the business loan lending process simple and faster are presented.

44582 ■ "'Groundhog Day' B & B Likely Will Be Converted Into One In Real Life" in *Chicago Tribune* (October 21, 2008)
Pub: McClatchy-Tribune Information Services
Ed: Carolyn Starks. **Description:** Everton Martin and Karla Stewart Martin have purchased the Victorian house that was featured as a bed-and-breakfast in the 1993 hit move "Groundhog Day"; the couple was initially unaware of the structure's celebrity status when they purchased it with the hope of fulfilling their dream of owning a bed-and-breakfast.

44583 ■ "A Growing Dilemma" in *Crain's Cleveland Business* (Vol. 28, October 8, 2007, No. 40, pp. 19)
Pub: Crain Communications, Inc.
Ed: Kimberly Bonvissuto. **Description:** Discusses small business owners who often have to grapple with the decision on whether or not to expand their operations and the importance of a business plan which may help owners with that decision.

44584 ■ "Have High-Tech Tax Credits Helped or Hurt Hawaii?" in *Hawaii Business* (Vol. 53, December 2007, No. 6, pp. 28)
Pub: Hawaii Business Publishing
Description: Presents the opinons of Channel Capital LLC's Walter R. Roth and Hawaii Venture Capital Association's Bill Spencer concerning the impacts of tax credits. Roth thinks that Act 221 appeals to investors who can earn despite business failure while Spencer thinks that the legislation promotes investments in innovative technology firms. The need to support tax credits is also discussed.

44585 ■ "Hawaii Business 2008 SB Success Awards" in *Hawaii Business* (Vol. 53, February 2008, No. 8, pp. 43)
Pub: Hawaii Business Publishing
Description: Winners in the Hawaii Business 2008 SB Success Awards are presented; the awards give recognition for Hawaii small businesses with less than 100 employees and are based on four criteria, namely: unique service or product; rapid expansion or sales growth; longevity; and competency in overcoming challenges.

44586 ■ "Hawaii's Identity Crisis" in *Hawaii Business* (Vol. 53, November 2007, No. 5, pp. 10)
Pub: Hawaii Business Publishing
Ed: Kelli Abe Trifonovitch. **Description:** Some Hawaiians have shown that the Superferry controversy makes it seem to the rest of the world as if they do

not know what they are doing, and intensifies several issues regarding the stability of investing in Hawaii. With or without the Superferry, there is still no evidence that investors are afraid to put their money in Hawaii.

44587 ■ "Head of the Class" in *Entrepreneur* **(Vol. 37, October 2009, No. 10, pp. 59)**
Pub: Entrepreneur Media, Inc.
Description: Top 25 graduate and undergraduate entrepreneurship programs in the US for 2009 as ranked by The Princeton Review are listed. Babson College in Wellesley, Massachusetts topped both categories.

44588 ■ "How Green Is The Valley?" in *Barron's* **(Vol. 88, July 4, 2008, No. 28, pp. 13)**
Pub: Dow Jones & Co., Inc.
Description: San Jose, California has made a good start towards becoming a leader in alternative energy technology through the establishment of United Laboratories' own lab in the city. The certification process for photovoltaic cells will be dramatically shortened with this endeavor.

44589 ■ "Intrepid Souls: Meet a Few Who've Made the Big Leap" in *Crain's Chicago Business* **(Vol. 31, November 10, 2008, No. 45, pp. 26)**
Pub: Crain Communications, Inc.
Ed: Meredith Landry. **Description:** Advice is given from entrepreneurs who have launched businesses in the last year despite the economic crisis. Among the types of businesses featured are a cooking school, a child day-care center, a children's clothing store and an Internet-based company.

44590 ■ "Kid-Friendly Business Sources" in *Black Enterprise* **(Vol. 37, January 2007, No. 6, pp. 40)**
Pub: Earl G. Graves Publishing Co. Inc.
Ed: Carolyn M. Brown. **Description:** Financial or business camps are a great way to encourage a child who interested in starting his or her own business. A number of these camps are available each year including Kidpreneurs Conference and Bull and Bear Investment Camp. Other resources are available online. Resources included.

44591 ■ "Legislators Must Cut Cost of Government" in *Crain's Detroit Business* **(Vol. 24, October 6, 2008, No. 40, pp. 6)**
Pub: Crain Communications, Inc.
Description: Southeast and West Michigan business leaders are setting aside their differences and have proposed clear agendas, ranging from eliminating the Michigan Business Tax to overhauling public employee and retiree benefits and pensions. Lawmakers must also come together to find solutions for the state's economy and discover an entirely new vision for the future of Michigan business.

44592 ■ "Live and Learn" in *Canadian Business* **(Vol. 80, April 23, 2007, No. 9, pp. 76)**
Pub: Rogers Media
Ed: Chris Buck. **Description:** Paul Anka, a musician, feels that ground work is essential before establishing a company.

44593 ■ "Local Knowledge" in *Hawaii Business* **(Vol. 53, December 2007, No. 6, pp. 40)**
Pub: Hawaii Business Publishing
Ed: David K. Choo. **Description:** Rules and facts business professionals need to know about the local life in Hawaii are presented. The important components in island life include knowledge Hawaiian high schools' histories and image, the local sports scene, special events, potluck ethics, and locals' favorite destination, which is Las Vegas.

44594 ■ "Look Before You Lease" in *Women Entrepreneur* **(February 3, 2009)**
Pub: Entrepreneur Media Inc.
Ed: Nina L. Kaufman. **Description:** Top issues to consider before leasing an office space are discussed including: additional charges that may be expected

on top of the basic rental price; determining both short- and long-term goals; the cost of improvements to the space; the cost of upkeep; and the conditions of the lease.

44595 ■ "Mandel Site Favored For UWM Hall" in *The Business Journal-Milwaukee* **(Vol. 25, September 19, 2008, No. 52, pp. A1)**
Pub: American City Business Journals, Inc.
Description: University of Wisconsin-Milwaukee student residence hall's leading location is a site pushed by Mandel Group Inc. Real estate sources say that the developer's proposal offers the best opportunity for business development and the least conflict with nearby neighborhoods. Plans for the Mandel site are presented.

44596 ■ "Minority Auto Suppliers Get Help Diversifying" in *Crain's Detroit Business* **(Vol. 26, January 11, 2010, No. 2, pp. 3)**
Pub: Crain Communications, Inc.
Ed: Sherri Welch. **Description:** Displaced minority auto suppliers are being given assistance by the Kauffman's Foundation Urban Entrepreneur Partnership Detroit program, a three-year effort to assist 150 of the region's suppliers into more diversified businesses.

44597 ■ "More Offices Planned For Percheron Square" in *The Business Journal-Milwaukee* **(Vol. 25, August 22, 2008, No. 48, pp. A1)**
Pub: American City Business Journals, Inc.
Ed: Pete Millard. **Description:** More office projects are under way at Percheron Square. Ryan Cos. US Inc., for example, plans to build over 200,000 square feet of office space at the area. Details of new office projects in Wisconsin are presented.

44598 ■ "Northern Kentucky Adds 1,355 Jobs in '07" in *Business Courier* **(Vol. 24, February 15, 2008, No. 45, pp. 3)**
Pub: American City Business Journals, Inc.
Ed: Lucy May. **Description:** Jobs generated by new and expanding businesses in Northern Kentucky in 2007 totaled to 1,355, which boosted total business sales to $410 million. The ripple effects of the businesses are expected to create 5,432 new jobs and increase business sales to more than $888 million.

44599 ■ "Ohio's Reputation Lags Its Business Ranking" in *Business Courier* **(Vol. 24, November 23, 2008, No. 32, pp. 1)**
Pub: American City Business Journals, Inc.
Ed: Jon Newberry. **Description:** Site Selection magazine's annual ranking of the top states for new business facilities has ranked Ohio and Kentucky in seventh and eight place respectively, but an opinion survey of real estate executives had placed Ohio much lower at 14. The survey asked 6,000 executives if Ohio's conditions were best for new building projects.

44600 ■ "Part-Time Office Space" in *Hawaii Business* **(Vol. 53, December 2007, No. 6, pp. 132)**
Pub: Hawaii Business Publishing
Ed: Ashley Hamershock. **Description:** My Office is one of the companies that are renting space office not only by the month, but by the hour. Such setup is beneficial to small businesses that do not need a whole office all to themselves, and are interested in cutting the cost of office space rental. The prices of office space in Hawaii are mentioned.

44601 ■ "People/Calendar" in *Brandweek* **(Vol. 49, April 21, 2008, No. 16, pp. 30)**
Pub: VNU Business Media, Inc.
Description: Listing of current conferences, tradeshows and events concerning the marketing industry.

44602 ■ "Pick A Name, Not Just Any Name" in *Women Entrepreneur* **(December 17, 2008)**
Pub: Entrepreneur Media Inc.
Ed: Maria Falconer. **Description:** Craft business owners must choose a name that sounds personal since customers who buy hand-made products want to feel that they are buying from an individual rather than an institution. Tips for choosing a name are provided.

44603 ■ "Playing to Win" in *Entrepreneur* **(Vol. 36, May 2008, No. 5, pp. 40)**
Pub: Entrepreneur Media, Inc.
Ed: Robert Kiyosaki. **Description:** Four personality types needed by entrepreneurs to drive their leadership in business are given. 'I must be liked' are social directors and go-betweens; 'I must be comfortable' are those who seek job security and are not at ease with deadlines; I must be right are those strong in opinion; and 'I must win' are people in charge.

44604 ■ "Population Growing Faster Than Retail, Service Sector" in *Crain's New York Business* **(Vol. 24, January 14, 2008, No. 2, pp. 30)**
Pub: Crain Communications, Inc.
Ed: Andrew Marks. **Description:** Downtown Manhattan is seeing more residential development; however, as more families call the area home the need for more retail and services is becoming evident.

44605 ■ "Region and City Need Influx of Youth" in *Crain's Detroit Business* **(Vol. 24, April 14, 2008, No. 15, pp. 8)**
Pub: Crain Communications, Inc.
Description: Discusses an upcoming report from Michigan Future Inc. which finds that young professionals, including those with children, are interested in living in an active urban environment. It also states that because many of those young professionals are entrepreneurial in nature, oftentimes businesses follow.

44606 ■ "Resource Line" in *Black Enterprise* **(Vol. 37, January 2007, No. 6, pp. 6)**
Pub: Earl G. Graves Publishing Co. Inc.
Description: Interactive Media Editor, Philana Patterson, writes a column for blackenterprise.com that offers advice and provides resources for entrepreneurs, corporate executives, business owners, and budding investors.

44607 ■ "SBA-Backed Lending Slides; Economy, Close Scrutiny of Applications Cited" in *Crain's Detroit Business* **(March 10, 2008)**
Pub: Crain Communications, Inc.
Ed: Nancy Kaffer. **Description:** Due to the state of the economy and a closer scrutiny on applications, Small Business Administration-backed loans are down by a significant margin in one loan program and have decreased slightly across the board. Statistical data included.

44608 ■ "Scottsdale Bank Plans 4Q Opening" in *The Business Journal - Serving Phoenix and the Valley of the Sun* **(Vol. 28, August 15, 2008, No. 50)**
Pub: American City Business Journals, Inc.
Ed: Chris Casacchia. **Description:** Arizona's Department of Financial Institutions has approved Scottsdale Business Bank, a community bank which plans to open in the fourth quarter of 2008. The bank, which is to be located near McCormick Ranch in Scottsdale, Arizona, will cater to small business owners in the professional sector, such as accountants and doctors.

44609 ■ "The Seat-Of-The-Pants School of Marketing" in *Brandweek* **(Vol. 49, April 21, 2008, No. 16, pp. 24)**
Pub: VNU Business Media, Inc.
Ed: David Vinjamuri. **Description:** Excerpt from the book "Accidental Branding: How Ordinary People Build Extraordinary Brands," by David Vinjamuri, discusses six shared principles for creating a brand that is unique and will be successful over the long-term.

44610 ■ "A Second Chance to Make a Living" in *The Business Journal-Milwaukee* **(Vol. 25, September 19, 2008, No. 52, pp. A1)**
Pub: American City Business Journals, Inc.
Description: Unemployed workers and baby boomers are driving interest in purchasing small businesses. BizBuySell general manager Mike Handelsman reveals that the supply of small businesses for sale is decreasing due to the increased demand. The trends in the small business market are analyzed.

44611 ■ "Senate OKs Funds for Promoting Tourism" in *Crain's Detroit Business* (Vol. 24, March 31, 2008, No. 13, pp. 6)
Pub: Crain Communications, Inc.
Ed: Amy Lane. **Description:** Discusses the Senate proposal which allocates funds for Michigan tourism and business promotion as well as Michigan's No Worker Left Behind initiative, a program that provides free tuition at community colleges and other venues to train displaced workers for high-demand occupations.

44612 ■ "Setting Out on Your Own? Think Franchises" in *Crain's Cleveland Business* (Vol. 28, October 8, 2007, No. 40, pp. 20)
Pub: Crain Communications, Inc.
Description: Franchisers are targeting baby boomers due to their willingness to put up some of their own money to open their own business. According to local franchising expert, Joel Libava, entrepreneurs should expect to pay about 15 to 30 percent of the total cost of starting the franchise out of their own pocket.

44613 ■ "Seven Ways to Fail Big" in *Harvard Business Review* (Vol. 86, September 2008, No. 9, pp. 82)
Pub: Harvard Business School Press
Ed: Paul B. Carroll; Chunka Mui. **Description:** Seven factors involved in business failures are identified, and ways to avoid them are described. These factors include flawed financial engineering, hurrying into consolidation, and investing in technology that is not a good fit.

44614 ■ "Sharing the Micro Wealth" in *Entrepreneur* (Vol. 37, July 2009, No. 7, pp. 46)
Pub: Entrepreneur Media, Inc.
Ed: Jennie Dorris. **Description:** Step-by-step guide is presented on how Kiva.org, a website which allows people to make microloans to entrepreneurs across the world, works. The website, founded by Matt Flannery, raises $1 million weekly and it will add U.S. entrepreneurs to its list of loan recipients in June 2010. Other features of Kiva.org are discussed.

44615 ■ "Shoe's On Other Foot" in *Business Courier* (Vol. 24, November 30, 2008, No. 33, pp. 1)
Pub: American City Business Journals, Inc.
Ed: Description: Ronald Hummons was fresh out of prison for felony in 2000, and through the help of spiritual non-profit group the Lord's Gym he was able to turn his life around and start his own company Grapevine Ltd. LLC, which makes C-town athletic shoes.

44616 ■ "Six Tips To Maximize Networking Opportunities" in *Women Entrepreneur* (November 3, 2008)
Pub: Entrepreneur Media Inc.
Ed: Tamara Monosoff. **Description:** Networking events fall into the realm of business development as opposed to immediate sales opportunities. It is important to remember that these events provide a chance to build relationships that may someday help one's business. Tips to help make the most out of networking events are provided.

44617 ■ "Small-Business Agenda: Increase Capital, Education, Tax Breaks" in *Crain's Detroit Business* (Vol. 24, March 17, 2008)
Pub: Crain Communications, Inc.
Ed: Nancy Kaffer. **Description:** Discusses the policy suggestions detailed in the Small Business Association of Michigan's entrepreneurial agenda which include five main categories of focus: making entrepreneurial education a higher state priority; increasing capital available to entrepreneurs; using the state's tax structure as an incentive for entrepreneurial growth; getting university research from the lab to the market; and limiting government regulation that's burdensome to small businesses and getting legislative support of entrepreneurial assistance efforts.

44618 ■ "Small Business: Just When Hopes Were High" in *Business Week* (January 8, 2007)
Pub: McGraw-Hill Companies
Ed: James Mehring. **Description:** Overview of the reasons for a fall in confidence concerning the economy among small businesses and the affect this could have in the coming year.

44619 ■ "The Solution" in *Entrepreneur* (Vol. 37, October 2009, No. 10, pp. 71)
Pub: Entrepreneur Media, Inc.
Ed: Jennifer Wang. **Description:** Ford's 2010 Transit Connect is a compact commercial van developed specifically for small business owners. The compact van offers an integrated in-dash computer system providing a cellular broadband connection.

44620 ■ "Soured Relationship Plays Out in Courts" in *The Business Journal-Serving Greater Tampa Bay* (Vol. 28, September 19, 2008, No. 39)
Pub: American City Business Journals, Inc.
Ed: Janet Leiser. **Description:** Heirs of developer Julian Hawthorne Lifset won a court battle to end a 50-year lease with Specialty Restaurants Corp. in Rocky Point. The decision opens the Tampa Bay prime waterfront property for new development.

44621 ■ "Spending on Innovation Down Sharply in State" in *Crain's Detroit Business* (Vol. 24, March 10, 2008, No. 10, pp. 7)
Pub: Crain Communications, Inc.
Ed: Chad Halcom. **Description:** Due to such issues as Michigan's uncertain tax structure, a shaky national economy, the credit crunch and mortgage lending crisis, investments in innovation for the state have sharply declined.

44622 ■ "Start or Buy? It's a Tough Question for Eager Entrepreneurs" in *Crain's Cleveland Business* (Vol. 28, October 8, 2007, No. 40)
Pub: Crain Communications, Inc.
Ed: David Prizinsky. **Description:** Discusses different approaches to becoming a small business owner.

44623 ■ "Success Products" in *Black Enterprise* (Vol. 37, February 2007, No. 7, pp. 135)
Pub: Earl G. Graves Publishing Co. Inc.
Ed: Tanisha A. Sykes. **Description:** Using innovative resources that are already at your fingertips instead of trying to reach out to companies first is a great way to discover whether you have a viable idea or product. Be motivated to start an e-newsletter letting people know about your products and attend conferences like The Motivation Show, the world's largest exhibition of motivational products and services related to performance in business.

44624 ■ "Survive the Small-to-Big Transition" in *Entrepreneur* (November 4, 2008)
Pub: Entrepreneur Media Inc.
Ed: Elizabeth Wilson. **Description:** Transitioning a small company to a large company can be a challenge, especially during the time when it is too big to be considered small and too small to be considered big. Common pitfalls during this time are discussed as well as techniques business owners should implement when dealing with this transitional period.

44625 ■ "Tee Off Online" in *Black Enterprise* (Vol. 37, January 2007, No. 6, pp. 52)
Pub: Earl G. Graves Publishing Co. Inc.
Ed: James C. Johnson. **Description:** The E-Com Resource Center is one of many resources that are available for those interested in starting an e-commerce business. One of the first steps is to create a business plan, of which there are free samples available at BPlans.com.

44626 ■ "The Thinker" in *Canadian Business* (Vol. 81, March 31, 2008, No. 5, pp. 52)
Pub: Rogers Media
Ed: Andrew Wahl. **Description:** Mihnea Moldoveanu provides much of the academic rigor that underpins Roger Martin's theories on how to improve the way business leaders think. Moldoveanu is also a classically trained pianist and founder of Redline Communications and has a mechanical engineering degree from MIT on top of his astounding knowledge on many academic fields.

44627 ■ "TMC Development Closes $1.1 Million Real Estate Purchase" in *Internet Wire* (September 17, 2009)
Pub: Comtex News Network, Inc.
Description: TMC Development announced the closing of a $1.1 million real estate purchase for Mansa, LLC dba Kwikee Mart, a Napa-based convenience store; TMC helped the company secure a Small Business Administration 504 loan in order to purchase the acquisition of a 3,464 square foot building. SBA created the 504 loan program to provide financing for growing small and medium-sized businesses.

44628 ■ "Top of the Food Chain" in *Entrepreneur* (Vol. 37, October 2009, No. 10, pp. 19)
Pub: Entrepreneur Media, Inc.
Ed: Jennifer Wang. **Description:** Television producer Mark Burnett discusses his latest reality television production, Shark Tank. The show pits venture capitalists against entrepreneurs in a contest to obtain business funding.

44629 ■ "Transform Your Life" in *Black Enterprise* (Vol. 37, January 2007, No. 6, pp. 14)
Pub: Earl G. Graves Publishing Co. Inc.
Description: Through the magazine, television and radio programs, events, and the website, the various platforms of Black Enterprise will provide the tools necessary to achieve success in business ventures, career aspirations, and personal goals.

44630 ■ "Tying the Knot" in *Entrepreneur* (Vol. 36, April 2008, No. 4, pp. 48)
Pub: Entrepreneur Media, Inc.
Ed: Guy Kawasaki. **Description:** Tips to consider when forming business partnerships are presented.

44631 ■ "The Union of Town and Gown" in *Entrepreneur* (Vol. 37, October 2009, No. 10, pp. 47)
Pub: Entrepreneur Media, Inc.
Ed: Jason Daley. **Description:** Ten of the best entrepreneurial initiatives involving cities and local universities in the US are described. Cities and universities are joining up for these efforts to strengthen local economies and stop brain drain.

44632 ■ "Venture Capital's Capital Infusion: Federal Incentives Mean More Money for VC Firms" in *Entrepreneur* (Vol. 37, August 2009)
Pub: Entrepreneur Media, Inc.
Ed: Carol Tice. **Description:** American Recovery and Reinvestment Act of 2009 changed the rules for the Small Business Investment Corporations (SBIC) program under the Small Business Authority. The rule changes are meant to put more money from the program into circulation and it increases funding to existing SBICs.

44633 ■ "Venture Gap" in *Canadian Business* (Vol. 81, March 17, 2008, No. 4, pp. 82)
Pub: Rogers Media
Ed: Joe Castaldo. **Description:** Money raised by Canadian venture capitalist firms has been declining since 2001. A strong venture capital market is important if Canada is to build innovative companies. Fixing Canada's tax policy on foreign investments is a start in reviving the industry.

44634 ■ "Wait a Minute!" in *Entrepreneur* (Vol. 37, September 2009, No. 9, pp. 76)
Pub: Entrepreneur Media, Inc.
Ed: Jennifer Wang. **Description:** Advice on how entrepreneurs in the United States should secure funding in view of the economic crisis is presented. Enough interest should be stimulated so as to secure a follow-up meeting. Investors should be asked questions that would encourage them to tell stories related to the downturn.

44635 ■ "Wayne, Oakland Counties Create Own 'Medical Corridor'" in *Crain's Detroit Business* (Vol. 24, October 6, 2008, No. 40, pp. 8)
Pub: Crain Communications, Inc.
Ed: Jay Greene. **Description:** Woodward Medical Corridor that runs along Woodward Avenue and currently encompasses twelve hospitals and is rapidly

growing with additional physician offices, advanced oncology centers and new hospitals. Beaumont Hospital is building a $160 million proton-beam therapy cancer center on its Royal Oak campus in a joint venture with Procure Treatment Centers of Bloomington Ind. That is expected to open in 2010 and will employ approximately 145 new workers.

44636 ■ "What Are Your Party's Legislative Priorities for 2008?" in *Hawaii Business* **(Vol. 53, January 2008, No. 7, pp. 22)**
Pub: Hawaii Business Publishing
Description: Discusses the Democratic Party of Hawaii which will prioritize giving more opportunities to earn a living a wage in 2008, according to the party chairwoman Jeani Withington. The Republican Party chairman Willes K. Lee, meanwhile, states that his party will seek to enhance the local business climate. The political parties' plans for Hawaii for the year 2008 are presented in detail.

44637 ■ "What's Cooking?" in *Entrepreneur* **(Vol. 36, April 2008, No. 4, pp. 98)**
Pub: Entrepreneur Media, Inc.
Ed: Eileen Figure Sandlin. **Description:** Unique and unusual restaurants have the potential to attract customers and provide them with fresh menu options. Outlining goals, strategies and details on proposed concept and target market can also help in restaurant planning. Other tips on how to plan launching your own restaurant are provided.

44638 ■ "The WIN Library" in *Women In Business* **(Vol. 61, August-September 2009, No. 4, pp. 36)**
Pub: American Business Women's Association
Ed: Leigh Elmore. **Description:** Women's Instructional Network (WIN) offers members of the American Business Women's Association with information about the organization and 15 Team Tools learning modules to help further the learning of business women. Other training programs and services offered by WIN are presented.

44639 ■ "Your Guide to Local Style Business" in *Hawaii Business* **(Vol. 53, December 2007, No. 6, pp. 36)**
Pub: Hawaii Business Publishing
Ed: David K. Choo. **Description:** Discusses the importance of studying the Hawaiian culture when doing business locally. It was observed that geographical aspects increase emphasis on culture and lifestyle more than the need to rectify false imaging do. Details of how locals adhere to their culture are supplied.

TRADE PERIODICALS

44640 ■ Business Opportunities Journal
Pub: Business Service Corp.
Ed: Mark Adkins, Editor, news@boj.com. **Released:** Monthly. **Description:** Newspaper covering businesses for sale.

44641 ■ Entrepreneur Magazine
Pub: Entrepreneur Media Inc.
Contact: Rieva Lesonsky, Editorial Dir.
Released: Monthly. **Price:** $11.97. **Description:** Magazine covering small business management and operation.

44642 ■ Entrepreneurship Theory and Practice
Pub: Baylor University
Released: Bimonthly. **Price:** $511 institutions Americas, print & online; $394 institutions UK, print & online; $772 institutions, other countries print & online; $500 institutions Europe print & online; $129 Americas, print & online; $122 other countries UK, print & online; $122 Europe (non-euro zone) print & online; $182 Europe (non-euro zone) print & online; $465 institutions Americas, online only. **Description:** Journal of the United States Association for Small Business and Entrepreneurship.

44643 ■ Journal of Entrepreneurial and Small Firm Finance
Pub: University of California Press
Released: 3/yr. **Description:** Journal that focuses on small business and financial issues.

44644 ■ SBANE Enterprise
Pub: Smaller Business Association of New England
Ed: Julie Scofield, Editor. **Released:** 8-9/year. **Price:** Included in membership; $49, nonmembers. **Description:** Reports on matters of concern to those who are engaged in small businesses in the New England area. Includes news of government actions and legislation and economic trends. Recurring features include items on business education opportunities, members, and Association activities.

44645 ■ The Small Business Advisor
Pub: Small Business Advisors Inc.
Contact: Joseph Gelb, Publisher
Ed: Ann Liss, Editor. **Released:** Monthly. **Price:** $35. **Description:** Seeks to help emerging growth companies increase profits. Considers small business issues, including marketing sales, finance, taxes, organizing, competition, management, and human resources. Recurring features include letters to the editor, interviews, and columns titled Info Bank, In the Mail Box, Taxes, Human Resources, Marketing, Insurance, and Law. Remarks: Publication suspended in 1980; resumed publication Fall 1993.

44646 ■ Small Business Opportunities
Pub: Harris Publications Inc.
Contact: Melissa Zinker
E-mail: melissa@harris-pub.com
Ed: Susan Rakowski, Editor, sr@harris-pub.com. **Released:** Bimonthly, (plus 4 special editions). **Price:** $14.97 U.S. and Canada; $29.94 other countries. **Description:** How-to magazine for small business owners.

VIDEOCASSETTES/ AUDIOCASSETTES

44647 ■ American Institute of Small Business: Setting Up a Home-Based Business
American Institute of Small Business (AISB)
23075 Highway 7, Ste. 200
Shorewood, MN 55331
Ph:(952)545-7001
Free: 800-328-2906
Fax:(952)545-7020
Co. E-mail: judy@aisb.biz
URL: http://www.pfa.com/AISB.htm
Released: 199?. **Price:** $69.95. **Description:** Step-by-step guide to operating a business out of your home. **Availability:** VHS.

44648 ■ American Institute of Small Business: Starting a Business—Advice from Experts
American Institute of Small Business (AISB)
23075 Highway 7, Ste. 200
Shorewood, MN 55331
Ph:(952)545-7001
Free: 800-328-2906
Fax:(952)545-7020
Co. E-mail: judy@aisb.biz
URL: http://www.pfa.com/AISB.htm
Released: 199?. **Price:** $69.95. **Description:** Business commentators from Money, Fortune, and Newsweek magazines give tips on taxes, obtaining financing, and other issues. **Availability:** VHS.

44649 ■ Beyond Start-Up: Management Lessons for Growing Companies
Video Arts, Inc.
c/o Aim Learning Group
8238-40 Lehigh
Morton Grove, IL 60053-2615
Free: 877-444-2230
Fax:(416)252-2155
Co. E-mail: service@aimlearninggroup.com
URL: http://www.aimlearninggroup.com
Released: 1989. **Price:** $395.00. **Description:** Don't settle for being a small company—find out what it takes to expand your business. **Availability:** VHS; 3/4U.

44650 ■ Changing Values: Moving Toward the Future - Trends That Will Affect Your Business
Encyclopedia Britannica
331 N. LaSalle St.
Chicago, IL 60654
Ph:(312)347-7159
Free: 800-323-1229
Fax:(312)294-2104
URL: http://www.britannica.com
Price: $595. **Description:** Explains the importance of identifying change in an everchanging culture. Introduces new values emerging in the workplace. **Availability:** VHS.

44651 ■ The Entrepreneurs: Risk Takers
RMI Media
1365 N. Winchester St.
Olathe, KS 66061-5880
Ph:(913)768-1696
Free: 800-745-5480
Fax:800-755-6910
Co. E-mail: actmedia@act.org
URL: http://www.actmedia.com
Released: 1989. **Price:** $70.00. **Description:** College and high school students gain a special understanding of small business from this series. **Availability:** VHS; 3/4U.

44652 ■ Finding a Niche: Determining Business Potential
Instructional Video
2219 C St.
Lincoln, NE 68502
Ph:(402)475-6570
Free: 800-228-0164
Fax:(402)475-6500
Co. E-mail: feedback@insvideo.com
URL: http://www.insvideo.com
Price: $99.00. **Description:** Outlines the process of selecting an appropriate market for your product, including profile development of potential customers and planning and implementing a feasability study. **Availability:** VHS.

44653 ■ Growing a Business
Ambrose Video Publishing, Inc.
145 W. 45th St., Ste. 1115
New York, NY 10036
Ph:(212)768-7373
Free: 800-526-4663
Fax:(212)768-9282
Co. E-mail: customerservice@ambrosevideo.com
URL: http://www.ambrosevideo.com
Released: 1989. **Price:** $1295.00. **Description:** This video shows the steps taken by different people to start up a business. **Availability:** VHS.

44654 ■ How to Start Your Own Successful Business
Instructional Video
2219 C St.
Lincoln, NE 68502
Ph:(402)475-6570
Free: 800-228-0164
Fax:(402)475-6500
Co. E-mail: feedback@insvideo.com
URL: http://www.insvideo.com
Price: $29.95. **Description:** Illustrates correct procedures for establishing and maintaining an effective business. Covers marketing, managing, financing, business insurance, buying an existing business, franchising, home-based business, youth entrepreneurial business, negotiating deals, and projecting your ideas. **Availability:** VHS.

44655 ■ I Can Do It! Stew Leonard
Direct Cinema Ltd.
PO Box 10003
Santa Monica, CA 90410-1003
Ph:(310)636-8200
Free: 800-525-0000

Fax:(310)636-8228
Co. E-mail: orders@directcinemalimited.com
URL: http://www.directcinema.com
Released: 1985. **Description:** The dairy king explains the details and knowledge he used to devise a phenomenonally successful business. **Availability:** VHS; 3/4U; Special order formats.

44656 ■ *Inc. Magazine Business Success Programs*
Cambridge Educational
c/o Films Media Group
132 West 31st Street, 17th Floor
Ste. 124
New York, NY 10001
Free: 800-257-5126
Fax:(609)671-0266
Co. E-mail: custserve@films.com
URL: http://www.cambridgeol.com
Released: 1987. **Price:** $99.95. **Description:** These four programs contain a step-by-step explanation of what must be done to succeed in business. **Availability:** VHS; CC.

44657 ■ *Inc. Magazine's How to (Really) Start Your Own Business*
Cambridge Educational
c/o Films Media Group
132 West 31st Street, 17th Floor
Ste. 124
New York, NY 10001
Free: 800-257-5126
Fax:(609)671-0266
Co. E-mail: custserve@films.com
URL: http://www.cambridgeol.com
Released: 1986. **Price:** $29.95. **Description:** An authoritative guide to starting a small business, including tips on investment acquisition, business planning, financing and more. **Availability:** VHS.

44658 ■ *Inside Business Today*
GPN Educational Media
1550 Executive Drive
Elgin, IL 60123
Ph:(402)472-2007
Free: 800-228-4630
Fax:800-306-2330
Co. E-mail: askgpn@smarterville.com
URL: http://www.shopgpn.com
Released: 1989. **Description:** Leaders in business and industry tell their success stories in this extensive series. **Availability:** VHS; 3/4U.

44659 ■ *Inside Business Today...The '90s*
GPN Educational Media
1550 Executive Drive
Elgin, IL 60123
Ph:(402)472-2007
Free: 800-228-4630
Fax:800-306-2330
Co. E-mail: askgpn@smarterville.com
URL: http://www.shopgpn.com
Released: 1990. **Price:** $2765.00. **Description:** Second part of the Inside Business series. Contains 30 sections which discusses various areas of business concerns in the 1990s. **Availability:** VHS.

44660 ■ *New or Used? Buying a Firm or Starting Your Own*
Instructional Video
2219 C St.
Lincoln, NE 68502
Ph:(402)475-6570
Free: 800-228-0164
Fax:(402)475-6500
Co. E-mail: feedback@insvideo.com
URL: http://www.insvideo.com
Price: $99.00. **Description:** Details the different options open to anyone wanting to start or obtain their own business. Discusses the various factors to be considered when putting a value on a company, negotiating price and terms, and closing the deal. **Availability:** VHS.

44661 ■ *Small Business in a Big World*
Instructional Video
2219 C St.
Lincoln, NE 68502
Ph:(402)475-6570

Free: 800-228-0164
Fax:(402)475-6500
Co. E-mail: feedback@insvideo.com
URL: http://www.insvideo.com
Price: $99.00. **Description:** Demonstrates how small business has contributed to the overall economy. Includes profiles of small retail, service, manufacturing, professional, high tech, wholesale, and warehousing operations at work. **Availability:** VHS.

44662 ■ *The Ten Commandments of Networking*
Encyclopedia Britannica
331 N. LaSalle St.
Chicago, IL 60654
Ph:(312)347-7159
Free: 800-323-1229
Fax:(312)294-2104
URL: http://www.britannica.com
Released: 1994. **Price:** $39.95. **Description:** One-part seminar and one-part live demonstration of various networking situations, geared toward the entrepreneur who wants to expand and cultivate personal and business relationships. **Availability:** VHS.

44663 ■ *Understanding Business Valuation*
Chesney Communications
2302 Martin St., Ste. 125
Irvine, CA 92612
Ph:(949)263-5500
Free: 800-223-8878
Fax:(949)263-5506
Co. E-mail: videocc@aol.com
URL: http://www.videocc.com
Released: 1987. **Description:** A look for the small businessman at how to plan the future of his company-growth, reinvestment and possible sale. **Availability:** VHS; 3/4U.

CONSULTANTS

44664 ■ *2010 Fund 5*
24351 Spartan St.
Mission Viejo, CA 92691-3920
Ph:(949)583-1992
Fax:(949)583-0474
Contact: Wally Eater, Principle
Scope: Funds in formation that will invest in technologies licensed from 30 universities.

44665 ■ *Aurora Management Partners Inc.*
4485 Tench Rd., Ste. 340
Suwanee, GA 30024
Ph:(770)904-5209
Co. E-mail: rturcotte@auroramp.com
URL: http://www.auroramp.com
Contact: William A. Barbee, Director
E-mail: abarbee@atsauroramp.com
Scope: Firm specializes in turnaround management and reorganization consulting. Firm develop strategic initiatives, organize and analyze solutions, deal with creditor issues, review organizational structure and develop time frames for decision making. Turnaround services offered include Recovery plans and their implementation, Viability analysis, Crisis management, Financial restructuring, Corporate and organizational restructuring, Facilities rationalization, Liquidation management, Loan workout, Litigation support and Expert testimony, Contract renegotiation, Sourcing loan refinancing and Sourcing equity investment. **Publications:** "TMA Turnaround of the Year Award, Small Company, Honorable Mention," Nov, 2005; "Back From The Brink - Bland Farms," Progressive Farmer, Oct, 2004; "New Breed of Turnaround Managers," Catalyst Magazine, Aug, 2004; "Key Performance Drivers - Bland Farms," The Produce News, Apr, 2004; "Corporate Governance: Averting Crisis's Before They Happen," ABJ journal, Feb, 2004.

44666 ■ *Biomedical Management Resources*
PO Box 10977
Conway, AR 72034
Ph:(801)272-4668

Fax:(801)277-3290
Co. E-mail: SeniorManagement@BiomedicalManagement.com
URL: http://www.biomedicalmanagement.com
Contact: Ping Fong Jr., President
E-mail: pingfong@biomedicalmanagement.com
Scope: Provides business development, interim management, and executive search services. Assists companies in strategic alliances, corporate partnering, business acquisition. Demonstrated success in identifying recruiting, and placing key managers in difficult to hire positions.

44667 ■ *BPT Consulting Associates Ltd.*
12 Parmenter Rd., Ste. B-6
Londonderry, NH 03053
Ph:(603)437-8484
Free: 888-278-0030
Fax:(603)434-5388
Co. E-mail: bptcons@tiac.net
Contact: John Kuczynski, President
E-mail: bptcons@tiac.net
Scope: Provides management consulting expertise and resources to cross-industry clients with services for: Business Management consulting, People/Human Resources Transition and Training programs, and a full cadre of multi-disciplined Technology Computer experts. Virtual consultants with expertise in e-commerce, supply chain management, organizational development, and business application development consulting.

44668 ■ *CEO Advisors*
848 Brickell Ave., Ste. 603
Miami, FL 33131
Ph:(305)371-8560
Fax:(305)371-8563
Co. E-mail: ciaizpurua@ceoadvisors.us
URL: http://www.ceoadvisors.us
Contact: Mario Castro, Vice President
E-mail: mcastro@atsceoadvisors.us
Scope: Business consulting firm offering clients services in strategy, mergers and acquisitions, corporate finance, corporate advisory, supply chain management, government relations and public affairs. Specializes in strategic planning, profit enhancement, start-up businesses, venture capital, appraisals and valuations.

44669 ■ *Chamberlain & Cansler Inc.*
2251 Perimeter Park Dr.
Atlanta, GA 30341
Ph:(770)457-5699
Contact: Charles L. Cansler, Owner
Scope: Firm specializes in strategic planning; profit enhancement; small business management; interim management; crisis management; turnarounds.

44670 ■ *Chartered Management Co.*
125 S Wacker Dr.
Chicago, IL 60606
Ph:(312)214-2575
Contact: William B. Avellone, President
Scope: Operations improvement consultants. Specializes in strategic planning; feasibility studies; management audits and reports; profit enhancement; start-up businesses; mergers and acquisitions; joint ventures; divestitures; interim management; crisis management; turnarounds; business process re-engineering; venture capital; and due diligence.

44671 ■ *Clayton/Curtis/Cottrell*
1722 Madison Ct.
Louisville, CO 80027-1121
Ph:(303)665-2005
Contact: Robert Cottrell, President
Scope: Market research firm specializes in providing consultations for packaged goods, telecommunications, direct marketing and printing, and packaging industries. Services include strategic planning; profit enhancement; startup businesses; mergers and acquisitions; joint ventures; divestitures; interim management; crisis management; turnarounds; market size, segmentation and rates of growth; competitor intelligence; image and reputation, and competitive analysis. **Publications:** "Turn an attitude into a purchase," Jul, 1995; "Mixed results for private label; price assaults by the national brands are get-

ting heavy, but there's still a place for private label," Jun, 1995; "In-store promotion goes high-tech: is the conventional coupon destined for obsolescence?," Jun, 1995.

44672 ■ Colmen Menard Company Inc.
The Woods, 994 Old Eagle School Rd., Ste. 1000
Wayne, PA 19087
Ph:(484)367-0300
Fax:(484)367-0305
Co. E-mail: cmci@colmenmenard.com
URL: http://www.colmenmenard.com
Contact: David W. Menard, Managing Director
E-mail: dmenard@atscolmenmenard.com
Scope: Merger and acquisition corporate finance and business advisory services for public and private companies located in North America. **Publications:** "Success in Selling a Troubled Company," Nov, 2002; "Savvy Dealmakers," May, 2001; "Truisms," M&A Today, Nov, 2000.

44673 ■ Comer & Associates L.L.C.
5255 Holmes Pl.
Boulder, CO 80303
Ph:(303)786-7986
Free: 888-950-3190
Fax:(303)895-2347
URL: http://www.comerassociates.com
Contact: Jerry C. Comer, President
E-mail: jcomer@comer-associates.com
Scope: Specialize in developing markets and businesses. Marketing support includes: Developing and writing strategic and tactical business plans; developing and writing focused, effective market plans; researching market potential and competition; implementing targeted marketing tactics to achieve company objectives; conducting customer surveys to determine satisfaction and attitudes toward client. Organization development support includes: Executive/management training programs; executive coaching; team building; developing effective organization structures; and management of change in dynamic and competitive environments; individual coaching for management and leadership effectiveness. **Seminars:** Developing a Strategic Market Plan; Market Research: Defining Your Opportunity; Management and Leadership Effectiveness; Team Building; Developing a Business Plan; How to Close; Using Questions to Sell; Sales System Elements and Checklist; Working With Independent Reps; Features vs. Benefits; Overcoming Objections; Sales Force Automation.

44674 ■ The Corlund Group L.L.C.
101 Federal St., Ste. 310
Boston, MA 02110
Ph:(617)423-9364
Fax:(617)423-9371
Co. E-mail: info@corlundgroup.com
URL: http://www.corlundgroup.com
Contact: Deborah J. Cornwall, Managing Director
E-mail: dcornwall@atscorlundgroup.com
Scope: Boutique firm offering services in the areas of leadership, governance, and change with a particular focus on CEO and senior executive succession planning, including assessment, development, and orchestrating succession processes with management and Boards of Directors. Also Board governance effectiveness. **Publications:** "Are You Rolling the Dice on CEO Succession?" Center for Healthcare Governance, 2006; "Leadership Due Diligence: The Neglected Governance Frontier," Directorship, Sep, 2001; "Leadership Due Diligence: Managing the Risks," The Corporate Board, Aug, 2001; "Succession: The need for detailed insight," Directors and Boards, 2001; "CEO Succession: Who's Doing Due Diligence?," 2001.

44675 ■ Corporate Consulting Inc.
3333 Belcaro Dr.
Denver, CO 80209-4912
Ph:(303)698-9292
Fax:(303)698-9292
Co. E-mail: corpcons@compuserve.com
Contact: Devereux C. Josephs, President
E-mail: corpcons@compuserve.com
Scope: Specializes in feasibility studies, organizational development, small business management, mergers and acquisitions, joint ventures, divestitures,

interim management, crisis management, turnarounds, financing, appraisals valuations and due diligence studies.

44676 ■ Crystal Clear Communications Inc.
1633 W Winslow Dr., Ste. 210
Mequon, WI 53092
Ph:(262)240-0072
Fax:(262)240-0073
Co. E-mail: contact@crystalclear1.com
URL: http://www.crystalclear1.com
Contact: Chez Fogel, Principle
E-mail: chfogel@atscrystalclear.com
Scope: Specialize in helping executives identify impediments to success, and then develop strategies to surmount them. Serves to identify core problems, suggest appropriate business changes, work with the organization to support these changes, and help executives articulate the behavior that will uphold these changes. Specializes in strategic planning; organizational development; small business management; executive coaching. **Publications:** "Weakest Link"; "Aware Leadership"; "Integrity"; "When Your Plate is Full"; "Problem Solving"; "Strategic Thinking".

44677 ■ Development Resource Consultants
PO Box 118
Rancho Cucamonga, CA 91729
Ph:(909)902-7655
Fax:(909)476-6942
Co. E-mail: drc@gotodrc.com
URL: http://www.gotodrc.com
Contact: Jerry R. Frey, Partner
E-mail: jfrey@atsgotodrc.com
Scope: Specializes in office re-organization, employee training in office organization, communication skills, sales training and career counseling. **Publications:** "Institute of Management Consultants Southern California Chapter," Jan, 2006.

44678 ■ Dimond Hospitality Consulting Group Inc.
5710 Stoneway Trl.
Nashville, TN 37209
Ph:(615)353-0033
Fax:(615)352-5290
Co. E-mail: drew@dimondhotelconsulting.com
URL: http://www.dimondhotelconsulting.com
Contact: Drew W. Dimond, President
E-mail: drew@dimondhotelconsulting.com
Scope: Specializes in strategic planning; start-up businesses; business process re-engineering; team building; competitive analysis; venture capital; competitive intelligence; and due diligence. Offers litigation support. Comprehensive hospitality consulting firm that serves as an adviser to leading hotel companies, independent hotels, lending institutions, trustees, law firms, investment companies and municipalities in the areas of: Asset management, Acquisition due diligence, Arbitration, Disposition advisory services, Exit strategies, Financial review and analysis, Impact studies, Mediation. **Publications:** "The distressed debt conundrum," Jul, 2009; "How to buy distressed assets," Apr, 2009; "Cmbs Loans: A History and the Future," Apr, 2009; "Opportunity Knocks," Apr, 2009; "Another Reality Check," Mar, 2009; "An Inkling of Hope," Mar, 2009; "Strong World Tourism Growth in 2007," 2007; "Les U.S. Construction Pipeline Sets Another Record at 5011 Hotels with 654503 Rooms"; "Hotel Capitalization Rates Hold for Now"; "Winning Cornell Hotel and Restaurant Administration Quarterly Article Provides Hotel Brand Analysis"; "Breaking News for Lifestyle Hotels. Ian Schrager and Bill Marriott Announce Their Marriage Will the Schrager-Marriott Marriage Lead to Eternal Bliss Or End in Divorce What Will the M Hotels Children Be Named"; "Brands Vs Independents"; "Nyu Conf Takes Industry Temp"; "Economy Hotel Performance Indication of Travel Trends"; "Hotel Sales Continue at Brisk Pace"; "Fundamentals Strong, Weakening Undercurrent"; "Hotel Investments: Where Do We Go From Here"; "On the Road: Aahoa Panel Commits to Change"; "Cuba Not Ready, But Expecting U.S. Tourists".

44679 ■ donphin.com Inc.
1001 B Ave., Ste. 200
Coronado, CA 92118
Ph:(619)550-3533

Free: 800-234-3304
Fax:(619)600-0096
Co. E-mail: inquiry@donphin.com
URL: http://www.donphin.com
Contact: Donald A. Phin, CEO
E-mail: don@donphin.com
Scope: Offers a comprehensive approach to understanding and applying a broad range of business principles: legal compliance issues, management concerns, health and safety, customer service, marketing, information management. Industries served: All developing small businesses. **Publications:** "Doing Business Right!"; "HR That Works!"; "Lawsuit Free! How to Prevent Employee Lawsuits"; "Building Powerful Employment Relationships!"; "Victims, Villains and Heroes: Managing Emotions in The Workplace". **Seminars:** Doing Business Right!; HR That Works!; Building Powerful Employment Relationships; Lawsuit Free!.

44680 ■ Dropkin & Co.
390 George St.
New Brunswick, NJ 08901
Ph:(732)828-3211
Fax:(732)828-4118
Co. E-mail: murray@dropkin.com
URL: http://www.dropkin.com
Contact: Mel Nusbaum, Principle
E-mail: mel@atsdropkin.com
Scope: Firm specializes in feasibility studies; business management; business process re-engineering; and team building, health care and housing. **Publications:** "Bookkeeping for Nonprofits," Jossey Bass, 2005; "Guide to Audits of Nonprofit Organizations," PPC; "The Nonprofit Report," Warren, Gorham & Lamont; "The Budget Building Book for Nonprofits," Jossey-Bass; "The Cash Flow Management Book for Nonprofits," Jossey-Bass.

44681 ■ Dubuc Lucke & Company Inc.
120 W 5th St.
Cincinnati, OH 45202-2713
Ph:(513)579-8330
Fax:(513)241-6669
Contact: Kenneth E. Dubuc, President
Scope: Provides consulting services in the areas of profit enhancement; small business management; mergers and acquisitions; joint ventures; divestitures; interim management; crisis management; turnarounds; appraisals; valuations; due diligence; and international trade.

44682 ■ The DuMond Group
5282 Princeton Ave.
Westminster, CA 92683-2753
Ph:(714)373-0610
Contact: David L. Dumond, Principle
Scope: Human resources and executive search consulting firm that specializes in organizational development; small business management; employee surveys and communication; performance appraisals; and team building.

44683 ■ Dunelm International
437 Colebrook Ln.
Bryn Mawr, PA 19010-3216
Ph:(610)989-0144
Fax:(610)964-9524
Co. E-mail: jecdunelm@worldnet.att.net
Contact: John E. Crowther, President
E-mail: jecdunelm@dunelm.org.uk
Scope: Firm specializes in feasibility studies; start-up businesses; interim management; crisis management; turnarounds; business process re-engineering; sales forecasting; supply chain solution and project management.

44684 ■ Facility Directions Inc.
PO Box 761
Manchester, MO 63011
Ph:(636)256-4400
Free: 800-536-0044
Fax:(636)227-2868
Co. E-mail: walty@facilitydirections.com
URL: http://www.facilitydirections.com
Contact: Walter E. Yesberg, President
E-mail: walty@facilitydirections.com
Scope: Firm specializes in service to financial institutions; strategic planning; feasibility studies; facility and space planning; attitude surveys; site selection.

44685 ■ First Strike Management Consulting Inc.
401 Loblolly Ave.
PO Box 1188
Little River, SC 29566-1188
Ph:(843)385-6338
Fax:(843)390-1004
Co. E-mail: fsmc.hq@fsmc.com
URL: http://www.fsmc.com
Contact: J.D. Lewis, President
E-mail: jd.lewis@fsmc.com
Scope: Offers proposal management and program management services. Specializes in enterprise systems, management systems, and staff augmentation. Serves the following industries: Nuclear/Fossil Power, Petro-Chemical, Aerospace and Defense, Telecommunications, Engineering and Construction, Information Technology, Golf Course Construction/ Management, Utility Engineering/Construction, Civil Works, and Housing Development. **Publications:** "Project Management for Executives"; "Project Risk Management"; "Project Communications Management"; "Winning Proposals, Four Computer Based Training (CBT) courses"; "Principles of Program Management". **Seminars:** Preparing Winning Proposals in Response to Government RFPs.

44686 ■ Global Technology Transfer L.L.C.
1500 Dixie Hwy.
Park Hills, KY 41011-2819
Ph:(859)431-1262
Fax:(859)431-5148
Co. E-mail: arzembrodt@worldnet.att.net
Contact: Michelle Hartley, CFO
Scope: Firm specializes in product development; quality assurance; new product development; and total quality management focusing on household chemical specialties, especially air fresheners. Utilizes latest technology from global resources. Specializes in enhancement products for home and automobile.

44687 ■ Great Lakes Consulting Group Inc.
54722 Little Flower Trl.
Mishawaka, IN 46545
Ph:(574)287-4500
Fax:(574)233-2688
Contact: James E. Schrager, President
Scope: Provides consulting services in the areas of strategic planning; feasibility studies; start-up businesses; small business management; mergers and acquisitions; joint ventures; divestitures; interim management; crisis management; turnarounds; business process re-engineering; venture capital; and international trade.

44688 ■ Grimmick Consulting Services
455 Donner Way
San Ramon, CA 94582
Ph:(925)735-1036
Fax:(925)735-1100
Co. E-mail: hank@grimmickconsulting.com
URL: http://www.grimmickconsulting.com
Contact: Henry Grimmick, President
E-mail: hank@grimmickconsulting.com
Scope: Provides consulting services in the areas of strategic planning; organizational assessment; organizational development; leadership and management development Baldridge criteria, process improvement and balanced scorecards and team dynamics.

44689 ■ Harvey C. Skoog
7151 E Addis Ave.
Prescott Valley, AZ 86314
Ph:(928)772-1448
Co. E-mail: hskoog@pvaz.net
E-mail: hskoog@pvaz.net
Scope: Firm has expertise in taxes, payroll, financial planning, budgeting, buy/sell planning, business start-up, fraud detection, troubled business consulting, acquisition, and marketing. Serves the manufacturing, construction, and retailing industries in Arizona.

44690 ■ Health Strategy Group Inc.
46 River Rd.
Chatham, NY 12037
Ph:(518)392-6770
Contact: John Fiorillo, Principle
Scope: Provides consulting services in the areas of strategic planning, feasibility studies, start-up businesses, organizational development, market research, customer service audits, new product development, marketing, public relations. **Publications:** "Online Consumer Surveys as a Methodology for Assessing the Quality of the United States Health Care System," 2004.

44691 ■ Hewitt Development Enterprises
18 Lindley Ave.
North Kingstown, RI 02852
Ph:(305)372-0941
Free: 800-631-3098
Fax:(305)372-0941
Co. E-mail: info@hewittdevelopment.com
URL: http://www.hewittdevelopment.com
Contact: Robert G. Hewitt, Principal
E-mail: bob@hewittdevelopment.com
Scope: Specializes in strategic planning; profit enhancement; start-up businesses; interim management; crisis management; turnarounds; production planning; just-in-time inventory management; and project management. Serves senior management (CEOs, CFOs, division presidents, etc.) and acquirers of distressed businesses.

44692 ■ Holt Capital
1916 Pike Pl., Ste. 12-344
Seattle, WA 98101
Ph:(206)484-0403
Fax:(206)789-8034
Co. E-mail: info@holtcapital.com
URL: http://www.holtcapital.com
Contact: David Brazeau, Principle
E-mail: mjholt@holtcapital.com
Scope: Registered investment advisory firm. Services include: Debt planning, private equity, mergers, divestitures and acquisitions, transaction support services. Connects companies with capital. **Publications:** "Early Sales Key to Early-Stage Funding"; "Financial Transactions: Who Should Be At Your Table"; "Get the Deal Done: The Four Keys to Successful Mergers and Acquisitions"; "Is Your First Paragraph a Turn-off"; "Bubble Rubble: Bridging the Price Gap for an Early-Stage Business"; "Are You Ready For The new Economy"; "Could I Get Money or Jail Time With That The Sarbanes-Oxley Act Of 2002 gives early-stage companies More Risks". **Seminars:** Attracting Private Investors; Five Proven Ways to Finance Your Company; How to Get VC Financing; Venture Packaging; How to Finance Company Expansion.

44693 ■ The Institute for Management Excellence
PO Box 5459
Lacey, WA 98509-5459
Ph:(360)412-0404
Co. E-mail: pwoc@itstime.com
URL: http://www.itstime.com
Contact: Michael Anthony, Director
E-mail: btaylor@itstime.com
Scope: Management consulting and training focuses on improving productivity, using practices and creative techniques. Practices based on the company's theme: It's time for new ways of doing business. Industries served: public sector, law enforcement, finance or banking, non profit, computers or high technology, education, human resources, utilities. **Publications:** "Income Without a Job," 2008; "The Other Side of Midnight, 2000: An Executive Guide to the Year 2000 Problem"; "Concordance to the Michael Teachings"; "Handbook of Small Business Advertising"; "The Personality Game"; "How to Market Yourself for Success". **Seminars:** The Personality Game; Power Path Seminars; Productivity Plus; Sexual Harassment and Discrimination Prevention; Worker's Comp Cost Reduction; Americans with Disabilities Act; In Search of Identify: Clarifying Corporate Culture.

44694 ■ Interminds & Federer Resources Inc.
106 E 6th St., Ste. 310
Austin, TX 78701-3659
Ph:(512)476-8800
Fax:(512)476-8811
URL: http://www.interminds.com
Contact: Salvador Apud, Partner
E-mail: sapud@atsintegra100.com
Scope: Firm specializes in feasibility studies; startup businesses; small business management; mergers and acquisitions; joint ventures; divestitures; interim management; crisis management; turnarounds; production planning; team building; appraisals and valuations.

44695 ■ International Management Consulting Group Inc.
1309 Harlan Dr., Ste. 205
Bellevue, NE 68005
Ph:(402)291-4545
Free: 800-665-4624
Fax:(402)291-4343
Co. E-mail: imcg@neonramp.com
Contact: Shawn Bengston, Mgr
Scope: Offers the following operational effectiveness programs: productivity improvement programs directed toward any sized business; business and strategic planning for executives; executive and employee seminars; work measurement and performance accounting; relocation planning and management services; job design, job analysis and human resources selection consulting; executive out placement services; and total quality management business processes re-engineering, procurement and purchasing practices. Also provides analysis of business problems faced by entrepreneurs and small business owners. Consultants seek cost savings for clients while expanding into new markets and managed growth opportunities for any sized businesses. Industries served: nearly all; but specialize in the following: insurance, transportation (passenger), family-owned businesses, and light manufacturing heavy production environment and wholesale/retail. **Publications:** "Why Every Executive Needs a Coach," 1997; "The Professional Job Finding System," 1997; "Why Small Business Is Where It's AT in the 1990's"; "It's All in the Plan," Small Business Reports, Jun, 1994; "Six Tips for Picking a Consultant," Small Business Reports, Jan, 1994. **Seminars:** Why Every Executive Needs a Coach; Strategic Planning for the 21st Century Executive; Mistakes Managers Make: And How to Avoid Them; Entrepreneurship in the 1990's; How to Start a Small Business and Survive; Time Management for Business Owners; Stress Management: How to Live With Stress; How to Select a Consultant in the 1990's; Total Quality Management: What's It All About; Business Process Reengineering; Activity-Based Learning. **Special Services:** Activity-based learning™.

44696 ■ Investor Voices L.L.C.
120A N Main Ave.
Newton, NC 28658
Ph:(717)626-3991
Fax:(570)227-7038
URL: http://www.investorvoices.com
Contact: Timothy Shannon, CEO
Scope: A due diligence based business development advisor. Seeks to partner with growing but underexposed small-cap companies. Provides business development, investor relations, advertising, and financial advisory services.

44697 ■ Johnston Co.
1646 Massachusetts Ave., Ste. 22
Lexington, MA 02420
Ph:(781)862-7595
Fax:(781)862-9066
Co. E-mail: info@johnstoncompany.com
URL: http://www.johnstoncompany.com
Contact: Terry Sugrue, Mgr
E-mail: tzsugrue@atshotmail.com
Scope: Firm specializes in management audits and reports; start-up businesses; small business management; mergers and acquisitions; joint ventures; divestitures; interim management; crisis management; turnarounds; cost controls; financing; venture capital; controller services; financial management,

strategic and advisory services. **Publications:** "Why are board meetings such a waste of time," Boston Business Journal, Apr, 2004.

44698 ■ Keiei Senryaku Corp.
19191 S Vermont Ave., Ste. 530
Torrance, CA 90502-1049
Ph:(310)366-3331
Free: 800-951-8780
Fax:(310)366-3330
Co. E-mail: takenakaes@earthlink.net
Contact: Kurt Miyamoto, President
Scope: Offers consulting services in the areas of strategic planning; feasibility studies; profit enhancement; organizational development; start-up businesses; mergers and acquisitions; joint ventures; divestitures; executive searches; sales management; and competitive analysis.

44699 ■ Key Communications Group Inc.
5617 Warwick Pl.
Chevy Chase, MD 20815-5503
Ph:(301)656-0450
Free: 800-705-5353
Fax:(301)656-4554
Co. E-mail: mr.dm@verizon.net
Contact: Carol A. Jason, Principle
E-mail: mr.dm@verizon.net
Scope: Direct marketing and publishing consultants specializing in subscriber and member acquisition for newsletters and other niche B2B publications, organizations and associations. Specialties: small and start-up businesses; mergers and acquisitions; joint ventures; divestitures; product development; employee surveys and communication; market research; customer service audits; new product development; direct marketing and competitive intelligence. **Publications:** "How I Tripled Site License Sales in One Year," Pma, Jul, 2004.

44700 ■ M-Squared Inc.
7101 Creedmoor Rd., Ste. 120
Raleigh, NC 27615
Ph:(919)848-4300
Fax:(919)848-1125
Co. E-mail: hdraddo@m2i.com
Contact: Robin Lombard, Vice President
Scope: Consultants will develop business plans and critiques, business goals and objectives, and strategic and operational planning, and assist with new business start-ups. Business negotiation including buy/sell businesses, contract negotiation, debt negotiation, mediation, and arbitration. Expertise with loan packaging and counseling, management training seminars and coaching, motivational training and team-building, and design and implementation of financial and operational controls. Industries served: All small businesses (under 50 employees), as well as government agencies. **Seminars:** Exploring Entrepreneurship; Strategic Planning for Small Business; Financial Analysis and Projections; Company Team Building.

44701 ■ Management Resource Partners
181 2nd Ave., Ste. 542
San Mateo, CA 94401
Ph:(650)401-5850
Fax:(650)401-5850
Contact: John C. Roberts, Principle
Scope: Firm specializes in strategic planning; small business management; mergers and acquisitions; joint ventures; divestitures; interim management; crisis management; turn around; venture capital; appraisals and valuations.

44702 ■ Mefford, Knutson & Associates Inc.
6437 Lyndale Ave. S, Ste. 103
Richfield, MN 55423-1465
Ph:(612)869-8011
Free: 800-831-0228
Fax:(612)869-8004
Co. E-mail: info@mkaonline.net
URL: http://www.mkaonline.net
Contact: Jennifer Thompson, Director
E-mail: jthompson@atsmkaonline.com
Scope: A consulting and licensed business brokerage firm specializing in start-up businesses; strategic planning; mergers and acquisitions; joint ventures;

divestitures; business process re-engineering; personnel policies and procedures; market research; new product development and cost controls.

44703 ■ Miller, Hellwig Associates
150 W End Ave.
New York, NY 10023-5713
Ph:(212)799-0471
Fax:(212)877-0186
Co. E-mail: millerhelwig@earthlink.net
Contact: Ernest C. Miller, President
Scope: Consulting services in the areas of start-up businesses; small business management; employee surveys and communication; performance appraisals; executive searches; team building; personnel policies and procedures; market research. Also involved in improving cross-cultural and multi-cultural relationships, particularly with Japanese clients. **Seminars:** Objectives and standards/recruiting for boards of directors.

44704 ■ Organization Counselors Inc.
44 W Broadway, Ste. 1102
PO Box 987
Salt Lake City, UT 84101
Ph:(801)363-2900
Fax:(801)363-0861
Co. E-mail: jpanos@xmission.com
Contact: John E. Panos, President
E-mail: jpanos@xmission.com
Scope: Organizational development; employee surveys and communication; outplacement; team building; total quality management and continuous improvement. **Seminars:** Correcting Performance Problems; Total Quality Management; Employee Selection; Performance Management.

44705 ■ Parker Consultants Inc.
230 Mason St.
Greenwich, CT 06830-6633
Ph:(203)869-9400
Contact: William P. Hartl, Chairman of the Board
Scope: Firm specializes in strategic planning; organizational development; small business management; performance appraisals; executive searches; team building; and customer service audits.

44706 ■ Partners for Market Leadership Inc.
400 Galleria Pky., Ste. 1500
Atlanta, GA 30339
Ph:(770)850-1409
Free: 800-984-1110
Co. E-mail: dcarpenter@market-leadership.com
URL: http://www.market-leadership.com
Contact: Nancy Surdyka, Mgr
E-mail: nsurdyka@atsmarket-leadership.com
Scope: Boutique consulting firm focused on assisting clients to develop sustainable market leadership in geographic, practice area and/or industry markets. Provides consulting on market leadership, revenue enhancement, strategic development and change facilitation. Additional services are offered to legal, accounting, valuation and financial firms.

44707 ■ Performance Consulting Group Inc.
8031 SW 35th Terr.
Miami, FL 33155-3443
Ph:(305)264-5577
Fax:(305)264-9079
Contact: Patrick J. O'Brien, President
Scope: Firm provides consulting services in the areas of strategic planning; profit enhancement; product development; and production planning.

44708 ■ Rose & Crangle Ltd.
117 N 4th St.
PO Box 285
Lincoln, KS 67455
Ph:(785)524-5050
Fax:(785)524-3130
Co. E-mail: rcltd@nckcn.com
URL: http://www.roseandcrangle.com
Contact: Jeanne Crangle, Principle
E-mail: rcltd@nckcn.com
Scope: Firm provides evaluation, planning and policy analyzes for universities, associations, foundations, governmental agencies and private companies engaged in scientific, technological or educational activities. Special expertise in the development of

new institutions. Special skills in providing planning and related group facilitation workshops. **Publications:** "Preface to Bulgarian Integration Into Europe and NATO: Issues of Science Policy And research Evaluation Practice," Ios Press, 2006; "Allocating Limited National Resources for Fundamental Research," 2005.

44709 ■ Rothschild Strategies Unlimited L.L.C.
19 Thistle Rd.
PO Box 7568
Norwalk, CT 06851-1909
Ph:(203)846-6898
Fax:(203)847-1426
Co. E-mail: bill@strategyleader.com
URL: http://www.strategyleader.com
Contact: William Rothchild, CEO
E-mail: billrothschild@atsoptonline.net
Scope: Consults with senior management and business level strategy teams to develop overall strategic direction, set priorities and creates sustainable competitive advantages and differentiators. Enables organizations to enhance their own strategic thinking and leadership skills so that they can continue to develop and implement profitable growth strategies. **Publications:** "Putting It All Together-a guide to strategic thinking"; "Competitive Advantage"; "Ristaker, Caretaker, Surgeon & Undertaker four faces of strategic leadership"; "The Secret to GE's Success"; "Having the Right Strategic Leader and Team". **Seminars:** Who is going the WRONG way?; Learning from your Successes and Failures. **Special Services:** StrategyLeader[R].

44710 ■ Sklar and Associates Inc.
242 Laurel Bay Dr.
Murrells Inlet, SC 29576
Ph:(202)257-5061
Fax:(843)651-3090
Co. E-mail: sklarincdc@aol.com
URL: http://www.sklarinc.com
Contact: Tim Sklar, President
Scope: Provides consulting services for business acquisitions, business development and project finance. Provides audit oversight services to listed corporations on Sarbanes-Oxley compliance. Services include: Due diligence analyses and corporate governance. Industries served: transportation sectors, energy sector and commercial real estate industries. **Seminars:** Financial Analysis in MBA; Emerging Company Finance; Due Diligence in Business Acquisition; Business Valuation.

44711 ■ Strategic MindShare Consulting
1401 Brickell Ave., Ste. 640
Miami, FL 33131
Ph:(305)377-2220
Fax:(305)377-2280
Co. E-mail: dee@strategicmindshare.com
URL: http://www.strategicmindshare.com
Contact: Cynthia R. Cohen, President
E-mail: cohen@strategicmindshare.com
Scope: Firm specializes in strategic planning; feasibility studies; profit enhancement; organizational development; start-up businesses; mergers and acquisitions; joint ventures; divestitures; interim management; crisis management; turnarounds; new product development and competitive analysis. **Publications:** "Top Ten CEO Burning Issues for 2005"; "Top Ten Consumer Behavioral Trends for 2005"; "The Influence Factors"; "New Profit Opportunities for Retailers and Consumer Product Companies".

44712 ■ Turnaround Inc.
3415 A St. NW
Gig Harbor, WA 98335
Ph:(253)857-6730
Fax:(253)857-6344
Co. E-mail: info@turnround-inc.com
URL: http://www.turnaround-inc.com
Contact: Miles Stover, President
E-mail: mstover@turnaround-inc.com
Scope: Firm provides interim executive management assistance and management advisory to small, medium and family-owned businesses that are not meeting their goals. Services include acting as an interim executive or on-site manager. Extensive practices in arena of bankruptcy management. **Publi-**

cations: "How to Identify Problem and Promising Management"; "How to Tell if Your Company is a Bankruptcy Candidate"; "Signs that Your Company is in Trouble"; "The Turnaround Specialist: How to File a Petition Under 11 USC 11". **Seminars:** Competitive Intelligence Gathering.

44713 ■ ValueNomics Value Specialists
50 W San Fernando St., Ste. 600
San Jose, CA 95113
Ph:(408)200-6400
Fax:(408)200-6401
Co. E-mail: info@amllp.com
Contact: Jeff A. Stegner, Partner
Scope: Consulting is offered in the areas of financial management, process re-engineering, growth business services; governance, risk/compliance, SOX readiness and compliance, SAS 70, enterprise risk management, system security, operational and internal audit; business advisory services; valuation services; CORE assessment; contract assurance; transaction advisory services, IT solutions and litigation support services. **Publications:** "Dueling Appraisers: How Differences in Input and Assumptions May Control the Value," Apr, 2005; "The Business of Business Valuation and the CPA as an expert witness"; "The Business of Business Valuation," McGraw-Hill Professional Publishers Inc.

44714 ■ Venture Marketing Associates L.L.C.
800 Palisade Ave., Ste. 907
Fort Lee, NJ 07024
Ph:(201)924-7435
Fax:(201)224-8757
Co. E-mail: venturemkt@aol.com
URL: http://www.venturemarketingassociates.com
Contact: Shep Altshuler, Principle
E-mail: shep@myventure.biz
Scope: Provides consulting services in business development and franchising. Provides hands-on assistance in planning and implementing strategic marketing/management plans. Clients include franchisers, small business owners and individuals. Cost-effective fees for those in transition, facing unemployment, researching a franchise or starting a business. Industries served: service, retail and distribution. **Seminars:** Franchise Your Business; How to Research a Franchise Services.

44715 ■ Young & Associates Inc.
121 E Main St.
PO Box 711
Kent, OH 44240
Ph:(330)678-0524
Free: 800-525-9775
Fax:(330)678-6219
Co. E-mail: online@younginc.com
URL: http://www.younginc.com
Contact: Mike Detrow, Principle
E-mail: mdetrow@atsyounginc.com
Scope: Provides a variety of management consulting, outsourcing, educational, and research services, including strategic planning, risk management, capital planning, mergers and acquisitions, internal audit, branching and expansion, loan review, information technology, marketing, market research, human resources planning and management, site/location feasibility studies, development of business plans, and organizational analysis and development and regulatory compliance. Specialists in small and mid-size companies. Industries served: financial institutions, manufacturers (business-to-business and consumer), banking, healthcare (hospitals and practitioners), retailers, and services. **Publications:** "An Avalanche of New Compliance Regulations," Oct, 2009; "Fair Lending Risk Assessment," May, 2009. **Special Services:** The Compliance Monitoring System™; Compliance Monitoring Update Service™; The Compliance Review Program™; Compliance Review Program Update Service™.

COMPUTERIZED DATABASES

44716 ■ SBA Online
U.S. Small Business Administration
409 3rd St. SW
Washington, DC 20416

Free: 800-U-ASK-SBA
Co. E-mail: answerdesk@sba.gov
URL: http://www.sba.gov
Description: Contains information of use to owners of small businesses, including an overview of U.S. Small Business Administration (SBA) programs, business development programs, financial services/loans, government contracting opportunities, legislation and regulations, small business facts, small business minority programs, and a listing of SBA offices. Includes a calendar of events, information files on special targeted SBA programs, and message areas for networking with the small business community. Enables the user to obtain gateway access to other U.S. federal agency bulletin board services. **Availability:** Online: U.S. Small Business Administration. **Type:** Bulletin board; Full text; Directory.

COMPUTER SYSTEMS/ SOFTWARE

44717 ■ Business Simulator
Strategic Management Group, Inc.
6 Tower Bridge, Ste. 540
Conshohocken, PA 19428
Ph:(484)391-2900
Free: 800-445-7089
Co. E-mail: rommin.adl@smginc.com
URL: http://www.smginc.com
Price: $69.95. **Description:** Software program allowing the user to simulate running a start-up company through the various phases of development.

LIBRARIES

44718 ■ Boston Public Library–Kirstein Business Branch
Copley Sq.
700 Boylston St.
Boston, MA 02116
Ph:(617)859-2142
Co. E-mail: ask@bpl.org
URL: http://www.bpl.org/research/kbb/kbbhome.htm
Contact: Laura Pattison, Econ.Dev.Libn.
Scope: Business administration, retailing, advertising, finance, marketing, real estate, insurance, banking, taxation, accounting, investments, economics, business law, small business. **Services:** Copying is available through the library's interlibrary loan department; reference faxing up to three pages. **Holdings:** Moody's Manuals (1935 to present in print; 1909-1997 in microfiche); Commercial and Financial Chronicle, 1957-1987; Bank and Quotation Record, 1928-1987; Standard and Poor's Daily Stock Price Record: New York and American Stock Exchanges, 1962 to present; over-the-counter stocks, 1968 to present; domestic and foreign trade directories; city directories; telephone directories for New England and U.S. cities with populations over 100,000 for New England cities and towns; Standard Stock Market Service, 1921-1922; Standard Stock Offerings, 1925-1939; National Stock Summary, 1927 to present; Standard & Poor's Stock Guide, 1943 to present; New York and American Stock Exchange companies Annual and 10K reports on microfiche (1987-1996); Wall Street Journal on microfilm (latest 10 years); Wall Street Transcript on microfilm (latest 5 years); D-U-N-S Business Identification Service (November 1973 -1995). **Subscriptions:** 700 journals and other serials; 13 newspapers.

44719 ■ Business Development Bank of Canada Research & Information Centre
5 Place Ville Marie, Ste. 300
Montreal, QC, Canada H3B 5E7
Ph:(514)283-7632
Fax:(514)283-2304
Co. E-mail: odette.lavoie@bdc.ca
Contact: Odette Lavoie, Sr.Info.Spec.
Scope: Small business, management, Canadian business and industry, banking and finance, development banking. **Services:** Interlibrary loan; Library not open to the public. **Holdings:** 5000 books. **Subscriptions:** 100 journals and other serials; 7 newspapers.

44720 ■ Canada–Newfoundland and Labrador Business Service Centre
West Block, Confederation Bldg.
PO Box 8700
St. John's, NL, Canada A1B 4J6
Ph:(709)729-7000
Fax:(709)729-0654
Co. E-mail: mike.howley@acoa-apeca.gc.ca
URL: http://www.intrd.gov.nl.ca/intrd/department/ branches/sibd/cnlbsc.html
Contact: Mike Howley, Mgr.
Scope: Marketing, small business, economic and regional development. **Services:** Copying; SDI; centre open to the public. **Holdings:** 10,000 books; 20 VF drawers of subject files; Standard Industrial Classification (SIC) files. **Subscriptions:** 300 journals and other serials.

44721 ■ Carnegie Library of Pittsburgh–Downtown & Business
612 Smithfield St.
Pittsburgh, PA 15222-2506
Ph:(412)281-7141
Fax:(412)471-1724
Co. E-mail: business@carnegielibrary.org
Contact: Karen Rossi, Br.Mgr.
Scope: Investments, small business, entrepreneurship, management, marketing, insurance, advertising, personal finance, accounting, real estate, job and career, International business. **Services:** Library open to the public. **Holdings:** 13,000 business volumes; VF materials; microfilm; looseleaf services; AV materials.

44722 ■ Chicago Public Library Central Library–Business/Science/Technology Division
Harold Washington Library Center
400 S. State St., 4th Fl.
Chicago, IL 60605
Ph:(312)747-4450
Fax:(312)747-4975
URL: http://www.chipublib.org/branch/details/library/ harold-washington/p/Bst
Contact: Marcia Dellenbach, BST Div.Chf.
Scope: Small business, marketing, technology, corporate reports, investments, management, personnel, patents, physical and biological sciences, medicine, health, computer science, careers, environmental information, gardening, cookbooks. **Services:** Interlibrary loan; copying; division open to the public. **Holdings:** 415,000 books; 52,100 bound periodical volumes; 33,000 reels of microfilm; Securities and Exchange Commission (SEC) reports; federal specifications and standards; American National Standards Institute standards; corporate Annual reports. **Subscriptions:** 4000 journals and other serials; 8 newspapers.

44723 ■ Employment Support Center Library
1556 Wisconsin Ave., NW
Washington, DC 20007
Ph:(202)628-2919
Fax:(703)790-1469
Co. E-mail: escjobclubs@yahoo.com
URL: http://jobclubs.angelfire.com/
Contact: Ellie Wegener, Exec.Dir.
Scope: Employment networking, self-esteem, starting your own business, setting up job clubs, training facilitators, maintaining a large job bank, providing job-searching skills. **Services:** Library open to the public. **Holdings:** 150 articles; books; periodicals; videos on job search; interviews; reports; manuscripts. **Subscriptions:** 4 journals and other serials; 2 newspapers.

44724 ■ Greater Oviedo Chamber of Commerce Business Library
PO Box 621236
Oviedo, FL 32765
Ph:(407)365-6500
Fax:(407)650-2712
Co. E-mail: cory@oviedowintersprings.org
URL: http://www.oviedowintersprings.org/pages/ home/default.aspx
Contact: Corydon G. Skeates, Exec.Dir.
Scope: Small business; central Florida business. **Services:** Copying; Library open to the public. **Holdings:** 3 books; 10 reports; periodicals. **Subscriptions:** 3 newspapers.

44725 ■ Indian River Area Library
PO Box 160
Indian River, MI 49749
Ph:(231)238-8581
Fax:(231)238-9494
Co. E-mail: indrivl@northland.lib.mi.us
URL: http://www.libnet.org/iriver/
Contact: Cindy Lou Poquette, Dir.
Scope: Small business, careers, fine arts, music, dance. **Services:** Interlibrary loan; copying; Library open to the public (fee for non-residents to check out materials). **Holdings:** 52,000 books; 2500 videocassettes; 2000 microfiche; videocassettes; sound cassettes; DVDs; CDs; periodicals; large print books. **Subscriptions:** 78 journals and other serials; 3 newspapers.

44726 ■ National Small Business Benefits Association Library
2244 N. Grand Ave., E.
Springfield, IL 62702
Ph:(217)544-0881
Fax:(217)544-5816
Co. E-mail: t-shirtz@t-shirtz.com
URL: http://www.t-shirtz.com
Scope: Small businesses. **Services:** Library open to the public with restrictions. **Holdings:** 300 volumes.

44727 ■ Nations Bank–Business Resource Center
3401 Westend Ave., Ste. 110
Nashville, TN 37203
Ph:(615)749-4088
Fax:(615)749-3685
Co. E-mail: Lillie.Taylor@NationsBank.com
Contact: Lillie Taylor, Libn.
Scope: Small business. **Services:** Copying; Library open to the public with restrictions. **Holdings:** 2000 books; 6 VF drawers of archives. **Subscriptions:** 160 journals and other serials.

44728 ■ New York State Small Business Development Center–Research Network
22 Corporate Woods Bldg., 3rd Fl.
Albany, NY 12246
Ph:(518)443-5398
Free: 800-732-SBDC
URL: http://www.nyssbdc.org/resources/researchnetwork.html
Contact: Mr. James King, State Dir.
Scope: Small business. **Services:** Copying; faxing; document delivery. **Holdings:** 1000 books; 20 CD-ROMs. **Subscriptions:** 40 journals and other serials; 10 newspapers.

44729 ■ Newfoundland Department of Industry, Trade and Technology–Registry
PO Box 8700
St. John's, NL, Canada A1B 4J6
Ph:(709)729-5982
Fax:(709)729-5936
Scope: Economics, energy, small business, oil and gas. **Holdings:** Figures not available.

44730 ■ Piedmont Technical College Library
Lex Walters Campus
Bldg. K, 2nd Fl.
PO Box 1467
Greenwood, SC 29648-1467

Ph:(864)941-8441
Free: 800-868-5528, x8441
Fax:(864)941-8558
Co. E-mail: librarian@ptc.edu
URL: http://www.ptc.edu/library/
Contact: Cindy Davies, Dean of Lrng.Rsrcs.
Scope: Economics, technology, allied health, nursing, small business, computer science, criminal justice. **Services:** Interlibrary loan; copying; Library open to the public. **Holdings:** 30,000 books; 400 bound periodical volumes; 3500 reels of microfilm; 2000 AV programs. **Subscriptions:** 325 journals and other serials; 10 newspapers.

44731 ■ Saskatchewan Research Council–Information Services
125-15 Innovation Blvd.
Saskatoon, SK, Canada S7N 2X8
Ph:(306)933-5400
Fax:(306)933-7446
Co. E-mail: library@src.sk.ca
URL: http://www.src.sk.ca
Contact: Colleen Marshall, Info.Mgt.Coord.
Scope: Agriculture, biotechnology and food, alternative energy and manufacturing, energy, the environment and forestry, mining and minerals. **Services:** Interlibrary loan (with other libraries) **Holdings:** 8600 monographs; 3300 SRC-authored publications. **Subscriptions:** 55 periodicals.

44732 ■ South College Library
3904 Lonas Dr.
Knoxville, TN 37909
Ph:(865)251-1800
Co. E-mail: mmchugh@southcollegetn.edu
URL: http://www.southcollegetn.edu/library/
Contact: Mel McHugh, Hd.Libn.
Scope: Business, physical therapy, occupational therapy, administration, medical administration, legal administration, small business, secretarial science, paralegal, hotel and restaurant management. **Services:** Interlibrary loan; copying; SDI. **Holdings:** 6700 books; 10 VF drawers; 214 volumes on microfilm; 1 cabinet of microfiche. **Subscriptions:** 106 journals and other serials.

44733 ■ U.S.D.A.–National Agricultural Library–Rural Information Center (10301)
10301 Baltimore Ave., Rm. 132
Beltsville, MD 20705
Ph:(301)504-5547
Free: 800-633-7701
Fax:(301)504-5181
Co. E-mail: ric@nal.usda.gov
URL: http://ric.nal.usda.gov
Contact: William Thomas, Coord.
Scope: Economic development; small business development; city and county government services; government and private grants and funding sources; rural communities; community leadership; natural resources. **Services:** Center open to the public. **Holdings:** Figures not available.

44734 ■ University of Colorado—Boulder–William M. White Business Library
Leeds School of Business
Campus Box 184
Boulder, CO 80309-0184

Ph:(303)492-8367
Fax:(303)735-0333
Co. E-mail: buslib@colorado.edu
URL: http://ucblibraries.colorado.edu/business
Contact: Gene Hayworth, Faculty Dir.
Scope: Ethics, information systems, business policy, economics and law, small business, management and Organization, finance and accounting, marketing, transportation, management science, real estate, insurance, taxation. **Services:** Interlibrary loan; copying; Library open to the public. **Holdings:** 80,000 volumes; 160,000 microforms. **Subscriptions:** 660 journals; 15 newspapers.

44735 ■ Warren County Community College Library Special Collections
475 Rte. 57 W.
Washington, NJ 07882-4343
Ph:(908)835-2440
Co. E-mail: abaker@warren.edu
URL: http://www.warren.edu
Contact: Ariana Baker, Ref.Libn.
Scope: Business, humanities, American history, law. **Services:** Interlibrary loan; Q&ANJ; copying; services for the deaf; closed-captioned videos available; Library open to the public. **Holdings:** 26,600 books; 18 lin.ft. of archival materials; 1100 videos/DVD; 45 CDs. **Subscriptions:** 200 journals and other serials.

RESEARCH CENTERS

44736 ■ Laval University–Centre for Entrepreneurship and Small Business–Centre d'Entrpreneuriat et de PME
Faculty of Science of the Administration
Pavilion Palasis Prince, local 1663
Ste. Foy, QC, Canada G1K 7P4
Ph:(418)656-2490
Fax:(418)656-2624
Co. E-mail: yvon.gasse@fsa.ulaval.ca
URL: http://www.fsa.ulaval.ca/cepme
Contact: Yvon Gasse PhD, Dir.
E-mail: yvon.gasse@fsa.ulaval.ca
Scope: Small and medium-sized businesses and entrepreneurship, including growth strategies and technological innovations to promote development. **Educational Activities:** Training sessions and seminars.

44737 ■ University of Quebec at Trois-Rivieres–Research Institute for Small and Medium-Sized Enterprises
Pavillon Desjardins-Hydro-Quebec
3351, Blvd. des Forges
PO Box 500
Trois-Rivieres, QC, Canada G9A 5H7
Ph:(819)376-5235
Fax:(819)376-5138
Co. E-mail: inrpme@uqtr.ca
URL: http://oraprdnt.uqtr.uquebec.ca/pls/public/gscw030?owa_no_site=861
Contact: Claire V. de la Durantaye, Dir.
E-mail: inrpme@uqtr.ca
Scope: Small business and entrepreneurship, including management, strategy, finance, operation, marketing, information systems innovation, regional sciences, and economics. **Publications:** Revue Internationale PME Scientific Magazine (3/year). **Educational Activities:** Postgraduate assistance; Weekly research seminars, in fall and winter terms.

Small Business Software

START-UP INFORMATION

44738 ■ *The 100 Best Businesses to Start When You Don't Want To Work Hard Anymore*
Pub: Career Press Inc.
Ed: Lisa Rogak. **Price:** $16.99. **Description:** Author helps burned-out workers envision a new future as a small business owner. Systems analysis, adventure travel outfitting, bookkeeping, food delivery, furniture making, and software development are among the industries examined.

44739 ■ "Aptitudes for Apps" in *Boston Business Journal* (Vol. 31, July 1, 2011, No. 23, pp. 3)
Pub: Boston Business Journal
Ed: Kyle Alspach. **Description:** Startups Apperian Inc. and Kinvey Inc. are aiming to accelerate the development and deployment of mobile applications and have received fund pledges from Boston-area venture capital firms.

44740 ■ "Local Startup Hits Big Leagues" in *Austin Business JournalInc.* (Vol. 28, December 19, 2008, No. 40, pp. 1)
Pub: American City Business Journals
Ed: Christopher Calnan. **Description:** Qcue LLC, an Austin, Texas-based company founded in 2007 is developing a software system that can be used by Major League Baseball teams to change the prices of their single-game tickets based on variables affecting demand. The company recently completed a trial with the San Francisco Giants in 2008.

44741 ■ "OtherInbox Ready for Revenue: Software Startup Expects Profits in '09" in *Austin Business JournalInc.* (Vol. 28, January 2, 2009)
Pub: American City Business Journals
Ed: Christopher Calnan. **Description:** Founder of Austin, Texas-based OtherBox Inc. expects the company to generate revenue through subscriptions and advertising and also reach profitability in 2009. The company's email management tool sends secondary mail to an alternate location thereby freeing up the work inbox for more urgent messages.

44742 ■ "Probability Processing Chip: Lyric Semiconductor" in *Inc.* (Volume 32, December 2010, No. 10, pp. 52)
Pub: Inc. Magazine
Ed: Christine Lagorio. **Description:** Lyric Semiconductor, a start up located in Cambridge, Massachusetts, has developed a computer chip that also uses values that fall between zero and one, resulting in a chip that can process information using probabilities, considering many possible answers that find the best fit.

ASSOCIATIONS AND OTHER ORGANIZATIONS

44743 ■ **Business Software Alliance**
1150 18th St. NW, Ste. 700
Washington, DC 20036

Ph:(202)872-5500
Fax:(202)872-5501
Co. E-mail: info@bsa.org
URL: http://www.bsa.org
Contact: Robert Holleyman II, Pres./CEO
Description: Computer software publishers. Promotes the free world trade of business software by combating international software piracy, advancing intellectual property protection, and increasing market access. **Publications:** *Guide to Software Management* (annual); *Software Review* (quarterly).

44744 ■ **TechAmerica**
601 Pennsylvania Ave. NW
North Bldg., Ste. 600
Arlington, VA 22209
Ph:(202)682-9110
Fax:(202)682-9111
Co. E-mail: olga.grkavac@techamerica.org
URL: http://www.itaa.org
Contact: Phil Bond, Pres./CEO
Description: A division of the Information Technology Association of America; software companies involved in the development or marketing of software for personal, midrange, and mainframe computers. Promotes the software industry and addresses specific problems of the industry. Represents the industry before various governmental units; provides educational programs to members; conducts research and makes available legal services. Develops standards. **Publications:** *Financial Operating Ratios for Software Companies*; *ITAA Software Industry Briefing Book*; *Quality Goes Global: An ITAA Guide to ISO 9,000 Standard Series for Information Technology Companies*; *Software Industry Executive Newsletter* (bimonthly).

EDUCATIONAL PROGRAMS

44745 ■ **Accessible Web Design: Complying with Section 508**
EEI Communications
66 Canal Ctr. Plz., Ste. 200
Alexandria, VA 22314-5507
Ph:(703)683-7453
Free: 888-253-2762
Fax:(703)683-7310
Co. E-mail: train@eeicom.com
URL: http://www.eeicom.com/training
Price: $425.00. **Description:** Covers what the law is and whom it applies, using HTML and CSS coding techniques to meet the guidelines, creating fluid design that adapts to user needs, using free validation to check site for accessibility, and putting the compliance icon on completed site. **Locations:** Silver Spring, MD; Alexandria, VA; Hunt Valley, MD; and Columbia, MD.

44746 ■ **Adobe Acrobat 9 for Legal Professionals**
EEI Communications
66 Canal Center Plz., Ste. 200
Alexandria, VA 22314
Ph:(703)683-7453
Free: 888-253-2762

Fax:(703)683-7310
Co. E-mail: train@eeicom.com
URL: http://www.eeicom.com/training
Price: $425.00. **Description:** Designed for lawyers and paralegals who need to incorporate specific legal procedures into their document workflow, including Redaction and Bates numbering. **Locations:** Alexandria, VA; Silver Spring, MD; Hunt Valley, MD; and Columbia, MD.

44747 ■ **Adobe Acrobat II**
EEI Communications
66 Canal Ctr. Plz., Ste. 200
Alexandria, VA 22314-5507
Ph:(703)683-7453
Free: 888-253-2762
Fax:(703)683-7310
Co. E-mail: train@eeicom.com
URL: http://www.eeicom.com/training
Price: $745.00. **Description:** Seminar that covers the advanced features of Adobe Acrobat, focusing on making documents accessible and flexible, incorporating digital signatures and security settings, creating and modifying PDF forms and multimedia presentations, using the engineering and technical features, and using Adobe Acrobat for professional publishing. **Locations:** Silver Spring, MD; and Alexandria, VA.

44748 ■ **Adobe Acrobat Section 508 Accessibility**
EEI Communications
66 Canal Ctr. Plz., Ste. 200
Alexandria, VA 22314-5507
Ph:(703)683-7453
Free: 888-253-2762
Fax:(703)683-7310
Co. E-mail: train@eeicom.com
URL: http://www.eeicom.com/training
Price: $425.00. **Description:** Covers the regulations by the Federal Government's Section 508 accessibility and the features of Adobe Acrobat software designed to meet the regulations, including definition of accessibility, authoring for accessibility, working with existing PDF files, forms, and scanned documents, using the accessibility checker, and tags palette, and testing your PDF files for accessibility. **Locations:** Alexandria, VA.

44749 ■ **Adobe After Effects II**
EEI Communications
66 Canal Ctr. Plz., Ste. 200
Alexandria, VA 22314-5507
Ph:(703)683-7453
Free: 888-253-2762
Fax:(703)683-7310
Co. E-mail: train@eeicom.com
URL: http://www.eeicom.com/training
Price: $1,065.00. **Description:** Seminar that builds on the foundation of After Effects I that covers the techniques that production environments use and learn to reverse-engineer popular effects seen on TV, including working with Rotoscoping techniques, keying and mattes, motion matching and video stabilization, 3D layers, cameras, and lights, titling effects

and filters, altering time and displacement, and rendering the movies and batching. **Locations:** Silver Spring, MD; and Alexandria, VA.

44750 ■ Adobe Bridge
EEI Communications
66 Canal Center Plz., Ste. 200
Alexandria, VA 22314
Ph:(703)683-7453
Free: 888-253-2762
Fax:(703)683-7310
Co. E-mail: train@eeicom.com
URL: http://www.eeicom.com/training
Price: $425.00. **Description:** Learn the many useful features hidden in Adobe Bridge, the command central for your Creative Suite 4 software, include the settings that help you get the most out of workflow. **Locations:** Alexandria, VA.

44751 ■ Adobe Captivate 3
EEI Communications
66 Canal Ctr. Plz., Ste. 200
Alexandria, VA 22314-5507
Ph:(703)683-7453
Free: 888-253-2762
Fax:(703)683-7310
Co. E-mail: train@eeicom.com
URL: http://www.eeicom.com/training
Price: $745.00. **Description:** Seminar that teaches how to create professional quality, interactive simulations and software demonstrations without any programming or multimedia knowledge, including basics, captions and timelines, images, pointer paths, buttons, and highlight boxes, movies, rollover captions and rollover images, slide labels and notes, audio, animation, and question slides. **Remarks:** Formerly known as Macromedia Authorware. **Locations:** Alexandria, VA.

44752 ■ Adobe ColdFusion II
EEI Communications
66 Canal Ctr. Plz., Ste. 200
Alexandria, VA 22314-5507
Ph:(703)683-7453
Free: 888-253-2762
Fax:(703)683-7310
Co. E-mail: train@eeicom.com
URL: http://www.eeicom.com/training
Price: $745.00. **Description:** Seminar that covers advanced programming techniques, including complex programming concepts such as arrays and loops, deploy application-level security, read information from and write information to text files on server, use the Verify search engine, schedule templates to run on a recurring basis, perform multiple queries as a transaction, and build intelligent "agents" for the Web. **Remarks:** Formerly known as Macromedia Authorware. **Locations:** Alexandria, VA.

44753 ■ Adobe Creative Suite 4 Bootcamp Training
EEI Communications
66 Canal Center Plz., Ste. 200
Alexandria, VA 22314
Ph:(703)683-7453
Free: 888-253-2762
Fax:(703)683-7310
Co. E-mail: train@eeicom.com
URL: http://www.eeicom.com/training
Price: $745.00. **Description:** Covers the interoperability and productively possible between Adobe Photoshop, Illustrator, InDesign, and Acrobat PDF. **Locations:** Silver Spring, MD; and Alexandria, VA.

44754 ■ Adobe Fireworks II
EEI Communications
66 Canal Ctr. Plz., Ste. 200
Alexandria, VA 22314-5507
Ph:(703)683-7453
Free: 888-253-2762
Fax:(703)683-7310
Co. E-mail: train@eeicom.com
URL: http://www.eeicom.com/training
Price: $745.00. **Description:** Covers Web page designs, including masks to create photomontages, create vector graphics, slicing advanced page designs, generate HTML and JavaScript code, swap images, and create pop-up images. **Remarks:** Formerly known as Macromedia Authorware. **Locations:** Silver Spring, MD.

44755 ■ Adobe Flash III
EEI Communications
66 Canal Ctr. Plz., Ste. 200
Alexandria, VA 22314-5507
Ph:(703)683-7453
Free: 888-253-2762
Fax:(703)683-7310
Co. E-mail: train@eeicom.com
URL: http://www.eeicom.com/training
Price: $745.00. **Description:** Covers project creation from planning and development, working with XML, advanced animation and interaction concepts and sound applications, and integrating video with Flash. **Remarks:** Formerly known as Macromedia Authorware. **Locations:** Silver Spring, MD; and Alexandria, VA.

44756 ■ Adobe Flash Media Server
EEI Communications
66 Canal Center Plz., Ste. 200
Alexandria, VA 22314
Ph:(703)683-7453
Free: 888-253-2762
Fax:(703)683-7310
Co. E-mail: train@eeicom.com
URL: http://www.eeicom.com/training
Price: $745.00. **Description:** Provides experienced Flash developers with the knowledge and hands-on experience they need to build and deliver Streaming and Social Media applications with Flash Media Server 3, with focus on Server Side ActionScript, ActionScript 3 and Flash skills required to build real-world media applications with audio, video, and data that interact with the user. **Locations:** Alexandria, VA.

44757 ■ Adobe Flex I - Developing Rich Internet Client Applications
EEI Communications
66 Canal Center Plz., Ste. 200
Alexandria, VA 22314
Ph:(703)683-7453
Free: 888-253-2762
Fax:(703)683-7310
Co. E-mail: train@eeicom.com
URL: http://www.eeicom.com/training
Price: $1,245.00. **Description:** Introduction to the Flex technology teaches how to develop fully functional, well architected front end for a Rich Internet Application (RIA). **Locations:** Alexandria, VA.

44758 ■ Adobe Flex II - Data and Communications
EEI Communications
66 Canal Center Plz., Ste. 200
Alexandria, VA 22314
Ph:(703)683-7453
Free: 888-253-2762
Fax:(703)683-7310
Co. E-mail: train@eeicom.com
URL: http://www.eeicom.com/training
Price: $995.00. **Description:** Learn how your Flex applications exchange data and communicate with remote objects in this hands-on course. **Locations:** Alexandria, VA.

44759 ■ Adobe Flex III - Building Dashboard Applications
EEI Communications
66 Canal Center Plz., Ste. 200
Alexandria, VA 22314
Ph:(703)683-7453
Free: 888-253-2762
Fax:(703)683-7310
Co. E-mail: train@eeicom.com
URL: http://www.eeicom.com/training
Price: $995.00. **Description:** Learn how to build dashboard applications using Adobe Flex 3 to create highly interactive charts and graphs for data visualization, including creating interactive charts and dynamically controlling the chart data. **Locations:** Alexandria, VA.

44760 ■ Adobe FrameMaker I
EEI Communications
66 Canal Center Plz., Ste. 200
Alexandria, VA 22314
Ph:(703)683-7453
Free: 888-253-2762
Fax:(703)683-7310
Co. E-mail: train@eeicom.com
URL: http://www.eeicom.com/training
Price: $1,065.00. **Description:** Learn how to design FrameMaker publication in its entirety, as well as work on a variety of FrameMaker documents. Some topics include understanding FrameMaker interface and screen elements, using paragraph designer to control paragraph formatting, working with character designer, adding color to character and paragraph formats, working with master pages and anchored frames, creating running headers and footers, creating and editing variables and working with table designer and customizing tables. **Locations:** Alexandria, VA.

44761 ■ Adobe FrameMaker III: Structured
EEI Communications
66 Canal Ctr. Plz., Ste. 200
Alexandria, VA 22314-5507
Ph:(703)683-7453
Free: 888-253-2762
Fax:(703)683-7310
Co. E-mail: train@eeicom.com
URL: http://www.eeicom.com/training
Price: $745.00. **Description:** Seminar using Adobe FrameMaker as an authoring tool for creating XML documents, including structured interface and add and edit elements and attributes, documents with structured content EDD (Element Definition Document) and DTD (Document Type Definitions), converting unstructured documents, and the latest tools availible for cross-media publishing. **Locations:** Alexandria, VA.

44762 ■ Adobe InDesign CS4 Master Class for Designers Training
EEI Communications
66 Canal Center Plz., Ste. 200
Alexandria, VA 22314
Ph:(703)683-7453
Free: 888-253-2762
Fax:(703)683-7310
Co. E-mail: train@eeicom.com
URL: http://www.eeicom.com/training
Price: $895.00. **Description:** Master Adobe InDesign CS4's styles, text processing capabilities, table-creation tools, automation features, and in-document creativity enhancements to free up countless hours from smaller tasks and concentrate on designing. **Locations:** Silver Spring, MD; Hunt Valley, MD; Columbia, MD; and Alexandria, VA.

44763 ■ Adobe InDesign III
EEI Communications
66 Canal Ctr. Plz., Ste. 200
Alexandria, VA 22314-5507
Ph:(703)683-7453
Free: 888-253-2762
Fax:(703)683-7310
Co. E-mail: train@eeicom.com
URL: http://www.eeicom.com/training
Price: $745.00. **Description:** 2-day seminar that explores the advanced features within Adobe InDesign, including transparency features, feathering, and drop shadows, hyperlinks for PDF or DHTML, create a book list, formatting an index, generate a table of contents, advanced frame techniques and color management, and XML and other cross-media publishing support. **Locations:** Alexandria, VA.

44764 ■ Adobe InDesign with InCopy for Workgroups Training
EEI Communications
66 Canal Center Plz., Ste. 200
Alexandria, VA 22314
Ph:(703)683-7453
Free: 888-253-2762

Fax:(703)683-7310
Co. E-mail: train@eeicom.com
URL: http://www.eeicom.com/training
Price: $425.00. **Description:** Learn a professional writing and editing program that tightly integrates with Adobe InDesign for a complete solution, including assigning editors to work on parts of pages, spreads, or entire documents in parallel with designers, significantly decreasing the production time for projects. **Locations:** Alexandria, VA.

44765 ■ Adobe InDesign IV
EEI Communications
66 Canal Center Plz., Ste. 200
Alexandria, VA 22314
Ph:(703)683-7453
Free: 888-253-2762
Fax:(703)683-7310
Co. E-mail: train@eeicom.com
URL: http://www.eeicom.com/training
Price: $795.00. **Description:** Examine ways to speed up productivity in your workflow by taking advantage of the many advanced features throughout InDesign CS4, including an interactive Data Merge project for joining graphic design with data from an external file. **Locations:** Alexandria, VA.

44766 ■ Adobe InDesign for Long Documents I
EEI Communications
66 Canal Center Plz., Ste. 200
Alexandria, VA 22314
Ph:(703)683-7453
Free: 888-253-2762
Fax:(703)683-7310
Co. E-mail: train@eeicom.com
URL: http://www.eeicom.com/training
Price: $795.00. **Description:** Learn to publish long documents, such as books or annual reports. Also, explore Adobe InDesign CS4 options in numbering, position figures in relation to text automatically, create running headers or footers, and much more. **Locations:** Alexandria, VA; and Silver Spring, MD.

44767 ■ Adobe InDesign for Long Documents II
EEI Communications
66 Canal Center Plz., Ste. 200
Alexandria, VA 22314
Ph:(703)683-7453
Free: 888-253-2762
Fax:(703)683-7310
Co. E-mail: train@eeicom.com
URL: http://www.eeicom.com/training
Price: $795.00. **Description:** Learn all you need to know to work effectively with InDesign CS4, including advanced features. **Locations:** Silver Spring, MD; and Alexandria, VA.

44768 ■ Adobe InDesign for Long Documents III
EEI Communications
66 Canal Center Plz., Ste. 200
Alexandria, VA 22314
Ph:(703)683-7453
Free: 888-253-2762
Fax:(703)683-7310
Co. E-mail: train@eeicom.com
URL: http://www.eeicom.com/training
Price: $795.00. **Description:** Learn to fully exploit all the advanced featured of InDesign CS4 as your integrated workflow and publishing environment. **Locations:** Alexandria, VA.

44769 ■ Adobe Lightroom Photo Workflow
EEI Communications
66 Canal Center Plz., Ste. 200
Alexandria, VA 22314
Ph:(703)683-7453
Free: 888-253-2762
Fax:(703)683-7310
Co. E-mail: train@eeicom.com
URL: http://www.eeicom.com/training
Price: $745.00. **Description:** Covers importing and arranging photos, quick edits, developing modules' array of image correction controls, tone curves, black and white conversions, working with Photoshop,

slideshow's customizable features, exporting images, and print controls and custom print layouts. **Locations:** Silver Spring, MD; and Alexandria, VA.

44770 ■ Adobe Photoshop for Beginners
Seminar Information Service, Inc.
20 Executive Park, Ste. 120
Irvine, CA 92614
Ph:(949)261-9104
Free: 877-SEM-INFO
Fax:(949)261-1963
Co. E-mail: info@seminarinformation.com
URL: http://www.seminarinformation.com
Price: $179.00. **Description:** Learn how to manipulate images, retouch photos, and cut down time through the entire design process. **Locations:** Houston, TX; Dallas, TX; Cromwell, CT; and Boston, MA.

44771 ■ Adobe Photoshop Channels and Masks
EEI Communications
66 Canal Center Plz., Ste. 200
Alexandria, VA 22314
Ph:(703)683-7453
Free: 888-253-2762
Fax:(703)683-7310
Co. E-mail: train@eeicom.com
URL: http://www.eeicom.com/training
Price: $745.00. **Description:** Learn how to make masks using channels in Adobe Photoshop CS3 to create high quality and accurate selections like the professionals do. **Locations:** Alexandria, VA.

44772 ■ Adobe Photoshop Digital Mastery I
EEI Communications
66 Canal Ctr. Plz., Ste. 200
Alexandria, VA 22314-5507
Ph:(703)683-7453
Free: 888-253-2762
Fax:(703)683-7310
Co. E-mail: train@eeicom.com
URL: http://www.eeicom.com/training
Price: $745.00. **Description:** Covers techniques for photo recovery, image enhancements, and professional portrait work. **Locations:** Alexandria, VA.

44773 ■ Adobe Photoshop Digital Painting
EEI Communications
66 Canal Center Plz., Ste. 200
Alexandria, VA 22314
Ph:(703)683-7453
Free: 888-253-2762
Fax:(703)683-7310
Co. E-mail: train@eeicom.com
URL: http://www.eeicom.com/training
Price: $745.00. **Description:** Learn digital painting techniques from adding colors and effects to line art to creating full-on digital paintings in various artistic styles, including watercolor and oil. **Locations:** Silver Spring, MD; Hunt Valley, MD; Columbia, MD; and Alexandria, VA.

44774 ■ Adobe Photoshop Extended
EEI Communications
66 Canal Center Plz., Ste. 200
Alexandria, VA 22314
Ph:(703)683-7453
Free: 888-253-2762
Fax:(703)683-7310
Co. E-mail: train@eeicom.com
URL: http://www.eeicom.com/training
Price: $425.00. **Description:** Covers 3D compositing and texture editing, enhanced vanishing point with 3D support, movie paint, the new animation palette, importing and playing video in Photoshop, video layers, using 2D and 3D measurement tools, scale marker, count tool and combining image stacks. **Locations:** Silver Spring, MD; Hunt Valley, MD; Columbia, MD; and Alexandria, VA.

44775 ■ Advanced Training for Microsoft Excel (Onsite)
Padgett-Thompson Seminars
Rockhurst University CEC
14502 W. 105th St.
Lenexa, KS 66215

Free: 800-349-1935
URL: http://www.findaseminar.com/tpd/Padgett-Thompson-Seminars.asp
Price: $179.00. **Description:** An intensive one-day seminar that teaches the most advanced features of Microsoft Excel. **Locations:** Duluth, MN.

44776 ■ AJAX Development I
EEI Communications
66 Canal Center Plz., Ste. 200
Alexandria, VA 22314
Ph:(703)683-7453
Free: 888-253-2762
Fax:(703)683-7310
Co. E-mail: train@eeicom.com
URL: http://www.eeicom.com/training
Price: $745.00. **Description:** Learn how to make dynamic and interactive Web applications using Asynchronous JavaScript and XML (AJAX), including a review of the essential elements of XHTML, CSS, and XML. **Locations:** Alexandria, VA.

44777 ■ AJAX Development II
EEI Communications
66 Canal Center Plz., Ste. 200
Alexandria, VA 22314
Ph:(703)683-7453
Free: 888-253-2762
Fax:(703)683-7310
Co. E-mail: train@eeicom.com
URL: http://www.eeicom.com/training
Price: $745.00. **Description:** In this advanced class explore AJAX in greater depth through topics that include addressing security concerns inherent to AJAX, using XPath and XSLT in your AJAX development, validating form data, managing user sessions, and explore the available AJAX frameworks. **Locations:** Alexandria, VA.

44778 ■ Apple DVD Studio Pro I
EEI Communications
66 Canal Ctr. Plz., Ste. 200
Alexandria, VA 22314-5507
Ph:(703)683-7453
Free: 888-253-2762
Fax:(703)683-7310
Co. E-mail: train@eeicom.com
URL: http://www.eeicom.com/training
Price: $745.00. **Description:** Seminar that covers creating menus within DVD Studio Pro, creating slide shows, adding subtitles and closed captioning, multiple language/audio streams, DVD-ROM content and Internet access, options to encode high quality video, creating and working with buttons, overlays, markers, and stories, basic scripting, advanced menu design, working with and creating transitions, using alternate and mixed angles, and Dolby, surround, and PCM audio encoding. **Locations:** Alexandria, VA.

44779 ■ Apple Final Cut Pro Bootcamp
EEI Communications
66 Canal Center Plz., Ste. 200
Alexandria, VA 22314
Ph:(703)683-7453
Free: 888-253-2762
Fax:(703)683-7310
Co. E-mail: train@eeicom.com
URL: http://www.eeicom.com/training
Price: $1,625.00. **Description:** Course includes an introduction to Final Cut Pro Interface, basic video editing, importing and exporting video footage, introduction to Soundtrack Pro Interface, basic audio editing, post-production techniques with video, introduction to DVD Studio Pro, introduction to motion, post-production techniques with video, introduction to DVD Studio Pro, and authoring DVDs to your own specifications. **Locations:** Alexandria, VA.

44780 ■ Apple Final Cut Pro I
EEI Communications
66 Canal Ctr. Plz., Ste. 200
Alexandria, VA 22314-5507
Ph:(703)683-7453
Free: 888-253-2762

Fax:(703)683-7310
Co. E-mail: train@eeicom.com
URL: http://www.eeicom.com/training
Price: $745.00. **Description:** Seminar that covers editing using Apple, including working with interface, video standard and HD basics, marking and editing, timeline control, single- and double-sided trimming, master clips, subclips and working with markers, capturing video, importing and exporting assets, working with audio and mixing audio tracks, applying transitions, adding and working with filters, build a composite image, change clip speeds, create motion effects, adding text and graphics, working with and creating animated titles, and finishing and outputting. **Locations:** Alexandria, VA.

44781 ■ Apple Final Cut Pro II
EEI Communications
66 Canal Center Plz., Ste. 200
Alexandria, VA 22314
Ph:(703)683-7453
Free: 888-253-2762
Fax:(703)683-7310
Co. E-mail: train@eeicom.com
URL: http://www.eeicom.com/training
Price: $745.00. **Description:** Learn all you need to know to create your video from concept to completion, including working with the interface, video standard and HD basics, timeline control, single- and double-sided trimming, capturing video and much more. **Locations:** Alexandria, VA.

44782 ■ Apple Motion I
EEI Communications
66 Canal Ctr. Plz., Ste. 200
Alexandria, VA 22314-5507
Ph:(703)683-7453
Free: 888-253-2762
Fax:(703)683-7310
Co. E-mail: train@eeicom.com
URL: http://www.eeicom.com/training
Price: $745.00. **Description:** Covers real-time motion graphics, including using generators, working with layers and objects, use and create customized templates, particles and parameter behaviors, blend modes, nonlinear editing and motion, key-framing, audio and setting markers, and create text effects. **Locations:** Alexandria, VA.

44783 ■ ASP.NET with VB.NET and C I
EEI Communications
66 Canal Center Plz., Ste. 200
Alexandria, VA 22314
Ph:(703)683-7453
Free: 888-253-2762
Fax:(703)683-7310
Co. E-mail: train@eeicom.com
URL: http://www.eeicom.com/training
Price: $1,065.00. **Description:** Learn to write dynamic, high-performance Web applications with Microsoft's ASP.NET. Topics include introduction of Web forms, controls (HTML, Server, Web), ASP.NET application state management, and error handling. **Locations:** Alexandria, VA.

44784 ■ ASP.NET with VB.NET and C II
EEI Communications
66 Canal Center Plz., Ste. 200
Alexandria, VA 22314
Ph:(703)683-7453
Free: 888-253-2762
Fax:(703)683-7310
Co. E-mail: train@eeicom.com
URL: http://www.eeicom.com/training
Price: $1,065.00. **Description:** Hands-on class with those with knowledge of HTML and some programming who want to study data binding, data controls and templates, consuming and manipulating data, and creating and managing .NET components and assemblies. **Locations:** Alexandria, VA.

44785 ■ ASP.NET with VB.NET C III
EEI Communications
66 Canal Center Plz., Ste. 200
Alexandria, VA 22314
Ph:(703)683-7453
Free: 888-253-2762

Fax:(703)683-7310
Co. E-mail: train@eeicom.com
URL: http://www.eeicom.com/training
Price: $1,065.00. **Description:** Hands-on class for those with the knowledge of HTML and some programming background who want to study Web services, localization, Web accessibility, testing and debugging a Web application, and configuring a Web application. **Locations:** Alexandria, VA.

44786 ■ Auditing Business Application Systems
Seminar Information Service, Inc.
20 Executive Park, Ste. 120
Irvine, CA 92614
Ph:(949)261-9104
Free: 877-SEM-INFO
Fax:(949)261-1963
Co. E-mail: info@seminarinformation.com
URL: http://www.seminarinformation.com
Price: $1,950.00. **Description:** Three-day seminar attendees will learn how to audit and how to develop controls for complex automated applications which use online/real-time, distributed processing, and/or database technologies, including an opportunity to actually prepare an audit plan for a complex application system. **Locations:** Chicago, IL; New York, NY; San Francisco, CA; and Boston, MA.

44787 ■ Business Analysis Essentials
Seminar Information Service, Inc.
20 Executive Park, Ste. 120
Irvine, CA 92614
Ph:(949)261-9104
Free: 877-SEM-INFO
Fax:(949)261-1963
Co. E-mail: info@seminarinformation.com
URL: http://www.seminarinformation.com
Price: $1,195.00. **Description:** Learn to define the scope of work and master requirements-gathering techniques that will work for a variety of projects and audiences. **Locations:** Cities throughout Canada.

44788 ■ Cascading Style Sheets II
EEI Communications
66 Canal Ctr. Plz., Ste. 200
Alexandria, VA 22314-5507
Ph:(703)683-7453
Free: 888-253-2762
Fax:(703)683-7310
Co. E-mail: train@eeicom.com
URL: http://www.eeicom.com/training
Price: $425.00. **Description:** Covers the conversion of an HTML Web site to a site that uses Cascading Style Sheets, including text enhancements, link color control, table conversion to precise positioning, layering with text and graphics, DHTML effects, a watermark background image, and validation CSS code. **Locations:** Alexandria, VA.

44789 ■ Color Management for Adobe Creative Suite 4 (CS4)
EEI Communications
66 Canal Center Plz., Ste. 200
Alexandria, VA 22314
Ph:(703)683-7453
Free: 888-253-2762
Fax:(703)683-7310
Co. E-mail: train@eeicom.com
URL: http://www.eeicom.com/training
Price: $795.00. **Description:** Learn how to get predictable, accurate, and stable color from scratch to screen to proof and printed output, including assessing your system for improvement by calibration. **Locations:** Alexandria, VA.

44790 ■ Color Management for Digital Publishing
EEI Communications
66 Canal Ctr. Plz., Ste. 200
Alexandria, VA 22314-5507
Ph:(703)683-7453
Free: 888-253-2762

Fax:(703)683-7310
Co. E-mail: train@eeicom.com
URL: http://www.eeicom.com/training
Price: $795.00. **Description:** Covers color theory and color models, build and edit ICC profiles, color management at the OS level, and setup. **Locations:** Alexandria, VA.

44791 ■ Deploying Microsoft Windows Vista Business Desktops (Onsite)
Seminar Information Service, Inc.
20 Executive Park, Ste. 120
Irvine, CA 92614
Ph:(949)261-9104
Free: 877-SEM-INFO
Fax:(949)261-1963
Co. E-mail: info@seminarinformation.com
URL: http://www.seminarinformation.com
Price: $2,095.00. **Description:** Three-day training to get the knowledge and skills you needed to successfully deploy Windows Vista business desktops throughout your organization. **Locations:** Morristown, NJ; Ottawa, CN; Washington, DC; and Toronto, CN.

44792 ■ Designing and Building Great Web Pages: Hands-On (Onsite)
Seminar Information Service, Inc.
20 Executive Park, Ste. 120
Irvine, CA 92614
Ph:(949)261-9104
Free: 877-SEM-INFO
Fax:(949)261-1963
Co. E-mail: info@seminarinformation.com
URL: http://www.seminarinformation.com
Price: $2,890.00. **Description:** Learn to build powerful Web content that effectively conveys your message; Create graphical content using Photoshop CS2, Fireworks 8 and Flash 8; Develop Web page content with FrontPage and Dreamweaver 8; Generate complex Web pages using Cascading Style Sheets, tables and layers; and Enhance Web pages with special effects and DHTML. **Locations:** Rockville, MD; Ottawa, CN; Reston, VA; and New York, NY.

44793 ■ Developing Effective Software Estimation Techniques (Onsite)
Seminar Information Service, Inc.
20 Executive Park, Ste. 120
Irvine, CA 92614
Ph:(949)261-9104
Free: 877-SEM-INFO
Fax:(949)261-1963
Co. E-mail: info@seminarinformation.com
URL: http://www.seminarinformation.com
Price: $2,490.00. **Description:** Learn how to prepare a software project estimate through an iterative process; Develop an initial estimate using the expert judgment method; Apply historical data for greater precision in an estimate; Refine the size or scope estimate using a component-based method; Perform Function Point calculations to determine the magnitude of a project; Translate a size or scope estimate into a time, schedule and cost estimate. **Locations:** Toronto and Ottawa, CN.

44794 ■ Developing SQL Queries for SQL Server: Hands-On (Onsite)
Seminar Information Service, Inc.
20 Executive Park, Ste. 120
Irvine, CA 92614
Ph:(949)261-9104
Free: 877-SEM-INFO
Fax:(949)261-1963
Co. E-mail: info@seminarinformation.com
URL: http://www.seminarinformation.com
Price: $2,890.00. **Description:** Learn how to develop complex and robust SQL queries for SQL Server 2005 and SQL Server 2000; Query multiple tables with inner joins, outer joins and self joins; Transform data with built-in functions; Summarize data using aggregation and grouping; Execute analytic functions to calculate ranks; Build simple and correlated subqueries. **Locations:** Cities throughout the United States.

44795 ■ Digital Scanning for Production
EEI Communications
66 Canal Ctr. Plz., Ste. 200
Alexandria, VA 22314-5507

Ph:(703)683-7453
Free: 888-253-2762
Fax:(703)683-7310
Co. E-mail: train@eeicom.com
URL: http://www.eeicom.com/training
Price: $745.00. **Description:** Seminar designed for those using any digital purpose, including direct reproduction or inclusion in page layout programs. **Locations:** Alexandria, VA; Silver Spring, MD; and Washington, DC.

44796 ■ Digital Video Production for Streaming and DVD
EEI Communications
66 Canal Ctr. Plz., Ste. 200
Alexandria, VA 22314-5507
Ph:(703)683-7453
Free: 888-253-2762
Fax:(703)683-7310
Co. E-mail: train@eeicom.com
URL: http://www.eeicom.com/training
Price: $1,065.00. **Description:** Seminar the teaches the process of producing video for distribution via the Web, CD, DVD and computer-based presentations, including writing, directing, shooting, recording, capture, edit, and encode/compress effective digital video for training, marketing, internal communications, public information, and other uses. Also, communicate effectively with internal clients/staff, video crews, and editing facilities. **Locations:** Alexandria, VA.

44797 ■ Dynamic Web Development I
EEI Communications
66 Canal Center Plz., Ste. 200
Alexandria, VA 22314
Ph:(703)683-7453
Free: 888-253-2762
Fax:(703)683-7310
Co. E-mail: train@eeicom.com
URL: http://www.eeicom.com/training
Price: $1,065.00. **Description:** Those already familiar with HTML and how to do some programming will learn to write high-performance Web applications with Microsoft's ASP.NET. Topics include Web forms, controls (HTML, server, Web), ASP.NET application state management, and error handling. **Locations:** Alexandria, VA.

44798 ■ Dynamic Web Development II
EEI Communications
66 Canal Center Plz., Ste. 200
Alexandria, VA 22314
Ph:(703)683-7453
Free: 888-253-2762
Fax:(703)683-7310
Co. E-mail: train@eeicom.com
URL: http://www.eeicom.com/training
Price: $1,065.00. **Description:** Explore data binding, data controls and templates, consuming and manipulating data, and creating and managing .NET components and assemblies. **Locations:** Alexandria, VA.

44799 ■ Enhanced and Video Podcasts
EEI Communications
66 Canal Center Plz., Ste. 200
Alexandria, VA 22314
Ph:(703)683-7453
Free: 888-253-2762
Fax:(703)683-7310
Co. E-mail: train@eeicom.com
URL: http://www.eeicom.com/training
Price: $745.00. **Description:** Course includes the pros and cons of enhanced podcasts and video poscasts, creating enhanced podcasts with GarageBand (Mac), creating enhanced podcasts on a PC, creating video podcasts with Funal Cut Pro (Mac) with Adobe Audition (PC), Using QuickTime Pro (Mac/PC) in post-production, compression and other troubleshooting issues, keeping production values simple but professional, how to keep video podcasts, and quick, easy downloads. **Locations:** Alexandria, VA.

44800 ■ The Essentials Of Crystal Reports
Seminar Information Service, Inc.
20 Executive Park, Ste. 120
Irvine, CA 92614
Ph:(949)261-9104
Free: 877-SEM-INFO

Fax:(949)261-1963
Co. E-mail: info@seminarinformation.com
URL: http://www.seminarinformation.com
Price: $199.00. **Description:** Learn to create complex reports containing huge amounts of information to simple reports without being an expert in databases. **Locations:** Cities throughout the United States.

44801 ■ Forensic Photoshop
EEI Communications
66 Canal Center Plz., Ste. 200
Alexandria, VA 22314
Ph:(703)683-7453
Free: 888-253-2762
Fax:(703)683-7310
Co. E-mail: train@eeicom.com
URL: http://www.eeicom.com/training
Price: $745.00. **Description:** Designed for law enforcement and Homeland Security personnel that outlines the processes for using Photoshop in a forensic environment. **Locations:** Silver Spring, MD; Hunt Valley, MD; Columbia, MD; and Alexandria, VA.

44802 ■ How to Manage an Information Security Program
Seminar Information Service, Inc.
20 Executive Park, Ste. 120
Irvine, CA 92614
Ph:(949)261-9104
Free: 877-SEM-INFO
Fax:(949)261-1963
Co. E-mail: info@seminarinformation.com
URL: http://www.seminarinformation.com
Price: $2,050.00. **Description:** Learn the components of a comprehensive plan, covering access control software applications; telecom/network security measures; physical protection of the computer facility; and the legal and regulatory aspects of information security. **Locations:** New York, NY; and Orlando, FL.

44803 ■ Introduction to ASP.NET 2.0 Applications
EEI Communications
66 Canal Ctr. Plz., Ste. 200
Alexandria, VA 22314-5507
Ph:(703)683-7453
Free: 888-253-2762
Fax:(703)683-7310
Co. E-mail: train@eeicom.com
URL: http://www.eeicom.com/training
Price: $745.00. **Description:** Seminar designed for ASP.NET programmers, includes ASP.NET 2.0 applications, master pages, Web parts and personalized API, ADO.NET 2.0 and data-bound controls, membership and role management API, and Web form wizards. **Locations:** Silver Spring, MD; Alexandria, VA; Hunt Valley, MD; and Columbia, MD.

44804 ■ Introduction to .Net and ASP.NET
EEI Communications
66 Canal Ctr. Plz., Ste. 200
Alexandria, VA 22314-5507
Ph:(703)683-7453
Free: 888-253-2762
Fax:(703)683-7310
Co. E-mail: train@eeicom.com
URL: http://www.eeicom.com/training
Price: $745.00. **Description:** Covers Microsoft.NET and ASP.NET Web pages in both Visual Basic.NET and C (pronounced C-sharp), including Microsoft.Net framework, common language run-time, base framework classes, ADO.NET, ASP.NET, .NET compact framework, XML Web services, and .NET languages **Locations:** Silver Spring, MD; Alexandria, VA; Hunt Valley, MD; and Columbia, MD.

44805 ■ Introduction to PHP and MySQL
EEI Communications
66 Canal Ctr. Plz., Ste. 200
Alexandria, VA 22314-5507
Ph:(703)683-7453
Free: 888-253-2762

Fax:(703)683-7310
Co. E-mail: train@eeicom.com
URL: http://www.eeicom.com/training
Price: $745.00. **Description:** Seminar that covers an open-source scripting language for developing database-driven Web sites, including how to download and install PHP on Web server, using PHP to respond to HTML form submissions, sending e-mail messages with PHP, SQL and querying databases with PHP, and managing state information with cookies and sessions. **Locations:** Silver Spring, MD; Alexandria, VA; Hunt Valley, MD; and Columbia, MD.

44806 ■ Layout Software Basics
EEI Communications
66 Canal Ctr. Plz., Ste. 200
Alexandria, VA 22314-5507
Ph:(703)683-7453
Free: 888-253-2762
Fax:(703)683-7310
Co. E-mail: train@eeicom.com
URL: http://www.eeicom.com/training
Price: $425.00. **Description:** Seminar that provides an introduction to publishing and graphics software, including a step-by-step introduction through the terms and tools of applications used by graphic designers, illustrators, photographers, and editors. **Locations:** Alexandria, VA.

44807 ■ Mastering Microsoft Excel
Fred Pryor Seminars & CareerTrack
5700 Broadmoor St., Ste. 300
Mission, KS 66202
Free: 800-780-8476
Fax:(913)967-8849
Co. E-mail: customerservice@pryor.com
URL: http://www.pryor.com
Price: $299.00; $279.00 for groups of 3 or more. **Description:** Seminar designed to deliver the most information in the least amount of time, including how to create spreadsheets, input data, perform mathematical calculations, develop workbooks, edit cells, and use formulas, functions, Wizards, and more. **Locations:** Cities throughout the United States.

44808 ■ Microsoft Access: A 2-Day Hands-On Workshop
Fred Pryor Seminars & CareerTrack
5700 Broadmoor St., Ste. 300
Mission, KS 66202
Free: 800-780-8476
Fax:(913)967-8849
Co. E-mail: customerservice@pryor.com
URL: http://www.pryor.com
Price: $299.00; $279.00 for groups of 3 or more. **Description:** Learn how to use features, how to solve problems, and customize Access for the way you work. **Locations:** Cities throughout the United States.

44809 ■ Microsoft Excel
Padgett-Thompson Seminars
Rockhurst University CEC
14502 W. 105th St.
Lenexa, KS 66215
Free: 800-349-1935
URL: http://www.findaseminar.com/tpd/Padgett-Thompson-Seminars.asp
Price: $199.00. **Description:** One-day workshop covering ways to get the most out of Excel's features and functions. **Locations:** Cities throughout the United States.

44810 ■ Microsoft Excel 2003/2007 - II
EEI Communications
66 Canal Ctr. Plz., Ste. 200
Alexandria, VA 22314-5507
Ph:(703)683-7453
Free: 888-253-2762
Fax:(703)683-7310
Co. E-mail: train@eeicom.com
URL: http://www.eeicom.com/training
Price: $745.00. **Description:** Seminar covering the advanced features of Excel, including advanced formulas, PivotTables, and analysis tools, including customizing workbook and toolbars, working with multiple data sources, edit macros, test data, and protect worksheets. **Locations:** Silver Spring, MD; and Alexandria, VA.

44811 ■ Microsoft Excel Basics
Fred Pryor Seminars & CareerTrack
5700 Broadmoor St., Ste. 300
Mission, KS 66202
Free: 800-780-8476
Fax:(913)967-8849
Co. E-mail: customerservice@pryor.com
URL: http://www.pryor.com

Price: $79.00; $74.00 for groups of 5 or more. **Description:** Seminar for Excel 2007 and 2010 starting with the basics and moving to more advanced features. **Locations:** Cities throughout the United States.

44812 ■ Microsoft PowerPoint 2007
Fred Pryor Seminars & CareerTrack
5700 Broadmoor St., Ste. 300
Mission, KS 66202
Free: 800-780-8476
Fax:(913)967-8849
Co. E-mail: customerservice@pryor.com
URL: http://www.pryor.com

Price: $149.00; $149.00 for groups of 5 or more. **Description:** Learn to put together well constructed, engaging and entertaining, pleasing to the eye, properly paced, and unmistakable clear in message presentations. **Locations:** Cities throughout the United States.

44813 ■ Microsoft Project 2003/2007 - II
EEI Communications
66 Canal Ctr. Plz., Ste. 200
Alexandria, VA 22314-5507
Ph:(703)683-7453
Free: 888-253-2762
Fax:(703)683-7310
Co. E-mail: train@eeicom.com
URL: http://www.eeicom.com/training

Price: $745.00. **Description:** Seminar that covers workload adjustments and developing tracking skills to ensure a successful project completion, including fine-tuning task, resource, and assignment information, reorganizing phases and tasks, analyzing the critical path, leveling over-allocated resources, documenting resource details with reports, create consumption rates, track project progress, create an interim plan, and documenting the project's progress with reports. **Locations:** Alexandria, VA.

44814 ■ Microsoft SharePoint I
EEI Communications
66 Canal Center Plz., Ste. 200
Alexandria, VA 22314
Ph:(703)683-7453
Free: 888-253-2762
Fax:(703)683-7310
Co. E-mail: train@eeicom.com
URL: http://www.eeicom.com/training

Price: $745.00. **Description:** Learn practical hands-on exercise techniques for using the document and project collaboration tools in Windows SharePoint Services. **Locations:** Alexandria, VA.

44815 ■ Microsoft SharePoint II
EEI Communications
66 Canal Center Plz., Ste. 200
Alexandria, VA 22314
Ph:(703)683-7453
Free: 888-253-2762
Fax:(703)683-7310
Co. E-mail: train@eeicom.com
URL: http://www.eeicom.com/training

Price: $1,065.00. **Description:** Hands-on class you will learn the skills to design, maintain, and publish a custom SharePoint site. **Locations:** Alexandria, VA.

44816 ■ Microsoft SharePoint III
EEI Communications
66 Canal Ctr. Plz., Ste. 200
Alexandria, VA 22314
Ph:(703)683-7453
Free: 888-253-2762

Fax:(703)683-7310
Co. E-mail: train@eeicom.com
URL: http://www.eeicom.com/training

Price: $1,065.00. **Description:** Hands-on class you learn how to create and make modifications that can be applied to all users on the site or to individual users using Microsoft SharePoint controls. **Locations:** Alexandria, VA.

44817 ■ Migrating to Structured Authoring in Adobe Framemaker
EEI Communications
66 Canal Center Plz., Ste. 200
Alexandria, VA 22314
Ph:(703)683-7453
Free: 888-253-2762
Fax:(703)683-7310
Co. E-mail: train@eeicom.com
URL: http://www.eeicom.com/training

Price: $745.00. **Description:** Learn to work with structured interface view, element catalogs, an understanding of elements and their attributes, edit structured documents, change, merge, split and wrapping of elements, working with paragraph, character, graphic, and table elements, validating documents, adding and editing element definitions, setting up elements with automatic insertion of children, and convert unstructured to structured documents. **Locations:** Alexandria, VA.

44818 ■ Object-Oriented Programming (OOP) Boot Camp
EEI Communications
66 Canal Ctr. Plz., Ste. 200
Alexandria, VA 22314-5507
Ph:(703)683-7453
Free: 888-253-2762
Fax:(703)683-7310
Co. E-mail: train@eeicom.com
URL: http://www.eeicom.com/training

Price: $425.00. **Description:** Seminar that teaches what it means to give objects characteristics that can be transferred to, added to, and combined with other objects to make a complete program, including classes and objects, fields, properties, methods, and events, encapsulating, inheritance and polymorphisms, overloading, overriding, and shadowing. **Locations:** Silver Spring, MD; Alexandria, VA; Hunt Valley, MD; and Columbia, MD.

44819 ■ Professional Design Techniques with Adobe Creative Suite 4 (CS4)
EEI Communications
66 Canal Center Plz., Ste. 200
Alexandria, VA 22314
Ph:(703)683-7453
Free: 888-253-2762
Fax:(703)683-7310
Co. E-mail: train@eeicom.com
URL: http://www.eeicom.com/training

Price: $745.00. **Description:** Covers design principles and workflow techniques in real-life projects, including the management of numerous parts, such as stories, data, charts, and images. **Locations:** Alexandria, VA.

44820 ■ C Programming: Hands-On (Onsite)
Seminar Information Service, Inc.
20 Executive Park, Ste. 120
Irvine, CA 92614
Ph:(949)261-9104
Free: 877-SEM-INFO
Fax:(949)261-1963
Co. E-mail: info@seminarinformation.com
URL: http://www.seminarinformation.com

Price: $2,890.00. **Description:** Learn how to: Create, compile and run C programs using Visual Studio 2005; Write and understand C language constructs, syntax and classes; Leverage the architecture and namespaces of the .NET Framework library; Manage the Common Language Infrastructure (CLI) to integrate C with Visual Basic 2005 and C++; Develop .NET components in C for desktop and distributed multi-tier applications. **Locations:** Toronto, CN; Rockville, MD; Irving, TX; New York, NY; El Segundo, CA; Alexandria, VA; Schaumburg, IL; Reston, VA; and Roseland, NJ.

44821 ■ Project Management for Software Development - Planning and Managing Successful Projects (Onsite)
Seminar Information Service, Inc.
20 Executive Park, Ste. 120
Irvine, CA 92614
Ph:(949)261-9104
Free: 877-SEM-INFO
Fax:(949)261-1963
Co. E-mail: info@seminarinformation.com
URL: http://www.seminarinformation.com

Price: $2,890.00. **Description:** Learn how to: Deliver successful software projects that support your organization's strategic goals; Match organizational needs to the most effective software development model; Plan and manage projects at each stage of the software development life cycle (SDLC); Create project plans that address real-world management challenges; Develop the skills for tracking and controlling the project deliverables; Focus on key tasks for the everyday management of software projects; Build an effective and committed team and keep them motivated day to day. **Locations:** Schaumburg, IL; Irving, TX; New York, NY; Ottawa, CN; Waltham, MA; Philadelphia, PA; Belmont, CA; Rockville, MD; and Atlanta, GA.

44822 ■ Structured Query Language (SQL) I
EEI Communications
66 Canal Ctr. Plz., Ste. 200
Alexandria, VA 22314-5507
Ph:(703)683-7453
Free: 888-253-2762
Fax:(703)683-7310
Co. E-mail: train@eeicom.com
URL: http://www.eeicom.com/training

Price: $745.00. **Description:** Seminar that covers how to organize and extract information from relational databases, including design relational databases, proper syntax for SQL statements, analyze and organize data, retrieve, insert, update, and delete data, use aggregate functions, write queries from multiple tables, and normalize data. **Locations:** Silver Spring, MD; Alexandria, VA; Hunt Valley, MD; and Columbia, MD.

44823 ■ Structured Query Language (SQL) II
EEI Communications
66 Canal Ctr. Plz., Ste. 200
Alexandria, VA 22314-5507
Ph:(703)683-7453
Free: 888-253-2762
Fax:(703)683-7310
Co. E-mail: train@eeicom.com
URL: http://www.eeicom.com/training

Price: $745.00. **Description:** Seminar that provides critical information for writing advanced database queries using complex databases, including design sub-queries, data dictionaries, establish database security, create and manage sequences and indexes, and create stored procedures. **Locations:** Silver Spring, MD; Alexandria, VA; Hunt Valley, MD; and Columbia, MD.

44824 ■ Typography and Font Management
EEI Communications
66 Canal Ctr. Plz., Ste. 200
Alexandria, VA 22314-5507
Ph:(703)683-7453
Free: 888-253-2762
Fax:(703)683-7310
Co. E-mail: train@eeicom.com
URL: http://www.eeicom.com/training

Price: $425.00. **Description:** Covers the various electronic typefaces used in desktop publishing applications, including installing, managing, and troubleshooting fonts. **Locations:** Alexandria, VA.

44825 ■ VMware Ultimate Bootcamp
EEI Communications
66 Canal Center Plz., Ste. 200
Alexandria, VA 22314
Ph:(703)683-7453
Free: 888-253-2762

Fax:(703)683-7310
Co. E-mail: train@eeicom.com
URL: http://www.eeicom.com/training
Price: $4,500.00. **Description:** Hands-on labs designed to expose you to advanced virtualization concepts with VMware V13.5 product suite. Comprehensive class prepares students to become professional virtualization experts with the certification Certified Virtualization Expert (CVE). **Locations:** Silver Spring, MD; Alexandria, VA; and Herndon, VA.

44826 ■ Web Design with Adobe Dreamweaver and Photoshop
EEI Communications
66 Canal Center Plz., Ste. 200
Alexandria, VA 22314
Ph:(703)683-7453
Free: 888-253-2762
Fax:(703)683-7310
Co. E-mail: train@eeicom.com
URL: http://www.eeicom.com/training
Price: $745.00. **Description:** Learn how to create attractive navigation elements and add texture and depth to your Web design, including how to create color palettes, and design clean and well-organized Web page layouts. **Locations:** Alexandria, VA; and Silver Spring, MD.

44827 ■ Web Graphics with Adobe Photoshop
EEI Communications
66 Canal Ctr. Plz., Ste. 200
Alexandria, VA 22314-5507
Ph:(703)683-7453
Free: 888-253-2762
Fax:(703)683-7310
Co. E-mail: train@eeicom.com
URL: http://www.eeicom.com/training
Price: $745.00. **Description:** Covers creating high-quality, low-bandwidth graphics for the Web, including optimizing GIFs and JPEGs, creating transparent GIF graphics and animated GIFs and rollovers, create background tiles and sliced graphics, create navigation bars and buttons, image maps, and correct photographs for the Web. **Locations:** Silver Spring, MD; and Alexandria, VA.

44828 ■ Website Optimization
Seminar Information Service, Inc.
20 Executive Park, Ste. 120
Irvine, CA 92614
Ph:(949)261-9104
Free: 877-SEM-INFO
Fax:(949)261-1963
Co. E-mail: info@seminarinformation.com
URL: http://www.seminarinformation.com
Price: $199.00. **Description:** Learn how to deliver exceptional service to site visitors, including a friendlier environment, obtain more leads, and integrate social media into your site. **Locations:** Oak Brook, IL; Milwaukee, WI; Madison, WI; Madison, WI; Chicago, IL; and Bloomington, MN.

44829 ■ Windows Vista: A Hands-On Introduction (Onsite)
Seminar Information Service, Inc.
20 Executive Park, Ste. 120
Irvine, CA 92614
Ph:(949)261-9104
Free: 877-SEM-INFO
Fax:(949)261-1963
Co. E-mail: info@seminarinformation.com
URL: http://www.seminarinformation.com
Price: $2,890.00. **Description:** Learn how to: Install and maintain Windows Vista in a professional environment; Navigate and configure Windows Vista; Create and manage users and groups; Protect resources with rights, access control and encryption; Implement and troubleshoot network and Internet connectivity; Improve application compatibility to maximize user productivity. **Locations:** Cities throughout the United States; Ottawa, CN; and Toronto, CN.

44830 ■ Writing for the Web II
EEI Communications
66 Canal Ctr. Plz., Ste. 200
Alexandria, VA 22314-5507
Ph:(703)683-7453
Free: 888-253-2762

Fax:(703)683-7310
Co. E-mail: train@eeicom.com
URL: http://www.eeicom.com/training
Price: $745.00. **Description:** Seminar for persons with 3-5 years' experience as a Web writer or editor, or have completed Writing for the Web I, covering how to define your genre and audience, develop a structure for your Web content, working with subject matter experts who aren't writers, making the most of your writing project, giving and getting feedback, writing links that work for your client, how to write menus so clients can use them, and recasting a print article for the Web. **Locations:** Silver Spring, MD; and Alexandria, VA.

44831 ■ XML Development I
EEI Communications
66 Canal Ctr. Plz., Ste. 200
Alexandria, VA 22314-5507
Ph:(703)683-7453
Free: 888-253-2762
Fax:(703)683-7310
Co. E-mail: train@eeicom.com
URL: http://www.eeicom.com/training
Price: $745.00. **Description:** Covers Extensible Markup Language (XML) that enables the Web designer to create information that is evolvable, including XML structure and syntax, create well-formed XML documents and document type definitions (DTDs) and schemas, valid XML documents, using entities, display using Cascading Style Sheets, data binding, and object model scripts. **Locations:** Silver Spring, MD; and Alexandria, VA.

44832 ■ XML Development II
EEI Communications
66 Canal Ctr. Plz., Ste. 200
Alexandria, VA 22314-5507
Ph:(703)683-7453
Free: 888-253-2762
Fax:(703)683-7310
Co. E-mail: train@eeicom.com
URL: http://www.eeicom.com/training
Price: $745.00. **Description:** Covers XSLT and how it is used to convert XML data for presentational purposes, modify data structure, and to create non-XML files, including building XSLT applications, transforming XML to HTML, PDF, and Word. **Locations:** Silver Spring, MD; Alexandria, VA; and Hunt Valley, MD.

44833 ■ XML Development III
EEI Communications
66 Canal Ctr. Plz., Ste. 200
Alexandria, VA 22314-5507
Ph:(703)683-7453
Free: 888-253-2762
Fax:(703)683-7310
Co. E-mail: train@eeicom.com
URL: http://www.eeicom.com/training
Price: $1,065.00. **Description:** Covers the integration of XML into Web applications using ASP, Cold Fusion, PHP and Java, including guidelines for translating XML structure to a relational database model, rules for modeling, common techniques for storing, transmitting, and displaying content, data access mechanisms that expose relational data as XML, and how to use related technologies when processing XML data. **Locations:** Silver Spring, MD; Alexandria, VA; Hunt Valley, MD; and Columbia, MD.

44834 ■ XML Web Services
EEI Communications
66 Canal Center Plz., Ste. 200
Alexandria, VA 22314
Ph:(703)683-7453
Free: 888-253-2762
Fax:(703)683-7310
Co. E-mail: train@eeicom.com
URL: http://www.eeicom.com/training
Price: $1,065.00. **Description:** Learn how Web services can enhance your Web site and communication with other companies. **Locations:** Alexandria, VA.

REFERENCE WORKS

44835 ■ "Abacast, Citadel Strike Radio Ad Deal" in *Business Journal Portland* (Vol. 27, December 31, 2010, No. 44, pp. 3)
Pub: Portland Business Journal
Ed: Erik Siemers. **Description:** Software firm Abacast Inc. has partnered with Citadel Media to aid the latter's advertising sales. Citadel provides radio networks and syndicated programs to 4,200 affiliate stations.

44836 ■ "ACC Game Development Program Opens" in *Austin Business JournalInc.* (Vol. 28, October 31, 2008, No. 33, pp. 1)
Pub: American City Business Journals
Ed: Sandra Zaragoza. **Description:** Austin, Texas-based Austin Community College has launched its Game Development Institute. The institute was created to meet the gaming industry's demand for skilled workers. One hundred students have enrolled with the institute.

44837 ■ "AMT's Partner Program Enables New Security Business Models" in *Internet Wire* (August 12, 2010)
Pub: Comtex
Description: AMT, technical provider of physical access control Software as a Service (Saas) solutions, has developed a new Partner Program that allows partners to outsource any technical abilities lacking to AMT with no upfront fees.

44838 ■ "Angel Investments Tripled in 2009" in *Austin Business JournalInc.* (Vol. 29, January 8, 2010, No. 44, pp. 1)
Pub: American City Business Journals
Ed: Christopher Calnan. **Description:** Central Texas Angel Network (CTAN) has invested $3.5 million in 12 ventures, which include 10 in Austin, Texas in 2009 to triple the amount it invested during 2008. The largest recipient of CTAN's investments is life sciences, which attracted 20 percent of the capital, while software investments fell to 18 percent. The new screening process that helps startups secure CTAN capital is explored.

44839 ■ "Apps For Anybody With an Idea" in *Advertising Age* (Vol. 79, October 20, 2008, No. 39, pp. 29)
Pub: Crain Communications, Inc.
Ed: Beth Snyder Bulik. **Description:** Apple's new online App Store is open to anyone with an idea and the ability to write code and many of these developers are not only finding a sense of community through this venue but are also making money since the sales are split with Apple, 30/70 in the developer's favor.

44840 ■ "Arctic IT Honored" in *Alaska Business Monthly* (Vol. 27, October 2011, No. 10, pp. 10)
Pub: Alaska Business Publishing Company
Ed: Nancy Pounds. **Description:** Arctic Information Technology Inc. was named to Everything Channel's 2011 Computer Reseller News (CRN) Next-Generation 250 list. The firm provides business software and network infrastructure solutions.

44841 ■ "Arizona Firms In Chicago Go For Gold With '08 Games" in *The Business Journal - Serving Phoenix and the Valley of the Sun* (Vol. 28, August 8, 2008, No. 49, pp. 1)
Pub: American City Business Journals, Inc.
Ed: Patrick O'Grady. **Description:** More than 20 U.S. athletes will wear Arizona-based eSoles LLC's custom-made insoles to increase their performance at the 2008 Beijing Olympics making eSoles one of the beneficiaries of the commercialization of the games. Translation software maker Auralog Inc saw a 60 percent jump in sales from its Mandarin Chinese language applications.

44842 ■ "Attivio Brings Order to Data" in *Information Today* (Vol. 26, February 2009, No. 2, pp. 14)
Pub: Information Today, Inc.
Ed: Marji McClure. **Description:** Profile of Attivio, the high tech firm offering next-generation software that helps businesses to consolidate data and eliminate enterprise silos.

44843 ■ "AVG Introduces Security Software Suite for SMBs 551179" in *eWeek* **(October 12, 2010)**
Pub: Ziff Davis Enterprise
Description: AVG Technologies is offering its AVG Internet Security 2011 Business Edition and AVG Anti-Virus Business Edition designed to give Internet-active SMB owners protection. The system protects online transactions and email communications as well as sensitive customer data and AVG Anti-Virus 2011 Business edition offers real-time protection against the latest online threats.

44844 ■ "BancVue to Expand" in *Austin Business JournalInc.* **(Vol. 29, November 27, 2009, No. 38, pp. 1)**
Pub: American City Business Journals
Ed: Kate Harrington. **Description:** Significant growth of BancVue in the past six years has prompted the company to look for a site that could increase its office space from 25,000 square feet to 65,000 square feet. BancVue offers bank and credit union software solutions and is planning to lease or buy a property in Austin, Texas.

44845 ■ "Bar Hopping: Your Numbers At a Glance" in *Inc.* **(January 2008, pp. 44-45)**
Pub: Gruner & Jahr USA Publishing
Ed: Michael Fitzgerald. **Description:** Software that helps any company analyze data include Crystal Xcelsius, a program that takes data from Excel documents and turns them into animated gauges, charts and graphs; CashView, a Web-based application that tracks receivables and payables; iDashboards, a Web-based programs that produces animated gauges, maps, pie charts and graphs; Corda Human Capital Management, that transforms stats like head count, productivity, and attrition into graphs and dials; NetSuite, a Web-based application that tracks key indicators; and Cognos Now, that gauges, dials, and graphs data.

44846 ■ "BayTSP, NTT Data Corp. Enter Into Reseller Pact to Market Online IP Monitoring" in *Professional Services Close-Up* **(Sept. 11, 2009)**
Pub: Close-Up Media
Description: Due to incredible interest from distributors and content owners across Asia, NTT Data Corp. will resell BayTSP's online intellectual property monitoring, enforcement, business intelligence and monetization services in Japan.

44847 ■ "Behind the Scenes: Companies At the Heart of Everyday Life" in *Inc.* **(February 2008, pp. 26-27)**
Pub: Gruner & Jahr USA Publishing
Ed: Athena Schindelheim. **Description:** Profiles of companies providing services to airports, making the environment safer and more efficient, as well as more comfortable for passengers and workers. Centerpoint Manufacturing provides garbage bins that can safely contain explosions producing thousands of pounds of pressure; Infax, whose software displays arrival and departure information on 19-foot-wide screens; Lavi Industries, whose products include security barricades, hostess stands, and salad-bar sneeze guards; and SATech maker of rubber flooring that helps ease discomfort for workers having to stand for long periods of time.

44848 ■ "Being all a-Twitter" in *Canadian Business* **(Vol. 81, December 8, 2008, No. 21, pp. 22)**
Pub: Rogers Media Ltd.
Ed: Andrew Wahl. **Description:** Marketing experts suggest that advertising strategies have to change along with new online social media. Companies are advised to find ways to incorporate social software because workers and customers are expected to continue its use.

44849 ■ "Best Managed Companies (Canada)" in *Canadian Business* **(Vol. 82, Summer 2009, No. 8, pp. 38)**
Pub: Rogers Media
Ed: Calvin Leung. **Description:** Agrium Inc. and Barrick Gold Corporation are among those that are found to be the best managed companies in Canada. Best

managed companies also include software firm Open Text Corporation, which has grown annual sales by 75 percent and annual profits by 160 percent since 1995. Open Text markets software that allow firms to manage word-based data, and has 46,000 customers in 114 countries.

44850 ■ "Beyond Microsoft and Yahoo!: Some M&A Prospects" in *Barron's* **(Vol. 88, March 17, 2008, No. 11, pp. 39)**
Pub: Dow Jones & Company, Inc.
Ed: Eric J. Savitz. **Description:** Weak quarterly earnings report for Yahoo! could pressure the company's board to cut a deal with Microsoft. Electronic Arts is expected to win its hostile $26-a-share bid for Take-Two Interactive Software. Potential targets and buyers for mergers and acquisitions are mentioned.

44851 ■ "Beyond YouTube: New Uses for Video, Online and Off" in *Inc.* **(October 2007, pp. 53-54)**
Pub: Gruner & Jahr USA Publishing
Ed: Leah Hoffmann. **Description:** Small companies are using video technology for embedding messages into email, broadcasting live interactive sales and training seminars, as well as marketing campaigns. Experts offer insight into producing and broadcasting business videos.

44852 ■ *The Big Switch*
Pub: W. W. Norton & Company, Inc.
Ed: Nicholas Carr. **Released:** January 19, 2009. **Price:** $16.95 paperback. **Description:** Today companies are dismantling private computer systems and tapping into services provided via the Internet. This shift is remaking the computer industry, bringing competitors such as Google to the forefront ant threatening traditional companies like Microsoft and Dell. The book weaves together history, economics, and technology to explain why computing is changing and what it means for the future.

44853 ■ *Business Feasibility Analysis Pro*
Pub: Prentice Hall PTR
Ed: Palo Alto Software. **Released:** August 2006. **Price:** $28.40. **Description:** Profile of software developed to support small business management and/or entrepreneurship text. Step-by-step instructions are provided.

44854 ■ "BusinessOnLine Launches a New Web-Based Search Engine Optimization Tool" in *Internet Wire* **(October 19, 2009)**
Pub: Comtex News Network, Inc.
Description: First Link Checker, a complimentary new search engine optimization tool that helps site owners optimize their on-page links by understanding which of those links are actually being counted in Google's relevancy algorithm, was developed by BusinessOnLine, a rapidly growing Internet marketing agency. This tool will make it easy for the average web master to ensure that their internal link structure is optimized.

44855 ■ "A Case Study: Real-Life Business Planning" in *Entrepreneur* **(February 3, 2009)**
Pub: Entrepreneur Media Inc.
Ed: Tim Berry. **Description:** Provides a case study of a two-day planning meeting for Palo Alto Software in which the executives of the company met for their annual planning cycle and discussed ways in which the company needed to change in order to stay viable in today's tough economic climate.

44856 ■ "Cerner Works the Business Circuit" in *Business Journal-Serving Metropolitan Kansas City* **(Vol. 26, October 5, 2007, No. 4, pp. 1)**
Pub: American City Business Journals, Inc.
Ed: Rob Roberts. **Description:** Cerner Corporation is embracing the coming of the electronic medical record exchange by creating a regional health information organization (RHIO) called the CareEntrust. The RHIO convinced health insurers to share claims data with patients and clinicians. At the Center Health Conference, held October 7 to 10, Cerner will demonstrate the software it developed for CareEntrust to the 40,000 healthcare and information technology professionals.

44857 ■ "ChemSW Software Development Services Available for Outsourcing" in *Information Today* **(Vol. 26, February 2009, No. 2, pp. 30)**
Pub: Information Today, Inc.
Description: ChemSW software development services include requirements analysis, specification development, design, development, testing, and system documentation as an IT outsourcing solution. The company can also develop software tracking systems for satellite stockrooms, provide asset management integration solutions and more.

44858 ■ "ClickFuel Launches New Products to Help Small and Mid-Sized Businesses Bolster Their Brand Online" in *Internet Wire* **(Dec. 3,2009)**
Pub: Comtex News Network, Inc.
Description: Boostability, a provider of Enterprise Search Engine Optimization (SEO) software technology, has partnered with ClickFuel, a firm that designs, tracks and manages Internet marketing campaigns in order to leverage Boostability's technology in order to deliver comprehensive SEO solutions to small and mid-size businesses; three new products will also become available for these business clients to help them manage all facets of their online presence.

44859 ■ "ClickFuel Unveils Internet Marketing Tools for Small Businesses" in *Internet Wire* **(October 19, 2009)**
Pub: Comtex News Network, Inc.
Description: ClickFuel, a firm that manages, designs and tracks marketing campaigns has unveiled a full software suite of affordable services and technology solutions designed to empower small business owners and help them promote and grow their businesses through targeted Internet marketing campaigns.

44860 ■ "Clouds in the Forecast" in *Information Today* **(Vol. 28, September 2011, No. 8, pp. 10)**
Pub: Information Today, Inc.
Ed: Paula J. Hane. **Description:** Cloud computing is software, applications, and data stored remotely and accessed via the Internet with output displayed on a client device. Recent developments in cloud computing are explored.

44861 ■ *Computer Accounting Essentials with Microsoft Office Accounting 2010*
Pub: McGraw-Hill Higher Education
Ed: Carol Yacht, Susan Crosson. **Released:** March 10, 2010. **Description:** Step-by-step guide to using Microsoft's Office Professional 2007 Accounting program.

44862 ■ "Cut Energy Waste" in *Inc.* **(Vol. 31, January-February 2009, No. 1, pp. 42)**
Pub: Mansueto Ventures LLC
Description: Carbon Control, Edison, and Saver software programs help companies cut carbon emissions by reducing the amount of energy consumed by computers while they are idle.

44863 ■ "Dear Customer: Managing E-Mail Campaigns" in *Inc.* **(March 2008, pp. 58-59)**
Pub: Gruner & Jahr USA Publishing
Ed: Ryan Underwood. **Description:** Internet services that help firms manage their online business including email marketing, to manage subscriber lists, comply with spam regulations, monitor bouncebacks, and track potential customers are profiled. Constant Contact, MobileStorm Stun, Campaign Monitor, Pop Commerce, Emma, and StrongMail E-mail Server are among software and services highlighted.

44864 ■ "Design Center Shows Quality of Digital Paper" in *American Printer* **(Vol. 128, June 1, 2011, No. 6)**
Pub: Penton Media Inc.
Description: Digital Design Centers allows printers to customize marketing tools in order to promote their own digital printing capabilities.

44865 ■ "Design Programs for HVAC Sizing Solutions" in *Contractor* **(Vol. 57, January 2010, No. 1, pp. 44)**
Pub: Penton Media, Inc.
Ed: William Feldman; Patti Feldman. **Description:** Rhvac 8 is an HVAC design program that lets users calculate peak heating and cooling load requirements

for rooms, zones, systems, and entire buildings. The HVAC Pipe Sizer software for the iPhone enables quick sizing of a simple piping system.

44866 ■ "Don't Touch My Laptop, If You Please Mr. Customs Man" in *Canadian Electronics* **(Vol. 23, June-July 2008, No. 4, pp. 6)**
Pub: Action Communication Inc.
Ed: Mark Borkowski. **Description:** Canadian businessmen bringing electronic devices to the US can protect the contents of their laptops by hiding their data from US border agents. They can also choose to clean up the contents of their laptop using file erasure programs.

44867 ■ "DST Turns to Banks for Credit" in *The Business Journal-Serving Metropolitan Kansas City* **(Vol. 27, October 3, 2008, No. 3, pp. 1)**
Pub: American City Business Journals, Inc.
Ed: Rob Roberts. **Description:** Kansas City, Missouri-based DST Systems Inc., a company that provides sophisticated information processing, computer software services and business solutions, has secured a new five-year, $120 million credit facility from Enterprise Bank and Bank of the West. The deal is seen to reflect that the region and community-banking model remain stable. Comments from executives are also provided.

44868 ■ "Eagles Measure Suite Success" in *Philadelphia Business Journal* **(Vol. 30, September 9, 2011, No. 30, pp. 1)**
Pub: American City Business Journals Inc.
Ed: John George. **Description:** Philadelphia Eagles have a new software program that helps suite holders keep track of how their suite is being used and whether they are getting a return on their investment. The software allows suite holders to better utilize and distribute their tickets.

44869 ■ "EBSCO Adds New Features to EBSCOhost Content Viewer" in *Information Today* **(Vol. 26, February 2009, No. 2, pp. 31)**
Pub: Information Today, Inc.
Description: EBSCOhost Content Viewer historical digital archive collection provides a visual overview of a displayed document, highlighting search keywords on the page as well as providing a document map that shows the number of times a given keyword is mentioned in a periodical, monograph, article, or other document. For periodical content, the viewer lets users browse multiple issues in a volume without leaving the interface; features include zoom and pan technology similar to online maps.

44870 ■ "Elastic Path Software Joins Canada in G20 Young Entrepreneur Summit" in *Internet Wire* **(June 14, 2010)**
Pub: Comtex
Description: The Canadian Youth Business Foundation hosted the G20 Young Entrepreneur Summit and announced that Harry Chemko of British Columbia's Elastic Path Software will be a member of the Canadian delegation at the G20 Young Entrepreneur Summit. Details are included.

44871 ■ "Elemental Nabs $5.5 Million" in *The Business Journal-Portland* **(Vol. 25, July 18, 2008, No. 19, pp. 1)**
Pub: American City Business Journals, Inc.
Ed: Aliza Earnshaw. **Description:** Elemental Technologies Inc., a Portland, Oregon-based software company got $5.5 million in new funding, bringing its total invested capital to $7.1 million in nine months since October 2008. The company plans to launch Badaboom, software for converting video into various formats, later in 2008.

44872 ■ "The Emergence of Governance In an Open Source Community" in *Academy of Management Journal* **(Vol. 50, No. 5, October 2007, pp. 1079)**
Pub: Academy of Management
Ed: Siiobhan O'Mahony, Fabrizio Ferraro. **Description:** Study examined the method of self-governance among small communities producing collective goods, focusing on an open source software com-

munity. Results revealed that a combination of bureaucratic and democratic practices helped its governance system.

44873 ■ "Empire of Pixels" in *Entrepreneur* **(Vol. 37, September 2009, No. 9, pp. 50)**
Pub: Entrepreneur Media, Inc.
Ed: Jason Daley. **Description:** Entrepreneur Jack Levin has successfully grown Imageshack, an image-hosting Web service. The Website currently gets 50 million unique visitors a month. Levin has launched Y-Frog, an application that uses Imageshack to allow Twitter users to add images to their posts.

44874 ■ *The Entrepreneurial Culture Network Advantage Within Chinese and Irish Software Firms*
Pub: Edward Elgar Publishing, Incorporated
Ed: Tsang. **Released:** October 2006. **Price:** $95.00. **Description:** Ways national cultural heritage influences entrepreneurial ventures are discussed.

44875 ■ "Ex Libris Rosetta Hits the Market" in *Information Today* **(Vol. 26, February 2009, No. 2, pp. 30)**
Pub: Information Today, Inc.
Description: Ex Libris Rosetta, the latest version of the Ex Libris Group's Digital Preservation System supports the acquisition, validation, ingest, storage, management, preservation, and dissemination of digital objects, allowing libraries the infrastructure and technology to preserve and facilitate access to digital collections. The firm's Ex Libris Rosseta Charter Program helps users develop strategic collaboration between Ex Libris and its customers to improve the product.

44876 ■ "Fly Phishing" in *Canadian Business* **(Vol. 80, October 22, 2007, No. 21, pp. 42)**
Pub: Rogers Media
Ed: Andy Holloway. **Description:** Symantec Corporation's report shows consumers and companies have effectively installed network defenses that prevent unwanted access. Phishing packages are readily available and are widely used. Other details of the Internet Security Threat Report are presented.

44877 ■ "The Folly of Google's Latest Gambit" in *Barron's* **(Vol. 89, July 13, 2009, No. 28, pp. 23)**
Pub: Dow Jones & Co., Inc.
Ed: Eric J. Savitz. **Description:** Google will enter the operating systems business with the introduction of the Google Chrome OS but its success is dubious because the project is still a year or so away while Microsoft will release an updated version of Windows by then; another problem is that Google already has another OS called Android which will overlap with the Chrome OS's market.

44878 ■ "German Win Through Sharing" in *Canadian Business* **(Vol. 83, September 14, 2010, No. 15, pp. 16)**
Pub: Rogers Media Ltd.
Ed: Jordan Timm. **Description:** German economic historian Eckhard Hoffner has a two-volume work showing how German's relaxed attitude toward copyright and intellectual property helped it catch up to industrialized United Kingdom. Hoffner's research was in response to his interest in the usefulness of software patents. Information on the debate regarding Canada's copyright laws is given.

44879 ■ "Getting Rid of Global Glitches: Choosing Software For Trade Compliance" in *Black Enterprise* **(Vol. 41, September 2010, No. 2, pp. 48)**
Pub: Earl G. Graves Publishing Co. Inc.
Ed: Marcia Wade Talbert. **Description:** Compliance software for trading with foreign companies must be compatible with the U.S. Census Bureau's Automated Export System (www.aesdirect.gov). It has to be current with regulatory requirements for any country in the world. Whether owners handle their own compliance or hire a logistics company, they need to be familiar with this software in order to access reports and improve transparency and efficiency of theft supply chain.

44880 ■ "Ghouls, Goblins, and Harry Potter: Cashing In On Halloween" in *Inc.* **(Vol. 33, October 2011, No. 8, pp. 24)**
Pub: Inc. Magazine
Ed: Darren Dahl. **Description:** Costume Craze, an online costume retailer reports $13.2 million in sales last year. Originally the family business started out as a software company called StaticAdvantage, but switched gears.

44881 ■ "Global: Put It on Autopilot" in *Entrepreneur* **(Vol. 35, October 2007, No. 10, pp. 110)**
Pub: Entrepreneur Media Inc.
Ed: Laurel Delaney. **Description:** A business that aims to enter the global market must first streamline its global supply chain (GSC). A streamlined GSC can be achieved by laying out the company's processes and by automating it with supply chain management software. Advantages of GSC automation such as credibility are provided.

44882 ■ "A Hacker in India Hijacked His Website Design and Was Making Good Money Selling It" in *Inc.* **(December 2007, pp. 77-78, 80)**
Pub: Gruner & Jahr USA Publishing
Ed: Darren Dahl. **Description:** John Anton, owner of an online custom T-shirt business and how a company in India was selling software Website templates identical to his firm's Website.

44883 ■ "His Banking Industry Software Never Caught On, so Bill Randle is Now Targeting the Health Care Market" in *Inc.* **(March 2008)**
Pub: Gruner & Jahr USA Publishing
Ed: Alex Salkever. **Description:** Profile of Bill Randle, bank executive turned entrepreneur; Randle tells how he changed his focus for his company from banking software to healthcare software. The firm employs ten people who secure online billing and recordkeeping systems for hospitals and insurers. Randle discusses critical decisions that will impact his firm in the coming year. Three experts offer advice.

44884 ■ "Holiday Sales Look Uncertain for Microsoft and PC Sellers" in *Puget Sound Business Journal* **(Vol. 29, November 28, 2008, No. 32)**
Pub: American City Business Journals
Ed: Todd Bishop. **Description:** Personal computer makers face uncertain holiday sales for 2008 as a result of the weak U.S. economy and a shift toward low-cost computers. Personal computer shipments for the fourth quarter 2008 are forecast to drop 1 percent compared to the same quarter 2007.

44885 ■ "How Hard Could It Be? Adventures In Software Demol'ling" in *Inc.* **(December 2007, pp. 99-100)**
Pub: Gruner & Jahr USA Publishing
Ed: Joel Spolsky. **Description:** Founder and CEO of Fog Creek Software, a New York City software developer shares insight into his software demo tour used to promote his firm's products.

44886 ■ "HR Tech on the Go" in *Workforce Management* **(Vol. 88, November 16, 2009, No. 12, pp. 1)**
Pub: Crain Communications, Inc.
Ed: Ed Frauenheim. **Description:** Examination of the necessity of mobile access of human resources software applications that allow managers to recruit, schedule and train employees via their mobile devices; some industry leaders believe that mobile HR applications are vital while others see this new technology as hype.

44887 ■ "iControl Networks Powers Comcast's XFINITY (Reg) Home Security Service" in *Benzinga.com* **(June 9, 2011)**
Pub: Benzinga.com
Ed: Benzinga Staff. **Description:** Comcast's XFINITY Home Security Service is powered by iControl Networks' OpenHome (TM) software platform. The service provides intrusion and fire protection along

44888 ■ "Image Conscious" in *Canadian Business* (Vol. 81, March 17, 2008, No. 4, pp. 36)
Pub: Rogers Media
Ed: Andrew Wahl. **Description:** Idee Inc. is testing an Internet search engine for images that does not rely on tags but compares its visual data to a database of other images. The company was founded and managed by Leila Boujnane as an off-shoot of their risk-management software firm. Their software has already been used by image companies to track copyrighted images and to find images within their own archives.

44889 ■ "iMozi Integrates Esprida LiveControl for Advanced DVD Kiosk Hardware" in *Wireless News* (December 20, 2010)
Pub: Close-Up Media Inc.
Description: Provider of self-service entertainment technology, iMozi Canada has partnered with Esprida to make its automated DVD Kiosk solutions Esprida-enabled. Esprida develops remote device management solutions and will offer enhanced capabilities and to improve customer experience for users.

44890 ■ "Inside Intel's Effectiveness System for Web Marketing" in *Advertising Age* (Vol. 81, January 25, 2010, No. 4, pp. 4)
Pub: Crain's Communications
Ed: Beth Snyder Bulik. **Description:** Overview of Intel's internally developed program called Value Point System in which the company is using in order to evaluate and measure online marketing effectiveness.

44891 ■ "Intel to Buy McAfee Security Business for 768B" in *eWeek* (August 19, 2010)
Pub: Ziff Davis Enterprise
Description: Intel will acquire security giant McAfee for approximately $7.68 billion, whereby McAfee would become a wholly owned subsidiary of Intel and would report to Intel's Software and Services Group.

44892 ■ "iPhone Apps Big Business" in *Austin Business JournalInc.* (Vol. 28, November 14, 2008, No. 35, pp. 1)
Pub: American City Business Journals
Ed: Christopher Calnan. **Description:** Members of the computer software industry in Austin, Texas have benefited from developing applications for Apple Inc.'s iPhone. Pangea Software Inc.'s revenues have grown by developing iPhone applications. Lexcycle LLC, on the other hand, has created an application that enables users to read books on the iPhone.

44893 ■ "iPhone Apps In a Flash" in *Entrepreneur* (Vol. 37, October 2009, No. 10, pp. 38)
Pub: Entrepreneur Media, Inc.
Description: Ansca is developing Corona, a software development kit for the Apple iPhone. The kit reduces development time and allows individuals with knowledge of software to develop iPhone applications.

44894 ■ "Is It Time to Ban Swearing at Work?" in *HR Specialist* (Vol. 8, September 2010, No. 9, pp. 2)
Pub: Capitol Information Group Inc.
Description: Screening software has been developed to identify profanity used in business correspondence.

44895 ■ "Is It Time for a Change?" in *Rental Product News* (Vol. 33, October 2011)
Pub: Cygnus Business Media
Ed: Jenny Lescohier. **Description:** Management software for running a rental business is examined.

44896 ■ "iSymmetry's Technological Makeover Or, How a Tech Company Finally Grew Up and Discovered the World Wide Web" in *Inc.* (October 2007)
Pub: Gruner & Jahr USA Publishing
Description: Profile of iSymmetry, an Atlanta, Georgia-based IT recruiting firm, covering the issues the company faces keeping its technology equipment

up-to-date. The firm has devised a program that will replace its old server-based software systems with on-demand software delivered via the Internet, known as software-as-a-service. Statistical information included.

44897 ■ "Johnny Royal of Luthier Society Unveils Archimedes 1.0 Trailer" in *Internet Wire* (October 22, 2009)
Pub: Comtex News Network, Inc.
Description: Luthier Society, a social media and viral branding agency, has released the first viral video for the company's ROI weighted-value software platform named Archimedes 1.0; users of the software will be able to determine the depth of their outreach efforts, saturation rate, value of their Internet presence and the geo-spatial location of their audience; this will give a true, monetized value for ROI (Return on Investment) in social media marketing.

44898 ■ "Keeping Up With the Joneses: Outfitting Your Company With Up-To-Date Technology is Vital" in *Black Enterprise* (November 2007)
Pub: Earl G. Graves Publishing Co. Inc.
Ed: Sonya A. Donaldson. **Description:** Small businesses, whether home-based or not, need to keep up with new technological developments including hardware, software, and the Internet.

44899 ■ "Lights, Camera, Action: Tools for Creating Video Blogs" in *Inc.* (Volume 32, December 2010, No. 10, pp. 57)
Pub: Inc. Magazine
Ed: John Brandon. **Description:** A video blog is a good way to spread company news, talk about products, and stand out among traditional company blogs. New editing software can create two- to four-minute blogs using a webcam and either Windows Live Essentials, Apple iLife 2011, Powerdirector 9 Ultra, or Adobe Visual Communicator 3.

44900 ■ "Make Relationships Count: CRM Software That Works" in *Black Enterprise* (Vol. 38, February 2008, No. 7, pp. 60)
Pub: Earl G. Graves Publishing Co. Inc.
Ed: Fiona Haley. **Description:** Customer relationship management (CRM) software can help any small business keep track of clients. Descriptions of the latest CRM software offered are profiled, including Salesforce.com, Microsoft Dynamics, and Saga Software.

44901 ■ "Media Software and Data Services" in *MarketingMagazine* (Vol. 115, September 27, 2010, No. 13, pp. 78)
Pub: Rogers Publishing Ltd.
Description: Media software and data services information in Canada is presented.

44902 ■ "Meetings Go Virtual" in *HRMagazine* (Vol. 54, January 2009, No. 1, pp. 74)
Pub: Society for Human Resource Management
Ed: Elizabeth Agnvall. **Description:** Microsoft Office Live Meeting conferencing software allows companies to schedule meetings from various company locations, thus saving travel costs.

44903 ■ "Metallics Education" in *American Printer* (Vol. 128, June 1, 2011, No. 6)
Pub: Penton Media Inc.
Description: Guide 'Curious About Print: Your Guide to the World of Curious Metallics' provides hints and tips to help printers maximize selection and reproduction, advice on working with metallic and UV inks, and recommendations for gaining quantity without sacrificing quality.

44904 ■ "Microsoft Clicks Into High Speed" in *Hispanic Business* (Vol. 30, July-August 2008, No. 7-8, pp. 54)
Pub: Hispanic Business, Inc.
Ed: Derek Reveron. **Description:** Microsoft's diversity hiring and vendor diversity program to capture more Hispanic consumer and business-to-business market is described. One of the main goals of these programs is to hire more Hispanic executives and

managers who will help the company develop and market products and services that will appeal and benefit Hispanic consumers.

44905 ■ "Microsoft Goes Macrosoft" in *Barron's* (Vol. 89, July 27, 2009, No. 30, pp. 25)
Pub: Dow Jones & Co., Inc.
Ed: Mark Veverka. **Description:** Microsoft reported a weak quarter on the heels of a tech rally which suggests the economy has not turned around. Marc Andreesen describes his new venture-capital fund as focused on "classic tech" and that historical reference places him in the annals of the last millennium.

44906 ■ "Microsoft Releases Office Security Updates" in *Mac World* (Vol. 27, November 2010, No. 11, pp. 66)
Pub: Mac Publishing
Ed: David Dahlquist. **Description:** Office for Mac and Mac Business Unit are Microsoft's pair of security- and stability-enhancing updates for Office 2008 and Office 2004. The software will improve the stability and compatibility and fixes vulnerabilities that would allow attackers to overwrite Mac's memory with malicious code.

44907 ■ *Microsoft Windows Small Business Server 2003 R2 Administrator's Companion*
Pub: Microsoft Press
Ed: Charlie Russel; Sharon Crawford. **Released:** July 2006. **Price:** $80.99. **Description:** Profile of Microsoft's Small Business Server R2.

44908 ■ "Mimosa Systems Gains 150,000 New NearPoint Users" in *Information Today* (Vol. 26, February 2009, No. 2, pp. 31)
Pub: Information Today, Inc.
Description: Mimosa System's NearPoint archive solution features email and file archiving, e-discovery, archive virtualization, and disaster recovery capabilities.

44909 ■ "MindLeaders' Online Training Courses Come to ePath Learning" in *Information Today* (Vol. 26, February 2009, No. 2, pp. 4)
Pub: Information Today, Inc.
Description: MindLeaders has partnered with ePath Learning to provide clients with over 2,200 new online courses. ePath's integrated Learning Management Service (iLMS) allows organizations to create online training programs for employees.

44910 ■ "More Leading Retailers Using Omniture Conversion Solutions to Boost Sales and Ecommerce Performance" in *Internet Wire* (Sept. 22,2009)
Pub: Comtex News Network, Inc.
Description: Many retailers are utilizing Omniture conversion solutions to improve the performance of their ecommerce businesses; recent enhancements to Omniture Merchandising and Omniture Recommendations help clients drive increased conversion to their Internet ventures.

44911 ■ "My Favorite Tool for Organizing Data" in *Inc.* (Vol. 33, November 2011, No. 9, pp. 46)
Pub: Inc. Magazine
Ed: Abram Brown. **Description:** Intelligence software firm uses Roambi, a Web-based service that turns spreadsheet data into interactive files for iPhones and iPads.

44912 ■ "New Database Brings Doctors Out of the Dark" in *Business Courier* (Vol. 26, October 23, 2009, No. 26, pp. 1)
Pub: American City Business Journals, Inc.
Ed: James Ritchie. **Description:** A database created by managed care consulting firm Praesentia allows doctors in Cincinnati to compare average reimbursements from health insurance companies to doctors in different areas. Specialist doctors in the city are paid an average of $172.25 for every office consultation.

44913 ■ **"New Sprint Phone Whets Appetite for Applications" in** *The Business Journal-Serving Metropolitan Kansas City* **(Vol. 26, July 25, 2008)**
Pub: American City Business Journals, Inc.
Ed: Suzanna Stagemeyer. Description: Firms supporting the applications of the new Samsung Instinct, which was introduced by Sprint Nextel Corp. in June 2008, have reported usage rates increase for their products. Handmark, whose mobile services Pocket Express comes loaded with Instinct, has redirected employees to meet the rising demand for the services. Other views and information on Instinct, are presented.

44914 ■ **"New Wave of Business Security Products Ushers in the Kaspersky Anti-Malware Protection System" in** *Internet Wire* **(October 26, 2010)**
Pub: Comtex
Description: Kaspersky Anti-Malware System provides anti-malware protection that requires minimal in-house resources for small businesses. The system offers a full range of tightly integrated end-to-end protection solutions, ensuring unified protection across an entire network, from endpoint and mobile device protection to file server, mail server, network storage and gateway protection. It provides flexible centralized management, immediate threat visibility and a level of responsiveness not seen in other anti-malware approaches.

44915 ■ **"Nonprofit NAIC Acquires Software Developer as For-Profit Arm" in** *Crain's Detroit Business* **(Vol. 25, June 22, 2009, No. 25, pp. 10)**
Pub: Crain Communications Inc. - Detroit
Ed: Sherri Begin Welch. Description: Details of National Association of Investors Corporation's acquisition of a Massachusetts investment software developer in order to offer more products to investment clubs and individual investors nationwide.

44916 ■ **"Not Your Father's Whiteboard" in** *Inc.* **(Vol. 33, November 2011, No. 9, pp. 50)**
Pub: Inc. Magazine
Ed: Adam Baer. Description: Sharp's new interactive whiteboard is really a 70-inch touch screen monitor with software for importing presentations from any Windows 7 computer.

44917 ■ **"Note-Taking App, Supercharged" in** *Inc.* **(Vol. 33, October 2011, No. 8, pp. 48)**
Pub: Inc. Magazine
Ed: Adam Baer. Description: Note Taker HD is an iPad app that lets the user text by typing with finger or stylus with various colors, fonts and sizes; Extensive Notes creates notes, records audio memos, and takes photos and videos; Evernote allows users to create notes, take snapshots, and record voice memos.

44918 ■ **"Nothing Like a Weak Team Or An Unrealistic Schedule To Start a Project Off Right" in** *Inc.* **(November 2007, pp. 85-87)**
Pub: Gruner & Jahr USA Publishing
Ed: Joel Spolsky. Description: Five easy ways to fail meeting a project deadline are discussed by the owner of a software development company: start with second-rate team of developers, set weekly milestones, negotiate a deadline, divide tasks equitably, and work until midnight.

44919 ■ **"OCE Boosts JetStream Productivity" in** *American Printer* **(Vol. 128, August 1, 2011, No. 8)**
Pub: Penton Media Inc.
Description: New Oce JetStream 1400 and 3000 digital full-color inkjet presses are profiled. The new models promise higher speed to grow print volume.

44920 ■ **"Oce Business Services: Discovery Made Easy" in** *Information Today* **(Vol. 26, February 2009, No. 2, pp. 31)**
Pub: Information Today, Inc.
Ed: Barbara Brynko. Description: Oce Business Services provides document process management and electronic discovery through its CaseData repertoire of legal management solutions.

44921 ■ **"Omniture's Next Version of SearchCenter Delivers Landing Page Optimization" in** *Internet Wire* **(September 24, 2009)**
Pub: Comtex News Network, Inc.
Description: Omniture, Inc., a leading provider of online business optimization software, has announced a new release of Omniture SearchCenter; this latest version will allow search engine marketers to test landing pages across campaigns and ad groups.

44922 ■ **"On Beyond Powerpoint: Presentations Get a Wake-Up Call" in** *Inc.* **(November 2007, pp. 58-59)**
Pub: Gruner & Jahr USA Publishing
Ed: Michael Fitzgerald. Description: New software that allows business presentations to be shared online are profiled, including ProfCast, audio podcasts for sales, marketing, and training; SmartDraw2008, software that creates professional graphics; Dimdim, an open-Web conferencing tool; Empressr, a hosted Web service for creating, managing, and sharing multimedia presentations; Zentation, a free tool that allows users to watch slides and a videos of presenter; Spresent, a Web-based presentation tool for remote offices or conference calls.

44923 ■ *Open Source Solutions for Small Business Problems*
Pub: Charles River Media
Ed: John Locke. Released: May 2004. Price: $35.95. Description: Open source software provides solutions to many small business problems such as tracking electronic documents, scheduling, accounting functions, managing contact lists, and reducing spam.

44924 ■ **"Oracle and Tauri Group Honored by Homeland Security and Defense Business Council" in** *Wireless News* **(December 15, 2009)**
Pub: Close-Up Media
Description: Selected as members of the year by the Homeland Security and Defense Business Council were Oracle, a software company that has provided thought leadership and strategic insights as well as The Tauri Group, an analytical consultancy, that has demonstrated a unique understanding of the role of small business and its vital contribution to the success of the country's security.

44925 ■ **"Our Gadget of the Week" in** *Barron's* **(Vol. 88, March 24, 2008, No. 12, pp. 47)**
Pub: Dow Jones & Company, Inc.
Ed: Tiernan Ray. Description: Review of the $299 Apple Time Capsule, which is a 500-megabyte hard disk drive and a Wi-Fi router, rolled into one device. The device allows users to create backup files without the need for sophisticated file management software.

44926 ■ **"Owner of IT Firm MK2 Tying Future to Software" in** *Crain's Cleveland Business* **(Vol. 30, June 15, 2009, No. 23, pp. 3)**
Pub: Crain Communications, Inc.
Ed: Chuck Soder. Description: Donald Kasper, owner of MK2 Technologies LLC of Cleveland, Ohio discusses his recent acquisition of a portion of ProSource Solution. The move will help expand the two companies' custom software development plans.

44927 ■ **"Panda Security for Business 4.05" in** *SC Magazine* **(Vol. 21, July 2010, No. 7, pp. 50)**
Pub: Haymarket Media Inc.
Description: Profile of Panda Security for Business, software offering endpoint security protection for computer desktops and servers is presented.

44928 ■ **"The Paper Shredder" in** *Business Courier* **(Vol. 26, September 11, 2009, No. 20, pp. 1)**
Pub: American City Business Journals, Inc.
Ed: Dan Monk. Description: DotLoop Company, owned by entrepreneur Austin Allison, is developing the DotLoop software, which eliminates paperwork in

the processing of real estate contracts. The software allows realtors to take control of the negotiation process and is adaptable to the rules of different US states.

44929 ■ **"Paperless Bookkeeping Program" in** *Fleet Owner Online* **(February 15, 2011)**
Pub: Penton Business Media Inc.
Description: TruckTax launched its new paperless bookkeeping system to help manage bookkeeping tasks, accounting and business tax information and filings for truckers.

44930 ■ **"PC Connection Acquires Cloud Software Provider" in** *New Hampshire Business Review* **(Vol. 33, March 25, 2011, No. 6, pp. 8)**
Pub: Business Publications Inc.
Description: Merrimack-based PC Connection Inc. acquired ValCom Technology, a provider of cloud-based IT service management software. Details of the deal are included.

44931 ■ **"PC Running Slowly? How to Rev Up Your Machine" in** *Inc.* **(Vol. 33, November 2011, No. 9, pp. 46)**
Pub: Inc. Magazine
Ed: John Brandon. Description: Software that keeps PCs tuned up and running smoothing are profiled: AUSLO6ICS BOOSTSPEED 5, $50; Tuneup Utilities 2011, $40; Slimware Slimcleaner 1.9, free; and IOBIT Advanced Systemcare Pro 4, $20 a year.

44932 ■ **"PopCap Games Achieves Significant Increase in Return on Ad Spend With Omniture SearchCenter" in** *Internet Wire* **(September 15, 2009)**
Pub: Comtex News Network, Inc.
Description: PopCap Games, a leading computer games provider, is using Omniture SearchCenter together with Omniture SiteCatalyst to increase revenue from its search engine marketing campaign. Omniture, Inc. is a leading provider of Internet business optimization software.

44933 ■ **"The Power of Negative Thinking" in** *Inc.* **(Volume 32, December 2010, No. 10, pp. 43)**
Pub: Inc. Magazine
Ed: Jason Fried. Description: A Website is software and most businesses have and need a good Website to generate business. Understanding for building a powerful Website is presented.

44934 ■ **"Power Ranger" in** *Inc.* **(November 2007, pp. 131)**
Pub: Gruner & Jahr USA Publishing
Ed: Nitasha Tiku. Description: Surveyor software is designed to power down computers when not in use, in order to save energy.

44935 ■ *Practical Tech for Your Business*
Pub: Kiplinger Books and Tapes
Ed: Michael J. Martinez. Released: 2002. Description: Advice is offered to help small business owners choose the right technology for their company. The guide tells how to get started, network via the Internet, create an office network, use database software, and conduct business using mobile technology.

44936 ■ **"Precision Crop Control with Valley Irrigation/CropMetrics Partnership" in** *Farm Industry News* **(January 6, 2011)**
Pub: Penton Business Media Inc.
Description: Irrigation systems have become a precision farming tool since partnering with agronomic software systems to apply products across the field by prescription. Valley Irrigation and CropMetrics have partnered in order to variably control water, fertilizer and other crop management products through a center pivot irrigation system.

44937 ■ **"Press Release: Trimble Introduces CFX-750 Display" in** *Farm Industry News* **(January 4, 2011)**
Pub: Penton Business Media Inc.
Description: Trimble is offering a touch screen display called the CFX-750. The new 8-inch full-color display allows farmers to choose the specific guidance, steering and precision agriculture capabilities

that best fit their farm's particular needs. The display can be upgraded as business needs change, including the addition of GLONASS capabilities, or the addition of section and rate control for crop inputs such as seed, chemicals and fertilizer.

44938 ■ "Programs Provide Education and Training" in *Contractor* **(Vol. 56, September 2009, No. 9, pp. 56)**
Pub: Penton Media, Inc.
Ed: William Feldman; Patti Feldman. **Description:** Opportunity Interactive's Showroom v2 software provides uses computer graphics to provide education and training on HVAC equipment and systems. It can draw heat pump balance points for a specific home. Meanwhile, Simutech's HVAC Training Simulators provide trainees with 'hands-on' HVACR training.

44939 ■ "Protection One Introduces Home and Business Security iPhone App" in *Wireless News* **(November 13, 2009)**
Pub: Close-Up Media
Description: Protection One, Inc., a provider of security systems to business and residential customers, has developed an application that allows users to access their security panels and receive real-time updates from their iPhone or iPod touch devices.

44940 ■ "Providers Ride First Wave of eHealth Dollars" in *Boston Business Journal* **(Vol. 31, June 10, 2011, No. 20, pp. 1)**
Pub: Boston Business Journal
Ed: Julie M. Donnelly. **Description:** Health care providers in Massachusetts implementing electronic medical records technology started receiving federal stimulus funds. Beth Israel Deaconess Medical Center was the first hospital to qualify for the funds.

44941 ■ "Publishing Technology Introduces IngentaConnect Mobile" in *Information Today* **(Vol. 26, February 2009, No. 2, pp. 33)**
Pub: Information Today, Inc.
Description: College undergraduates will find Publishing Technology's newest publisher product, IngentaConnect Mobile helpful. The product allows users to read articles and abstracts on mobile devices. According to a recent study, 73 percent of young adults with wireless hand-held devices use them to access non-voice data on any given day.

44942 ■ "Putting the App in Apple" in *Inc.* **(Vol. 30, November 2008, No. 11, pp.)**
Pub: Mansueto Ventures LLC
Ed: Nitasha Tiku. **Description:** Aftermarket companies are scrambling to develop games and widgets for Apple's iPhone. Apple launched a kit for developers interested in creating iPhone-specific software along with the App Store, and an iTunes spinoff. Profiles of various software programs that may be used on the iPhone are given.

44943 ■ *QuickBooks All-in-One Desk Reference for Dummies*
Pub: John Wiley & Sons, Incorporated
Ed: Stephen L. Nelson. **Released:** January 2007. **Price:** $29.99 (US), $42.99 (Canadian). **Description:** Compilation of nine self-contained minibooks to get the most from QuickBooks accounting software. Companion Web site with sample business plan workbook and downloadable profit-volume cost analysis workbook included.

44944 ■ *QuickBooks for the New Bean Counter: Business Owner's Guide 2006*
Pub: Wheatmark
Ed: Joseph L. Catallini. **Released:** July 2006. **Price:** $21.95. **Description:** Profile of QuickBooks software, offering insight into using the software's accounting and bookkeeping functions.

44945 ■ *QuickBooks Simple Start for Dummies*
Pub: John Wiley & Sons, Incorporated
Ed: Stephen L. Nelson. **Released:** October 2004. **Price:** $21.99. **Description:** Profile of Intuits new accounting software geared to micro businesses. Advice is offered on daily, monthly, and yearly accounting activities covering records, sales tax, and reports.

44946 ■ *QuickBooks X on Demand*
Pub: Que
Ed: Gail Perry. **Released:** December 2006. **Price:** $34.99. **Description:** Step-by-step training for using various small business financial software programs; includes illustrated, full color explanations.

44947 ■ *QuickBooks X for Dummies*
Pub: John Wiley & Sons, Incorporated
Ed: Stephen L. Nelson. **Released:** November 2006. **Price:** $21.99. **Description:** Key features of Quick-Books software for small business are introduced. Invoicing and credit memos, recoding sales receipts, accounting, budgeting, taxes, payroll, financial reports, job estimating, billing, tracking, data backup, are among the features.

44948 ■ "Quickoffice's MobileFiles Pro App Enables Excel Editing On-the-Go" in *Information Today* **(Vol. 26, February 2009, No. 2, pp. 31)**
Pub: Information Today, Inc.
Description: Quickoffice Inc. introduced MobileFiles Pro, which features editable Microsoft Office functionality for the iPone and iPod touch. The application allows users to edit and save Microsoft Excel files in .xls format, transfer files to and from PC and Mac desktops via Wi-Fi, and access and synchronize with Apple MobileMe accounts.

44949 ■ "Remote Control: Working From Wherever" in *Inc.* **(February 2008, pp. 46-47)**
Pub: Gruner & Jahr USA Publishing
Ed: Ryan Underwood. **Description:** New technology allows workers to perform tasks from anywhere via the Internet. Profiles of products to help connect to your office from afar include, LogMein Pro, a Web-based service that allowsaccess to a computer from anywhere; Xdrive, an online service that allows users to store and swap files; Basecamp, a Web-based tools that works like a secure version of MySpace; MojoPac Freedom, is software that allows users to copy their computer's desktop to a removable hard drive and plug into any PC; WatchGuard Firebox X Core e-Series UTM Bundle, hardware that blocks hackers and viruses while allowing employees to work remotely; TightVNC, a free open-source software that lets you control another computer via the Internet.

44950 ■ "RES Stakes Its Claim in Area" in *Philadelphia Business Journal* **(Vol. 28, January 29, 2010, No. 50, pp. 1)**
Pub: American City Business Journals
Ed: Peter Key. **Description:** RES Software Company Inc. of Amsterdam, Netherlands appointed Jim Kirby as president for the Americas and Klaus Besier as chairman in an effort to boost the firm's presence in the US. Brief career profiles of Kirby and Besier are included. RES develops software that allows management of information flow between an organization and its employees regardless of location.

44951 ■ "Route Optimization Impacts the Bottom Line" in *Contractor* **(Vol. 56, November 2009, No. 11, pp. 48)**
Pub: Penton Media, Inc.
Ed: Dave Beaudry. **Description:** Plumbing and HVAC businesses can save a significant amount of money from route optimization. The process begins with gathering information on a fleet and a routing software tool can determine the effectiveness of current route configurations and identify preferable route plans.

44952 ■ *Salesforce.com Secrets of Success: Best Practices for Growth and Profitability*
Pub: Prentice Hall Business Publishing
Ed: David Taber. **Released:** May 15, 2009. **Price:** $34.99. **Description:** Guide for using Salesforce. com; it provides insight into navigating through user groups, management, sales, marketing and IT departments in order to achieve the best results.

44953 ■ "Save the Date" in *Barron's* **(Vol. 90, September 13, 2010, No. 37, pp. 35)**
Pub: Barron's Editorial & Corporate Headquarters
Ed: Mark Veverka. **Description:** Mark Hurd is the new Co-President of Oracle after being forced out at Hewlett-Packard where he faced a harassment complaint. HP fired Hurd due to expense account malfeasance. Hurd is also set to speak at an Oracle trade show in San Francisco on September 20, 2010.

44954 ■ "Scitable Puts Nature Education on the Map" in *Information Today* **(Vol. 26, February 2009, No. 2, pp. 29)**
Pub: Information Today, Inc.
Description: Nature Education, a division of the Nature Publishing Group, released its first product, Scitable, a free online resource for undergraduate biology students and educators. The service includes over 180 overviews of key genetics concepts as well as social networking features, including groups and functionality, that lets students work with classmates and others. Teachers can use the service to set up public or private groups for students.

44955 ■ "Second Cup?" in *Canadian Business* **(Vol. 81, July 21, 2008, No. 11, pp. 50)**
Pub: Rogers Media Ltd.
Ed: Calvin Leung. **Description:** Profile of James Gosling who is credited as the inventor of the Java programming language; however, the 53-year-old software developer feels ambivalent for being credited as inventor since many people contributed to the language. Netscape and Sun Microsystems incorporation of the programming language into Java is presented.

44956 ■ "Sense of Discovery" in *Business Journal Portland* **(Vol. 27, November 19, 2010, No. 38, pp. 1)**
Pub: Portland Business Journal
Ed: Erik Siemers. **Description:** Tigard, Oregon-based Exterro Inc. CEO Bobby Balachandran announced plans to go public without the help of an institutional investor. Balachandran believes Exterro could grow to a $100 million legal compliance software company in the span of three years. Insights on Exterro's growth as market leader in the $1 billion legal governance software market are also given.

44957 ■ "Serials Solutions Launches 360 Resource Manager Consortium Edition" in *Information Today* **(Vol. 26, February 2009, No. 2, pp. 32)**
Pub: Information Today, Inc.
Description: Serials Solutions new Serials Solutions 360 Resource Manager Consortium Edition helps consortia, groups and member libraries with their e-resource management services. The products allows users to consolidate e-resource metadata and acquisition information into one place, which enables groups to manage holdings, subscriptions, licensing, contacts, and cost information and to streamline delivery of information to members.

44958 ■ "A Side Project Threatens To Get Totally Out of Control and I Think, 'How Fun'" in *Inc.* **(October 2007, pp. 81-82)**
Pub: Gruner & Jahr USA Publishing
Ed: Joel Spolsky. **Description:** Profile of Fog Creek Software, makers of project-management software for other software developers. Fog Creek's owner discusses his idea to create a new product for his firm.

44959 ■ "Skype on Steroids" in *Inc.* **(Vol. 31, January-February 2009, No. 1, pp. 46)**
Pub: Mansueto Ventures LLC
Ed: Nitasha Tiku. **Description:** Free software called VoxOx allows users to make calls over the Internet and connects all email and IM accounts.

44960 ■ "Slow but Steady into the Future" in *Barron's* **(Vol. 88, July 7, 2008, No. 27, pp. M)**
Pub: Dow Jones & Co., Inc.
Ed: Mark Veverka. **Description:** Investors are advised to maintain their watch on the shares of business software company NetSuite. The company's chief executive officer, Zach Nelson, claims that the company has a 10-year lead on its competitors with the development of software-as-a service.

44961 ■ "Small is Bountiful for Intuit" in *Barron's* **(Vol. 90, September 13, 2010, No. 37, pp. 22)**
Pub: Barron's Editorial & Corporate Headquarters
Ed: Mark Veverka. **Description:** Finance software maker Intuit wants to tap the underserved small busi-

ness market. One analyst sees Intuit's shares rising 25 percent to 55 percent in the next 12 months from September 2010.

44962 ■ **"A Software Company's Whimsical Widgets Were an Instant Hit. But Its Core Product Was Getting Overshadowed" in** *Inc.* **(Jan. 2008)**
Pub: Gruner & Jahr USA Publishing
Ed: Alex Salkever. **Description:** A widget designed as a marketing tool tuned into a hit on Facebook. Should ChipIn shift its focus?

44963 ■ **"Software Solutions Increase Productivity" in** *Contractor* **(Vol. 57, February 2010, No. 2, pp. 26)**
Pub: Penton Media, Inc.
Ed: William Feldman; Patti Feldman. **Description:** Singletouch is a real-time data capture solution for mechanical and other contractors that work in jobs that require materials and workload tracking. Contractors get information on extreme weather and sudden changes in the cost of materials. The OptimumHVAC optimization software by Optimum Energy is designed to optimize energy savings in commercial buildings.

44964 ■ **"Software Solutions from Trane and Carrier" in** *Contractor* **(Vol. 56, July 2009, No. 7, pp. 38)**
Pub: Penton Media, Inc.
Ed: William Feldman; Patti Feldman. **Description:** Trane Trace 700 software helps HVAC contractors optimize the design of a building's HVAC system and aids in the evaluation of various key energy-saving concepts, including daylighting, high-performance glazing, and other optimization strategies. Carrier's E20-II family of software programs lets contractors increase the accuracy of an HVAC system estimate.

44965 ■ **"Software's Last Hurrah" in** *Canadian Business* **(Vol. 81, December 24, 2007, No. 1, pp. 27)**
Pub: Rogers Media
Ed: Andrew Wahl. **Description:** Canada's software industry could be facing a challenge with IBM's acquisition of Cognos, which was the country's last major independent business intelligence company and was also IBM's largest acquisition ever. Next in line to Cognos in terms of prominence is Open Text Corporation, which could also be a possible candidate for acquisition, as analysts predict.

44966 ■ **"Speaking In Tongues: Rosetta Stone's TOTALE Adds 'Social' To Language Learning" in** *Black Enterprise* **(Vol. 41, September 2010, No. 2)**
Pub: Earl G. Graves Publishing Co. Inc.
Ed: Sonya A. Donaldson. **Description:** As small businesses become more globalized, it is necessary to learn new languages in order to compete. Rosetta Stone's TOTALe is profiled.

44967 ■ **"Startup on Cusp of Trend" in** *Austin Business JournalInc.* **(Vol. 29, January 8, 2010, No. 44, pp. 1)**
Pub: American City Business Journals
Ed: Christopher Calnan. **Description:** Austin-based Socialware Inc. introduced a new business called social middleware, which is a software that is layered between the company network and social networking Website used by workers. The software was designed to give employers a measure of control over content while allowing workers to continue using online social networks.

44968 ■ **"The State of the Art in End-User Software Engineering" in** *ACM Computing Surveys* **(Vol. 43, Fall 2011, No. 3, pp. 21)**
Pub: Association for Computing Machinery
Description: Most programs today are not written by professional software developers but by people with expertise in other domains working towards goals for which they need computational support. A discussion of empirical research about end-user software engineering activities and the technologies designed to support them is presented. Several crosscutting issues in the design of EUSE tools, including the roles of risk, reward, and domain complexity, and self-

efficacy in the design of EUSE tools and the potential of educating users about software engineering principles are also examined.

44969 ■ **"The Story Of Diane Greene" in** *Barron's* **(Vol. 88, July 14, 2008, No. 28, pp. 31)**
Pub: Dow Jones & Co., Inc.
Ed: Mark Veverka. **Description:** Discusses the ousting of Diane Greene as a chief executive of VMWare, a developer of virtualization software, after the firm went public; in this case Greene, a brilliant engineer, should not be negatively impacted by the decision because it is common for companies to bring in new executive leadership that is more operations oriented after the company goes public.

44970 ■ **"A Survey of Combinatorial Testing" in** *ACM Computing Surveys* **(Vol. 43, Summer 2011, No. 2, pp. 11)**
Pub: Association for Computing Machinery
Ed: Changhai Nie, Hareton Leung. **Description:** Combinatorial Testing (CT) can detect failures triggered by interactions of parameters in the Software Under Test (SUT) with a covering array test suite generated by some sampling mechanisms. Basic concepts and notations of CT are covered.

44971 ■ **"A Survey of Comparison-Based System-Level Diagnosis" in** *ACM Computing Surveys* **(Vol. 43, Fall 2011, No. 3, pp. 22)**
Pub: Association for Computing Machinery
Ed: Elias P. Duarte Jr., Roverli P. Ziwich, Luiz C.P. Albini. **Description:** The growing complexity and dependability requirements of hardware, software, and networks demand efficient techniques for discovering disruptive behavior in those systems. Comparison-based diagnosis is a realistic approach to detect faulty units based on the outputs of tasks executed by system units. This survey integrates the vast amount of research efforts that have been produced in this field.

44972 ■ **"Taking the Steps Into the Clouds" in** *New Hampshire Business Review* **(Vol. 33, March 25, 2011, No. 6, pp. 19)**
Pub: Business Publications Inc.
Ed: Tim Wessels. **Description:** Cloud services include Internet and Web security, spam filtering, message archiving, work group collaboration, IT asset management, help desk and disaster recovery backup.

44973 ■ **"Tech Deal Couples Homegrown Firms" in** *The Business Journal-Serving Greater Tampa Bay* **(Vol. 28, July 4, 2008, No. 28, pp. 1)**
Pub: American City Business Journals, Inc.
Ed: Michael Hinman. **Description:** Tampa Bay, Florida-based Administrative Partners Inc. was acquired by Tribridge Inc. resulting in the strengthening of the delivery of Microsoft products to clients. Other details of the merger of the management consulting services companies are presented.

44974 ■ **"Technology to the Rescue" in** *Contractor* **(Vol. 56, July 2009, No. 7, pp. 22)**
Pub: Penton Media, Inc.
Ed: Candace Ruolo. **Description:** Features of several products that will make the job of a mechanical contractor easier are discussed. These include Ridgid's line of drain and sewer inspection cameras and monitors, Motion Computing's Motion F5 tablet rugged tablet PC, the JobClock from Exaktime, and the TeleNav Track tool for mobile workforce management.

44975 ■ **"Technology: What Seems To Be the Problem? Self Service Gets a Tune-Up" in** *Inc.* **(February 2008, pp. 43-44)**
Pub: Gruner & Jahr USA Publishing
Ed: Darren Dahl. **Description:** Self-service software can save companies money when responding to customer service phone calls, text or email messages. More companies are relying on alternatives such as automated Web-based self-service systems.

44976 ■ **"Ted Stahl: Executive Chairman" in** *Inside Business* **(Vol. 13, September-October 2011, No. 5, pp. NC6)**
Pub: Great Lakes Publishing Company
Ed: Miranda S. Miller. **Description:** Profile of Ted Stahl, who started working in his family's business when he was ten years old is presented. The firm makes dies for numbers and letters used on team uniforms. Another of the family firms manufactures stock and custom heat-printing products, equipment and supplies. It also educates customers on ways to decorate garments with heat printing products and offers graphics and software for customers to create their own artwork.

44977 ■ **"Tell Us What You Really Think Collecting Customer Feedback" in** *Inc.* **(Vol. 30, December 2008, No. 12, pp. 52)**
Pub: Mansueto Ventures LLC
Ed: Ryan Underwood. **Description:** According to a recent survey, nearly 77 percent of online shoppers review consumer-generated reviews of products before making a purchase.

44978 ■ **"Thinking Strategically About Technology" in** *Franchising World* **(Vol. 42, August 2010, No. 8, pp. 9)**
Pub: International Franchise Association
Ed: Bruce Franson. **Description:** Nearly 25 percent of companies waste money from their technology budget. Most of the budget is spent on non-strategic software. Ways to spend money on technology for any franchise are examined.

44979 ■ **"A Timely Boon for Small Investors" in** *Barron's* **(Vol. 88, March 24, 2008, No. 12, pp. 48)**
Pub: Dow Jones & Company, Inc.
Ed: Theresa W. Carey. **Description:** Nasdaq Data Store's new program called Market Replay allows investors to accurately track stock price movements. The replay can be as long as a day of market time and allows investors to determine whether they executed stock trades at the best possible price.

44980 ■ **"Touching the Future" in** *Canadian Business* **(Vol. 81, July 21, 2008, No. 11, pp. 41)**
Pub: Rogers Media Ltd.
Ed: Matt McClearn. **Description:** Microsoft Corp. has launched a multi-touch product which is both a software and hardware technology called Microsoft Surface. The innovative product allows people to use it at the same time, however touch-based computers are reported to be around $100,000. Other features and benefits of the product are presented.

44981 ■ **"Trust But Verify: FMLA Software Isn't Foolproof, So Apply a Human Touch" in** *HR Specialist* **(Vol. 8, September 2010, No. 9, pp. 3)**
Pub: Capitol Information Group Inc.
Description: Employers are using software to track FMLA information, however, it is important for employers to review reasons for eligibility requirements, particularly when an employee is reportedly overstepping the bounds within leave regulations due to software error.

44982 ■ **"Two Field Service Management Solutions" in** *Contractor* **(Vol. 56, November 2009, No. 11, pp. 37)**
Pub: Penton Media, Inc.
Ed: William Feldman; Patti Feldman. **Description:** Bella Solutions Field Service Software v. 4.2 is a web based solution for HVAC service contractors that enables scheduling of emergency, one-time, multivisit or periodically recurring jobs with drag and drop appointments. VaZing is another web based solution that costs $99 per month for contractors. It can handle line-item discounting and invoices aside from scheduling.

44983 ■ **"Two Ways to Find New Customers" in** *Inc.* **(Vol. 31, January-February 2009, No. 1, pp. 41)**
Pub: Mansueto Ventures LLC
Description: Latest software programs that help sales staff connect to new leads are profiled. Salesconx provides online leads while Demandbase reports users on a particular Website.

44984 ■ **"Unbound ID Raises $2 Million" in** *Austin Business JournalInc.* **(Vol. 28, December 12, 2008, No. 39, pp. 1)**
Pub: American City Business Journals
Ed: Christopher Calnan. **Description:** Austin, Texas-based Unbound ID Corporation has secured $2 million in funding from venture capital firm Silverton Partners. The company has developed identity management software for network directories. The market for identity management technology is expected to grow to more than $12.3 billion by 2014.

44985 ■ **"uTest Discusses the Evolution of Crowdsourcing Models at CrowdConf 2010" in** *Internet Wire* **(October 1, 2010)**
Pub: Comtex
Description: World's largest software testing marketplace, uTest, announces its first conference dedicated to the emerging field of crowdsourcing along with the future of distributed work. A panel of experts will discuss common misconceptions about crowdsourcing using real-world examples.

44986 ■ **"Video Surveillance Enters Digital Era, Makes Giant Strides" in** *Arkansas Business* **(Vol. 26, September 28, 2009, No. 39, pp. 1)**
Pub: Journal Publishing Inc.
Ed: Jamie Walden. **Description:** Arkansas business owners are finding that the newest technology in video surveillance is leading to swift apprehension of thieves due to the high-quality digital imagery now being captured on surveillance equipment. Motion detection software for these systems is enhancing the capabilities of these systems and providing opportunities for businesses that would normally have problems integrating these systems.

44987 ■ **"A Virtual Jog Mode for CAM" in** *Modern Machine Shop* **(Vol. 84, November 2011, No. 6, pp. 22)**
Pub: Gardner Publications
Ed: Edwin Gasparraj. **Description:** In many cases, CAM programming required a specific, user-defined path. Siemens PLMs Generic Motion Controller is an alternative that defines the tool path within CAM. The program is a virtual 'teach' mode that enables the user to capture cutter locations by jogging machines axes within CAM.

44988 ■ **"Web Translation Made Simple" in** *Inc.* **(Vol. 33, October 2011, No. 8, pp. 44)**
Pub: Inc. Magazine
Ed: Adam Baer. **Description:** Smartling is a Web-based service that translates sites into more than 50 foreign languages. The software will begin translation right after setting up the account.

44989 ■ **"Website Backup Made Simple" in** *Inc.* **(Vol. 33, September 2011, No. 7, pp. 52)**
Pub: Inc. Magazine
Ed: John Brandon. **Description:** Tools to back up content on a Website are profiled. Vaultpress works only with sites that run on the WordPress publishing platform and CodeGuard works with a variety of publishing platforms and hosting services.

44990 ■ **"Wegmans Uses Database for Recall" in** *Supermarket News* **(Vol. 56, September 22, 2008, No. 38)**
Pub: Penton Business Media, Inc.
Ed: Carol Angrisani. **Description:** Wegmans used data obtained through its loyalty card that, in turn, sent automated telephone calls to every customer who had purchased tainted pet food when Mars Petcare recalled dog food products.

44991 ■ **"Will the Force Be With Salesforce?" in** *Barron's* **(Vol. 88, March 24, 2008, No. 12, pp. 20)**
Pub: Dow Jones & Company, Inc.
Ed: Mark Veverka. **Description:** Shares of Salesforce.com are likely to drop from the $44.83-a-share level in the face of a deteriorating economy and financial sector and thus lower demand for business software. The company is unlikely to deliver on its ambitious earnings forecasts for 2008 especially with strengthening competition from Oracle.

44992 ■ **"Women Losing IT Ground" in** *Marketing to Women* **(Vol. 21, February 2008, No. 2, pp. 6)**
Pub: EPM Communications, Inc.
Description: According to a study conducted by The National Center for Women & Information Technology, women in technology are losing ground. Statistical data included.

44993 ■ **"Yammer Gets Serious" in** *Inc.* **(Volume 32, December 2010, No. 10, pp. 58)**
Pub: Inc. Magazine
Ed: Eric Markowitz. **Description:** Yammer, an internal social network for companies, allows coworkers to share ideas and documents in real-time. Details of this service are included.

44994 ■ **"Yes, No, and Somewhat Likely: Survey the World with Web Polls" in** *Inc.* **(October 2007, pp. 58-59)**
Pub: Gruner & Jahr USA Publishing
Ed: Don Steinberg. **Description:** Online tools for surveying customers, employees and the general public include Zoomergan zPro and Zoomerang Sample, software designed to send surveys and allows viewing results; SurveyMonkey software creates, administers and allows viewing online surveys and results; Vizu software places a one-question poll on a particular Website; and Vovici EFM Feedback, a subscription service providing ongoing surveys to customers or employees.

44995 ■ **"Zeon Solutions Teams with Endeca for SaaS Version of Endeca InFront" in** *Entertainment Close-Up* **(October 25, 2011)**
Pub: Close-Up Media
Description: Zeon Solutions, an enterprise e-commerce and Website development firm announced a special licensing partnership with Endecca Technologies. Endeca is an information management software company that provides small and mid-size retailers with high-performance Customer Experience Management technology.

TRADE PERIODICALS

44996 ■ *Business Computer Report*
Pub: Lawrence Oakly
Ed: Lawrence Oakly, Editor. **Released:** Monthly. **Description:** Reviews business applications software and hardware for IBM and compatible computers.

44997 ■ *PC Business Products*
Pub: Worldwide Videotex
Contact: Mark Wright
Released: Monthly. **Price:** $165, U.S. and Canada; $180, elsewhere outside North America. **Description:** Covers developments in software and hardware products and services. Includes list of performance ratings and prices.

44998 ■ *Technology Trends*
Pub: Enterprise Technology Corp.
Ed: Kevin J. Merz, Editor. **Released:** 6/year. **Description:** Discusses news on computer software technology and its perceived value to the business community.

CONSULTANTS

44999 ■ **Business Resource Software Inc.**
1779 Wells Branch Pky.
Austin, TX 78728
Ph:(512)251-7541
Free: 800-423-1228
Fax:(512)251-4401
Co. E-mail: sales@brs-inc.com
URL: http://www.brs-inc.com
Contact: Larry Nesbit, President
E-mail: brown@brs-inc.com
Scope: Provides marketing and business planning software. Provides an evaluation of business conditions and advises the users about situations in their specific business. **Special Services:** Plan Write[R]; Quick Insight[R]; Business Insight[R].

45000 ■ **CheckMark Software Inc.**
724 Whalers Way, Bldg. H, Ste. 101
Fort Collins, CO 80525-7578
Ph:(970)225-0522
Free: 800-444-9922
Fax:(970)225-0611
Co. E-mail: info@checkmark.com
URL: http://www.checkmark.com
Contact: Terry Stone, Dir of Sales
E-mail: rgilmore@checkmark.com
Scope: Developer of accounting software tools for small businesses and provides fast, easy to use, affordable accounting and payroll solutions to small and medium sized businesses. Provides payroll software and multiledger integrated accounting software. **Special Services:** MultiLedger[TM]; Payroll.

45001 ■ **Claremont Consulting Group**
4525 Castle Ln.
La Canada, CA 91011-1436
Ph:(818)249-0584
Fax:(818)249-5811
Contact: Donald S. Remer, Partner
E-mail: amruskin@compuserve.com
Scope: Consulting, coaching, training, and litigation support in project management, engineering management, system engineering and cost estimating. **Publications:** "What Every Engineer Should Know About Project Management"; "100% product-oriented work breakdown structures and their importance to system engineering". **Seminars:** Project Management, System Engineering and Cost Estimating.

45002 ■ **DacEasy Inc.**
1715 N Brown Rd.
Lawrenceville, GA 30043
Ph:(770)492-6414
Free: 800-322-3279
Fax:(770)724-2874
Co. E-mail: sales@daceasy.com
URL: http://www.daceasy.com
Contact: Marchell Gillis
E-mail: marchell.gillis@sage.com
Scope: Develops an accounting system for small businesses that integrates accounting, invoicing, payroll, communications, and management software into a single package. **Seminars:** DacEasy Training. **Special Services:** DacEasy.

45003 ■ **Global Business Consultants**
200 Lake Hills Rd.
PO Box 776
Pinehurst, NC 28374-0776
Ph:(910)295-5991
Fax:(910)295-5991
Co. E-mail: gbc@pinehurst.net
Contact: Gerd Hofielen, Partner
E-mail: mcoin@atsyourculturecoach.com
Scope: Firm specializes in human resources management; project management; software development; and international trade. Offers litigation support. **Publications:** "Culture to Culture: Mission Trip Do's and Don'ts," Jul, 2005; "Rules of the Game: Global Business Protocol". **Seminars:** Cross-Cultural Training.

45004 ■ **MoneySoft Inc.**
1 E Camelback Rd., Ste. 550
Phoenix, AZ 85012-1650
Ph:(602)266-7710
Free: 800-966-7797
Fax:(602)230-1864
Co. E-mail: info@moneysoft.com
URL: http://www.moneysoft.com
Contact: Michael Bray, Principle
E-mail: mbray@moneysoft.com
Scope: Specializes in the publication of software for the corporate acquisition and development community. Assists businesses develop acquisition goals and criteria that build shareholder value; determine whether an acquisition candidate meets their criteria; conduct analysis of the candidate's historic performance and position; estimate the candidate's future earning capacity; prepare professional-quality valuations and appraisal reports for tax, business planning or litigation related matters; determine purchase price and optimal terms. Prepare a detailed plan to finance

the acquisition; estimate the future earnings of the candidate after the acquisition; generate fact-filled acquisition proposals for presentation to management and funding sources; and manage and track fixed assets and depreciation. **Publications:** "The Price is Right- Or is It?"; "Preparing Financial Projections and Valuations"; "Negotiating Business Acquisitions"; "Managing the Process of Buying a Business"; "The Overpayment Trap"; "Strategies to Avoid the Overpayment Trap"; "The Value, Price and Cost of an Acquisition"; "The Trouble with EBITDA". **Special Services:** Corporate Valuation Professional™; DealSense^R; Buy-OutPlan^R; Corporate Valuation™; Lightning Deal Reviewer^R; Fixed Asset Pro™; Benchmark Pro 2006™; DealSense Plus; Mergerstat^R.

45005 ■ On-Q Software Inc.
13764 SW 11th St.
Miami, FL 33184

Ph:(305)553-2400
Free: 800-553-2862
Fax:(305)220-2666
Co. E-mail: info@on-qsoftware.com
URL: http://www.on-qsoftware.com
Contact: Terry Cajigas, Principle
E-mail: hcajigas@on-qsoftware.com
Scope: Provides the small business community with simple to use, feature rich software. Provides software solutions including time and fixed fee billing, due date tracking and practice manager.

COMPUTERIZED DATABASES

45006 ■ *TecTrends*
Information Sources Inc.
PO Box 8120
Berkeley, CA 94707

Ph:(510)525-6220
Co. E-mail: tectrendsinfo@tectrends.com
URL: http://www.tectrends.com

Description: Contains information on the information technology industry, with detailed descriptions on more than 12,000 information technology products. Includes company information, including personnel names, addresses, telephone numbers, URLs, e-mails, and a description of the company. Product information includes system requirements, availability, vendor support, and a product description. These product and company descriptions are linked to independent third-party reviews abstracted from more than 200 trade journals and industry magazines. **Availability:** Online: Information Sources Inc., ProQuest LLC, ProQuest LLC. **Type:** Bibliographic; Directory.

START-UP INFORMATION

45007 ■ *How to Start Your Own Business for Entrepreneurs*
Pub: FT Press
Ed: Robert Ashton. **Released:** December 9, 2010. **Price:** $24.99. **Description:** More than 300,000 individuals start a business every year. That number will rise over the next year or two if the current economic downturn leads to widespread job losses.

45008 ■ "The Next Generation: African Americans Are Successfully Launching Businesses Earlier In Life" in *Black Enterprise* (January 2008)
Pub: Earl G. Graves Publishing Co. Inc.
Ed: Tennille M. Robinson. **Description:** According to a survey conducted by OPEN, a team dedicated small business at American Express, Generation Y individuals are three times more likely to start their own company. Three African American individuals who did just that are profiled.

ASSOCIATIONS AND OTHER ORGANIZATIONS

45009 ■ **Academy of Legal Studies in Business**
Miami University
Dept. of Finance
3111 Farmer School of Business
Oxford, OH 45056
Free: 800-831-2903
Co. E-mail: herrondj@muohio.edu
URL: http://www.alsb.org
Contact: Prof. Daniel J. Herron, Exec. Sec.
Description: Teachers of business law and legal environment in colleges and universities. Promotes and encourages business law scholarship and teaching outside of the law school environment. **Publications:** *American Business Law Journal* (quarterly); *Journal of Legal Studies Education* (semiannual).

45010 ■ **Association for Consumer Trends**
7076 Drinkard Way
Mechanicsville, VA 23111
Ph:(804)559-6519
Fax:(804)559-4087
Co. E-mail: info@consumerexpert.org
URL: http://www.consumerexpert.org
Contact: Ms. Kimberly Thies, Exec. Dir.
Description: Provides global trend information and networking resources to assist members to identify and integrate trends into the design and marketing of consumer goods and services; educates businesses to interpret impact of trends on consumer needs and expectations. Hosts an annual Consumer Trends Forum with speakers addressing consumer trends. **Publications:** *Trendline* (biweekly).

45011 ■ **Small Business Legislative Council**
1100 H St. NW, Ste. 540
Washington, DC 20005
Ph:(202)639-8500

Fax:(202)296-5333
Co. E-mail: email@sblc.org
URL: http://www.sblc.org
Contact: John Satagaj, Pres./Gen. Counsel
Description: Serves as an independent coalition of trade and professional associations that share a common commitment to the future of small business. Represents the interests of small businesses in such diverse economic sectors as manufacturing, retailing, distribution, professional and technical services, construction, transportation, and agriculture. .

REFERENCE WORKS

45012 ■ "Burner Handles Everything From 2 to B100" in *Indoor Comfort Marketing* (Vol. 70, May 2011, No. 5, pp. 24)
Pub: Industry Publications Inc.
Description: A new oil burner being offered by AMERIgreen Energy is profiled.

45013 ■ "10 Trends That Are Shaping Global Media Consumption" in *Advertising Age* (Vol. 81, December 6, 2010, No. 43, pp. 3)
Pub: Crain Communications, Inc.
Ed: Ann Marie Kerwin. **Description:** Ad Age offers the statistics from the TV penetration rate in Kenya to the number of World Cup watchers and more.

45014 ■ "The ABCs of a Good Show" in *Playthings* (Vol. 106, October 1, 2008, No. 9, pp. 18)
Pub: Reed Business Information
Ed: Karyn M. Peterson. **Description:** ABC Kids Expo 2008 made a strong showing with products for babies, kids and new/expecting parents. The new Naturally Kids section promoting eco-friendly products was the highlight of the show.

45015 ■ "Abroad, Not Overboard" in *Entrepreneur* (Vol. 36, April 2008, No. 4, pp. 68)
Pub: Entrepreneur Media, Inc.
Ed: Crystal Detamore-Rodman. **Description:** Export-Import Bank is an agency created by the U.S. government to help exporters get credit insurance and capital loans by providing them with loan guarantees. The bank, being criticized as supporting more the bigger exporters, has allotted to smaller businesses a bigger portion of the annual credit being approved.

45016 ■ *The Age Curve: How to Profit from the Demographic Storm*
Pub: AMACOM
Ed: Kenneth W. Gronbach. **Released:** July 3, 2008. **Price:** $24.95. **Description:** Reveals how America's largest generations are redefining consumer behavior and how businesses can anticipate their growing needs more effectively.

45017 ■ "Age-Old System of Bartering Is Being Revolutionized by Phoenix Company, Premier Barter" in *Internet Wire* (July 12, 2010)
Pub: Comtex
Description: Premier Barter is helping entrepreneurs rediscover the system of bartering as a method of exchanging goods and services without cash or credit.

45018 ■ "Agribusiness: How to Get Rich in Farming" in *Canadian Business* (Vol. 80, January 29, 2007, No. 3, pp. 42)
Pub: Rogers Media
Ed: Peter Shawn Taylor. **Description:** The trends pertaining to the income of Canadian farmers are examined. The methods of increasing the profits of Canadian agribusinesses are discussed.

45019 ■ "ALA: Hot Topics for Librarianship" in *Information Today* (Vol. 28, September 2011, No. 8, pp. 17)
Pub: Information Today, Inc.
Ed: Barbara Brynko. **Description:** Highlights from the American Library Association Annual Conference and Exhibition are listed. Thousands of attendees sought out services, displays, demos, new product rollouts, and freebies. Emerging technology for librarians, staff development, gray literature, interlibrary loans, and next-generation interfaces were among the topics discussed.

45020 ■ "All Eyes On Iris" in *Canadian Business* (Vol. 81, July 22, 2008, No. 12-13, pp. 20)
Pub: Rogers Media Ltd.
Ed: Jack Mintz. **Description:** Provincial governments in Canada are believed to be awaiting Alberta Finance Minister Iris Evans' financial and investment policies as well as Evans' development of a new saving strategy. Alberta is the only Canadian province that is in position to invest in sovereign wealth funds after it eliminated its debt in 2005.

45021 ■ "Alternative Energy Calls for Alternative Marketing" in *Indoor Comfort Marketing* (Vol. 70, June 2011, No. 6, pp. 8)
Pub: Industry Publications Inc.
Ed: Richard Rutigliano. **Description:** Advice for marketing solar energy products and services is given.

45022 ■ "Amid Recession, Companies Still Value Supplier Diversity Programs" in *Hispanic Business* (July-August 2009, pp. 34)
Pub: Hispanic Business
Ed: Joshua Molina. **Description:** The decline of traditionally strong industries, from automotive manufacturing to construction, has shaken today's economy and has forced small businesses, especially suppliers and minority-owned firms, turn to diversity programs in order to make changes.

45023 ■ "Amount Md. Pays to Unemployed Dips to Lowest Level Since '08" in *Baltimore Business Journal* (Vol. 28, November 12, 2010, No. 27)
Pub: Baltimore Business Journal
Ed: Scott Dance. **Description:** Maryland paid out $50 million for unemployment benefits in September 2010 for its lowest payout since 2008. The drop in unemployment payout could mean lower taxes for employers who pay for the benefits. The unemployment rate in Maryland, however, increased to 7.5 percent.

45024 ■ "Analysts: Intel Site May Be Last Major U.S.-Built Fab" in *Business Journal-Serving Phoenix and the Valley of the Sun* **(Oct. 19, 2007)**
Pub: American City Business Journals, Inc.
Ed: Ty Young. **Description:** Intel's million-square-foot manufacturing facility, called Fab 32, is expected to open in 2007. The plant will mass-produce the 45-nanometer microchip. Industry analysts believe Fab 32 may be the last of its kind to be built in the U.S., as construction costs are higher in America than in other countries. Intel's future in Chandler is examined.

45025 ■ "Analysts: More Mergers for the Region's Hospitals" in *Boston Business Journal* **(Vol. 30, October 15, 2010, No. 36, pp. 1)**
Pub: Boston Business Journal
Ed: Julie M. Donnelly. **Description:** A number of hospitals in Boston, Massachusetts are engaging in mergers and acquisitions. Caritas Christi Health Care is set to be purchased by Cerberus Capital Management. The U.S. healthcare reform law is seen to drive the development.

45026 ■ "App Time: Smartphone Applications Aren't Just for Fun and Games Anymore" in *Inc.* **(Volume 32, December 2010, No. 10, pp. 116)**
Pub: Inc. Magazine
Ed: Jason Del Rey. **Description:** Smart phone technology can help any small business market their products and services.

45027 ■ "Apparel" in *Retail Merchandiser* **(Vol. 51, July-August 2011, No. 4, pp. 14)**
Pub: Phoenix Media Corporation
Description: NPD Group Inc. released current sales statistics for the women's apparel market along with men's apparel. It also reported annual shoes sales for 2010. Statistical data included.

45028 ■ "Are Movie Theaters Doomed?" in *Business Horizons* **(November-December 2007, pp. 491)**
Pub: Elsevier Technology Publications
Ed: Jon Silver, John McDonnell. **Description:** Theater operators must embrace new technologies and more diverse target markets if they are to stem the decline in theatergoers. Movie theaters remain highly vulnerable to trends in the home entertainment industry.

45029 ■ "Are You Ignoring Trends That Could Shake Up Your Business?" in *Harvard Business Review* **(Vol. 88, July-August 2010, No. 7-8, pp. 124)**
Pub: Harvard Business School Publishing
Ed: Elie Ofek, Luc Wathieu. **Description:** Ways for firms to capitalize on trends that might otherwise negatively affect their business are spotlighted. These include using certain aspects of the trend to augment traditional product/service offerings, and combining the trend with the offerings to transcend its traditional category.

45030 ■ "As Capital Gains Tax Hike Looms, Merger Activity Percolates" in *Baltimore Business Journal* **(Vol. 28, August 27, 2010, No. 16, pp. 1)**
Pub: Baltimore Business Journal
Ed: Scott Dance. **Description:** Concerns for higher capital gains taxes in 2011 have been provoking buyers and sellers to engage in mergers and acquisitions activity, which is expected to gain momentum before the end of 2010. Companies that had saved cash during the recession have been taking advantage of the buyer's market. Other trends in local and national mergers and acquisitions activity are presented.

45031 ■ "As Technology Changes, So Must African American Business" in *Black Enterprise* **(Vol. 41, August 2010, No. 1, pp. 61)**
Pub: Earl G. Graves Publishing Co. Inc.
Ed: Sonya A. Donaldson. **Description:** Social media is essential to compete in today's business environment, especially for African American firms.

45032 ■ "Ask Inc." in *Inc.* **(October 2007, pp. 73-74)**
Pub: Gruner & Jahr USA Publishing
Description: An online marketing research firm investigates the use of online communities such as MySpace and Second life in order to recruit individuals to answer surveys.

45033 ■ "Athletes Face Wins and Losses After Pro Sport" in *The Business Journal - Serving Phoenix and the Valley of the Sun* **(Vol. 29, September 19, 2008, No. 3, pp. 1)**
Pub: American City Business Journals, Inc.
Ed: Chris Casacchia. **Description:** Professional athletes like hockey star Jeremy Roenick start businesses, while others like Joel Adamson work to boost local communities. Former athletes were found to be particularly interested with real estate businesses. Other views and information on former athletes and their life after sports are presented.

45034 ■ "Attend To Your Corporate Housekeeping" in *Women Entrepreneur* **(December 4, 2008)**
Pub: Entrepreneur Media Inc.
Ed: Nina Kaufman. **Description:** Business owners can lose all the benefits and privileges of the corporate form if they do not follow proper corporate formalities such as holding an annual meeting, electing officers and directors and adopting or passing corporate resolutions. Creditors are able to take from one's personal assets if such formalities have not been followed.

45035 ■ "Attract More Online Customers: Make Your Website Work Harder for You" in *Black Enterprise* **(Vol. 37, November 2006, No. 4, pp. 66)**
Pub: Earl G. Graves Publishing Co. Inc.
Ed: **Description:** Having an impressive presence on the Internet has become crucial. Detailed advice on making your website serve your business in the best way possible is included.

45036 ■ "Attracting Veteran-Franchisees To Your System" in *Franchising World* **(Vol. 42, November 2010, No. 11, pp. 53)**
Pub: International Franchise Association
Ed: Mary Kennedy Thompson. **Description:** As military servicemen and women return home, the franchising industry expects an increase in veterans as franchise owners. The Veterans Transition Franchise Initiative, also known as VetFran, is described.

45037 ■ "Auto Supplier Stock Battered In Wake Of Wall Street Woes" in *Crain's Detroit Business* **(Vol. 24, September 29, 2008, No. 39, pp. 4)**
Pub: Crain Communications, Inc.
Ed: Ryan Beene. **Description:** Due to the volatility of the stock market and public perception of the $700 billion banking bailout, auto suppliers are now facing a dramatic drop in their shares. Statistical data included.

45038 ■ "AVT Launches New ExpressPay Vending Systems" in *Benzinga.com* **(July 13, 2011)**
Pub: Benzinga.com
Ed: Benzinga Staff. **Description:** AVT Inc. has developed a new high-tech vending system that features a touch screen interface and a cashless payment system so users can find what they want easily and pay using a credit card.

45039 ■ "A Baby Step to the South" in *Canadian Business* **(Vol. 81, July 22, 2008, No. 12-13, pp. 21)**
Pub: Rogers Media Ltd.
Ed: Jane Bao. **Description:** Canada's free trade agreement (FTA) with Colombia is seen as Canada's re-engagement with Latin America. Some politicians believe that the FTA is more of a political agreement than a trade agreement with Colombia. Key information on Canada's trade agreements, as well as trade with Colombia and Latin American countries, is presented.

45040 ■ *Back on the Career Track: A Guide for Stay-At-Home Moms Who Want to Return to Work*
Pub: Warner Books Inc.
Ed: Carol Fishman Cohen; Vivian Steir Rabin. **Released:** 2008. **Price:** $14.99 paperback. **Description:** For women like themselves who have rejoined the workforce after a prolonged absence, the authors detail seven main steps for reentry; profiles of six women who have successfully re-launched their careers are included.

45041 ■ "Back on Track-Or Off the Rails?" in *Business Week* **(September 22, 2008, No. 4100, pp. 22)**
Pub: McGraw-Hill Companies, Inc.
Ed: Peter Coy; Tara Kalwarski. **Description:** Discusses the possible scenarios the American economy may undergo due to the takeover of Fannie Mae and Freddie Mac. Statistical data included.

45042 ■ "Bailout Forgets the 'Little Guys'" in *The Business Journal-Milwaukee* **(Vol. 25, September 26, 2008, No. 53, pp. A1)**
Pub: American City Business Journals, Inc.
Ed: Rich Kirchen. **Description:** Community Bankers of Wisconsin and the Wisconsin Bankers Association are urging members to approach congressional representatives and remind them to include local banks in building the $700 billion bailout plan. WBA president and CEO Kurt Bauer thinks that it is only fair to include smaller institutions in the bailout. The initial bailout plan and its benefit for the smaller banks are examined.

45043 ■ "Banking Bailout: Boost or Bust?" in *Crain's Detroit Business* **(Vol. 24, September 29, 2008, No. 39, pp. 1)**
Pub: Crain Communications, Inc.
Ed: Amy Lane. **Description:** Economic insiders discuss the banking bailout and how it might impact the state of Michigan.

45044 ■ "Banking Crisis Rattles Local Businesses" in *Puget Sound Business Journal* **(Vol. 29, October 10, 2008, No. 25, pp. 1)**
Pub: American City Business Journals
Ed: Kirsten Grind. **Description:** Customers of Washington Mutual in the Puget Sound region started withdrawing large sums of cash due to fears of the banks unstable condition.

45045 ■ "Banking on Twitter" in *Baltimore Business Journal* **(Vol. 27, February 6, 2010, No. 40, pp. 1)**
Pub: American City Business Journals
Ed: Gary Haber. **Description:** Ways that banks are using Twitter, Facebook and other social networking sites to provide customer services is discussed. First Mariner Bank is one of those banks that are finding the social media platform as a great way to reach customers. Privacy issues regarding this marketing trend are examined.

45046 ■ "Bankruptcy Blowback" in *Business Week* **(September 22, 2008, No. 4100, pp. 36)**
Pub: McGraw-Hill Companies, Inc.
Ed: Jessica Silver-Greenberg. **Description:** Changes to bankruptcy laws which were enacted in 2005 after banks and other financial institutions lobbied hard for them are now suffering the consequences of the laws which force more troubled borrowers to let their homes go into foreclosure; lenders suffer financially every time they have to take on a foreclosure and the laws in which they lobbied so hard to see enacted are now becoming a problem for these lending institutions. Details of the changes in the laws are outlined as are the affects on the consumer, the economy and the lenders.

45047 ■ "Banks Lower Rates on CDs, Deposits" in *Baltimore Business Journal* **(Vol. 27, January 1, 2010, No. 35, pp. 1)**
Pub: American City Business Journals
Ed: Gary Haber. **Description:** Greater Baltimore area banks in Maryland have lowered their rates on certificates of deposits (CDs) and money market accounts, which could indicate the incoming trend for

the first half of 2010. A banking industry forecast shows that lower Federal Funds rate, low inflation, and a new Federal Deposit Insurance Corporation (FDIC) rule might cause the rates to drop even further. Details on the FDIC rule are given.

45048 ■ **"Bartering Makes a Return in Hard Times"** in *Atlanta Journal-Constitution* (October 2, 2010, pp. A15)
Pub: Atlanta Journal-Constitution
Ed: Bill York. **Description:** The advantages of bartering are explored.

45049 ■ **"Bartering Trades on Talents"** in *Reading Eagle* (June 20, 2010)
Pub: Reading Eagle/Reading Times
Ed: Tony Lucia. **Description:** Bartering is not just a way of trading goods and services, it can be an essential tool for small business to survive in a bad economy.

45050 ■ **"Be Wary of Legal Advice on Internet, Lawyers Warn"** in *Crain's Detroit Business* (Vol. 24, September 22, 2008, No. 38, pp. 16)
Pub: Crain Communications, Inc.
Ed: Harriet Tramer. **Description:** While some lawyers feel that the proliferation of legal information on the Internet can point people in the right direction, others maintain that it simply results in giving false hope, may bring about confusion or worse yet, it sometimes makes their jobs even harder.

45051 ■ *Behind the Cloud*
Pub: Jossey-Bass
Ed: Marc Benioff, Carlye Adler. **Released:** 2010. **Price:** $27.95. **Description:** Salesforce.com is the world's most successful business-to-business cloud-computing company that sells an online service that helps businesses manage sales, customer service, and marketing functions.

45052 ■ **"Beyond YouTube: New Uses for Video, Online and Off"** in *Inc.* (October 2007, pp. 53-54)
Pub: Gruner & Jahr USA Publishing
Ed: Leah Hoffmann. **Description:** Small companies are using video technology for embedding messages into email, broadcasting live interactive sales and training seminars, as well as marketing campaigns. Experts offer insight into producing and broadcasting business videos.

45053 ■ *Big-Box Swindle: The True Cost of Mega-Retailers and the Fight for America's Independent Businesses*
Pub: Beacon Press
Ed: Stacy Mitchell. **Released:** October 2007. **Price:** $15.00. **Description:** Examination of the economic, environmental, and social damage done by big-box retailers like Wal-Mart, Costco, and Home Depot. Labor policies of these retailers, particularly those enforced by Wal-Mart, are discussed at length.

45054 ■ *The Big Switch*
Pub: W. W. Norton & Company, Inc.
Ed: Nicholas Carr. **Released:** January 19, 2009. **Price:** $16.95 paperback. **Description:** Today companies are dismantling private computer systems and tapping into services provided via the Internet. This shift is remaking the computer industry, bringing competitors such as Google to the forefront ant threatening traditional companies like Microsoft and Dell. The book weaves together history, economics, and technology to explain why computing is changing and what it means for the future.

45055 ■ *The Big Switch: Rewiring the World, From Edison to Google*
Pub: W.W. Norton & Company
Ed: Nicholas Carr. **Released:** 2009. **Price:** $25.95. **Description:** Companies such as Google, Microsoft, and Amazon.com are building huge centers in order to create massive data centers. Together these centers form a giant computing grid that will deliver the digital universe to scientific labs, companies and homes in the future. This trend could bring about a new, darker phase for the Internet, one where these networks could operate as a fearsome entity that will dominate the lives of individuals worldwide.

45056 ■ **"Bigger is Definitely Not Better When It Comes to Cooling"** in *Indoor Comfort Marketing* (Vol. 70, May 2011, No. 5, pp. 49)
Pub: Industry Publications Inc.
Ed: Eugene Silberstein. **Description:** Efficiency is more important when installing air conditioning equipment over size of the unit. Details are provided.

45057 ■ **"Bill Kaneko"** in *Hawaii Business* (Vol. 53, December 2007, No. 6, pp. 32)
Pub: Hawaii Business Publishing
Ed: David K. Choo. **Description:** Hawaii Institute for Public Affairs chief executive officer and president Bill Kaneko believes that the Hawaiian economy is booming, however, he also asserts that the economy is too focused on tourism and real estate. Kaneko has also realized the that the will of the people is strong while he was helping with the Hawaiian 2050 Sustainability Plan. The difficulties of making a sustainable Hawaii are discussed.

45058 ■ **"Biodiesel Poised to Regain Growth"** in *Farm Industry News* (January 21, 2011)
Pub: Penton Business Media Inc.
Description: According to Gary Haer, vice president of sales and marketing for Renewable Energy Group, the biodiesel industry is positioned to regain growth in 2011 with the reinstatement of the biodiesel blendersa tax credt of $1 per gallon.

45059 ■ **"Bioheat – Alternative for Fueling Equipment"** in *Indoor Comfort Marketing* (Vol. 70, May 2011, No. 5, pp. 14)
Pub: Industry Publications Inc.
Ed: Gary Hess. **Description:** Profile of Worley and Obetz, supplier of biofuels used as an alternative for fueling industry equipment.

45060 ■ **"Biotechs Are Using Back Door to Go Public"** in *Boston Business Journal* (Vol. 31, May 27, 2011, No. 18, pp. 1)
Pub: Boston Business Journal
Ed: Julie M. Donnelly. **Description:** Members of Massachusetts' biotechnology sector have been engaging in reverse mergers as an alternative to initial public offerings. Reverse mergers provide access to institutional investors and hedge funds.

45061 ■ **"Birdcage Optimization"** in *Pet Product News* (Vol. 64, November 2010, No. 11, pp. 54)
Pub: BowTie Inc.
Description: Manufacturers have been emphasizing size, security, quality construction, stylish design, and quick cleaning when guiding consumers on making birdcage options. Selecting a birdcage is gaining importance considering that cage purchases have become the highest expense associated with owning a bird. Other avian habitat trends are also examined.

45062 ■ **"Blue Hill Tavern to Host Baltimore's First Cupcake Camp"** in *Daily Record* (August 10, 2011)
Pub: Dolan Company
Ed: Rachel Bernstein. **Description:** Cities joining the trend to host cupcake camps are listed. The camps are open to all individuals wishing to share and eat cupcakes in an open environment.

45063 ■ **"Branding Your Way"** in *Canadian Business* (Vol. 80, February 12, 2007, No. 4, pp. 31)
Pub: Rogers Media
Ed: Erin Pooley. **Description:** The trend in involving consumers in brand marketing by seeking their views through contests or inviting them to produce and submit commercials through Internet is discussed.

45064 ■ **"Burger Market Sizzling with Newcomers"** in *Boston Business Journal* (Vol. 29, June 10, 2011, No. 5, pp. 1)
Pub: American City Business Journals Inc.
Ed: Ryan Sharrow. **Description:** The burger trend in Maryland is on the rise with burger joints either opening up or expanding into several branches. Startup costs for this kind of business range between $250,000 to $400,000. With a growth rate of roughly

17 percent in 2009, this so-called better burger segment of the burger categories is expected to dominate the market for quite some time.

45065 ■ **"Business Forecast: Stormy and Successful"** in *Women In Business* (Vol. 62, June 2010, No. 2, pp. 12)
Pub: American Business Women's Association
Ed: Kathleen Leighton. **Description:** Stormy Simon, vice president of customer service at Overstock.com is a self-made career woman who started out as a temporary employee in the company in 2001. She was not able to attend college because she had two sons to care for after her divorce. Simon got involved in advertising and media buying and shares her love for business.

45066 ■ **"Business Must Stand Up And Be Counted"** in *Crain's Detroit Business* (Vol. 24, October 6, 2008, No. 40, pp. 6)
Pub: Crain Communications, Inc.
Description: Discusses the challenges that the new mayor of Detroit faces concerning business, the state of the economy and the exceptionally tight budget the city is running on, which includes a lot of red ink. It is very likely that the city is going to see tax revenues fall substantially in the next few months and business leaders may find it in their favor to lend their support to the new mayor as well as provide him with the executive talent necessary to overcome some of these crucial issues.

45067 ■ **"Business Stands Firm for Reform"** in *Crain's Detroit Business* (Vol. 26, January 4, 2010, No. 1, pp. 3)
Pub: Crain Communications, Inc.
Ed: Amy Lane. **Description:** As Michigan faces a new year of budgetary problems, many business groups are preparing to hold firm against tax increases and instead push for enacting spending reforms.

45068 ■ **"Businesses Keep a Watchful Eye on Worker's Comp"** in *The Business Journal-Serving Greater Tampa Bay* (September 5, 2008)
Pub: American City Business Journals, Inc.
Ed: Jane Meinhardt. **Description:** Pending a ruling from the Florida Supreme Court that could uphold the 2003 changes on workers' compensation law, the outcome would include restrictions on claimant attorneys' fees and allow the competitive workers' compensation insurance rates to remain low. However, insurance rates are expected to go up if the court overturns the changes.

45069 ■ **"Buyers' Market"** in *Baltimore Business Journal* (Vol. 27, November 20, 2009, No. 28, pp. 1)
Pub: American City Business Journals
Ed: Daniel J. Sernovitz. **Description:** Some business owners in Maryland are removing their leases and purchasing buildings due to the lower costs of real estate. This trend has enabled small business owners to avoid rent hikes, while setting equity into their companies. The pros and cons of owning buildings and how business owners assess their return on investment are examined.

45070 ■ **"Buying Power of Hispanics Growing"** in *Austin Business JournalInc.* (Vol. 29, November 27, 2009, No. 38, pp. 1)
Pub: American City Business Journals
Ed: Sandra Zaragoza. **Description:** Hispanic Marketing Symposium presented a report stating that the buying power of Hispanics of Austin, Texas has grown by 54 percent in last five years to $9.4 billion in 2009. Details on the projected growth of the Hispanic market in the are is covered.

45071 ■ **"Buying Seed by Weight or By Count"** in *Farm Industry News* (October 20, 2010)
Pub: Penton Business Media Inc.
Ed: Mark Moore. **Description:** Soybean producers have the option of buying seeds by count or by weight; tips for either method of purchase are outlined.

45072 ■ "Call of Prepaid Heard by More" in *Chicago Tribune* **(November 26, 2008)**
Pub: McClatchy-Tribune Information Services

Ed: Wailin Wong. **Description:** Due to the economic downturn, more consumers are switching to no-contract, prepaid cell phone service. Customers find that the cost savings, flexibility and lack of contract are appealing in such uncertain times.

45073 ■ "Campaigner Survey: 46 Percent of Small Businesses Use Email Marketing" in *Wireless News* **(November 21, 2009)**
Pub: Close-Up Media

Description: Almost half (46 percent) of small businesses surveyed by Campaigner's 2009 State of Small Business Online Marketing, say that they rely on email marketing to help them find new customers, keep existing ones and grow their businesses. The survey also found that 36 percent of small businesses plan to begin using email marketing over the next year. The trend to utilize Internet marketing tools is allowing small businesses to grow faster and generate higher revenues than those that are not using these mediums.

45074 ■ "Can HOAs Stop You From Going Green?" in *Contractor* **(Vol. 56, July 2009, No. 7, pp. 39)**
Pub: Penton Media, Inc.

Ed: Susan Linden McGreevy. **Description:** There have been cases concerning homeowners' associations objections to the installation of wind turbines and solar panels. Precedence with the courts show that they will look at several factors when deciding to uphold restrictions on property use including whether the item encroaches on the rights of others, is likely to adversely affect property values, and also the state of enforcement.

45075 ■ "Canada Tomorrow" in *Canadian Business* **(Vol. 80, October 8, 2007, No. 20, pp. 14)**
Pub: Rogers Media

Ed: Donald J. Johnston. **Description:** An assessment of Canada's future in terms of its educational, social, and economic environment is presented. Concerns regarding the country's educational system such as the declining interest in science and technology and the possible lack of teachers in the future are discussed. In terms of its social and economic aspects, the need to support entrepreneurs and other qualified people is explained.

45076 ■ "Canada's Oil Rush" in *Canadian Business* **(Vol. 81, October 13, 2008, No. 17, pp. 58)**
Pub: Rogers Media Ltd.

Description: Excerpt from Andrew Nikiforuk's 'Tar Sands' details the exploration and development of oil sands in Alberta, Canada and its significance to the U.S. Canada has been the United State's largest supplier of oil since 2002, accounting for 18 percent of U.S. oil imports. Details regarding Canada's oil sand are examined.

45077 ■ "Canadian Hydronics Businesses Promote 'Beautiful Heat'" in *Indoor Comfort Marketing* **(Vol. 70, September 2011, No. 9, pp. 20)**
Pub: Industry Publications Inc.

Description: Canadian hydronics companies are promoting their systems as beautiful heat. Hydronics is the use of water as the heat-transfer medium in heating and cooling system.

45078 ■ "Capital Ideas: Regions to Lansing: Focus on Taxes, Reform, Keeping Talent" in *Crain's Detroit Business* **(Vol. 24, October 6, 2008)**
Pub: Crain Communications, Inc.

Ed: Amy Lane. **Description:** Michigan must make bold and dramatic changes in public policy regarding business legislation. The tax structure, unemployment issues and attracting and retaining talent are among the issues the state must confront, especially in this tough economic climate.

45079 ■ "Capturing Generation Y: Ready, Set, Transform" in *Credit Union Times* **(Vol. 21, July 14, 2010, No. 27, pp. 20)**
Pub: Summit Business Media

Ed: Senthil Kumar. **Description:** The financial services sector recognizes that Generation Y will have a definite impact on the way business is conducted in the future. The mindset of Generation Y is social and companies need to use networking tools such as Facebook in order to reach this demographic.

45080 ■ "Car Dealers Shift Gears to Survive" in *Puget Sound Business Journal* **(Vol. 29, November 14, 2008, No. 30, pp. 1)**
Pub: American City Business Journals

Ed: Gregg Lamm. **Description:** Washington-based automobile dealers are offering incentives such as repairs, parts and used cars in order to supplement the decline in new car sales.

45081 ■ "Carbon Trading: Current Schemes and Future Developments" in *Energy Policy* **(Vol. 39, October 2011, No. 10, pp. 6040-6054)**
Pub: Reed Elsevier Reference Publishing

Ed: Slobodan Perdan, Adisa Azapagic. **Description:** Current and future developments regarding carbon trading is highlighted.

45082 ■ *The Catalyst Code: The Strategies Behind the World's Most Dynamic Companies*
Pub: Harvard Business School Press

Ed: David S. Evans; Richard Schmalensee. **Released:** May 9, 2007. **Price:** $29.95. **Description:** Economic catalysts businesses can bring consumers and merchants together in order to survive in an economy where markets, consumers and technology are always changing.

45083 ■ "Cents and Sensibility" in *Playthings* **(Vol. 107, January 1, 2009, No. 1, pp. 19)**
Pub: Reed Business Information

Ed: Pamela Brill. **Description:** Recent concerns over safety, phthalate and lead paint and other toxic materials, as well as consumers going green, are issues discussed by toy manufacturers. Doll manufacturers also face increase labor and material costs and are working to design dolls that girls will love.

45084 ■ *Change in SMEs: The New European Capitalism*
Pub: Palgrave Macmillan

Ed: Katharina Bluhm; Rudi Schmidt. **Released:** October 2008. **Price:** $95.00. **Description:** Effects of global change on corporate governance, management, competitive strategies and labor relations in small-to-medium sized enterprises in various European countries are discussed.

45085 ■ "Changing Fuel Compositions: What It Means To You and Your Business" in *Indoor Comfort Marketing* **(Vol. 70, June 2011, No. 6, pp. 30)**
Pub: Industry Publications Inc.

Ed: Paul Nazzaro. **Description:** Biofuels are outlined and the way it is changing the HVAC/R industry are discussed.

45086 ■ *Chief Culture Officer: How to Create a Living, Breathing Corporation*
Pub: Basic Books

Ed: Grant McCracken. **Price:** $26.95. **Description:** Business consultant argues that corporations need to focus on 'reading' what's happening in the culture around them. Otherwise, companies will suffer the consequences, as Levi Strauss did when it missed out on the rise of hip-hop (and the baggy pants that are part of that lifestyle).

45087 ■ "Child-Care Policy and the Labor Supply of Mothers with Young Children" in *University of Chicago Press* **(Vol. 26, July 2008, No. 3)**
Pub: University of Chicago Press

Ed: Pierre Lefebvre, Philip Merrigan. **Description:** In 1997, the provincial government of Quebec, the second most populous province in Canada, initiated a new childcare policy. Licensed childcare service

providers began offering day care spaces at the reduced fee of $5 per day per child for children aged four. By 2000, the policy applied to all children not in kindergarten. Using annual data (1993-2002) drawn from Statistics Canada's Survey of Labour and Income Dynamics, the results show that the policy had a large and statistically significant impact on the labor supply of mothers with preschool children.

45088 ■ "Cincinnati's Senior Moment" in *Business Courier* **(Vol. 27, June 11, 2010, No. 6, pp. 1)**
Pub: Business Courier

Ed: James Ritchie. **Description:** It is believed that the high demand in housing that will accompany the aging population has yet to arrive, and is not due for years to come. The next few years could lead to leaner times for long-standing independent-living properties and a slow climb for newer centers looking to build occupancy.

45089 ■ *Cities from the Arabian Desert: The Building of Jubail and Yanbu in Saudi Arabia*
Pub: Turnaround Associates

Ed: Andrea H. Pampanini. **Released:** May 2005. **Price:** $35.00. **Description:** An overview of Saudi Arabia's government to take control of the nation's natural resources and change the government, educational system, and its culture by evolving into a modern industrial society.

45090 ■ "ClickFuel Unveils Internet Marketing Tools for Small Businesses" in *Internet Wire* **(October 19, 2009)**
Pub: Comtex News Network, Inc.

Description: ClickFuel, a firm that manages, designs and tracks marketing campaigns has unveiled a full software suite of affordable services and technology solutions designed to empower small business owners and help them promote and grow their businesses through targeted Internet marketing campaigns.

45091 ■ "Closing the Marketing Capabilities Gap" in *Journal of Marketing* **(Vol. 75, July 2011, No. 4, pp. 183)**
Pub: American Marketing Association

Ed: George S. Day. **Description:** A look at the growing gap between the demands of the market and the capacity of organizations is presented. New thinking about marketing capabilities is needed to close the gap between the accelerating complexities of their market needs. The adaptive capabilities needed are vigilant market learning, adaptive market experimentation, and open marketing.

45092 ■ "Clouds in the Forecast" in *Information Today* **(Vol. 28, September 2011, No. 8, pp. 10)**
Pub: Information Today, Inc.

Ed: Paula J. Hane. **Description:** Cloud computing is software, applications, and data stored remotely and accessed via the Internet with output displayed on a client device. Recent developments in cloud computing are explored.

45093 ■ "Collection Agency Issues Whitepaper on Legal and Ethical Methods of Collecting on Overdue Accounts" in *Internet Wire* **(July 20, 2009)**
Pub: Comtex News Network, Inc.

Description: American Profit Recovery, a collection agency based in Massachusetts and Michigan, has updated and reissued a whitepaper on what businesses can and cannot do regarding conversing with their customers in an attempt to collect on overdue accounts and payments. A detailed summary of the federal laws associated with collecting on overdue accounts is outlined in such a way that any business owner, manager, or responsible party can easily understand.

45094 ■ "Commentary. Economic Trends for Small Business" in *Small Business Economic Trends* **(April 2008, pp. 3)**
Pub: National Federation of Independent Business

Ed: William C. Dunkelberg, Holly Wade. **Description:** Commentary on the economic trends for small businesses in the U.S. is presented. Analysis of recession possibilities is given. Reports indicate that the number of business owners citing inflation as their number one problem is at its highest point since 1982.

45095 ■ **"Commentary. On Federal Reserve's Cut of Interest Rates" in** *Small Business Economic Trends* **(January 2008, pp. 3)**
Pub: National Federation of Independent Business

Description: Federal Reserve cut interest rates and announced its economic outlook on September 18, 2007 to stimulate spending. The cut in interest rates, however, may not help in supporting consumer spending because savers may lose interest income. The expected economic impact of the interest rate cuts and the U.S. economic outlook are also discussed.

45096 ■ **"Commentary. Small Business Economic Trends" in** *Small Business Economic Trends* **(February 2008, pp. 3)**
Pub: National Federation of Independent Business

Ed: William C. Dunkelberg, Holly Wade. **Description:** Commentary on the economic trends for small businesses in the U.S. is presented. Analysis of the U.S. Federal Reserve Board's efforts to prevent a recession is given. Reduction in business inventories is also discussed.

45097 ■ **"Commotion Pictures; Bill C-10: Is It Censorship or Merely Inept?" in** *Canadian Business* **(Vol. 81, March 31, 2008, No. 5, pp. 10)**
Pub: Rogers Media

Ed: Denis Seguin. **Description:** Filmmakers are claiming that Bill C-10 amounts to censorship as it could retract a production's eligibility for a tax credit if it is deemed offensive. However, the bill's backers say that the bill protects against tax dollars being directed at productions that run contrary to public policy.

45098 ■ *The Company We Keep: Reinventing Small Business for People, Community, and Place*
Pub: Chelsea Green Publishing

Ed: John Abrams, William Grieder. **Released:** June 2006. **Price:** $18.00. **Description:** The new business trend in social entrepreneurship as a business plan enables small business owners to meet the triple bottom line of profits for people (employees and owners), community, and the environment.

45099 ■ **"Competition At Last?" in** *Canadian Business* **(Vol. 81, July 22, 2008, No. 12-13, pp. 7)**
Pub: Rogers Media Ltd.

Description: Competition Policy Review Panel's 'Compete to Win' report revealed that Canada is being 'hollowed-out' by foreign acquisitions. The panel investigated competition and foreign investment policies in Canada. Key information on the report, as well as views on the Investment Canada Act and the Competition Act, is presented.

45100 ■ **"Congress Ponders Annuity Trusts" in** *National Underwriter Life & Health* **(Vol. 114, June 21, 2010, No. 12, pp. 10)**
Pub: Summit Business Media

Ed: Arthur D. Postal. **Description:** Congress is looking over several bills, including the Small Business Jobs Tax Relief Act that would significantly narrow the advantages of using grantor-retained annuity trusts (GRATs) to avoid estate and gift taxes.

45101 ■ **"Consumers Like Green, But Not Mandates" in** *Business Journal-Milwaukee* **(Vol. 28, December 10, 2010, No. 10, pp. A1)**
Pub: Milwaukee Business Journal

Ed: Sean Ryan. **Description:** Milwaukee, Wisconsin consumers are willing to spend more on green energy, a survey has revealed. Respondents also said they will pay more for efficient cars and appliances. Support for public incentives for homeowners and businesses that reduce energy use has also increased.

45102 ■ **"Consumers Who Saw a Food Truck This Summer" in** *Nation's Restaurant News* **(Vol. 45, September 26, 2011, No. 20, pp. 8)**
Pub: Penton Media Inc.

Description: A guide to the number of customers encountering food trucks during summer 2011 is presented by region.

45103 ■ **"Convenience Store Deal for Cardtronics" in** *American Banker* **(Vol. 174, July 28, 2009, No. 143, pp. 12)**
Pub: SourceMedia, Inc.

Description: Royal Buying Group, Inc., a convenience store marketing company, has agreed to recommend automated teller machine services from Cardtronics Inc., to its clients.

45104 ■ **"Corporate Diversity Driving Profits" in** *Hispanic Business* **(Vol. 30, September 2008, No. 9, pp. 12)**
Pub: Hispanic Business, Inc.

Ed: Michael Bowker. **Description:** U.S. businesses are beginning to appreciate the importance of diversity and are developing strategies to introduce a diverse workforce that reflects the cultural composition of their customers. The realization that diversity increases profits and the use of professional networks to recruit and retain skilled minority employees are two other new trends impacting corporate diversity in the U.S.

45105 ■ **"COSE: More Small Companies Offering Wellness Plans" in** *Crain's Cleveland Business* **(Vol. 28, December 3, 2007, No. 48, pp. 22)**
Pub: Crain Communications, Inc.

Ed: Shannon Mortland. **Description:** Discusses the Council of Smaller Enterprises (COSE) which is offering incentives to companies who implement wellness programs and can show that their employees are living healthier lives.

45106 ■ **"Countdown" in** *Canadian Business* **(Vol. 81, March 3, 2008, No. 3, pp. 27)**
Pub: Rogers Media

Ed: Al Rosen. **Description:** According to a recent poll only 42 percent of portfolio managers in Canada are aware that the country is planning to adopt the International Financial Reporting Standards beginning 2011. The shift to the new standards will have significant impacts on investment values and will be the biggest revolution in Canadian financial reporting. The effects of the transition on portfolio managers and investors are analyzed.

45107 ■ **"Counter Service" in** *Nation's Restaurant News* **(Vol. 45, September 26, 2011, No. 20, pp. 8)**
Pub: Penton Media Inc.

Description: As food trucks continue their momentum, a study was conducted showing how many consumer would visit a food truck. Nearly two thirds of 18-44 year olds would likely visit a food truck, while individuals over the age of 65 only 38 percent would eat from a food truck.

45108 ■ **"Counter Service: We Gear Up Some Food Truck Stats" in** *Nation's Restaurant News* **(Vol. 45, August 8, 2011, No. 16, pp. 6)**
Pub: Penton Media Inc.

Description: According to a recent survey, people do not see food truck service as a trend and 84 percent of social media users said they would visit food trucks at least once a week.

45109 ■ *Creating a World without Poverty: Social Business and the Future of Capitalism*
Pub: Basic Books

Released: April 26, 2009. **Price:** $26.00. **Description:** Explanation of how microcredit lending practices and more collaborative business strategies can be used to alleviate poverty worldwide.

45110 ■ **"Credit Crunch Gives, Takes Away" in** *The Business Journal-Serving Metropolitan Kansas City* **(Vol. 27, October 17, 2008, No. 5, pp. 1)**
Pub: American City Business Journals, Inc.

Ed: Suzanna Stagemeyer. **Description:** Although many Kansas City business enterprises have been adversely affected by the U.S. credit crunch, others

have remained relatively unscathed. Examples of how local businesses are being impacted by the crisis are provided including: American Trailer & Storage Inc., which declared bankruptcy after failing to pay a long-term loan; and NetStandard, a technology firm who, on the other hand, is being pursued by prospective lenders.

45111 ■ **"Credit Unions Buck Trend, Lend Millions More" in** *Saint Louis Business Journal* **(Vol. 32, September 9, 2011, No. 2, pp. 1)**
Pub: Saint Louis Business Journal

Ed: Greg Edwards. **Description:** St. Louis, Missouri-based credit unions have been making more loans despite the weak economy. Credit unions have made a total of $3.46 billion in outstanding loans as of June 30, 2011.

45112 ■ **"Credit Unions Gain: New Members Sign Up, Fleeing Banks" in** *Puget Sound Business Journal* **(Vol. 29, October 10, 2008, No. 25, pp. 1)**
Pub: American City Business Journals

Ed: Kirsten Grind. **Description:** Credit unions are gaining new members due to customers' lack of confidence in federal banks.

45113 ■ **"The Critical Need to Reinvent Management" in** *Business Strategy Review* **(Vol. 21, Spring 2010, No. 1, pp. 4)**
Pub: Wiley-Blackwell

Ed: Julian Birkinshaw. **Description:** The author believes that management is undervalued today - and for good reasons. Management, he says, has failed at the big-picture level and thinks it is time to reinvent the profession.

45114 ■ *Crowdsourcing: Why the Power of the Crowd is Driving the Future of Business*
Pub: Crown Business

Ed: Jeff Howe. **Released:** 2009. **Price:** $26.95. **Description:** Small businesses are shown how to use social networks online to promote goods and services.

45115 ■ **"Crude Awakening" in** *Canadian Business* **(Vol. 81, October 27, 2008, No. 18, pp. 14)**
Pub: Rogers Media Ltd.

Ed: Jeff Sanford. **Description:** Jim Grays believes that a global liquid fuels crisis is coming and hopes the expected transition from oil dependence will be smooth. Charles Maxwell, on the other hand, predicts that a new world economy will arrive in three waves. Views of both experts are examined.

45116 ■ **"Cupcake Craze" in** *Mail Tribune* **(March 2, 2011)**
Pub: Southern Oregon Media Group

Ed: Sarah Lemon. **Description:** Gourmet cupcake shops are sprouting up in large cities in Oregon. The Cupcake Company, a family business, is profiled.

45117 ■ **"A Curious Appeal (Market for Scientific Toys)" in** *Playthings* **(Vol. 106, October 1, 2008, No. 9, pp. 26)**
Pub: Reed Business Information

Ed: Pamela Brill. **Description:** Science and nature toys are still popular with children. Kits allow kids to make candy, soap, grow miniature gardens, catch bugs and more. These hands-on kits have manufacturers watching trends to create more toys in this category.

45118 ■ **"Currency: I'm Otta Here" in** *Entrepreneur* **(Vol. 35, October 2007, No. 10, pp. 72)**
Pub: Entrepreneur Media Inc.

Ed: C.J. Prince. **Description:** Liberum Research revealed that 193 chief financial officers (CFOs) at small companies have either resigned or retired during the first half of 2007. A survey conducted by Tatum found that unreasonable expectations from the management and compliance to regulations are the main reasons why CFOs are leaving small firms. The chief executive officer's role in making CFOs stay is also discussed.

45119 ■ *Currency Internationalization: Global Experiences and Implications for the Renminbi*
Pub: Palgrave Macmillan
Ed: Wensheng Peng, Chang Shu. **Released:** January 5, 2010. **Price:** $100.00. **Description:** A collection of academic studies relating to the potential internationalization of China's remninbi. It also discusses the increasing use of China's remninbi currency in international trade and finance.

45120 ■ "Daddy's Home! Fathers Stay Home To Watch the Kids and Build Businesses To Suit Their Values" in *Black Enterprise* (October 2007)
Pub: Earl G. Graves Publishing Co. Inc.
Ed: George Alexander. **Description:** Fathers are staying home and running home-based businesses in order to spend more time with their families.

45121 ■ "A Day Late and a Dollar Short" in *Indoor Comfort Marketing* (Vol. 70, March 2011, No. 3, pp. 30)
Pub: Industry Publications Inc.
Ed: Philip J. Baratz. **Description:** A discussion involving futures options and fuel oil prices is presented.

45122 ■ "Dealers Trying Not to Fold" in *Business First Columbus* (Vol. 25, December 5, 2008, No. 15, pp. A1)
Pub: American City Business Journals
Ed: Dan Eaton. **Description:** Increase in the number of automobile dealer closures in Ohio is seen to impact the state's economy. The trend of consolidation is forecasted to adversely affect employment and sales. Statistical data included.

45123 ■ "Death of the PC" in *Canadian Business* (Vol. 83, October 12, 2010, No. 17, pp. 44)
Pub: Rogers Media Ltd.
Ed: Joe Castaldo. **Description:** The future of the personal computer (PC) is looking bleak as consumers are relying more on new mobile devices instead of their PC. A 'Wall Street Journal' article published in September 2010 reported that the iPad had cannibalized sales of laptops by as much as 50 percent. The emergence of tablet computers running alternative operating systems is also explained.

45124 ■ "Defying Gravity?" in *Canadian Business* (Vol. 81, October 13, 2008, No. 17, pp. 17)
Pub: Rogers Media Ltd.
Ed: Joe Castaldo. **Description:** Airlines around the world are expected to lose $4.1 billion in 2009, but experts believe Canadian airlines will be able to survive the economic challenges. Lower demand for air travel and uncertainty on oil prices are also expected to make the conditions more challenging. Views and key information on airlines in Canada and around the world are cited.

45125 ■ "Despite Economic Upheaval Generation Y is Still Feeling Green: RSA Canada Survey" in *CNW Group* (October 28, 2010)
Pub: CNW Group
Description: Canadian Generation Y individuals believe it is important for their company to be environmentally-friendly and one-third of those surveyed would quit their job if they found their employer was environmentally irresponsible, despite the economy.

45126 ■ "The Digital Revolution is Over. Long Live the Digital Revolution!" in *Business Strategy Review* (Vol. 21, Spring 2010, No. 1, pp. 74)
Pub: Wiley-Blackwell
Ed: Gianvito Lanzolla, Jamie Anderson. **Description:** Many businesses are now involved in the digital marketplace. The authors argue that the new reality of numerous companies offering overlapping products means that it is critical for managers to understand digital convergence and to observe the imperatives for remaining competitive.

45127 ■ "Do the Math on Discounts" in *Entrepreneur* (Vol. 37, October 2009, No. 10, pp. 82)
Pub: Entrepreneur Media, Inc.
Ed: Jennifer Lawler. **Description:** Small business owners should consider all effects of discounts before implementing them. Some entrepreneurs do not discount prices for fear of damaging brands or their company's reputation.

45128 ■ "Docs Might Hold Cure for Real Estate, Banks" in *Baltimore Business Journal* (Vol. 28, November 5, 2010, No. 26, pp. 1)
Pub: Baltimore Business Journal
Ed: Gary Haber. **Description:** Health care providers, including physicians are purchasing their office space instead of renting it as banks lower interest rates to 6 percent on mortgages for medical offices. The rise in demand offers relief to the commercial real estate market. It has also resulted in a boom in building new medical offices.

45129 ■ "Doctors Buy In to Medical Timeshares" in *Houston Business Journal* (Vol. 40, December 11, 2009, No. 31, pp. 1)
Pub: American City Business Journals
Ed: Mary Ann Azevedo. **Description:** Memorial Hermann Hospital System has leased to doctors three examination rooms and medical office space in the Memorial Hermann Medical Plaza in line with its new timeshare concept. The concept was designed to bring primary care physicians to its Texas Medical Center campus.

45130 ■ "Doctors Eye Rating Plan With Caution" in *The Business Journal-Portland* (Vol. 25, July 4, 2008, No. 17, pp. 1)
Pub: American City Business Journals, Inc.
Ed: Robin J. Moody. **Description:** Doctors in Portland, Oregon are wary of a new Providence Health Plan system that rates their performance on patients with certain medical conditions. The system is expected to discourage wasteful procedures, thereby, saving employers' money. Other mechanics of the rating system are also discussed.

45131 ■ "DOE Proposes New Water Heater Efficiency Standards" in *Contractor* (Vol. 57, January 2010, No. 1, pp. 3)
Pub: Penton Media, Inc.
Ed: Robert P. Mader. **Description:** U.S. Department of Energy is proposing higher efficiency standards for gas and electric water heaters which will not take effect until 2015. The proposal calls for gas-fired storage water heaters less than 60 gallons to have an Energy Factor of 0.675 and those larger than 60 gallons to have an Energy Factor of 0.717.

45132 ■ "Doing the Right Thing" in *Black Enterprise* (Vol. 38, July 2008, No. 12, pp. 50)
Pub: Earl G. Graves Publishing Co. Inc.
Ed: Tamara E. Holmes. **Description:** More business owners are trying to become more environmentally friendly, either due to their belief in social responsibility or for financial incentives or for both reasons. Tips for making one's business more environmentally responsible are included as well as a listing of resources that may be available to help owners in their efforts.

45133 ■ "Doing Without" in *Baltimore Business Journal* (Vol. 28, June 11, 2010, No. 5, pp. 1)
Pub: Baltimore Business Journal
Ed: Scott Graham. **Description:** Maryland Health Care Commission report figures have shown only 47,661 small businesses provided some level of health coverage to 381,517 employees in 2009. These numbers are down from 51,283 employers who offered benefits to 407,983 employees in 2008 to highlight a disturbing trend in Maryland's small-group insurance market. Reasons for the drop are discussed.

45134 ■ "Don't Expect Quick Fix" in *The Business Journal-Serving Metropolitan Kansas City* (Vol. 27, October 3, 2008, No. 3, pp. 1)
Pub: American City Business Journals, Inc.
Ed: James Dornbrook. **Description:** United States governmental entities cannot provide a quick fix solution to the current financial crisis. The economy

requires a systemic change in the way people think about credit. The financial services industry should also focus on core lending principles.

45135 ■ *Earth: The Sequel*
Pub: W. W. Norton & Company, Inc.
Ed: Fred Krupp; Miriam Horn. **Released:** March 16, 2009. **Price:** $15.95. **Description:** President of the Environmental Defense Fund offers suggestions for small businesses to help solve global warming. Investigation into the new industries, jobs, and opportunities is provided.

45136 ■ "eBay Introduces Open Commerce Ecosystem" in *Entertainment Close-Up* (October 24, 2011)
Pub: Close-Up Media
Description: eBay's new X.commerce is an open commerce ecosystem that will arm developers and merchants with the technology tools required to keep pace with the ever-changing industry. X.commerce brings together the technology assets and developer communities of eBay, PayPal, Magento and partners to expand on eBays vision for enabling commerce.

45137 ■ "Economic Outlook 2009" in *Hispanic Business* (January-February 2009, pp. 30, 32)
Pub: Hispanic Business
Ed: Dr. Juan Solana. **Description:** Successful business policies of the past no longer work in this economic climate. New tools and initiatives regarding monetary policy, fiscal policy and a higher multiplier are required to survive the crisis.

45138 ■ "Economic Trends for Small Business" in *Small Business Economic Trends* (April 2008, pp. 1)
Pub: National Federation of Independent Business
Ed: William C. Dunkelberg, Holly Wade. **Description:** Summary of economic trends for small businesses in the U.S. is presented. Economic indicators such as capital spending, inventories and sales, inflation, and profits are given. Analysis of credit markets is also provided.

45139 ■ *Ecopreneuring: Putting Purpose and the Planet Before Profits*
Pub: New Society Publishers
Ed: John Ivanko; Lisa Kivirist. **Released:** July 1, 2008. **Price:** $17.95 paperback. **Description:** Ecopreneurs in America are shifting profits and market share towards green living. The book provides a guideline for ecopreneurs in the areas of eco-business basics, purposeful management, marketing in the green economy, and running a lifestyle business.

45140 ■ "Effort Is Growing to Offer Healthier Choices in Vending Machines" in *Philadelphia Inquirer* (July 29, 2011)
Pub: Philadelphia Media Network Inc.
Ed: Don Sapatkin. **Description:** Since Boston's mayor announced a ban on the sale of all sugar sweetened beverages on city properties, it seems more cities, states, hospitals, businesses, and even park systems are following suit. Thus, vending machines are beginning to offer healthier snacks and drinks to consumers.

45141 ■ "Election Could Undo Renewable Energy Quotas" in *The Business Journal - Serving Phoenix and the Valley of the Sun* (Vol. 28, July 11, 2008, No. 45, pp. 1)
Pub: American City Business Journals, Inc.
Ed: Patrick O'Grady. **Description:** Competition for the three open seats in the Arizona Corporation Commission is intense, with 12 candidates contesting for the three slots. The commission's mandates for renewable energy and infrastructure investment will also be at stake.

45142 ■ *Electronic Commerce*
Pub: Course Technology
Ed: Gary Schneider, Bryant Chrzan, Charles McCormick. **Released:** May 1, 2010. **Price:** $117.95. **Description:** E-commerce can open the door to more opportunities than ever before for small business. Packed with real-world examples and cases, the book delivers comprehensive coverage of emerging online

technologies and trends and their influence on the electronic marketplace. It details how the landscape of online commerce is evolving, reflecting changes in the economy and how business and society are responding to those changes. Balancing technological issues with the strategic business aspects of successful e-commerce, the new edition includes expanded coverage of international issues, social networking, mobile commerce, Web 2.0 technologies, and updates on spam, phishing, and identity theft.

45143 ■ *The Elephant and the Dragon: The Rise of India and China and What It Means to All of Us*

Pub: W.W. Norton & Company

Ed: Robyn Meredith. **Released:** 2008. **Price:** $15.95. **Description:** The author illustrates how both China and India have followed their own economic path, and examines the countries' similarities and considers the repercussions of their growing involvement in the world market.

45144 ■ *Emerging Business Online: Global Markets and the Power of B2B Internet Marketing*

Pub: FT Press

Ed: Lara Fawzy, Lucas Dworksi. **Released:** October 1, 2010. **Price:** $49.99. **Description:** An introduction into ebocube (emerging business online), a comprehensive proven business model for Internet B2B marketing in emerging markets.

45145 ■ *The Emerging Digital Economy: Entrepreneurship, Clusters, and Policy*

Pub: Springer

Ed: Borje Johansson; Charlie Karlsson; Roger Stough. **Released:** August 2006. **Price:** $119.00. **Description:** The new economy, or digital economy, and its impact on the way industries and firms choose to locate and cluster geographically.

45146 ■ *The Emerging Markets Century: How a New Breed of World-Class Companies is Overtaking the World*

Pub: Free Press/Simon & Schuster Inc.

Ed: Antoine van Agtmael. **Released:** 2007. **Price:** $29.00. **Description:** An exploration of how companies like Lenovo and Haier who are presently in emerging economies are already competing with household name brands like Ford and Sony, thus proving globalization is here to stay.

45147 ■ "Eminent Domain Fight Looks Imminent" in *The Business Journal-Serving Metropolitan Kansas City* (Vol. 26, August 1, 2008, No. 47)

Pub: American City Business Journals, Inc.

Ed: Rob Roberts. **Description:** Views and information on the proposed constitutional amendments that will limit the use of eminent domain in Missouri, are presented. The proposals are expected to largely ban the taking of private property for private development. It may be included in a November 4,2008 statewide vote for approval.

45148 ■ "Employers See Workers' Comp Rates Rising" in *Sacramento Business Journal* (Vol. 28, April 8, 2011, No. 6, pp. 1)

Pub: Sacramento Business Journal

Ed: Kelly Johnson. **Description:** Employers in California are facing higher workers compensation costs. Increased medical costs and litigation are seen to drive the trend.

45149 ■ "Employers Tied in Knots" in *Sacramento Business Journal* (Vol. 25, August 15, 2008, No. 24, pp. 1)

Pub: American City Business Journals, Inc.

Ed: Kathy Robertson. **Description:** Conflicting laws on same sex marriage have been posing problems for companies, and insurers in California. The court ruling that allowed gay marriages has created differences between state and federal laws. Federal laws on same-sex spouse taxation are also seen to complicate the issue.

45150 ■ "EPA 'Finalizes' WaterSense for Homes" in *Contractor* (Vol. 57, January 2010, No. 1, pp. 70)

Pub: Penton Media, Inc.

Ed: Bob Mader. **Description:** U.S. Environmental Protection Agency released its "final" version of the WaterSense for Homes standard. The standard's provisions that affect plumbing contractors includes the specification that everything has to be leak tested and final service pressure cannot exceed 60 psi.

45151 ■ "An Equity Fund of Their Own" in *Entrepreneur* (Vol. 35, October 2007, No. 10, pp. 68)

Pub: Entrepreneur Media Inc.

Ed: Lee Gimpel. **Description:** About 100 new private equity funds have formed since 2002, proof that private equity investing is becoming popular among companies. There is also an increase in competition to close deals owing to the large number of investors that companies can choose; advantages of smaller funds over the larger one is explained.

45152 ■ "Every Year, Thousands of People Are Killed By Pathogens In Food. William Hanson Wants To Help" in *Inc.* (November 2007, pp. 46-47)

Pub: Gruner & Jahr USA Publishing

Ed: Dalia Fahmy. **Description:** OmniFresh 1000 System tests produce for pathogens such as E.coli and salmonella. The firm is able to test for these pathogens in two hours compared to traditional tests that take as many as three days. Each year some 5,000 Americans die from food-borne diseases.

45153 ■ "Exiting Stage Left" in *Baltimore Business Journal* (Vol. 28, June 18, 2010, No. 6, pp. 1)

Pub: Baltimore Business Journal

Ed: Scott Dance. **Description:** Film professionals including crew members and actors have been leaving Maryland to find work in other states such as Michigan, Louisiana, and Georgia where bigger budgets and film production incentives are given. Other consequences of this trend in local TV and film production are discussed.

45154 ■ "Expert Sees No Radical Reform of 401(K) System" in *Workforce Management* (Vol. 88, November 16, 2009, No. 12, pp. 12)

Pub: Crain Communications, Inc.

Ed: Ed Frauenheim. **Description:** Although many would like to see an overhaul of the 401(k) retirement system, it is unlikely to occur anytime soon; however, the drastic stock market drop of 2008 has raised pointed questions about the 401(k) system and if it enables a secure retirement for American workers.

45155 ■ "Experts Strive to Educate on Proper Pet Diets" in *Pet Product News* (Vol. 64, November 2010, No. 11, pp. 40)

Pub: BowTie Inc.

Ed: John Hustace Walker. **Description:** Pet supply manufacturers have been bundling small mammal food and treats with educational sources to help retailers avoid customer misinformation. This action has been motivated by the customer's quest to seek proper nutritional advice for their small mammal pets.

45156 ■ "Experts Take the Temp of Obama Plan" in *The Business Journal-Serving Metropolitan Kansas City* (Vol. 27, November 14, 2008, No. 10)

Pub: American City Business Journals, Inc.

Ed: Rob Roberts. **Description:** Kansas City, Missouri-based employee benefits experts say president-elect Barack Obama's health care reform plan is on track. Insurance for children and capitalization for health information technology are seen as priority areas. The plan is aimed at reducing the number of uninsured people in the United States.

45157 ■ "Face Values: Responsibility Inc" in *Business Strategy Review* (Vol. 21, Summer 2010, No. 2, pp. 66)

Pub: Wiley-Blackwell

Ed: John Connolly. **Description:** Investment and growth in emerging markets will bring new opportunities, but with them added responsibility. Will companies be able to rise to meet the new responsibility agenda?

45158 ■ "Facebook: A Promotional Budget's Best Friend" in *Women Entrepreneur* (February 1, 2009)

Pub: Entrepreneur Media Inc.

Ed: Tamara Monosoff. **Description:** Facebook began as a social networking website but has become a valuable marketing tool for all types of businesses, organizations and causes. Tips are provided for creating a Facebook account and growing one's network on Facebook.

45159 ■ *The Facebook Effect: The Inside Story of the Company That Is Connecting the World*

Pub: Simon & Shuster

Ed: David Kirkpatrick. **Released:** June 8, 2010. **Price:** $26.00. **Description:** There's never been a Website like Facebook: more than 350 million people have accounts, and if the growth rate continues, by 2013 every Internet user worldwide will have his or her own page. No one's had more access to the inner workings of the phenomenon than Kirkpatrick, a senior tech writer at Fortune magazine. Written with the full cooperation of founder Mark Zuckerberg, the book follows the company from its genesis in a Harvard dorm room through its successes over Friendster and MySpace, the expansion of the user base, and Zuckerberg's refusal to sell.

45160 ■ "Fair Tax Backers Hope MBT Anger Will Bring Votes" in *Crain's Detroit Business* (Vol. 24, March 31, 2008, No. 13, pp. 32)

Pub: Crain Communications, Inc.

Ed: **Description:** Discusses the Michigan Fair Tax Proposal which would eliminate Michigan's business taxes and income tax, raise the state sales tax to 9.75 percent and expand it to services.

45161 ■ "Falling Local Executive Pay Could Suggest a Trend" in *Tampa Bay Business Journal* (Vol. 30, January 15, 2010, No. 4, pp. 1)

Pub: American City Business Journals

Ed: Margie Manning. **Description:** Tampa Bay, Florida-based Raymond James Financial Inc. and MarineMax Inc.'s proxy statements have shown the decreasing compensation of the companies' highest paid executives. The falling trend in executive compensation was a result of intensified shareholder scrutiny and the economy.

45162 ■ "Family Business Research" in *International Journal of Entrepreneurship and Small Business* (Vol. 12, December 3, 2010, No. 1)

Pub: Publishers Communication Group

Ed: A. Bakr Ibrahim, Jean B. McGuire. **Description:** Assessment of the growing field of family business and suggestions for an integrated framework. The paper addresses a number of key issues facing family business research.

45163 ■ "Faster and Shorter" in *Canadian Business* (Vol. 81, October 13, 2008, No. 17, pp. 25)

Pub: Rogers Media Ltd.

Ed: Terri Goveia. **Description:** Study revealed that instant messaging (IM) technologies are slowly becoming legitimate in the corporate world. IM is traditionally considered as a distraction, but it was found to let workers make targeted inquiries that gives them what they need in an instant. Other views and information about IMs is included.

45164 ■ "Fifty Percent of Global Online Retail Visits Were to Amazon, eBay and Alibaba in June 2011" in *Benzinga.com* (October 29, 2011)

Pub: Benzinga.com

Ed: Benzinga Staff. **Description:** Current statistics and future forecasts through the year 2015 for Amazon, eBay and Alibaba are explored.

45165 ■ "Fight Against Fake" in *The Business Journal-Portland* (Vol. 25, July 18, 2008, No. 19, pp. 1)

Pub: American City Business Journals, Inc.

Ed: Erik Siemers. **Description:** Companies, such as Columbia Sportswear Co. and Nike Inc., are fighting the counterfeiting of their sportswear and footwear products through the legal process of coordinating with law enforcement agencies to raid factories. Most of the counterfeiting factories are in China and India. Other details on the issue are discussed.

45166 ■ "Film Incentives: A Hit or a Flop?" in *Michigan Vue* **(Vol. 13, July-August 2008, No. 4, pp. 10)**
Pub: Entrepreneur Media Inc.
Description: Michigan's new film incentive legislation is fulfilling its core purpose, according to Lisa Dancsok of the Michigan Economic Development Corp. (MEDC), by kickstarting the state's entry into the multi-billion dollar industry; the initiative is considered to be very competitive with other states and countries and is thought to be a way in which to help revitalize Michigan's struggling economy.

45167 ■ "Final State Budget Is a Mixed Bag of Key Industries" in *The Business Journal - Serving Phoenix and the Valley of the Sun* **(Vol. 28, July 4, 2008, No. 44, pp. 3)**
Pub: American City Business Journals, Inc.
Ed: Mike Sunnucks; Patrick O'Grady. **Description:** Approved by Governor Janet Napolitano and passed by the Arizona Legislature, the $9.9 billion state budget is beneficial to some industries in the business community. The tax cap for on Arizona Lottery has been removed which is beneficial to the industry, while the solar energy industry and real estate developers stand to lose from the spending bill. Other details of the finance budget are presented.

45168 ■ "Fitter from Twitter" in *Boston Business Journal* **(Vol. 30, December 17, 2010, No. 47, pp. 1)**
Pub: Boston Business Journal
Ed: Lisa van der Pool. **Description:** Small businesses are increasing their use of the Twitter microblogging platform to attract and retain customers. Lisa Johnson, who owns Modern Pilates studios, managed to raise awareness of her personal brand nationally through the social media platform.

45169 ■ "Five Ways to Make RTK Pay" in *Farm Industry News* **(March 25, 2011)**
Pub: Penton Business Media Inc.
Ed: David Hest. **Description:** It is important for farmers to decide whether they are seeking greater accuracy or faster payback when upgrading navigation systems. The trend towards higher accuracy continues to grow.

45170 ■ "Flying the Unfriendly Skies" in *Crain's Chicago Business* **(Vol. 31, April 21, 2008, No. 16, pp. 26)**
Pub: Crain Communications, Inc.
Ed: Sarah A. Klein. **Description:** Due to the number of Chicago companies and entrepreneurs who are traveling overseas more frequently in order to strengthen ties with customers, companies and oftentimes even business partners, the number of flights leaving O'Hare International Airport for destinations abroad has surged; In 2007, international passengers departing O'Hare totaled 5.7 million, up from 2.4 million in 1990.

45171 ■ "Food as Nature Intended" in *Pet Product News* **(Vol. 64, November 2010, No. 11, pp. 30)**
Pub: BowTie Inc.
Ed: Nikki Moustaki. **Description:** Dog owners have been extending their health-consciousness to their pets by seeking natural products that will address their pets' raw food diet. Retailers response to this trend are outlined.

45172 ■ "Foods for Thought" in *Pet Product News* **(Vol. 64, December 2010, No. 12, pp. 16)**
Pub: BowTie Inc.
Ed: Maddy Heleine. **Description:** Manufacturers have been focused at developing species-specific fish foods due to consumer tendency to assess the benefits of the food they feed their fish. As retailers stock species-specific fish foods, manufacturers have provided in-store items and strategies to assist in efficiently selling these food products. Trends in fish food packaging and ingredients are also discussed.

45173 ■ "For All It's Worth" in *Entrepreneur* **(Vol. 36, April 2008, No. 4, pp. 46)**
Pub: Entrepreneur Media, Inc.
Ed: Farnoosh Torabi. **Description:** Discusses the federal estate tax system requires that 45 percent of the money beyond $2 million be given to the government. Ways on how to minimize the effects of estate tax on assets include: creating bypass trusts for married couples; setting up an irrevocable life insurance trust to avoid taxation of estate for insurance benefactors; and having annual gift tax exclusion.

45174 ■ "For MySpace, A Redesign to Entice Generation Y" in *The New York Times* **(October 27, 2010, pp. B3)**
Pub: The New York Times Company
Ed: Miguel Helft. **Description:** MySpace is redesigning its Website in order to attract individuals from the Generation Y group.

45175 ■ "Franchising Lures Boomers" in *Business Journal-Portland* **(Vol. 24, November 9, 2007, No. 36, pp. 1)**
Pub: American City Business Journals, Inc.
Ed: Wendy Culverwell. **Description:** Popularity of franchising has increased, and investors belonging to the baby boom generation contribute largely to this growth. The number of aging baby boomers is also increasing, particularly in Oregon, which means further growth of franchises can be expected. Reasons why franchising is a good investment for aging baby boomers are given.

45176 ■ "Freshman Lawmaker Graves Keeping Busy" in *Atlanta Journal-Constitution* **(June 20, 2010, pp. A6)**
Pub: Atlanta Journal Constitution
Ed: Bob Keefe. **Description:** Newly elected Republican Representative Tom Graves of Ranger supports the Small Business Jobs Tax Relief Act.

45177 ■ "From Fat to Fit" in *Canadian Business* **(Vol. 79, September 25, 2006, No. 19, pp. 100)**
Pub: Rogers Media
Ed: Graham Scott. **Description:** The increase in physical fitness clubs across Canada is discussed.

45178 ■ "FTC Takes Aim At Foreclosure 'Rescue' Firm" in *The Business Journal-Serving Greater Tampa Bay* **(Vol. 28, September 19, 2008, No. 39)**
Pub: American City Business Journals, Inc.
Ed: Michael Hinman. **Description:** United Home Savers LLP has been ordered to halt its mortgage foreclosure rescue services after the Federal Trade Commission accused it of deceptive advertising. The company is alleged to have charged customers $1,200 in exchange for unfulfilled promises to keep them in their homes.

45179 ■ "Fuel for Thought; Canadian Business Leaders on Energy Policy" in *Canadian Business* **(Vol. 81, September 15, 2008, No. 14-15, pp. 12)**
Pub: Rogers Media Ltd.
Ed: Joe Castaldo. **Description:** Most Canadian business leaders worry about the unreliability of the oil supply but feel that Canada is in a better position to benefit from the energy supply crisis than other countries. Many respondents also highlighted the need to invest in renewable energy sources.

45180 ■ "Fueling Business" in *The Business Journal-Milwaukee* **(Vol. 25, July 25, 2008, No. 44, pp. A1)**
Pub: American City Business Journals, Inc.
Ed: David Doege. **Description:** Several businesses in Wisconsin's Milwaukee area are offering gas cards in order to attract customers. Examples of this include apartment manager Nancy Randle offering a $400 gas card to new tenants with a 1 year lease and dentist Perry Sukowatey giving a $25 gas card after examining patients. Other details on gas card promotions are discussed.

45181 ■ "Funny Business" in *Canadian Business* **(Vol. 82, April 27, 2009, No. 7, pp. 27)**
Pub: Rogers Media
Ed: Rachel Pulfer. **Description:** Companies are advised to use humor in marketing to drive more revenue. IBM Canada, for example, commissioned Second City Communications for a marketing campaign that involved humor. While IBM Canada declined to give sales or traffic figures, firm executives rank the marketing campaign as an overall success.

45182 ■ "Furniture Making May Come Back—Literally" in *Business North Carolina* **(Vol. 28, March 2008, No. 3, pp. 32)**
Pub: Business North Carolina
Description: Due to the weak U.S. dollar and the fact that lumber processors never left the country, foreign furniture manufacturers are becoming interested in moving manufacturing plants to the U.S.

45183 ■ "Future Autoworkers will Need Broader Skills" in *Crain's Detroit Business* **(Vol. 25, June 8, 2009, No. 23, pp. 13)**
Pub: Crain Communications Inc. - Detroit
Ed: Ryan Beene. **Description:** Auto industry observers report that new workers in the industry will need advanced skills and educational backgrounds in engineering and technical fields because jobs in the factories will become more technology-based and multidisciplinary.

45184 ■ "Future of Diversity: Cultural Inclusion Is a Business Imperative" in *Black Enterprise* **(Vol. 41, August 2010, No. 1, pp. 75)**
Pub: Earl G. Graves Publishing Co. Inc.
Ed: Annya M. Lott. **Description:** As globalization continues to make the world a smaller place, workforce diversity will be imperative to any small company in order to be sustainable.

45185 ■ "The Future Is Another Country; Higher Education" in *The Economist* **(Vol. 390, January 3, 2009, No. 8612, pp. 43)**
Pub: The Economist Newspaper Inc.
Description: Due to the growth of the global corporation, more ambitious students are studying at universities abroad; the impact of this trend is discussed.

45186 ■ "The Future of Work" in *Black Enterprise* **(Vol. 41, August 2010, No. 1, pp. 65)**
Pub: Earl G. Graves Publishing Co. Inc.
Ed: Annya M. Lott. **Description:** Technology, globalization, and outsourcing will continue to shape the future of work. Social media is a means for small companies to market goods and services.

45187 ■ "The Future of Work" in *Business Strategy Review* **(Vol. 21, Autumn 2010, No. 3, pp. 16)**
Pub: Wiley-Blackwell
Ed: Lynda Gratton. **Description:** Work is universal. Buy, how, why, where and when we work has never been so open to individual interpretation. The certainties of the past have been replaced by ambiguity, questions and the steady hum of technology. Research covering 21 global companies and more than 200 executives covers the future of work.

45188 ■ "Futures Shock for the CME" in *Crain's Chicago Business* **(Vol. 31, November 10, 2008, No. 45, pp. 8)**
Pub: Crain Communications, Inc.
Ed: Ann Saphir. **Description:** Chicago-based CME Group Inc., the largest futures exchange operator in the U.S., is facing a potentially radically altered regulatory landscape as Congress weighs sweeping reform of financial oversight. The possible merger of the CFTC and the Securities and Exchange Commission are among CME's concerns. Other details of possible regulatory measures are provided.

45189 ■ "Generation Y Chooses the Mobile Web" in *PR Newswire* **(November 24, 2010)**
Pub: PR Newswire Association LLC
Description: Generation Y individuals between the ages of 18 - 27 use their mobile phones to browse

the Internet more often than a desktop or laptop computer, according to a survey conducted by Opera, a Web browser company.

45190 ■ "Generation Y Driving Portland Multifamily Market" in *Daily Journal of Commerce, Portland* (October 29, 2010)
Pub: Dolan Media Newswires

Ed: Nick Bjork. **Description:** Generation Y, young adults between the ages of 18-30, are interested in multifamily residents in the Portland, Oregon area. Developers in the area, particularly North Portland, have recognized this trend and are looking into multifamily investments.

45191 ■ "Generation Y Goes To Work; Management" in *The Economist* (Vol. 390, January 3, 2009, No. 8612, pp. 48)
Pub: The Economist Newspaper Inc.

Description: Unemployment rates among people in their 20s has increased significantly and there is a lower turnover in crisis-hit firms, which has made it more difficult to simply find another job if one is unsatisfied with the management style of his or her company. Managers are adopting a more command-and-control approach which is the antithesis of the open, collaborative style that younger employees prefer.

45192 ■ "Getting the Bioheat Word Out" in *Indoor Comfort Marketing* (Vol. 70, September 2011, No. 9, pp. 32)
Pub: Industry Publications Inc.

Description: Ways to market advanced liquid fuels to the public are outlined.

45193 ■ "The GHG Quandary: Whose Problem Is It Anyway?" in *Canadian Business* (Vol. 81, September 15, 2008, No. 14-15, pp. 72)
Pub: Rogers Media Ltd.

Ed: Matthew McClearn. **Description:** Nongovernmental organizations were able to revoke the permit for Imperial Oil Ltd's Kearl oilsands project on the grounds of its expected greenhouse gas emission but the court's ruling was rendered irrelevant by bureaucratic paper-shuffling shortly after. The idea of an environmental impact assessment as a guide to identify the consequences of a project is also discussed.

45194 ■ "Go Beyond Local Search With Hyper-Local" in *Women Entrepreneur* (October 30, 2008)
Pub: Entrepreneur Media Inc.

Ed: Lena West. **Description:** According to Forrester Research, as much as $500 billion in local spending in 2007 was influenced by the Internet and industry analysts report that consumers spend approximately 80 percent of their income within 50 miles of their home. Discussion of ways in which to capitalize on the hyper-local trend that is being driven by greater Internet connectivity and use of the web to find information is provided.

45195 ■ "Going Green, Going Slowly" in *Playthings* (Vol. 106, September 1, 2008, No. 8, pp. 17)
Pub: Reed Business Information

Ed: Nancy Zwiers. **Description:** Sustainability and greener materials for both product and packaging in the toy industry has become important for protecting our environment. However, in a recent survey nearly 60 percent of responders stated environmental issues did not play a part in purchasing a toy or game for their children.

45196 ■ "Grave Concerns" in *Canadian Business* (Vol. 81, July 21 2008, No. 11, pp. 25)
Pub: Rogers Media Ltd.

Ed: Andrew Nikiforuk. **Description:** Air pollution control regulations to reduce greenhouse gasses have been implemented by the Canadian government. The federal government is planning to construct a carbon funeral industry that will store the global

warming gases, however the expenditure for the project will be shifted to the taxpayers. Details of the Bruce Peachy's initiative on how to reduce GHGs are presented.

45197 ■ "Gray, Gray, & Gray: a Difficult Year for Oilheat" in *Indoor Comfort Marketing* (Vol. 70, September 2011, No. 9, pp. 30)
Pub: Industry Publications Inc.

Description: According to the 20th Annual Oilheat Industry Survey, 2011 will be another dismal year for the industry sector.

45198 ■ "Green Acres" in *Hawaii Business* (Vol. 54, September 2008, No. 3, pp. 48)
Pub: Hawaii Business Publishing

Ed: Jan Tenbruggencate. **Description:** Bill Cowern's Hawaiian Mahogany is a forestry business that processes low-value trees to be sold as wood chips, which can be burned to create biodiesel. Cowern is planning to obtain certification to market carbon credits and is also working with Green Energy Hawaii for the permit of a biomass-fueled power plant. Other details about Cowern's business are discussed.

45199 ■ *Green Business: A Five-Part Model for Creating an Environmentally Responsible Company*
Pub: Schiffer Publishing

Ed: Amy K. Townsend. **Released:** 2006. **Price:** $29.95 paperback. **Description:** Five-part model for small companies to become a green business; the book discusses the advantages to following the current trend using environmentally-friendly practices.

45200 ■ "Green Business Push Blooms" in *Charlotte Observer* (February 7, 2007)
Pub: Knight-Ridder/Tribune Business News

Ed: Christopher D. Kirkpatrick. **Description:** Many energy companies are capitalizing on corporate guild about global warming. Companies offering environmental peace of mind are discussed.

45201 ■ "Green Counting" in *Canadian Business* (Vol. 81, October 13, 2008, No. 17, pp. 27)
Pub: Rogers Media Ltd.

Ed: Joe Castaldo. **Description:** Procter and Gamble research revealed that only 10 percent of North American consumers are willing to accept trade-offs for a greener product. Three out of four North American consumers will not accept a higher price or a decrease in a product's performance for an environmental benefit. Details on green marketing are also discussed.

45202 ■ *Green Your Small Business: Profitable Ways to Become an Ecopreneur*
Pub: McGraw-Hill

Ed: Scott Cooney. **Released:** November 7, 2008. **Price:** $19.95 paperback. **Description:** Advice and guidance is given to help any entrepreneur start, build or grow a green business, focusing on green business basics, market research and financing, as well as handling legal and insurance issues.

45203 ■ "Greening the Auto Industry" in *Business Journal-Serving Phoenix & the Valley of the Sun* (Vol. 30, July 23, 2010, No. 46, pp. 1)
Pub: Phoenix Business Journal

Ed: Patrick O'Grady. **Description:** Thermo Fluids Inc. has been recycling used oil products since 1993 and could become Arizona's first home for oil filter recycling after retrofitting its Phoenix facility to include a compaction machine. The new service could help establish Thermo Fluids as a recycling hub for nearby states.

45204 ■ "Groomers Eye Profit Growth Through Services" in *Pet Product News* (Vol. 64, December 2010, No. 12, pp. 26)
Pub: BowTie Inc.

Ed: Kathleen M. Mangan. **Description:** Pet groomers can successfully offer add-on services by taking into account insider customer knowledge, store image, and financial analysis in the decision-making process. Many pet groomers have decided to add services such as spa treatments and training due to

a slump in the bathing and grooming business. How some pet groomers gained profitability through add-on services is explored.

45205 ■ *Groundswell: Winning in a World Transformed by Social Technologies*
Pub: Harvard Business School Press

Ed: Charlene Li; Josh Bernoff. **Released:** April 21, 2008. **Price:** $29.95. **Description:** Individuals are using online social technologies such as blogs, social networking sites, YouTube, and podcasts to discuss products and companies, write their own news, and find their own deals. When consumers you've never met are rating your company's products in public forums with which you have no experience or influence, your company is vulnerable. This book teaches the tools and data necessary to turn this treat into an opportunity.

45206 ■ *Grown Up Digital: How the Net Generation Is Changing Your World*
Pub: The McGraw-Hill Companies

Ed: Don Tapscott. **Released:** 2009. **Price:** $27.95. **Description:** As baby boomers retire, business needs to understand what makes the Internet work for business.

45207 ■ "H&M Offers a Dress for Less" in *Canadian Business* (Vol. 83, September 14, 2010, No. 15, pp. 20)
Pub: Rogers Media Ltd.

Ed: Laura Cameron. **Description:** Swedish clothing company H&M has implemented loss leader strategy by pricing some dresses at extremely low prices. The economy has forced retailers to keep prices down despite the increasing cost of manufacturing, partly due to Chinese labor becoming more expensive. How the trend will affect apparel companies is discussed.

45208 ■ "Hank Paulson On the Housing Bailout and What's Ahead" in *Business Week* (September 22, 2008, No. 4100, pp. 19)
Pub: McGraw-Hill Companies, Inc.

Ed: Maria Bartiromo. **Description:** Interview with Treasury Secretary Henry Paulson in which he discusses the bailout of Fannie Mae and Freddie Mac as well as the potential impact on the American economy and foreign interests and investments in the country. Paulson has faith that the government's actions will help to stabilize the housing market.

45209 ■ "Health Job Shift Looms" in *Boston Business Journal* (Vol. 31, June 3, 2011, No. 19, pp. 3)
Pub: Boston Business Journal

Ed: Julie M. Donnelly. **Description:** Pending health care payment reform in Massachusetts is seen to adversely impact hospital staff. Hospitals are also seen to serve more patients once the bill is approved.

45210 ■ "Health Nuts and Bolts" in *Entrepreneur* (Vol. 36, April 2008, No. 4, pp. 24)
Pub: Entrepreneur Media, Inc.

Ed: Jacquelyn Lynn. **Description:** Encouraging employees to develop good eating habits can promote productivity at work. Ways on how to improve employee eating habits include employers setting a good example themselves and offering employees healthy options. Other details about the topic are discussed.

45211 ■ "Helping Customers Fight Pet Waste" in *Pet Product News* (Vol. 64, November 2010, No. 11, pp. 52)
Pub: BowTie Inc.

Ed: Sandy Robins. **Description:** Pet cleaning products manufacturers have been enjoying high sales figures by paying attention to changing pet ownership trends and environmental awareness. Meanwhile, the inclusion of user-friendly features in these products has also been boosted by the social role of pets and the media attention to pet waste. How manufacturers have been responding to this demand is explored.

45212 ■ "Helping Small Businesses Create Jobs" in *America's Intelligence Wire* (August 27, 2010)
Pub: HighBeam Research

Ed: Ross Raihala. **Description:** Ways the Small Business Jobs Tax Relief Act will help small businesses create jobs are investigated.

45213 ■ "Henry Mintzberg: Still the Zealous Skeptic and Scold" in *Strategy and Leadership* **(Vol. 39, March-April 2011, No. 2, pp. 4)**

Pub: Emerald Group Publishing Inc.

Ed: Robert J. Allio. **Description:** Henry Mintzberg, professor at the McGill University in Montreal, Canada, shares his thoughts on issues such as inappropriate methods in management education and on trends in leadership and management. Mintzberg believes that US businesses are facing serious management and leadership challenges.

45214 ■ "His Record, Not Polls, Is What Matters" in *Bangor Daily News* **(October 13, 2010)**

Pub: Bangor Daily News

Ed: Nick Sambides Jr. **Description:** The Small Business Jobs Tax Relief Act could spur investment in small businesses by increasing capital gains tax cuts for investors in small business in 2010 and increase to $20,000 from $5,000 the deduction for start-up businesses.

45215 ■ "Hispantelligence Report" in *Hispanic Business* **(January-February 2009, pp. 10)**

Pub: Hispanic Business

Description: U.S. Hispanic purchasing power is expected to reach $958 billion in 2009 and projected to reach $1.25 trillion by 2015, a rate of more than two times the overall national rate. Statistical data included.

45216 ■ "Holiday Cheer" in *Business Journal-Serving Phoenix & the Valley of the Sun* **(Vol. 31, December 3, 2010, No. 13, pp. 1)**

Pub: Phoenix Journal

Ed: Lynn Ducey, Mike Sunnucks. **Description:** Results of a study conducted by Challenger, Gray & Christmas Inc., shows that 68 percent of companies are planning holiday parties in 2010, up slightly from 62 percent in 2009. About 53 percent of those having holiday parties are holding them on company premises.

45217 ■ "The Hollow Debate" in *Canadian Business* **(Vol. 81, March 3, 2008, No. 3, pp. 26)**

Pub: Rogers Media

Ed: Thomas Watson. **Description:** According to a report conducted by the Conference Board of Canada, the Canadian business community is not being hollowed out by acquisitions made by foreign companies. Findings further showed that local businesses are protected by dual shares and that the economy can benefit more from foreign acquisitions than local mergers. The need to relax foreign ownership restrictions and other recommendations are presented.

45218 ■ "Holy Wasabi! Sushi Not Just For Parents Anymore" in *Chicago Tribune* **(March 13, 2008)**

Pub: McClatchy-Tribune Information Services

Ed: Christopher Borrelli. **Description:** Wicker Park cooking school, The Kid's Table, specializes in cooking classes for pre-teens; Elena Marre who owns the school was surprised when she was asked to plan a children's party in which she would teach a course in sushi making. More and more adolescents and small children are eating sushi.

45219 ■ "The Home Game" in *Canadian Business* **(Vol. 80, October 8, 2007, No. 20, pp. 68)**

Pub: Rogers Media

Ed: Rachel Pulfer. **Description:** Analysis of Canada's banking industry is presented. Trends show that Canadian banks avoid risks in their investments, and usually choose to take safer paths. Experts believe these trends affect the country's economy and that Canadian banks do not play a significant role in economic development.

45220 ■ "A Home of Her Own" in *Hawaii Business* **(Vol. 53, October 2007, No. 4, pp. 51)**

Pub: Hawaii Business Publishing

Ed: Maria Torres-Kitamura. **Description:** It was observed that the number of single women in Hawaii purchasing their own home has increased, as that in the whole United States where the percentage has increased from 14 percent in 1995 to 22 percent in 2006. However, First Hawaiian Bank's Wendy Lum thinks that the trend will not continue in Hawaii due to lending restrictions. The factors that women consider in buying a home of their own are presented.

45221 ■ "Home Improvement Marketers Target Women With New Products, New Campaigns and Plenty of Pink" in *Marketing to Women* **(March 2008)**

Pub: EPM Communications, Inc.

Description: From creating tools that fit a woman's ergonomics to designs that fit a woman's fashion sense, home improvement is finding new ways in which to market to women.

45222 ■ "Home Sweet Home?" in *Canadian Business* **(Vol. 79, September 11, 2006, No. 18, pp. 17)**

Pub: Rogers Media

Ed: David Wolf. **Description:** Fading attractiveness of the Canadian stock market for its domestic investors is discussed. Changing investor's trends toward cross-border investments are presented.

45223 ■ "A Home's Identity in Black and White" in *Crain's Chicago Business* **(Vol. 31, April 21, 2008, No. 16, pp. 35)**

Pub: Crain Communications, Inc.

Ed: Lisa Bertagnoli. **Description:** Real estate agents are finding that showing customers a written floor plan is a trend that is growing since many buyers feel that Online virtual tours distort a room. Although floor plans cost up to $500 to have drawn up, they clearly show potential buyers the exact dimensions of rooms and how they connect.

45224 ■ *Hoover's Vision*

Pub: Cengage Learning

Ed: Gary Hoover. **Description:** Founder of Bookstop Inc. and Hoover's Inc. provides a plan to turn an enterprise into a success by showing entrepreneurs how to address inputs with an open mind in order to see more than what other's envision. Hoover pushes business owners to create and feed a clear and consistent vision by recognizing the importance of history and trends, then helps them find the essential qualities of entrepreneurial leadership.

45225 ■ "Hospitals See Major Shift To Outpatient Care" in *The Business Journal-Milwaukee* **(Vol. 25, September 12, 2008, No. 51, pp. A1)**

Pub: American City Business Journals, Inc.

Ed: Corrinne Hess. **Description:** Statistics show that the revenue of Wisconsin hospitals from outpatient medical care is about to surpass revenue from hospital patients who stay overnight. This revenue increase is attributed to new technology and less-invasive surgery. Trends show that the shift toward outpatient care actually started in the late 1980s and early 1990s.

45226 ■ "Hot Air" in *Canadian Business* **(Vol. 81, July 22, 2008, No. 12-13, pp. 16)**

Pub: Rogers Media Ltd.

Ed: Joe Castaldo. **Description:** Over half of 101 business leaders who were recently surveyed oppose Liberal leader Stephane Dion's carbon-tax proposal, saying that manufacturers in Canada are likely to suffer from the plan. Additional key results of the survey are presented.

45227 ■ "House Committee on Small Business Calls for Sweeping Changes to SBIR Program" in *Hispanic Business* **(Vol. 30, March 2008, No. 3)**

Pub: Hispanic Business

Description: Proposals suggested by the House Committee on small business to revamp the Small Business Innovation and Research Program (SBIR) are reported. These include allowing participating firms greater flexibility to use venture capital funds, increasing SBIR grants and faster processing of applications.

45228 ■ "Housing Markets Still Struggling" in *Montana Business Quarterly* **(Vol. 49, Spring 2011, No. 1, pp. 17)**

Pub: Bureau of Business & Economic Research

Ed: Scott Rickard. **Description:** Montana's economic conditions are a bit better than national averages. Data ranked by state, year-over-year price change, and total price peak is presented, along with statistical data for the entire nation.

45229 ■ "How to Boost Your Super Bowl ROI" in *Advertising Age* **(Vol. 80, December 7, 2009, No. 41, pp. 3)**

Pub: Crain's Communications

Ed: Abbey Klaassen. **Description:** Internet marketing is essential, even for the corporations that can afford to spend $3 million on a 30-second Super Bowl spot; last year, Super Bowl advertising reached an online viewership of 99.5 million while 98.7 million people watched the game on television validating the idea that public relations must go farther than a mere television ad campaign. Social media provides businesses with a longer shelf life for their ad campaigns. Advice is also given regarding ways in which to strategize a smart and well-thought plan for utilizing the online marketing options currently available.

45230 ■ "How Growers Buy" in *Farm Industry News* **(Vol. 42, January 1, 2009, No. 1)**

Pub: Penton Media, Inc.

Ed: Karen McMahon. **Description:** According to a survey regarding the buying habits among large commercial growers, most prefer to purchase from local retailers, customer service is important concerning their decision on who to buy products from, and price and convenience seem to be more important then brand.

45231 ■ "How In the World?" in *Business Strategy Review* **(Vol. 21, Spring 2010, No. 1, pp. 12)**

Pub: Wiley-Blackwell

Ed: Stuart Crainer. **Description:** We may think of management as a recent phenomenon, but its roots lie in the first organizing activities of our ancestors. The author looks a the emergence of management as a profession. He finds that the road to modern management leads to a paradox and questions ways to change that.

45232 ■ "How Marketers Can Tap the Web" in *Sales and Marketing Management* **(November 12, 2009)**

Pub: Nielsen Business Media, Inc.

Description: Internet marketing strategies require careful planning and tools in order to track success. Businesses are utilizing this trend to attract new clients as well as keep customers they already have satisfied. Advice on website development and design is provided.

45233 ■ "How to Survive This Mess" in *Crain's Chicago Business* **(Vol. 31, April 14, 2008, No. 15, pp. 18)**

Pub: Crain Communications, Inc.

Ed: Christina Le Beau. **Description:** Small business owners can make it through a possible recession with preparations such as reviewing their balance sheet and cash flow every week and spotting trends then reacting quickly to them.

45234 ■ "How To Get a Loan the Web 2.0 Way" in *Black Enterprise* **(Vol. 41, December 2010, No. 5, pp. 23)**

Pub: Earl G. Graves Publishing Co. Inc.

Ed: John Simons. **Description:** People are turning to online peer-to-peer network for personal loans as banks are lending less money.

45235 ■ "How-To Workshops Teach Sewing, Styles" in *St. Louis Post-Dispatch* **(September 14, 2010)**

Pub: St. Louis Post-Dispatch

Ed: Kalen Ponche. **Description:** Profile of DIY Style Workshop in St. Charles, Missouri, where sewing, designing and teaching is offered. The shop is home base for DIY Style, a Website created by mother and daughter to teach younger people how to sew.

45236 ■ "The Human Factor" in *Canadian Business* (Vol. 80, October 8, 2007, No. 20, pp. 22)
Pub: Rogers Media
Ed: Alex Mynek. **Description:** David Foot, a demographer and an economics professor at the University of Toronto, talks about Canada's future, including economic and demographic trends. He discusses activities that should be done by businessmen in order to prepare for the future. He also addresses the role of the Canadian government in economic development.

45237 ■ "HVAC/R Evolution" in *Indoor Comfort Marketing* (Vol. 70, March 2011, No. 3, pp. 14)
Pub: Industry Publications Inc.
Ed: Gene Bartholomew. **Description:** Tools and techniques for heating, ventilation, air conditioning and refrigeration are examined.

45238 ■ *IBM on Demand Technology for the Growing Business: How to Optimize Your Computing Environment for Today and Tomorrow*
Pub: Maximum Press
Ed: Jim Hoskins. **Released:** June 2005. **Price:** $29.95. **Description:** IBM is offering computer solutions to small companies entering the On Demand trend in business.

45239 ■ "ICC Works on Prescriptive Green Construction Code" in *Contractor* (Vol. 56, October 2009, No. 10, pp. 1)
Pub: Penton Media, Inc.
Ed: Robert P. Mader. **Description:** International Code Council launched an initiative to create a green construction code that focuses on existing commercial buildings. The initiative's timeline will include public meetings leading up to a final draft that will be available in 2010.

45240 ■ "An Ill Wind: Icelandic Bank Failures Chill Atlantic Canada" in *Canadian Business* (Vol. 81, November 10, 2008, No. 19, pp. 10)
Pub: Rogers Media Ltd.
Ed: Charles Mandel. **Description:** Bank failures in Iceland have put a stop to flights ferrying Icelanders to Newfoundland to purchase Christmas gifts, thereby threatening Newfoundland's tourism industry. The credit of Newfoundland's fisheries is also being squeezed since most of Atlantic Canadian seafood processors hold lines of credit from Icelandic banks.

45241 ■ "Illinois Bets On Recycling Program" in *Chicago Tribune* (November 29, 2008)
Pub: McClatchy-Tribune Information Services
Ed: Joel Hood. **Description:** Traditionally the holiday gift-giving season is one of the most wasteful times of year and the state of Illinois is granting $760,000 to small businesses and cities in an attempt to expand curbside recycling programs and hire additional workers to address electronic waste.

45242 ■ "Imax Becomes Toast of Movie Industry" in *Globe & Mail* (January 10, 2006, pp. B2)
Pub: CTVglobemedia Publishing Inc.
Ed: Grant Robertson. **Description:** The United States-based mainstream theatres company Imax Corp., has reported a 35 percent rise in its ticket sales, showing the growing interest of the American audience in the Imax formatted films. A complete focus on this trend is presented.

45243 ■ "Immigration Issues Frustrate Owners From Overseas" in *The Business Journal-Serving Greater Tampa Bay* (Vol. 28, August 15, 2008)
Pub: American City Business Journals, Inc.
Ed: Margie Manning. **Description:** Investors who availed the E-2 visa program believe that the tightened restrictions on the visa program has trapped them in the United States. The E-2 investor visa program was designed to attract investors into the U.S., but restrictions were tightened after the September 11, 2001 attacks. Other views and information on E-2 and its impact on investors are presented.

45244 ■ *Import/Export for Dummies*
Pub: John Wiley and Sons, Inc.
Ed: John J. Capela. **Released:** June 2008. **Price:** $19.99. **Description:** Provides entrepreneurs and small- to medium-size businesses with information required to start exporting products globally and importing goods to the U.S. Topics covered include the ins and outs of developing or expanding operations to gain market share, with details on the top ten countries in which America trades, from Canada to Germany to China.

45245 ■ "Incentives Debate Rages On Unabated" in *The Business Journal-Serving Metropolitan Kansas City* (Vol. 26, September 5, 2008, No. 52)
Pub: American City Business Journals, Inc.
Ed: Rob Roberts. **Description:** Debate on the new economic development and incentives policy adopted by the Kansas City Council is still on. The city's Planned Industrial Expansion Authority has rejected a standard property tax abatement proposal. The real estate development community has opposed the rejection of proposed the tax incentives policy.

45246 ■ "Inch by Inch, Employees Lose Ground" in *Business Courier* (Vol. 26, November 13, 2009, No. 29, pp. 1)
Pub: American City Business Journals, Inc.
Ed: James Ritchie. **Description:** Employees in Ohio who retained their jobs have suffered losses in salary and other benefits, as companies exert efforts to save money. Thirty-four percent of employees experienced pay cuts. Statistical data included.

45247 ■ "Indigenous Tourism Operators" in *International Journal of Entrepreneurship and Small Business* (Vol. 10, July 6, 2010, No. 4)
Pub: Publishers Communication Group
Ed: Andrews Cardow, Peter Wiltshier. **Description:** Emergent enthusiasm for tourism as a savior for economic development in the Chatham Islands of New Zealand is highlighted.

45248 ■ "Indoor Air Quality – a Tribute to Efficiency" in *Indoor Comfort Marketing* (Vol. 70, August 2011, No. 8, pp. 8)
Pub: Industry Publications Inc.
Ed: Matthew Maleske. **Description:** Efficiency of new HVAC/R equipment has helped improve indoor air quality.

45249 ■ "Industry Escalates Lobbying Efforts For Loan Program" in *Crain's Detroit Business* (Vol. 24, September 22, 2008, No. 38, pp. 22)
Pub: Crain Communications, Inc.
Ed: Jay Greene; Ryan Beene; Harry Stoffer. **Description:** Auto suppliers such as Lear Corp., which is best known for vehicle seating, also supplies high-voltage wiring for Ford hybrids and is developing other hybrid components. These suppliers are joining automakers in lobbying for the loan program which would promote the accelerated development of fuel-efficient vehicles.

45250 ■ "The Influencers" in *Entrepreneur* (Vol. 36, March 2008, No. 3, pp. 66)
Pub: Entrepreneur Media Inc.
Ed: Andrea Cooper. **Description:** Among the 25 people, events, and trends that will influence business in 2008 are: the 2008 U.S. presidential elections, climate change, China, weakening U.S. dollar, mortgage crisis, generational shift, Bill Drayton, and Bill Gates. Other 2008 influencers are presented.

45251 ■ "Innovation Can Be Imperative for Those in Hands-On Trades" in *Crain's Cleveland Business* (Vol. 28, November 12, 2007, No. 45)
Pub: Crain Communications, Inc.
Ed: Harriet Tramer. **Description:** Discusses the importance of networking and innovative marketing concerning those in art and restoration trades.

45252 ■ "Insider" in *Canadian Business* (Vol. 81, Summer 2008, No. 9, pp. 170)
Pub: Rogers Media Ltd.
Ed: Thomas Watson; Jeff Sanford. **Description:** Oil peak theory posits that the world has consumed half of the non-renewable resources is indicated by the

surging oil prices. However, critics argued that the high oil prices are effects of market speculation and not the depletion of the supply. Ten reasons on why to buy and not buy peak oil are presented.

45253 ■ "Intel Joins Movement to Turn Cube Farms Into Wide-Open Spaces" in *Sacramento Business Journal* (Vol. 28, May 27, 2011, No. 13, pp. 1)
Pub: Sacramento Business Journal
Ed: Melanie Turner. **Description:** Intel Corporation has remodeled its facility in Folsom, California. The renovation has required some workers to give up their cubicles. Comments from executives are included.

45254 ■ "Interest in 'Encore Careers' is Growing" in *HRMagazine* (Vol. 53, November 2008, No. 11, pp. 22)
Pub: Society for Human Resource Management
Description: Unexpectedly large numbers of baby boomers are looking for jobs that can provide them with 'means and meaning', according to a survey by MetLife and Civic Ventures. They can find those jobs in encore careers, an opportunity to do work that has a social impact and personal meaning.

45255 ■ "Interested in 12 Billion Dollars?" in *Indoor Comfort Marketing* (Vol. 70, March 2011, No. 3, pp. 18)
Pub: Industry Publications Inc.
Ed: Matthew Maleske. **Description:** Trends in the indoor quality industry are cited, with insight into expanding an existing indoor heating and cooling business.

45256 ■ "Internet Marketing and Social Media Knowledge Vital for SMBs" in *Internet Wire* (November 24, 2009)
Pub: Comtex News Network, Inc.
Description: Small and medium-size businesses must learn to market themselves over the Internet in order to succeed and grow in today's marketplace. Web Marketing Today offers the largest source of the most important information concerning doing business on the Internet including e-commerce, email marketing and social networking opportunities.

45257 ■ "Investigation Hints at Workers' Comp Trouble" in *Sacramento Business Journal* (Vol. 25, July 4, 2008, No. 18, pp. 1)
Pub: American City Business Journals, Inc.
Ed: Kelly Johnson. **Description:** In 500 California firms, a survey of worker compensation revealed that 38 percent of the companies had problems with required coverage. Government investigators are bothered that 107 companies did not respond to the official inquiry. Other views and information on the survey and on the expected economic implications of the findings are presented.

45258 ■ "Is Business Ethics Getting Better? A Historical Perspective" in *Business Ethics Quarterly* (Vol. 21, April 2011, No. 2, pp. 335)
Pub: Society for Business Ethics
Ed: Joanne B. Ciulla. **Description:** The question 'Is Business Ethics Getting Better?' as a heuristic for discussing the importance of history in understanding business and ethics is answered. The article uses a number of examples to illustrate how the same ethical problems in business have been around for a long time. It describes early attempts at the Harvard School of Business to use business history as a means of teaching students about moral and social values. In the end, the author suggests that history may be another way to teach ethics, enrich business ethics courses, and develop the perspective and vision in future business leaders.

45259 ■ "Is this a Buying Opportunity?" in *Canadian Business* (Vol. 82, April 27, 2009, No. 7, pp. 46)
Pub: Rogers Media
Ed: Andy Holloway. **Description:** Home prices in Canada are down by as much as 14.2 percent in 2009 compared to prices in 2008, making homes more affordable now. Some housing experts believe that homes are still good investments as prices of

rent and properties always recover. Meanwhile, a survey found that Canadians under 35 plan to buy a home within two years.

45260 ■ "Is Hawaii Ready for Universal Health Care?" in *Hawaii Business* **(Vol. 53, February 2008, No. 8, pp. 26)**
Pub: Hawaii Business Publishing
Description: Representative Lyn Finnegan does not believe that a universal health is good for Hawaii as health insurance for everyone will be difficult to achieve. Representative John M. Mizuno says that House Bill 1008 introduced in the state was a landmark for Hawaii as it will provide the people with health care insurance. Other details about their opinion on the topic are presented.

45261 ■ "Jobs Data Show Wild Card" in *Barron's* **(Vol. 90, September 6, 2010, No. 36, pp. M12)**
Pub: Barron's Editorial & Corporate Headquarters
Ed: Gene Epstein. **Description:** August 2010 jobs report revealed a 54,000 decline in non-farm payrolls and that the unemployment rate remains unchanged at 9.6 percent. The report also shows a welcome rise of 848,999 in the household-data category. The unemployment rate shows a reversed trend where men's 10.6 percent unemployment is higher than women's 8.6 percent rate.

45262 ■ "The Keeper of Records" in *Black Enterprise* **(Vol. 41, December 2010, No. 5, pp. 54)**
Pub: Earl G. Graves Publishing Co. Inc.
Ed: Denise Campbell. **Description:** Medical billing and coding, submission of claims to health insurance companies and Medicare or Medicaid for payment is one of the fastest growing disciplines in healthcare.

45263 ■ "Kenyans Embrace Moving Money By Text Message" in *Chicago Tribune* **(October 7, 2008)**
Pub: McClatchy-Tribune Information Services
Ed: Laurie Goering. **Description:** Cell phone banking services are becoming more common, especially for foreign residents; customers are able to establish a virtual cell phone bank account through companies such as M-Pesa which allows their customers to pay bills, withdraw cash, pay merchants or text money to relatives.

45264 ■ "Know the Facts About Natural Gas!" in *Indoor Comfort Marketing* **(Vol. 70, August 2011, No. 8, pp. 26)**
Pub: Industry Publications Inc.
Description: AEC Activity Update is presented on the American Energy Coalition's Website.

45265 ■ "LA Passes HET Ordinance, California Greens Code" in *Contractor* **(Vol. 56, September 2009, No. 9, pp. 1)**
Pub: Penton Media, Inc.
Ed: Candace Ruolo. **Description:** Los Angeles City Council has passed a Water Efficiency Requirements ordinance. The law mandates lower low-flow plumbing requirements for plumbing fixtures installed in new buildings and retrofits. Under the ordinance, a toilet's maximum flush volume may not exceed 1.28-gpf.

45266 ■ "A Late Night Run: After-Hours Pediatric Practice Fills Void for Affordable Urgent Care" in *Black Enterprise* **(February 2008)**
Pub: Earl G. Graves Publishing Co. Inc.
Ed: Erinn R. Johnson. **Description:** Practicing pediatricians in Texas founded the Night Light After Hours Pediatrics facility in order to provide urgent care to children without the trauma witnessed in emergency rooms at hospitals.

45267 ■ "Lawyers Lock Up Cops as Clients" in *Sacramento Business Journal* **(Vol. 28, April 8, 2011, No. 6, pp. 1)**
Pub: Sacramento Business Journal
Ed: Kathy Robertson. **Description:** Sacramento-based law firm Mastagni, Holstedt and Chiurazzi has grown its client base by specializing in law enforcement labor issues. The firm represents 80,000 public

sector correctional officers in the US. The firm has been experiencing an increase in new business as public sector employers face huge budget deficits.

45268 ■ "Layoffs Continue to Be a Drag on Region's Recovery" in *Philadelphia Business Journal* **(Vol. 28, January 22, 2010, No. 49, pp. 1)**
Pub: American City Business Journals
Ed: Athena D. Merritt. **Description:** Mass layoffs continue to hamper Pennsylvania's economic recovery. Job losses are predicted to decline in 2010.

45269 ■ "Lead-Free Products must Meet Requirements" in *Contractor* **(Vol. 56, September 2009, No. 9, pp. 30)**
Pub: Penton Media, Inc.
Ed: Robert Gottermeier. **Description:** United States Environmental Protection Agency's adoption of the Safe Drinking Water Act is aimed at lowering lead extraction levels from plumbing products. Manufacturers have since deleaded brass and bronze potable water products. Meanwhile, California and Vermont have passed a law limiting lead content for potable water conveying plumbing products.

45270 ■ "Legislation Introduced" in *Indoor Comfort Marketing* **(Vol. 70, July 2011, No. 7, pp. 6)**
Pub: Industry Publications Inc.
Description: New industry legislation is examined by the National Oilheat Research Alliance.

45271 ■ "Legislators Must Cut Cost of Government" in *Crain's Detroit Business* **(Vol. 24, October 6, 2008, No. 40, pp. 6)**
Pub: Crain Communications, Inc.
Description: Southeast and West Michigan business leaders are setting aside their differences and have proposed clear agendas, ranging from eliminating the Michigan Business Tax to overhauling public employee and retiree benefits and pensions. Lawmakers must also come together to find solutions for the state's economy and discover an entirely new vision for the future of Michigan business.

45272 ■ "Lending Act Touted by Michaud" in *Morning Sentinel* **(June 21, 2010)**
Pub: Morning Sentinel
Ed: Doug Harlow. **Description:** If passed, the Small Business Jobs Tax Relief Act will leverage up to $300 billion in loans for small businesses through a $30 billion lending fund for small and medium-sized community banks, which focus on lending to small firms.

45273 ■ "Lending Stays Down at Local Banks" in *Business Courier* **(Vol. 27, October 1, 2010, No. 22, pp. 1)**
Pub: Business Courier
Ed: Steve Watkins. **Description:** Greater Cincinnati's largest banks have experienced decreases in loans in the past year due to weak economy and sagging loan demands. Analysis of mid-year data has shown that loans drop by a total of $3.6 billion or 4 percent at the ten largest banks as of June 30, 2010 compared to same period in 2009.

45274 ■ "Let the Online Games Begin" in *Canadian Business* **(Vol. 80, January 29, 2007, No. 3, pp. 23)**
Pub: Rogers Media
Ed: Andy Holloway. **Description:** The trends pertaining to the promotion of the products and services of different Canadian companies on the internet are discussed.

45275 ■ "A Little Less Hot Air" in *Canadian Business* **(Vol. 81, March 17, 2008, No. 4, pp. 9)**
Pub: Rogers Media
Description: British Columbia will levy an extra tax on all carbon-emitting fuels starting July 1, 2008. The tax will raise $1.8 billion in three years and in effect, the province will reduce general corporate income tax from 12 percent to 11 percent. The tax on small businesses and personal income will also be reduced.

45276 ■ "Local Firms Will Feel Impact Of Wall St. Woes" in *The Business Journal-Milwaukee* **(Vol. 25, September 19, 2008, No. 52, pp. A1)**
Pub: American City Business Journals, Inc.
Ed: Rich Kirchen. **Description:** Wall Street's crisis is expected to affect businesses in Wisconsin, in terms of decreased demand for services and products and increased financing costs. Businesses in Milwaukee area may face higher interest rates and tougher loan standards. The potential impacts of the Wall Street crisis on local businesses are examined further.

45277 ■ "Local Lending Tumbles $10 Billion Since '08" in *Saint Louis Business Journal* **(Vol. 31, August 26, 2011, No. 53, pp. 1)**
Pub: Saint Louis Business Journal
Ed: Greg Edwards. **Description:** St. Louis, Missouri-based banks lending fell by more than 30 percent in less than three years, from about $30 billion in third and fourth quarters 2008 to about $20 billion in the most recent quarter. However, community banks revealed that they want to lend but there is no loan demand.

45278 ■ "Location, Location" in *Black Enterprise* **(Vol. 38, February 2008, No. 7, pp. 64)**
Pub: Earl G. Graves Publishing Co. Inc.
Ed: Marcia Reed-Woodard. **Description:** Overseas work assignments are increasing, especially for workers in the U.S., Canada and Latin America.

45279 ■ "The Lost Opportunity for a Canadian Steel Giant" in *Globe & Mail* **(April 23, 2007, pp. B1)**
Pub: CTVglobemedia Publishing Inc.
Ed: Greg Keenan. **Description:** The efforts of Algoma Steel Inc. to create a Canadian steel manufacturer that could survive the global trends of consolidation in the steel industry are described. The company's efforts to acquire Stelco Inc., Ivaco Inc. and Slater Steel Inc. are discussed.

45280 ■ "A Love of Likes" in *Boston Business Journal* **(Vol. 31, July 8, 2011, No. 24, pp. 1)**
Pub: Boston Business Journal
Ed: Lisa van der Pool. **Description:** An increasing number of companies in Boston, Massachusetts have been keen on getting Facebook 'likes' from people. Business owners realize that Facebook 'likes' could generate sales and based on some studies, equate to specific dollar values.

45281 ■ "Lunch Box Maker Gives Back" in *Marketing to Women* **(Vol. 23, November 2010, No. 11, pp. 5)**
Pub: EPM Communications, Inc.
Description: Female entrepreneurs launched a new program called, "Share Your Lunch Project" that encourages mothers to give back and replace their child's lunchbox with their eco-friendly lunch boxes, which are available at select retailers. All proceeds from the project will benefit the World Food Program USA, which feeds children in developing countries.

45282 ■ "The Major Leagues: Have Front-Office Positions Opened Up for Blacks?" in *Black Enterprise* **(Vol. 37, February 2007, No. 7, pp.)**
Pub: Earl G. Graves Publishing Co. Inc.
Ed: Alexis McCombs. **Description:** Major leave sports teams are hiring more African Americans to manage and coach teams. Statistical data included.

45283 ■ "Make It Yourself: Home Sewing, Gender, and Culture, 1890-1930" in *Business History Review* **(Vol. 84, Autumn 2010, No. 3, pp. 602)**
Pub: Harvard Business School
Ed: Alexis McCrossen. **Description:** Review of the publication, 'Make It Yourself: Home Sewing, Gender, and Culture, 1890-1930, a nonfiction work.

45284 ■ "Managers as Visionaries: a Skill That Can Be Learned" in *Strategy and Leadership* **(Vol. 39, September-October 2011, No. 5, pp. 56-58)**
Pub: Emerald Group Publishing Inc.
Ed: Stephen M. Millett. **Description:** A study uses research findings to examine whether visionary

management can be learned. Results conclude that managers can learn visionary management through intuitive pattern recognition of trends and by using scenarios for anticipating and planning for likely future occurrences.

45285 ■ *Managing the Older Worker: How to Prepare for the New Organizational Order*
Pub: Harvard Business Press
Ed: Peter Cappelli, Bill Novelli. **Price:** $29.95. **Description:** Your organization needs older workers more than ever: They transfer knowledge between generations, transmit your company's values to new hires, make excellent mentors for younger employees, and provide a 'just in time' workforce for special projects.

45286 ■ "Manufacturing Jobs Go Begging in Downturn" in *Puget Sound Business Journal* (Vol. 29, December 26, 2008, No. 36, pp. 1)
Pub: American City Business Journals
Ed: Steve Wilhelm. **Description:** Trends show that skilled jobs in aerospace and other technology manufacturing industries are in a state of decline as layoffs hit broad sectors of the economy. Too few people are entering the field, prompting companies to try to maintain these skilled workers, thus creating problems that could affect the sector's vitality.

45287 ■ "A Manufacturing Revival" in *Boston Business Journal* (Vol. 31, May 27, 2011, No. 18, pp. 1)
Pub: Boston Business Journal
Ed: Kyle Alspach. **Description:** Massachusetts' manufacturing sector has grown despite the high cost of labor, real estate and electricity. Manufacturing jobs in the state have increased to 2,800 in April 2011.

45288 ■ "Many Retailers Soften Return Policies" in *Austin Business JournalInc.* (Vol. 28, December 26, 2008, No. 41, pp. 1)
Pub: American City Business Journals
Ed: Jean Kwon. **Description:** National Retail Federation reported the percentage of retailers saying their holiday return policy in 2008 will slacken compared to last season has increased from 3.4 percent to 11 percent. An increasing percentage of retailers are also getting stingier, as 17.1 percent revealed that their return policies will be stricter.

45289 ■ "Mapping Out a Career" in *Occupational Outlook Quarterly* (Vol. 54, Fall 2010, No. 3, pp. 12)
Pub: U.S. Bureau of Labor Statistics
Ed: Audrey Watson. **Description:** Geographic distribution of occupations is studied, along with lifestyle considerations when choosing a career.

45290 ■ "Market Squeezes Some Lawyers" in *Austin Business JournalInc.* (Vol. 28, December 12, 2008, No. 39, pp. 1)
Pub: American City Business Journals
Ed: Jean Kwon. **Description:** Austin, Texas-based lawyers have been adversely affected by the economic downturn. Fewer works for lawyers in mergers and acquisitions and other activities are being offered. Lawyers are refinancing debts and offering other services.

45291 ■ "Marketing in the Digital World: Here's How to Craft a Smart Online Strategy" in *Black Enterprise* (Vol. 40, July 2010, No. 12, pp. 47)
Pub: Earl G. Graves Publishing Co. Inc.
Ed: Sonya A. Donaldson. **Description:** Social media is an integral part of any small business plan in addressing marketing, sales, and branding strategies.

45292 ■ "Marketing Scholarship 2.0" in *Journal of Marketing* (Vol. 75, July 2011, No. 4, pp. 225)
Pub: American Marketing Association
Ed: Richard J. Lutz. **Description:** A study of the implications of changing environment and newer collaborative models for marketing knowledge production and dissemination is presented. Crowdsourcing has become a frequently employed strategy in

industry. Academic researchers should collaborate more as well as the academe and industry, to make sure that important problems are being investigated.

45293 ■ "Maryland Hospitals Cope with Rare Drop in Patient Admissions" in *Boston Business Journal* (Vol. 29, September 23, 2011, No. 20, pp. 1)
Pub: American City Business Journals Inc.
Ed: Scott Dance. **Description:** Admissions to Maryland hospitals have dropped to less than 700,000 in fiscal year 2010 and initial figures for fiscal 2011 show in-patient admissions are now nearing 660,000. The decline can be partly attributed to new ways health insurers are paying hospitals for care and to the financial reward hospitals get for cutting back on admissions.

45294 ■ "Mass-Transit Backers: Change in State Funding Needed" in *Crain's Detroit Business* (Vol. 24, October 6, 2008, No. 40, pp. 19)
Pub: Crain Communications, Inc.
Ed: Bill Shea. **Description:** Options to reform transportation and infrastructure funding in the state of Michigan are examined. Transit revitalization investment zones are also discussed.

45295 ■ "MBT Add On: Gone by 2012?" in *Crain's Detroit Business* (Vol. 24, October 6, 2008, No. 40, pp. 1)
Pub: Crain Communications, Inc.
Ed: Amy Lane. **Description:** Discusses the Michigan Business Tax (MBT), which has angered many businesses in the state due to the addition of a 21.99 percent surcharge. Although the tax policy will cut taxes on 63 percent of businesses in the state and represent no tax liability change for another nine percent of firms, other businesses will see increases of 100 percent or more. This increase means that many business owners will be forced to relocate or close their establishment and others will have to eliminate jobs. Lawmakers are attempting to find a solution to this problem.

45296 ■ "McD's Dollar-Menu Fixation Sparks Revolt" in *Advertising Age* (Vol. 79, June 2, 2008, No. 22, pp. 1)
Pub: Crain Communications, Inc.
Ed: Emily Bryson York. **Description:** McDonald's franchisees say that low-cost dollar-menu offerings are impacting their bottom line and many have discontinued the dollar-menu altogether due to rising commodity costs, an increase in minimum wage and consumers trading down to the lower-price items.

45297 ■ "Medicaid Insurers See Growth in Small Business Market" in *Boston Business Journal* (Vol. 31, July 15, 2011, No. 25, pp. 1)
Pub: Boston Business Journal
Ed: Julie M. Donnelly. **Description:** BMC HealthNet Plan announced plans to launch small business products to serve small businesses that are priced out of rising premium rates at large Massachusetts insurers. BMC joined competitors CeltiCare Health Plan and Neighborhood Health Plan in augmenting its core business.

45298 ■ "The Medium 150" in *Canadian Business* (Vol. 81, Summer 2008, No. 9, pp. 129)
Pub: Rogers Media Ltd.
Description: Medium-sized companies are ranked based on market capitalization and stock performance. Timminico Ltd. topped the roster with 1,294.2 percent returns, while Petrominerales Ltd. ranked second with 325.4 percent. A table showing the 2008 rankings of the companies is presented.

45299 ■ "Meet Rebecca. She's Here to Fire You" in *Inc.* (November 2007, pp. 25-26)
Pub: Gruner & Jahr USA Publishing
Ed: Max Chafkin. **Description:** Amid liability concerns as well as CEO guilt, more and more firms are using consulting companies to fire workers. These outsourced firms help small companies structure severance and document information in order to limit legal liability when firing an employee.

45300 ■ "Meet the White-Label Cash Kings" in *Globe & Mail* (April 23, 2007, pp. B1)
Pub: CTVglobemedia Publishing Inc.
Ed: Tara Perkins; Tavia Grant. **Description:** The services provided by the independent Canadian companies managing automated banking machines are described. The trends of ownership of automated banking machines in Canada are discussed.

45301 ■ "Michaud Touts Small-Business Credentials" in *Bangor Daily News* (September 10, 2010)
Pub: Bangor Daily News
Ed: Nick Sambides Jr. **Description:** Mike Michaud, Democrat, is running against a Republican challenger in the 2nd District and states he will support the Small Business Jobs Tax Relief Act if reelected.

45302 ■ "Micro-Cap Companies" in *Canadian Business* (Vol. 81, Summer 2008, No. 9, pp. 157)
Pub: Rogers Media Ltd.
Description: Micro-cap companies have lower than $221 million in terms of market capitalization. Burnaby, British Columbia-based Fancamp Exploration Ltd. topped the roster with 1,116.7 percent in return. A table showing the 2008 rankings of the companies is presented.

45303 ■ *Microtrends*
Pub: Twelve Books/Hachette Book Group USA
Ed: Mark J. Pen with E. Kinney Zalesne. **Released:** September 2007. **Price:** $25.99. **Description:** Detecting small patterns the great impact they can have on business.

45304 ■ *Microtrends: The Small Forces Behind Tomorrow's Big Changes*
Pub: Business Plus
Ed: Mark J. Penn. **Released:** 2007. **Price:** $25.99. **Description:** Political pollster and lead presidential campaign strategist for Hillary Clinton, identifies seventy-five microtrends he believes are changing the social and cultural landscape in the U.S. and globally. The book covers the areas of health and wellness, technology, education and more.

45305 ■ "Minimizing Import Risks" in *Canadian Sailings* (July 7, 2008)
Pub: Commonwealth Business Media
Ed: Jack Kohane. **Description:** New food and product safety laws may be enacted by Canada's Parliament; importers, retailers and manufacturers could face huge fines if the new laws are passed.

45306 ■ "Misguided" in *Canadian Business* (Vol. 81, July 22, 2008, No. 12-13, pp. 30)
Pub: Rogers Media Ltd.
Ed: Al Rosen. **Description:** Canada's securities regulations are discussed; differing views on using principles-based and rules-based securities regulations are also presented.

45307 ■ *The Missing Class: Portraits of the Near Poor in America*
Pub: Houghton Mifflin
Ed: Katherine S. Newman; Victor Tan Chen. **Released:** 2007. **Description:** Information regarding the 57 million Americans existing on the razor-thin margin between poverty and middle class.

45308 ■ "More Ad Shops Link Payment to Results" in *Boston Business Journal* (Vol. 30, November 12, 2010, No. 42, pp. 1)
Pub: Boston Business Journal
Ed: Lisa van der Pool. **Description:** A growing number of advertising firms are proposing a 'value-based' payment scheme where they are paid a base fee plus a bonus if certain sales goals or other targets are met. The proposed shift in payment scheme is seen as reminiscent of the dot-com boom about ten years ago. Advertising firms are traditionally paid by the hour.

45309 ■ "More Brides, Grooms Say 'I Do' to Interracial Marriage" in *Black Enterprise* (Vol. 41, August 2010, No. 1, pp. 36)
Pub: Earl G. Graves Publishing Co. Inc.
Description: According to a recent survey conducted by Pew Research Center, a record 14.6 percent of all new marriages in the U.S. in 2008 were interracial. Statistical data included.

45310 ■ **"More Businesses Will Shift Health Costs to Workers"** in *Business Review, Albany New York* **(Vol. 34, November 16, 2007, No. 33, pp. 1)**
Pub: American City Business Journals, Inc.
Ed: Barbara Pinckney. **Description:** Survey conducted by consulting firm Benetech Inc. showed that sixty percent of employers are planning to increase payroll deductions to pay for health insurance premiums. More than ninety percent of the employers prefer HMO plans, followed by Preferred Provider Organizations. Other details of the survey are discussed.

45311 ■ **"More Callers Are Cutting Their Landlines"** in *Chicago Tribune* **(December 30, 2008)**
Pub: McClatchy-Tribune Information Services
Ed: Eric Benderoff. **Description:** Despite sporadic outages for cell phone users, the trend for consumers to cut out the expense of a landline does not appear to be slowing; experts believe that the recession will further increase the number of consumers who decide to go completely wireless.

45312 ■ **"More Law Partners Jumping Ship"** in *Boston Business Journal* **(Vol. 27, October 5, 2007, No. 36, pp. 1)**
Pub: American City Business Journals Inc.
Ed: Lisa van der Pool. **Description:** Boston lawyers are moving from one law firm to another, a practice becoming more prevalent than in recent times. Loss of revenue, clients and poor partner morale are some of the reasons for these actions. Details of this profound trend are discussed.

45313 ■ **"More Small Businesses Willing to Fund Employees' Benefits"** in *Baltimore Business Journal* **(Vol. 28, June 18, 2010, No. 6, pp. 1)**
Pub: Baltimore Business Journal
Ed: Scott Graham. **Description:** An increasing number of small businesses in Maryland are tapping into potentially cheaper self-funded health plans instead of providing fully insured benefits to employees through traditional health plans. Self-funded health plans charge employers for health care up to a specified level. Economic implications of self-funded plans to small businesses are discussed.

45314 ■ **"Mortgages Going Under"** in *Black Enterprise* **(Vol. 41, December 2010, No. 5, pp. 20)**
Pub: Earl G. Graves Publishing Co. Inc.
Description: Nearly one-fifth of the country's homeowners are underwater in their mortgages, which means they owe more on their home than the home's worth. Statistical data included.

45315 ■ **"Most Viewed Stories, Videos on farmindustrynews.com in 2010"** in *Farm Industry News* **(January 4, 2011)**
Pub: Penton Business Media Inc.
Description: The top ten most popularly viewed stories and videos presented on farmindustrynews. com Website are listed.

45316 ■ **"Move Over - Or Out"** in *Puget Sound Business Journal* **(Vol. 29, November 28, 2008, No. 32, pp. 1)**
Pub: American City Business Journals
Ed: Kirsten Grind. **Description:** Real estate agents in the state of Washington are either moving to smaller real estate firms or quitting the industry due to the weak housing market. Lesser-known firms are experiencing an influx of experienced real estate agents, while 2,800 agents in the state have left the industry.

45317 ■ **"Moving Into the Digital Space: How New Media Create Opportunities for Minorities"** in *Black Enterprise* **(February 2008)**
Pub: Earl G. Graves Publishing Co. Inc.
Ed: Sonia Alleyne. **Description:** The Internet is becoming an alternative to traditional sources of entertainment; nearly 16 percent of American households who use the Internet watch television online. One such Internet show features a variety of African American lifestyles.

45318 ■ **"Must Work for Food"** in *Pet Product News* **(Vol. 64, November 2010, No. 11, pp. 24)**
Pub: BowTie Inc.
Ed: Wendy Bedwell-Wilson. **Description:** Pet supply retailers can benefit from stocking foods and treats that address obesity, which according to the American Veterinary Medical Association, has become the most prevalent nutritional disorder in dogs. With the rise in dog obesity, products like work-for-their food toys have been sought by dog owners.

45319 ■ **"Myths of Deleveraging"** in *Barron's* **(Vol. 90, August 23, 2010, No. 34, pp. M14)**
Pub: Barron's Editorial & Corporate Headquarters
Ed: Gene Epstein. **Description:** The opposite is true against reports about deleveraging or the decrease in credit since inflation-adjusted-investment factories and equipment rose 7.8 percent in the first quarter of 2010. On consumer deleveraging, sales of homes through credit is weak but there is a trend towards more realistic homeownership and consumer spending on durable goods rose 8.8 percent.

45320 ■ **"NAWBO Takes the Stage at Press Conference for Small Business Jobs, Credit and Tax Relief Acts"** in *Internet Wire* **(June 17, 2010)**
Pub: Comtex
Description: A survey of the National Association of Women Business Owners reported optimism returning and women business owners are ready to invest in job creation. The Small Business Jobs Tax Relief Act will aid in their progress.

45321 ■ **"Need Fiber in Your Diet? Pour Some Milk"** in *Globe & Mail* **(April 10, 2007, pp. B7)**
Pub: CTVglobemedia Publishing Inc.
Ed: William Illsey Atkinson. **Description:** The growing market and demand for functional foods and neutraceuticals in Canada is discussed. The research being conducted by University of Manitoba's Richardson Centre for Functional Foods and Nutraceuticals to explore new health compounds in food is highlighted.

45322 ■ **"New Approach Could Boost Ivory Tower Innovation"** in *Business Journal-Portland* **(Vol. 24, November 16, 2007, No. 37, pp. 1)**
Pub: American City Business Journals, Inc.
Ed: Aliza Earnshaw. **Description:** New approach which aims to help universities move to a corporate structure, secure funds, and find professional managers is being explored. Accelerator Corporation was able to help six companies through its funding. Joe Tanous who is behind Oregon's State University's enhanced commercialization, would like to apply the same approach Accelerator used to help Oregon State University, the University of Oregon, Portland State University and Oregon Health and Science University.

45323 ■ **"A New Day is Dawning"** in *Indoor Comfort Marketing* **(Vol. 70, August 2011, No. 8, pp. 18)**
Pub: Industry Publications Inc.
Ed: Paul Nazzaro. **Description:** New trends in the HVAC/R industry regarding biofuels and bioheat are explored.

45324 ■ **"The New Face of Social Media"** in *Hispanic Business* **(December 2010)**
Pub: Hispanic Business
Ed: Gary D. Fackler. **Description:** Latina bloggers carve out a new niche in social media that helps preserve their unique cultural identities.

45325 ■ **"New Global Hot Spots: Look Beyond Shanghai for the Next Big Thing"** in *Inc.* **(October 2007, pp. 40-41)**
Pub: Gruner & Jahr USA Publishing
Description: The Chinese government is investing money to lure U.S. companies to start doing business in Chengdu, China. The government is upgrading Chengdu's infrastructure and establishing free trade zones in a less polluted environment. Other cities profiled in the article include: Yekaterinburg, Russia; Poznan, Poland; Ahmadabad and Kolkata, India; Suzhou, China; Belo Horizonte, Brazil; Ras Al Khaimah, United Arab Emirates; and Aguascalientes, Mexico.

45326 ■ **"New Health Care Sector"** in *Hispanic Business* **(July-August 2009, pp. 10-12)**
Pub: Hispanic Business
Ed: Rob Kuznia. **Description:** Despite the recession and reform, the health care sector continues to grow at a fast rate. The top ten health care organizations are outlined.

45327 ■ **"New Jobless Claims Filed in December Soar"** in *Baltimore Business Journal* **(Vol. 27, January 29, 2010, No. 39, pp. 1)**
Pub: American City Business Journals
Ed: Scott Dance. **Description:** Maryland received 48,693 new claims for unemployment benefits in December 2009, reaching its highest monthly total since 1974. The number of claims was up 49 percent from November and 13 percent from the same period in 2008. Labor officials and economists discuss this trend.

45328 ■ **"A New Mix of Tenants Settles In"** in *Crain's New York Business* **(Vol. 24, January 14, 2008, No. 2, pp. 26)**
Pub: Crain Communications, Inc.
Ed: Andrew Marks. **Description:** More and more nonfinancial firms are relocating downtown due to the new retailers and restaurants that are reshaping the look and feel of lower Manhattan.

45329 ■ **"The New Nimble"** in *Barron's* **(Vol. 90, August 30, 2010, No. 35, pp. S12)**
Pub: Barron's Editorial & Corporate Headquarters
Ed: Suzanne McGee. **Description:** Financial advisors are making investments based on short-lived market trends due to the uncertainty in the long-term market. This strategy can be demanding and advisors should only try it if they are confident about their skill in spotting short-term trends.

45330 ■ **"New Recession-Proof Internet Marketing Package Allows Businesses to Ramp Up Web Traffic and Profits"** in *PR Newswire* **(Jan. 25, 2010)**
Pub: PR Newswire Association, LLC
Description: Profile of Reel Web Design, a leading marketing firm in New York City that caters to small to medium sized businesses with smaller budgets that need substantial return on investment; Reel Web Design offers video production and submission, web design and maintenance and press release writing among additional services.

45331 ■ *The New Role of Regional Management*
Pub: Palgrave Macmillan
Ed: Bjorn Ambos, Bodo B. Schlegelmilch. **Released:** January 19, 2010. **Price:** $95.00. **Description:** Regional management is becoming more important to companies as they expand globally. This book explores the challenges of European, United States and Asian companies and outlines how regional headquarters can develop into Dynamic Competence Relay centers to master these issues.

45332 ■ **"The New Schools"** in *Black Enterprise* **(February 2008)**
Pub: Earl G. Graves Publishing Co. Inc.
Ed: Kinsley Kanu, Jr. **Description:** Ten educational programs to help top executives keep pace with the ever-changing market trends while gaining perspective on innovation and new ideas are examined.

45333 ■ **"New Technology, Growing Fan Base Fuel Truck Trend"** in *Nation's Restaurant News* **(Vol. 45, June 13, 2001, No. 12, pp. 16)**
Pub: Penton Media Inc.
Ed: Ron Ruggless. **Description:** Food trucks drove more interest at this year's National Restaurant Association Restaurant Hotel-Motel Show in Chicago. The trend continues to show long-term growth.

45334 ■ *The New Wellness Revolution: Make a Fortune in the Next Trillion Dollar Industry*
Pub: John Wiley & Sons, Incorporated
Ed: Paul Zane Pilzer. **Released:** February 16, 2007. **Price:** $24.95. **Description:** Tips for starting and running a healthcare business.

45335 ■ **"Nexstar Super Meeting Breaks Business Barriers"** in *Contractor* **(Vol. 56, November 2009, No. 11, pp. 3)**
Pub: Penton Media, Inc.
Ed: Candace Roulo. **Description:** Around 400 Nexstar members met to discuss the trends in the HVAC industry and the economic outlook for 2010. Former lead solo pilot John Foley for the Blue Angels made a presentation on how a business can increase overall productivity based on the culture of the Blue Angels. Some breakout sessions tackled how to optimize workflow and marketing.

45336 ■ **"No Matter the Workplace Size, Handbooks Can Play a Vital Role"** in *Crain's Cleveland Business* **(Vol. 28, November 12, 2007, No. 45)**
Pub: Crain Communications, Inc.
Ed: David Prizinsky. **Description:** Employee handbooks are important for even small businesses that wish to remain relatively informal since that documentation can help a company with a defense when confronted by employee or government lawsuits; they also demonstrate a consistency in policy which is a vital way in which employees, managers and owners remain focused on the company's prime goals.

45337 ■ **"No Place Like Home"** in *Small Business Opportunities* **(Winter 2010)**
Pub: Harris Publications Inc.
Ed: Description: Five reasons to start a home-staging business in any economy are listed. Home staging is listed as the top emerging career on Website, Careerbuilder.com.

45338 ■ **"No Shortage of Challenges for Cross-Border Trade"** in *Canadian Sailings* **(June 30, 2008)**
Pub: Commonwealth Business Media
Ed: Kathlyn Horibe. **Description:** Pros and cons of the North American Free Trade Agreement are examined. The agreement between the U.S. and Canada concerning trade was an essential step toward securing economic growth for Canadian citizens. Two-way trade between the counties has tripled since the agreement and accounts for 7.1 million American and 3 million Canadian jobs.

45339 ■ *Non-Standard Employment under Globalization*
Pub: Palgrave Macmillan
Ed: Koichi Usami. **Released:** January 19, 2010. **Price:** $100.00. **Description:** Expansion of non-standard employment under globalization is being recognized in all of the newly industrialized countries. The book examines deregulation of labor markets, social protection for nonstandard workers, and social security reforms in accordance with the transformation of employment.

45340 ■ **"Nortel Makes Customers Stars in New Campaign"** in *Brandweek* **(Vol. 49, April 21, 2008, No. 16, pp. 8)**
Pub: VNU Business Media, Inc.
Ed: Mike Beirne. **Description:** Nortel has launched a new television advertising campaign in which the business-to-business communications technology provider cast senior executives in 30-second TV case studies that show how Nortel's technology helped their businesses innovate.

45341 ■ **"North American Pet Health Insurance Market Poised for Growth"** in *Pet Product News* **(Vol. 64, December 2010, No. 12, pp. 4)**
Pub: BowTie Inc.
Ed: David Lummis. **Description:** The pet health insurance market is expected to further grow after posting about $350 million in sales in 2009, a gain of more than $40 million. Pet insurance firms have offered strategies such as product humanization in

response to this growth forecast. Meanwhile, pet insurance shoppers have been provided more by insurance firms with wider choices.

45342 ■ **"Not Your Dad's Business Card"** in *Small Business Opportunities* **(July 2008)**
Pub: Entrepreneur Media Inc.
Ed: Rob Schlacter. **Description:** Provides tips on how to effectively design and use business cards.

45343 ■ **"Now Entering A Secure Area"** in *Women Entrepreneur* **(January 14, 2009)**
Pub: Entrepreneur Media Inc.
Ed: Aliza Sherman. **Description:** Despite the fact that the field of government intelligence and security is dominated by males, many women entrepreneurs are finding opportunities for their products and services in homeland security. Profiles of several women who have found such opportunities are included.

45344 ■ **"Nowspeed and OneSource to Conduct Webinar"** in *Internet Wire* **(December 14, 2009)**
Pub: Comtex News Network, Inc.
Description: OneSource, a leading provider of global business information, and Nowspeed, an Internet marketing agency, will conduct a webinar titled "How to Develop Social Media Content That Gets Results" in order to provide marketers insight into how to develop and optimize effective social media content to get consumer results that translate into purchases and lead generation.

45345 ■ *On the Make: Clerks and the Quest for Capital in Nineteenth-Century America*
Pub: NYU Press
Ed: Brian Luskey. **Released:** January 1, 2010. **Price:** $48.00. **Description:** Through exploration into the diaries, newspapers, credit reports, census data, advice literature and fiction, the book presents the origins of the white collar culture, the antebellum clerk.

45346 ■ **"On tap: More Could Get MEGA Credits; Need to Look Outside State May Be Cut"** in *Crain's Detroit Business* **(April 7, 2008)**
Pub: Crain Communications, Inc.
Ed: Amy Lane. **Description:** In order to qualify for Michigan Economic Growth Authority tax credits Michigan businesses may no longer have to shop outside the state due to a new bill which has already passed the state Senate and will move on to the House; the bill, along with further changes to the MEGA program, is designed to provide incentives for investments that would add relevance and make Michigan more competitive.

45347 ■ **"On Target"** in *Canadian Business* **(Vol. 81, July 22, 2008, No. 12-13, pp. 45)**
Pub: Rogers Media Ltd.
Ed: Calvin Leung. **Description:** Companies such as LavalifePRIME, a dating website devoted to singles 45 and older, discuss the value of marketing and services aimed at Canada's older consumers. One-third of Canada's 33 million people are 50-plus, controlling 77 percent of the countries wealth.

45348 ■ **"On Their Own"** in *Crain's Cleveland Business* **(Vol. 28, November 12, 2007, No. 45, pp. 19)**
Pub: Crain Communications, Inc.
Ed: Eileen Beal. **Description:** Discusses the reasons more physicians with entrepreneurial spirit are opening their own practices as well the added challenges and responsibilities that comes with owning one's own practice.

45349 ■ **"One Hundred Years of Excellence in Business Education: What Have We Learned?"** in *Business Horizons* **(January-February 2008)**
Pub: Elsevier Advanced Technology Publications
Ed: Frank Acito, Patricia M. McDougall, Daniel C. Smith. **Description:** Business schools have to be more innovative, efficient and nimble, so that the quality of the next generation of business leaders is improved. The Kelley School of Business, Indiana

University ahs long been a leader in business education. The trends that influence the future of business education and useful success principles are discussed.

45350 ■ **"One on One With SEIA's President, CEO"** in *Contractor* **(Vol. 57, January 2010, No. 1, pp. 40)**
Pub: Penton Media, Inc.
Ed: Dave Yates. **Description:** Solar Energy Industries Association President and CEO Rhone Resch says that the deployment of solar systems in the U.S. has exploded since 2005 and that there is a need to make inroads for shaping the U.S. energy policy. Resch says one of the hurdles they face is that there are no universal standards.

45351 ■ **"Online Book Sales Surpass Bookstores"** in *Information Today* **(Vol. 28, September 2011, No. 8, pp. 11)**
Pub: Information Today, Inc.
Ed: Cindy Martine. **Description:** Online book sales outpaced bookstore purchases in the United States, signaling a shift in the US book industry. Statistical data included.

45352 ■ **"Opportunity Knocks"** in *Small Business Opportunities* **(September 2008)**
Pub: Entrepreneur Media Inc.
Description: Profile of YourOffice USA, a franchise that provides home-based and small businesses cost-effective and efficient support through "virtual" offices that are available as much or as little as the client needs it; they also supply necessary tools such as a professional business address, private mailbox service, personalized telephone answering and more that supports clients who want to look, act and operate with an advanced business image.

45353 ■ **"Optimism Index"** in *Black Enterprise* **(Vol. 41, September 2010, No. 2, pp. 24)**
Pub: Earl G. Graves Publishing Co. Inc.
Description: According to a Pew Research Center report, 81 percent of African Americans expect to improve their finances in 2011. Blacks have carried a disproportionate share of job losses and housing foreclosures in the recession that began in 2007.

45354 ■ **"Optimize.ca Supplies Free Online Financial Advice"** in *Entertainment Close-Up* **(October 9, 2010)**
Pub: Close-Up Media Inc.
Description: Optimize.ca provides free online financial advice, focusing on instant savings for their mutual funds and other banking products while improving rates of return and overall financial health.

45355 ■ **"Ordering Pizza Hut From Your Facebook Page?"** in *Advertising Age* **(Vol. 79, November 10, 2008, No. 42, pp. 50)**
Pub: Crain Communications, Inc.
Ed: Emily Bryson York. **Description:** Fast-food chains are experimenting with delivery/takeout services via social networks such as Facebook and iPhone applications. This also allows the chains to build valuable databases of their customers.

45356 ■ **"Organic Chain Scouting Tri-State Sites, Including Kenwood"** in *Business Courier* **(Vol. 27, December 3, 2010, No. 31, pp. 1)**
Pub: Business Courier
Ed: Tom Demeropolis. **Description:** Asheville, North Carolina-based Earth Fare has been planning to add a total of six stores in 2011, including the potential opening of more than one store in the Greater Cincinnati area market. Earth Fare has not named specific locations but Kenwood area was reportedly being considered for its first location. Insights on growing trends toward health food stores are also given.

45357 ■ **"Organic Dairy Farmers Wanted"** in *Canadian Business* **(Vol. 80, April 23, 2007, No. 9, pp. 11)**
Pub: Rogers Media
Ed: Wendy Glauser. **Description:** The growth of the Harmony Organic due to demand for organic dairy products is presented.

45358 ■ "Our Hoarder Mentality: Blame the Hard Disk" in *PC Magazine* **(Vol. 30, November 2011, No. 11, pp. 46)**
Pub: Ziff Davis Inc.

Ed: John C. Dvorak. **Description:** Computer programmers, once referred to as computer users, are slowly being replaced by passive consumers of products and content of tablets and handheld mobile phones and devices of the future. Understanding is garnered as this article examines this industry trend.

45359 ■ "Outpouring of Outreach" in *Crain's Cleveland Business* **(Vol. 30, June 15, 2009, No. 23, pp. 3)**
Pub: Crain Communications, Inc.

Ed: Shannon Mortland. **Description:** Nonprofit organizations are experiencing a higher number of volunteers than in the past. People are willing to donate their skills and services rather than contributing money.

45360 ■ *Over the Counter*
Pub: The Mercier Press, Ltd.

Ed: Keogh. **Released:** January 1, 2009. **Price:** $54. 95. **Description:** An overview of the changing landscape of Cork, Ireland's retail stores is presented.

45361 ■ "Overheating Taking Place? Pay Attention to Details..." in *Indoor Comfort Marketing* **(Vol. 70, March 2011, No. 3, pp.)**
Pub: Industry Publications Inc.

Ed: George R. Carey. **Description:** Boiler facts are outlined to help the small HVAC company when servicing customers.

45362 ■ "Overview - Small Business Optimism" in *Small Business Economic Trends* **(July 2010, pp. 4)**
Pub: National Federation of Independent Business

Description: An optimism index among small businesses surveyed in the U.S. from 1986 to 2010 is presented in graph form. A small business optimism index from January 2005 to June 2010 is also given in tabular form. The index value was seasonally adjusted at 1986=100.

45363 ■ "Paper Replaces PVC for Gift Cards" in *American Printer* **(Vol. 128, June 1, 2011, No. 6)**
Pub: Penton Media Inc.

Description: Monadnock Envi Card Stock replaces paper for gift cards, loyalty cards, membership cards, hotel keys and durable signage. This renewable wood fiber alternative to PVC card materials comes from Monadock Paper Mills.

45364 ■ "Part-Time Assignments" in *Black Enterprise* **(Vol. 37, December 2006, No. 5, pp. 70)**
Pub: Earl G. Graves Publishing Co. Inc.

Description: During critical change initiatives interim management, an employment model which uses senior-level executives to manage a special project or specific business function on a temporary basis, can have many benefits.

45365 ■ "Part-Time Office Space" in *Hawaii Business* **(Vol. 53, December 2007, No. 6, pp. 132)**
Pub: Hawaii Business Publishing

Ed: Ashley Hamershock. **Description:** My Office is one of the companies that are renting space office not only by the month, but by the hour. Such setup is beneficial to small businesses that do not need a whole office all to themselves, and are interested in cutting the cost of office space rental. The prices of office space in Hawaii are mentioned.

45366 ■ "Patients: Make Mine a Single" in *Business Courier* **(Vol. 24, March 28, 2008, No. 51, pp. 1)**
Pub: American City Business Journals, Inc.

Ed: James Ritchie. **Description:** Hospitals in the Tri-State area are switching from double to private rooms since patients heal better in private rooms and also they provide peace and quiet to patients. Private rooms also contribute to the reduction of medical errors and hospital acquired infection rates.

45367 ■ "Peak Show" in *Canadian Business* **(Vol. 81, December 24, 2007, No. 1, pp. 28)**
Pub: Rogers Media

Ed: Thomas Watson. **Description:** Factors affecting oil prices could include political instability and economic slowdown, but peak oil is not one of them as it is believed there is still plenty of oil in supply. Details on the oil supply and demand, trend for higher prices, and peak oil expert Matthew Simmons' prediction on the issue are discussed.

45368 ■ "Phoenix Conference Reveals Opportunities are Coming" in *Indoor Comfort Marketing* **(Vol. 70, March 2011, No. 3, pp. 24)**
Pub: Industry Publications Inc.

Ed: Paul J. Nazzaro. **Description:** Advanced liquid fuels were spotlighted at the Phoenix conference revealing the opportunities for using liquid fuels.

45369 ■ "Pioneers Get All The Perks" in *Canadian Business* **(Vol. 81, March 3, 2008, No. 3, pp. 18)**
Pub: Rogers Media

Description: Suncor Energy Inc. will face royalty payments from 25% to 30% of net profits as it signs a new deal with Alberta. Biovail Corp., meanwhile, is under a U.S. grand jury investigation for supposed improprieties in Cardizem LA heart drug launch. The Conference Board of Canada's proposal to impose taxes on greenhouse gas emissions and other developments in the business community are discussed.

45370 ■ "Point, Click, Buy" in *Barron's* **(Vol. 90, September 6, 2010, No. 36, pp. 11)**
Pub: Barron's Editorial & Corporate Headquarters

Ed: Vito J. Racanelli. **Description:** Non-travel online retail sales from January to July 2010 increased nine percent which indicates that online shopping for the coming holidays will be good. Online sales are outpacing traditional shopping, but pricing is still critical.

45371 ■ "Positive Transformational Change" in *Indoor Comfort Marketing* **(Vol. 70, April 2011, No. 4, pp. 30)**
Pub: Industry Publications Inc.

Ed: Blaine Fox. **Description:** Management changes taking place at Shark Bites HVAC firm are discussed.

45372 ■ *The Post-American World*
Pub: W.W. Norton & Company

Ed: Fareed Zakaria. **Released:** 2009. **Price:** $25.95. **Description:** Analysis of the changes taking place as new countries are rising as status players challenging American dominance.

45373 ■ "The Power of Innovation" in *Canadian Business* **(Vol. 81, March 17, 2008, No. 4, pp. 57)**
Pub: Rogers Media

Ed: Andrew Wahl. **Description:** Canada ranks badly in terms innovation yardsticks that directly translate to economic growth such as business R&D as a percentage of GDP and R&D per capita. Canada's reliance on natural resources does not provide incentives to innovate unlike smaller countries with little natural resources. Canada could spur innovation through regulations that encourage industrial research.

45374 ■ *The Power of Social Innovation: How Civic Entrepreneurs Ignite Community Networks for Good*
Pub: John Wiley & Sons, Inc.

Ed: Stephen Goldsmith, Tim Burke, Gigi Georges. **Released:** March 10, 2010. **Price:** $35.00. **Description:** This seminal book provides tools for civic entrepreneurs to create healthier communities and promote innovative solutions to public and social problems. It shows how to effectively tackle the intractable issues facing the country.

45375 ■ "PPC's Major Commitment to Biofuel Infrastructure" in *Indoor Comfort Marketing* **(Vol. 70, April 2011, No. 4, pp. 6)**
Pub: Industry Publications Inc.

Description: Petroleum Products Corporation's commitment to the biofuel infrastructure is outlined.

45376 ■ "Pre-K Pressure" in *Hawaii Business* **(Vol. 53, October 2007, No. 4, pp. 32)**
Pub: Hawaii Business Publishing

Ed: David K. Choo. **Description:** Kindergarten admission in Hawaii is becoming more competitive. Parents, for example, prepare their children for the kindergarten admissions process by bringing them to the schools before the interview or by paying for tutorial services. The impacts of increased competition in school admissions on the life of Hawaiian children are discussed.

45377 ■ "A Precious Resource: Investing In the Fate of Fresh Water" in *Black Enterprise* **(Vol. 38, February 2008, No. 7, pp. 44)**
Pub: Earl G. Graves Publishing Co. Inc.

Ed: Charles Keenan. **Description:** Despite rising oil prices, water may become the most precious commodity in years to come because the world's supply of drinkable water is dwindling.

45378 ■ *Predictably Irrational: The Hidden Forces That Shape Our Decisions*
Pub: HarperCollins Publishers

Ed: Dan Ariely. **Released:** 2009. **Price:** $25.95. **Description:** Behaviorists are bringing the economics profession around to realizing that human beings are impulsive, shortsighted and procrastinating in behavior. Economists are using this information to market products to consumers.

45379 ■ "Prescription for Health: Choosing the Best Healthcare Plan" in *Black Enterprise* **(Vol. 38, July 2008, No. 12, pp. 48)**
Pub: Earl G. Graves Publishing Co. Inc.

Ed: Tamara E. Holmes. **Description:** According to a survey of small-business owners conducted by Sure-Payroll Inc., 20 percent of respondents have had a prospective employee refuse a job offer because healthcare benefits did not come with it. Cost is not the only reason many small-business owners do not offer these benefits. Guidelines to help take some of the confusion out of the guesswork that comes with trying to find the proper fit concerning healthcare benefits are outlined.

45380 ■ "Price Data" in *Montly Labor Review* **(Vol. 133, September 2010, No. 9, pp. 128)**
Pub: Bureau of Labor Statistics

Description: Consumer price indexes for all urban consumers and for urban wage earners and clerical workers is presented with U.S. city average, by expenditure category and commodity or service group.

45381 ■ "Private Equity Firms Focus on Failing Banks" in *Baltimore Business Journal* **(Vol. 28, July 16, 2010, No. 10, pp. 1)**
Pub: Baltimore Business Journal

Ed: Gary Haber. **Description:** Four deals in which assets of failed banks were acquired by private equity firms have been approved by the Federal Deposit Insurance Corporation in the past couple of years. Bay Bank FSK, for example, purchased Bay National Bank's assets in July 2010. Forecasts on more private equity acquisitions in the community banking industry are given.

45382 ■ "Profit Predictions Look Too Plump" in *Barron's* **(Vol. 88, March 31, 2008, No. 13, pp. 37)**
Pub: Dow Jones & Company, Inc.

Ed: Johanna Bennett. **Description:** Full-year forecast points to a 14 percent gain for 2008 but the second-half profit increases would have to grow at a fast rate and peak at 61 percent in the fourth quarter to achieve this. Trends in the U.S. economic conditions are also discussed.

45383 ■ *Profiting from Diversity: The Business Advantages and the Obstacles to Achieving Diversity*
Pub: Palgrave Macmillan

Ed: Gloria Moss. **Released:** January 5, 2010. **Price:** $95.00. **Description:** Although the benefits of diversity in small business are often discussed, specific ways in which organizations can profit from diversity and some of the obstacles faced are defined.

45384 ■ **"Protection, Flexibility Make Single-Member LLCs Attractive"** in *Crain's Cleveland Business* (Vol. 28, November 12, 2007, No. 45)

Pub: Crain Communications, Inc.

Ed: Peter DeMarco. **Description:** Discusses the reasons why single-member limited liability companies are gaining popularity; LLC structure allows a great deal of flexibility and protects the owner from liability.

45385 ■ **"Provinces Tackle E-Waste Problem"** in *Canadian Electronics* (Vol. 23, June-July 2008, No. 4, pp. 1)

Pub: Action Communication Inc.

Ed: Ken Manchen. **Description:** Canadian provinces are implementing measures concerning the safe and environmentally friendly disposal of electronic waste. Alberta, British Columbia, Nova Scotia, and Saskatchewan impose an e-waste recycling fee on electronic equipment purchases.

45386 ■ **"Psst...Spread the Word"** in *Boston Business Journal* (Vol. 27, November 23, 2007, No. 43, pp. 1)

Pub: American City Business Journals Inc.

Ed: Lisa van der Pool. **Description:** More and more Boston companies are using word-of-mouth marketing to boost sales, and spending on it rose to $981 million in 2006. It is projected that spending on word-of-mouth marketing will reach $1.4 billion in 2007, and marketing companies using this type of method are getting higher funding. Trends in word-of-mouth marketing are discussed.

45387 ■ **"Quality at Bargain Prices"** in *Black Enterprise* (Vol. 41, December 2010, No. 5, pp. 30)

Pub: Earl G. Graves Publishing Co. Inc.

Ed: James A. Anderson. **Description:** Monica L. Walker, CEO of Holland Capital Management, suggests investors to watch prevailing trends in the financial market and to focus on using bottom-up analysis to identify companies meeting their investment criteria.

45388 ■ **"Quits Versus Layoffs"** in *Occupational Outlook Quarterly* (Vol. 55, Fall 2011, No. 3, pp. 36)

Pub: U.S. Bureau of Labor Statistics

Description: Data from the U.S. Bureau of Labor Statistics provides data from the Job Openings and Labor Turnover Survey regarding quits and layoffs.

45389 ■ **"The Rabbi Trust"** in *Barron's* (Vol. 88, March 24, 2008, No. 12, pp. 55)

Pub: Dow Jones & Company, Inc.

Ed: Joseph F. Gelband. **Description:** Discusses a rabbi trust which is a method of deferring taxes on compensation allowed by the Internal Revenue Service. Funding of the trust is not considered taxable. Other regulations concerning tax deferment are also discussed.

45390 ■ *Race and Entrepreneurial Success: Black-, Asian-, and White-Owned Businesses in the United States*

Pub: MIT Press

Ed: Robert W. Fairlie. **Released:** September 30, 2008. **Price:** $35.00. **Description:** Trends in minority small business ownership are explored, focusing on the importance of human capital, financial capital, and family business background in successful business ownership.

45391 ■ **"The Racial Divide and the Class Struggle in the United States"** in *WorkingUSA* (Vol. 11, September 2008, No. 3, pp. 311)

Pub: Blackwell Publishers Ltd.

Ed: Michael Goldfield. **Description:** An examination of questions of race that continue to play such a prominent role in contemporary society is presented, focusing on the undermining of potential solidarity and strength of the working class movement, what sustains racists attitudes, practices and institutions, especially in the face of trends in world economic development.

45392 ■ **"Radiant – the Hottest Topic in ... Cooling"** in *Indoor Comfort Marketing* (Vol. 70, February 2011, No. 2, pp. 8)

Pub: Industry Publications Inc.

Description: Examination of radiant cooling systems, a new trend in cooling homes and buildings.

45393 ■ *Reading Financial Reports for Dummies*

Pub: John Wiley and Sons, Inc.

Ed: Lita Epstein. **Released:** January 2009. **Price:** $21.99. **Description:** This second edition contains more new and updated information, including new information on the separate accounting and financial reporting standards for private/small businesses versus public/large businesses; updated information reflecting 2007 laws on international financial reporting standards; new content to match SEC and other governmental regulatory changes over the last three years; new information about how the analyst-corporate connection has changed the playing field; the impact of corporate communications and new technologies; new examples that reflect the current trends; and updated Websites and resources.

45394 ■ **"Real Estate Defaults Top $300M"** in *Business Courier* (Vol. 26, January 15, 2010, No. 39, pp. 1)

Pub: American City Business Journals, Inc.

Ed: Dan Monk. **Description:** Cincinnati commercial real estate owners defaulting in securitized loans reached $306 million at the end of 2009. The trend has lifted the region's default rate to nearly 9 percent. National average for commercial real estate default is examined.

45395 ■ **"Real Estate Funds Swell Past $350M"** in *Business Journal Portland* (Vol. 27, December 31, 2010, No. 44, pp. 1)

Pub: Portland Business Journal

Ed: Wendy Culverwell. **Description:** Oregon-based real estate funds have raised around half of the $735 million that was raised by local companies. Investors have been purchasing distressed properties. Commercial real estate prices have declined since 2007.

45396 ■ **"Real Estate Market Still in a Slump"** in *Montana Business Quarterly* (Vol. 49, Summer 2011, No. 2, pp. 15)

Pub: Bureau of Business & Economic Research

Ed: Patrick M. Barkey. **Description:** Montana's housing market is still in decline with no sign of improving in the near future. Statistical data included.

45397 ■ **"The Reality of Fantasy Sports"** in *Entrepreneur* (Vol. 37, September 2009, No. 9, pp. 52)

Pub: Entrepreneur Media, Inc.

Ed: Jason Ankeny. **Description:** United States fantasy sports business has grown into a $1 billion industry. Fantasy gaming in the country remains affordable and accessible despite the increase in prices of tickets to sports games. Comments from analysts are also presented.

45398 ■ **"Realtors Signing Out"** in *The Business Journal-Serving Metropolitan Kansas City* (Vol. 27, November 21, 2008, No. 11, pp. 1)

Pub: American City Business Journals, Inc.

Ed: Rob Roberts. **Description:** The Kansas City Regional Association of Realtors has lost 1,000 of its members due to the downturn in the housing market. Applications for realtor licenses have dropped by 159 percent. Changes in Missouri's licensing requirements are seen as additional reasons for the declines.

45399 ■ **"A Recipe for Change"** in *Canadian Business* (Vol. 80, October 22, 2007, No. 21, pp. 25)

Pub: Rogers Media

Ed: Erin Pooley. **Description:** Market conditions have changed and customers around the world are demanding low-fat alternatives. Labor costs have risen and so did the price of foodstuffs. The impacts of this on fast food restaurants as well as the measures they have taken to cope with the new demands are discussed.

45400 ■ **"Recruiting 2.0"** in *Entrepreneur* (Vol. 35, November 2007, No. 11, pp. 100)

Pub: Entrepreneur Media Inc.

Ed: Andrea Cooper. **Description:** Technology is becoming a tool to help small companies find the best employees. Firms can look into social networking sites to see recommendations from the applicants' colleagues. Tips on how to select the employees online are listed.

45401 ■ **"Red, Pink and More: Cause Marketing Surges as a Prime Tactic to Reach Female Customers"** in *Marketing to Women* (April 2008)

Pub: EPM Communications, Inc.

Description: According to the American Marketing Association, forty percent of women say they are more likely to purchase a product or service if they know a certain amount of the price is being donated directly to a cause or campaign that they believe in supporting.

45402 ■ **"Research and Markets Adds: 2011 U.S. Women's & Children's Clothing Wholesale Report"** in *Health & Beauty Close-Up* (October 16, 2010)

Pub: Close-Up Media Inc.

Description: The Women's & Children's Clothing Wholesale Report is an annual report containing timely and accurate industry statistics, forecasts and demographics.

45403 ■ **"Research and Markets Adds Report: Credit and Collection Practices 2009"** in *Wireless News* (August 12, 2009)

Pub: Close-Up Media

Description: Research and Markets announced the addition of the "Credit and Collection Practices 2009" report which will highlight credit and collection industry practices and technologies. The report also includes an overview of the best practices in the field.

45404 ■ **"Research and Markets: Wedding Statistics and Industry Reports"** in *Benzinga.com* (June 24, 2011)

Pub: Benzinga.com

Ed: Benzinga Staff. **Description:** The latest trends and statistics regarding weddings and the wedding industry are spotlighted.

45405 ■ **"Resource Line"** in *Black Enterprise* (Vol. 37, January 2007, No. 6, pp. 6)

Pub: Earl G. Graves Publishing Co. Inc.

Description: Interactive Media Editor, Philana Patterson, writes a column for blackenterprise.com that offers advice and provides resources for entrepreneurs, corporate executives, business owners, and budding investors.

45406 ■ **"Rest Easy, Retailers"** in *Pet Product News* (Vol. 64, December 2010, No. 12, pp. S1)

Pub: BowTie Inc.

Ed: Wendy Bedwell-Wilson. **Description:** Pointers on how retailers can market all-natural beds and bedding products for pets are provided. The demand for these pet beds and bedding products has been increasing as customers become aware of the benefits of natural rest and relaxation products.

45407 ■ **"Restaurants Dish Up Meal Deals To Attract Customers"** in *Crain's Detroit Business* (Vol. 24, October 6, 2008, No. 40, pp. 1)

Pub: Crain Communications, Inc.

Ed: Nathan Skid. **Description:** Restaurateurs are devising many creative and rewarding incentives to get customers to frequent their establishments during this economic crisis. Innovative ways in which even higher-end establishments are drawing in business are discussed.

45408 ■ **"A Rise in Rental Units"** in *Philadelphia Business Journal* (Vol. 30, October 7, 2011, No. 34, pp. 1)

Pub: American City Business Journals Inc.

Ed: Natalie Kostelni. **Description:** Housing developers have been stepping up the construction of new apartment complexes throughout the suburbs of

Pennsylvania in order to capture growing demand for rental properties. BPG Properties Ltd. has nearly 1,000 new apartments under construction.

45409 ■ "Running On Empty" in *The Business Journal-Milwaukee* (Vol. 25, July 4, 2008, No. 41, pp. A1)

Pub: American City Business Journals, Inc.

Ed: David Doege. **Description:** Employers are more engaged in offering incentives designed to offset commuting costs. Among the incentives offered are gas cards, parking reimbursement and midyear wage increases. The other efforts to help employees with the costs of going to work are discussed.

45410 ■ "Safeway" in *Ice Cream Reporter* (Vol. 23, September 20, 2010, No. 10, pp. 8)

Pub: Ice Cream Reporter

Description: Safeway supermarkets have upsized their private label ice cream to a full half gallon, thus reversing the trend where most brands were shrinking their containers.

45411 ■ "Sales of Pension Income Targeted by Senator" in *Wall Street Journal Eastern Edition* (November 21 , 2011, pp. C7)

Pub: Dow Jones & Company Inc.

Ed: Leslie Scism. **Description:** Senator Tom Harkin is concerned about a widening business in which retirees and veterans sell pension income to investors in the secondary market. The business provides major profits for middlemen. Harkin wants those who are considering such a sale to have adequate information provided and knowledge in order to avoid unscrupulous dealings.

45412 ■ *Sarbanes-Oxley for Dummies, 2nd Ed.*

Pub: John Wiley and Sons, Inc.

Ed: Jill Gilbert Welytok. **Released:** February 2008. **Price:** $21.99. **Description:** Provides the latest Sarbanes-Oxley (SOX) legislation with procedures to safely and effectively reduce compliance costs. Topics include way to: establish SOX standards for IT professionals, minimize compliances costs for every aspect of a business, survive a Section 404 audit, avoid litigation under SOX, anticipate future rules and trends, create a post-SOX paper trail, increase a company's standing and reputation, work with SOX in a small business, meet new SOX standards, build a board that can't be bought, and to comply with all SOX management mandates.

45413 ■ *Say Everything: How Blogging Began, What It's Becoming, and Why It Matters*

Pub: Crown Business

Ed: Scott Rosenberg. **Released:** 2009. **Price:** $26. 00. **Description:** A history of Internet blogs that explains how they started and why they matter to any small business.

45414 ■ "Scottsdale Bank Plans 4Q Opening" in *The Business Journal - Serving Phoenix and the Valley of the Sun* (Vol. 28, August 15, 2008, No. 50)

Pub: American City Business Journals, Inc.

Ed: Chris Casacchia. **Description:** Arizona's Department of Financial Institutions has approved Scottsdale Business Bank, a community bank which plans to open in the fourth quarter of 2008. The bank, which is to be located near McCormick Ranch in Scottsdale, Arizona, will cater to small business owners in the professional sector, such as accountants and doctors.

45415 ■ "SEC Report On Rating Agencies Falls Short" in *Barron's* (Vol. 88, July 14, 2008, No. 28, pp. 35)

Pub: Dow Jones & Co., Inc.

Ed: Jack Willoughby. **Description:** The Securities and Exchange Commissions report on credit-rating firms should have drawn attention to the slipshod practices in the offerings of collateralized debt obligations. The report fell short of prescribing correctives for the flawed system of these agencies' relationship with their clients.

45416 ■ "A Second Chance to Make a Living" in *The Business Journal-Milwaukee* (Vol. 25, September 19, 2008, No. 52, pp. A1)

Pub: American City Business Journals, Inc.

Description: Unemployed workers and baby boomers are driving interest in purchasing small businesses. BizBuySell general manager Mike Handelsman reveals that the supply of small businesses for sale is decreasing due to the increased demand. The trends in the small business market are analyzed.

45417 ■ "Seeing Green in Going Green" in *The Business Journal-Serving Greater Tampa Bay* (Vol. 28, July 4, 2008, No. 28, pp. 1)

Pub: American City Business Journals, Inc.

Ed: Janet Leiser. **Description:** Atlanta, Georgia-based developer IDI Corp. is pushing for Leadership in Energy and Environmental Design certification for the warehouse that is currently under construction at Madison Business Center along Port Sutton and U.S. 41. The industrial building is the first in Tampa Bay to seek certification for LEED as set by the U.S. Green Building Council.

45418 ■ "Self-Employment in the United States" in *Montly Labor Review* (Vol. 133, September 2010, No. 9, pp. 17)

Pub: Bureau of Labor Statistics

Description: Self employment in 2009 in the U.S. continued to be more common among men, Whites, Asians, and older workers and in the agriculture, construction, and services industries.

45419 ■ "Senate Bill Would Eliminate MBT Surcharge in 2011" in *Crain's Detroit Business* (Vol. 24, April 7, 2008, No. 14, pp. 33)

Pub: Crain Communications, Inc.

Ed: Amy Lane. **Description:** Discusses possible changes to the new Michigan Business Tax, including a proposed bill which would phase out a 21.99 percent surcharge on the tax.

45420 ■ "Senate OKs Funds for Promoting Tourism" in *Crain's Detroit Business* (Vol. 24, March 31, 2008, No. 13, pp. 6)

Pub: Crain Communications, Inc.

Ed: Amy Lane. **Description:** Discusses the Senate proposal which allocates funds for Michigan tourism and business promotion as well as Michigan's No Worker Left Behind initiative, a program that provides free tuition at community colleges and other venues to train displaced workers for high-demand occupations.

45421 ■ "Senators Predict Online School Changes" in *Puget Sound Business Journal* (Vol. 29, September 19, 2008, No. 22, pp. 1)

Pub: American City Business Journals

Ed: Clay Holtzman. **Description:** State senators promise to create new legislation that would tighten the monitoring and oversight of online public schools. The officials are concerned about the lack of oversight of the programs as well as lack of knowledge about content of the lessons.

45422 ■ "Setting Out on Your Own? Think Franchises" in *Crain's Cleveland Business* (Vol. 28, October 8, 2007, No. 40, pp. 20)

Pub: Crain Communications, Inc.

Description: Franchisers are targeting baby boomers due to their willingness to put up some of their own money to open their own business. According to local franchising expert, Joel Libava, entrepreneurs should expect to pay about 15 to 30 percent of the total cost of starting the franchise out of their own pocket.

45423 ■ "Sewing Resurgence" in *Northeast Mississippi Daily Journal* (June 11, 2010)

Pub: Northeast Mississippi Daily Journal

Ed: Ginna Parsons. **Description:** Information about the growing trend in sewing is discussed.

45424 ■ *Shedworking: The Alternative Workplace Revolution*

Pub: Frances Lincoln Limited

Ed: Alex Johnson. **Released:** June 10, 2010. **Price:** $29.95. **Description:** Shedworking is an alternative office space for those working at home. The book features shedworkers and shedbuilders from around the world who are leading this alternative workplace revolution and why this trend is working.

45425 ■ "Shoestring-Budget Marketing" in *Women Entrepreneur* (January 5, 2009)

Pub: Entrepreneur Media Inc.

Ed: Maria Falconer. **Description:** Pay-per-click search engine advertising is the traditional type of e-marketing that may not only be too expensive for certain kinds of businesses but also may not attract the quality customer base a business looking to grow needs to find. Social networking websites have become a mandatory marketing tool for business owners who want to see growth in their sales; tips are provided for utilizing these networking websites in order to gain more visibility on the Internet which can, in turn, lead to the more sales.

45426 ■ "Should I or Shouldn't I?" in *Indoor Comfort Marketing* (Vol. 70, February 2011, No. 2, pp. 30)

Pub: Industry Publications Inc.

Ed: Philip J. Baratz. **Description:** Investment tips are shared for investing in futures options.

45427 ■ "Sick of Trends? You Should Be" in *Brandweek* (Vol. 49, April 21, 2008, No. 16, pp. 22)

Pub: VNU Business Media, Inc.

Ed: Eric Zeitoun. **Description:** Eric Zeitoun, the president of Dragon Rouge, a global brand consultancy, discusses the importance of macrotrends as opposed to microtrends which he feels are often irrelevant, create confusion and cause marketers to lose site of the larger picture of their industry. Macrotrends, on the other hand, create a fundamental, societal shift that influences consumer attitudes over a long period of time.

45428 ■ "Sign of the Times: Temp-To-Perm Attorneys" in *HRMagazine* (Vol. 54, January 2009, No. 1, pp. 24)

Pub: Society for Human Resource Management

Ed: Bill Leonard. **Description:** A growing number of law firms are hiring professional staff on a temp-to-perm basis according to the president of Professional Placement Services in Florida. Firms can save money while testing potential employees on a temporary basis.

45429 ■ "Single Most Important Problem" in *Small Business Economic Trends* (January 2008, pp. 18)

Pub: National Federation of Independent Business

Description: Table of the single most important problem among small businesses surveyed in the U.S. in December 2007 is presented. Taxes were selected by 21 percent of firms as the single most important problem, followed by cost and availability of insurance at 16 percent. Graphs comparing selected single most important problem from January 1986 to December 2007 are also given.

45430 ■ "Skinny Jeans Sticking Around for Fall" in *Charlotte Observer* (February 5, 2007)

Pub: Knight-Ridder/Tribune Business News

Ed: Crystal Dempsey. **Description:** Clothing designers were showing skinny jeans in the fall/winter fashion shows for 2007.

45431 ■ "Slimmer Interiros Make Small Cars Seem Big" in *Automotive News* (Vol. 86, October 31, 2011, No. 6488, pp. 16)

Pub: Crain Communications Inc.

Ed: David Sedgwick. **Description:** Cost-conscious buyers want luxury car amenities in their smaller vehicles, so automakers are rethinking interiors. Style, efficiency and value could be the next trend in vehicles.

45432 ■ "The Small 300" in *Canadian Business* (Vol. 81, Summer 2008, No. 9, pp. 137)

Pub: Rogers Media Ltd.

Description: Small cap-companies are ranked based on market capitalization and stock performance. Calgary-based Grande Cache Coal Corp. topped the roster with 1,000 percent of return resulting from strong sales. A table showing the 2008 rankings of the companies is presented.

45433 ■ **"Small Business Capital Outlays"** in *Small Business Economic Trends* **(January 2008, pp. 16)**
Pub: National Federation of Independent Business
Description: Graph representing actual and planned capital expenditures among small businesses surveyed in the U.S. from January 1986 to December 2007 is given. Tables showing actual capital expenditures, type of capital expenditures made, amount of capital expenditures made, and capital expenditure plans are also presented.

45434 ■ **"Small Business Compensation"** in *Small Business Economic Trends* **(July 2010, pp. 10)**
Pub: National Federation of Independent Business
Description: A graph from a survey of small businesses in the U.S. is given representing small business compensation from January 1986 to June 2010. Tables showing actual compensation changes and compensation plans are also presented. A graph comparing small business prices and labor compensation is supplied.

45435 ■ **"Small Business Credit Conditions"** in *Small Business Economic Trends* **(July 2010, pp. 12)**
Pub: National Federation of Independent Business
Description: Graphs representing loan availability and interest rates among U.S. small businesses surveyed from January 1986 to June 2010 are given. Tables showing regular borrowers, availability of loans, satisfied borrowing needs, expected credit conditions, relative interest rate paid by regular borrowers, and actual interest rate paid on short-term loans by borrowers are also presented.

45436 ■ **"Small Business Earnings"** in *Small Business Economic Trends* **(July 2010, pp. 6)**
Pub: National Federation of Independent Business
Description: A graph from a survey of small businesses in the U.S. is given representing actual small business earnings from January 1986 to June 2010. Tables showing actual earnings changes and most important reason for lower earnings are also presented.

45437 ■ **"Small Business Employment"** in *Small Business Economic Trends* **(March 2008, pp. 9)**
Pub: National Federation of Independent Business
Ed: William C. Dunkelberg, Holly Wade. **Description:** Four tables and a graph that present employment rates of small businesses in the U.S. are provided. The tables include figures on employment changes, number of qualified applicants, job openings and hiring plans.

45438 ■ *The Small Business Guide to HSAs*
Pub: Brick Tower Press
Ed: JoAnn Mills Laing. **Released:** September 2004. **Price:** $14.95. **Description:** Government-assisted Health Savings Accounts (HSAs) offer employees a tax-free way to accumulate savings to be used for qualified medical expenses, they can be rolled over without penalty for future spending, or invested to accumulate savings to pay for health needs after retirement. Employers offering HSAs can save up to two-thirds of business expenses on health insurance costs.

45439 ■ **"Small Business Inventories"** in *Small Business Economic Trends* **(July 2010, pp. 14)**
Pub: National Federation of Independent Business
Description: A graph representing actual and planned inventories among small businesses surveyed in the U.S. from January 1986 to June 2010 is presented. A graph comparing inventory satisfaction and inventory plans over the same time period is also given. Tables showing actual inventory changes, inventory satisfaction, and inventory plans are also supplied.

45440 ■ **"Small Business Outlook"** in *Small Business Economic Trends* **(March 2008, pp. 4)**
Pub: National Federation of Independent Business
Ed: William C. Dunkelberg, Holly Wade. **Description:** Three tables and a graph representing forecasts in business expansions of small businesses in the U.S. are presented. The figures presented in the graph include data from 1986 to 2008.

45441 ■ **"Small Business Prices"** in *Small Business Economic Trends* **(July 2010, pp. 8)**
Pub: National Federation of Independent Business
Description: A graph from a survey of small businesses in the U.S. is given representing business prices from January 1986 to June 2010. Actual prices (last three months) and planned prices (next three months) were compared in the graph. Tables of actual price changes and price plans from January 2005 to June 2010 are also supplied.

45442 ■ **"Small Business Sales"** in *Small Business Economic Trends* **(March 2008, pp. 7)**
Pub: National Federation of Independent Business
Ed: William C. Dunkelberg, Holly Wade. **Description:** Two tables and a graph that present sales figures for small businesses in the U.S. are given. Statistics for sales changes and sales expectations are provided. The figures in the graph include data from 1986 to 2008.

45443 ■ **"Small Changes Can Mean Big Energy Savings"** in *Crain's Cleveland Business* **(Vol. 28, November 5, 2007, No. 44, pp. 21)**
Pub: Crain Communications, Inc.
Ed: Harriet Tramer. **Description:** Many Northeast Ohio businesses are taking their cues from the residential real estate market to draw and capitalize on interest in energy efficiency and is regularly taken into account by local architects.

45444 ■ **"Smaller Banks Could Face Tough 2008"** in *Austin Business JournalInc.* **(Vol. 28, January 2, 2009, No. 1, pp. 3)**
Pub: American City Business Journals
Ed: Christopher Calnan. **Description:** The turbulence in the banking industry is expected to reach Texas in 2009 and industry insiders believe there will be a shift in deposits from small, regional banks to larger banks due to low consumer confidence. One economist says that a large number of banks are going to go out of business in 2009.

45445 ■ *So You Want to Start a Business?*
Pub: Pearson Education
Ed: Edward D. Hess; Charles Goetz. **Released:** August 30, 2008. **Price:** $18.99. **Description:** Over sixty percent of Americans say they would like to own their own business and more than five million business startups are launched annually. However, fifty to seventy percent of new businesses fail. This book identifies the eight mistakes that cause these business failures and offers entrepreneurs the knowledge, tools, templates, strategies, and hands-on how-to advice needed to avoid these errors and succeed.

45446 ■ *Social Enterprise: Developing Sustainable Businesses*
Pub: Palgrave Macmillan
Ed: Frank Martin, Marcus Thompson. **Released:** January 1, 2010. **Price:** $106.00. **Description:** Social enterprises bring people and communities together for economic development and social gain and represent a growing sector of the business community.

45447 ■ **"Social Media By the Numbers: Social-Media Marketing Is All the Rage"** in *Inc.* **(Vol. 33, November 2011, No. 9, pp. 70)**
Pub: Inc. Magazine
Ed: J.J. McCorvey, Issie Lapowsky. **Description:** Six strategies to help small businesses use social media sites such as Facebook and Twitter to promote their companies are presented.

45448 ■ **"Social Networks in the Workplace"** in *Strategy & Leadership* **(Vol. 38, July-August 2010, No. 4, pp. 50-53)**
Pub: Emerald Inc.
Ed: Daniel Burrus. **Description:** The opinions of futurist Daniel Burrus on a novel trend called 'Business 2.0', which involves the use of social networking applications as business tools, are presented. His suggestion that personal social networking technology can be used by businesses to improve collaboration, problem solving, and leadership communications to achieve continuous value innovation is discussed.

45449 ■ **"Sole Proprietorship Returns, 2008 Part 2"** in *SOI Bulletin* **(Vol. 30, Summer 2010, No. 1, pp. 27)**
Pub: Government Printing Office
Description: Table of Nonfarm Sole Proprietorships is presented. Statistics are broken down by sector reporting all nonfarm industries as well as agriculture, forestry, hunting and fishing.

45450 ■ **"Sole Proprietorship Returns, 2008"** in *SOI Bulletin* **(Vol. 30, Summer 2010, No. 1, pp. 6)**
Pub: Government Printing Office
Ed: Adrian Dungan. **Description:** Approximately 22.6 million individual income tax returns reported nonfarm sole proprietorship activity, a 2.2 percent decrease from 2007. Statistical data included.

45451 ■ **"Solidarity UAW Forever"** in *Crain's Detroit Business* **(Vol. 25, June 1, 2009, No. 22, pp. M001)**
Pub: Crain Communications Inc. - Detroit
Ed: Ryan Beene. **Description:** United Auto Workers union has made it difficult for certain businesses to move to Michigan. Discussion is made about the issues involved and changes that need to be made in the way labor and management do business.

45452 ■ **"Solo, But Not Alone"** in *Entrepreneur* **(Vol. 37, October 2009, No. 10, pp. 99)**
Pub: Entrepreneur Media, Inc.
Ed: David Port. **Description:** Co-working spaces are emerging in different US cities, allowing entrepreneurs and other independent workers to co-exist. These work spaces, which can be availed for about $500 a month or $25 a day, also afford networking opportunities.

45453 ■ **"Some Big Biotechs Buying Own Stock"** in *Boston Business Journal* **(Vol. 30, November 5, 2010, No. 41, pp. 1)**
Pub: Boston Business Journal
Ed: Julie M. Donnelly. **Description:** Biotechnology companies such as Biogen Idec and Genzyme Corporation are conducting stock buybacks as they look to invest their cash holdings. Other analysts see the buybacks as reluctance in committing to longer-term investments.

45454 ■ **"Sorry: Good Defense for Mal Offense"** in *The Business Journal-Serving Metropolitan Kansas City* **(Vol. 26, July 4, 2008, No. 43, pp. 1)**
Pub: American City Business Journals, Inc.
Ed: Rob Roberts. **Description:** According to a survey conducted by the Kansas City Business Journal, ten hospitals in Kansas City showed that they have adopted disclosure policies that include prompt apologies and settlement offers. The policy is effective in minimizing medical malpractice lawsuits. Other details of the survey are presented.

45455 ■ **"Sprinkler Advocates Beat Builders Again"** in *Contractor* **(Vol. 56, November 2009, No. 11, pp. 58)**
Pub: Penton Media, Inc.
Ed: Bob Mader. **Description:** Proponents of residential fire sprinklers were able to fend off the attempt by the National Association of Home Builders to do away with mandated fire sprinklers on the International Residential Code by the International Code Council (ICC). The ICC's vote on the issue is good news for fire sprinkler contractors and plumbing contractors.

45456 ■ "Staging a Martini-and-GQ Lifestyle; Faux Possessions Play to Buyer's Aspirations" in *Crain's Chicago Business* (April 21, 2008)
Pub: Crain Communications, Inc.
Ed: Kevin Davis. **Description:** Due to the competition of the slumping housing market, home stagers are becoming more prominent and are using creative ways to make an impression beyond de-cluttering, painting and cleaning by using accents such as casually placed magazines, candles and table settings.

45457 ■ "The Start of a Beautiful Friendship: Partnering with Your Customers on R&D" in *Inc.* (March 2008, pp. 37-38)
Pub: Gruner & Jahr USA Publishing
Ed: Leigh Buchanan. **Description:** Joint research and development projects between customers and suppliers are a growing trend in the small business community; these ventures can help keep new product development costs lower. Four tips to maintain a good working relationship in these ventures are outlined.

45458 ■ "Start Connecting Today" in *Indoor Comfort Marketing* (Vol. 70, May 2011, No. 5, pp. 34)
Pub: Industry Publications Inc.
Ed: Paul Nazzaro. **Description:** An in-depth discussion regarding the use of biofuels on bioheat use and dealership.

45459 ■ "Startup on Cusp of Trend" in *Austin Business JournalInc.* (Vol. 29, January 8, 2010, No. 44, pp. 1)
Pub: American City Business Journals
Ed: Christopher Calnan. **Description:** Austin-based Socialware Inc. introduced a new business called social middleware, which is a software that is layered between the company network and social networking Website used by workers. The software was designed to give employers a measure of control over content while allowing workers to continue using online social networks.

45460 ■ "State Film Business Tops $1.3 Billion" in *The Business Journal-Portland* (Vol. 25, August 22, 2008, No. 24, pp. 1)
Pub: American City Business Journals, Inc.
Ed: Andy Giegerich. **Description:** Oregon's film industry has generated $1.39 billion in direct and indirect economic impact in 2007, a 55 percent rise from 2005 levels. The growth of the industry is attributed to tax incentives issued in 2007, which attracted film production companies from other states.

45461 ■ "The State of the Stores" in *Playthings* (Vol. 106, November 1, 2008, No. 10, pp. 8)
Pub: Reed Business Information
Ed: Dana French. **Description:** Investigation into the top twenty-five toy and game retailers shows that video games and related handheld and console systems as well as computer games were number one with America's children in 2007.

45462 ■ "State Unemployment Fraud Rising Sharply" in *Sacramento Business Journal* (Vol. 28, October 21, 2011, No. 34, pp. 1)
Pub: Sacramento Business Journal
Ed: Michael Shaw. **Description:** California's Employment Development Department has reported that overpayments, especially due to fraud or misrepresentation, have increased from $88 million in 2008 to more than $250 million in 2010. However, criminal prosecutions in 2010 were fewer than in 2008 as the agency struggles to recover the money.

45463 ■ "Stimulating Fare at the SBA" in *Barron's* (Vol. 89, July 20, 2009, No. 29, pp. 12)
Pub: Dow Jones & Co., Inc.
Ed: Jim McTague. **Description:** Internet access at the Small Business Administration slowed down on 7 July 2009, apparently caused by employees streaming videos of the Michael Jackson tribute. The agency claims that the event did not disrupt its operations.

45464 ■ "Stop the Madness" in *Hawaii Business* (Vol. 53, October 2007, No. 4, pp. 10)
Pub: Hawaii Business Publishing
Ed: Kelli Abe Trifonovitch. **Description:** Discusses the number of parents paying for kindergarten admissions tutorials for their kids which has increased, as parents want to improve their children's chances of being admitted at a prestigious school. Some schools in Hawaii are not in favor of this trend, and they actually rate an applicant negatively if his or her answers seem to be too rehearsed. Some of the lessons in the admissions tutorials are discussed.

45465 ■ "Storm Takes Toll On Area Businesses" in *The Business Journal - Serving Phoenix and the Valley of the Sun* (Vol. 28, September 5, 2008, No. 52, pp. 1)
Pub: American City Business Journals, Inc.
Ed: Chris Casacchia. **Description:** Many small businesses in Phoenix, Arizona have lost sales and goods from storms and power outages. Retailers were forced to dispose of spoiled products. Details of damages inflicted by the storm are also presented.

45466 ■ "Struggling Community Banks Find Little Help In Wall Street Bailout" in *Crain's Detroit Business* (Vol. 24, September 29, 2008)
Pub: Crain Communications, Inc.
Ed: Tom Henderson. **Description:** Both public and private Michigan bands have been hit hard by poorly performing loan portfolios and although their problems were not caused by high-risk securities but by a longtime statewide recession and a housing slump, these community banks have little hope of seeing any of the bailout money that has been allotted for the larger institutions.

45467 ■ "Succeed With the Right Equipment" in *Pet Product News* (Vol. 64, November 2010, No. 11, pp. 42)
Pub: BowTie Inc.
Ed: Sandi Cain. **Description:** Grooming shop owners have been focusing on obtaining ergonomic, durable, and efficient products such as restraints, tables, and tubs. These products enhance the way grooming tasks are conducted. Ways pet supply manufacturers have responded to this trend are examined.

45468 ■ "Sudden Shift Leaves Wells Vendor Scrambling" in *Charlotte Business Journal* (Vol. 25, July 9, 2010, No. 16, pp. 1)
Pub: Charlotte Business Journal
Ed: Adam O'Daniel. **Description:** Rubber stamps vendor Carolina Marking Devices is facing a 30 percent drop in business after banking firm Wells Fargo & Company decided to buy its rubber stamps from another vendor. Carolina Marking Devices had provided rubber to First Union Corporation and its successor Wachovia Corporation, which was eventually acquired by Wells Fargo. Other reactions from Carolina Marking Device owners are given.

45469 ■ "Suddenly, Sewing Is Hip Again for Kids, Moms and Crafters" in *Atlanta Journal-Constitution* (August 29, 2010)
Pub: Atlanta Journal-Constitution
Ed: Rosalind Bentley. **Description:** Across Atlanta, Georgia, along with the entire nation, sewing classes are increasing in popularity.

45470 ■ "Summary. Economic Trends for Small Business" in *Small Business Economic Trends* (February 2008, pp. 1)
Pub: National Federation of Independent Business
Ed: William C. Dunkelberg, Holly Wade. **Description:** Summary of economic trends for small businesses in the U.S. is provided. Economic indicators such as capital spending, inventories and sales, inflation, and profits are given. Analysis of credit markets is also provided.

45471 ■ "Survey Finds State Execs Cool On Climate Change" in *The Business Journal-Milwaukee* (Vol. 25, August 8, 2008, No. 46, pp. A1)
Pub: American City Business Journals, Inc.
Ed: David Doege. **Description:** According to a survey of business executives in Wisconsin, business leaders do not see climate change as a pressing concern, but businesses are moving toward more energy-efficient operations. The survey also revealed that executives believe that financial incentives can promote energy conservation. Other survey results are provided.

45472 ■ "Survey Profile" in *Small Business Economic Trends* (February 2008, pp. 19)
Pub: National Federation of Independent Business
Ed: William C. Dunkelberg, Holly Wade. **Description:** Two graphs and a table that present the profile of small businesses that participated in the National Federation of Independent Business (NFIB) survey are provided. The actual number of firms, their industry types, and the number of full and part-time employees are also given.

45473 ■ "Sustaining Health" in *Pet Product News* (Vol. 64, November 2010, No. 11, pp. 28)
Pub: BowTie Inc.
Ed: Angela Pham. **Description:** How pet supply retailers have responded to dog owners' interest in health supplements and their ingredients is discussed. Dog owners are showing interest in the ingredients inside the supplements and are reading labels. Retailers must now prove the beneficial effects of these ingredients in order to make the sale.

45474 ■ "A Switch in the Kitchen" in *Barron's* (Vol. 88, March 24, 2008, No. 12, pp. 17)
Pub: Dow Jones & Company, Inc.
Description: Men are doing more kitchen duties, with 18 percent of meals at home being made by men in 2007 compared to 11 percent four years previously. Young wives, however, choose to forgo work and stay at home.

45475 ■ "Take the Right Approach to Concrete Polishing Rentals" in *Rental Product News* (Vol. 33, June 2011)
Pub: Cygnus Business Media
Ed: Jenny Lescohier. **Description:** A recent trend in flooring is concrete polishing for a practical, beautiful and sustainable way to decorate homes and businesses. Things to keep in mind when assessing the value of adding concrete polishing equipment to an existing rental store are evaluated.

45476 ■ "Tap Into Food Truck Trend to Rev Up Sales, Build Buzz" in *Nation's Restaurant News* (Vol. 45, February 7, 2011, No. 3, pp. 18)
Pub: Penton Media Inc.
Ed: Brian Sacks. **Description:** Food truck trend is growing, particularly in New York City, Philadelphia, Washington DC, and Los Angeles, California. Man entrepreneurs are using a mobile food component to market their food before opening a restaurant.

45477 ■ "Tapping the 'Well' in Wellness" in *Pet Product News* (Vol. 64, November 2010, No. 11, pp. 1)
Pub: BowTie Inc.
Ed: Wendy-Bedwell Wilson. **Description:** Healthy food and treats are among the leading wellness products being sought by customers from specialty retailers to keep their pets healthy. With this demand for pet wellness products, retailers suggest making sure that staff know key ingredients to emphasize to customers. Other insights into this trend and ways to engage customers are discussed.

45478 ■ "Tax Talk; Usual Election-Year Obstacles to Income Tax May Not Apply This Time" in *Crain's Chicago Business* (March 24, 2008)
Pub: Crain Communications, Inc.
Ed: Greg Hinz. **Description:** Discusses the possible raising of the state's income tax; The latest version of the income tax hike bill, sponsored by Senator James Meeks, D-Chicago, would boost individual rates to 5 percent from 3 percent, with the corporate rate rising to a total of 8 percent from 4.8 percent; about $3 billion of the projected $8 billion that would be brought in would be used to cut local property taxes and experts believe the business community overall would benefit.

45479 ■ "Taxes, Right-To-Work Top West Michigan Concerns" in *Crain's Detroit Business* (Vol. 24, September 22, 2008, No. 38, pp. 6)

Pub: Crain Communications, Inc.

Ed: Amy Lane. **Description:** Two of the top priorities of business leaders in Western Michigan are the new business tax which they want to end as well as making the state a "right-to-work" one through laws to prohibit unions from requiring workers to pay dues and membership as a condition of their employment.

45480 ■ "Taxis Are Set to Go Hybrid" in *Philadelphia Business Journal* (Vol. 30, September 16, 2011, No. 31, pp. 1)

Pub: American City Business Journals Inc.

Ed: Natalie Kostelni. **Description:** Taxis are going hybrid in several major states such as New York, California and Maryland where it is mandated, but it is yet to happen in Philadelphia, Pennsylvania with the exception of one taxi company. Freedom Taxi is awaiting Philadelphia Parking Authority's sign off.

45481 ■ "Tell Us What You Really Think Collecting Customer Feedback" in *Inc.* (Vol. 30, December 2008, No. 12, pp. 52)

Pub: Mansueto Ventures LLC

Ed: Ryan Underwood. **Description:** According to a recent survey, nearly 77 percent of online shoppers review consumer-generated reviews of products before making a purchase.

45482 ■ "Texas State Poised for Boom" in *Austin Business JournalInc.* (Vol. 29, January 29, 2010, No. 47, pp. 1)

Pub: American City Business Journals

Ed: Sandra Zaragoza. **Description:** Texas State University, San Marcos has seen its student population grow to 30,800 and the university is set for $633 million in construction projects to address demand for student housing and building expansions and renovations. Details on the buildings and student housing plans for the projects are provided.

45483 ■ "The Next 20 Years: How Customer and Workforce Attitudes Will Evolve" in *Harvard Business Review* (Vol. 85, July-August 2007, No. 7-8)

Pub: Harvard Business School Publishing

Ed: Neil Howe, William Strauss. **Description:** Identification of social categories inhabited by age groups is used to calculate how consumer and employee opinions and behavior will change, and how this will impact economic development and corporate growth.

45484 ■ "Tied to Home: Female Owned Businesses Export Less, And It's Not Just Because They're Smaller" in *Canadian Business* (April 14, 2008)

Pub: Rogers Media

Ed: Lauren McKeon. **Description:** Only 12 percent of small and midsized enterprises that are run by women export their products and services. Government agencies can be more proactive in promoting the benefits of exporting by including women in case studies and recruiting women as mentors. Exporting provides great growth potential especially for the service sector where women have an advantage.

45485 ■ "Time for State Tax Restructure?" in *Crain's Detroit Business* (Vol. 26, January 18, 2010, No. 3, pp. 3)

Pub: Crain Communications, Inc.

Ed: Amy Lane. **Description:** Business Leaders for Michigan, a statewide CEO group, launched a proposal to cut the Michigan Business Tax by about $1.1 billion and replace the revenue by taxing services. Statistical data included.

45486 ■ *The Tipping Point: How Little Things Can Make a Big Difference*

Pub: Little Brown & Company

Ed: Malcolm Gladwell. **Released:** January 2002. **Price:** $14.95. **Description:** Correlation between societal changes and marketing and business trends.

45487 ■ "TiVo, Domino's Team to Offer Pizza Ordering by DVR" in *Advertising Age* (Vol. 79, November 17, 2008, No. 43, pp. 48)

Pub: Crain Communications, Inc.

Ed: Brian Steinberg. **Description:** Domino's Pizza and TiVo are teaming up to make it possible for customers to order from the restaurant straight from their DVR. The companies see that this kind of interactive television and consumer experience will only serve to generate more sales as the customer can be exposed to a fuller range of menu selections and will not have to interrupt their viewing, while workers can spend more time making the product.

45488 ■ "Tough Sell: Senior Projects Hustle to Keep Buyers" in *Puget Sound Business Journal* (Vol. 29, November 21, 2008, No. 31, pp.)

Pub: American City Business Journals

Ed: Heidi Dietrich. **Description:** Plans to move to retirement communities are being postponed by seniors in Washington's Puget Sound area due to difficulty selling their current homes in the slow economy. Retirement communities are trying to lure clients by offering new finance programs and sales plans.

45489 ■ "Toughen Up, Cupcake: You Know Who Plays for Keeps These Days? Cupcake Makers" in *Inc* (Vol. 33, May 2011, No. 4, pp. 100)

Pub: Inc. Magazine

Ed: Burt Helm. **Description:** Cupcake shops are sprouting up everywhere across the nation and Washington, DC seems to be the epicenter for the trend. Profile of a new bakery called Sprinkles, that offers cupcake creations, is featured.

45490 ■ "Tower City Hopes Restrictions on Minors Boost Retail Center" in *Crain's Cleveland Business* (Vol. 28, November 5, 2007, No. 44)

Pub: Crain Communications, Inc.

Ed: John Booth. **Description:** Tower City Center, a shopping mall in downtown Cleveland, hopes to generate more business with their new rules restricting the access of unaccompanied minors after 2:30 p.m.

45491 ■ "The Transparent Supply Chain" in *Harvard Business Review* (Vol. 88, October 2010, No. 10, pp. 76)

Pub: Harvard Business School Publishing

Ed: Steve New. **Description:** Examination of the use of new technologies to create a transparent supply chain, such as next-generation 2D bar codes in clothing labels that can provide data on a garment's provenance.

45492 ■ *True Green at Work: 100 Ways You Can Make the Environment Your Business*

Pub: National Geographic

Ed: Kim McKay; Jenny Bonnin; Tim Wallace. **Released:** February 19, 2008. **Price:** $19.95 paperback. **Description:** Manual to help any small business minimize its carbon footprint by reducing waste.

45493 ■ "Turbulent Skies" in *The Business Journal-Portland* (Vol. 25, August 29, 2008, No. 25, pp. 1)

Pub: American City Business Journals, Inc.

Ed: Erik Siemers. **Description:** Small airlines are struggling to keep their commercial services amid the troubled commercial airline sector. Small communities, for example, were expected to pony up about $650,000 in revenue guarantees each in order to convince SkyWest Airlines to offer two direct flights to Portland daily beginning October 12, 2008. The trends in the commercial airline industry are analyzed.

45494 ■ "Turfway Slowing its Gait" in *Business Courier* (Vol. 26, November 6, 2009, No. 28, pp. 1)

Pub: American City Business Journals, Inc.

Ed: Jon Newberry. **Description:** Kentucky's Turfway Park will be decreasing its weekly race schedule from five days to three days in the first two months of 2010, and to four days in March 2010. The decision to make reductions in the schedule is attributed to the reloca-

tion of thoroughbred racing to states that allow casino gambling. As a result, Turfway Park's resources and purse money would be focused on less days.

45495 ■ "Turmoil Means Changes For Retailers" in *The Business Journal-Serving Metropolitan Kansas City* (Vol. 27, October 10, 2008, No. 4)

Pub: American City Business Journals, Inc.

Ed: Suzanna Stagemeyer. **Description:** Impacts of the financial crisis on Kansas Metropolitan Area retailers are varied. Rob Dalzell, for instance, found it difficult to secure a loan for his new self-serve yogurt store Yummo. The trends in retailing in the area are examined further as well as ways in which local businesses are changing in an attempt to stay solvent during the economic downturn.

45496 ■ "Ultra Green Energy Services Opens NJ Biodiesel Transload Facility" in *Indoor Comfort Marketing* (Vol. 70, June 2011, No. 6, pp. 35)

Pub: Industry Publications Inc.

Description: Profile of Ultra Green Energy Services and the opening of their new biodiesel facility in New Jersey is discussed.

45497 ■ "Ultra Low Sulfur Diesel: The Promise and the Reality" in *Indoor Comfort Marketing* (Vol. 70, July 2011, No. 7, pp. 22)

Pub: Industry Publications Inc.

Ed: Ed Kitchen. **Description:** Impacts of ultra low sulfur diesel are examined.

45498 ■ "Unions and Upward Mobility for Low-Wage Workers" in *WorkingUSA* (Vol. 11, September 2008, No. 3, pp. 337)

Pub: Blackwell Publishers Ltd.

Ed: John Schmitt, Margy Waller, Shawn Fremstad, Ben Zipperer. **Description:** Examination of the impact of unionization on the pay and benefits in fifteen important low-wage occupations is outlined. Even after controlling for important differences between union and nonunion workers, including such factors as age and education level, unionization improves the pay and benefits offered in what are otherwise low-paying occupations.

45499 ■ "U.S. Recession Officially Over: Is Recovery Ever Going to Arrive?" in *Montana Business Quarterly* (Vol. 49, Spring 2011, No. 1, pp. 6)

Pub: Bureau of Business & Economic Research

Ed: Patrick M. Barkey. **Description:** Ten predictions regarding American's economy for 2012 are listed.

45500 ■ "Univest Charter Switch Signals Banking Trend" in *Philadelphia Business Journal* (Vol. 30, September 2, 2011, No. 29, pp. 1)

Pub: American City Business Journals Inc.

Ed: Jeff Blumenthal. **Description:** Univest Corporation of Pennsylvania changed from a federal to state charter because of cost savings and state agency has greater understanding of the intricacies of the local economy. The Pennsylvania Department of Banking has also received inquiries from seven other banks about doing the same this year.

45501 ■ *Upstarts! How GenY Entrepreneurs Are Rocking the World of Business and 8 Ways You Can Profit from Their Success*

Pub: The McGraw-Hill Companies

Ed: Donna Fenn. **Released:** September 1, 2009. **Price:** $25.95. **Description:** An inside glance at the GenY startup companies that are changing the way the world conducts business.

45502 ■ "USAmeriBank Deals for Growth" in *The Business Journal-Serving Greater Tampa Bay* (Vol. 28, September 26, 2008, No. 40, pp. 1)

Pub: American City Business Journals, Inc.

Ed: Margie Manning. **Description:** It is believed that the pending $14.9 million purchase of Liberty Bank by USAmeriBank could be at the forefront of a trend. Executives of both companies expect the deal to close by the end of 2008. USAmeriBank will have $430 million in assets and five offices in Pinellas, Florida once the deal is completed.

45503 ■ "Use Ink Presets to Minimize Makeready" in *American Printer* **(Vol. 128, July 1, 2011, No. 7)**
Pub: Penton Media Inc.
Description: Automatic registration systems enable most printers to be in register very quickly after press startup. If the paper, ink and press time wasted during makeready can be reduced, these savings will flow directly to the bottom line. Ink presetting as an economical solution to set color quickly is a trend that continues to gain momentum.

45504 ■ "Vacation, What Vacation?" in *Black Enterprise* **(Vol. 41, August 2010, No. 1, pp. 36)**
Pub: Earl G. Graves Publishing Co. Inc.
Description: Nearly 50 percent of employers expect employees to check in with the office while they are away on vacation.

45505 ■ "Valenti: Roots of Financial Crisis Go Back to 1998" in *Crain's Detroit Business* **(Vol. 24, October 6, 2008, No. 40, pp. 25)**
Pub: Crain Communications, Inc.
Ed: Tom Henderson; Nathan Skid. **Description:** Interview with Sam Valenti III who is the chairman and CEO of Valenti Capital L.L.C., a wealth-management firm; Valenti discusses in detail the history that led up to the current economic crisis as well as his prediction for the future of the country.

45506 ■ *Values and Opportunities in Social Entrepreneurship*
Pub: Palgrave Macmillan
Ed: Kai Hockerts. **Released:** November 1, 2009. **Price:** $90.00. **Description:** Social entrepreneurship has grown as a research field. This book discusses social entrepreneurship as well as the identification and exploitation of social venturing opportunities.

45507 ■ "Verdict: Few Legal Jobs" in *Boston Business Journal* **(Vol. 31, June 17, 2011, No. 21, pp. 1)**
Pub: Boston Business Journal
Ed: Lisa van der Pool. **Description:** Law school graduates in Massachusetts are finding it harder to find work as the legal job market remains weak. The national employment rate for the 2010 law school class fell to 87.6 percent, while only 68.4 percent held jobs that require passing the bar examination.

45508 ■ "Video Surveillance Enters Digital Era, Makes Giant Strides" in *Arkansas Business* **(Vol. 26, September 28, 2009, No. 39, pp. 1)**
Pub: Journal Publishing Inc.
Ed: Jamie Walden. **Description:** Arkansas business owners are finding that the newest technology in video surveillance is leading to swift apprehension of thieves due to the high-quality digital imagery now being captured on surveillance equipment. Motion detection software for these systems is enhancing the capabilities of these systems and providing opportunities for businesses that would normally have problems integrating these systems.

45509 ■ "Vistaprint Survey Indicates that Online Marketing Taking Hold Among Small Businesses" in *Internet Wire* **(December 10, 2009)**
Pub: Comtex News Network, Inc.
Description: According to a comprehensive survey from Vistaprint N.V., small businesses are very likely to increase their use of Internet marketing strategies such as paid and organic search, email marketing, social media networking and custom websites over the next year. Trends continue to show that more small businesses are indeed adapting to the changing marketplace and are more willing to diversify their marketing strategies than ever before.

45510 ■ "Vive La Resistance: Competing Logics and the Consolidation of U.S. Community Banking" in *Academy of Management Journal* **(August 2007)**
Pub: Academy of Management
Ed: Christopher Marquis, Michael Lounsbury. **Description:** Ways in which competing logics facilitate

resistance to institutional change is presented, highlighting on banking professionals' resistance to large, national banks acquisitions of smaller, local banks.

45511 ■ "Volunteers Needed" in *Canadian Business* **(Vol. 81, October 27, 2008, No. 18, pp. 60)**
Pub: Rogers Media Ltd.
Ed: Megan Harman. **Description:** Emissions-targeting regulations focus on the biggest polluters, missing out on other companies that leave carbon footprints in things such as shipping and travel. Some companies in Canada have initiated programs to offset their carbon emissions. Critics claim that offsetting does not reduce emissions and the programs merely justify pollution.

45512 ■ "The War for Talent" in *Canadian Business* **(Vol. 80, January 29, 2007, No. 3, pp. 60)**
Pub: Rogers Media
Ed: Erin Pooley. **Description:** The recruitment policies of Canadian businesses are described. The trends pertaining to the growth of executive salaries in Canada are discussed.

45513 ■ "Web-Based Marketing Excites, Challenges Small Business Use" in *Colorado Springs Business Journal* **(January 20, 2010)**
Pub: Dolan Media Co.
Ed: Becky Hurley. **Description:** Business-to-business and consumer-direct firms alike are using the fast-changing Web technologies to increase sales, leads and track consumer behavior but once a company commits to an Online marketing plan, experts believe, they must be prepared to consistently tweak and overhaul content and distribution vehicles in order to keep up.

45514 ■ "Welcome to a New Kind of Cubicle Culture" in *Boston Business Journal* **(Vol. 29, August 19, 2011, No. 15, pp. 1)**
Pub: American City Business Journals Inc.
Ed: Alexander Jackson. **Description:** Beehive Baltimore offers a co-working space where independent freelancers and entrepreneurs can work. There are two other companies that provide the same service and the value of these services to these professional is that it provides them with an office that is both convenient and affordable aside from letting them network with peers.

45515 ■ "What is the Future of Disk Drives, Death or Rebirth?" in *ACM Computing Surveys* **(Vol. 43, Fall 2011, No. 3, pp. 23)**
Pub: Association for Computing Machinery
Ed: Yuhui Deng. **Description:** Disk drives have experienced dramatic development to meet performance requirements since the IBM 1301 disk drive was announced in 1961. However, the performance gap between memory and disk drives has widened to 6 orders of magnitude and continues to widen by about 50 percent per year. Challenges and opportunities facing these storage devices are explored.

45516 ■ "What the Future Holds for Consumers" in *Black Enterprise* **(Vol. 41, August 2010, No. 1, pp. 47)**
Pub: Earl G. Graves Publishing Co. Inc.
Ed: Sheiresa Ngo. **Description:** The way people purchase goods and service has changed with technology. With an increased focus on security (as well as privacy and fairness) the U.S. Congress began regulating the credit card industry with the Fair Credit Reporting Act of 1970 and the Credit Card Accountability, Responsibility, and Disclosure (CARD) Act of 2009.

45517 ■ "What Is a Geothermal Heat Pump" in *Indoor Comfort Marketing* **(Vol. 70, August 2011, No. 8, pp. 14)**
Pub: Industry Publications Inc.
Ed: George Carey. **Description:** Examination of geothermal heat pumps is provided, citing new trends in the industry.

45518 ■ "What Moms Want" in *Marketing to Women* **(Vol. 21, February 2008, No. 2, pp. 6)**
Pub: EPM Communications, Inc.
Description: According to a survey conducted by Eureka's Spa, moms would rather have an experience gift than flowers or chocolate. The top five dream gifts include a spa day, a weekend getaway, maid service, a bathroom makeover or a getaway weekend with girlfriends.

45519 ■ "What Will Green Power Cost? Surcharge, Spending Cap Considered" in *Crain's Detroit Business* **(Vol. 24, March 10, 2008, No. 10, pp. 1)**
Pub: Crain Communications, Inc.
Ed: Amy Lane. **Description:** Due to a proposed mandate, which states that 10 percent of power will have to come from renewable sources by 2015 in the state of Michigan, concern is being raised about the higher electricity prices this legislation will undoubtedly cause to business and residential customers.

45520 ■ "What You Should Know If Your Bank Fails" in *Black Enterprise* **(Vol. 41, December 2010, No. 5, pp. 29)**
Pub: Earl G. Graves Publishing Co. Inc.
Ed: John Simons. **Description:** The Federal Deposit Insurance Corporation announced that the number of banks in trouble has reached the highest level since March 1993. Advice from the FDIC is cited. Statistical data included.

45521 ■ "What's Holding Down Small Business?" in *Business Owner* **(Vol. 35, November-December 2011, No. 6, pp. 3)**
Pub: DL Perkins Company
Description: According to a recent survey conducted by the National Federation of Independent Business, demand is the number one reason for slow growth to any small business in today's economy.

45522 ■ "Where the Future is Made" in *Indoor Comfort Marketing* **(Vol. 70, May 2011, No. 5, pp. 48)**
Pub: Industry Publications Inc.
Description: Research being performed at Brookhaven National Laboratory, located in Upton, New York, is discussed, focusing on new energy sources for our nation.

45523 ■ "Where Next?" in *Business Strategy Review* **(Vol. 21, Summer 2010, No. 2, pp. 20)**
Pub: Wiley-Blackwell
Description: The emergence of large, vibrant and seemingly unstoppable new markets has been the good news story of the past decade. Brazil, Russia, India and China (BRIC) are among those who have emerged blinking into the new economy.

45524 ■ "Where Women Work" in *Marketing to Women* **(Vol. 21, April 2008, No. 4, pp. 8)**
Pub: EPM Communications, Inc.
Description: According to the U.S. Census Bureau, 60 percent of America's professional tax preparers are women. Also features additional trends concerning women in the workplace. Statistical data included.

45525 ■ "Which Direction are Herbicides Heading?" in *Farm Industry News* **(October 11, 2011)**
Pub: Penton Business Media Inc.
Ed: Jennifer Shike. **Description:** Currently, one of the best solutions for growers fighting weed resistance may be 2,4-D or other auxin herbicides.

45526 ■ "Wikinomics: The Sequel" in *Business Strategy Review* **(Vol. 21, Summer 2010, No. 2, pp. 64)**
Pub: Wiley-Blackwell
Description: Ever-optimistic Don Tapscott and Anthony Williams, coauthors of Wikinomics and individually, of a number of other books that study the Internet and its relation to society, are now working on a new book, one for which they're using the Internet to determine its title.

45527 ■ **"Will Home Buyers Pay for Green Features?"** in *Contractor* (Vol. 56, October 2009, No. 10, pp. 70)

Pub: Penton Media, Inc.

Ed: Bob Mader. **Description:** National Association of Home Builders commissioned a survey which shows that homeowners are interested in green as long as they do no have to pay much for it. The association did not allow a board member to read the survey which raises questions about how the questions were phrased and how the sample was selected.

45528 ■ **"Will Small Business be Stimulated"** in *Entrepreneur* (Vol. 37, July 2009, No. 7, pp. 18)

Pub: Entrepreneur Media, Inc.

Ed: Jennifer Wang. **Description:** Steven Strauss, Alberto G. Alvarado, Jeff Rosenweig, Al Gordon, and Theresa Alfaro Daytner share their views on how the American Recovery and Reinvestment Act of 2009, also known as the economic stimulus, will affect small businesses. Their backgrounds are also provided.

45529 ■ **"Will Workers Be Left To Build It Here?"** in *Boston Business Journal* (Vol. 31, June 3, 2011, No. 19, pp. 1)

Pub: Boston Business Journal

Ed: Kyle Alspach. **Description:** Lack of skilled workers has resulted in delayed expansion of local manufacturing operations in Massachusetts. Acme Packet Inc. expects to add only 10 jobs by the end of 2011.

45530 ■ *Winner Take All: How Competitiveness Shapes the Fate of Nations*

Pub: Basic Books

Ed: Richard J. Elkus Jr. **Released:** 2009. **Price:** $27.00. **Description:** American government and misguided business practices has allowed the U.S. to fall behind other countries in various market sectors such as cameras and televisions, as well as information technologies. It will take a national strategy to for America to regain its lead in crucial industries.

45531 ■ **"Women Board Number Stagnates"** in *Boston Business Journal* (Vol. 30, November 26, 2010, No. 44, pp. 1)

Pub: Boston Business Journal

Ed: Mary Moore. **Description:** The 2010 data in 'Census of Women Directors and Executive Officers of Massachusetts Public Companies' showed little change in the number of executive officers and board members in the state's top 100 firms. The data was compiled by Bentley University, The Boston Club, and Mercer. Key information on 2010 Women on Boards is also provided.

45532 ■ **"Women Clicking to Earn Virtual Dollars"** in *Sales and Marketing Management* (November 11, 2009)

Pub: Nielsen Business Media, Inc.

Ed: Stacy Straczynski. **Description:** According to a new report from Internet marketing firm Q Interactive, women are increasingly playing social media games where they are able to click on an ad or sign up for a promotion to earn virtual currency. Research is showing that this kind of marketing may be a potent tool, especially for e-commerce and online stores.

45533 ■ **"Women Workers Spend Lunchtime on Fridays Shopping Online"** in *Marketing to Women* (Vol. 23, November 2010, No. 11, pp. 8)

Pub: EPM Communications, Inc.

Description: Forty percent of women shop online during work hours, particularly on Fridays. The largest number of women make these purchases during their lunch break. Demographics are included.

45534 ■ **"Words at Work"** in *Information Today* (Vol. 26, February 2009, No. 2, pp. 25)

Pub: Information Today, Inc.

Description: Current new buzzwords include the following: digital amnesia, or overload by availability, speed and volume of digital information; maternal profiling, a form a discrimination against women; recipe malpractice, a reminder that just because you can turn on a stove it doesn't make you a chef; ringxi-

ety, the act when everyone reaches for their cell phone when one rings; verbing, the practice of turning good nouns into verbs.

45535 ■ **"Work/Family Balance Boosts Business"** in *Marketing to Women* (Vol. 21, February 2008, No. 2, pp. 8)

Pub: EPM Communications, Inc.

Description: Flexibility in the workplace is becoming a more important issue to both women and men. Statistical data included.

45536 ■ **"Workers' Comp System Cuts Through Paper"** in *Sacramento Business Journal* (Vol. 25, July 11, 2008, No. 19, pp. 1)

Pub: American City Business Journals, Inc.

Ed: Kelly Johnson. **Description:** California has started testing a new paperless system for handling disputed workers' compensation claims. It is believed that the shift will affect people both inside and outside of the state Division of Workers' Compensation and the state Workers' Compensation Appeals Board. The other details of the planned system are also presented.

45537 ■ **"WQA's Leadership Conference Tackles Industry Issues"** in *Contractor* (Vol. 56, October 2009, No. 10, pp. 3)

Pub: Penton Media, Inc.

Ed: Candace Roulo. **Description:** Water Quality Association's Mid-Year Leadership Conference held in Bloomingdale, Illinois in September 2009 tackled lead regulation, water softeners, and product efficiency. The possibility of a WQA green seal was discussed by the Water Sciences Committee and the Government Relations Committee meeting.

45538 ■ **"Xbox 360 Excels as a Media Hub"** in *Hispanic Business* (October 2009, pp. 40)

Pub: Hispanic Business

Ed: Jeremy Nisen. **Description:** Xbox 360 video game console from Microsoft offers games, amazing graphics and state-of-the-art accessories. The trend towards purchase of the Xbox includes more than teenagers.

45539 ■ **"Yao Ming Courts China's Wine Boom"** in *Wall Street Journal Eastern Edition* (November 28, 2011, pp. B4)

Pub: Dow Jones & Company Inc.

Ed: Jason Chow. **Description:** Yao Ming, the former NBA 7-foot 6-inch Chinese basketball star, is set to cash in on the market potential for wine in China. He has created his own winery in California, Yao Family Wines, which will produce wines solely for the Chinese market.

45540 ■ **"Year-End Tax Tips"** in *Hawaii Business* (Vol. 53, December 2007, No. 6, pp. 136)

Pub: Hawaii Business Publishing

Ed: Kathleen Bryan. **Description:** Tax planning tips for the end of 2007, in relation to the tax breaks that are scheduled to expire, are presented. Among the tax breaks that will be expiring at the 2007 year-end are sales tax deduction in the state and local level, premiums on mortgage insurance, and deduction on tuition. The impacts of these changes are discussed.

45541 ■ **"Young Adults Choose to go Without Health Insurance"** in *Business Review, Albany New York* (Vol. 34, November 30, 2007, No. 35, pp. 1)

Pub: American City Business Journals, Inc.

Ed: Barbara Pinckney. **Description:** U.S. Census Bureau revealed that in 2006, 19 million people between the ages of 18 and 34 were without health insurance, or 40 percent of the uninsured individuals in the country. College graduation usually means the end of health coverage, since most fresh graduates opt to not get any health insurance plan. Solutions to this growing issue are also addressed.

45542 ■ **"Your Guide to Local Style Business"** in *Hawaii Business* (Vol. 53, December 2007, No. 6, pp. 36)

Pub: Hawaii Business Publishing

Ed: David K. Choo. **Description:** Discusses the importance of studying the Hawaiian culture when doing business locally. It was observed that geo-

graphical aspects increase emphasis on culture and lifestyle more than the need to rectify false imaging do. Details of how locals adhere to their culture are supplied.

45543 ■ **"Your Place: Housing Developers Try to Read Generation Y"** in *Philadelphia Inquirer* (December 2, 2010)

Pub: Philadelphia Media Network Inc.

Ed: Al Heavens. **Description:** Results of a survey conducted with Generation Y individuals are examined, focusing on housing developments and whether this particular generation prefers suburban or rural lifestyles. Generation Y encompasses people ages 18 to 32 years old. Statistical data included.

45544 ■ *YouTube and Video Marketing: An Hour a Day*

Pub: Sybex

Ed: Greg Jarboe. **Released:** August 10, 2009. **Price:** $29.99. **Description:** The importance of online video marketing for businesses is stressed. Tips for developing and implementing video marketing are outlined.

TRADE PERIODICALS

45545 ■ *Business Trends*

Pub: Bowes Publishers Ltd.

Contact: Gord Bowes, Gp. Ed.

Released: Monthly. **Price:** $24 Canadian (GST included); $2 single issue outside of our regular delivery area; $48 Canadian funds (surface mail only). **Description:** Magazine featuring local business-related articles for the Sarnia, Ontario area in Canada.

CONSULTANTS

45546 ■ **Sklar and Associates Inc.**

242 Laurel Bay Dr.

Murrells Inlet, SC 29576

Ph:(202)257-5061

Fax:(843)651-3090

Co. E-mail: sklarincdc@aol.com

URL: http://www.sklarinc.com

Contact: Tim Sklar, President

Scope: Provides consulting services for business acquisitions, business development and project finance. Provides audit oversight services to listed corporations on Sarbanes-Oxley compliance. Services include: Due diligence analyses and corporate governance. Industries served: transportation sectors, energy sector and commercial real estate industries. **Seminars:** Financial Analysis in MBA; Emerging Company Finance; Due Diligence in Business Acquisition; Business Valuation.

COMPUTERIZED DATABASES

45547 ■ *Stern's Management Review*

Stern & Associates

11260 Overland Ave., Ste. 16A

Culver City, CA 90230

Ph:(310)838-0551

Co. E-mail: info@hrconsultant.com

URL: http://www.hrconsultant.com

Description: Contains business management information and ideas from the print version of Stern's Management Review, a quarterly management newsletter. Includes the full text of editorials from the newsletter since 1992. Covers such issues as business trends, leadership, corporate downsizing, management, compensation, and much more. **Availability:** Online: Stern & Associates. **Type:** Full text.

LIBRARIES

45548 ■ **Colorado Mountain College–Alpine Campus Library**

1330 Bob Adams Dr.

Steamboat Springs, CO 80477

Ph:(970)870-4445

Free: 800-621-8559

Co. E-mail: dwillis@coloradomtn.edu

URL: http://www.coloradomtn.edu/current_students/
library/about/alpine/

Contact: David Willis, Lib.Dir.

Scope: Small business, hotel and restaurant management, health and fitness, U.S. history and literature, American music, skiing. **Services:** Interlibrary loan; Library open to the public. **Holdings:** 30,000 books; 580 CDs; maps; state documents; CD-ROMs. **Subscriptions:** 225 journals and other serials; 15 newspapers.

45549 ■ Greater Oviedo Chamber of Commerce Business Library
PO Box 621236
Oviedo, FL 32765
Ph:(407)365-6500
Fax:(407)650-2712
Co. E-mail: cory@oviedowintersprings.org
URL: http://www.oviedowintersprings.org/pages/
home/default.aspx
Contact: Corydon G. Skeates, Exec.Dir.

Scope: Small business; central Florida business. **Services:** Copying; Library open to the public. **Holdings:** 3 books; 10 reports; periodicals. **Subscriptions:** 3 newspapers.

45550 ■ Indian River Area Library
PO Box 160
Indian River, MI 49749
Ph:(231)238-8581
Fax:(231)238-9494
Co. E-mail: indrivl@northland.lib.mi.us
URL: http://www.libnet.org/iriver/
Contact: Cindy Lou Poquette, Dir.

Scope: Small business, careers, fine arts, music, dance. **Services:** Interlibrary loan; copying; Library open to the public (fee for non-residents to check out materials). **Holdings:** 52,000 books; 2500 videocassettes; 2000 microfiche; videocassettes; sound cassettes; DVDs; CDs; periodicals; large print books. **Subscriptions:** 78 journals and other serials; 3 newspapers.

45551 ■ Small Business Administration Reference Library
409 3rd St., SW
Washington, DC 20416
Ph:(202)205-7033
Fax:(202)481-5881
Co. E-mail: answerdesk@sba.gov
URL: http://www.sba.gov
Contact: Margaret Hickey, Adm.Libn.

Scope: Small business, finance, management, venture capital. **Services:** Interlibrary loan; Library open to the public for reference use only. **Holdings:** 8000 volumes. **Subscriptions:** 72 journals and other serials.

RESEARCH CENTERS

45552 ■ Alabama Law Institute
PO Box 861425
Tuscaloosa, AL 35486-0013
Ph:(205)348-7411
Fax:(205)348-8411
Co. E-mail: rmccurley@ali.state.al.us
URL: http://ali.state.al.us
Contact: Robert L. McCurley Jr., Dir.
E-mail: rmccurley@ali.state.al.us

Scope: Statutes of Alabama, including studies of existing laws with systematic revision of laws to be proposed to Alabama legislature. Conducts investigations into state tax structure, evidence, criminal law, business law, probate law, real property, and family law. Develops manuals for legislators, county commissioners, tax assessors and collectors, and other governmental offices. **Publications:** Annual Report. **Educational Activities:** Basic and advanced law courses, for probate judges; Capital Intern Program, allowing three students to work at the State Legislature.

45553 ■ Bradley University–Center for Business and Economic Research
Foster College of Business Administration
1501 W Bradley Ave.
Peoria, IL 61625
Ph:(309)677-2262
Fax:(309)677-3257
Co. E-mail: bjg@bradley.edu
URL: http://www.bradley.edu/academic/colleges/fcba/
centers/economic
Contact: Dr. Bernard Goitein, Dir.
E-mail: bjg@bradley.edu

Scope: Coordinates faculty research projects in program evaluation, consumer confidence, economic development, market research, needs assessment, impact analysis, modeling, forecasting, survey research, cost and price modeling, accounting and special purpose information systems, location analysis, financial planning, cost-benefit analysis, performance evaluation and productivity analysis. **Publications:** Peoria MSA Business Database Report (quarterly); Peoria MSA Consumer Sentiment (3/ year).

45554 ■ Central Connecticut State University–Connecticut Small Business Development Center
Downtown Bldg.
185 Main St.
New Britain, CT 06051
Ph:(860)832-0650
Fax:(860)832-0656
Co. E-mail: csbdc@ccsu.edu
URL: http://www.ctsbdc.org
Contact: Ginne Rae Clay-Gilmore, State Dir.
E-mail: csbdc@ccsu.edu

Scope: Provides business management research service to small and mid-size firms in Connecticut, including studies of pre-venture feasibility, the business plan, marketing, record-keeping, financial planning, production, loan packaging, general management, foreign developments with respect to national laws, product demands, available distribution channels, business customs and regulations, product export evaluation, and export sales strategies. **Services:** Technical assistance and education for business owners and entrepreneurs. **Publications:** Reports (periodically). **Educational Activities:** Professional counseling; Seminars.

45555 ■ East Tennessee State University–Tennessee Small Business Development Center
College of Business & Technology
2109 W Market St.
Johnson City, TN 37604
Ph:(423)439-8505
Fax:(423)439-8506
Co. E-mail: bjustice@mail.tsbdc.org
URL: http://www.tsbdc.org
Contact: Dr. Robert A. Justice, Dir.
E-mail: bjustice@mail.tsbdc.org

Scope: Small business assistance in the areas of business plans and strategies, financial forecasts, feasibility studies, financial statement analysis, credit establishment and collection policies, inventory control analysis, marketing plans, accounting and record-keeping systems, licenses, permits, tax authorities, organizational structure, management succession, professional development, and buying and selling. **Services:** Provides free Internet access to clients (daily). **Educational Activities:** Consulting, technical assistance, and management assistance (daily); Workshops, seminars and conferences (weekly).

45556 ■ Indiana State University–Small Business Development Center
Scott College of Business, Rm. 510
800 Sycamore St.
Terre Haute, IN 47809-5402
Ph:(812)237-7676
Free: 800—227-7232

Fax:(812)237-7675
Co. E-mail: westcentral@isbdc.org
URL: http://www.westcentralindianasbdc.com
Contact: Heather Penney, Regional Dir.
E-mail: westcentral@isbdc.org

Scope: Small business development and entrepreneurship. **Services:** Counseling; Training and referral services, to new and emerging small businesses.

45557 ■ Michigan State University–Institute for Public Policy and Social Research
321 Berkey Hall
East Lansing, MI 48824-1111
Ph:(517)355-6672
Fax:(517)432-1544
Co. E-mail: douglas.roberts@ssc.msu.edu
URL: http://www.ippsr.msu.edu
Contact: Douglas B. Roberts PhD, Dir.
E-mail: douglas.roberts@ssc.msu.edu

Scope: Conducts social and policy research at the national, state, and local levels, focusing on improving the policy process to make governance more effective and developing better policies. **Services:** Public policy forums (quarterly). **Publications:** Policy briefs; SOSS Bulletins. **Educational Activities:** Conference, seminars, and special events; Political leadership program (monthly); Public Policy Seminars (monthly).

45558 ■ Pennsylvania Small Business Development Centers
3819-33 Chestnut St., Ste. 325
Philadelphia, PA 19104-3238
Ph:(215)898-1219
Fax:(215)573-2135
Co. E-mail: cconroy@wharton.upenn.edu
URL: http://pasbdc.org
Contact: Christian Conroy, Dir.
E-mail: cconroy@wharton.upenn.edu

Scope: Helps small businesses improve profitability and increase employment through programs of procurement, international trade, product development, and business law. **Services:** Free management consulting to entrepreneurs and prospective business owners. **Educational Activities:** Training programs, workshops, and seminars.

45559 ■ University of Mississippi–Small Business Development Center
122 Jeanette Phillips Dr.
PO Box 1848
University, MS 38677-1848
Ph:(662)915-5001
Free: 800—725-7232
Fax:(662)915-5650
Co. E-mail: msbdc@olemiss.edu
URL: http://mssbdc.org
Contact: James Carden, Dir.
E-mail: msbdc@olemiss.edu

Scope: Small business management, including feasibility studies, business law, venture capital, government contracting, and financial, production, and personnel management. **Services:** Management counseling and marketing assistance for entrepreneurs and small business owners and managers. **Educational Activities:** Seminars and training on small business development.

45560 ■ University of New Hampshire–New Hampshire Small Business Development Center
110 McConnell Hall
Whittemore School of Business & Economics
Durham, NH 03824
Ph:(603)862-2200
Fax:(603)862-4876
Co. E-mail: mary.collins@unh.edu
URL: http://www.nhsbdc.org
Contact: Mary E. Collins, Dir.
E-mail: mary.collins@unh.edu

Scope: Provides research support services to small businesses in New Hampshire. **Services:** Consulting and technical assistance. **Publications:** Annual report. **Educational Activities:** Conferences, workshops and seminars.

45561 ■ World Jurist Association
7910 Woodmont Ave., Ste. 1440
Bethesda, MD 20814
Ph:(202)466-5428

Fax:(202)452-8540
Co. E-mail: wja@worldjurist.org
URL: http://www.worldjurist.org
Contact: Sona N. Pancholy, Exec.VP
E-mail: wja@worldjurist.org
Scope: International law and legal institutions, includ

ing studies on world peace through law, communications law, an international court system, international treaties and agreements, foreign investment disputes, real estate and business law, and legal education. Serves as a voluntary international association of the legal profession. **Publications:** Directory of law and

judicial systems of nations; Law/Technology (quarterly); Pamphlets Series (occasionally); Report Series on Law-making Activities of International Organizations; Workpapers; The World Jurist (bimonthly). **Educational Activities:** World conferences (biennially), in odd years.

Socially Responsible Business Practices

START-UP INFORMATION

45562 ■ **"Making Social Ventures Work" in** *Harvard Business Review* **(Vol. 88, September 2010, No. 9, pp. 66)**
Pub: Harvard Business School Publishing
Ed: James D. Thompson, Ian C. MacMillan. **Description:** Five steps are to define, examine the political aspects, focus on discovery-driven planning, develop an appropriate exit strategy, and anticipate unexpected consequences when starting a new social venture.

ASSOCIATIONS AND OTHER ORGANIZATIONS

45563 ■ **As You Sow Foundation**
311 California St., Ste. 510
San Francisco, CA 94104
Ph:(415)391-3212
Fax:(415)391-3245
Co. E-mail: michael@asyousow.org
URL: http://www.asyousow.org
Contact: Michael Passoff
Description: Dedicated to promoting corporate social responsibility. **Publications:** *Proxy Season Preview* (quarterly); *Unlocking the Power of the Proxy* .

45564 ■ **Business for Social Responsibility**
111 Sutter St., 12th Fl.
San Francisco, CA 94104
Ph:(415)984-3200
Fax:(415)984-3201
Co. E-mail: web@bsr.org
URL: http://www.bsr.org
Contact: Mats Lederhausen, Chm.
Description: Large, small, and medium-sized businesses. Promotes responsible business behavior and serves as a resource to companies striving to make ethical business decisions. **Publications:** *BSR Weekly* (weekly).

45565 ■ **Women's Healthy Environments Network**
215 Spadina Ave., Ste. 400
Toronto, ON, Canada M5T 2C7
Ph:(416)928-0880
Fax:(416)644-0116
Co. E-mail: office@womenshealthyenvironments.ca
URL: http://www.womenshealthyenvironments.ca
Contact: Marie Lorenzo, Co-Chair
Description: Women experts in environmental studies and issues. Works to implement community development projects to improve the environment. Provides a forum for discussion, information exchange, and the conducting of research related to women in the fields of planning, health, workplace, design, economy, urban and rural sociology, and community development. Initiates and organizes community projects. Advocates environmental protection, anti-discriminatory zoning practices, and the development of affordable housing. **Publications:** *Whitewash*; *Women and Environments* (quarterly).

EDUCATIONAL PROGRAMS

45566 ■ **Social Media Overview**
EEI Communications
66 Canal Center Plz., Ste. 200
Alexandria, VA 22314
Ph:(703)683-7453
Free: 888-253-2762
Fax:(703)683-7310
Co. E-mail: train@eeicom.com
URL: http://www.eeicom.com/training
Price: $425.00. **Description:** Learn how to model your website and online initiatives to the new Web 2.0 movement, including working with Facebook and Twitter, pros and cons of MySpace, Wikis, working with blogs, and podcasting in a nutshell. **Locations:** Alexandria, VA.

REFERENCE WORKS

45567 ■ **"2008 Woman of the Year Gala" in** *Hispanic Business* **(Vol. 30, July-August 2008, No. 7-8, pp. 58)**
Pub: Hispanic Business, Inc.
Ed: Brynne Chappell. **Description:** Brief report on the sixth annual Women of the Year Awards gala which was held at JW Marriott Desert Ridge Resort and Spa is given; 20 women were honored with these awards for their professional contribution, commitment to the advancement of the Hispanic community and involvement with charitable organizations.

45568 ■ **"Active Duty" in** *Crain's Cleveland Business* **(Vol. 28, November 26, 2007, No. 47, pp. 3)**
Pub: Crain Communications, Inc.
Ed: David Bennett. **Description:** Discusses the Veteran Workforce Training Program, sponsored by the Volunteers of America - Greater Ohio; the program is meant to provide employment training for military veterans and to assist them in transitioning back into the work force.

45569 ■ **"Alliance to End Hunger to Hold Press Conference on Fasting, Prayer and Budget Cuts" in** *Food & Beverage Close-Up* **(March 28, 2011)**
Pub: Close-Up Media
Description: A coalition of religious and other leaders are launching a new campaign to protect programs for vulnerable people. Partners include: Alliance to End Hunger, American Jewish World Service, Bread for the World, Congressional Hunger Center, Feeding America, Food for the Hungry, Islamic Relief USA, Meals on Wheels Association of America, New Manna Inc., ONE, Society of Saint Andrews, Sojourners, and World Food Program USA.

45570 ■ **"Alliance Offers to Help Italian Workers Settle In" in** *Crain's Detroit Business* **(Vol. 25, June 15, 2009, No. 24, pp. 21)**
Pub: Crain Communications Inc. - Detroit
Ed: Nancy Kaffer. **Description:** Italian American Alliance for Business and Technology will help workers arriving from Italy to transition to their new homes in the Detroit area.

45571 ■ **"Also Active in the Fight Against Cancer is Dreyer's Grand Ice Cream" in** *Ice Cream Reporter* **(Vol. 23, October 20, 2010, No. 11, pp. 8)**
Pub: Ice Cream Reporter
Description: Dreyer's Grand Ice Cream partnered with Experience Project's BroadCause.com to raise awareness around pediatric cancer research.

45572 ■ **"Are EO Programs Right for Your Business?" in** *Contractor* **(Vol. 56, October 2009, No. 10, pp. 49)**
Pub: Penton Media, Inc.
Ed: Susan Linden McGreevy. **Description:** Some of the laws regarding equal opportunity programs are discussed. Suggestions for mechanical contractors who are considering certification to qualify for these programs are presented.

45573 ■ **"Are There Material Benefits To Social Diversity?" in** *Hispanic Business* **(Vol. 30, September 2008, No. 9, pp. 10)**
Pub: Hispanic Business, Inc.
Ed: Brigida Benitez. **Description:** Diversity in American colleges and universities, where students view and appreciate their peers as individuals and do not judge them on the basis of race, gender, or ethnicity is discussed. The benefits of diversity in higher education are also acknowledged by the U.S. Supreme Court and by leading American corporations.

45574 ■ **"Are You a Young Canadian Entrepreneur Looking for Recognition?" in** *CNW Group* **(November 10, 2010)**
Pub: Comtex
Description: Business Development Bank of Canada is looking for young Canadian entrepreneurs ages 19 to 35 for its 2011 Young Entrepreneur Awards. The awards pay tribute to remarkable young Canadian entrepreneurs for their creativity, innovative spirit and community development, as well as business success.

45575 ■ *The Art of the Start*
Pub: Portfolio Publishing
Ed: Guy Kawasaki. **Price:** $26.95. **Description:** Apple's Guy Kawasaki offers information to help would-be entrepreneurs create new enterprises. As founder and CEO of Garage Technology Ventures, he has field-tested his ideas with newly hatched companies and he takes readers through every phase of creating a business, from the very basics of raising money and designing a business model through the many stages that eventually lead to success and thus giving back to society.

45576 ■ **"'The Asian Decade'" in** *Hawaii Business* **(Vol. 53, January 2008, No. 7, pp. 19)**
Pub: Hawaii Business Publishing
Ed: Cathy S. Cruz-George. **Description:** Chaney Brooks, a Hawaiian real estate company, has affiliated with commercial real estate network NAI Global. The NAI partnership will improve Hawaii's interna-

tional business, particularly its Asian investments. Hawaii's diverse workforce is evaluated, with regards to being an asset for international businesses.

45577 ■ "At This Bakery, Interns' Hope Rises Along With the Bread" in *Chicago Tribune* **(October 31, 2008)**
Pub: McClatchy-Tribune Information Services
Ed: Mary Schmich. **Description:** Profile of Sweet Miss Givings Bakery and its diverse founder, interns and employees; the bakery was founded by Stan Sloan, an Episcopal priest who started the business to help fund his ministry; Sloan saw a need for jobs for those living with HIV and other disabilities and through the bakery the interns learn the skills needed to eventually find work elsewhere.

45578 ■ "Athletes Face Wins and Losses After Pro Sport" in *The Business Journal - Serving Phoenix and the Valley of the Sun* **(Vol. 29, September 19, 2008, No. 3, pp. 1)**
Pub: American City Business Journals, Inc.
Ed: Chris Casacchia. **Description:** Professional athletes like hockey star Jeremy Roenick start businesses, while others like Joel Adamson work to boost local communities. Former athletes were found to be particularly interested with real estate businesses. Other views and information on former athletes and their life after sports are presented.

45579 ■ "Attracting Veteran-Franchisees To Your System" in *Franchising World* **(Vol. 42, November 2010, No. 11, pp. 53)**
Pub: International Franchise Association
Ed: Mary Kennedy Thompson. **Description:** As military servicemen and women return home, the franchising industry expects an increase in veterans as franchise owners. The Veterans Transition Franchise Initiative, also known as VetFran, is described.

45580 ■ "Automaker Foundations Run Leaner" in *Crain's Detroit Business* **(Vol. 26, January 11, 2010, No. 2, pp. 1)**
Pub: Crain Communications, Inc.
Ed: Sherri Welch. **Description:** Overview of the Detroit automobile industry includes restoring profitability, smarter marketing strategies and philanthropy. Each company comprising the Big 3 is examined, as is their vision for the future.

45581 ■ "Back Talk With Terrie M. Williams" in *Black Enterprise* **(Vol. 38, December 2007, No. 5, pp. 204)**
Pub: Earl G. Graves Publishing Co. Inc.
Ed: Tennille M. Robinson. **Description:** Profile of Terrie M. Williams, president of a public relations agency as well as founder of a youth empowerment organization called Stay Strong Foundation. Williams reflects on her bouts with depression and how the disease impacts sufferers and talks about her book that will inspire others dealing with depression.

45582 ■ "Banking on Cord Blood" in *Business Journal-Serving Phoenix & the Valley of the Sun* **(Vol. 31, September 10, 2010, No. 1, pp. 1)**
Pub: Phoenix Business Journal
Ed: Angela Gonzales. **Description:** Celebration Stem Cell Centre obtained contracts from Mercy Gilbert Medical Center and its two sister hospitals, St. Joseph Hospital and Medical Center in Phoenix, Arizona and Chandler Regional Medical Center. The contract will facilitate the donation of unused umbilical cord blood for research.

45583 ■ "Become A Brand" in *Women Entrepreneur* **(September 14, 2008)**
Pub: Entrepreneur Media Inc.
Ed: Suzy Girard-Ruttenberg. **Description:** Powerful brands are effective, innovative, exclusive or even socially conscious; it is important for small businesses to understand the power of becoming a brand since it is one of the best ways in which to position one's company and drive its growth.

45584 ■ "The Believer" in *Inc.* **(December 2007, pp. 130-138)**
Pub: Gruner & Jahr USA Publishing
Ed: Leigh Buchanan. **Description:** Profile of Selena Cuffe, wine importer and socially conscious woman entrepreneur, who is focusing her talents on helping South Africa get wine products to America.

45585 ■ "The Best Advice I Ever Got" in *Harvard Business Review* **(Vol. 86, September 2008, No. 9, pp. 29)**
Pub: Harvard Business School Press
Ed: Daisy Wademan Dowling. **Description:** Bright Horizons Family Solutions founder and chair Linda Mason illustrates how letting one's life passion direct entrepreneurship and business success. She describes how her humanitarian interests and efforts gave her the drive to launch a childcare service.

45586 ■ "Bethesda Stepping Out" in *Business Courier* **(Vol. 27, October 15, 2010, No. 24, pp. 1)**
Pub: Business Courier
Ed: James Ritchie. **Description:** Nonprofit organization Bethesda Inc. is planning to donate $5 million a year for the next three years to Greater Cincinnati health care reforms. Bethesda revealed that it announced its donations to pressure other organizations to help.

45587 ■ *Big-Box Swindle: The True Cost of Mega-Retailers and the Fight for America's Independent Businesses*
Pub: Beacon Press
Ed: Stacy Mitchell. **Released:** October 2007. **Price:** $15.00. **Description:** Examination of the economic, environmental, and social damage done by big-box retailers like Wal-Mart, Costco, and Home Depot. Labor policies of these retailers, particularly those enforced by Wal-Mart, are discussed at length.

45588 ■ "Big Shoes to Fill for New United Way Chairman" in *Business Courier* **(Vol. 27, June 25, 2010, No. 8, pp. 4)**
Pub: Business Courier
Ed: Lucy May. **Description:** David Dougherty, chairman of the nonprofit United Way of Greater Cincinnati, explains how he can surpass the nonprofit's 2009 campaign kickoff that raised $62 million. For 2010, Dougherty has prepared a $2 million matching grant from a group of local individuals, corporations, and foundations. Dougherty also discusses what he learned from participating in the 2009 campaign.

45589 ■ "Billion-Dollar Impact" in *Business First Buffalo* **(November 9, 2007, pp. 1)**
Pub: American City Business Journals, Inc.
Ed: Tracey Dury. **Description:** Western New York has thousands of nonprofit organizations, 240 of which have collective revenue of $1.74 billion based on federal tax returns for the 2005 and 2006 fiscal years. The nonprofit sector has a large impact on WNY's economy, but it is not highly recognized. The financial performance of notable nonprofit organizations is given.

45590 ■ "Bits 'n' Pieces: Shelter Gives Out Pet Food to Keep Animals At Home" in *Columbian* **(January 19, 2009)**
Pub: The Columbian
Ed: Elisa Williams. **Description:** Lend a Paw program gives surplus food to pet owners in need; since August 2008 they distributed over 7,000 pounds of dry and wet food to shelters and pet owners.

45591 ■ "Blue Cross Confronts Baby Blues" in *Marketing to Women* **(Vol. 21, March 2008, No. 3, pp. 3)**
Pub: EPM Communications, Inc.
Description: Blue Cross of California has launched a Maternity Depression Program aimed at educating mothers suffering from postpartum depression.

45592 ■ "Boxing, Tech Giants Team to Help Teens" in *Hispanic Business* **(January-February 2009, pp. 44)**
Pub: Hispanic Business
Ed: Daniel Soussa. **Description:** Microsoft and Oscar de la Hoya are providing teens a head start for careers in the sciences by offering a competition in the categories of photography, short films or Web-based games.

45593 ■ "Brewing a Love-Haiti Relationship" in *The Business Journal - Serving Phoenix and the Valley of the Sun* **(Vol. 28, July 4, 2008, No. 44)**
Pub: American City Business Journals, Inc.
Ed: Yvonne Zusel. **Description:** Jean and Alicia Marseille have ventured into a coffee distribution

company called Ka Bel LLC which markets Marabou brand of coffee imported from Haiti. Part of the proceeds of the business is donated to entrepreneurs from Jean's country, Haiti. Details of the Marseille's startup business and personal mission to help are discussed.

45594 ■ "Bringing Charities More Bang for Their Buck" in *Crain's Chicago Business* **(Vol. 34, May 23, 2011, No. 21, pp. 31)**
Pub: Crain Communications Inc.
Ed: Lisa Bertagnoli. **Description:** Marcy-Newberry Association connects charities with manufacturers in order to use excess items such as clothing, janitorial and office supplies.

45595 ■ *Business, Occupations, Professions and Vocations in the Bible*
Pub: ABC Book Publishing
Ed: Rich Brott. **Released:** 2008. **Price:** $19.99. **Description:** The important role small business has played in all societies and cultures throughout history is examined. The ingenuity of individuals and their ability to design, craft, manufacture and harvest has kept countries and kingdoms prosperous.

45596 ■ "Business Through Hollywood's Lens" in *Harvard Business Review* **(Vol. 88, October 2010, No. 10, pp. 146)**
Pub: Harvard Business School Publishing
Ed: Batia Wiesnefeld, Gino Cattani. **Description:** The authors contend that businesses are likely to be portrayed as villains in movies because corruption has higher entertainment draw. However, movies also depict popular opinion, which encourages businesses to be accountable and to help build communities.

45597 ■ *Business as Usual*
Pub: HarperBusiness
Ed: Anita Roddick. **Released:** 2005. **Price:** $12.95. **Description:** Founder of The Body Shop shares her story and gives her opinion on everything from cynical cosmetic companies to destructive consultants.

45598 ■ "CBC and Chrysler Strike Deal" in *Black Enterprise* **(Vol. 37, December 2006, No. 5, pp. 36)**
Pub: Earl G. Graves Publishing Co. Inc.
Ed: Kiara Ashanti. **Description:** Congressional Black Foundation and Chrysler Financial have partnered to provide financial education to students at historically black colleges and universities. The prime objective of the program is to reduce the number of college students that graduate with poor credit scores and high debt.

45599 ■ "Coming Up Short" in *Boston Business Journal* **(Vol. 30, October 15, 2010, No. 36, pp. 1)**
Pub: Boston Business Journal
Ed: Tim McLaughlin, Mary Moore. **Description:** Boston, Massachusetts-based nonprofits have been profiting less from charity golf tournaments. Nonprofits have been collecting less than 50 cents on the dollar from such events. But nonprofits have been restructuring golf tournaments in order to boost profits.

45600 ■ "Community Commitment Safeguards Franchising Industry" in *Franchising World* **(Vol. 42, November 2010, No. 11, pp. 38)**
Pub: International Franchise Association
Description: Individuals who are dedicated to committing time and resources to bring to the attention of legislators those laws and proposals affecting franchise small businesses are highlighted in a monthly format.

45601 ■ *The Company We Keep: Reinventing Small Business for People, Community, and Place*
Pub: Chelsea Green Publishing
Ed: John Abrams, William Grieder. **Released:** June 2006. **Price:** $18.00. **Description:** The new business trend in social entrepreneurship as a business plan enables small business owners to meet the triple bottom line of profits for people (employees and owners), community, and the environment.

45602 ■ *The Complete Idiot's Guide to Starting and Running a Thrift Store*
Pub: Alpha Publishing House

Ed: Ravel Buckley, Carol Costa. **Released:** January 5, 2010. **Price:** $18.95. **Description:** Thrift stores saw a 35 percent increase in sales during the falling economy in 2008. Despite the low startup costs, launching and running a thrift store is complicated. Two experts cover the entire process, including setting up a store on a nonprofit basis, choosing a location, funding, donations for saleable items, recruiting and managing staff, sorting items, pricing, and recycling donations.

45603 ■ "Conversation" in *Harvard Business Review* (Vol. 86, September 2008, No. 9, pp. 32)
Pub: Harvard Business School Press

Ed: Susan Donovan. **Description:** Danish software entrepreneur Thorkil Sonne has helped improve employment for individuals with autism after discovering the perception of detail and remarkable memory skills in his own son, who has autism. His company, Specialisterne, was built via focusing on these strengths.

45604 ■ "Corporate Diversity Driving Profits" in *Hispanic Business* (Vol. 30, September 2008, No. 9, pp. 12)
Pub: Hispanic Business, Inc.

Ed: Michael Bowker. **Description:** U.S. businesses are beginning to appreciate the importance of diversity and are developing strategies to introduce a diverse workforce that reflects the cultural composition of their customers. The realization that diversity increases profits and the use of professional networks to recruit and retain skilled minority employees are two other new trends impacting corporate diversity in the U.S.

45605 ■ "Corporate Responsibility" in *Professional Services Close-Up* (July 2, 2010)
Pub: Close-Up Media

Description: List of firms awarded the inaugural Best Corporate Citizens in Government Contracting by the Corporate Responsibility Magazine is presented. The list is based on the methodology of the Magazine's Best Corporate Citizen's List, with 324 data points of publicly-available information in seven categories which include: environment, climate change, human rights, philanthropy, employee relations, financial performance, and governance.

45606 ■ "Corporate Social Responsibility: A Process Model of Sensemaking" in *Academy of Management Review* (January 2008, pp. 122)
Pub: ScholarOne, Inc.

Ed: Kunal Basu, Guido Palazzo. **Description:** A novel process model of corporate social responsibility is presented. It uses organizational sensemaking to educate managers about elements of appropriate relationships with stakeholders and others.

45607 ■ "Corporation, Be Good! The Story of Corporate Social Responsibility" in *Business and Society* (December 2007, pp. 479-485)
Pub: Sage Publications USA

Ed: David M. Wasieleski. **Description:** Review of the book, "Corporation, Be Good! The Story of Corporate Social Responsibility" is presented. The book examines the importance of corporate responsibility and its economic impact.

45608 ■ "Could This Be Your Next Office Building?" in *Austin Business Journal* (Vol. 31, May 13, 2011, No. 10, pp. A1)
Pub: American City Business Journals Inc.

Ed: Cody Lyon. **Description:** Falcon Containers moved to a 51-acre site in Far East Austin, Texas and started construction of a 2,500-square-foot headquarters made from eight 40-foot shipping containers. Falcon's CEO Stephen Shang plans to use his headquarters building as a showroom to attract upscale, urban hipsters. Insights on the construction's environmental and social impact are shared. ■

45609 ■ "CR Magazine Taps ITT As a 'Best Corporate Citizen' in Government Contracting" in *Profesisonal Services Close-Up* (July 30, 2010)
Pub: Close-Up Media

Description: ITT Corporation was named by Corporate Responsibility Magazine as a Best Corporate Citizen in Government Contracting. The list recognizes publicly-traded companies that exemplify transparency and accountability while serving the U.S. government.

45610 ■ *Creating a World without Poverty: Social Business and the Future of Capitalism*
Pub: Basic Books

Released: April 26, 2009. **Price:** $26.00. **Description:** Explanation of how microcredit lending practices and more collaborative business strategies can be used to alleviate poverty worldwide.

45611 ■ "Diana Bonta: Keeping People Healthy and Thriving" in *Hispanic Business* (Vol. 30, April 2008, No. 4, pp. 30)
Pub: Hispanic Business

Ed: Leanndra Martinez. **Description:** Diana Bonta serves as vice president of public affairs for Kaiser Permanente and is a strong advocate for health reform and improving access to health care. In order to better serve the underinsured and uninsured, she directs Kaiser's Community Benefit division that devoted $369 million last year to this cause.

45612 ■ "Do-Gooder Finance: How a New Crop of Investors Is Helping Social Entrepreneurs" in *Inc.* (February 2008, pp. 29-30)
Pub: Gruner & Jahr USA Publishing

Ed: Nitasha Tiku. **Description:** Social venture firms are not seeking to sell companies as quickly as traditional venture companies. Four socially minded venture capital firms and banks profiled include, Underdog Venture, Island Pond, Vermont; Root Capital, Cambridge, Massachusetts; ShoreBank Pacific, Ilwaco, Washington; and TBL Capital, Sausalito, California.

45613 ■ "Doing Good: Cause and Effect" in *Entrepreneur* (Vol. 36, February 2008, No. 2, pp. 23)
Pub: Entrepreneur Media Inc.

Description: Lisa Knoppe established Art for a Cause LLC that employs people with mental and physical disabilities. The company makes hand-painted tools and furniture to be sold at gift retailers and hardware stores.

45614 ■ "Doing the Right Thing" in *Black Enterprise* (Vol. 38, July 2008, No. 12, pp. 50)
Pub: Earl G. Graves Publishing Co. Inc.

Ed: Tamara E. Holmes. **Description:** More business owners are trying to become more environmentally friendly, either due to their belief in social responsibility or for financial incentives or for both reasons. Tips for making one's business more environmentally responsible are included as well as a listing of resources that may be available to help owners in their efforts.

45615 ■ "Donated Sprinkler System Honors Fallen Firefighter" in *Contractor* (Vol. 56, July 2009, No. 7, pp. 3)
Pub: Penton Media, Inc.

Ed: Steve Spaulding. **Description:** Capital City District Habitat for Humanity has constructed a home with a residential fire sprinkler system in honor of Ted Abriel, a firefighter who died on the job. Albany Fire Protection donated the labor for the installation of the fire sprinkler system.

45616 ■ "Doubletree Finds a Niche for Giving Back" in *Hotel and Motel Management* (Vol. 225, July 2010, No. 8, pp. 6)
Pub: Questex Media Group Inc.

Ed: Paul J. Heney. **Description:** Profile of Doubletree Hotel's community outreach programs that help employee volunteers work to educate children and the public about issues important to the environment.

45617 ■ "Doubtful Donors" in *Canadian Business* (Vol. 81, December 8, 2008, No. 21, pp. 8)
Pub: Rogers Media Ltd.

Ed: Dennis Seguin. **Description:** Key information on fundraising consultancy Inspire, as well as views and information on charitable organizations in Canada is presented. Inspire designs the financial architecture of charitable foundations in Canada, which was affected by the current financial crisis. Inspire advises foundations to keep existing donors.

45618 ■ "Dragon, but..." in *Canadian Business* (Vol. 81, December 8, 2008, No. 21, pp. 45)
Pub: Rogers Media Ltd.

Ed: Matthew McLearn. **Description:** The greatest challenge in smooth trade relations between China and Canada is believed to be lukewarm relations with China over human rights issues. Australia on the other hand, has attracted huge Chinese outward direct investments because of strong trade relations.

45619 ■ *The Dream Manager*
Pub: Hyperion

Ed: Matthew Kelly. **Price:** $19.95. **Description:** A business fable about the virtues of helping those working for and with you to achieve their dreams. Managers can boost morale and control turnover by adopting this policy.

45620 ■ *Ecopreneuring: Putting Purpose and the Planet Before Profits*
Pub: New Society Publishers

Ed: John Ivanko; Lisa Kivirist. **Released:** July 1, 2008. **Price:** $17.95 paperback. **Description:** Ecopreneurs in America are shifting profits and market share towards green living. The book provides a guideline for ecopreneurs in the areas of eco-business basics, purposeful management, marketing in the green economy, and running a lifestyle business.

45621 ■ "Editor's Note" in *Canadian Business* (Vol. 81, March 17, 2008, No. 4, pp. 7)
Pub: Rogers Media

Ed: Joe Chidley. **Description:** Canadian Consolidated government expenditures increased by an average of 4.5 percent annually from 2003 to 2007. Health care, housing, and the environment were some of the areas which experienced higher spending. However, government spending in labor, employment, and immigration dropped 6.6 percent.

45622 ■ "Elder Care At Work" in *HRMagazine* (Vol. 53, September 2008, No. 9, pp. 111)
Pub: Society for Human Resource Management

Ed: Pamela Babcock. **Description:** Many employers are helping workers who face sudden, short-term elder care needs.

45623 ■ *Entrepreneurship As Social Change: A Third New Movements in Entrepreneurship Book*
Pub: Edward Elgar Publishing, Incorporated

Ed: Steyaert. **Released:** February 2007. **Price:** $120.00. **Description:** Third book in a series, the edition examines entrepreneurship as a societal phenomenon.

45624 ■ *Entrepreneurship and Small Business*
Pub: Palgrave Macmillan

Ed: Paul Burns. **Released:** January 2007. **Price:** $74.95. **Description:** Entrepreneurial skills, focusing on good management practices are discussed. Topics include family businesses, corporate, international and social entrepreneurship.

45625 ■ "Everybody Wants To Save the World: But When You Start a Charity Overseas, Good Intentions Often Go Awry" in *Inc.* (December 2007)
Pub: Gruner & Jahr USA Publishing

Ed: Dalia Fahmy. **Description:** Unique set of challenges faced by small businesses wanting to create a charity overseas. Five key issues to explore before starting a charity overseas are examined.

45626 ■ "The Evolution of Corporate Social Responsibility" in *Business Horizons* **(November-December 2007, pp. 449)**
Pub: Elsevier Technology Publications
Ed: Philip L. Cochran. **Description:** Corporate social responsibility is now perceived as vital in enhancing the profitability of businesses while improving their reputation. It has changed business practices such as philanthropy, investment, and entrepreneurship.

45627 ■ "Fairness First" in *Canadian Business* **(Vol. 80, April 23, 2007, No. 9, pp. 45)**
Pub: Rogers Media
Ed: Erin Pooley. **Description:** The need for the fair treatment of employees from the perspective of employee compensation is discussed.

45628 ■ "Family Matters: Founding Family Firms and Corporate Political Activity" in *Business and Society* **(December 2007, pp. 395-428)**
Pub: Sage Publications USA
Ed: Michael Hadani. **Description:** The impact of publicly traded family founding firms and their inclination for corporate political activity is examined. Publicly traded family founding firms are more predisposed to engage in corporate political activity when the founder is in an executive position. Details of these findings are reported.

45629 ■ "Festivals Press on Despite Loss of Sponsors" in *Crain's Detroit Business* **(Vol. 25, June 22, 2009, No. 25, pp. 3)**
Pub: Crain Communications Inc. - Detroit
Ed: Sherri Began Welch. **Description:** Organizers of local festivals are experiencing a decrease in sponsorship this summer due to the slow economy. These events help keep areas vibrant and stress the importance of community and cultural events.

45630 ■ "Fire Destroys Veterans' Kiosk" in *Houston Chronicle* **(November 24, 2010, pp. 14)**
Pub: Houston Chronicle
Description: A leaking propane heater is believed to have started a fire that destroyed a kiosk near the Vietnam Veterans Memorial in Washington DC. The kiosk, manned by volunteers from the Rolling Thunder veterans group, provide education to the public about those individuals still missing from the Vietnam War.

45631 ■ "FIS-Metavante Deal Paying Off for Many" in *Business Journal-Milwaukee* **(Vol. 28, December 17, 2010, No. 11, pp. A1)**
Pub: Milwaukee Business Journal
Ed: Rich Kirchen. **Description:** Jacksonville, Florida-based Fidelity National Information Services Inc., also known as FIS, has remained committed to Milwaukee, Wisconsin more than a year after purchasing Metavante Technologies Inc. FIS has transferred several operations into Metropolitan Milwaukee and has continued its contribution to charitable organizations in the area.

45632 ■ "Food Bank to Move, Double in Size" in *Austin Business Journal* **(Vol. 31, July 8, 2011, No. 18, pp. 1)**
Pub: American City Business Journals Inc.
Ed: Sandra Zaragoza. **Description:** The Capital Area Food Bank (CAFB) of Texas intends to construct a 125,000-square-foot hub on the land it purchased in East Texas. The hub will accommodate administrative offices, warehouse and refrigeration space, and a production kitchen.

45633 ■ "Give Until It Works" in *Hispanic Business* **(March 2008, pp. 26-27)**
Pub: Hispanic Business
Ed: Rick Munarriz. **Description:** Ways to maximize a tax advantage from charitable contributions for small business owners are addressed.

45634 ■ *Giving*
Pub: Knopf Publishing/Random House
Ed: Bill Clinton. **Price:** $24.95. **Description:** The former president describes people and projects that save lives and solve problems around the world.

45635 ■ "The Global Talent Hunt" in *Business Strategy Review* **(Vol. 21, Spring 2010, No. 1, pp. 78)**
Pub: Wiley-Blackwell
Ed: Richard Emerton. **Description:** Richard Emerton explains how the new 'triple context' of economy, environment and society will have profound implications for human resource practices. He suggests that viewing talent as abundant is the right perspective for a manager.

45636 ■ "Gloria Christiansen: Tennessee's Unselfish Citizen" in *Women In Business* **(Vol. 61, December 2009, No. 6, pp. 10)**
Pub: American Business Women's Association
Description: Gloria Christiansen, a Colombian-born secretary of the Knoxville Area American Business Women's Association (ABWA) Council, shares her experiences as an immigrant in Tennessee who has been provided with the opportunity to grow professionally through ABWA. Aside from participating in community development projects, she deems her American citizenship as an inspiring and honorable experience.

45637 ■ *The Go-Giver: A Little Story About a Powerful Business Idea*
Pub: Penguin Group
Ed: Bob Burg; John David Mann. **Released:** December 27, 2007. **Price:** $19.95. **Description:** Story of an ambitious young man named Joe who years for success. The book is a heartwarming tale that brings new relevance to the old proverb, "Give and you shall receive".

45638 ■ "GoodNews.com and the Little Cupcake Shoppe Support Calgary Food Bank With Unique $1.00 Deal" in *Marketwire Canada* **(March 9, 2011)**
Pub: Marketwire Canada
Description: Socially-conscious group-buying Website, GoodNews.com has partnered with The Little Cupcake Shoppe in Calgary, to raise funds for the Inter-Faith Food Bank. The fundraiser will feature a half dozen, pre-packaged assorted miniature cupcakes for $1.00. The entire amount is donated to the Calgary Food Bank.

45639 ■ *Grassroots NGOs by Women for Women: The Driving Force of Development in India*
Pub: SAGE Publications, Incorporated
Ed: Femida Handy; Meenaz Kassam; Suzanne Feeney; Bhagyashree Ranade. **Released:** July 2006. **Price:** $29.95. **Description:** Understanding the role of non-governmental organizations in women's development is offered through interviews with twenty women in India who have founded NGOs serving women.

45640 ■ *Groundswell: Winning in a World Transformed by Social Technologies*
Pub: Harvard Business School Press
Ed: Charlene Li; Josh Bernoff. **Released:** April 21, 2008. **Price:** $29.95. **Description:** Individuals are using online social technologies such as blogs, social networking sites, YouTube, and podcasts to discuss products and companies, write their own news, and find their own deals. When consumers you've never met are rating your company's products in public forums with which you have no experience or influence, your company is vulnerable. This book teaches the tools and data necessary to turn this treat into an opportunity.

45641 ■ "Group Sewing for Area Charities" in *Messenger-Inquirer* **(July 7, 2010)**
Pub: Messenger-Inquirer
Ed: Beth Wilberding. **Description:** Hobby Lobby in Owensboro, Kentucky features a weekly sewing group that made 656 pillowcases for area agencies.

45642 ■ *Growing Local Value: How to Build Business Partnerships That Strengthen Your Community*
Pub: Berrett-Koehler Publishers, Incorporated
Ed: Laury Hammel; Gun Denhart. **Released:** December 2006. **Price:** $15.00. **Description:** Advice and examples are provided for building socially responsible entrepreneurship.

45643 ■ "Halls Give Hospital Drive $11 Million Infusion" in *The Business Journal-Serving Metropolitan Kansas City* **(Vol. 26, July 18, 2008)**
Pub: American City Business Journals, Inc.
Ed: Rob Roberts. **Description:** Don Hall, chairman of Hallmark Cards Inc., and eight family members have announced that they will give $11 million to Children's Mercy Hospitals and Clinics for its $800 million expansion plan. Hall Family Foundation president Bill Hall that contributions such as that for Children's Mercy reflect the charitable interests of the foundation's board and founders. The possible impacts of the Hall's donation are analyzed.

45644 ■ "Hansen Mechanical Performs Boiler Upgrade at Brookfield Zoo" in *Contractor* **(Vol. 57, February 2010, No. 2, pp. 7)**
Pub: Penton Media, Inc.
Description: Hansen Mechanical installed a donated boiler in the Brookfield Zoo from Weil-McLain. The boilers were installed in the zoo's 'The Swamp' and 'The Living Coast' exhibits.

45645 ■ "Help Employees Give Away Some Of That Bonus" in *Harvard Business Review* **(Vol. 86, July-August 2008, No. 8, pp. 1)**
Pub: Harvard Business School Press
Ed: Michael I. Norton; Elizabeth W. Dunn. **Description:** Research indicates that how employees spend their bonuses is key to their resultant happiness, rather than simply receiving the bonus itself. Firms that offer donation options can thereby increase employee satisfaction.

45646 ■ "Higher Thread Count for Metropole" in *Business Courier* **(Vol. 26, September 25, 2009, No. 22, pp. 1)**
Pub: American City Business Journals, Inc.
Ed: Lisa Biank Fasig, Lucy May. **Description:** Cincinnati Center City Development Corporation is under contract to buy the 225-unit apartment building called Metropole Apartments and 21c Museum Hotel is the lead candidate for the space. Advocates of some residents of the low-income rental complex complain that this move could leave them homeless.

45647 ■ "Hourly Payment and Volunteering" in *Academy of Management Journal* **(August 2007)**
Pub: Academy of Management
Ed: Sanford E. DeVoe, Jeffrey Pfeffer. **Description:** Brief description about theoretically important class of work, which is freely undertaken without remuneration, is presented.

45648 ■ *How Come That Idiot's Rich and I'm Not?*
Pub: Crown Publishing/Random House
Ed: Robert Shemin. **Released:** April 2009. **Price:** $13.95. **Description:** The book shows the average person not only how to get rich, but to create, connect and contribute greatly.

45649 ■ *How To Change the World*
Pub: Oxford University Press
Ed: David Bornstein. **Released:** September 2007. **Price:** $15.95. **Description:** Social entrepreneurs are individuals with powerful ideas that improve other people's lives and have implemented these ideas across cities, countries and in some cases, around the world. These are doctors, lawyers, engineers, teachers, journalists and parents who solve social problems on a large scale and have a profound effect on society.

45650 ■ "Howl-o-ween" in *Decatur Daily* **(October 25, 2011)**
Pub: Decatur Daily
Ed: Catherine Godbey. **Description:** Animal Friends Humane Society provides free pet food and cat litter to Meals on Wheels clients.

45651 ■ "Innovating Globally" in *Business Strategy Review* **(Vol. 21, Spring 2010, No. 1, pp. 24)**
Pub: Wiley-Blackwell
Ed: Costas Markides, Stuart Crainer. **Description:** Costas Markides has spent over two decades studying business strategy and innovation. Recently, he

has been focusing on the bigger picture of how people can address major social problems. Can the techniques used by managers to create innovation inside organizations work with global change?

45652 ■ "The Innovator: Rob McEwen's Unique Vision of Philanthropy and Business" in *Canadian Business* (Vol. 81, November 10, 2008, No. 19)
Pub: Rogers Media Ltd.
Ed: Alex Mlynek. **Description:** Rob McEwen says that his donation to the Schulich School of Business is his first large donation. He went to the University Health Network and was told about their pan for regenerative medicine, helping him make the decision. McEwan wants to be involved in philanthropy in the areas of leadership and education.

45653 ■ "Institutional Logics in the Study of Organizations" in *Business Ethics Quarterly* (Vol. 21, July 2011, No. 3, pp. 409)
Pub: Society for Business Ethics
Ed: Marc Orlitzky. **Description:** Examination into whether the empirical evidence on the relationship between corporate social performance (CSP) and corporate financial performance (CFP) differs depending on the publication outlet in which that evidence appears.

45654 ■ "Interest in 'Encore Careers' is Growing" in *HRMagazine* (Vol. 53, November 2008, No. 11, pp. 22)
Pub: Society for Human Resource Management
Description: Unexpectedly large numbers of baby boomers are looking for jobs that can provide them with 'means and meaning', according to a survey by MetLife and Civic Ventures. They can find those jobs in encore careers, an opportunity to do work that has a social impact and personal meaning.

45655 ■ "Is Globalization Threatening U.S. Hispanic Progress?" in *Hispanic Business* (Vol. 30, September 2008, No. 9, pp. 16)
Pub: Hispanic Business, Inc.
Ed: Jessica Haro. **Description:** Talented Hispanic employees are making progress within the increasingly diverse American corporate scenario. However, while some experts believe the induction of foreign professionals through globalization will not impact this progress, others feel it could hamper opportunities for American Hispanics.

45656 ■ "Janet Froetscher, CEO, United Way of Metropolitan Chicago" in *Crain's Chicago Business* (Vol. 31, May 5, 2008, No. 18, pp. 26)
Pub: Crain Communications, Inc.
Ed: Emily Stone. **Description:** Profile of Janet Froetscher who is the CEO of United Way of Metropolitan Chicago who organized the country's largest-ever merger of non-profits with 53 smaller suburban chapters consolidating with the Chicago one. The consolidation saves $4 million a year with departments such as finance, information technology and communications which allows that money be spent funding job training, after-school programs and aid for 7,000 Hurricane Katrina evacuees living in the Chicago area.

45657 ■ "Kelvin Taketa" in *Hawaii Business* (Vol. 53, October 2007, No. 4, pp. 30)
Pub: Hawaii Business Publishing
Ed: Scott Radway. **Description:** Hawaii Community Foundation chief executive officer Kelvin Taketa believes that the leadership shortage for nonprofit sector in Hawaii is a result of leaders retiring or switching to part-time work. Taketa adds that the duties of a nonprofit organization leader are very challenging, with the organizations being usually thinly staffed. His opinion on the prospects of young leadership in Hawaii is also given.

45658 ■ *The Leadership Challenge*
Pub: Jossey-Bass Publishers
Ed: James M. Kouzes, Barry Z. Posner. **Released:** June 30, 1995. **Price:** $22.00. **Description:** According to research by the authors, people can make extraordinary things happen by liberating the leader

within everyone around them. This handbook gives practical tips to aspire leaders in retail, manufacturing, government, community, church and school settings.

45659 ■ "Let It Shine: Organization Helps Disadvantaged Girls See Their Worth" in *Black Enterprise* (Vol. 38, February 2008, No. 7, pp. 142)
Pub: Earl G. Graves Publishing Co. Inc.
Ed: George Alexander. **Description:** Wilson Mourning, founder of the clothing label Honey Child, attributes her success to her mother and other positive women who helped her through her adolescence. Mourning created a mentoring organization that helps young girls in the Miami, Florida area to develop life skills.

45660 ■ "A Lifetime of Giving: Food Bank CEO Fights Hunger One Mouth At a Time" in *Black Enterprise* (Vol. 41, November 2010, No. 4, pp. 86)
Pub: Earl G. Graves Publishing Co. Inc.
Ed: Tamara E. Holmes. **Description:** Profile of Valerie Traore, CEO of Food Bank of South Jersey. Traore stresses the importance of volunteerism that she learned from her grandparents. Hunger relief became her passion when she served as a temp office worker for the Maryland Food Bank in Baltimore. She earned her Bachelor's of Science in management and has dedicated herself to a career in nonprofit service.

45661 ■ *Living Above the Store: Building a Business That Creates Value, Inspires Change, and Restores Land and Community*
Pub: Chelsea Green Publishing
Ed: Martin Melaver. **Released:** May 1, 2009. **Price:** $27.95. **Description:** Martin Melaver shares insight into building a business plan that utilizes diversity, shared values, common purpose and land-community ethics that are restorative for humankind and nature.

45662 ■ "The Loan Arranger" in *Canadian Business* (Vol. 80, October 22, 2007, No. 21, pp. 15)
Pub: Rogers Media
Ed: Rachel Pulfer. **Description:** Muhammad Yunus received the Nobel Prize in 2006 for the organization that he founded, the Grameen Bank. The bank has helped women in developing countries and has also begun helping millions of individuals to make loans in the U.S. through the Grameen Bank. An evaluation of the Grameen model is provided.

45663 ■ "Lunch Box Maker Gives Back" in *Marketing to Women* (Vol. 23, November 2010, No. 11, pp. 5)
Pub: EPM Communications, Inc.
Description: Female entrepreneurs launched a new program called, "Share Your Lunch Project" that encourages mothers to give back and replace their child's lunchbox with their eco-friendly lunch boxes, which are available at select retailers. All proceeds from the project will benefit the World Food Program USA, which feeds children in developing countries.

45664 ■ "Make a Resolution: ADA Training" in *HRMagazine* (Vol. 54, January 2009, No. 1, pp. 81)
Pub: Society for Human Resource Management
Ed: Victoria Zellers. **Description:** Americans with Disabilities Act (ADA) Amendments Act took effect January 1, 2009. The ADA Amendments Act means that more applicants and employees are eligible for reasonable accommodations and that employers need to develop a new ADA compliance strategy.

45665 ■ "McDonald's Founders Fund $80 Million Project" in *The Business Journal - Serving Phoenix and the Valley of the Sun* (Vol. 28, September 12, 2008, No. 53, pp. 1)
Pub: American City Business Journals, Inc.
Ed: Jan Buchholz. **Description:** Construction will begin in early 2009 on an $80 million Ray and Joan Kroc Community Center in Phoenix, Arizona. It will be located adjacent to the Salvation Army, which received a $1.9 billion contribution from Joan Kroc after her death in 2003. This fund will be divided to construct 30 community centers across the country.

45666 ■ *Memos to the Prime Minister: What Canada Could Be in the 21st Century*
Pub: John Wiley & Sons, Incorporated
Ed: Harvey Schacter. **Released:** April 11, 2003. **Price:** $16.95. **Description:** A look into the business future of Canada. Topics include business, healthcare, think tanks, policy groups, education, the arts, economy, and social issues.

45667 ■ *Microfranchising: Creating Wealth at the Bottom of the Pyramid*
Pub: Edward Elgar Publishing, Incorporated
Ed: W. Gibb Dyer; Jason Fairbourne; Stephen W. Gibson. **Released:** July 2008. **Price:** $35.00. **Description:** Ideas from researchers and social entrepreneurs discusses the movement that moves microfranchising into a mechanism for sustainable poverty reduction on a scale to match microfinance.

45668 ■ "Military Brides Can Get Free Wedding Gowns" in *Virginian-Pilot* (November 10, 2010)
Pub: The Virginia-Pilot
Ed: Jamesetta Walker. **Description:** Seventy-five designer wedding gowns will be given to military brides on a first-come, first-served basis at Maya Couture through the Brides Across America's wedding gown giveaway program. Gowns are valued between $500 to $3,000 and are donated by designers Maggie Sottero, Pronovias and Essense of Australia.

45669 ■ "Minority Entrepreneurs, Business Advocate of the Year Named" in *Daily News* (November 1, 2010)
Pub: Daily News
Ed: Aniesa Holmes. **Description:** Jacksonville-Onslow Chamber of Commerce Minority Enterprise Development Day honored outstanding entrepreneurs from the region. Candidates were chosen based on criteria such as business accomplishments, chamber involvement and dedication as well as their commitment to serving people in the community.

45670 ■ "Model Citizen" in *Entrepreneur* (Vol. 36, February 2008, No. 2, pp. 42)
Pub: Entrepreneur Media Inc.
Ed: Guy Kawasaki. **Description:** A mensch is a person of noble character, as defined by Leo Rosten. Tips on how to be a mensch and a better person, in relation to being an entrepreneur, are given. These include: helping others without expecting something in return, giving back to society, and knowing the line between right and wrong.

45671 ■ *The Mom and Pop Store: How the Unsung Heroes of the American Economy Are Surviving and Thriving*
Pub: Walker & Company
Ed: Robert Spector. **Released:** September 1, 2009. **Price:** $26.00. **Description:** The history of small independent retail enterprises and how mom and pop stores in the U.S. continue to thrive through customer service and renewed community support for local businesses.

45672 ■ "More Volunteers Needed to Make a Difference" in *Times-News* (October 18, 2011)
Pub: Times-News
Ed: Roselee Papandrea. **Description:** Meals on Wheels program in the Burlington, North Carolina area is seeking volunteers to deliver meals to senior citizens.

45673 ■ "New Economy Initiative Gains Partners" in *Crain's Detroit Business* (Vol. 25, June 1, 2009, No. 22, pp. M014)
Pub: Crain Communications Inc. - Detroit
Ed: Sherri Begin Welch. **Description:** New Economy Initiative is a $100 million philanthropic initiative that focuses on regional economic development. Recent grants awarded to Michigan companies are outlined.

45674 ■ *The New Social Entrepreneurship What Awaits Social Entrepreneurship Ventures?*
Pub: Edward Elgar Publishing, Incorporated
Ed: Perrini. **Released:** October 2006. **Price:** $120.00. **Description:** Social entrepreneurship seeks to improve societal well-being within entrepreneurial organizations.

45675 ■ "Nonprofit to Grow" in *Austin Business JournalInc.* (Vol. 29, January 22, 2010, No. 46, pp. 1)
Pub: American City Business Journals
Ed: Sandra Zaragoza. **Description:** Southwest Key Programs Inc. received a $2.1 million grant from the U.S. Economic Development Administration to help finance the building of a $3.6 million 'Social Enterprise Complex'. The complex is expected to create at least 100 jobs in East Austin, Texas. Details of the plan for the complex are presented.

45676 ■ "Nonprofit NAIC Acquires Software Developer as For-Profit Arm" in *Crain's Detroit Business* (Vol. 25, June 22, 2009, No. 25, pp. 10)
Pub: Crain Communications Inc. - Detroit
Ed: Sherri Begin Welch. **Description:** Details of National Association of Investors Corporation's acquisition of a Massachusetts investment software developer in order to offer more products to investment clubs and individual investors nationwide.

45677 ■ "Nonprofits Find Plenty of Optimism for the Future" in *Business Courier* (Vol. 26, January 1, 2010, No. 37, pp. 1)
Pub: American City Business Journals, Inc.
Ed: Lucy May. **Description:** Forecasts of various nonprofits in Cincinnati, Ohio such as the United Way of Greater Cincinnati, the Greater Cincinnati Foundation and The Fine Arts Fund for 2010 are presented.

45678 ■ "Nonprofits Hope Employees Dig Deep" in *Austin Business JournalInc.* (Vol. 28, December 5, 2008, No. 38, pp. A1)
Pub: American City Business Journals
Ed: Sandra Zaragoza. **Description:** Nonprofit organizations in Austin, Texas are stepping up workplace giving drives in the hope that workers will continue giving donations to them. Corporations are cutting costs due to the recession, reducing donations to nonprofit organizations in the process.

45679 ■ "Nonprofits Pressured to Rein in Fundraising Events" in *Crain's Detroit Business* (Vol. 25, June 15, 2009, No. 24, pp. 1)
Pub: Crain Communications Inc. - Detroit
Ed: Sherri Begin Welch. **Description:** Local corporations have asked nonprofit= s to limit fundraising events in order to cut costs during the recession.

45680 ■ "OHC Aids Long Island Family" in *Indoor Comfort Marketing* (Vol. 70, May 2011, No. 5, pp. 45)
Pub: Industry Publications Inc.
Ed: Judy Garber. **Description:** Ways Community Oil Heat helped a customer living in Long Island heat their home during desperate times.

45681 ■ "Oil Rich" in *Canadian Business* (Vol. 79, Winter 2006, No. 24, pp. 57)
Pub: Rogers Media
Ed: Calvin Leung. **Description:** The efforts of John Risley, the Chairman of the Candaian firm Clearwater Fine Foods Inc., to educate consumers about the health aspects of seafood, are described.

45682 ■ "On the Clock" in *Canadian Business* (Vol. 82, April 27, 2009, No. 7, pp. 28)
Pub: Rogers Media
Ed: Sarka Halas. **Description:** Survey of 100 Canadian executives found that senior managers can be out of a job for about nine months before their careers are adversely affected. The nine month mark can be avoided if job seekers build networks even before they lose their jobs. Job seekers should also take volunteer work and training opportunities to increase their changes of landing a job.

45683 ■ "On the Economic Dimensions of Corporate Social Responsibility" in *Business and Society* (December 2007, pp. 457-478)
Pub: Sage Publications USA
Ed: Fabienne Fortanier, Ans Kolk. **Description:** Economic impact of Fortune Global 250 firms analyzing concern for corporate social responsibility is discussed, focusing on an illustration of mechanisms by which multinational enterprises affect economic developed.

45684 ■ "One Laptop Per Child Weighs Going For-Profit" in *Boston Business Journal* (Vol. 31, May 20, 2011, No. 17, pp. 1)
Pub: Boston Business Journal
Ed: Mary Moore. **Description:** Nonprofit organization One Laptop Per Child is thinking of shifting into a for-profit structure in order to raise as much as $10 million in capital to achieve its goal of distributing more XO laptops to poor children worldwide. The organization has distributed 2 million computers since 2008 with Uruguay, Peru and Rwanda as its biggest markets.

45685 ■ "Online Pet Medication Store Supports Free Vaccinations for Cats" in *Internet Wire* (August 31, 2010)
Pub: Comtex
Description: Pethealth Inc., The Petango Store will help to support The Humane Society of Tampa Bay's efforts by offering free feline vaccinations for the cat's entire lifetime that is adopted between September 1, 2010 and February 28, 2010. The cat must be one year or older at time of adoption.

45686 ■ "OPSEU: Developmental Service Workers Picketing Across Ontario to Raise Community Awareness" in *Canadian Corporate News* (May 16, 2007)
Pub: Comtex News Network Inc.
Description: Across Ontario staff who support people with developmental disabilities are picketing local MPP offices and other community hubs to highlight the Ontario government's inadequate response to the crisis in developmental services.

45687 ■ "Outpouring of Outreach" in *Crain's Cleveland Business* (Vol. 30, June 15, 2009, No. 23, pp. 3)
Pub: Crain Communications, Inc.
Ed: Shannon Mortland. **Description:** Nonprofit organizations are experiencing a higher number of volunteers than in the past. People are willing to donate their skills and services rather than contributing money.

45688 ■ "Pet Food Bank 'Shares the Love'" in *Pet Product News* (Vol. 64, December 2010, No. 12, pp. 6)
Pub: BowTie Inc.
Description: Winston-Salem, North Carolina-based nonprofit Share the Love Pet Food Bank has donated 60,000 pounds of pet food since its establishment in 2009. It has been linking pet food manufacturers and rescue groups to supply unsold pet food to needy animals. The nonprofit intends to reach out to more animal welfare groups by building more warehouses.

45689 ■ "Pet Kiosk Offers Search Options" in *Times-News* (October 14, 2010)
Pub: Times-News Publishing Company
Ed: Roselee Papandrea. **Description:** Chameleon Pet Kiosk located at the Spay and Neuter Clinic of Alamance County in Burlington, North Carolina allows users to see and read about animals available for adoption at the center.

45690 ■ "Philanthropy Good For Business" in *Crain's Detroit Business* (Vol. 24, February 18, 2008, No. 7, pp. 14)
Pub: Crain Communications Inc. - Detroit
Ed: Sheena Harrison. **Description:** Profile of Burce McCully, founder of Dynamic Edge Inc., and his views on philanthropy as a key to any small company's success. The Ann Arbor, Michigan information technology firm has volunteered and raised funds for many causes since 1999 when the company was founded.

45691 ■ "A Place to Call Home" in *Business Courier* (Vol. 24, March 7, 2008, No. 48, pp. 1)
Pub: American City Business Journals, Inc.
Ed: Lucy May. **Description:** Discusses a new type of housing for Cincinnati's chronically homeless that will be developed by the Over-the-Rhine Community Housing Network and the Cincinnati Center City Development Corp. Advocates believe that it is the missing link in the community's efforts to eradicate homelessness. The details of the project are also presented.

45692 ■ "Planning Ahead" in *Crain's Cleveland Business* (Vol. 30, June 15, 2009, No. 23, pp. 12)
Pub: Crain Communications, Inc.
Ed: Shannon Mortland. **Description:** Cleveland area nonprofit organizations are developing new strategies for raising donations, while keeping costs down in the slow economy.

45693 ■ "Post-Prison Center Idea Rankles OTR" in *Business Courier* (Vol. 26, November 27, 2009, No. 31, pp. 1)
Pub: American City Business Journals, Inc.
Ed: Lucy May. **Description:** Cincinnati officials and community leaders oppose Firetree Ltd.'s plan to launch a residential program for federal offenders near the School for the Creative and Performing Arts in Over-the-Rhine. Firetree, a Pennsylvania-based reentry center services firm, proposed a five-year contract with the Federal Bureau of Prisons based on a letter to Cincinnati Police Chief Thomas Streicher.

45694 ■ *The Power of Social Innovation: How Civic Entrepreneurs Ignite Community Networks for Good*
Pub: John Wiley & Sons, Inc.
Ed: Stephen Goldsmith, Tim Burke, Gigi Georges. **Released:** March 10, 2010. **Price:** $35.00. **Description:** This seminal book provides tools for civic entrepreneurs to create healthier communities and promote innovative solutions to public and social problems. It shows how to effectively tackle the intractable issues facing the country.

45695 ■ "Preserving a Nonprofit's Mission" in *Boston Business Journal* (Vol. 31, June 17, 2011, No. 21, pp. 3)
Pub: Boston Business Journal
Ed: Mary Moore. **Description:** Young Women's Christian Association Boston (YWCA) agreed to absorb the LeadBoston social issues and youth programs operated by the Boston Center for Community Justice. The BCCJ is scheduled to close after failing to stabilize its finances.

45696 ■ "Pride Lands Janitorial Work at New Terminal" in *Sacramento Business Journal* (Vol. 28, June 10, 2011, No. 15, pp. 1)
Pub: Sacramento Business Journal
Ed: Kelly Johnson. **Description:** Pride Industries Inc. won the five-year $9.4 million contract to clean the Sacramento International Airport's new Terminal B, which will open in fall 2011. The nonprofit organization posts a revenue of $191 million for 2011 and currently employs more than 2,400 people with disabilities. The contract is expected to provide savings of over $3 million a year to the airport.

45697 ■ "Priority: In Memoriam" in *Inc.* (December 2007, pp. 25-26, 28, 30)
Pub: Gruner & Jahr USA Publishing
Ed: Ryan McCarthy. **Description:** Profiles of entrepreneurs who died in 2007; these individuals helped to create some major business trends in the last fifty years, from the advent of socially responsible business to development of quality manufacturing.

45698 ■ "The Progressive Pet Shop: Showcasing Strays" in *Animals' Agenda* (March-April 1993, pp. 34)
Pub: Animal Rights Network Inc.
Ed: Athena Rhiannon Schaffer. **Description:** Brothers Pets stopped selling cats and dogs in order to donate kennel space to the Aspen Hill, Maryland animal shelter. The events leading to this small business decision and its success are presented.

45699 ■ "Proud Out Loud" in *Canadian Business* (Vol. 80, April 23, 2007, No. 9, pp. 52)
Pub: Rogers Media
Description: The role of accomplishments of employees in improving workplace conditions is presented.

45700 ■ "Readers Share How Sewing Shaped the Fabric of Their Lives" in *Virginian-Pilot* (September 14, 2010)
Pub: Virginian-Pilot
Ed: Jamesetta Walker. **Description:** People discuss the ways sewing has help enrich their lives, from public service projects and conventions centered on sewing.

45701 ■ **"Religious Revival" in** *Canadian Business* **(Vol. 81, December 8, 2008, No. 21, pp. 57)**
Pub: Rogers Media Ltd.
Ed: Paul Webster. **Description:** Canada-based lawyer Cyndee Todgham Cherniak believes that Canadians wishing to do business in China should have professional competence, as well as cultural and spiritual sensitivity. Chinese government officials also acknowledge the role of religion in China's economy.

45702 ■ **"The Romance of Good Deeds: a Business With a Cause Can Do Good in the World" in** *Inc.* **(Volume 32, December 2010, No. 10, pp. 47)**
Pub: Inc. Magazine
Ed: Meg Cadoux Hirshberg. **Description:** Entrepreneurship and family relationships are discussed. When a small business has a passion for philanthropy it can help any marriage by creating even greater passion for each other.

45703 ■ **"Sage Advice" in** *Canadian Business* **(Vol. 80, October 22, 2007, No. 21, pp. 70)**
Pub: Rogers Media
Ed: John Gray. **Description:** Seymour Schulich, one of Canada's richest men and generous philanthropist, wrote the book, "Get Smarter: Life and Business Lessons". The business book sold more than 50,000 copies and now sits on Canada's bestseller's list. Its popularity is attributed to the marketing efforts of the entrepreneur and author.

45704 ■ **"Second Chance Counselor" in** *Business Courier* **(Vol. 27, July 2, 2010, No. 9, pp. 1)**
Pub: Business Courier
Ed: Lucy May. **Description:** Stephen Tucker, director of workforce development for the Urban League of Greater Cincinnati, is an example of how ex-offenders can be given chances for employment after service jail sentences. How the Urban Leagues' Solid Opportunities for Advancement job training program helped Tucker and other ex-offenders is discussed.

45705 ■ **"Seymour Schulich" in** *Canadian Business* **(Vol. 79, Winter 2006, No. 24, pp. 144)**
Pub: Rogers Media
Ed: John Gray. **Description:** The views of the Canadian billionaire Seymour Schulich, on the evaluation of donations and gifts, are presented.

45706 ■ **"Silver Key Seeks Volunteer Drivers in Colorado Springs" in** *Colorado Springs Business Journal* **(October 21, 2011)**
Pub: Dolan Media
Ed: Amy Gillentine. **Description:** Silver Keyis look for drivers to use their own vehicles to deliver Meals on Wheels to area seniors. For many of these senior citizens, it is the only outside contact they have an entire day.

45707 ■ **"Small Is Best, Says Housing Officials" in** *Business First Buffalo* **(November 16, 2007, pp. 1)**
Pub: American City Business Journals, Inc.
Ed: Tracey Drury. **Description:** Nonprofit organizations in some parts of the U.S. are moving senior citizens from larger institutions into smaller housing. The benefits of smaller housing for the elderly are evaluated.

45708 ■ *Social Enterprise: Developing Sustainable Businesses*
Pub: Palgrave Macmillan
Ed: Frank Martin, Marcus Thompson. **Released:** January 1, 2010. **Price:** $106.00. **Description:** Social enterprises bring people and communities together for economic development and social gain and represent a growing sector of the business community.

45709 ■ *Social Entrepreneurship*
Pub: Palgrave Macmillan
Ed: Johanna Mair; Jeffrey Robinson; Kai Hockerts. **Released:** June 2006. **Price:** $80.00. **Description:** Social entrepreneurship is the process involving innovative approaches to solving social problems while creating economic value.

45710 ■ *Social Entrepreneurship For Dummies*
Pub: John Wiley & Sons
Ed: Mark Derieux, Robert Stebbins. **Released:** April 10, 2010. **Price:** $24.99. **Description:** Discover ways to bring social entrepreneurship to a small company in today's business environment. Today, a company is not measured by financial performance alone, but also on social entrepreneurship.

45711 ■ *Social Entrepreneurship: What Everyone Needs to Know*
Pub: Oxford University Press, Inc.
Ed: David Bornstein, Susan Davis. **Released:** April 10, 2010. **Price:** $16.95. **Description:** In development circles, there is now a widespread consensus that social entrepreneurs represent a far better mechanism to respond to needs than we have ever had before, a decentralized and emergent force that remains the best hope for solutions.

45712 ■ *The Spiritual Entrepreneur*
Pub: New Paradigm Media
Ed: Robert Morgen. **Released:** January 1, 2010. **Price:** $16.95. **Description:** Step-by-step guide to start a small business and then use that business to create various streams of passive income to support yourself and charities is presented.

45713 ■ *The Starbucks Experience*
Pub: McGraw-Hill
Ed: Joseph A. Michelli. **Released:** September 14, 2006. **Price:** $24.95. **Description:** Boardroom strategies, employee motivation tips, community involvement, and customer satisfaction are issues addressed, using Starbucks as a model.

45714 ■ **"Still on the Block" in** *Entrepreneur* **(Vol. 35, November 2007, No. 11, pp. 22)**
Pub: Entrepreneur Media Inc.
Ed: Laura Tiffany. **Description:** Neighborhoods where business enterprises are located sometimes go into decline, particularly in low-income communities with high crime rates. Some entrepreneurs share stories about getting involved to help revive the community and keep their businesses thriving.

45715 ■ *SuperCorp: How Vanguard Companies Create Innovation, Profits, Growth, and Social Good*
Pub: Crown Business
Ed: Rosabeth Moss Kanter. **Released:** 2009. **Price:** $27.50. **Description:** Harvard professor makes a persuasive case showing how social good is good for any company's bottom line.

45716 ■ **"Survey: Most Approve of Donating Used Pacemakers to Medically Underserved" in** *Crain's Detroit Business* **(Vol. 25, June 1, 2009)**
Pub: Crain Communications Inc. - Detroit
Description: According to a survey conducted by University of Michigan Cardiovascular Center, 87 percent of those with pacemakers and 71 percent of the general population would donate the device to patients in underserved nations.

45717 ■ **"The Tapestry of Life" in** *Women In Business* **(Vol. 61, December 2009, No. 6, pp. 8)**
Pub: American Business Women's Association
Ed: Kathleen Leighton. **Description:** Suzanne Fanch, co-owner of the Devil's Thumb Ranch, discusses the family and career-related influences that helped her to achieve success as a small business proprietor. She advises that opportunities should be treated as building blocks towards success. Fanch's involvement in advocacies that take care of the welfare of community, children, and environment is also discussed.

45718 ■ **"Taxpayer Says a Simple Thank-You Would Help" in** *Boston Business Journal* **(Vol. 27, November 16, 2007, No. 42, pp. 1)**
Pub: American City Business Journals Inc.
Ed: Jesse Noyes. **Description:** Bill Freza founded the ThankTheTaxpayer.org, a Website and incorporated organization. The non-partisan group aims to

induce gratitude and civility as a tax reform and attitude among taxpayers, particularly those in the top wage category.

45719 ■ **"Tech Giving 2.0" in** *Boston Business Journal* **(Vol. 31, August 5, 2011, No. 28, pp. 1)**
Pub: Boston Business Journal
Ed: Mary Moore. **Description:** Entrepreneurs and venture capitalists in Boston have launched Technology Underwriting Greater Good, the tech industry's answer to the criticism that they are not charitable. The foundation finances nonprofits that aid young people through entrepreneurship, education and life experience. Other tech firms in Boston doing charitable works are discussed.

45720 ■ **"Tenacious Trailblazer" in** *Hispanic Business* **(Vol. 30, April 2008, No. 4, pp. 26)**
Pub: Hispanic Business
Ed: Melinda Burns. **Description:** Dr. Sandra Hernandez has been named as Hispanic Business Woman of the Year for her pioneering work in health care reform. Dr. Hernandez is the first Hispanic and the first woman to serve as public health director for the city and county of San Francisco.

45721 ■ **"This Just In" in** *Crain's Detroit Business* **(Vol. 25, June 1, 2009, No. 22, pp. 1)**
Pub: Crain Communications Inc. - Detroit
Description: Three veterans of the auto industry have partnered to create, Revitalizing Michigan, a nonprofit dedicated to help manufacturers improve their processes. The firm is seeking federal, state and private grants to fund the mission.

45722 ■ **"To Help Maintain an Adequate Blood Supply During the Summer Months" in** *Ice Cream Reporter* **(Vol. 21, August 20, 2008, No. 9, pp. 8)**
Pub: Ice Cream Reporter
Description: Friendly's and the American Red Cross have partnered to offer blood donors a coupon for one free carton of Friendly's ice cream in order to maintain an adequate supply during summer months.

45723 ■ **"Toward a Political Conception of Corporate Responsibility" in** *Academy of Management Review* **(October 2007, pp. 1096)**
Pub: ScholarOne, Inc.
Ed: Andreas Georg Scherer, Guido Palazzo. **Description:** The limitations of studies on corporate social responsibility and a new theory based on Jurgen Habermas theory of democracy are highlighted. The key role played by the business firm in globalization of society is presented.

45724 ■ **"Tualatin Senior Center Under Construction" in** *Daily Journal of Commerce* **(October 21, 2011)**
Pub: Dolan Media
Ed: Angela Webber. **Description:** Juanita Pohl Center in Tualatin Community Park is the home to TualatinAEs Meals on Wheels program that delivers meals to seniors in the area.

45725 ■ *Values-Centered Entrepreneurship*
Pub: Routledge
Ed: David Y. Choi, Edmund Gray. **Released:** August 10, 2010. **Price:** $39.95. **Description:** A new brand of entrepreneurs has arrived on the business scene, carrying with them a new set of values. They possess a sense of social responsibility, the need to protect the planet, and to do the right thing for all stakeholders.

45726 ■ *Values and Opportunities in Social Entrepreneurship*
Pub: Palgrave Macmillan
Ed: Kai Hockerts. **Released:** November 1, 2009. **Price:** $90.00. **Description:** Social entrepreneurship has grown as a research field. This book discusses social entrepreneurship as well as the identification and exploitation of social venturing opportunities.

45727 ■ *Values Sell: Transforming Purpose into Profit through Creative Sales and Distribution Strategies*
Pub: Berrett-Koehler Publishers, Incorporated
Ed: Nadine A. Thompson; Angela E. Soper. **Released:** March 28, 2007. **Price:** $16.95. **Descrip-

tion: Sales and distribution are the lifeblood of any business, socially responsible businesses are no different.

45728 ■ "Wal-Mart Sharpens Focus on Roxbury" in *Boston Business Journal* **(Vol. 31, July 8, 2011, No. 24, pp. 1)**
Pub: Boston Business Journal
Ed: Mary Moore. **Description:** Wal-Mart Stores is boosting its search for a possible location in the Roxbury section of Boston, Massachusetts. The search is focused on underserved communities in terms of jobs and access to reasonably-priced merchandise. The extent Boston's African American community has clashed with Mayor Thomas M. Memino over the accommodations of the retailer in Roxbury is discussed.

45729 ■ "Water Distiller" in *Canadian Business* **(Vol. 81, September 29, 2008, No. 16, pp. 52)**
Pub: Rogers Media Ltd.
Ed: Matthew McClearn. **Description:** Les Fairn's invention of a water distiller called a Solarsphere was recognized in the Great Canadian Invention Competition. Fairn's invention resembles a buoy that uses the sun's energy to vaporize dirty water then leaves the impurities behind in a sump. The invention has an application for producing potable water in impoverished countries.

45730 ■ *The Way We'll Be: The Zogby Report on the Transformation of the American Dream*
Pub: Crown Business
Ed: John Zogby. **Released:** 2009. **Price:** $26.00. **Description:** According to a recent poll, the next generation of Americans are not as concerned about making money as they are about making a difference in the world.

45731 ■ "Weaving a Stronger Fabric: Organizing a Global Sweat-Free Apparel Production Agreement" in *WorkingUSA* **(Vol. 11, June 2008, No. 2)**
Pub: Blackwell Publishers Ltd.
Ed: Eric Dirnbach. **Description:** Tens of millions of workers working under terrible sweatshop conditions in the global apparel industry. Workers are employed at apparel contractors and have been largely unsuccessful in organizing and improving their working conditions. The major apparel manufacturers and retailers have the most power in this industry, and they have adopted corporate social responsibility programs as a false solution to the sweatshop problem. The major North American apparel unions dealt with similar sweatshop conditions a century ago by organizing the contractors and brands into joint association contracts that significantly raised standards. Taking inspiration from their example, workers and their anti-sweatshop allies need to work together to coordinate a global organizing effort that builds worker power and establishes a global production agreement that negotiates with both contractors and the brands for improved wages, benefits, and working conditions.

45732 ■ "When Profit Is Not the Incentive" in *Business North Carolina* **(Vol. 28, February 2008, No. 2, pp. 42)**
Pub: Business North Carolina
Ed: Amanda Parry. **Description:** Novant Health is North Carolina's fifth-largest private-sector employer and one of the largest nonprofit companies. Nonprofits grew 35 percent in North Carolina from 1995 to 2003.

45733 ■ "Where New Economy Initiative Grants Have Gone" in *Crain's Detroit Business* **(Vol. 25, June 1, 2009, No. 22, pp. M014)**
Pub: Crain Communications Inc. - Detroit
Description: Listing of grants totaling $20.5 million focusing on talent development, attraction and retention; innovation and entrepreneurship; and shifting to a culture that values learning, work and innovation, is presented.

45734 ■ "Winner Nonprofit, Hospitals" in *Crain's Detroit Business* **(Vol. 25, June 22, 2009, No. 25, pp. E002)**
Pub: Crain Communications Inc. - Detroit
Ed: Jay Greene. **Description:** James Connelly, CFO for Henry Ford Health System, discusses the financial status of the system. Statistical data included.

45735 ■ "Winner: Nonprofit, Human Services" in *Crain's Detroit Business* **(Vol. 25, June 22, 2009, No. 25, pp. E002)**
Pub: Crain Communications Inc. - Detroit
Ed: Sherri Begin Welch. **Description:** Profile of Lighthouse of Oakland County, located in Pontiac, Michigan. The nonprofit and its three subsidiaries are operating on a consolidated 2009 budget of $8.5 million.

45736 ■ *Women Count: A Guide to Changing the World*
Pub: Purdue University Press
Ed: Susan Bulkeley Butler, Bob Keefe. **Released:** August 26, 2010. **Price:** $24.95. **Description:** Throughout history, women have struggled to change the workplace, change government, change society. It's time for women to change the world! Whether on the job, in politics, or in their community, there has never been a better time for women to make a difference in the world.

45737 ■ *The Working Man and Woman's Guide to Becoming a Millionaire*
Pub: Prentiss Publishing
Ed: Al Herron. **Released:** November 2006. **Description:** President and CEO of a Century 21 office in Dallas, Texas shares insight into financial security and commitment to community.

45738 ■ "Your Big Give" in *Small Business Opportunities* **(September 2008)**
Pub: Entrepreneur Media Inc.
Ed: Michael Guld. **Description:** Cause related marketing is beneficial to businesses as well as the communities they inhabit; three small businesses that are elevating their standing in the community while at the same time increasing their customer base are profiled.

TRADE PERIODICALS

45739 ■ *Business Ethics*
Pub: Business Ethics
Released: Quarterly. **Description:** Business newsletter.

RESEARCH CENTERS

45740 ■ Bentley College–Center for Business Ethics
175 Forest St., AAC 108
Waltham, MA 02452-4705
Ph:(781)891-2981
Fax:(781)891-2988
Co. E-mail: cbeinfo@bentley.edu
URL: http://www.bentley.edu/cbe
Contact: W. Michael Hoffman PhD, Exec.Dir.
E-mail: cbeinfo@bentley.edu
Scope: Business ethics in an industrial society, particularly in relationship to the activities of academe, corporations, labor, government, special interest groups, and various professions. Conducts surveys on topics such as business ethics curriculum and instilling ethical values in corporations. **Services:** Consulting. **Publications:** Bibliographies on business ethics topics; CBE News/Books and surveys; Conference proceedings. **Educational Activities:** Executive education and training programs. **Awards:** Executive Scholar and Research Fellow Programs; Hoffman Prize in Business Ethics.

45741 ■ Ethics Resource Center, Inc.
2345 Crystal Dr., Ste. 201
Arlington, VA 22202
Ph:(703)647-2185
Fax:(703)647-2180
Co. E-mail: pat@ethics.org
URL: http://www.ethics.org
Contact: Patricia Harned PhD, Pres.
E-mail: pat@ethics.org
Scope: Serves as a resource center for information, advice, and educational products and services intended to strengthen interest in organizational ethics and character education. Helps governments, companies, and associations establish standards of ethical conduct and design and implement educational programs that effectively communicate organizational values and personal responsibilities. **Publications:** Annual report; Ethics for Life Video Series; Ethics Today (10/year); Ethics at Work Video Series; National Business Ethics survey reports; Survey reports. **Educational Activities:** Produces films and other instructional materials, for use in public schools to help teachers develop and reinforce positive values and character traits in students; Seminars, on business ethics and character education; Teacher training institutes; Workshops designed to assist in the development and implementation of corporate ethics programs. **Awards:** Stanley C. Pace Distinguished Award to Lecture on Leadership in Ethics.

45742 ■ Santa Clara University–Markkula Center for Applied Ethics
500 El Camino Real
Santa Clara, CA 95053-0633
Ph:(408)554-5319
Fax:(408)554-2373
Co. E-mail: ethics@scu.edu
URL: http://www.scu.edu/ethics
Contact: Kirk O. Hanson, Exec.Dir.
E-mail: ethics@scu.edu
Scope: Ethics in the areas of biotechnology and health care, education, business, and government. Seeks to increase the understanding of the role of ethics in private and public decision-making processes. **Services:** Consulting (weekly), for hospitals, businesses, schools, and nonprofit groups; Curriculum Development in K-12 Character Education. **Publications:** At the Center (annually). **Educational Activities:** Business and Organizational Ethics Partnership (quarterly), between businesses and ethics scholars; Symposia, workshops, lectures (weekly), on applied ethics.

45743 ■ University of Florida–Center for Applied Philosophy and Ethics in the Professions
332 Griffin-Floyd Hall
PO Box 118545
Gainesville, FL 32611-8545
Ph:(352)392-2084
Fax:(352)392-5577
Co. E-mail: rbaum@ufl.edu
Contact: Dr. Robert J. Baum, Dir.
E-mail: rbaum@ufl.edu
Scope: Professional and business ethics. **Publications:** Business and Professional Ethics Journal (quarterly); Professional Ethics (quarterly). **Educational Activities:** Conferences.

45744 ■ University of Virginia–Olsson Center for Applied Ethics
Darden School of Business
100 Darden Blvd.
PO Box 6550
Charlottesville, VA 22906
Ph:(434)924-7247
Fax:(434)924-6378
Co. E-mail: wicksa@darden.virginia.edu
URL: http://www.darden.virginia.edu/web/Olsson-Center-for-Applied-Ethics
Contact: Prof. Andrew C. Wicks, Dir.
E-mail: wicksa@darden.virginia.edu
Scope: Socio/ethical issues relating to business, including standards of conduct. **Educational Activities:** Lectures and seminars, conducive to the exchange of ethical concepts among business executives, academia, and others.

START-UP INFORMATION

45745 ■ *Corporation: Small Business Start-Up Kit*
Pub: Nova Publishing Company
Ed: Daniel Sitarz. **Released:** February 2005. **Price:** $29.95. **Description:** Guidebook to help entrepreneurs start up and run a small business corporation. Book includes state and federal forms with instructions.

45746 ■ *How to Form Your Own California Corporation*
Pub: NOLO
Ed: Anthony Mancuso. **Released:** March 2009. **Price:** $39.99. **Description:** Instructions and forms required to incorporate any business in the State of California.

45747 ■ *How to Start and Run Your Own Corporation: S-Corporations For Small Business Owners*
Pub: HCM Publishing
Ed: Peter I. Hupalo. **Released:** March 6, 2003. **Price:** $22.95. **Description:** Basics of corporate business structure are explained. Topics include discovering the best business structure for your company; how to decided between an S-Corporation and LLC; choosing the state in which to incorporate, how to form a corporation, angel investing, special issues for one-person corporations, the role of bylaws and corporate minutes, board of directors, taxes, workers' compensation issues, retirement plans, and more.

45748 ■ *The Small Business Start-Up Kit*
Pub: NOLO
Ed: Peri Pakroo. **Released:** January 2008. **Price:** $29.99. **Description:** Entrepreneurial advice for launching a new business. Topics include compliance with state regulations, sole proprietorships, partnerships, corporations, limited liability companies, as well as accounting and tax information.

45749 ■ *Structuring Your Business*
Pub: Adams Media Corporation
Ed: Michele Cagan. **Released:** 2004. **Price:** $19.95. **Description:** Accountant and author shares insight into starting a new company. The guide assists entrepreneurs through the process, whether it is a corporation, an LLC, a sole proprietorship, or a partnership. Tax codes, accounting practices and legislation affecting every business as well as tips on managing finances are among the topics covered.

ASSOCIATIONS AND OTHER ORGANIZATIONS

45750 ■ **National Association for the Self-Employed**
PO Box 241
Annapolis Junction, MD 20701-0241
Free: 800-232-6273
URL: http://www.nase.org
Contact: Kristie Arslan, Pres.
Description: Self-employed and small independent businesspersons. Acts as an advocate at the state and federal levels for self-employed people. Provides discounts on products and services important to self-employed and small business owners. **Publications:** *Self-Employed America* (bimonthly); *Washington Watch* (weekly).

REFERENCE WORKS

45751 ■ *Breaking Free: How to Work at Home with the Perfect Small Business Opportunity*
Pub: Lulu.com
Ed: Brian Armstrong. **Released:** June 2007. **Price:** $24.95. **Description:** Three ways to smooth the transition from working for someone else to starting your own business are outlined. Seven exercises to help discover the type of business you should start, how to incorporate, get important tax benefits, and start accepting payments immediately are examined.

45752 ■ *Choosing the Right Legal Form of Business: The Complete Guide to Becoming a Sole Proprietor, Partnership, LLC, or Corporation*
Pub: Atlantic Publishing Company
Ed: Pat Mitchell. **Released:** January 1, 2009. **Price:** $24.95. **Description:** According to the U.S. Small Business Administration, nearly 250,000 new businesses start up annually; currently there are over nine million small companies in the nation. The importance of choosing the proper legal form of business is stressed.

45753 ■ *Deduct It!: Lower Your Small Business Taxes*
Pub: NOLO
Ed: Stephen Fishman. **Released:** November 2009. **Price:** $34.99. **Description:** Ways to maximize business tax deductions for any type of small business owner (sole proprietor, partnership, LLC, corporation).

45754 ■ *Entrepreneurial Finance*
Pub: Pearson Education, Limited
Ed: Philip J. Adelman; Alan M. Marks. **Released:** July 2006. **Price:** $87.35. **Description:** Financial aspects of running a small business are covered; topics include sole proprietorships, partnerships, limited liability companies, and private corporations.

45755 ■ *Fast-Track Business Start-Up Kit: California*
Pub: DP Group, Incorporated
Ed: Carolyn Usinger. **Released:** September 2006. **Price:** $29.00. **Description:** Step-by-step guide for starting and running a business in California, including information on sole proprietors, partnerships, limited liability companies, S and C corporations, as well as details concerning business entities, sales taxes, environmental issues, human resources, and more.

45756 ■ *Getting Rich In Your Underwear: How To Start and Run a Profitable Home-Based Business*
Pub: HCM Publishing
Ed: Peter I. Hupalo. **Released:** April 1, 2005. **Price:** $17.95. **Description:** Book offers insight into starting a home-based business. Entrepreneurs will learn about business models and the home business; distribution and fulfillment of product or service; marketing and sales; how to overcome the fear of starting a business; personal success characteristics; naming a business; zoning and insurance; intellectual capital; copyrights, trademarks, and patents; limited liability companies and S-corporations; business expenses and accounting; taxes; fifteen basic steps for starting a home-based business, state resources for starting a home company; and seven home-based business ideas.

45757 ■ *How to Form Your Own Corporation without a Lawyer for Under $75.00*
Pub: Dearborn Trade Publishing Inc.
Ed: Ted Nicholas; Sean P. Melvin. **Price:** $19.95.

45758 ■ *Own Your Own Corporation: Why the Rich Own Their Own Companies and Everyone Else Works for Them*
Pub: Business Plus
Ed: Garrett Sutton; Robert T. Kiyosaki; Ann Blackman. **Released:** June 2008. **Price:** $17.99 paperback. **Description:** Part of the Rich Dad Advisor's Series, this edition shows how individuals can incorporate themselves and their businesses to save thousands of dollars in taxes and protect against financial disaster.

45759 ■ *"Protect Your Assets" in Black Enterprise* (Vol. 38, January 2008, No. 6, pp. 38)
Pub: Earl G. Graves Publishing Co. Inc.
Ed: Trevor Delaney. **Description:** Owner of rental properties seeks advice for incorporating versus getting an LLC for the business.

45760 ■ *Small Business: An Entrepreneur's Plan*
Pub: Nelson Thomson Learning
Ed: Ronald A. Knowles. **Released:** December 2006. **Description:** Entrepreneur's guide to planning a small business.

45761 ■ *"Sole Proprietorship Returns, 2008 Part 2" in SOI Bulletin* (Vol. 30, Summer 2010, No. 1, pp. 27)
Pub: Government Printing Office
Description: Table of Nonfarm Sole Proprietorships is presented. Statistics are broken down by sector reporting all nonfarm industries as well as agriculture, forestry, hunting and fishing.

45762 ■ *"Sole Proprietorship Returns, 2008" in SOI Bulletin* (Vol. 30, Summer 2010, No. 1, pp. 6)
Pub: Government Printing Office
Ed: Adrian Dungan. **Description:** Approximately 22.6 million individual income tax returns reported nonfarm sole proprietorship activity, a 2.2 percent decrease from 2007. Statistical data included.

45763 ■ *"Startup Makes Attempt to 'Reform' Health Insurance" in Austin Business JournalInc.* (Vol. 29, January 15, 2010, No. 45, pp. 1)
Pub: American City Business Journals
Ed: Sandra Zaragoza. **Description:** Health insurance provider ETMG LLC of Austin, Texas plans to

act as a managing general agent and a third-party administrator that can facilitate customized plans for small businesses and sole proprietors. According to CEO Mark Adams, profitability is expected for ETMG, which have also clinched $1.5 million worth of investments. Entities that have agreed to do business with ETMG are presented.

45764 ■ **"Symbility Solutions Joins Motion Computing Partner Program" in** *Canadian Corporate News* **(May 14, 2007)**
Pub: Comtex News Network Inc.
Description: Symbility Solutions Inc., a wholly owned subsidiary of Automated Benefits Corp., announced an agreement with Alliance Partner of Motion Computing, a leader in wireless communications and mobile computing, in which both companies will invest in a sales and marketing strategy that focuses specifically on the insurance market.

45765 ■ *Working Solo*
Pub: John Wiley & Sons Inc.
Contact: Terri Lonier, Author
Price: $21.95, individuals paperback. **Covers:** Over 1,000 solo business opportunities, as well as a resource section on publications, organizations, and other essential contacts for solo professionals.

VIDEOCASSETTES/ AUDIOCASSETTES

45766 ■ *Be Your Own Boss: Start a Business*
The Learning Seed
641 W. Lake St., Ste. 301
Chicago, IL 60661
Free: 800-634-4941
Fax:800-998-0854
Co. E-mail: info@learningseed.com
URL: http://www.learningseed.com
Released: 1992. **Price:** $89.00. **Description:** Four Chicago-area entrepreneurs offer advice on starting your own business and cover topics such as market research, location selection, promotion, financial planning, legal requirements and more. **Availability:** VHS.

45767 ■ *Doing Business*
The Cinema Guild
115 West 30th St., Ste. 800
New York, NY 10001
Ph:(212)685-6242
Free: 800-723-5522
Fax:(212)685-4717
Co. E-mail: info@cinemaguild.com
URL: http://www.cinemaguild.com
Released: 1981. **Description:** This documentary offers an insightful examination of self-managed businesses. The film is frank about the problems involved in going into business for oneself, including the delicacy of managing employees, arranging non-stressful working conditions, and balancing the desire for growth with a sense of family. **Availability:** 3/4U; Special order formats.

45768 ■ *How to Beat the Odds*
National Audiovisual Center
5301 Shawnee Rd.
Alexandria, VA 22312
Ph:(703)605-6000
Free: 800-553-6847
Fax:(703)321-8547
Co. E-mail: customerservice@ntis.gov
URL: http://www.ntis.gov/products/nac.aspx
Released: 1980. **Price:** $95.00. **Description:** This video is designed to be an aid to small business own-ers trying to get ahead, and includes many strategies and tips from those entrepreneurs in the government bureaucracy. **Availability:** VHS; 3/4U.

45769 ■ *How to Start Your Own Successful Business*
Instructional Video
2219 C St.
Lincoln, NE 68502
Ph:(402)475-6570
Free: 800-228-0164
Fax:(402)475-6500
Co. E-mail: feedback@insvideo.com
URL: http://www.insvideo.com
Price: $29.95. **Description:** Illustrates correct procedures for establishing and maintaining an effective business. Covers marketing, managing, financing, business insurance, buying an existing business, franchising, home-based business, youth entrepreneurial business, negotiating deals, and projecting your ideas. **Availability:** VHS.

45770 ■ *New or Used? Buying a Firm or Starting Your Own*
Instructional Video
2219 C St.
Lincoln, NE 68502
Ph:(402)475-6570
Free: 800-228-0164
Fax:(402)475-6500
Co. E-mail: feedback@insvideo.com
URL: http://www.insvideo.com
Price: $99.00. **Description:** Details the different options open to anyone wanting to start or obtain their own business. Discusses the various factors to be considered when putting a value on a company, negotiating price and terms, and closing the deal. **Availability:** VHS.

ASSOCIATIONS AND OTHER ORGANIZATIONS

45771 ■ Alcoholics Anonymous World Services
PO Box 459
New York, NY 10163
Ph:(212)870-3400
URL: http://www.aa.org
Description: Individuals recovering from alcoholism. Maintains that members can solve their common problem and help others achieve sobriety through a twelve step program that includes sharing their experience, strength, and hope with each other. Self-supported through members' contributions, not an allied with any sect, denomination, political organization, or institution and does not endorse nor oppose any cause. .

45772 ■ Institute for a Drug-Free Workplace
10701 Parkridge Blvd., Ste. 300
Reston, VA 20191
Ph:(703)391-7222
Fax:(703)391-7223
Co. E-mail: institute@drugfreeworkplace.org
URL: http://www.drugfreeworkplace.org
Contact: Mark A. de Bernardo, Exec. Dir.
Description: Businesses, organizations, and individuals united to preserve the rights of employers and employees involved in corporate drug abuse prevention programs. Seeks to influence public policy pertaining to drug-abuse prevention in the workplace. Conducts surveys. **Publications:** *Avoiding Legal Liability: The 25 Most Common Employer Mistakes in Addressing Drug Abuse*; *Does Drug Testing Work?*; *Drug and Alcohol Abuse Prevention and the ADA: An Employer's Guide*; *Drug Testing in the Workplace: Basic Issues, Answers, and Options for Employees*; *Employee Assistance Programs: An Employer's Development and Implementation Guide*; *Employee Drug Education and Awareness and Supervisor Training: An Employer's Development and Implementation Guide*; *Guide to Dangerous Drugs*; *Guide to State and Federal Drug Testing Laws* (annual); *International Guide to Workplace Substance Abuse Prevention*; *Policy on Drug and Alcohol Abuse Prevention: An Employer's Development and Implementation Guide*; *What Every Employee Should Know About Alcohol Abuse: Answer to 25 Good Questions* .

45773 ■ Institute on Global Drug Policy
5999 Central Ave., Ste. 301
St. Petersburg, FL 33704-2744
Ph:(727)828-0211
Fax:(727)828-0212
Co. E-mail: info@globaldrugpolicy.org
URL: http://www.globaldrugpolicy.org
Contact: Lana Beck, Managing Ed.
Description: Works to exchange information about drug policy and practice while sharing different cultural attitudes and perspective on the drug issue. Disseminates accurate scientific information on drugs. **Publications:** *Journal of Global Drug Policy and Practice* (quarterly).

45774 ■ NAADAC: The Association for Addiction Professionals
1001 N Fairfax St., Ste. 201
Alexandria, VA 22314
Ph:(703)741-7686
Free: 800-548-0497
Fax:(703)741-7698
Co. E-mail: naadac@naadac.org
URL: http://www.naadac.org
Contact: Donald P. Osborn, Pres.
Description: Promotes excellence in care by promoting up-to-date and science-based services to clients, families, and communities. Provides education, clinical training and certification. Among the organization's national certification programs are the National Certified Addiction Counselor, Tobacco Addiction Credential and the Masters Addiction Counselor designations. **Publications:** *The Basics of Addiction Counseling: A Desk Reference and Study Guide* (periodic); *Basics of Addiction Counseling Independent Study Course* (periodic); *NAADAC News* (bimonthly).

45775 ■ Narcotics Anonymous
PO Box 9999
Van Nuys, CA 91409
Ph:(818)773-9999
Fax:(818)700-0700
Co. E-mail: fsmail@na.org
URL: http://www.na.org
Contact: Jeff Gershoff, Service Coor.
Description: Aims to recover addicts throughout the world, works to offer help to fellow addicts seeking recovery. Meets regularly to facilitate and stabilize their recovery. Uses 12-step program adapted from Alcoholics Anonymous to aid in the recovery process. **Publications:** *A Guide to Public Information*; *Just For Today: Daily Meditations for Recovering Addicts*; *The NA Way Magazine: The International Journal of Narcotics Anonymous* (quarterly).

45776 ■ National Association of Addiction Treatment Providers
313 W Liberty St., Ste. 129
Lancaster, PA 17603-2748
Ph:(717)392-8480
Fax:(717)392-8481
Co. E-mail: kcarpenterpalumbo@naatp.org
URL: http://www.naatp.org
Contact: Karen Carpenter-Palumbo, Pres./CEO
Description: Corporate and private institutional alcohol and/or drug dependency treatment facilities. Promotes awareness of chemical dependency as a treatable disease; advocates high standards of health care in substance abuse treatment facilities. Encourages member education. Maintains contact with U.S. Congress and state and local governments. Serves in an advisory capacity to the Joint Commission on Accreditation of Healthcare Organizations and to the Commission on Accreditation of Rehabilitation Facilities. Compiles statistics on chemical dependency treatment and recovery. **Publications:** *Benchmark Survey* (annual).

45777 ■ National Association on Drug Abuse Problems
355 Lexington Ave.
New York, NY 10017
Ph:(212)986-1170
Fax:(212)697-2939
Co. E-mail: info@nadap.org
URL: http://www.nadap.org
Contact: John A. Darin, Pres./CEO
Description: Serves as an information clearinghouse and referral bureau for corporations and local communities interested in prevention of substance abuse and treatment of substance abusers. Provides: resources to local communities seeking to combat drug and alcohol abuse; corporate services for employers interested in creating a drug-free workplace. Makes available vocational education services including training in job hunting, job interview workshops, training programs for substance abuse treatment professionals, and individual consultations for recovering substance abusers seeking to return to the job market. Provides placement services; has conducted surveys on the employability of rehabilitated drug users and found that former addicts perform comparably with others hired for similar jobs. Operates Neighborhood Prevention Network, through which local communities develop parent support groups and youth peer leadership groups dedicated to combating drug and alcohol abuse. Maintains speakers' bureau. **Publications:** *NADAP News/Report* (quarterly).

45778 ■ Substance Abuse Librarians and Information Specialists
PO Box 9513
Berkeley, CA 94709-0513
Ph:(510)769-1831
Fax:(510)865-2467
Co. E-mail: salis@salis.org
URL: http://www.salis.org
Contact: Andrea Mitchell, Exec. Dir.
Description: Individuals and organizations interested in the collection, organization, dissemination, exchange, and retrieval of materials concerning substance abuse, including alcohol, tobacco, and other drugs. Provides professional development and exchange of information and concerns about access to and dissemination of information on substance abuse. Offers information on films, books, articles, pamphlets, reports, government publications, libraries, clearinghouses, and information centers. **Publications:** *SALIS News* (quarterly).

REFERENCE WORKS

45779 ■ *Case Management Resource Guide*
Pub: Access Intelligence L.L.C.
Released: Annual, latest edition 2005-2006. **Price:** $60, individuals for additional copy, per volume. **Entries Include:** Facility name, address, phone names and titles of key personnel; number of employees, geographical area served, type of service or programs provided branch office or parent organization name and phone, and credentials. **Database Covers:** In four regional volumes, lists 110,000 health care facili-

ties and support services, including homecare, rehabilitation, psychiatric, and addiction treatment program; hospices, adult day care, and burn and cancer centers. **Arrangement:** Classified by service provided and location. **Indexes:** Company name, advertiser.

TRADE PERIODICALS

45780 ■ Forensic Drug Abuse Advisor
Pub: Forensic Drug Abuse Advisor Inc.
Ed: Steven B. Karch, M.D., Editor. **Released:** 10/year. **Price:** $197, individuals. **Description:** Acts as a drug information source. Emphasizes the latest scientific discoveries in drug abuse, workplace drug testing, federal drug law, and forensic pathology. An absolute necessity in drug related litigation. Recurring features include letters to the editor, news of research, a calendar of events, reports of meetings, news of educational opportunities, book reviews, and notices of publications available. Continuing medical education available.

45781 ■ Hazelden Voice
Pub: Hazelden Foundation
Ed: Marty Duda, Editor, mduda@hazelden.org. **Released:** 2/year. **Price:** Free. **Description:** Reports on Hazelden activities and programs, and discusses developments and issues in chemical dependency treatment and prevention.

45782 ■ ICPA Reporter
Pub: International Commission for the Prevention of Alcoholism and Drug Dependency
Contact: Gary B. Swanson, Managing Editor
Ed: Peter H. Landless, Editor. **Released:** DependencySemiannual. **Price:** Free. **Description:** Reports on activities of the Commission worldwide, which seeks to prevent alcoholism and drug dependency. Recurring features include a calendar of events and notices of publications available.

45783 ■ Journal of Drug Education
Pub: Baywood Publishing Company Inc.
Contact: James Robinson, Exec. Ed.
Released: 4/yr. **Price:** $402 institutions; $381 institutions online. **Description:** Peer-reviewed journal on the behavioral consequences of drug use and abuse for education professionals, health professionals, social service and Armed Forces personnel.

45784 ■ The Prevention Researcher
Pub: Integrated Research Services Inc.
Ed: Steven Ungerleider, Ph.D., Editor, suinteg@attglobal.net. **Released:** Quarterly, 4/year. **Price:** $36, individuals; $48 libraries. **Description:** Specializes in prevention topics for at-risk youth.

VIDEOCASSETTES/ AUDIOCASSETTES

45785 ■ Creating a Drug-Free Workplace
Coastal Training Technologies Corp.
500 Studio Dr.
Virginia Beach, VA 23452
Ph:(757)498-9014
Free: 877-262-7825
Fax:(757)498-3657
Co. E-mail: info@training.dupont.com
URL: http://www.coastal.com
Released: 1993. **Price:** $395. **Description:** Two acted stories illustrate workers having problems with drug and alcohol problems and who create problems for their companies. **Availability:** VHS.

45786 ■ Disease Concept of Alcoholism/EAP
New Dimension Media, Inc.
307 N Michigan Ave., Ste. 500
Chicago, IL 60601
Ph:(312)642-9400
Free: 800-288-4456
Fax:(312)642-9805
Co. E-mail: Info@NDMquestar.com
URL: http://www.ndmquestar.com
Released: 1986. **Price:** $50.00. **Description:** Information designed for supervisory training that stresses communication and motivation. **Availability:** VHS; 3/4U.

45787 ■ The Drug-Free Workplace
Learning Communications LLC
5520 Trabuco Rd.
Irvine, CA 92620
Free: 800-622-3610
Fax:(949)727-4323
Co. E-mail: sales@learncom.com
URL: http://www.learncomhr.com
Released: 1991. **Price:** $175.00. **Description:** A two-part program designed to make employees and managers aware of the provisions of the Drug-Free Workplace Act. Includes a Compliance and Implementation Guide, as well as participants manuals. **Availability:** VHS; 3/4U.

45788 ■ Drug Testing in the Workplace
American Bar Association
321 N. Clark St.
Chicago, IL 60654-7598
Ph:(312)988-5000
Free: 800-285-2221
Fax:(312)988-5494
Co. E-mail: abapubed@abanet.org
URL: http://www.abanet.org/publiced/
Released: 1987. **Price:** $295.00. **Description:** The story of what one company did about drug testing after a suspicious on-the-job accident. Urine and blood testing are demonstrated. **Availability:** VHS; 3/4U.

45789 ■ Drugs in the Workplace
Curtis, Inc.
1105 Western Ave.
Cincinnati, OH 45203
Ph:(513)621-8895
Free: 800-733-2878
Fax:(513)621-0942
Co. E-mail: info@curtisinc.com
URL: http://www.curtisinc.com
Description: A four-part series for supervisors demonstrating how to handle workers who engage in substance abuse. **Availability:** VHS.

45790 ■ Drugs in the Workplace 2: What Every Manager and Supervisor Must Know
Aspen Publishers
7201 McKinney Circ.
Frederick, MD 21704
Ph:(301)698-7100
Free: 800-234-1660
Fax:800-901-9075
URL: http://www.aspenpublishers.com
Released: 1987. **Price:** $495.00. **Description:** Supervisors see what must be done to stop drug abuse in the workplace, and they also learn what, legally, they can and can't do about the problem. **Availability:** VHS; 3/4U.

45791 ■ Managing a Drug-Free Work Environment
Encyclopedia Britannica
331 N. LaSalle St.
Chicago, IL 60654
Ph:(312)347-7159
Free: 800-323-1229
Fax:(312)294-2104
URL: http://www.britannica.com
Released: 1989. **Price:** $495.00. **Description:** This film focuses on the role and responsibility of managers in counteracting drug abuse in the workplace. **Availability:** VHS; 3/4U.

45792 ■ The Physiological Effects of Cocaine
Phoenix Learning Group
2349 Chaffee Dr.
St. Louis, MO 63146-3306
Ph:(314)569-0211
Free: 800-221-1274
Fax:(314)569-2834
URL: http://www.phoenixlearninggroup.com
Released: 198?. **Description:** Provides the professional with information on the physiological effects of cocaine. Also includes information on the history and physical properties of cocaine. **Availability:** VHS; 3/4U.

45793 ■ Substance Abuse: Everyone's Problem
AJN Video Library/Lippincott Williams & Wilkins
American Journal of Nursing
345 Hudson St., 16th Fl.
New York, NY 10014
Ph:(212)886-1200
Free: 800-256-4045
Fax:(212)886-1276
Co. E-mail: info@nursingcenter.com
URL: http://www.nursingcenter.com
Price: $250.00. **Description:** Describes the signs of drug and alcohol abuse and the steps to take if a staff member is suspected of having these problems. Also discusses how to plan and conduct a management conference, what to do when immediate action is needed, and how to motivate the staff member to seek help. Emphasis is placed on getting the employee to acknowledge that they have a problem and need help. **Availability:** VHS.

45794 ■ Taking Action: Substance Abuse in the Workplace
Phoenix Learning Group
2349 Chaffee Dr.
St. Louis, MO 63146-3306
Ph:(314)569-0211
Free: 800-221-1274
Fax:(314)569-2834
URL: http://www.phoenixlearninggroup.com
Released: 1989. **Price:** $600.00. **Description:** This video will help managers implement an effective substance abuse prevention program for the workplace. **Availability:** VHS; 8mm; 3/4U.

45795 ■ Taking Action 2: Frontline Against Drugs
Aspen Publishers
7201 McKinney Circ.
Frederick, MD 21704
Ph:(301)698-7100
Free: 800-234-1660
Fax:800-901-9075
URL: http://www.aspenpublishers.com
Released: 1991. **Price:** $600. **Description:** A follow-up video to "Taking Action," this program creates scenarios where workers at various levels are advised what to do when co-workers are abusing drugs or alcohol. **Availability:** VHS.

45796 ■ Working Drug Free
Cambridge Educational
c/o Films Media Group
132 West 31st Street, 17th Floor
Ste. 124
New York, NY 10001
Free: 800-257-5126
Fax:(609)671-0266
Co. E-mail: custserve@films.com
URL: http://www.cambridgeol.com
Price: $475.00. **Description:** The physiological effects of drugs on the brain are examined to illustrate the dangers involved and how this may hamper work performance. Produced in compliance with the Federal Drug-Free Workplace Act. **Availability:** VHS; 3/4U; Special order formats.

CONSULTANTS

45797 ■ Aantia Kersey & Associates
17716 Oak Park Ave.
Tinley Park, IL 60477-3936
Ph:(708)460-6060
Fax:(708)460-6060
Co. E-mail: antia@juno.com
Contact: Dr. Kersey H. Antia, Owner
E-mail: antia@juno.com
Scope: Human resources development consultants offering employee assistance programs in alcohol and substance abuse for employees with problems, psychological services to industry and public and private organizations and on-the-spot or by-mail psychological testing programs for selection, promotion and transfer of employees. Serves private industries as well as government agencies. **Semi-**

nars: Stress; Time Management; Smoking Cessation; Morale Improvement; Detection of Substance Abuse Among Employees.

45798 ■ Bensinger, Du Pont & Associates
134 N LaSalle St., Ste. 2200
Chicago, IL 60602
Ph:(312)726-8620
Free: 800-227-8620
Fax:(312)726-1061
Co. E-mail: marie.apke@bensingerdupont.com
URL: http://www.bensingerdupont.com
Contact: Dr. Al Beaubier, Vice President
E-mail: abeaubier@atsaol.com
Scope: Employee Assistance Program EAP provider, gambling help line provider, consultant on substance abuse, drug testing and gambling addiction. **Publications:** "Drug Testing in Treatment Settings, Drug Testing in Schools," 2005; "Drug Testing in Correctional Settings," 2005; "Getting Tough on Gateway Drugs: A Guide for the Family"; "A Bridge to Recovery: An Introduction to Twelve-Step Programs"; "The Selfish Brain: Learning from Addiction".

45799 ■ Birenbaum & Associates
906 Olive St., Ste. 1200
Saint Louis, MO 63101-1448
Ph:(314)241-1445
Fax:(314)241-1449
Co. E-mail: birenbaum@birenbaum.org
Contact: Mark S. Birenbaum, President
Scope: Multi-association management firm and industrial relations specialists offering consultation to management in public and private sectors. Specializes in meeting management. Clients include manufacturing, service industry, fire protection districts, and government. **Seminars:** Alcohol/Drug Abuse Policies for Employers.

45800 ■ Chris Frings & Associates
633 Winwood Dr.
Birmingham, AL 35226-2837
Ph:(205)823-5044
Fax:(205)823-4283
Co. E-mail: chris@chrisfrings.com
URL: http://www.chrisfrings.com
Contact: Christopher S. Frings, President
E-mail: cfrings@compuserve.com
Scope: Provides expert testimony and consultation for court and arbitration regarding abused drug testing. Consultant to industry and labor relations attorneys with abused drug testing needs and problems. Also offers seminars and workshops and keynote speeches on management issues. **Publications:** "The Hitchhikers Guide to Effective Time Management: The Only Time Management Book You Will Ever Need," Aacc Press, 2004. **Seminars:** Workplace Drug Testing; Effective Time Management; Stress Management; Managing Change; Management and Leadership Strategies for Succeeding in the 21st Century; Increasing Productivity Through Effective Time &Information Management; Mastering Change; Management Q & A.

45801 ■ Cook International Inc.
5659 Thicket Ln.
PO Box 2128
Columbia, MD 21044-2557
Ph:(410)992-7318
Contact: Clarence Cook, Owner
Scope: Offers both consultation and operational field services for both basic and complex security problems required by government and private industry. Services include security surveys and vulnerability studies, personnel background investigations, security guard training, pre-board screening for airlines, internal/external investigations, building security planning and design and drug abuse programs. Industries served: Automobile dealers, retail stores, U.S. and local governments and military installations. **Seminars:** Drug Abuse in Industry.

45802 ■ Drug Testing Consultants Inc.
10875 Main St., Ste. 107
PO Box 706
Fairfax, VA 22030-0706
Ph:(703)273-1757
Free: 800-944-8378

Fax:(703)352-7124
Contact: Vern Jones, Principle
E-mail: rschoening@comdt.uscg.mil
Scope: Conducts workplace drug testing programs for government and private sectors.

45803 ■ DW Smothers and Associates
3137 Castro Valley Blvd., Ste. 215
PO Box 2804
Castro Valley, CA 94546
Ph:(510)728-9861
Free: 800-818-7654
Fax:(510)728-9802
Co. E-mail: dwsl@flash.net
URL: http://www.picoop.com
Contact: David W. Smothers, President
E-mail: dws1@flash.net
Scope: Provides investigative consulting regarding loss prevention in areas of personnel safety and physical security. Active in systems and procedures design as well as development of same. Serves private industries as well as government agencies.

45804 ■ Healy & Associates Inc.
3033 W Jefferson St., Apt. W
Joliet, IL 60435-6449
Ph:(815)741-0102
Fax:(815)744-5412
Contact: Richard Kelling, President
Scope: Personal development consultant with experience in alcoholism and family treatment; employee assistance program consultation and implementation; health promotion programming on stress, smoking cessation, weight control; alcohol and drug related prevention and educational programming; and individual, group and family counseling. Serves private industries as wells government agencies. **Seminars:** Assertive Communication; Alcohol and Drug Problems in the Workplace; Chemical Dependency: Enabling vs. Intervention; Stress Management; Employee Assistance Programs; Smoking Cessation in the Workplace; Eating and Weight Issues; Cultural Diversity Training; Adapting to Change in the Workplace; Adapting to Shift Work.

45805 ■ National Scientific Services
3411 Philips Dr.
Baltimore, MD 21208-1827
Ph:(410)486-7486
Fax:(410)653-4824
Co. E-mail: fortox@aol.com
Contact: Yale H. Caplan, Director
Scope: Consultant in toxicology, drug and chemical analysis, workplace drug testing, and interpretation of toxicology information. Serves as expert witness in drunk driving and drug testing cases. **Publications:** "Garriott's Medicolegal Aspects of Alcohol," Lawyers & Judges Publishing Co.

45806 ■ Professional Alternative Inc.
101 Derby St., Ste. 200
Hingham, MA 02043
Ph:(617)722-6020
Fax:(617)722-6029
Co. E-mail: info@profalt.com
URL: http://www.profalt.com
Contact: Patrick Cox, Principal
E-mail: pcox@profalt.com
Scope: Human resources consulting firm specializes in technical industries.

45807 ■ Recovery Communications Inc.
PO Box 19910
Baltimore, MD 21211
Ph:(410)243-8352
Fax:(410)243-8558
Co. E-mail: tdrews3879@aol.com
URL: http://www.gettingthemsober.com
Contact: Toby Rice Drews, President
E-mail: tdrews3879@aol.com
Scope: Acts as expert witness and offers consultation in the field of substance abuse and addiction. Industries served: legal, health care and government. **Publications:** "Getting Them Sober, Volume One"; "Getting Them Sober: You Can Help," Recovery Communications, Apr. 1998; "Getting Your Children Sober"; "Sex and the Sober Alcoholic: A Healing Guide and Workbook"; "Get Rid of Anxiety and

Stress". **Seminars:** Attachments and Excited Miseries in the Workplace; Getting Past Stuck-Points in Recovery; Replacing the Excitement of Sickness.

45808 ■ Richard C. Webber Associates L.L.C.
3760 S Highland Dr., Ste. 431
Salt Lake City, UT 84106
Ph:(801)273-3322
Fax:(801)273-3321
Co. E-mail: rickcwebber@cs.com
Contact: Richard C. Webber, President
E-mail: rickcwebber@cs.com
Scope: Consulting firm that provides public safety, law enforcement and expert witness testimony services. Specializing in the development and presentation of drug and substance abuse programs, as well as executive and employee development programs. Specializes in instructor development (train-the-trainer), curriculum design and development, presentation skills and stage fright coping skills, and media relations. Leadership and motivation seminars are offered for both middle management and executives. Industries served include city, county, state, and federal law enforcement agencies; energy and oil; aerospace and aircraft; motion picture; and government agencies. **Publications:** "Drugs/Alcohol in the Workplace"; "Employment change and individual career marketing when looking to change careers". **Seminars:** Drugs/Alcohol in the Workplace; Instructor Development; Media Relations; Leadership; Stress Management; Time Management; Outplacement and Job Searching Skill Enhancement.

45809 ■ Richard Haynes & Associates L.L.C.
1021 Temple St.
Charleston, WV 25312-2153
Ph:(304)346-6228
Fax:(304)346-9135
Co. E-mail: captrah@citynet.net
Contact: Suzanne E. Haynes, Principle
E-mail: captrah@citynet.net
Scope: Security management consultant. Offers the following services: security surveys and audits; security readiness for labor disputes; investigations; security training and awareness programs; special projects. Industries served: mining, petroleum, law enforcement, private security companies and government agencies. **Publications:** "Let's Talk Security," Kanawha Valley Business Monthly; "The SWAT Cyclopedia" Aug, 1999. **Seminars:** Personal Protection Workshop: Workplace Violence.

45810 ■ Safety & Loss Control Associates
515 Arbor Ln.
PO Box 611
South Elgin, IL 60177
Ph:(847)622-1690
Fax:(847)622-1695
Co. E-mail: donneslund@aol.com
URL: http://www.safetyandlosscontrolassoc.com
Contact: Donald A. Neslund, Owner
E-mail: donneslund@aol.com
Scope: Assists contractors and industrial operators in reducing worker injuries and illnesses. Safety and training consulting includes employee training, supervisor and management seminars, OSHA compliance audits, pre-job inspections, expert witness work, accident investigation and reconstruction. Also provides expertise in ladders and scaffolds, fall protection, drugs and alcohol in work place, confined space entry, blasting and man produced vibration, driving, trench safety, Hazcom and lockout and tag out. Serves the construction, insurance, legal profession and manufacturing industries. **Seminars:** Hazard Communication-Construction, Trench Safety, OSHA 30-hour Hazard Recognition Course; Communication and Interpersonal Skills Workshops.

45811 ■ VMC Consulting Service
12 S Division St.
Peekskill, NY 10566-3608
Ph:(914)737-1977
Fax:(914)838-2331
Contact: Vail M. Conn, Director
Scope: Social issues counseling offered on family problems, dysfunctional disorders, and drug and alcohol abuse. Also provides expertise to companies including EAP consulting and assessment-referral services. Training extended to human resource

management and staff on substance abuse problems. **Seminars:** Substance Abuse Problems: How to Deal With Them; Alcoholism in the Family and Workplace; Drug Addiction and the Consequences; Recognizing and Dealing With Substance Abuse Problems.

COMPUTERIZED DATABASES

45812 ■ *ETOH, the Alcohol and Alcohol Problems Science Database*
U.S. National Institutes of Health
5635 Fishers Ln.
MSC 9304
Bethesda, MD 20892-9304
Ph:(301)443-3860
Fax:(301)443-6077
Co. E-mail: niaaweb-r@exchange.nih.gov
URL: http://www.niaaa.nih.gov
Description: Contains more than 130,000 citations, with abstracts, to worldwide literature on alcoholism research. Sources include periodicals, monographs, conference proceedings, reports, and dissertation abstracts. **Availability:** Online: Wolters Kluwer Health, U.S. National Institutes of Health. **Type:** Bibliographic.

LIBRARIES

45813 ■ Addictions Foundation of Manitoba–William Potoroka Memorial Library
1031 Portage Ave.
Winnipeg, MB, Canada R3G 0R8
Ph:(204)944-6233
Free: (866)638-2568
Fax:(204)772-0225
Co. E-mail: library@afm.mb.ca
URL: http://www.afm.mb.ca
Scope: Alcohol and drug use and abuse, gambling, psychology, education, treatment, counseling, FASD. **Services:** Interlibrary loan; copying; Library open to the public. **Holdings:** 5500 books; 36 pamphlet titles; 1020 videocassettes/DVDs. **Subscriptions:** 30 journals and other serials.

45814 ■ Akeela Inc. Library
4111 Minnesota Dr.
Anchorage, AK 99503
Ph:(907)565-1200
Fax:(907)258-6052
Co. E-mail: library@akeela.org
URL: http://www.akeela.org/
Contact: Anjana Roy, Libn.
Scope: Alcohol and other drugs. **Services:** Library open to the public. **Holdings:** 1500 curriculum and training materials; 4000 books; 1000 videotapes. **Subscriptions:** 160 journals and other serials.

45815 ■ Alcohol Research Group Library
Public Health Inst.
6475 Christie Ave., Ste. 400
Emeryville, CA 94608-1010
Ph:(510)597-3440
Fax:(510)985-6459
Co. E-mail: library@arg.org
URL: http://www.arg.org/resources/library.php
Contact: Jeff Schiller, Libn.
Scope: Alcohol use and abuse, epidemiology of alcohol use and allied problems, drug use and abuse, tobacco and use. **Services:** Copying; SDI; Library open to the public by appointment. **Holdings:** 6000 books; 60,000 reprints, reports, dissertations. **Subscriptions:** 300 journals and other serials.

45816 ■ Centre for Addiction and Mental Health Library
33 Russell St.
Toronto, ON, Canada M5S 2S1
Ph:(416)595-6144
Fax:(416)595-6601
Co. E-mail: library@camh.net
URL: http://www.camh.net/About_Addiction_Mental_Health/CAMH_Library/index.html
Contact: Sheila Lacroix, Lib.Coord.
Scope: Alcoholism, substance abuse, psychiatric disorders, mental illness, mental health. **Services:** Interlibrary loan (in Canada only); AV loan (Ontario

only); copying; SDI; Library open to the public. **Holdings:** 30,000 books; 11,000 reprints; 1250 audio/visual items. **Subscriptions:** 300 journals and other serials.

45817 ■ Drug & Alcohol Treatment Association of Rhode Island–In-Rhodes Library Library
102 Dupont Dr.
Providence, RI 02907
Ph:(401)521-5759
Fax:(401)751-7850
Co. E-mail: dcohen@dataofri.org
URL: http://www.dataofri.org/
Contact: Debra Cohen-Estes, Libn.
Scope: Alcohol, tobacco, drugs, HIV, sexually transmitted diseases, domestic violence, mental health, parenting, mentoring, other isms and disorders, self-esteem gambling. **Services:** Library open to the public. **Holdings:** 1700 books; 1400 videocassettes; 375 audiocassettes; 4100 reference materials. **Subscriptions:** 2 journals and other serials.

45818 ■ Hazelden Library–Library CO-4
15251 Pleasant Valley Rd.
Center City, MN 55012
Ph:(651)213-4093
Free: 800-257-7810
Fax:(651)213-4411
Co. E-mail: bweiner@hazelden.org
URL: http://www.hazelden.org/web/go/library
Contact: Barbara S. Weiner, MLS, Mgr.
Scope: Chemical dependency, alcoholism, treatment, chronic illness, spirituality, twelve steps, recovery, self-help, addictions, personal growth, family, counseling. **Services:** Library open to the public with restrictions. **Holdings:** 15,000 books; 600 cassette tapes; 700 videos. **Subscriptions:** 90 journals and other serials.

45819 ■ Lakeview Center, Inc. Library
1221 W. Lakeview Ave.
Pensacola, FL 32501
Ph:(850)432-1222
URL: http://www.ebaptisthealthcare.org/Lakeview-Center/
Scope: Psychiatry, psychology, alcoholism, drug addiction, children's and young adults' problems, management. **Services:** Interlibrary loan; copying; Library open to adult practitioners and interns. **Holdings:** 1921 books; 106 videocassettes; 75 kits; 227 government documents; 5 games. **Subscriptions:** 33 journals and other serials.

45820 ■ Maine State Office of Substance Abuse–Information and Resource Center
11 State House Station
41 Anthony Ave.
Augusta, ME 04333-0011
Ph:(207)287-8900
Free: 800-499-0027
Fax:(207)287-8910
Co. E-mail: osa.ircosa@maine.gov
URL: http://www.maine.gov/dhhs/osa/irc
Contact: Jo McCaslin, Coord.
Scope: Alcohol and drugs - use, abuse, dependency, education, prevention, and training; youth suicide prevention. **Services:** Center open to school systems, community organizations, agencies, and professionals. **Holdings:** 5800 books; 1600 videotapes and DVDs. **Subscriptions:** 20 journals and other serials.

45821 ■ National Clearinghouse for Alcohol and Drug Information Library
PO Box 2345
Rockville, MD 20847-2345
Ph:(301)468-2600
Free: 800-729-6686
Fax:(301)468-6433
Co. E-mail: info@health.org
URL: http://ftp.health.org
Contact: Lizabeth J. Foster, Libn.
Scope: Alcohol, tobacco, and other drug abuse. **Services:** Interlibrary loan; copying; SDI; Library open to the public for reference use only. **Holdings:** 3721 books; 80,000 cataloged items; 80,000 accessioned items; digitized documents; reports; manuscripts. **Subscriptions:** 141 journals and other serials; 8 newspapers.

45822 ■ North Conway Institute–Resource Center - Alcohol and Drugs
168 Mt. Vernon St.
West Newton, MA 02165-2517
Ph:(617)742-0424
Contact: Rev. David A. Works, Pres.
Scope: Alcohol, drugs. **Services:** Center open to the public. **Holdings:** 800 books. **Subscriptions:** 50 journals and other serials.

45823 ■ Nova Scotia Department of Education–Drug Dependency Services Division Library
Lord Nelson Bldg.
5675 Spring Garden Rd.
Halifax, NS, Canada B3J 1H1
Ph:(902)424-7214
Fax:(902)425-0550
Contact: Ruth Vaughan
Scope: Health. **Services:** Interlibrary loan; copying. **Holdings:** 5000 books. **Subscriptions:** 50 journals and other serials; 3 newspapers.

45824 ■ Ohio Center for Prevention Studies–Ohio Safe Schools Center
Teachers Bldg., Rm. 439
PO Box 210109
Cincinnati, OH 45221-0109
Free: 800-788-7254
Fax:(513)556-0782
Co. E-mail: robert.canning@uc.edu
URL: http://www.ebasedprevention.org
Contact: Bonnie Hedrick, Prin. Investigator
Scope: Safe School trainings, school climate, violence, drug abuse, alcohol, AIDS.

45825 ■ Prevention Research Center–Library and Information Services
1995 University Ave., Ste. 450
Berkeley, CA 94704
Ph:(510)486-1111
Fax:(510)644-0594
Co. E-mail: center@prev.org
URL: http://www.prev.org/
Contact: Julie Murphy, Mgr. of Lib. & Info.Svcs.
Scope: Alcohol and drug abuse prevention research. **Services:** Library not open to the public. **Holdings:** 1500 books; 4000 reprints; 2000 reports. **Subscriptions:** 35 journals and other serials.

45826 ■ Rebok Memorial Library
12501 Old Columbia Pike
PO Box 4999
Silver Spring, MD 20904
Ph:(301)680-6495
Fax:(301)680-6090
Co. E-mail: ahecht@capaccess.org
URL: http://www.loc.gov/rr/main/religion/sevadv.html
Contact: Alan Hecht, Dir.
Scope: Social problems - alcohol, tobacco, narcotics; health and temperance general, history, religion, women's studies, family life. **Services:** Interlibrary loan; copying; SDI; Library open to the public with restrictions (appointment required for first visit). **Holdings:** 9700 books. **Subscriptions:** 50 journals and other serials; 6 newspapers.

45827 ■ Research Institute on Addictions Library
University at Buffalo
1021 Main St.
Buffalo, NY 14203-1016
Ph:(716)887-2511
Fax:(716)887-2490
Co. E-mail: sawusch@ria.buffalo.edu
URL: http://www.ria.buffalo.edu
Contact: Ann Mina Sawusch, MSW, MLS, Hd.Libn.
Scope: Alcoholism, drug dependence, and alcohol and drug abuse physiological, psychological, sociological, biochemical, pharmacological aspects. **Services:** Interlibrary loan; copying; Library open to the public for reference use only. **Holdings:** 4000 books; 400 periodical titles. **Subscriptions:** 130 journals and other serials.

45828 ■ Rutgers University–Rutgers Center of Alcohol Studies
Smithers Hall
607 Allison Rd.
Piscataway, NJ 08854-8001
Ph:(732)445-4442
Fax:(732)445-5944
Co. E-mail: alclib@rci.rutgers.edu
URL: http://alcoholstudies.rutgers.edu
Contact: Dr. Judit H. Ward, Dir., Info.Svcs.
Scope: Alcohol and drug use (biomedical and psychosocial aspects), alcohol and drug education, substance abuse prevention and treatment. **Services:** Interlibrary loan; copying; Center and Library open to the public. **Holdings:** 15,000 books and pamphlets; 250 videos; 500 research instruments. **Subscriptions:** 220 journals and other serials.

45829 ■ South Carolina Department of Alcohol and Other Drug Abuse Services–The Drugstore Information Clearinghouse
101 Executive Center Dr., Ste. 215
Columbia, SC 29210
Ph:(803)896-5555
Fax:(803)896-5557
Co. E-mail: lfrederick@daodas.state.sc.us
URL: http://www.daodas.org/web/infosite
Contact: Lachelle Frederick, Prog.Asst.
Scope: Alcohol and other drug abuse - education, prevention, intervention, treatment.

45830 ■ South Carolina Department of Mental Health–Earle E. Morris, Jr. Alcohol & Drug Addiction Treatment Center Library
610 Faison Dr.
Columbia, SC 29203
Ph:(803)935-7791
Fax:(803)935-6222
Contact: Michael Blanck, Lib.Hd.
Scope: Alcoholism, drug addiction, group and family therapy. **Services:** Interlibrary loan; Library not open to the public. **Holdings:** 2000 books. **Subscriptions:** 31 journals and other serials.

45831 ■ U.S. Drug Enforcement Administration Library
8701 Morrissette Dr.
Springfield, VA 22152
Ph:(202)307-7787
Free: 800-882-9539
URL: http://www.justice.gov/dea
Contact: Michele M. Leonhart, Adm.
Scope: Narcotic addiction, dangerous drug abuse, law and legislation, law enforcement, drug abuse education, International control. **Services:** Interlibrary loan; Library not open to the public. **Holdings:** 10,000 books; 40 VF drawers. **Subscriptions:** 225 journals and other serials.

45832 ■ University of Washington–Alcohol & Drug Abuse Institute Library
1107 NE 45th St., Ste. 120
Box 354805
Seattle, WA 98105-4631
Ph:(206)543-0937
Fax:(206)543-5473
Co. E-mail: adai@u.washington.edu
URL: http://lib.adai.washington.edu
Contact: Nancy Sutherland, Lib.Dir.
Scope: Alcohol and drug abuse. **Services:** Interlibrary loan; Library open to the public. **Holdings:** 3800 books; 10,000 reprints; 210 videos. **Subscriptions:** 100 journals and other serials.

45833 ■ West Central Georgia Regional Hospital Library
PO Box 12435
Columbus, GA 31917-2435
Ph:(706)568-5204
Co. E-mail: wcgrh@dhr.state.ga.us
URL: http://www.wcgrh.org
Scope: Alcohol and drug abuse, bibliotherapy, brief and short-term therapy/counseling, consumer/patient education, forensic psychiatry, psychiatric nursing, psychiatric social work, psychology. **Holdings:** 4500 books; 246 bound periodical volumes; 325 AV programs.

45834 ■ Western State Psychiatric Center Library
Box 1
Fort Supply, OK 73841
Ph:(580)766-2311
Fax:(580)766-2168
Contact: Karen Connell, Lib.Techn.
Scope: Substance abuse, psychiatry, psychology. **Services:** Interlibrary loan; copying; Library open to the public for reference use only. **Holdings:** 2778 books; 23 bound periodical volumes; 50 boxes of booklets, pamphlets, and reports; 59 audiotapes; 49 video recordings. **Subscriptions:** 20 journals and other serials; 10 newspapers.

RESEARCH CENTERS

45835 ■ Columbia University–Center for Social Policy and Practice in the Workplace
1255 Amsterdam Ave., 11th Fl.
New York, NY 10027
Ph:(212)851-2256
Fax:(212)851-2262
Co. E-mail: sa12@columbia.edu
URL: http://www.workplacecenter.org
Contact: Prof. Sheila H. Akabas PhD, Dir.
E-mail: sa12@columbia.edu
Scope: Policy and program issues in the area of work and social welfare policy, including job maintenance of the disabled in the workplace, analysis of Employee Assistance Programs, studies of gender integration, substance abuse in the workplace and programs. Provides a laboratory to test and evaluate service delivery patterns for occupational social workers and offers interdisciplinary training. **Services:** Counseling at the workplace on family and work related problems; Employment of people with disabilities; Regional Information Clearinghouses; Written training packages on new social service ideas. **Educational Activities:** Continuing education courses and workshops for social workers; Seminars on the organization and delivery of services to workers, open to human service, union, and personnel professionals; Training in the social management of employee benefits.

45836 ■ Indiana University Bloomington–Center for Studies of Law in Action
Sycamore Hall, Rm. 302
1033 E 3rd St.
Bloomington, IN 47405
Ph:(812)855-1783
Fax:(812)855-7542
Co. E-mail: slfreder@indiana.edu
URL: http://www.borkensteincourse.org
Contact: Suz Frederickson, Prog.Coord.
E-mail: slfreder@indiana.edu
Scope: Alcohol and transportation, the effects of drugs, pharmacology, and toxicology. **Educational Activities:** Scientific testing personnel training on alcohol and drug use, and highway safety (3/year), 1 week courses held at Indiana University usually in April, May and December, provided by international experts in toxicology.

45837 ■ North Charles Mental Health Research and Training Foundation, Inc.
955 Massachusetts Ave., Ste. 301
Cambridge, MA 02139
Ph:(617)864-0941
Fax:(617)876-9760
Co. E-mail: wmcauliffe@ntc.org
URL: http://www.northcharles.org
Contact: William McAuliffe PhD, Dir.
E-mail: wmcauliffe@ntc.org
Scope: Mental health and addictions/substance abuse, including behavioral studies and evaluations of substance abuse trends and treatments.

45838 ■ Oregon Research Institute
1715 Franklin Blvd.
Eugene, OR 97403
Ph:(541)484-2123

Fax:(541)484-1108
Co. E-mail: cynthia@ori.org
URL: http://www.ori.org
Contact: Cynthia Guinn, Exec.Dir.
E-mail: cynthia@ori.org
Scope: Behavioral sciences, including studies in tobacco prevention and cessation, compliance with diabetic regimens, children's social skills, personality structure, drug abuse prevention, depression and family interaction, special education technology, adolescent depression, and community child-rearing practices. Provides behavioral research and consultation services to other public and private agencies in fields of education, health, and mental health. **Publications:** Annual report (annually); Research bulletin (periodically). **Educational Activities:** Colloquia (occasionally), provides an opportunity ORI scientists and visiting colleagues to present findings to the research community; Research to Practice Annual Conference, one-day conference to share research-based practices with health and educational professionals and policy makers.

45839 ■ Rutgers University–Center of Alcohol Studies
607 Allison Rd.
Piscataway, NJ 08854-8001
Ph:(732)445-2190
Fax:(732)445-3500
Co. E-mail: alclib@rci.rutgers.edu
URL: http://alcoholstudies.rutgers.edu
Contact: Robert J. Pandina PhD, Dir.
E-mail: alclib@rci.rutgers.edu
Scope: Causes and treatment of alcoholism and drug abuse, diverse actions of alcohol and other drugs on the body, means to prevent alcohol and other drug misuse, and the incidence and prevalence of normal and problem alcohol consumption in the U.S. and the world, including human enzyme systems important in alcohol metabolism, development of tolerance and physical dependence on alcohol, and hormonal changes. **Services:** Consulting; Outpatient clinical services. **Publications:** Journal of Studies on Alcohol (bimonthly); Monographs of the Rutgers Center of Alcohol Studies; National Institute of Alcohol Abuse and Alcoholism-Rutgers University Center of Alcohol Studies (NIAAA-RUCAS) Treatment Series. **Educational Activities:** Community and industrial workshops; Cooper Colloquium Series, during the academic year; Institute of Alcohol and Drug Studies (annually), in July; Summer School of Alcohol and Drug Studies, in August.

45840 ■ Stanford University–Stanford Prevention Research Center
Medical School Office Bldg., MC 5411
251 Campus Dr.
Stanford, CA 94305-5411
Ph:(650)723-6254
Fax:(650)723-6254
Co. E-mail: fortmann@stanford.edu
URL: http://prevention.stanford.edu
Contact: Stephen P. Fortmann MD, Dir.
E-mail: fortmann@stanford.edu
Scope: Prevention and control of chronic disease. Stresses a public health or community approach to disease prevention and health promotion and seeks methods to improve the overall level of community health by favorably modifying the environmental and personal factors known to influence chronic disease incidence, including blood pressure, blood cholesterol, cigarette use, nutrition, obesity, physical activity, and stress. **Services:** Health Improvement Classes (daily), classes offered in exercise, smoking cessation, stress management, weight control, and nutrition for University faculty, staff, and families; Technical assistance, education, and training (daily), for the public, educators, health professionals, and communities; Worksite-based strategic planning and research (daily), in managed care. **Educational Activities:** Postdoctoral research training program; Research seminars (weekly); Undergraduate and graduate level teaching activities at the University.

45841 ■ State University of New York at Buffalo–Research Institute on Addictions
1021 Main St.
Buffalo, NY 14203-1014
Ph:(716)887-2566

Fax:(716)887-2252
Co. E-mail: connors@ria.buffalo.edu
URL: http://www.ria.buffalo.edu
Contact: Gerard J. Connors PhD, Dir.
E-mail: connors@ria.buffalo.edu
Scope: Etiology, course, treatment, and prevention of alcoholism and substance abuse. Studies the following six aspects of substance abuse: normative patterns; biochemical, physiological, psychological, and social antecedents and consequences; biopsychosocial aspects of consumption in early and middle adulthood; family aspects; alcohol-drug interactions; and treatment and prevention strategies. **Services:** RIA Clinical Research Center, outpatient facilities. **Publications:** RIA Annual Report; RIA Report (quarterly). **Educational Activities:** Seminars (10/year),

for researchers, treatment professionals, and interested persons; Substance Abuse Research Seminars.

45842 ■ University of Kentucky–Center on Drug and Alcohol Research
643 Maxwelton Ct.
Lexington, KY 40506-0350
Ph:(859)257-6485
Fax:(859)257-5232
Co. E-mail: sharon.walsh@uky.edu
URL: http://cdar.uky.edu
Contact: Sharon Walsh PhD, Dir.
E-mail: sharon.walsh@uky.edu
Scope: Biological, social, and psychological aspects of alcohol and drug abuse; and HIV/AIDS. Conducts

household and other surveys. **Services:** Consulting and technical assistance for the community.

45843 ■ University of Washington–Addictive Behaviors Research Center
Department of Psychology, Box 351629
Seattle, WA 98195-1629
Ph:(206)685-1200
Fax:(206)685-1310
Co. E-mail: abrc@u.washington.edu
URL: http://depts.washington.edu/abrc
Contact: Dr. Mary Larimer, Assoc.Dir.
E-mail: abrc@u.washington.edu
Scope: Addictive behaviors, including topics such as alcohol abuse, smoking, relapse prevention, harm reduction, and skills training. **Educational Activities:** Postdoctoral program in addictive behaviors.

START-UP INFORMATION

45844 ■ **"His Record, Not Polls, Is What Matters"** in *Bangor Daily News* (October 13, 2010)
Pub: Bangor Daily News
Ed: Nick Sambides Jr. **Description:** The Small Business Jobs Tax Relief Act could spur investment in small businesses by increasing capital gains tax cuts for investors in small business in 2010 and increase to $20,000 from $5,000 the deduction for start-up businesses.

45845 ■ *Legal Guide for Starting and Running a Small Business*
Pub: NOLO
Ed: Fred Steingold. **Released:** April 2008. **Price:** $34.99. **Description:** Information for starting a new business focusing on choosing a business structure, taxes, employees and independent contractors, trademark and service marks, licensing and permits, leasing and improvement of commercial space, buying and selling a business, and more.

45846 ■ *The Small Business Start-Up Kit*
Pub: NOLO
Ed: Peri Pakroo. **Released:** January 2008. **Price:** $29.99. **Description:** Entrepreneurial advice for launching a new business. Topics include compliance with state regulations, sole proprietorships, partnerships, corporations, limited liability companies, as well as accounting and tax information.

45847 ■ *Structuring Your Business*
Pub: Adams Media Corporation
Ed: Michele Cagan. **Released:** 2004. **Price:** $19.95. **Description:** Accountant and author shares insight into starting a new company. The guide assists entrepreneurs through the process, whether it is a corporation, an LLC, a sole proprietorship, or a partnership. Tax codes, accounting practices and legislation affecting every business as well as tips on managing finances are among the topics covered.

45848 ■ *Working for Yourself: An Entrepreneur's Guide to the Basics*
Pub: Kogan Page, Limited
Ed: Jonathan Reuvid. **Released:** September 2006. **Description:** Guide for starting a new business venture, focusing on raising financing, legal and tax issues, marketing, information technology, and site location.

ASSOCIATIONS AND OTHER ORGANIZATIONS

45849 ■ **American Taxation Association**
9201 University City Blvd.
Charlotte, NC 28223
Ph:(704)687-7696
Co. E-mail: americantaxationassociation@aaahq.org
URL: http://aaahq.org/ata/index.htm
Contact: Hughlene Burton, Pres.
Description: Membership comprises primarily university professors teaching federal income tax, federal estate, and/or gift tax courses; other members are

practitioners, including certified public accountants. Seeks to further taxation education. Researches the impact of the tax process, particularly tax code sections, on the social and economic structure of the U.S. Maintains speakers' bureau. .

45850 ■ **Tax Executives Institute**
1200 G St. NW, Ste. 300
Washington, DC 20005-3814
Ph:(202)638-5601
Fax:(202)638-5607
Co. E-mail: asktei@tei.org
URL: http://www.tei.org
Contact: Timothy J. McCormally, Exec. Dir.
Description: Professional society of executives administering and directing tax affairs for corporations and businesses. Maintains TEI Education Fund.
Publications: *The Tax Executive* (bimonthly); *Value-Added Taxes - A Comparative Analysis* .

REFERENCE WORKS

45851 ■ **"3CDC's Biggest Year"** in *Business Courier* (Vol. 26, December 18, 2009, No. 34, pp. 1)
Pub: American City Business Journals, Inc.
Ed: Lucy May. **Description:** Cincinnati Center City Development Corporation (3CDC) will make 2010 its biggest year with nearly $164 million projects in the works. Historic tax credits and continued help from the city have allowed the private nonprofit organization to finance mega projects such as the $43 million renovation and expansion of Washington Park. Other projects that 3CDC will start or complete in 2010 are presented.

45852 ■ **"$100 Million Plan for Jefferson Arms"** in *Saint Louis Business Journal* (Vol. 32, October 14, 2011, No. 7, pp. 1)
Pub: Saint Louis Business Journal
Ed: Evan Binns. **Description:** Teach for America is planning a $100 million renovation project of the former Jefferson Arms hotel in St. Louis, Missouri. The organization has signed a letter of intent to occupy the space. Financing of the project will be mainly through tax credits.

45853 ■ **"$100 Million in Projects Jeopardized"** in *Business Courier* (Vol. 24, March 28, 2008, No. 51, pp. 1)
Pub: American City Business Journals, Inc.
Ed: Dan Monk. **Description:** Ohio's historic preservation tax credit program may be reinstated after some companies planned to sue over its stoppage. The Ohio Department of Development said the program was halted because it exceeded the allocated budget for the credit. $34 million in credits are at stake for more than two dozen local projects if the program is reinstated.

45854 ■ **"100 Percent Equipment Tax Deduction Deadline Nears"** in *Farm Industry News* (December 1, 2010)
Pub: Penton Business Media Inc.
Description: Farmers and small business owners are warned that the first deadline for taking advantage

of the tax code provision that allows them to deduct the full purchase price of qualified capital expenditures up to $500,000 during the tax year is nearing.

45855 ■ **"2011 Tax Information of Interest"** in *Business Owner* (Vol. 35, November-December 2011, No. 6, pp. 10)
Pub: DL Perkins Company
Description: Compilation of 2011 tax information to help small business take advantage of all tax incentives.

45856 ■ **"Alberta Slashes Tax Rate to Ten Percent"** in *Globe & Mail* (March 23, 2006, pp. B1)
Pub: CTVglobemedia Publishing Inc.
Ed: Patrick Brethour. **Description:** Alberta province has slashed its corporate taxes from 11.5 to 10 percent to draw more business to the state. Details of the tax cut and its impact is analyzed.

45857 ■ **"Alberta Warns Ottawa On Taxes"** in *Globe & Mail* (March 9, 2007, pp. B1)
Pub: CTVglobemedia Publishing Inc.
Ed: Steven Chase. **Description:** Ottawa's proposal to remove the tax break for oil sands projects has been criticized by Alberta finance minister Lyle Oberg. The cancelling of tax breaks could hamper development in oil sands and thus hit Alberta's economy.

45858 ■ **"All-Star Advice 2010"** in *Black Enterprise* (Vol. 41, October 2010, No. 3, pp. 97)
Pub: Earl G. Graves Publishing Co. Inc.
Ed: Renita Burns, Sheiresa Ngo, Marcia Wade Talbert. **Description:** Financial experts share tips on real estate, investing, taxes, insurance and debt management.

45859 ■ **"Allowing Ethanol Tax Incentive to Expire Would Risk Jobs, RFAas Dinneen Says"** in *Farm Industry News* (November 3, 2010)
Pub: Penton Business Media Inc.
Description: Jobs would be at risk if the ethanol tax incentive expires.

45860 ■ **"The Annual Entitlement Lecture: Trustees of Medicare and Social Security Issue Another Dismal Report"** in *Barron's* (March 31, 2008)
Pub: Dow Jones & Company, Inc.
Ed: Thomas G. Donlan. **Description:** Expenditures on Medicare hospital insurance and the revenues available to pay for it have led to a gap of capital valued at $38.6 trillion. Slashing the benefits or raising taxes will not solve the gap which exists unless the government saves the money and invests it in private markets.

45861 ■ **"Another Baby Step"** in *Canadian Business* (Vol. 81, March 31, 2008, No. 5, pp. 32)
Pub: Rogers Media
Ed: Andrew Wahl. **Description:** Discusses the Canadian government's federal budget which makes it easier to tap into tax credits for corporate research

and development. However, these steps do not really go far enough to boost industrial research levels in Canada. Making these incentives at least partially refundable could help during tough economic times.

45862 ■ "As Capital Gains Tax Hike Looms, Merger Activity Percolates" in *Baltimore Business Journal* **(Vol. 28, August 27, 2010, No. 16, pp. 1)**
Pub: Baltimore Business Journal

Ed: Scott Dance. **Description:** Concerns for higher capital gains taxes in 2011 have been provoking buyers and sellers to engage in mergers and acquisitions activity, which is expected to gain momentum before the end of 2010. Companies that had saved cash during the recession have been taking advantage of the buyer's market. Other trends in local and national mergers and acquisitions activity are presented.

45863 ■ "Austin Ponders Annexing FI Racetrack" in *Austin Business Journal* **(Vol. 31, July 8, 2011, No. 18, pp. 1)**
Pub: American City Business Journals Inc.

Ed: Vicky Garza. **Description:** City planners in Austin, Texas are studying the feasibility of annexing the land under and around the Circuit of the Americas Formula One Racetrack being constructed east of the city. The annexation could generate at least $13 million in financial gain over 25 years from property taxes alone.

45864 ■ "BABs in Bond Land" in *Barron's* **(Vol. 89, July 6, 2009, No. 27, pp. 14)**
Pub: Dow Jones & Co., Inc.

Ed: Jim McTague. **Description:** American Recovery and Reinvestment Act has created taxable Build America Bonds (BAB) to finance new construction projects. The issuance of the two varieties of taxable BABs is expected to benefit the municipal bond market.

45865 ■ "Bank on It" in *Hawaii Business* **(Vol. 53, November 2007, No. 5, pp. 60)**
Pub: Hawaii Business Publishing

Ed: Kathleen Bryan. **Description:** Many Baby Boomers that are preparing to retire would like to give back and make a difference. One way is to make gifts of Individual Retirement Assets (IRA). During 2007 people over 70 years can make withdrawals from an IRA and donate it without realizing the income as taxable.

45866 ■ *Beat the Taxman 2006: Easy Ways to Save Tax in Your Small Business*
Pub: John Wiley & Sons, Incorporated

Ed: Stephen Thompson. **Released:** May 2006. **Price:** $21.95. **Description:** Tax advice is given to help small businesses maximize returns for 2006.

45867 ■ *Beat the Taxman 2007: Easy Ways to Save Tax in Your Small Business, 2007 Edition For the 2006 Tax Year*
Pub: John Wiley & Sons, Incorporated

Ed: Stephen Thompson. **Released:** December 2006. **Price:** $26.99. **Description:** Year-round tax planner for entrepreneurs; the book is written in a question and answer format to help small business owners save money on annual taxes.

45868 ■ *Beat the Taxman: Easy Ways to Tax Save in Your Small Business*
Pub: John Wiley & Sons, Incorporated

Ed: Stephen Thompson. **Released:** May 2008. **Price:** $26.95. **Description:** Concise tax planner to help entrepreneurs take advantage of current tax laws.

45869 ■ *Being Self-Employed: How to Run a Business Out of Your Home, Claim Travel and Depreciation and Earn a Good Income Well into Your 70s or 80s*
Pub: Allyear Tax Guides

Ed: Holmes F. Crouch, Irma Jean Crouch, Barbara J. MacRae. **Released:** September 2004. **Price:** $24.95 (US), $37.95 (Canadian). **Description:** Guide for small business to keep accurate tax records.

45870 ■ "Best Income Trusts" in *Canadian Business* **(Vol. 82, Summer 2009, No. 8, pp. 36)**
Pub: Rogers Media

Ed: Calvin Leung. **Description:** Boardwalk REIT and Can. Apartment Properties REIT are among the income trusts in Canada that are found to have the potential as a good investment. Suggested income trusts also include the Yellow Pages Income Fund, which recently reported a 19.4 percent yield. The income trusts however, are expected to be affected by the Conservatives' tax that will take effect in 2011.

45871 ■ "BETC Backers Plot Future" in *Business Journal Portland* **(Vol. 27, December 10, 2010, No. 41, pp. 1)**
Pub: Portland Business Journal

Ed: Erik Siemers. **Description:** A coalition of clean energy groups and industrial manufacturers have spearheaded a campaign aimed at persuading Oregon legislators that the state's Business Energy Tax Credit (BETC) is vital in job creation. Oregon's BETC grants tax credits for 50 percent of an eligible renewable or clean energy project's cost. However, some legislators propose BETC's abolition.

45872 ■ "Big Trouble at Sony Ericsson" in *Barron's* **(Vol. 88, March 24, 2008, No. 12, pp. M9)**
Pub: Dow Jones & Company, Inc.

Ed: Angelo Franchini. **Description:** Sony Ericsson is facing trouble as it warned that its sales and net income before taxes will fall by nearly half for the first quarter of 2008. The joint venture of Sony and Ericsson has a global mobile phone market share of nine percent as of 2007, fourth largest in the world.

45873 ■ "Bigger TIF Makes Development Inroads" in *The Business Journal-Serving Metropolitan Kansas City* **(Vol. 26, July 11, 2008, No. 44)**
Pub: American City Business Journals, Inc.

Ed: Rob Roberts. **Description:** On July 9, 2008 the Tax Increment Financing Commission voted to expand a TIF district to Tiffany Springs Road. The plan for the TIF district close to Kansas City International Airport is to include a-half mile of the road. The impacts of the expansion on construction projects and on the road network are analyzed.

45874 ■ "Bills Raise Blues Debate; An Unfair Edge or Level Playing Field?" in *Crain's Detroit Business* **(Vol. 24, January 21, 2008, No. 3)**
Pub: Crain Communications Inc. - Detroit

Ed: Sherri Begin. **Description:** Changes in Michigan state law would change the way health insurance can be sold to individuals. Michigan Blue Cross Blue Shield is working to keep its tax-exempt status while staying competitive against for-profit insurers and nonprofit HMOs.

45875 ■ "Biodiesel Poised to Regain Growth" in *Farm Industry News* **(January 21, 2011)**
Pub: Penton Business Media Inc.

Description: According to Gary Haer, vice president of sales and marketing for Renewable Energy Group, the biodiesel industry is positioned to regain growth in 2011 with the reinstatement of the biodiesel blend-ersa tax credt of $1 per gallon.

45876 ■ "BK Franchisees Lose Sleep Over Late-Night Rule" in *Advertising Age* **(Vol. 79, August 11, 2008, No. 31, pp. 1)**
Pub: Crain Communications, Inc.

Ed: Emily Bryson York. **Description:** Burger King's corporate headquarters mandates that franchisees remain open until at least 2 a.m. Three Miami operators have filed a lawsuit that alleges the extended hours can be dangerous, do not make money and overtax the workforce.

45877 ■ *Breaking Free: How to Work at Home with the Perfect Small Business Opportunity*
Pub: Lulu.com

Ed: Brian Armstrong. **Released:** June 2007. **Price:** $24.95. **Description:** Three ways to smooth the transition from working for someone else to starting

your own business are outlined. Seven exercises to help discover the type of business you should start, how to incorporate, get important tax benefits, and start accepting payments immediately are examined.

45878 ■ "Business Execs Await Walker's Tax Cut Plan" in *Business Journal-Milwaukee* **(Vol. 28, December 17, 2010, No. 11, pp. A1)**
Pub: Milwaukee Business Journal

Ed: Rich Kirchen. **Description:** Wisconsin governor-elect Scott Walker has to tackle the state's projected $3.3 billion budget deficit, which became the subject of speculation among business groups and state politic watchers. Walker has pledged to reduce the state taxes without driving costs down to the local government and school district level.

45879 ■ "Business Must Stand Up And Be Counted" in *Crain's Detroit Business* **(Vol. 24, October 6, 2008, No. 40, pp. 6)**
Pub: Crain Communications, Inc.

Description: Discusses the challenges that the new mayor of Detroit faces concerning business, the state of the economy and the exceptionally tight budget the city is running on, which includes a lot of red ink. It is very likely that the city is going to see tax revenues fall substantially in the next few months and business leaders may find it in their favor to lend their support to the new mayor as well as provide him with the executive talent necessary to overcome some of these crucial issues.

45880 ■ "Business Owners Lien Trinity Project" in *The Business Journal-Serving Greater Tampa Bay* **(Vol. 28, July 25, 2008, No. 31, pp. 1)**
Pub: American City Business Journals, Inc.

Ed: Janet Leiser. **Description:** The Internal Revenue Service is trying to collect $2.9 million from the developer of the Trinity Town Center, William Plaines, due to the delays in the project. This is in addition to a $5.2 million lien by the project's subcontractors.

45881 ■ *Business Owner's Toolkit Tax Guide*
Pub: Toolkit Media Group

Released: January 2009. **Price:** $17.95. **Description:** Resource addresses the tax-filing process while helping to minimize bills. Discussions are focused on important issues pertaining to the small business owner. Topics cover include: personal and business expenses and how they are differentiated, how employee benefit plans are handled on tax returns, and what the IRS looks for when conducting audits. Free online information and support is also included.

45882 ■ "Business Stands Firm for Reform" in *Crain's Detroit Business* **(Vol. 26, January 4, 2010, No. 1, pp. 3)**
Pub: Crain Communications, Inc.

Ed: Amy Lane. **Description:** As Michigan faces a new year of budgetary problems, many business groups are preparing to hold firm against tax increases and instead push for enacting spending reforms.

45883 ■ "Business Tax Complaints Prompt Action" in *Sacramento Business Journal* **(Vol. 28, July 29, 2011, No. 22, pp. 1)**
Pub: Sacramento Business Journal

Ed: Michael Shaw. **Description:** California's Board of Equalization has amended a program to collect taxes from businesses for out-of-state purchases due to a flood of complaints from owners who find the paperwork costly and time consuming. The program was created in 2009 and fell short of expectations as it only brought in $56 million in the first two years against the projected $264 million.

45884 ■ "Business Warns Against Tax Hike" in *Puget Sound Business Journal* **(Vol. 29, November 14, 2008, No. 30, pp. 1)**
Pub: American City Business Journals

Ed: Deirdre Gregg. **Description:** Washington-based businesses have warned state lawmakers against imposing new taxes because of the economic decline. They suggest the government should focus on spending cuts to address the $3 billion shortfall.

45885 ■ "Businesses Balk at 1099 Provision in Health Reform Law" in *Baltimore Business Journal* **(Vol. 28, August 13, 2010, No. 14, pp. 1)**
Pub: Baltimore Business Journal

Ed: Scott Dance. **Description:** Small business advocates and accountants have criticized the Internal Revenue Service Form 1099 provision in the health care reform law as not worth the cost of time and money. Critics believe the policy would create a deluge of the documents that is too much for the companies or the IRS to handle. Details of the provision are also discussed.

45886 ■ "Cabela's Repays Incentives as Sales Lag" in *Business Journal-Milwaukee* **(Vol. 28, November 19, 2010, No. 7, pp. A1)**
Pub: Milwaukee Business Journal

Ed: Stacy Vogel Davis. **Description:** Cabela's has given back $266,000 to the government of Wisconsin owing to its failure to meet projected revenue goals for its Richfield, Wisconsin store. It has also failed to meet sales tax and hiring projection. The company received $4 million in incentives from Washington County.

45887 ■ "Calendar" in *Crain's Detroit Business* **(Vol. 24, October 6, 2008, No. 40, pp. 22)**
Pub: Crain Communications, Inc.

Description: Listing of events in the Detroit area include conferences addressing entrepreneurialism, economic development, manufacturing, marketing, the housing crisis and women business ownership.

45888 ■ "Canada Wins Second NAFTA Decision on Softwood Tariffs" in *Globe & Mail* **(March 18, 2006, pp. B2)**
Pub: CTVglobemedia Publishing Inc.

Ed: Steven Chase; Peter Kennedy. **Description:** Canada has won a second major North American Free Trade Agreement (NAFTA) victory in five years of legal battles over U.S. tariffs on softwood. Details of the controversy and ruling are presented.

45889 ■ *Canadian Small Business Kit for Dummies*
Pub: John Wiley & Sons, Incorporated

Ed: Margaret Kerr; JoAnn Kurtz. **Released:** May 2006. **Price:** $28.99. **Description:** Resources include information on changes to laws and taxes for small businesses in Canada.

45890 ■ "Candidates Differ On State's Green Streak" in *Business Journal Portland* **(Vol. 27, October 22, 2010, No. 34, pp. 1)**
Pub: Portland Business Journal

Ed: Andy Giegerich. **Description:** The views of Oregon gubernatorial candidates Chris Dudley and John Kitzhaber on the state's economy and on environmental policies are presented. Both Dudley, who is a Republican, and his Democratic challenger believe that biomass could help drive the state's economy. Both candidates also pledged changes in Oregon's business energy tax credit (BETC) program.

45891 ■ "The Carbon Equation" in *Canadian Business* **(Vol. 81, October 27, 2008, No. 18, pp. 109)**
Pub: Rogers Media Ltd.

Ed: Jack M. Mintz. **Description:** Economic and environmental impacts of the likely rejection of a carbon tax for the cap-and-trade system in Canada are discussed. The Conservative Party is expected tow in the 2008 elections and would likely pursue the cap-and-trade system.

45892 ■ "Cashing in Before You Join: Negotiating a Signing Bonus" in *Black Enterprise* **(Vol. 37, October 2006, No. 3, pp. 90)**
Pub: Earl G. Graves Publishing Co. Inc.

Ed: Chauntelle Folds. **Description:** Information on how to research and negotiate a signing deal, including how to avoid a tax hit.

45893 ■ "Cautions On Loans With Your Business" in *Business Owner* **(Vol. 35, July-August 2011, No. 4, pp. 5)**
Pub: DL Perkins Company

Description: Caution must be used when borrowing from or lending to any small business. Tax guidelines for the borrowing and lending practice are also included.

45894 ■ *CCH Toolkit Tax Guide 2007*
Pub: CCH, Inc.

Ed: Paul Gada. **Released:** January 2007. **Price:** $17.95. **Description:** Guide for filing 2007 tax forms for both personal and small businesses with expert line-by-line explanations.

45895 ■ "CEOs Decry Budget Taxation Change" in *Globe & Mail* **(April 2, 2007, pp. B1)**
Pub: CTVglobemedia Publishing Inc.

Ed: Steven Chase. **Description:** The views of the chief executive officers of Canadian firms, on the changes in the country's policy governing the taxation of foreign deals, are presented.

45896 ■ "Channeling for Growth" in *The Business Journal-Serving Greater Tampa Bay* **(Vol. 28, July 11, 2008, No. 29, pp. 1)**
Pub: American City Business Journals, Inc.

Ed: Margie Manning. **Description:** HSN Inc., one of the largest employers in Tampa Bay, Florida, is expected to spend an additional $9.7 million annually as it plans to hire more accounting, internal audit, legal, treasury and tax personnel after its spin-off to a public company. Details on the company's sales growth are provided.

45897 ■ "The China Tax" in *Forbes* **(Vol. 180, October 1, 2007, No. 6, pp. 35)**
Pub: Forbes Inc.

Ed: Robyn Meredith. **Description:** U.S. consumers can see a rise in prices for goods made in China due to growing pressure from Congress to ensure safe products from that country. Taxing products imported from China could be levied in five different forms listed.

45898 ■ "City, County May Kill VC Tax" in *Business Journal-Portland* **(Vol. 24, October 12, 2007, No. 33, pp. 1)**
Pub: American City Business Journals, Inc.

Ed: Aliza Earnshaw. **Description:** City of Portland and Multnomah County in Oregon may soon kill taxes levied on venture capital (VC) firms, which is expected to take place in late October 2007. Capitalists have long been saying that taxation is driving them out of town, but this change is expected to generate more investments and persuade VC firms to relocate within city limits.

45899 ■ "City Eyeing Tax Breaks for Arena" in *Boston Business Journal* **(Vol. 29, June 3, 2011, No. 4, pp. 1)**
Pub: American City Business Journals Inc.

Ed: Daniel J. Sernovitz. **Description:** Baltimore City is opting to give millions of dollars in tax breaks and construction loans to a group of private investors led by William Hackerman who is proposing to build a new arena and hotel at the Baltimore Convention Center. The project will cost $500 million with the state putting up another $400 million for the center's expansion.

45900 ■ "Clock Ticking for Hotel Berry" in *Sacramento Business Journal* **(Vol. 25, July 25, 2008, No. 21, pp. 1)**
Pub: American City Business Journals, Inc.

Ed: Michael Shaw. **Description:** Federal tax credits worth $13.6 million have been awarded to boost the renovation project for the aging Hotel Berry in downtown Sacramento, California. The owners of the hotel have five months before the expiration of the tax credits to raise the remaining funding for the $20 million renovation.

45901 ■ "Commentary: US Economic Recovery and Policy" in *Small Business Economic Trends* **(July 2010, pp. 3)**
Pub: National Federation of Independent Business

Description: U.S. Government is making economic recovery difficult, with one of the largest tax increases in history arriving in six months. Meanwhile, Congress

is looking into taxing successful businesses, which will potentially hamper growth and real investment. Other insights on the government's role in the country's economic growth are presented.

45902 ■ "Commotion Pictures; Bill C-10: Is It Censorship or Merely Inept?" in *Canadian Business* **(Vol. 81, March 31, 2008, No. 5, pp. 10)**
Pub: Rogers Media

Ed: Denis Seguin. **Description:** Filmmakers are claiming that Bill C-10 amounts to censorship as it could retract a production's eligibility for a tax credit if it is deemed offensive. However, the bill's backers say that the bill protects against tax dollars being directed at productions that run contrary to public policy.

45903 ■ *The Complete Guide to Buying a Business*
Pub: NOLO

Ed: Fred S. Steingold. **Released:** November 2007. **Price:** $24.99. **Description:** Key steps in buying a business are highlighted, focusing on legal issues, tax considerations, approaches for valuing a business, financing, structuring the deal, along with forms and documents for taking ownership are included.

45904 ■ "Confidence High, But Lenders More Cautious" in *Farmer's Weekly* **(March 28, 2008, No. 320)**
Pub: Reed Business Information

Description: Discusses the effect of the global credit crunch on farmers as well as recent auctions which were timed to beat changes to capital gains tax.

45905 ■ "Congress Ponders Annuity Trusts" in *National Underwriter Life & Health* **(Vol. 114, June 21, 2010, No. 12, pp. 10)**
Pub: Summit Business Media

Ed: Arthur D. Postal. **Description:** Congress is looking over several bills, including the Small Business Jobs Tax Relief Act that would significantly narrow the advantages of using grantor-retained annuity trusts (GRATs) to avoid estate and gift taxes.

45906 ■ "Council Power Shift Could Benefit Business" in *Business Courier* **(Vol. 26, November 6, 2009, No. 28, pp. 1)**
Pub: American City Business Journals, Inc.

Ed: Lucy May. **Description:** A majority in the Cincinnati City Council, which is comprised of reelected members, might be created by Charlie Winburn's impending return to the council. It would be empowered to decide on public safety, stock options taxes, and environmental justice. How the presumed majority would affect the city's economic progress is discussed.

45907 ■ "Countywide Tax Could Fund Metro" in *Business Courier* **(Vol. 26, January 15, 2010, No. 39, pp. 1)**
Pub: American City Business Journals, Inc.

Ed: Lucy May, Dan Monk. **Description:** Cincinnati officials are considering a new countywide tax to fund the Metro bus system and extend healthcare to the poor.

45908 ■ *Craft, Inc.*
Pub: Chronicle Books LLC

Ed: Meg Mateo Ilasco. **Released:** August 2007. **Price:** $16.95. **Description:** Business primer for entrepreneurial crafters wishing to turn their hobbies into a small business, including tips for developing products, naming the company, writing a business plan, applying for licenses, and paying taxes.

45909 ■ "Daley's Efforts to Ease Traffic Woes Fall Short" in *Crain's Chicago Business* **(Vol. 31, May 5, 2008, No. 18, pp. 18)**
Pub: Crain Communications, Inc.

Description: Discusses some of the inherent problems of Mayor Daley's plan to reduce traffic congestion by creating a tax on drivers who park their cars downtown during peak traffic periods and putting articulated buses on new bus-only lanes on major arterial streets leading into the Loop.

45910 ■ "Datebook" in *Crain's Chicago Business* (Vol. 31, April 28, 2008, No. 17, pp. 18)
Pub: Crain Communications, Inc.
Description: Listing of events in the Detroit area include conferences addressing entrepreneurialism, economic development, and women business ownership.

45911 ■ *Deduct It!: Lower Your Small Business Taxes*
Pub: NOLO
Ed: Stephen Fishman. **Released:** November 2009. **Price:** $34.99. **Description:** Ways to make the most of tax deductions for any small business are covered. The book is organized into categories featuring common deductions, start-up expenses, health deductions, entertainment, travel, inventory, equipment and more. Current tax laws and numbers for 2008 are included.

45912 ■ "Defer Tax with Installment Sale Election" in *Business Owner* (Vol. 35, September-October 2011, No. 5, pp. 12)
Pub: DL Perkins Company
Description: It is critical to consult with a tax professional before selling any high-value asset in order to minimize taxes.

45913 ■ "The Design of Tax Policy in Canada" in *Canadian Journal of Economics* (Vol. 44, November 2011, No. 4, pp. 1184)
Pub: Blackwell Publishers Ltd.
Ed: Kevin Milligan. **Description:** Empirical evidence and tax policy design are presented by Richard Blundell.

45914 ■ "The Display Group Is Super-Sized" in *Michigan Vue* (Vol. 13, July-August 2008, No. 4, pp. 34)
Pub: Entrepreneur Media Inc.
Description: Profile of the Display Group, located in downtown Detroit, this company provides custom designed mobile marketing displays as well as special event production services for trade show displays. The rental house and design service is also beginning to see more business due to the film initiative, which provides incentives for films that are shooting in Michigan.

45915 ■ "Dodge Slashes Growth Estimate" in *Globe & Mail* (January 19, 2007, pp. B3)
Pub: CTVglobemedia Publishing Inc.
Ed: Heather Scoffield. **Description:** Bank of Canada Governor David Dodge decision to keep the interest rate 4.25 percent despite a slowdown in the economy is discussed.

45916 ■ "Does it Add Up?" in *Canadian Business* (Vol. 81, October 13, 2008, No. 17, pp. 18)
Pub: Rogers Media Ltd.
Ed: Jack Mintz. **Description:** Views on Canada's tax policy, as well as on tax reforms planned by major parties and their expected economic impact are discussed. The Tories' proposal to cut federal diesel fuel tax is seen as politically smart, but reforms on other taxes could help generate economic growth. High income tax rates are believed to discourage talented individuals from working in Canada.

45917 ■ "Down to the Wire for Your Taxes" in *Women In Business* (Vol. 63, Spring 2011, No. 1, pp. 22)
Pub: American Business Women's Association
Ed: Maureen Sullivan. **Description:** A look at a last-minute checklist to consult before filing annual corporate tax returns for a small business owner is presented. Enlisting professional help for small business taxes is always a good investment. However, small business owners have to make sure their records back up their filing when planning to go it alone.

45918 ■ "Duro Bag to Expand, Add 130 Jobs" in *Business Courier* (Vol. 27, August 6, 2010, No. 14, pp. 1)
Pub: Business Courier
Ed: Jon Newberry. **Description:** Duro Bag Manufacturing Company will expand capacity at its Florence, Kentucky plant and will add around 130 jobs over the

next few years. The state of Kentucky has given preliminary approval for up to $1 million in tax incentives over 10 years, tied to the creation of new jobs. The company's investment will include new production and packaging equipment and building improvements.

45919 ■ "Easy to be Queasy" in *Canadian Business* (Vol. 81, December 24, 2007, No. 1, pp. 25)
Pub: Rogers Media
Ed: Jack Mintz. **Description:** Canada could be facing a slowdown in economic growth for 2008 as the country's economy depends on the U.S. economy, which is still facing recession in the subprime market. Details on Canada's economic growth, the impact of the weak U.S. dollar, increase in the unemployment rate, and decline in tax revenue are explored.

45920 ■ *EBay Income: How ANYONE of Any Age, Location, and/or Background Can Build a Highly Profitable Online Business with eBay (Revised 2nd Edition)*
Pub: Atlantic Publishing Company
Released: December 1, 2010. **Price:** $24.95. **Description:** A complete overview of eBay is given and guides any small company through the entire process of creating the auction and auction strategies, photography, writing copy, text and formatting, multiple sales, programming tricks, PayPal, accounting, creating marketing, merchandising, managing email lists, advertising plans, taxes and sales tax, best time to list items and for how long, sniping programs, international customers, opening a storefront, electronic commerce, buy-it now pricing, keywords, Google marketing and eBay secrets.

45921 ■ *The Ebay Seller's Tax and Legal Answer Book*
Pub: AMACOM
Ed: Cliff Ennico. **Released:** April 30, 2007. **Price:** $19.95. **Description:** Helps sellers using Ebay to file taxes properly, while saving money.

45922 ■ *Electronic Commerce: Technical, Business, and Legal Issues*
Pub: Prentice Hall PTR
Ed: Oktay Dogramaci; Aryya Gangopadhyay; Yelena Yesha; Nabil R. Adam. **Released:** August 1998. **Description:** Provides insight into the goals of using the Internet to grow a business in the areas of networking and telecommunication, security, and storage and retrieval; business areas such as marketing, procurement and purchasing, billing and payment, and supply chain management; and legal aspects such as privacy, intellectual property, taxation, contractual and legal settlements.

45923 ■ "Eliminating All of Your Estate Tax Burden" in *Contractor* (Vol. 57, January 2010, No. 1, pp. 48)
Pub: Penton Media, Inc.
Ed: Irv Blackman. **Description:** Suggestions on how family owned businesses can minimize their estate tax burdens are discussed. One of these includes not using life insurance in a business succession plan to move stocks to the children and to never use Section 6166 as part of the overall estate tax plan.

45924 ■ "Employer Jobless Tax Could Rise" in *Sacramento Business Journal* (Vol. 28, May 27, 2011, No. 13, pp. 1)
Pub: Sacramento Business Journal
Ed: Kathy Robertson. **Description:** The government of California is facing an estimated $16 billion deficit in its unemployment insurance fund. Unemployment insurance spending has exceeded employer contributions to the fund. Statistics on unemployment insurance is included.

45925 ■ "Employers Tied in Knots" in *Sacramento Business Journal* (Vol. 25, August 15, 2008, No. 24, pp. 1)
Pub: American City Business Journals, Inc.
Ed: Kathy Robertson. **Description:** Conflicting laws on same sex marriage have been posing problems for companies, and insurers in California. The court ruling that allowed gay marriages has created differ-

ences between state and federal laws. Federal laws on same-sex spouse taxation are also seen to complicate the issue.

45926 ■ "EPA Grants E15 Waiver for 2001-2006 Vehicles" in *Farm Industry News* (January 21, 2011)
Pub: Penton Business Media Inc.
Description: U.S. Environmental Protection Agency waived a limitation on selling gasoline that contains more than 10 percent ethanol for model year 2001-2006 cars and light trucks, allowing fuel to contain up to 15 percent ethanol (E15) for these vehicles.

45927 ■ "Escape the AMT Trap" in *Entrepreneur* (Vol. 36, February 2008, No. 2, pp. 64)
Pub: Entrepreneur Media Inc.
Ed: Scott Bernard Nelson. **Description:** Alternative Minimum Tax (AMT), developed by the Internal Revenue Service for taxation of high-income people, has also affected other taxpayers regarding thresholds for inflation. The goal to escape the AMT trap is to defer payments and push off saving strategies into the next year. Details about deferring payments are discussed.

45928 ■ "Estate Tax Problems may Soon Disappear" in *Contractor* (Vol. 56, September 2009, No. 9, pp. 60)
Pub: Penton Media, Inc.
Ed: Irv Blackman. **Description:** Advice on how to effectively plan estate tax in the United States. Pending changes to US estate tax laws are seen to resolve inheritance problems. Captive insurance firms can lower property and casualty insurance costs to transfer businesses to children.

45929 ■ "Expect Action on Health Care and the Economy" in *Contractor* (Vol. 57, January 2010, No. 1, pp. 30)
Pub: Penton Media, Inc.
Ed: Kevin Schwalb. **Description:** The Plumbing-Heating-Cooling Contractors National Association is working to solidify its standing in the public policy arena as the legislative agenda will focus on health care reform, estate tax and immigration reform, all of which will impact the industries.

45930 ■ "Expert Sees No Radical Reform of 401(K) System" in *Workforce Management* (Vol. 88, November 16, 2009, No. 12, pp. 12)
Pub: Crain Communications, Inc.
Ed: Ed Frauenheim. **Description:** Although many would like to see an overhaul of the 401(k) retirement system, it is unlikely to occur anytime soon; however, the drastic stock market drop of 2008 has raised pointed questions about the 401(k) system and if it enables a secure retirement for American workers.

45931 ■ "Experts Discuss New Tax Rules in Webinar to Help Farmers With Year-End Tax Planning" in *Farm Industry News* (November 22, 2011)
Pub: Penton Business Media Inc.
Description: Section 179 deductions and Bonus Depreciation tax rules for years 2011 and 2012 and how they impact farming operations are available at TractorLife.com. The Website helps farmers maintain and extend the operating lives of their tractors.

45932 ■ "Exposed?" in *Mergers & Acquisitions: The Dealmaker's Journal* (March 1, 2008)
Pub: SourceMedia, Inc.
Ed: Jerry Abejo. **Description:** State-run pension plans' contributions are declining due to a loss of tax revenue from plummeting home values.

45933 ■ *Facing Financial Dysfunction*
Pub: Infinity Publishing
Ed: Bert Whitehead. **Released:** April 2004. **Description:** Handbook to help individuals manage their finances, investments, taxes and retirement.

45934 ■ "Fair Play? China Cheats, Carney Talks and Rankin Walks; Here's the Latest" in *Canadian Business* (Vol. 81, March 17, 2008, No. 4)
Pub: Rogers Media
Description: Discusses the World Trade Organization which says that China is breaking trade rules by taxing imports of auto parts at the same rate as

foreign-made finished cars. Mark Carney first speech as the governor of the Bank of Canada made economists suspect a rate cut on overnight loans. Andre Rankin was ordered by the Ontario Securities Commission to pay $250,000 in investigation costs.

45935 ■ "Fair Tax Backers Hope MBT Anger Will Bring Votes" in *Crain's Detroit Business* **(Vol. 24, March 31, 2008, No. 13, pp. 32)**
Pub: Crain Communications, Inc.
Ed: Description: Discusses the Michigan Fair Tax Proposal which would eliminate Michigan's business taxes and income tax, raise the state sales tax to 9.75 percent and expand it to services.

45936 ■ *Family Limited Partnership Deskbook*
Pub: American Bar Association
Ed: David T. Lewis; Andrea C. Chomakos. **Released:** March 25, 2008. **Price:** $169.95. **Description:** Forming and funding a family limited partnership or limited liability company is complicated. In-depth analysis of all facets of this business entity are examined using detailed guidance on the basic principles of drafting, forming, funding, and valuing an FLP or LLC and also covers tax concerns. Examples and extensive sample forms are included on a CD-ROM included with the book.

45937 ■ *Family Limited Partnerships Deskbook: Forming and Funding FLPs and Other Closely Held Business Entities*
Pub: American Bar Association
Ed: David T. Lewis. **Released:** March 2008. **Price:** $169.95. **Description:** Forming and funding a family limited partnership (FLP) or limited liability company (LLC) is common and complicated. This handbook offers in-depth analysis of issues facing these types of businesses. Guidance is given on the principles of drafting, forming, funding, and valuing an FLP or LLC as well as tax matters. Examples and sample forms are included on a CD-ROM.

45938 ■ *A Family Matter: A Guide to Operating Your Personal Estate*
Pub: Brown Books Publishing Group
Ed: William A. Verkest. **Released:** May 2003. **Price:** $22.95 **Description:** Guidebook to financial management of personal assets is presented. Important documents must be maintained in a safe, secure place for family members or attorneys to access when necessary. The author suggests that a personal diary be kept with important information regarding records of investment accounts and financial summaries for every year in order to calculate taxes and manage financial matters more efficiently.

45939 ■ *Fast-Track Business Start-Up Kit: California*
Pub: DP Group, Incorporated
Ed: Carolyn Usinger. **Released:** September 2006. **Price:** $29.00. **Description:** Step-by-step guide for starting and running a business in California, including information on sole proprietors, partnerships, limited liability companies, S and C corporations, as well as details concerning business entities, sales taxes, environmental issues, human resources, and more.

45940 ■ "Feds to Pay University $20M" in *Business Courier* **(Vol. 27, July 23, 2010, No. 12, pp. 3)**
Pub: Business Courier
Ed: James Ritchie. **Description:** The U.S. government is set to pay University Hospital and medical residents who trained there $20 million as part of a tax dispute settlement. Around 1,000 former residents are to receive tax refunds. But the hospital must provide the U.S. Internal Revenue Service with extensive documentation.

45941 ■ "Film Incentives: A Hit or a Flop?" in *Michigan Vue* **(Vol. 13, July-August 2008, No. 4, pp. 10)**
Pub: Entrepreneur Media Inc.
Description: Michigan's new film incentive legislation is fulfilling its core purpose, according to Lisa Dancsok of the Michigan Economic Development Corp. (MEDC), by kickstarting the state's entry into the multi-billion dollar industry; the initiative is

considered to be very competitive with other states and countries and is thought to be a way in which to help revitalize Michigan's struggling economy.

45942 ■ "Final State Budget Is a Mixed Bag of Key Industries" in *The Business Journal - Serving Phoenix and the Valley of the Sun* **(Vol. 28, July 4, 2008, No. 44, pp. 3)**
Pub: American City Business Journals, Inc.
Ed: Mike Sunnucks; Patrick O'Grady. **Description:** Approved by Governor Janet Napolitano and passed by the Arizona Legislature, the $9.9 billion state budget is beneficial to some industries in the business community. The tax cap for on Arizona Lottery has been removed which is beneficial to the industry, while the solar energy industry and real estate developers stand to lose from the spending bill. Other details of the finance budget are presented.

45943 ■ "Finding Room for Financing" in *The Business Journal-Serving Metropolitan Kansas City* **(Vol. 26, August 1, 2008, No. 47, pp. 1)**
Pub: American City Business Journals, Inc.
Ed: Rob Roberts. **Description:** Kansas City officials are expecting to receive financing recommendations for a new 1,000-room convention headquarters hotel. The $300-million project could be financed either through private ownership with public subsidies, or through public ownership with tax-exempt bond financing. Other views and information on the project and its expected economic impact, are presented.

45944 ■ "First-Time Homebuyer Credit May Add Some Momentum to Market" in *Crain's Cleveland Business* **(Vol. 30, May 18, 2009, No. 20)**
Pub: Crain Communications, Inc.
Ed: Stan Bullard. **Description:** Federal tax credits for first-time homebuyers have increased the number of homes being sold. Details of the tax credit are defined.

45945 ■ "Five Area Businesses Win State Tax Breaks" in *Crain's Detroit Business* **(Vol. 25, June 22, 2009, No. 25, pp. 9)**
Pub: Crain Communications Inc. - Detroit
Ed: Amy Lane. **Description:** Michigan Economic Growth Authority approved tax breaks for five area businesses among 15 across the state. Details of the tax credits are provided.

45946 ■ "For All It's Worth" in *Entrepreneur* **(Vol. 36, April 2008, No. 4, pp. 46)**
Pub: Entrepreneur Media, Inc.
Ed: Farnoosh Torabi. **Description:** Discusses the federal estate tax system requires that 45 percent of the money beyond $2 million be given to the government. Ways on how to minimize the effects of estate tax on assets include: creating bypass trusts for married couples; setting up an irrevocable life insurance trust to avoid taxation of estate for insurance benefactors; and having annual gift tax exclusion.

45947 ■ "Foreign (In)Direct Investment and Corporate Taxation" in *Canadian Journal of Economics* **(Vol. 44, November 2011, No. 4, pp. 1497)**
Pub: Blackwell Publishers Ltd.
Ed: Georg Wamser. **Description:** Foreign investments of multinational firms are often complex in that they involve conduit entities. In particular, a multinational can pursue either a direct or an indirect investment strategy, where the latter involves an intermediate corporate entity and is associated with enhanced opportunities for international tax planning. As a consequence, in the case of indirect investments, the role of corporate taxation in destination countries may change. An investigation into the effects of corporation taxation on foreign investment decisions of German multinationals, taking explicitly into account that firms choose in a first stage the investment regime, (direct vs. indirect) is provided.

45948 ■ "Formaspace Finds a Bigger Home" in *Austin Business JournalInc.* **(Vol. 29, December 4, 2009, No. 39, pp. 1)**
Pub: American City Business Journals
Ed: Kate Harrington. **Description:** Formaspace Technical Furniture has signed a lease for 56,700 square feet in Harris Ridge Business Center at

Northeast Austin, Texas, which represents one of the area's largest leases for 2009. The new lease enables Formaspace to hire new employees, invest in new equipment, and take advantage of a taxing designation created for manufacturers.

45949 ■ *Free Lunch: How the Wealthiest Americans Enrich Themselves at Government Expense (an Stick You with the Bill)*
Pub: Portfolio
Ed: Released: Price: Description: Johnston uses the case of the Texas Rangers as an example to support his belief that the nation's monied elite bend the rules of capitalism for their own benefit.

45950 ■ "Freshman Lawmaker Graves Keeping Busy" in *Atlanta Journal-Constitution* **(June 20, 2010, pp. A6)**
Pub: Atlanta Journal Constitution
Ed: Bob Keefe. **Description:** Newly elected Republican Representative Tom Graves of Ranger supports the Small Business Jobs Tax Relief Act.

45951 ■ "Fuel for Thought" in *Canadian Business* **(Vol. 81, April 14, 2008, No. 6, pp. 18)**
Pub: Rogers Media
Ed: John Gray. **Description:** Discusses a web poll of 133 CEOs and other business leaders that shows that they predict oil prices to increase to US $113 per barrel over the 2008 to 2010 timeframe. Most of the respondents did not favor cutting gas taxes but this group wants the government to cut taxes on fuel-efficient vehicles and increase subsidies to local transit systems.

45952 ■ "Getting More Out of Retirement" in *Agency Sales Magazine* **(Vol. 39, November 2009, No. 10, pp. 48)**
Pub: MANA
Ed: Joshua D. Mosshart. **Description:** Overview of the Tax Increase Prevention and Reconciliation Act, which lets employees convert to a Roth IRA in 2010. The benefits of conversion depend on age and wealth and it is best to consult a tax advisor to determine the best strategy for retirement planners.

45953 ■ "Getting Out of an IRS Mess" in *Black Enterprise* **(Vol. 37, December 2006, No. 5, pp. 53)**
Pub: Earl G. Graves Publishing Co. Inc.
Ed: Carolyn M. Brown. **Description:** Owing back taxes to the IRS can lead to huge penalties and interest. Here are some tips on how to handle paying the IRS what you owe them.

45954 ■ *Getting Rich In Your Underwear: How To Start and Run a Profitable Home-Based Business*
Pub: HCM Publishing
Ed: Peter I. Hupalo. **Released:** April 1, 2005. **Price:** $17.95. **Description:** Book offers insight into starting a home-based business. Entrepreneurs will learn about business models and the home business; distribution and fulfillment of product or service; marketing and sales; how to overcome the fear of starting a business; personal success characteristics; naming a business; zoning and insurance; intellectual capital; copyrights, trademarks, and patents; limited liability companies and S-corporations; business expenses and accounting; taxes; fifteen basic steps for starting a home-based business, state resources for starting a home company; and seven home-based business ideas.

45955 ■ "Give a Little Back" in *Canadian Business* **(Vol. 79, November 20, 2006, No. 23, pp. 17)**
Pub: Rogers Media
Ed: Jack Mintz. **Description:** The plans of Jim Flaherty, Canada's minister of finance, to remove the corporate tax bias on income paid to pension plans are discussed.

45956 ■ "Give Until It Works" in *Hispanic Business* **(March 2008, pp. 26-27)**
Pub: Hispanic Business
Ed: Rick Munarriz. **Description:** Ways to maximize a tax advantage from charitable contributions for small business owners are addressed.

45957 ▪ "Global-Preneuring: Tax Ramifications Can Make or Break a Worldwide Enterprise" in *Small Business Opportunities* (May 2008)
Pub: Harris Publications Inc.
Description: It is imperative to consider the tax ramifications when starting or expanding a global enterprise.

45958 ▪ "Goodwill Haunts Local Companies; Bad Buyouts During Boom Times Producing Big Writedowns" in *Crain's Chicago Business* (Apr. 28, 2008)
Pub: Crain Communications, Inc.
Ed: Ann Saphir. **Description:** Many companies are having to face the reality that they overpaid for acquisitions made in better economic times; investors often dismiss such one-time charges as mere accounting adjustments but writeoffs related to past acquisitions can signal future problems because they mean the expected profits that justified the purchase have not materialized. Writeoffs are particularly worrisome for firms with a lot of debt and whose banks require them to have enough assets to back up their borrowings.

45959 ▪ "Government Intervention" in *Canadian Business* (Vol. 79, November 6, 2006, No. 22, pp. 116)
Pub: Rogers Media
Description: The effects of income trust tax on economic conditions and investment of Canada are presented.

45960 ▪ "Grave Concerns" in *Canadian Business* (Vol. 81, July 21 2008, No. 11, pp. 25)
Pub: Rogers Media Ltd.
Ed: Andrew Nikiforuk. **Description:** Air pollution control regulations to reduce greenhouse gasses have been implemented by the Canadian government. The federal government is planning to construct a carbon funeral industry that will store the global warming gases, however the expenditure for the project will be shifted to the taxpayers. Details of the Bruce Peachy's initiative on how to reduce GHGs are presented.

45961 ▪ "Green Shift Sees Red" in *Canadian Business* (Vol. 81, September 29, 2008, No. 16)
Pub: Rogers Media Ltd.
Ed: Jeff Sanford. **Description:** Green Shift Inc. is suing the Liberal Party of Canada in an $8.5 million lawsuit for using the phrase "green shift" when they rolled out their carbon tax and climate change policy. The company has come to be recognized as a consultant and provider of green products such as non-toxic, biodegradable cups, plates, and utensils for events.

45962 ▪ "Have High-Tech Tax Credits Helped or Hurt Hawaii?" in *Hawaii Business* (Vol. 53, December 2007, No. 6, pp. 28)
Pub: Hawaii Business Publishing
Description: Presents the opinons of Channel Capital LLC's Walter R. Roth and Hawaii Venture Capital Association's Bill Spencer concerning the impacts of tax credits. Roth thinks that Act 221 appeals to investors who can earn despite business failure while Spencer thinks that the legislation promotes investments in innovative technology firms. The need to support tax credits is also discussed.

45963 ▪ "Helping Small Businesses Create Jobs" in *America's Intelligence Wire* (August 27, 2010)
Pub: HighBeam Research
Ed: Ross Raihala. **Description:** Ways the Small Business Jobs Tax Relief Act will help small businesses create jobs are investigated.

45964 ▪ "The Hidden Tax" in *Canadian Business* (Vol. 81, April 14, 2008, No. 6, pp. 28)
Pub: Rogers Media
Ed: Al Rosen. **Description:** Accounting fraud could take out a sizable sum from one's retirement fund when computed over a long period of time. The much

bigger tax on savings is the collective impact of the smaller losses that do not attract the attention they deserve. Ensuring that investors are not unnecessarily taxed 2 percent of their total investments every year outweighs the benefit of a 2 percent reduction in personal tax rates.

45965 ▪ "High-Tech Job-Apalooza!" in *Orlando Business Journal* (Vol. 26, January 15, 2010, No. 33, pp. 1)
Pub: American City Business Journals
Ed: Christopher Boyd. **Description:** Science Applications International Corporation, Saab Training USA LLC, CAE USA, and Pelliconi &C.SPA attempt to obtain $939,000 in tax incentives to generate 222 technology and defense-related jobs in Orange County, Florida. Each job will provide an average salary of $67,000. Future plans of each technology and defense firm are also presented.

45966 ▪ "Hike in Md.'s Alcohol Tax May Be Hard For Lawmakers to Swallow" in *Baltimore Business Journal* (Vol. 28, November 19, 2010, No. 28)
Pub: Baltimore Business Journal
Ed: Emily Mullin. **Description:** Maryland's General Assembly has been reluctant to support a dime-per-drink increase in alcohol tax that was drafted in the 2009 bill if the tax revenue goes into a separate fund. The alcohol tax increase is considered unnecessary by some lawmakers and business leaders due to impending federal spending boosts.

45967 ▪ "Hilliard Scans Horizon, Finds Defense Contractor" in *Business First Columbus* (Vol. 25, October 17, 2008, No. 8, pp. A1)
Pub: American City Business Journals
Ed: Brian R. Ball. **Description:** An incentive package being offered by Hilliard may prompt a Powell defense contractor to relocate in 2009. The package offered to Star Dynamics Corporation incorporates incentives that return a sizeable amount of income taxes to the company.

45968 ▪ "Historic Tax Credit Plan Gains Support" in *Baltimore Business Journal* (Vol. 27, January 8, 2010, No. 36, pp. 1)
Pub: American City Business Journals
Ed: Heather Harlan Warnack. **Description:** Maryland Governor Martin O'Malley plans to push legislation in the General Assembly to extend for three more years the tax credit program for rehabilitation of obsolete buildings. The Maryland Heritage Structure Rehabilitation Tax Credit Program has declined from almost $75 million in expenses in 2001 to roughly $5 million in 2010 fiscal year. Details on the projects that benefited from the program are explored.

45969 ▪ *Home Business Tax Deductions: Keep What You Earn*
Pub: NOLO
Ed: Stephen Fishman. **Released:** November 2006. **Price:** $34.99. **Description:** Home business tax deductions are outlined. Basic information on the ways various business structures are taxed and how deductions work is included.

45970 ▪ "Hospital Tax Could Be a Separate Bill" in *Business Journal-Milwaukee* (Vol. 25, October 26, 2007, No. 4, pp. A1)
Pub: American City Business Journals, Inc.
Ed: Elizabeth Sanders. **Description:** Hospital officials are working on reintroducing a hospital tax proposal that would increase Medicaid reimbursement, thereby generating millions of dollars of revenue for the Milwaukee-area hospitals. The bill sponsored by Governor Jim Doyle was supported by the Wisconsin Hospital Association. Details of the proposed hospital tax are presented.

45971 ▪ "Hospitals Face Big Whammy From State Fees" in *Business Courier* (Vol. 26, October 2, 2009, No. 23, pp. 1)
Pub: American City Business Journals, Inc.
Ed: James Ritchie. **Description:** Ohio hospitals are facing losses of nearly $145 million in franchise fees which are set to be levied by the state. Ohio hospitals will be responsible for a total of $718 million franchise

fees as required by 2010-2011 state budget but will recover only 80 percent of the amount in increased Medicaid fees. Possible effects of anticipated losses to Ohio hospitals are examined.

45972 ▪ "Hot Air" in *Canadian Business* (Vol. 81, July 22, 2008, No. 12-13, pp. 16)
Pub: Rogers Media Ltd.
Ed: Joe Castaldo. **Description:** Over half of 101 business leaders who were recently surveyed oppose Liberal leader Stephane Dion's carbon-tax proposal, saying that manufacturers in Canada are likely to suffer from the plan. Additional key results of the survey are presented.

45973 ▪ "Hot Air: On Global Warming and Carbon Tax" in *Canadian Business* (Vol. 81, October 13, 2008, No. 17, pp. 12)
Pub: Rogers Media Ltd.
Ed: Joe Castaldo. **Description:** Survey of Canadian business leaders revealed that the environment is a key issue in Canada's federal elections. Respondents believe that Prime Minister Stephen Harper's views on global warming and climate change are closer to their own views. Other key information on the survey is presented.

45974 ▪ "Hotel Tax Eyed For Waukesha" in *The Business Journal-Milwaukee* (Vol. 25, August 29, 2008, No. 49, pp. A1)
Pub: American City Business Journals, Inc.
Ed: Rich Kirchen. **Description:** Midwest Airlines Center chairman Frank Gimbel wants Waukesha County to help in the funding of the $200-million expansion of the convention center through a hotel room tax. The Waukesha hotel industry is expected to oppose the new room tax. Other views and information on the planned new room tax in Waukesha are presented.

45975 ▪ "Housing Hedge" in *Canadian Business* (Vol. 79, July 17, 2006, No. 14-15, pp. 66)
Pub: Rogers Media
Ed: Jeff Sanford. **Description:** The idea of starting a hedge scheme for housing is presented using the advent of pension schemes as an example to follow.

45976 ▪ "How About Trying a Foreclosure Tax?" in *Crain's Detroit Business* (Vol. 24, January 28, 2008, No. 4, pp. 9)
Pub: Crain Communications Inc. - Detroit
Ed: Mark Goodell. **Description:** According to a recent study, local communities could see a $100 million decrease in property tax revenues, and the state could lose as much as $12 million in lower sales tax proceeds. Experts discuss options for Michigan's government to institute a foreclosure tax.

45977 ▪ "How to Maximize Your Investment Income" in *Contractor* (Vol. 56, December 2009, No. 12, pp. 33)
Pub: Penton Media, Inc.
Ed: Irv Blackman. **Description:** Private placement life insurance (PPLI) can minimize taxes and protect assets. PPLI is a form of variable universal insurance that is offered privately. Risk of insurance company illiquidity is avoided as investments are placed in separate accounts.

45978 ▪ *How to Start an Internet Sales Business*
Pub: Lulu.com
Ed: Dan Davis. **Released:** August 2005. **Price:** $19.95. **Description:** Small business guide for launching an Internet sales company. Topics include business structure, licenses, and taxes.

45979 ▪ *How to Start and Run a Small Book Publishing Company: A Small Business Guide to Self-Publishing and Independent Publishing*
Pub: HCM Publishing
Ed: Peter I. Hupalo. **Released:** August 30, 2002. **Price:** $18.95. **Description:** The book teaches all aspects of starting and running a small book publishing company. Topics covered include: inventory accounting in the book trade, just-in-time inventory management, turnkey fulfillment solutions, tax deductible costs, basics of sales and use tax, book pricing,

standards in terms of the book industry, working with distributors and wholesalers, cover design and book layout, book promotion and marketing, how to select profitable authors to publish, printing process, printing on demand, the power of a strong backlist, and how to value copyright.

45980 ■ How to Start and Run Your Own Corporation: S-Corporations For Small Business Owners

Pub: HCM Publishing

Ed: Peter I. Hupalo. **Released:** March 6, 2003. **Price:** $22.95. **Description:** Basics of corporate business structure are explained. Topics include discovering the best business structure for your company; how to decided between an S-Corporation and LLC; choosing the state in which to incorporate, how to form a corporation, angel investing, special issues for one-person corporations, the role of bylaws and corporate minutes, board of directors, taxes, workers' compensation issues, retirement plans, and more.

45981 ■ "The HST Hornet's Nest" in Canadian Business (Vol. 83, September 14, 2010, No. 15, pp. 17)

Pub: Rogers Media Ltd.

Ed: Michael McCullough. **Description:** Canadian Premier Gordon Campbell's Harmonized Sales Tax (HST) initiative has left British Columbia's economic and political future stuck in uncertainty. The petition of a coalition group forced a bill to abolish the HST through legislation or referendum. How the HST's abolition will affect British Columbia's revenues is also discussed.

45982 ■ "Incentives Debate Rages On Unabated" in The Business Journal-Serving Metropolitan Kansas City (Vol. 26, September 5, 2008, No. 52)

Pub: American City Business Journals, Inc.

Ed: Rob Roberts. **Description:** Debate on the new economic development and incentives policy adopted by the Kansas City Council is still on. The city's Planned Industrial Expansion Authority has rejected a standard property tax abatement proposal. The real estate development community has opposed the rejection of proposed the tax incentives policy.

45983 ■ "An Insurance Roll-Up In Danger of Unraveling" in Barron's (Vol. 88, March 17, 2008, No. 11, pp. 51)

Pub: Dow Jones & Company, Inc.

Ed: Bill Alpert. **Description:** Shares of National Financial Partners have fallen below their initial offering price as sputtering sales and management turnover leave many investors wondering. One of the company's star brokers is being sued for their "life settlement" contracts while another broker is being pursued by the IRS for unpaid taxes.

45984 ■ "Intel: Tax Breaks Key" in Business Journal Portland (Vol. 27, October 22, 2010, No. 34, pp. 1)

Pub: Portland Business Journal

Ed: Erik Siemers. **Description:** Intel Corporation believes that state tax incentives will be critical, especially in the purchase of manufacturing equipment, as they build a new chip factory in Hillsboro, Oregon. The tax breaks would help Intel avoid paying 10 times more in property taxes compared to average Washington County firms. Critics argue that Intel has about $15 billion in cash assets, and can afford the factory without the tax breaks.

45985 ■ "International Benefits Roundup" in Employee Benefit News (Vol. 25, December 1, 2011, No. 15)

Pub: SourceMedia Inc.

Description: Employee contributions to an employer-sponsored defined contribution plan in Japan will allowed on a tax-deductible basis; however, currently employee contributions are not allowed. The defined contribution plan is outlined for better understanding.

45986 ■ "Investment Firms Unite: Coalition Fights New Tax Law" in Black Enterprise (Vol. 38, December 2007, No. 5, pp. 52)

Pub: Earl G. Graves Publishing Co. Inc.

Ed: Joyce Jones. **Description:** Minorities working in private equity, real estate and investment management firms have united to form the Access to Capital

Coalition to oppose legislation that they feel would adversely affect their ability to attract investments and executives. Details of the group are included.

45987 ■ "Iowa Tax Case Could Cost Nation's Franchises" in Franchising World (Vol. 42, September 2010, No. 9, pp. 38)

Pub: International Franchise Association

Ed: Bruce A. Ackerman, Adam B. Thimmesch. **Description:** Ruling by the Iowa Supreme Court could have a financial impact on franchisors across the U.S. Iowa asserted that Kentucky Fried Chicken is subject to Iowa corporate income tax based solely on the fact that it received royalties from franchises in the state.

45988 ■ "It's Not Perfect; But Illinois a Good Home for Business" in Crain's Chicago Business (Vol. 34, October 24, 2011, No. 42, pp. 18)

Pub: Crain Communications Inc.

Description: Focusing on all factors that encompass Illinois' business environment, findings show that Illinois is a good place to start and grow a business. The study focused on corporate income tax rates and the fact that talent, access to capital and customers along with transportation connections are among the important factors the state has for small businesses.

45989 ■ J. K. Lasser's Small Business Taxes 2008: Your Complete Guide to a Better Bottom Line

Pub: John Wiley & Sons, Incorporated

Ed: Barbara Weltman. **Released:** November 2007. **Description:** Comprehensive guide providing tax strategies for any small business in the U.S. Sample forms and checklists are included.

45990 ■ JK Lasser's Small Business Taxes 2077: Your Complete Guide to a Better Bottom Line

Pub: John Wiley & Sons, Incorporated

Ed: Barbara Weltman. **Released:** November 2006. **Price:** $17.95. **Description:** J.K. Lasser's guide that offers tax facts and strategies for small businesses. The book helps to maximize deductions while learning tax planning strategies.

45991 ■ "Know Your Numbers" in Inc. (Volume 32, December 2010, No. 10, pp. 39)

Pub: Inc. Magazine

Ed: Norm Brodsky. **Description:** Ways to maximize profit and minimize tax burden are presented.

45992 ■ "Lean on Me" in Entrepreneur (Vol. 36, February 2008, No. 2, pp. 40)

Pub: Entrepreneur Media Inc.

Ed: Farnoosh Torabi. **Description:** Investing in tax liens is booming with the growth in the number of homeowners missing property tax payments. Details on how to bid for and when to redeem tax liens are outlined.

45993 ■ "Legislators Must Cut Cost of Government" in Crain's Detroit Business (Vol. 24, October 6, 2008, No. 40, pp. 6)

Pub: Crain Communications, Inc.

Description: Southeast and West Michigan business leaders are setting aside their differences and have proposed clear agendas, ranging from eliminating the Michigan Business Tax to overhauling public employee and retiree benefits and pensions. Lawmakers must also come together to find solutions for the state's economy and discover an entirely new vision for the future of Michigan business.

45994 ■ "Legislature Passes Increased Tax Credit for Urban Brownfield Projects" in Crain's Detroit Business (Vol. 24, March 31, 2008, No. 13)

Pub: Crain Communications, Inc.

Ed: Amy Lane. **Description:** Discusses the bill passed by the Legislature that creates a tax credit of up to 20 percent for projects in urban development areas.

45995 ■ "Lending Act Touted by Michaud" in Morning Sentinel (June 21, 2010)

Pub: Morning Sentinel

Ed: Doug Harlow. **Description:** If passed, the Small Business Jobs Tax Relief Act will leverage up to $300 billion in loans for small businesses through a $30 billion lending fund for small and medium-sized community banks, which focus on lending to small firms.

45996 ■ "Lifetime Planning with a Twist" in Contractor (Vol. 56, July 2009, No. 7, pp. 40)

Pub: Penton Media, Inc.

Ed: Irv Blackman. **Description:** Private Placement Life Insurance lets wealthy investors make their investment gains tax-free and can be set up so investors can make tax-free loans from the policy. This can be used on a younger member of the family as a wealth-building strategy if the investor is uninsurable.

45997 ■ "Lights, Camera...Incentive" in Austin Business JournalInc. (Vol. 28, October 10, 2008, No. 30, pp. 1)

Pub: American City Business Journals

Ed: Sandra Zaragoza. **Description:** Film industry insiders are saying that state level tax breaks are needed to boost the sector, together with the help of the $700 billion bailout bill, which is expected to provide $470 million in tax incentives to the movie industry. Other details on filmmakers' call for more tax incentives for Texas' film industry are discussed.

45998 ■ "Like Mom and Apple Pie" in Canadian Business (Vol. 79, October 9, 2006, No. 20, pp. 19)

Pub: Rogers Media

Ed: Peter Shawn Taylor. **Description:** Impact of paying huge tax bills on the social benefits of family income is discussed. Income splitting as an effective way to lower household's overall tax bill is presented.

45999 ■ "A Little Less Hot Air" in Canadian Business (Vol. 81, March 17, 2008, No. 4, pp. 9)

Pub: Rogers Media

Description: British Columbia will levy an extra tax on all carbon-emitting fuels starting July 1, 2008. The tax will raise $1.8 billion in three years and in effect, the province will reduce general corporate income tax from 12 percent to 11 percent. The tax on small businesses and personal income will also be reduced.

46000 ■ "Local Manufacturers See Tax Proposal Hurting Global Operations" in Crain's Cleveland Business (Vol. 30, May 18, 2009, No. 20)

Pub: Crain Communications, Inc.

Ed: Dan Shingler. **Description:** New tax laws proposed by the Obama Administration could hinder the efforts of some Northeast Ohio industrial companies from expanding their overseas markets. The law is designed to prevent companies from moving jobs overseas.

46001 ■ "Looking for a Sales Tax Extension" in Milwaukee Business Journal (Vol. 27, January 29, 2010, No. 18, pp. A1)

Pub: American City Business Journals

Ed: Mark Kass. **Description:** Milwaukee, Wisconsin-area business executives believe the extension of the Miller Park 0.1 percent sales tax could help fund a new basketball arena to replace the 21-year-old Bradley Center in downtown Milwaukee. However, any sales tax expansion that includes the new basketball arena would need approval by Wisconsin's legislature.

46002 ■ "Major Advances in Heat Pump Technology" in Contractor (Vol. 57, January 2010, No. 1, pp. 42)

Pub: Penton Media, Inc.

Ed: Mark Eatherton. **Description:** Tax credits make ground-source heat pump technology more economically feasible. Suggestions on how to choose the right ground-source heat pump technology to install in a house are discussed.

46003 ■ *Make Sure It's Deductible*
Pub: McGraw-Hill Inc.
Ed: Evelyn Jacks. **Released:** November 2006. **Price:** $22.95. **Description:** Tax planning, strategies are provided to help small businesses maximize deductions.

46004 ■ *Make Your Life Tax Deductible: Easy Techniques to Reduce Your Taxes and Start Building Wealth Immediately*
Pub: McGraw-Hill Companies
Ed: David Meier. **Released:** December 2005. **Price:** $16.95 (US), $22.95 (Canadian). **Description:** Over 150 tax deductions are listed to help small business owners lower taxes and boost profits.

46005 ■ "Maryland Senate Gets Read to Talk Taxes" in *Boston Business Journal* (Vol. 29, July 1, 2011, No. 8, pp. 1)
Pub: American City Business Journals Inc.
Ed: Scott Dance. **Description:** Maryland Senate Budget and Taxation Committee will meet July 26, 2011 to discuss some of business community's concerns including sales tax expansion to cover services, a restructuring of the corporate income tax brackets and an answer to questions regarding transportation funding project.

46006 ■ "Mayor Unveils Business Plan" in *Boston Business Journal* (Vol. 29, September 16, 2011, No. 19, pp. 1)
Pub: American City Business Journals Inc.
Ed: Gary Haber. **Description:** Mayor Stephanie Rawlings-Blake of Baltimore, Maryland unveiled her plan to push the economy forward. Her key objectives include giving more support for the city's technology companies and refocusing the Baltimore Development Corporation on job creation and retention.

46007 ■ "MBT 'Sticker Shock' Surprises Business; Reaction? 'You Can't Print It,' Owner Says" in *Crain's Detroit Business* (March 17, 2008)
Pub: Crain Communications, Inc.
Ed: Amy Lane. **Description:** Overview of the new Michigan Business Tax which is raising many middle-sized businesses' taxes by up to 400 percent.

46008 ■ "Medicaid Expansion Could Prompt New Taxes, Program Cuts" in *Baltimore Business Journal* (Vol. 27, October 23, 2009, No. 24, pp. 1)
Pub: American City Business Journals
Ed: Julekha Dash. **Description:** Effects of the expected federal expansion of Medicaid under federal health care reform on Maryland tax policy are presented. Health care executives believe new taxes are necessary for the state to pay for an expansion that could cost over $400 million to $600 million.

46009 ■ *Mergers and Acquisitions from A to Z*
Pub: Amacom
Ed: Andrew J. Sherman, Milledge A. Hart. **Released:** January 2006. **Price:** $35.00. **Description:** Guide for the entire process of mergers and acquisitions, including taxes, accounting, laws, and projected financial gain.

46010 ■ "Michaud Touts Small-Business Credentials" in *Bangor Daily News* (September 10, 2010)
Pub: Bangor Daily News
Ed: Nick Sambides Jr. **Description:** Mike Michaud, Democrat, is running against a Republican challenger in the 2nd District and states he will support the Small Business Jobs Tax Relief Act if reelected.

46011 ■ *Minding Her Own Business, 4th Ed.*
Pub: Sphinx Publishing
Ed: Jan Zobel. **Released:** January 1, 2005. **Price:** $16.95. **Description:** A guide to taxes and financial records for women entrepreneurs is presented.

46012 ■ "More Corporate Welfare?" in *Canadian Business* (Vol. 80, February 12, 2007, No. 4, pp. 96)
Pub: Rogers Media
Description: The burden on Canadian taxpayers by governmental efforts to finance loss-making companies in the name of corporate welfare is discussed.

46013 ■ "More Jobs Moving Out of City" in *Business Courier* (Vol. 24, March 14, 2008, No. 49, pp. 1)
Pub: American City Business Journals, Inc.
Ed: Steve Watkins; Laura Baverman. **Description:** UBS Financial Services Inc. is moving Gradison to Kenwood Town Place in Sycamore Township a year after UBS acquired Gradison. The township does not have a tax on earnings so the move will save Gradison's employees the 2.1 percent Cincinnati tax.

46014 ■ "NAWBO Takes the Stage at Press Conference for Small Business Jobs, Credit and Tax Relief Acts" in *Internet Wire* (June 17, 2010)
Pub: Comtex
Description: A survey of the National Association of Women Business Owners reported optimism returning and women business owners are ready to invest in job creation. The Small Business Jobs Tax Relief Act will aid in their progress.

46015 ■ "New Rule Rankles In Jersey" in *Philadelphia Business Journal* (Vol. 30, September 16, 2011, No. 31, pp. 1)
Pub: American City Business Journals Inc.
Ed: Jeff Blumenthal. **Description:** A new rule in New Jersey which taxes out-of-state companies that conduct business in the state earned the ire of several banks, mortgage lenders and credit card companies and prompted opponents to threaten to file lawsuits. The new rule is an amendment to New Jersey Division of Taxation's corporate business tax regulation and is retroactive to 2002. Details are given.

46016 ■ "New Tax Sends Biz Scrambling; Service Levy Will Affect 16,000 Businesses" in *Crain's Detroit Business* (October 8, 2007)
Pub: Crain Communications Inc. - Detroit
Ed: Amy Lane. **Description:** Legislation that imposes a tax on services in Michigan has business leaders upset. The new law exerts a 6 percent tax on 57 categories of services that affects 16,000 businesses in the state.

46017 ■ "New Year, New Estate Plan" in *Hawaii Business* (Vol. 53, February 2008, No. 8, pp. 54)
Pub: Hawaii Business Publishing
Ed: Antony M. Orme. **Description:** Discusses the start of the new year which can be a time to revise wills and estate plans as failure to do so may create problems of unequal inheritance and increase in estate tax exemption, which could disinherit beneficiaries. Other circumstances that can prompt changes in wills and estate plans are presented.

46018 ■ "Now You See It..." in *Canadian Business* (Vol. 81, November 10, 2008, No. 19, pp. 20)
Pub: Rogers Media Ltd.
Ed: Sharda Prashad. **Description:** Total return swaps were offered by Deutsche Bank AG and UBS AG to foreign investors for them to avoid paying taxes on the proceeds of their shares of Fording Canadian Coal Trust when Teck Cominco offered to buy the company. This means that the Canadian government is losing tax revenue from foreigners and it is argued that a simpler tax system would avoid this practice.

46019 ■ "Ohio Business Incentives Lag Offerings By Other States" in *Crain's Cleveland Business* (Vol. 30, May 18, 2009, No. 20, pp. 1)
Pub: Crain Communications, Inc.
Ed: Jay Miller. **Description:** Incentives designed to attract business and promote business expansion in Ohio has not done their job. According to a new study, despite tax changes made four years ago, the state's ability to attract new business has gone unchanged.

46020 ■ "On tap: More Could Get MEGA Credits; Need to Look Outside State May Be Cut" in *Crain's Detroit Business* (April 7, 2008)
Pub: Crain Communications, Inc.
Ed: Amy Lane. **Description:** In order to qualify for Michigan Economic Growth Authority tax credits Michigan businesses may no longer have to shop

outside the state due to a new bill which has already passed the state Senate and will move on to the House; the bill, along with further changes to the MEGA program, is designed to provide incentives for investments that would add relevance and make Michigan more competitive.

46021 ■ "Ottawa Advised to Underwrite Carbon Technology" in *Globe & Mail* (March 10, 2007, pp. B3)
Pub: CTVglobemedia Publishing Inc.
Ed: Shawn McCarthy. **Description:** A federal panel's suggestion that carbon tax in Canada was not adequate to encourage oil companies and utilities to take up costly technologies to reduce carbon emissions is discussed.

46022 ■ "Ottawa Attacks!" in *Canadian Business* (Vol. 79, November 6, 2006, No. 22, pp. 21)
Pub: Rogers Media
Ed: Jeff Sanford. **Description:** The effects of new tax policy developed by Jim Flaherty, Finance Minister of Canada, on income trusts are presented.

46023 ■ *Overcoming Barriers to Entrepreneurship in the United States*
Pub: Lexington Books
Ed: Diana Furchtgott-Roth. **Released:** March 28, 2008. **Price:** $24.95. **Description:** Real and perceived barriers to the founding and running of small businesses in America are discussed. Each chapter outlines how policy and economic environments can hinder business owners and offers tips to overcome these obstacles. Starting with venture capital access in Silicon Valley during the Internet bubble, the book goes on to question the link between personal wealth and entrepreneurship, examines how federal tax rates affect small business creation and destruction, explains the low rate of self-employment among Mexican immigrants, and suggests ways pension coverage can be increased in small businesses.

46024 ■ *Own Your Own Corporation: Why the Rich Own Their Own Companies and Everyone Else Works for Them*
Pub: Business Plus
Ed: Garrett Sutton; Robert T. Kiyosaki; Ann Blackman. **Released:** June 2008. **Price:** $17.99 paperback. **Description:** Part of the Rich Dad Advisor's Series, this edition shows how individuals can incorporate themselves and their businesses to save thousands of dollars in taxes and protect against financial disaster.

46025 ■ "PA Tax Reforms See Some Progress" in *Philadelphia Business Journal* (Vol. 28, October 16, 2009, No. 35, pp. 1)
Pub: American City Business Journals
Ed: Athena D. Merritt. **Description:** It was reported that Pennsylvania's $27.8 billion budget arrived 101 days late, but business groups are encouraged that progress continues to be made on long-called-for tax reforms. The Research and Development Tax Credit, currently at $40 million, will drop to $20 million in 2009-2010.

46026 ■ "Pain Ahead as Profit Pressure Increases" in *Crain's Chicago Business* (Vol. 31, May 5, 2008, No. 18, pp. 4)
Pub: Crain Communications, Inc.
Ed: Daniel Rome Levine. **Description:** Interview with David Klaskin, the chairman and chief investment officer at Oak Ridge Investments LLC, who discusses the outlook for the economy and corporate earnings, particularly in the housing and auto industries, the impact of economic stimulus checks, the weakness of the dollar and recommendations of stocks that individual investors may find helpful.

46027 ■ "P&G vs. IRS: Split Decision" in *Business Courier* (Vol. 27, July 16, 2010, No. 11, pp. 1)
Pub: Business Courier
Ed: Jon Newberry. **Description:** Implications of a court ruling in a $435 million legal dispute between Procter & Gamble Company (P&G) and the Internal Revenue Service (IRS) are discussed. A $21 million win has been realized for P&G for its interpretation of research and development tax credits. However, the

said case might involve more than $700 million in P&G tax deductions from 2001 through 2004 that the IRS had disallowed.

46028 ■ "P&L Building Owner Nears Start of $157M Condo Plan" in *Business Journal-Serving Metropolitan Kansas City* **(November 23, 2007)**
Pub: American City Business Journals, Inc.
Ed: Jim Davis. **Description:** The owner of Power and Light Building is ready to begin a $157 million plan to refurbish the Kansas City landmark and redevelop a property right next to it after receiving tax increment refinancing for the project.

46029 ■ "Paperless Bookkeeping Program" in *Fleet Owner Online* **(February 15, 2011)**
Pub: Penton Business Media Inc.
Description: TruckTax launched its new paperless bookkeeping system to help manage bookkeeping tasks, accounting and business tax information and filings for truckers.

46030 ■ "Pick and Save" in *Entrepreneur* **(Vol. 36, April 2008, No. 4, pp. 66)**
Pub: Entrepreneur Media, Inc.
Ed: C.J. Prince. **Description:** Business owners can purchase the needed big equipment to offset this year's expected profit. They can also switch to annualized computing of quarterly income and estimated tax payments to pay less estimated taxes for the first half of the year. Other tips on tax planning are provided.

46031 ■ "Pinellas Leaders Want First Leg of Light Rail" in *The Business Journal-Serving Greater Tampa Bay* **(Vol. 28, August 8, 2008, No. 33)**
Pub: American City Business Journals, Inc.
Ed: Larry Halstead. **Description:** Proposed routes for the first leg of the planned light railway system in the Tampa Bay, Florida area are being presented as the Tampa Bay Area Regional Transportation Authority is about to make its master plan for the project. A sales tax for transit is being proposed to fund the project, as well as an expansion of the accompanying bus system.

46032 ■ "Pioneers Get All The Perks" in *Canadian Business* **(Vol. 81, March 3, 2008, No. 3, pp. 18)**
Pub: Rogers Media
Description: Suncor Energy Inc. will face royalty payments from 25% to 30% of net profits as it signs a new deal with Alberta. Biovail Corp., meanwhile, is under a U.S. grand jury investigation for supposed improprieties in Cardizem LA heart drug launch. The Conference Board of Canada's proposal to impose taxes on greenhouse gas emissions and other developments in the business community are discussed.

46033 ■ "Poor Economy Inspires Rich Alternatives In a Modern, and Tax-Free, Twist on Bartering" in *Houston Chronicle* **(June 7, 2010)**
Pub: Houston Chronicle Publishing Company
Ed: Michael Rubinkam. **Description:** Time banking helps individuals and firms receive goods or services by depositing time dollars into a bank reserved for receipt of goods and services.

46034 ■ *PPC's Small Business Tax Guide*
Pub: Practitioners Publishing Company
Ed: Douglas L. Weinbrenner, Virginia R. Bergman, Toni M. Greenwall, James A. Keller, Scott Mayfield, Linda A. Markwood. **Released:** January 2005. **Price:** $189.00. **Description:** Business tax laws are covered in an easy to understand format.

46035 ■ *PPC's Small Business Tax Guide, Vol. 2*
Pub: Practitioners Publishing Company
Ed: Douglas L. Weinbrenner, Virginia R. Bergman, Toni M. Greenwall, James A. Keller, Scott Mayfield, Linda A. Markwood. **Released:** January 2005. **Price:** $189.00. **Description:** Second volume containing technical guide covering business tax laws.

46036 ■ "Praise for Tax Cuts" in *Canadian Business* **(Vol. 80, November 19, 2007, No. 23, pp. 16)**
Pub: Rogers Media
Ed: Joe Castaldo. **Description:** A Compas Inc. survey found that most of the 158 business leaders polled are in favor of federal tax cuts. The findings revealed that the respondents gave an average of 74 percent to the mini-budget, an unusual score for a government initiative. Other opinions on the government's tax relief are presented.

46037 ■ *Principles of Private Firm Valuation*
Pub: John Wiley & Sons, Incorporated
Ed: Stanley J. Feldman. **Released:** April 2005. **Price:** $85.00. **Description:** Tools and techniques to correctly perform private firm valuation, including value and how to measure it, valuing control, determining the size of the marketability discount, creating transparency and the implications for value, the value of tax pass-through entities versus a C corporation, etc.

46038 ■ "Private Pitfalls" in *Canadian Business* **(Vol. 80, October 22, 2007, No. 21, pp. 34)**
Pub: Rogers Media
Ed: Al Rosen. **Description:** Guidelines on how minority shareholders can avoid drawbacks at the time of purchase, during ownership, and when selling shares are discussed; contractual protection, sales taxation and share price are also presented. Investment in a private company entails knowing the party you are buying share from.

46039 ■ "Proposed Transit Legislation" in *Crain's Detroit Business* **(Vol. 24, October 6, 2008, No. 40, pp. 19)**
Pub: Crain Communications, Inc.
Description: Breakdown of state Representative Marie Donigan's proposed transit legislation includes tax increment financing. Other pieces of the proposed legislation are examined.

46040 ■ *QuickBooks Simple Start for Dummies*
Pub: John Wiley & Sons, Incorporated
Ed: Stephen L. Nelson. **Released:** October 2004. **Price:** $21.99. **Description:** Profile of Intuits new accounting software geared to micro businesses. Advice is offered on daily, monthly, and yearly accounting activities covering records, sales tax, and reports.

46041 ■ *QuickBooks X for Dummies*
Pub: John Wiley & Sons, Incorporated
Ed: Stephen L. Nelson. **Released:** November 2006. **Price:** $21.99. **Description:** Key features of Quick-Books software for small business are introduced. Invoicing and credit memos, recoding sales receipts, accounting, budgeting, taxes, payroll, financial reports, job estimating, billing, tracking, data backup, are among the features.

46042 ■ "Quicken Starter Edition 2008" in *Black Enterprise* **(Vol. 38, March 2008, No. 8, pp. 54)**
Pub: Earl G. Graves Publishing Co. Inc.
Ed: Sonya A. Donaldson. **Description:** Profile of Quicken Starter Edition 2008 offering programs that track spending; it will also categorize tax deductible expenses.

46043 ■ "The Rabbi Trust" in *Barron's* **(Vol. 88, March 24, 2008, No. 12, pp. 55)**
Pub: Dow Jones & Company, Inc.
Ed: Joseph F. Gelband. **Description:** Discusses a rabbi trust which is a method of deferring taxes on compensation allowed by the Internal Revenue Service. Funding of the trust is not considered taxable. Other regulations concerning tax deferment are also discussed.

46044 ■ "Raising Money: the Bond that Lasts" in *Entrepreneur* **(Vol. 35, October 2007, No. 10, pp. 73)**
Pub: Entrepreneur Media Inc.
Ed: Crystal Detamore-Rodman. **Description:** Tax-exempt bonds can be the solution to long-term financing needs of entrepreneurs. However, high initial costs may discourage some entrepreneurs to apply

for these bonds, with transactions usually costing $3 mor more. How tax-exempt bonds work, and how rules vary with different states are discussed.

46045 ■ "Real Estate Wheeling and Dealing Picks Up" in *Business Journal Portland* **(Vol. 27, October 29, 2010, No. 35, pp. 1)**
Pub: Portland Business Journal
Ed: Wendy Culverwell. **Description:** LoopNet has listed 33 prominent commercial properties for sale in Portland, Oregon's real estate market. However, reasons for the sales rush are not totally clear, but speculations point to the end of the Bush tax cuts in 2010 that prompted real estate investors to close the deals and avoid the increase in capital gains taxes.

46046 ■ "Red Tape Ties Detroit Housing Rehab Plan" in *Crain's Detroit Business* **(Vol. 24, September 22, 2008, No. 38, pp. 1)**
Pub: Crain Communications, Inc.
Ed: Ryan Beene. **Description:** Venture-capital firm Wilherst Oxford LLC is a Florida-based company that has purchased 300 inner-city homes which were in foreclosure in Detroit. Wilherst Oxford is asking the city to forgive the existing tax and utility liens so the firm can utilize the money for home improvements. The city, however, is reluctant but has stated that they are willing to negotiate.

46047 ■ "Retailers, Your Will, and More" in *Agency Sales Magazine* **(Vol. 39, July 2009, No. 7, pp. 46)**
Pub: MANA
Ed: Melvin H. Daskal. **Description:** IRS audit guide for small retail businesses is presented. Tips on how to make a will with multiple beneficiaries are discussed together with medical expenses that can not be deducted.

46048 ■ *Retire Dollar Smart*
Pub: Trafford Publishing
Ed: Jim Miller. **Released:** July 2006. **Price:** $25.99. **Description:** The difference between savings and investments and their importance is examined, along with four rules for converting good investments into even greater ones. Contingency plans for healthcare costs as well as ways to manage taxes on investments are discussed. Five methods to control the costs of investing and saving include the use of smart strategies; getting independent, accurate, complete information; investing passively; asking for a discount; and taking off your blinders. Ten steps for designing a foolproof retirement investment portfolio are also provided.

46049 ■ "Revenue Shortfall Leads to Budget Uncertainty" in *Crain's Detroit Business* **(Vol. 24, March 10, 2008, No. 10, pp. 26)**
Pub: Crain Communications, Inc.
Ed: Amy Lane. **Description:** Michigan's current-year budget may face a $134 million shortfall due to such issues as lower-than-anticipated payment from a 1999 national settlement with the U.S. tobacco industry, overestimated growth in property-tax revenue, the impact of the federal stimulus package and the potential settlement of a Midland property-tax dispute. The governor's proposed budget for fiscal year for 2009 may face a $249.6 million shortfall.

46050 ■ "S3 Entertainment Group Partners with WFW International for Film Services in Michigan" in *Michigan Vue* **(July-August 2008)**
Pub: Entrepreneur Media Inc.
Description: William F. White (WFW), one of North America's largest production equipment providers has partnered with S3 Entertainment Group (S3EG), a Michigan-based full-service film production services company due to the new incentives package which currently offers the highest incentives in the United States, up to 42 percent. S3EG will actively store, lease, manage, distribute and sell WFW's equipment to the growing number of production teams that are filming in the state.

46051 ■ "SABMiller Deal Hit by Tax Ruling" in *Wall Street Journal Eastern Edition* **(November 21 , 2011, pp. B9)**
Pub: Dow Jones & Company Inc.
Ed: David Fickling, Simon Zekaria. **Description:** SABMiller PLC, the giant brewer in the United Kingdom, is acquiring Australian beer icon Foster's

Group Ltd. for US$9.9 billion, but will have to come up with another A$582 million following a tax ruling by the Australian Taxation Office in order that shareholders of Foster's don't lose.

46052 ■ "Sales Tax Proposed to Revive KRM" in *Business Journal-Milwaukee* **(Vol. 25, October 26, 2007, No. 4, pp. A1)**
Pub: American City Business Journals, Inc.
Ed: Rich Kirchen. **Description:** City and county officials are proposing a $13 increase in rental car fees to finance the Kenosha-Racine-Milwaukee line. The Alliance of Cities proposed sales tax are backed by Milwaukee-area business groups, however it failed to generate support from the public.

46053 ■ "Samsung 'Holding Breath'" in *Austin Business JournalInc.* **(Vol. 29, January 29, 2010, No. 47, pp. 1)**
Pub: American City Business Journals
Ed: Jacob Dirr. **Description:** Samsung Austin Semiconductor LLC entered into an incentives agreement with the State of Texas in 2005, which involved $230 million in tax breaks and public financing. Terms of the agreement have been met, but some are questioning whether the company will be able to meet its goals for the Austin operations in 2010.

46054 ■ "Saratoga Eagle Project Quenches Thirst To Grow" in *Business Review, Albany New York* **(Vol. 34, November 30, 2007, No. 35, pp. 3)**
Pub: American City Business Journals, Inc.
Ed: Robin K. Cooper. **Description:** Saratoga Eagle Sales and Service will be searching for contractors for the construction of its new beverage distribution center at the WJ Grande Industrial Park in Saratoga Springs, New York. The $8 million, 107,000 square foot facility is part of Saratoga Eagle's expansion plan. The company's growth in the Capital Region market and $1.3 million tax break are discussed.

46055 ■ *Sarbanes-Oxley for Small Businesses: Leveraging Compliance for Maximum Advantage*
Pub: John Wiley & Sons, Incorporated
Ed: Peggy M. Jackson. **Released:** November 2006. **Price:** $39.95. **Description:** Book lists five ways the Sarbane Oxley Act helps small businesses.

46056 ■ *Save $2000 to $8000 in Taxes with a Home-Based Business*
Pub: TKG Publishing
Ed: Greco Garcia. **Released:** February 2007. **Price:** $16.99. **Description:** Tax advice for a home-based business is given.

46057 ■ *Schaum's Outline Financial Management, Third Edition*
Pub: McGraw-Hill
Ed: Jae K. Shim; Joel G. Siegel. **Released:** May 2007. **Price:** $22.95 (CND). **Description:** Rules and regulations governing corporate finance, including the Sarbanes-Oxley Act are discussed.

46058 ■ "Seasonal Franchises" in *Franchising World* **(Vol. 42, August 2010, No. 8, pp. 50)**
Pub: International Franchise Association
Ed: Jennifer Lemcke. **Description:** Seasonal franchises, such as tax businesses can be slow during the summer months. Restaurants are slow during the months of January and February. The various challenges faced by seasonal franchises are examined.

46059 ■ "SEC Extends Small Business Deadline for SOX Audit Requirement" in *HRMagazine* **(Vol. 53, August 2008, No. 8, pp. 20)**
Pub: Society for Human Resource Management
Description: Securities and Exchange Commission has approved a one-year extension of the compliance date for smaller public companies to meet the Section 404(b) auditor attestation requirement of the Sarbanes-Oxley Act.

46060 ■ *The Secret of Exiting Your Business Under Your Terms!*
Pub: Outskirts Press, Incorporated
Ed: Gene H. Irwin. **Released:** August 2005. **Price:** $29.95. **Description:** Topics include how to sell a business for the highest value, tax laws governing the sale of a business, finding the right buyer, mergers and acquisitions, negotiating the sale, and using a limited auction to increase future value of a business.

46061 ■ *Self-Employed Tax Solutions: Quick, Simple, Money-Saving, Audit-Proof Tax and Recordkeeping Basics*
Pub: The Globe Pequot Press
Ed: June Walker. **Released:** January 1, 2009. **Price:** $17.95. **Description:** A simple system for maintaining tax records and filing tax forms for any small business is explored.

46062 ■ "Senate Bill Would Eliminate MBT Surcharge in 2011" in *Crain's Detroit Business* **(Vol. 24, April 7, 2008, No. 14, pp. 33)**
Pub: Crain Communications, Inc.
Ed: Amy Lane. **Description:** Discusses possible changes to the new Michigan Business Tax, including a proposed bill which would phase out a 21.99 percent surcharge on the tax.

46063 ■ "Several Studio Projects in Production" in *Crain's Detroit Business* **(Vol. 26, January 18, 2010, No. 3, pp. 21)**
Pub: Crain Communications, Inc.
Ed: Bill Shea. **Description:** Overview of several projects in development in the metro Detroit area due to Michigan's film industry incentives which include a 25 percent tax credit for infrastructure projects.

46064 ■ "Shear Profit" in *Crain's Cleveland Business* **(Vol. 28, October 29, 2007, No. 43, pp. 3)**
Pub: Crain Communications, Inc.
Ed: David Bennett. **Description:** Alpaca farms are becoming a very profitable business for a number of Northeast Ohio entrepreneurs due to the high return on initial investments, tax incentives and the rise in demand for the animals. Ohio leads the country in the number of alpaca farms with roughly one-third located in Northeast Ohio.

46065 ■ *A Simplified Guide to Small Business Tax Deductions*
Pub: Frontline Publishers, Incorporated
Ed: Gladson I. Nwanna. **Released:** December 2005. **Price:** $39.99. **Description:** An overview of federal tax deductions allowed for small businesses; also lists tax schedules and forms and the line to claim the deductions.

46066 ■ "Single Most Important Problem" in *Small Business Economic Trends* **(July 2010, pp. 18)**
Pub: National Federation of Independent Business
Description: A table showing the single most important problem among small businesses surveyed in the U.S. for June 2010 is presented. Poor sales was selected by 30 percent of firms as the single most important problem, followed by taxes and government requirements and red tape. Graphs comparing selected single most important problem from January 1986 to June 2010 are also given.

46067 ■ "Small-Business Agenda: Increase Capital, Education, Tax Breaks" in *Crain's Detroit Business* **(Vol. 24, March 17, 2008)**
Pub: Crain Communications, Inc.
Ed: Nancy Kaffer. **Description:** Discusses the policy suggestions detailed in the Small Business Association of Michigan's entrepreneurial agenda which include five main categories of focus: making entrepreneurial education a higher state priority; increasing capital available to entrepreneurs; using the state's tax structure as an incentive for entrepreneurial growth; getting university research from the lab to the market; and limiting government regulation that's burdensome to small businesses and getting legislative support of entrepreneurial assistance efforts.

46068 ■ *Small Business Desk Reference*
Pub: Penguin Books (USA) Incorporated
Ed: Gene Marks. **Released:** December 2004. **Description:** Comprehensive guide for starting or running a successful small business, focusing on buying a business or franchise, writing a business plan, financial management, accounting, legal issues, human resources management, operations, marketing, sales, customer service, taxes, insurance, and ethics. Information for launching a restaurant, property management firm, retail outlet, consulting firm, and service business is included.

46069 ■ *Small Business Legal Tool Kit*
Pub: Entrepreneur Press
Ed: Ira Nottonson; Theresa A. Pickner. **Released:** May 2007. **Price:** $36.95. **Description:** Legal expertise is provided by two leading entrepreneurial attorneys. Issues covered include forming and operating a business: taxes, contracts, leases, bylaws, trademarks, small claims court, etc.

46070 ■ *Small Business Management*
Pub: John Wiley & Sons, Incorporated
Ed: Margaret Burlingame. **Released:** March 2007. **Price:** $44.95. **Description:** Advice for starting and running a small business as well as information on the value and appeal of small businesses, is given. Topics include budgets, taxes, inventory, ethics, e-commerce, and current laws.

46071 ■ *The Small Business Start-Up Kit for California*
Pub: NOLO
Ed: Peri Pakroo. **Released:** March 2008. **Price:** $29.99. **Description:** Handbook covering all aspects of starting a business in California, including information about necessary fees, forms, and taxes.

46072 ■ *Small Business Survival Guide: Starting, Protecting, and Securing Your Business for Long-Term Success*
Pub: Adams Media Corporation
Ed: Cliff Ennico. **Released:** September 2005. **Price:** $12.95 (US), $17.95 (Canadian). **Description:** Entrepreneurship in the new millennium. Topics include creditors, taxes, competition, business law, and accounting.

46073 ■ *Small Business Tax Deductions 2006*
Pub: Continuing Education of the Bar-California
Ed: Stephen Fishman. **Released:** June 2006. **Price:** $99.00. **Description:** Allowable tax deductions for small business in 2006 are explained.

46074 ■ *Small Business Taxes 2006: Your Complete Guide to a Better Bottom Line*
Pub: John Wiley & Sons, Incorporated
Ed: Barbara Weltman. **Released:** November 2008. **Price:** $18.95. **Description:** Detailed information on new tax laws and IRS rules for small businesses.

46075 ■ *Small Business Taxes Made Easy: How to Increase Your Deductions, Reduce What You Owe, and Boost Your Profits*
Pub: McGraw-Hill Companies
Ed: Eva Rosenberg. **Released:** December 2004. **Price:** $16.95. **Description:** Tax expert gives advice to small business owners regarding tax issues. TaxMamma.com, run by Eva Rosenberg, is one of the top seven tax advice Websites on the Internet.

46076 ■ "Small Business Unsure of Impact of New Tax Law" in *Crain's Detroit Business* **(Vol. 23, October 15, 2007, No. 42, pp. 13)**
Pub: Crain Communications Inc. - Detroit
Ed: Sheena Harrison. **Description:** Small business owners in Michigan are concerned with issues surrounding the proposed increases in state taxes geared at small business, which includes a 6 percent service tax.

46077 ■ "Small Businesses Benefiting from Movie-Struck Hub" in *Boston Business Journal* **(Vol. 27, October 12, 2007, No. 37, pp. 1)**
Pub: American City Business Journals Inc.
Ed: Naomi R. Kooker. **Description:** Revision of the Massachusetts' film tax credits has attracted filming of major motion pictures in the state and local businesses have benefited. A list of businesses that saw boosts from the movie-making industry's presence is presented.

46078 ■ *Small Time Operator: How to Start Your Own Business, Keep Your Books, Pay Your Taxes, and Stay Out of Trouble*
Pub: Bell Springs Publishing
Ed: Bernard B. Kamoroff. **Released:** January 2008. **Price:** $18.95. **Description:** Comprehensive guide for starting any kind of business.

46079 ■ *Smart Tax Write-Offs, 5th Ed.*
Pub: Rayve Productions, Inc.
Ed: Norm Ray. **Released:** February 2008. **Price:** $15.95. **Description:** Guidebook to help small business owners take advantage of legitimate tax deductions for home-based and other entrepreneurial businesses.

46080 ■ "Smart Year-End Tax Moves" in *Business Owner* (Vol. 35, November-December 2011, No. 6, pp. 8)
Pub: DL Perkins Company
Description: Managing small business and individual taxes is more important in a bad economy. It is imperative to seek all tax incentives that apply to your business.

46081 ■ "A Smarter Kind of Taxes" in *Canadian Business* (Vol. 80, October 8, 2007, No. 20, pp. 203)
Pub: Rogers Media
Ed: Jack Mintz. **Description:** Forecasts on Canada's tax system by 2020 are analyzed. It is expected that the country's aging society will place great demands on elderly-related spending such as pensions and healthcare. And, since the elderly pay fewer taxes, the revenue available to the government will be reduced. Other trends also show that several factors will cause significant change to the country's tax system.

46082 ■ "A Socko Payout Menu: Rural Phone Carrier Plots to Supercharge Its Shares" in *Barron's* (Vol. 88, June 30, 2008, No. 26, pp. M5)
Pub: Dow Jones & Co., Inc.
Ed: Shirley A. Lazo. **Description:** CenturyTel boosted its quarterly common payout to 70 cents from 6.75 cents per share die to its strong cash flows and solid balance sheet. Eastman Kodak's plan for a buyback will be partially funded by its $581 million tax refund. CME Group will buyback stocks through 2009 worth $1.1 billion.

46083 ■ "Solace for the Freshly Flaherty'd" in *Canadian Business* (Vol. 79, November 6, 2006, No. 22, pp. 114)
Pub: Rogers Media
Ed: Ian McGugan. **Description:** Tips to manage investments with relation to cash distribution tax on income trusts are presented.

46084 ■ "Solar Credit Lapse Spur Late Demand" in *The Business Journal - Serving Phoenix and the Valley of the Sun* (Vol. 28, July 18, 2008)
Pub: American City Business Journals, Inc.
Ed: Patrick O'Grady. **Description:** Businesses looking to engage in the solar energy industry are facing the problems of taxation and limited solar panel supply. Solar panels manufacturers are focusing more on the European market. Political issues surrounding the federal tax credit policy on solar energy users are also discussed.

46085 ■ "Solutions to Family Business Problems" in *Contractor* (Vol. 56, October 2009, No. 10, pp. 51)
Pub: Penton Media, Inc.
Ed: Irv Blackman. **Description:** Several common business problems that family owned firms face are presented together with their solutions. These problems include giving the children stock bonus options while another discusses the tax burden when a father wants to transfer the business to his son.

46086 ■ "Something to Like" in *Canadian Business* (Vol. 81, April 14, 2008, No. 6, pp. 22)
Pub: Rogers Media
Ed: Jack Mintz. **Description:** Jim Flaherty's policy on tax-free savings account (TFSA) will allow Canadians to accumulate wealth at a much faster rate and

these accounts could be especially good for people who are subject to high effective taxes on savings. Investors should put their money into a Registered Retirement Savings Plan (RRSP) when it comes to risky investments but the TFSA is better than an RRSP if investors expect very high taxes on withdrawals from their RRSP.

46087 ■ "Spending on Innovation Down Sharply in State" in *Crain's Detroit Business* (Vol. 24, March 10, 2008, No. 10, pp. 7)
Pub: Crain Communications, Inc.
Ed: Chad Halcom. **Description:** Due to such issues as Michigan's uncertain tax structure, a shaky national economy, the credit crunch and mortgage lending crisis, investments in innovation for the state have sharply declined.

46088 ■ "Stadium Developers Seek a Win With the State" in *The Business Journal-Serving Metropolitan Kansas City* (Vol. 26, August 22, 2008)
Pub: American City Business Journals, Inc.
Ed: Rob Roberts. **Description:** Three Trails Redevelopment LLC is hoping to win $30 million in state tax credits from the Missouri Development Finance Board for the construction of an 18,500-seat Wizards stadium. The project is contingent on state tax incentives and the company remains optimistic about their goal.

46089 ■ *Starting and Running Your Own Horse Business*
Pub: Storey Publishing, LLC
Ed: Mary Ashby McDonald. **Released:** November 1, 2009. **Price:** $19.95. **Description:** Insight into starting and running a successful equestrian business is given. The book covers safety, tips for operating a riding school or horse camp, strategies for launching a carriage business, along with tax and insurance advice.

46090 ■ "State Aviation Fuel Tax Proposal Runs Into Turbulence" in *Crain's Detroit Business* (Vol. 25, June 15, 2009, No. 24, pp. 5)
Pub: Crain Communications Inc. - Detroit
Ed: Amy Lane. **Description:** Delta Airlines Inc. is concerned about a proposal that would change the way Michigan taxes aviation fuel. The plan would go from the current cents-per-gallon tax to a percentage tax on the wholesale price of fuel, which would raise the taxes significantly.

46091 ■ "State Expects Increase of $50 Million from Film Bills; Come Back, Al Roker" in *Crain's Detroit Business* (March 24, 2008)
Pub: Crain Communications, Inc.
Ed: Bill Shea. **Description:** Overview of the new film initiative and its incentives designed to entice more film work to Michigan; the measures could bring $50 million to $100 million in movie production work for the rest of this year compared to the $4 million total the state saw last year. Also discusses the show "DEA" which was filmed in Detroit and stars Al Roker.

46092 ■ "State Film Business Tops $1.3 Billion" in *The Business Journal-Portland* (Vol. 25, August 22, 2008, No. 24, pp. 1)
Pub: American City Business Journals, Inc.
Ed: Andy Giegerich. **Description:** Oregon's film industry has generated $1.39 billion in direct and indirect economic impact in 2007, a 55 percent rise from 2005 levels. The growth of the industry is attributed to tax incentives issued in 2007, which attracted film production companies from other states.

46093 ■ "State Lawmakers Should Try Raising Jobs, Not Taxes" in *Crain's Chicago Business* (Vol. 31, March 24, 2008, No. 12, pp. 20)
Pub: Crain Communications, Inc.
Ed: Diug Whitley. **Description:** According to U.S. Department of Labor figures through December 2007, Illinois has ranked 45th in the nation in job growth for seven straight months. Many feel that the state would not need to raise taxes if they spent more time working to keep and attract employers that create jobs.

46094 ■ "State Reaps $440M with Small-Biz Tax Crackdown" in *Boston Business Journal* (Vol. 27, October 19, 2007, No. 38, pp. 1)
Pub: American City Business Journals Inc.
Ed: Lisa van der Pool. **Description:** Massachusetts Department of Revenue has generated $440 million from businesses who have not filed or paid enough taxes. Discover Tax is a database program that targets tax evaders. Small businesses are impacted by this system most.

46095 ■ "Statistical Data of Interest" in *Business Owner* (Vol. 35, July-August 2011, No. 4, pp. 7)
Pub: DL Perkins Company
Description: Sources of federal tax revenue are presented; payroll taxes, 36 percent; corporate income tax, 12 percent, other 4 percent, excise taxes, 3 percent, individual income tax, 45 percent.

46096 ■ "Super Bowl Events Get Tax Breaks" in *Business Journal-Serving Phoenix and the Valley of the Sun* (Vol. 7, October 12, 2007, No. 28)
Pub: American City Business Journals, Inc.
Ed: Mike Sunnucks. **Description:** Cities of Glendale and Phoenix, Arizona increased sales taxes in September 2007 and have issued tax exemptions for professional sporting events like the Super Bowl. Phoenix is planning to exempt events included in the 2009 NBA All-Star Game. National Football League's tax abatement requirement to cities hosting the Super Bowl is discussed.

46097 ■ "Surviving an IRS Audit: Tips for Small Businesses" in *Agency Sales Magazine* (Vol. 39, July 2009, No. 7, pp. 52)
Pub: MANA
Ed: Joshua D. Mosshart. **Description:** It is a good idea to enlist the services of a tax professional even if an audit is expected to go smoothly since the IRS is likely to scrutinize the unreported income and personal as well as business expenses of a small business during an audit.

46098 ■ "Suspense Hangs Over Fledging Film Industry" in *Crain's Detroit Business* (Vol. 26, January 18, 2010, No. 3, pp. 3)
Pub: Crain Communications, Inc.
Ed: Bill Shea. **Description:** Overview of the film incentive package which has fostered a growth in the industry with 52 productions completed in 2009, bringing in $223.6 million in gross in-state production expenditures of which the state will refund $87.2 million. Opposition to the incentives has been growing among legislatures who believe that the initiatives cost more than they ultimately bring into the state. Experts believe that the initiatives will remain since they have already fostered economic growth and are good for the state's image.

46099 ■ "Sweet Harmony" in *Canadian Business* (Vol. 82, April 27, 2009, No. 7, pp. 6)
Pub: Rogers Media
Description: Canada will harmonize its 5 percent federal goods and services tax wit the 8 percent provincial sales tax effective July 1, 2010. Meanwhile, provinces like Ontario and Quebec have switched the sales taxes that are charged in new investments into a value-added tax. The conversion has led to an 11 percent increase in investments in Quebec and the three other provinces that made the conversion.

46100 ■ "Take the Wheel: the Pension Protection Act Doesn't Mean You Can Sit Back and Relax" in *Black Enterprise* (October 2007)
Pub: Earl G. Graves Publishing Co. Inc.
Ed: Mellody Hobson. **Description:** Pension Protection Act provides multiple benefits and tax advantages for retirement, however the investment options and contribution rates are very conservative.

46101 ■ "Tax Abatement Changes Seen as Home Run for Cleveland Condo Market" in *Crain's Cleveland Business* (Vol. 30, June 15, 2009, No. 23)
Pub: Crain Communications, Inc.
Ed: Jay Miller. **Description:** Condominium ownership became a bit more affordable for Cleveland

residents since changes in both state and local tax abatement policy changes. The tax credits are examined.

46102 ■ "Tax Credit Crunch" in *Miami Daily Business Review* **(March 26, 2008)**
Pub: ALM Media Inc.
Ed: Paula Iuspa-Abbott. **Description:** Uncertainty is growing over the future of the low-income housing project in South Florida and the tax credit program that helps fuel the projects.

46103 ■ "Tax Deal Yields Polaris Offices" in *Business First-Columbus* **(October 26, 2007, pp. A1)**
Pub: American City Business Journals, Inc.
Ed: Brian R. Ball. **Description:** Speculation on a possible office building construction is increasing with the expansion of tax incentives to build at the Polaris Centers of Commerce. Details of community reinvestment in the Columbus, Ohio area along with possible 15-year 100 percent tax abatements for Polaris office buildings are discussed.

46104 ■ "Tax-Free Zones Need Shows; Out-of-State Shoppers Are Key To Success" in *Crain's Detroit Business* **(Vol. 24, January 28, 2008, No. 4)**
Pub: Crain Communications Inc. - Detroit
Ed: Daniel Duggan. **Description:** Sales tax-free zones are being considered by Michigan's legislators in order to promote the state as a conference destination.

46105 ■ "Tax Reform Analysis: Reforms Equal Smaller 401(k)s" in *Employee Benefit News* **(Vol. 25, December 1, 2011, No. 15, pp. 19)**
Pub: SourceMedia Inc.
Ed: Lisa V. Gillespie. **Description:** According to a new analysis by the Employee Benefit Research Institute, two recent proposals to change existing tax treatment of 401(k) retirement plans could cost workers because they would lower their account balances towards retirement.

46106 ■ *Tax Savvy for Small Business*
Pub: NOLO
Ed: Frederick W. Daily. **Released:** November 2006. **Price:** $36.99. **Description:** Strategies to help small business owners claim all legitimate deductions and keep accurate records.

46107 ■ *Tax Savvy for Small Business: Year-Round Tax Strategies to Save You Money*
Pub: NOLO
Ed: Frederick W. Daily, Bethany K. Laurence. **Released:** September 2005. **Price:** $36.99. **Description:** Tax strategies for small business. Includes the latest tax numbers and laws as well as current Internal Revenue Service forms and publications.

46108 ■ *Tax Smarts for Small Business*
Pub: Sourcebooks, Incorporated
Ed: James O. Parker. **Released:** December 2006. **Price:** $27.95. **Description:** Tax guide for small businesses.

46109 ■ "Tax Talk; Usual Election-Year Obstacles to Income Tax May Not Apply This Time" in *Crain's Chicago Business* **(March 24, 2008)**
Pub: Crain Communications, Inc.
Ed: Greg Hinz. **Description:** Discusses the possible raising of the state's income tax; The latest version of the income tax hike bill, sponsored by Senator James Meeks, D-Chicago, would boost individual rates to 5 percent from 3 percent, with the corporate rate rising to a total of 8 percent from 4.8 percent; about $3 billion of the projected $8 billion that would be brought in would be used to cut local property taxes and experts believe the business community overall would benefit.

46110 ■ "Tax Thriller in D.C." in *Barron's* **(Vol. 90, August 30, 2010, No. 35, pp. 17)**
Pub: Barron's Editorial & Corporate Headquarters
Ed: Jim McTague. **Description:** There are speculations on how Senator Harry Reid can push his bill to raise taxes on the wealthy while retaining the George W. Bush tax rates for the rest. Reid's challenge is to get the 60 votes needed to pass the bill.

46111 ■ "Taxes, Right-To-Work Top West Michigan Concerns" in *Crain's Detroit Business* **(Vol. 24, September 22, 2008, No. 38, pp. 6)**
Pub: Crain Communications, Inc.
Ed: Amy Lane. **Description:** Two of the top priorities of business leaders in Western Michigan are the new business tax which they want to end as well as making the state a "right-to-work" one through laws to prohibit unions from requiring workers to pay dues and membership as a condition of their employment.

46112 ■ "Taxing Position: Yoga Studios Hit for Back Sales Tax" in *Puget Sound Business Journal* **(Vol. 29, August 29, 2008, No. 19, pp. 1)**
Pub: American City Business Journals
Ed: Deirdre Gregg. **Description:** Several yoga studies were audited and told they owe several years worth of back taxes. A spokesman from the Washington Department of Revenue stated the yoga studies should be collecting the tax in general and that yoga classes given for the purpose of physical fitness are taxable.

46113 ■ "A Taxing Proposition" in *Black Enterprise* **(Vol. 37, January 2007, No. 6, pp. 6)**
Pub: Earl G. Graves Publishing Co. Inc.
Description: Learn how to avoid tax problems on Black Enterprise's website, blackenterprise.com.

46114 ■ "Taxpayer Says a Simple Thank-You Would Help" in *Boston Business Journal* **(Vol. 27, November 16, 2007, No. 42, pp. 1)**
Pub: American City Business Journals Inc.
Ed: Jesse Noyes. **Description:** Bill Freza founded the ThankTheTaxpayer.org, a Website and incorporated organization. The non-partisan group aims to induce gratitude and civility as a tax reform and attitude among taxpayers, particularly those in the top wage category.

46115 ■ "Taxpayers' Banks Share Even Higher" in *Business Courier* **(Vol. 24, October 26, 2008, No. 28, pp. 1)**
Pub: American City Business Journals, Inc.
Ed: Dan Monk; Lucy May. **Description:** Banks Working Group originally announced that it needs $106 million in public funds to build the Banks riverfront development but then declared it needs $45 million more from Cincinnati and Hamilton County after it approved a deal for the project. It would not be easy for the city and the county to come up with the money but many decision-makers think it's worth it.

46116 ■ "Tech Tax Heroes Go from Political Neophytes to Savvy Fundraisers" in *Baltimore Business Journal* **(Vol. 27, November 20, 2009, No. 28)**
Pub: American City Business Journals
Ed: Scott Dance. **Description:** A group of computer services and information technology executives in Maryland have arranged a private dinner that will function as a fundraiser for Governor Martin O'Malley and Lieutenant Governor Anthony Brown. The event is seen as an effort to ensure the industry's involvement in the state after fighting for the repeal of the tech tax in 2007.

46117 ■ "Tempel Steel To Expand Its Chicago Plant" in *Chicago Tribune* **(August 22, 2008)**
Pub: McClatchy-Tribune Information Services
Ed: James P. Miller. **Description:** Tempel Steel Co. is no longer considering transferring a Libertyville factory's production to Mexico; the company has responded to government incentives and will instead shift that work to its plant on Chicago's North Side.

46118 ■ "Test Your Structural Integrity" in *Entrepreneur* **(Vol. 37, August 2009, No. 8, pp. 60)**
Pub: Entrepreneur Media, Inc.
Ed: Jennifer Lawler. **Description:** Tax considerations can be important when choosing a business structure. For example, profits are taxed to the corporation in a

C corp while profits are taxed only once at an S corp or a limited liability company. Meeting a tax professional should be done prior to switching to a different structure.

46119 ■ "That Vision Thing" in *Canadian Business* **(Vol. 80, December 25, 2006, No. 1, pp. 78)**
Pub: Rogers Media
Description: Suggestions for better Canadian tax policy and making airspace competitive among other things, to improve the economy in 2007, are presented.

46120 ■ "They're Hopping Mad" in *Canadian Business* **(Vol. 80, October 22, 2007, No. 21, pp. 20)**
Pub: Rogers Media
Description: Alberta Review Panel is calling for a 20 percent increase in oil and gas development taxes. SABMiller and Molson Coors Brewing Company combined its U.S. and Puerto Rican operations, though the deal is still subject to regulatory approvals. Montreal Exchange Inc. filed for approval of the trade of Montreal Climate Exchange futures contracts.

46121 ■ "Three Trails Blazes Tax Credit Deal" in *The Business Journal-Serving Metropolitan Kansas City* **(Vol. 27, November 7, 2008, No. 9)**
Pub: American City Business Journals, Inc.
Ed: Rob Roberts. **Description:** Three Trails Redevelopment LLC plans to redevelop the Bannister Mall area. The Missouri Development Finance Board is expected to approve $30 million in tax credits for the project. A verbal agreement on the terms and conditions has already been reached according to the agency's executive director.

46122 ■ "Time to Engage Europe" in *Canadian Business* **(Vol. 79, June 19, 2006, No. 13, pp. 19)**
Pub: Rogers Media
Ed: Jack Mintz. **Description:** European and Canadian governments improved their trade and investment relations with the March 18, 2004 frame work to develop a Trade and Investment Enhancement Agreement. Still there is lot of opportunities to solve tax and trade issues.

46123 ■ "Time for State Tax Restructure?" in *Crain's Detroit Business* **(Vol. 26, January 18, 2010, No. 3, pp. 3)**
Pub: Crain Communications, Inc.
Ed: Amy Lane. **Description:** Business Leaders for Michigan, a statewide CEO group, launched a proposal to cut the Michigan Business Tax by about $1.1 billion and replace the revenue by taxing services. Statistical data included.

46124 ■ "To Be or Not To Be an S Corporation" in *Modern Machine Shop* **(Vol. 84, September 2011, No. 4, pp. 38)**
Pub: Gardner Publications
Ed: Irving L. Blackman. **Description:** The definitions of both C corporations and S corporations are defined to help any machine shop discover which best suits the owner's business plan.

46125 ■ *Top Tax Savings Ideas: How to Survive in Today's Tough Tax Environment*
Pub: Entrepreneur Press
Ed: Thomas J. Stemmy. **Released:** March 2004. **Price:** $18.95 (US), $26.95 (Canadian). **Description:** Tax deductions, fringe benefits, and tax deferrals for small businesses.

46126 ■ "Tourism Bureau Seeks Hotel Tax Hike" in *Baltimore Business Journal* **(Vol. 27, December 18, 2009, No. 32, pp. 1)**
Pub: American City Business Journals
Ed: Rachel Bernstein. **Description:** Baltimore, Maryland's tourism agency, Visit Baltimore, has proposed a new hotel tax that could produce $2 million annually for its marketing budget, fund improvements to the city's 30-year-old convention center and help it compete for World Cup soccer games. Baltimore hotel leaders discuss the new tax.

46127 ■ "Tourism Push Rising in Fall" in *Philadelphia Business Journal* **(Vol. 30, August 26, 2011, No. 28, pp. 1)**
Pub: American City Business Journals Inc.
Ed: Peter Van Allen. **Description:** Philadelphia is offering events for tourists this fall despite massive cuts for tourism promotion. Governor Tim Corbet slashed $5.5 million in funding for the state's tourism-promotion agencies which received $32 million in 2009. The agencies were forced to cooperate and fend for themselves using the hotel taxes that sustain them.

46128 ■ "The Trader's Edge" in *Barron's* **(Vol. 88, March 31, 2008, No. 13, pp. 56)**
Pub: Dow Jones & Company, Inc.
Ed: Dan McGuire. **Description:** There is a $3,000 a year annual limit to deducting investor's losses and normal investment expenses are purportedly deductible as miscellaneous expenses on Schedule A only to the extent that they exceed two percent of adjusted gross income. Professional gamblers who can use Schedule C are unable deduct a net gaming loss against income from any other sources.

46129 ■ "Tradeshow Attendance Incentives Add Up" in *Pet Product News* **(Vol. 64, December 2010, No. 12, pp. 14)**
Pub: BowTie Inc.
Ed: Mark E. Battersby. **Description:** Pointers on how pet specialty retailers can claim business travel tax and income tax deductions for expenses paid or incurred in participation at tradeshows, conventions, and meetings are presented. Incentives in form of these deductions could allow pet specialty retailers to gain business benefits, aside from the education and enjoyment involved with the travel.

46130 ■ "Traditional VS. Roth IRA" in *Black Enterprise* **(Vol. 37, October 2006, No. 3, pp. 58)**
Pub: Earl G. Graves Publishing Co. Inc.
Ed: K. Parker; Carolyn M. Brown. **Description:** Government taxes the traditional IRAs different than it taxes Roth IRAs.

46131 ■ "Transborder Short-Sea Shipping: Hurdles Remain" in *Canadian Sailings* **(June 30, 2008)**
Pub: Commonwealth Business Media
Ed: Kathlyn Horibe. **Description:** Legislation that would exempt non-bulk commercial cargo by water in the Great Lakes region from U.S. taxation is discussed.

46132 ■ "Travel Tears" in *Crain's Chicago Business* **(Vol. 31, November 17, 2008, No. 46, pp. 3)**
Pub: Crain Communications, Inc.
Ed: Bob Tita. **Description:** Hotels, restaurants and conventions are seeing a decline in profits due to corporate travel cutbacks and the sagging economy. City and state revenues derived from taxes on tourism-related industries are also suffering.

46133 ■ "Trust Tax Under Fire as Drain on Revenue" in *Globe & Mail* **(April 9, 2007, pp. B1)**
Pub: CTVglobemedia Publishing Inc.
Ed: Steven Chase. **Description:** The economic aspects of the implementation of the trust levy by the Canadian government are discussed. The acquisition of Canadian income trusts by Canadian and international financial institutions is described.

46134 ■ *Ultimate Small Business Advisor*
Pub: Entrepreneur Press
Ed: Andi Axman. **Released:** May 2007. **Price:** $30.95. **Description:** Tip for starting and running a small business, including new tax rulings and laws affecting small business, are shared.

46135 ■ "Unemployment Tax Surge Could Hit Businesses Hard" in *Orlando Business Journal* **(Vol. 26, January 1, 2010, No. 31, pp. 1)**
Pub: American City Business Journals
Ed: Christopher Boyd. **Description:** Consequences of the almost 1,100 percent increase in Florida's minimum unemployment compensation insurance tax

to businesses in the state are discussed. Employers pay for the said tax, which is used to fund the state's unemployment claims.

46136 ■ "U.S. Buyer Rescues KCP From Trust Tax Burden" in *Globe & Mail* **(April 3, 2007, pp. B1)**
Pub: CTVglobemedia Publishing Inc.
Ed: Richard Blackwell. **Description:** The economic aspects of the buyout of KCP Income Fund by Caxton-Iseman Capital Inc. are discussed.

46137 ■ *United States Taxes and Tax Policy*
Pub: Cambridge University Press
Ed: David G. Davies. **Released:** January 22, 2010. **Price:** $34.99. **Description:** This book expands the information on taxes found in public finance texts by using a combination of institutional, factual, theoretical and empirical information. It also stresses the economic effects of taxes and tax policy.

46138 ■ "Up In the Air" in *The Business Journal-Serving Greater Tampa Bay* **(Vol. 28, July 18, 2008, No. 30, pp. 1)**
Pub: American City Business Journals, Inc.
Ed: Margie Manning. **Description:** Views and information on Busch Gardens and on its future, are presented. The park's 3,769 employees worry for their future, after tourism industry experts have expressed concerns on possible tax cuts and other cost reductions. The future of the park, which ranks number 19 as the most visited park in the world, is expected to have a major impact on the tourism industry.

46139 ■ "VC Tax Almost Gone" in *Business Journal-Portland* **(Vol. 24, November 23, 2007, No. 38, pp. 1)**
Pub: American City Business Journals, Inc.
Ed: Aliza Earnshaw. **Description:** Portland Revenue Bureau's proposal to repeal a business income tax is scheduled to be approved by the Portland City Council and Multnomah County Council. Despite the good decision on the part of the city, the removal of the tax policy is not a guarantee that venture capital firms will relocate to the city.

46140 ■ "Venture Gap" in *Canadian Business* **(Vol. 81, March 17, 2008, No. 4, pp. 82)**
Pub: Rogers Media
Ed: Joe Castaldo. **Description:** Money raised by Canadian venture capitalist firms has been declining since 2001. A strong venture capital market is important if Canada is to build innovative companies. Fixing Canada's tax policy on foreign investments is a start in reviving the industry.

46141 ■ "Verizon Comes Calling With 500 Jobs" in *Business First Columbus* **(Vol. 25, September 15, 2008, No. 4, pp. 1)**
Pub: American City Business Journals
Ed: Brian R. Ball. **Description:** Hilliard, Ohio offered Verizon Wireless a 15-year incentive package worth $3.4 million for the company to move 300 customer financial services jobs to the city in addition to the 200 jobs from their facility in Dublin, Ohio. The incentives include a return of 15 percent of the income tax generated by the jobs.

46142 ■ "Wanted: Angels in the Country" in *Austin Business JournalInc.* **(Vol. 28, July 18, 2008, No. 18, pp. 1)**
Pub: American City Business Journals
Ed: Laura Hipp. **Description:** A proposal is being pushed forward by managers of Texas' Emerging Technology Fund to create an angel investors' network. The proposal is asking that tax credits for those who invest in research and development projects be granted in order to boost the number of technology companies in the state.

46143 ■ "Was Mandating Solar Power Water Heaters For New Homes Good Policy?" in *Hawaii Business* **(Vol. 54, August 2008, No. 2, pp. 28)**
Pub: Hawaii Business Publishing
Description: Senator Gary L. Kooser of District 7 Kauai-Niihau believes that the mandating of energy-efficient water heaters for new single-family homes starting in 2010 will help cut Hawaii's oil consump-

tion. Ron Richmond of the Hawaii Solar Energy Association says that the content of SB 644 has negative consequences as it allows for choice of energy and not just solar, and it also eliminates tax credits for new homebuyers.

46144 ■ "Water Efficiency Bill Move Through Congress" in *Contractor* **(Vol. 56, July 2009, No. 7, pp. 20)**
Pub: Penton Media, Inc.
Ed: Kevin Schwalb. **Description:** National Association, a plumbing-heating-cooling contractor, was instrumental in drafting the Water Advanced Technologies for Efficient Resource Use Act of 2009 and they are also backing the Water Accountability Tax Efficiency Reinvestment Act. The first bill promotes WaterSense-labeled products while the other promotes water conservation through tax credits.

46145 ■ "The Weeks Ahead" in *Crain's New York Business* **(Vol. 24, January 14, 2008, No. 2, pp. 20)**
Pub: Crain Communications, Inc.
Description: Listing of events in the Detroit area include conferences addressing entrepreneurialism, economic development, and women business ownership.

46146 ■ "Weighing the Write-Off" in *Baltimore Business Journal* **(Vol. 28, September 10, 2010, No. 18, pp. 1)**
Pub: Baltimore Business Journal
Ed: Daniel J. Sernovitz. **Description:** President Barrack Obama has proposed to let business write off their investments in plant and equipment upgrades under a plan aimed at getting the economy going. The plan would allow a company to write off 100 percent of the depreciation for their new investments at one time instead of over several years.

46147 ■ "Weyerhaeuser's REIT Decision Shouldn't Scare Investors Away" in *Barron's* **(Vol. 88, June 30, 2008, No. 26, pp. 18)**
Pub: Dow Jones & Co., Inc.
Ed: Christopher Williams. **Description:** Weyerhaeuser Co.'s management said that a conversion to a real estate investment trust was not likely in 2009 since the move is not tax-efficient as of the moment and would overload its non-timber assets with debt. The company's shares have fallen by 19.5 percent. However, the company remains an asset-rich outfit and its activist shareholder is pushing for change.

46148 ■ *Working for Yourself: Law and Taxes for Independent Contractors, Freelancers and Consultants*
Pub: NOLO Publications
Ed: Stephen Fishman. **Released:** March 2008. **Price:** $39.99 paperback. **Description:** In-depth information is shared for contractors, freelancers and consultants involving business law and small business taxes.

46149 ■ "Year-End Tax Tips" in *Hawaii Business* **(Vol. 53, December 2007, No. 6, pp. 136)**
Pub: Hawaii Business Publishing
Ed: Kathleen Bryan. **Description:** Tax planning tips for the end of 2007, in relation to the tax breaks that are scheduled to expire, are presented. Among the tax breaks that will be expiring at the 2007 year-end are sales tax deduction in the state and local level, premiums on mortgage insurance, and deduction on tuition. The impacts of these changes are discussed.

TRADE PERIODICALS

46150 ■ *Corporate Directions*
Pub: CCH Inc.
Ed: Charles W. Edwards, Editor. **Released:** Biweekly. **Price:** $213. **Description:** Discusses coverage of SEC news and regulations affecting publicly-traded companies and their officers and directors. Follows trends in corporate goverance and investor relations. Recurring features include interviews, news of research, reports of meetings, news of educational opportunities, notices of publications available, analyses of SEC regulations and court opinions, industry surveys, and columns titled Litigation Update and News from the States.

46151 ■ *Intertax*
Pub: Kluwer Academic/Plenum Publishing Corp.
Contact: Michael A. Olesnicky, Assoc. Ed.
Released: Monthly. **Price:** $901 print or online; $1,201 print or online; $662 print or online; $1,171 print & online; $1,562 print & online; $861 print & online. **Description:** Journal covering tax information worldwide.

46152 ■ *Small Business Council of America—Alert*
Pub: Small Business Council of America Inc.
Ed: Released: Quarterly. **Price:** Included in membership. **Description:** Monitors federal tax legislation affecting small business. Reports on the Council's advocacy in support of legislation creating economic incentives for small businesses. Encourages members to participate in the legislative process. Recurring features include Council news and a calendar of events.

46153 ■ *Small Business Taxes and Management*
Pub: A/N Group Inc.
Contact: Steven A. Hopfenmuller, Publisher
Released: Semimonthly, Daily (Mon. thru Fri.). **Price:** $49.95. **Description:** Offers current tax news, reviews of recent cases, tax saving tips, and personal financial planning for small business owners. Includes articles on issues such as finance and management. Remarks: Available online only

VIDEOCASSETTES/ AUDIOCASSETTES

46154 ■ *CPE Network: Tax & Accounting Report*
Bisk Education
9417 Princess Palm Ave.
Tampa, FL 33619
Free: 800-874-7877
Co. E-mail: info@bisk.com
URL: http://www.bisk.com
Price: $1200.00. **Description:** Provides information on current tax regulations and current accounting and auditing changes. Video newsletter published 11 times per year. **Availability:** VHS.

46155 ■ *Tax Season Update: Small Businesses and Their Owners*
Bisk Education
9417 Princess Palm Ave.
Tampa, FL 33619
Free: 800-874-7877
Co. E-mail: info@bisk.com
URL: http://www.bisk.com
Price: $199.00. **Description:** Discusses year-end tax tips and the upcoming tax legislation affecting small businesses and their owners. Furnishes information on choice of entity, new tax rates, private pension plans, trusts, planning and strategies for small business, bankruptcy law, tax planning issues, and new penalty and compliance provisions. Includes workbook and quizzer. **Availability:** VHS.

CONSULTANTS

46156 ■ Donald C. Wright
3906 Lawndale Ln. N
Plymouth, MN 55446-2940
Ph:(763)478-6999
Co. E-mail: donaldwright@compuserve.com
URL: http://www.donaldwrightcpa.com
Contact: Donald C. Wright, President
E-mail: donaldwright@compuserve.com
Scope: Offers accounting, tax, and small business consulting services. Services include cash flow and budgeting analysis; financial forecast and projections; financial statements; reviews and compilations; tax planning, tax preparation; IRS and state/local representation; international taxation; estate, gift and trust tax return preparation; benefit plan services; business succession planning; estate planning; financial planning; management advisory services, pension and profit sharing plans, retirement planning, expert witness services and employee benefits plans.

Serves individuals, corporations, partnerships, and non-profit organizations. **Seminars:** Qualified pension plans and employee welfare benefit plans.

46157 ■ General Business Services Corp.
1020 N University Parks Dr.
PO Box 3146
Waco, TX 76707
Ph:(817)745-2525
Free: 800-583-6181
Fax:(817)745-2544
Scope: Firm provides financial management, business counseling, and tax-related products and services to business owners and professionals. Additional services include proper record-keeping systems, accurate tax return preparation, computer software services, and financial planning services. Initial and continuous training is available to franchisees in all areas: Business and tax counseling, client acquisition and business operations. **Publications:** "Tax Tips for the Small Business Owner and Professional," 1993.

46158 ■ Gordian Concepts & Solutions
16 Blueberry Ln.
Lincoln, MA 01773
Ph:(617)259-8341
Co. E-mail: gordian@usa1.com
Contact: Stephen R. Low, President
Scope: Engineering and management consultancy offering general, financial, and valuation services, civil and tax litigation support. Assists clients in entering new businesses, planning new products and services, and evaluating feasibility. Targets industrial concerns engaged in manufacturing, assembly, warehousing, energy production, process systems and biotechnology, steel, paper, and electronics. Serves businesses such as retailing, financial services, health care, satellite broadcasting and cable television, outdoor advertising and professional practices. **Publications:** "Establishing Rural Cellular Company Values," Cellular Business.

46159 ■ Harvey C. Skoog
7151 E Addis Ave.
Prescott Valley, AZ 86314
Ph:(928)772-1448
Co. E-mail: hskoog@pvaz.net
E-mail: hskoog@pvaz.net
Scope: Firm has expertise in taxes, payroll, financial planning, budgeting, buy/sell planning, business start-up, fraud detection, troubled business consulting, acquisition, and marketing. Serves the manufacturing, construction, and retailing industries in Arizona.

46160 ■ Horwath International Association
420 Lexington Ave., Ste. 526
New York, NY 10170-0526
Ph:(212)808-2000
Fax:(212)808-2020
Co. E-mail: contactus@horwath.com
URL: http://www.horwath.com
Contact: Mark Hildebrand, CEO
E-mail: mhildebrand@atshorwath.com
Scope: Services include: Accounting, auditing, tax and management consulting. Provides innovative business solutions in the area of assurance, business services, consulting, corporate finance, risk management, tax and technology. **Publications:** "Does Your Business Have an E-Commerce Strategy"; "Americas Tax Facts", 2007; "Caring Sharing Investing Growing: The Story of Horwath International," Nov, 2006; "How To Franchise Internationally"; "International Tax Planning Manual: Expatriates and Migrants"; "Americas Tax Facts 2007"; "European and Middle East Tax Facts 2008"; "International Offshore Financial Services"; "International Tax Planning Manual: Corporations"; "Asia or Pacific Tax News 2008: Issue 2"; "FOMB: A Quiz for Business Owners". **Seminars:** Demand Creation Training, Dec, 2006; Marketing, Dec, 2006.

46161 ■ Marion S. Rice
5281 Pinnacle Rd.
Dayton, OH 45417
Ph:(937)859-7763

Fax:(937)847-0046
Scope: Provides consultation to individuals and small businesses on tax management and bookkeeping activities.

46162 ■ Pioneer Business Consultants
9042 Garfield Ave., Ste. 312
Huntington Beach, CA 92646
Ph:(714)964-7600
Fax:(714)962-6585
Contact: Ron von Freyman, Mgr
Scope: Offers general management consulting specializing in business acquisitions, tax and business planning, cash flow analyses, business valuations and business sales and expert witness court testimony regarding business sales, valuations and accounting.

FRANCHISES AND BUSINESS OPPORTUNITIES

46163 ■ Cash Plus
Cash Plus, Inc.
3002 Dow Ave., Ste, 120
Tustin, CA 92780
Ph:(714)731-2274
Free: 888-707-2274
Fax:(714)731-2099
No. of Franchise Units: 91. **No. of Company-Owned Units:** 2. **Founded:** 1984. **Franchised:** 1988. **Description:** Check cashing service and related services, including money orders, wire transfers, cash advances, mailboxes, notary, UPS, fax, snacks, tax filing and other items. **Equity Capital Needed:** $190,200-$269,700. **Franchise Fee:** $35,000. **Financial Assistance:** Provides guidance on credit applications and business plans used by franchisees seeking third party financing. **Training:** Provides training including easy-to-run computerized operating system, promotions and check verification and payday advance process.

COMPUTERIZED DATABASES

46164 ■ *CCH Tax Protos*
CCH Canadian Ltd.
90 Sheppard Ave. E, Ste. 300
Toronto, ON, Canada M2N 6X1
Ph:(416)224-2224
Free: 800-268-4522
Fax:(416)224-2243
Co. E-mail: cservice@cch.ca
URL: http://www.cch.ca
Description: Contains current information on taxes in Canada. Includes updates on legislation, interpretation bulletins, information circulars, rulings, Department of Finance releases, Revenue Canada releases, court cases, Internal Revenue Canada documents, draft legislation and explanatory notes, CCH Tax newsletters, and more. **Availability:** Online: CCH Canadian Ltd. **Type:** Bulletin board.

46165 ■ *e-JEP*
American Economic Association
2014 Broadway, Ste. 305
Nashville, TN 37203
Ph:(615)322-2595
Fax:(615)343-7590
Co. E-mail: aeainfo@vanderbilt.edu
URL: http://www.vanderbilt.edu/AEA
Description: Contains the full text of the *Journal of Economic Perspectives*. Includes articles, reports, and other material for economists and economics professionals. Features analysis and critiques of recent research findings and developments in public policy. Includes coverage of global economics issues and developments. Features articles on education in economics, employment issues for economists, and other issues of concern to professional economists. **Availability:** Online: American Economic Association, Thomson Reuters; CD-ROM: American Economic Association. **Type:** Full text.

46166 ■ *Federal Income Taxation of Corporations and Shareholders*
Thomson Reuters
395 Hudson St., 4th Fl.
New York, NY 10014
Ph:(212)367-6300
Free: 800-431-9025
Co. E-mail: ria@thomson.com
URL: http://ria.thomsonreuters.com
Description: Contains the full text of the seventh edition of *Federal Income Taxation of Corporations and Shareholders*, a treatise on the subject of corporate taxation. Covers all areas of corporate income taxation. Focuses on tax issues in the life-cycle of corporations. Includes details and analysis of how shareholders and corporations are affected by the Internal Revenue Code, the IRS, and by tax-related court decisions. **Availability:** Online: Thomson Reuters, Thomson Reuters. **Type:** Full text.

46167 ■ *Federal Income Taxation of S Corporations*
Thomson Reuters
395 Hudson St., 4th Fl.
New York, NY 10014
Ph:(212)367-6300
Free: 800-431-9025
Co. E-mail: ria@thomson.com
URL: http://ria.thomsonreuters.com
Description: Contains the full text of the fourth edition of *Federal Income Taxation of S Corporations*. Covers income tax issues spanning the entire life of an S corporation, from election to operation to termination. Provides authoritative interpretations and insights into rules and regulations controlling S corporations. Includes guidance on daily operation and long-term maintenance of the S corporation. **Availability:** Online: Thomson Reuters, Thomson Reuters. **Type:** Full text.

46168 ■ *Federal Taxes Weekly Alert*
Thomson Reuters
395 Hudson St., 4th Fl.
New York, NY 10014
Ph:(212)367-6300
Free: 800-431-9025
Co. E-mail: ria@thomson.com
URL: http://ria.thomsonreuters.com
Description: Contains weekly updates, news, and time-critical information on U.S. federal taxes and taxation. Includes details on the latest actions and developments in Congress, as well as decisions and opinions from the courts, the federal treasury, the IRS, and other agencies. Includes updates on pending and current legislation. Includes comprehensive and authoritative analysis of federal tax laws, regulations, and issues, with specific attention given to their application and impact. **Availability:** Online: Thomson Reuters, Thomson Reuters. **Type:** Full text.

46169 ■ *IRS Practice and Procedure*
Thomson Reuters
395 Hudson St., 4th Fl.
New York, NY 10014
Ph:(212)367-6300
Free: 800-431-9025
Co. E-mail: ria@thomson.com
URL: http://ria.thomsonreuters.com
Description: Contains the full text of the second edition of *IRS Practice and Procedure*, a treatise on the subject of IRS procedures. Clarifies IRS procedures and policies. Includes detailed procedural information on such activities as drafting a ruling request, prepar-

ing for an appeals conference, and dealing with an IRS revenue officer. Covers recent changes in tax laws, civil and criminal penalties, and IRS access to foreign-based records. **Availability:** Online: Thomson Reuters, Thomson Reuters. **Type:** Full text.

46170 ■ *Limited Liability Companies: Tax & Business Law*
Thomson Reuters
395 Hudson St., 4th Fl.
New York, NY 10014
Ph:(212)367-6300
Free: 800-431-9025
Co. E-mail: ria@thomson.com
URL: http://ria.thomsonreuters.com
Description: Contains the full text of Limited Liability Companies, a treatise on the subject. Includes in-depth and comprehensive analysis of tax rules and regulations for limited liability companies (LLCs) and limited liability partnerships (LLPs). Includes coverage of issues related to forming, operating, transferring, and dissolving LLCs and LLPs. Includes business and tax planning guidelines specifically designed to take advantage of the tax breaks available to LLCs and LLPs. Corresponds to the print volume of the same name. **Availability:** Online: Thomson Reuters, Thomson Reuters. **Type:** Full text.

46171 ■ *State Tax Notes*
Tax Analysts
400 S Maple Ave., Ste. 400
Falls Church, VA 22046
Ph:(703)533-4400
Free: 800-955-2444
Co. E-mail: cservice@tax.org
URL: http://www.taxanalysts.com
Description: Follows tax developments in every state, and keeps track of interstate trends. Covers multi-state Organizations, state tax conferences, tax decisions from courts nationwide, rulings and regulations from revenue departments, and legislation from all 50 states each week. **Availability:** Online: LexisNexis Group. **Type:** Full text.

46172 ■ *State Tax Today*
Tax Analysts
400 S Maple Ave., Ste. 400
Falls Church, VA 22046
Ph:(703)533-4400
Free: 800-955-2444
Co. E-mail: cservice@tax.org
URL: http://www.taxanalysts.com
Description: Covers tax news and documents from every state, the District of Columbia, and all U.S. possessions, complete with summaries and full text of legislation. Includes proposed and finalized regulations, *Revenue Rulings & Procedures*, supreme, appellate, and tax court opinions, and private letter rulings. **Availability:** Online: Tax Analysts. **Type:** Full text.

46173 ■ *The Tax Directory*
Tax Analysts
400 S Maple Ave., Ste. 400
Falls Church, VA 22046
Ph:(703)533-4400
Free: 800-955-2444
Co. E-mail: cservice@tax.org
URL: http://www.taxanalysts.com
Description: Contains information on more than 20,000 tax professionals. Vol. One Government Officials Worldwide including state and federal officials, including taxwriting committees U.S. Department of

Treasury and IRS, Tax Court Judges, International Financial Specialists, Tax and Business Journalists, Professional Associations, and Tax Groups and Coalitions. Vol. Two Corporate Tax Managers including names and contact information for tax managers in largest U.S corporations. Entries including industry description derived from the Securities and Exchange Commission's four-digit Standard Industry Classification code used by the listed companies for filing purposes. **Availability:** Online: LexisNexis Group; CD-ROM: Tax Analysts. **Type:** Directory.

LIBRARIES

46174 ■ Arnold & Porter LLP Library
399 Park Ave.
New York, NY 10022-4690
Ph:(212)715-1382
Fax:(212)715-1399
Co. E-mail: kim.fenty@aporter.com
Contact: Kim R. Fenty, Lib.Mgr.
Scope: Litigation; law - tax, corporate, and environmental. **Services:** Interlibrary loan; Library not open to the public. **Holdings:** 20,000 books; 400 bound periodical volumes. **Subscriptions:** 205 journals and other serials; 15 newspapers.

46175 ■ Gardiner Roberts LLP Library
Scotia Plaza, Ste. 3100
40 King St., W.
Toronto, ON, Canada M5H 3Y2
Ph:(416)865-6600
Fax:(416)865-6636
URL: http://www.gardiner-roberts.com
Scope: Law - administrative, civil, commercial, insurance, municipal, real estate, tax; intellectual property; information technology. **Services:** Interlibrary loan; copying. **Holdings:** 2000 books; 300 bound periodical volumes; 500 reports; CD-ROMs. **Subscriptions:** 200 journals and other serials; 6 newspapers.

46176 ■ Greene Radovsky Maloney Share Library
4 Embarcadero Ctr., Ste. 4000
San Francisco, CA 94111
Ph:(415)981-1400
Fax:(415)777-4961
Co. E-mail: info@grmslaw.com
URL: http://www.greeneradovsky.com
Scope: Taxation. **Services:** Interlibrary loan; copying; Library not open to the public. **Holdings:** 1200 books; 75 bound periodical volumes. **Subscriptions:** 150 journals and other serials; 10 newspapers.

46177 ■ Ross & McBride Library
PO Box 907
Hamilton, ON, Canada L8N 3P6
Ph:(905)526-9800
Fax:(905)526-0732
Co. E-mail: contact@rossmcbride.com
URL: http://www.rossmcbride.com/
Scope: Law, taxation. **Holdings:** Figures not available.

46178 ■ Southeastern University Library
501 I St., SW
Washington, DC 20024
Ph:(202)478-8225
Fax:(202)488-8093
Co. E-mail: library@seu.edu
URL: http://www.seuniversity.edu/library
Contact: Jamila Kader, Actg.Dir.
Scope: Science, technology, humanities, health, social sciences **Services:** Interlibrary loan; Library open to the public. **Holdings:** 50,000 books.

ASSOCIATIONS AND OTHER ORGANIZATIONS

46179 ■ APQC
123 N Post Oak Ln., 3rd Fl.
Houston, TX 77024
Ph:(713)681-4020
Free: 800-776-9676
Fax:(713)681-8578
Co. E-mail: apqcinfo@apqc.org
URL: http://www.apqc.org
Contact: Carla O'Dell PhD, Pres.
Description: Resource for process and performance improvement. Helps organizations adapt to rapidly changing environments, build new and better ways to work, and succeed in a competitive marketplace. Focuses on productivity, knowledge management, benchmarking, and quality improvement initiatives. Works with member organizations to identify best practices, discover effective methods of improvement, broadly disseminate findings, and connect individuals with one another and the knowledge and tools they need to succeed. Serves approximately 500 organizations worldwide in all sectors of business, education, and government. **Publications:** *APQC Center View* (monthly); *Best Practice* .

46180 ■ Center for Creative Leadership
PO Box 26300
Greensboro, NC 27438-6300
Ph:(336)545-2810
Fax:(336)282-3284
Co. E-mail: info@ccl.org
URL: http://www.ccl.org
Contact: John R. Ryan, Pres.
Description: Promotes behavioral science research and leadership education. **Publications:** *Center for Creative Leadership Catalog* (annual); *Leadership in Action* (bimonthly); *Research Reports* (periodic).

46181 ■ Employers Group
1150 S Olive St., Ste. 2300
Los Angeles, CA 90015
Free: 800-748-8484
Co. E-mail: serviceone@employersgroup.com
URL: http://www.employersgroup.com
Contact: Mark Wilbur, Pres./CEO
Description: Provides human resources management services including wage, salary, and benefit surveys; personnel practices surveys; management counseling; management education programs; litigation surveillance; government relations; and research library service. Provides customized human resources services including employee opinion surveys and employee communications programs through its subsidiary, The Employers Group Service Corp. Offers unemployment insurance services, workers' compensation programs, and in-house management training programs. Conducts research and educational programs; maintains speakers' bureau. **Publications:** *California Wage and Hour GuideAL* (annual).

46182 ■ Human Resource Planning Society
401 N Michigan Ave., Ste. 2200
Chicago, IL 60611
Ph:(312)321-6805
Fax:(312)673-6944
Co. E-mail: info@hrps.org
URL: http://www.hrps.org
Contact: Tom Nicholson, Exec. Dir.
Description: Human resource planning professionals representing 160 corporations and 3,000 individual members, including strategic human resources planning and development specialists, staffing analysts, business planners, line managers, and others who function as business partners in the application of strategic human resource management practices. Seeks to increase the impact of human resource planning and management on business and organizational performance. Sponsors program of professional development in human resource planning concepts, techniques, and practices. Offers networking opportunities. **Publications:** *Human Resource Planning Society—Membership Directory* (annual); *People & Strategy* (quarterly); *Restoring Trust: HR's Role In Corporate Governance* .

46183 ■ Institute of Management Accountants, Cost Management Group
10 Paragon Dr.
Montvale, NJ 07645-1773
Ph:(201)573-9000
Free: 800-638-4427
Fax:(201)474-1600
Co. E-mail: ima@imanet.org
URL: http://www.imanet.org
Contact: Paul A. Sharman ACMA, Pres./CEO
Description: A group within the Institute of Management Accountants. Seeks to improve the quality of corporate cost management systems. Educates business professionals about decision-making and productivity improvement. Provides a means of exchanging opinions and experiences about cost management systems. Conducts surveys; compiles statistics. .

46184 ■ Institute for Operations Research and the Management Sciences
7240 Parkway. Dr., Ste. 300
Hanover, MD 21076-1310
Ph:(443)757-3500
Free: 800-446-3676
Fax:(443)757-3515
Co. E-mail: informs@informs.org
URL: http://www.informs.org
Contact: Rina R. Schneur, Pres.
Description: International scientific society dedicated to improving operational processes, decision-making and management through the application of methods from science and mathematics. Represents operations researchers, management scientists and those working in related fields within engineering and the information, decision, mathematical and social sciences. **Publications:** *Information Systems Research* (quarterly); *Informs Transactions on Education* (periodic); *Interfaces* (bimonthly); *Management Science* (monthly); *Manufacturing and Service Operations Management* (quarterly); *Marketing Science* (quarterly); *Mathematics of Operations Research* (quarterly); *Operations Research* (bimonthly); *Organization Science* (bimonthly); *Transportation Science* (quarterly).

46185 ■ International Production Planning and Scheduling Association
PO Box 5031
Incline Village, NV 89450
Ph:(775)833-3922
Co. E-mail: billk@ippsa.org
URL: http://www.ippsa.org
Description: Seeks to expand the knowledge of advanced planning and scheduling technology among manufacturing companies. Conducts educational planning and scheduling seminars and integrates Material and Capacity Management in its workshops. **Publications:** *Evaluating Scheduling Performance*; *FCS Book Description*; *Scheduling Methods that Work*; *Seminar Presenters Biography* .

46186 ■ International Society for the Study of Time
St. Joseph's University
English Department
5600 City Ave.
Philadelphia, PA 19131-1395
Co. E-mail: membership@studyoftime.org
URL: http://www.studyoftime.org
Contact: Paul Harris, Pres.
Description: Scientists and humanists. Explores the idea and experience of time and the role time plays in the physical, organic, intellectual, and social worlds. Encourages interdisciplinary study; provides a forum for exchange of ideas among members. **Publications:** *KronoScope* (semiannual); *Time's News* (annual).

46187 ■ Project Management Institute
14 Campus Blvd.
Newtown Square, PA 19073-3299
Ph:(610)356-4600
Fax:(610)482-9971
Co. E-mail: customercare@pmi.org
URL: http://www.pmi.org
Contact: Mark Langley, Pres./CEO
Description: Corporations and individuals engaged in the practice of project management; project management students and educators. Seeks to advance the study, teaching and practice of project management. Establishes project management standards; conducts educational and professional certification courses; bestows Project Management Professional credential upon qualified individuals. Offers educational seminars and global congresses. **Publications:** *PM Network* (monthly); *PMI Today* (monthly); *Project Management Institute—Annual Proceedings* (annual); *Project Management Journal* (quarterly).

46188 ■ Society for Advancement of Management
6300 Ocean Dr.
OCNR 330, Unit 5807
Corpus Christi, TX 78412

Ph:(361)825-6045
Free: 888-827-6077
Fax:(361)825-2725
Co. E-mail: sam@samnational.org
URL: http://www.samnational.org
Contact: Dr. Moustafa H. Abdelsamad, Pres./CEO
Description: Represents management executives in industry commerce, government, and education. Fields of interest include management education, policy and strategy, MIS, international management, administration, budgeting, collective bargaining, distribution, incentives, materials handling, quality control, and training. **Publications:** *SAM Advanced Management Journal* (quarterly); *SAM Management In Practice* (quarterly); *The SAM News International* (quarterly); *Society for Advancement of Management—International Business Conference Proceedings* (annual).

EDUCATIONAL PROGRAMS

46189 ■ Basics of Time Management Workshop (Onsite)
Seminar Information Service, Inc.
20 Executive Park, Ste. 120
Irvine, CA 92614
Ph:(949)261-9104
Free: 877-SEM-INFO
Fax:(949)261-1963
Co. E-mail: info@seminarinformation.com
URL: http://www.seminarinformation.com
Price: $895.00. **Description:** Identify and overcome barriers to effective time management issues, including proven time management and prioritizing skills to help you concentrate on how to determine how much time, energy and resources is needed. **Locations:** Houston and Dallas, TX.

46190 ■ Brain-Based Time Management
Seminar Information Service, Inc.
20 Executive Park, Ste. 120
Irvine, CA 92614
Ph:(949)261-9104
Free: 877-SEM-INFO
Fax:(949)261-1963
Co. E-mail: info@seminarinformation.com
URL: http://www.seminarinformation.com
Price: $795.00. **Description:** Determine your Time Type; understand how you accomplish your work; develop strategies to maximize your Time Type; apply Time Type strategies to daily tasks and activities. **Locations:** New York, NY.

46191 ■ Effective Time Management: Prioritizing for Success (Onsite)
Seminar Information Service, Inc.
20 Executive Park, Ste. 120
Irvine, CA 92614
Ph:(949)261-9104
Free: 877-SEM-INFO
Fax:(949)261-1963
Co. E-mail: info@seminarinformation.com
URL: http://www.seminarinformation.com
Price: $1,890.00. **Description:** Learn how to: Set goals and priorities that enable you to effectively manage your time; Monitor daily work habits and determine areas for improvement; Plan daily tasks and goals that align with your mission statement; Identify, evaluate and select tools that help with time and priority management; Avoid over-committing yourself and combat procrastination; Balance your professional and personal lives; Implement a personal time-management action plan. **Locations:** Toronto, CN; Reston, VA; New York, NY; Alexandria, VA; Irving, TX; and Rockville, MD.

46192 ■ Essential Time Management & Organizational Skills (Onsite)
Seminar Information Service, Inc.
20 Executive Park, Ste. 120
Irvine, CA 92614
Ph:(949)261-9104
Free: 877-SEM-INFO

Fax:(949)261-1963
Co. E-mail: info@seminarinformation.com
URL: http://www.seminarinformation.com
Price: $179.00. **Description:** Time management plan that you will design for yourself; allowing you to build in the flexibility you need to meet work and home commitments. **Locations:** Cities throughout the United States.

46193 ■ How to Manage Inventories and Cycle Counts
Fred Pryor Seminars & CareerTrack
5700 Broadmoor St., Ste. 300
Mission, KS 66202
Free: 800-780-8476
Fax:(913)967-8849
Co. E-mail: customerservice@pryor.com
URL: http://www.pryor.com
Price: $199.00; $189.00 for groups of 5 or more. **Description:** Cost saving methods and time saving techniques to ensure accurate counts and inventories. **Locations:** Cities throughout the United States.

46194 ■ The Indispensable Assistant
Seminar Information Service, Inc.
20 Executive Park, Ste. 120
Irvine, CA 92614
Ph:(949)261-9104
Free: 877-SEM-INFO
Fax:(949)261-1963
Co. E-mail: info@seminarinformation.com
URL: http://www.seminarinformation.com
Price: $149.00; $139.00 each for 4 or more. **Description:** Learn how to juggle multiple projects and priorities; how to keep things running smoothly when the boss is away; how to save time by delegating; and how to identify and overcome personal productivity roadblocks. **Locations:** Cities throughout the United States.

46195 ■ Managing Information Overload: Techniques for Working Smarter (Onsite)
Seminar Information Service, Inc.
20 Executive Park, Ste. 120
Irvine, CA 92614
Ph:(949)261-9104
Free: 877-SEM-INFO
Fax:(949)261-1963
Co. E-mail: info@seminarinformation.com
URL: http://www.seminarinformation.com
Price: $1,890.00. **Description:** Learn how to increase your productivity with effective information management skills, apply creative strategies, including mind maps, for processing information, adopt speed-reading techniques to quickly digest reports, and develop advanced memory skills to retain important information. **Locations:** Toronto, CN; Ottawa, CN; and New York, NY.

46196 ■ Managing Multiple Priorities
Seminar Information Service, Inc.
20 Executive Park, Ste. 120
Irvine, CA 92614
Ph:(949)261-9104
Free: 877-SEM-INFO
Fax:(949)261-1963
Co. E-mail: info@seminarinformation.com
URL: http://www.seminarinformation.com
Price: $1,495.00. **Description:** Focus on practical techniques for setting priorities and goals and on how to manage ongoing projects from start to finish. Topics include: handling paperwork systematically, realistic ways to decrease interruptions, and learning to say no. **Locations:** New York, NY.

46197 ■ Managing Multiple Priorities, Projects and Deadlines
Seminar Information Service, Inc.
20 Executive Park, Ste. 120
Irvine, CA 92614
Ph:(949)261-9104
Free: 877-SEM-INFO

Fax:(949)261-1963
Co. E-mail: info@seminarinformation.com
URL: http://www.seminarinformation.com
Price: $99.00; $89.00 for five or more. **Description:** An intensive one-day seminar that helps participants gain more control over their time, tasks, and priorities. **Locations:** Cities throughout the United States.

46198 ■ Managing Multiple Projects, Competing Priorities & Tight Deadlines
Seminar Information Service, Inc.
20 Executive Park, Ste. 120
Irvine, CA 92614
Ph:(949)261-9104
Free: 877-SEM-INFO
Fax:(949)261-1963
Co. E-mail: info@seminarinformation.com
URL: http://www.seminarinformation.com
Price: $199.00. **Description:** Skills you need to immediately and effectively deal with multiple projects, expectations, and deadlines without backlog, burnout, and stress. **Locations:** Cities throughout the United States.

46199 ■ Managing Multiple Projects, Objectives and Deadlines
Seminar Information Service, Inc.
20 Executive Park, Ste. 120
Irvine, CA 92614
Ph:(949)261-9104
Free: 877-SEM-INFO
Fax:(949)261-1963
Co. E-mail: info@seminarinformation.com
URL: http://www.seminarinformation.com
Price: $199.00; $189.00 for four or more. **Description:** Learn organizational skills to help you get more accomplished.. **Locations:** Cities throughout the United States.

46200 ■ The Strategic Speed-Reading Advantage for Executives & Legal Professionals
Fred Pryor Seminars & CareerTrack
5700 Broadmoor St., Ste. 300
Mission, KS 66202
Free: 800-780-8476
Fax:(913)967-8849
Co. E-mail: customerservice@pryor.com
URL: http://www.pryor.com
Price: $149.00; $139.00 for groups of 5 or more. **Description:** Learn to organize, prioritize, and absorb volumes of information for effortlessly making critical decisions. **Locations:** Cities throughout the United States.

46201 ■ Superior Time Planning: The Organizer (Onsite)
Seminar Information Service, Inc.
20 Executive Park, Ste. 120
Irvine, CA 92614
Ph:(949)261-9104
Free: 877-SEM-INFO
Fax:(949)261-1963
Co. E-mail: info@seminarinformation.com
URL: http://www.seminarinformation.com
Price: $285.00. **Description:** Participants learn to organize information to increase overall effectiveness through comprehensive long range planning and documentation, including how to monitor activities and track results. **Locations:** Waukesha, WI.

46202 ■ Time Management
Seminar Information Service, Inc.
20 Executive Park, Ste. 120
Irvine, CA 92614
Ph:(949)261-9104
Free: 877-SEM-INFO
Fax:(949)261-1963
Co. E-mail: info@seminarinformation.com
URL: http://www.seminarinformation.com
Price: $1,895.00. **Description:** Learn to determine how your time is being spent, develop strategies for time allocation, create a structure to control time spent on tasks and activities, and prioritize what matters most in your life. **Locations:** Chicago, IL; Arlington, VA; New York, NY; San Francisco, CA; and Atlanta, GA.

46203 ■ Time Management Survival Skills
Seminar Information Service, Inc.
20 Executive Park, Ste. 120
Irvine, CA 92614
Ph:(949)261-9104
Free: 877-SEM-INFO
Fax:(949)261-1963
Co. E-mail: info@seminarinformation.com
URL: http://www.seminarinformation.com
Price: $845.00. **Description:** Develop a step-by-step action plan and use the latest tools for accomplishing your important goals, objectives, and activities. **Locations:** Chelmsford, MA; and Boston, MA.

REFERENCE WORKS

46204 ■ *10 Steps to Successful Social Networking for Business*
Pub: American Society for Training and Development
Ed: Darin Hartley. **Released:** July 1, 2010. **Price:** $19.95. **Description:** Designed for today's fast-paced, need-it-yesterday business environment and for the thousands of workers who find themselves faced with new assignments, responsibilities, and requirements and too little time to learn what they must know.

46205 ■ "2007 Fittest CEOs" in *Hawaii Business* (Vol. 53, October 2007, No. 4, pp. 40)
Pub: Hawaii Business Publishing
Description: Discusses the outcome of the fittest chief executive officers in Hawaii competition for 2007. Hawaii Capital Management's David Low leads the list while Group Pacific (Hawaii) Inc.'s Chip Doyle and Greater Good Inc.'s Kari Leong placed second and third, respectively. The CEO's routines, eating habits, and inspirations for staying fit are provided.

46206 ■ "The Balancing Act: How Busy Executives Make Their Lives Work" in *Black Enterprise* (Vol. 37, February 2007, No. 7, pp. 118)
Pub: Earl G. Graves Publishing Co. Inc.
Ed: Marcia A. Reed-Woodard. **Description:** More than 70 percent of women with children work outside the home, according to a 2005 survey conducted by the U.S. Department of Labor Bureau. One of the biggest struggles these women face is balancing family with career aspirations and climbing the corporate ranks.

46207 ■ "Cyberwise" in *Black Enterprise* (Vol. 40, July 2010, No. 12, pp. 48)
Pub: Earl G. Graves Publishing Co. Inc.
Description: Tools to effectively manage time are explored.

46208 ■ "Desk-Bound No More" in *Charlotte Business Journal* (Vol. 25, August 13, 2010, No. 21, pp. 1)
Pub: Charlotte Business Journal
Ed: Adam O' Daniel. **Description:** Bank of America has launched a program that encourages employees to work on their own schedules. The program encourages productivity and health work-life balance. A survey has also revealed that employees feel more productive under the program.

46209 ■ "Dick Haskayne" in *Canadian Business* (Vol. 81, March 31, 2008, No. 5, pp. 72)
Pub: Rogers Media
Ed: Andy Holloway. **Description:** Dick Haskayne says that he learned a lot about business from his dad who ran a butcher shop where they had to make a decision on buying cattle and getting credit. Haskayne says that family, friends, finances, career, health, and infrastructure are benchmarks that have to be balanced.

46210 ■ "The Early Bird Really Does Get the Worm" in *Harvard Business Review* (Vol. 88, July-August 2010, No. 7-8, pp. 30)
Pub: Harvard Business School Publishing
Ed: Christoph Randler. **Description:** Research indicates that those who identify themselves as 'morning people' tend to be more proactive, and thus

have a career-development advantage over those who identify themselves as 'night people'. Implications of the research are also discussed.

46211 ■ "The End of Clock-Punching" in *Canadian Business* (Vol. 83, September 14, 2010, No. 15, pp. 96)
Pub: Rogers Media Ltd.
Ed: Lyndsie Bourgon. **Description:** Workplace consultant Peter Hadwen is pushing for the transformation of Canada's government departments into results-only work environments (ROWE). ROWE does not require employees to show up to work at a certain time as long as they are meeting goals and achieving results in their jobs. Details of studies regarding ROWE in US companies are examined.

46212 ■ *Enlightened Leadership: Best Practice Guidelines and Time Tools for Easily Implementing Learning Organizations*
Pub: Learning House Publishing, Inc.
Ed: Ralph LoVuolo; Alan G. Thomas. **Released:** May 2006. **Price:** $79.99. **Description:** Innovation and creativity are essential for any successful small business. The book provides owners, managers, and team leaders with the tools necessary to produce "disciplined innovation".

46213 ■ *Enlightened Leadership: Best Practice Guidelines and Timesaving Tools for Easily Implementing Learning Organizations*
Pub: Learning House Publishing, Incorporated
Ed: Alan G. Thomas; Ralph L. LoVuolo; Jeanne C. Hillson. **Released:** September 2006, printable 3 times/year. **Price:** $21.00. **Description:** Book provides the tools required to create a learning organization management model along with a step-by-step guide for team planning and learning. The strategy works as a manager's self-help guide as well as offering continuous learning and improvement for company-wide success.

46214 ■ *Getting Things Done: The Art of Stress-Free Productivity*
Pub: Penguin Books (USA) Incorporated
Ed: David Allen. **Released:** December 2002. **Price:** $16.00. **Description:** Coach and management consultant recommends methods for stress-free performance under the premise that productivity is directly related to our ability to relax.

46215 ■ "Heavy Duty: The Case Against Packing Lightly" in *Crain's Chicago Business* (Vol. 31, April 21, 2008, No. 16, pp. 29)
Pub: Crain Communications, Inc.
Ed: Sarah A. Klein. **Description:** Penelope Biggs, a Northern Trust executive who manages sales teams in North America, Europe and Asia gives advice on traveling abroad for business including time management skills, handling time-zone hops and avoiding jet-lag.

46216 ■ *Home-Based Business for Dummies*
Pub: John Wiley and Sons, Inc.
Ed: Paul Edwards, Sarah Edwards, Peter Economy. **Released:** February 25, 2005. **Price:** $19.99. **Description:** Provides all the information needed to start and run a home-based business. Topics include: selecting the right business; setting up a home office; managing money, credit, and financing; marketing; and ways to avoid distractions while working at home.

46217 ■ "How To Turn Your Efforts Into Results" in *Green Industry Pro* (Vol. 23, September 2011)
Pub: Cygnus Business Media
Ed: Bob Coulter. **Description:** Working Smarter Training Challenge teaches that leaders are able to carry out solutions directly into their organization, develop skills and drive business results in key areas by creating a culture of energized workers who are able to take ownership of their performance as well as the performance of the company as a whole.

46218 ■ "Ian Delaney" in *Canadian Business* (Vol. 81, Summer 2008, No. 9, pp. 168)
Pub: Rogers Media Ltd.
Ed: Joe Castaldo. **Description:** Interview with Ian Delaney who is the executive chairman of chemical company Sherritt International Corp.; Delaney previ-

ously worked as chief executive for a holding company owned by Peter Munk. Details of his beliefs, profession and family life are discussed.

46219 ■ "Integrating Business Core Knowledge through Upper Division Report Composition" in *Business Communication Quarterly* (December 2007)
Pub: Sage Publications USA
Ed: Joy Roach, Daniel Tracy, Kay Durden. **Description:** An assignment that integrates subjects and encourages the use of business communication report-writing skills is presented. This assignment is designed to complement business school curricula and help develop critical thinking and organizational skills.

46220 ■ "Interview Advisory; Warning! Do YOU Have VD?" in *Canadian Corporate News* (May 18, 2007)
Pub: Comtex News Network Inc.
Description: Interview with Beverly Beuermann-King, a stress and wellness specialist, who provides insights on the problems associated with Vacation Deprivation.

46221 ■ *Lean Six Sigmas That Works: A Powerful Action Plan for Dramatically Improving Quality, Increasing Speed, and Reducing Waste*
Pub: American Management Association
Ed: Bill Carreira; Bill Trudell. **Released:** 2006. **Price:** $21.95.

46222 ■ "Leave It Behind; Novel Packing Strategy" in *Crain's Chicago Business* (Vol. 31, April 21, 2008, No. 16, pp. 32)
Pub: Crain Communications, Inc.
Ed: Sarah A. Klein. **Description:** Patrick Brady who investigates possible violations of the Foreign Corrupt Practices Act has a novel approach when traveling to frequent destinations which allows him to travel with only a carry-on piece of luggage: he leaves suits at dry cleaners in the places he visits most often and since he mainly stays at the same hotels, he also leaves sets of workout clothes and running shoes with hotel staff.

46223 ■ "Madeleine Paquin" in *Canadian Business* (Vol. 81, March 3, 2008, No. 3, pp. 92)
Pub: Rogers Media
Ed: Regan Ray. **Description:** Madeleine Paquin, chief executive officer and president of Logistec Corp., talks about how she balanced her career and her life as a mother to two girls. Paquin thinks that working mothers need to focus on some things instead of trying to do everything. Her career in the marine cargo handling industry is also discussed.

46224 ■ "Make It Easier On Yourself" in *Women In Business* (Vol. 63, Fall 2011, No. 3, pp. 28)
Pub: American Business Women's Association
Ed: Maureen Sullivan. **Description:** Getting and staying organized helps avoid wasting time on deciding which priorities to address first. Taking help and avoiding hoarding are examples of how to become organized. The use of technology for organizing priorities is also explained.

46225 ■ "Make It Easy" in *Entrepreneur* (Vol. 36, May 2008, No. 5, pp. 49)
Pub: Entrepreneur Media, Inc.
Ed: Mike Hogan. **Description:** Zoho has a Planner that keep contacts, notes and reminders and a DB & Reports feature for reports, data analysis and pricing comparisons. WebEx WebOffice Workgroup supports document management and templates for contacts lists, time sheets and sales tracking. Other online data manages are presented.

46226 ■ "The Middle Ages" in *Hawaii Business* (Vol. 53, October 2007, No. 4, pp. 42)
Pub: Hawaii Business Publishing
Ed: Cathy S. Cruz-George. **Description:** Starcom Builders Inc.'s Theodore "Ted" Taketa, School Kine Cookies' Steven Gold And Sharon Serene of Sharon

Serene Creative are among the participants in Hawaii's Fittest CEO competition for executives over 50 years old. Taketa takes yoga classes, and also goes to the gym while Serne has Mike Hann as her professional trainer. Eating habits of the aforementioned executives are also described.

46227 ■ "Mobility: So Happy Together" in *Entrepreneur* **(Vol. 35, October 2007, No. 10, pp. 64)**
Pub: Entrepreneur Media Inc.
Ed: Heather Clancy. **Description:** Joshua Burnett, CEO and founder of 9ci, uses index cards to keep track of what he needs to do despite the fact that he has a notebook computer, cell phone and PDA. Kim Hahn, a media entrepreneur, prefers jotting her ideas down in a spiral notebook, has a team that would organize her records for her, and a personal assistant that would keep track of changes to her schedule. Reasons why these entrepreneurs use old-fashioned methods along with new technology are given.

46228 ■ "Monday Organizer: Clean and De-Clutter in 15 Minutes" in *Tulsa World* **(June 13, 2011)**
Pub: McClatchy Company
Ed: Kim Brown. **Description:** New weekly series highlights practical tips and helpful ideas to simply life by taking 15 minutes to de-clutter your home or office. Paper clutter can be eliminated in 15 minutes by gathering up newspapers and magazines to recycle; sort mail as soon as you receive it and throw away any junk mail at that time. If watching TV, use commercial time to accomplish small tasks.

46229 ■ "Our Gadget of the Week" in *Barron's* **(Vol. 89, July 27, 2009, No. 30, pp. 26)**
Pub: Dow Jones & Co., Inc.
Ed: Jay Palmer. **Description:** Zeo Sleep Coach has a lightweight headband with built-in sensors which measures the user's brain waves and records their sleep patterns. The device details the time the users spends in deep sleep, light sleep and the restorative REM (rapid eye movement) sleep mode. Users can get lifestyle change recommendations from a website to improve their sleep.

46230 ■ "Pack Mentality" in *Crain's Chicago Business* **(Vol. 31, April 21, 2008, No. 16, pp. 31)**
Pub: Crain Communications, Inc.
Ed: Sarah A. Klein. **Description:** Jill Smart, the head of human resources for a company with 170,000 employees worldwide, frequently travels to India, London and Singapore; Ms. Smart provides advice concerning efficiency, time management and avoiding jet-lag.

46231 ■ "Pau Hana" in *Hawaii Business* **(Vol. 53, December 2007, No. 6, pp. 118)**
Pub: Hawaii Business Publishing
Ed: Cathy Cruz-George. **Description:** Presented are the hobbies of four Hawaii executives as well as the reason these hobbies are an important part of their lives and add to their ability to manage effectively. Mike Wilkins, for example, is not only Turtle Bay Resort's director of sales and marketing, but is also a glider pilot, while Aubrey Hawk Public Relations president Aubrey Hawk loves baking. The interests of Queen Liliuokalani Trust's Thomas K. Kaulukukui Jr., Reyn Spooner's Tim McCullough, and Heide and Cook Ltd.'s Dexter S. Kekua, are discussed.

46232 ■ *The Power of Full Engagement: Managing Energy, Not Time, is the Key to High Performance and Personal Renewal*
Pub: Free Press/Simon & Schuster
Ed: Jim Loehr; Tony Schwartz. **Released:** December 21, 2004. **Price:** $15.95 paperback. **Description:** The book presents a program to help stressed individuals find more purpose in their work and ways to better handle overburdened relationships.

46233 ■ "Power Play" in *Harvard Business Review* **(Vol. 88, July-August 2010, No. 7-8, pp. 84)**
Pub: Harvard Business School Publishing
Ed: Jeffrey Pfeffer. **Description:** Guidelines include in-depth understanding of resources at one's dis-

posal, relentlessness that still provides opponents with opportunities to save face, and a determination not to be put off by the processes of politics.

46234 ■ "Pressed for Time" in *Marketing to Women* **(Vol. 21, March 2008, No. 3, pp. 1)**
Pub: EPM Communications, Inc.
Description: Statistical data concerning the tools women use for time management which include gadgets as well as traditional media such as calendars.

46235 ■ "Professional Help: Cross That Off Your To-Do List" in *Inc.* **(November 2007, pp. 89-90, 92)**
Pub: Gruner & Jahr USA Publishing
Ed: Alison Stein Wellner. **Description:** Small business owners are finding that it pays to hire someone to takeover the personal tasks of daily living, including hiring a personal assistant, chauffeur, chef, stylist, pet caregiver, or concierge service.

46236 ■ "The Sweet Spot: A Sugar-Coated Pitch Paid Off Big Time" in *Black Enterprise* **(Vol. 37, November 2006, No. 4, pp. 71)**
Pub: Earl G. Graves Publishing Co. Inc.
Ed: Laura Egodigwe. **Description:** In an interview with Debra Sandler, president of McNeil Nutritionals L.L.C., Sandler talks about the challenges of bringing a new product to the marketplace, how her personal experiences effect her business decisions, and the difficulties of re-entering the workforce.

46237 ■ *Table Talk: The Savvy Girl's Alternative to Networking*
Pub: AuthorHouse
Ed: Diane Danielson. **Released:** April 1, 2003. **Price:** $17.50. **Description:** Let's face it. Women and men are different. So why should we all have to network in the same way? And, why should women have to 'network' at all? Between family and work responsibilities, the idea of pressing flesh at some not-very-festive cocktail party is right up there in appeal with a root canal. But what if women could find a way to make career boosting connections that are actually fun? Enter 'table talk', a new way to network for time-pressed, professional women.

46238 ■ *Take Back Your Time: How to Regain Control of Work, Information and Technology*
Pub: St. Martin's Press LLC
Ed: Jan Jasper. **Released:** November 1999. **Price:** $16.99. **Description:** Strategies to become more organized and productive.

46239 ■ "Time Value of Money Rate of Return" in *Business Owner* **(Vol. 35, September-October 2011, No. 5, pp. 8)**
Pub: DL Perkins Company
Description: Estimating value of an income-generating asset or group of assets requires the small business owner to consider concepts such as the time value of money, risk and required rate of return. A brief summary explaining this theory is presented.

46240 ■ "Transform Your Life" in *Black Enterprise* **(Vol. 37, January 2007, No. 6, pp. 14)**
Pub: Earl G. Graves Publishing Co. Inc.
Description: Through the magazine, television and radio programs, events, and the website, the various platforms of Black Enterprise will provide the tools necessary to achieve success in business ventures, career aspirations, and personal goals.

46241 ■ "Use Ink Presets to Minimize Makeready" in *American Printer* **(Vol. 128, July 1, 2011, No. 7)**
Pub: Penton Media Inc.
Description: Automatic registration systems enable most printers to be in register very quickly after press startup. If the paper, ink and press time wasted during makeready can be reduced, these savings will flow directly to the bottom line. Ink presetting as an economical solution to set color quickly is a trend that continues to gain momentum.

46242 ■ "What Are You Afraid Of?" in *Entrepreneur* **(Vol. 37, July 2009, No. 7, pp. 79)**
Pub: Entrepreneur Media, Inc.
Ed: Lindsay Holloway. **Description:** According to a survey of entrepreneurs in the US, failure, economic uncertainty, not having enough personal time, being their own boss, and staying afloat are the biggest fears when starting a business. Advice on how to deal with these fears is also given.

46243 ■ "What Brain Science Tells Us About How to Excel" in *Harvard Business Review* **(Vol. 88, December 2010, No. 12, pp. 123)**
Pub: Harvard Business School Publishing
Ed: Edward M. Hallowell. **Description:** Relevant discoveries in brain research as they apply to boosting employee motivation and organizational effectiveness are explained. Included is a checklist of 15 items for use in assessing the fitness of a person for a particular job, focusing on the intersection of what one likes to do, what one does best, and what increases organizational value.

46244 ■ "What Moms Want" in *Marketing to Women* **(Vol. 21, February 2008, No. 2, pp. 6)**
Pub: EPM Communications, Inc.
Description: According to a survey conducted by Eureka's Spa, moms would rather have an experience gift than flowers or chocolate. The top five dream gifts include a spa day, a weekend getaway, maid service, a bathroom makeover or a getaway weekend with girlfriends.

46245 ■ *What Self-Made Millionaires Really Think, Know and Do: A Straight-Talking Guide to Business Success and Personal Riches*
Pub: John Wiley & Sons, Incorporated
Ed: Richard Dobbins; Barrie Pettman. **Released:** September 2006. **Price:** $24.95. **Description:** Guide for understanding the concepts of entrepreneurial success; the book offers insight into bringing an idea into reality, marketing, time management, leadership skills, and setting clear goals.

46246 ■ "When Virtue Is A Vice" in *Harvard Business Review* **(Vol. 86, July-August 2008, No. 8, pp. 22)**
Pub: Harvard Business School Press
Ed: Anat Keinan; Ran Kivetz. **Description:** Negative consequences of habitually denying self-indulgence, from work and life balance to consumer shopping behaviors are discussed.

46247 ■ "Why Mumbai at 1PM is the Center of the Business World" in *Harvard Business Review* **(Vol. 88, October 2010, No. 10, pp. 38)**
Pub: Harvard Business School Publishing
Ed: Michael Segalla. **Description:** A time zone chart is presented for assisting in the planning of international conference calls.

46248 ■ "Work/Family Balance Boosts Business" in *Marketing to Women* **(Vol. 21, February 2008, No. 2, pp. 8)**
Pub: EPM Communications, Inc.
Description: Flexibility in the workplace is becoming a more important issue to both women and men. Statistical data included.

VIDEOCASSETTES/ AUDIOCASSETTES

46249 ■ *Analyzing Our Time Usage*
Resources for Education & Management, Inc.
1804 Montreal Ct., Ste. A
Tucker, GA 30084
Released: 1972. **Description:** Two methods for managing time-breaking down the types of work we do and setting priorities-are discussed. **Availability:** VHS; 3/4U.

46250 ■ *Another Meeting*
Exec-U-Service Associates
4326 US Highway 1
Princeton, NJ 08540
Released: 1978. **Description:** Gives practical ideas on how to improve the results and time efficiency of meetings. A solid basis for analyzing the meeting process is explored. **Availability:** 3/4U.

46251 ■ Do It Now!
Aspen Publishers
7201 McKinney Circ.
Frederick, MD 21704
Ph:(301)698-7100
Free: 800-234-1660
Fax:800-901-9075
URL: http://www.aspenpublishers.com
Released: 197?. **Description:** This program examines what procrastination is, what causes it, and suggests techniques for breaking the habit. **Availability:** VHS; 3/4U.

46252 ■ Don't Agonize—Organize Series with Dr. John Wayne Lee
Instructional Video
2219 C St.
Lincoln, NE 68502
Ph:(402)475-6570
Free: 800-228-0164
Fax:(402)475-6500
Co. E-mail: feedback@insvideo.com
URL: http://www.insvideo.com
Price: $179.10. **Description:** Dr. John Wayne Lee teaches his techniques on time and self management. Only available in the U.S. **Availability:** VHS.

46253 ■ The Effective Manager
Nightingale-Conant Corp.
6245 W. Howard St.
Niles, IL 60714
Ph:(847)647-0300
Free: 800-560-6081
URL: http://www.nightingale.com
Price: $95.00. **Description:** A series of award-winning programs designed to promote effective management and help increase sales. Audio tapes and booklets are included, and the series can be purchased individually or as a set. **Availability:** VHS.

46254 ■ Empowerment: Managing Your Time
International Training Consultants, Inc.
1838 Park Oaks
Kemah, TX 77565
Free: 800-998-8764
Co. E-mail: itc@trainingitc.com
URL: http://www.trainingitc.com
Price: $495.00. **Description:** Part of the "Empowerment: The Employee Development Series." Teaches employees to become aware of how they manage their time and offers advice on how they can manage it better. Also discusses priority setting, daily planning, long-range planning, scheduling, and other time management functions. **Availability:** VHS.

46255 ■ Empowerment: The Employee Development Series
International Training Consultants, Inc.
1838 Park Oaks
Kemah, TX 77565
Free: 800-998-8764
Co. E-mail: itc@trainingitc.com
URL: http://www.trainingitc.com
Price: $10350.00. **Description:** Employee development series which prepares employees to meet the demands of today's workplace with skill and confidence. Covers such topics as time management, team work, communication, career advancement, working together, and problem solving. Comes with leader's guide, overhead transparencies, five participant booklets, and a complete participant's manual. **Availability:** VHS.

46256 ■ Get the Edge with Time Management/Rick Barrera
Instructional Video
2219 C St.
Lincoln, NE 68502
Ph:(402)475-6570
Free: 800-228-0164
Fax:(402)475-6500
Co. E-mail: feedback@insvideo.com
URL: http://www.insvideo.com
Price: $95.00. **Description:** Rick Barrera discusses time management skills. Points out how time management team affect success. Only available in the U.S. **Availability:** VHS.

46257 ■ Getting Things Done: An Achiever's Guide to Better Time-Management
Instructional Video
2219 C St.
Lincoln, NE 68502
Ph:(402)475-6570
Free: 800-228-0164
Fax:(402)475-6500
Co. E-mail: feedback@insvideo.com
URL: http://www.insvideo.com
Price: $79.95. **Description:** Offers a systematic approach to achieving goals through the use of time management, stressing the importance of proper prioritization. **Availability:** VHS.

46258 ■ How to Get Control of Your Time and Your Job
Aspen Publishers
7201 McKinney Circ.
Frederick, MD 21704
Ph:(301)698-7100
Free: 800-234-1660
Fax:800-901-9075
URL: http://www.aspenpublishers.com
Released: 1983. **Description:** This is a complete program designed by time management expert Alan La Kein to help you learn to use your time effectively. **Availability:** VHS.

46259 ■ How to Get Things Done
Nightingale-Conant Corp.
6245 W. Howard St.
Niles, IL 60714
Ph:(847)647-0300
Free: 800-560-6081
URL: http://www.nightingale.com
Price: $95.00. **Description:** Time-management and time-allocation skills are presented, to help workers accomplish more in less time. Includes an audio cassette and book. **Availability:** VHS.

46260 ■ Manage Your Time to Build Your Territory
Dartnell Corp.
2222 Sedwick Drive, Ste. 101
Durham, NC 27713
Free: 800-233-8720
Fax:800-508-2592
Co. E-mail: customerservice@dartnellcorp.com
URL: http://www.dartnellcorp.com
Released: 1974. **Description:** An examination of time thieves that rob salespeople of both hours and sales volume. From the "Tough-Minded Salesmanship" series. **Availability:** VHS; 3/4U; Special order formats.

46261 ■ Management of Time
Resources for Education & Management, Inc.
1804 Montreal Ct., Ste. A
Tucker, GA 30084
Released: 1972. **Description:** Teaches supervisors how to manage time effectively. It consists of four modules: The Time of Our Lives; Analyzing Our Time Usage; Using Others to Save Time; and Our Time Is Our Time. **Availability:** VHS; 3/4U.

46262 ■ Managing Time
Learning Communications LLC
5520 Trabuco Rd.
Irvine, CA 92620
Free: 800-622-3610
Fax:(949)727-4323
Co. E-mail: sales@learncom.com
URL: http://www.learncomhr.com
Released: 1968. **Description:** Stimulates the day-to-day planning of work, use of personnel, staff, and use of time. **Availability:** VHS; 3/4U.

46263 ■ Managing Your Time
Resources for Education & Management, Inc.
1804 Montreal Ct., Ste. A
Tucker, GA 30084
Released: 1970. **Description:** Shows office workers more than 20 ways to manage their time more effectively. Time-saving suggestions are given for typing, filing, and dictation that pay off in increased productivity and efficiency. **Availability:** VHS; 3/4U.

46264 ■ A Perfectly Normal Day
Aspen Publishers
7201 McKinney Circ.
Frederick, MD 21704
Ph:(301)698-7100
Free: 800-234-1660
Fax:800-901-9075
URL: http://www.aspenpublishers.com
Released: 197?. **Description:** Helps develop a new attitude toward interruptions and crises-and teaches us how to reduce and manage them. **Availability:** VHS; 3/4U.

46265 ■ Personal Achievement Series—Time Management: How to Increase Your Productivity and Get the Results You Want
Instructional Video
2219 C St.
Lincoln, NE 68502
Ph:(402)475-6570
Free: 800-228-0164
Fax:(402)475-6500
Co. E-mail: feedback@insvideo.com
URL: http://www.insvideo.com
Price: $69.95. **Description:** Outlines ways to eliminate time-wasting elements of daily life. Includes guidebook. **Availability:** VHS.

46266 ■ Personal Time Management Video
Instructional Video
2219 C St.
Lincoln, NE 68502
Ph:(402)475-6570
Free: 800-228-0164
Fax:(402)475-6500
Co. E-mail: feedback@insvideo.com
URL: http://www.insvideo.com
Price: $59.95. **Description:** Brian Tracy illustrates techniques to help put short-term goals in focus to gain long-term aspirations, overcome anxieties related to time restraints, and move on to complete any task. **Availability:** VHS.

46267 ■ Time Is Money!
Aspen Publishers
7201 McKinney Circ.
Frederick, MD 21704
Ph:(301)698-7100
Free: 800-234-1660
Fax:800-901-9075
URL: http://www.aspenpublishers.com
Released: 197?. **Description:** Helps solve salespeople's time problems by teaching them good habits, and provides them with timesaving techniques so they'll spend their time more profitably. **Availability:** VHS; 3/4U.

46268 ■ Time Management: Keeping the Monkey off Your Back
Excellence in Training Corp.
c/o ICON Training
804 Roosevelt St.
Polk City, IA 50226
Free: 800-609-0479
Co. E-mail: info@icontraining.com
URL: http://www.icontraining.com
Released: 1991. **Price:** $595.00. **Description:** A discussion of ways to manage events, rather than being managed by events. **Availability:** VHS; 3/4U; Special order formats.

46269 ■ Time Management for Managers
Time-Life Video and Television
1450 Palmyra Ave.
Richmond, VA 23227-4420
Ph:(804)266-6330
Free: 800-950-7887
Fax:(757)427-7905
URL: http://www.timelife.com
Released: 1980. **Description:** This six-part series of untitled programs covers the principles of time management, including decision-making, delegating, scheduling, and managing interruptions. It is designed to help managers become more productive in both personal and professional time. Available only as a set. **Availability:** VHS; 3/4U; Special order formats.

46270 ■ Time Management for Managers and Professionals (41-1XX)
Skillsoft
107 Northeastern Blvd.
Nashua, NH 03062
Free: 877-545-5763
Co. E-mail: info@netg.com
URL: http://www.skillsoft.com/
Released: 1979. **Description:** Part of an integrated course aimed at teaching a strategy for time management which will enable participants to make better contributions to their organization. **Availability:** 3/4U.

46271 ■ Time Management for Women
Instructional Video
2219 C St.
Lincoln, NE 68502
Ph:(402)475-6570
Free: 800-228-0164
Fax:(402)475-6500
Co. E-mail: feedback@insvideo.com
URL: http://www.insvideo.com
Price: $79.95. **Description:** Kay Cronkite Waldo offers time management training for women, focusing on behavior patterns, energy cycles, efficiency vs. effectiveness, time wasters, decision-making factors, and the superwoman theory. **Availability:** VHS.

46272 ■ The Time of Our Lives
Resources for Education & Management, Inc.
1804 Montreal Ct., Ste. A
Tucker, GA 30084
Released: 1972. **Description:** Good planning is necessary if work is to fit into the time available. The keys of proper time management are introduced. **Availability:** VHS; 3/4U.

46273 ■ The Time Trap
American Media, Inc.
4621 121st St.
Urbandale, IA 50323-2311
Ph:(515)224-0919
Free: 888-776-8268
Fax:(515)327-2555
Co. E-mail: custsvc@ammedia.com
URL: http://www.ammedia.com
Released: 1982. **Description:** This program dramatically demonstrates techniques that can help individuals to manage their time better, avoiding those everyday time-wasting problems at the office. **Availability:** VHS; 3/4U.

46274 ■ The Time of Your Life
Aspen Publishers
7201 McKinney Circ.
Frederick, MD 21704
Ph:(301)698-7100
Free: 800-234-1660
Fax:800-901-9075
URL: http://www.aspenpublishers.com
Released: 1985. **Price:** $570.00. **Description:** Based on Alan Lakein's bestseller, outlines 60 simple ideas on how to make more effective use of your time. A meeting guide and optional support materials are available. Revised and updated in 1991. **Availability:** VHS; 3/4U.

46275 ■ The Two-Minute Drill
Aspen Publishers
7201 McKinney Circ.
Frederick, MD 21704
Ph:(301)698-7100
Free: 800-234-1660
Fax:800-901-9075
URL: http://www.aspenpublishers.com
Released: 1979. **Description:** A program hosted by Fran Tarkenton, retired Minnesota Viking quarterback, that explores how to use time. Time is an ally—a positive approach to use the clock to your advantage. **Availability:** VHS; 3/4U.

46276 ■ Using Others to Save Time
Resources for Education & Management, Inc.
1804 Montreal Ct., Ste. A
Tucker, GA 30084
Released: 1972. **Description:** Delegation is defined as more than giving other people more work to do. It is shown to save time, and in the process, develop others' abilities. **Availability:** VHS; 3/4U.

CONSULTANTS

46277 ■ Associations Plus
50 Laurelton Rd.
Mount Kisco, NY 10549-4218
Ph:(914)241-3917
Fax:(914)946-2674
Co. E-mail: mtrossi@aol.com
Contact: Marie T. Rossi, President
Scope: Offers human resource development services specializing in sales training, support staff training, trade show selling, time management skills and stress management training. **Seminars:** Non-verbal Communications; Time/Stress Management; Better Selling Techniques; Trade Show Sales Techniques.

46278 ■ Carson Research Center
2957 Flamingo Dr.
Miami Beach, FL 33140-3916
Ph:(305)534-8846
Free: 800-541-8846
Fax:(305)532-8826
Co. E-mail: gayle@gaylecarson.com
URL: http://www.spunkyoldbroad.com
Contact: Gayle Carson, President
E-mail: gayle@atsgaylecarson.com
Scope: Human performance improvement consultants offering a wide variety of training opportunities for personnel of businesses of all kinds, state and national association and government agencies. General areas of training include management training, assertiveness, time management, change management, sales training, supervisory skills, coping with difficult people, stress management and strategic quality management and customer service, negotiation and shoe string marketing. Serves clients worldwide. Facilitation of board retreats, web-based programs available 24/7. **Publications:** "Creating a Winning Image"; "Making Meetings Work"; "How to Turn Customer Service Into an Ongoing Profit Center"; "Business 2005-Six Traits of Success"; "The Leading Edge"; "Communication Cash: How to Earn Fame & Fortune As a Professional Speaker"; "Winning Ways"; "How To Energize Your Life And Make The Difference You Want". **Seminars:** Dynamic Leadership; Business 2005; Negotiating to Win; How to Energize Your Life and Make the Difference You Want; Dealing with Difficult People; How to be A Great Coach; How To Turn Customer Service Into An Ongoing Profit Center; The Virtual Classroom.

46279 ■ David L. Ward and Associates Inc.
1951 - 47th St., Ste. 179
San Diego, CA 92102
Ph:(619)266-2701
Fax:(773)935-3779
Co. E-mail: dward@wardmosaic.com
URL: http://www.wardmosaic.com
Contact: David L. Ward, President
E-mail: dward@wardmosaic.com
Scope: Specializes in mosaic glass art consulting. The firm provides various seminars on mosaic glass art. **Publications:** "Mosaic Glue Comparison Testing". **Seminars:** Mosaic Glass Art Workshop; How to Turn Your Glass Hobby Into a Money-Making Business.

46280 ■ Dr. Donald Kirkpatrick
842 Kirkland Ct.
Pewaukee, WI 53072
Ph:(262)695-5851
Fax:(262)784-7994
Co. E-mail: dleekirk@aol.com
Contact: Dr. Donald L. Kirkpatrick, Owner
Scope: Gives presentations for professional societies including ASTD, IQPC, Training and linkage, and conducts in-house seminars for all levels of management on various subjects including: leadership and motivation, communications, managing change, time management, supervisory/management selection, training and development, performance appraisal, coaching, managing conflict, decision making, how to conduct productive meetings, and Evaluating Training Programs: The Four Levels. Serves private industries as well as government agencies. **Publications:** "Evaluating Training Programs; the Four Levels," Bennett-Koehler Publishers, 2006; "Developing Supervisors and Team Leaders," Butterworth-

Heinemann, Jun, 2006. **Seminars:** Effective Communication; Leadership and Motivation; Teambuilding; Decision Making and Empowerment; Performance Appraisal and Coaching; How to Conduct Productive Meetings; How to Manage Change; Time Management; Orienting and Training Employees; Evaluating Training Programs; Training Tools/Supervisory; Management Inventories on Human Relations; Communications; Managing Change; Time Management; Performance Approval and Coaching; Modern Management; Leadership Motivation and Decision Making, Evaluating Training Programs: The Four Levels.

46281 ■ Harold Taylor Time Consultants Inc.
1176 N Shore Dr.
Dunnville, ON, Canada N1A 2W5
Ph:(905)853-9328
Free: 800-361-8463
Fax:(905)701-0970
Co. E-mail: info@taylorintime.com
URL: http://www.taylorintime.com
Contact: Yvonne Bottcher, Mgr
E-mail: harold@taylorintime.com
Scope: Offers time management seminars or workshops for managers, salespeople and support staff in all industries and organizations. Also available for keynote addresses. **Publications:** "Benefits of Time Management"; "The Truth About Multitasking"; "Schedule, Don't List"; "Put Off Procrastination"; "Am I a Workaholic?"; "Don't Be a Perfectionist"; "Shortcuts Through Life"; "Ten Principles of Scheduling"; "The Road to Success is Paved with Goals"; "Time Management for Creative People"; "The High Cost of Complexity"; "Scheduling is the Key to Goal Achievement"; "Sleep Deprivation, the Latest Time Waster"; "Pareto Visits a Retail Store". **Seminars:** Making Time Work For You, May, 2007; Time Management Tele class for Professional Organizers, Mar, 2007; Time management with the Palm; Managing Paperwork; Time Management for Students.

46282 ■ Leadership Training Associates
10022 Oak Tree Ct.
Littleton, CO 80124-9714
Ph:(303)706-9590
Contact: Randy M. Bauer, President
Scope: Provides training and consulting services to organizations across the country in the areas of: Effective supervision, total quality management, leadership skills, managing time, coaching and counseling skills, stress management, effective communication, productivity improvement, and managing conflict. Serves private industries as well as government agencies. **Seminars:** Better Communication At Work; Skills for the Newly Appointed Manager; How to Beat Job Burnout; Dealing With Upset Customers and the Public; The Skill of Listening; Managing Conflict; Motivation and Positive Discipline; Time Management Strategies; Stress Management Techniques; Total Quality Management.

46283 ■ Organization Plus
14 Palmer Rd.
Beverly, MA 01915-2710
Ph:(978)922-6136
Fax:(978)922-0143
Co. E-mail: information@organizationplus.com
URL: http://www.organizationplus.com
Contact: Susan Lannis, President
E-mail: nancy@organizationplus.com
Scope: Organizing consultant specializing in time management, clutter control, office organization and as a business consultant. Serves individuals and small businesses (including home based). **Seminars:** Get Organized, Get Energized!; Triumph Over Time; The 3 Hour Transformation; The National Association of Professional Organizers (NAPO); The National Association of Women Business Owners; Wellspring Working Capital; Home Based Businesswomen's Network; Cape Ann Chamber of Commerce; Small Business Administration.

46284 ■ Quma Learning Systems Inc.
505 S Val Vista Dr., Ste. 4
Mesa, AZ 85204-3215
Ph:(480)545-8311
Free: 800-622-6463

Fax:(480)545-8233
Co. E-mail: info@quma.net
URL: http://www.quma.net
Contact: C. Spencer Reynolds, Principle
E-mail: chip@atsquma.net
Scope: Business management firm that works with corporations in developing empowering cultures by laying the foundation of ownership spirit. Specializes in providing principles and tools for maximizing full potential in one's self by becoming more accountable, responsible and committed. **Publications:** "The Book On Mind Management Discussion Guide"; "The Ownership Spirit Handbook"; "The Book on Mind Management"; "Money: An Owner's Manual". **Seminars:** The Ownership Spirit; Visioneering; Life Management; Money: An Owner's Manual; Communicating For Success; Sustaining Peak Performance.

46285 ■ Smart Ways to Work
1441 Franklin St., Ste. 301
Oakland, CA 94612-3219
Ph:(510)763-8482
Free: 800-599-8463
Fax:(510)763-0790
Co. E-mail: odette@smartwaystowork.com
URL: http://www.smartwaystowork.com
Contact: Odette Pollar, President
E-mail: odette@smartwaystowork.com
Scope: A management consulting firm specializing in the training of supervisors, managers and professional staff in the area of time management, problem solving, decision making and strategic planning. Assists businesses and corporations in developing and implementing programs for increased productivity, greater profit and improved employee morale. Serves private industries as well as government agencies. **Publications:** "Surviving Information Overload driv-ing Information Overload: How to Find, Filter, and Focus on What's Important," Crisp Publications, Sep, 2003; "Take Back Your Life: Smart Ways to Simplify Daily Living," Conari Press, Apr, 1999; "365 Ways to Simplify Your Work Life," Kaplan Business, Aug, 1996; "Dynamics of Diversity: Strategic Programs for Your Organization," Crisp Publications, 1994; "Organizing Your Workspace: A Guide to Personal Productivity," Crisp Publications, May, 1992. **Seminars:** Managing Multiple Demands: Surviving Ground Zero; Defending Your Life: Balancing Work And Home; Desktop Sprawl: Conquer Your Paper Pile-Up; Getting It All Done: Breaking The Time Bind; To Give or Not To Give: The Delegation Dilemma; Information Happens: Don't Let It Happen On You; Take The Terror Out Of Talk: Secrets To Successful Speaking; To Give or Not To Give: The Delegation Dilemma; Managing Meetings.

46286 ■ SunCoach Inc.
6 Aberdeen Pl.
Fair Lawn, NJ 07410
Ph:(201)791-2396
Free: 800-764-3047
Fax:(201)796-5490
Co. E-mail: sunny@suncoach.com
URL: http://www.sunnyschlenger.com
Contact: Kathy Smith, Mgr
E-mail: kathy@atssuncoach.com
Scope: Consults with corporate and individual clients in the areas of time management and office space organization. Offers group seminars and personal counseling in time management and related topics. **Publications:** "Organizing for the Spirit," Jossey-Bass J.Wiley & Sons, Apr, 2004; "How To Be Organized In Spite Of Yourself," Penguin Putnam, 1999; "Connections "; "What Are You Afraid Of"; "Redefining Yourself "; "When Old Dreams Change "; "What Do You Do When You've Run Out of Room"; "Get Organized: Heal the World"; "Reframing the Past "; "Giving Through Hospice"; "The Day The Ceiling Fell In". **Seminars:** Organizing as Self-Discovery: Preserving Your Legacy, Oct, 2009.

46287 ■ Time Masters - The Institute for Personal Excellence
55-220 Kulanui St.
Laie, HI 96762
Ph:(801)785-1105
Fax:(801)785-5035
Contact: Todd L. Pearson, President
Scope: Employs a telephone coaching approach to teaching personal productivity, one-on-one, to any location in the world. Focuses on implementation and application of success principles over four months. Training course focuses on motivation, personal leadership, time management, sales, and entrepreneurship. **Seminars:** The Time Masters Personal Productivity Seminars; Personal Skills One-on-One Coaching.

46288 ■ TWD & Associates
431 S Patton Ave.
Arlington Heights, IL 60005-2253
Ph:(847)398-6410
Fax:(847)255-5095
Co. E-mail: tdoo@aol.com
Contact: Thomas W. Dooley, President
E-mail: twhdoo@yahoo.com
Scope: Consulting specialists in small business management particularly in the areas of personnel, training, marketing, franchising, sales, time management, budgeting, raising capital, and long-range planning. **Seminars:** Alternative Methods of Financing for Franchising; Effectiveness of Organizational Development Training Programs for Hourly-Hire Workers in Manufacturing Plants. **Special Services:** ABR[R].

ASSOCIATIONS AND OTHER ORGANIZATIONS

46289 ■ Exhibit Designers and Producers Association
10 Norden Pl.
Norwalk, CT 06855
Ph:(203)852-5698
Fax:(203)854-6735
Co. E-mail: jprovost@edpa.com
URL: http://www.edpa.com
Contact: Jeff Provost, Exec. Dir.
Description: Firms designing and building exhibits for trade shows and museums. Conducts educational and research programs. **Publications:** *EDP Action News* (bimonthly); *EDPA.COMmunications* (monthly); *EDPA Today* (quarterly).

46290 ■ Trade Show Exhibitors Association
2301 S Lake Shore Dr., Ste. 1005
Chicago, IL 60616
Ph:(312)842-8732
Fax:(312)842-8744
Co. E-mail: membership@tsea.org
URL: http://www.tsea.org
Contact: Margit B. Weisgal CME, Pres./CEO
Description: Exhibitors working to improve the effectiveness of trade shows as a marketing tool. Purposes are to promote the progress and development of trade show exhibiting; to collect and disseminate trade show information; conduct studies, surveys, and stated projects designed to improve trade shows; to foster good relations and communications with organizations representing others in the industry; to undertake other activities necessary to promote the welfare of member companies. Sponsors Exhibit Industry Education Foundation and professional exhibiting seminars; the forum series of educational programs on key issues affecting the industry. Maintains placement services; compiles statistics. **Publications:** *Trade Show Ideas Magazine* (monthly);Membership Directory (annual).

REFERENCE WORKS

46291 ■ "$3 Million in Repairs Prep Cobo for Auto Show" in *Crain's Detroit Business* (Vol. 26, January 4, 2010, No. 1, pp. 1)
Pub: Crain Communications, Inc.
Ed: Nancy Kaffer. **Description:** Overview of the six projects priced roughly at $3 million which were needed in order to host the North American International Auto Show; show organizers stated that the work was absolutely necessary to keep the show in the city of Detroit.

46292 ■ "2008 Woman of the Year Gala" in *Hispanic Business* (Vol. 30, July-August 2008, No. 7-8, pp. 58)
Pub: Hispanic Business, Inc.
Ed: Brynne Chappell. **Description:** Brief report on the sixth annual Women of the Year Awards gala which was held at JW Marriott Desert Ridge Resort and Spa is given; 20 women were honored with these awards for their professional contribution, commitment to the advancement of the Hispanic community and involvement with charitable organizations.

46293 ■ "ALA: Hot Topics for Librarianship" in *Information Today* (Vol. 28, September 2011, No. 8, pp. 17)
Pub: Information Today, Inc.
Ed: Barbara Brynko. **Description:** Highlights from the American Library Association Annual Conference and Exhibition are listed. Thousands of attendees sought out services, displays, demos, new product rollouts, and freebies. Emerging technology for librarians, staff development, gray literature, interlibrary loans, and next-generation interfaces were among the topics discussed.

46294 ■ "And In This Briefcase" in *Mergers & Acquisitions: The Dealmaker's Journal* (March 1, 2008)
Pub: SourceMedia, Inc.
Description: ACG San Diego decided to address the impact the changes in the economy will have on potential private equity transactions as well as what criteria private equity firms are looking for when assessing a company. At the opening of the chapter's 2008 breakfast meeting, real-world case studies were utilized with the audiences' participation in order to assess pre-deal risk scenarios.

46295 ■ Annual Trade Show Directory
Pub: Forum Publishing Co.
Released: Annual, Latest edition 2011. **Price:** $39.95, individuals. **Covers:** over 2,400 merchandise trade shows throughout the United States and Canada. **Entries Include:** Company name, address, phone, estimated attendance and number of exhibitors, show description. **Arrangement:** Classified by product, then chronological. **Indexes:** Product, type of show.

46296 ■ "AREE Meets in Atlantic City" in *Indoor Comfort Marketing* (Vol. 70, June 2011, No. 6, pp. 28)
Pub: Industry Publications Inc.
Description: Highlights of the Atlantic Region Energy Expo are provided.

46297 ■ "Around the World in a Day" in *Agency Sales Magazine* (Vol. 39, August 2009, No. 8, pp. 36)
Pub: MANA
Ed: Jack Foster. **Description:** Highlights of Manufacturer's Agents National Association (MANA) member Les Rapchak one-day visit to Basra, Iraq are presented. Rapchak completed the trip via Frankfurt, Germany and Kuwait with a stop afterwards in Istanbul, Turkey. His purpose for the trip was to take part in a seminar at the State Company for Petrochemical Industries.

46298 ■ "Art Attack 2007 Comes to Minneapolis" in *Art Business News* (Vol. 34, November 2007, No. 11, pp. 11)
Pub: Pfingsten Publishing, LLC
Description: Overview of Art Attack 2007, an open studio and gallery crawl in the Northeast Minneapolis Arts District which featured artists working in glass, ceramics, jewelry, mosaics, mixed media, photography, painting, pottery, sculpture, textiles and wood.

46299 ■ "Art Miami Comes to Miami's Wynwood Art District" in *Art Business News* (Vol. 34, November 2007, No. 11, pp. 18)
Pub: Pfingsten Publishing, LLC
Description: In December, The Art Group will hold its Art Miami fair in the Wynwood Art District; the exhibitors range from painting, sculpture, video and works on paper.

46300 ■ "The Art of War for Women" in *Hawaii Business* (Vol. 54, July 2008, No. 1, pp. 23)
Pub: Hawaii Business Publishing
Description: Business consultant Chi-Ning Chu talks about her new book 'The Art of War for Women: Sun Tzu's Ancient Strategies and Wisdom for Winning at Work', which discusses how women can more effectively win in business. She also shares her thoughts about the advantages that women have, which they can use in businesses decisions.

46301 ■ "Artexpo Celebrates 30th Anniversary" in *Art Business News* (Vol. 34, November 2007, No. 11, pp. 18)
Pub: Pfingsten Publishing, LLC
Description: In honor of its 30th anniversary Artexpo New York 2008 will be an unforgettable show offering a collection of fine-art education courses for both trade and consumer attendees and featuring a variety of artists working in all mediums.

46302 ■ "An Artwork in Progress" in *Hawaii Business* (Vol. 53, March 2008, No. 9, pp. 45)
Pub: Hawaii Business Publishing
Ed: Jolyn Okimoto Rosa. **Description:** Art galleries in Honolulu, Hawaii holds the First Friday Gallery Walk and other special events, which draw crowd to and increase sales activities in the city's downtown. The district also advocates for the reintroduction of Honolulu's Chinatown to the people. Details regarding the art galleries' Chinatown revival and its local economic impact are discussed.

46303 ■ "Attorney Panel Tackles Contract Questions" in *Agency Sales Magazine* (Vol. 39, September-October 2009, No. 9, pp. 8)
Pub: MANA
Ed: Jack Foster. **Description:** MANAfest conference tackled issues regarding a sales representative's contract. One attorney from the panel advised reps to go through proposed agreements with attorneys who are knowledgeable concerning rep laws. Another attorney advised reps to communicate with a company to ask about their responsibilities if that company is facing financial difficulty.

46304 ■ "Auto Show Aims to Electrify" in *Crain's Detroit Business* (Vol. 26, January 11, 2010, No. 2, pp. 1)
Pub: Crain Communications, Inc.
Ed: Ryan Beene. **Description:** Overview of the North American International Auto show include sixteen production and concept vehicles including eight from the Detroit 3. High-tech battery suppliers as well as hybrid and electric vehicles will highlight the show.

46305 ■ "Avanti Hosts Users Conference" in *American Printer* (Vol. 128, July 1, 2011, No. 7)

Pub: Penton Media Inc.

Description: Avanti Computer Systems Ltd. hosted its 19th annual users conference in Washington DC. In-plant and commercial printers were in attendance.

46306 ■ "BBB Hires Marketing Firm to Attract More Businesses" in *Baltimore Business Journal* (Vol. 27, January 1, 2010, No. 35, pp. 1)

Pub: American City Business Journals

Ed: Julekha Dash. **Description:** Better Business Bureau (BBB) of Greater Maryland hired Bystry Carson & Associates Ltd. to assist in its rebranding efforts in order to entice more businesses. Bystry Carson will promote BBB's new mission at lectures, seminars, and networking events, as well as educate businesses about the agency through blogs and Twitter. BBB's services are also outlined.

46307 ■ "Biz Assesses 'Textgate' Fallout; Conventions, Smaller Deals Affected" in *Crain's Detroit Business* (Vol. 24, March 31, 2008)

Pub: Crain Communications, Inc.

Ed: Tom Henderson. **Description:** Businesspeople who were trying to measure the amount of economic damage is likely to be caused due to Mayor Kwame Kilpatrick's indictment on eight charges and found that: automotive and other large global deals are less likely to be affected than location decisions by smaller companies and convention site decisions. Also being affected are negotiations in which Mexican startup companies were planning a partnership with the TechTown incubator to pursue opportunities in the auto sector; those plans are being put on hold while they look at other sites.

46308 ■ "Bottom-Fishing and Speed-Dating in India" in *Barron's* (Vol. 88, March 24, 2008, No. 12, pp. M12)

Pub: Dow Jones & Company, Inc.

Ed: Elliot Wilson. **Description:** Indian stocks have fallen hard in 2008, with Mumbai's Sensex 30 down 30 percent from its January 2008 peak of 21,000 to 14,995 in March. The India Private Equity Fair 2008 attracted 140 of the world's largest private equity firms and about 24 of India's fastest-growing corporations. Statistical data included.

46309 ■ "The British Aren't Coming" in *Crain's Chicago Business* (Vol. 34, October 24, 2011, No. 42, pp. 3)

Pub: Crain Communications Inc.

Ed: Brigid Sweeney. **Description:** In a move to attract tourists back to Chicago, its Convention and Tourism Bureau is marketing in London, England, Mexico, and Canada, but not Germany or France because of budget constraints.

46310 ■ "Calendar" in *Crain's Detroit Business* (Vol. 24, March 24, 2008, No. 12, pp. 25)

Pub: Crain Communications, Inc.

Description: Listing of events in the Detroit area include conferences addressing entrepreneurialism, economic development, and women business ownership.

46311 ■ "CarBiz Inc. Speaking At NABD" in *Canadian Corporate News* (May 14, 2007)

Pub: Comtex News Network Inc.

Description: CarBiz Inc., a leading provider of software, consulting, and training solutions to the United States' automotive industry, had two of its executive officers speak at the National Alliance of Buy Here - Pay Here Dealers (NABD), a conference that draws over 2,000 dealers, service providers, and experts from across the United States.

46312 ■ "Celebrate Success. Embrace Innovation" in *Black Enterprise* (Vol. 37, February 2007, No. 7, pp. 145)

Pub: Earl G. Graves Publishing Co. Inc.

Description: 2007 Women of Power Summit provides networking opportunities, empowerment sessions, and nightly entertainment. More than 500 executive women of color are expected to attend this inspiring summit in Phoenix, February 7-10.

46313 ■ "Change Is in the Air" in *Agency Sales Magazine* (Vol. 39, August 2009, No. 8, pp. 30)

Pub: MANA

Ed: Jack Foster. **Description:** Highlights of the Power-Motion Technology Representatives Association (PTRA) 37th Annual Conference, which projected an economic upturn, are presented. Allan Bealulieu of the Institute for Trend Research gave the positive news while Manufacturer's Agents National Association (MANA) president Brain Shirley emphasized the need to take advantage of a turnaround.

46314 ■ "Chattanooga at a Glance" in *Women In Business* (Vol. 62, June 2010, No. 2, pp. 29)

Pub: American Business Women's Association

Ed: Jill Yates Bagby. **Description:** City of Chattanooga, Tennessee is the location of the 2010 American Business Women's Association (ABWA) National Women's Leadership Conference. The city offers historical sites, parks and tourist attractions, as well as dining options.

46315 ■ "City's Hilton Hotel Still Losing Money" in *Baltimore Business Journal* (Vol. 28, October 15, 2010, No. 23, pp. 1)

Pub: Baltimore Business Journal

Ed: Danile J. Sernovitz. **Description:** Baltimore, Maryland-owned Hilton Baltimore Convention Center Hotel has been expected by Baltimore Hotel Corporation to wrap up 2010 with a $9.8 million deficit after completing its first year in operation in the red. The forecast would mark the controversial project's third-straight year of losses.

46316 ■ "Clinic to Use Medical Summit to Pump Up Cardiology Center" in *Crain's Cleveland Business* (Vol. 28, October 1, 2007, No. 39, pp. 6)

Pub: Crain Communications, Inc.

Ed: Chuck Soder. **Description:** Overview of the Medical Innovation Summit, sponsored by the Cleveland Clinic and regional business recruitment group Team NEO, whose theme was cardiology. The goal for this year's summit went beyond finding companies for the cardiovascular center, it also looked to market the region to other industries with growth potential.

46317 ■ "Clusters Last Stand?" in *Canadian Electronics* (Vol. 23, February 2008, No. 1, pp. 6)

Pub: CLB Media Inc.

Description: Survival of technology clusters was the focus of Strategic Microelectronics Council's conference entitled, "The Power of Community: Building Technology Clusters in Canada". Clusters can help foster growth in the microelectronics sector, and it was recognized that government intervention is needed to maintain these clusters.

46318 ■ "Conference Calendar" in *Marketing to Women* (Vol. 21, February 2008, No. 2, pp. 1)

Pub: EPM Communications, Inc.

Description: Listing of current conferences and events concerning women, marketing and business.

46319 ■ "Convention Budgeting Best Practice" in *Franchising World* (Vol. 42, November 2010, No. 11, pp. 11)

Pub: International Franchise Association

Ed: Steve Friedman. **Description:** Franchise conventions can offer benefits to both franchisor and franchisee in terms of culture-building, professional education and networking. However, these conventions can be costly. Tips for planning a successful franchising convention on a budget are outlined.

46320 ■ "Convention Calendar" in *Black Enterprise* (Vol. 37, December 2006, No. 5, pp. 74)

Pub: Earl G. Graves Publishing Co. Inc.

Description: Listing of conferences and summits targeting African American business owners and executives.

46321 ■ *Craft Inc: Turn Your Creative Hobby into a Business*

Pub: Chronicle Books LLC

Ed: Meg Mateo Ilasco. **Released:** September 2007. **Price:** $16.95. **Description:** Guide to help any crafter turn their hobby into a successful business. The book covers all aspects including pricing, sales and marketing, trade shows, as well as interviews with successful craft artisans Jonathan Adler, Lotta Jansdotter, Denyse Schmidt and Jill Bliss.

46322 ■ "Datebook" in *Crain's Chicago Business* (Vol. 31, April 28, 2008, No. 17, pp. 18)

Pub: Crain Communications, Inc.

Description: Listing of events in the Detroit area include conferences addressing entrepreneurialism, economic development, and women business ownership.

46323 ■ "Datran Media Executives to Lead Industry Debates Across Q1 Conferences" in *Internet Wire* (January 22, 2010)

Pub: Comtex News Network, Inc.

Description: Datran Media, an industry-leading digital marketing technology company, will be sending members of its management team to several conferences in the early part of the first quarter of 2010; discussions will include Internet marketing innovations, e-commerce and media distribution.

46324 ■ "Designing Events Updates Online Suite" in *Wireless News* (October 25, 2009)

Pub: Close-Up Media

Description: Designing Events, an outsourcing and consulting firm for conferences and meetings, announced the release of an update to its Designing Events Online suite of web-based management and marketing tools; features include enhanced versions of online registration and collaboration, content management, session development, social media and conference websites.

46325 ■ "Detroit Hosts Conferences on Green Building, IT, Finance" in *Crain's Detroit Business* (Vol. 25, June 1, 2009, No. 22, pp. 9)

Pub: Crain Communications Inc. - Detroit

Ed: Tom Henderson. **Description:** Detroit will host three conferences in June 2009, one features green technology, one information technology and the third will gather black bankers and financial experts from across the nation.

46326 ■ "Developer Banks On East Submarket, Slowdown Not a Hinderance" in *The Business Journal-Serving Greater Tampa Bay* (August 1, 2008)

Pub: American City Business Journals, Inc.

Ed: Janet Leiser. **Description:** CLW Industrial Group and Cobalt Industrial REIT II have teamed up to develop a 14-acre area in northeast Hillsborough County, Florida. The $15 million industrial park project includes the 175,000-square-foot New Tampa Commerce Center, scheduled for completion in the first quarter of 2009.

46327 ■ "Developers Await Hotel" in *The Business Journal-Portland* (Vol. 25, July 11, 2008, No. 18, pp. 1)

Pub: American City Business Journals, Inc.

Ed: Wendy Culverwell. **Description:** Developers are eager to start the construction of a new hotel at the Oregon Convention Center in Portland, Oregon as hey say that the project will help boost the convention center neighborhood. The project, called The Westin Portland at the Convention Center, is partly handled by Ashforth Pacific Inc.

46328 ■ "The Display Group Is Super-Sized" in *Michigan Vue* (Vol. 13, July-August 2008, No. 4, pp. 34)

Pub: Entrepreneur Media Inc.

Description: Profile of the Display Group, located in downtown Detroit, this company provides custom designed mobile marketing displays as well as special event production services for trade show displays. The rental house and design service is also beginning to see more business due to the film initiative, which provides incentives for films that are shooting in Michigan.

46329 ■ "Dow Champions Innovative Energy Solutions for Auto Industry at NAIAS" in *Business of Global Warming* **(January 25, 2010, pp. 7)**
Pub: Investment Weekly News
Description: This year's North American International Auto Show in Detroit will host the "Electric Avenue" exhibit sponsored by the Dow Chemical Company. The display will showcase the latest in innovative energy solutions from Dow as well as electric vehicles and the technology supporting them. This marks the first time a non-automotive manufacturer is part of the main floor of the show.

46330 ■ "Downtowns Must Court Young, CEOs for Cities President Says" in *Crain's Detroit Business* **(Vol. 24, October 6, 2008, No. 40, pp. 18)**
Pub: Crain Communications, Inc.
Ed: Amy Lane. **Description:** It is important to produce more college graduates, and keep them in Michigan, according to CEOs for Cities President Carol Coletta when she spoke to a session at the West Michigan Regional Policy Conference which was held in September in Grand Rapids. Ways in which city leaders can connect students to communities, resulting in employees who have vested interest in the region, are also discussed.

46331 ■ "The Early Bird Gets the Worm" in *Black Enterprise* **(Vol. 37, January 2007, No. 6, pp. 111)**
Pub: Earl G. Graves Publishing Co. Inc.
Ed: Tykisha N. Lundy. **Description:** General Motors hosts the Black Enterprise Conference And Expo: Where Deals Are Made at Walt Disney World's Swan and Dolphin Resort, May 9-12. The conference will offer great information to entrepreneurs.

46332 ■ "East-Side Real Estate Forum Detours To Grand Rapids" in *Crain's Detroit Business* **(Vol. 24, October 6, 2008, No. 40, pp. 17)**
Pub: Crain Communications, Inc.
Ed: Daniel Duggan. **Description:** Tom Wackerman was elected chairman of the University of Michigan-Urban Land Institute Real Estate Forum and proposed that the annual conference be held in Grand Rapids due to the brisk economic activity he was finding there; although the idea was initially met with resistance, the plan to introduce East-siders to the West side began receiving more enthusiasm due to the revitalization of the area, which was once considered to have a bleak outlook. Many are hoping to learn the lessons of those who were able to change a negative economic climate into a positive one in which the cooperation of private business and government can work together to accomplish goals.

46333 ■ "Economy Forcing Meeting Planners to Think Fast" in *Crain's Cleveland Business* **(Vol. 30, June 15, 2009, No. 23, pp. 15)**
Pub: Crain Communications, Inc.
Ed: Amy Ann Stoessel. **Description:** Meeting planners are working hard to meet lower corporate budgets when planning events.

46334 ■ "Entrepreneurs Conference" in *Black Enterprise* **(Vol. 38, February 2008, No. 7, pp. 163)**
Pub: Earl G. Graves Publishing Co. Inc.
Description: Black Enterprise Entrepreneurs Conference and Expo will be held May 14-17, 2008 at the Charlotte Westin Hotel and Charlotte Convention Center in North Carolina. Entrepreneurs are given the opportunity to present their business ideas in the Bevator Pitch Competition for a chance to win products and services.

46335 ■ "Events Struggling with Fees" in *Philadelphia Business Journal* **(Vol. 28, November 20, 2009, No. 40, pp. 1)**
Pub: American City Business Journals
Ed: Peter van Allen. **Description:** Dad Vail Regatta organizers told Philadelphia officials their plans to move the rowing event out of Philadelphia into Rum-

son, New Jersey was due to rising fees from the city and the loss of corporate sponsorship. Smaller events have been left out of funding or transferred to other locations due, in part, to higher fees also.

46336 ■ "Facebook, Adobe, Kenshoo, Outright and Cignex Datamatics Sign On to X.commerce" in *Entertainment Close-Up* **(October 24, 2011)**
Pub: Close-Up Media
Description: Facebook, Adobe, Kenshoo, Outright and Cignex Datamatics have all partnered with X.commerce's ecosystem, where developers build and merchants can come to shop for new technologies and services.

46337 ■ "Finding Room for Financing" in *The Business Journal-Serving Metropolitan Kansas City* **(Vol. 26, August 1, 2008, No. 47, pp. 1)**
Pub: American City Business Journals, Inc.
Ed: Rob Roberts. **Description:** Kansas City officials are expecting to receive financing recommendations for a new 1,000-room convention headquarters hotel. The $300-million project could be financed either through private ownership with public subsidies, or through public ownership with tax-exempt bond financing. Other views and information on the project and its expected economic impact, are presented.

46338 ■ "Four Exhibition Considerations" in *American Printer* **(Vol. 128, August 1, 2011, No. 8)**
Pub: Penton Media Inc.
Description: Four questions to ask at the Graph Expo will help printers improve their own business.

46339 ■ "Grainger Show Highlights Building Green, Economy" in *Contractor* **(Vol. 57, February 2010, No. 2, pp. 3)**
Pub: Penton Media, Inc.
Ed: Candace Roulo. **Description:** chief U.S. economist told attendees of the Grainger's 2010 Total MRO Solutions National Customer Show that the economic recovery would be subdued. Mechanical contractors who attended the event also learned about building sustainable, green products, and technologies, and economic and business challenges.

46340 ■ "Grand Action Makes Grand Changes in Grand Rapids" in *Crain's Detroit Business* **(Vol. 25, June 1, 2009, No. 22, pp. M012)**
Pub: Crain Communications Inc. - Detroit
Ed: Amy Lane. **Description:** Businessman Dick DeVos believes that governments are not always the best to lead certain initiatives. That's why, in 1991, he gathered 50 west Michigan community leaders and volunteers to look consider the construction of an arena and expanding or renovating local convention operations. Grand Action has undertaken four major projects in the city.

46341 ■ "Half a World Away" in *Tampa Bay Business Journal* **(Vol. 30, December 4, 2009, No. 50, pp. 1)**
Pub: American City Business Journals
Ed: Jane Meinhardt. **Description:** Enterprise Florida has offered four trade grants for Florida's marine industry businesses to give them a chance to tap into the Middle East market at the Dubai International Boat Show on March 9 to 13, 2010. The grants pay for 50 percent of the exhibition costs for the qualifying business.

46342 ■ "Here's the Deal" in *Crain's Cleveland Business* **(Vol. 30, June 15, 2009, No. 23, pp. 14)**
Pub: Crain Communications, Inc.
Description: Incentives being offered by hotels, restaurants, golf courses and major chains in order to promote bookings for meetings or conferences in the Cleveland area are listed.

46343 ■ "Herrell's Launches New Corporate Identity at Fancy Food Show" in *Ice Cream Reporter* **(Vol. 23, July 20, 2010, No. 8, pp. 3)**
Pub: Ice Cream Reporter
Description: Herrell's ice cream introduced a new corporate branding at the Summer 2010 Fancy Food

Show last summer. Slightly Mad Communications advertising agency developed the new brand to reflect the era of the early 1970s.

46344 ■ "Hotel Tax Eyed For Waukesha" in *The Business Journal-Milwaukee* **(Vol. 25, August 29, 2008, No. 49, pp. A1)**
Pub: American City Business Journals, Inc.
Ed: Rich Kirchen. **Description:** Midwest Airlines Center chairman Frank Gimbel wants Waukesha County to help in the funding of the $200-million expansion of the convention center through a hotel room tax. The Waukesha hotel industry is expected to oppose the new room tax. Other views and information on the planned new room tax in Waukesha are presented.

46345 ■ "How to Declutter Your Life Closet Cleanup: Putting a Lid on Clutter" in *Atlanta Journal-Constitution* **(May 1, 2011)**
Pub: Atlanta Journal-Constitution
Ed: Felicia Feaster. **Description:** The annual Closets and Home Organization Convention and Expo spotlights new products and services designed to help people get organized at home or the workplace. The organization sector is holding steady despite the recession and is expected to expand into garage organization.

46346 ■ "IFA-AAG Professional Athlete Franchise Summit Scores" in *Franchising World* **(Vol. 42, August 2010, No. 8, pp. 56)**
Pub: International Franchise Association
Ed: Miriam L. Brewer. **Description:** The first International Franchise Association-Allied Athlete Group Franchise summit spotlighted athletes turned business owners addressing peers on franchising. The summit is expected to become an annual event.

46347 ■ "Industry/Events 2011" in *American Printer* **(Vol. 128, July 1, 2011, No. 7)**
Pub: Penton Media Inc.
Description: PMA, the Worldwide Community of Imaging Association launched its new CliQ with how-to tips, product reviews and monthly photo contests. PMA formed a partnership with the Consumer Electronics Association to make changes to this year's annual convention.

46348 ■ "IPEX Moves to London Venue" in *American Printer* **(Vol. 128, July 1, 2011, No. 7)**
Pub: Penton Media Inc.
Description: IPES 2014 is being relocated to London's ExCeL International Exhibition and Conference Centre from March 26 to April 2, 2014.

46349 ■ "Javo Beverage to Feature On-Demand Coffee System" in *GlobeNewswire* **(October 20, 2009)**
Pub: Comtex News Network, Inc.
Description: During the National Association of Convenience Store Show (NACS) at the Las Vegas Convention Center, Javo Beverage Company, Inc., a leading provider of premium dispensable coffee and tea-based beverages to the foodservice industry, will introduce its on-demand hot coffee system as well as a new line of products for the convenience store industry.

46350 ■ "Jay Berkowitz to Present Making Social Media Money Seminar at Affiliate Summit West" in *Entertainment Close-Up* **(January 15, 2010)**
Pub: Close-Up Media
Description: Highlights of Jay Berkowitz's conference, "Making Social Media Make Money" include ways in which to develop Internet marketing strategies that will maximize Website traffic and convert that traffic to sales.

46351 ■ "Kent Officials Seek Further KSU, City Unity" in *Crain's Cleveland Business* **(Vol. 28, December 3, 2007, No. 48, pp. 3)**
Pub: Crain Communications, Inc.
Ed: Jay Miller. **Description:** Kent State University and Portage County are searching for a developer who will use a three-acre parcel to bring new life to the city's sagging downtown and create an area that

will better link the town and the Kent State campus. The project will include a hotel and conference center as well as retail and restaurant space.

46352 ■ **"Kuno Creative to Present B2B Social Media Campaign Webinar" in** *Entertainment Close-Up* **(August 25, 2011)**
Pub: Close-Up Media

Description: Kuno Creative, an inbound marketing agency, will host Three Steps of a Successful B2B Social Media Campaign. The firm is a provider of Website development, branding, marketing strategy, public relations, Internet marketing, and inbound marketing.

46353 ■ **"Let's Put On a Show" in** *Inc.* **(November 2007, pp. 127)**
Pub: Gruner & Jahr USA Publishing

Ed: Elaine Appleton Grant. **Description:** Profile of Jeff Baker, CEO of Image 4, designer of trade show exhibits. Baker shares details of the firm's commitment to being green.

46354 ■ **"Local Green Technology on Display" in** *Crain's Detroit Business* **(Vol. 26, January 18, 2010, No. 3, pp. 1)**
Pub: Crain Communications, Inc.

Ed: Ryan Beene. **Description:** Detroit's 2010 North American International Auto Show put the newest, most innovative green technologies on display showing that the Southeast Michigan automobile industry is gaining traction with its burgeoning e-vehicle infrastructure. Think, a Norwegian electric city-car manufacturer is eyeing sites in Southeast Michigan in which to locate its corporate headquarters and technical center for its North American branch.

46355 ■ **"Look, Leap, and License" in** *Retail Merchandiser* **(Vol. 51, July-August 2011, No. 4, pp. 16)**
Pub: Phoenix Media Corporation

Description: Toys highlighting the Licensing International Expo 2011 included a life-sized Cookie Monster, Papa Smurf, Power Rangers, Transformer, and margarita wrestlers. Taking licensed properties international was a common theme at this year's show.

46356 ■ *Mail Order in the Internet Age*
Pub: Morgan James Publishing, LLC

Ed: Ted Ciuba. **Released:** May 2004. **Price:** $19.95. **Description:** Direct response market, or mail order, for marketing and selling a product or service is discussed, with emphasis on how direct marketing compares favorably to other methods in terms of speed, ease, profitability, and affordability. Advice is given for writing ads; seminars to attend; and newsletters, mailing lists and magazines in which to subscribe.

46357 ■ **"Major Golf Retail Show in the Rough for 2010" in** *Orlando Business Journal* **(Vol. 26, January 15, 2010, No. 33, pp. 1)**
Pub: American City Business Journals

Ed: Anjali Fluker. **Description:** The 57th Annual PGA Merchandise Show in Orlando, Florida is projected to attract 39,000 attendees in 2010, compared with 41,000 in 2009. According to the Orange County Convention Center, economic benefits that could be obtained from the 2010 edition of the golf retail show might reach only $77 million, compared with $78 million generated last year.

46358 ■ **"MANAfest Provides Reps with Tools for the Future" in** *Agency Sales Magazine* **(Vol. 39, September-October 2009, No. 9, pp. 36)**
Pub: MANA

Ed: Jack Foster. **Description:** Former Harley Davidson director of communications Ken Schmidt was the keynote speaker at the MANAfest conference; he discussed how the company delivered itself from bankruptcy. Selling Power magazine publisher Gerhard Gschwandtner also made a presentation; he believes that there will be opportunities for sales people involved in relationship selling.

46359 ■ **"Minnesota ABC Event Looks at Government Contracting" in** *Finance and Commerce Daily Newspaper* **(November 23, 2010)**
Pub: Dolan Media Newswires

Ed: Brian Johnson. **Description:** Minnesota Associated Builders and Contractors hosted an event focusing on doing business with government agencies. Topics included bidding work, awarding jobs, paperwork, guidelines, certifications and upcoming projects.

46360 ■ **"More Than 1,000 Attend Second WaterSmart" in** *Contractor* **(Vol. 56, November 2009, No. 11, pp. 3)**
Pub: Penton Media, Inc.

Description: Over 1,000 plumbing and water conservation professionals attended the second WaterSmart Innovations Conference and Exposition in Las Vegas. Plumbing industry personalities made presentations during the conference and several innovative products were displayed at the trade show.

46361 ■ **"Nobody Knows What To Do" in** *Barron's* **(Vol. 88, March 17, 2008, No. 11, pp. 40)**
Pub: Dow Jones & Company, Inc.

Ed: Mark Veverka. **Description:** Attendees of the South by Southwest Interactive conference failed to get an insight on how to make money on the Web from former Walt Disney CEO Michael Eisner when Eisner said there's no proven business model for financing projects. Eisner said he finances his projects with the help of his connections to get product-placement deals.

46362 ■ **"Norvax University Health Insurance Sales Training and Online Marketing Conference" in** *Internet Wire* **(January 27, 2010)**
Pub: Comtex News Network, Inc.

Description: Overview of the Norvax University Marketing and Sales Success Conference Tour which includes insurance sales training seminars, proven and innovative online marketing techniques and a host of additional information and networking opportunities.

46363 ■ **"Not Enough Room" in** *Austin Business JournalInc.* **(Vol. 29, November 13, 2009, No. 36, pp. A1)**
Pub: American City Business Journals

Ed: Jacob Dirr. **Description:** Hotel and convention business in downtown Austin, Texas lost nearly $5.3 million when Dell Inc. relocated its annual convention to Las Vegas. However, lack of capital caused the postponement of various hotel projects which need to be finished in order to attract well-attended conventions. Makeover projects on Austin's Waller Creek and Sixth Street are discussed.

46364 ■ **"Now See This" in** *Entrepreneur* **(Vol. 36, April 2008, No. 4, pp. 53)**
Pub: Entrepreneur Media, Inc.

Ed: Mike Hogan. **Description:** New high definition (HD) products are to be introduced in 2008 at the Consumer Electronics Show and the Macworld Conference & Expo. HD lineup from companies such as Dell Inc. and Hewlett-Packard Co. are discussed.

46365 ■ **"Nowspeed and OneSource to Conduct Webinar" in** *Internet Wire* **(December 14, 2009)**
Pub: Comtex News Network, Inc.

Description: OneSource, a leading provider of global business information, and Nowspeed, an Internet marketing agency, will conduct a webinar titled "How to Develop Social Media Content That Gets Results" in order to provide marketers insight into how to develop and optimize effective social media content to get consumer results that translate into purchases and lead generation.

46366 ■ **"Nowspeed's David Reske to Speak at SolidWorks World 2010 in Anaheim" in** *Internet Wire* **(January 7, 2010)**
Pub: Comtex News Network, Inc.

Description: David Reske, managing director at Nowspeed, an Internet marketing agency based in the Boston area, will be presenting at SolidWorks World 2010; the convention's presentation will focus on proven methodologies, practical tips and real-world case studies in order to help attendees leverage the powerful Internet marketing innovations that are proving effective for businesses.

46367 ■ **"O'Loughlin Cuts $6 Million for Chesterfield Doubletree" in** *Saint Louis Business Journal* **(Vol. 32, September 2, 2011, No. 1, pp. 1)**
Pub: Saint Louis Business Journal

Ed: Angela Mueller. **Description:** Lodging Hospitality Management (LHM) acquired the Doubletree Hotel and Conference Center in Chesterfield, Missouri and added it as the 18th hotel in its portfolio. LHM chairman and CEO Bob O'Loughlin plans to invest nearly $15 million in the hotel, including $9 for renovation.

46368 ■ **"One World" in** *American Printer* **(Vol. 128, August 1, 2011, No. 8)**
Pub: Penton Media Inc.

Description: Graph Expo will highlight entrepreneurs focused on the connection between content, technology and business models.

46369 ■ **"The Open Mobile Summit Opens in San Francisco Today: John Donahoe CEO eBay to Keynote" in** *Benzinga.com* **(November 2, 2011)**
Pub: Benzinga.com

Ed: Benzinga Staff. **Description:** eBay's CEO, John Donahoe was keynote speaker at the 4th Annual Open Mobile Summit held in San Francisco, California. eBay is one of the 130 companies participating as speakers at the event.

46370 ■ **"Other First Place Winners From the Expo" in** *Ice Cream Reporter* **(Vol. 23, September 20, 2010, No. 10, pp. 8)**
Pub: Ice Cream Reporter

Description: Sassy Cow Creamery, Columbus, Wisconsin; Stewarts, Saratoga Springs, New York; Purity Dairies, Nashville, Tennessee; Kemps, Cedarburg, Wisconsin, and Kelly Country Creamery also won first place awards for various categories at the 2010 World Dairy Expo.

46371 ■ **"People/Calendar" in** *Brandweek* **(Vol. 49, April 21, 2008, No. 16, pp. 30)**
Pub: VNU Business Media, Inc.

Description: Listing of current conferences, tradeshows and events concerning the marketing industry.

46372 ■ **"People and Places" in** *Entrepreneur* **(Vol. 36, February 2008, No. 2, pp. 12)**
Pub: Entrepreneur Media Inc.

Ed: Rieva Lesonsky. **Description:** Websites of different organizations that can provide entrepreneurs with business help are presented. Business-related events such as the Women in Charge conference and Xerox Smart Business Symposium are mentioned.

46373 ■ **"PHCC Convention, Show Gets High Marks" in** *Contractor* **(Vol. 56, December 2009, No. 12, pp. 1)**
Pub: Penton Media, Inc.

Ed: Robert P. Mader. **Description:** Plumbing-Heating-Cooling Contractors National Association has held its first convention and trade show in New Orleans, Louisiana. Attendees were treated to a variety of seminars and exhibitors during the event. Comments from event organizers are also given.

46374 ■ **"Pipe Show Finds a Way for Smokers to Light Up" in** *Crain's Chicago Business* **(Vol. 31, April 28, 2008, No. 17, pp. 57)**
Pub: Crain Communications, Inc.

Ed: H. Lee Murphy. **Description:** With the help of attorneys within its local membership of 150 pipe collectors, the Chicagoland Pipe Collectors Club will be allowed to smoke at its 13th International Pipe & Tobacciana Show at Pheasant Run Resort. The event is expected to draw 4,000 pipe enthusiasts from as far as China and Russia.

46375 ■ **"Plan Your Next Event at Newport News Marriott at City Center" in** *Benzinga.com* **(July 29, 2011)**
Pub: Benzinga.com

Ed: Benzinga Staff. **Description:** Newport News Marriott at City Center is promoting itself as the premier venue for business meetings, conventions and weddings.

46376 ■ **"Plumbing, Heating Products Shine at Greenbuild"** in *Contractor* (Vol. 57, January 2010, No. 1, pp. 3)
Pub: Penton Media, Inc.

Ed: Robert P. Mader. **Description:** Among the many exhibitors at Greenbuild 2009 was T&S Brass which showcased their low-flow pre-rinse spray valves and Watts Water Technologies which showed off their hot water recirculating system. Aquatherm and Acorn Engineering were also at the show.

46377 ■ **"Plumbing, Heating Products Shine at Greenbuild Expo"** in *Contractor* (Vol. 56, December 2009, No. 12, pp. 1)
Pub: Penton Media, Inc.

Ed: Robert P. Mader. **Description:** Greenbuild Show held in Phoenix, Arizona has showcased the latest in plumbing and heating products. Zurn displayed its EcoVantage line of fixtures and valves during the event. Meanwhile, Sloan Valve offered its washdown 1-pint/flush Alphine urinal.

46378 ■ **"Polite Conversation"** in *Mergers & Acquisitions: The Dealmaker's Journal* (March 1, 2008)
Pub: SourceMedia, Inc.

Description: In January, industry leaders and dealmakers met at Davos to discuss topics ranging from the possibility of a recession to what lies ahead in the deal market.

46379 ■ **"Prepping for the Unpredictable"** in *Crain's Cleveland Business* (Vol. 30, June 15, 2009, No. 23, pp. 16)
Pub: Crain Communications, Inc.

Ed: Joel Hammond. **Description:** Michael Ferrara, event planner and designer for Executive Caterers discusses the many events he has planned.

46380 ■ **"Proposal for a Macomb County Visitors Bureau Draws Mixed Reaction"** in *Crain's Detroit Business* (Vol. 24, March 31, 2008, No. 13)
Pub: Crain Communications, Inc.

Ed: Chad Halcom. **Description:** Discusses the newly formed M-59 Corridor Business Association and its proposal to create a convention and visitors bureau dedicated to the county's interests.

46381 ■ **"Real-Life Coursework for Real-Life Business People"** in *Women In Business* (Vol. 63, Summer 2011, No. 2, pp. 22)
Pub: American Business Women's Association

Ed: Leigh Elmore. **Description:** American Business Women's Association National Women's Leadership Conference provides members with academic business training courses. Members can take a variety of MBA-level courses that are taught by University of Kansas School of Business professors. Courses include marketing, management, leadership and communication and decision making.

46382 ■ **"Renren Partners With Recruit to Launch Social Wedding Services"** in *Benzinga.com* (June 7, 2011)
Pub: Benzinga.com

Ed: Benzinga Staff. **Description:** Renren Inc. and Recruit Company Ltd. partnered to build a wedding social media catering to engaged couples and newlyweds in China. The platform will integrate online wedding related social content and offline media such as magazine and wedding exhibitions.

46383 ■ **"Rock Festival: High Spirited Conventioneers Celebrate Their Good Fortune"** in *Canadian Business* (Vol. 81, March 31, 2008, No. 5)
Pub: Rogers Media

Ed: Jeff Sanford. **Description:** Soaring prices of commodities in the mining industry have been very good for the attendees of the 76th annual conference of the Prospectors & Developers Association of Canada. A speaker at the conference expects commodity prices to come off a bit but not fall dramatically as it did in the 1980's.

46384 ■ **"RPA Preps for Building Radiant Conference, Show"** in *Contractor* (Vol. 57, January 2010, No. 1, pp. 5)
Pub: Penton Media, Inc.

Description: Radiant Panel Association is accepting registrations for its Building Radiant 2010 Conference and Trade Show. The conference will discuss radiant heating as well as insurance and other legal matters for mechanical contractors.

46385 ■ **"A Safe Bet"** in *Entrepreneur* (Vol. 35, October 2007, No. 10, pp. 26)
Pub: Entrepreneur Media Inc.

Ed: Carol Tice. **Description:** U.S. Department of Defense has developed a program, called the Defense Venture Catalyst Initiative or DeVenCI, that will match defense officials to the products that they need. DeVenCI uses conferences to showcase the defense contractors and their technologies to defense managers. Details of how this program helps both contractors and defense officials are overviewed.

46386 ■ **"Save the Date"** in *Barron's* (Vol. 90, September 13, 2010, No. 37, pp. 35)
Pub: Barron's Editorial & Corporate Headquarters

Ed: Mark Veverka. **Description:** Mark Hurd is the new Co-President of Oracle after being forced out at Hewlett-Packard where he faced a harassment complaint. HP fired Hurd due to expense account malfeasance. Hurd is also set to speak at an Oracle trade show in San Francisco on September 20, 2010.

46387 ■ **"Save the Date"** in *Mergers & Acquisitions: The Dealmaker's Journal* (March 1, 2008)
Pub: SourceMedia, Inc.

Description: Listing of conferences and forums that deal with business and investing, particularly with mergers and acquisitions. Includes dates, locations and Internet addresses.

46388 ■ **"Secrets To Trade Show Success"** in *Women Entrepreneur* (September 12, 2008)
Pub: Entrepreneur Media Inc.

Ed: Lesley Spencer Pyle. **Description:** Trade shows require an enormous amount of work, but they are an investment that can pay off handsomely because they allow a business to get their product or service in front of their target market. Advice regarding trade shows is given including selecting the correct venue, researching the affair and following up on leads obtained at the event.

46389 ■ **"Sherwin-Williams Workers Forgo Travel for Virtual Trade Show"** in *Crain's Cleveland Business* (Vol. 28, October 15, 2007, No. 41)
Pub: Crain Communications, Inc.

Ed: John Booth. **Description:** Overview of Cyber-Coating 2007, a cutting-edge virtual three-dimensional trade show that exhibitors such as Sherwin-Williams Co.'s Chemical Coatings Division will take part in by chatting verbally or via text messages in order to exchange information and listen to pitches just like they would on an actual trade show floor.

46390 ■ **"Show Dates"** in *Art Business News* (Vol. 34, November 2007, No. 11, pp. 18)
Pub: Pfingsten Publishing, LLC

Description: Listing of conferences, trade shows and gallery openings for artists and those in the art industry.

46391 ■ **"Silverdome Bidders Bring New Proposals"** in *Crain's Detroit Business* (Vol. 24, March 17, 2008, No. 11, pp. 23)
Pub: Crain Communications, Inc.

Ed: Daniel Duggan. **Description:** Discusses the seven plans which have been proposed as part of the third round of bidding for the Pontiac Silverdome; proposals range from Global Baseball Inc., a baseball league that would pit a team from every country against one another, to an Indian casino, a musical "hall of fame", a convention center, a horse track, a hotel and an indoor water park.

46392 ■ **"Six Tips To Maximize Networking Opportunities"** in *Women Entrepreneur* (November 3, 2008)
Pub: Entrepreneur Media Inc.

Ed: Tamara Monosoff. **Description:** Networking events fall into the realm of business development as opposed to immediate sales opportunities. It is important to remember that these events provide a chance to build relationships that may someday help one's business. Tips to help make the most out of networking events are provided.

46393 ■ **"Social Media Event Slated for March 25"** in *Bellingham Business Journal* (Vol. February 2010, pp. 3)
Pub: Sound Publishing Inc.

Description: Center for Economic Vitality (CEV) and the Technology Alliance Group (TAG) will host the 2010 Social Media Conference at the McIntyre Hall Performing Arts & Conference Center in Mt. Vernon, Washington. The event will provide networking opportunities for attendees.

46394 ■ **"Speak Better: Five Tips for Polished Presentations"** in *Women Entrepreneur* (September 19, 2008)
Pub: Entrepreneur Media Inc.

Ed: Suzannah Baum. **Description:** Successful entrepreneurs agree that exemplary public speaking skills are among the core techniques needed to propel their business forward. A well-delivered presentation can result in securing a new distribution channel, gaining new customers, locking into a new referral stream or receiving extra funding.

46395 ■ **"Sponsorship, Booths Available for Spring Business Showcase"** in *Bellingham Business Journal* (Vol. February 2010, pp. 3)
Pub: Sound Publishing Inc.

Description: Third Annual Spring Business Showcase still have space available for vendors and sponsors. The event gives local businesses the opportunity to increase their visibility and provides a means to increase sales and build relationships.

46396 ■ **"State of a Fair!"** in *Small Business Opportunities* (March 2008)
Pub: Harris Publications Inc.

Ed: Shelly Buss. **Description:** State fairs are money-making venues; one company made $2 million in 12 days at the Minnesota State Fair.

46397 ■ **"State Fairgrounds Adding Year-Round Attractions"** in *Crain's Detroit Business* (Vol. 24, February 18, 2008, No. 7, pp. 17)
Pub: Crain Communications Inc. - Detroit

Ed: Robert Ankeny. **Description:** Michigan State Fairgrounds and Exposition Center shares its plans to become a year-round recreation, entertainment and education center.

46398 ■ **"Success Products"** in *Black Enterprise* (Vol. 37, February 2007, No. 7, pp. 135)
Pub: Earl G. Graves Publishing Co. Inc.

Ed: Tanisha A. Sykes. **Description:** Using innovative resources that are already at your fingertips instead of trying to reach out to companies first is a great way to discover whether you have a viable idea or product. Be motivated to start an e-newsletter letting people know about your products and attend conferences like The Motivation Show, the world's largest exhibition of motivational products and services related to performance in business.

46399 ■ **"Tax-Free Zones Need Shows; Out-of-State Shoppers Are Key To Success"** in *Crain's Detroit Business* (Vol. 24, January 28, 2008, No. 4)
Pub: Crain Communications Inc. - Detroit

Ed: Daniel Duggan. **Description:** Sales tax-free zones are being considered by Michigan's legislators in order to promote the state as a conference destination.

46400 ■ "Teachable Moments: Worth Every Penny" in *Pet Product News* **(Vol. 64, December 2010, No. 12, pp. 34)**
Pub: BowTie Inc.
Ed: Cheryl Reeves. **Description:** Pet bird retailers can attain both outreach to customers and enhanced profitability by staging educational events such as the annual Parrot Palooza event of Burlington, New Jersey-based Bird Paradise. Aside from attracting a global audience, Parrot Palooza features seminars, workshops, classes, and bird-related contests.

46401 ■ "Tic-Tac-Show" in *American Printer* **(Vol. 128, August 1, 2011, No. 8)**
Pub: Penton Media Inc.
Description: Graph Expo has become the US print industry's main event. There will be as many as 500 exhibitors at this year's event and the Graphic Arts Show Company lists over 30 co-located events as well as 53 new sessions in the seminar program's 28 education categories.

46402 ■ "Tightening Economy Squeezes Business Travel" in *HRMagazine* **(Vol. 53, August 2008, No. 8, pp. 19)**
Pub: Society for Human Resource Management
Ed: Kathy Gurchiek. **Description:** New surveys show that some companies are not cutting out business travel, they are using cheaper hotels and cutting back on trade shows and conference travel. Statistical data included.

46403 ■ "Tool Time" in *Entrepreneur* **(Vol. 36, March 2008, No. 3, pp. 90)**
Pub: Entrepreneur Media Inc.
Ed: Nichole A. Torres. **Description:** DaVinci Institute holds an annual event in Colorado to display new products and inventions. Innovative Design Engineering Animation is a consulting company that helps inventors develop product through various stages. NineSigma Inc. has an online marketplace where inventors can post ideas for clients needing new products.

46404 ■ "Tourism Bureau Seeks Hotel Tax Hike" in *Baltimore Business Journal* **(Vol. 27, December 18, 2009, No. 32, pp. 1)**
Pub: American City Business Journals
Ed: Rachel Bernstein. **Description:** Baltimore, Maryland's tourism agency, Visit Baltimore, has proposed a new hotel tax that could produce $2 million annually for its marketing budget, fund improvements to the city's 30-year-old convention center and help it compete for World Cup soccer games. Baltimore hotel leaders discuss the new tax.

46405 ■ *Trade Shows Worldwide*
Pub: Gale
Released: Annual, Latest edition 30th, April 2012. **Price:** $645, individuals. **Covers:** Over 10,000 trade shows and exhibitions, including those held at conferences, conventions, meetings, trade and industrial events, merchandise marts, and national expositions; 6,000 trade show sponsors and organizers; of trade show facilities, services, and information sources, approximately 5,900 conference and convention centers, about 600 visitor and convention bureaus, 400 World Trade Centers; sources of information for the trade show industry, including professional associations, consulting organizations, and publications; and 1,900 trade show industry service suppliers. **Entries Include:** name, address, phone, fax, e-mail, website, toll-free, phone, fax, name and title of contact; show frequency; founding date; audience; number of attendees; price for display space; description of exhibits; registration fees; industry programs; social events; square feet/meters of exhibition space; number of meeting rooms needed; number of hotel rooms and nights needed; publications, dates and locations of future shows. **Arrangement:** Separate sections for shows and exhibitions, for sponsors/organizers, and for trade show facilities, services, and information sources. **Indexes:** Chronological (show date), geographical (show location), subject, name and keyword.

46406 ■ "Tradeshow Attendance Incentives Add Up" in *Pet Product News* **(Vol. 64, December 2010, No. 12, pp. 14)**
Pub: BowTie Inc.
Ed: Mark E. Battersby. **Description:** Pointers on how pet specialty retailers can claim business travel tax and income tax deductions for expenses paid or incurred in participation at tradeshows, conventions, and meetings are presented. Incentives in form of these deductions could allow pet specialty retailers to gain business benefits, aside from the education and enjoyment involved with the travel.

46407 ■ *The Tradeshow Week Calendar*
Pub: Tradeshow Week Inc.
Contact: Adam Schaffer, Publisher
E-mail: aschaffer@reedbusiness.com
Released: Annual, Latest edition December, 2003. **Price:** $10; Free. **Publication Includes:** About 100 major North American trade shows and expositions for a one-week period six months from the date of the issue and one year from date of the issue; overseas trade shows and expositions for a one-week period eight months from the date of the issue. **Entries Include:** Exposition name, dates, location, frequency of meeting, number of booths, number of companies exhibiting in show, expected attendance, name, address, phone and fax of show management. Principal content of publication is news and statistics on the tradeshow industry. **Arrangement:** Chronological.

46408 ■ *Tradeshow Week Data Book*
Pub: Tradeshow Week Inc.
Contact: Larry Dunn, Publisher
E-mail: ldunn@reedbusiness.com
Released: Annual, Latest edition 2010. **Price:** $305, individuals plus $25 shipping and handling. **Covers:** Nearly 5,300 trade and public shows with at least 5,000 net square feet of exhibit space scheduled in the United States and Canada up to five years from publication date. **Entries Include:** Show title, show management and sponsor, show description, location, dates, general contractor, estimated net square feet of exhibit space, number and profile of exhibitors and participants, fees, associated seminars, meetings and conferences, show history, future dates and sites. **Arrangement:** Classified by industry category. **Indexes:** Geographical, alphabetical, chronological, show management, show size, rotation pattern, new shows.

46409 ■ "Travel Tears" in *Crain's Chicago Business* **(Vol. 31, November 17, 2008, No. 46, pp. 3)**
Pub: Crain Communications, Inc.
Ed: Bob Tita. **Description:** Hotels, restaurants and conventions are seeing a decline in profits due to corporate travel cutbacks and the sagging economy. City and state revenues derived from taxes on tourism-related industries are also suffering.

46410 ■ "A Vegas Sensation Inaugural Artexpo Las Vegas" in *Art Business News* **(Vol. 34, November 2007, No. 11, pp. 1)**
Pub: Pfingsten Publishing, LLC
Ed: Jennifer Dulin. **Description:** Overview of the first Artexpo Las Vegas which featured exhibitors, artists and buyers and was a wonderful place for networking.

46411 ■ "Wal-Mart Doesn't Sell Council" in *The Business Journal-Serving Metropolitan Kansas City* **(Vol. 26, July 4, 2008, No. 43, pp. 1)**
Pub: American City Business Journals, Inc.
Ed: Steve Vockrodt. **Description:** Wal-Mart Stores Inc. announced that it will move the location of its annual convention from Kansas City, Missouri to Orlando, Florida. The change of venue came after Rick Hughes, Kansas City Convention and Visitors Association president rejected Wal-Mart's proposal to subsidize a new hotel in the downtown area that is needed for the event.

46412 ■ "The Weeks Ahead" in *Crain's New York Business* **(Vol. 24, January 14, 2008, No. 2, pp. 20)**
Pub: Crain Communications, Inc.
Description: Listing of events in the Detroit area include conferences addressing entrepreneurialism, economic development, and women business ownership.

46413 ■ "Welcome to Babesland" in *Women In Business* **(Vol. 62, June 2010, No. 2, pp. 33)**
Pub: American Business Women's Association
Ed: Leigh Elmore. **Description:** Music group, Four Bitchin' Babes will be performing at the 2010 American Business Women's Association's National Women's Leadership Conference. The group has been in the industry for 20 years and has released nine albums. The Four Bitchin' Babes consist of Sally Fingerett, Nancy Moran, Deirdre Flint, and Debi Smith.

46414 ■ "Women of Power" in *Black Enterprise* **(Vol. 41, November 2010, No. 4, pp. 94)**
Pub: Earl G. Graves Publishing Co. Inc.
Description: Black Enterprise Women of Power Summit will be held February 23-26, 2011 at the Ritz Carlton in Orlando, Florida. Speakers will offer insight on career, household, and life in general.

46415 ■ "Women of Power Summit" in *Black Enterprise* **(Vol. 38, February 2008, No. 7, pp. 163)**
Pub: Earl G. Graves Publishing Co. Inc.
Description: Third annual Women of Power Summit, hosted by State Farm, will host over 700 executive women of color offering empowerment sessions, tips for networking, along with entertainment.

46416 ■ "Worry No. 1 at Auto Show" in *Crain's Detroit Business* **(Vol. 24, January 21, 2008, No. 3, pp. 1)**
Pub: Crain Communications Inc. - Detroit
Ed: Brent Snavely. **Description:** Recession fears clouded activity at the 2008 North American International Auto Show. Automakers are expecting to see a drop in sales due to slow holiday retail spending as well as fallout from the subprime lending crisis.

46417 ■ "WQA's Leadership Conference Tackles Industry Issues" in *Contractor* **(Vol. 56, October 2009, No. 10, pp. 3)**
Pub: Penton Media, Inc.
Ed: Candace Roulo. **Description:** Water Quality Association's Mid-Year Leadership Conference held in Bloomingdale, Illinois in September 2009 tackled lead regulation, water softeners, and product efficiency. The possibility of a WQA green seal was discussed by the Water Sciences Committee and the Government Relations Committee meeting.

46418 ■ "Your Turn in the Spotlight" in *Inc.* **(March 2008, pp. 30)**
Pub: Gruner & Jahr USA Publishing
Ed: Elaine Appleton Grant. **Description:** Profile of a Tennessee business that produces events and concerts. The company offers a complete package of services handling staging, lighting, video, musical instrument rentals, and audio support. The founder has decided to sell the business and details of the asking price, price rationale, the pros and cons of buying the firm and its bottom line are examined.

TRADE PERIODICALS

46419 ■ *Exhibit Builder*
Pub: Exhibit Builder Magazine
Contact: Judy Pomerantz, Managing Editor
E-mail: judyp@exhibitbuilder.net
Released: Periodic, 7/yr. **Price:** $45; $50 Canada; $70 other countries; $90 other countries 2 years.
Description: Magazine covering new product information and research related to the exhibit building, including museums and trade shows.

46420 ■ *Expo*
Pub: EXPO Magazine Inc.
Contact: Donna Sanford, Publisher
E-mail: dsanford@red7media.com
Ed: Danica Tormohlen, Editor, dtormohlen@red7media.com. **Released:** Monthly. **Description:** Trade magazine for those in the exposition industry.

46421 ■ *Successful Meetings*
Pub: Successful Meetings
Contact: Vincent Alonzo, Editor-in-Chief
E-mail: valonzo@ntmllc.com
Released: Monthly. **Price:** $79; $95 Canada; $195 other countries. **Description:** Magazine focusing on conventions, meetings, exhibits, training, trade shows and incentive travel. Includes annual directory issue.

VIDEOCASSETTES/ AUDIOCASSETTES

46422 ■ It'll Be O.K. on the Day
Video Arts, Inc.
c/o Aim Learning Group
8238-40 Lehigh
Morton Grove, IL 60053-2615
Free: 877-444-2230
Fax:(416)252-2155
Co. E-mail: service@aimlearninggroup.com
URL: http://www.aimlearninggroup.com
Released: 1989. **Price:** $695.00. **Description:** Understand the best way to set up an exhibition booth so that it will be most efficient. **Availability:** VHS; 3/4U.

46423 ■ That's Show Business: The Rules of Exhibiting
Video Arts, Inc.
c/o Aim Learning Group
8238-40 Lehigh
Morton Grove, IL 60053-2615
Free: 877-444-2230
Fax:(416)252-2155
Co. E-mail: service@aimlearninggroup.com
URL: http://www.aimlearninggroup.com
Released: 1991. **Price:** $790.00. **Description:** A sensible yet humorous approach to business exhibitions show the most common mistakes and how to avoid them. **Availability:** VHS; 8mm; 3/4U; Special order formats.

46424 ■ The Trade Show Advantage
Creative Training Solutions
5 Timberline Dr.
Voorhees, NJ 08043
Ph:(856)784-3468
Free: 800-515-4114
Fax:(856)784-7087
Co. E-mail: mail@creativetraining.com
URL: http://www.creativetraining.com
Price: $395.00. **Description:** Shows how to set up a booth at a trade show. Includes everything from personal comportment to information on the typical trade show environment. Includes planning guide, handout, and audiocassette. **Availability:** VHS.

46425 ■ Working the Booth: Trade Show Success
American Media, Inc.
4621 121st St.
Urbandale, IA 50323-2311
Ph:(515)224-0919
Free: 888-776-8268
Fax:(515)327-2555
Co. E-mail: custsvc@ammedia.com
URL: http://www.ammedia.com
Released: 1992. **Price:** $395.00. **Description:** Details techniques on successfully setting up and maintaining a booth at a trade show. Stresses etiquette, professionalism, positivity, correct prospect handling, and salesmanship. **Availability:** VHS; 3/4U; 8mm.

TRADE SHOWS AND CONVENTIONS

46426 ■ ABA/BMA National Conference for Community Bankers
American Bankers Association
1120 Connecticut Ave. NW
Washington, DC 20036
Free: 800-BAN-KERS
Co. E-mail: custserv@aba.com
URL: http://www.aba.com
Released: Annual. **Audience:** Chairmen and presidents, mainly of banks with less than $500 million in assets, community bank CEOs, bank directors, and other community bank executives. **Principal Exhibits:** Products and services related to investment management, customer service improvements, advertising, asset/liability management, bank management, electronic data interchange, employee recruitment/training, insurance, strategic planning models, including preparation for the 21st century,

new revenue sources, cost control techniques, mainframe computers, market research, MCIF technology, minicomputers in community banking applications, software: platform, optical disk, and loan pricing, sweep accounts, and relationship banking for community bankers. **Dates and Locations:** 2011 Feb 20-23, San Diego, CA.

46427 ■ ABA Sales Management Workshop
American Bankers Association
1120 Connecticut Ave. NW
Washington, DC 20036
Free: 800-BAN-KERS
Co. E-mail: custserv@aba.com
URL: http://www.aba.com
Released: Annual. **Audience:** Senior community bank executives, marketing directors, mid-level bank retail managers, sales managers. **Principal Exhibits:** Services related to creating and maintaining customers.

46428 ■ American Public Health Association Public Health Expo
American Public Health Association
800 I St. NW
Washington, DC 20001
Ph:(202)777-2742
Fax:(202)777-2534
Co. E-mail: comments@apha.org
URL: http://www.apha.org/
Released: Annual. **Audience:** Public health professionals, physicians, nurses, and health administrators. **Principal Exhibits:** Medical, products-related and pharmaceutical, health services, publishers, computer/software, educational, government, schools of public health. **Dates and Locations:** 2011 Oct 29 - Nov 02, Washington, DC; 2012 Oct 27-31, San Francisco, CA; 2013 Nov 02-06, Boston, MA; 2014 Nov 15-19, New Orleans, LA.

46429 ■ American Quilt Study Group Seminar
American Quilt Study Group
1610 L St.
Lincoln, NE 68508-2509
Ph:(402)477-1181
Fax:(402)477-1181
Co. E-mail: aqsg2@americanquiltstudygroup.org
URL: http://www.americanquiltstudygroup.org
Released: Annual. **Principal Exhibits:** Quilt-related articles.

46430 ■ American Real Estate Society Annual Meeting
American Real Estate Society
5353 Parkside Dr.
Cleveland State Univ.
Coll. of Bus.
Dept. of Finance, UC513
Jupiter, FL 33458
Ph:(561)799-8664
Fax:(561)799-8535
Co. E-mail: dcooper@fau.edu
URL: http://www.aresnet.org
Released: Annual. **Audience:** College and university professors; high-level practicing professionals involved in all aspects real estate. **Principal Exhibits:** Exhibits relating to decision-making within real estate finance, real estate market analysis, investment, valuation, development, and other areas related to real estate in the private sector. Data providers, book publishers, etc.

46431 ■ American School Health Association National School Health Conference
American School Health Association
7263 State Rte. 43
PO Box 708
Kent, OH 44240
Ph:(330)678-1601
Fax:(330)678-4526
Co. E-mail: asha@ashaweb.org
URL: http://www.ashaweb.org
Released: Annual. **Audience:** School nurses, health educators, physicians, teachers, school administrators, dentists, school counselors, physical educators, and school health coordinators. **Principal Exhibits:** Publications, pharmaceuticals, clinical and medical equipment and supplies, information on health

organizations, and health education methods and materials. **Dates and Locations:** 2011 Oct 12-15, Louisville, KY; 2012 Oct 10-13, San Antonio, TX; 2013 Oct 09-12, Myrtle Beach, SC.

46432 ■ American Technical Education Association National Conference on Technical Education
American Technical Education Association
c/o North Dakota State College of Science
800 N. 6th St.
Wahpeton, ND 58076-0002
Ph:(701)671-2301
Fax:(701)671-2260
URL: http://www.ateaonline.org
Released: Annual. **Audience:** Technical educators and administrators of post-secondary technical education. **Principal Exhibits:** Supplies and services related to post secondary technical education.

46433 ■ ApEx
Canadian Restaurant and Food Services Association
316 Bloor St. W.
Toronto, ON, Canada M5S 1W5
Ph:(416)923-8416
Free: 800-387-5649
Fax:(416)923-1450
Co. E-mail: info@crfa.ca
URL: http://www.crfa.ca
Audience: Trade. **Principal Exhibits:** Products and services for the restaurant and hospitality industry, as well as institutions, convenience stores, delis and bakeries. **Dates and Locations:** 2011 Apr 03-04, Moncton, NB.

46434 ■ Association for Research on Nonprofit Organizations and Voluntary Action Conference
Association for Research on Nonprofit Organizations and Voluntary Action
550 W N St., Ste. 301
Indianapolis, IN 46202
Ph:(317)684-2120
Fax:(317)684-2128
URL: http://www.arnova.org
Released: Annual. **Audience:** Scholars and nonprofit organization professionals. **Principal Exhibits:** Exhibits for citizen participation and voluntary action, including social movements, interest groups, consumer groups, political participation, community development, and religious organizations.

46435 ■ Baltimore Women's Show
S & L Productions, Inc.
1916 Crain Hwy., Ste. 16
Glen Burnie, MD 21061
Ph:(410)863-1180
Fax:(410)863-1187
URL: http://www.mdhomeandgarden.com
Released: Annual. **Audience:** Women 25-65 yrs. **Principal Exhibits:** Products and services for women.

46436 ■ BMA Annual Marketing Forum
American Bankers Association
1120 Connecticut Ave. NW
Washington, DC 20036
Free: 800-BAN-KERS
Co. E-mail: custserv@aba.com
URL: http://www.aba.com
Released: Annual. **Audience:** Bankers including community bank CEO's, marketing directors, sales managers, advertising directors, public relations managers. **Principal Exhibits:** Financial services marketing offering banking solutions in advertising services, bank equipment/systems, computer software, database marketing, direct marketing/sales, incentive/premium programs, insurance services, investment services, marketing consulting, merchandising, publishing, research, retail delivery, sales training, service quality, signage, and telemarketing.

46437 ■ BMA Private Wealth Sales Management Workshop, an ABA Program
American Bankers Association
1120 Connecticut Ave. NW
Washington, DC 20036

Free: 800-BAN-KERS
Co. E-mail: custserv@aba.com
URL: http://www.aba.com
Released: Annual. **Audience:** Trust, private banking and asset management officers, bank brokerage managers, sales managers, business development managers, and regional department managers. **Principal Exhibits:** Provides marketing education and information, professional growth and networking resources to marketing professionals in the financial services industry. **Dates and Locations:** 2011 Mar 06-08, Miami, FL.

46438 ■ Broadcast Cable Financial Management Association Conference
Broadcast Cable Financial Management Association
550 Frontage Rd., Ste. 3600
Northfield, IL 60093
Ph:(847)716-7000
Fax:(847)716-7004
Co. E-mail: info@bcfm.com
URL: http://www.bcfm.com
Released: Annual. **Audience:** Business managers, CFOs. **Principal Exhibits:** Exhibits relating to the financial management of radio, television, and cable television operations, including issues such as industry - specific software, collection agencies, insurance, investments, banking, accounting firms and music licensing. **Dates and Locations:** 2011 May 15-17, Atlanta,, GA.

46439 ■ Cabletelevision Advertising Bureau - Cable Advertising Conference
Cabletelevision Advertising Bureau
830 3rd Ave., 2nd Fl.
New York, NY 10022
Ph:(212)508-1200
Fax:(212)832-3268
URL: http://www.thecab.tv/
Released: Annual. **Audience:** Cable television and advertising trade. **Principal Exhibits:** Cable television and advertising equipment, supplies, and services.

46440 ■ Canadian Real Estate Association Annual Conference and Trade Show
Canadian Real Estate Association
Canada Bldg.
200 Catherine St.
Ottawa, ON, Canada K2P 2K9
Ph:(613)237-7111
Free: 800-842-2732
Fax:(613)234-2567
Co. E-mail: info@crea.ca
URL: http://www.crea.ca
Released: Annual. **Audience:** Real estate professionals, brokers, managers, corporate representatives from real estate boards across the country. **Principal Exhibits:** Real Estate, financial, printing, and computer business equipment.

46441 ■ Computer Game Developers' Conference
CMP Media LLC (San Mateo, California)
2800 Campus Dr.
San Mateo, CA 94403
Ph:(650)513-4300
Co. E-mail: cmp@cmp.com
URL: http://www.cmp.com
Released: Annual. **Principal Exhibits:** Equipment, supplies, and services for developers and producers of computer games.

46442 ■ Estuarine Research Federation Conference
Estuarine Research Federation
PO Box 510
University of Southwest Louisiana
Dept. of Biology
Port Republic, MD 20676
Ph:(410)326-7467
Fax:(410)326-7466
Co. E-mail: info@erf.org
URL: http://www.erf.org
Released: Biennial. **Principal Exhibits:** Exhibits for persons actively engaged in biological, hydrographic, or related investigations of estuarine problems.

46443 ■ Expo Comm Wireless Korea
E.J. Krause & Associates, Inc.
6550 Rock Spring Dr., Ste. 500
Bethesda, MD 20817
Ph:(301)493-5500
Fax:(301)493-5705
Co. E-mail: ejkinfo@ejkrause.com
URL: http://www.ejkrause.com
Released: Annual. **Principal Exhibits:** Equipment, supplies, and services for computers.

46444 ■ Florida RV Supershow
Florida RV Trade Association
10510 Gibsonton Dr.
Riverview, FL 33578
Ph:(813)741-0488
Fax:(813)741-0688
Co. E-mail: info@frvta.org
URL: http://www.frvta.org
Released: Annual. **Audience:** First time buyers as well as current owners. **Principal Exhibits:** Recreational vehicle supplies and accessories. **Dates and Locations:** 2011 Jan 11-16, Tampa, FL.

46445 ■ GMC Philadelphia Home Show
dmg world media (USA) inc. (Philadelphia, Pennsylvania)
200 Haddonfield-Berlin Rd., Ste. 302
High Ridge Commons
Gibbsboro, NJ 08026
Ph:(856)784-4774
Free: 800-756-5692
Fax:(856)435-5920
URL: http://www.dmgworldmedia.com
Released: Annual. **Audience:** Home owners and apartment dwellers. **Principal Exhibits:** House and apartment products, supplies, and services.

46446 ■ Handmade - A Division of the San Francisco International Gift Fair
George Little Management, LLC (New York, New York)
1133 Westchester Ave., Ste. N136
White Plains, NY 10606
Ph:(914)421-3200
Free: 800-272-SHOW
Co. E-mail: cathy_steel@glmshows.com
URL: http://www.glmshows.com
Released: Semiannual. **Audience:** Specialty, department, stationery, juvenile, and jewelry stores, interior designers, gift shops, mail order catalogs, importers/distributors of home products. **Principal Exhibits:** Handmade merchandise, including functional and decorative home furnishings, fashion accessories, jewelry plus an array of other unique craft objects. All merchandise is selected by a panel of craft professionals for uniqueness, originality and marketability.

46447 ■ Home Entertainment Show
Trigger Agency
3539 Clipper Mill Rd.
Baltimore, MD 21211
Free: 800-830-3976
Fax:(410)878-9911
Co. E-mail: info@triggeragency.com
URL: http://www.triggeragency.com/
Released: Biennial. **Audience:** Consumers, trade and press. **Principal Exhibits:** Home theater and high-fidelity audio equipment, supplies, and services.

46448 ■ HSMAI - Affordable Meetings West
George Little Management, LLC (New York, New York)
1133 Westchester Ave., Ste. N136
White Plains, NY 10606
Ph:(914)421-3200
Free: 800-272-SHOW
Co. E-mail: cathy_steel@glmshows.com
URL: http://www.glmshows.com
Released: Annual. **Audience:** Trade professionals. **Principal Exhibits:** Equipment, supplies, and services for the hospitality and marketing industry. **Dates and Locations:** 2011 Jun 15-16, Long Beach, CA.

46449 ■ The Imprinted Sportswear Show, Atlantic City
Nielsen Business Media
770 Broadway
New York, NY 10003-9595

Ph:(646)654-4500
Co. E-mail: bmcomm@nielsen.com
URL: http://www.nielsenbusinessmedia.com/
Released: Annual. **Audience:** Trade only. **Principal Exhibits:** Trade show source for the imprinted sportswear/textile screen printing/embroidery industry; t-shirts, pre-prints, and other apparel; design software; screen printing supplies and equipment; transfers, lettering embroidery equipment and supplies. **Dates and Locations:** 2011 Mar 11-13, Atlantic City, NJ.

46450 ■ International Conference on Fundraising
Association of Fundraising Professionals
4300 Wilson Blvd., Ste. 300
Arlington, VA 22203-4168
Ph:(703)684-0410
Fax:(703)684-0540
URL: http://www.afpnet.org
Released: Annual. **Audience:** Decision makers for development offices for nonprofits. **Principal Exhibits:** Fund raising tools.

46451 ■ International Restaurant & Foodservice Show of New York
Reed Exhibitions North American Headquarters
383 Main Ave.
Norwalk, CT 06851
Ph:(203)840-4800
Fax:(203)840-5805
Co. E-mail: export@reedexpo.com
URL: http://www.reedexpo.com
Released: Annual. **Principal Exhibits:** Equipment, supplies, and services for the food products, foodservice, restaurant, and institutional food service industries.

46452 ■ International Sport Summit
E.J. Krause & Associates, Inc.
6550 Rock Spring Dr., Ste. 500
Bethesda, MD 20817
Ph:(301)493-5500
Fax:(301)493-5705
Co. E-mail: ejkinfo@ejkrause.com
URL: http://www.ejkrause.com
Released: Annual. **Audience:** Trade professionals. **Principal Exhibits:** Equipment, supplies, and services for sports facilities and events.

46453 ■ JAGEN UND FISCHEN - International Exhibition for Hunters, Fishermen and Marksmen
Kallman Worldwide, Inc.
4 North St., Ste. 800
Waldwick, NJ 07463-1842
Ph:(201)251-2600
Fax:(201)251-2760
Co. E-mail: info@kallman.com
URL: http://www.kallman.com
Principal Exhibits: Equipment, supplies, and services for hunters, fishermen, and marksmen.

46454 ■ Maryland Municipal League Convention
Maryland Municipal League
1212 West St.
Annapolis, MD 21401
Ph:(410)268-5514
Free: 800-492-7121
Fax:(410)268-7004
Co. E-mail: mml@mdmunicipal.org
URL: http://www.mdmunicipal.org
Released: Annual. **Audience:** Municipal officials and other county and state officials. **Principal Exhibits:** Office equipment, public works equipment, insurance companies, consulting firms, recreation equipment, computers, engineering firms, police equipment, and code publishers. **Dates and Locations:** 2011 Jun 26-29, Ocean City, MD.

46455 ■ Memories Expo
Offinger Management Co.
1100-H Brandywine Blvd.
PO Box 3388
Zanesville, OH 43702-3388
Ph:(740)452-4541
Free: 888-878-6334

Fax:(740)452-2552
Co. E-mail: OMC.Info@Offinger.com
URL: http://www.offinger.com
Released: 5/year. **Audience:** Trade and public. **Principal Exhibits:** Scrapbook supplies. **Dates and Locations:** 2011 Mar 25-26, Columbus, OH.

46456 ■ Michigan Association for Computer Users in Learning Conference
Michigan Association for Computer Users in Learning
3410 Belle Chase Way, Ste. 100
Holt, MI 48842-0518
Ph:(517)694-9756
Fax:(517)694-9773
Co. E-mail: macul@macul.org
URL: http://www.macul.org
Released: Annual. **Audience:** Educational technology professionals. **Principal Exhibits:** Computer and educational equipment, supplies, and services.

46457 ■ Michigan Interscholastic Athletic Administrators Mid-Winter Conference
Michigan Interscholastic Athletic Administrator Association
35445 Hathaway
Livonia, MI 48150-2513
Ph:(734)422-3569
Fax:(734)762-9957
URL: http://www.miaaa.com
Released: Annual. **Audience:** Educators in the field of secondary interscholastic athletic administration. **Principal Exhibits:** Sports supplies, athletic equipment, clothing, publications, fund raisers, and athletic training supplies, and awards companies.

46458 ■ Michigan Restaurant Show
Michigan Restaurant Association
225 W. Washtenaw St.
Lansing, MI 48933
Ph:(517)482-5244
Free: 800-968-9668
Fax:(517)482-7663
URL: http://www.michiganrestaurant.org
Released: Annual. **Audience:** Food service industry professionals. **Principal Exhibits:** Equipment, supplies, and services for the food service industry.

46459 ■ Minneapolis International Motorcycle Show
Advanstar Communications
641 Lexington Ave., 8th Fl.
New York, NY 10022
Ph:(212)951-6600
Fax:(212)951-6793
Co. E-mail: info@advantstar.com
URL: http://www.advanstar.com
Audience: Public: Motorcycle, watercraft and ATV enthusiasts. **Principal Exhibits:** A marketplace where manufacturers and retailers can display and sell their products such as motorcycles, all-terrain vehicles (ATV), scooters, watercraft, apparel, parts and accessories.

46460 ■ National Agricultural Bankers Conference
American Bankers Association
1120 Connecticut Ave. NW
Washington, DC 20036
Free: 800-BAN-KERS
Co. E-mail: custserv@aba.com
URL: http://www.aba.com
Released: Annual. **Audience:** Bank CEOs, mainly from community banks in rural areas, executive vice presidents, senior vice presidents, economists, analysts. **Principal Exhibits:** The latest developments in the agricultural lending business, as well as strategies for better market share, profitability and customer service.

46461 ■ Natural Products Expo East
New Hope Natural Media
1401 Pearl St.
Boulder, CO 80302-5346
Ph:(303)939-8440

Fax:(303)998-9020
Co. E-mail: info@newhope.com
URL: http://www.newhope.com
Released: Annual. **Audience:** Retailers, wholesalers, distributors, and brokers from the natural products industry. **Principal Exhibits:** Natural, organic and environmentally sound products, including: alternative health care, vegetarian and allergy-free personal care recycled/recyclable products, biodegradable products, and organic meats. **Dates and Locations:** 2011 Sep 21-24, Baltimore, MD.

46462 ■ New Jersey League of Municipalities Annual Conference
New Jersey League of Municipalities
222 West State St.
Trenton, NJ 08608
Ph:(609)695-3481
Fax:(609)695-0151
Co. E-mail: league@njslom.com
URL: http://www.njslom.com
Released: Annual. **Audience:** Municipal officials. **Principal Exhibits:** Municipal products and services.

46463 ■ North American Association of State and Provincial Lotteries Conference and Trade Show
North American Association of State and Provincial Lotteries
6 N. Broadway
Geneva, OH 44041
Ph:(440)466-5630
Fax:(440)466-5649
Co. E-mail: info@nasplhq.org
URL: http://www.naspl.org
Released: Annual. **Audience:** Lottery industry professionals. **Principal Exhibits:** Lottery equipment, supplies, and services.

46464 ■ Old House/New House Home Show
Kennedy Productions, Inc.
1208 Lisle Pl.
Lisle, IL 60532-2262
Ph:(630)515-1160
Fax:(630)515-1165
Co. E-mail: kp@corecomm.net
URL: http://www.kennedyproductions.com
Released: Semiannual. **Audience:** Trade professionals and general public. **Principal Exhibits:** Products and services for home remodeling, improvement, enhancement, decorating, landscaping and more. Hundreds of ideas to improve and beautify every home.

46465 ■ ON DEMAND Digital Printing & Publishing Strategy Conference and Exposition
Advanstar Communications
641 Lexington Ave., 8th Fl.
New York, NY 10022
Ph:(212)951-6600
Fax:(212)951-6793
Co. E-mail: info@advantstar.com
URL: http://www.advanstar.com
Released: Annual. **Audience:** Corporate executives, print providers, government users. **Principal Exhibits:** Addresses the digitalization of workflow in the printing and publishing marketplace.

46466 ■ Outdoor Retailer Summer Market
VNU Expo (Laguna Beach, California)
310 Broadway
Laguna Beach, CA 92651
Ph:(946)376-6200
Free: 800-486-2701
Fax:(949)497-5290
Co. E-mail: interbike@wyoming.com
URL: http://www.vnuexpo.com
Released: Annual. **Audience:** Owners and managers of the specialty sports retail stores. **Principal Exhibits:** Human-powered outdoor sports goods. **Dates and Locations:** 2011 Aug 04-07, Salt Lake City, UT.

46467 ■ Outdoor Retailer Winter Market
VNU Expo (Laguna Beach, California)
310 Broadway
Laguna Beach, CA 92651
Ph:(946)376-6200

Free: 800-486-2701
Fax:(949)497-5290
Co. E-mail: interbike@wyoming.com
URL: http://www.vnuexpo.com
Released: Annual. **Audience:** Owners and managers of specialty sports retail stores. **Principal Exhibits:** Human-powered outdoor sports goods. **Dates and Locations:** 2011 Jan 19-23, Salt Lake City, UT.

46468 ■ Pittsburgh Women's Show
Trigger Agency
3539 Clipper Mill Rd.
Baltimore, MD 21211
Free: 800-830-3976
Fax:(410)878-9911
Co. E-mail: info@triggeragency.com
URL: http://www.triggeragency.com/
Released: Annual. **Audience:** Trade and public. **Principal Exhibits:** Products and services for women relating to health, fitness, business, careers, and finance.

46469 ■ Rocky Mountain Snowmobile & Icefishing Expo
Industrial Expositions, Inc.
1675 Larimer St., No.700
PO Box 480084
Denver, CO 80248-0084
Ph:(303)892-6800
Free: 800-457-2434
Fax:(303)892-6322
Co. E-mail: info@iei-expos.com
URL: http://www.iei-expos.com/
Released: Annual. **Audience:** Snowmobilers. **Principal Exhibits:** Snowmobiles, clothing and accessories, recreational vehicles, travel and accommodations.

46470 ■ Scuba ExtaSea Expo
Industrial Expositions, Inc.
1675 Larimer St., No.700
PO Box 480084
Denver, CO 80248-0084
Ph:(303)892-6800
Free: 800-457-2434
Fax:(303)892-6322
Co. E-mail: info@iei-expos.com
URL: http://www.iei-expos.com/
Released: Annual. **Audience:** General public. **Principal Exhibits:** Scuba diving, snorkeling, travel and accessories.

46471 ■ Society of Craft Designers Educational Seminar
Offinger Management Co.
1100-H Brandywine Blvd.
PO Box 3388
Zanesville, OH 43702-3388
Ph:(740)452-4541
Free: 888-878-6334
Fax:(740)452-2552
Co. E-mail: OMC.Info@Offinger.com
URL: http://www.offinger.com
Released: Annual. **Audience:** Designers, manufacturers, editors, and publishers. **Principal Exhibits:** Craft designer showcases and education.

46472 ■ Society for Human Resource Management (SHRM) The HRM Marketplace Exposition
Society for Human Resource Management
1800 Duke St.
Alexandria, VA 22314
Ph:(703)548-3440
Free: 800-283-SHRM
Fax:(703)535-6490
Co. E-mail: shrm@shrm.org
URL: http://www.shrm.org
Released: Annual. **Audience:** Human resource management and related professionals. **Principal Exhibits:** Human resource management products and services; including relocation human resource information systems, recruitment, executive search, temporary/contact personnel employee compensation and benefits, incentive program information, childcare/eldercare, and drug testing information.

46473 ■ South Dakota Association of Realtors Convention
South Dakota Association of Realtors
204 N. Euclid Ave.
Pierre, SD 57501
Ph:(605)224-0554
Fax:(605)224-8975
Co. E-mail: sdar@sdrealtor.org
URL: http://www.sdrealtor.org
Released: Annual. **Audience:** Industry professionals. **Principal Exhibits:** Real estate. **Dates and Locations:** 2011 Sep 14-16, Pierre, SD.

46474 ■ Texas Apartment Association Annual Education Conference and Lone Star Expo
Texas Apartment Association, Inc.
1011 San Jacinto Blvd., Ste. 600
Austin, TX 78701-1951
Ph:(512)479-6252
Fax:(512)479-6291
URL: http://www.taa.org
Released: Annual. **Audience:** Owners and management company reps of multi-housing communities from Texas. **Principal Exhibits:** Goods and services geared to multi-housing professionals, including software, soft goods, and property supplies.

46475 ■ TS2 - The Trade Show About Trade Shows
National Trade Productions, Inc.
313 S. Patrick St.
Alexandria, VA 22314-3567
Free: 800-687-7469
Fax:(703)836-4486
Co. E-mail: ntpinfo@ntpshow.com
URL: http://www.ntpshow.com
Released: Annual. **Audience:** Exhibit managers. **Principal Exhibits:** Equipment, supplies, and services for the trade show industry, including moving companies, booths and other structures, publications, audiovisual equipment, and related items.

46476 ■ Virginia Health Care Association Annual Convention and Trade Show
Virginia Health Care Association
2112 W. Laburnum Ave., Ste. 206
Richmond, VA 23227
Ph:(804)353-9101
Fax:(804)353-3098
Co. E-mail: kathy.robertson@vhca.org
URL: http://www.vhca.org
Released: Annual. **Audience:** Nursing homeowners, administrators, purchasing agents, and nurses; dietary, housekeeping, social services, and activities departments' heads. **Principal Exhibits:** Equipment, supplies, and services for nursing home operations, including food, medical supplies, furniture, computer systems, linen, medical equipment, insurance, pharmaceuticals, optometrists, psychologists, and transportation.

46477 ■ West Ex: The Rocky Mountain Regional Hospitality Exposition
Colorado Restaurant Association
430 E. 7th Ave.
Denver, CO 80203

Ph:(303)830-2972
Free: 800-522-2972
Fax:(303)830-2973
Co. E-mail: info@coloradorestaurant.com
URL: http://www.coloradorestaurant.com
Released: Annual. **Audience:** Food service and restaurant industry personnel. **Principal Exhibits:** Food service and lodging products, equipment, and services.

46478 ■ Western Food Service & Hospitality Expo Los Angeles
California Restaurant Association
1011 10th St.
Sacramento, CA 95814
Ph:(916)447-5793
Free: 800-765-4842
Fax:(916)447-6182
URL: http://www.calrest.org
Audience: Food service hospitality and lodging industry professionals. **Principal Exhibits:** Food, equipment, supplies, and services for food service and lodging industries. **Dates and Locations:** 2011 Aug 28-30, San Diego, CA.

CONSULTANTS

46479 ■ Featherlite Exhibits
545 E Algonquin Rd., Ste. E
Arlington Heights, IL 60005
Ph:(763)537-5533
Free: 800-229-5533
Fax:(763)923-6041
Co. E-mail: marketing@featherlite.com
URL: http://www.featherlite.com
Contact: Linda Nelson, Principal
Scope: Trade show consultancy includes full-service rentals, installation and dismantling, accessories and complete graphic design services. **Special Services:** Computer-aided drafting and design service; Featherlite[R].

46480 ■ International Training and Management Co.
60 Prue Ave.
Toronto, ON, Canada M6B 1R5
Ph:(416)783-5200
Free: 800-358-6079
Fax:(416)783-6200
Co. E-mail: info@siskindtraining.com
URL: http://www.siskindtraining.com
Contact: Barry Siskind, President
E-mail: barry@atssiskindtraining.com
Scope: Provides both exhibitor training products as well as consulting services. Industries served: private and public companies who exhibit at trade or consumer shows. **Publications:** "A Strategic Approach to Trade Show Staffing"; "Approach Your Show Selection Strategically"; "Approaching Prospects on the Show Floor"; "Powerful exhibit marketing: the complete guide to successful trade shows, conferences and consumer shows," J. Wiley and Sons Canada, 2005; "Bumblebees can't fly: 7 simple strategies for making the impossible pos,"Wiley and Sons Canada, 2004; "Eagles must soar: 7 strategies for living alife with certainty," Wiley and Sons Canada, 2004;

"Bumblebees Can't Fly, a Practical Guide to Making Everyday Work," Stoddart, 2001; "Take the stress out of show planning"; "Avoid convention overload"; "Making Contact"; "Seminars to Build Your Business"; "Making Trade Shows Work". **Seminars:** The Successful Exhibitor.

46481 ■ Intex Exhibit Systems L.L.C.
1846 Sequoia Ave.
Orange, CA 92868
Ph:(714)940-0369
Free: 800-331-6633
Fax:(714)935-0223
Co. E-mail: info@intexexhibits.com
URL: http://www.intexexhibits.com
Contact: Sue Bonas, Owner
E-mail: mdk@intexexhibits.com
Scope: Firm specializes in the design and production of exhibits, displays and pavilions for world fairs, tradeshows and similar events. Services include product design, industrial and engineering design for educational exhibits, museum exhibits and science and technology museology. Serves private industry as well as government agencies. **Publications:** "Trade Show Marketing," Sep, 2000; "Exhibitor Times," 1998. **Special Services:** Fastpack[TM]; Panelflo[TM]; affordable-1[TM]; thegraphic arm[TM]; Expression[TM]; TigerMark[TM].

46482 ■ Reed
701 Deming Way
Madison, WI 53717-1937
Ph:(608)827-0701
Free: 800-373-0043
Fax:(608)827-0702
Co. E-mail: info@rsandk.com
URL: http://www.rsandk.com
Contact: Kathleen Mitchell, Principal
E-mail: jallen@atsrsandk.com
Scope: Provides marketing, advertising and design. Communications agency that specializes in creating image and awareness programs for business-to-business clients in the life sciences, computer technology, power quality, filtration, medical equipment, financial services and telecommunications industries.

46483 ■ Together Inc.
802 E 6th St.
PO Box 52528
Tulsa, OK 74120-3610
Ph:(918)587-2405
Free: 800-282-0085
Fax:(918)382-0906
Co. E-mail: pinrus@aol.com
URL: http://www.positivepins.com
Contact: Michelle L. Gentry-Anderson, Vice President
Scope: Offers services in employee and client self development training, logo development, lapel pin design, fund raising, public relations, conference and exhibit planning, direct marketing, association management, human resource development, and photography. Industries served: Government agencies, education, association and business, public and private schools. **Seminars:** Adventures in Attitudes; Diversity and Board Training for non-profits. **Special Services:** The Pin Man[R].

ASSOCIATIONS AND OTHER ORGANIZATIONS

46484 ■ Agricultural Producers Union–Union des Producteurs Agricoles
555 Roland-Therrien Blvd.
Longueuil, QC, Canada J4H 3Y9
Ph:(450)679-0530
Co. E-mail: upa@upa.qc.ca
Contact: Christian Lacasse, Pres. Gen.
Description: Promotes and supports the interests of agricultural producers throughout Canada. Provides information on updated developments on the farming industry. Works as a communications network among Quebec farmers. Protects the rights of individuals within the agricultural producing community. **Publications:** *Terre de Chez Nous* (weekly).

46485 ■ Association des Aides Familiales du Quebec
2348, Jean talon est, Local 407
Montreal, QC, Canada H2E 1V7
Ph:(514)272-2670
Fax:(514)272-8338
Co. E-mail: info@aafq.ca
URL: http://www.aafq.ca
Description: Domestic workers. Seeks to obtain optimal conditions of employment for members. Advocates for increased recognition of the rights of domestic workers; represents members in negotiations with employers. **Publications:** *Standing Tall* (bimonthly).

46486 ■ Building and Construction Trades Department - Canadian Office–Departement des Metiers de la Construction - Bureau Canadien
130 Albert St., Ste. 1902
Ottawa, ON, Canada K1P 5G4
Ph:(613)236-0653
Fax:(613)230-5138
Co. E-mail: rblakely@buildingtrades.ca
URL: http://www.buildingtrades.ca
Contact: Mark H. Ayers, Pres./Sec.-Treas.
Description: Individuals working in the building trades. Seeks to obtain optimal conditions of employment for members. Represents members in negotiations with employers.

46487 ■ Canadian Association of Labour Media
76 Westmount Ave.
Toronto, ON, Canada M6H 3K1
Ph:(416)656-2256
Free: 888-290-CALM
Fax:(416)656-7649
Co. E-mail: editor@calm.ca
URL: http://www.calm.ca
Contact: Rosemarie Bahr, Ed.
Description: Media organizations operated by labor unions. Promotes increased awareness of the trade union movement and issues affecting workers. Serves as a clearinghouse on trade unionism and labor issues. **Publications:** *CALMideas* (annual).

46488 ■ Canadian Association of Professional Employees–Association Canadienne des employes professionels
100 Queen St., 4th Fl.
Ottawa, ON, Canada K1P 1J9
Ph:(613)236-9181
Free: 800-265-9181
Fax:(613)236-6017
Co. E-mail: general@acep-cape.ca
URL: http://www.acep-cape.ca
Contact: Claude Poirier, Pres.
Description: Professional and technical employees. Seeks to obtain optimal conditions of employment for members. Represents members in negotiations with employers.

46489 ■ Canadian Auto Workers
205 Placer Ct.
Toronto, ON, Canada M2H 3H9
Ph:(416)497-4110
Free: 800-268-5763
Fax:(416)495-6552
Co. E-mail: cawpres@caw.ca
URL: http://www.caw.ca
Contact: Ken Lewenza, Pres.
Description: Represents the economic and workplace safety interests of Canadian automobile workers. Conducts economic and social action activities; maintains educational, charitable and research programs. Operates speakers' bureau. **Publications:** *Contact* (weekly).

46490 ■ Canadian Industrial Relations Association–Association Canadienne des Relations Industrielles
Dept. des Relations Industrielles
Universite de Laval, Pavillon J.-A.-DeSeve
Quebec, QC, Canada G1V 0A6
Ph:(418)656-2468
Fax:(418)656-7688
Co. E-mail: acri-cira@rlt.ulaval.ca
URL: http://www.cira-acri.ca
Contact: Dr. Larry Haiven, Pres.
Description: Industrial relations' professionals. Seeks to advance the study and practice of industrial relations. Serves as a forum for the exchange of ideas and information among members; sponsors research.

46491 ■ Canadian Labour Congress–Congres du travail du Canada
2841 Riverside Dr.
Ottawa, ON, Canada K1V 8X7
Ph:(613)521-3400
Fax:(613)521-4655
URL: http://www.canadianlabour.ca/home
Contact: Ken Georgetti, Pres.
Description: Works to ensure that all Canadians are able to find employment at fair wages, with union representation and the right to collective bargaining, in a safe environment. Seeks to create a just and equitable society. Joins with other organizations for advocacy and action on behalf of working Canadians. Facilitates establishment of grass roots organizations. Conducts research and educational programs; maintains speakers' bureau; compiles statistics. **Publications:** *C.L.C. Fax-Press* (weekly); *Sweatshop Alert* (periodic); *UI Bulletin* (periodic).

46492 ■ Canadian Media Guild–Guilde Canadienne des Medias
310 Front St. W, Ste. 810
Toronto, ON, Canada M5V 3B5
Ph:(416)591-5333
Free: 800-465-4149
Fax:(416)591-7278
Co. E-mail: info@cmg.ca
URL: http://www.cmg.ca
Contact: Carmel Smyth, Pres.
Description: Employees of press and broadcasting companies and other media outlets. Seeks to secure optimal conditions of employment for members. Represents members in negotiations with employers. **Publications:** *G-Force* (quarterly).

46493 ■ Canadian Teachers' Federation–Federation canadienne des enseignantes et des enseignants
2490 Don Reid Dr.
Ottawa, ON, Canada K1H 1E1
Ph:(613)232-1505
Free: (866)283-1505
Fax:(613)232-1886
Co. E-mail: info@ctf-fce.ca
URL: http://www.ctf-fce.ca
Contact: Dr. Calvin Fraser, Sec. Gen.
Description: Provincial and territorial teachers' organizations. Works to ensure that teachers' opinions are considered when national government bodies debate educational legislation. Facilitates communication and cooperation among members. Conducts research, educational, and lobbying activities.

46494 ■ Canadian Union of Public Employees–Le Syndicat Canadien de la Fonction Publique
1375 St. Lauren Blvd.
Ottawa, ON, Canada K1G 0Z7
Ph:(613)237-1590
Fax:(613)237-5508
URL: http://cupe.ca
Contact: Paul Moist, Natl. Pres.
Description: Seeks to protect the rights and improve the conditions of employment of members. Promotes fairness in hiring and promotion without regard to race or gender. Represents members in collective bargaining; makes available legal, educational, research, job evaluation, and communications services. **Publications:** *CUPE: It's Your Union*; *Organize* (periodic).

46495 ■ Communications, Energy and Paperworkers Union of Canada–Syndicat Canadien des Communications, de l'Energie et du Papier
301 Laurier Ave. W
Ottawa, ON, Canada K1P 6M6
Ph:(613)230-5200
Free: 877-230-5201

Fax:(613)230-5801
Co. E-mail: info@cep.ca
URL: http://www.cep.ca
Contact: Dave Coles, Pres.
Description: Trade union. Organizes and conducts collective bargaining for individuals employed in the telecommunications, electrical, electronics, pulp and paper, energy, print and broadcast media, and chemical industries in Canada.

46496 ■ Communications Workers of America/Canada–Syndicat des Communications d'Amerique
7B-1050 Baxter Rd.
Ottawa, ON, Canada K2C 3P1
Ph:(613)820-9777
Free: 877-486-4292
Fax:(613)820-8188
Co. E-mail: info@cwa-scacanada.ca
URL: http://www.cwa-scacanada.ca
Contact: Arnold Amber, Chm.
Description: Primarily union of journalists and media workers in Canada, as well as social workers and employees in the manufacturing industry. **Publications:** *TNG Canada Today* (monthly).

46497 ■ Confederation of National Trade Unions–Confederation des Syndicats Nationaux
1601 Ave. de Lorimier
Montreal, QC, Canada H2K 4M5
Ph:(514)598-2283
Free: (866)646-7760
Fax:(514)598-2476
Co. E-mail: csnexecutif@csn.qc.ca
URL: http://www.csn.qc.ca
Contact: Louis Roy, Pres.
Description: National trade unions representing 235,000 workers. Promotes advancement of the Canadian labor movement. Represents workers in collective bargaining. **Publications:** *Nouvelles CSN* (biweekly).

46498 ■ Editors' Association of Canada–Association canadienne des reviseurs
502-27 Carlton St.
Toronto, ON, Canada M5B 1L2
Ph:(416)975-1379
Free: (866)226-3348
Fax:(416)975-1637
Co. E-mail: info@editors.ca
URL: http://www.editors.ca
Contact: Michelle Boulton, Pres.
Description: Editors, proofreaders, copy editors, and researchers working on both English and French language printed materials. Promotes advancement of the profession of editing, and of members' capabilities. Conducts professional development courses for members; makes available to members job hotline services and discount long-term disability, extended health, and dental and life insurance. Sets and enforces editorial standards of practice; establishes payment levels and conditions of employment for editorial work. Cooperates with other organizations pursuing similar goals. **Publications:** *Active Voice* (bimonthly).

46499 ■ Labor Union Congress of Quebec–Centrale des Syndicats du Quebec
9405 rue Sherbrooke E
Montreal, QC, Canada H1L 6P3
Ph:(514)356-8888
Free: 800-465-0897
Fax:(514)356-9999
Co. E-mail: organisation_syndicale@csq.qc.net
URL: http://www.csq.qc.net
Contact: Gabriel Marchand, Dir. Gen.
Description: Professional unions representing teachers and other educational personnel. Represents members in collective bargaining negotiations; promotes members' professional interests. Conducts union education, political action, and research activities. Serves as liaison between French-speaking educational organizations in the world through the Comite Syndical Francophone de L'Education et de la Formation. **Publications:** *Nouvelles CSQ* (bimonthly).

46500 ■ Union of Canadian Transportation Employees
233 Gilmour St., Ste. 702
Ottawa, ON, Canada K2P 0P2
Ph:(613)238-4003
Fax:(613)236-0379
Co. E-mail: buschml@psac-afpc.com
URL: http://www.ucte.com
Contact: Christine Collins, Natl. Pres.
Description: Individuals employed in the transportation industries. Seeks to obtain optimal conditions of employment for members. Represents members in negotiations with employers. **Telecommunication Services:** electronic mail, collinc@psac-afpc.com.

46501 ■ United Steelworkers of America - Canadian Branch–Metallurgistes Unis d'Amerique
800-234 Eglinton Ave. E
Toronto, ON, Canada M4P 1K7
Ph:(416)487-1571
Fax:(416)482-5548
Co. E-mail: usw@usw.ca
URL: http://www.usw.ca
Contact: Ken Neumann, Natl. Dir.
Description: Represents the interests of workers in a variety of sectors in Canada. Maintains charitable program. **Publications:** *Steelabor - Canadian Edition* (monthly); *Steeleader* (periodic); *Unionbuilder* (periodic).

EDUCATIONAL PROGRAMS

46502 ■ Investigation Tools and Techniques: Developing Facts and Evidence
Seminar Information Service, Inc.
20 Executive Park, Ste. 120
Irvine, CA 92614
Ph:(949)261-9104
Free: 877-SEM-INFO
Fax:(949)261-1963
Co. E-mail: info@seminarinformation.com
URL: http://www.seminarinformation.com
Price: $795.00. **Description:** Interactive workshop provides valuable information and tools on how to conduct an investigation of major workplace offenses that may result in immediate termination and that may be the subject of employment litigation. **Locations:** New York, NY.

46503 ■ The Law of Equal Employment Opportunity
Seminar Information Service, Inc.
20 Executive Park, Ste. 120
Irvine, CA 92614
Ph:(949)261-9104
Free: 877-SEM-INFO
Fax:(949)261-1963
Co. E-mail: info@seminarinformation.com
URL: http://www.seminarinformation.com
Price: $1,795.00. **Description:** Participants examine Equal Employment Opportunity/affirmative action laws and obligations of employers, recent legislation, guidelines, compliance agencies' interpretations, and court decisions and the impact of Equal Employment laws on policies, procedures, and day-to-day operations. **Locations:** New York, NY.

46504 ■ Legal Issues for Managers (Onsite)
Seminar Information Service, Inc.
20 Executive Park, Ste. 120
Irvine, CA 92614
Ph:(949)261-9104
Free: 877-SEM-INFO
Fax:(949)261-1963
Co. E-mail: info@seminarinformation.com
URL: http://www.seminarinformation.com
Price: $1,990.00. **Description:** Using a case study, practical examples, and discussions participants will explore the law as it relates to making nondiscriminatory employment decisions, compliance with wage and hour laws, safety and health rights and responsibilities, required versus discretionary leaves of absence, managing employees covered by labor agreements, and individual rights and wrongful discharge. **Locations:** New York, NY.

46505 ■ The Service Contract Act
Seminar Information Service, Inc.
20 Executive Park, Ste. 120
Irvine, CA 92614
Ph:(949)261-9104
Free: 877-SEM-INFO
Fax:(949)261-1963
Co. E-mail: info@seminarinformation.com
URL: http://www.seminarinformation.com
Price: $995.00. **Description:** This course covers the applicable labor requirements, how they are enforced, and how to efficiently incorporate them into contract activities. **Locations:** Washington, DC; and Las Vegas, NV.

46506 ■ Wage and Hour Law Compliance
Seminar Information Service, Inc.
20 Executive Park, Ste. 120
Irvine, CA 92614
Ph:(949)261-9104
Free: 877-SEM-INFO
Fax:(949)261-1963
Co. E-mail: info@seminarinformation.com
URL: http://www.seminarinformation.com
Price: $199.00. **Description:** Learn the latest decisions and applications of the Fair Labor Standards Act. **Locations:** Pasco, WA; Spokane, WA; Everett, WA; Seattle, WA; and Tacoma, WA.

REFERENCE WORKS

46507 ■ "ACTRA Phones It In" in *Canadian Business* (Vol. 80, January 15, 2007, No. 2, pp. 8)
Pub: Rogers Media
Ed: Denis Seguin. **Description:** The strike held by the members of the ACTRA or Canadian Cinema, Television and Radio Artists from January 8 2007, due to the contract dispute with the trade association representing Canadian producers, is discussed.

46508 ■ "Air Canada to Slash 600 Non-Union Jobs" in *Globe & Mail* (February 11, 2006, pp. B3)
Pub: CTVglobemedia Publishing Inc.
Ed: Brent Jang. **Description:** The reasons behind workforce reduction by ACE Aviation Holdings Inc. at Air Canada are presented.

46509 ■ "Airline Mergers: United Next?" in *Crain's Chicago Business* (Vol. 31, April 21, 2008, No. 16, pp. 12)
Pub: Crain Communications, Inc.
Description: Discusses a potential merger between United and Continental airlines; unions representing 48,900 pilots, mechanics, flight attendants, ticket agents and ramp workers at United have put the management on notice that they expect to be a factor in any merger discussions if the company wants their cooperation.

46510 ■ "An Analysis of Three Labor Unions' Outreach to Brazilian Immigrant Workers in Boston" in *WorkingUSA* (Vol. 11, June 2008, No. 2)
Pub: Blackwell Publishers Ltd.
Ed: Joshua Kirshner. **Description:** Author seeks to shed light on the conditions under which labor unions can include immigrants in their ranks as a means to regain their strength. It does so by focusing on the example of Brazilian immigrants in Boston and compares the approaches of three union locals in Boston toward organizing Brazilian workers, the Painters, the Teamsters, and the United Food and Commercial Workers Union. While previous studies argue that ethnicity and social networks can account for immigrants' receptivity to unions, this article highlights strategic choice on the part of union officials as an important factor in facilitating unionization of Brazilian workers.

46511 ■ "Apprenticeship: Earn While You Learn" in *Occupational Outlook Quarterly* (Vol. 54, Fall 2010, No. 3, pp. 24)
Pub: U.S. Bureau of Labor Statistics
Description: Paid training, or apprenticeships, are examined. Registered apprenticeship programs conform to certain guidelines and industry-established

training standards and may be run by businesses, trade or professional associations, or partnerships with business and unions.

46512 ■ **"As Tradesmen Age, New Workers In Short Supply"** in *Boston Business Journal* **(Vol. 27, November 9, 2007, No. 41, pp. 1)**
Pub: American City Business Journals Inc.
Ed: Jackie Noblett. **Description:** It is becoming more difficult to find young people who have the skills for installation and maintenance businesses. Some businesses are unable to complete contracts on time due to lack of staff. Unions are making efforts to address the expected shortfall of laborers in the coming years through apprenticeship programs.

46513 ■ **"Back to Business"** in *Retail Merchandiser* **(Vol. 51, September-October 2011, No. 5, pp. 18)**
Pub: Phoenix Media Corporation
Ed: Eric Slack. **Description:** National Football League owners and players have reached a labor agreement for the next ten years. America's football league can once again focus on providing fans with a great product both on and off the field.

46514 ■ *Big-Box Swindle: The True Cost of Mega-Retailers and the Fight for America's Independent Businesses*
Pub: Beacon Press
Ed: Stacy Mitchell. **Released:** October 2007. **Price:** $15.00. **Description:** Examination of the economic, environmental, and social damage done by big-box retailers like Wal-Mart, Costco, and Home Depot. Labor policies of these retailers, particularly those enforced by Wal-Mart, are discussed at length.

46515 ■ **"Boeing's Next Flight May Well Be to the South"** in *Puget Sound Business Journal* **(Vol. 29, November 21, 2008, No. 31, pp.)**
Pub: American City Business Journals
Ed: Steve Wilhelm. **Description:** Southern states in the U.S. are luring Boeing Company to locate a new plant in their region which is experiencing a growing industrial base while offering permissive labor laws as selling points.

46516 ■ **"The Bottom Line: Did CN Push Too Hard?"** in *Globe & Mail* **(February 23, 2007, pp. B1)**
Pub: CTVglobemedia Publishing Inc.
Ed: Brett Jang. **Description:** The effect of the efficiency drive started by Hunter Harrison at Canadian National Railway Company on the company's labor relations is discussed.

46517 ■ **"Brief: Janitorial Company Must Pay Back Wages"** in *Buffalo News* **(September 24, 2011)**
Pub: The Buffalo News
Ed: Jonathan D. Epstein. **Description:** Knights Facilities Management, located in Michigan, provides grounds maintenance and janitorial services at the Ralph Wilson Stadium in Buffalo, New York. The US Department of Labor ordered the firm to pay $22,000 in back wages and damages to 26 employees for overtime and minimum wage compensation. Details of the company's violation of the Fair Labor Standards Act are included.

46518 ■ **"Builders, Unions Aim to Cut Costs; Pushing Changes to Regain Share of Residential Market; Seek Council's Help"** in *Crain's New York Business*
Pub: Crain Communications, Inc.
Ed: Erik Engquist. **Description:** Union contractors and workers are worried about a decline in their market share for housing so they intend to ask the City Council to impose new safety and benefit standards on all contractors to avoid being undercut by nonunion competitors.

46519 ■ **"Businesses Keep a Watchful Eye on Worker's Comp"** in *The Business Journal-Serving Greater Tampa Bay* **(September 5, 2008)**
Pub: American City Business Journals, Inc.
Ed: Jane Meinhardt. **Description:** Pending a ruling from the Florida Supreme Court that could uphold the 2003 changes on workers' compensation law, the

outcome would include restrictions on claimant attorneys' fees and allow the competitive workers' compensation insurance rates to remain low. However, insurance rates are expected to go up if the court overturns the changes.

46520 ■ **"Car Trouble"** in *Canadian Business* **(Vol. 80, October 22, 2007, No. 21, pp. 27)**
Pub: Rogers Media
Ed: Thomas Watson. **Description:** Contract between General Motors Corporation and the United Auto Workers Union has created a competitive arm for the U.S. Big Three automakers. Data on the market and production data of car companies are presented.

46521 ■ **"CAW Boss Troubled Over 'Vulnerable' Ford Plants"** in *Globe & Mail* **(January 19, 2006, pp. B6)**
Pub: CTVglobemedia Publishing Inc.
Ed: Greg Keenan. **Description:** The concerns of president Buzz Hargrove of Canadian Auto Workers on the impact of Ford Motor Co.'s restructuring efforts on closure of automotive plants in Canada, are presented.

46522 ■ **"CAW Hopes to Beat Xstrata Deadline"** in *Globe & Mail* **(January 30, 2007, pp. B3)**
Pub: CTVglobemedia Publishing Inc.
Ed: Andy Hoffman. **Description:** The decision of Canadian Auto Workers to strike work at Xstrata PLC over wage increase is discussed.

46523 ■ **"Centerpoint Nurses Unionize Despite Change In Hospital CEO"** in *Business Journal-Serving Metropolitan Kansas City* **(November 16, 2007)**
Pub: American City Business Journals, Inc.
Ed: Rob Roberts. **Description:** The change in Centerpoint Medical Center's CEO did not stop the hospital's 336 registered nurses from joining Nurses United for Improved Patient Care. Carolyn Caldwell was named CEO of Centerpoint on October 8, 2007, one week after Dan Jones announced his resignation. Poor communications are pointed out as the reason why the nurses joined the union.

46524 ■ *Change in SMEs: The New European Capitalism*
Pub: Palgrave Macmillan
Ed: Katharina Bluhm; Rudi Schmidt. **Released:** October 2008. **Price:** $95.00. **Description:** Effects of global change on corporate governance, management, competitive strategies and labor relations in small-to-medium sized enterprises in various European countries are discussed.

46525 ■ **"Chrysler Unions Set Up Roadblocks to Private Equity"** in *Globe & Mail* **(March 20, 2007, pp. B3)**
Pub: CTVglobemedia Publishing Inc.
Ed: Greg Keenan. **Description:** The opposition to the Canadian Auto Workers union and the United Auto Workers to any proposal to sell Chrysler Group is discussed.

46526 ■ **"CN Aims for Regional Pacts to Halt Labor Row"** in *Globe & Mail* **(April 17, 2007, pp. B2)**
Pub: CTVglobemedia Publishing Inc.
Ed: Brent Jang. **Description:** The decision of Canadian National Railway Co. to settle labor dispute with regional unions is discussed.

46527 ■ **"CN Rail Strike Ends With Fragile Truce"** in *Globe & Mail* **(February 26, 2007, pp. B1)**
Pub: CTVglobemedia Publishing Inc.
Ed: Brent Jang. **Description:** The agreement between Canadian National Railway Co. and the United Transportation Union on wage increase that ended employee strike is discussed.

46528 ■ **"Coherent Laying Off 144 As It Prepares To Shut Auburn Plant"** in *Sacramento Business Journal* **(Vol. 25, August 1, 2008, No. 22, pp. 1)**
Pub: American City Business Journals, Inc.
Ed: Melanie Turner. **Description:** Sacramento, California-based Coherent Inc. is planning to lay off 144 workers at its Auburn facility. Coherent has been cutting payroll and its real estate holdings. Statistics on the company's earnings are also provided.

46529 ■ **"Collateral Damage"** in *Business Courier* **(Vol. 26, October 16, 2009, No. 25, pp. 1)**
Pub: American City Business Journals, Inc.
Ed: Jon Newberry. **Description:** Non-union construction firms representing Ohio Valley Associated Builders and Contractors Inc. have filed cases against unionized shops claiming violations of wage law in Ohio. Defendants say the violations are minor, however, they believe they are caught in the middle of the group's campaign to change the state's wage law.

46530 ■ **"Companies Must Set Goals for Diversity"** in *Crain's Detroit Business* **(Vol. 24, April 14, 2008, No. 15, pp. 16)**
Pub: Crain Communications, Inc.
Ed: Laura Weiner. **Description:** Diversity programs should start with a plan that takes into account exactly what the company wants to accomplish; this may include wanting to increase the bottom line with new contracts or wanting a staff that is more innovative in their ideas due to their varied backgrounds.

46531 ■ **"Companies Press Ottawa to End CN Labor Dispute"** in *Globe & Mail* **(April 16, 2007, pp. B1)**
Pub: CTVglobemedia Publishing Inc.
Ed: Brent Jang. **Description:** The plea of several industries to the Canadian parliament to end the labor dispute at the Canadian National Railway Co. is discussed.

46532 ■ **"Compulsory Proportional Representation: Allaying Potential Concerns"** in *WorkingUSA* **(Vol. 11, September 2008, No. 3, pp. 349)**
Pub: Blackwell Publishers Ltd.
Ed: Mark Harcourt, Helen Lam. **Description:** Present union certification system has many faults, the most important of which is its failure to deliver employee representation to all but a small and declining minority of workers. As an alternative, compulsory proportional representation (CPR) would have many advantages, particularly when compared with other reform proposals, most of which are designed to only reinvigorate, modify, or supplement the existing system.

46533 ■ **"Contractors Can't Do It Alone, PHCC's Pfeffer Says"** in *Contractor* **(Vol. 56, October 2009, No. 10, pp. 3)**
Pub: Penton Media, Inc.
Ed: Robert P. Mader. **Description:** President Herbert "Skip" Pfeffer of the Plumbing-Heating-Cooling Contractors National Association says lobbying and education are the services that the association offers that a contractor cannot do individually. Pfeffer says the dues for the association are set up in a manner that allows members to pay monthly.

46534 ■ **"Councilman May Revive Labor Bill"** in *Baltimore Business Journal* **(Vol. 28, August 13, 2010, No. 14, pp. 1)**
Pub: Baltimore Business Journal
Ed: Daniel J. Sernovitz. **Description:** Baltimore, Maryland Councilman Bill Henry has started reviving controversial legislation that would force developers and contractors to give preference to union labor. The legislation requires contractors to give preference to city workers in order to lower Baltimore's unemployment rate.

46535 ■ **"Counting on Engagement at Ernst and Young"** in *Workforce Management* **(Vol. 88, November 16, 2009, No. 12, pp. 25)**
Pub: Crain Communications, Inc.
Ed: Ed Frauenheim. **Description:** Employee engagement has been difficult to maintain through the recession but firms such as Ernst & Young have found that the effort to keep their employees loyal has paid off.

46536 ■ **"Cultural Due Diligence"** in *Canadian Business* **(Vol. 80, April 23, 2007, No. 9, pp. 60)**
Pub: Rogers Media
Ed: Graham Lowe. **Description:** The factors to be considered by job seekers during judging good workplace with relation to corporate culture are presented.

46537 ■ "CVRD Inco Strike Shuts Sudbury Mines" in *Globe & Mail* (April 2, 2007, pp. B1)

Pub: CTVglobemedia Publishing Inc.

Ed: Andy Hoffman. **Description:** The closure of nickel mining operations at the Sudbury mines due to the strike by employees of CVRD Inco Ltd. is described. The prospects of a rise in the prices of nickel are discussed, besides the production of metals in Canada.

46538 ■ "Defensive Training" in *Crain's Detroit Business* (Vol. 24, September 22, 2008, No. 38, pp. 11)

Pub: Crain Communications, Inc.

Ed: Robert Ankeny. **Description:** Rising retaliation claims in regards to discrimination complaints are creating an atmosphere in which managers must learn how to avoid or deal with these lawsuits as well as the retaliation that often follows. Examples of cases are given as well as advice for dealing with such problems that may arise in the workplace.

46539 ■ "Dirty Work Required" in *Workforce Management* (Vol. 88, November 16, 2009, No. 12, pp. 34)

Pub: Crain Communications, Inc.

Ed: John Hollon. **Description:** Due to salary freezes, pay cuts, layoffs, buyouts and a number of other stress factors brought about by the recession, employee engagement has been difficult to maintain by managers.

46540 ■ "Downturn Tests HCL's Pledge to Employees" in *Workforce Management* (Vol. 88, November 16, 2009, No. 12, pp. 23)

Pub: Crain Communications, Inc.

Ed: Ed Frauenheim. **Description:** HCL Technologies has kept its promise to keep from laying any employees off during the recession which served as a test for the tech firm's Employee First program, which seeks to give workers greater income security as well as a stronger voice in the firm.

46541 ■ "Empathy: An Entrepreneur's Killer App" in *Women Entrepreneur* (February 3, 2009)

Pub: Entrepreneur Media Inc.

Ed: Kristi Hedges. **Description:** It is just as important to treat employees with courtesy and respect during bad economic times as it is in a good economy. Employers sometimes take advantage of such bad economic times since they realize that employees are grateful to have a job and cannot just quit and easily find work elsewhere. The importance of empathy in a company's leadership personnel is discussed.

46542 ■ "Energy Sparks Job Growth" in *The Business Journal-Serving Greater Tampa Bay* (Vol. 28, August 8, 2008, No. 33, pp. 1)

Pub: American City Business Journals, Inc.

Ed: Margie Manning. **Description:** Energy infrastructure projects in Tampa Bay, Florida, are increasing the demand for labor in the area. Energy projects requiring an increase in labor include TECO Energy Inc.'s plan for a natural gas pipeline in the area and the installation of energy management system in Bank of America's branches in the area.

46543 ■ "Fairness First" in *Canadian Business* (Vol. 80, April 23, 2007, No. 9, pp. 45)

Pub: Rogers Media

Ed: Erin Pooley. **Description:** The need for the fair treatment of employees from the perspective of employee compensation is discussed.

46544 ■ "For Yung, Lady Luck a Fickle Mistress" in *Business Courier* (Vol. 24, November 30, 2008, No. 33, pp. 1)

Pub: American City Business Journals, Inc.

Ed: Dan Monk. **Description:** Bill Yung's Columbia Sussex Corp. won the bid for the parent company of Tropicana casinos in November 2006, and a year after, the company is facing regulatory and labor issues.

46545 ■ "Ford Executive Pay Could Fuel Tensions" in *Globe & Mail* (April 6, 2007, pp. B7)

Pub: CTVglobemedia Publishing Inc.

Ed: John D. Stoll; Terry Kosdrosky; Chad Clinton. **Description:** The likely tension between workers and management over the $62 million offer of Ford Motor Co. to its top executives is discussed.

46546 ■ "Fresh Direct's Crisis" in *Crain's New York Business* (Vol. 24, January 14, 2008, No. 2, pp. 3)

Pub: Crain Communications, Inc.

Ed: Lisa Fickenscher. **Description:** Freshdirect, an Internet grocery delivery service, finds itself under siege from federal immigration authorities, customers and labor organizations due to its employment practice of hiring illegals. At stake is the grocer's reputation as well as its ambitious growth plans, including an initial public offering of its stock.

46547 ■ "Generation Y Goes To Work; Management" in *The Economist* (Vol. 390, January 3, 2009, No. 8612, pp. 48)

Pub: The Economist Newspaper Inc.

Description: Unemployment rates among people in their 20s has increased significantly and there is a lower turnover in crisis-hit firms, which has made it more difficult to simply find another job if one is unsatisfied with the management style of his or her company. Managers are adopting a more command-and-control approach which is the antithesis of the open, collaborative style that younger employees prefer.

46548 ■ "Get Back To Business Planning Fundamentals" in *Entrepreneur* (October 24, 2008)

Pub: Entrepreneur Media Inc.

Ed: Tim Berry. **Description:** During a recession it is important to know what adjustment to make to your business plan. Some fundamentals to remember include: watching things more closely by tracking progress on cash, sales, new projects, customer satisfaction, ad spending and expenses; looking for built-in indicators such as what drives sales or expenses; watching what drives cash flow; and do not make mistakes such as laying off experienced employees too soon.

46549 ■ "Get Prepared for New Employee Free Choice Act" in *HRMagazine* (Vol. 53, December 2008, No. 12, pp. 22)

Pub: Society for Human Resource Management

Ed: Allen Smith. **Description:** According to the director of global labor and employee relations with Ingersoll Rand Company, unions may have started having employees signing authorization cards in anticipation of the Employee Free Choice Act. Once signed, the cards are good for one year and employers would have only ten days in which to prepare for bargaining with unions over the first labor contract. The Act also requires these negotiations be subject to mandatory arbitration if a contract is not reached within 120 days of negotiations with unions, resulting in employers' wage rates, health insurance, retirement benefits and key language about flexibility would be determined by an arbitrator with no vested interest in the success of the company.

46550 ■ "Hot-Button Ordinances May Go Up for Review" in *Crain's Detroit Business* (Vol. 26, January 18, 2010, No. 3, pp. 1)

Pub: Crain Communications, Inc.

Ed: Nancy Kaffer. **Description:** Detroit's economic fate may be tied to the city's anti-privatization ordinance and its policy of giving contract preference to Detroit-based businesses. The new administration feels that it is time to put everything on the table in an attempt to look for ways in which to save the city money.

46551 ■ "How Much Profit is Enough?" in *Automotive News* (Vol. 86, October 31, 2011, No. 6488, pp. 12)

Pub: Crain Communications Inc.

Ed: Keith Crain. **Description:** Workers at the big three automobile companies are unhappy about the issues of class wealth, like the high compensations offered to CEOs.

46552 ■ "How to Protect Your Job in a Recession" in *Harvard Business Review* (Vol. 86, September 2008, No. 9, pp. 113)

Pub: Harvard Business School Press

Ed: Janet Banks; Diane Coutu. **Description:** Strategies are presented for enhancing one's job security. These include being a team player, empathizing with management, preserving optimism, and concentrating on the customer.

46553 ■ "In Everyone's Interests" in *Canadian Business* (Vol. 80, April 23, 2007, No. 9, pp. 62)

Pub: Rogers Media

Ed: Rachel Pulfer. **Description:** The need of strategic negotiations during a labor contract to prevent disputes with employer is emphasized.

46554 ■ "Investigation Hints at Workers' Comp Trouble" in *Sacramento Business Journal* (Vol. 25, July 4, 2008, No. 18, pp. 1)

Pub: American City Business Journals, Inc.

Ed: Kelly Johnson. **Description:** In 500 California firms, a survey of worker compensation revealed that 38 percent of the companies had problems with required coverage. Government investigators are bothered that 107 companies did not respond to the official inquiry. Other views and information on the survey and on the expected economic implications of the findings are presented.

46555 ■ "Is Raising CPP Premiums a Good Idea?" in *Canadian Business* (Vol. 83, July 20, 2010, No. 11-12, pp. 37)

Pub: Rogers Media Ltd.

Description: Big labor is pushing for an increase in Canada Pension Plan premiums but pension consultants believe this system is not broken and that the government needs to focus on addressing the low rate of personal retirement savings. If the premiums go up, even those with high savings will be forced to pay more and it could block other plans that really address the real issue.

46556 ■ "It's All in the Details" in *Canadian Business* (Vol. 80, December 25, 2006, No. 1, pp. 11)

Pub: Rogers Media

Description: The failure of several Canadian clothing retailers to disclose their labor practices is discussed.

46557 ■ "Just Shut The Hell Up" in *Canadian Business* (Vol. 81, July 22, 2008, No. 12-13, pp. 33)

Pub: Rogers Media Ltd.

Ed: Jane Bao. **Description:** Employees desire better communication as opposed to more communication from their managers. Advice regarding managing communication in the workplace is given including ways in which speakers can say more with fewer words.

46558 ■ "KC Plants Downshift" in *The Business Journal-Serving Metropolitan Kansas City* (Vol. 27, November 7, 2008, No. 9, pp. 1)

Pub: American City Business Journals, Inc.

Ed: James Dornbrook. **Description:** Discusses Ford Motor Co. and General Motors' factories in the region; Ford Motor Co. removed the second shift on the F-150 line at the Kansas City Assembly Plant but added a shift to the production of the Ford Escape and Mercury Mariner in an attempt to avoid layoffs. One spokesman for General Motors, however, states that they cannot guarantee that they won't make any production cuts and layoffs in the future.

46559 ■ "Labor Compensation and Collective Bargaining Data" in *Montly Labor Review* (Vol. 133, September 2010, No. 9, pp. 116)

Pub: Bureau of Labor Statistics

Description: Employment cost index is presented, citing compensation by occupation and industry group.

46560 ■ "Labor and Management: Working Together for a Stable Future" in *Alaska Business Monthly* **(Vol. 27, October 2011, No. 10, pp. 130)**
Pub: Alaska Business Publishing Company

Ed: Nicole A. Bonham Colby. **Description:** Alaska unions and employers are working to ensure a consistent flow of skilled Alaska workers as current the current workforce reaches retirement age.

46561 ■ "LaSalle Street Firms Cherry-Pick Talent As Wall Street Tanks" in *Crain's Chicago Business* **(Vol. 31, November 17, 2008, No. 46)**
Pub: Crain Communications, Inc.

Ed: H. Lee Murphy. **Description:** Many local businesses are taking advantage of the lay offs that many major Wall Street firms are undergoing in their workforces; these companies see the opportunity to woo talent and expand their staff with quality executives.

46562 ■ "Law Firms Troll for Complaints Among Disgruntled Workers" in *The Business Journal-Serving Greater Tampa Bay* **(Vol. 28, July 11, 2008)**
Pub: American City Business Journals, Inc.

Ed: Jane Meinhardt. **Description:** Economic slowdown has affected businesses as they downsize, seeing an increase in wage and hour complaints using loopholes in the Fair Labor Standards Act, from which several law firms are recently generating revenue. Federal judges notice the increase in lawsuits and ordered that law firms show cause for non-compliance.

46563 ■ "Law Reform, Collective Bargaining, and the Balance of Power: Results of an Empirical Study" in *WorkingUSA* **(June 2008)**
Pub: Blackwell Publishers Ltd.

Ed: Ellen Dannin, Michelle Dean, Gangaram Singh. **Description:** Despite Congress' having made clear policy statements in the National Labor Relations Act that the law was intended to promote equality of bargaining power between employers and employees, to promote the practice and procedure of collective bargaining as the method of setting workplace terms and conditions of employment, and forbidding construing the law "so as to either interfere with or impede or diminish in any way the right to strike," by early 1940, the courts had given employers the right to permanently replace strikers and implement their final offer at impasse. Judges have often justified these doctrines as promoting balance in bargaining. Critics contend that the doctrines have the capacity to destroy the right to strike, unbalance bargaining power, and divert parties from the process of bargaining collectively. Some have proposed allowing temporary but not permanent striker replacement. The article uses a bargaining simulation followed by a survey and debriefing comments to test these opposing claims.

46564 ■ "Lawyers Lock Up Cops as Clients" in *Sacramento Business Journal* **(Vol. 28, April 8, 2011, No. 6, pp. 1)**
Pub: Sacramento Business Journal

Ed: Kathy Robertson. **Description:** Sacramento-based law firm Mastagni, Holstedt and Chiurazzi has grown its client base by specializing in law enforcement labor issues. The firm represents 80,000 public sector correctional officers in the US. The firm has been experiencing an increase in new business as public sector employers face huge budget deficits.

46565 ■ "Legislators Must Cut Cost of Government" in *Crain's Detroit Business* **(Vol. 24, October 6, 2008, No. 40, pp. 6)**
Pub: Crain Communications, Inc.

Description: Southeast and West Michigan business leaders are setting aside their differences and have proposed clear agendas, ranging from eliminating the Michigan Business Tax to overhauling public employee and retiree benefits and pensions. Lawmakers must also come together to find solutions for the state's economy and discover an entirely new vision for the future of Michigan business.

46566 ■ "Living in a 'Goldfish Bowl'" in *WorkingUSA* **(Vol. 11, June 2008, No. 2, pp. 277)**
Pub: Blackwell Publishers Ltd.

Ed: John Lund. **Description:** Recent changes in laws, regulations and even the reporting format of labor organization annual financial reports in both the U.S. and Australia have received surprisingly little attention, yet they have significantly increased the amount of information available both to union members and the public in general, as reports in both countries are available via government Websites. While such financial reporting laws are extremely rare in European countries, with the exception of the UK and Ireland, the U.S. and Australian reporting systems have become among the most detailed in the world. After reviewing these changes in financial reporting and the availability of these reports, as well as comparing and contrasting the specific reporting requirements of each country, this paper then examines the cost-benefit impact of more detailed financial reporting.

46567 ■ "Making Diverse Teams Click" in *Harvard Business Review* **(Vol. 86, July-August 2008, No. 8, pp. 20)**
Pub: Harvard Business School Press

Ed: Jeffrey T. Polzer. **Description:** 360-degree feedback to increase the efficacy of diverse-member workplace teams, which involves each member providing feedback to the others on the team is discussed.

46568 ■ "Managing the Facebookers; Business" in *The Economist* **(Vol. 390, January 3, 2009, No. 8612, pp. 10)**
Pub: Economist Newspaper Ltd.

Description: According to a report from PricewaterhouseCoopers, a business consultancy, workers from Generation Y, also known as the Net Generation, are more difficult to recruit and integrate into companies that practice traditional business acumen. 61 percent of chief executive managers say that they have trouble with younger employees who tend to be more narcissistic and more interested in personal fulfillment with a need for frequent feedback and an over-precise set of objectives on the path to promotion which can be hard for managers who are used to a different relationship with their subordinates. Older bosses should prepare to make some concessions to their younger talent since some of the issues that make them happy include cheaper online ways to communicate and additional coaching, both of which are good for business.

46569 ■ "Mentoring Support" in *Black Enterprise* **(Vol. 38, July 2008, No. 12, pp. 64)**
Pub: Earl G. Graves Publishing Co. Inc.

Description: With his relocation from his multicultural team in New York to the less diverse Scripps Networks' headquarters in Knoxville, Earl Cokley has made it a top priority to push for more diversity and mentoring opportunities within the management of the media and marketing company.

46570 ■ "The Mobile Workforce Revolution" in *Canadian Business* **(Vol. 81, March 31, 2008, No. 5, pp. 28)**
Pub: Rogers Media

Ed: Diane Horton. **Description:** Diane Horton explains how a mobile workforce helps companies cut costs, increase productivity, and boost employee motivation. Horton says that employees believe they usually become more productive by 15 to 30 percent after their companies go mobile.

46571 ■ "New Jobless Claims Filed in December Soar" in *Baltimore Business Journal* **(Vol. 27, January 29, 2010, No. 39, pp. 1)**
Pub: American City Business Journals

Ed: Scott Dance. **Description:** Maryland received 48,693 new claims for unemployment benefits in December 2009, reaching its highest monthly total since 1974. The number of claims was up 49 percent from November and 13 percent from the same period in 2008. Labor officials and economists discuss this trend.

46572 ■ "New Race Suit at Local Coke Plant" in *Business Courier* **(Vol. 24, February 1, 2008, No. 43, pp. 1)**
Pub: American City Business Journals, Inc.

Ed: Jon Newberry. **Description:** Another racial harassment lawsuit has been filed against the Coca-Cola Enterprises Inc. plant in Madisonville by its 23 black workers. The lawsuit alleges that the working environment at the plant continues to be offensive, abusive, intimidating and hostile. Details of the class-action suit are provided.

46573 ■ "NFL Labor, Legal Issues Hang Over Detroit Lions' Rebuilding Efforts" in *Crain's Detroit Business* **(Vol. 26, January 11, 2010, No. 2)**
Pub: Crain Communications, Inc.

Ed: Bill Shea. **Description:** Overview of the possible outcomes regarding labor talks with Detroit Lion's players as well as the outcome of a U.S. Supreme Court decision that could boost franchise values but at the expense of fans and corporate sponsors.

46574 ■ "Nine Sectors to Watch: Automotive" in *Canadian Business* **(Vol. 81, December 24, 2007, No. 1, pp. 47)**
Pub: Rogers Media

Ed: Thomas Watson. **Description:** Forecasts on the Canadian automotive sector for 2008 are presented. Details on contract concessions made by American unions, the industry's Big Three (General Motors, Chrysler, and Ford) operations in Canada, and Canadian Auto Workers demand for higher wages are also discussed.

46575 ■ "No End to the Nightmare; America's Car Industry" in *The Economist* **(Vol. 390, January 3, 2009, No. 8612, pp. 46)**
Pub: The Economist Newspaper Inc.

Description: Detroit's struggling auto industry and the government loan package is discussed as well as the United Auto Worker union, which is loathed by Senate Republicans.

46576 ■ *No Place Like Home: Organizing Home-Based Labor in the Era of Structural Adjustment*
Pub: Routledge Inc.

Ed: David Staples. **Released:** November 2006. **Price:** $70.00. **Description:** The book examines the role of home-based women workers in contemporary capitalism.

46577 ■ "OPSEU: Developmental Service Workers Picketing Across Ontario to Raise Community Awareness" in *Canadian Corporate News* **(May 16, 2007)**
Pub: Comtex News Network Inc.

Description: Across Ontario staff who support people with developmental disabilities are picketing local MPP offices and other community hubs to highlight the Ontario government's inadequate response to the crisis in developmental services.

46578 ■ "Randy Perreira" in *Hawaii Business* **(Vol. 53, February 2008, No. 8, pp. 28)**
Pub: Hawaii Business Publishing

Ed: David K. Choo. **Description:** Randy Perreira is recently named executive director of Hawaii Government Employees Association. He talks about how he was shaped growing up with a father who was a labor leader and how the challenges in 2008 compare with those in the time of his father. He also shares his thoughts about the importance of employees fighting for their rights.

46579 ■ "Recession Survival Tip: Less Is More" in *Women Entrepreneur* **(December 31, 2008)**
Pub: Entrepreneur Media Inc.

Ed: Suzy Girard-Ruttenberg. **Description:** These trying economic times can be an opportunity to make bold changes in one's business that may yield lasting results, not just short-term survival; simplification, accountability and shoring up one's margins are things to look at when determining the goals of the company.

46580 ■ **"Ronald Taketa"** in *Hawaii Business* (Vol. 54, September 2008, No. 3, pp. 28)

Pub: Hawaii Business Publishing

Ed: Shara Enay. **Description:** Interview with Ronald Taketa of the Hawaii Carpenters Union who states that the economic downturn has affected the construction industry as 20 percent of the union's 7,800 members are unemployed. He shares his thoughts about the industry's economic situation, the union's advertisements, and his role as a leader of the union.

46581 ■ **"Running On Empty"** in *The Business Journal-Milwaukee* (Vol. 25, July 4, 2008, No. 41, pp. A1)

Pub: American City Business Journals, Inc.

Ed: David Doege. **Description:** Employers are more engaged in offering incentives designed to offset commuting costs. Among the incentives offered are gas cards, parking reimbursement and midyear wage increases. The other efforts to help employees with the costs of going to work are discussed.

46582 ■ **"The Rypple Effect; Performance Management"** in *The Economist* (Vol. 390, January 3, 2009, No. 8612, pp. 48)

Pub: The Economist Newspaper Inc.

Description: New companies such as Rypple, a new, web-based service, claim that they can satisfy the Net Generation's need for frequent assessments while easing the burden this creates for management.

46583 ■ **"Scouting and Keeping Good Talent in the Workplace"** in *Hawaii Business* (Vol. 53, January 2008, No. 7, pp. 50)

Pub: Hawaii Business Publishing

Ed: Christie Dermegian. **Description:** Tips on improving employee selection and retention are presented. The strategies in choosing and keeping the right employees include identifying which type of people the company needs and improving the workplace environment.

46584 ■ **"Solidarity UAW Forever"** in *Crain's Detroit Business* (Vol. 25, June 1, 2009, No. 22, pp. M001)

Pub: Crain Communications Inc. - Detroit

Ed: Ryan Beene. **Description:** United Auto Workers union has made it difficult for certain businesses to move to Michigan. Discussion is made about the issues involved and changes that need to be made in the way labor and management do business.

46585 ■ **"Sorry: Good Defense for Mal Offense"** in *The Business Journal-Serving Metropolitan Kansas City* (Vol. 26, July 4, 2008, No. 43, pp. 1)

Pub: American City Business Journals, Inc.

Ed: Rob Roberts. **Description:** According to a survey conducted by the Kansas City Business Journal, ten hospitals in Kansas City showed that they have adopted disclosure policies that include prompt apologies and settlement offers. The policy is effective in minimizing medical malpractice lawsuits. Other details of the survey are presented.

46586 ■ **"A Stalled Culture Change?"** in *Workforce Management* (Vol. 88, December 14, 2009, No. 13, pp. 1)

Pub: Crain Communications, Inc.

Ed: Jeremy Smerd. **Description:** General Motors CEO Fritz Henderson's abrupt resignation shocked employees and signaled that Henderson had not done enough to change the company's culture, especially in dealing with its top management.

46587 ■ **"Star Power"** in *Small Business Opportunities* (September 2008)

Pub: Entrepreneur Media Inc.

Description: Employee retention is an important factor for corporate executives to consider because the impact of excessive turnovers can be devastating to a company causing poor morale, unemployment claims, hiring costs, lost production and customer loss. Although there is no specific formula for retaining employees, there are several things every organization can do to keep their workers happy and increase the chances that they will stay loyal and

keep working for the company for years to come; tips aimed at management regarding good employee relationships are included.

46588 ■ **"Steeling for Battle"** in *Crain's Chicago Business* (Vol. 31, April 21, 2008, No. 16, pp. 3)

Pub: Crain Communications, Inc.

Ed: Bob Tita. **Description:** Discusses contract negotiations between the United Steelworkers union and ArcelorMittal USA Inc., the nation's largest steelmaker, and U.S. Steel Corp., the third-largest; the union sees these negotiations as the best chance in two decades to regain lost ground but industry experts predict the companies will try to reduce benefits, demand a separate, lower wage scale for new hires and look for relief from the rising costs for retirees' health insurance coverage.

46589 ■ **"The Story Of Diane Greene"** in *Barron's* (Vol. 88, July 14, 2008, No. 28, pp. 31)

Pub: Dow Jones & Co., Inc.

Ed: Mark Veverka. **Description:** Discusses the ousting of Diane Greene as a chief executive of VMWare, a developer of virtualization software, after the firm went public; in this case Greene, a brilliant engineer, should not be negatively impacted by the decision because it is common for companies to bring in new executive leadership that is more operations oriented after the company goes public.

46590 ■ **"Taxes, Right-To-Work Top West Michigan Concerns"** in *Crain's Detroit Business* (Vol. 24, September 22, 2008, No. 38, pp. 6)

Pub: Crain Communications, Inc.

Ed: Amy Lane. **Description:** Two of the top priorities of business leaders in Western Michigan are the new business tax which they want to end as well as making the state a "right-to-work" one through laws to prohibit unions from requiring workers to pay dues and membership as a condition of their employment.

46591 ■ **"Truckers Walk Strike Line"** in *Puget Sound Business Journal* (Vol. 29, October 24, 2008, No. 27, pp. 1)

Pub: American City Business Journals

Ed: Steve Wilhelm. **Description:** Teamsters Local 174 went on strike against Oak Harbor Freight Lines Inc. over alleged company violations of federal labor laws. The union also accuses the company of engaging directly with employees and holding mandatory meetings about contract negotiations.

46592 ■ **"U Overhauling Its Janitorial Program, but Custodians Taking Exception"** in *Saint Paul Pioneer Press* (August 20, 2011)

Pub: McClatchy-Tribune Regional News

Ed: Mila Koumpilova. **Description:** University of Minnesota developed a new team cleaning approach for its campus. The new custodian program will save $3.1 million annually while providing a cleaner campus. The union representing the custodians questions both claims.

46593 ■ **"Union Ethics Training: Building the Legitimacy and Effectiveness of Organized Labor"** in *WorkingUSA* (Vol. 11, September 2008, No. 3)

Pub: Blackwell Publishers Ltd.

Ed: Maggie Cohen. **Description:** Arguments are presented for the implementation of serious ethics training at all levels of labor unions and their contribution to union effectiveness by enhancing union legitimacy-understood as an amalgam of legal, pragmatic, and moral legitimacy and by paving the way to stable recognition of the labor movement as an integral part of American society, necessary to economic prosperity and the realization of fundamental American moral and social values.

46594 ■ **"Union, Heal Thyself"** in *Canadian Business* (Vol. 81, July 21, 2008, No. 11, pp. 9)

Pub: Rogers Media Ltd.

Description: General Motors Corp. was offered by the federal government a $250 million fund after the company declared plans to close its facility in On-

tario. The government move is geared towards supporting the workers who have refused to support the automotive company. Details of the labor contract between General Motors and the Canadian Auto Workers are presented.

46595 ■ **"Union Questions Patrick Cudahy Layoffs"** in *Business Journal-Milwaukee* (Vol. 28, December 3, 2010, No. 9, pp. A1)

Pub: Milwaukee Business Journal

Ed: Rich Ravito. **Description:** United Food and Commercial Workers Local 1473 is investigating Patrick Cudahy Inc.'s termination of 340 jobs. The union said the company has violated the law for failing to issue proper notice of a mass layoff.

46596 ■ **"Unions Pony Up $1 Million for McBride Stimulus"** in *Saint Louis Business Journal* (Vol. 31, July 29, 2011, No. 49, pp. 1)

Pub: Saint Louis Business Journal

Ed: Evan Binns. **Description:** Carpenters District Council of Greater St. Louis and International Brotherhood of Electrical Workers Local 1 were among the nine unions that agreed to split the cost of nearly $1 million in incentives for homebuyers who purchase homes in McBride communities. McBride & Son has spent over $100,000 to promote the incentive program.

46597 ■ **"Unions and Upward Mobility for Low-Wage Workers"** in *WorkingUSA* (Vol. 11, September 2008, No. 3, pp. 337)

Pub: Blackwell Publishers Ltd.

Ed: John Schmitt, Margy Waller, Shawn Fremstad, Ben Zipperer. **Description:** Examination of the impact of unionization on the pay and benefits in fifteen important low-wage occupations is outlined. Even after controlling for important differences between union and nonunion workers, including such factors as age and education level, unionization improves the pay and benefits offered in what are otherwise low-paying occupations.

46598 ■ **"UnitedHealthcare Resists Prognosis"** in *The Business Journal-Serving Metropolitan Kansas City* (Vol. 26, August 29, 2008, No. 51)

Pub: American City Business Journals, Inc.

Ed: Rob Roberts. **Description:** Saint Luke's Hospital Systems terminated UnitedHealthcare from its insurance provider network on July 25, 2008. Negotiators with both parties have stopped speaking, and employees under UnitedHealthcare plans will have to pay higher bills unless Saint Luke's reconsiders its decision. The parties' previous negotiations are discussed.

46599 ■ **"Unmasking Manly Men"** in *Harvard Business Review* (Vol. 86, July-August 2008, No. 8, pp. 20)

Pub: Harvard Business School Press

Ed: Robin J. Ely; Debra Meyerson. **Description:** Oil rig work is used to explore how focusing on job requirements and performance successfully challenged stereotypical views of masculinity and competence.

46600 ■ **"Verizon, Union Dispute is a Vestige of the Past"** in *Philadelphia Business Journal* (Vol. 30, August 26, 2011, No. 28, pp. 1)

Pub: American City Business Journals Inc.

Ed: Peter Key. **Description:** Verizon is arguing that some of the provisions of its unionized workers' contracts date back to the days before AT&T were forced to spin off its local phone-service providers in 1984. The evolution of Verizon through the years and its relations with its unions are discussed.

46601 ■ **"Vicki Avril; Senior Vice-President of Tubular Division, Ipsco Inc."** in *Crain's Chicago Business* (Vol. 31, May 5, 2008, No. 18)

Pub: Crain Communications, Inc.

Ed: Miriam Gottfried. **Description:** Profile of Vicki Avril who is the senior vice-president of the tubular division at Ipsco Inc. where she supervises 2,800 employees and 13 mills throughout the United States and Canada.

46602 ■ "Wal-Mart Expansion Plans Hit Roadblock" in *Crain's Chicago Business* (Vol. 31, March 24, 2008, No. 12, pp. 2)
Pub: Crain Communications, Inc.
Ed: Monee Fields-White. **Description:** Wal-Mart Stores Inc.'s expansion plans in Chicago have suffered a series of setbacks due to a shifting political landscape in which may require the company to pay higher wages. Wal-Mart claims that its hourly pay and benefits are fair; however, the labor force does not agree.

46603 ■ "Weaving a Stronger Fabric: Organizing a Global Sweat-Free Apparel Production Agreement" in *WorkingUSA* (Vol. 11, June 2008, No. 2)
Pub: Blackwell Publishers Ltd.
Ed: Eric Dirnbach. **Description:** Tens of millions of workers working under terrible sweatshop conditions in the global apparel industry. Workers are employed at apparel contractors and have been largely unsuccessful in organizing and improving their working conditions. The major apparel manufacturers and retailers have the most power in this industry, and they have adopted corporate social responsibility programs as a false solution to the sweatshop problem. The major North American apparel unions dealt with similar sweatshop conditions a century ago by organizing the contractors and brands into joint association contracts that significantly raised standards. Taking inspiration from their example, workers and their anti-sweatshop allies need to work together to coordinate a global organizing effort that builds worker power and establishes a global production agreement that negotiates with both contractors and the brands for improved wages, benefits, and working conditions.

46604 ■ "Whistleblower or Manipulator?" in *Canadian Business* (Vol. 81, July 22, 2008, No. 12-13, pp. 11)
Pub: Rogers Media Ltd.
Ed: John Gray. **Description:** Discusses Maria Messina who is portrayed by prosecutors of the Livent Inc. trial as a whistleblower, while defense lawyers insist that she is a manipulator. Defense lawyers allege that Messina, who was Livent's chief financial officer, is a character assassin that made money out of Livent's bankruptcy. Other views on Messina, as well as information on the case, are presented.

46605 ■ "Will Call Center Servicing Solve Labor's Customer Satisfaction Problems?" in *WorkingUSA* (Vol. 11, September 2008, No. 3, pp. 383)
Pub: Blackwell Publishers Ltd.
Ed: Steve Early. **Description:** Service Employees International Union (SEIU) has launched an ambitious plan to service hundreds of thousands of members through a network of Member Resource Centers (MRCs). This call center servicing strategy draws on the experience of unions in Australia and the customer service centers operated by major corporations. Call center critics fear the role of union stewards and shop floor activity will be undermined by the introduction of this system in SEIU workplaces in the U.S.

46606 ■ "Women's Union Leadership: Closing the Gender Gap" in *WorkingUSA* (Vol. 11, December 2008, No. 4, pp. 459)
Pub: Blackwell Publishers Ltd.
Ed: Michelle Kaminski, Elaine K. Yakura. **Description:** Women make up 44 percent of the labor movement, but a smaller percentage of union leaders. The importance of having a leadership representative of membership, some differences between male and female leadership, and why the labor movement needs more women leaders is discussed.

46607 ■ "Worth His Salt" in *Hawaii Business* (Vol. 53, January 2008, No. 7, pp. 45)
Pub: Hawaii Business Publishing
Ed: Jolyn Okimoto Rosa. **Description:** Bryan Zada owns three PretzelMaker franchises, whose total loss amounted to $40,000 in 2003. Zada believes that listening to employees was one of the key steps in turning the business around. The efforts made to improve the franchises' products are also given.

46608 ■ "Xstrata and CAW Get Tentative Deal" in *Globe & Mail* (February 2, 2007, pp. B3)
Pub: CTVglobemedia Publishing Inc.
Ed: Andy Hoffman. **Description:** The agreement between Xstrata PLC and Canadian Auto Workers union over wage hike is discussed.

TRADE PERIODICALS

46609 ■ *Collective Bargaining Negotiations and Contracts*
Pub: Bureau of National Affairs Inc.
Contact: Leslie Goldman, Managing Editor
Released: Biweekly. **Price:** $246. **Description:** Presents news of developments in collective bargaining, including contract settlements, bargaining techniques and trends, and contract interpretations by the courts. Recurring features include columns titled Clause Talk, Arbitrating the Contract, Facts & Figures, and Perspective.

46610 ■ *Daily Labor Report*
Pub: Bureau of National Affairs Inc.
Contact: Susan Sala, Managing Editor
Released: Daily. **Price:** $6,160. **Description:** Covers labor developments in Congress, the courts, federal agencies, unions, management, and the National Labor Relations Board.

46611 ■ *Human Resources Report*
Pub: Bureau of National Affairs Inc.
Contact: Gail Moorstein, Managing Editor
Released: Weekly. **Price:** $875. **Description:** Monitors employee and labor relations in the United States. Follows private sector developments in compensation, health benefits, Equal Employment Opportunity (EEO), labor economics, legislation, and regulatory issues. Recurring features include a calendar of events, and weekly analysis.

46612 ■ *IRC Newsletter*
Pub: Industrial Relations Center (IRC)
Released: Bimonthly. **Description:** Focuses on industrial relations and collective bargaining, with summaries of court decisions in the field and of decisions of the National Labor Relations Board and other boards and commissions. Covers pending legislation pertaining to work, labor-management relations, and similar subjects. Recurring features include bibliographic information, statistics, announcements of appointments, and synopses of significant reports and studies.

46613 ■ *Labor Center Reporter*
Pub: Center for Labor Research and Education
Released: Quarterly. **Price:** $20 (Donation). **Description:** Supplies economic and social analysis of issues of concern to the trade union community.

46614 ■ *Labor Relations Week*
Pub: Bureau of National Affairs Inc.
Contact: Susan Sala, Managing Editor
Released: Weekly. **Price:** $944. **Description:** Provides a comprehensive overview of developments influencing labor relations in the private sector.

46615 ■ *School of Labor and Industrial Relations eNewsletter*
Pub: School of Labor and Industrial Relations
Ed: Released: Semiannual. **Price:** Free. **Description:** Reports news of the School, including the status of various programs and services and statistics on growth. Contains articles on manpower, organizational behavior and personnel management, international and comparative labor and industrial relations, social structure and community organization, and social and industrial psychology. Recurring features include notices of job opportunities for graduates, courses offered, activities of the faculty, and meetings; book reviews; and recent reprints.

46616 ■ *Union Labor Report Weekly Newsletter*
Pub: Bureau of National Affairs Inc.
Contact: Jeff Day, Managing Editor
Released: Weekly. **Price:** $162. **Description:** Provides a roundup of developments of concern to organized labor. Includes summaries of arbitration

awards and court cases. Recurring features include sections titled Special Report, Labor Facts, and Grievance Guide. Included with subscription to Union Labor Report or available separately. Subscription price includes Union Labor Report's On The Line newsletter.

VIDEOCASSETTES/ AUDIOCASSETTES

46617 ■ *Labor Management*
New Dimension Media, Inc.
307 N Michigan Ave., Ste. 500
Chicago, IL 60601
Ph:(312)642-9400
Free: 800-288-4456
Fax:(312)642-9805
Co. E-mail: Info@NDMquestar.com
URL: http://www.ndmquestar.com
Released: 1987. **Price:** $50.00. **Description:** Shows the importance of cooperation between union workers and management. Because it supplies solutions for handling employee situations, it is aimed towards management. **Availability:** VHS; 3/4U.

COMPUTERIZED DATABASES

46618 ■ *Construction Labor Report*
The Bureau of National Affairs Inc.
1801 S Bell St.
Arlington, VA 22202
Free: 800-372-1033
Co. E-mail: customercare@bna.com
URL: http://www.bna.com
Description: Contains labor and employment issues for all segments of the construction industry, including union, non-union, dual shop, and government officials tracking the industry. Topics include apprentices, arbitration decisions, collective bargaining, contractor associations, court and administrative decisions, EEO, employee benefits, federal and state legislation, government regulations, health and safety, independent contractors, jobsite accidents, jurisdictional disputes, labor laws, union organizing, worker shortages, workers' compensation insurance, workforce demographics, regulatory, legislative, and industry developments impacting the construction industry; legal news, state news, economic statistics, lists of relevant meetings, seminars, and conferences; and full text of court decisions, legislation approved by Congress, minority business enterprises, mixed crews, NLRB decisions, pension and benefits matters, prevailing wage laws, productivity, project labor agreements, substance abuse and control, training, transportation, and union job targeting programs. Includes summaries of all reports covered in each issue. **Availability:** Online: The Bureau of National Affairs Inc., Thomson Reuters. **Type:** Full text.

46619 ■ *Human Resources Report*
The Bureau of National Affairs Inc.
1801 S Bell St.
Arlington, VA 22202
Free: 800-372-1033
Co. E-mail: customercare@bna.com
URL: http://www.bna.com
Description: Contains detailed reporting and news of developments and trends affecting human resources and employee relations. Covers relevant national news, legislative and regulatory developments, labor economics, developments in training and technology, health benefits, employee-management relations, compensation, and legal developments. Provides conference reports, status reports on legislation and regulations, and state, local, and international news. Covers issues such as grievances, EEO/diversity, compensation and benefits, comparable worth, job security, flexible employment, right-to-know, maternity/paternity benefits, employment at will, employee privacy rights, pay equity, drug screening, child care benefits, smoking restrictions, early retirement, immigration reform, benefits taxation, and healthcare cost containment. **Availability:** Online: The Bureau of National Affairs Inc. **Type:** Full text.

46620 ■ *Labor Relations Week*
The Bureau of National Affairs Inc.
1801 S Bell St.
Arlington, VA 22202
Free: 800-372-1033
Co. E-mail: customercare@bna.com
URL: http://www.bna.com
Description: Contains the latest information on congressional, judicial, legislative, and economic developments affecting private-sector labor relations. Includes coverage of collective bargaining, National Labor Relations Board (NLRB) and court rulings, Equal Employment Opportunity (EEO) policy, health issues, safety, technology issues, and legislative and regulatory news. Covers state and federal labor trends and laws, contracts and grievances, union organization, labor management, and more. **Availability:** Online: The Bureau of National Affairs Inc. **Type:** Full text; Numeric.

LIBRARIES

46621 ■ Canadian Labour Congress Library
2841 Riverside Dr.
Ottawa, ON, Canada K1V 8X7
Ph:(613)521-3400
Fax:(613)521-4655
URL: http://www.canadianlabour.ca
Contact: Ken Georgetti, Pres.
Scope: Labor, labor history, industrial relations, trade unions, economics. **Services:** Interlibrary loan. **Holdings:** 4000 books; CLC Convention documents. **Subscriptions:** 36 journals and other serials.

46622 ■ Federation des Travailleurs et Travailleuses du Quebec–Centre de Documentation
565 boul Cremazie E. Bureau 12100
Montreal, QC, Canada H2M 2W3
Ph:(514)383-8025
Fax:(514)383-0502
Co. E-mail: ireny@ftq.qc.ca
URL: http://www.ftq.qc.ca
Contact: Isabelle Reny, Doc.
Scope: Work, unions, sociology, economy. **Services:** Copying; Library open to the public. **Holdings:** 10,200 books. **Subscriptions:** 150 journals and other serials; 3 newspapers.

46623 ■ Manitoba Department of Labour–Manitoba Labour Board Library
500-175 Hargrave St.
Winnipeg, MB, Canada R3C 3R8
Ph:(204)945-5046

Fax:(204)945-1296
Co. E-mail: mlb@gov.mb.ca
URL: http://www.gov.mb.ca/labour/labbrd/
Contact: Jodi Gilmore, Res.
Scope: Labor. **Services:** Library open to the public. **Holdings:** 100 books; 1080 bound periodical volumes. **Subscriptions:** 5 journals and other serials.

46624 ■ York University–Centre for Research in Work and Society
276 York Lanes
4700 Keele St.
Toronto, ON, Canada M3J 1P3
Ph:(416)736-2100 x70494
Co. E-mail: paszter@yorku.ca
URL: http://www.yorku.ca/crws
Contact: Dr. Norene Pupo, Dir.
Scope: Work and society, unions, arbitration. **Services:** Library open to students, faculty and staff; open by appointment only from May to August. **Holdings:** 500 books; journals; primary and secondary documents and sources.

RESEARCH CENTERS

46625 ■ International Labor Rights Forum
1634 I St. NW, No. 1001
Washington, DC 20006
Ph:(202)347-4100
Fax:(202)347-4885
Co. E-mail: laborrights@ilrf.org
URL: http://www.laborrights.org
Contact: Judy Gearhart, Exec.Dir.
E-mail: laborrights@ilrf.org
Scope: Labor rights in the U.S. and abroad, including child labor exploitation, forced labor, attacks on and imprisonment of union leaders, and other violations of international labor standards, trade unions, democracy in developing countries, global trade, and economic integration. **Services:** Information and analyses regarding labor rights conditions internationally. **Publications:** Books and papers (quarterly). **Educational Activities:** Conferences (periodically). **Awards:** Award for leadership in defending labor rights (occasionally).

46626 ■ Labor and Employment Relations Association
121 Labor & Employment Relations Bldg.
504 E Armory Ave.
Champaign, IL 61820
Ph:(217)333-0072

Fax:(217)265-5130
Co. E-mail: leraoffice@illinois.edu
URL: http://www.leraweb.org
Contact: Paula D. Wells, Exec.Dir.
E-mail: leraoffice@illinois.edu
Scope: Labor, employment, and the workplace, including employer and employee organization, employment and labor relations, human resources, labor markets, income security, and related fields, including international and comparative dimensions in all pertinent disciplines, including industrial relations, history, economics, political science, psychology, sociology, law, management, labor studies, and others. **Publications:** LERA proceedings of the annual meeting (annually); LERA Newsletter (quarterly); Perspectives on Work magazine (annually); Research Volume (annually). **Educational Activities:** LERA jobs announcement service (weekly); LERA PhD Student Consortium (annually). **Awards:** LERA Best Dissertation Award (annually); LERA Excellence in Education Awards (annually); LERA Lifetime Achievement Award (annually); LERA Outstanding Young Practitioner Award (annually); LERA Outstanding Young Scholar Awards (annually).

46627 ■ Labor Research Association
330 W 42nd St., 13th Fl.
New York, NY 10001
Ph:(212)714-1677
Fax:(212)714-1674
Co. E-mail: info@lra-ny.com
URL: http://www.laborresearch.org/about.php
Contact: Jonathan Tasini, Exec.Dir.
E-mail: info@lra-ny.com
Scope: Economic, social, and political conditions, focusing on labor relations.

46628 ■ University of Louisville–Labor-Management Center
Patterson Hall, Rm. 113
Louisville, KY 40292
Ph:(502)852-6482
Fax:(502)852-6453
Co. E-mail: carrie.donald@louisville.edu
URL: http://louisville.edu/labormanagement/
Contact: Prof. Carrie G. Donald, Dir.
E-mail: carrie.donald@louisville.edu
Scope: Labor-management relations, equal employment opportunity, economic development issues, and public perceptions of labor relations. **Services:** Arbitration Advocacy Institute; Institute for ADA Medication; Planning and consulting services. **Publications:** Newsletter (quarterly); Research publications series. **Educational Activities:** Symposia and seminars. **Awards:** Labor-Management Annual Award, honors a workplace where management and the union(s) have promoted and demonstrated positive labor-management relations.

Venture Capital and Other Funding

START-UP INFORMATION

46629 ■ *Angel Financing: How to Find and Invest in Private Equity*
Pub: John Wiley and Sons, Inc.

Ed: Gerald A. Benjamin; Joel B. Margulis. **Price:** $65.00. **Description:** The book provides a proven strategy to help entrepreneurs find angel investors. Interviews with angel investors as well as information about investors' hedging strategies, risk assessments, syndication orientation, financial return expectations, deal structuring preferences, monitoring investments, harvesting returns, and realist exit strategies are covered.

46630 ■ **"ATI Now Ready to Pounce on Biotech" in** *Austin Business JournalInc.* **(Vol. 28, August 22, 2008, No. 23, pp. 1)**
Pub: American City Business Journals

Ed: Laura Hipp. **Description:** Austin Technology Incubator has entered the biotechnology sector through a program of the University of Texas incubator. The company's bioscience program was set off by a grant from the City of Austin worth $125,000. The growth of Austin's biotechnology sector is examined.

46631 ■ **"EDCO Doling Out Capital Along Border" in** *Austin Business JournalInc.* **(Vol. 28, August 1, 2008, No. 20, pp. 1)**
Pub: American City Business Journals

Ed: Sandra Zaragoza. **Description:** Non-profit business incubator Economic Development Catalyst Organization Ventures is searching for promising startup companies. The company is targeting startups in green energy, technology and consumer markets. EDCO has partnered with consumer electronics repair company CherryFusion and technology firm MiniDonations.

46632 ■ **"EMU, Spark Plan Business Incubator for Ypsilanti" in** *Crain's Detroit Business* **(Vol. 23, October 15, 2007, No. 42, pp. 3)**
Pub: Crain Communications Inc. - Detroit

Ed: Chad Halcom. **Description:** Eastern Michigan University is seeking federal grants and other funding for a new business incubator program that would be in cooperation with Ann Arbor Spark. The site would become a part of a network of three Spark incubator programs with a focus on innovation in biotechnology and pharmaceuticals.

46633 ■ **"Friends With Money" in** *Entrepreneur* **(Vol. 37, August 2009, No. 8, pp. 74)**
Pub: Entrepreneur Media, Inc.

Ed: Asheesh Advani. **Description:** Providing a strong introduction to an investor will maximize a startup's chances of getting a second meeting. Startups should also pick an achievable fund raising goal and to keep track of their labor-adjusted net capital when fund raising.

46634 ■ **"Macomb County, OU Eye Business Incubator" in** *Crain's Detroit Business* **(Vol. 24, February 11, 2008, No. 6, pp. 1)**
Pub: Crain Communications Inc. - Detroit

Ed: Chad Halcom. **Description:** Officials in Macomb County, Michigan are discussing plans to create a defense-themed business incubator in the county. Macomb County was awarded $282,000 in federal budget appropriation for the project.

46635 ■ *Mommy Millionaire: How I Turned My Kitchen Table Idea Into a Million Dollars and How You Can, Too!*
Pub: St. Martin's Press LLC

Ed: Kim Lavine. **Released:** February 19, 2008. **Price:** $14.95. **Description:** Advice, secrets and lessons for making a million dollars from a mom who turned her kitchen into a successful business; tools cover developing and patenting an idea, cold calling, trade shows, QVC, big retailers, manufacturing, and raising venture capital.

46636 ■ **"New Program for Entrepreneurs" in** *Austin Business JournalInc.* **(Vol. 29, February 12, 2010, No. 29, pp. 1)**
Pub: American City Business Journals

Ed: Christopher Calnan. **Description:** Nonprofit group Economic Development Catalyst Organization (ECDO) is formalizing its BizLaunch mentoring program, which was stated in 2009. The program aims to offer support networks to entrepreneurs and assistance regarding early-stage venture capital.

46637 ■ **"Oversubscribed: Startup Funds Pour In" in** *Boston Business Journal* **(Vol. 31, July 22, 2011, No. 26, pp. 1)**
Pub: Boston Business Journal

Ed: Kyle Alspach. **Description:** Companies in Boston, Massachusetts are attracting strong interest from venture capital companies, resulting in increased venture capital funding. About $1.14 billion was invested in local companies during second quarter 2011.

46638 ■ *Raising Capital*
Pub: Kiplinger Books and Tapes

Ed: Andrew J. Sherman. **Price:** $34.95. **Description:** Corporate attorney provides a comprehensive guide using in-depth, practical advice on raising money to start and grow a business. A 115-page appendix contains samples of financing agreements, forms and questionnaires.

46639 ■ *Seed-Stage Venture Investing: The Ins and Outs for Entrepreneurs, Start-Ups, and Investors on Successfully Starting a New Business*
Pub: Aspatore Books, Incorporated

Ed: William J. Robbins. **Released:** July 2006. **Price:** $199.95. **Description:** Ideas for starting, funding, and managing technology-based firms, also known as, venture capitalists, are featured.

46640 ■ **"Spread Your Wings" in** *Canadian Business* **(Vol. 81, March 17, 2008, No. 4, pp. 31)**
Pub: Rogers Media

Ed: Megan Harman. **Description:** Financing from angel investors is one avenue that should be explored by startups. Angel investors are typically affluent individuals who invest their own money. Angel investors usually want at least 10 times their initial investment within eight years but they benefit the businesses through their help in decision-making and the industry expertise they provide.

46641 ■ **"State Fund That Aids New Companies Likely To Wither" in** *Crain's Detroit Business* **(Vol. 24, February 25, 2008, No. 8, pp. 16)**
Pub: Crain Communications Inc. - Detroit

Ed: Tom Henderson. **Description:** Officials are committed to fighting to save funding for the statewide Strategic Economic Investment and Commercialization Board which provides pre-seed money to start-up firms.

46642 ■ **"UM-Dearborn to Launch Program for Entrepreneurs" in** *Crain's Detroit Business* **(Vol. 24, April 14, 2008, No. 15, pp. 7)**
Pub: Crain Communications, Inc.

Ed: Chad Halcom. **Description:** Starting this fall the University of Michigan-Dearborn will begin its Product Realization and Technology Commercialization Program for entrepreneurs and innovators with lab-tested, high-technology products. Ultimately, 20 businesses will each work with the university in creating a customer base, commercializing a new high-tech product or process and connecting with venture capitalists who may invest in the new companies.

46643 ■ **"The Y Factor" in** *Entrepreneur* **(Vol. 35, November 2007, No. 11, pp. 58)**
Pub: Entrepreneur Media Inc.

Ed: Sara Wilson. **Description:** Venture capital company Y Cominbator hosts a three-month program wherein the firm's founders select technology entrepreneurs from across the U.S. to help and to mentor them on starting a business.

ASSOCIATIONS AND OTHER ORGANIZATIONS

46644 ■ **Canada's Venture Capital and Private Equity Association–Association Canadienne du Capital de Risque et d'Investissement**
MaRS Centre
Heritage Bldg.
101 College St., Ste. 120 J
Toronto, ON, Canada M5G 1L7
Ph:(416)487-0519
Fax:(416)487-5899
Co. E-mail: cvca@cvca.ca
URL: http://www.cvca.ca
Contact: Richard M. Remillard, Exec. Dir.
Description: Ventures and risks capital companies. Promotes economic growth through provision of capital to emerging businesses. Conducts research; facilitates exchange of information among members; represents the venture capital industry before government agencies, industrial and financial organizations, and the public. **Publications:** *Enterprise* (quarterly).

46645 ■ Center for Venture Research
University of New Hampshire
Whittemore School of Business and Economics
15 Academic Way
Durham, NH 03824-2602
Ph:(603)862-3341
Fax:(603)862-4468
Co. E-mail: cvr@unh.edu
URL: http://wsbe.unh.edu/cvr
Contact: Jeffrey E. Sohl, Dir.
Description: Encourages and conducts research into methods of financing new technology-based industries and firms. .

46646 ■ Coleman Foundation
651 W Washington Blvd., Ste. 306
Chicago, IL 60661
Ph:(312)902-7120
Fax:(312)902-7124
Co. E-mail: info@colemanfoundation.org
URL: http://www.colemanfoundation.org
Contact: Michael W. Hennessy, Pres./CEO
Description: Strives to support entrepreneurship, cancer research, housing and education for the handicapped, and diverse educational programs. .

46647 ■ Commercial Finance Association
370 7th Ave., Ste. 1801
New York, NY 10001-3979
Ph:(212)792-9390
Fax:(212)564-6053
Co. E-mail: info@cfa.com
URL: http://www.cfa.com
Contact: Randolph T. Abrahams, Pres./CEO
Description: Organizations engaged in asset-based financial services including commercial financing and factoring and lending money on a secured basis to small- and medium-sized business firms. Acts as a forum for information and consideration about ideas, opportunities and legislation concerning asset-based financial services. Seeks to improve the industry's legal and operational procedures. Offers job placement and reference services for members. Sponsors School for Field Examiners and other educational programs. Compiles statistics; conducts seminars and surveys; maintains speakers' bureau and 21 committees. .

46648 ■ Council of Development Finance Agencies
85 E Gay St., Ste. 700
Columbus, OH 43215
Ph:(614)224-1300
Fax:(614)224-1343
Co. E-mail: info@cdfa.net
URL: http://www.cdfa.net
Contact: Toby Rittner, Pres./CEO
Description: Works for the advancement of development finance concerns and interests. Represents members of the development finance community from the public, private and non-profit sectors. **Publications:** *Development Finance Review Weekly* (weekly).

46649 ■ National Association of Development Companies
6764 Old McLean Village Dr.
McLean, VA 22101
Ph:(703)748-2575
Fax:(703)748-2582
Co. E-mail: chris@nadco.org
URL: http://www.nadco.org
Contact: Christopher L. Crawford, Pres./CEO
Description: Small Business Administration Section 504 certified development companies. Provides long-term financing to small and medium-sized businesses. Represents membership in negotiations with the SBA, Congress, and congressional staff members; negotiates changes in legislation, regulations, operation procedures, and other matters such as prepayments problems, reporting requirements, and loan servicing procedures. Provides technical assistance and information regarding special training programs, marketing techniques, audit checklists, and loan closing and processing procedures. Compiles statistics. **Publications:** *NADCO News* (monthly).

46650 ■ National Association of Equity Source Banks
5432 Price Ave.
Baltimore, MD 21215
Ph:(410)367-5309
Co. E-mail: nahbb@msn.com
Contact: Rudolph Lewis, Pres.
Description: Private investors and venture capital firms. Promotes investments in micro-economic enterprises from urban and rural areas with certified business models and franchises (these models must be third party verified from a business development institution authorized by the Association). .

46651 ■ National Association of Investment Companies
1300 Pennsylvania Ave. NW, Ste. 700
Washington, DC 20004
Ph:(202)204-3001
Fax:(202)204-3022
Co. E-mail: admin@naicvc.com
URL: http://www.naicvc.com
Contact: Samuel J. Boyd Jr., Pres./CEO
Description: Aims to: represent the minority small business investment company industry in the public sector; provide industry education and develop research material on the activities of the industry. Collects and disseminates relevant business and trade information to members; facilitates the exchange of new ideas and financing strategies; assists organizing groups attempting to form or acquire minority enterprise small business investment companies; provide management and technical assistance to members. **Publications:** *NAIC Membership Directory* (annual).

46652 ■ National Association of Small Business Investment Companies
1100 H St. NW, Ste. 610
Washington, DC 20005
Ph:(202)628-5055
Fax:(202)628-5080
Co. E-mail: bpalmer@nasbic.org
URL: http://www.nasbic.org
Contact: Brett Palmer, Pres.
Description: Firms licensed as Small Business Investment Companies (SBICs) under the Small Business Investment Act of 1958. **Publications:** *NASBIC Membership Directory* (annual); *NASBIC News* (quarterly); *Today's SBICs: Investing in America's Future* .

46653 ■ National Venture Capital Association
1655 N Ft. Myer Dr., Ste. 850
Arlington, VA 22209
Ph:(703)524-2549
Fax:(703)524-3940
Co. E-mail: mheesen@nvca.org
URL: http://www.nvca.org
Contact: Mark G. Heesen, Pres.
Description: Venture capital organizations, corporate financiers, and individual venture capitalists who are responsible for investing private capital in young companies on a professional basis. Fosters a broader understanding of the importance of venture capital to the vitality of the U.S. economy and to stimulate the free flow of capital to young companies. Seeks to improve communications among venture capitalists throughout the country and to improve the general level of knowledge of the venturing process in government, universities, and the business community. **Publications:** *National Venture Capital Association—Annual Membership Directory* (annual); *The Venture Capital Review* (semiannual);*Yearbook* (annual).

REFERENCE WORKS

46654 ■ "75 Most Powerful Blacks on Wall Street" in *Black Enterprise* (Vol. 37, October 2006, No. 3, pp. 136)
Pub: Earl G. Graves Publishing Co. Inc.
Ed: Carolyn M. Brown. **Description:** Profiles of seventy-five African American top executives. The listing is a compilation of the brightest and best venture capitalists, asset managers, CEOs, traders, and investment bankers.

46655 ■ "AIC To Buy $350M of Real Estate" in *Austin Business JournalInc.* (Vol. 28, November 14, 2008, No. 35, pp. 1)
Pub: American City Business Journals
Ed: Kate Harrington. **Description:** Austin-based AIC Ventures LP is planning to buy $350 million worth of commercial real estate. The company's move will double its acquisitions. It is also planning to acquire 30 assets for its eight fun in 2009 from middle-market companies.

46656 ■ "Alberta Star Begins Phase 2 Drilling On Its Eldorado & Contact Lake IOCG & Uranium Projects" in *Canadian Corporate News* (May 16, 2007)
Pub: Comtex News Network Inc.
Description: Profile of Alberta Star Development Corp., a Canadian mineral exploration company that identifies, acquires, and finances advanced stage exploration projects in Canada, and its current undertaking of its 2007 drill program in which the company intends to begin accelerating its uranium and poly-metallic exploration and drilling activities on all of its drill targets for 2007 now that it has been granted its permits.

46657 ■ "All Indicators in Michigan Innovation Index Drop in 4Q" in *Crain's Detroit Business* (Vol. 25, June 22, 2009, No. 25, pp. 9)
Pub: Crain Communications Inc. - Detroit
Ed: Ryan Beene. **Description:** Economic indicators that rate Michigan's innovation fell in the fourth quarter of 2008. The index of trademark applications, SBA loans, venture capital funding, new incorporations and other indicators traced dropped 12.6 points.

46658 ■ "Angel Investing 2009" in *Inc.* (Vol. 31, January-February 2009, No. 1, pp. 83)
Pub: Mansueto Ventures LLC
Ed: Kasey Wehrum. **Description:** Tips for finding funding in tough economic times are presented, including secrets for closing second-round deals.

46659 ■ "Angel Investments Tripled in 2009" in *Austin Business JournalInc.* (Vol. 29, January 8, 2010, No. 44, pp. 1)
Pub: American City Business Journals
Ed: Christopher Calnan. **Description:** Central Texas Angel Network (CTAN) has invested $3.5 million in 12 ventures, which include 10 in Austin, Texas in 2009 to triple the amount it invested during 2008. The largest recipient of CTAN's investments is life sciences, which attracted 20 percent of the capital, while software investments fell to 18 percent. The new screening process that helps startups secure CTAN capital is explored.

46660 ■ "Aptitudes for Apps" in *Boston Business Journal* (Vol. 31, July 1, 2011, No. 23, pp. 3)
Pub: Boston Business Journal
Ed: Kyle Alspach. **Description:** Startups Apperian Inc. and Kinvey Inc. are aiming to accelerate the development and deployment of mobile applications and have received fund pledges from Boston-area venture capital firms.

46661 ■ "Ardesta Venture-Capital Fund Folds" in *Crain's Detroit Business* (Vol. 24, September 22, 2008, No. 38, pp. 24)
Pub: Crain Communications, Inc.
Ed: Tom Henderson. **Description:** Due to the downturn in the local economy, Ann Arbor-based Ardesta LLC, a venture-capital firm specializing in micro- and nanotechnology research, has pulled the plug on its planned fund of $100 million and said no to an investment of up to $15 million from the state.

46662 ■ "Area VCs Take Praise, Lumps, on Web site" in *Boston Business Journal* (Vol. 27, October 26, 2007, No. 39, pp. 1)
Pub: American City Business Journals Inc.
Ed: Jesse Noyes. **Description:** TheFunded.com is a social networking site that allows entrepreneurs to rate venture capitalists and post their comments. Information about venture capitalist firms such as size and the partners behind it are also provided.

46663 ■ *The Art of the Start*
Pub: Portfolio Publishing

Ed: Guy Kawasaki. **Price:** $26.95. **Description:** Apple's Guy Kawasaki offers information to help would-be entrepreneurs create new enterprises. As founder and CEO of Garage Technology Ventures, he has field-tested his ideas with newly hatched companies and he takes readers through every phase of creating a business, from the very basics of raising money and designing a business model through the many stages that eventually lead to success and thus giving back to society.

46664 ■ "ATS Secures Investment From Goldman Sachs" in *The Business Journal - Serving Phoenix and the Valley of the Sun* (Vol. 29, September 26, 2008, No. 4, pp. 1)
Pub: American City Business Journals, Inc.

Ed: Patrick O'Grady. **Description:** Goldman Sachs made an investment to American Traffic Solutions Inc. (ATS) which will allow it to gain two seats on the board of the red-light and speed cameras maker. The investment will help ATS maintain its rapid growth which is at 83 percent over the past 18 months leading up to September 2008.

46665 ■ "Attorney Guides Biotech Company in $6 Million Initial Public Offering" in *Miami Daily Business Review* (March 26, 2008)
Pub: ALM Media Inc.

Description: In order to raise capital to engage in a full-scale trial of MyoCell to receive clinical approval, Bioheart Inc., launched an initial public offering. Bioheart researches and develops cell therapies to treat heart damage.

46666 ■ *Attracting Investors: A Marketing Approach to Finding Funds for Your Business*
Pub: John Wiley & Sons, Incorporated

Ed: Philip Kotler, Hermawan Kartajaya, S. David Young. **Released:** August 2004. **Price:** $29.95 (US), $42.99 (Canadian). **Description:** Marketing experts advise entrepreneurs in ways to find investors in order to raise capital for their companies.

46667 ■ "Austin Ventures: Is It a VC Firm?" in *Austin Business Journal* (Vol. 31, June 17, 2011, No. 15, pp. 1)
Pub: American City Business Journals Inc.

Ed: Christopher Calnan. **Description:** Investment firm Austin Ventures could lose its classification as a venture capital firm under a new definition of venture capital by the Securities and Exchange Commission. The reclassification could result in additional expenses for Austin Ventures, which has two-thirds of its investments in growth equity transactions.

46668 ■ "Bigger TIF Makes Development Inroads" in *The Business Journal-Serving Metropolitan Kansas City* (Vol. 26, July 11, 2008, No. 44)
Pub: American City Business Journals, Inc.

Ed: Rob Roberts. **Description:** On July 9, 2008 the Tax Increment Financing Commission voted to expand a TIF district to Tiffany Springs Road. The plan for the TIF district close to Kansas City International Airport is to include a-half mile of the road. The impacts of the expansion on construction projects and on the road network are analyzed.

46669 ■ "Boise-based Highway 12 Invests in Crowdsourcing Platform" in *Idaho Business Review* (September 24, 2010)
Pub: Dolan Media Newswires

Ed: Simon Shifrin. **Description:** The only venture capital fund in Idaho, Highway 12 Ventures, is funding Kapost a new company that helps news Websites, blogs and other online venues to pull content from a larger network of writers.

46670 ■ "Catching Creatives; Detroit Group Gets Grant to Attract 1,000 Design Pros" in *Crain's Detroit Business* (March 24, 2008)
Pub: Crain Communications, Inc.

Ed: Sherri Begin. **Description:** Design Detroit was given a $200,000 planning grant by the Knight Foundation, an organization that strives to back initia-

tives that leverage talent and resources in each of the 26 U.S. cities it funds, to inspire strategies to attract up to 1,000 creative professionals to live in Detroit.

46671 ■ "Centerpoint Funding In Limbo" in *The Business Journal - Serving Phoenix and the Valley of the Sun* (Vol. 28, August 1, 2008, No. 48)
Pub: American City Business Journals, Inc.

Ed: Jan Buchholz. **Description:** Avenue Communities LLC has threatened to file a case against Mortgages Ltd. over the finance of the Centerpoint development project in Tempe, Arizona. Avenue Communities want Mortgages Ltd. to file a motion with the U.S. Bankruptcy Court so that it can secure financing for the project. Other views and information on the finance of Centerpoint, are presented.

46672 ■ "The Chips Are In" in *Business Journal-Portland* (Vol. 24, November 2, 2007, No. 35, pp. 1)
Pub: American City Business Journals, Inc.

Ed: Aliza Earnshaw. **Description:** The $30 million funding round of Ambric Inc., which brings a total investment of $51 million, is about to close, and its clients are releasing over half-dozen products containing Ambric chips in January 2008. The features of Ambric's semiconductors, its market sectors and market positioning, as well as its investor relations, are discussed.

46673 ■ "City, County May Kill VC Tax" in *Business Journal-Portland* (Vol. 24, October 12, 2007, No. 33, pp. 1)
Pub: American City Business Journals, Inc.

Ed: Aliza Earnshaw. **Description:** City of Portland and Multnomah County in Oregon may soon kill taxes levied on venture capital (VC) firms, which is expected to take place in late October 2007. Capitalists have long been saying that taxation is driving them out of town, but this change is expected to generate more investments and persuade VC firms to relocate within city limits.

46674 ■ "ClearEdge Hums Along" in *Business Journal Portland* (Vol. 26, December 18, 2009, No. 41, pp. 1)
Pub: American City Business Journals Inc.

Ed: Erik Siemers. **Description:** Hillsboro-based ClearEdge Power Inc. expanded its workforce and facilities with $15M capital from investors. Since May 2009, the number of employees increased from 40 to 150 and headquarters expanded from 5,000 to 80,000 square feet.

46675 ■ "Columbia's JPB Raising $175M to Acquire Companies, Real Estate" in *Boston Business Journal* (Vol. 29, May 27, 2011, No. 3, pp. 1)
Pub: American City Business Journals Inc.

Ed: Gary Haber. **Description:** JPB Enterprises is preparing to raise $175 million in its goal of acquiring companies and real estate that are major names in America. The $75 million will be raised for a buyout fund that will target wide range of industries while the $100 million will be used for land investment projects in the Florida Panhandle. Baltimore firms are expected to benefit from this deal.

46676 ■ "Commensurate with Experience" in *Entrepreneur* (Vol. 37, October 2009, No. 10, pp. 84)
Pub: Entrepreneur Media, Inc.

Ed: Carol Tice. **Description:** RingRevenue, a firm that specializes in pay-per-call technology that allows affiliate networks and advertising agencies to track purchases, began a funding round in June 2009 which it closed quickly after obtaining $3.5 million in venture capital. The round was closed earlier than the projections of its owners due to their track record.

46677 ■ "Company Goes High-Tech To Attack Some Sore Spots" in *Boston Business Journal* (Vol. 27, December 7, 2007, No. 45, pp. 10)
Pub: American City Business Journals, Inc.

Ed: Mark Hollmer. **Description:** Transport Pharmaceuticals Inc. hopes to raise $35 million to fund a drug and a treatment device for treating cold sores,

and seek federal regulatory approval. Dennis Goldberg, the company's CEO, believes that existing treatments that use acyclovir cream are relatively weak. Transport's drug uses a soluble gel cartridge with a higher concentration of acyclovir.

46678 ■ *Directory of Operating Small Business Investment Companies*
Pub: Investment Div.

Released: Semiannual, April and October. **Covers:** About 300 operating small business investment companies holding regular licenses and licenses under the section 301(d) of the Small Business Investment Act covering minority enterprise SBICs. **Entries Include:** Company name, address, phone, branch offices, type of ownership, date licensed by SBA, license number, amount of obligation to the Small Business Administration, amount of private capital held, and type of investments made. **Arrangement:** Separate geographical sections for each type of license.

46679 ■ *Directory of Venture Capital*
Pub: John Wiley & Sons Inc.
Contact: Kate Lister, Author

Released: Latest edition March 2000. **Price:** $59.95, individuals paperback. **Covers:** More than 600 actively investing venture capital firms and funding sources. **Entries Include:** Company name, address, phone, types of investments, geographic preference.

46680 ■ *The Directory of Venture Capital and Private Equity Firms: 2009*
Pub: Grey House Publishing

Ed: Laura Mars-Proietti. **Released:** April 1, 2009. **Price:** $450.00. **Description:** Updated and expanded edition that includes new entries offering access to more than 3,500 domestic and international venture capital and private equity firms; detailed contact information and extensive data on investments and funds is included.

46681 ■ "Do-Gooder Finance: How a New Crop of Investors Is Helping Social Entrepreneurs" in *Inc.* (February 2008, pp. 29-30)
Pub: Gruner & Jahr USA Publishing

Ed: Nitasha Tiku. **Description:** Social venture firms are not seeking to sell companies as quickly as traditional venture companies. Four socially minded venture capital firms and banks profiled include, Underdog Venture, Island Pond, Vermont; Root Capital, Cambridge, Massachusetts; ShoreBank Pacific, Ilwaco, Washington; and TBL Capital, Sausalito, California.

46682 ■ *Doing Business with Beauty: Black Women, Hair Salons, and the Racial Enclave Economy*
Pub: Rowman and Littlefield Publishers, Inc.

Ed: Adia Harvey Wingfield. **Released:** June 28, 2008. **Price:** $19.95. **Description:** Factors that draw black women into the hair industry are examined. Interviews with hair salon owners explore aspects of owning a salon, owner-employee relationships, and the black female owner's struggle for autonomy and success in entrepreneurship.

46683 ■ "EDF Ventures Dissolves Fund, Begins Anew On Investment" in *Crain's Detroit Business* (Vol. 24, February 25, 2008, No. 8, pp. 14)
Pub: Crain Communications Inc. - Detroit

Ed: Tom Henderson. **Description:** EDF Ventures is Michigan's oldest venture capital firm and was part of the second round of investments by the state's 21st Century Investment Fund and the Venture Michigan Fund.

46684 ■ "Elemental Nabs $5.5 Million" in *The Business Journal-Portland* (Vol. 25, July 18, 2008, No. 19, pp. 1)
Pub: American City Business Journals, Inc.

Ed: Aliza Earnshaw. **Description:** Elemental Technologies Inc., a Portland, Oregon-based software company got $5.5 million in new funding, bringing its total invested capital to $7.1 million in nine months since October 2008. The company plans to launch Badaboom, software for converting video into various formats, later in 2008.

46685 ■ **"The Emerging Capital Market for Nonprofits"** in *Harvard Business Review* (Vol. 88, October 2010, No. 10, pp. 110)
Pub: Harvard Business School Publishing
Ed: Robert S. Kaplan, Allen S. Grossman. **Description:** Demonstration of how nonprofits can use intermediaries to grow their organizational structures, giving them improved scale and impact is offered. Some intermediaries play a mutual-fund role and conduct due diligence, while others act as venture capital funds and implement strategy.

46686 ■ **"Emerging Tech Fund Strong in 2009"** in *Austin Business JournalInc.* (Vol. 29, December 25, 2009, No. 42, pp. 1)
Pub: American City Business Journals
Ed: Christopher Calnan. **Description:** Texas' Emerging Technology Fund (ETF) has seen an increase in applications from the state's technology companies in 2009. ETF received 87 applications in 2009 from Central Texas companies versus 50 during 2008 while $10.5 million was given to seven Texas companies compared with $10.6 million to ten companies in 2008.

46687 ■ **"Fight Ensues Over Irreplaceable Gowns"** in *Tampa Bay Business Journal* (Vol. 30, January 15, 2010, No. 4, pp. 1)
Pub: American City Business Journals
Ed: Janet Leiser. **Description:** People's Princess Charitable Foundation Inc. founder Maureen Rorech Dunkel has sought Chapter 11 bankruptcy protection before a state court decides on the fate of the five of 13 Princess Diana Gowns. Dunkel and the nonprofit were sued by Patricia Sullivan of HRH Venture LLC who claimed they defaulted on $1.5 million in loans.

46688 ■ *Financing Your Small Business*
Pub: Barron's Educational Series, Incorporated
Ed: Robert Walter. **Released:** December 2003. **Description:** Tips for raising venture capital, dealing with bank officials, and initiating public offerings of stock shares for small business.

46689 ■ **"Finding Room for Financing"** in *The Business Journal-Serving Metropolitan Kansas City* (Vol. 26, August 1, 2008, No. 47, pp. 1)
Pub: American City Business Journals, Inc.
Ed: Rob Roberts. **Description:** Kansas City officials are expecting to receive financing recommendations for a new 1,000-room convention headquarters hotel. The $300-million project could be financed either through private ownership with public subsidies, or through public ownership with tax-exempt bond financing. Other views and information on the project and its expected economic impact, are presented.

46690 ■ **"Former Mayor Driving $500 Million Real Estate Equity Fund"** in *The Business Journal - Serving Phoenix and the Valley of the Sun* (Vol. 28, August 15, 2008, No. 50, pp. 1)
Pub: American City Business Journals, Inc.
Ed: Jan Buchholz. **Description:** Paul John, the former mayor of Phoenix, is establishing a $500 million real estate asset management fund. The fund is dubbed Southwest Next Capital Management and has attracted three local partners, namely Joseph Meyer, Jay Michalowski, and James Mullany, who all have background in finance and construction.

46691 ■ **"Friends With Money"** in *Canadian Business* (Vol. 81, Summer 2008, No. 9, pp. 22)
Pub: Rogers Media Ltd.
Description: Two of the most well connected managers in Canadian capital markets Rob Farquharson and Brian Gibson will launch Panoply Capital Asset Management in June. The investment management company aims to raise a billion dollars from institutions and high-net worth individuals.

46692 ■ **"Funding Drought Stalls Biotech Incubators"** in *Saint Louis Business Journal* (Vol. 31, July 29, 2011, No. 49, pp. 1)
Pub: Saint Louis Business Journal
Ed: Angela Mueller. **Description:** Economic slowdown took its toll on cash-strapped startups that fill incubators such as the Bio-Research and Development Growth (BRDG) Park in Creve Coeur, Missouri and the Center for Emerging Technologies in Midtown St. Louis. BRDG put a hold on construction of of its two buildings.

46693 ■ **"Get With the Program"** in *Entrepreneur* (Vol. 36, April 2008, No. 4, pp. 130)
Pub: Entrepreneur Media, Inc.
Ed: Nichole L. Torres. **Description:** Entrepreneurship initiatives help college students get connected with other students, teach them about how to start their own business while still in school, and help with funding. Some of these programs are the Harold Grinspoon Charitable Foundation's Entrepreneurship Initiative and the Syracuse Campus-Community Entrepreneurship Initiative.

46694 ■ **"Graduates to the TSX in 2008"** in *Canadian Business* (Vol. 81, Summer 2008, No. 9, pp. 79)
Pub: Rogers Media Ltd.
Ed: Calvin Leung. **Description:** Table showing the market capitalization and stock performance of the companies that jumped to the TSX Venture Exchange is presented. The 17 companies that made the leap to the list will have an easier time raising capital, although leeway must be made in investing since they are still new businesses.

46695 ■ **"Greener Pastures"** in *Canadian Business* (Vol. 80, February 12, 2007, No. 4, pp. 69)
Pub: Rogers Media
Ed: Thomas Watson. **Description:** The effort of venture capitalists, including chief executive officer of Fun Technologies Lorne Abony, in successful running of several ventures in diverse fields is discussed.

46696 ■ **"Growing Field"** in *Crain's Detroit Business* (Vol. 26, January 11, 2010, No. 2, pp. 3)
Pub: Crain Communications, Inc.
Description: Detroit's TechTown was awarded a combination loan and grant of $4.1 million from the U.S. Department of Housing and Urban Development to build a 15,000-square-foot stem cell center, a collection of laboratories that will be available to both for-profit companies and university researchers.

46697 ■ **"Health Care Leads Sectors Attracting Capital"** in *Hispanic Business* (March 2008, pp. 14-16, 18)
Pub: Hispanic Business
Ed: Scott Williams. **Description:** U. S. Hispanic healthcare, media, and food were the key industries in the U.S. gaining investors in 2007.

46698 ■ **"House Committee on Small Business Calls for Sweeping Changes to SBIR Program"** in *Hispanic Business* (March 2008, pp. 44)
Pub: Hispanic Business
Description: Changes in the Small Business Innovation and Research Program would allow greater flexibility for firms participating in the program to leverage venture capital funds.

46699 ■ **"How to Not Get Fired"** in *Entrepreneur* (Vol. 37, September 2009, No. 9, pp. 62)
Pub: Entrepreneur Media, Inc.
Ed: Brad Feld. **Description:** Advice on how chief executive officers (CEO) of venture capital funded firms can avoid being replaced is presented. A CEO should not be defensive of the prospect of being replaced. The CEO may also work with the investors and the board for a smooth transition.

46700 ■ *How to Start and Run Your Own Corporation: S-Corporations For Small Business Owners*
Pub: HCM Publishing
Ed: Peter I. Hupalo. **Released:** March 6, 2003. **Price:** $22.95. **Description:** Basics of corporate business structure are explained. Topics include discovering the best business structure for your company; how to decided between an S-Corporation and LLC; choosing the state in which to incorporate, how to form a corporation, angel investing, special issues for one-person corporations, the role of bylaws and corporate minutes, board of directors, taxes, workers' compensation issues, retirement plans, and more.

46701 ■ **"Human Bone Breakthrough"** in *Houston Business Journal* (Vol. 40, January 8, 2010, No. 35, pp. 1)
Pub: American City Business Journals
Ed: Casey Wooten. **Description:** Biotech startup company Osteosphere in Houston, Texas aims to market a technology in which laboratory-grown bone tissues can be processed to appear like a real human bone tissue. The technology was developed by a co-founder of the startup and it can be applied to bone disease and injury treatment. Osteophere's future plans, such as the search for possible investors, is also outlined.

46702 ■ **"I-5 Bridge Funding Unclear"** in *The Business Journal-Portland* (Vol. 25, July 11, 2008, No. 18, pp. 1)
Pub: American City Business Journals, Inc.
Ed: Andy Giegerich. **Description:** Financing for a new Interstate 5 bridge is unclear as Washington lawmakers identify two priority projects other than the planned bridge, which is shared with Oregon. An estimate says that the two states could pay between $487.6 million and $1.5 billion for the new bridge. Other details on the financing of the project are discussed.

46703 ■ **"In China, Railways to Riches"** in *Barron's* (Vol. 88, July 7, 2008, No. 27, pp. M9)
Pub: Dow Jones & Co., Inc.
Ed: Assif Shameen. **Description:** Shares of Chinese railway companies look to benefit from multimillion-dollar investments aimed at upgrading the Chinese railway network. Investment in the sector is expected to reach $210 billion for the 2006-2010 period.

46704 ■ **"In the Know?"** in *Entrepreneur* (Vol. 37, July 2009, No. 7, pp. 30)
Pub: Entrepreneur Media, Inc.
Ed: Brad Feld. **Description:** Tips on what entrepreneurs should and should not share with their venture capitalists (VCs) are given. Entrepreneurs must be transparent with their VCs, but they should not bombard VCs with too many details. The aspect of a business that a VC is concerned with varies from one VC to another, and it is important that entrepreneurs understand the best way to communicate with their VC.

46705 ■ **"Inside the Mind of an Investor: Lessons from Bill Draper"** in *Inc.* (Volume 32, December 2010, No. 10, pp. 140)
Pub: Inc. Magazine
Ed: Leigh Buchanan. **Description:** Profile of the three-generation Draper family, the first venture capital firm west of the Mississippi.

46706 ■ **"Inventive Doctor New Venture Partner"** in *Houston Business Journal* (Vol. 40, January 29, 2010, No. 38, pp. A2)
Pub: American City Business Journals
Ed: Ford Gunter. **Description:** Dr. Billy Cohn, a surgeon from Houston, Texas has been named as venture partner for venture firm Sante Ventures LLC of Austin, Texas. Cohn will be responsible for seeing marketable developing technologies in the medical industry. The motivation for Cohn's naming as venture partner is his development of a minimally invasive therapy for end-stage renal disease.

46707 ■ **"Investors Sue Jackson Properties for Fraud, Breach of Contract"** in *The Business Journal - Serving Phoenix and the Valley of the Sun* (Vol. 28, July 18, 2008, No. 46, pp. 1)
Pub: American City Business Journals, Inc.
Ed: Jan Buchholz. **Description:** Investors sued Jackson Properties EVB Inc. and Jackson Properties EVB LLC for fraud and breach of contract over a botched housing development deal. The investors also filed a complaint before the Arizona Corporation Commission. The investors stand to lose $8 million from the halted development deal.

46708 ■ "It's Not Easy Investing Green" in *Entrepreneur* **(Vol. 37, August 2009, No. 8, pp. 64)**
Pub: Entrepreneur Media, Inc.
Ed: Rosalind Resnick. **Description:** Some venture capitalists remain bullish on green investing despite signs of stagnation. One way for an investor to cash in on green investing is to invest in large public companies that are investing big in green initiatives. Being an angel investor to a local clean-tech company is another avenue.

46709 ■ "A Knack for Entrepreneurship" in *Hispanic Business* **(January-February 2008, pp. 42, 44-45)**
Pub: Hispanic Business
Ed: Hildy Medina. **Description:** Profile of Carlos Antonio Garcia, CEO of Kira, is investing in young companies.

46710 ■ "Lack of Support Drives Scientists Away from Valley" in *The Business Journal - Serving Phoenix and the Valley of the Sun* **(Vol. 28, August 1, 2008, No. 48, pp. 1)**
Pub: American City Business Journals, Inc.
Ed: Angela Gonzales. **Description:** Lack of support for scientists has caused scientists like Dietrich Stephan to depart from the city. Stephan is expected to relocate to California where he has found funding for his company Navigenics. Other views and information on the rising rate of the departure of scientists are presented.

46711 ■ "Lenders" in *The Business Journal - Serving Phoenix and the Valley of the Sun* **(Vol. 28, July 25, 2008, No. 47, pp. 1)**
Pub: American City Business Journals, Inc.
Ed: Jan Buchholz. **Description:** Private equity lender Investor Mortgage Holdings Inc. has continued growing despite the crisis surrounding the real estate and financial industries and has accumulated a $700 million loan portfolio. Private lending has become increasingly important in financing real estate deals as commercial credit has dried up.

46712 ■ "Lines of Communication" in *Entrepreneur* **(Vol. 37, October 2009, No. 10, pp. 80)**
Pub: Entrepreneur Media, Inc.
Ed: Brad Feld. **Description:** Entrepreneurial companies should establish a clear and open communication culture between their management teams and their venture capital backers. Chief executive officers should trust their leadership teams when it comes to communicating with venture capitalists.

46713 ■ "Looking For Financing?" in *Hispanic Business* **(Vol. 30, July-August 2008, No. 7-8, pp. 16)**
Pub: Hispanic Business, Inc.
Ed: Frank Nelson. **Description:** Investment firms want to know about businesses that need funding for either expansion or acquisition; companies fitting this profile are interviewed and their perceptions are discussed. Investment firms need businesses to be realistic in their expectations and business plans which show spending of funds and expected benefits, long term goals, track record and strong management teams.

46714 ■ "Losses Threaten Comp Care's Future Viability" in *The Business Journal-Serving Greater Tampa Bay* **(Vol. 28, August 15, 2008, No. 34)**
Pub: American City Business Journals, Inc.
Ed: Margie Manning. **Description:** Comprehensive Care Corp. expressed that it may have to cease or drastically curtail its operations if it won't be able to raise additional funding in the next two or three months. The firm, which provides managed behavioral health care services, is also believed to be exploring a sale. Other views and information on Comprehensive Care's finances and plans are presented.

46715 ■ "Making Waves" in *Business Journal Portland* **(Vol. 27, November 26, 2010, No. 39, pp. 1)**
Pub: Portland Business Journal
Ed: Erik Siemers. **Description:** Corvallis, Oregon-based Columbia Power Technologies LLC is about to

close a $2 million Series A round of investment initiated by $750,000 from Oregon Angel Fund. The wave energy startup company was formed to commercialize the wave buoy technology developed by Oregon State University researchers.

46716 ■ "The Marathon Club: Building a Bridge to Wealth" in *Hispanic Business* **(March 2008, pp. 24)**
Pub: Hispanic Business
Ed: Hildy Median. **Description:** Minority businesses find it more difficult to secure venture capital for entrepreneurial pursuits. Joe Watson, CEO of Without Excuses and Strategic Hire, suggests Hispanics and African Americans collaborate on issues of importance to minority entrepreneurs.

46717 ■ *McMafia: A Journey Through the Global Criminal Underworld*
Pub: Pantheon Books
Ed: Misha Glenny. **Released:** 2009. **Price:** $27.95. **Description:** Criminal entrepreneurs are using well-organized cosmopolitan networks to capitalize on globalization. Money from wars and illegal activities are being used to raise venture capital to finance criminal enterprises.

46718 ■ "MEDC: Put Venture Funds to Work" in *Crain's Detroit Business* **(Vol. 25, June 22, 2009, No. 25, pp. 1)**
Pub: Crain Communications Inc. - Detroit
Ed: Tom Henderson. **Description:** Michigan Strategic Fund board will finalize approval for ESP Holdings II LLC, Peninsula Capital Partners LLC, Triathlon Medical Ventures LLC and Arsenal Venture Partners Inc. are expected to share $35.5 million from the fund.

46719 ■ "Meet the Dropouts: the Students Who Chose Start-Ups Over College" in *Inc.* **(Vol. 33, September 2011, No. 7, pp. 32)**
Pub: Inc. Magazine
Ed: Eric Markowitz. **Description:** Profiles of 24 college students who left school in order to work on their own startup companies. Each new company is receiving $100,000 from Peter Thiel, cofounder of PayPal and an angel investor.

46720 ■ "Meet UT's New Business Mind" in *Austin Business Journal* **(Vol. 31, May 13, 2011, No. 10, pp. A1)**
Pub: American City Business Journals Inc.
Ed: Sandra Zaragoza. **Description:** University of Texas (UT) chief commercialization officer, Dr. Richard Miller, has opened a satellite office in Silicon Valley, California in the hopes of luring Californian investors to the science and technology at UT. The satellite office is just one of Miller's efforts to reshape and widen the commercialization of UT-Austin. Insights into Miller's long-term view approach to commercialization are also covered.

46721 ■ "Merkle Lands $75M" in *Baltimore Business Journal* **(Vol. 28, October 15, 2010, No. 23, pp. 1)**
Pub: Baltimore Business Journal
Ed: Gary Haber. **Description:** Baltimore, Maryland-based Merkle has received a $75 million investment from Silicon Valley-based Technology Crossover Ventures. The private equity firm's cash infusion was considered the biggest stake made in a company in the region and provides a healthy sign for Greater Baltimore's company.

46722 ■ "Microsoft Goes Macrosoft" in *Barron's* **(Vol. 89, July 27, 2009, No. 30, pp. 25)**
Pub: Dow Jones & Co., Inc.
Ed: Mark Veverka. **Description:** Microsoft reported a weak quarter on the heels of a tech rally which suggests the economy has not turned around. Marc Andreesen describes his new venture-capital fund as focused on "classic tech" and that historical reference places him in the annals of the last millennium.

46723 ■ "Millions Needed To Finish First Place" in *The Business Journal-Milwaukee* **(Vol. 25, August 15, 2008, No. 47, pp. A1)**
Pub: American City Business Journals, Inc.
Ed: Rich Kirchen. **Description:** First Place on the River condominium project in Milwaukee, Wisconsin,

needs $18.2 million before it can be completed. A total of $6.8 million have already been spent since the project went into receivership on 31 January 2008.

46724 ■ "Molycorp Funds Wind Energy Technology Company" in *Manufacturing Close-Up* **(September 19, 2011)**
Pub: Close-Up Media
Description: Molycorp Inc., producer of rare earth oxides (REO) and a REO producer outside of China, announced it will invest in Boulder Wind Power, which has designed a rare earth magnet powered wind turbine generator. This new generator can produce electricity as low as $0.04 per Kilowatt Hour. Boulder Wind Power's patented wind turbine technology allows for use of rare earth permanent magnets that do not require dysprosium, which is relatively scarce.

46725 ■ "Mr. Clean" in *Canadian Business* **(Vol. 81, October 27, 2008, No. 18, pp. 74)**
Pub: Rogers Media Ltd.
Ed: Rachel Pulfer. **Description:** Profile of Nicholas Parker, co-founder of Cleantech Group LLC, a pioneer in clean technology investing. Cleantech, now a global industry, accounts for 10 percent of all venture capital investments made by U.S. companies in 2007.

46726 ■ "Nanoready?" in *Entrepreneur* **(Vol. 36, May 2008, No. 5, pp. 20)**
Pub: Entrepreneur Media, Inc.
Ed: Andrea Cooper. **Description:** Experts predict that the medicine and energy sectors are among those that will see nanotechnology innovations in the coming years, and that nanotechnology will produce significant commercial value in new products. Some entrepreneurs are investing in nanotech and are partnering with universities. Details on nanotech funding concerns are discussed.

46727 ■ *National Venture Capital Association—Membership Directory*
Pub: National Venture Capital Association
Contact: Molly M. Myers, Vice President
Released: Annual, Latest edition 2009. **Price:** $195 hard copy; $325 CD-ROM one-user license (additional license $75). **Covers:** 480 venture capital firms, including subsidiaries of banks and insurance companies. **Entries Include:** Firm name, address, phone, contact names, fax number, investment preferences. **Arrangement:** Alphabetical. **Indexes:** Contact name.

46728 ■ "The New Face of Detroit" in *Inc.* **(Vol. 33, October 2011, No. 8, pp. 6)**
Pub: Inc. Magazine
Ed: Elizabeth Sile. **Description:** Basketball legend Magic Johnson has joined Detroit Venture Partners and Detroit will be one of the firm's three inaugural cities to host fellows from Venture for America, a new organization that places recent college graduates in start-up companies.

46729 ■ "Nobody Knows What To Do" in *Barron's* **(Vol. 88, March 17, 2008, No. 11, pp. 40)**
Pub: Dow Jones & Company, Inc.
Ed: Mark Veverka. **Description:** Attendees of the South by Southwest Interactive conference failed to get an insight on how to make money on the Web from former Walt Disney CEO Michael Eisner when Eisner said there's no proven business model for financing projects. Eisner said he finances his projects with the help of his connections to get product-placement deals.

46730 ■ "NYC Tops Hub in Tech VC Dollars" in *Boston Business Journal* **(Vol. 31, August 5, 2011, No. 28, pp. 1)**
Pub: Boston Business Journal
Ed: Kyle Alspach. **Description:** New York City has been outdoing Boston in terms of venture capital for technology firms since second quarter 2010. New York tech firms raised $865 million during the first two quarters of 2011 against Boston techs' $682 million. Boston has the edge, though, when it comes to hiring engineering talent as it is home to the Massachusetts Institute of Technology.

46731 ■ *Overcoming Barriers to Entrepreneurship in the United States*
Pub: Lexington Books
Ed: Diana Furchtgott-Roth. **Released:** March 28, 2008. **Price:** $24.95. **Description:** Real and perceived barriers to the founding and running of small businesses in America are discussed. Each chapter outlines how policy and economic environments can hinder business owners and offers tips to overcome these obstacles. Starting with venture capital access in Silicon Valley during the Internet bubble, the book goes on to question the link between personal wealth and entrepreneurship, examines how federal tax rates affect small business creation and destruction, explains the low rate of self-employment among Mexican immigrants, and suggests ways pension coverage can be increased in small businesses.

46732 ■ **"The Perks of Going Public"** in *Austin Business Journal* (Vol. 31, July 15, 2011, No. 19, pp. A17)
Pub: American City Business Journals Inc.
Ed: Christopher Calnan. **Description:** HomeAway Inc. launched a $216 million initial public offering. Austin Ventures has generated more than $32 million from the IPO.

46733 ■ **"Phoenix Company Realizing Dream of Global Growth"** in *The Business Journal - Serving Phoenix and the Valley of the Sun* (Vol. 28, July 18, 2008, No. 46, pp. 1)
Pub: American City Business Journals, Inc.
Ed: Chris Casacchia. **Description:** Phoenix, Arizona-based lubricant maker DreamBrands Inc. is realizing global growth. The company, which has been generating interest from institutional investors, is seeking a second round of funding. Details of the company's products and marketing plans are also discussed.

46734 ■ **"Private Equity Firm Links First Arizona Deal"** in *Business Journal-Serving Phoenix and the Valley of the Sun* (November 2, 2007)
Pub: American City Business Journals, Inc.
Ed: Chris Casacchia. **Description:** Pacific Investment Partners and Your Source Financial launched a $10 million fund and signed their first deal. The two companies acquires a minority stake in Dreambrands Inc. for $3 million. Dreambrands is using the capital to market its personal lubricant product Carrageenana.

46735 ■ **"Private Equity Party Fuelled by Cheap Debt"** in *Globe & Mail* (February 27, 2007, pp. B1)
Pub: CTVglobemedia Publishing Inc.
Ed: Sinclair Stewart. **Description:** The funding of private equity fund Kohlberg Kravis through cheap debt, during the buyout of the TXU Corp. is discussed.

46736 ■ **"PSU Launches $90 Million Project"** in *The Business Journal-Portland* (Vol. 25, July 18, 2008, No. 19, pp. 1)
Pub: American City Business Journals, Inc.
Ed: Aliza Earnshaw. **Description:** Portland State University (PSU) has launched a $90-million project for a new business school building, which is to be located at Southwest Market and Southwest Park. The business school is expected to move in to its new 130,000-suqare-foot building by 2013. PSU business school needs to raise $30 million for the project.

46737 ■ *Raising Capital*
Pub: Greenwood Publishing Group, Inc.
Ed: David Nour. **Released:** March 1, 2009. **Price:** $39.95. **Description:** An overview to help entrepreneurs find capital for starting and maintaining a small business is presented. The author shows how to develop long-term relationships with financial partners and ways to attract financing to fund the startup and growth phases of any business. Entrepreneurs tell how they raised money from friends, family, angel investors, banks and venture capitalists and private equity firms.

46738 ■ *Raising Venture Capital for the Serious Entrepreneur*
Pub: McGraw-Hill Inc.
Ed: Dermot Berkery. **Released:** September 2007. **Price:** $49.95. **Description:** Sourcebook to help entrepreneurs secure venture capital from investors.

46739 ■ **"Raptor Opens Consultancy"** in *Austin Business Journal* (Vol. 31, July 8, 2011, No. 18, pp. 1)
Pub: American City Business Journals Inc.
Ed: Christopher Calnan. **Description:** Boston hedge fund operator Raptor Group launched Raptor Accelerator, a consulting business providing sales and advisory services to early-stage companies in Central Texas. Aside from getting involved with the startups in which the Raptor Group invests, Raptor Accelerator will target firms operating in the sports, media, entertainment, and content technology sectors.

46740 ■ **"Rebels' Cause: Adult Stem Cell"** in *Austin Business Journal* (Vol. 31, June 3, 2011, No. 13, pp. 1)
Pub: American City Business Journals Inc.
Ed: Sandra Zaragoza. **Description:** MedRebels Foundation was launched in February 2011 with the goal of providing millions of dollars for research funding, education and advocacy for adult stem cell-focused medicine. The foundation, whose major contributor is SpineSmith LP, is a collaboration of other adult stem cell-related companies and nonprofit partners. It hopes to raise $200,000 by the end of 2011.

46741 ■ **"Recession-Proof Your Startup"** in *Crain's Chicago Business* (Vol. 31, November 10, 2008, No. 45, pp. 24)
Pub: Crain Communications, Inc.
Description: Detailed information concerning ways in which to start a business during an economic crisis is provided. Ways in which to find financing, the importance of a solid business plan, customer service, problem-solving and finding the right niche for the region are also discussed.

46742 ■ **"Red Tape Ties Detroit Housing Rehab Plan"** in *Crain's Detroit Business* (Vol. 24, September 22, 2008, No. 38, pp. 1)
Pub: Crain Communications, Inc.
Ed: Ryan Beene. **Description:** Venture-capital firm Wilherst Oxford LLC is a Florida-based company that has purchased 300 inner-city homes which were in foreclosure in Detroit. Wilherst Oxford is asking the city to forgive the existing tax and utility liens so the firm can utilize the money for home improvements. The city, however, is reluctant but has stated that they are willing to negotiate.

46743 ■ **"Running the Numbers"** in *Entrepreneur* (Vol. 37, July 2009, No. 7, pp. 87)
Pub: Entrepreneur Media, Inc.
Ed: Carol Tice. **Description:** Ways in which entrepreneurs can assess if they are ready to be a multi-unit franchisee are presented. Choosing the right locations, knowing how much assistance they can get from the franchisor, and financing are the key considerations when planning additional franchise units. Examples of success in multi-unit operations and multi-unit terms are also presented.

46744 ■ **"A Safe Bet"** in *Entrepreneur* (Vol. 35, October 2007, No. 10, pp. 26)
Pub: Entrepreneur Media Inc.
Ed: Carol Tice. **Description:** U.S. Department of Defense has developed a program, called the Defense Venture Catalyst Initiative or DeVenCI, that will match defense officials to the products that they need. DeVenCI uses conferences to showcase the defense contractors and their technologies to defense managers. Details of how this program helps both contractors and defense officials are overviewed.

46745 ■ **"Seed Funding"** in *Saint Louis Business Journal* (Vol. 31, July 29, 2011, No. 49, pp. 1)
Pub: Saint Louis Business Journal
Ed: Kelsey Volkmann. **Description:** Monsanto kicked off a new campaign, 'St. Louis Grown' to show its commitment to the St. Louis, Missouri region after spending millions in recent years on national advertising campaigns. Monsanto had a marketing budget totaling $839 million in 2010 for both brand and corporate marketing.

46746 ■ **"Small-Business Agenda: Increase Capital, Education, Tax Breaks"** in *Crain's Detroit Business* (Vol. 24, March 17, 2008)
Pub: Crain Communications, Inc.
Ed: Nancy Kaffer. **Description:** Discusses the policy suggestions identified in the Small Business Association of Michigan's entrepreneurial agenda which include five main categories of focus: making entrepreneurial education a higher state priority; increasing capital available to entrepreneurs; using the state's tax structure as an incentive for entrepreneurial growth; getting university research from the lab to the market; and limiting government regulation that's burdensome to small businesses and getting legislative support of entrepreneurial assistance efforts.

46747 ■ **"Speak Better: Five Tips for Polished Presentations"** in *Women Entrepreneur* (September 19, 2008)
Pub: Entrepreneur Media Inc.
Ed: Suzannah Baum. **Description:** Successful entrepreneurs agree that exemplary public speaking skills are among the core techniques needed to propel their business forward. A well-delivered presentation can result in securing a new distribution channel, gaining new customers, locking into a new referral stream or receiving extra funding.

46748 ■ **"Spending on Innovation Down Sharply in State"** in *Crain's Detroit Business* (Vol. 24, March 10, 2008, No. 10, pp. 7)
Pub: Crain Communications, Inc.
Ed: Chad Halcom. **Description:** Due to such issues as Michigan's uncertain tax structure, a shaky national economy, the credit crunch and mortgage lending crisis, investments in innovation for the state have sharply declined.

46749 ■ **"State VC Fund To Get At Least $7.5 Million"** in *Crain's Detroit Business* (Vol. 24, February 25, 2008, No. 8, pp. 14)
Pub: Crain Communications Inc. - Detroit
Description: Michigan's 21st Century Investment Fund is expected to receive $7.5 million, financed by tobacco-settlement money. The Michigan Strategic Fund Board will determine which firms will receive venture capital, which is mandated by legislation to invest the fund within three years.

46750 ■ **"Study Puts Hub On Top of the Tech Heap"** in *Boston Business Journal* (Vol. 30, November 26, 2010, No. 44, pp. 1)
Pub: Boston Business Journal
Ed: Galen Moore. **Description:** The Ewing Marion Kauffman Foundation ranked Massachusetts at the top in its evaluations of states' innovative industries, government leadership, and education. Meanwhile, research blog formDs.com also ranked Massachusetts number one in terms of venture-capital financings per capita.

46751 ■ **"Tech Giving 2.0"** in *Boston Business Journal* (Vol. 31, August 5, 2011, No. 28, pp. 1)
Pub: Boston Business Journal
Ed: Mary Moore. **Description:** Entrepreneurs and venture capitalists in Boston have launched Technology Underwriting Greater Good, the tech industry's answer to the criticism that they are not charitable. The foundation finances nonprofits that aid young people through entrepreneurship, education and life experience. Other tech firms in Boston doing charitable works are discussed.

46752 ■ **"Tech Godfather Steve Walker Winding Down Howard Venture Fund"** in *Baltimore Business Journal* (Vol. 27, December 11, 2009, No. 31)
Pub: American City Business Journals
Ed: Scott Dance. **Description:** Steve Walker, president of venture capital fund firm Walker Ventures, will be closing the Howard County, Maryland-based firm as the economic situation is finding it difficult to recover investor's money. According to Walker, the economy also constrained investors from financing venture funds. Despite the closure, Walker will continue his work in the local angel investing community.

46753 ■ "TechLift Strives to Fill in Gaps in Entrepreneurial Support Efforts" in *Crain's Cleveland Business* **(November 12, 2007)**
Pub: Crain Communications, Inc.

Ed: Marsha Powers. **Description:** Profile of the program, TechLift, a new business model launched by NorTech, that is aiming to provide assistance to technology-based companies that may not be a good fit for other entrepreneurial support venues.

46754 ■ *Technological Entrepreneurship*
Pub: Edward Elgar Publishing, Incorporated

Ed: Donald Siegel. **Released:** October 2006. **Price:** $230.00. **Description:** Technological entrepreneurship at universities is discussed. The book covers four related topics: university licensing and patenting; science parks and incubators; university-based startups; and the role of academic science in entrepreneurship.

46755 ■ "TELUS Says No Thanks to Joining BCE Fray" in *Globe & Mail* **(April 24, 2007, pp. B1)**
Pub: CTVglobemedia Publishing Inc.

Ed: Eric Reguly; Catherine McLean. **Description:** The causes of the refusal of TELUS Corp. to try and acquire BCE Inc. are discussed. The prospects of the acquisition of TELUS Corp. by private equity funds are discussed, besides the availability of cash with private equity funds.

46756 ■ *They Made America*
Pub: Little Brown Company/Time Warner Book Group

Ed: Harold Evans, Gail Buckland, David Lefer. **Released:** 2006. **Price:** $18.95. **Description:** Coffee table book highlighting entrepreneurship; this book is filled with interesting illustrated portraits of entrepreneurs and innovators like Thomas Edison, George Doriot (a venture capital pioneer), and Ida Rosenthal (inventor of the Maidenform bra).

46757 ■ "Top of the Food Chain" in *Entrepreneur* **(Vol. 37, October 2009, No. 10, pp. 19)**
Pub: Entrepreneur Media, Inc.

Ed: Jennifer Wang. **Description:** Television producer Mark Burnett discusses his latest reality television production, Shark Tank. The show pits venture capitalists against entrepreneurs in a contest to obtain business funding.

46758 ■ "Troubled Project In Court" in *The Business Journal-Portland* **(Vol. 25, July 25, 2008, No. 20, pp. 1)**
Pub: American City Business Journals, Inc.

Ed: Wendy Culverwell. **Description:** Views and information on Salpare Bay's Hayden Island project, as well as on financing problems and cases associated with the project, are presented. Construction of luxurious waterside condominiums stopped last fall, after the discovery of financing problems and subcontractors and other parties started filing claims and counterclaims.

46759 ■ "Unbound ID Raises $2 Million" in *Austin Business JournalInc.* **(Vol. 28, December 12, 2008, No. 39, pp. 1)**
Pub: American City Business Journals

Ed: Christopher Calnan. **Description:** Austin, Texas-based Unbound ID Corporation has secured $2 million in funding from venture capital firm Silverton Partners. The company has developed identity management software for network directories. The market for identity management technology is expected to grow to more than $12.3 billion by 2014.

46760 ■ *Values and Opportunities in Social Entrepreneurship*
Pub: Palgrave Macmillan

Ed: Kai Hockerts. **Released:** November 1, 2009. **Price:** $90.00. **Description:** Social entrepreneurship has grown as a research field. This book discusses social entrepreneurship as well as the identification and exploitation of social venturing opportunities.

46761 ■ *Valuing Early Stage and Venture Backed Companies*
Pub: John Wiley & Sons, Inc.

Ed: Neil J. Beaton. **Released:** December 1, 2009. **Price:** $110.00. **Description:** Valuation techniques that can be used to value early stage companies with complex capital structures are examined.

46762 ■ "VC Boosts WorkForce; Livonia Software Company to Add Sales, Marketing Staff" in *Crain's Detroit Business* **(March 24, 2008)**
Pub: Crain Communications, Inc.

Ed: Tom Henderson. **Description:** WorkForce Software Inc., a company that provides software to manage payroll processes and oversee compliance with state and federal regulations and with union rules, plans to use an investment of $5.5 million in venture capital to hire more sales and marketing staff.

46763 ■ "VC-Heavy, Revenue-Light Sensicore Sold to GE Division" in *Crain's Detroit Business* **(Vol. 24, April 14, 2008, No. 15, pp. 28)**
Pub: Crain Communications, Inc.

Ed: Tom Henderson. **Description:** General Electric has acquired Sensicore Inc., which although one of Michigan's most successful companies in raising venture capital was unable to generate significant revenue from its handheld water-testing devices. GE is capable of penetrating a larger market than a private company and will be able to take the devices to the municipal marketplace.

46764 ■ "VC Investing Down 63 Percent" in *Austin Business JournalInc.* **(Vol. 29, January 29, 2010, No. 47, pp. 1)**
Pub: American City Business Journals

Ed: Christopher Calnan. **Description:** Venture capital investments in the Austin, Texas area have declined by about 63 percent from $590.1 million in 2008 to $219.2 million in 2009. Deal volume remained steady at 53 local company fundings, but the median deal value declined from $6.5 million in 2008 to $3 million in 2009. Details on several local deals are presented.

46765 ■ "VC Money Down In State, Number of Deals Up" in *Crain's Detroit Business* **(Vol. 24, January 28, 2008, No. 4, pp. 18)**
Pub: Crain Communications Inc. - Detroit

Ed: Tom Henderson. **Description:** Despite the amount of money invested by venture capitalists in Michigan is down, the number of deals rose according to the annual Money Tree report. Venture capital firms invested a combined $105.4 million in 22 deals that involved 19 companies in the state.

46766 ■ "The VC Shakeout" in *Harvard Business Review* **(Vol. 88, July-August 2010, No. 7-8, pp. 21)**
Pub: Harvard Business School Publishing

Ed: Joseph Ghalbouni, Dominque Rouzies. **Description:** Authors argue that in order to be successful, venture capital needs to focus less on how to sell a newly acquired investment and more on ways to grow a good company.

46767 ■ "VC Tax Almost Gone" in *Business Journal-Portland* **(Vol. 24, November 23, 2007, No. 38, pp. 1)**
Pub: American City Business Journals, Inc.

Ed: Aliza Earnshaw. **Description:** Portland Revenue Bureau's proposal to repeal a business income tax is scheduled to be approved by the Portland City Council and Multnomah County Council. Despite the good decision on the part of the city, the removal of the tax policy is not a guarantee that venture capital firms will relocate to the city.

46768 ■ "Venture Capital's Capital Infusion: Federal Incentives Mean More Money for VC Firms" in *Entrepreneur* **(Vol. 37, August 2009)**
Pub: Entrepreneur Media, Inc.

Ed: Carol Tice. **Description:** American Recovery and Reinvestment Act of 2009 changed the rules for the Small Business Investment Corporations (SBIC) program under the Small Business Authority. The

rule changes are meant to put more money from the program into circulation and it increases funding to existing SBICs.

46769 ■ "Venture Gap" in *Canadian Business* **(Vol. 81, March 17, 2008, No. 4, pp. 82)**
Pub: Rogers Media

Ed: Joe Castaldo. **Description:** Money raised by Canadian venture capitalist firms has been declining since 2001. A strong venture capital market is important if Canada is to build innovative companies. Fixing Canada's tax policy on foreign investments is a start in reviving the industry.

46770 ■ "Wait a Minute!" in *Entrepreneur* **(Vol. 37, September 2009, No. 9, pp. 76)**
Pub: Entrepreneur Media, Inc.

Ed: Jennifer Wang. **Description:** Advice on how entrepreneurs in the United States should secure funding in view of the economic crisis is presented. Enough interest should be stimulated so as to secure a follow-up meeting. Investors should be asked questions that would encourage them to tell stories related to the downturn.

46771 ■ *The Wall Street Journal. Complete Small Business Guidebook*
Pub: Three Rivers Press

Ed: Colleen DeBaise. **Released:** December 29, 2009. **Price:** $15.00. **Description:** The mechanics of building, running and growing a profitable business are outlined, teaching how to write a business plan, ways to finding money during lean years, how to keep stress in check, time management, investment in technology, hiring, marketing, management basics, angel investing and venture capital, as well as an exit strategy.

46772 ■ "Wanted: Angels in the Country" in *Austin Business JournalInc.* **(Vol. 28, July 18, 2008, No. 18, pp. 1)**
Pub: American City Business Journals

Ed: Laura Hipp. **Description:** A proposal is being pushed forward by managers of Texas' Emerging Technology Fund to create an angel investors' network. The proposal is asking that tax credits for those who invest in research and development projects be granted in order to boost the number of technology companies in the state.

46773 ■ "Well-Heeled Startup" in *Business Journal Portland* **(Vol. 27, November 12, 2010, No. 37, pp. 1)**
Pub: Portland Business Journal

Ed: Erik Siemers. **Description:** Oh! Shoes LLC expects to receive about $1.5 million in funding from angel investors, while marketing a new line of high heel shoes that are comfortable, healthy, and attractive. The new line of shoes will use the technology of athletic footwear while having the look of an Italian designer. Oh! Shoes hopes to generate $35 million in sales by 2014.

46774 ■ *Western Association of Venture Capitalists—Directory of Members*
Pub: Western Association of Venture Capitalists

Released: Annual, February; Latest edition 2008. **Price:** $300, nonmembers. **Covers:** About 169 venture capital firms; coverage limited to the western United States. **Entries Include:** Company name, address, phone, name and title of contact; years experienced in venture capital field; description of investment preferences, desired maturity of company, desired investment position. **Arrangement:** Alphabetical.

46775 ■ "White Cat Media Tells You Where to Get a Bargain. Now It's Shopping for $1.5 Million" in *Inc.* **(March 2008, pp. 48)**
Pub: Gruner & Jahr USA Publishing

Ed: Athena Schindelheim. **Description:** Profile of White Cat Media which runs two shopping Websites: SheFinds.com for fashion and beauty items, and MomFinds.com for mothers. The New York City firm reported revenues for 2007 at $400,000 and is looking for funding capital in the amount of $1.7 million.

46776 ■ **"Will Work for Equity" in** *Inc.* **(March 2008, pp. 50, 52)**
Pub: Gruner & Jahr USA Publishing
Ed: Ryan McCarthy. **Description:** Profile of Dave Graham and his information technology company; Graham built his business by taking equity in client firms rather than charging fees. Four tips to consider before signing a work-for-equity business deal are outlined.

46777 ■ **"Women: Send Me An Angel" in** *Entrepreneur* **(Vol. 35, October 2007, No. 10, pp. 38)**
Pub: Entrepreneur Media Inc.
Ed: Aliza Sherman. **Description:** Golden Seeds has invested in Enter Artemis Woman LLC when the latter decided to put its products into Wal-Mart. Golden Seeds was formed by angel investors who aim to help women build their own businesses. Tips on how to approach angel investors and getting angel funding are given.

46778 ■ **"A World of Investors" in** *Entrepreneur* **(Vol. 35, November 2007, No. 11, pp. 72)**
Pub: Entrepreneur Media Inc.
Ed: Gail Dutton. **Description:** Information technology services company mPortal Inc. raised nearly $15 million in financing from venture capital company Friedli Corporate Finance. The biggest international investors are European companies, while the venture capital market is growing in Asia.

46779 ■ **"Xtium Has Its Head in the Clouds" in** *Philadelphia Business Journal* **(Vol. 30, September 23, 2011, No. 32, pp. 1)**
Pub: American City Business Journals Inc.
Ed: Peter Key. **Description:** Philadelphia-based cloud computing firm Xtium LLC received an $11.5 million first-round investment from Boston-Massachusetts-based OpenView Venture Partners. Catering to midsize businesses and unit of bigger firms, Xtium offers disaster-recovery, hosting, and managed-information-technology-infrastructure services.

46780 ■ **"Your Startup may be Worth Less than You Think" in** *Entrepreneur* **(Vol. 37, October 2009, No. 10, pp. 96)**
Pub: Entrepreneur Media, Inc.
Ed: Asheesh Advani. **Description:** Valuations of startups at the idea stage are dropping due to the effects of the recession. This drop is due to the decreasing availability of investment capital, the reduction in portfolio values of investors, and the increase in early stage startups.

46781 ■ **"Zit Zapper Lands New Funding" in** *Houston Business Journal* **(Vol. 40, November 27, 2009, No. 29, pp. 1)**
Pub: American City Business Journals
Ed: Mary Ann Azevedo. **Description:** Tyrell Inc. of Houston, Texas generated $20 million in funds for making a cheaper version of its acne-removing Zeno device. The upcoming product, Zeno Mini, will be targeted to a mass market with a price tag of about $89. In 2005, the original Zeno acne treatment device could only be bought through medical offices and spas at about $225.

TRADE PERIODICALS

46782 ■ *Venture Capital Journal*
Pub: Venture Economics Inc.
Contact: Kathleen Devlin, Editor-in-Chief
E-mail: Lawrence.Aragon@thomson.com
Released: Monthly. **Price:** $960, U.S. first year; $1650, elsewhere for combination of print and online edition. **Description:** Hard news, analysis and data on the North American private equity market.

CONSULTANTS

46783 ■ **Abrams Valuation Group Inc.**
7 Slevin Ct.
Monsey, NY 10952
Ph:(818)505-6008
Fax:(818)761-2148
Co. E-mail: ask.avg@abramsvaluation.com
URL: http://www.abramsvaluation.com
Contact: Scott Deifik, Principal
Scope: Valuators of businesses and intangible assets, providing expert analysis of difficult-to-resolve valuation issues for litigation, tax planning and business transactions. **Publications:** "Lost Inventory and Lost Profits Damage Formulas in Litigation," Sep, 2004; "The Bias in Annual (vs. Monthly) Discounting is Immaterial," Sep, 2003; "Forecasting Cash Flow: Mathematics of the Payout Ratio," Jun, 2003; "Problems in the QMDM and Comparison to Economic Components Model: A Response to Chris Mercer," Jun, 2002; "Discount Rates as a Function of Log Size and Valuation Error Measurement".

46784 ■ **Alimansky Capital Group Inc.**
12 E 44th St., Penthouse
New York, NY 10017-3606
Ph:(212)832-7300
Fax:(212)832-7338
Co. E-mail: info@alimansky.com
URL: http://www.alimansky.com
Contact: Sujit Chawla, Mgr
E-mail: nycrt4@atsnycrt.com
Scope: A private investment banking and advisory firm specializing in advising smaller middle market companies on raising equity and debt for acquisitions, expansion, and restructurings, and in sponsoring such businesses to appropriate sources of capital. Also works with management teams that seeking leveraged buyout or acquisition financing, and with private and institutional investors. Helps formulate investment strategies and evaluate venture capital and buyout opportunities. Serves companies in a broad range of industries, from leading edge technologies to consumer products and services.

46785 ■ **Alpha Capital Partners Ltd.**
3155 Research Blvd.
Dayton, OH 45420
Ph:(312)322-9800
Fax:(312)322-9808
Co. E-mail: kalnow@alphacapital.com
URL: http://www.alphacapital.com
Contact: Timm R. Reynolds, Principal
Scope: A venture capital management organization that provides equity financing for promising growth businesses and buyouts or recapitalization of established companies.

46786 ■ **American Document Examiners Inc.**
1208 Marine Way, Ste. 303-A
North Palm Beach, FL 33408
Ph:(248)681-7255
Fax:(248)681-5344
Co. E-mail: ritalord@aol.com
URL: http://www.americandocumentexaminers.com
Contact: Rita M. Lord, Principal
Scope: Document examiners specializing in handwriting and hand printing, signature verification, typewriter identification, alterations and obliterations, number identification, and forgery detection. Provides forensic examination of wills probate matters, bank checks and bank notes, insurance contracts, real estate documents, workers compensation matters, bomb threat notes, suicide notes and anonymous notes, election ballots, and deeds.

46787 ■ **Andrew Barile Consulting Corporation Inc.**
PO Box 9580
Rancho Santa Fe, CA 92067
Ph:(858)759-5039
Fax:(858)759-8436
Co. E-mail: abarile@abarileconsult.com
URL: http://www.abarileconsult.com
Contact: Andrew J. Barile, Principle
E-mail: abarile@abarileconsult.com
Scope: A strategic insurance and reinsurance consulting firm.

46788 ■ **Antares Capital Corp.**
PO Box 410730
Melbourne, FL 32941
Ph:(305)894-2888
Fax:(305)894-3227
Co. E-mail: info@antarescapital.com
URL: http://www.antarescapital.com
Contact: Thomas Domencich, Partner
Scope: Invests equity capital in developmental and expansion stage companies and in management buyout opportunities. Looks for firms that have an opportunity to deploy capital on an efficient basis to significantly alter their growth trajectory and create value for the founders, managers, and owners of the businesses.

46789 ■ **Antoinette Doyle Consulting**
695 42nd Ave.
San Francisco, CA 94121-2532
Ph:(415)752-2413
Fax:(415)752-2440
Co. E-mail: tdoyle@planeteria.net
Contact: Toni Doyle, Owner
E-mail: tdoyle@planeteria.net
Scope: Provides fundraising consulting services to non-profit organizations. Services include annual campaigns, capital and major gift campaigns, and foundation and corporate relations.

46790 ■ **Avery Business Development Services**
2506 St. Michel Ct.
Ponte Vedra Beach, FL 32082
Ph:(904)285-6033
Fax:(904)280-8840
Contact: Henry Avery, Owner
Scope: Offers general business and management consulting of business development from project conception to full commercialization. Scope of activities includes new venture development, business strategy planning, corporate development, licensing, and merger/acquisitions. Industries served: Chemical, plastics, and biotechnology coatings. **Seminars:** Constructing the Business Plan and Obtaining Financing For a New Business Venture; Business Strategy Planning.

46791 ■ **Blueprint Fundraising and Communications**
54 - 1101 Nicola St.
Vancouver, ON, Canada V6G 2E3
Ph:(604)682-6582
Free: 877-682-6582
Fax:(604)682-6580
Co. E-mail: andrea@blueprintfundraising.com
URL: http://www.blueprintfundraising.com
Contact: Andrea Seale, Principle
E-mail: andrea@blueprintfundraising.com
Scope: Firm provides fund raising-related consulting, coaching and workshops for nonprofits. Services include fund raising audits and plans; major gift, membership and planned giving programs; communications strategies and writing projects; campaign feasibility studies; hands-on campaign management; fund raising training and coaching for staff and boards; case statements, proposals, direct mail and other materials; donor stewardship program development; sponsorship development; and prospect research. **Seminars:** Your Major Gifts Campaign, Vancouver, Sep, 2010.

46792 ■ **Bridge Consulting Group**
3235 Ella Lee Ln.
Houston, TX 77019
Ph:(713)521-1352
Fax:(713)521-0025
Co. E-mail: dgehrman@bridgecons.com
Contact: Douglas B. Gehrman, Managing Director
E-mail: dgehrman@bridgecons.com
Scope: Consulting practice delivers strategic solutions for managing mergers, acquisitions and business transformations and developing leaders. Focuses on the human, organizational and cultural factors vital to corporate change and on programs for developing the leadership. **Publications:** "Navigating the Whitewater of a Merger Strategies for Success"; "The Leadership Promise Guideposts for Aspiring Leaders"; "The Rise of Intellectual Capitalism".

46793 ■ **Bridgewood Consultants**
20793 Farmington Rd., Ste. 21
Farmington, MI 48336
Ph:(248)426-0079

Fax:(248)426-0823
Co. E-mail: dbrann@bridgewoodcc.com
Contact: Dorothy Zynda Snyder, Principle
E-mail: dbrann@bridgewoodcc.com
Scope: Firm specializes in assisting service-oriented businesses develop a professional image, organizational skills and a structural foundation. **Publications:** "Don't Give Up Before You've Begun!"; "Invest in Your Success"; "Marketing Our Way"; "Marketing - Sorting Fact from Opinion; and Times, They are a Chang'in - What About You?". **Seminars:** Make Your Waiting Room Standing Room Only, Sep, 2007; Marketing 101, Sep, 2007; Creating a Lucrative Practice.

46794 ■ BSpudly Enterprises Inc.
524 W Portland St.
Phoenix, AZ 85003
Ph:(602)293-3474
Fax:(602)296-7270
Co. E-mail: bspudly@aol.com
URL: http://www.bspudly.com
Contact: Kurt Bloeser, President
E-mail: bspudly@aol.com
Scope: Consultant provides financial consulting, bank training and expert testimony.

46795 ■ Burns Innovation Group Inc.
Landmark Sq. II, 1708 Dolphin Ave., Ste. 806
Kelowna, BC, Canada V1Y 9S4
Ph:(250)763-4716
Free: 877-763-4022
Fax:877-353-8608
Co. E-mail: steve@burnsinnovation.com
Contact: Steve Burns, CEO
E-mail: steve@burnsinnovation.com
Scope: A full-service consulting firm dedicated to helping entrepreneurs build their businesses by providing hands-on consulting services. Provides services in finance, marketing and sales, and human resources. Business strategy services include evaluating the strategy of a business, conducting strategic planning sessions, development of strategic performance indicators, development of full business plans, and facilitation of planning sessions/business builder system. Financial services include mergers and acquisitions, cash flow management, profit improvement analysis, financial statement analysis, financial ratio analysis assistance in obtaining financing, and negotiation of new business arrangements including sales or purchase of a business, joint ventures, and partnerships and strategic alliances. Marketing and sales services include development and execution of marketing plans, development and execution of sales strategies, marketing mix, product and pricing strategies, and providing focus groups and customer advisory boards. Human resource services include recruitment and selection of key personnel, recruitment strategies, online recruitment, establishing compensation strategies, assistance in hiring and selection, assistance in developing and executing employee retention strategies, employee satisfaction surveys, and customized training programs. Process and technology services include review and improvement of key processes in the business, development of key indicators to better manage key business processes, utilization of technology to improve process management, and development and execution of e-commerce strategies. **Publications:** "Entrepreneurialism Okanagan Style"; "Burns Business Builder - Beyond the Box"; "The Sales Overhaul - Step 1 - The Sales Audit"; "Overhauling Your Sales Effort"; "The Inside/Outside Marketing Measurement System"; "Overhauling Your Marketing Efforts"; "Why You Need A Leadership Overhaul"; "The Three Most Important Measures of Business Success"; "It is Never Too Late to Start Action Oriented Listening"; "Mid Year Reality Check"; "Thinking Beyond the Box"; "Growing Your Leadership"; "Creating Your Own Fresh Start"; "Identifying Your Defining Moments"; "Achieving a Balanced Life". **Seminars:** One Page Performance Management Plan; Employee Self-Evaluation Performance Assessment; Marketing Intelligence Part 1; Human Resource Planning/Policies; Four Ways To Grow Your Business; How To Effectively Recruit High Technology Personnel; How To Interview, Select And Hire High Technology Personnel; Making Your Business Really Fly.

46796 ■ Burt Bernstein Insurance Litigation Consultants
626 Carlo Dr.
Goleta, CA 93117
Ph:(805)692-1978
Fax:(805)964-8041
Co. E-mail: burtins@cox.net
URL: http://www.burtbernstein.com
Contact: Burt Bernstein, Principle
E-mail: burtins@cox.net
Scope: An insurance litigation consultant offering services for disputes involving life, disability, and health insurance.

46797 ■ The Business Continuity Group Inc.
101 Federal St., Ste. 1900
Boston, MA 02110
Ph:(617)342-7260
Free: 888-438-0224
Co. E-mail: websales@bcragent.com
URL: http://www.continuityhost.com
Contact: Roy T. Weston, CEO
E-mail: rweston@bcgit.com
Scope: Provides expertise in international business contingency. Offers technical consulting and training services as well as specialized consulting services in the areas of continuity, such as security and regulatory compliance, storage and networking, and contract negotiations. Also provides support services in site hosting, monitoring services. Typical services cover continuity planning, security issues, compliance and litigation, vendor due diligence, disaster recovery, integration issues and research and training.

46798 ■ The Business Place Ltd.
10 Kingsbridge Garden Cir., Ste. 506
Mississauga, ON, Canada L5R 3K6
Ph:(905)890-9245
Fax:(905)890-3229
Co. E-mail: gary.landa@thebusinessplace.com
URL: http://www.thebusinessplace.com
Contact: Gary R. Landa, President
E-mail: gary.landa@thebusinessplace.com
Scope: Assists in the buying and selling of businesses, arranging bank financing, venture capital loans/investments, mergers and acquisitions. **Publications:** "Did you find the right business for sale Part II," Feb, 2009; "Did you find the right business," Feb, 2009; "Buying a business what do you look for when looking at financial statements," Feb, 2009; "Business brokers how do you know if you found the right business broker," Feb, 2009; "Businesses how do you determine if you found the right one," Feb, 2009; "Start up businesses how do you value them when you are looking for equity," Feb, 2009; "Business locations time to move intone space, Feb, 2009; Business brokers are they helpful," Feb, 2009.

46799 ■ The Business Success Group L.L.C.
1033 NE 17th Way, Ste. 1704
Fort Lauderdale, FL 33304
Ph:(248)703-6013
Co. E-mail: info@businessadvisorygrp.com
URL: http://www.businessadvisorygrp.com
Contact: Roberta S. Socall, Principal
E-mail: tsocall@businessadvisorygrp.com
Scope: Firm offers business and training services to companies. Business programs include Business Success Planning; Financial Business Planning and Assistance with Search for Funding Sources; Strategic Market Planning; Human Resource Services; Recruiting with a Guarantee; Career/Life Success Planning; One-On-One Career Counseling; and Retreat and Strategic Planning Facilitation. Training services include E-learning That is Award-Winning; Business Improvement Training and Organizational Development; Formal Personal Training; and Personal Assessment (Profile) Instruments. **Seminars:** Starting Your Business the Right Way - The First Time. **Special Services:** BSP^R; CLSP^R; The Fish Philosophy^R; Inscape Publishing^R; DiSC^R.

46800 ■ Business Systems Consulting
15 Lincoln St., 330 Main St., Ste. 210
Wakefield, MA 01880
Ph:(781)683-4040

Fax:(781)683-4040
Co. E-mail: info@bizsysconsulting.com
URL: http://www.bizsysconsulting.com
Contact: Len Levin, Principle
E-mail: len@bizsysconsulting.com
Scope: IT consultancy providing a range of services to companies. Services include analysis, planning and implementation; procurement management; outsourcing services; ongoing support; process and work flow development and training.

46801 ■ Butterflies in Progress L.L.C.
9352 Rockfish Gap Tpke.
Afton, VA 22920
Ph:(540)447-6823
Fax:(540)456-6758
Co. E-mail: cynthia@butterfliesinprogress.com
URL: http://www.butterfliesinprogress.com
Contact: Cynthia Hurst, Owner
E-mail: cynthia@butterfliesinprogress.com
Scope: Consultant specializes in raising corporate and foundation funds, the development of annual fundraising campaigns and overseeing special fund raising.

46802 ■ Canadian Association of Professional Speakers
1370 Don Mills Rd., Ste. 300
PO Box 3491, Sta. B
Toronto, ON, Canada M3B 3N7
Ph:(416)847-3355
Free: 877-847-3350
Fax:(416)441-0591
Co. E-mail: info@canadianspeakers.org
URL: http://www.canadianspeakers.org
Contact: Shelle Rose Charvet, President
E-mail: shari@atscanadianspeakers.org
Scope: Canadian speakers, trainers, consultants and facilitators. Specialists in a range of topics and responsive to media. Seeks to raise the profile and professionalism of members. Helps members hone their skills at securing more business and in delivering their expertise through education, focused programming and networking.

46803 ■ Concept Development Associates Inc.
PO Box 15245
Evansville, IN 47716-0245
Ph:(812)471-3334
Fax:(812)477-6499
Contact: Deborah Clark, Principal
Scope: A globally-connected venture capital group.

46804 ■ Crosslink Capital
Two Embarcadero Ctr., Ste. 2200
San Francisco, CA 94111
Ph:(415)617-1800
Co. E-mail: ewinterhalter@crosslinkcapital.com
URL: http://www.crosslinkcapital.com
Contact: Eric Winterhalter, Partner
E-mail: ewinterhalter@atscrosslinkcapital.com
Scope: An independent venture capital and investment firm. Firm focuses on strategic business and technology questions as well as to discuss tactical approaches to addressing these challenges.

46805 ■ Design Financial Inc.
5 Belleview St., Ste. 100
Mount Clemens, MI 48043-2238
Ph:(586)469-7788
Fax:(586)469-4700
Co. E-mail: anthony.forlini@designfinancial.com
URL: http://www.designfinancial.com
Contact: Sondra Dean, Mgr
E-mail: sondra.dean@atsdesignfinancial.com
Scope: Firm provides individual and business financial planning services. Services offered include business succession strategies, charitable donation strategies, estate analysis, and retirement strategies. **Publications:** "Estates & Trusts"; "Tax Planning"; "Cash Management"; "Retirement"; "Investing"; "Risk Management". **Seminars:** Retirement; Estate Planning; Tax Strategies; Long Term Care; Financial Management.

46806 ■ Disability Income Concepts Inc.
1433 Camellia Cir.
PO Box 266257
Weston, FL 33326
Ph:(954)217-8260
Free: 877-776-3948
Fax:(954)217-8241
Co. E-mail: disability@disabilityconcepts.com
URL: http://www.disabilityconcepts.com
Contact: Gerald Katz, President
Scope: Firm specializes in disabled insured claims and consulting services. Services include expert witness testimony for disability insurance claim disputes; independent and comprehensive review, analysis and summary of current disability and/or long term care insurance coverage; consultation on how to complete initial disability claim forms and ongoing progress reports; coordination of disability policy information and claims status with personal attorneys; and review and coordination of financial claims information with accountants.

46807 ■ ECG Advisors L.L.C.
200 Business Park Dr., Ste. 101
Armonk, NY 10504
Ph:(310)251-0860
Fax:(310)459-0615
Co. E-mail: info@ecgadvisors.com
Contact: Randolph O. Ramirez, Owner
Scope: Firm advises boards of directors and their compensation committees, large share holders/investors and other stake holders on executive compensation, directors pay, corporate governance and other compensation issues such as linking compensation strategy with corporate strategy, equity and pseudo-equity pay, competitive bench marking, pay systems, regulatory compliance and performance measurement. Firm also provides litigation and arbitration support, assisting clients in IRS proceedings, divorce and asset division disputes, defense contract audit agency (DCAA) action, expert testimony and corporate and individual bankruptcy proceedings.

46808 ■ ECnow.com Inc.
20660 Stevens Creek Blvd., Ste. 210
Cupertino, CA 95014
Ph:(408)257-3000
Fax:(408)843-0769
Co. E-mail: info@ecnow.com
URL: http://www.ecnow.com
Contact: Mitchell Levy, CEO
E-mail: mitchell.levy.sjsupd@ecnow.com
Scope: A management consulting firm specializing in strategic consulting and targeted business education. **Publications:** "E-Volve-or-Die.com"; "Happy About Outsourcing"; "Happy About Knowing What to Expect in 2005, 2006, 2007 & 2008". **Seminars:** Business and Management Issues. **Special Services:** Value Framework[R]; Happy About[R].

46809 ■ Elliott Appraisers L.L.C.
3000 Richmond Ave., Ste. 240
Houston, TX 77098-3188
Ph:(713)530-9919
Fax:(713)337-0919
Co. E-mail: quenton@appraiser4jewelry.com
URL: http://www.appraiser4jewelry.com
Contact: Quenton T. Elliott Jr., Principle
E-mail: quenton@appraiser4jewelry.com
Scope: Provides independent valuation of gems and fine jewelry, forensic gemology services, and consulting.

46810 ■ Equity Partners of America Ltd.
1450 W Long Lake Rd., Ste. 340
Troy, MI 48098-6351
Ph:(248)952-0300
Fax:(248)952-0314
Co. E-mail: equitypartners@email.msn.com
Contact: Albert A. Koch, Managing Director
Scope: Private investment bank specializing in debt and equity capital procurement; buying and selling businesses; shareholder value enhancement strategies; and litigation and alternative dispute resolution assistance; including expert witness assistance. Serves manufacturing, distribution and service industries. **Seminars:** Preparation of a business plan;

Use of financial statements in damage claims; Determining the value of a business; When to sell a family business.

46811 ■ The Hotel Experts L.L.C.
PO Box 113
Stratham, NH 03885
Ph:(561)775-4990
Fax:(561)622-9223
Co. E-mail: saltriverfarm@yahoo.com
URL: http://member.expertpages.com/thehotelexperts
Contact: Steve Stearns, Partner
E-mail: stevest50@aol.com
Scope: Attorney case consultants and expert witnesses in hotel litigation. Guides through discovery, depositions and case strategy, submitting detailed opinions, and offering trial testimony both for and against hotel properties, owners, operators, franchisers and individual litigants.

46812 ■ Integrated Development Consulting
1115 W Mead Ave.
Salt Lake City, UT 84104
Ph:(801)533-8375
Co. E-mail: amyoconnor@earthlink.net
URL: http://www.integrated-development.biz
Contact: Amy O'Connor, Principle
E-mail: amyoconnor@earthlink.net
Scope: Provides organizational development consulting to nonprofits through training, coaching and facilitation. Areas include strategic planning, organizational assessments, board development, membership acquisition, message development, and communication.

46813 ■ Investor Voices L.L.C.
120A N Main Ave.
Newton, NC 28658
Ph:(717)626-3991
Fax:(570)227-7038
URL: http://www.investorvoices.com
Contact: Timothy Shannon, CEO
Scope: A due diligence based business development advisor. Seeks to partner with growing but underexposed small-cap companies. Provides business development, investor relations, advertising, and financial advisory services.

46814 ■ Jewels by Stacy Appraisals
712 Bancroft Rd., Ste. 436
Walnut Creek, CA 94598
Ph:(925)939-4367
Fax:(925)939-4567
Co. E-mail: nancy@appraiser.net
URL: http://www.jewelry-appraisal.com
Contact: Carole Richbourg, Mgr
E-mail: carole.richbourg@atscomcast.net
Scope: An independent jewelry appraiser specializing in appraisal of modern and antique fine jewelry, diamonds, gemstones and watches. **Publications:** "Gem print Goes Hollywood"; "Some Good Advice on Buying Diamonds"; "Gold Buying Scams"; "Cruise Purchases of Jewelry"; "Buying Gemstones in Afghanistan"; "Red Labradorite Scams"; "Tanzanite Scams"; "Shipping jewelry". **Seminars:** Conquering Comps workshop, San Francisco, Oct, 2009.

46815 ■ Mara Perez, Ph.D. Fund Development and Planning Services
320 Via Casitas, Ste. 107
Greenbrae, CA 94904
Ph:(415)461-0141
Fax:(415)461-7741
Co. E-mail: mperez@svn.net
URL: http://www.svn.net/mperez
Contact: Mara Perez, Owner
E-mail: mperez@svn.net
Scope: Consultant works with boards and staff leadership of non profit organizations and educational institutions. Areas include Latino affairs, diversity, health, the arts, education, spirituality, the environment and international affairs. Services in fund development, strategic planning, and coalition development. **Publications:** "Democratization's: Comparisons, Confrontations, and Contrasts," MIT Press, 2009; "International migration and the Latino

population in the U.S".. **Seminars:** International migration; Wednesday Morning Dialogue; National Association of Hispanic Realtors.

46816 ■ Micro Cap et Al
470 Granville St., Ste. 1120
Vancouver, BC, Canada V6C 1V5
Ph:(604)713-8010
Free: 877-642-7622
Fax:(604)713-8018
Co. E-mail: info@microcapetal.com
URL: http://www.microcapetal.com
Contact: Robert Bell, President
E-mail: bbell@atsmicrocapetal.com
Scope: Strategic business solutions partners specializing in investor relations (lead generation programs, pro-active IR programs, maintenance IR Programs, and shareholder audits); capital placement (private placements, debt placements, and seed stock offerings); and consulting (corporate structure, syndication strategies, and merger and acquisition advice).

46817 ■ New York Grant Co.
29 Broadway, Ste. 2222
New York, NY 10006
Ph:(212)227-8283
Fax:(212)214-0814
Co. E-mail: marsha@nygrants.com
URL: http://www.nygrants.com
Contact: Ann Kayman, Office Manager, Information Systems
E-mail: ann@atsnygrants.com
Scope: Consultants in economic development to assist clients in navigating the maze of economic incentives in New York, such as tax breaks, wage tax credits, energy discounts, real estate tax exemptions, investment tax credits and other benefits from local, state, and federal agencies.

46818 ■ Newmarket Capital Advisors
5310 Harvest Hill Rd.
Dallas, TX 75230
Ph:(972)386-3860
Fax:(972)503-1519
Contact: Frank Cole, President
Scope: Venture capitalists that offer assistance in strategic decisions and long range planning.

46819 ■ Pacific Century Group Ventures Ltd.
105-150 Crowfoot Cres. NW, Ste. 700
Calgary, AB, Canada T3G 3T2
Ph:(604)871-0452
Fax:(604)871-0451
Co. E-mail: info@pcentury.com
URL: http://www.pcentury.com
Contact: Harish C. Consul, Accounting Manager
E-mail: hconsul@atspcentury.com
Scope: Experienced in fund management, venture capital and corporate finance. Specializes in information technology and real estate sectors.

46820 ■ Predictable Futures Inc.
10104 103 Ave., Ste. 1211
Edmonton, AB, Canada T5J 0H8
Ph:(780)702-2499
Free: (866)241-2221
Fax:(780)428-1410
Co. E-mail: solutions@predictablefutures.com
URL: http://www.predictablefutures.com
Contact: Barbara Benoliel, Principle
Scope: Firm partners with clients to design and coordinate succession, estate and wealth management strategies. Specialists in the fields of strategic planning, governance, mediation, facilitation, law, taxation, and business and insurance planning. **Publications:** "Beyond Survival: A Guide for Business Owners and their Families"; "Achieving Authentic Success"; "Halftime"; "Game Plan"; "How to RETIRE Happy, Wild & Free". **Seminars:** Family Business Succession-It's All About Planning, Hawaii, Mar, 2006.

46821 ■ Samuel E. Bodily Associates
Office:172, 100 Darden Blvd.
PO Box 6550
Charlottesville, VA 22903
Ph:(434)924-4813

Fax:(434)243-7677
Co. E-mail: bodilys@virginia.edu
Contact: Samuel E. Bodily, Principle
E-mail: bodilys@virginia.edu
Scope: Consultant specializes in financial analysis, capital investment, business/product/market planners, financial risk analysis and decision sciences. **Publications:** "I Can't Get No Satisfaction: How Bundling and Multi-Part Pricing Can Satisfy Consumers and Suppliers," Feb, 2006; "Organizational Use of Decision Analysis," Oct, 2004; "Real Options," Oct, 2004.

46822 ■ Seacoast Capital
455 Market St., Ste. 2000
San Francisco, CA 94105
Ph:(978)750-1300
Fax:(978)750-1301
Co. E-mail: gdeli@seacoastcapital.com
URL: http://www.seacoastcapital.com
Contact: Walter H. Leonard, CFO & Treas
E-mail: wleonard@seacoastcapital.com
Scope: Invests growth capital in small companies led by strong, entrepreneurial management teams. Provides follow-on financing for acquisitions, internal growth or the execution of roll-out strategies. Assists portfolio companies develop and refine strategic plans, recruit additional management or board talent, access debt or equity capital markets, identify and negotiate acquisitions, develop compensation and incentive programs, and maximize value for all stakeholders upon exit.

46823 ■ SG Capital
1825 Century Pk. E, 17th Fl.
Los Angeles, CA 90067
Ph:(310)556-9900
Fax:(310)861-9901
Contact: Mike Plotnik, Managing Director
E-mail: mikep@atssgcapital.com
Scope: Venture capital firm that provides secured asset based funding to companies experiencing fast growth exceeding normal debt to equity ratios and companies being re-structured due to losses.

46824 ■ Spherix Inc.
12051 Indian Creek Ct.
Beltsville, MD 20705
Ph:(301)897-2540
Free: (866)774-3749
Fax:(301)897-2567
Co. E-mail: info@spherix.com
URL: http://www.biospherics.com
Contact: Thomas B. Peter, Director
Scope: Provides health sciences consulting services that provides scientific and strategic support for suppliers, manufacturers, distributors and retailers of: Conventional foods, biotechnology-derived foods, medical foods, infant formulas, food ingredients, dietary supplements, food contact substances, pharmaceuticals, medical devices, consumer products and industrial chemicals and pesticides. Provides teleservices, ebusinesses, and IT solutions for the health and information industries. **Publications:** "Viking found no life on Mars, and, just as important, it found why there can be no life". **Special Services:** Naturlose^R.

46825 ■ Sprout Group
11 Madison Ave., 13th Fl.
New York, NY 10010-3698
Ph:(212)538-3600
Fax:(212)538-8245
Co. E-mail: info@sproutgroup.com
URL: http://www.sproutgroup.com
Contact: Tracy Urquiaga, CFO
E-mail: janet.hickey@atssproutgroup.com
Scope: The firm invests in stages from start-ups through buyouts in high growth areas such as information technology, medical products and services, business services and retail.

46826 ■ Strategies for Social Change L.L.C.
50 Broad St., Ste. 1937
New York, NY 10004
Ph:(212)785-0544

Fax:(212)785-0669
Co. E-mail: info@communityimpactconsulting.com
URL: http://www.CommunityImpactConsulting.com
Contact: Andrea Williams, Principle
Scope: Culture-minded firm develops capacity building services, strategies and solutions to help nonprofits increase their resources, maximize strategic impact and achieve their mission. Services include strategic planning, board development, executive coaching, fund development and grant writing, executive transition planning, leadership skills training, needs assessment and program evaluation, program planning, outcomes management, retreat facilitation, financial management consultation, and website development. **Publications:** "The Do's and Don'ts of Hiring a Consultant"; "Executive Coaching Works!"; "Characteristics of Highly Effective Organizations". **Seminars:** Grant Writing and Fund Development Training; Board Governance and Training Retreat Facilitation; Strategic Planning Training; Cultural Competency Training and Retreat Facilitation; Leadership Training and Retreat Facilitation.

46827 ■ Thomson Venture Economics Inc.
395 Hudson St., Ste. 3
New York, NY 10014
Ph:(212)807-5000
Free: 888-989-8373
Fax:(212)807-5122
Contact: Adam Reinebach, Vice President
E-mail: adam.reinebach@atstfn.com
Scope: Venture capital and business development specialists providing customized research for industrial and financial corporations. Services include: identification of high-potential companies for investment, alliance or acquisition; assistance in establishing venture capital or strategic alliance programs; and assistance with specific acquisition searches. Services for institutional investors in venture capital include: Basic education and due diligence evaluation of venture capital as an investment; development of venture capital investment strategy; and identification of investment opportunities, portfolio monitoring, analysis, performance; and benchmarking for the venture capital asset class. Serves private industries as well as government agencies. **Seminars:** Performance Monitoring Workshop.

46828 ■ Venture Planning Associates Inc.
2515 Glen Eagles Dr.
PO Box 33219
Reno, NV 89533
Ph:(775)747-8829
Free: 888-404-1212
Co. E-mail: capital@ventureplan.com
URL: http://www.ventureplan.com
Contact: Todd Smith, CFO
Scope: Provides venture capital consulting services for all phases of business development, from start-ups to IPOs. Investment criteria and participation in projects include: the ability to purchase founders stock convertible preferred or warrants; direct participation in management either on the board of directors or as an officer business market large enough to go national; exit strategy via buyout or acquisition by larger firms; fee for services paid following seed capital funding. Provides entrepreneurial training, consulting, executive search, marketing assistance and referral services to other professionals.

46829 ■ Wall Street Services Inc.
11 Broadway, Ste. 910
New York, NY 10004
Ph:(212)509-7200
Fax:(212)943-1597
Co. E-mail: info@wallstreetservices.com
URL: http://www.wallstreetservices.com
Contact: Peter Laughter, CEO
E-mail: pjlaughter@atswallstreetservices.com
Scope: A staffing agency catering to top tier Manhattan investment banks and legal firms. Specializes in personnel placement and executive search. Proprietary systems include an instrument for measuring key work place attributes, a method for determining what position will inspire and challenge the best available workers, and tools for rapidly matching the right candidate to the job. **Publications:** "Wall Street Services Editorial".

46830 ■ Western Capital Financial Services Inc.
63 East 11400 South, Bldg. 221
Sandy, UT 84070
Ph:(801)619-4700
Free: 877-517-9555
Fax:(408)889-2415
Co. E-mail: support@mycollector.com
URL: http://www.mycollector.com
Contact: Robert Paisola, CEO
E-mail: robert@mycollector.com
Scope: Firm specializes in debt collection and portfolio recovery business. **Publications:** "The art of getting paid".

46831 ■ Western Capital Holdings Inc.
10050 E Applwood Dr.
Parker, CO 80138
Ph:(303)841-1022
Fax:(303)770-1945
Contact: Patrick T. Frasco, President
Scope: Specialists in all phases of financial and management consulting. Provide strong emphasis in strategic planning and corporate development, financial analysis, acquisitions, investment banking and corporate finance. Projects range in size and duration to fit clients needs. Services can be applied to many diverse financial projects that may include the following: Business plan development, budgeting and forecasting, strategic planning, cash flow analysis, cash flow management, corporate development, banking relations, asset management, and financial analysis. Industries served: Food industry, manufacturing, distribution, retailing, computer services, agribusiness, financial services, insurance, and government agencies. **Seminars:** Buy Low, Sell High, Collect Early and Pay Late; Preparing Your Company for Sale; Venture Capital - Finding an Angel.

FRANCHISES AND BUSINESS OPPORTUNITIES

46832 ■ The Entrust Group
Entrust
555 12th St., Ste. 1250
Oakland, CA 94607
Free: 888-340-8977
Fax:(510)251-2847
Description: Administrators of self directed IRAs. **Financial Assistance:** No. **Training:** Yes.

46833 ■ Innovative Lease Services, Inc.
5931 Priestly Dr., Ste. 205
Carlsbad, CA 92008
Ph:(760)438-1470
Free: 800-298-2882
Fax:(760)438-2046
Founded: 1987. **Description:** Equipment financing for franchises.

46834 ■ Wirth Business Credit
Winmark Corporation
605 Hwy. 169 N, Ste. 400
Minneapolis, MN 55441
Free: 800-567-6600
Fax:(763)520-8501
No. of Franchise Units: 56. **Founded:** 2005. **Franchised:** 2005. **Description:** Equipment leasing and financing. **Equity Capital Needed:** $39,630-$74,510. **Franchise Fee:** $35,000. **Royalty Fee:** No. **Financial Assistance:** No.

COMPUTER SYSTEMS/ SOFTWARE

46835 ■ *Loan Express*
Entrepreneur, Inc.
2445 McCabe Way
Irvine, CA 92614
Ph:(949)261-2325
Free: 800-421-2300
Fax:(949)261-7729
URL: http://www.entrepreneur.com
Price: $99.95. **Description:** Software program providing step-by-step information for writing a loan proposal.

LIBRARIES

46836 ■ Innovation Ontario Corporation Information Centre
56 Wellesley St. W, 7th Fl.
Toronto, ON, Canada M7A 2E7
Ph:(416)326-1041
Fax:(416)326-1109
Scope: Venture capital, innovation, new technology licensing. **Services:** Copying; Library not open to the public. **Holdings:** Figures not available.

46837 ■ Loan Brokers Association–Information Services
917 S. Park St.
Owosso, MI 48867-4422
Contact: Ben Campbell, Dir.
Scope: Loan brokers, loan consulting, credit repair, lending, credit cards, venture capital. **Services:** Copying; SDI; Library to members or by permission.

46838 ■ Sentron Medical Inc.–Senmed Medical Ventures Library
4445 Lake Forest Dr., No. 600
Cincinnati, OH 45242-3798
Ph:(513)563-3240
Fax:(513)563-3261
URL: http://www.senmed.com/organization.htm
Contact: Rosanne Wohlwender
Scope: Biotechnology, medical devices and diagnostics, technology transfer, pharmaceuticals, venture capital, licensing. **Services:** Library not open to the public. **Holdings:** 800 books; 50 reports. **Subscriptions:** 100 journals and other serials; 2 newspapers.

RESEARCH CENTERS

46839 ■ St. Louis University–Smurfit-Stone Center for Entrepreneurship
John Cook School of Business
3674 Lindell Blvd.
St. Louis, MO 63108
Ph:(314)977-3850
Fax:(314)977-3627
Co. E-mail: rhodesja@slu.edu
URL: http://www.slu.edu/ssce.xml
Contact: Jeanne Rhodes, Admin.Asst.
E-mail: rhodesja@slu.edu
Scope: Venture capital, endowed positions in entrepreneurship. **Educational Activities:** Billiken Angel Network; Collegiate Entrepreneurship Organizations; Gateway Series for Entrepreneurship Research for faculty (annually), in spring; Habitat for Neighborhood Business; Idea to Product Competition for Missouri and Illinois universities; Summer Entrepreneurship Academy for high school students. **Awards:** Smurfit-Stone Entrepreneurial Alumni Hall of Fame.

START-UP INFORMATION

46840 ■ *Scrapbooking for Profit: Cashing in on Retail, Home-Based and Internet Opportunities*
Pub: Allworth Press
Ed: Rebecca Pittman. **Released:** June 2005. **Price:** $19.95 (US), $22.95 (Canadian). **Description:** Eleven strategies for starting a scrapbooking business, including brick-and-mortar stores, home-based businesses, and online retail and wholesale outlets.

ASSOCIATIONS AND OTHER ORGANIZATIONS

46841 ■ International Federation of Pharmaceutical Wholesalers
10569 Crestwood Dr.
Manassas, VA 20109
Ph:(703)331-3714
Fax:(703)331-3715
Co. E-mail: info@ifpw.com
URL: http://www.ifpw.com
Contact: Eric V. Zwisler, Vice Chm.
Description: Wholesalers and distributors of pharmaceutical products. Promotes efficient delivery of pharmaceuticals to hospitals, physicians, and pharmacists; seeks to increase public awareness of the role played by members in the health care system. Facilitates cooperation and exchange of information among members; represents members' commercial and regulatory interests; sponsors educational and promotional programs. .

46842 ■ National Association of Wholesaler-Distributors
1325 G St. NW, Ste. 1000
Washington, DC 20005
Ph:(202)872-0885
Fax:(202)785-0586
Co. E-mail: naw@naw.org
URL: http://www.naw.org
Contact: Dirk Van Dongen, Pres.
Description: Federation of national, state, and regional associations, and individual wholesaler-distributor firms. Represents industry's views to the federal government. Analyzes current and proposed legislation and government regulations affecting the industry. Maintains public relations and media programs and a research foundation. Conducts wholesale executive management courses. **Publications:** *NAW Report* (bimonthly); *SmartBrief* .

46843 ■ NAW Institute for Distribution Excellence
1325 G St. NW, Ste. 1000
Washington, DC 20005
Ph:(202)872-0885
Fax:(202)785-0586
Co. E-mail: naw@naw.org
URL: http://www.naw.org/institute/iindex.php
Contact: Dirk Van Dongen, Pres.
Description: Firms that are members of the National Association of Wholesaler-Distributors, wholesalers, and trade associations. Seeks to advance knowledge in the field of wholesale distribution by means of long-range research projects. **Publications:** *Connect with Your Suppliers: A Wholesaler-Distributor's Guide to Electronic Communications Systems*; *Facing the Forces of Change: The Road to Opportunity* (triennial); *Price for Success: A Practical Guide for Improving Margins in Wholesale Distribution* .

REFERENCE WORKS

46844 ■ *American Wholesalers and Distributors Directory*
Pub: Gale
Released: Annual, Latest edition 22nd; April, 2011. **Price:** $410, individuals. **Covers:** Name and address, fax number, SIC code, principal product lines, total number of employees, estimated annual sales volume and principal officers' information of 27,000 large and small wholesalers and distributors in the U.S. and Puerto Rico. **Arrangement:** By broad subject from principal product line, by Standard Industrial Classification code (SIC index), by state and city (geographical index), and by company name (alphabetic index). **Indexes:** SIC, geographical, alphabetical.

46845 ■ *The Big Payback: The History of the Business of Hip-Hop*
Pub: New American Library/Penguin Group
Ed: Dan Charnas. **Price:** $24.95. **Description:** The complete history of hip-hop music is presented, by following the money and the relationship between artist and merchant. In its promise of economic security and creative control for black artist-entrepreneurs, it is the culmination of dreams of black nationalists and civil rights leaders.

46846 ■ *"From Craft Biz To Wholesale Giant"* in *Women Entrepreneur* (January 19, 2009)
Pub: Entrepreneur Media Inc.
Ed: Maria Falconer. **Description:** Advice is given on how to turn a small craft business into a full-time venture; tips to help one transition from a part-time designer to a full-time wholesaler and brand are also included.

46847 ■ *"Ground Floor Opportunity"* in *Small Business Opportunities* (July 2008)
Pub: Entrepreneur Media Inc.
Description: Profile of Doug Disney, the founder of the booming franchise Tile Outlet Always in Stock, which sells ceramic and porcelain tile and stone products at wholesale prices; Disney found inspiration in a book he read in two days and that motivated him to expand his venture into a huge franchise opportunity.

46848 ■ *"Home Depot Eyes Wholesale Spinoff"* in *Globe & Mail* (February 13, 2007, pp. B13)
Pub: CTVglobemedia Publishing Inc.
Description: Home Depot Inc. is planning to sell or spinoff its professional supply business to focus on retail stores. The weakening sales and profits are the main driving force behind the company's decision.

46849 ■ *How to Start and Run a Small Book Publishing Company: A Small Business Guide to Self-Publishing and Independent Publishing*
Pub: HCM Publishing
Ed: Peter I. Hupalo. **Released:** August 30, 2002. **Price:** $18.95. **Description:** The book teaches all aspects of starting and running a small book publishing company. Topics covered include: inventory accounting in the book trade, just-in-time inventory management, turnkey fulfillment solutions, tax deductible costs, basics of sales and use tax, book pricing, standards in terms of the book industry, working with distributors and wholesalers, cover design and book layout, book promotion and marketing, how to select profitable authors to publish, printing process, printing on demand, the power of a strong backlist, and how to value copyright.

46850 ■ *"Identify and Conquer"* in *Black Enterprise* (Vol. 38, December 2007, No. 5, pp. 76)
Pub: Earl G. Graves Publishing Co. Inc.
Ed: Tennille M. Robinson. **Description:** Twenty-two-year-old entrepreneur wants to expand her wholesale body oil and skincare products business.

46851 ■ *"Merchants Association Working on Deal for Large Wholesale Warehouse"* in *Austin Business JournalInc.* (September 19, 2008)
Pub: American City Business Journals
Ed: Jean Kwon. **Description:** Greater Austin Merchants Association planning to buy a former Dell Outlet Factory in Austin, Texas and convert it into a warehouse for convenience stores and gas stations.

46852 ■ *"Printers to the Trade"* in *American Printer* (Vol. 128, July 1, 2011, No. 7)
Pub: Penton Media Inc.
Description: Wholesale printing is discussed. Two wholesale printers share insight into their success, from business philosophies in general to practices that build strong relationships.

46853 ■ *"Research and Market Adds: 2010 US Women's and Children's Clothing Wholesale Report"* in *Wireless News* (November 8, 2009)
Pub: Close-Up Media
Description: Highlights of the annual Research and Markets "2010 U.S. Women's and Children's Clothing Wholesale Report" include industry statistics, demographics and forecasts.

46854 ■ *"Research and Markets Adds: 2011 U.S. Women's & Children's Clothing Wholesale Report"* in *Health & Beauty Close-Up* (October 16, 2010)
Pub: Close-Up Media Inc.
Description: The Women's & Children's Clothing Wholesale Report is an annual report containing timely and accurate industry statistics, forecasts and demographics.

STATISTICAL SOURCES

46855 ■ *RMA Annual Statement Studies*
Pub: Robert Morris Associates (RMA)
Released: Annual. **Price:** $175.00 2006-07 edition, $105.00. **Description:** Contains composite balance sheets and income statements for more than 360 industries, including the accounting, auditing, and bookkeeping industries. Also contains five years of comparative historical data for discerning trends. Includes 16 commonly used ratios, computed for most of the size groupings for nearly every industry.

TRADE PERIODICALS

46856 ■ *NAW Report*
Pub: National Association of Wholesaler-Distributors (NAW)
Ed: Ruth Stadius, Editor. **Released:** Bimonthly. **Description:** Publishes information on government issues and actions affecting wholesaler-distributors

specifically and the business community generally. Recurring features include reports on federal legislative and regulatory developments; legal and insurance trends; industry research and statistics; and business services offered through the association's group purchasing program. Remarks: Available online only

FRANCHISES AND BUSINESS OPPORTUNITIES

46857 ■ Business Cards Tomorrow
Business Cards Tomorrow, Inc.
3000 NE 30th Pl., 5th Fl.
Ft. Lauderdale, FL 33306
Ph:(954)563-1224
Free: 800-627-9998
Fax:(954)565-0742
No. of Franchise Units: 64. **No. of Company-Owned Units:** 5. **Founded:** 1975. **Franchised:** 1977. **Description:** Professional, niche wholesale

service business. **Equity Capital Needed:** $991,700-$1,100,000. **Franchise Fee:** $35,000. **Financial Assistance:** Third party financing available. **Training:** Provides 2 weeks at headquarters, 4 weeks onsite and ongoing support.

46858 ■ Prosource Wholesale Floorcoverings
CCA Global Partners
4301 Earth City Expy.
Earth City, MO 63045
Free: 800-466-6984
Fax:(314)506-0953
Co. E-mail: mjameson@pswwholesale.com
URL: http://www.prosourcefloors.com
No. of Franchise Units: 138. **No. of Company-Owned Units:** 3. **Founded:** 1990. **Franchised:** 1991. **Description:** Members-only wholesale flooring showroom. **Equity Capital Needed:** $750,000 net worth; $375,000 minimum investment. **Franchise Fee:** $46,450. **Financial Assistance:** Yes. **Training:** Initial training provided at headquarters in St. Louis and ongoing support.

START-UP INFORMATION

46859 ■ *Birthing the Elephant: A Woman's Go-For-It Guide to Overcoming the Big Challenges of Launching a Business*
Pub: Ten Speed Press

Ed: Karin Abarbanel; Bruce Freeman. **Released:** 2008. **Price:** $15.95. **Description:** Consultants help women think like an entrepreneur in order to successfully launch any new business.

46860 ■ *Birthing the Elephant: The Woman's Go-for-It! Guide to Overcoming the Big Challenges of Launching a Business*
Pub: Ten Speed Press

Ed: Karin Abarbanel; Bruce Freeman. **Released:** March 2008. **Price:** $15.95. **Description:** Advice for women entrepreneurs is given. The book explores the emotional challenges faced by women starting businesses, along with advice for reshaping image. This handbook helps women survive and succeed in business.

46861 ■ "Find the Upside to a Down Economy" in *Women Entrepreneur* (September 30, 2008)
Pub: Entrepreneur Media Inc.

Ed: Tamara Monosoff. **Description:** Starting a new business in this economic crisis may not be as daunting of a pursuit as one might think. Aspiring entrepreneurs may find success by looking for opportunities in unusual places and relying on what they do best.

46862 ■ "Getting Others To Take Your Startup Seriously" in *Women Entrepreneur* (August 1, 2008)
Pub: Entrepreneur Media Inc.

Ed: Tamara Monosoff. **Description:** Writing a serious business plan is essential if you want others to take your startup endeavor seriously. As friends, family and acquaintances see you taking positive steps toward your goal they will begin to lend their support and may even help get the business off the ground.

46863 ■ *The Girl's Guide to Starting Your Own Business: Candid Advice, Frank Talk, and True Stories*
Pub: Collins Publications

Ed: Caitlin Friedman; Kimberly Yorio. **Released:** January 1, 2005. **Price:** $14.95. **Description:** Advice is given to help any woman start her own company. Every chapter includes interviews, charts, quizzes and witty directives about self-employment. Topics include, choosing a name and logo, business law, communication and information about business associations.

46864 ■ "I Have A Business Idea. What Now?" in *Women Entrepreneur* (October 15, 2008)
Pub: Entrepreneur Media Inc.

Ed: Cheryl Isaac. **Description:** Four pre-planning steps to take before launching a new business are discussed in detail.

46865 ■ *Mommy Millionaire: How I Turned My Kitchen Table Idea Into a Million Dollars and How You Can, Too!*
Pub: St. Martin's Press LLC

Ed: Kim Lavine. **Released:** February 19, 2008. **Price:** $14.95. **Description:** Advice, secrets and lessons for making a million dollars from a mom who turned her kitchen into a successful business; tools cover developing and patenting an idea, cold calling, trade shows, QVC, big retailers, manufacturing, and raising venture capital.

46866 ■ "Mount Laurel Woman Launches Venture Into Children's Used Clothing" in *Philadelphia Inquirer* (September 17, 2010)
Pub: Philadelphia Media Network

Ed: Maria Panaritis. **Description:** Profile of Jennifer Frisch, stay-at-home mom turned entrepreneur. Frisch started a used-clothing store Once Upon a Child after opening her franchised Plato's Closet, selling unwanted and used baby clothing and accessories at her new shop, while offering used merchandise to teens at Plato's Closet.

46867 ■ "Secure Future" in *Small Business Opportunities* (November 2010)
Pub: Harris Publications Inc.

Ed: Stan Roberts. **Description:** Fed up with the corporate world, this first-time business owner sells security equipment over the phone. Last year, sales hit $4 million. Profile of the founder of SmartWatch Security & Sound, Madelaine Lock is included.

46868 ■ *Small Business Savvy*
Pub: Adams Media Corporation

Ed: Norma J. Rist; Katina Z. Jones. **Released:** 2002. **Description:** Advice is given to women wishing to start their own companies using guidance and real-world examples to help position themselves for future growth. Tips to survive through a bad economic environment, breaking into a market, working with less money, accepting change, and ways to balance success with personal life are explored.

46869 ■ *There's a Business In Every Woman: A 7-Step Guide to Discovering, Starting, and Building the Business of Your Dreams*
Pub: Ballantine/Random House

Ed: Ann M. Holmes. **Released:** 2008. **Price:** $15.00 paperback. **Description:** Economist and workplace expert provides a no-nonsense guide detailing seven steps to creating a successful business, based on her own experiences and on those of her employees. She highlights the importance of understanding and using your core competencies, building an organized infrastructure from the start, and planning for and managing your growth.

46870 ■ "Time for a Leap Of Faith?" in *Women Entrepreneur* (November 18, 2008)
Pub: Entrepreneur Media Inc.

Ed: Cynthia McKay. **Description:** Starting a new business, despite the downturn in the economy, can prove to be a successful endeavor if one has the time, energy and most importantly a good idea.

46871 ■ "Try a Little Piece of Heaven at this Suffolk Cupcakery" in *Virginia-Pilot* (February 13, 2011)
Pub: McClatchy Company

Ed: Hattie Brown Garrow. **Description:** Profile of Tanya West, owner of the new startup called Divine Creations Cupcakery and Desserts located in Suffolk, Virginia. West is a full-time baker and mother of three children.

46872 ■ "Victoria Colligan; Co-Founder, Ladies Who Launch Inc., 38" in *Crain's Cleveland Business* (Vol. 28, November 19, 2007, No. 46)
Pub: Crain Communications, Inc.

Ed: Jay Miller. **Description:** Profile of Victoria Colligan who is the co-founder of Ladies Who Launch Inc., an organization with franchises in nearly 50 cities; the company offers women entrepreneurs workshops and a newsletter to help women balance their businesses with other aspects of their lives. Ms. Colligan found that women were learning about being business owners differently than men and she felt that there was a need to create opportunities for networking for women launching businesses that had more of a lifestyle purpose.

46873 ■ *Work@home: A Practical Guide for Women Who Want to Work from Home*
Pub: Woman's Missionary Union

Ed: Glynnis Whitwer. **Released:** March 2007. **Price:** $15.99. **Description:** Fifty-three percent of all small business are home-based. The book provides tips to women for starting a home-based business.

ASSOCIATIONS AND OTHER ORGANIZATIONS

46874 ■ **American Academy of Professional Coders**
2480 S 3850 W, Ste. B
Salt Lake City, UT 84120
Ph:(801)236-2200
Free: 800-626-2633
Fax:(801)236-2258
Co. E-mail: info@aapc.com
URL: http://www.aapc.com
Contact: Reed Pew, Chm.
Description: Works to elevate the standards of medical coding by providing ongoing education, certification, networking and recognition. Promotes high standards of physician and outpatient facility coding through education and certification. **Publications:** *Physician Coding Book Bundle 1* .

46875 ■ **American Business Women's Association**
PO Box 8728
Kansas City, MO 64114-0728
Free: 800-228-0007
Fax:(913)732-5100
Co. E-mail: abwa@abwa.org
URL: http://www.abwa.org
Contact: Lynn Drowne, Natl. Pres.
Description: Women in business, including women owning or operating their own businesses, women in

professions and women employed in any level of government, education, or retailing, manufacturing and service companies. Provides opportunities for businesswomen to help themselves and others grow personally and professionally through leadership, education, networking support and national recognition. Offers leadership training, business skills training and business education; special membership options for retired businesswomen and the Company Connection for business owners, a resume service, credit card and programs, various travel and insurance benefits. Sponsors American Business Women's Day and National Convention and regional conferences held annually. **Publications:** *The Leadership Edge* (quarterly); *Women in Business* (bimonthly).

46876 ■ Asian Women in Business
42 Broadway, Ste. 1748
New York, NY 10004
Ph:(212)868-1368
Fax:(212)868-1373
Co. E-mail: info@awib.org
URL: http://www.awib.org
Contact: Julie Azuma, Chair
Description: Asian-American women in business. Seeks to enable Asian-American women to achieve their entrepreneurial potential. Serves as a clearinghouse on issues affecting small business owners; provides technical assistance and other support to members; sponsors business and entrepreneurial education courses. **Publications:** Newsletter (quarterly).

46877 ■ Canadian Association of Women Executives and Entrepreneurs–Association Canadienne des Femmes Cadres et Entrepreneurs
401 Bay St., Ste. 1600
Toronto, ON, Canada M5K 2Y4
Ph:(416)756-0000
Fax:(416)756-0000
Co. E-mail: contact@cawee.net
URL: http://www.cawee.net
Contact: Dr. Melvine Baird, Pres.
Description: Seeks to provide opportunities for women to empower other women in the development and advancement of their business and professional lives; which fosters financial independence, professional development and personal satisfaction. **Publications:** *Acclaim* (quarterly).

46878 ■ Canadian Federation of Business and Professional Women's Clubs
45 Brixham Rd.
London, ON, Canada N6K 1P5
Ph:(519)473-3505
Co. E-mail: bpwcanada@bpwcanada.com
URL: http://www.bpwcanada.com
Contact: Doris Hall, Pres.
Description: Canadian women engaged in business, the professions, or industry. Works to enhance the economic, social, and employment status of women. Encourages women to become active in government at every level. Strives to improve business service standards. Networks with related organizations to promote common concerns. **Publications:** *Business and Professional Women* (quarterly).

46879 ■ Center for Economic Options
910 Quarrier St., Ste. 206
Charleston, WV 25301
Ph:(304)345-1298
Fax:(304)342-0641
Co. E-mail: info@economicoptions.org
URL: http://www.centerforeconomicoptions.org
Contact: Pam Curry, Exec. Dir.
Description: Seeks to improve the economic position and quality of life for women, especially low-income and minority women. Works to provide access to job training and employment options to women. Supports self-employed women and small business owners by offering training and technical assistance and information. Advocates women's legal right to employment, training, education, and credit. Seeks to inform the public on economic issues related to women; while activities are conducted on local and state levels, group cooperates with national and international organizations on issues relating to

employment and economic justice for women. Maintains speakers' bureau and library. Compiles statistics; conducts research. **Publications:** *Women and Employment News* (quarterly).

46880 ■ Center for Women's Business Research
1760 Old Meadow Rd., Ste. 500
McLean, VA 22102
Ph:(703)556-7162
Fax:(703)506-3266
URL: http://www.cfwbr.org
Contact: Dr. Patricia G. Greene, Chair
Description: Women business owners. Supports the growth of women business owners and their enterprises by conducting research, sharing information and increasing knowledge. Offers marketing consulting and seminars. **Publications:** *Key Facts about Women-Owned Businesses* .

46881 ■ Commission on the Status of Women
Division for the Advancement of Women
2 UN Plz., DC2-12th Fl.
New York, NY 10017
Fax:(212)963-3463
Co. E-mail: daw@un.org
URL: http://www.un.org/womenwatch/daw/csw
Description: Consists of representatives from forty-five member states of the United Nations. Promotes women's rights in political, economic, civil, social, and educational fields. Encourages cooperation between organizations seeking to advance the status of women, and advises the U.N. and member bodies on situations requiring immediate attention. Acts as a preparatory body for the world conference on women. .

46882 ■ Educational Foundation for Women in Accounting
136 S Keowee St.
Dayton, OH 45402
Ph:(937)424-3391
Fax:(937)222-5749
Co. E-mail: info@efwa.org
URL: http://www.efwa.org
Contact: Gail Anikouchine CPA, Pres.
Description: Women in the accounting field. Supports the advancement of women in the accounting profession through funding of education, research, career literature, publications, and other projects. **Publications:** *The Educator* (semiannual).

46883 ■ National Association for Female Executives
PO Box 3052
Langhorne, PA 19047
Free: 800-927-6233
Co. E-mail: roxanne.natale@nafe.com
URL: http://www.nafe.com
Contact: Dr. Betty Spence, Pres.
Description: Represents and supports professional women and women business owners; provides resources and services through education, networking and public advocacy to empower members to achieve career success and financial security. **Publications:** *NAFE E-Newsletter* (biweekly).

46884 ■ National Association of Women Business Owners
601 Pennsylvania Ave. NW
South Bldg., Ste. 900
Washington, DC 20004
Free: 800-556-2926
Fax:(202)403-3788
Co. E-mail: national@nawbo.org
URL: http://www.nawbo.org
Contact: Helen Han, Pres./CEO
Description: Represents and promotes women-owned businesses to shape economic and public policy. **Publications:** *NAWBOTime* (bimonthly).

46885 ■ National Association of Women MBAs
PO Box 2932
Houston, TX 77251-2932
Co. E-mail: director@mbawomen.org
URL: http://www.mbawomen.org
Contact: Stacey A. Gordon, Managing Dir.
Description: Provides networking opportunities for its members. Increases communication among gradu-

ate business schools regarding their initiatives to educate and support women in business. .

46886 ■ National Women's Business Council
409 3rd St. SW, Ste. 210
Washington, DC 20024
Ph:(202)205-3850
Fax:(202)205-6825
Co. E-mail: info@nwbc.gov
URL: http://www.nwbc.gov
Contact: Dana M. Lewis, Exec. Dir.
Description: Women business owners. Strives to promote initiatives, policies, and programs designed to support women's business enterprises. **Publications:** *Engage* (bimonthly); *Study of Women-Owned and Led Businesses*; *Support for Women's Enterprise Development in the United States: Lessons Learned, by the Council's Executive Director, Julie Weeks* .

46887 ■ Women in Franchising
53 W Jackson Blvd., Ste. 1157
Chicago, IL 60604
Ph:(312)431-1467
Co. E-mail: spkezios@womeninfranchising.com
URL: http://www.womeninfranchising.com
Contact: Susan P. Kezios, Pres.
Description: Assists women interested in all aspects of franchise business development including those buying a franchised business and those expanding their businesses via franchising. Provides franchise technical assistance in both of these areas. Surveys the industry on the status of women. **Publications:** *Buying a Franchise: How to Make the Right Choice*; *Growing Your Business: The Franchise Option* .

46888 ■ Women in Packaging
4290 Bells Ferry Rd., Ste. 106-17
Kennesaw, GA 30144-1300
Ph:(678)594-6872
Co. E-mail: joann@womeninpackaging.org
URL: http://womeninpackaging.org
Contact: JoAnn R. Hines, Founder
Description: Works to promote and encourage women in the packaging industry. Educates the packaging industry about the contributions of women to the industry; helps to eliminate stereotypes and discrimination in the profession; offers networking opportunities; conducts career enhancement programs; compiles statistics; maintains speakers' bureau. **Publications:** *Packaging Horizons* .

46889 ■ Women's Regional Publications of America
PO Box 12955
Albuquerque, NM 87195
Ph:(505)247-9195
Free: 800-282-8749
Co. E-mail: kgreen@womsdigest.net
URL: http://www.womensyellowpages.org
Contact: Karen Green, Pres.
Description: Provides a forum where publishers of women's publications and business directories share information and resources. Increases the visibility, authority, influence and status of women's business for the purpose of promoting growth and support of women. Educates the general public about the need to support women-owned businesses, including equal opportunity employers and contractors. .

REFERENCE WORKS

46890 ■ "2008 Woman of the Year Gala" in *Hispanic Business* (Vol. 30, July-August 2008, No. 7-8, pp. 58)
Pub: Hispanic Business, Inc.
Ed: Brynne Chappell. **Description:** Brief report on the sixth annual Women of the Year Awards gala which was held at JW Marriott Desert Ridge Resort and Spa is given; 20 women were honored with these awards for their professional contribution, commitment to the advancement of the Hispanic community and involvement with charitable organizations.

46891 ■ "ABWA Through the Years: Extending the Hand of Friendship" in *Women In Business* (Vol. 63, Spring 2011, No. 1, pp. 8)
Pub: American Business Women's Association
Ed: Rene Street, Leigh Elmore. **Description:** A look back at the history of the American Business Wom-

en's Association (ABWA) as they celebrate March as Women's History month is presented. Looking back at the archives has revealed how several veteran ABWA members came to join the sisterhood of ABWA through the Hand of Friendship Tea.

46892 ■ The Accidental Entrepreneur: The 50 Things I Wish Someone Had Told Me About Starting a Business
Pub: AMACOM

Ed: Susan Urpuhart-Brown. **Released:** May 26, 2008. **Price:** $17.95. **Description:** Entrepreneur shares insight into launching her company and answers eight questions everyone considering starting a small business should ask up front, along with the top ten traits of a successful entrepreneur.

46893 ■ "Ace Every Introduction" in Women Entrepreneur (September 10, 2008)
Pub: Entrepreneur Media Inc.

Ed: Cynthia McKay. **Description:** Making a powerful first impression is one of the most important marketing tools a business owner can possess. Advice about meeting new business contacts is given.

46894 ■ "AG Warns Slots MBE Plan Risky" in Boston Business Journal (Vol. 29, May 27, 2011, No. 3, pp. 1)
Pub: American City Business Journals Inc.

Ed: Scott Dance. **Description:** Attorney General Doug Gansler states that the law extending the minority business program on slots parlors contracting through 2018 could be open to lawsuits. He recommended that the state should conduct a study proving that minority- and women-owned businesses do not get a fair share in the gaming industry before it signs the bill to avoid lawsuits from majority-owned firms.

46895 ■ "The AHA Moment" in Hispanic Business (December 2010)
Pub: Hispanic Business

Ed: Rebecca Vallaneda. **Description:** An interview with Gisela Girard on how competitive market conditions push buttons. Girard stepped down from her 18-month position as chairwoman the Association of Hispanic Advertising Agencies. She has more than 20 years of experience in advertising and research marketing.

46896 ■ "Are You Ready for a Transformation?" in Women Entrepreneur (November 28, 2008)
Pub: Entrepreneur Media Inc.

Ed: Aliza Sherman. **Description:** Marlene J. Waldock, an expert in women's empowerment and reinvention, discusses brand modification and what a business owner should consider before attempting to change or modify their brand.

46897 ■ The Art of War for Women
Pub: Doubleday

Ed: Chin-ning Chu. **Released:** April 10, 2007. **Price:** $21.95. **Description:** According to the author, the workplace is a battlefield for women. She offers a strategy for women to succeed in business.

46898 ■ Avon: Building the World's Premier Company for Women
Pub: John Wiley & Sons, Incorporated

Ed: Laura Klepacki. **Released:** May 2006. **Price:** $21.99. **Description:** Profile of Avon, the world's largest direct sales company. Avon representatives number four million in over 140 countries.

46899 ■ Back on the Career Track: A Guide for Stay-At-Home Moms Who Want to Return to Work
Pub: Warner Books Inc.

Ed: Carol Fishman Cohen; Vivian Steir Rabin. **Released:** 2008. **Price:** $14.99 paperback. **Description:** For women like themselves who have rejoined the workforce after a prolonged absence, the authors detail seven main steps for reentry; profiles of six women who have successfully re-launched their careers are included.

46900 ■ "Back Talk With Terrie M. Williams" in Black Enterprise (Vol. 38, December 2007, No. 5, pp. 204)
Pub: Earl G. Graves Publishing Co. Inc.

Ed: Tennille M. Robinson. **Description:** Profile of Terrie M. Williams, president of a public relations agency as well as founder of a youth empowerment organization called Stay Strong Foundation. Williams reflects on her bouts with depression and how the disease impacts sufferers and talks about her book that will inspire others dealing with depression.

46901 ■ "Barbara West" in Crain's Cleveland Business (Vol. 30, June 29, 2009, No. 25, pp. 14)
Pub: Crain Communications, Inc.

Ed: Shannon Mortland. **Description:** Profile of Barbara West, administrative director of emergency medicine at MetroHealth Medical Center in Ohio. Ms. West manages Metro Life Flight that uses helicopters to transport patients to MetroHealth. She discusses the challenges of taking care of patients when big emergencies occur.

46902 ■ "Baxter Baker Wins in Hot Finale of 'Cupcake Wars'" in Fort Mill Times (September 13, 2011)
Pub: McClatchy Company

Ed: Jenny Overmann. **Description:** Heather McDonnell, owner of Cupcrazed Cakery, and her assistant Debbie McDonnell, vied for a chance to win $10,000 on the cable network show called "Cupcake Wars", and to serve cupcakes at the album release party for country singer Jennette McCurdy. At the end of the show, the sisters-in-law won the top prize.

46903 ■ "Because Kids Need To Be Heard: Tina Wells: Buzz Marketing Group: Voorhees, New Jersey" in Inc. (Volume 32, December 2010)
Pub: Inc. Magazine

Ed: Tamara Schweitzer. **Description:** Profile of Tina Wells, founder and CEO of Buzz Marketing Group, who writes a tween book series called Mackenzie Blue to reach young girls.

46904 ■ "Become A Brand" in Women Entrepreneur (September 14, 2008)
Pub: Entrepreneur Media Inc.

Ed: Suzy Girard-Ruttenberg. **Description:** Powerful brands are effective, innovative, exclusive or even socially conscious; it is important for small businesses to understand the power of becoming a brand since it is one of the best ways in which to position one's company and drive its growth.

46905 ■ "The Believer" in Inc. (December 2007, pp. 130-138)
Pub: Gruner & Jahr USA Publishing

Ed: Leigh Buchanan. **Description:** Profile of Selena Cuffe, wine importer and socially conscious woman entrepreneur, who is focusing her talents on helping South Africa get wine products to America.

46906 ■ "Best Practices Award-Winning Teams 2010-2011" in Women In Business (Vol. 63, Fall 2011, No. 3, pp. 19)
Pub: American Business Women's Association

Description: List of American Business Women's Association's best practices award winning teams for 2010-2011 is given. Coral Springs Charter Chapter, Emerald Coast Chapter, and Golden Dome Chapter are some of the winners for level one. Level two and level three winners are also presented.

46907 ■ Big Vision, Small Business
Pub: Ivy Sea, Inc.

Ed: Jamie S. Walters. **Released:** October 10, 2002. **Price:** $17.95. **Description:** The power of the small enterprise is examined. The author shares her expertise as an entrepreneur and founder of a business consulting firm to help small business owners successfully run their companies. Interviews with more than seventy small business owners provide insight into visioning, planning, and establishing a small company, as well as strategies for good employee and customer relationships.

46908 ■ Boss of You: Everything a Woman Needs to Know to Start, Run, and Maintain Her Own Business
Pub: Seal Press

Ed: Lauren Bacon; Emira Mears. **Released:** June 2008. **Price:** $15.95. **Description:** Women entrepreneurs start businesses at twice the rate of male counterparts. Information is shared to help a woman start, run and maintain a successful company.

46909 ■ "Business Forecast: Stormy and Successful" in Women In Business (Vol. 62, June 2010, No. 2, pp. 12)
Pub: American Business Women's Association

Ed: Kathleen Leighton. **Description:** Stormy Simon, vice president of customer service at Overstock.com is a self-made career woman who started out as a temporary employee in the company in 2001. She was not able to attend college because she had two sons to care for after her divorce. Simon got involved in advertising and media buying and shares her love for business.

46910 ■ Business as Usual
Pub: HarperBusiness

Ed: Anita Roddick. **Released:** 2005. **Price:** $12.95. **Description:** Founder of The Body Shop shares her story and gives her opinion on everything from cynical cosmetic companies to destructive consultants.

46911 ■ "Calendar" in Crain's Detroit Business (Vol. 24, March 10, 2008, No. 10, pp. 21)
Pub: Crain Communications, Inc.

Description: Listing of events in the Detroit area include conferences addressing entrepreneurialism, economic development, and women business ownership.

46912 ■ "Car Dealer Closings: Immoral, Slow-Death" in Crain's Detroit Business (Vol. 25, June 8, 2009, No. 23)
Pub: Crain Communications Inc. - Detroit

Ed: Daniel Duggan. **Description:** Colleen McDonald discusses the closing of her two Chrysler dealerships located in Taylor and Livonia, Michigan, along with her Farmington Hills store, Holiday Chevrolet.

46913 ■ "Celebrate Success. Embrace Innovation" in Black Enterprise (Vol. 37, February 2007, No. 7, pp. 145)
Pub: Earl G. Graves Publishing Co. Inc.

Description: 2007 Women of Power Summit provides networking opportunities, empowerment sessions, and nightly entertainment. More than 500 executive women of color are expected to attend this inspiring summit in Phoenix, February 7-10.

46914 ■ "Chattanooga at a Glance" in Women In Business (Vol. 62, June 2010, No. 2, pp. 29)
Pub: American Business Women's Association

Ed: Jill Yates Bagby. **Description:** City of Chattanooga, Tennessee is the location of the 2010 American Business Women's Association (ABWA) National Women's Leadership Conference. The city offers historical sites, parks and tourist attractions, as well as dining options.

46915 ■ "City Seeks More Minorities" in Austin Business JournalInc. (Vol. 28, November 7, 2008, No. 34, pp. A1)
Pub: American City Business Journals

Ed: Jean Kwon. **Description:** Austin, Texas is planning to increase the participation of minority- and women-owned businesses in government contracts. Contractors are required to show 'good faith' to comply with the specified goals. The city is planning to effect the changes in the construction and professional services sector.

46916 ■ "Common Thread" in Entrepreneur (Vol. 36, March 2008, No. 3, pp. 144)
Pub: Entrepreneur Media Inc.

Ed: Sara Wilson. **Description:** Profile of Stacey Benet and her business, Alice and Olivia, and how she jumpstarted her career in the clothing industry after she wore a self-designed pair of pants that caught the attention of a Barney's New York representative is presented.

46917 ■ **"Conference Calendar" in** *Marketing to Women* **(Vol. 21, March 2008, No. 3, pp. 7)**
Pub: EPM Communications, Inc.
Description: Listing of current conferences and events aimed at women entrepreneurs and leaders.

46918 ■ **"Congratulations to the 2010 Top Ten Business Women of ABWA" in** *Women In Business* **(Vol. 61, August-September 2009, No. 4, pp. 12)**
Pub: American Business Women's Association
Description: Listing of the top 10 members of the American Business Women's Association (ABWA) for 2010 is presented. The lists of the top ten 2010 members selected by each of the six ABWA chapters are also provided.

46919 ■ **"Congratulations to the 2012 Top Ten Business Women of ABWA" in** *Women In Business* **(Vol. 63, Fall 2011, No. 3, pp. 14)**
Pub: American Business Women's Association
Description: Geri Bertram, Patti Bigger, and Susan Crowther are among the top ten businesswomen of the American Business Women's Association recognized for their contribution to the group, community involvement, and career achievements. Bertram is the manager for procurement planning control in Ingalls Shipbuilding while Bigger is Specialty Screw Corporation's corporate relations manager. Also on the list are Virginia DeGiorgi and Geanna Kincanon.

46920 ■ **"Convention Calendar" in** *Black Enterprise* **(Vol. 37, February 2007, No. 7, pp. 68)**
Pub: Earl G. Graves Publishing Co. Inc.
Description: Listing of conventions and trade show of interest to minority and women business leaders.

46921 ■ **"A Conversation with; Renea Butler, Real Estate One Inc." in** *Crain's Detroit Business* **(Vol. 25, June 8, 2009, No. 23, pp. 12)**
Pub: Crain Communications Inc. - Detroit
Ed: Ryan Beene. **Description:** Renea Butler, vice president of administration and human resources for Real Estate One Inc. in Southfield as well as vice president for public relations for the Human Resource Association of Greater Detroit, talks about how the economy has affected human resource services.

46922 ■ **"Crafting Kinship at Home and Work: Women Miners in Wyoming" in** *WorkingUSA* **(Vol. 11, December 2008, No. 4, pp. 439)**
Pub: Blackwell Publishers Ltd.
Ed: Jessica M. Smith. **Description:** Institutional policies and social dynamics shaping women working in the northeastern Wyoming mining industry are examined. Ethnographic research suggests that the women's successful integration into this nontraditional workplace is predicated on their ability to craft and maintain kin-like social relationships in two spheres. First, women miners have addressed the challenges of managing their home and work responsibilities by cultivating networks of friends and family to care for their children while they are at work. Second, women miners craft close relationships with coworkers in what are called 'crew families'. These relationships make their work more enjoyable and the ways in which they create camaraderie prompt a reconsideration of conventional accounts of sexual harassment in the mining industry.

46923 ■ **"Cupcake Maker Explains Tricks of the Trade" in** *Chattanooga Times/Free Press* **(September 6, 2011)**
Pub: Chattanooga Publishing Company
Ed: Holly Leber. **Description:** Sunny Burden, head baker at Whipped Cupcakes in Chattanooga, Tennessee creates themed cupcakes as well as traditional ones. Burden finds baking therapeutic.

46924 ■ **"Cupcake Maker Grabs Outpost" in** *Crain's New York Business* **(Vol. 27, August 15, 2011, No. 33, pp. 16)**
Pub: Crain Communications Inc.
Ed: Jermaine Taylor. **Description:** Family-owned miniature cupcake maker, Baked by Melissa, singed a ten-year lease, expanding their stores to five. The business was started three years ago by advertising executive Melissa Bushell.

46925 ■ **"'Cupcake Wars' TV Show Returns to Hampton Roads" in** *Virginian-Pilot* **(September 11, 2011)**
Pub: McClatchy Company
Ed: Carolyn Shapiro. **Description:** Virginia Beach, Virginia sweet shop called Just Cupcakes and Carolina Cupcakery will compete for prizes on cable TV's Food Network Channel. Carla Hesseltine, owner of Just Cupcakes made it to the final rounds.

46926 ■ **"Datebook" in** *Crain's Chicago Business* **(Vol. 31, April 28, 2008, No. 17, pp. 18)**
Pub: Crain Communications, Inc.
Description: Listing of events in the Detroit area include conferences addressing entrepreneurialism, economic development, and women business ownership.

46927 ■ **"Developing the Next Generation of Rosies" in** *Employee Benefit News* **(Vol. 25, November 1, 2011, No. 14, pp. 36)**
Pub: SourceMedia Inc.
Ed: Kathleen Koster. **Description:** According to the research group Catalyst, women made up 46.7 percent of the American workforce in 2010, however only 14.4 percent was Fortune 500 executive officers and 15.7 percent held Fortune 500 board seats. Statistical data included.

46928 ■ *Divas Doing Business: What the Guidebooks Don't Tell You About Being A Woman Entrepreneur*
Pub: Nouveau Connoisseurs Corporation
Ed: Monique Hayward. **Released:** February 14, 2009. **Price:** $19.95. **Description:** A must-read for any woman who's currently running a business or is thinking of starting one.

46929 ■ *Doing Business with Beauty: Black Women, Hair Salons, and the Racial Enclave Economy*
Pub: Rowman and Littlefield Publishers, Inc.
Ed: Adia Harvey Wingfield. **Released:** June 28, 2008. **Price:** $19.95. **Description:** Factors that draw black women into the hair industry are examined. Interviews with hair salon owners explore aspects of owning a salon, owner-employee relationships, and the black female owner's struggle for autonomy and success in entrepreneurship.

46930 ■ **"Doing Good: Cause and Effect" in** *Entrepreneur* **(Vol. 36, February 2008, No. 2, pp. 23)**
Pub: Entrepreneur Media Inc.
Description: Lisa Knoppe established Art for a Cause LLC that employs people with mental and physical disabilities. The company makes hand-painted tools and furniture to be sold at gift retailers and hardware stores.

46931 ■ **"Don't Quit When The Road Gets Bumpy" in** *Women Entrepreneur* **(November 25, 2008)**
Pub: Entrepreneur Media Inc.
Ed: Bonnie Price. **Description:** Discusses techniques four women entrepreneurs are utilizing to keep their businesses successful despite the credit crunch and the economic downturn.

46932 ■ **"Dress Professionally Cool for Summer" in** *Women In Business* **(Vol. 62, June 2010, No. 2, pp. 38)**
Pub: American Business Women's Association
Ed: Maureen Sullivan. **Description:** Summer clothing for business and career women is discussed with regard to traditional and relaxed work places. Fabric considerations, tips on choosing blazers and a list of clothes and other items that are not appropriate for the workplace are presented.

46933 ■ **"Edible Endeavors" in** *Black Enterprise* **(March 2008)**
Pub: Earl G. Graves Publishing Co. Inc.
Ed: Carolyn M. Brown. **Description:** Profile of Jacqueline Frazer, woman entrepreneur who turned her love for cooking into a catering business. She is chef

and owner of Command Performance in New York City. The firm works with more than 50 clients annually and generates annual revenues of about $350,000.

46934 ■ *Enterprising Women in Urban Zimbabwe: Gender, Microbusiness, and Globalization*
Pub: Indiana University Press
Ed: Mary Johnson Osirim. **Released:** April 1, 2009. **Price:** $39.95. **Description:** An investigation into the business and personal experiences of women entrepreneurs in the microenterprise sector in Zimbabwe. Many of these women work as market traders, crocheters, seamstresses, and hairdressers.

46935 ■ **"Entrepreneur Says Spirituality Has Been a Key to Her Success" in** *Business First Columbus* **(Vol. 25, October 17, 2008, No. 8, pp. 1)**
Pub: American City Business Journals
Ed: Scott Rawdon. **Description:** Profile of Carolyn Williams Francis, CEO of Williams Interior Designs Inc. She outlines her mantra for success in her furniture design business, but emphasizes that faith has taken her business to greater heights.

46936 ■ **"Every Resume Tells a Story" in** *Women In Business* **(Vol. 62, September 2010, No. 3, pp. 26)**
Pub: American Business Women's Association
Ed: Kathleen Leighton. **Description:** Ways in which job applicants can write a good resume and promote themselves are discussed. It is believed that applicants should be proud of their accomplishments and they need to add details that will make them stand out. The importance of including a professional narrative in the resume is also explained.

46937 ■ **"The Evolution of Carolyn Elman" in** *Women In Business* **(Vol. 62, September 2010, No. 3, pp. 11)**
Pub: American Business Women's Association
Ed: Leigh Elmore. **Description:** Carolyn Elman, former executive director of the American Business Women's Association (ABWA), provides an overview of her career. Elman grew up with the Association, and it was part of her family's existence. She believes that the ABWA provides women the opportunity to learn and improve their skills in business.

46938 ■ **"Fall Wardrobe on a Budget" in** *Women In Business* **(Vol. 62, September 2010, No. 3, pp. 38)**
Pub: American Business Women's Association
Ed: Kathleen Leighton. **Description:** Things women should keep in mind when putting together a fall wardrobe are discussed. Women should aim for at least two jackets, five tops, four pants or skirts, two twin sets, five pairs of pantyhose, and two pair of shoes. They should also be ruthless when it comes to quality and practicality.

46939 ■ *Female Enterprise in the New Economy*
Pub: University of Toronto Press
Ed: Karen D. Hughes. **Released:** January 2006. **Price:** $67.00, paperback $27.50. **Description:** Examination of whether the increasingly entrepreneurial economy is offering women more opportunity or increases their risk for poverty and economic insecurity.

46940 ■ *Female Entrepreneurship in East and South-East Asia: Opportunities and Challenges*
Pub: Woodhead Publishing Limited
Ed: Philippe Debroux. **Released:** February 10, 2010. **Description:** A detailed study of female entrepreneurship in Asia, where public authorities are slowly realizing the importance of women as workers and entrepreneurs.

46941 ■ **"Female Hispanic Professionals by the Number" in** *Hispanic Business* **(Vol. 30, April 2008, No. 4, pp. 8)**
Pub: Hispanic Business
Description: More executive opportunities are presenting themselves for future generations of Hispanic women who are more frequently being found in high-level positions. Statistical data included.

46942 ■ "Filling the Business Gap" in *Hispanic Business* **(December 2010)**
Pub: Hispanic Business
Ed: Richard Larsen. **Description:** New York group seeks to increase state diversity supplier spending to help create jobs and boost the economy. According to a recent study, six out of 10 small business owners will increase capital spending but delay hiring in 2011. However, potential job creation is good among businesses owned by women and minorities.

46943 ■ "The Final Say" in *Hispanic Business* **(Vol. 30, March 2008, No. 3, pp. 52)**
Pub: Hispanic Business
Ed: Hildy Medina. **Description:** Vice-Chairwoman of the pensions and investments committee and Illinois State Senator Iris Martinez is the first Hispanic woman to be elected Senator and is advocating for pension funds to include Hispanic money managers and minority- and female-owned businesses in the investment plans.

46944 ■ "Fitter from Twitter" in *Boston Business Journal* **(Vol. 30, December 17, 2010, No. 47, pp. 1)**
Pub: Boston Business Journal
Ed: Lisa van der Pool. **Description:** Small businesses are increasing their use of the Twitter microblogging platform to attract and retain customers. Lisa Johnson, who owns Modern Pilates studios, managed to raise awareness of her personal brand nationally through the social media platform.

46945 ■ "Five Low-Cost Home Based Startups" in *Women Entrepreneur* **(December 16, 2008)**
Pub: Entrepreneur Media Inc.
Ed: Lesley Spencer Pyle. **Description:** During tough economic times, small businesses have an advantage over large companies because they can adjust to economic conditions more easily and without having to go through corporate red tape that can slow the implementation process. A budding entrepreneur may find success by taking inventory of his or her skills, experience, expertise and passions and utilizing those qualities to start a business. Five low-cost home-based startups are profiled. These include starting an online store, a virtual assistant service, web designer, sales representative and a home staging counselor.

46946 ■ "Floral-Design Kiosk Business in Colorado Springs Blossoming" in *Colorado Springs Business Journal* **(September 24, 2010)**
Pub: Dolan Media Newswires
Ed: Monica Mendoza. **Description:** Profile of Shellie Greto and her mother Jackie Martin who started a wholesale flower business in their garage. The do-it-yourself floral arrangement firm started a kiosk business in supermarkets called Complete Design.

46947 ■ "For Giving Us a Way To Say Yes To Solar: Lynn Jurich and Edward Fenster" in *Inc.* **(Volume 32, December 2010, No. 10, pp. 110)**
Pub: Inc. Magazine
Description: Profile of entrepreneurs Lynn Jurich and Edward Fenster, cofounders of SunRun. The firm installs solar panels at little or no cost and homeowners sign 20-year contracts to buy power at a fixed price.

46948 ■ "For Putting Down Roots in Business: Amy Norquist: Greensulate, New York City" in *Inc.* **(Volume 32, December 2010, No. 10, pp. 106)**
Pub: Inc. Magazine
Ed: Christine Lagorio. **Description:** Profile of Amy Norquist who left her position at an environmental nonprofit organization to found Greensulate. Her firm insulates rooftops with lavender, native grasses and succulents called sedum in order to eliminate carbon from the atmosphere.

46949 ■ *The Foundations of Female Entrepreneurship: Women in Business in Mid-Victorian London*
Pub: Routledge
Ed: Alison Kay. **Released:** April 1, 2009. **Price:** $130.00. **Description:** This book argues that active business did not exclude women from 1747 to 1880,

although careful representation was necessary and this has obscured the similarities of women's businesses to those of many male business owners.

46950 ■ "From Craft Biz To Wholesale Giant" in *Women Entrepreneur* **(January 19, 2009)**
Pub: Entrepreneur Media Inc.
Ed: Maria Falconer. **Description:** Advice is given on how to turn a small craft business into a full-time venture; tips to help one transition from a part-time designer to a full-time wholesaler and brand are also included.

46951 ■ "Game Changer" in *Canadian Business* **(Vol. 83, June 15, 2010, No. 10, pp. 52)**
Pub: Rogers Media Ltd.
Ed: Jordan Timm. **Description:** Ubisoft chose Ontario to be the site for its new development studio and it has appointed Jade Raymond as its managing director. Raymond was born in Montreal in 1975 and studied computer science at McGill. Raymond is said to possess the understanding of the game industry's technical, art, and business components.

46952 ■ *The Girl's Guide to Being a Boss (Without Being a Bitch): Valuable Lessons, Smart Suggestions, and True Stories for Succeeding*
Pub: Random Housing Publishing Group
Ed: Caitlin Friedman; Kimberly Yorio. **Released:** April 2006.

46953 ■ *The Girl's Guide to Building a Million-Dollar Business*
Pub: AMACOM
Ed: Susan Wilson Solovic. **Released:** 2008. **Price:** $21.95. **Description:** Success plan for women business owners; the book includes tips for determination, managing changing relationships, keeping employees and customers happy, getting and maintaining credit, overcoming gender bias, and creating a good business plan and solid brand.

46954 ■ "Going for the APEX" in *Women In Business* **(Vol. 62, September 2010, No. 3, pp. 28)**
Pub: American Business Women's Association
Description: Information about the American Business Women's Association (ABWA) professional development tools, which keep members focused on personal excellence, is presented. The organization recently launched the APEX (Achieving Personal Excellence) Award to honor women who are making a commitment to themselves.

46955 ■ "The Good Guys of ABWA" in *Women In Business* **(Vol. 63, Fall 2011, No. 3, pp. 9)**
Pub: American Business Women's Association
Ed: Rene Street. **Description:** The American Business Women's Association (ABWA) was an all-woman group since its founding in 1949. However, a Supreme Court ruling in 1987 opened all-male and all-female organizations of the opposite sex. Some of the male members of the ABWA are Bill Hense, James Drager, and John Lester.

46956 ■ *Grassroots NGOs by Women for Women: The Driving Force of Development in India*
Pub: SAGE Publications, Incorporated
Ed: Femida Handy; Meenaz Kassam; Suzanne Feeney; Bhagyashree Ranade. **Released:** July 2006. **Price:** $29.95. **Description:** Understanding the role of non-governmental organizations in women's development is offered through interviews with twenty women in India who have founded NGOs serving women.

46957 ■ "Grooming Your Online Persona" in *Women In Business* **(Vol. 62, June 2010, No. 2, pp. 36)**
Pub: American Business Women's Association
Ed: Diane Stafford. **Description:** Employees' use of online social networks could become a basis on how their employers, clients, or business partners would judge them. Personal details, pictures and other on-

line data should be filtered to avoid inappropriate or uncomfortable situations and distinguish personal from professional or work life.

46958 ■ "Growing Strong" in *Entrepreneur* **(Vol. 35, November 2007, No. 11, pp. 36)**
Pub: Entrepreneur Media Inc.
Ed: Nichole L. Torres. **Description:** Amy Langer founded Salo LL with partner John Folkestad. The company is growing fast since its 2002 launch, with over $40 million in projections for 2007. The finance and accounting staffing company tops the list of the fastest-growing women-led companies in North America.

46959 ■ *Growth Oriented Women Entrepreneurs and Their Businesses: A Global Research Perspective*
Pub: Edward Elgar Publishing, Incorporated
Ed: Candida G. Brush. **Released:** June 2006. **Price:** $135.00. **Description:** Roles women play in entrepreneurship globally and their economic impact are examined.

46960 ■ "Helping Women Grow Their Businesses One Entrepreneur at a Time" in *Hispanic Business* **(July-August 2007, pp. 56-57)**
Pub: Hispanic Business
Ed: Hildy Medina. **Description:** American Express OPEN is a program focusing on women business owners whose companies report revenues of $200,000 or more. The program offers the chance to win a free year of mentoring, marketing and technology assistance along with a $50,000 line of credit.

46961 ■ "The Hispanic Business 100 Most Influential Hispanics" in *Hispanic Business* **(October 2007, pp. 30)**
Pub: Hispanic Business
Description: Profiles of the one hundred Hispanic business leaders are presented.

46962 ■ "Honoring Creativity" in *Playthings* **(Vol. 107, January 1, 2009, No. 1, pp. 28)**
Pub: Reed Business Information
Ed: Cliff Annicelli. **Description:** Toy & Game Inventors Expo is held annually in conjunction with the Chicago Toy & Game Fair. The event honors toy inventors in the categories of Game Design, Toy Design and Rising Stars, plus a lifetime achievement award. Profile of the company, Toying With Games, founded by Joyce Johnson and Colleen McCarthy-Evans are included in the article.

46963 ■ "How I Did It: It Just Came Naturally" in *Inc.* **(November 2007, pp. 110-112)**
Pub: Gruner & Jahr USA Publishing
Ed: Athena Schindelheim. **Description:** Profile of Bobbi Brown, CEO and founder of Bobbi Brown Cosmetics, designed to highlight a woman's natural look. Brown opened her first freestanding retail store recently that houses a makeup artistry school in the back.

46964 ■ "How I Did It: Laurel Touby Mediabistro" in *Inc.* **(March 2008, pp. 124-126)**
Pub: Gruner & Jahr USA Publishing
Ed: Eric Schine. **Description:** Profile of Laurel Touby and her business plan; Touby started Mediabistro as a series of parties that turned into an influential job listing and training Website for journalists. Last year she sold it for $23 million.

46965 ■ "How Investors React When Women Join Boards" in *Harvard Business Review* **(Vol. 88, July-August 2010, No. 7-8, pp. 24)**
Pub: Harvard Business School Publishing
Ed: Andrew O'Connell. **Description:** Research reveals a cognitive bias in blockholders regarding the presence of women on boards of directors despite evidence showing that diversity improves results.

46966 ■ "How Not to Build a Website" in *Women Entrepreneur* **(December 24, 2008)**
Pub: Entrepreneur Media Inc.
Ed: Erica Ruback; Joanie Reisen. **Description:** Tips for producing a unique and functional Website are given as well as a number of lessons a pair of entrepreneurs learned while trying to launch their networking website, MomSpace.com.

46967 ■ *How Remarkable Women Lead: A Breakthrough Model for Work and Life*
Pub: Crown Business
Ed: Joanna Barsh, Susie Cranston. **Released:** September 24, 2009. **Price:** $27.50. **Description:** An introduction to remarkable women, from Time Inc.'s Ann Moore to Xerox's Anne Mulcahy, who recount their inspiring struggles.

46968 ■ *How to Run Your Business Like a Girl: Successful Strategies from Entrepreneurial Women Who Made It Happen*
Pub: Adams Media Corporation
Ed: Elizabeth Cogswell Baskin. **Released:** September 2005. **Description:** Tour of three women entrepreneurs and their successful companies.

46969 ■ "How to Set Up an Effective Home Office" in *Women Entrepreneur* (August 22, 2008)
Pub: Entrepreneur Media Inc.
Ed: Laura Stack. **Description:** Checklist provides ways in which one can arrange their home office to provide the greatest efficiency which will allow maximum productivity and as a result the greater the chance of success.

46970 ■ "How Sweet It Is: a Health Hardship Leads to Cupcake Commerce" in *Black Enterprise* (Vol. 41, August 2010, No. 1, pp. 56)
Pub: Earl G. Graves Publishing Co. Inc.
Ed: Tamara E. Holmes. **Description:** Profile of Andra Hall, entrepreneur who started her cupcake business when her one-year-old daughter suffered from sleep apnea and wanted the flexibility to be with her baby. Hall and her husband refinanced their home in order to start the bakery

46971 ■ *How Women Make Money: Inspirational Stories and Practical Advice from Successful Canadian Entrepreneurs*
Pub: Dundurn Press
Ed: Julie V. Watson. **Released:** April 1, 2004. **Price:** $24.99. **Description:** Collection of profiles, anecdotes, and practical advice and guides to help women take control of their lives, start a new business, and reach financial goals.

46972 ■ *If You Have to Cry, Go Outside: And Other Things Your Mother Never Told You*
Pub: HarperOne
Ed: Kelly Cutrone. **Released:** February 2, 2010. **Price:** $22.99. **Description:** Women's mentor advices on how to make it in one of the most competitive industries in the world, fashion. She has kicked people out of fashion shows, forced some of reality television's shiny start to fire their friends, and built her own company which is one of the most powerful public relations firms in the fashion business.

46973 ■ *In the Company of Women: Canadian Women Talk About What It Takes to Start and Manage a Successful Business*
Pub: HarperCollins Publishers Inc.
Ed: Katherine Gay. **Released:** 1998. **Description:** Information to help women start and run a small business in Canada.

46974 ■ "In It For the Long Run" in *Business Journal-Serving Phoenix & the Valley of the Sun* (Vol. 30, August 20, 2010, No. 50, pp. 1)
Pub: Phoenix Business Journal
Ed: Angela Gonzales. **Description:** Cancer survivor Helene Neville has finished a record-breaking 2,520-mile run in 93 days and then celebrated her 50th birthday despite being diagnosed with Hodgkins' lymphoma in 1991. Neveille, who is also a Phoenix area registered nurse, made stops along the way to promote her book, 'Nurses in Shape'. Neville also discusses how she fought her cancer through running.

46975 ■ "In the Raw: Karyn Calabrese Brings Healthy Dining to a New Sophisticated Level" in *Black Enterprise* (Vol. 41, September 2010)
Pub: Earl G. Graves Publishing Co. Inc.
Ed: Sonia Alleyne. **Description:** Profile of Karyn Calabrese whose businesses are based in Chicago, Illinois. Calabrese has launched a complete line of

products (vitamins and beauty items), services (spa, chiropractic, and acupuncture treatments), and restaurants to bring health dining and lifestyles to a better level.

46976 ■ *International Handbook of Women and Small Business Entrepreneurship*
Pub: Edward Elgar Publishing, Incorporated
Ed: Fielden. **Released:** December 2006. **Price:** $50.00. **Description:** Practical initiatives and strategies for women entering small business entrepreneurial ventures are examined.

46977 ■ "The Interview" in *Crain's Cleveland Business* (Vol. 30, June 22, 2009, No. 24, pp. 9)
Pub: Crain Communications, Inc.
Description: In an interview with Mary K. Whitmer, partner at Kohrman Jackson & Krantz, she addresses issues facing the Northeast Ohio legal community. Ms. Whitmer is the new president of the Cleveland Metropolitan Bar Association.

46978 ■ "Is It Time to Move to a Real Office?" in *Women Entrepreneur* (December 30, 2008)
Pub: Entrepreneur Media Inc.
Ed: Aliza Sherman. **Description:** Before moving a company from a home-office to a real office it is important to make sure that the additional overhead that will be incurred by the move is comfortably covered and that the move is being done for the right reasons. Several women entrepreneurs who have moved their businesses from their homes to an actual rental space are profiled.

46979 ■ "It's Not Rocket Science" in *Hispanic Business* (September 2007, pp. 30, 32)
Pub: Hispanic Business
Ed: Hildy Medina. **Description:** Profile of France Cordova, president of Purdue University. Cordova has established many diversity programs at the school.

46980 ■ "Kaminsky Back in the Business of Selling Her Chocolate Treats" in *Business First Buffalo* (October 5, 2007, pp. 4)
Pub: American City Business Journals, Inc.
Ed: Tracey Drury. **Description:** Loretta Kaminsky, the original owner of Lou-Retta's Custom Chocolates brand, has decided to bring her products back into the market after winning a breach of contract lawsuit against Art Coco. Kaminsky sold her business to Art Coco in 2003, agreeing to the deal that Kaminsky will promote the products for two years in exchange for royalties and Art Coco's maintaining of product quality. Details of the distribution agreement with Wegmans, which will reintroduce Kaminsky's products are presented.

46981 ■ "Katie's Cupcakes to Celebrate One-Year Anniversary" in *Bellingham Business Journal* (Vol. March 2010, pp. 3)
Pub: Sound Publishing Inc.
Description: Katie Swanson, owner of Katie's Cupcakes, celebrated her firm's one-year anniversary with a fundraiser for the Whatcom Humane Society by offering free specialty cupcakes and other special events to the public. The specialty cupcakes will feature either a paw or bone and will be available throughout the month of March.

46982 ■ *Kitchen Table Entrepreneurs: How Eleven Women Escaped Poverty and Became Their Own Bosses*
Pub: Westview Press
Ed: Martha Shirk, Anna S. Wadia. **Released:** October 2008. **Price:** $16.95. **Description:** Profile of eleven successful women entrepreneurs.

46983 ■ "Know Your Bones: Take Your Bone Health Seriously" in *Women In Business* (Vol. 62, June 2010, No. 2, pp. 40)
Pub: American Business Women's Association
Description: Bone health for women with postmenopausal osteoporosis is encouraged to help create an appropriate health plan that includes exercise, diet and medication. Questions to consider when discussing possible plans with health care providers are presented.

46984 ■ *Lessons of a Lipstick Queen: Finding and Developing the Great Idea That Can Change Your Life*
Pub: Simon & Schuster
Ed: Poppy King. **Released:** May 1, 2009. **Price:** $14.00. **Description:** Poppy King tells how she started her lipstick brand at age eighteen. She reveals how she managed to launch her business using a good idea and finding financing, marketing the product and how she became successful.

46985 ■ "Let It Shine: Organization Helps Disadvantaged Girls See Their Worth" in *Black Enterprise* (Vol. 38, February 2008, No. 7, pp. 142)
Pub: Earl G. Graves Publishing Co. Inc.
Ed: George Alexander. **Description:** Wilson Mourning, founder of the clothing label Honey Child, attributes her success to her mother and other positive women who helped her through her adolescence. Mourning created a mentoring organization that helps young girls in the Miami, Florida area to develop life skills.

46986 ■ "A Lifetime of Giving: Food Bank CEO Fights Hunger One Mouth At a Time" in *Black Enterprise* (Vol. 41, November 2010, No. 4, pp. 86)
Pub: Earl G. Graves Publishing Co. Inc.
Ed: Tamara E. Holmes. **Description:** Profile of Valerie Traore, CEO of Food Bank of South Jersey. Traore stresses the importance of volunteerism that she learned from her grandparents. Hunger relief became her passion when she served as a temp office worker for the Maryland Food Bank in Baltimore. She earned her Bachelor's of Science in management and has dedicated herself to a career in nonprofit service.

46987 ■ "Lunch Box Maker Gives Back" in *Marketing to Women* (Vol. 23, November 2010, No. 11, pp. 5)
Pub: EPM Communications, Inc.
Description: Female entrepreneurs launched a new program called, "Share Your Lunch Project" that encourages mothers to give back and replace their child's lunchbox with their eco-friendly lunch boxes, which are available at select retailers. All proceeds from the project will benefit the World Food Program USA, which feeds children in developing countries.

46988 ■ *Martha, Inc.*
Pub: John Wiley and Sons, Inc.
Ed: Christopher Byron. **Released:** 2002. **Price:** $28.00. **Description:** Profile of Martha Stewart's rise from working class to a billionaire businesswoman is presented. The book covers Stewart's power struggles and personal conflicts as well as her triumphs.

46989 ■ *Minding Her Own Business, 4th Ed.*
Pub: Sphinx Publishing
Ed: Jan Zobel. **Released:** January 1, 2005. **Price:** $16.95. **Description:** A guide to taxes and financial records for women entrepreneurs is presented.

46990 ■ "Mixing Business and Pleasure On the Green" in *Black Enterprise* (Vol. 41, October 2010, No. 3, pp. 65)
Pub: Earl G. Graves Publishing Co. Inc.
Ed: Annya M. Lott. **Description:** Glow Golf, sponsored by Glow Sports, will offer instruction to 150 female corporate executives and entrepreneurs to learn the fundamentals of the game of golf.

46991 ■ "Mom of Eight Named Regional Minority Small Business Person of the Year" in *Daily News* (November 8, 2010)
Pub: Daily News
Ed: Suzanne Ulbrich. **Description:** Profile of Melissa Leifheit, mother of eight and named Regional Minority Small Business Person of the Year by the North Carolina Small Business Administration.

46992 ■ *The Mommy Manifesto: How to Use Our Power to Think Big, Break Limitations and Achieve Success*
Pub: John Wiley & Sons, Inc.
Ed: Kim Lavine. **Released:** September 1, 2009. **Price:** $24.95. **Description:** A new women's revolution will help women take control of their careers,

their lives, and their economic future. The book shows how mom's control the economy and have the power to become successful entrepreneurs.

46993 ■ *More Than a Pink Cadillac*
Pub: McGraw-Hill
Ed: Jim Underwood. **Released:** 2002. **Price:** $23.95. **Description:** Profile of Mary Kay Ash who turned her $5,000 investment into a billion-dollar corporation. Ash's nine principles that form the foundation of her company's global success are outlined. Stories from her sales force leaders share ideas for motivating employees, impressing customers and building a successful company. The book emphasizes the leadership skills required to drive performance in any successful enterprise.

46994 ■ "My Day" in *Business Strategy Review* (Vol. 21, Autumn 2010, No. 3, pp. 77)
Pub: Wiley-Blackwell
Ed: Julie Meyer. **Description:** Julie Meyer shot to prominence as cofounder of the entrepreneurial network, First Tuesday. The firm was sold for $50 million in 2000.

46995 ■ *My Life From Scratch: A Sweet Journey of Starting Over, One Cake at a Time*
Pub: Broadway Books
Released: June 8, 2010. **Price:** $14.00. **Description:** Lively account of Old World recipes, Bullock-Prado, a former Hollywood film developer and sister to actress Sandra Bullock, recounts the joys and heartbreak of running her own patisserie in Montpelier, Vermont. Having fled Los Angeles with her husband, Ray for the simpler pleasures of a small town near the Green Mountains, she opened her own bake shop, Gesine Confectionary in 2004, mostly on the fame of the macaroons she refashioned from her German mother's favorite almond treat, mandelhoernchen (and the casual mention of her sister in an interview). Her memoir follows one day in a busy baker's life, from waking at 3 a.m. to prepare the batter and bake her croissants, scones, and sticky buns, before opening her shop at 7 a.m., through the hectic lunch, and 3 p.m. tea time.

46996 ■ *My So-Called Freelance Life: How to Survive and Thrive as a Creative Professional for Hire*
Pub: Seal Press
Ed: Michelle Goodman. **Released:** October 1, 2008. **Price:** $15.95. **Description:** Guidebook for women wishing to start a freelancing business; tips, advice, how-to's and all the information needed to survive working from home are included.

46997 ■ "Nancy Hughes Anthony" in *Canadian Business* (Vol. 81, October 13, 2008, No. 17, pp. 104)
Pub: Rogers Media Ltd.
Ed: Andy Holloway. **Description:** Profile of Nancy Hughes Anthony, who believes her experience operating large enterprises as a public servant helped her earn positions that ultimately brought her to her current position as chief executive and president of the Canadian Bankers Association. She also thinks there should be more public-private sector coordination within industries.

46998 ■ *National Directory of Woman-Owned Business Firms*
Pub: Business Research Services Inc.
Released: Annual, Latest edition 13th. **Price:** $295, individuals paperback. **Covers:** 30,000 woman-owned businesses. **Entries Include:** Company name, address, phone, name and title of contact, minority group, certification status, date founded, number of employees, description of products or services, sales volume, government contracting experience, references. **Arrangement:** Standard Industrial Classification (SIC) code, geographical. **Indexes:** Alphabetical by company.

46999 ■ "Natural Attraction: Bath and Body Products Maker Delivers Wholesome Goodness" in *Black Enterprise* (Vol. 38, November 2007, No. 4)
Pub: Earl G. Graves Publishing Co. Inc.
Ed: Kaylyn Kendall Dines. **Description:** Profile of Dawn Fitch, creator of Pooka Inc., manufacturer of

handmade bath and body products that contain no preservatives. Sales are expected to reach $750,000 for 2007.

47000 ■ "NAWBO Takes the Stage at Press Conference for Small Business Jobs, Credit and Tax Relief Acts" in *Internet Wire* (June 17, 2010)
Pub: Comtex
Description: A survey of the National Association of Women Business Owners reported optimism returning and women business owners are ready to invest in job creation. The Small Business Jobs Tax Relief Act will aid in their progress.

47001 ■ "Need a Course Correction? Let ABWA Be Your Navigator" in *Women In Business* (Vol. 62, September 2010, No. 3, pp. 6)
Pub: American Business Women's Association
Ed: Rene Street. **Description:** It is believed that the American Business Women's Association (ABWA) has the ability to help women in their quest for greater success. The organization also has the energy needed to move on to the next stage for women in business. ABWA's members have taken the initiative to embrace the group's potential.

47002 ■ "Negotiating Muscle" in *Black Enterprise* (Vol. 38, February 2008, No. 7, pp. 70)
Pub: Earl G. Graves Publishing Co. Inc.
Ed: Sonia Alleyne. **Description:** Negotiating historically has been a barrier for women in business, the book, "Ask For It: How Women Can Use the Power of Negotiation to Get What They Really Want" helps professional females identify and create great business opportunities.

47003 ■ "New York Collection Agency's Bribery Case Resolved" in *Collections & Credit Risk* (Vol. 15, August 1, 2010, No. 7, pp. 19)
Pub: SourceMedia Inc.
Description: Criminal conviction and civil settlement in a bribery case and Medicaid scam involving H.I.S. Holdings Inc. and owner Deborah Kantor is examined.

47004 ■ "NJ Tries to Push Stimulus Funds to Minorities" in *Philadelphia Business Journal* (Vol. 28, September 25, 2009, No. 32, pp. 1)
Pub: American City Business Journals
Ed: Athena D. Merritt. **Description:** New Jersey Governor Jon S. Corzine signed an executive order that seeks to ease the way for minority and women-owned business to take on federal stimulus-funded work. New Jersey has also forged new relations with different organizations to reduce the time and cost of certifications for businesses.

47005 ■ "Nonprofit Ready to Get More Girls into 'STEM' Jobs" in *Austin Business JournalInc.* (Vol. 29, December 25, 2009, No. 42, pp. 1)
Pub: American City Business Journals
Ed: Sandra Zaragoza. **Description:** Girlstart has completed its $1.5 million capital campaign to buy the building it will care the Girlstart Tech Center. Girlstart is a nonprofit organization that prepares girls for science, technology, engineering and mathematics or STEM careers. Details of the program are highlighted.

47006 ■ "Nonprofits May Lose MBE Status in MD" in *Boston Business Journal* (Vol. 29, September 2, 2011, No. 17, pp. 1)
Pub: American City Business Journals Inc.
Ed: Scott Dance. **Description:** A business group has been pushing to bar nonprofits from Maryland's Minority Business program. Nonprofits have been found to take a large portion of state contracts intended for women- and minority-owned businesses. The group is also crafting proposed legislation to remove nonprofits from the program.

47007 ■ "Now Entering A Secure Area" in *Women Entrepreneur* (January 14, 2009)
Pub: Entrepreneur Media Inc.
Ed: Aliza Sherman. **Description:** Despite the fact that the field of government intelligence and security is dominated by males, many women entrepreneurs

are finding opportunities for their products and services in homeland security. Profiles of several women who have found such opportunities are included.

47008 ■ *Off-Ramps and On-Ramps: Keeping Talented Women on the Road to Success*
Pub: Harvard Business School Press
Ed: Sylvia Ann Hewlett. **Price:** $29.95. **Description:** Hewlett (founding president for the Center for Work-Life Policy) examines why many women exit their careers, taking 'off-ramps' (leaving altogether) or 'scenic routes' (opting to work part-time), often during critical, competitive times. She also provides valuable suggestions for companies hoping to retain talented employees of any gender.

47009 ■ "On the Green: Sheila Johnson Adds $35 Million Golf Resort To Her Expanding Portfolio" in *Black Enterprise* (January 2008)
Pub: Earl G. Graves Publishing Co. Inc.
Ed: Donna M. Owens. **Description:** Profile of Sheila Johnson, CEO of Salamander Hospitality LLC, made history when she purchased the Innisbrook Resort and Golf Club, making her the first African American woman to own this type of property. The resort includes four championship golf courses, six swimming pools, four restaurants, eleven tennis courts, three conference halls, and a nature preserve.

47010 ■ "On Your Marks, American Airlines, Now Vote!" in *Benzinga.com* (, 2011)
Pub: Benzinga.com
Ed: Benzinga Staff. **Description:** Wedding planner, Aviva Samuels, owner of Kiss the Planner boutique wedding and event planning agency in Florida, says that winning this contest would help her increase her knowledge base and provide in-depth, personal experience offering more destination wedding destinations.

47011 ■ "The One Thing That's Holding Back Your Wellness Program" in *Employee Benefit News* (Vol. 25, December 1, 2011, No. 15, pp. 8)
Pub: SourceMedia Inc.
Ed: Kelley M. Butler. **Description:** A 13-year study shows that women who sat for more than six hours a day were 94 percent more likely to die during the study period. Most women sit at their desks an average of 7.7 hours while at work.

47012 ■ "Out Front and Strong" in *WorkingUSA* (Vol. 11, December 2008, No. 4, pp. 477)
Pub: Blackwell Publishers Ltd.
Ed: Jessica Wilkerson. **Description:** History of the Tennessee Committee on Occupational Safety and Health that formed in East Tennessee in 1979 is explored. The article addresses how local women contributed to the organization at the grassroots.

47013 ■ "Packing Chic" in *Black Enterprise* (Vol. 38, February 2008, No. 7, pp. 154)
Pub: Earl G. Graves Publishing Co. Inc.
Ed: Sonai Alleyne. **Description:** Profile of Angela Theodora's leather overnight bags that offer a variety of smart compartments for the business traveler.

47014 ■ *The Pampered Chef*
Pub: Doubleday Broadway Publishing Group
Ed: Doris Christopher. **Description:** The Pampered Chef has been selling high quality kitchen tools through in-home cooking demonstration for twenty-five years. CEO and founder explains how she turned her one woman company into a a business with sales approaching $1 billion. Christopher shares her story by providing the foundation, strategies for entrepreneurs, setting priorities, knowing when to expand and when to slow growth, and dealing with adversity.

47015 ■ "Passionate About Empowering Women" in *Women In Business* (Vol. 63, Spring 2011, No. 1, pp. 24)
Pub: American Business Women's Association
Ed: Leigh Elmore. **Description:** Krazy Coupon Ladies cofounder Joanie Demer shares her views about her book, 'Pick Another Checkout Lane, Honey', which she coauthored with Heather Wheeler.

Demer believes using coupons is for everyone who wants to save money. She also believes that extreme couponing is not an exercise for those who lack organizational ability since it requires planning and discipline.

47016 ■ "Pedal to the Medal" in *Small Business Opportunities* **(Summer 2010)**
Pub: Harris Publications Inc.
Ed: Chuck Green. **Description:** Profile of Darlene Miller who became and partner and eventually took over Permac Industries, a firm that specializes in precision machine products.

47017 ■ "People and Places" in *Entrepreneur* **(Vol. 36, February 2008, No. 2, pp. 12)**
Pub: Entrepreneur Media Inc.
Ed: Rieva Lesonsky. **Description:** Websites of different organizations that can provide entrepreneurs with business help are presented. Business-related events such as the Women in Charge conference and Xerox Smart Business Symposium are mentioned.

47018 ■ "The People Who Influence You the Most - Believe In You" in *Women In Business* **(Vol. 62, September 2010, No. 3, pp. 9)**
Pub: American Business Women's Association
Description: The president of the American Business Women's Association (ABWA) talks about her experiences in the organization. She believes that the dynamic women with whom she worked with helped her shape the organization into one that her predecessors believed it could become. The importance of dealing with challenges while making each experience an opportunity to learn is also discussed.

47019 ■ "Physics for Females" in *Occupational Outlook Quarterly* **(Vol. 55, Summer 2011, No. 2, pp. 22)**
Pub: U.S. Bureau of Labor Statistics
Description: Free resources to help females investigate careers in medical physics and health physics are available from the American Physical Society. The booklet is designed for girls in middle and high school and describes the work of 15 women who use physics to solve medical mysteries, discover planets, research new materials, and more.

47020 ■ "Pick A Trademark You Can Protect" in *Women Entrepreneur* **(November 3, 2008)**
Pub: Entrepreneur Media Inc.
Ed: Nina L. Kaufman. **Description:** Provides information regarding trademarks, how to choose a name that will win approval from the U.S. Patent and Trademark Office, and how to choose a trademark that one can protect.

47021 ■ "Play It Safe or Take a Stand?" in *Harvard Business Review* **(Vol. 88, November 2010, No. 11, pp. 139)**
Pub: Harvard Business School Publishing
Ed: Trish Gorman Clifford, Jay Barney. **Description:** A fictitious leadership scenario is presented, with contributors providing comments and recommendations. A female executive ponders whether to assert a point of view on a new venture. Both experts agree that after providing careful analysis of pros and cons, the executive should come to a well-informed conclusion.

47022 ■ "The Power of ABWA" in *Women In Business* **(Vol. 62, September 2010, No. 3, pp. 36)**
Pub: American Business Women's Association
Ed: Leigh Elmore. **Description:** Information about the internship received by Erica Rockley at American Business Women's Association (ABWA) headquarters is presented. Rockley received heartfelt professional advice the days she spent at the office. She also learned the importance of networking.

47023 ■ "The Power of Commitment: Mere Motivation Is Often Not Enough To Achieve Your Goals" in *Black Enterprise* **(November 2007)**
Pub: Earl G. Graves Publishing Co. Inc.
Ed: Tamara E. Holmes. **Description:** Profile of Michelle Tucker Kirk who opened her bridal shop in 2006. Kirk explains how her commitment and determi-

nation were keys to the company's success. Five signs to help any would-be entrepreneur discover if they are truly committed to a business idea are listed.

47024 ■ *Prepare to Be a Teen Millionaire*
Pub: Health Communications, Inc.
Ed: Robyn Collins; Kimberly Spinks Burleson. **Released:** April 1, 2008. **Price:** $16.95. **Description:** Business reference for any teenager wishing to become a successful entrepreneur; advice is given from successful teenage millionaires. Topics covered include: choosing a business name, type, and location; use of the Internet; legal issues; branding, sales, and marketing; funding and financial management; return on investment; retirement; development of a sound business plan; and certification for minority or women-owned companies.

47025 ■ "Profile: Lynda Gratton" in *Business Strategy Review* **(Vol. 21, Autumn 2010, No. 3, pp. 74)**
Pub: Wiley-Blackwell
Ed: Stuart Crainer. **Description:** The early 20th Century marked the dawn of modern enterprise management, and no one influenced its practice more than Frederick W. Taylor, inventor of 'scientific management'. This radical transformation of management and among the few thinkers most influencing this transformation is Lynda Gratton, London Business School Professor of Management Practice.

47026 ■ "Program for Women Entrepreneurs: Tips for Surviving this Economy" in *Crain's Detroit Business* **(Vol. 25, June 22, 2009, No. 25)**
Pub: Crain Communications Inc. - Detroit
Description: Michigan Leadership Institute for Women Entrepreneurs will hold its third and final program, "Tough Times are Temporary, but Tough People are Permanent" at the Davenport University in Livonia, Michigan.

47027 ■ "Public Opinion" in *Entrepreneur* **(Vol. 36, April 2008, No. 4, pp. 28)**
Pub: Entrepreneur Media, Inc.
Ed: Aliza Sherman. **Description:** According to a 2007 report from Group and Organization Management, women in top positions can lead publicly traded companies to stock price and earnings growth. Some women business owners say that going public has provided them with the capital to grow. Details on the potential of women-managed publicly traded companies are discussed.

47028 ■ "Queen Bees: All Sting, No Honey" in *Business Horizons* **(September-October 2007, pp. 348)**
Pub: Elsevier Technology Publications
Ed: Catherine M. Dalton. **Description:** Female rivalry or competition in the workplace and other domains are explained and compared to the behavior of honeybees. Novels and other works on the topic of competition among women are discussed.

47029 ■ "Real-Life Coursework for Real-Life Business People" in *Women In Business* **(Vol. 63, Summer 2011, No. 2, pp. 22)**
Pub: American Business Women's Association
Ed: Leigh Elmore. **Description:** American Business Women's Association National Women's Leadership Conference provides members with academic business training courses. Members can take a variety of MBA-level courses that are taught by University of Kansas School of Business professors. Courses include marketing, management, leadership and communication and decision making.

47030 ■ "The Right Remedy: Entrepreneur's Success Is a Matter of Life and Death" in *Black Enterprise* **(Vol. 38, February 2008, No. 7, pp. 46)**
Pub: Earl G. Graves Publishing Co. Inc.
Ed: Tamara E. Holmes. **Description:** Profile of Leah Brown, whose company conducts clinical trials to determine if specific drugs will relieve particular symptoms. Her company will also visit physician's offices to make certain doctors are following proper protocol for a clinical trial or will collect data from patients.

47031 ■ "The Role of Human and Financial Capital in the Profitability and Growth of Women-Owned Small Firms" in *Journal of Small Business Management*
Pub: Blackwell Publishing, Inc.
Ed: Susan Coleman. **Description:** Examines the relationship between the human and financial capital in both men and women-owned businesses and firm performance in the service and retail sectors.

47032 ■ *The Savvy Gal's Guide to Online Networking (Or What Would Jane Austen Do?)*
Pub: Booklocker.com Inc.
Ed: Diane K. Daneilson, Lindsey Pollak. **Released:** August 10, 2007. **Price:** $14.95. **Description:** It is a truth universally acknowledged that a woman in search of a fabulous career must be in want of networking opportunities. Or so Jane Austen would say if she were writing, or more likely, blogging today. So begins the must-read guide to networking in the 21st Century. Authors and networking experts share the nuts, bolts and savvy secrets that businesswomen need in order to use technology to build professional relationships.

47033 ■ *The Savvy Girl's Guide to Online Networking (Or What Would Jane Austen Do?)*
Pub: Booklocker.com Inc.
Ed: Diane K. Danielson; Lindsey Pollak. **Released:** August 10, 2007. **Price:** $14.95. **Description:** The book offers tips, tactics and etiquette for businesswomen wishing to build professional relationships via email, online networks, blogs, and message boards.

47034 ■ *Secrets of Millionaire Moms*
Pub: McGraw-Hill
Ed: Tamara Monosoff. **Released:** March 2007. **Price:** $16.95. **Description:** Profiles of successful women/mother entrepreneurs are presented, including Julie Clark, Lane Nemeth, Lillian Vernon, Victoria Knight, Rachel Ashwell and other powerful businesswomen.

47035 ■ "The Secret's Out About Kansas City" in *Women In Business* **(Vol. 61, August-September 2009, No. 4, pp. 26)**
Pub: American Business Women's Association
Ed: Leigh Elmore. **Description:** Missouri's Kansas City offers various attractions, such as public fountains, the 18th and Vine Historic Districts for jazz enthusiasts, and the Crossroads Arts District with a variety of art galleries. Details on other cultural attractions and neighborhoods in the city are presented.

47036 ■ "Secrets To Trade Show Success" in *Women Entrepreneur* **(September 12, 2008)**
Pub: Entrepreneur Media Inc.
Ed: Lesley Spencer Pyle. **Description:** Trade shows require an enormous amount of work, but they are an investment that can pay off handsomely because they allow a business to get their product or service in front of their target market. Advice regarding trade shows is given including selecting the correct venue, researching the affair and following up on leads obtained at the event.

47037 ■ "Shari's Berries Founder Shuts Last of Her Stores" in *Sacramento Business Journal* **(Vol. 28, September 2, 2011, No. 27, pp. 1)**
Pub: Sacramento Business Journal
Ed: Kelly Johnson. **Description:** Sacramento, California-based Shari's Berries owner Shari Fitzpatrick closed the company's last three stores called The Berry Factory. Fitzpatrick also filed for business bankruptcy protection. The weak economy is blamed for the company's failure.

47038 ■ "Shop Around" in *Houston Chronicle* **(December 7, 2010, pp. 3)**
Pub: Houston Chronicle
Ed: Tara Dooley. **Description:** Profile of Diana Candida and Maria Martinez who partnered to open Beatniks, a shop carrying vintage clothing, art from various artists, dance shoes, and jewelry.

47039 ■ "Sign Up To Grow Your Business, Generate Jobs" in *Women Entrepreneur* (November 25, 2008)
Pub: Entrepreneur Media Inc.
Ed: Eve Gumpel. Description: Nell Merlino has announced the new Make Mine A Million-Dollar Race, which aims to encourage hundreds of thousands of women entrepreneurs to grow their business to revenue goals of $250,00, $500,000 or $1 million and more as well as create 800,000 new jobs in an attempt to stimulate the nation's economy.

47040 ■ "Six Tips To Maximize Networking Opportunities" in *Women Entrepreneur* (November 3, 2008)
Pub: Entrepreneur Media Inc.
Ed: Tamara Monosoff. Description: Networking events fall into the realm of business development as opposed to immediate sales opportunities. It is important to remember that these events provide a chance to build relationships that may someday help one's business. Tips to help make the most out of networking events are provided.

47041 ■ "So You Want to Start a Business?" in *Women Entrepreneur* (August 5, 2008)
Pub: Entrepreneur Media Inc.
Ed: Cynthia McKay. Description: Advice for taking an idea and turning it into a legitimate business is given.

47042 ■ "Some Women Warming Up to Economy's Prospects" in *Crain's Cleveland Business* (Vol. 30, June 1, 2009, No. 21, pp. 9)
Pub: Crain Communications, Inc.
Ed: Mark Dodosh. Description: According to a recent survey conducted by the Center for Women's Business Research and KeyBank focusing on the experience and opinions of women business owners, 48 percent of respondents believe the economy will improve over the next six months. Statistical data included.

47043 ■ "Speak Better: Five Tips for Polished Presentations" in *Women Entrepreneur* (September 19, 2008)
Pub: Entrepreneur Media Inc.
Ed: Suzannah Baum. Description: Successful entrepreneurs agree that exemplary public speaking skills are among the core techniques needed to propel their business forward. A well-delivered presentation can result in securing a new distribution channel, gaining new customers, locking into a new referral stream or receiving extra funding.

47044 ■ "The Stars Align: Trail Blazers, Headline Makers on 2007 List Set Example for Others" in *Hispanic Business* (October 2007, pp. 22)
Pub: Hispanic Business
Description: Top one hundred most influential Hispanic business leaders comprise of 66 percent men and 34 percent women, distributed by 27 percent in government, 42 percent corporate, 11 percent education, five percent art and entertainment, and 15 percent in other sectors. Statistical data included.

47045 ■ "State's Glass Ceiling Gets Higher" in *Business Journal-Milwaukee* (Vol. 25, October 5, 2007, No. 1, pp. A1)
Pub: American City Business Journals, Inc.
Ed: Jennifer Batog. Description: Report showed that more than a third of Wisconsin's fifty largest companies have no female executive officers, and the number of companies with at least one woman at top departments has also decreased since 2005. Companies lacking women at upper management levels risk jeopardizing their firms' vitality as diversity in executive offices leads to diverse ideas that can help in relating better to customers and clients.

47046 ■ "A Step Up" in *Black Enterprise* (Vol. 38, January 2008, No. 6, pp. 53)
Pub: Earl G. Graves Publishing Co. Inc.
Description: Professional black women can get advice from a nonprofit program called ASCENT: Leading Multicultural Women to the Top. ASCENT's

sessions last six months and are held at both Tuck School of Business at Dartmouth and UCLA Anderson School of Management.

47047 ■ "Stylish Successes" in *Women In Business* (Vol. 61, October-November 2009, No. 5, pp. 12)
Pub: American Business Women's Association
Ed: Leigh Elmore; Megan L. Reese. Description: Amanda Horan Kennedy, Angela Samuels, Barbara Nast Saletan, and Patty Nast Canton are career women who ventured into entrepreneurship. They are deemed to possess networking and teamwork skills that ensured their success in the garment industry.

47048 ■ "Susan Leger Ferraro Built a $7.2 Million Day Care Business. Now She Wants To Expand-And Cash Out" in *Inc.* (January 2008, pp. 50-53)
Pub: Gruner & Jahr USA Publishing
Ed: Dalia Fahmy. Description: Profile of Susan Leger Ferraro who wants to expand her chain of day care centers into Florida and California and sell part of her 87 percent stake to reduce financial risk.

47049 ■ "Sylvie Collection Offers a Feminine Perspective and Voice in Male Dominated Bridal Industry" in *Benzinga.com* (October 29, 2011)
Pub: Benzinga.com
Ed: Benzinga Staff. Description: Bridal jewelry designer Sylvie Levine has created over 1,000 customizable styles of engagement rings and wedding bands and is reaching out to prospective new brides through a new Website, interactive social media campaign and monthly trunk show appearances.

47050 ■ *Table Talk: The Savvy Girl's Alternative to Networking*
Pub: AuthorHouse
Ed: Diane Danielson. Released: April 1, 2003. Price: $17.50. Description: Let's face it. Women and men are different. So why should we all have to network in the same way? And, why should women have to 'network' at all? Between family and work responsibilities, the idea of pressing flesh at some not-very-festive cocktail party is right up there in appeal with a root canal. But what if women could find a way to make career boosting connections that are actually fun? Enter 'table talk', a new way to network for time-pressed, professional women.

47051 ■ "Tamara Vrooman" in *Canadian Business* (Vol. 80, November 19, 2007, No. 23, pp. 9)
Pub: Rogers Media
Ed: Regan Ray. Description: Profile of Tamara Vrooman, newly appointed CEO of Canada's largest credit union, Vancity. Vrooman believes that Vancity has an advantage over big bank when it comes to the flexibility of products the company offers. The role of Vancity and credit unions in the banking sector of Canada is discussed.

47052 ■ "The Tapestry of Life" in *Women In Business* (Vol. 61, December 2009, No. 6, pp. 8)
Pub: American Business Women's Association
Ed: Kathleen Leighton. Description: Suzanne Fanch, co-owner of the Devil's Thumb Ranch, discusses the family and career-related influences that helped her to achieve success as a small business proprietor. She advises that opportunities should be treated as building blocks towards success. Fanch's involvement in advocacies that take care of the welfare of community, children, and environment is also discussed.

47053 ■ "Teaneck Resident Chairs National Minority Business Group" in *Record* (January 5, 2011)
Pub: Record
Ed: Andrew Tangel. Description: National Minority Business Council Inc. is a trade group for minority women- and veteran-owned small businesses. Ben Jones began his term as chairman of the group in January 2011.

47054 ■ "Ten Ways to Save on Business Travel" in *Women Entrepreneur* (November 21, 2008)
Pub: Entrepreneur Media Inc.
Ed: Julie Moline. Description: Advice regarding ways in which to save money when traveling for business is given.

47055 ■ "The Way I Work: Kim Kleeman" in *Inc.* (October 2007, pp. 110-112, 114)
Pub: Gruner & Jahr USA Publishing
Ed: Leigh Buchanan. Description: Profile of Kim Kleeman, founder and president of ShakespeareSquared, a firm that develops educational materials, including lesson plans, teacher guides, activity workbooks, and discussion guides for large publishers. Kleeman talks about the challenges she faces running her nearly all-women company while maintaining a balance with her family.

47056 ■ "Tied to Home: Female Owned Businesses Export Less, And It's Not Just Because They're Smaller" in *Canadian Business* (April 14, 2008)
Pub: Rogers Media
Ed: Lauren McKeon. Description: Only 12 percent of small and midsized enterprises that are run by women export their products and services. Government agencies can be more proactive in promoting the benefits of exporting by including women in case studies and recruiting women as mentors. Exporting provides great growth potential especially for the service sector where women have an advantage.

47057 ■ "To Live and Thrive in L.A." in *Canadian Business* (Vol. 81, October 13, 2008, No. 17, pp. 78)
Pub: Rogers Media Ltd.
Ed: Rachel Pulfer. Description: Toronto entrepreneur Shereen Arazm thrived in Los Angeles, California as the queen of nightlife. Arazm holds or has held ownership stakes in bars, nightspots and restaurants that include the Geisha House, Concorde, Shag, Parc and Central, and Terroni L.A.

47058 ■ "Toes for Business" in *Hispanic Business* (October 2007, pp. 10, 12)
Pub: Hispanic Business
Ed: Gabriel Rodriguez. Description: Prima ballerinas, Lorena and Lorna Feijoo, have increased box office sales by at least 30 to 40 percent. A discussion with Pedro Pablo Pena, artistic director of the Miami Hispanic Ballet Corps and founder of the first Choreographic Workshop of Havana is included.

47059 ■ "Too Much Information?" in *Black Enterprise* (Vol. 37, December 2006, No. 5, pp. 59)
Pub: Earl G. Graves Publishing Co. Inc.
Ed: James C. Johnson. Description: African American business owners often face the dilemma of whether or not to divulge their minority status when soliciting new customers and financial institutions. The quality of the products or services is always the key factor and race should never define one's business; however, it is appropriate to market oneself as a minority or women-owned business, especially if the company is in an industry where those clients are offered top-tier contracts.

47060 ■ "Top 50" in *Entrepreneur* (Vol. 35, November 2007, No. 11, pp. 38)
Pub: Entrepreneur Media Inc.
Description: List of the 50 fastest-growing women-led businesses in North America is presented.

47061 ■ *Tough Choices: A Memoir*
Pub: Penguin Group
Ed: Carly Florina. Released: October 2006. Price: $24.95. Description: Former woman CEO at Hewlett-Packard is profiled.

47062 ■ "Transform Your Life" in *Black Enterprise* (Vol. 37, January 2007, No. 6, pp. 14)
Pub: Earl G. Graves Publishing Co. Inc.
Description: Through the magazine, television and radio programs, events, and the website, the various platforms of Black Enterprise will provide the tools necessary to achieve success in business ventures, career aspirations, and personal goals.

47063 ■ *The Trump Card: Playing to Win in Work and Life*
Pub: Touchstone/Simon & Schuster Inc.
Ed: Ivanka Trump. **Released:** October 12, 2009. **Price:** $24.99. **Description:** Profile of Ivanka Trump, the daughter of Donald and Ivana Trump; she shares the life lessons and hard-won insights that have made her successful in the business world.

47064 ■ "Turning Bright Ideas Into Profitable Businesses" in *Inside Business* (Vol. 13, September-October 2011, No. 5, pp. SS6)
Pub: Great Lakes Publishing Company
Ed: Susan Keen Flynn. **Description:** Startup Lakewood was launched by Mickie Rinehart. She provides free resources to entrepreneurs in the city in order to help them turn their small business vision into reality.

47065 ■ "Twenty Years of Advocacy and Education" in *Women Entrepreneur* (January 18, 2009)
Pub: Entrepreneur Media Inc.
Ed: Eve Gumpel. **Description:** Profile of Sharon Hadary who served as executive director of the Center for Women's Business Research for two decades; Hadary discusses what she has learned about women business owners, their impact on the economy and what successful business owners share in common.

47066 ■ "Two Local Bakers Winners of TV's 'Cupcake Wars'" in *Toledo Blade* (July 6, 2011)
Pub: Toledo Times
Description: Winners of cable network Food Channel's Cupcake Wars, Lori Jacobs and Dana Iliev own Cake in a Cup in Toledo, Ohio. The partners shop features creative cupcakes with names such as Monkey Business, Pretty in Pink, and Tropical Getaway.

47067 ■ *Use What You've Got*
Pub: Portfolio Publishing
Ed: Barbara Corcoran, Bruce Littlefield. **Released:** 2003. **Price:** $24.95. **Description:** Founder and chairman of New York's premier real estate company, the Corcoran Group, shares her successes in the real estate industry. The book offers tips and pointers to salespeople, entrepreneurs and business people alike. Corcoran explains how she went from waiting tables and borrowed $1,000 from a boyfriend to build her real estate company into the industry's powerhouse.

47068 ■ "Virginia Albanese: President and CEO" in *Inside Business* (Vol. 13, September-October 2011, No. 5, pp. NC4)
Pub: Great Lakes Publishing Company
Ed: Jeannie Roberts. **Description:** Profile of Virginia Albanese, CEO of FedEx's Custom Critical Division in Akron, Ohio. Albanese discusses her philosophy on business leadership.

47069 ■ "Want a Facial With That Steak?" in *Charlotte Observer* (February 5, 2007)
Pub: Knight-Ridder/Tribune Business News
Ed: Jen Aronoff. **Description:** Profile of Burke Myotherapy Massage & Spa and Schell's Bistro. Lynn Shell moved her massage therapy business into a 106-year old home that had been used as a restaurant. She opened her own eatery on the first floor and offers massage therapy upstairs.

47070 ■ "We Were Strutting Our Stuff" in *Women In Business* (Vol. 63, Summer 2011, No. 2, pp. 10)
Pub: American Business Women's Association
Ed: Rene Street, Leigh Elmore. **Description:** American Business Women's Association's STRUT relay race event helped raise awareness of the group in the United States. The event also provided excellent team-building exercises for ABWA chapters. It also helped participants boost their leadership and business skills.

47071 ■ "The Weeks Ahead" in *Crain's New York Business* (Vol. 24, January 14, 2008, No. 2, pp. 20)
Pub: Crain Communications, Inc.
Description: Listing of events in the Detroit area include conferences addressing entrepreneurialism, economic development, and women business ownership.

47072 ■ "Welcome to Babesland" in *Women In Business* (Vol. 62, June 2010, No. 2, pp. 33)
Pub: American Business Women's Association
Ed: Leigh Elmore. **Description:** Music group, Four Bitchin' Babes will be performing at the 2010 American Business Women's Association's National Women's Leadership Conference. The group has been in the industry for 20 years and has released nine albums. The Four Bitchin' Babes consist of Sally Fingerett, Nancy Moran, Deirdre Flint, and Debi Smith.

47073 ■ *What Men Don't Tell Woman about Business: Opening Up the Heavily Guarded Alpha Male Playbook*
Pub: John Wiley and Sons, Inc.
Ed: Christopher V. Fleet. **Released:** October 26, 2007. **Description:** Valuable guide for any woman in business, this book helps reveal everything a woman needs to know in order to understand, communicate, and compete with men in business.

47074 ■ "The Whole Package" in *Entrepreneur* (Vol. 36, February 2008, No. 2, pp. 24)
Pub: Entrepreneur Media Inc.
Description: Holy Bohn, owner of The Honest Statute, developed an environmentally-friendly packaging for her pet food products. The company hired a packaging consultant and spent $175,000. Big corporations also spend money and plunge into the latest trends in packaging ranging from lighter and flexible to temperature-sensitive labels.

47075 ■ "Why Men Still Get More Promotions Than Women" in *Harvard Business Review* (Vol. 88, September 2010, No. 9, pp. 80)
Pub: Harvard Business School Publishing
Ed: Herminia Ibarra, Nancy M. Carter, Christine Silva. **Description:** Sponsorship, rather than mentoring, is identified as the main difference in why men still receive more promotions than women. Active executive sponsorship is key to fostering career advancement.

47076 ■ "The WIN Library" in *Women In Business* (Vol. 61, August-September 2009, No. 4, pp. 36)
Pub: American Business Women's Association
Ed: Leigh Elmore. **Description:** Women's Instructional Network (WIN) offers members of the American Business Women's Association with information about the organization and 15 Team Tools learning modules to help further the learning of business women. Other training programs and services offered by WIN are presented.

47077 ■ "Women as 21st Century Leaders" in *Women In Business* (Vol. 63, Summer 2011, No. 2, pp. 26)
Pub: American Business Women's Association
Ed: Leigh Elmore. **Description:** American Business Women's Association and Park University have partnered to provide a leadership training program to attendees of the 2011 National Women's Leadership Conference. The courses will incorporate introduction to concepts, development of critical thinking skills and direct application through exercises. Comments from executives are also included.

47078 ■ "Women: the Alpha Advantage" in *Entrepreneur* (Vol. 36, February 2008, No. 2, pp. 34)
Pub: Entrepreneur Media Inc.
Ed: Aliza Sherman. **Description:** Women entrepreneurs are said to be mistaken with the belief that they need to display aggression and compete with other women to gain power. Workshops and books address this issue and discuss how women could be alpha entrepreneurs. Recommendations with regard to the topic are explored.

47079 ■ "Women Board Number Stagnates" in *Boston Business Journal* (Vol. 30, November 26, 2010, No. 44, pp. 1)
Pub: Boston Business Journal
Ed: Mary Moore. **Description:** The 2010 data in 'Census of Women Directors and Executive Officers of Massachusetts Public Companies' showed little change in the number of executive officers and board

members in the state's top 100 firms. The data was compiled by Bentley University, The Boston Club, and Mercer. Key information on 2010 Women on Boards is also provided.

47080 ■ *Women Count: A Guide to Changing the World*
Pub: Purdue University Press
Ed: Susan Bulkeley Butler, Bob Keefe. **Released:** August 26, 2010. **Price:** $24.95. **Description:** Throughout history, women have struggled to change the workplace, change government, change society. It's time for women to change the world! Whether on the job, in politics, or in their community, there has never been a better time for women to make a difference in the world.

47081 ■ *Women Entrepreneurs*
Pub: Edward Elgar Publishing, Incorporated
Ed: Andrea Smith-Hunter. **Released:** October 2006. **Price:** $120.00. **Description:** Focus is on women entrepreneurs; information includes human capital, network structures and financial capital, with comparative analysis across racial lines.

47082 ■ "Women and Higher Education" in *Montly Labor Review* (Vol. 133, September 2010, No. 9, pp. 70)
Pub: Bureau of Labor Statistics
Description: The increase in people going to college has been mostly among women. Statistical data included.

47083 ■ *Women-Owned & Home-Based Businesses*
Pub: DIANE Publishing Co.
Ed: Christopher S. Bond. **Released:** 1999. **Price:** $40.00.

47084 ■ "Women of Power" in *Black Enterprise* (Vol. 41, November 2010, No. 4, pp. 94)
Pub: Earl G. Graves Publishing Co. Inc.
Description: Black Enterprise Women of Power Summit will be held February 23-26, 2011 at the Ritz Carlton in Orlando, Florida. Speakers will offer insight into career, household, and life in general.

47085 ■ "Women of Power Summit" in *Black Enterprise* (Vol. 38, February 2008, No. 7, pp. 163)
Pub: Earl G. Graves Publishing Co. Inc.
Description: Third annual Women of Power Summit, hosted by State Farm, will host over 700 executive women of color offering empowerment sessions, tips for networking, along with entertainment.

47086 ■ "Women: Send Me An Angel" in *Entrepreneur* (Vol. 35, October 2007, No. 10, pp. 38)
Pub: Entrepreneur Media Inc.
Ed: Aliza Sherman. **Description:** Golden Seeds has invested in Enter Artemis Woman LLC when the latter decided to put its products into Wal-Mart. Golden Seeds was formed by angel investors who aim to help women build their own businesses. Tips on how to approach angel investors and getting angel funding are given.

47087 ■ "Women's Union Leadership: Closing the Gender Gap" in *WorkingUSA* (Vol. 11, December 2008, No. 4, pp. 459)
Pub: Blackwell Publishers Ltd.
Ed: Michelle Kaminski, Elaine K. Yakura. **Description:** Women make up 44 percent of the labor movement, but a smaller percentage of union leaders. The importance of having a leadership representative of membership, some differences between male and female leadership, and why the labor movement needs more women leaders is discussed.

47088 ■ "Work Together" in *Entrepreneur* (Vol. 35, November 2007, No. 11, pp. 34)
Pub: Entrepreneur Media Inc.
Ed: Aliza Sherman. **Description:** Marsha Firestone founded Women Presidents' Organization, creating small groups of women who head their own busi-

nesses. The idea was for each chapter of the organization to have businesswomen share experiences to help others learn from running their own business.

47089 ■ "The Workplace Generation Gaps" in Women In Business (Vol. 62, June 2010, No. 2, pp. 8)
Pub: American Business Women's Association
Ed: Leigh Elmore. **Description:** Generation gaps among baby boomers, Generation X and Generation Y in the workplace are attributed to technological divides and differences in opinions. These factors could lead to workplace misunderstandings, employee turnover and communication difficulties. Details on managing such workplace gaps are discussed.

47090 ■ "Wowing Her Customers" in Women In Business (Vol. 61, August-September 2009, No. 4, pp. 34)
Pub: American Business Women's Association
Ed: Kathleen Leighton. **Description:** Gail Worth, together with her brother, bought her parents' Harley-Davidson motorcycle dealership in Grandview, Missouri. She eventually had the dealership to herself when her brother broke out of the partnership. Gail says she is comfortable in a man's world kind of business and has expanded the business with a 10-acre site.

TRADE PERIODICALS

47091 ■ Business Woman Magazine
Pub: Business and Professional Women/USA
Contact: Ayoka Blandford, Dir. of Communication
E-mail: ablandford@bpwfoundation.org
Released: 3/yr. **Price:** $30; $35 two years. **Description:** Magazine for working women that promotes workplace equity issues.

47092 ■ CWC Communicator
Pub: California Women's Caucus
Ed: Dr. Pat Nellor Wickwire, Editor. **Released:** 2-4/year. **Price:** $15, Included in membership. **Description:** Discusses issues affecting women, particularly regarding careers and especially women in counseling careers. Recurring features include news of research, a calendar of events, news of educational opportunities, and notices of publications available.

47093 ■ The Facilitator
Pub: Nurre Ink
Contact: Susan M. Nurre, Editor & Publisher
E-mail: snurre@thefacilitator.com
Released: Quarterly. **Price:** $35, U.S.; $35, institutions; $40, out of country. **Description:** Provides articles written by facilitators that are designed to link facilitators from around the world in a forum of sharing, networking, and communicating. Includes updates on training, automated meeting tools, and resources. Recurring features include tips and techniques, a calendar of events, reports of meetings, news of educational opportunities, book reviews, and notices of publications available.

47094 ■ Multicultural Marketing News
Pub: Multicultural Marketing Resources Inc.
Contact: Lisa Skriloff, Editor-in-Chief
Released: Bimonthly. **Price:** $1050 for Multicultural Marketing News only; $250 for MMN Online only. **Description:** Covers minority- and women-owned businesses and corporations that sell to them. Provides story ideas, diverse resources for journalists, and contacts for marketing executives. Recurring features include a calendar of events, business profiles, and a feature on a trend in multicultural marketing.

47095 ■ Women in Business
Pub: The ABWA Company Inc.
Contact: Cynthia Bell, Business Devel. managing editorager
E-mail: cbell@abwa.org
Released: Bimonthly. **Price:** $32 nonmembers. **Description:** Women's business magazine.

47096 ■ Women Chemists
Pub: American Chemical Society
Ed: Teri Quinn Gray, Editor. **Released:** Semiannual. **Description:** Aims "to be leaders in attracting, developing, and promoting women in the chemical sciences." Reports on women's achievements in the chemical sciences, as well as grants available, symposiums, and current events.

VIDEOCASSETTES/ AUDIOCASSETTES

47097 ■ American Institute of Small Business: Women in Business
American Institute of Small Business (AISB)
23075 Highway 7, Ste. 200
Shorewood, MN 55331
Ph:(952)545-7001
Free: 800-328-2906
Fax:(952)545-7020
Co. E-mail: judy@aisb.biz
URL: http://www.pfa.com/AISB.htm
Released: 199?. **Price:** $69.95. **Description:** Female small business owners discuss success, overcoming stereotypes, obtaining financing, and other issues. **Availability:** VHS.

47098 ■ Change Your Mind: Inner Training for Women in Business
American Bar Association
321 N. Clark St.
Chicago, IL 60654-7598
Ph:(312)988-5000
Free: 800-285-2221
Fax:(312)988-5494
Co. E-mail: abapubed@abanet.org
URL: http://www.abanet.org/publiced/
Released: 1988. **Price:** $495.00. **Description:** Dr. Kay Porter and Judy Foster give steps that will help women become better and more confident in the business world. **Availability:** VHS.

47099 ■ Enterprising Women
American Bar Association
321 N. Clark St.
Chicago, IL 60654-7598
Ph:(312)988-5000
Free: 800-285-2221
Fax:(312)988-5494
Co. E-mail: abapubed@abanet.org
URL: http://www.abanet.org/publiced/
Released: 1989. **Price:** $395.00. **Description:** Profiles of five different businesses and the women who run them. **Availability:** VHS; 3/4U.

47100 ■ Inc. Magazine Business Success Programs
Cambridge Educational
c/o Films Media Group
132 West 31st Street, 17th Floor
Ste. 124
New York, NY 10001
Free: 800-257-5126
Fax:(609)671-0266
Co. E-mail: custserve@films.com
URL: http://www.cambridgeol.com
Released: 1987. **Price:** $99.95. **Description:** These four programs contain a step-by-step explanation of what must be done to succeed in business. **Availability:** VHS; CC.

47101 ■ Special Issues for Women Entrepreneurs
Instructional Video
2219 C St.
Lincoln, NE 68502
Ph:(402)475-6570
Free: 800-228-0164
Fax:(402)475-6500
Co. E-mail: feedback@insvideo.com
URL: http://www.insvideo.com
Price: $89.95. **Description:** Contains panel discussion on the problems women face when starting and running their own business. Includes insight from honored women entrepreneurs. **Availability:** VHS.

47102 ■ Time Management for Women
Instructional Video
2219 C St.
Lincoln, NE 68502
Ph:(402)475-6570
Free: 800-228-0164
Fax:(402)475-6500
Co. E-mail: feedback@insvideo.com
URL: http://www.insvideo.com
Price: $79.95. **Description:** Kay Cronkite Waldo offers time management training for women, focusing on behavior patterns, energy cycles, efficiency vs. effectiveness, time wasters, decision-making factors, and the superwoman theory. **Availability:** VHS.

47103 ■ Woman Entrepreneur: Do You Have What it Takes?
Cambridge Educational
c/o Films Media Group
132 West 31st Street, 17th Floor
Ste. 124
New York, NY 10001
Free: 800-257-5126
Fax:(609)671-0266
Co. E-mail: custserve@films.com
URL: http://www.cambridgeol.com
Released: 1987. **Price:** $29.95. **Description:** A motivational look at starting a business for women, featuring interviews with a half-dozen women who have made it. **Availability:** VHS.

TRADE SHOWS AND CONVENTIONS

47104 ■ Annual NAIW Convention - National Association of Insurance Women International
National Association of Insurance Women International
9343 E. 95th Ct. S.
Tulsa, OK 74133
Ph:(918)294-3700
Free: 800-766-6249
Fax:(918)743-1968
Co. E-mail: joinnaiw@naiw.org
URL: http://www.naiw.org
Released: Annual. **Principal Exhibits:** Equipment, supplies, and services for insurance industry professionals. **Dates and Locations:** 2011 Jun 05-08, Flamingo, NV.

CONSULTANTS

47105 ■ Association of Home-Based Women Entrepreneurs
PO Box 31561
Saint Louis, MO 63131-1561
Ph:(314)805-9519
Fax:(314)909-8179
Co. E-mail: aschaefer@advbizsol.com
URL: http://www.hbwe.org
Contact: Sue Lunnemann, Treasurer
E-mail: sue@atssl-solutions.biz
Scope: Organization dedicated to women working from home-based offices. Focuses on the needs and interests of women doing their own business. It also focuses on business-related programs and issues, networking, leads and mentoring for professional growth in a dynamic and friendly atmosphere. **Publications:** "Taking Your Business International"; "Dressing For Success"; "Web 2.0 The Future of the Internet"; "Assertiveness Skills for Women in Business". **Seminars:** Making Connections, Jul, 2008; One Inch Wide, One Mile Deep, Jun, 2008; Accelerating Your Business, May, 2008; Change is Good, Apr, 2008; Pyro Marketing, Jan, 2007; Twenty Five Key Steps To Maintaining A Successful Home-Based Business, Nov, 2006.

47106 ■ Donna Cornell Enterprises Inc.
68 N Plank Rd., Ste. 204
Newburgh, NY 12550-2122
Ph:(845)565-0088
Free: 888-769-3792

Fax:(845)565-0084
Co. E-mail: rc@cornellcareercenter.com
Contact: Donna Cornell, President
E-mail: rc@cornellcareercenter.com
Scope: Offers services in career consultant, professional search, job placement and national professional search. **Publications:** "The Power of the Woman Within"; "Juggling it All!"; "Journey: A Woman's Guide to Success"; "Shatter the Traditions".

47107 ■ Joel Greenstein & Associates
6212 Nethercombe Ct.
McLean, VA 22101
Ph:(703)893-1888
Co. E-mail: jgreenstein@contractmasters.com
Contact: Joel Greenstein, Principle
E-mail: jgreenstein@contractmasters.com
Scope: Provides services to minority and women-owned businesses and government agencies. Specializes in interpreting federal, agency-specific acquisition regulations and contract terms and conditions. Offers assistance with preparing technical, cost proposals and sealed bids.

COMPUTERIZED DATABASES

47108 ■ *National Directory of Woman-Owned Business Firms*
Business Research Services Inc.
7720 Wisconsin Ave., Ste. 213
Bethesda, MD 20814
Ph:(301)229-5561
Free: 800-845-8420
Fax:(301)229-6133
Co. E-mail: brspubs@sba8a.com
URL: http://www.sba8a.com
Description: Contains information on more than 30,000 woman-owned businesses in the United States. Provides name, address, telephone number, name and title of contact, minority group, certification status, date founded, number of employees, description of products or services, U.S. Standard Industrial Classification (SIC) codes, sales volume, government contracting experience, and references. Regional subsets and custom databases also available. Corresponds to the *National Directory of Woman-Owned Business Firms.* **Availability:** CD-ROM: Business

Research Services Inc; Diskette: Business Research Services Inc;Batch: Business Research Services Inc.
Type: Directory.

RESEARCH CENTERS

47109 ■ HEC Montreal–Group for Women, Management and Organizations–Groupe Femmes, Gestion et Entreprises
3000 Chemin de la Cote-Sainte-Catherine
Montreal, QC, Canada H3T 2A7
Ph:(514)340-6015
Fax:(514)340-3825
Co. E-mail: louise.st-cyr@hec.ca
URL: http://neumann.hec.ca/groupefge/
Contact: Louise St-Cyr, Dir.
E-mail: louise.st-cyr@hec.ca
Scope: Women in a changing world: sources, development and practices of leadership; women entrepreneurs: characteristics, motivations, management practices and access to financing; women's succession; and reconciling family and career. **Publications:** Research. **Educational Activities:** Conference.

ASSOCIATIONS AND OTHER ORGANIZATIONS

47110 ■ National Safety Council
1121 Spring Lake Dr.
Itasca, IL 60143-3201
Ph:(630)285-1121
Free: 800-621-7615
Fax:(630)285-1315
Co. E-mail: info@nsc.org
URL: http://www.nsc.org
Contact: Janet P. Froetscher, Pres./CEO
Description: Promotes injury reduction by providing a forum for the exchange of safety and health ideas, techniques, and experiences and the discussion of injury prevention methods. Offers courses in first aid, occupational safety and traffic safety. Maintains extensive library on health and safety subjects. **Publications:** *Family Safety and Health* (quarterly); *Safety and Health* (monthly).

47111 ■ National Safety Management Society
PO Box 4460
Walnut Creek, CA 94596-0460
Free: 800-321-2910
Co. E-mail: nsmsinc@yahoo.com
URL: http://www.nsms.us
Contact: Roosevelt Smith, Pres.
Description: Individuals with managerial responsibilities related to safety/loss control management, including professionals in the fields of education, medicine, computer technology, security, personnel, law, and other disciplines. Advances new concepts of accident prevention and loss control and promotes the role of safety management in the total management effort. Advises concentration in areas where a favorable cost/benefit return can be achieved with these new concepts while being cognizant of humanitarian considerations. Participates in local, state, and regional safety conferences; conducts regional management improvement and executive safety training seminars. **Publications:** *Journal of Safety Management* (quarterly); *NSMS Digest* (monthly).

47112 ■ Voluntary Protection Programs Participants' Association
7600-E Leesburg Pike, Ste. 100
Falls Church, VA 22043
Ph:(703)761-1146
Fax:(703)761-1148
Co. E-mail: administration@vpppa.org
URL: http://www.vpppa.org
Contact: R. Davis Layne, Exec. Dir.
Description: Companies participating in Voluntary Protection Programs and other workplace environmental protection, health, and safety programs. Promotes cooperation between labor, management, and government agencies to insure safe and environmentally sustainable workplaces. Works closely with federal environmental and safety agencies to develop and implement cooperative programs; provides information on environmental health and workplace safety to congressional committees considering legislation. **Publications:** *On the Wire* (bimonthly); *Safety News Network* (biweekly); *Washington Update* (monthly).

EDUCATIONAL PROGRAMS

47113 ■ The Essentials of OSHA Compliance
Seminar Information Service, Inc.
20 Executive Park, Ste. 120
Irvine, CA 92614
Ph:(949)261-9104
Free: 877-SEM-INFO
Fax:(949)261-1963
Co. E-mail: info@seminarinformation.com
URL: http://www.seminarinformation.com
Price: $299.00. **Description:** A comprehensive update on changes in OSHA rules and guidelines and more. **Locations:** Concord, CA; Sacramento, CA; Little Rock, AR; and Dallas, TX.

47114 ■ OSHA 30-Hour Compliance Course
Fred Pryor Seminars & CareerTrack
5700 Broadmoor St., Ste. 300
Mission, KS 66202
Free: 800-780-8476
Fax:(913)967-8849
Co. E-mail: customerservice@pryor.com
URL: http://www.pryor.com
Price: $1,999.00; $1,099.00 for groups of 3 or more. **Description:** A practical, handson experience you need to pinpoint hidden or overlooked safety and health issues, address them, and become fully compliant with OSHA's general industry standards. **Locations:** Cities throughout the United States.

47115 ■ OSHA Compliance
Fred Pryor Seminars & CareerTrack
5700 Broadmoor St., Ste. 300
Mission, KS 66202
Free: 800-780-8476
Fax:(913)967-8849
Co. E-mail: customerservice@pryor.com
URL: http://www.pryor.com
Price: $199.00; $189.00 for groups of 5 or more. **Description:** Learn cost effective methods for getting your organization into compliance, how to expand the effectiveness of your safety training program, learn how to keep records required by OSHA, and how to assess your organization for a variety of hazards. **Locations:** Cities throughout the United States.

47116 ■ OSHA Compliance and Training for Medical and Dental 2010
Seminar Information Service, Inc.
20 Executive Park, Ste. 120
Irvine, CA 92614
Ph:(949)261-9104
Free: 877-SEM-INFO
Fax:(949)261-1963
Co. E-mail: info@seminarinformation.com
URL: http://www.seminarinformation.com
Price: $319.00. **Description:** Covers everything you need to ensure compliance with all OSHA standards and requirements. **Locations:** Cities throughout the United States.

47117 ■ OSHA Compliance & Workplace Safety
Seminar Information Service, Inc.
20 Executive Park, Ste. 120
Irvine, CA 92614
Ph:(949)261-9104
Free: 877-SEM-INFO
Fax:(949)261-1963
Co. E-mail: info@seminarinformation.com
URL: http://www.seminarinformation.com
Price: $199.00. **Description:** Comprehensive update in OSHA's ever-changing requirements and innovative methods other organizations are successfully using to meet these stringent standards. **Locations:** Cities throughout the United States.

REFERENCE WORKS

47118 ■ "BC Forest Safety Council Unveils Supervisor Course to Respond to Industry Demands" in *Canadian Corporate News* (May 14, 2007)
Pub: Comtex News Network Inc.
Description: BC Forest Safety Council launched the sector's first supervisor training program that will lead to certification of forest supervisors in response to an industry-wide demand for standardized safety training for supervisors

47119 ■ "Be Safe: CSE Requires a Series of Steps" in *Contractor* (Vol. 56, October 2009, No. 10, pp. 40)
Pub: Penton Media, Inc.
Ed: Dave Yates. **Description:** Confined Space Entry claims 91 lives each year and plumbers can prevent this by following several steps starting with the use of a four-gas analyzer which costs $1,262. It measures oxygen levels, as well as combustible gases, carbon monoxide, and hydrogen sulfide.

47120 ■ "Blast Blame" in *The Business Journal-Milwaukee* (Vol. 25, September 5, 2008, No. 50, pp. 1)
Pub: American City Business Journals, Inc.
Description: Rexnord Industries LLC and J.M. Brennan Inc.'s property damage trial in connection with the explosion at the Falk Corp. plant in Menomonee Valley, Wisconsin is set to begin. Lawyers for the two companies have failed to reach a settlement. A leaking propane line was seen as the cause of the blast.

47121 ■ "Businesses Keep a Watchful Eye on Worker's Comp" in *The Business Journal-Serving Greater Tampa Bay* (September 5, 2008)
Pub: American City Business Journals, Inc.
Ed: Jane Meinhardt. **Description:** Pending a ruling from the Florida Supreme Court that could uphold the 2003 changes on workers' compensation law, the outcome would include restrictions on claimant attorneys' fees and allow the competitive workers' compensation insurance rates to remain low. However, insurance rates are expected to go up if the court overturns the changes.

47122 ■ "Connectors for Space, Mil/Aero and Medical Applications" in *Canadian Electronics* (Vol. 23, June-July 2008, No. 4, pp. 13)
Pub: Action Communication Inc.
Ed: Gilles Parguey. **Description:** Product information on electrical connectors for use in space, military, aeronautics, and medical applications is provided. These connectors are built to withstand the extreme conditions offered by the harsh working environments in those applications.

47123 ■ "CSE: Contractors Are Always Responsible" in *Contractor* (Vol. 56, November 2009, No. 11, pp. 34)
Pub: Penton Media, Inc.
Ed: Dave Yates. **Description:** Plumbing contractors should purchase a long snorkel hose, a tripod with manual-crank hoist, and a sump pump in order to prevent accidents associated with Confined Space Entry. Liability issues surrounding confined space entry prevention and accidents are discussed.

47124 ■ "Don't Fall Foul of Farming's Workplace Killer" in *Farmer's Weekly* (March 28, 2008, No. 320)
Pub: Reed Business Information
Description: Discusses the Work at Height Regulations that were introduced to reduce the risk of injury and death caused by accidental falls in the workplace.

47125 ■ "Employers See Workers' Comp Rates Rising" in *Sacramento Business Journal* (Vol. 28, April 8, 2011, No. 6, pp. 1)
Pub: Sacramento Business Journal
Ed: Kelly Johnson. **Description:** Employers in California are facing higher workers compensation costs. Increased medical costs and litigation are seen to drive the trend.

47126 ■ "Employers Waking Up to Effects of Workers' Sleep Problems" in *Crain's Cleveland Business* (Vol. 28, December 3, 2007, No. 48, pp. 18)
Pub: Crain Communications, Inc.
Ed: Jennifer Keirn. **Description:** Employers are beginning to realize that poor sleep quality can impact their bottom lines with higher health care costs and more lost-time accidents. The National Institutes of Health estimates that sleep deprivation, sleep disorders and excessive daytime sleepiness add about $15 billion to our national health care bill and cost employers $50 billion in lost productivity.

47127 ■ *Enabling Environments for Jobs and Entrepreneurship: The Role of Policy and Law in Small Enterprise Employment*
Pub: International Labour Office
Ed: Gerhard Reinecke. **Released:** February 2004. **Price:** $83.25. **Description:** National policies, laws and regulations governing workplace safety.

47128 ■ "Fewer People Dying At Work" in *Sacramento Business Journal* (Vol. 25, August 29, 2008, No. 26, pp. 1)
Pub: American City Business Journals, Inc.
Ed: Kathy Robertson. **Description:** Statistics show that workplace deaths in California dropped by 24 percent in 2007 compared with the previous year. Much of the decline was observed in the construction industry, where a slowing economy affected employment and dangerous work. The number of workplace deaths in the state also declined in all major categories except fires and explosions.

47129 ■ "Grace Puma; Senior Vice-President of Strategic Sourcing, United Airlines" in *Crain's Chicago Business* (May 5, 2008)
Pub: Crain Communications, Inc.
Ed: John Rosenthal. **Description:** Profile of Grace Puma who is the senior vice-president of strategic sourcing at United Airlines and is responsible for cutting costs at the company in a number of ways including scheduling safety inspections at the same time as routine maintenance, thereby reducing the downtime of each aircraft by five days as well as replacing a third of her staff with outside talent.

47130 ■ "Hot For All The Wrong Reasons" in *Canadian Business* (Vol. 81, March 31, 2008, No. 5, pp. 19)
Pub: Rogers Media
Ed: Andrea Jezovit. **Description:** Soaring platinum prices are due to South Africa's platinum mining industry's safety issues and power supply disruptions that exacerbate the metal's supply problems. South Africa supplies 80 percent of the world's platinum. South Africa's power utility has said that it cannot guarantee the industry's power needs until 2013.

47131 ■ "Huberman Failing to Keep CTA on Track" in *Crain's Chicago Business* (Vol. 31, April 21, 2008, No. 16, pp. 22)
Pub: Crain Communications, Inc.
Description: Discusses the deplorable service of CTA, the Chicago Transit Authority, as well as CTA President Ron Huberman who, up until last week had riders hoping he had the management skills necessary to fix the system's problems; Tuesday's event left hundreds of riders trapped for hours and thousands standing on train platforms along the Blue Line waiting for trains that never came.

47132 ■ "Injured Workers Caught in the Middle" in *Sacramento Business Journal* (Vol. 28, June 10, 2011, No. 15, pp. 1)
Pub: Sacramento Business Journal
Ed: Kelly Johnson. **Description:** A bill that would extend the cap on disability payments to nearly five years is in the works, but employers and insurance companies fear it would increase their costs. Proponents of the bill say, however, that it would correct unfairness suffered by the employees. Features of the bill are discussed as well as its effects on both parties and the State of California.

47133 ■ *Law for the Small and Growing Business*
Pub: Jordans Publishing Limited
Ed: P. Bohm. **Released:** February 2007. **Price:** $59.98. **Description:** Legal and regulatory issues facing small businesses, including employment law, health and safety, commercial property, company law and finance are covered.

47134 ■ "Marine Act Amendments Gain Parliamentary Approval" in *Canadian Sailings* (July 7, 2008)
Pub: Commonwealth Business Media
Ed: Alex Binkley. **Description:** Changes to the Canada Marine Act provides better borrowing deals as well as an ability to tap into federal infrastructure funding for environmental protection measures, security improvements and other site enhancements.

47135 ■ *National Directory of Safety Consultants*
Pub: American Society of Safety Engineers
Contact: Fred Fortman, Exec. Dir.
E-mail: ffortman@asse.org
Released: latest edition 18th ed. **Price:** Free. **Covers:** Over 2,000 occupational health and safety consultants who are members of the society's consultants division. **Entries Include:** Name, office address and phone, highest degree held, areas of occupational specialization, memberships, licenses and registrations held. **Arrangement:** Alphabetical. **Indexes:** Geographical, area of expertise.

47136 ■ "Omniplex on the Case" in *Black Enterprise* (Vol. 37, December 2006, No. 5, pp. 38)
Pub: Earl G. Graves Publishing Co. Inc.
Ed: Glenn Townes. **Description:** Office of Personnel Management in Washington D.C. recently awarded a service contract to Omniplex World Services Corp. Virginia-based, The Chantilly, will perform security investigations and background checks on current and prospective federal employees and military personnel and contractors.

47137 ■ "The One Thing That's Holding Back Your Wellness Program" in *Employee Benefit News* (Vol. 25, December 1, 2011, No. 15, pp. 8)
Pub: SourceMedia Inc.
Ed: Kelley M. Butler. **Description:** A 13-year study shows that women who sat for more than six hours a

day were 94 percent more likely to die during the study period. Most women sit at their desks an average of 7.7 hours while at work.

47138 ■ "OSHA Proposes Historic Safety Penalty on BP" in *Workforce Management* (Vol. 88, November 16, 2009, No. 12, pp. 8)
Pub: Crain Communications, Inc.
Ed: Mark Schoeff Jr. **Description:** Labor Secretary Hilda Solis has warned that she aims to toughen the enforcement of workplace laws; OSHA, the Occupational Safety and Health Administration, an agency within the Department of Labor, is penalizing BP Products North America Inc. for their failure to improve workplace safety.

47139 ■ "The Price of Citizenship" in *Canadian Business* (Vol. 79, August 14, 2006, No. 16-17, pp. 13)
Pub: Rogers Media
Ed: Jack Mintz. **Description:** Safety and insurance benefits provided by the Canadian government to Canadian passport holders returning from Lebanon, is discussed.

47140 ■ "Project Managers' Creed: Learn It, Live It" in *Contractor* (Vol. 56, November 2009, No. 11, pp. 46)
Pub: Penton Media, Inc.
Ed: Kent Craig. **Description:** Project managers should take the health and safety of their subordinates above all else. A manager should deal with the things that distract him from his job before starting a day on the site. The manager should maintain a comfortable and relaxed attitude with his employees.

47141 ■ *Small Businesses and Workplace Fatality Risk: An Exploratory Analysis*
Pub: RAND Corporation
Ed: John F. Mendelhoff; Christopher Nelson; Kilkon Ko. **Released:** June 2006. **Price:** $20.00. **Description:** According to previous research, small business worksites report higher rates of deaths or serious injuries than larger corporations. Statistical data included.

47142 ■ "Solar Hot Water Sales Are Hot, Hot, Hot" in *Contractor* (Vol. 56, December 2009, No. 12, pp. 22)
Pub: Penton Media, Inc.
Ed: Dave Yates. **Description:** Plumbing contractors in the United States can benefit from the increased sales of solar thermal water systems. Licensed plumbers have the base knowledge on the risks associated from heating and storing water. Safety issues associated with solar water heaters are also included.

47143 ■ "United's Next Hurdle: Costly Repairs" in *Crain's Chicago Business* (Vol. 31, April 14, 2008, No. 15, pp. 1)
Pub: Crain Communications, Inc.
Ed: John Pletz. **Description:** Discusses the recent crackdown by aviation regulators concerning airline safety at United Airlines as well as other carriers. Maintenance costs at United for the upkeep on the company's older planes is severely affecting its bottom line which is already sagging under heavy fuel costs.

TRADE PERIODICALS

47144 ■ *EHS Today*
Pub: Penton Media Inc.
Released: Monthly. **Price:** Free to qualified subscribers; $72 Canada print only; $50 Canada digital only; $99 other countries print only; $80 other countries digital only. **Description:** Monthly publication for safety professionals featuring information to meet OSHA and EPA compliance requirements, improve management of safety, industrial hygiene and environmental programs and find products and services to protect employees and property.

47145 ■ *Industrial Safety and Hygiene News*
Pub: BNP Media
Contact: Randy Green, Publisher
E-mail: greenr@bnpmedia.com
Released: Monthly. **Price:** $64; $128 two years; $87 Canada; $173 Canada 2 years; $102 other countries; $204 other countries 2 years. **Description:** Magazine

for corporate managers and specialists responsible for employee safety and health, environmental programs, and regulatory compliance.

47146 ■ Inside OSHA

Pub: Inside Washington Publishers
Contact: Bob Cusack, Managing Editor
Released: Biweekly, every other Monday. **Price:** $725, U.S. and Canada; $775, elsewhere. **Description:** Reports on news of the Occupational Safety and Health Administration.

47147 ■ Occupational Health & Safety

Pub: 1105 Media, Inc.
Contact: Laura Swift, Assoc. Ed.
Ed: Jerry Laws, Editor, jlaws@1105media.com. **Released:** Monthly. **Price:** $99. **Description:** Magazine covering federal and state regulation of occupational health and safety.

47148 ■ OSHA Compliance Advisor

Pub: Business & Legal Reports Inc.
Contact: Robert L. Brady, Editor-in-Chief
E-mail: rbrady@blr.com
Released: Semimonthly, 24/year. **Price:** $299.95, individuals. **Description:** Provides information on employee safety issues, Occupational Safety and Health Act (OSHA), programs, accident incidents, and job hazards. Recurring features include columns titled Compliance Report, Federal Register Digest, From the States, Washington Watch, News Roundup.

47149 ■ OSHAWeek

Pub: Stevens Publishing Corp.
Contact: Ralph Jensen, Editor-in-Chief
Ed: Katie Hooten, Editor. **Released:** Weekly, 48/year. **Price:** $399. **Description:** Reports on news and updates on safety issues. Recurring features include news of research and a calendar of events.

47150 ■ Safety Compliance Alert

Pub: Progressive Business Publications
Ed: Rebecca Cavanaugh, Editor, cavanaugh@pbp.com. **Released:** Semimonthly. **Price:** $299, individuals. **Description:** Presents real world examples to help safety professionals avoid accidents and fires, reduce costs, and comply with changing OSHA rules. Recurring features include news of research, a calendar of events, news of educational opportunities, and a column titled Sharpen Your Judgment.

47151 ■ Safety Update

Pub: Ontario Safety League
Contact: Wendy Williams, Ed.Coor.
Ed: Kira Vermond, Editor. **Released:** Quarterly. **Price:** $30. **Description:** Newsletter on the Ontario Safety League's activities and news related to transportation and safety education.

47152 ■ Work & Stress

Pub: Taylor & Francis Group Journals
Contact: Philip Dewe, Assoc. Ed.
Released: Quarterly. **Price:** $558 institutions print and online; $530 institutions online only; $277 print only; $82 society; $337 institutions print and online; $321 institutions online only; $50 society. **Description:** Peer-reviewed journal focusing on psychological, social, organizational aspects of occupational and environmental Health stress and safety Management.

VIDEOCASSETTES/ AUDIOCASSETTES

47153 ■ Accident Investigation: A Tool for Effective Prevention

Learning Communications LLC
5520 Trabuco Rd.
Irvine, CA 92620
Free: 800-622-3610
Fax:(949)727-4323
Co. E-mail: sales@learncom.com
URL: http://www.learncomhr.com
Released: 1992. **Description:** Provides accident investigation techniques for supervisors and managers. Includes Leader's Guide. **Availability:** VHS; 3/4U.

47154 ■ Back Injury Prevention Through Ergonomics

Film Library/National Safety Council California Chapter
4553 Glencoe Ave., Ste. 150
Marina Del Rey, CA 90292
Ph:(310)827-9781
Free: 800-421-9585
Fax:(310)827-9861
Co. E-mail: California@nsc.org
URL: http://www.nsc.org/nsc_near_you/FindYourLocalChapter/Pages/California.aspx
Released: 198?. **Description:** This is a demonstration of how a total ergonomics program can reduce workers' on-the-job injuries. **Availability:** VHS; 3/4U.

47155 ■ Brace Your Space: Earthquake Safety in the Work Environment

AJN Video Library/Lippincott Williams & Wilkins
American Journal of Nursing
345 Hudson St., 16th Fl.
New York, NY 10014
Ph:(212)886-1200
Free: 800-256-4045
Fax:(212)886-1276
Co. E-mail: info@nursingcenter.com
URL: http://www.nursingcenter.com
Released: 1993. **Price:** $150.00. **Description:** Uses earthquake footage from the 1989 Loma Prieta quake to demonstrate the need for seismic safety in the school and business workplace, including the three basic principles of earthquake workplace safety and simple techniques for bracing and securing common office equipment and furnishings. **Availability:** VHS; 3/4U.

47156 ■ CHEMSAFE

Learning Communications LLC
5520 Trabuco Rd.
Irvine, CA 92620
Free: 800-622-3610
Fax:(949)727-4323
Co. E-mail: sales@learncom.com
URL: http://www.learncomhr.com
Released: 1991. **Price:** $175.00. **Description:** A nine-module program designed to help companies comply with OSHA's Hazard Communication Standard. Each module covers a different type of chemical hazard. A leader's guide and participants' handouts are included. **Availability:** VHS; 3/4U.

47157 ■ 80% Preventable (Burn Injury Prevention)

Bergwall Productions, Inc.
1 DIckinson Drive, Brandywine BUilding 5, Ste. 105
PO Box 1481
Chadds Ford, PA 19317
Ph:(610)361-0334
Free: 800-934-8696
Fax:(610)361-0092
URL: http://www.bergwall.com
Released: 1992. **Price:** $99.00. **Description:** Dramatizes what can happen when a lazy and careless worker goofs around once too often. Testimony from a nurse reaffirms the message of the title—that 80% of burn accidents are preventable. **Availability:** VHS.

47158 ■ Electrical Safety in the Lab

Film Library/National Safety Council California Chapter
4553 Glencoe Ave., Ste. 150
Marina Del Rey, CA 90292
Ph:(310)827-9781
Free: 800-421-9585
Fax:(310)827-9861
Co. E-mail: California@nsc.org
URL: http://www.nsc.org/nsc_near_you/FindYourLocalChapter/Pages/California.aspx
Released: 1995. **Price:** $99.95. **Description:** Explains how electricity works and its potential hazards. **Availability:** VHS.

47159 ■ Electrical Safety Related Work Practices

Gulf Publishing Co.
PO Box 2608
Houston, TX 77252
Ph:(713)529-4301

Free: 800-231-6275
Fax:(713)520-4433
Co. E-mail: customerservices@gulfpub.com
URL: http://www.gulfpub.com
Released: 1992. **Price:** $1495.00. **Description:** Six-part training program that offers educational material on electrical safety. Centers on the new OSHA requirements for work performed on or near exposed energized and de-energized parts of electrical equipment, the use of electrical protective equipment, and the safe use of electrical equipment. **Availability:** VHS; 3/4U; Special order formats.

47160 ■ Emergency Planning and Crisis Management Series

Gulf Publishing Co.
PO Box 2608
Houston, TX 77252
Ph:(713)529-4301
Free: 800-231-6275
Fax:(713)520-4433
Co. E-mail: customerservices@gulfpub.com
URL: http://www.gulfpub.com
Released: 1992. **Price:** $995.00. **Description:** Three-part vocational series that helps facilities develop an emergency plan and provide for employee training regarding this plan. Comes with detailed leader's guide. **Availability:** VHS; 3/4U.

47161 ■ ErgoKinetics: Safety in Motion

Aspen Publishers
7201 McKinney Circ.
Frederick, MD 21704
Ph:(301)698-7100
Free: 800-234-1660
Fax:800-901-9075
URL: http://www.aspenpublishers.com
Released: 1994. **Description:** Training program that offers ergonomic solutions for preventing three of the most common types of complaints in the workplace: back and neck injuries; hand, wrist, and arm injuries; and VDT-related visual problems. Contains two separate modules: one for the plant and one for the office. Comes with leader's guide and participants' workbooks. **Availability:** VHS.

47162 ■ Ergonomics: Low-Cost, Common-Sense Training Solutions

Learning Communications LLC
5520 Trabuco Rd.
Irvine, CA 92620
Free: 800-622-3610
Fax:(949)727-4323
Co. E-mail: sales@learncom.com
URL: http://www.learncomhr.com
Released: 1991. **Description:** A 3-tape guide to reducing cumulative trauma disorders (also known as repetitive motion illnesses), reduce stress, and increase productivity—all without costly engineering controls or job redesigns. A set of three tapes, complete with Leader's Guides and Participant Workbooks. **Availability:** VHS; 3/4U.

47163 ■ Ergonomics at Work

Film Library/National Safety Council California Chapter
4553 Glencoe Ave., Ste. 150
Marina Del Rey, CA 90292
Ph:(310)827-9781
Free: 800-421-9585
Fax:(310)827-9861
Co. E-mail: California@nsc.org
URL: http://www.nsc.org/nsc_near_you/FindYourLocalChapter/Pages/California.aspx
Released: 198?. **Description:** This tape looks at how ergonomics can aid in creating safer working conditions. **Availability:** VHS; 3/4U.

47164 ■ Explosives

Learning Communications LLC
5520 Trabuco Rd.
Irvine, CA 92620
Free: 800-622-3610

Workplace Safety ■ 47181

Fax:(949)727-4323
Co. E-mail: sales@learncom.com
URL: http://www.learncomhr.com
Price: $395.00. **Description:** Employees learn how to prevent accidental fires and explosions while working around highly combustible materials. Includes a trainer's manual and ten handbooks. **Availability:** VHS; 8mm; 3/4U; CC.

47165 ■ The Extra Step
Cambridge Educational
c/o Films Media Group
132 West 31st Street, 17th Floor
Ste. 124
New York, NY 10001
Free: 800-257-5126
Fax:(609)671-0266
Co. E-mail: custserve@films.com
URL: http://www.cambridgeol.com
Price: $445.00. **Description:** A program for both new and veteran employees about the potential danger in handling and working around chemicals. Emphasizes the need for proper safety attitudes and the importance of personal protection from chemical hazards. **Availability:** VHS; 3/4U; Special order formats.

47166 ■ Facts about OSHA Inspections
Film Library/National Safety Council California Chapter
4553 Glencoe Ave., Ste. 150
Marina Del Rey, CA 90292
Ph:(310)827-9781
Free: 800-421-9585
Fax:(310)827-9861
Co. E-mail: California@nsc.org
URL: http://www.nsc.org/nsc_near_you/FindYourLocalChapter/Pages/California.aspx
Released: 1995. **Price:** $195.00. **Description:** Explains compliance procedures for conducting OSHA inspections. Aids workers, supervisors and managers to improve the workplace in order to avoid fines, penalties and citations. **Availability:** VHS.

47167 ■ First Aid on the Job
Audio Graphics Training Systems
301 West Broome St., Suite 100
Lagrange, GA 30240
Ph:(404)507-2487
Free: 800-814-9792
Fax:(706)883-7136
Co. E-mail: customerservice@agts-web.com
URL: http://www.agts-web.com
Released: 199?. **Price:** $395.00. **Description:** Covers when and how to move a victim, stopping bleeding, symptoms of shock and prevention, and bloodborne precautions. **Availability:** VHS.

47168 ■ Foreman's Accident Protection Series
Gulf Publishing Co.
PO Box 2608
Houston, TX 77252
Ph:(713)529-4301
Free: 800-231-6275
Fax:(713)520-4433
Co. E-mail: customerservices@gulfpub.com
URL: http://www.gulfpub.com
Released: 1988. **Price:** $375.00. **Description:** An 11-tape series on setting up an effective industrial safety program. **Availability:** VHS; 3/4U.

47169 ■ Handle with Care
Bergwall Productions, Inc.
1 DIckinson Drive, Brandywine BUilding 5, Ste. 105
PO Box 1481
Chadds Ford, PA 19317
Ph:(610)361-0334
Free: 800-934-8696
Fax:(610)361-0092
URL: http://www.bergwall.com
Released: 1992. **Price:** $99.00. **Description:** Short story segments dramatize dangerous situations a variety of people can find themselves in on any given day. Impacts viewers in a more direct way than many lectures devoted to safety. **Availability:** VHS.

47170 ■ The Hazard Awareness Training Series
Genium Group Inc.
79 The Mall
PO Box 46
Amsterdam, NY 12010
Ph:(518)842-4111
Free: 877-284-1963
Fax:(518)842-1843
Co. E-mail: info@genium.com
URL: http://www.genium.com
Released: 1989. **Price:** $534.00. **Description:** OSHA laws, how to read and label material safety data sheets, and other industrial health threats are covered in this series. **Availability:** VHS; 3/4U.

47171 ■ Identifying the UN/DOT Hazard Classes: Labels and Placards (Revised)
American Media, Inc.
4621 121st St.
Urbandale, IA 50323-2311
Ph:(515)224-0919
Free: 888-776-8268
Fax:(515)327-2555
Co. E-mail: custsvc@ammedia.com
URL: http://www.ammedia.com
Released: 1992. **Price:** $175.00. **Description:** Helps workers identify hazardous materials with labels and placards. Highlights information on hazard classes, containers, packaging, and emergency information resources. Includes an instructor's guide, discussion questions, a quiz, and a study guide. A discount is available to those who trade-in the original version. **Availability:** VHS.

47172 ■ Industrial Safety
Agency for Instructional Technology (AIT)
1800 N. Stonelake Dr.
Box A
Bloomington, IN 47402-0120
Ph:(812)339-2203
Free: 800-457-4509
Fax:(812)333-4218
Co. E-mail: info@ait.net
URL: http://www.ait.net
Released: 1986. **Price:** $1095.00. **Description:** A series of ten programs about things that can be done to make the workplace safer. **Availability:** VHS; 3/4U.

47173 ■ Making It Better: How Everyone Can Create a Safer Workplace
Learning Communications LLC
5520 Trabuco Rd.
Irvine, CA 92620
Free: 800-622-3610
Fax:(949)727-4323
Co. E-mail: sales@learncom.com
URL: http://www.learncomhr.com
Price: $295.00. **Description:** Shows examples of safety measures created and implemented by employees. Encourages employees to take an active role in workplace safety. Includes leader guide and 10 workbooks. **Availability:** VHS; 3/4U; 8mm.

47174 ■ The Man from OSHA
Film Library/National Safety Council California Chapter
4553 Glencoe Ave., Ste. 150
Marina Del Rey, CA 90292
Ph:(310)827-9781
Free: 800-421-9585
Fax:(310)827-9861
Co. E-mail: California@nsc.org
URL: http://www.nsc.org/nsc_near_you/FindYourLocalChapter/Pages/California.aspx
Released: 198?. **Description:** This is an explanation of the OSHA program and what an OSHA inspector does. **Availability:** VHS; 3/4U.

47175 ■ Office Safety and Workplace Ergonomics
Gulf Publishing Co.
PO Box 2608
Houston, TX 77252
Ph:(713)529-4301
Free: 800-231-6275

Fax:(713)520-4433
Co. E-mail: customerservices@gulfpub.com
URL: http://www.gulfpub.com
Released: 1992. **Price:** $495.00. **Description:** Training program that centers on ways of fostering awareness among office employees regarding safety in the office. **Availability:** VHS; 3/4U.

47176 ■ OSHA Confined Space Entry
Williams Learning Network
15400 Calhoun Dr.
Rockville, MD 20855-2762
Fax:(301)315-6880
Co. E-mail: mait@willearn.com
URL: http://www.willearn.com
Released: 1993. **Description:** Outlines OSHA regulations for permit required confined spaces covering such topics as isolating, testing, and preparing permit spaces; properly equipping workers; maintaining entry conditions and employee duties. Includes Leader's Guide and 25 Program Guides. **Availability:** VHS; 3/4U.

47177 ■ OSHA Electrical Safety for Non-Electrical Workers
Williams Learning Network
15400 Calhoun Dr.
Rockville, MD 20855-2762
Fax:(301)315-6880
Co. E-mail: mait@willearn.com
URL: http://www.willearn.com
Description: Describes basic electrical safety for employees with little or no training. Explains basic properties of electricity, avoidance of electrical hazards, and steps to take in an electrical emergency. Helps meet OSHA 29 CFR 1910.331-335 training requirements. Includes Leader's Guide and 25 Program Guides. **Availability:** VHS; 3/4U.

47178 ■ Right-to-Know: Working Around Hazardous Substances
Learning Communications LLC
5520 Trabuco Rd.
Irvine, CA 92620
Free: 800-622-3610
Fax:(949)727-4323
Co. E-mail: sales@learncom.com
URL: http://www.learncomhr.com
Price: $295.00. **Description:** Employees learn how to properly handle hazardous chemicals to eliminate or minimize accidents. Includes leader's guide and 10 workbooks. **Availability:** VHS; 8mm; 3/4U.

47179 ■ Take Two ... for Safety
DuPont Safety Resources
PO Box 80013
Wilmington, DE 19880-0013
Free: 800-532-7233
Fax:888-644-7233
URL: http://www2.dupont.com/Sustainable_Solutions/en_US/practice_areas/safety_consultants/index.html
Released: 1993. **Description:** A series about industrial safety precautions. **Availability:** VHS; 3/4U.

47180 ■ What's Your Risk?
Gulf Publishing Co.
PO Box 2608
Houston, TX 77252
Ph:(713)529-4301
Free: 800-231-6275
Fax:(713)520-4433
Co. E-mail: customerservices@gulfpub.com
URL: http://www.gulfpub.com
Released: 1991. **Price:** $395.00. **Description:** A look at the three categories of risk infection as defined by OSHA, and the safe work practices and protective equipment necessary to minimize exposure. **Availability:** VHS; 3/4U.

TRADE SHOWS AND CONVENTIONS

47181 ■ Ohio Safety Congress and Expo
Bureau of Workers Compensation
30 W. Spring St.
Columbus, OH 43215-2256
Ph:800-292-4833

Free: 800-644-6292
Fax:877-520-6446
Co. E-mail: ombudsperson@bwc.state.oh.us
URL: http://www.ohiobwc.com
Released: Annual. **Audience:** Occupational safety and health professionals. **Principal Exhibits:** Occupational safety and health equipment, supplies, and services.

47182 ■ Wisconsin Safety and Health Congress/Exposition

Wisconsin Council of Safety, Division WMC Foundation
501 E Washington Ave.
PO Box 352
Madison, WI 53703-2944
Ph:(608)258-3400
Fax:(608)258-3413
URL: http://www.wmc.org
Released: Annual. **Audience:** Safety professionals; executives; local representatives; occupational health and industrial hygiene personnel. **Principal Exhibits:** Safety, health and compliance products/services for industry.

CONSULTANTS

47183 ■ American Forensic Engineers

34 Sammis Ln.
White Plains, NY 10605
Ph:(914)949-5978
Fax:(914)949-0350
Co. E-mail: gusmundel@aol.com
Contact: August B. Mundel, President
E-mail: gusmundel@aol.com
Scope: Provides industrial, safety, and forensic consulting services. Services include relevant engineering studies, sampling, statistical studies, quality and reliability efforts, industrial hygiene, human factors analysis, industrial experimentation, product safety analysis and product liability causes in the electrical, electronic, electro-chemical, chemical, mechanical, and battery industrial areas. Also offers building inspection services. Serves private industries as well as government agencies in the U.S. **Publications:** "Ethics in Quality," Marcell Dekker.

47184 ■ Caliche Ltd.

800 N Shoreline Blvd., Ste. 700N
PO Box 107
Corpus Christi, TX 78401
Ph:(281)356-6038
Free: 800-683-1046
Fax:(281)356-6224
Co. E-mail: calicheltd@calicheltd.com
URL: http://www.calicheltd.com
Contact: Thomas G. Luther Jr., Vice President
E-mail: gerryluther@envirtech.com
Scope: Safety, health and environmental management consulting company. Provides comprehensive environmental services including air, soil and water monitoring and analysis, emission and ventilation studies, asbestos and lead-based paint consulting, environmental site assessments, industrial hygiene and safety audits, indoor air quality and underground storage tank closures. Industries served: all. **Seminars:** How You Can Get the Most of Your Industrial Hygiene Assessment: A Systematic and Comprehensive Approach to Exposure Assessment, Aug, 2007.

47185 ■ Charp Associates Inc.

39 Maple Ave.
Upper Darby, PA 19082-1902
Ph:(610)789-7498
Fax:(610)789-7499
Co. E-mail: charp@seas.upenn.edu
Contact: Solomon Charp, President
Scope: Consulting engineers providing analysis of designs, technical analyses, investigations and reports primarily on electrical, mechanical and electro-mechanical equipment. Experienced in communications equipment, instrumentation and sensing systems, production processes and controls, quality control and performance characteristics, occupational and industrial safety, statistical data processing and equipment, accident reconstruction, failure analysis, and analysis of causes of fires. Also offers consulting in training and development, especially in relation to

the needs and applications of computers in education. Expertise in applications of computers and technology in educational institutions/systems and to commercial suppliers. Industries served: manufacturing and industrial, transportation, occupational safety, legal and insurance industries. **Publications:** "Technological Horizons in Education".

47186 ■ Claymore Engineering

1308 Valle Vista Dr.
Fullerton, CA 92831-1944
Ph:(714)870-4521
Fax:(714)870-7051
Co. E-mail: claymoreengr@cs.com
Contact: Denison W. York, Vice President
Scope: Practice limited to solving air pollution and industrial safety compliance problems. Serves private industries as well as government agencies.

47187 ■ Cocciardi & Associates Inc.

4 Kacey Ct.
Mechanicsburg, PA 17055-5596
Ph:(717)766-4500
Free: 800-377-3024
Fax:(717)766-3999
Co. E-mail: jcocciardi@cocciardi.com
URL: http://www.cocciardi.com
Contact: Rocco DiPietro, Mgr
E-mail: rdipietro@atscocciardi.com
Scope: Firm provides safety, health and environmental consulting and training. It handles such issues as Hazardous Waste Operations and Emergency Response Regulation (HAZWOPER), asbestos and lead training (for licensing requirements), environmental auditing, and health and safety investigations. It serves all industries worldwide. **Publications:** "Terrorism Response Field Guide," Jones and Bartlett, 2003; "Terrorism Response Training Manual," Jones and Bartlett, 2003; "Emergency Response Team Manual," National Fire Protection Association, 2004.

47188 ■ donphin.com Inc.

1001 B Ave., Ste. 200
Coronado, CA 92118
Ph:(619)550-3533
Free: 800-234-3304
Fax:(619)600-0096
Co. E-mail: inquiry@donphin.com
URL: http://www.donphin.com
Contact: Donald A. Phin, CEO
E-mail: don@donphin.com
Scope: Offers a comprehensive approach to understanding and applying a broad range of business principles: legal compliance issues, management concerns, health and safety, customer service, marketing, information management. Industries served: All developing small businesses. **Publications:** "Doing Business Right!"; "HR That Works!"; "Lawsuit Free! How to Prevent Employee Lawsuits"; "Building Powerful Employment Relationships!"; "Victims, Villains and Heroes: Managing Emotions in The Workplace". **Seminars:** Doing Business Right!; HR That Works!; Building Powerful Employment Relationships; Lawsuit Free!.

47189 ■ Environmental Assessment Services Inc.

124 S Main St.
Middletown, OH 45044-4002
Ph:(513)424-3400
Fax:(513)424-2020
Co. E-mail: easdave@aol.com
Contact: David W. Armentrout, President
Scope: Offers environmental and health and safety services in compliance auditing, program management and implementation, field services (monitoring/testing) and real estate assessment.

47190 ■ Environmental Support Network Inc.

5376 Fulton Dr. NW
Canton, OH 44718-1808
Ph:(330)494-0905
Fax:(330)494-1650
Co. E-mail: esn@sssnet.com
Contact: William P. Racine, President
Scope: Provides environmental, health, and safety consulting and project management services. These include compliance auditing and remediation specifications concerning air, groundwater, and soil quality.

Also offers health and safety reviews, asbestos and lead-based paint handling, noise sampling, industrial permitting, and UST management. Industries served: education, finance, industry and government. **Seminars:** Environmental Health and Safety Management in Ohio; Managing Compliance in Ohio; Environmental Site Remediation in Ohio and Surrounding States; Conducting ESAs by ASTM Standards; Health and Safety Management in the Medical Setting; Exposure Monitoring in Schools and Public Buildings.

47191 ■ Error Analysis Inc.

5173 Waring Rd., Ste. 157
San Diego, CA 92120-2705
Ph:(619)464-4427
Fax:(619)464-4992
Co. E-mail: info@erroranalysis.com
URL: http://www.erroranalysis.com
Contact: Cynthia A. Larue, Principle
E-mail: clarue@atserroranalysis.com
Scope: Firm dedicated to research and consulting in the fields of human factors, safety and accident reconstruction. Provides consulting and expert witness services to attorneys, the insurance industry and businesses throughout the world. **Publications:** "Stairway falls: An ergonomics analysis of 80 cases," Professional Safety, 2009; "The practice of forensic human factors/ergonomics and related safety professions," Lawyers & Judges Publishing Company, 2009. **Seminars:** The role of a just culture, American Society of Safety Engineers, Costa Mesa, CA, Jan, 2009; Common trends in slip and falls, Las Vegas, NV, Sep, 2008; Safety; Risk Management; Premises and Product Liability.

47192 ■ Fox Fire Safety Inc.

4605 Lincoln Way E
PO Box 1901
Mishawaka, IN 46544
Ph:(574)258-5479
Free: 800-919-0410
Fax:(574)674-0911
Co. E-mail: ffsinfo@foxfiresafety.com
URL: http://www.foxfiresafety.com
Contact: Robert E. Murray, President
Scope: Provides fire protection and fire suppression needs in a range of systems. Also offers service and installation of fire protection equipment. Serves all industries.

47193 ■ Humanics ErgoSystems Inc.

PO Box 17388
Encino, CA 91416-7388
Ph:(818)345-3746
Fax:(818)705-3903
Co. E-mail: ergonomics@humanics-es.com
URL: http://www.humanics-es.com
Contact: Rani Lueder, Principle
E-mail: rani@humanics-es.com
Scope: Specializes in occupational ergonomics; ergonomic workplace evaluations; ergonomics research; ergonomic seminars and training; psychological and biomechanics testing (EMG, dynamic lumbar motion, strength assessment, nerve conduction); product evaluations; compliance with ergonomic standards; and expert witnessing. **Publications:** "The Future of Ergonomics in Children's Education," IEA 2009; "Ergonomics for Children; designing products and places for toddlers to teens," 2007; "Are Children just Little Adults? Child growth, development and age-related risk," Dec, 2003; "Rethinking Sitting," Oct, 2003; "Revisiting Ergonomics," May, 2003. **Seminars:** Teaching elder design, Las Vegas, Jul, 2008; Ergonomic considerations in seated work activities, University of California, Los Angeles, Jun, 2008; Rethinking back support: Sacral, lumbar or live backs, Dec, 2007; Adjunct Faculty, Human Factors and Design, 2006; Zen sitting and Western seating, 2005; Behavioral ergonomics, Oct, 2005; Sitting & seating in Zenmonasteries, Sep, 2005; Walking in their shoe.

47194 ■ John Smithkey, III, RN

1271 Overland Ave. NE
North Canton, OH 44720-1731
Ph:(330)494-3729
Co. E-mail: schoolnurse007@aol.com
E-mail: schoolnurse007@aol.com
Scope: Specializes in public and occupational health, HIV/AIDS education and prevention programs, grant and proposal writing, and programs for businesses

and employees. **Publications:** "The Strange World of Head Lice Information," Jun, 2003. **Seminars:** CPR; Communicable Diseases; Bloodborne Pathogen Training; Delegation of Nursing Tasks and Medication Administration Certification; Anaphylactic Shock and EpiPen Training.

47195 ■ Leonard R. Friedman Risk Management Inc.
170 Great Neck Rd., Ste. 140
Great Neck, NY 11021-3337
Ph:(516)466-0750
Fax:(516)466-0997
Co. E-mail: info@lrfrm.com
URL: http://www.lrfrm.com
Contact: Alice B. Weiss, Vice President
E-mail: refrati@atslrfrm.com
Scope: Provides risk and insurance management and safety and claims managements services to corporations across the country. Analyzes exposure to loss, audits insurance contracts, structures competitive bidding, reviews contracts and leases, implements and monitors safety and claims management programs and recommends risk transfer programs to reduce exposure to loss. Industries served: profit and nonprofit companies engaged in retail, manufacturing, distributing, hospitality, real estate and service.

47196 ■ Retail Safety Consortium
640 N Main St., Ste. 1256
Bountiful, UT 84010
Ph:(801)951-2566
Free: 800-370-9168
Contact: Michael E. Howell, President
Scope: Specializes in safety and human factors for retail industries.

47197 ■ Roy C. Craft
1707 Pecan St.
Bay City, TX 77414-4648
Ph:(409)245-9991
Fax:(409)245-9991
Co. E-mail: rcraft@tgn.net
Contact: Roy Craft, Owner
E-mail: rcraft@tgn.net
Scope: Consultant in health physics concerning control, protection, contamination, regulation and environmental impact.

47198 ■ Safety Management Services
4012 Santa Nella Pl.
San Diego, CA 92130-2291
Ph:(858)259-0591
Fax:(858)792-2350
Contact: Bob Harrell, President
E-mail: bharrell1@san.rr.com
Scope: Offers safety consulting services: Evaluates safety policies and procedures to determine degree of effectiveness; advises on compliance with OSHA standards; and provides safety programs for managers, supervisors, and workers. Industries served: general contractors in new construction, renovation, and demolition; and tenant improvement companies which hire general contractors to perform construction activities on their premises. Also assists litigation as construction safety expert witness. Safety training programs customized to meet clients needs. **Publications:** "What Can Go Wrong?," International Cranes magazine, Apr, 1994; **Seminars:** Federal OSHA Construction Safety and Health Course for Trainers, University of California, San Diego; OSHA 10-Hour Construction Safety Course; 90-Hour Construction Safety Management Certificate Course - 1991 to 1993; Fall Protection; Confined Space Standards; Cranes and Rigging; Scaffold or Trenching and Excavation; and Safe Construction Work Practices.

47199 ■ Vaccari & Associates Inc.
17 Cypress St. 1
Marblehead, MA 01945-1925
Ph:(781)639-0946
Fax:(781)639-0946
Co. E-mail: rvaccari1@verizon.net
Contact: Ralph J. Vaccari, President
E-mail: rvaccari@rcn.com
Scope: A provider of appraisals for primary and secondary mortgages, mortgage refinancing, employee relocation, private mortgage insurance removal, estate planning and divorce settlement.

47200 ■ Verk Consultants Inc.
1527 Industrial Way SW
PO Box 11277
Albany, OR 97322
Ph:(541)687-9170
Fax:(541)687-9758
Co. E-mail: larry@verk.com
Contact: Larry H. Malmgren, President
E-mail: larry@verk.com
Scope: Specializes in vocational rehabilitation, work-site evaluations for managing workers compensation and the Americans with Disabilities Act, Title I. **Seminars:** ADA Title I, Workers Compensation, Disability Management.

COMPUTERIZED DATABASES

47201 ■ *Environment & Safety Library*
The Bureau of National Affairs Inc.
1801 S Bell St.
Arlington, VA 22202
Free: 800-372-1033
Co. E-mail: customercare@bna.com
URL: http://www.bna.com
Description: Contains reports on current laws and regulations, news, and developments in the environment and safety field worldwide. Covers air pollution; ANSI standards scopes; Canadian laws and regulations; chemical manufacturing and regulation; compliance deadlines; environmental due diligence; European Union directives and regulations; federal statutes; regulations; guidance/agency documents and executive orders; food and drug regulation; food safety; hazmat transport; international treaties; bilateral agreements; conventions; environmental laws and regulations; contacts; Mexican laws and regulations; mines and mining safety; NAFTA; occupational safety and health; OSWER directives; pesticides; right-to-know; solid, hazardous, and radioactive waste; state environmental statutes and regulations; state safety statutes and regulations for OSHA-approved states; test methods; toxic substances; waste management, disposal, and cleanup; and water pollution. Includes the full text of federal statutes, codified regulations, and the *Federal Register*; the full text of state statutes and regulations; full text of international treaties, Canadian and Mexican laws, country profiles, and European Union directives; legal decisions; BNA analysis; BNA reports; more than 3,000 federal and state forms; and data on more than 80,000 regulated chemical substances. Also contains an index of more than 275,000 cross-referenced entries. **Availability:** Online: The Bureau of National Affairs Inc; CD-ROM: The Bureau of National Affairs Inc. **Type:** Full text.

47202 ■ *Health and Safety Science Abstracts*
ProQuest LLC
789 E Eisenhower Pkwy.
Ann Arbor, MI 48103
Ph:(734)761-4700
Fax:(734)997-4222
Co. E-mail: info@proquest.com
URL: http://www.csa.com
Description: Contains more than 176,000 citations, with abstracts, to the worldwide literature on safety science and hazard control, with an emphasis on the identification, evaluation, and elimination or control of hazards. Includes coverage of issues related to liability. Sources include books, periodicals, government reports, conference proceedings, patents, and dissertations. Corresponds to *Health and Safety Science Abstracts*. **Availability:** Online: ProQuest LLC, STN International. **Type:** Bibliographic.

47203 ■ *State Health Care Regulatory Developments*
The Bureau of National Affairs Inc.
1801 S Bell St.
Arlington, VA 22202
Free: 800-372-1033
Co. E-mail: customercare@bna.com
URL: http://www.bna.com
Description: Contains information on health care regulatory news and developments in the United States. Subjects include community-based care, home care, emergency care, infectious diseases, managed care, insurance, laboratories, Medicaid,

mental health, medical waste, nursing homes, pharmaceuticals, physician services, professional licensing, provider relationships, worker protection and compensation. Entries are organized by state, topic, and register citation. **Availability:** Online: The Bureau of National Affairs Inc., Thomson Reuters. **Type:** Full text.

LIBRARIES

47204 ■ Ameren Corporation Library
1901 Chouteau Ave.
Box 66149
St. Louis, MO 63166-6149
Ph:(314)554-3094
Fax:(314)554-2888
Co. E-mail: khayes2@ameren.com
Contact: Katharine A. Hayes, Tech.Libn.
Scope: Business, the environment, engineering, occupational safety and health, nuclear power, public utilities, public-private power. **Holdings:** Figures not available. **Subscriptions:** 400 journals and other serials.

47205 ■ BNA Library
1801 S. Bell St.
Arlington, VA 22202-4501
Ph:(703)341-3303
Free: 800-372-1033
Fax:(703)341-1610
Co. E-mail: mbromley@bna.com
URL: http://www.bna.com
Contact: Catherine Kitchell, Ref.Libn.
Scope: Law, labor-management relations, economics, government regulation, business, the environment, industrial safety and health. **Services:** Interlibrary loan; Library open by special arrangement only. **Holdings:** 20,000 volumes. **Subscriptions:** 650 journals and other serials; 20 newspapers.

47206 ■ CELOTEX Technical Center Library
10301 9th St., N.
St. Petersburg, FL 33716
Ph:(813)576-4171
Fax:(813)576-0318
Contact: David Brzana, Info.Spec.
Scope: Polymer chemistry, specialty chemicals, building materials, materials science. **Services:** Interlibrary loan; center not open to the public. **Holdings:** 2000 books. **Subscriptions:** 150 journals and other serials.

47207 ■ CIGNA Corporation Philadelphia Research Library
2 Liberty Pl.
1601 Chestnut St.
Philadelphia, PA 19192
Ph:(215)761-1000
Fax:(215)761-5588
Co. E-mail: daniel.mullan@cigna.com
URL: http://www.cigna.com
Contact: Dan Mullan, Mgr.
Scope: Insurance, management, occupational and environmental safety and health. **Services:** Interlibrary loan; Library not open to the public. **Holdings:** 2000 books. **Subscriptions:** 400 journals and other serials.

47208 ■ Cogswell College Library
1175 Bordeaux Dr.
Sunnyvale, CA 94089-9772
Ph:(408)541-0100, x-144
Fax:(408)747-0764
Co. E-mail: library@cogswell.edu
URL: http://www.cogswell.edu/library.htm
Contact: Bruce G. Dahms, Libn.
Scope: Fire science, electrical engineering, software engineering, computer and video imaging, digital motion pictures, digital audio technology. **Services:** Interlibrary loan; copying; Library open to the public for reference use only. **Holdings:** 13,024 books. **Subscriptions:** 100 journals and other serials; 3 newspapers.

47209 ■ Consad Research Corporation Library
211 N. Whitfield St., Ste. 250
Pittsburgh, PA 15206
Ph:(412)363-5500
Fax:(412)363-5509
Co. E-mail: info@consad.com
URL: http://www.consad.com
Contact: Wilbur Steger, Pres.
Scope: Social science methodology, statistics, urban planning, drug abuse, healthcare, economics, occupational safety and health. **Services:** Library open to the public with restrictions. **Holdings:** 10,000 books; 10,000 reports. **Subscriptions:** 54 journals and other serials.

47210 ■ Cornell University–School of Industrial and Labor Relations–Martin P. Catherwood Library (239 I)
239 Ives Hall
Ithaca, NY 14853-3901
Ph:(607)255-5435
Fax:(607)255-9641
Co. E-mail: smb6@cornell.edu
URL: http://www.ilr.cornell.edu/library/
Contact: Stuart Basefsky, Sr.Ref.Libn.
Scope: Labor-management relations, labor law and legislation, labor Organization, industrial and labor conditions, labor economics, human resources, income security, human resources management, supervision, occupational safety and health, International and comparative labor relations, organizational behavior and negotiation, and conflict resolution. **Services:** Interlibrary loan; Library open to the public. **Holdings:** 232,000 volumes; 44,368 microforms; 19,000 cubic feet of manuscripts; 647 motion pictures; 1016 filmstrips and slides; 878 videotapes; 2123 sound recordings; 373 computer files; 350,000 images. **Subscriptions:** 3998 serials; 4 newspapers.

47211 ■ Exxon Research and Engineering Company Information, Computing, and Business Systems
PO Box 998
Rte. 22 E.
Annandale, NJ 08801
Ph:(908)730-2924
Fax:(908)730-3344
Co. E-mail: mjbarne@erenj.com
Contact: Mary Jo Barnello, Sr.Anl.
Scope: Petroleum refining processes and products, petrochemical processes and products, chemistry, physics, metallurgy, mathematics, industrial safety. **Services:** Services not open to the public. **Holdings:** 35,000 volumes and microforms; patent holdings. **Subscriptions:** 350 journals and other serials.

47212 ■ The Hartford Financial Services Company–Loss Control Library
690 Asylum Ave.
Hartford Plaza
COGS 2-45
Hartford, CT 06105
Ph:(860)547-5000
Fax:(860)547-6004
Co. E-mail: lynn.zweiflet@thehartford.com
URL: http://www.thehartford.com/corporate/losscontrol/aboutlc.html
Contact: Lynn A. Zweifler, MLS
Scope: Safety engineering, toxicology, chemistry, fire protection, transportation, occupational safety and health, industrial hygiene, ergonomics, risk management. **Services:** Interlibrary loan; Library open to the public by special arrangement only. **Holdings:** 2000 books; government documents; 15 VF drawers. **Subscriptions:** 200 journals and other serials.

47213 ■ Industrial Health Foundation, Inc. Library
34 Penn Cir., W.
Pittsburgh, PA 15206
Ph:(412)363-6600
Fax:(412)363-6605
Co. E-mail: admin@infipcorp.com
Contact: Janice O'Polka, Proj.Mgr., Info.Svcs.
Scope: Industrial hygiene, occupational safety and health, toxicology, environmental issues. **Services:** Interlibrary loan; Library not open to the public. **Hold-**

ings: 3000 books; 100 bound periodical volumes; 78,000 abstracts; 50 VF drawers of pamphlets and reprints. **Subscriptions:** 60 journals and other serials.

47214 ■ Institute for Business and Home Safety Library
4775 E. Fowler Ave.
Tampa, FL 33617
Ph:(813)286-3400
Fax:(813)286-9960
Co. E-mail: info@ibhs.org
URL: http://www.disastersafety.org/
Contact: Hilary B. Thomson, Lib.Hd.
Scope: Insurance, natural disasters, building codes, wind and seismic engineering. **Services:** Interlibrary loan; research for member companies. **Holdings:** 3000 books, periodicals, and audio/visuals. **Subscriptions:** 159 journals and other serials; 3 newspapers.

47215 ■ International Union of Operating Engineers–Research Department Library
1125 17th St., NW
Washington, DC 20036
Ph:(202)429-9100
Fax:(202)778-2613
URL: http://www.iuoe.org/index.asp
Contact: David Treanor, Dir.
Scope: Union history, productivity of heavy equipment, industrial safety. **Services:** Library not open to the public. **Holdings:** 2000 books; industrial surveys; slides; motion pictures; microfiche.

47216 ■ J.J. Keller & Associates, Inc.–Editorial Resource Center–Research & Technical Library (3003)
3003 W. Breezewwod Ln.
PO Box 368
Neenah, WI 54957-0368
Free: 800-558-5011, x-7308
Co. E-mail: library@jjkeller.com
URL: http://www.jjkeller.com
Contact: Webb A. Shaw, Corp.Ed.Dir.
Scope: Transportation, motor carrier regulations, workplace safety regulations and practices, hazardous materials, hazardous wastes, industry regulations and compliance, food safety, human resources. **Services:** Copying; Library open to the public by referral. **Holdings:** 8000 books, 500 periodicals; 7600 books, AV programs, and government documents (Department of Transportation, Environmental Protection Agency, and Department of Labor). **Subscriptions:** 1100 journals and other serials.

47217 ■ Lakehead University–Resource Centre for Occupational Health and Safety
University Ctr., Rm. 3
955 Oliver Rd.
Thunder Bay, ON, Canada P7B 5E1
Ph:(807)343-8334
Fax:(807)343-7701
Co. E-mail: ursula.macdonald@lakeheadu.ca
URL: http://hr.lakeheadu.ca/wp/?pg=140
Contact: Ursula MacDonald, Hea. & Safety Off.
Scope: Occupational health and safety, the environment. **Services:** Interlibrary loan; copying; Library open to the public. **Holdings:** 10,000 books and articles. **Subscriptions:** 10 journals and other serials; 2 newspapers.

47218 ■ Manitoba Department of Labour & Immigration–Workplace Safety and Health Division–Client Resource Centre (200-4)
200-401 York Ave.
Winnipeg, MB, Canada R3C 0P8
Ph:(204)945-3446
Free: 800-282-8069
URL: http://www.gov.mb.ca/labour/safety/index.html
Contact: Darlene Muise, Ed.
Scope: Toxicology, occupational health and safety, industrial hygiene. **Services:** Library not open to the public. **Holdings:** Figures not available.

47219 ■ Montana Tech of the University of Montana–Montana Tech Library
1300 W. Park St.
Butte, MT 59701-8997
Ph:(406)496-4281

Fax:(406)496-4133
Co. E-mail: astclair@mtech.edu
URL: http://www.mtech.edu/library
Contact: Ann St. Clair, Dir.
Scope: Geology, mining, mineral processing, geochemistry, geophysics, petroleum, environmental engineering, occupational safety, mineral economics, industrial hygiene, nursing, healthcare informatics. **Services:** Interlibrary loan; scanning; color copying. **Holdings:** 59,039 books; 81,794 bound periodical volumes. **Subscriptions:** 394 journals and other serials.

47220 ■ National Safety Council Library
1121 Spring Lake Dr.
Itasca, IL 60143-3201
Ph:(630)775-2199
Free: 800-621-7619
Fax:(630)285-0765
Co. E-mail: library@nsc.org
URL: http://www.nsc.org/
Contact: Alaina Kolosh, Libn.
Scope: Accident prevention in general, occupational safety and health, industrial hygiene, traffic/transportation safety, and safety research. **Services:** Interlibrary loan; copying; Library open to the public with prior contact suggested. **Holdings:** 4100 books; 500 bound periodical volumes; 94,600 other cataloged items; 40,300 research reports; 510 reels of microfilm; 4000 microfiche. **Subscriptions:** 200 journals and other serials.

47221 ■ New Mexico Department of Environment–NMED Library
1190 St. Francis Dr., Ste. N4050
PO Box 5469
Santa Fe, NM 87502
Ph:(505)827-2855
Free: 800-219-6157
Fax:(505)827-2818
Co. E-mail: ann_baumgarn@nmenv.state.nm.us
URL: http://www.nmenv.state.nm.us
Contact: Ms. Ann Baumgarn
Scope: Ground water protection, surface water protection, hazardous waste disposal, radiation protection, occupational health and safety, air quality protection. **Services:** Copying; Library open to the public for reference use only. **Holdings:** 700 books; 154 bound periodical volumes; 6500 reports and documents. **Subscriptions:** 35 journals and other serials.

47222 ■ New York Department of State–Office of Fire Prevention and Control–Academy of Fire Science - Library (600 C)
600 College Ave.
Montour Falls, NY 14865-9634
Ph:(607)535-7136, x-605
Fax:(607)535-4841
Co. E-mail: library@dos.state.ny.us
URL: http://www.dos.state.ny.us/fire/library.html
Contact: Diana Robinson, Libn.
Scope: Fire protection, prevention, and control; rescue; fire department administration and management; New York state codes, standards, and regulations; emergency medical services; hazardous materials; arson prevention; fire investigation; history of fire service in New York State. **Services:** Interlibrary loan; copying; answers to email, mail and telephone inquiries from patrons in New York state; Library open to the public. **Holdings:** 6000 books; 250 bound periodical volumes; 16 VF drawers; 200 microfiche; 3300 videocassettes; CDs and DVDs. **Subscriptions:** 45000 journals and other serials.

47223 ■ North Carolina Department of Labor–Charles H. Livengood, Jr. Memorial Library
1101 Mail Service Center
Raleigh, NC 27699-1101
Ph:(919)807-2850
Co. E-mail: dol.library@labor.nc.gov
URL: http://www.nclabor.com/lib/lib2.htm
Contact: Nick Vincelli, Libn.
Scope: Labor law and history, occupational safety, health, and training. **Services:** Interlibrary loan; copying; SDI. **Holdings:** 12,000 volumes; 533 bound

periodical volumes; 1200 audiocassettes; vertical files; state government documents. **Subscriptions:** 120 journals and other serials.

47224 ■ Ohio Bureau of Workers' Compensation–BWC Library
30 W. Spring St., 3rd Fl.
Columbus, OH 43215-2256
Ph:(614)466-7388
Free: 800-644-6292
Fax:(614)644-9634
Co. E-mail: library@bwc.state.oh.us
URL: http://www.ohiobwc.com
Contact: Melissa Hatfield, Lib.Adm.
Scope: Occupational safety, industrial hygiene, workers' compensation, occupational rehabilitation. **Services:** Interlibrary loan; copying; Center open to the public. **Holdings:** 6000 books; 850 standards; 200 microfiche; 20 VF drawers of pamphlets; 650 subject headings; 2 VF drawers of clippings; 600 videos. **Subscriptions:** 280 journals and other serials.

47225 ■ PACE International Union–Irene Glaus Memorial Library
3340 Perimeter Hill Dr.
Box 1475
Nashville, TN 37202
Ph:(615)834-8590
Fax:(615)831-6792
Co. E-mail: mdimoff@paceunion.org
URL: http://www.paceunion.org
Contact: Mary Alyce Dimoff, Info.Spec.
Scope: Labor relations, law, and history; occupational safety and health. **Services:** Interlibrary loan; Library open to the public for reference use only. **Holdings:** 10,100 books; 1600 bound periodical volumes; 12,250 microfiche; 60 audiotapes; 310 videotapes; 600 government documents; UPIU archival material (39 linear feet of folders, boxes, bound periodical volumes, microfilm), AIW, IWNA and OCAW archival material. **Subscriptions:** 183 journals and other serials; 44 newspapers.

47226 ■ Triodyne Inc.–Beth Hamilton Safety Library
450 Skokie Blvd.
Northbrook, IL 60062
Ph:(847)677-4730
Fax:(847)647-2047
Co. E-mail: infoserv@triodyne.com
URL: http://www.triodyne.com/Library.htm
Contact: John Kristelli, Info.Svcs.Mgr.
Scope: Engineering - forensic, mechanical, automotive, civil; industrial safety; materials science. **Services:** Interlibrary loan; Center not open to the public. **Holdings:** 3000 monograph titles; 600 VF drawers of technical reports; 1200 VF drawers of manufacturers' literature and catalogs; 800 VF of subject files, bibliographies, and ephemera, 120 VF drawers of engineering standards and specifications. **Subscriptions:** 212 journals and other serials.

47227 ■ U.S. Army–Public Health Command Library
5158 Blackhawk Rd.
Aberdeen Proving Ground, MD 21010
Ph:(410)436-4311
Free: 800-222-9698
Co. E-mail: usachppm-pao@amedd.army.mil
URL: http://phc.amedd.army.mil/Pages/default.aspx
Contact: Krishan S. Goel, Libn.
Scope: Occupational medicine, safety and health; chemistry and toxicology; audiology; medical entomology; laser, microwave, and radiological safety and health; air and water pollution; sanitary engineering. **Services:** Interlibrary loan; copying; SDI. **Holdings:** 9000 books; 8000 bound periodical volumes; 8400 R&D reports; 3000 microfiche. **Subscriptions:** 250 journals and other serials.

47228 ■ U.S. Bureau of Mines–Twin Cities Research Center Library
201 Federal Dr.
St. Paul, MN 55111
Ph:(612)725-4503

Fax:(612)725-4784
Contact: Marilynn R. Anderson, Libn.
Scope: Mining engineering, metallurgy, mineral industries, geology, industrial safety, environmental remediation. **Services:** Interlibrary loan; Library open to the public. **Holdings:** 8200 books; 2270 bound periodical volumes; 120 VF drawers of reports, documents, patents. **Subscriptions:** 190 journals and other serials.

47229 ■ U.S. Dept. of Labor–Occupational Safety and Health Administration–Region VIII Library (1999)
1999 Broadway, Ste. 1690
PO Box 46550
Denver, CO 80202-5716
Ph:(720)264-6550
Fax:(720)264-6585
Co. E-mail: leslie.carolyn@dol.gov
Contact: Carolyn Leslie, Libn.
Scope: Occupational safety, Occupational health, OSHA regulations, any questions about OSHA - federal or state. **Services:** Interlibrary loan; copying; Library open to the public for reference use only; OSHA publications are distributed from this office (one copy per request/title). Help with using OSHA's public website (http://www.osha.gov). **Holdings:** 600 books; 1100 reports.

47230 ■ U.S. Dept. of Labor–OSHA–Billings Area Office Library (2900)
2900 4th Ave. N., Ste. 303
Billings, MT 59101
Ph:(406)247-7494
Fax:(406)247-7499
URL: http://www.osha.gov
Contact: Bonnie Albright, Ck.
Scope: Safety and health in the workplace. **Services:** Library open to the public. **Holdings:** 500 books.

47231 ■ U.S. Dept. of Labor–OSHA–Region III Library (Curti)
Curtis Center, Ste. 740 W.
170 S. Independence Mall W.
Philadelphia, PA 19106
Ph:(215)861-4900
Fax:(215)861-4904
URL: http://www.osha.gov
Contact: Barbara Bray, Libn.
Scope: Occupational health and safety, industrial hygiene, toxic substances. **Services:** Library open to the public. **Holdings:** 2000 books. **Subscriptions:** 12 journals and other serials.

47232 ■ U.S. Dept. of Labor–OSHA–Region X Library (1111)
1111 3rd Ave., Ste. 715
Seattle, WA 98101-3216
Ph:(206)553-7620
Fax:(206)553-6499
URL: http://www.osha.gov
Contact: Laura Tippetts, Tech.Info.Spec.
Scope: Industrial hygiene, toxic substances, industrial safety, toxicology, safety, engineering. **Services:** Interlibrary loan; copying; Library open to the public for reference use only. **Holdings:** 1600 titles. **Subscriptions:** 10 journals and other serials.

47233 ■ U.S. Dept. of Labor–OSHA–Technical Data Center (200 C)
200 Constitution Ave. NW, Rm. N-2625
Washington, DC 20210
Ph:(202)693-2350
Fax:(202)693-1648
URL: http://www.osha.gov/dts/tdc/index.html
Contact: Robb Turnage, Ed.
Scope: Occupational safety, industrial hygiene, toxicology, control technology, hazardous materials, fire safety, electrical safety, noise, carcinogens, material safety, farm safety, process safety, ergonomics, occupational health nursing, blood-borne pathogens, indoor air quality, Occupational Safety & Health Administration (OSHA) rulemaking docket. **Services:** Interlibrary loan; Center open to the public for reference use only. **Holdings:** 6000 books and bound periodical volumes; 500,000 microfiche; standards from more than 370 organizations and societies. **Subscriptions:** 200 journals and other serials.

47234 ■ U.S. Dept. of Labor–OSHA - Office of Training & Education–H. Lee Saltsgaver Library (2020)
2020 S. Arlington Heights Rd.
Arlington Heights, IL 60005
Ph:(847)759-7736
Fax:(847)759-7748
Co. E-mail: perlman.elizabeth@dol.gov
URL: http://www.osha.gov/
Contact: Elizabeth Perlman, MSLIS
Scope: Industrial hygiene, occupational safety, industrial toxicology. **Services:** Library open to the public for reference use only. **Holdings:** 1550 government documents; 1250 standards. **Subscriptions:** 46 journals and other serials.

47235 ■ U.S. National Institute for Occupational Safety & Health–Library C-21
4676 Columbia Pkwy.
Cincinnati, OH 45226
Ph:(513)533-8302
Co. E-mail: cdcinfo@cdc.gov
URL: http://www.cdc.gov/niosh
Contact: Lawrence Q. Foster, Hd.Libn.
Scope: Occupational safety and health, industrial hygiene and toxicology. **Services:** Interlibrary loan; Library open to the public. **Holdings:** 8000 books; 10,000 bound periodical volumes. **Subscriptions:** 125 journals and other serials.

47236 ■ University of California, Berkeley–School of Public Health–Labor Occupational Health Program Library (2223)
2223 Fulton St., 4th Fl.
Berkeley, CA 94720-5120
Ph:(510)643-4335
Fax:(510)643-5698
Co. E-mail: andrews2@berkeley.edu
URL: http://www.lohp.org/library/
Contact: Karen Andrews, Libn.
Scope: Chemical and physical occupational hazards, medical and industrial hygiene, standards and regulations, workers' compensation and education. **Services:** Library open to the public for reference use only; technical assistance by phone and e-mail. **Holdings:** 10,000 books, pamphlets, periodicals, and videos; 180 unbound periodicals; newspaper clipping file. **Subscriptions:** 50 journals and other serials; 110 newspapers.

47237 ■ WorkSafeNB–Communications Department
1 Portland St.
PO Box 160
St. John, NB, Canada E2L 3X9
Ph:(506)632-2200
Free: 800-222-9775
Fax:(506)632-2830
Co. E-mail: communications@ws-ts.nb.ca
URL: http://www.worksafenb.ca
Contact: Jill Breen, Commun.Asst.
Scope: Social affairs, education, occupational health and safety, training, mining safety. **Holdings:** Figures not available.

RESEARCH CENTERS

47238 ■ National Farm Medicine Center
1000 N Oak Ave.
Marshfield, WI 54449-5790
Ph:(715)389-4999
Free: 800–662-6900
Fax:(715)389-4996
Co. E-mail: lee.barbara@mcrf.mfldclin.edu
URL: http://www.marshfieldclinic.org/nfmc/
Contact: Barbara C. Lee PhD, Dir.
E-mail: lee.barbara@mcrf.mfldclin.edu
Scope: Human health and safety associated with rural and agricultural work, life and environment. **Publications:** Cultivate newsletter; Nurture newsletter; Progress Report; Year in Review annual report.

47239 ■ University of Michigan–Center for Ergonomics
1205 Beal Ave.
Ann Arbor, MI 48109-2117
Ph:(734)763-2243

Fax:(734)764-3451
Co. E-mail: rrabourn@umich.edu
URL: http://www.engin.umich.edu/dept/ioe/C4E
Contact: Randy Rabourn
E-mail: rrabourn@umich.edu
Scope: Ergonomics and safety engineering, including studies on contemporary techniques and methods necessary to minimize occupational health and safety problems and maximize human-hardware performance capability. **Educational Activities:** 15 one- to five-day courses for engineers, managers, and occupational health professionals (annually).

47240 ■ University of Montreal–Health and Prevention Social Research Group–Groupe de Recherche sur les Aspects Sociaux de la Sante et de la Prevention
2801 Edouard-Montpetit Blvd., Ste. 168
Station Centre-ville, Box 6128
Montreal, QC, Canada H3C 3J7
Ph:(514)343-6193
Fax:(514)343-2334
Co. E-mail: andree.demers@umontreal.ca
URL: http://www.grasp.umontreal.ca
Contact: Andre Demers PhD, Dir.
E-mail: andree.demers@umontreal.ca
Scope: Social determinants of health and social dynamics in illness, health, and services, including collective choices in matters of health policy and health resource allocation; social control and regulation of social and health problems; social and ethical issues related to new medical technologies; sociology of health professions; social dynamics of drinking behavior; mental health policy development and implementation; community-based mental health care; sociology of mental health iatrogenic; psychotropic drug utilization; handicap and stigma; and critical mental health theory. Also studies prevention

strategies in occupational work and safety, including development and impact of occupational health and safety policies; organizational factors in occupational health and safety; work organization and mental health; management styles and types of occupational diseases; evaluation of efficacy of preventive measures in occupational health and safety; aging at work. **Services:** Policy consultation, to health and welfare organizations, advocacy groups, and government. **Educational Activities:** Multidisciplinary university seminars (monthly).

47241 ■ University of Utah–Rocky Mountain Center for Occupational and Environmental Health
391 Chipeta Way, Ste. C
Salt Lake City, UT 84108
Ph:(801)581-4800
Fax:(801)581-7224
Co. E-mail: kurt.hegmann@hsc.utah.edu
URL: http://medicine.utah.edu/rmcoeh
Contact: Dr. Kurt T. Hegmann, Dir.
E-mail: kurt.hegmann@hsc.utah.edu
Scope: Occupational and environmental health and safety with emphasis on exposure assessment, environmental epidemiology, asbestos-related health problems, musculoskeletal and other injury evaluation and prevention, and ergonomic aspects of the work environment. **Services:** Consulting, for federal, state, and local governments, industry, and other organizations. **Educational Activities:** Continuing education programs, in industrial hygiene, occupational medicine, and occupational safety and ergonomics, with more than 2,000 attendees yearly; Graduate programs in industrial hygiene and occupational medicine; Residency program in occupational medicine.

47242 ■ University of Waterloo–Ergonomics and Safety Consulting Services
200 University Ave. W
Waterloo, ON, Canada N2L 3G1

Ph:(519)888-4567
Fax:(519)886-5488
Co. E-mail: wells@healthy.uwaterloo.ca
URL: http://www.ergonomics.uwaterloo.ca
Contact: Prof. Richard Wells PhD, Dir.
E-mail: wells@healthy.uwaterloo.ca
Scope: Contract research and consulting for industry and government in occupational safety, and ergonomics. Studies include workplace hazard assessments, personal protective equipment evaluations, repetitive strain and over-exertion injury prevention, ergonomic intervention. **Services:** Information and advisory services, including interpretations and consultations, and other analytical services. **Educational Activities:** Seminars; Short courses; Symposia.

47243 ■ West Virginia University–Institute of Occupational and Environmental Health
Robert C. Byrd Health Sciences Ctr.
School of Medicine
PO Box 9190
Morgantown, WV 26506-9190
Ph:(304)293-3693
Fax:(304)293-2629
Co. E-mail: cmartin@hsc.wvu.edu
URL: http://www.hsc.wvu.edu/ioeh
Contact: Dr. Christopher J. Martin, Dir.
E-mail: cmartin@hsc.wvu.edu
Scope: Occupational and environmental health, including occupational medicine and environmental toxicology. **Services:** Community consultations, on toxic exposure risk; Patient care, for toxic exposure. **Publications:** Occupational Health. **Educational Activities:** Master's degree, in public health; Residencies, in preventive occupational and environmental medicine; Workshops.

START-UP INFORMATION

47244 ■ *101 Businesses You Can Start with Less Than One Thousand Dollars: for Students*
Pub: Atlantic Publishing Company
Ed: Heather Lee Shepherd. **Released:** September 2007. **Price:** $21.95. **Description:** More than 100 business ideas for busy students; these ideas can be started for very little money yet provide striving students with more money than they would make working a job paying an hourly wage. Web links for additional information are provides along with detailed instruction and examples for starting a successful business.

47245 ■ "On Their Own: Bronx High School Students Open a Bank Branch" in *Black Enterprise* (Vol. 38, February 2008, No. 7, pp. 42)
Pub: Earl G. Graves Publishing Co. Inc.
Ed: Jessica Jones. **Description:** Students at Fordham Leadership Academy for Business and Technology in New York City opened a student-run bank branch at their high school. The business paid high school seniors $11 per hour to work as tellers. Students were also taught interviewing basics.

47246 ■ *Prepare to Be a Teen Millionaire*
Pub: Health Communications, Inc.
Ed: Robyn Collins; Kimberly Spinks Burleson. **Released:** April 1, 2008. **Price:** $16.95. **Description:** Business reference for any teenager wishing to become a successful entrepreneur; advice is given from successful teenage millionaires. Topics covered include: choosing a business name, type, and location; use of the Internet; legal issues; branding, sales, and marketing; funding and financial management; return on investment; retirement; development of a sound business plan; and certification for minority or women-owned companies.

ASSOCIATIONS AND OTHER ORGANIZATIONS

47247 ■ Entrepreneurs' Organization
500 Montgomery St., Ste. 500
Alexandria, VA 22314
Ph:(703)519-6700
Fax:(703)519-1864
Co. E-mail: info@eonetwork.org
URL: http://www.eonetwork.org
Contact: Michael Caito, Chm.
Description: Entrepreneurs under the age of 50 who have either founded, co-founded, are a controlling shareholder of, or own a firm with annual gross revenues exceeding $1,000,000 (membership is by invitation only). Engages leading entrepreneurs to learn and grow. Serves as a focal point for networking and development of members through small group learning sessions, regular local chapter social and learning events, and global conference-based education programs. **Publications:** *Octane* (quarterly); *Overdrive* (monthly).

47248 ■ National Foundation for Teaching Entrepreneurship
120 Wall St., 18th Fl.
New York, NY 10005
Ph:(212)232-3333
Fax:(212)232-2244
URL: http://www.nfte.com
Contact: Steve Mariotti, Founder
Description: Devoted to teaching entrepreneurship education to low-income young people, ages 11 through 18. **Publications:** *NFTE News* (quarterly).

47249 ■ Young Presidents' Organization
600 E Las Colinas Blvd., Ste. 1000
Irving, TX 75039
Ph:(972)587-1500
Free: 800-773-7976
Fax:(972)587-1611
Co. E-mail: joinypo@ypo.org
URL: http://www.ypo.org
Description: Presidents or chief executive officers of corporations with minimum of 50 employees; each member must have been elected president before his/her 40th birthday and must retire by June 30th the year after his/her 50th birthday. Assists members in becoming better presidents through education and idea exchange. Conducts courses for members and spouses, in business, arts and sciences, world affairs, and family and community life, during a given year at various locations, including graduate business schools. .

REFERENCE WORKS

47250 ■ "Are You a Young Canadian Entrepreneur Looking for Recognition?" in *CNW Group* (November 10, 2010)
Pub: Comtex
Description: Business Development Bank of Canada is looking for young Canadian entrepreneurs ages 19 to 35 for its 2011 Young Entrepreneur Awards. The awards pay tribute to remarkable young Canadian entrepreneurs for their creativity, innovative spirit and community development, as well as business success.

47251 ■ "Biz U: Cool for School" in *Entrepreneur* (Vol. 35, October 2007, No. 10, pp. 144)
Pub: Entrepreneur Media Inc.
Ed: Nichole L. Torres. **Description:** Forming a high technology business while still in college has its advantages such as having information resources nearby and having students from various fields to ask for help and advice. School business competitions are also helpful in building networks with investors. Ways that the college environment can be useful to aspiring entrepreneurs, particularly to those who are into high technology business, are discussed.

47252 ■ "Business Start-Up a Learning Experience for Young Bellingham Entrepreneur" in *Bellingham Herald* (July 18, 2010)
Pub: Bellingham Herald
Ed: Dave Gallagher. **Description:** Profile of 21-year-old entrepreneur, Chase Larabee, who developed an online program that helps airport fixed-based operators handle refueling, hotel and transportation reservations and other requests from private airplane pilots.

47253 ■ *Capitalism for Kids: Growing Up to Be Your Own Boss*
Pub: Bluestocking Press
Ed: Karl Hess. **Released:** June 2006. **Price:** $8.95. **Description:** Capitalism, democratic socialism, socialism, communism, and totalitarianism is explained to children. The book explains to young people how to build a profitable business.

47254 ■ *Creating Success from the Inside Out: Develop the Focus and Strategy to Uncover the Life You Want*
Pub: John Wiley and Sons, Inc.
Ed: Ephren W. Taylor. **Released:** November 16, 2007. **Price:** $24.95. **Description:** Ephren Taylor founded his first business at age 12 and was a multimillionaire CEO ten years later. Taylor explains how he and other successful young entrepreneurs think about success and achievement.

47255 ■ "Creativity: A Key Link to Entrepreneurial Behavior" in *Business Horizons* (September-October 2007, pp. 365)
Pub: Elsevier Technology Publications
Ed: Stephen Ko, John E. Butler. **Description:** Importance of creativity and its link to entrepreneurial behavior is examined. In a study of various entrepreneurs, studies concluded that a solid knowledge base, a well-developed social network, and a strong focus on identifying opportunities are relevant to entrepreneurial behavior.

47256 ■ "Elastic Path Software Joins Canada in G20 Young Entrepreneur Summit" in *Internet Wire* (June 14, 2010)
Pub: Comtex
Description: The Canadian Youth Business Foundation hosted the G20 Young Entrepreneur Summit and announced that Harry Chemko of British Columbia's Elastic Path Software will be a member of the Canadian delegation at the G20 Young Entrepreneur Summit. Details are included.

47257 ■ "G20 Young Entrepreneur Alliance Signs Charter Outlining Commitment to Entrepreneurship" in *Internet Wire* (November 10, 2010)
Pub: Comtex
Description: G20 Young Entrepreneur Summit members created a charter document that outlines their support for the G20 process to include entrepreneurship on its agenda. Details of the Summit are included.

47258 ■ *Here Come the Regulars: How to Run a Record Label on a Shoestring Budget*
Pub: Faber & Faber, Inc.
Ed: Ian Anderson. **Released:** October 1, 2009. **Price:** $15.00. **Description:** Author, Ian Anderson launched his own successful record label, Afternoon Records

when he was 18 years old. Anderson shares insight into starting a record label, focusing on label image, budget, blogging, potential artists, as well as legal aspects.

47259 ■ "Identify and Conquer" in *Black Enterprise* **(Vol. 38, December 2007, No. 5, pp. 76)**
Pub: Earl G. Graves Publishing Co. Inc.
Ed: Tennille M. Robinson. **Description:** Twenty-two-year-old entrepreneur wants to expand her wholesale body oil and skincare products business.

47260 ■ "Kid-Friendly Business Sources" in *Black Enterprise* **(Vol. 37, January 2007, No. 6, pp. 40)**
Pub: Earl G. Graves Publishing Co. Inc.
Ed: Carolyn M. Brown. **Description:** Financial or business camps are a great way to encourage a child who interested in starting his or her own business. A number of these camps are available each year including Kidpreneurs Conference and Bull and Bear Investment Camp. Other resources are available online. Resources included.

47261 ■ "Labor of Love" in *Green Industry Pro* **(Vol. 23, March 2011, No. 3, pp. 14)**
Pub: Cygnus Business Media
Ed: Gregg Wartgow. **Description:** Profile of CLS Landscape Management in Chino, California and its owner who started the company when he was 21 years old. Kevin Davis built his landscape firm into a $20 million a year business without using any dedicated salesperson.

47262 ■ *Lessons of a Lipstick Queen: Finding and Developing the Great Idea That Can Change Your Life*
Pub: Simon & Schuster
Ed: Poppy King. **Released:** May 1, 2009. **Price:** $14.00. **Description:** Poppy King tells how she started her lipstick brand at age eighteen. She reveals how she managed to launch her business using a good idea and finding financing, marketing the product and how she became successful.

47263 ■ "Meet the Dropouts: the Students Who Chose Start-Ups Over College" in *Inc.* **(Vol. 33, September 2011, No. 7, pp. 32)**
Pub: Inc. Magazine
Ed: Eric Markowitz. **Description:** Profiles of 24 college students who left school in order to work on their own startup companies. Each new company is receiving $100,000 from Peter Thiel, cofounder of PayPal and an angel investor.

47264 ■ *My Start-Up Life: What a (Very) Young C.E.O. Learned on His Journey Through Silicon Valley*
Pub: Jossey-Bass Publishers
Ed: Ben Casnocha. **Released:** May 25, 2007. **Price:** $24.95. **Description:** Profile of Ben Casnocha, a young entrepreneur who shares insight into starting a running a new business.

47265 ■ "Screen Time" in *Canadian Business* **(Vol. 81, October 13, 2008, No. 17, pp. 93)**
Pub: Rogers Media Ltd.
Ed: Calvin Leung. **Description:** Young Canadian entertainment business up-and-comers like Ari Lantos and Brian Mossof plan to produce movies that cold earn and entertain audiences rather than focusing on winning awards. English movies continue to struggle in Canada, while French-language films continue to thrive. Details on Canada's movie industry are furnished.

47266 ■ "Tech Giving 2.0" in *Boston Business Journal* **(Vol. 31, August 5, 2011, No. 28, pp. 1)**
Pub: Boston Business Journal
Ed: Mary Moore. **Description:** Entrepreneurs and venture capitalists in Boston have launched Technology Underwriting Greater Good, the tech industry's answer to the criticism that they are not charitable. The foundation finances nonprofits that aid young people through entrepreneurship, education and life experience. Other tech firms in Boston doing charitable works are discussed.

47267 ■ *Young Bucks: How to Raise a Future Millionaire*
Pub: Thomas Nelson Inc.
Ed: Troy Dunn. **Released:** November 2007. **Price:** $17.99. **Description:** Advice is given to parents to teach their children how to save money, invest wisely and even start their own business.

47268 ■ "Young Entrepreneur Gets Some Recognition and Some Help for College" in *Philadelphia Inquirer* **(August 30, 2010)**
Pub: Philadelphia Inquirer
Ed: Susan Snyder. **Description:** Profile of Zachary Gosling, age 18, who launched an online auction Website from his bedroom, using advertising and sponsorship funds rather than charging fees to users.

47269 ■ "Young Entrepreneur's Business Plan? An Ice Cream Boat? Really Floats: Maine at Work" in *Portland Press Herald* **(August 9, 2010)**
Pub: Portland Press Herald
Ed: Ray Routhier. **Description:** Profile of Jake Viola, founder of and ice cream boat located near Portland,

Maine. Viola is a sophomore at Yale University and sells ice cream from his pontoon boat on Little Sebago lake.

47270 ■ "Young Millionaires" in *Entrepreneur* **(Vol. 35, October 2007, No. 10, pp. 76)**
Pub: Entrepreneur Media Inc.
Ed: Jessica Chen, Lindsay Hollway, Amanda C. Kooser, Kim Orr, James Park, Nichole L. Torres, and Sarah Wilson. **Description:** Young successful entrepreneurs of 2007 were chosen to talk about their success story and their business strategies in the past and those for the future. Among those featured are Kelly Flatley, Brendan Synnott, Herman Flores, Myles Kovacs, Haythem Haddad, Jim Wetzel, Lance Lawson, Jacob DeHart, Jake Nickell, Tim Vanderhook, Chris Vanderhook, Russell Vanderhook, Megan Duckett, Brad Sugars, John Vechey, Brian Fiete, Jason Kapalka, Nathan Jones, Devon Rifkin, Ryan Black, Ed Nichols, Jeremy Black, Amy Smilovic, Bob Shallenberger, and John Cavanagh.

TRADE PERIODICALS

47271 ■ *Futures*
Pub: Junior Achievement Inc.
Ed: Released: Quarterly. **Description:** Carries feature articles on various aspects of the Junior Achievement program and the volunteers and funders who support it. Promotes the principles of the free enterprise system. Recurring features include board member and volunteer profiles, and strategic initiatives.

VIDEOCASSETTES/ AUDIOCASSETTES

47272 ■ *Baby-Sitting the Responsible Way*
Cambridge Educational
c/o Films Media Group
132 West 31st Street, 17th Floor
Ste. 124
New York, NY 10001
Free: 800-257-5126
Fax:(609)671-0266
Co. E-mail: custserve@films.com
URL: http://www.cambridgeol.com
Price: $49.00. **Description:** Covers issues in responsible babysitting, including handling emergencies, keeping children on schedule, mealtime, handling behavior problems, and accident avoidance. Outlines behaviors to avoid such as talking extensively on the phone, failing to clean-up, and doing homework. Includes manual. **Availability:** VHS.

SMALL BUSINESS DEVELOPMENT CENTERS

47273 ■ Alabama A & M University Small Business Development Center
PO Box 429
Normal, AL 35762
URL: http://www.asbdc.org
Contact: Eric O'hene, Dir.

47274 ■ Alabama Small Business Development Consortium
1500 1st Ave. N, Ste. R118
Birmingham, AL 35203
Fax:(205)307-6511
URL: http://www.asbdc.org
Contact: William Campbell, Dir.

47275 ■ Alabama State University Small Business Development Center
915 S Jackson St.
Montgomery, AL 36104
Fax:(334)269-1102
Co. E-mail: lpatrick@alasu.edu
URL: http://www.cobanetwork.com/sbdc
Contact: Lorenza Patrick, Dir.

47276 ■ Auburn University Small Business Development Center
108 Lowder Business Bldg.
Auburn, AL 36849
Co. E-mail: dipofja@auburn.edu
URL: http://www.sbdc.auburn.edu
Contact: Jackie Alexander Di Pofi, Dir.

47277 ■ Jacksonville State University Small Business Development Center
College of Commerce and Business Administration
Merrill Hall, Rm. 114
700 Pelham Rd. N
Jacksonville, AL 36265
Co. E-mail: sbdc@jsu.edu
URL: http://www.jsu.edu/depart/sbdc
Contact: Pat Shaddix, Dir.

47278 ■ Troy University Small Business Development Center
Troy Campus
100 Industrial Blvd.
Troy, AL 36081
Co. E-mail: slucas@troy.edu
URL: http://cibed.troy.edu/sbdc
Contact: Sandra Lucas, Dir.

47279 ■ University of Alabama in Huntsville Small Business Development Center
301 Sparkman Dr.
Huntsville, AL 35899
Fax:(256)824-4339
Co. E-mail: sbdc@uah.edu
URL: http://sbdc.uah.edu
Contact: Kannan Grant, Dir.

47280 ■ University of Alabama Small Business Development Center
214 AIME Bldg.
720 2nd St.
Tuscaloosa, AL 35401
URL: http://www.asbdc.org
Contact: Paavo Hanninen, Dir.

47281 ■ University of North Alabama - Small Business Development Center
Keller Hall 135
1 Harrison Plz.
Florence, AL 35632
Fax:(256)765-4813
URL: http://business.una.edu/sbdc
Contact: Rick A. Lester, Dir.

47282 ■ University of South Alabama Small Business Development Center
MCOB, Rm. 118
307 University Blvd.
Mobile, AL 36688
Fax:(251)460-6246
Co. E-mail: sbdc@usouthal.edu
URL: http://www.southalabama.edu/sbdc
Contact: Thomas Tucker, Dir.

47283 ■ University of West Alabama Small Business Development Center
Guy Hunt Technical Complex, R122, Sta. 35
Livingston, AL 35470
URL: http://www.asbdc.org
Contact: Donald Mills, Dir.

SMALL BUSINESS ASSISTANCE PROGRAMS

47284 ■ Alabama Department of Economic and Community Affairs–Community and Economic Development Programs
401 Adams Ave.
PO Box 5690
Montgomery, AL 36103-5690
Ph:(334)242-5100
Fax:(334)242-5099
URL: http://www.adeca.state.al.us
Contact: Doni M. Ingram, Dir.
Description: Provides consultation services to small and developing businesses; provides information on federal grants and projects; and helps businesses to develop export contacts and markets.

47285 ■ U.S. Small Business Administration–Birmingham District Office
801 Tom Martin Dr., Ste. 201
Birmingham, AL 35211
Ph:(205)290-7101
Fax:(205)290-7404
URL: http://www.sba.gov
Contact: Tom Todt, Dir.
Description: Assists businesses planning new manufacturing, processing, warehousing, distribution, research, or office facilities, or expanding present facilities. Staff includes experts in research, tax,

finance, community data, and other areas. Helps in developing a finance package made up of bonds, grants, and loans. Services offered free of charge.

47286 ■ University of Alabama–Alabama International Trade Center
500 Colonial Dr., 201 Bidgood Hall
Box 870396
Tuscaloosa, AL 35487-0396
Ph:(205)348-7621
Free: 800-747-2482
Fax:(205)348-6974
Co. E-mail: aitc@ua.edu
URL: http://www.aitc.ua.edu
Contact: Brian K. Davis, Dir.
Description: Offers consulting services and seminars to help businesses develop international activities. Compiles information on foreign business climates. Services provided free of charge to smaller businesses; others must pay a fee.

SCORE OFFICES

47287 ■ Anniston SCORE
Path: www.anniston.scorechapter.org

BETTER BUSINESS BUREAUS

47288 ■ Better Business Bureau, Birmingham
PO Box 55268
Birmingham, AL 35255-5268
Ph:(205)558-2222
Free: 800-824-5274
Fax:(205)558-2239
Co. E-mail: info@centralalabama.bbb.org
URL: http://www.birmingham-al.bbb.org
Contact: David C. Smitherman, Pres.

47289 ■ Better Business Bureau of North Alabama
PO Box 383
Huntsville, AL 35804-0383
Ph:(256)533-1640
Free: 800-239-1642
Fax:(256)533-1177
Co. E-mail: info@northalabama.bbb.org
URL: http://northalabama.bbb.org
Contact: Ms. Michele McDaniel, Pres./CEO

47290 ■ Better Business Bureau of South Alabama
3361-E Cottage Hill Rd.
Mobile, AL 36606
Ph:(251)433-5494
Free: 800-544-4714
Fax:(251)438-3191
Co. E-mail: info@bbsouthal.org
URL: http://mobile.bbb.org
Contact: Tina Waller, Pres./CEO

CHAMBERS OF COMMERCE

47291 ■ Alabama Gulf Coast Area Chamber of Commerce
3150 Gulf Shores Pkwy.
PO Drawer 3869
Gulf Shores, AL 36547-3869
Ph:(251)968-6904
Fax:(251)968-5332
Co. E-mail: info@alagulfcoastchamber.com
URL: http://www.alagulfcoastchamber.com
Contact: Mark Berson, Pres.

47292 ■ Alexander City Chamber of Commerce
120 Tallapoosa St.
PO Box 926
Alexander City, AL 35010
Ph:(256)234-3461
Fax:(256)234-0094
Co. E-mail: susanfoy@charter.net
URL: http://www.alexandercity.org
Contact: Susan Foy, Pres./CEO

47293 ■ Aliceville Area Chamber of Commerce
PO Drawer A
Aliceville, AL 35442
Ph:(205)373-2820
Co. E-mail: acc@nctv.com
URL: http://www.cityofaliceville.com
Contact: Gale Ammerman, Chm.

47294 ■ Arab Chamber of Commerce
PO Box 626
1157 N Main St.
Arab, AL 35016
Ph:(256)586-3138
Fax:(256)586-0233
Co. E-mail: ddunn@arab-chamber.org
URL: http://www.arab-chamber.org
Contact: Deneille Dunn, Pres.

47295 ■ Athens-Limestone County Chamber of Commerce
101 S Beaty St.
PO Box 150
Athens, AL 35612
Ph:(256)232-2600
Fax:(256)232-5606
Co. E-mail: info@tourathens.com
URL: http://tourathens.com
Contact: Hugh Ball, Pres.

47296 ■ Atmore Area Chamber of Commerce
501 S Pensacola Ave.
Atmore, AL 36502
Ph:(251)368-3305
Fax:(251)368-0800
Co. E-mail: atmoreal@frontiernet.net
URL: http://www.atmorechamber.com

47297 ■ Auburn Chamber of Commerce
714 E Glenn Ave.
PO Box 1370
Auburn, AL 36831-1370
Ph:(334)887-7011
Fax:(334)821-5500
Co. E-mail: info@auburnchamber.com
URL: http://www.auburnchamber.com
Contact: Lolly Stainer, Pres.

47298 ■ Bayou La Batre Chamber of Commerce
PO Box 486
Bayou La Batre, AL 36509
Ph:(251)824-4088
Fax:(251)824-4088
Co. E-mail: info@bayoulabatrechamber.com
URL: http://www.bayoulabatrechamber.com

47299 ■ Birmingham Regional Chamber of Commerce
505 N 20th St.
Birmingham, AL 35203
Ph:(205)324-2100

Fax:(205)324-2560
Co. E-mail: russellc@birminghamchamber.com
URL: http://www.birminghamchamber.com
Contact: Russel Cunningham, Pres./CEO

47300 ■ Blount County-Oneonta Chamber of Commerce
PO Box 1487
Oneonta, AL 35121
Ph:(205)274-2153
Fax:(205)274-2099
Co. E-mail: info@blountoneontachamber.org
URL: http://www.blountoneontachamber.org
Contact: Charles R. Carr, Exec. Dir.

47301 ■ Boaz Chamber of Commerce
100 E Bartlett Ave.
PO Box 563
Boaz, AL 35957
Ph:(256)593-8154
Fax:(256)593-1233
Co. E-mail: boazchamber@charter.net
URL: http://www.boazchamberofcommerce.com
Contact: Keyesta Sherman, Pres.

47302 ■ Central Baldwin Chamber of Commerce
PO Box 587
Robertsdale, AL 36567
Ph:(251)947-5932
Fax:(251)947-2626
Co. E-mail: info@cbcchamber.org
URL: http://www.cbcchamber.org
Contact: Marian Mason, Pres./CEO

47303 ■ Chamber of Commerce - Bessemer Area
321 N 18th St.
Bessemer, AL 35020
Ph:(205)425-3253
Free: 888-423-7736
Fax:(205)425-4979
Co. E-mail: mmilan1@bellsouth.net
URL: http://www.bessemerchamber.com
Contact: Ronald W. Acker, Pres.

47304 ■ Chamber of Commerce of Huntsville/Madison County
225 Church St.
Huntsville, AL 35801
Ph:(256)535-2000
Fax:(256)535-2015
Co. E-mail: hcc@hsvchamber.org
URL: http://www.huntsvillealabamausa.com
Contact: Brian Hilson, Pres./CEO

47305 ■ Chamber of Commerce of Walker County
204 19th St. E, Ste. 101
Jasper, AL 35501
Ph:(205)384-4571
Fax:(205)384-4901
Co. E-mail: linda@walkerchamber.us
URL: http://www.walkerchamber.us
Contact: Linda Lewis, Pres.

47306 ■ Chamber of Commerce of West Alabama
2200 University Blvd.
Tuscaloosa, AL 35402
Ph:(205)758-7588
Fax:(205)391-0565
Co. E-mail: chamber@dbtech.net
URL: http://www.tuscaloosachamber.com
Contact: Johnnie R. Aycock, Pres.

47307 ■ Cherokee County Chamber of Commerce
801 Cedar Bluff Rd.
PO Box 86
Centre, AL 35960-0086
Ph:(256)927-8455
Fax:(256)927-2768
Co. E-mail: cccoc@tds.net
URL: http://www.cherokee-chamber.org
Contact: Kurt Duryea, Chair

47308 ■ Childersburg Chamber of Commerce
PO Box 527
Childersburg, AL 35044
Ph:(256)378-5482
Fax:(256)378-5833
Co. E-mail: pbstorey@childersburg.com
URL: http://www.childersburg.com
Contact: Pete Storey, Pres./CEO

47309 ■ Chilton County Chamber of Commerce
PO Box 66
Clanton, AL 35046
Ph:(205)755-2400
Fax:(205)755-8444
Co. E-mail: office@chiltonconcountychamber.com
URL: http://www.chiltoncountychamber.com
Contact: Pennie Broussard

47310 ■ Clay County Chamber of Commerce, Alabama
PO Box 85
Lineville, AL 36266
Ph:(256)396-2828
Fax:(256)396-5532
Co. E-mail: claychamber@centurytel.net
URL: http://claycochamber.com
Contact: Mary Patchunka-Smith, Exec. Dir.

47311 ■ Cullman Area Chamber of Commerce
PO Box 1104
Cullman, AL 35056-1104
Ph:(256)734-0454
Free: 800-313-5114
Fax:(256)737-7443
Co. E-mail: info@cullmanchamber.org
URL: http://www.cullmanchamber.org
Contact: Dr. Vicki Hawsey, Chair

47312 ■ Dadeville Area Chamber of Commerce
185 S Tallassee St., Ste. 103
Dadeville, AL 36853
Ph:(256)825-4019
Fax:(256)825-0547
Co. E-mail: chamber@dadeville.com
URL: http://www.dadeville.com
Contact: Steve Kerr, Pres.

47313 ■ Decatur Morgan County Chamber of Commerce
515 Sixth Ave. NE
Decatur, AL 35602-2003
Ph:(256)353-5312
Fax:(256)353-2384
Co. E-mail: john@dcc.org
URL: http://www.dcc.org
Contact: John Seymour, Pres./CEO

47314 ■ Demopolis Area Chamber of Commerce
102 E Washington St.
PO Box 667
Demopolis, AL 36732
Ph:(334)289-0270
Fax:(334)289-1382
Co. E-mail: dacc@westal.net
URL: http://www.demopolischamber.com
Contact: Kelley Smith, Pres.

47315 ■ Dothan Area Chamber of Commerce
102 Jamestown Blvd.
PO Box 638
Dothan, AL 36302-0638
Ph:(334)792-5138
Free: 800-221-1027
Fax:(334)794-4796
Co. E-mail: cshippey@dothan.com
URL: http://www.dothan.com
Contact: Matt Parker, Pres.

47316 ■ Eastern Shore Chamber of Commerce
29750 Larry Dee Cawyer Dr.
PO Drawer 310
Daphne, AL 36526
Ph:(251)621-8222

Fax:(251)621-8001
Co. E-mail: office@eschamber.com
URL: http://www.eschamber.com
Contact: Darrelyn J. Bender, Pres.

47317 ■ Enterprise Chamber of Commerce
PO Box 310577
Enterprise, AL 36331-0577
Ph:(334)347-0581
Free: 800-235-4730
Fax:(334)393-8204
Co. E-mail: chamberpresident@centurytel.net
URL: http://www.enterprisealabama.com
Contact: Phil Thomas, Pres.

47318 ■ Eufaula - Barbour County Chamber of Commerce
333 E Broad St.
PO Box 697
Eufaula, AL 36072-0697
Ph:(334)687-6664
Free: 800-524-7529
Fax:(334)687-5240
Co. E-mail: info@eufaulachamber.com
Contact: James D. Bradley, Exec. Dir.

47319 ■ Eutaw Area Chamber of Commerce
111 Main St.
Eutaw, AL 35462
Ph:(205)372-9002
Fax:(205)372-1393
Co. E-mail: eutawchamber@bellsouth.net
URL: http://www.eutawchamber.com
Contact: Ralph Banks III

47320 ■ Evergreen/Conecuh Chamber of Commerce
100 Depot Sq.
Evergreen, AL 36401
Ph:(251)578-1707
Fax:(251)578-5660
Co. E-mail: emma0916@bellsouth.net
URL: http://www.evergreenchamberofcommerce.org
Contact: Ms. Emma Johnson, Admin.

47321 ■ Fayette Area Chamber of Commerce
PO Box 247
102 2nd Ave.
Fayette, AL 35555
Ph:(205)932-4587
Co. E-mail: info@fayetteareachamber.org
URL: http://www.fayetteareachamber.org

47322 ■ Fort Payne Chamber of Commerce
300 Gault Ave. N
Fort Payne, AL 35968-0125
Ph:(256)845-2741
Fax:(256)845-5849
URL: http://www.fortpaynechamber.com
Contact: Carol Beddingfield, Dir.

47323 ■ Franklin County Chamber of Commerce
103 N Jackson Ave.
PO Box 44
Russellville, AL 35653
Ph:(256)332-1760
Fax:(256)332-1740
Co. E-mail: franklincounty@charter.net
URL: http://www.franklincountychamber.org
Contact: Cheryl Bradford, Exec. Dir.

47324 ■ Gadsden Area Chamber of Commerce
1 Commerce Sq.
Gadsden, AL 35901
Ph:(256)543-3472
Free: 800-238-6924
Co. E-mail: info@gadsdenchamber.com
URL: http://www.gadsdenchamber.com
Contact: Tom Quinn, Pres.

47325 ■ Gardendale Chamber of Commerce
2109 Moncrief Rd., Ste. 115
Gardendale, AL 35071
Ph:(205)631-9195
Free: 888-631-4422

Fax:(205)631-9034
Co. E-mail: joy@gardendalechamberofcommerce.com
URL: http://www.gardendalechamberofcommerce.com
Contact: Joy Clayton, Exec. Dir.

47326 ■ Greater Brewton Area Chamber of Commerce
1010 B Douglas Ave.
Brewton, AL 36426
Ph:(251)867-3224
Fax:(251)809-1793
Co. E-mail: jcrane@brewtonchamber.com
URL: http://www.brewtonchamber.com
Contact: Judy Crane, Exec. Dir.

47327 ■ Greater Geneva Area Chamber of Commerce
406 S Commerce St.
Geneva, AL 36340
Ph:(334)684-6582
Co. E-mail: genevachamber@aol.com
URL: http://www.genevaalabama.net
Contact: Olivia McCray

47328 ■ Greater Jackson County Chamber of Commerce
PO Box 973
Scottsboro, AL 35769
Ph:(256)259-5500
Free: 800-259-5508
Fax:(256)259-4447
Co. E-mail: roden@scottsboro.org
URL: http://www.jacksoncountychamber.com
Contact: Rick Roden, Pres./CEO

47329 ■ Greater Shelby County Chamber of Commerce
1301 County Services Dr.
Pelham, AL 35124
Ph:(205)663-4542
Fax:(205)663-4524
Co. E-mail: info@shelbychamber.org
URL: http://www.shelbychamber.org/GSCHome.asp?ID=2
Contact: Jennifer Trammell, Pres./CEO

47330 ■ Greater Talladega Area Chamber of Commerce
PO Box A
Talladega, AL 35161-0005
Ph:(256)362-9075
Fax:(256)362-9093
Co. E-mail: talladegachamber@yahoo.com
URL: http://www.talladegachamber.com
Contact: Heidi Edwards, Exec. Dir.

47331 ■ Greater Tallassee Area Chamber of Commerce
650 Gilmer Ave.
Tallassee, AL 36078
Ph:(334)283-5151
Fax:(334)252-0774
Co. E-mail: chamber@tallassee.al.us
URL: http://www.tallassee.al.us
Contact: George McCain, Exec. Dir.

47332 ■ Greater Valley Area Chamber of Commerce
PO Box 205
Lanett, AL 36863
Ph:(334)642-1411
Fax:(334)642-1410
Co. E-mail: info@greatervalleyarea.com
URL: http://www.greatervalleyarea.com
Contact: Kate Pruit, Pres.

47333 ■ Greenville Area Chamber of Commerce
1 Depot Sq.
Greenville, AL 36037
Ph:(334)382-3251
Free: 800-959-0717
Fax:(334)382-3181
Co. E-mail: chamber@greenville-alabama.com
URL: http://www.greenville-alabama.com
Contact: Francine Wasden, Exec. Dir.

47334 ■ Haleyville Area Chamber of Commerce
PO Box 634
Haleyville, AL 35565
Ph:(205)486-4611
Fax:(205)486-5074
Co. E-mail: info@haleyvillechamber.org
URL: http://www.haleyvillechamber.org
Contact: Bobby Taylor, Pres.

47335 ■ Hartselle Area Chamber of Commerce
PO Box 817
Hartselle, AL 35640
Ph:(256)773-4370
Free: 800-294-0692
Fax:(256)773-4379
Co. E-mail: hartsell@hiwaay.net
URL: http://www.hartsellechamber.com
Contact: Susan Hines, Pres.

47336 ■ Headland Chamber of Commerce
101 E King St.
Headland, AL 36345
Ph:(334)693-5094
URL: http://headlandal.org/index.php?option=com_contact&Itemid=3
Contact: William Snell, Pres.

47337 ■ Homewood Chamber of Commerce
1721 Oxmoor Rd.
Homewood, AL 35209
Ph:(205)871-5631
Co. E-mail: johnchristopher_batts@colonialbank.com
URL: http://www.homewoodchamber.org
Contact: John Christopher Batts, Exec. VP

47338 ■ Hoover Chamber of Commerce
PO Box 36005
Hoover, AL 35236
Ph:(205)988-5672
Fax:(205)988-8383
Co. E-mail: bill@hooverchamber.org
URL: http://www.hooverchamber.org
Contact: Bill Powell, Exec. Dir.

47339 ■ Hueytown Chamber of Commerce
2058-A High School Rd.
Hueytown, AL 35023
Ph:(205)491-8039
Co. E-mail: hueyoed@bellsouth.net
URL: http://www.hueytownchamber.com
Contact: George Hudson, Pres.

47340 ■ Lake Guntersville Chamber of Commerce
PO Box 577
Guntersville, AL 35976
Ph:(256)582-3612
Free: 800-869-LAKE
Fax:(256)582-3682
Co. E-mail: gcc@lakeguntersville.org
URL: http://www.lakeguntersville.org
Contact: Morri Yancy, Pres.

47341 ■ Lawrence County Chamber of Commerce, Alabama
PO Box 325
Moulton, AL 35650
Ph:(256)974-1658
Fax:(256)974-2400
Co. E-mail: lawrence@lawrencealabama.com
URL: http://www.lawrencealabama.com
Contact: Kim Hood, Exec. Dir.

47342 ■ Leeds Area Chamber of Commerce
PO Box 900
Leeds, AL 35094-0900
Ph:(205)699-5001
Fax:(205)699-1777
Co. E-mail: leedschamber@windstream.net
URL: http://www.leedsalabama.com
Contact: Bill Morris, Pres.

47343 ■ Mobile Area Chamber of Commerce
451 Government St.
Mobile, AL 36652-2187
Ph:(251)433-6951
Free: 800-422-6951

Fax:(251)432-1143
Co. E-mail: info@mobilechamber.com
URL: http://www.mobilechamber.com
Contact: Mr. Winthrop M. Hallett III, Pres.

47344 ■ Monroeville Area Chamber of Commerce
63 N Mt. Pleasant Ave.
Monroeville, AL 36460
Ph:(251)743-2879
Fax:(251)743-2189
Co. E-mail: sandy@monroecountyal.com
URL: http://www.monroecountyal.com
Contact: Sandy C. Smith, Exec. Dir.

47345 ■ Montevallo Chamber of Commerce
720 Oak St.
Montevallo, AL 35115
Ph:(205)665-1519
Fax:(205)665-0759
Co. E-mail: montevallocc@bellsouth.net
Contact: Ben McCrory, Pres.

47346 ■ Montgomery Area Chamber of Commerce
41 Commerce St.
PO Box 79
Montgomery, AL 36104-3502
Ph:(334)834-5200
Co. E-mail: rgeorge@montgomerychamber.com
URL: http://www.montgomerychamber.com/Page.
aspx?pid=195
Contact: Randall L. George CED, Pres.

47347 ■ North Baldwin Chamber of Commerce
301 McMeans Ave.
PO Box 310
Bay Minette, AL 36507
Ph:(251)937-5665
Fax:(251)937-5670
Co. E-mail: director@northbaldwinchamber.com
URL: http://www.northbaldwinchamber.com
Contact: Margo Allen, Exec. Dir.

47348 ■ Northwest Alabama Junior Chamber of Commerce
2808 Jackson Hwy.
Sheffield, AL 35660
Ph:(256)740-0255
Co. E-mail: nwajcc@mail.com
URL: http://nwajcc.tripod.com
Contact: Martin Dean, Pres.

47349 ■ Opelika Chamber of Commerce
601 Ave. A
PO Box 2366
Opelika, AL 36803-2366
Ph:(334)745-4861
Fax:(334)749-4740
Co. E-mail: coc@opelika.com
URL: http://www.opelika.com
Contact: Wendi Routhier, Pres.

47350 ■ Opp and Covington County Area Chamber of Commerce
PO Box 148
Opp, AL 36467
Ph:(334)493-3070
Free: 800-239-8054
Fax:(334)493-1060
Co. E-mail: info@oppchamber.com
URL: http://www.oppchamber.com
Contact: Dr. Joshua Driver, Pres.

47351 ■ Phenix City-Russell County Chamber of Commerce
1107 Broad St.
Phenix City, AL 36867
Ph:(334)298-3639
Free: 800-892-2248
Fax:(334)298-3846
Co. E-mail: pcrccham@ldl.net
URL: http://pc-rcchamber.com
Contact: Victor W. Cross, Pres.

47352 ■ Prattville Area Chamber of Commerce
131 N Court St.
Prattville, AL 36067
Ph:(334)365-7392
Free: 800-588-2796
Fax:(334)361-1314
Co. E-mail: jprochazka@prattvillechamber.com
URL: http://www.prattvillechamber.com
Contact: Connie Bainbridge, Pres.

47353 ■ Rainsville Chamber of Commerce
PO Box 396
Rainsville, AL 35986
Ph:(256)638-7800
Co. E-mail: timeberhart@farmerstel.com
URL: http://www.rainsville.info
Contact: Tim Eberhart, Publicity Dir.

47354 ■ Saraland Area Chamber of Commerce
939 Hwy. 43 S
Saraland, AL 36571
Ph:(251)675-4444
Fax:(251)675-2307
Co. E-mail: info@saralandcoc.com
URL: http://www.saralandcoc.com
Contact: Doug Roberts, Chm.

47355 ■ Shoals Chamber of Commerce
20 Hightower Pl.
Florence, AL 35630
Ph:(256)764-4661
Free: 877-764-4661
Fax:(256)766-9017
Co. E-mail: shoals@shoalschamber.com
URL: http://www.shoalschamber.com
Contact: Mr. Stephen B. Holt CCE, Pres.

47356 ■ South Baldwin Chamber of Commerce
104 N Mackenzie St.
PO Box 1117
Foley, AL 36536
Ph:(251)943-3291
Fax:(251)943-6810
Co. E-mail: info@southbaldwinchamber.com
URL: http://www.southbaldwinchamber.com
Contact: Donna H. Watts, Pres./CEO

47357 ■ Springville Area Chamber of Commerce
6496 U.S. Hwy. 11
Springville, AL 35146
Ph:(205)467-2339
Co. E-mail: bwisner@springvillealabama.org
URL: http://www.springvillealabama.org/sacoc/index.
html
Contact: Cason Catts, Pres.

47358 ■ Sylacauga Chamber of Commerce
PO Box 185
Sylacauga, AL 35150
Ph:(256)249-0308
Fax:(256)249-0315
Co. E-mail: jrichardson@sylacauga.net
URL: http://www.sylacauga.net/chamber
Contact: Joe Richardson, Dir.

47359 ■ Trussville Area Chamber of Commerce
225 Parkway Dr.
Trussville, AL 35173
Ph:(205)655-7535
Free: 800-949-8222
Fax:(205)655-3705
Co. E-mail: trusscoc@hiwaay.net
URL: http://www.trussvillechamber.com
Contact: Diane Poole, Exec. Dir.

47360 ■ Union Springs/Bullock County Chamber of Commerce
PO Box 5006
Union Springs, AL 36089
Ph:(334)738-2424
Co. E-mail: info@usacoc.com
URL: http://www.usacoc.com
Contact: Joyce Perrin, Pres.

47361 ■ Vestavia Hills Chamber of Commerce
1975 Merryvale Rd.
Vestavia Hills, AL 35216
Ph:(205)823-5011
Free: (866)402-VHCC
Fax:(205)823-8974
Co. E-mail: chamber@vestaviahills.org
URL: http://www.vestaviahills.org
Contact: Karen J. Odle, Exec. Dir.

47362 ■ Winfield Chamber of Commerce
PO Box 1557
Winfield, AL 35594
Ph:(205)487-8841
Co. E-mail: chamberofcommerce@winfieldcity.org
URL: http://www.winfieldcity.org
Contact: Chele Bussey, Pres.

MINORITY BUSINESS ASSISTANCE PROGRAMS

47363 ■ Alabama Minority Business Enterprise Center
450A Government St.
Mobile, AL 36602
Ph:(251)433-2250
Fax:(251)433-2208
Co. E-mail: pramos@mbecalabama.org
URL: http://www.mbecalabama.org
Contact: Pamela Ramos, Proj Mgr
Description: Provides business and technical support for emerging and existing minority businesses in Alabama.

47364 ■ Alabama Minority Business Opportunity Center
4715 Alton Ct.
Birmingham, AL 35210
Ph:(205)957-9779
Fax:(205)957-2114
Co. E-mail: info@mbocalabama.org
URL: http://www.mbocalabama.org
Contact: Henry A. Turner, Exec Dir
Description: Assists corporations, government agencies, and universities in developing business opportunites to support minority enterprises.

47365 ■ Birmingham Business Resource Center
1500 1st Ave. N, Ste. 106, Unit 2
Birmingham, AL 35203
Ph:(205)250-6380
Fax:(205)250-6384
Co. E-mail: info@bbrc.biz
URL: http://www.mybbrc.biz/
Contact: Andrew Mayo
Description: Offers small business finance and related technical assistance.

47366 ■ Women's Business Center Inc.
1301 Azalea Rd., Ste. 201A
Mobile, AL 36693
Ph:(251)660-2725
Fax:(251)660-8854
Co. E-mail: info@womenbiz.biz
URL: http://www.womenbiz.biz
Contact: Kathryn Kahalley Cariglino, Exec Dir
Description: Works to assist and empower women in starting or growing small businesses.

FINANCING AND LOAN PROGRAMS

47367 ■ Bonaventure Capital
3104 Blue Lake Dr., Ste. 120
Birmingham, AL 35243
Ph:(205)588-6024

Fax:(205)870-8050
URL: http://www.bonaventurecapital.net
Contact: Steve Dauphin, Partner
E-mail: sdauphin@bonaventurecapital.net
Preferred Investment Size: $500,000 to $1,500,000.
Investment Policies: Early stage. **Industry Preferences:** Computer software, industrial and energy, financial services, and utilities. **Geographic Preferences:** Southeast. **Principal Exhibits:**

47368 ▪ FHL Capital Corp.
2 20th Street N., Ste. 860
Birmingham, AL 35203
Ph:(205)328-3098
Fax:(205)323-0001
Co. E-mail: officemgr@fhlcapital.com
URL: http://www.fhlcapital.com
Contact: Edwin W. Finch III, Founder, President and Chief Executive O
E-mail: efinch@fhlcapital.com
Preferred Investment Size: $1,000,000 to $75,000,000. **Investment Types:** Mergers and acquisitions, divestitures, private placements, leveraged and management buyouts, recapitalization, and special situation. **Geographic Preferences:** U.S. **Principal Exhibits:**

47369 ▪ Harbert Management Corp.
2100 3rd Ave., N., Ste. 600
Birmingham, AL 35203
Ph:(205)987-5500
Fax:(205)987-5568
URL: http://www.harbert.net
Contact: Michael D. Luce, President and Chief Operating Officer
Preferred Investment Size: $1,000,000 to $4,000,000. **Investment Types:** Leveraged buyout, mezzanine, acquisition, special situation, and recapitalizations. **Industry Preferences:** Technology, semiconductors and other electronics, medical and health, biotechnology, communications, software and services. **Geographic Preferences:** Southeastern U.S. **Principal Exhibits:**

47370 ▪ Hickory Venture Capital Corp. / Hickory Venture Group
301 Washington St., Ste. 301
Huntsville, AL 35801
Ph:(256)539-1931
Fax:(256)539-5130
Co. E-mail: info@hvcc.com
URL: http://www.hvcc.com
Contact: J. Thomas Noojin, Principal
Preferred Investment Size: $1,000,000 to $7,000,000. **Investment Types:** First stage, later stage, balanced, and leverage buyout. **Industry Preferences:** Communications and media, computer software and services, computer hardware, Internet specific, consumer related, industrial and energy, semiconductors and other electronics, medical and health, other products, and biotechnology. **Geographic Preferences:** Southeast, Midwest, and Texas. **Principal Exhibits:**

47371 ▪ Southeastern Technology Fund
207 East Side Sq., 1st Fl.
Huntsville, AL 35801
Ph:(256)883-8711
Fax:(256)883-8558
URL: http://www.setfund.com
Contact: Chris Horgen, Senior Managing Partner
Preferred Investment Size: $1,000,000 to $3,000,000. **Investment Types:** Early, first and second stage, and expansion. **Industry Preferences:** Communications and media, Internet specific, computer software and services. **Geographic Preferences:** Southeast. **Principal Exhibits:**

PROCUREMENT ASSISTANCE PROGRAMS

47372 ▪ Alabama Department of Finance–Division of Purchasing
100 N Union St., Ste. 192
Montgomery, AL 36130-3620
Ph:(334)242-7250

Fax:(334)242-4419
URL: http://www.purchasing.state.al.us
Contact: Isaac Kervin, Purchasing Dir
Description: Contact for the state's list of bidders for government purchasing contracts. A small business representative is available.

47373 ▪ Alabama Procurement Center Representatives
Bldg. 5303, Rm. 3135 US SBA
Redstone Arsenal, AL 35898-5150
Ph:(256)842-6240
Fax:(256)842-0085
Co. E-mail: gary.heard@sba.gov
URL: http://www.sba.gov
Contact: Gary Heard, Prgm Rep
E-mail: gary.heard@sba.gov
Description: Covers activities for Army Aviation & Missile Command (Huntsville, AL).

47374 ▪ Alabama Procurement Technical Assistance Center–University of Alabama
Box 870396
Tuscaloosa, AL 35487-0396
Ph:(205)348-1687
Fax:(205)348-6974
Co. E-mail: asbdc@ua.edu
URL: http://www.al-ptac.org
Contact: Pat Phillips, Dir.
Description: Identifies and implements innovative procurement practices in support of the efforts of our customers, and assists the University with its mission of teaching, research and public service by safeguarding the integrity of the purchasing and payables process.

47375 ▪ Alabama Small Business Development Consortium
Box 870396
Tuscaloosa, AL 35487-0396
Ph:(205)348-1582
Free: 877-825-7232
Fax:(205)348-6974
Co. E-mail: rlgrover@ua.edu
URL: http://www.asbdc.org
Contact: William Campbell, Dir.
Description: Notifies businesses of bidding opportunities. Offers counseling in areas such as bid package preparation, minority programs, military packaging, pricing, bonding, and quality assurance. Holds training seminars and procurement conferences.

INCUBATORS/RESEARCH AND TECHNOLOGY PARKS

47376 ▪ Auburn University–Economic and Community Development Institute
Extension Hall
Auburn University, AL 36849-5252
Ph:(334)844-4704
Fax:(334)844-4709
Co. E-mail: sumneja@auburn.edu
URL: http://www.auburn.edu/outreach/ecdi
Contact: Joe A. Sumners PhD, Dir.
E-mail: sumneja@auburn.edu
Scope: Economic and community development, focusing on issues related to Alabama. **Services:** Intensive Economic Development Training Course (annually), two-week training program for economic developers; Rural Alabama Initiative Grant Program, mini-grants for local community and economic development projects.

47377 ▪ Auburn University–Office of Vice President for Research
202 Samford Hall
Auburn, AL 36849
Ph:(334)844-4784
Fax:(334)844-5971
Co. E-mail: jmason@auburn.edu
URL: http://fp.auburn.edu/vpr/default.aspx
Contact: John M. Mason Jr., VP, Res.
E-mail: jmason@auburn.edu
Scope: Administers and coordinates all research conducted at the University, including research in biological, physical, and social sciences, the arts, humanities, engineering, space, and related areas.
Publications: Annual Research Report.

47378 ▪ Baldwin County Business Incubator
PO Box 1340
Robertsdale, AL 36567
Ph:(251)947-2445
Free: 800-947-2445
Fax:(251)947-4229
Co. E-mail: info@baldwinincubator.com
URL: http://www.baldwinincubator.com/
Contact: Bob Higgins, Dir.
Description: A small business incubator that offers qualifying start-up companies a structured two-to-three-year program of advice and professional assistance to help ensure success.

47379 ▪ Bessemer Business Incubation System
1020 Ninth Ave. SW
Bessemer, AL 35022
Ph:(205)481-2000
Fax:(205)481-2100
Co. E-mail: Bessemerincubator@yahoo.com
URL: http://bessemerincubator.net
Description: A division of the Bessemer Development Board that provides in-house services for businesses with revenues up to $5,000,000. It serves not only startup operations, but challenged, former home-based, geographically-expanding and those operations still in the research/feasibility phase. Businesses can remain in the incubator for up to 5 years.

47380 ▪ Business Technology Development Center
515 Sparkman Dr.
Huntsville, AL 35816
Ph:(256)704-6000
Fax:(256)704-6002
URL: http://www.biztech.org/
Contact: Gary Tauss, Dir. & CEO
Description: BizTech is a technology incubator designed to help small companies develop emerging technologies for the global marketplace, providing mentoring, access to investors, training, a ready-made network of contacts, and various business support services designed to improve the likelihood of success.

47381 ▪ Cummings Research Park
Chamber of Commerce of Huntsville/Madison County
225 Church St.
Huntsville, AL 35801
Ph:(256)535-2018
Fax:(256)535-2015
Co. E-mail: rdavis@hsvchamber.org
URL: http://www.huntsvillealabamausa.com/new_exp/new_crp_toc.html
Contact: Rick Davis, Dir.
E-mail: rdavis@hsvchamber.org
Scope: Aerospace, missile defense research and development, electronics, telecommunications, applied optics, artificial intelligence, software development, data communications, and life sciences.

47382 ▪ Innovation Depot
1500 First Ave. N.
Birmingham, AL 35203
Ph:(205)250-8000
Fax:(205)250-8013
Co. E-mail: ecinfo@entrepreneurialctr.com
URL: http://www.innovationdepot.net
Contact: Kevin Herren, Dir.
Description: Innovation Depot is a business incubator housing 70 start-up businesses. The Depot is a non-profit partnership formed by the combination of the Entrepreneurial Center and the Univeristy of Alabama at Birmingham's Office for the Advancement of Developing Industries.

47383 ▪ Montgomery Area Chamber of Commerce Incubation Program
600 S Court St.
Montgomery, AL 36101
Ph:(334)834-5200

Fax:(334)265-4745
Co. E-mail: lmcginty@montgomerychamber.com
URL: http://www.montgomerychamber.com
Contact: Lisa McGinty, Dir.
Description: A non-profit small business incubator program for new service and light manufacturing businesses in the Montgomery area.

47384 ■ Northeast Alabama Entrepreneurial System
1400 Commerce Blvd., Ste. 1
Anniston, AL 36207
Ph:(256)831-5215
Fax:(256)831-8728
Co. E-mail: giles@neaes.org
URL: http://www.neaes.org
Contact: Giles McDaniel, Chairman
Description: The Entrepreneurial Center is a business incubator. A business incubator is a building in which start-up companies locate during their initial growth phase which can range from one to five years.

47385 ■ Shoals Entrepreneurial Center
3115 Northington Ct.
Florence, AL 35630
Ph:(256)760-9014
Fax:(256)740-5530
Co. E-mail: ContactUs@shoalsec.com
URL: http://www.shoalsec.com
Contact: Giles H. McDaniel, Exec. Dir.
Description: A private, non-profit corporation whose purpose is to assist new or fledgling businesses to grow in a sheltered environment until they are ready to be self-sustaining within the business community.

47386 ■ University of Alabama–Office for Sponsored Programs
152 Rose Administration, Box 870104
Tuscaloosa, AL 35487-0104
Ph:(205)348-5152

Fax:(205)348-8882
Co. E-mail: chope@fa.ua.edu
URL: http://www.osp.ua.edu/
Contact: Cynthia Hope, Dir.
E-mail: chope@fa.ua.edu
Scope: Coordinates contract and grant-sponsored research and development activities on campus of the University located in Tuscaloosa including engineering, mathematics, physics, chemistry, biology, sociology, psychology, business, highway engineering, computer science, geology, nutrition, child development, nursing, communications, law, community health, mining, energy, natural resources, social work, music, public administration, archeology, various center activities.

47387 ■ University of Alabama at Birmingham–Office of Grants and Contracts Administration
Administration Bldg. 1170
1530 3rd Ave. S
Birmingham, AL 35294-0111
Ph:(205)934-5266
Fax:(205)975-5977
Co. E-mail: stedman@uab.edu
URL: http://www.uab.edu/osp
Contact: Lynn W. Stedman, Dir.
E-mail: stedman@uab.edu
Scope: Administers and coordinates extramurally sponsored research conducted in all units of the University located in Birmingham.

LEGISLATIVE ASSISTANCE

47388 ■ Alabama State House of Representatives–Bill Status Office
Alabama State House, Rm. 512
11 S. Union St. 5th Fl.
Montgomery, AL 36130
Ph:(334)242-7627
Free: 800-499-3051

Fax:(334)353-9040
Co. E-mail: alsenate@mindspring.com
URL: http://www.legislature.state.al.us
Contact: Jennifer Dabbou, Bill Status Clerk

47389 ■ Alabama State House of Representatives–House Commerce Committee
Alabama State House
11 S. Union St., Rm. 522-B
Montgomery, AL 36130
Ph:(334)242-7697
Fax:(334)353-0828
Co. E-mail: house3@mindspring.com
URL: http://www.legislature.state.al.us
Contact: Frank McDaniel, Chair

PUBLICATIONS

47390 ■ *Atlanta Business Chronicle*
1801 Peachtree St., Ste. 150
Atlanta, GA 30309
Ph:(404)249-1000
Fax:(404)249-1048
Co. E-mail: atlanta@amcity.com
URL: http://www.amcity.com/atlanta

47391 ■ *Starting and Operating a Business in Alabama: A Step-by-Step Guide*
PSI Research
300 N. Valley Dr.
Grants Pass, OR 97526
Ph:(503)479-9464
Free: 800-228-2275
Fax:(503)476-1479
Co. E-mail: psi2@magick.net
Ed: Michael D. Jenkins. **Released:** Revised edition, 1992. **Price:** $29.95 (looseleaf binder); $24.95 (paper). **Description:** Part of the Successful Business Library series.

SMALL BUSINESS DEVELOPMENT CENTERS

47392 ■ Alaska Small Business Development Center - Central Region
201 N Lucille St., Ste. 2A
Wasilla, AK 99654
Free: 877-373-7232
Fax:(907)373-7234
Co. E-mail: anjad2@uaa.alaska.edu
URL: http://www.aksbdc.org
Contact: Jason Dinneen, Dir.

47393 ■ Alaska Small Business Development Center - Great North Region
UAF Tanana Valley Campus
604 Barnette St., Ste. 220
Fairbanks, AK 99701
Free: 800-478-1701
Fax:(907)456-7233
Co. E-mail: anmkt@uaa.alaska.edu
URL: http://www.tvc.uaf.edu/sbdc.html
Contact: Matt Tullar, Dir.

47394 ■ Alaska Small Business Development Center - South Central Region
430 W 7th Ave., Ste. 110
Anchorage, AK 99501
Free: 800-478-7232
Fax:(907)274-9524
Co. E-mail: anibv@uaa.alaska.edu
URL: http://www.aksbdc.org
Contact: Isaac Vanderburg, Dir.

47395 ■ Alaska Small Business Development Center - South West Region
43335 Kalifornsky Beach Rd., Ste. 12
Soldotna, AK 99669
Fax:(907)260-1695
Co. E-mail: inmeg@uaa.alaska.edu
URL: http://www.aksbdc.org
Contact: Mark Gregory, Dir.

47396 ■ Alaska Small Business Development Center - Southeast Region
3100 Channel Dr., Ste. 306
Juneau, AK 99801
Fax:(907)463-3430
Co. E-mail: anamd1@uaa.alaska.edu
URL: http://www.aksbdc.org
Contact: Amy Daugherty, Dir.

SMALL BUSINESS ASSISTANCE PROGRAMS

47397 ■ Alaska Department of Commerce, Community, and Economic Development
PO Box 110800
Juneau, AK 99811-0800
Ph:(907)465-2500
Fax:(907)465-3767
Co. E-mail: questions@alaska.gov
URL: http://www.commerce.state.ak.us
Contact: Emil Notti, Commissioner
Description: Assists entrepreneurs in starting new businesses or expanding existing businesses. Helps prepare applications for economic development programs. Holds seminars and workshops on various aspects of business management.

BETTER BUSINESS BUREAUS

47398 ■ Better Business Bureau of Alaska
3601 C St., Ste. 1378
Anchorage, AK 99503
Ph:(907)562-0704
Fax:(907)562-4061
Co. E-mail: info@thebbb.org
URL: http://www.alaska.bbb.org
Contact: Robert W.G. Andrew, Pres./CEO

CHAMBERS OF COMMERCE

47399 ■ Alaska State Chamber of Commerce
217 2nd St., Ste. 201
Juneau, AK 99801-1267
Ph:(907)586-2323
Fax:(907)463-5515
Co. E-mail: info@alaskachamber.com
URL: http://www.alaskachamber.com
Contact: Wayne A. Stevens, Pres.

47400 ■ Anchor Point Chamber of Commerce
PO Box 610
Anchor Point, AK 99556-0610
Ph:(907)235-2600
Fax:(907)235-2600
Co. E-mail: info@anchorpointchamber.org
URL: http://www.anchorpointchamber.org
Contact: Doug Ruzicka, Pres.

47401 ■ Anchorage Chamber of Commerce
1016 W 6th Ave., Ste. 303
Anchorage, AK 99501-2309
Ph:(907)272-2401
Fax:(907)272-4117
Co. E-mail: info@anchoragechamber.org
URL: http://www.anchoragechamber.org
Contact: Tony Izzo, Chm.-Elect

47402 ■ Big Lake Chamber of Commerce
PO Box 520067
Big Lake, AK 99652
Ph:(907)892-6109
Fax:(907)892-6189
Co. E-mail: info@biglakechamber.org
URL: http://www.biglakechamber.org
Contact: Bob DeLoach, Pres.

47403 ■ Chugiak-Eagle River Chamber of Commerce
11401 Old Glenn Hwy., Ste. 105
PO Box 770353
Eagle River, AK 99577-0353
Ph:(907)694-4702
Fax:(907)694-1205
Co. E-mail: info@cer.com
URL: http://www.cer.org
Contact: Susan Gorski, Exec. Dir.

47404 ■ Cordova Chamber of Commerce
PO Box 99
Cordova, AK 99574
Ph:(907)424-7260
Fax:(907)424-7259
Co. E-mail: cchamber@ctcak.net
URL: http://www.cordovachamber.com
Contact: Martin Moe, Exec. Dir.

47405 ■ Delta Chamber of Commerce
PO Box 987
Delta Junction, AK 99737-0987
Ph:(907)895-5068
Free: 877-895-5068
Fax:(907)895-5141
Co. E-mail: deltacc@deltachamber.org
URL: http://www.deltachamber.org
Contact: Brenda Peterson, Exec. Dir.

47406 ■ Funny River Chamber of Commerce
35850 Pioneer Rd.
Soldotna, AK 99669
Ph:(907)262-0879
Contact: Ray Price

47407 ■ Greater Copper Valley Chamber of Commerce
PO Box 469
Glennallen, AK 99588-0469
Ph:(907)822-5555
Fax:(907)822-5555
Co. E-mail: info@traveltoalaska.com
URL: http://www.coppervalleychamber.com
Contact: CD McCurry, Pres.

47408 ■ Greater Fairbanks Chamber of Commerce
100 Cushman St., Ste. 102
Fairbanks, AK 99701
Ph:(907)452-1105
Fax:(907)456-6968
Co. E-mail: info@fairbankschamber.org
URL: http://www.fairbankschamber.org
Contact: Barb Lorz-Wammack, Exec. Dir.

47409 ■ Greater Healy-Denali Chamber of Commerce
PO Box 437
Healy, AK 99743-0437
Ph:(907)683-4636
Co. E-mail: info@denalichamber.com
URL: http://www.denalichamber.com

47410 ■ Greater Ketchikan Chamber of Commerce
PO Box 5954
Ketchikan, AK 99901
Ph:(907)225-3184

Fax:(907)225-3187
Co. E-mail: info@ketchikanchamber.com
URL: http://www.ketchikanchamber.com
Contact: Rob Skinner, Pres.

47411 ■ Greater Palmer Chamber of Commerce
723 S Valley Way
Palmer, AK 99645
Ph:(907)745-2880
Fax:(907)746-4164
Co. E-mail: info@palmerchamber.org
URL: http://www.palmerchamber.org
Contact: Crystal Limbaugh, Exec. Dir.

47412 ■ Greater Sitka Chamber of Commerce
PO Box 638
Sitka, AK 99835
Ph:(907)747-8604
Fax:(907)747-7613
Co. E-mail: chamber@ptialaska.net
URL: http://www.sitkacoc.com
Contact: Sheila Finkenbinder, Exec. Dir.

47413 ■ Greater Soldotna Chamber of Commerce
44790 Sterling Hwy.
Soldotna, AK 99669
Ph:(907)262-9814
Fax:(907)262-3566
Co. E-mail: info@soldotnachamber.com
URL: http://visitsoldotna.com/chamber
Contact: Keri Hiler, Pres.

47414 ■ Greater Wasilla Chamber of Commerce
415 E Railroad Ave.
Wasilla, AK 99654
Ph:(907)376-1299
Fax:(907)373-2560
Co. E-mail: contact@wasillachamber.org
URL: http://www.wasillachamber.org
Contact: Erika M. Bills, Pres.

47415 ■ Haines Chamber of Commerce
PO Box 1449
Haines, AK 99827-1449
Ph:(907)766-2202
Fax:(907)766-2271
Co. E-mail: chamber@haineschamber.org
URL: http://www.haineschamber.org
Contact: Karl Heinz, Pres.

47416 ■ Homer Chamber of Commerce
201 Sterling Hwy.
Homer, AK 99603
Ph:(907)235-7740
Fax:(907)235-8766
Co. E-mail: info@homeralaska.org
URL: http://www.homeralaska.org
Contact: Tina Day, Exec. Dir.

47417 ■ Juneau Chamber of Commerce
3100 Channel Dr., Ste. 300
Juneau, AK 99801
Ph:(907)463-3488
Fax:(907)463-3489
Co. E-mail: jcc@alaska.com
URL: http://www.juneauchamber.com/page/page/
4494865.htm
Contact: Cathie Roemmich, CEO

47418 ■ Kenai Chamber of Commerce
402 Overland St.
Kenai, AK 99611
Ph:(907)283-7989
Fax:(907)283-7183
Co. E-mail: info@kenaichamber.org
URL: http://www.kenaichamber.org
Contact: Roy Wells, Pres.

47419 ■ Kodiak Chamber of Commerce
100 E Marine Way, Ste. 300
Kodiak, AK 99615-1485
Ph:(907)486-5557

Fax:(907)486-7605
Co. E-mail: chamber@kodiak.org
URL: http://www.kodiak.org/business/kodiak-
chamber-of-commerce.html
Contact: Deborah King, Exec. Dir.

47420 ■ Nome Chamber of Commerce
PO Box 250
Nome, AK 99762
Ph:(907)443-3879
Fax:(907)443-3892
Co. E-mail: nomechamber@gci.net
URL: http://www.nomechamber.org
Contact: Mitch Erickson, Exec. Dir.

47421 ■ Petersburg Chamber of Commerce
PO Box 649
Petersburg, AK 99833
Ph:(907)772-3646
Fax:(907)772-2453
Co. E-mail: chamber@petersburg.org
URL: http://www.petersburg.org
Contact: Rosann Dunham, Pres.

47422 ■ Prince of Wales Chamber of Commerce
PO Box 490
Klawock, AK 99925-0490
Ph:(907)755-2626
Fax:(907)755-2627
Co. E-mail: info@princeofwalescoc.org
URL: http://www.princeofwalescoc.org
Contact: Jan Bush, Pres.

47423 ■ Seldovia Chamber of Commerce
PO Drawer F
Seldovia, AK 99663
Ph:(907)234-7803
Fax:(907)234-7612
Co. E-mail: admin@harborsedge.com
URL: http://www.xyz.net/IAtseldovia
Contact: Peggy Keesecker, Pres.

47424 ■ Seward Chamber of Commerce
PO Box 749
Seward, AK 99664-0749
Ph:(907)224-8051
Fax:(907)224-5353
Co. E-mail: director@seward.net
URL: http://www.sewardak.org
Contact: Laura Cloward, Exec. Dir.

47425 ■ Skagway Chamber of Commerce
PO Box 194
Skagway, AK 99840-0194
Ph:(907)983-1898
Fax:(907)983-2031
Co. E-mail: chamber@aptalaska.net
URL: http://www.skagwaychamber.org
Contact: Marla Belisle, Office Admin.

47426 ■ Talkeetna Chamber of Commerce
PO Box 334
Talkeetna, AK 99676-0334
Ph:(907)733-2330
Fax:(907)733-4578
Co. E-mail: info@talkeetnachamber.org
URL: http://www.talkeetnachamber.org

47427 ■ Tok Chamber of Commerce
PO Box 389
Tok, AK 99780-0389
Ph:(907)883-5775
Co. E-mail: info@tokalaskainfo.com
URL: http://www.tokalaskainfo.com
Contact: Bonnie Jenkins, Mgr.

47428 ■ Willow Chamber of Commerce
PO Box 183
Willow, AK 99688
Ph:(907)495-6800
Fax:(907)495-6800
Co. E-mail: mail@willowchamber.org
URL: http://www.willowchamber.org
Contact: Mr. Houston Stanley, VP

47429 ■ Wrangell Chamber of Commerce
PO Box 49
Wrangell, AK 99929
Ph:(907)874-3901
Free: 800-367-9745
Fax:(907)874-3905
Co. E-mail: wchamber@gci.net
URL: http://www.wrangellchamber.org
Contact: Janell Privett, Pres.

MINORITY BUSINESS ASSISTANCE PROGRAMS

47430 ■ Alaska Minority Business Development Center–Tanana Chief Conference, Inc.
122 First Ave., Ste. 600
Fairbanks, AK 99701
Ph:(907)452-8251
Fax:(907)459-3851
Co. E-mail: info@tananachiefs.org
URL: http://www.tananachiefs.org

47431 ■ YWCA Anchorage Women's Business Solutions
324 E 5th Ave.
Anchorage, AK 99501
Ph:(907)644-9611
Fax:(907)644-9650
Co. E-mail: cailleo@ywcaak.org
URL: http://www.ywcaak.org/finances.htm
Contact: Caren Ailleo, Dir
Description: Provides business development services for women in Alaska who want to start or grow a business.

INCUBATORS/RESEARCH AND TECHNOLOGY PARKS

47432 ■ University of Alaska Fairbanks–Office of Sponsored Programs
West Ridge Research Bldg., Ste. 212
902 Koyukuk Dr.
PO Box 757270
Fairbanks, AK 99775-7270
Ph:(907)474-6000
Fax:(907)474-5444
Co. E-mail: uaf-osp@alaska.edu
URL: http://www.uaf.edu/osp
Contact: Dr. Andrew Parkerson-Gray, Dir.
E-mail: uaf-osp@alaska.edu
Scope: Responsible for coordination of research programs of the University involving geophysics, marine science, water resources, energy resources, agriculture, biology, social and economic concerns, education, environmental data, anthropology, archeology, fisheries, wildlife, forests, and minerals, emphasizing Northern, cold, and arctic regions. Approves all proposals for grants, locates funding sources, and maintains contact with federal and state agencies and private foundations interested in research. Administers special research projects not allocated to research institutes, centers, or laboratories; supervises support services, including aircraft, ships, land vehicles, and a rocket-launching facility; and operates numerous observational field sites in Alaska, its adjacent territories, and overseas. **Services:** Extension services, in agriculture, fisheries, mining, and small business development. **Educational Activities:** National and international symposia; Seminars, organized through research of the University.

EDUCATIONAL PROGRAMS

47433 ■ Matanuska-Susitna College
PO Box 2889
Palmer, AK 99645
Ph:(907)745-9774
Fax:(907)745-9711
Co. E-mail: info@matsu.alaska.edu
URL: http://www.matsu.alaska.edu
Description: Two-year college offering a program in small business management.

PUBLICATIONS

47434 ■ *Alaska Business Monthly*
P.O. Box 241288
Anchorage, AK 99524-1288
Ph:(907)276-4373

Fax:(907)279-2900
Co. E-mail: info@akbizmag.com
URL: http://www.akbizmag.com

47435 ■ *Starting and Operating a Business in Alaska: A Step-by-Step Guide*
PSI Research
300 N. Valley Dr.
Grants Pass, OR 97526

Ph:(503)479-9464
Free: 800-228-2275
Fax:(503)476-1479
Co. E-mail: psi2@magick.net
Ed: Michael D. Jenkins. **Released:** Revised edition, 1992. **Price:** $29.95 (looseleaf binder); $24.95 (paper). **Description:** Part of the Successful Business Library series.

Arizona

SMALL BUSINESS DEVELOPMENT CENTERS

47436 ■ Arizona Western College Small Business Development Center
1351 S Redondo Center Dr., Ste. 101
Yuma, AZ 85365
Co. E-mail: randy.nelson@azwestern.edu
URL: http://www.azsbdc.net
Contact: Randy Nelson, Dir.

47437 ■ Central Arizona College Small Business Development Center
540 N Camino Mercado, No. 1
Casa Grande, AZ 85222
Fax:(520)494-6612
Co. E-mail: sbdc@centralaz.edu
URL: http://www.centralaz.edu/biz
Contact: Jim Rhodes, Dir.

47438 ■ Cochise College Small Business Development Center
901 N Colombo Ave., Rm. 308
Sierra Vista, AZ 85635
Free: 800-966-7943
Co. E-mail: hollism@cochise.edu
URL: http://www.cochise.edu/conteducation/sbdc
Contact: Mignonne Hollis, Dir.

47439 ■ Coconino Community College Small Business Development Center
3000 N 4th St.
Flagstaff, AZ 86004
Fax:(928)526-8693
Co. E-mail: sbdc@coconino.edu
URL: http://www.coconino.edu/sbdc
Contact: Annette Zinky, Dir.

47440 ■ Eastern Arizona College Small Business Development Center
Student Services Bldg., Rm. 113
615 N Stadium Ave.
Thatcher, AZ 85552
Free: 888-322-5780
Fax:(928)428-8591
Co. E-mail: sbdc@eac.edu
URL: http://www.eac.edu/sbdc
Contact: Mike Fox, Dir.

47441 ■ Maricopa Community Colleges at Phoenix Small Business Development Center
2400 N Central Ave., Ste. 104
Phoenix, AZ 85004
Fax:(602)230-7989
Co. E-mail: rich.senopole@maricopasbdc.com
URL: http://www.maricopasbdc.com
Contact: Richard Senopole, Dir.

47442 ■ Mesa Minority/Micro Small Business Development Center
165 N Centennial Way, No. 209-213
Mesa, AZ 85201
Co. E-mail: luis.reynoso@domail.maricopa.edu
URL: http://www.maricopasbdc.com
Contact: Luis Reynoso, Dir.

47443 ■ Mohave Community College Small Business Development Center
1971 E Jagerson Ave.
Kingman, AZ 86409
Co. E-mail: kmarsh@mohave.edu
URL: http://www.mohave.edu/pages/195.asp
Contact: Kelley Marsh, Dir.

47444 ■ Northland Pioneer College's Small Business Development Center
PO Box 610
Holbrook, AZ 86025
Fax:(928)532-6171
Co. E-mail: mengle98@yahoo.com
URL: http://www.npcsbdc.com
Contact: Mark Engle, Dir.

47445 ■ Pima College's Small Business Development Center
PCC Community Campus
401 N Bonita Ave.
Tucson, AZ 85709
Fax:(520)206-6550
Co. E-mail: sbdc@pima.edu
URL: http://www.pima.edu/smallbusiness
Contact: Susan Kifer, Dir.

SMALL BUSINESS ASSISTANCE PROGRAMS

47446 ■ Arizona Department of Commerce
commerce@azcommerce.com
1700 W Washington, Ste. 600
Phoenix, AZ 85007
Ph:(602)771-1100
Fax:(602)771-1202
URL: http://www.azcommerce.com
Contact: Don Cardon, Dir.
Description: Offers assistance to businesses in various stages of growth; helps businesses establishing operations in Arizona; packages expansion financing for established companies; and helps with export financing.

SCORE OFFICES

47447 ■ Southern Arizona SCORE
Path: www.scoretucson.org

BETTER BUSINESS BUREAUS

47448 ■ Better Business Bureau, Central/ Northern Arizona
4428 N 12th St.
Phoenix, AZ 85014-4585
Ph:(602)264-1721
Free: 877-291-6222
Fax:(602)263-0997
Co. E-mail: info@arizonabbb.org
URL: http://central-northern-western-arizona.bbb.org
Contact: Matthew Fehling, Pres./CEO

47449 ■ Better Business Bureau of Tucson
434 S Williams Blvd., Ste. 102
Tucson, AZ 85711
Ph:(520)888-5353
Fax:(520)888-6262
Co. E-mail: info@tucson.bbb.org
URL: http://tucson.bbb.org
Contact: Kim States, Pres.

CHAMBERS OF COMMERCE

47450 ■ Ahwatukee Foothills Chamber of Commerce
10235 S 51st St., No. 185
Phoenix, AZ 85044
Ph:(480)753-7676
Fax:(480)753-3898
Co. E-mail: info@ahwatukeechamber.com
URL: http://www.ahwatukeechamber.com
Contact: Laura Rivers, Pres./Exec. Dir.

47451 ■ Ajo District Chamber of Commerce
400 Taladro St.
Ajo, AZ 85321
Ph:(520)387-7742
Fax:(520)387-3641
Co. E-mail: ajocofc@tabletoptelephone.com
URL: http://www.ajochamber.com
Contact: Silvia Howard, Exec. Dir.

47452 ■ Alpine Chamber of Commerce
PO Box 410
Alpine, AZ 85920
Ph:(928)339-4330
Co. E-mail: chamber@alpinearizona.com
URL: http://www.alpinearizona.com
Contact: Heidi Beaubriand, Pres.

47453 ■ Apache Junction Chamber of Commerce
PO Box 1747
Apache Junction, AZ 85217-1747
Ph:(480)982-3141
Fax:(480)982-3234
Co. E-mail: ajchamber@qwest.net
URL: http://www.apachejunctioncoc.com
Contact: Kevin Thompson, Chm.

47454 ■ Arizona Chamber of Commerce and Industry
1850 N Central Ave., Ste. 1433
Phoenix, AZ 85004
Ph:(602)248-9172
Free: 800-498-6973
Fax:(602)265-1262
Co. E-mail: info@azchamber.com
URL: http://www.azchamber.com
Contact: Glenn Hamer, Pres./CEO

47455 ■ Arizona City Chamber of Commerce
PO Box 5
Arizona City, AZ 85223-0005
Ph:(520)466-5141

Fax:(520)466-8204
Co. E-mail: azchamber@cgmailbox.com
URL: http://www.azcchamber.com

47456 ■ Arizona Hispanic Chamber of Commerce
255 E Osborne Rd., Ste. 201
Phoenix, AZ 85012
Ph:(602)279-1800
Fax:(602)279-8900
Co. E-mail: info@azhcc.com
URL: http://www.azhcc.com
Contact: Robert Espiritu, Chm.

47457 ■ Asian Chamber of Commerce
7217 N 6th St.
Phoenix, AZ 85020
Ph:(602)222-2009
Fax:(602)870-7562
Co. E-mail: asiansun@aol.com
URL: http://www.asianchamber.org
Contact: Madeline Ong-Sakata, Sec./Exec. Dir.

47458 ■ Benson - San Pedro Valley Chamber of Commerce
PO Box 2255
Benson, AZ 85602
Ph:(520)586-2842
Fax:(520)586-1972
Co. E-mail: info@bensonchamberaz.com
URL: http://www.bensonchamberaz.com
Contact: Robert Mucci, Exec. Dir.

47459 ■ Bisbee Chamber of Commerce and Visitor Center
PO Box BA
Bisbee, AZ 85603
Ph:(520)432-5421
Fax:(520)432-3308
Co. E-mail: chamber@bisbeearizona.com
URL: http://bisbeearizona.com/content
Contact: Clark Hay, Pres.

47460 ■ Bouse Chamber of Commerce
PO Box 817
Bouse, AZ 85325-0817
Ph:(928)851-2509
Co. E-mail: bousecofc@yahoo.com
URL: http://www.bousechamberofcommerce.com

47461 ■ Buckeye Valley Chamber of Commerce
508 E Monroe Ave.
Buckeye, AZ 85326
Ph:(623)386-2727
Free: 888-EZW-AY4U
Co. E-mail: jan@buckeyevalleychamber.org
URL: http://www.buckeyevalleychamber.org
Contact: Todd Hornback, Chm.

47462 ■ Bullhead Area Chamber of Commerce
1251 Hwy. 95
Bullhead City, AZ 86429
Ph:(928)754-4121
Free: 800-987-7457
Fax:(928)754-5514
Co. E-mail: info@bullheadchamber.com
URL: http://www.bullheadchamber.com
Contact: Michael K. Conner, Pres./CEO

47463 ■ Camp Verde Chamber of Commerce
385 S Main St.
Camp Verde, AZ 86322
Ph:(928)567-9294
Fax:(928)567-4793
Co. E-mail: info@campverde.org
URL: http://www.visitcampverde.com
Contact: Tracie Schimikowsky, Dir. of Operations

47464 ■ Chandler Chamber of Commerce
25 S Arizona Pl., No. 201
Chandler, AZ 85225
Ph:(480)963-4571
Free: 800-963-4571
Fax:(480)963-0188
Co. E-mail: president@chandlerchamber.com
URL: http://www.chandlerchamber.com
Contact: Jerry Bustamante, Pres./CEO

47465 ■ Chino Valley Area Chamber of Commerce
PO Box 419
Chino Valley, AZ 86323
Ph:(928)636-2493
Free: 877-523-1988
Fax:(928)636-4112
Co. E-mail: chamber@chinovalley.org
URL: http://www.chinovalley.org

47466 ■ Chloride Chamber of Commerce
PO Box 268
Chloride, AZ 86431-0268
Ph:(928)565-2204
Co. E-mail: contact@chloridearizona.com
URL: http://www.chloridearizona.com
Contact: Kate Woody, Sec.

47467 ■ Clarkdale Chamber of Commerce
PO Box 161
Clarkdale, AZ 86324
Ph:(928)634-9438
Fax:(928)634-9430
Co. E-mail: cccinfo@clarkdalechamber.com
URL: http://www.clarkdalechamber.com
Contact: Katie Canon, Pres.

47468 ■ Copper Basin Chamber of Commerce
PO Box 206
Kearny, AZ 85237
Ph:(520)363-7607
Fax:(520)363-7551
Co. E-mail: cbc@copperbasinaz.com
URL: http://www.copperbasinaz.com
Contact: Bobby Brosbin

47469 ■ Cottonwood Chamber of Commerce
1010 S Main St.
Cottonwood, AZ 86326
Ph:(928)634-7593
Fax:(928)634-7594
Co. E-mail: info@cottonwoodchamberaz.org
Contact: Debbie Wilden, Pres./CEO

47470 ■ Dolan Springs Chamber of Commerce
PO Box 274
Dolan Springs, AZ 86441
Ph:(928)767-4473
Co. E-mail: president@dolanspringschamberofcommerce.com
URL: http://www.dolanspringschamberofcommerce.com

47471 ■ Eloy Chamber of Commerce
305 N Stuart Blvd.
Eloy, AZ 85231
Ph:(520)466-3411
Fax:(520)466-4698
Co. E-mail: info@eloychamber.com
URL: http://www.eloychamber.com
Contact: Paula Lambert, Pres.

47472 ■ Flagstaff Chamber of Commerce
101 W Rte. 66
Flagstaff, AZ 86001
Ph:(928)774-4505
Fax:(928)779-1209
Co. E-mail: sznetko@flagstaffchamber.com
URL: http://www.flagstaffchamber.com
Contact: Julie Pastrick, Pres./CEO

47473 ■ Fountain Hills Chamber of Commerce
PO Box 17598
Fountain Hills, AZ 85269-7598
Ph:(480)837-1654
Fax:(480)837-3077
Co. E-mail: frank@fountainhillschamber.com
URL: http://www.fountainhillschamber.com
Contact: Frank S. Ferrara, Pres./CEO

47474 ■ Gilbert Chamber of Commerce
PO Box 527
Gilbert, AZ 85299-0527
Ph:(480)892-0056

Fax:(480)892-1980
Co. E-mail: info@gilbertchamber.com
URL: http://www.gilbertaz.com
Contact: Kathy Langdon, Pres./CEO

47475 ■ Glendale Chamber of Commerce
PO Box 249
Glendale, AZ 85311
Ph:(623)937-4754
Free: 800-437-8669
Fax:(623)937-3333
Co. E-mail: info@glendaleazchamber.org
URL: http://www.glendaleazchamber.org
Contact: Don Rinehart, Pres./CEO

47476 ■ Globe-Miami Regional Chamber of Commerce and Economic Development Corporation
1360 N Broad St.
Globe, AZ 85501
Ph:(928)425-4495
Free: 800-804-5623
Fax:(928)425-3410
Co. E-mail: gmr@cableone.net
URL: http://www.globemiamichamber.com
Contact: Russ Fetterman, Pres.

47477 ■ Golden Valley Chamber of Commerce
3395 Verde
Golden Valley, AZ 86413
Ph:(928)565-3311
Fax:(928)565-3133
URL: http://www.goldenvalleychamber.com
Contact: Pat Randolph, Pres.

47478 ■ Graham County Chamber of Commerce
1111 Thatcher Blvd.
Safford, AZ 85546
Ph:(928)428-2511
Free: 888-837-1841
Fax:(928)428-0744
Co. E-mail: info@graham-chamber.com
URL: http://www.graham-chamber.com
Contact: Steve Junion, Pres.

47479 ■ Grand Canyon Chamber of Commerce
PO Box 3007
Grand Canyon, AZ 86023
Ph:(530)283-5553
Free: 888-472-2696
Fax:(928)638-4095
Co. E-mail: info@grandcanyonchamber.org
URL: http://grandcanyonvisitorbureau.com

47480 ■ Greater Casa Grande Chamber of Commerce
575 N Marshall St.
Casa Grande, AZ 85222-5246
Ph:(520)836-2125
Free: 800-916-1515
Fax:(520)836-6233
Co. E-mail: chamber@cgmailbox.com
URL: http://www.casagrandechamber.org
Contact: Ms. Helen Neuharth, Pres./CEO

47481 ■ Greater Phoenix Black Chamber of Commerce
201 E Washington St., Ste. 350
Phoenix, AZ 85004
Ph:(602)307-5200
Fax:(602)307-5204
Co. E-mail: info@phoenixblackchamber.com
URL: http://www.phoenixblackchamber.com
Contact: Ron Busby, Pres./CEO

47482 ■ Greater Phoenix Chamber of Commerce
201 N Central Ave., 27th Fl.
Phoenix, AZ 85004
Ph:(602)495-2195
Fax:(602)495-8913
Co. E-mail: info@phoenixchamber.com
URL: http://www.phoenixchamber.com
Contact: Katie Pushor, Pres./CEO

47483 ■ Greater Sierra Vista Area Chamber of Commerce
21 E Wilcox Dr.
Sierra Vista, AZ 85635
Ph:(520)458-6940
Free: 888-399-2948
Fax:(520)452-0878
Co. E-mail: info@sierravistachamber.org
URL: http://www.sierravistachamber.org
Contact: Susan Tegmeyer, Pres./CEO

47484 ■ Heber - Overgaard Chamber of Commerce
PO Box 1926
Overgaard, AZ 85933
Ph:(928)535-5777
Fax:(928)535-3254
Co. E-mail: heberovergaard.coc@hotmail.com
URL: http://www.heberovergaard.org

47485 ■ Jerome Chamber of Commerce
PO Box K
Jerome, AZ 86331
Ph:(928)634-2900
Co. E-mail: jcc@jeromechamber.org
URL: http://www.jeromechamber.com
Contact: Christine Barag, Pres.

47486 ■ Kingman Area Chamber of Commerce
120 W Andy Devine Ave.
Kingman, AZ 86401
Ph:(928)753-6253
Fax:(928)753-1049
Co. E-mail: info@kingmanchamber.org
URL: http://www.kingmanchamber.org
Contact: Beverly J. Liles, Pres./CEO

47487 ■ Lake Havasu Area Chamber of Commerce
314 London Bridge Rd.
Lake Havasu City, AZ 86403-5772
Ph:(928)855-4115
Fax:(928)680-0010
Co. E-mail: info@havasuchamber.com
URL: http://www.havasuchamber.com
Contact: Lisa Krueger, Pres./CEO

47488 ■ Marana Chamber of Commerce
13881 N Casa Grande Hwy.
Marana, AZ 85653-9312
Ph:(520)682-4314
Fax:(520)682-2303
Co. E-mail: info@maranachamber.com
URL: http://www.maranachamber.com
Contact: Ed Stolmaker, Pres./CEO

47489 ■ McMullen Valley Chamber of Commerce
PO Box 700
Salome, AZ 85348-0700
Ph:(928)859-3846
Fax:(928)859-4399
Co. E-mail: mcmullencoc@tds.net
URL: http://www.azoutback.com

47490 ■ Mesa Chamber of Commerce
120 N Center St.
Mesa, AZ 85201
Ph:(480)969-1307
Fax:(480)827-0727
Co. E-mail: info@mesachamber.org
URL: http://www.mesachamber.org
Contact: Charles Deaton, Pres./CEO

47491 ■ Mohave Valley Chamber of Commerce
PO Box 5439
Mohave Valley, AZ 86446
Ph:(928)768-2777
Fax:(928)768-6610
Co. E-mail: info@mohavevalleychamber.com
URL: http://www.mohavevalleychamber.com
Contact: Emma J. Watson, Pres.

47492 ■ Nogales-Santa Cruz County Chamber of Commerce
123 W Kino Park Way
Nogales, AZ 85621
Ph:(520)287-3685
Fax:(520)287-3687
Co. E-mail: info@thenogaleschamber.com
URL: http://www.thenogaleschamber.com/portal
Contact: Olivia Ainza-Kramer, Pres./CEO

47493 ■ North Phoenix Chamber of Commerce
12601 N Cave Creek, Ste. 104
Phoenix, AZ 85022
Ph:(602)482-3344
Free: 888-EZW-AY4U
Fax:(623)321-0273
Co. E-mail: kathy@northphoenixchamber.com
URL: http://www.northphoenixchamber.com
Contact: Jean Lukens, Exec. Dir.

47494 ■ Northwest Valley Chamber of Commerce
12801 W Bell Rd., Ste. 14
Surprise, AZ 85374
Ph:(623)583-0692
Fax:(623)583-0694
Co. E-mail: danderson@surpriseregionalchamber.com
URL: http://www.surpriseregionalchamber.com
Contact: Jeanne Blackman, Chair

47495 ■ Oatman-Goldroad Chamber of Commerce
PO Box 423
Oatman, AZ 86433
Ph:(928)768-6222
Co. E-mail: oatman@oatmangoldroad.com
URL: http://www.oatmangoldroad.com
Contact: Jackie Rowland

47496 ■ Page-Lake Powell Chamber of Commerce
PO Box 727
Page, AZ 86040
Ph:(928)645-2741
Free: 888-261-PAGE
Fax:(928)645-3181
Co. E-mail: chamber@pagelakepowellchamber.org
URL: http://www.pagelakepowellchamber.org
Contact: Vin Paitoon, Exec. Dir.

47497 ■ Parker Area Chamber of Commerce
1217 S California Ave.
Parker, AZ 85344
Ph:(928)669-2174
Fax:(928)669-6304
Co. E-mail: info@parkerareachamberofcommerce.com
URL: http://www.parkerareachamberofcommerce.com
Contact: Tina Torelli, Pres.

47498 ■ Pearce - Sunsites Chamber of Commerce
PO Box 536
Pearce, AZ 85625-0536
Ph:(520)826-3535
Co. E-mail: info@pearcesunsiteschamber.org
URL: http://www.pearcesunsiteschamber.org/portal
Contact: Murray McClelland, Pres.

47499 ■ Peoria Chamber of Commerce
8765 W Kelton Ln., Bldg. C-1
Peoria, AZ 85382
Ph:(623)979-3601
Free: 800-580-2645
Fax:(623)486-4729
Co. E-mail: diana@peoriachamber.com
URL: http://www.peoriachamber.com
Contact: Diana Bedient, Exec. Dir.

47500 ■ Pinetop-Lakeside Chamber of Commerce
PO Box 4220
Pinetop, AZ 85935
Ph:(928)367-4290
Free: 800-573-4031

Fax:(928)367-1247
Co. E-mail: info@pinetoplakesidechamber.com
URL: http://www.pinetoplakesidechamber.com
Contact: Bev Stepp, Exec. Dir.

47501 ■ Prescott Chamber of Commerce
117 W Goodwin St.
Prescott, AZ 86303-3954
Ph:(928)445-2000
Free: 800-266-7534
Fax:(928)445-0068
Co. E-mail: dmaurer@prescott.org
URL: http://www.prescott.org
Contact: David Maurer, CEO

47502 ■ Prescott Valley Chamber of Commerce
3001 N Main St., Ste. 2A
Prescott Valley, AZ 86314
Ph:(928)772-8857
Fax:(928)772-4267
Co. E-mail: info@pvchamber.org
URL: http://www.pvchamber.org
Contact: Marnie Uhl, Pres./CEO

47503 ■ Quartzsite Chamber of Commerce
PO Box 2566
Quartzsite, AZ 85346-0085
Ph:(928)927-9321
Co. E-mail: info@qzchamber.com
URL: http://www.quartzsitechamber.org
Contact: Richard Oldham, Chamber Pres.

47504 ■ Rim Country Regional Chamber of Commerce
100 W Main St.
PO Box 1380
Payson, AZ 85547
Ph:(928)474-4515
Free: 800-672-9766
Fax:(928)474-8812
Co. E-mail: chamber@npgcable.com
URL: http://www.rimcountrychamber.com

47505 ■ St. Johns Regional Chamber of Commerce
PO Box 929
St. Johns, AZ 85936
Ph:(928)337-2000
Fax:(928)337-2020
Co. E-mail: info@stjohnschamber.com
URL: http://www.stjohnschamber.com
Contact: Kelly Gunnels, Exec. Dir.

47506 ■ Scottsdale Area Chamber of Commerce
4725 N Scottsdale Rd., No. 210
Scottsdale, AZ 85251-4498
Ph:(480)355-2700
Fax:(480)355-2710
Co. E-mail: info@scottsdalechamber.com
URL: http://www.scottsdalechamber.com
Contact: Rick Kidder, Pres./CEO

47507 ■ Sedona-Oak Creek Canyon Chamber of Commerce
PO Box 478
Sedona, AZ 86339
Ph:(928)282-7722
Free: 800-288-7336
Fax:(928)204-1064
Co. E-mail: info@sedonachamber.com
URL: http://www.sedonachamber.com
Contact: Jennifer Wesselhoff, Pres./CEO

47508 ■ Show Low Regional Chamber of Commerce
81 E Deuce of Clubs
Show Low, AZ 85901
Ph:(928)537-2326
Free: 888-SHO-WLOW
Fax:(928)532-7610
Co. E-mail: info@showlowchamberofcommerce.com
URL: http://www.showlowchamberofcommerce.com
Contact: Jerry Howell, Chm.

47509 ■ Snowflake - Taylor Chamber of Commerce
110 N Main St., Ste. A
Snowflake, AZ 85937
Ph:(928)536-4331
Fax:(928)536-5208
Co. E-mail: snowflaketaylorchamber@gmail.com
URL: http://www.snowflaketaylorchamber.org
Contact: Greg Hudson, Exec. Dir.

47510 ■ Southwest Valley Chamber of Commerce
289 N Litchfield Rd.
Goodyear, AZ 85338
Ph:(623)932-2260
Fax:(623)932-9057
Co. E-mail: info@southwestvalleychamber.org
URL: http://www.southwestvalleychamber.org
Contact: Sharolyn Hohman, CEO/Pres.

47511 ■ Springerville-Eagar Regional Chamber of Commerce
PO Box 31
Springerville, AZ 85938-0031
Ph:(928)333-2123
Fax:(928)333-5690
Co. E-mail: info@springerville-eagarchamber.com
URL: http://www.springerville-eagarchamber.com
Contact: Jennifer Prochnow, Exec. Dir.

47512 ■ Superior Chamber of Commerce
PO Box 95
Superior, AZ 85273-0095
Ph:(520)689-0200
Fax:(520)689-0200
Co. E-mail: support@superiorarizonachamber.org
URL: http://www.superiorazchamber.net

47513 ■ Swedish-American Chamber of Commerce, Arizona
4300 N Miller Rd., Ste. 125
Scottsdale, AZ 85251
Co. E-mail: contact@saccarizona.org
URL: http://www.saccarizona.org
Contact: Asa Undhagen, Sec.

47514 ■ Tempe Chamber of Commerce
PO Box 28500
Tempe, AZ 85285-8500
Ph:(480)967-7891
Fax:(480)966-5365
Co. E-mail: info@tempechamber.org
URL: http://www.tempechamber.org/index.php
Contact: Mary Ann Miller, Pres./CEO

47515 ■ Tombstone Chamber of Commerce
PO Box 995
Tombstone, AZ 85638
Free: 888-457-3929
Co. E-mail: info@tombstone.org
URL: http://www.tombstonechamber.com

47516 ■ Tubac Chamber of Commerce
PO Box 1866
Tubac, AZ 85646
Ph:(520)398-2704
Fax:(520)398-1704
Co. E-mail: assistance@tubacaz.com
URL: http://www.tubacaz.com
Contact: Carol Cullen, Exec. Dir.

47517 ■ Tucson Metropolitan Chamber of Commerce
PO Box 991
Tucson, AZ 85702
Ph:(520)792-2250
Fax:(520)882-5704
Co. E-mail: info@tucsonchamber.org
URL: http://www.tucsonchamber.org
Contact: John C. Camper CCE, Pres.

47518 ■ Wickenburg Chamber of Commerce
216 N Frontier St.
Wickenburg, AZ 85390
Ph:(928)684-5479
Free: 800-942-5242

Fax:(928)684-5470
Co. E-mail: info@wickenburgchamber.com
URL: http://www.wickenburgchamber.com
Contact: Ben Ruoti, Pres.

47519 ■ Willcox Chamber of Commerce and Agriculture
1500 N Circle I Rd.
Willcox, AZ 85643
Ph:(520)384-2272
Free: 800-200-2272
Fax:(520)384-0293
Co. E-mail: willcoxchamber@vtc.net
URL: http://www.willcoxchamber.com
Contact: Kathy Smith, Exec. Dir.

47520 ■ Williams-Grand Canyon Chamber of Commerce
200 W Railroad Ave.
Williams, AZ 86046
Ph:(928)635-0273
Fax:(928)635-1417
Co. E-mail: info@williamschamber.com
URL: http://www.williamschamber.com
Contact: Ms. Donna Eastman Liddle, Pres./CEO

47521 ■ Winslow Chamber of Commerce
PO Box 460
Winslow, AZ 86047
Ph:(928)289-2434
Fax:(928)289-5660
Co. E-mail: info@winslowarizona.org
URL: http://www.winslowarizona.org
Contact: Jim Currier, Pres.

47522 ■ Yuma County Chamber of Commerce
180 W 1st St., Ste. A
Yuma, AZ 85364
Ph:(928)782-2567
Free: 877-782-0438
Fax:(928)343-0038
Co. E-mail: info@yumachamber.org
URL: http://www.yumachamber.org
Contact: Ken Rosevear, Exec. Dir.

MINORITY BUSINESS ASSISTANCE PROGRAMS

47523 ■ Arizona Minority Business Enterprise Center
255 E Osborn Rd., Ste. 202
Phoenix, AZ 85012
Ph:(602)248-0007
Fax:(602)279-8900
Co. E-mail: info@azmbec.com
URL: http://www.azmbec.com
Contact: Alika Kumar, Dir

47524 ■ Arizona Native American Business Development Center–National Center for American Indian Enterprise Development Center
953 E Juanita Ave.
Mesa, AZ 85204
Ph:(480)545-1298
Fax:(480)545-4208
Co. E-mail: ncaiedcln@aol.com
URL: http://www.ncaied.org
Contact: Joan Notah, Dir

FINANCING AND LOAN PROGRAMS

47525 ■ Miller Capital Corp.
4909 E. McDowell Rd.
Phoenix, AZ 85008-4293
Ph:(602)225-0505
Fax:(602)225-9024
URL: http://www.themillergroup.net
Contact: Rudy R. Miller, President, Chief Executive Officer and C
Preferred Investment Size: $1,000,000 to $5,000,000. **Investment Types:** Second stage. **Industry Preferences:** Consumer related. **Geographic Preferences:** U.S. **Principal Exhibits:**

47526 ■ Valley Ventures / Arizona Growth Partners, L.P.
1275 W. Washington St., Ste. 101
PO Box 62798
Tempe, AZ 85281
Ph:(480)661-6600
Fax:(602)286-5284
Co. E-mail: businessplans@valleyventures.com
URL: http://www.valleyventures.com
Contact: Jock Holliman III, General Partner
Investment Types: Seed, early and second stage, balanced, expansion, mezzanine, private placement, recapitalizations, and leveraged buyout. **Industry Preferences:** Computer software, Internet specific, semiconductors and other electronics, biotechnology, and medical and health. **Geographic Preferences:** Arizona, Colorado, Nevada, New Mexico, Southern California, Southwest, Texas, and Utah. **Principal Exhibits:**

PROCUREMENT ASSISTANCE PROGRAMS

47527 ■ Arizona Procurement Technical Assistance Center–The National Center for AIED
National Center Headquarters
953 E Juanita Ave.
Mesa, AZ 85204
Ph:(480)545-1298
Free: 800-462-2433
Fax:(480)454-4208
Co. E-mail: ken.robbins@ncaied.org
URL: http://www.ncaied.org
Contact: Ken Robbins, Pres/CEO
Description: Committed to Business Development for Indian People.

47528 ■ Maricopa County Procurement Technical Assistance Center–APTAN - Bid Source
201 N Central Ave., 27th Fl.
Phoenix, AZ 85073
Ph:(602)495-6467
Fax:(602)495-8913
Co. E-mail: bidsource@phoenixchamber.com
URL: http://www.phoenixchamber.com
Contact: Daniel Ayala, Dir
E-mail: cmccroskey@phoenixchamber.com

INCUBATORS/RESEARCH AND TECHNOLOGY PARKS

47529 ■ Arizona Center for Innovation
9040 S Rita Rd., Ste. 1100
Tucson, AZ 85747
Ph:(520)382-3260
Fax:(520)382-3299
Co. E-mail: info@azinnovation.com
URL: http://www.azinnovation.org/
Contact: Marie Wesselhoft, Dir.
Description: A high-tech incubator promoting the development of high technology companies in Southern Arizona through a disciplined program of business development.

47530 ■ Arizona State University Research Park
8750 S Science Dr.
Tempe, AZ 85284-1828
Ph:(480)752-1000
Fax:(480)491-2273
Co. E-mail: michele.pino@asu.edu
URL: http://researchpark.asu.edu
Contact: Michele Pino, Exec.Dir.
E-mail: michele.pino@asu.edu
Scope: Seeks to link technological results of university and individual research with private industry. The Park provides tenants with leased land for construction of research and development facilities, laboratories, offices, pilot plants, facilities for production or assembly of prototype products, University and government research facilities, education and training

facilities, and corporate regional or national headquarters facilities related to these functions. **Educational Activities:** Conferences.

47531 ■ Association of University Research Parks
6262 N Swan Rd., Ste. 100
Tucson, AZ 85718
Ph:(520)529-2521
Fax:(520)529-2499
Co. E-mail: info@aurp.net
URL: http://www.aurp.net
Contact: Eileen Walker, CEO
E-mail: info@aurp.net
Scope: Serves as forum for the exchange of information on planning, construction, marketing, and managing of university-related research parks, particularly information on university-industry relations, innovation, technology incubators, and technology transfer to the private sector. Monitor legislative and regulatory actions affecting the development and operation of research parks. Act as a clearinghouse for career opportunities. **Publications:** The Research Park Forum (bimonthly). **Educational Activities:** Annual conference; Seminars; Workshops.

47532 ■ Northern Arizona Center for Entrepreneurship and Technology
2225 N Gemini Dr.
Flagstaff, AZ 86001
Ph:(928)213-9234
Fax:(928)213-9720
Co. E-mail: info@nacet.org
URL: http://www.nacet.org/
Contact: Russ Yelton, Pres. & CEO
Description: An incubator supporting the creation of science and technology-based businesses in Arizona.

47533 ■ Research Corporation Technologies
5210 E Williams Cir., Ste. 240
Tucson, AZ 85711-4410
Ph:(520)748-4400
Fax:(520)748-0025
Co. E-mail: csouvignier@rctech.com
URL: http://www.rctech.com
Contact: Chad W. Souvignier PhD, Mng.Dir.
E-mail: csouvignier@rctech.com
Scope: Appraises, protects, develops, and commercializes inventions from colleges, universities, medical research organizations, and other research laboratories. Among the variety of inventions that have been developed and marketed are agricultural and other chemicals, chemical processes, biotechnologies, bioprocessing, diagnostics, foods and additives, pharmaceuticals, plants, vaccines, veterinary products, agricultural equipment, analytical instruments, chemicals, electronics, materials, industrial processes, machines, medical/surgical diagnostics, and optics/optical instruments. Provides incentives for invention disclosure, funds selected applied research, new business formation.

47534 ■ Stealthmode Partners
260 S Arizona Ave.
Chandler, AZ 85225
Ph:(816)974-8836
Fax:(602)532-7087
Co. E-mail: francine@stealthmode.com
URL: http://stealthmode.com/
Contact: Francine Hardaway
Description: A network of people and companies working together behind the scenes (in "stealthmode") to help its portfolio companies grow bigger,

better, faster. Companies accepted into the Stealthmode Partners portfolio receive coaching, consulting, and connections to the people and resources they need to reach success.

47535 ■ Thunderbird Global Entrepreneurship Incubator
Thunderbird School of Global Management
Voris Bldg.
1 Global Pl.
Glendale, AZ 85306
Ph:(602)978-7571
Fax:(602)439-1435
Co. E-mail: cge@thunderbird.edu
URL: http://www.thunderbird.edu
Description: A small business incubator offering entrepreneurs a unique environment to increase their chances for success, providing low-cast office space, professional and support services, and fostering entrepreneurial ideas from the early stages of company development until the graduation from the incubator.

47536 ■ University of Arizona–Office of Vice President for Research, Graduate Studies and Economic Development
601 Administration Bldg.
1401 E University Dr.
Tucson, AZ 85721-0066
Ph:(520)621-3513
Fax:(520)621-7507
Co. E-mail: tolbert@email.arizona.edu
URL: http://www.vpr.arizona.edu
Contact: Prof. Leslie P. Tolbert PhD, VP
E-mail: tolbert@email.arizona.edu
Scope: Responsible for coordinating and administering extramurally supported research programs conducted in various departments and organized research units of the University.

47537 ■ University of Arizona Foundation
1111 N Cherry Ave.
PO Box 210109
Tucson, AZ 85721-0109
Ph:(520)621-9077
Fax:(520)621-8820
Co. E-mail: moore@al.arizona.edu
URL: http://www.uafoundation.org
Contact: James H. Moore Jr., Pres.
E-mail: moore@al.arizona.edu
Scope: Seeks private funds for support of educational and research programs at the University. **Publications:** Foundation report (semiannually). **Educational Activities:** Conferences.

EDUCATIONAL PROGRAMS

47538 ■ Eastern Arizona College
615 N Stadium Ave.
Thatcher, AZ 85552-0769
Ph:(928)428-8472
Free: 800-678-3808
Fax:(928)428-8462
URL: http://www.eac.edu
Description: Two-year college offering a small business management program.

47539 ■ Rio Salado Community College
2323 W 14th St.
Tempe, AZ 85281
Ph:(480)517-8000

Free: 800-729-1197
Fax:(480)517-8519
URL: http://www.rio.maricopa.edu
Description: Two-year college offering a program in small business management.

PUBLICATIONS

47540 ■ *Starting and Operating a Business in Arizona: A Step-by-Step Guide*
PSI Research
300 N. Valley Dr.
Grants Pass, OR 97526
Ph:(503)479-9464
Free: 800-228-2275
Fax:(503)476-1479
Co. E-mail: psi2@magick.net
Ed: Michael D. Jenkins. **Released:** Revised edition, 1992. **Price:** $29.95 (looseleaf binder); $24.95 (paper). **Description:** Part of the Successful Business Library series.

PUBLISHERS

47541 ■ Center for Competitiveness and Prosperity Research
W. P. Carey School of Business
PO Box 874011
Tempe, AZ 85287-4011
Ph:(480)965-3961
Fax:(480)965-5458
Co. E-mail: wpcarey.ccpr@asu.edu
URL: http://wpcarey.asu.edu/seid/ccpr
Contact: Tom R. Rex, Director
E-mail: tom.rex@asu.edu
Description: Publishes books on economics, real estate, consumer price index and demographics. Reports and documents in microform distributed by University Microfilms, Information Access Company and the Institute for Scientific Information. Printed publications available from the Center. Does not accept unsolicited manuscripts. **Founded:** 1954.

47542 ■ Sohnen-Moe Associates Inc.
8340 N Thornydale Rd., Ste. 110-261
Tucson, AZ 85741
Ph:(520)743-3936
Free: 800-786-4774
Fax:(520)743-3656
Co. E-mail: sma.info@sohnen-moe.com
URL: http://www.sohnen-moe.com
Contact: Virginia Anthony, President
Description: Publishes materials for small business owners, especially health care practitioners. **Founded:** 1984.

47543 ■ Success Showcase Publishing
10115 E Bell Rd., Ste. 107-616
PO Box 27946
Scottsdale, AZ 85260
Ph:(480)634-7691
Free: 800-359-4544
Fax:(480)634-7692
Co. E-mail: info@debbieallen.com
URL: http://www.debbieallen.com
Contact: Debbie Allen, President
E-mail: debbie@debbieAllen.com
Description: Publishes books on general business and marketing titles. Does not accept unsolicited manuscripts. Reaches market through direct mail, reviews and listings. **Founded:** 1996.

SMALL BUSINESS DEVELOPMENT CENTERS

47544 ■ Arkansas State University Small Business Development Center
PO Box 2650
State University, AR 72467
Co. E-mail: hlawrenc@astate.edu
URL: http://www.deltaced.astate.edu/asbdc.htm
Contact: Herb Lawrence, Dir.

47545 ■ Southern Arkansas University Small Business Development Center
PO Box 9192
Magnolia, AR 71754
Co. E-mail: tpconsidine@saumag.edu
URL: http://www.saumag.edu/sbdc
Contact: Felicia Bozeman

SCORE OFFICES

47546 ■ Garland County SCORE
Path: www.hotspringschamber.com/resources/sba.asp

47547 ■ Harrison SCORE
Path: www.nwascore.org/harrison.htm

47548 ■ River Valley SCORE
Path:

47549 ■ South Central Arkansas SCORE
Path: www.southcentralarkansas.scorechapter.org

BETTER BUSINESS BUREAUS

47550 ■ Better Business Bureau of Arkansas
12521 Kanis Rd.
Little Rock, AR 72211
Ph:(501)664-7274
Fax:(501)664-0024
Co. E-mail: info@bbbarkansas.org
URL: http://arkansas.bbb.org
Contact: Janet J. Robb, Pres.

CHAMBERS OF COMMERCE

47551 ■ Alma Area Chamber of Commerce
PO Box 2607
Alma, AR 72921
Ph:(479)632-4127
Fax:(479)632-4037
Co. E-mail: almachamber@centurytel.net
URL: http://www.almachamber.com

47552 ■ Arkadelphia Area Chamber of Commerce
PO Box 38
Arkadelphia, AR 71923-0038
Ph:(870)246-5542
Free: 800-874-4289
Fax:(870)246-5543
Co. E-mail: chamber@cityofarkadelphia.com
URL: http://www.arkadelphia.org
Contact: Mr. Connie D. Nelson, Exec. Dir.

47553 ■ Arkansas State Chamber of Commerce
PO Box 3645
Little Rock, AR 72203-3645
Ph:(501)372-2222
Fax:(501)372-2722
Co. E-mail: rzook@arkansasstatechamber.com
URL: http://ascc.weknowarkansas.org
Contact: Randy Zook, Pres./CEO

47554 ■ Bald Knob Area Chamber of Commerce
PO Box 338
Bald Knob, AR 72010
Ph:(501)724-3140
Fax:(501)724-8100
Co. E-mail: baldknobchamber@centurytel.net
URL: http://www.baldknobchamber.com/baldknob

47555 ■ Batesville Area Chamber of Commerce
409 Vine St.
Batesville, AR 72501
Ph:(870)793-2378
Fax:(870)793-3061
Co. E-mail: info@mybatesville.org
URL: http://www.mybatesville.org
Contact: Ms. Stacy Gunderman, Chair

47556 ■ Benton Area Chamber of Commerce
607 N Market St.
Benton, AR 72015
Ph:(501)315-8272
Fax:(501)315-8290
Co. E-mail: reception@bentonchamber.com
URL: http://www.bentonchamber.com
Contact: Connie Curry, Exec. Asst.

47557 ■ Bentonville-Bella Vista Chamber of Commerce
PO Box 330
Bentonville, AR 72712
Ph:(479)273-2841
Fax:(479)273-2180
Co. E-mail: info@bbvchamber.com
URL: http://www.bbvchamber.com
Contact: Ed Clifford, Pres./CEO

47558 ■ Blytheville-Gosnell Area Chamber of Commerce
PO Box 485
Blytheville, AR 72316-0485
Ph:(870)762-2012
Fax:(870)762-0551
Co. E-mail: info@blythevillegosnell.com
URL: http://www.blythevillegosnell.com
Contact: Elizabeth Smith, Exec. Dir.

47559 ■ Booneville Development Corporation - South Logan County Chamber of Commerce
PO Box 55
Booneville, AR 72927
Ph:(479)675-2666
Fax:(479)675-5158
Co. E-mail: information@booneville.com
URL: http://www.booneville.com
Contact: Stacey McCollough, Exec. Dir.

47560 ■ Bradley County Chamber of Commerce
104 N Myrtle St.
Warren, AR 71671
Ph:(870)226-5225
Fax:(870)226-6285
Co. E-mail: bcc.warren@sbcglobal.net
URL: http://www.bradleychamber.com
Contact: Grace Miller

47561 ■ Brinkley Chamber of Commerce
Brinkley Convention Center
1501 Weatherby Dr.
Brinkley, AR 72021
Ph:(870)734-1382
Co. E-mail: brinkleyar@msn.com
URL: http://www.brinkleyar.com
Contact: Barbara Skouras

47562 ■ Bryant Chamber of Commerce
PO Box 261
Bryant, AR 72089-0261
Ph:(501)847-4702
Fax:(501)847-7576
Co. E-mail: bryantcofc@aristotle.net
URL: http://www.bryant-ar.com/chamber/default.html
Contact: Rae Ann Fields, Exec. Dir.

47563 ■ Bull Shoals Lake - White River Chamber of Commerce
PO Box 354
Bull Shoals, AR 72619
Ph:(870)445-4443
Free: 800-447-1290
Co. E-mail: havefun@bullshoals.org
URL: http://www.bullshoals.org
Contact: Anne Mahoney, Exec. Dir.

47564 ■ Cabot Chamber of Commerce
PO Box 631
Cabot, AR 72023
Ph:(501)843-2136
Fax:(501)843-1861
Co. E-mail: chamber@cabotcc.org
URL: http://www.cabotarkansas.us
Contact: Billye Everett, Exec. Dir.

47565 ■ Cave City Chamber of Commerce
PO Box 274
Cave City, AR 72521
Ph:(870)283-7333
Free: (866)351-7333
Co. E-mail: laura@frontiercs.com
URL: http://www.cavecityarkansas.info
Contact: James Street, Pres.

47566 ■ Clarendon Chamber of Commerce
PO Box 153
Clarendon, AR 72029-0153
Ph:(870)747-5414
Co. E-mail: clarendoncityhall@centurytel.net
URL: http://www.clarendon-ar.com
Contact: Ladon Edens, Sec.-Treas.

47567 ■ Clarksville-Johnson County Chamber of Commerce
101 N Johnson St.
Clarksville, AR 72830
Ph:(479)754-2340
Fax:(479)754-4923
Co. E-mail: cjccofc@centurytel.net
URL: http://www.clarksvillearchamber.com
Contact: Vicki Lyons, Exec. Dir.

47568 ■ Clinton Chamber of Commerce
PO Box 52
Clinton, AR 72031
Ph:(501)745-6500
Fax:(501)745-6505
Co. E-mail: office@clintonchamber.com
URL: http://www.clintonchamber.com
Contact: Linda Fisher, contact

47569 ■ Conway Area Chamber of Commerce
900 Oak St.
Conway, AR 72032-4402
Ph:(501)327-7788
Fax:(501)327-7790
Co. E-mail: getsmart@conwayarkansas.org
URL: http://www.conwayarkcc.org
Contact: Brad Lacy, Pres./CEO

47570 ■ Corning Area Chamber of Commerce
1621 W Main St.
Corning, AR 72422-0093
Ph:(870)857-3874
URL: http://www.corningarchamber.org

47571 ■ Cotter Chamber of Commerce
PO Box 489
Cotter, AR 72626-0489
Ph:(870)321-1243
Co. E-mail: chamber@cotterarkansas.com
URL: http://www.cotterarkansas.com
Contact: Larry Barker, Pres.

47572 ■ Cross County Chamber of Commerce and Economic Development Corporation
PO Box 234
Wynne, AR 72396
Ph:(870)238-2601
Fax:(870)238-7844
Co. E-mail: info@crosscountychamber.com
URL: http://www.crosscountychamber.com
Contact: Joy Shepherd, Pres.

47573 ■ Crossett Area Chamber of Commerce
101 W 1st Ave.
Crossett, AR 71635
Ph:(870)364-6591
Fax:(870)364-7488
URL: http://www.crossettchamber.org
Contact: Darell Loveless, Pres.-Elect

47574 ■ De Queen/Sevier County Chamber of Commerce
315 W Stilwell Ave.
De Queen, AR 71832
Ph:(870)584-3225
Fax:(870)642-5533
Co. E-mail: dqscoc@ipa.net
URL: http://www.dequeenchamberofcommerce.com
Contact: Bonita Smith, Pres.

47575 ■ Dermott Area Chamber of Commerce
PO Box 147
Dermott, AR 71638-0147
Ph:(870)538-5656
Fax:(870)538-5493
Co. E-mail: email@dermottchamber.com
URL: http://www.dermottchamber.com
Contact: Frank Henry Jr., Exec. Dir.

47576 ■ Dierks Chamber of Commerce
PO Box 292
Dierks, AR 71833-0292
Ph:(870)286-3163
Co. E-mail: dierkscoc@alltel.net
URL: http://www.dierkschamberofcommerce.com
Contact: Brenda Ward, Pres.

47577 ■ Dumas Chamber of Commerce
PO Box 431
Dumas, AR 71639-0431
Ph:(870)382-5447
Fax:(870)382-3031
Co. E-mail: dumaschamber@dumasar.net
URL: http://www.dumasar.net
Contact: Sammye Owen, Exec. Dir.

47578 ■ El Dorado Chamber of Commerce
111 W Main St.
El Dorado, AR 71730
Ph:(870)863-6113
Free: 888-921-2666
Fax:(870)863-6115
Co. E-mail: info@goeldorado.com
URL: http://www.goeldorado.com
Contact: Don Wales, Pres./CEO

47579 ■ Fayetteville Chamber of Commerce
123 W Mountain St.
Fayetteville, AR 72701
Ph:(479)521-1710
Fax:(479)521-1791
Co. E-mail: chamber@fayettevillear.com
URL: http://www.fayettevillear.com
Contact: Steve Clark, Pres./CEO

47580 ■ Flippin Chamber of Commerce
PO Box 118
Flippin, AR 72634-0118
Ph:(870)453-8480
Co. E-mail: chicks@tlcbank.net
URL: http://www.flippinchamber.com
Contact: Claudia Hicks, Pres.

47581 ■ Fordyce Chamber of Commerce
101 S Main St.
Fordyce, AR 71742
Ph:(870)352-2198
Fax:(870)352-8610
Co. E-mail: cityoffordyce@alltel.net
Contact: Barbara M. Finley, Exec. Dir.

47582 ■ Forrest City Area Chamber of Commerce
203 N Izard
Forrest City, AR 72335
Ph:(870)633-1651
Fax:(870)633-9500
Co. E-mail: info@forrestcitychamber.com
URL: http://www.forrestcitychamber.com
Contact: David K. Dunn, Exec. Dir.

47583 ■ Fort Smith Chamber of Commerce
PO Box 1668
Fort Smith, AR 72902
Ph:(479)783-6118
Fax:(479)783-6110
Co. E-mail: info@fortsmithchamber.com
URL: http://www.fortsmithchamber.org
Contact: Tom Manskey, Pres./CEO

47584 ■ Grant County Chamber of Commerce
202 N Oak St.
Sheridan, AR 72150-2132
Ph:(870)942-3021
Fax:(870)942-3378
Co. E-mail: gccc@alltel.net
URL: http://www.grantcountychamber.com
Contact: LeAnn Williams, Exec. Sec.

47585 ■ Greater Eureka Springs Chamber of Commerce
PO Box 551
Eureka Springs, AR 72632-0551
Ph:(479)253-8737
Free: 800-6-EUREKA

Fax:(479)253-5037
Co. E-mail: jeff@eurekaspringschamber.com
URL: http://www.eurekaspringschamber.com
Contact: Jeffrey B. Feldman, Pres./CEO

47586 ■ Greater Hot Springs Chamber of Commerce
659 Ouachita Ave.
Hot Springs, AR 71901
Ph:(501)321-1700
Free: 800-467-INFO
Fax:(501)321-3551
Co. E-mail: info@hotspringschamber.com
URL: http://www.hotspringschamber.com
Contact: Dave Byerly, Pres./CEO

47587 ■ Greater Pine Bluff Chamber of Commerce
PO Box 5069
Pine Bluff, AR 71611
Ph:(870)535-0110
Fax:(870)535-1643
Co. E-mail: info@pinebluffchamber.com
URL: http://www.pinebluffchamber.com
Contact: Ford Trotter, Chm.

47588 ■ Greenwood Chamber of Commerce
PO Box 511
Greenwood, AR 72936
Ph:(479)996-6357
Fax:(479)996-1162
Co. E-mail: info@greenwoodchamber.net
URL: http://www.greenwoodarkansas.com
Contact: Dr. Kay Johnson, Sec.

47589 ■ Greers Ferry Area Chamber of Commerce
PO Box 1354
Greers Ferry, AR 72067
Ph:(501)825-7188
Free: 888-825-7199
Co. E-mail: ceswl-gf@usa.army.mil
URL: http://greersferry.com
Contact: Gene Eddleman, Pres.

47590 ■ Gurdon Chamber of Commerce
PO Box 187
Gurdon, AR 71743-0187
Ph:(870)353-2661
URL: http://www.gurdonchamberofcommerce.com
Contact: Bill O'Connell, Pres.

47591 ■ Hamburg Area Chamber of Commerce
PO Box 460
Hamburg, AR 71646
Ph:(870)853-8345
Fax:(870)853-8345
Co. E-mail: info@hamburgareachamber.org
URL: http://www.hamburgareachamber.org
Contact: Robin LaCaze, Exec. Dir.

47592 ■ Harrisburg Area Chamber of Commerce
PO Box 265
Harrisburg, AR 72432
Ph:(870)578-5461
Co. E-mail: hbgchamber@pcsii.com
URL: http://www.harrisburgchamber.com
Contact: Mildred Traynom, Sec.-Treas.

47593 ■ Harrison Chamber of Commerce
621 E Rush
Harrison, AR 72601
Ph:(870)741-2659
Free: 800-880-6265
Co. E-mail: cocinfo@harrison-chamber.com
URL: http://www.harrison-chamber.com
Contact: Mike Tucker, Pres.

47594 ■ Heber Springs Area Chamber of Commerce
1001 W Main St.
Heber Springs, AR 72543
Ph:(501)362-2444
Free: 800-774-3237
Co. E-mail: chamber@heber-springs.com
URL: http://www.heber-springs.com/content
Contact: Marilyn Wright, Exec. Dir.

47595 ■ Hope-Hempstead County Chamber of Commerce
PO Box 250
Hope, AR 71802-0250
Ph:(870)777-3640
Fax:(870)722-6154
Co. E-mail: hopemelonfest@yahoo.com
URL: http://www.hopechamberofcommerce.com
Contact: Mark Keith, Dir.

47596 ■ Horseshoe Bend Area Chamber of Commerce
811 2nd St., No. 18
Diamond B. Mall
Horseshoe Bend, AR 72512
Ph:(870)670-5433
Free: 800-239-9338
Co. E-mail: hsbcoc@gmail.com
URL: http://horseshoebendar-net.grayscustomsad-dlery.com
Contact: Paul Sulser, Pres.

47597 ■ Huntsville Chamber of Commerce
PO Box 950
104 E Main St.
Huntsville, AR 72740-0950
Ph:(479)738-6000
Co. E-mail: service@huntsvillearchamber.com
URL: http://www.huntsvillearchamber.com
Contact: Mr. Richard Gillham, Sec.

47598 ■ Jonesboro Regional Chamber of Commerce
1709 E Nettleton Ave.
Jonesboro, AR 72403-0789
Ph:(870)932-6691
Fax:(870)933-5762
Co. E-mail: myoung@jonesborocofc.org
URL: http://www.jonesborochamber.org
Contact: Mark Young, Pres./CEO

47599 ■ Lake Village Chamber of Commerce
PO Box 752
Lake Village, AR 71653
Ph:(870)265-5997
Fax:(870)265-5254
Co. E-mail: request@lakevillagechamber.com
URL: http://www.lakevillagechamber.com
Contact: Lisa V. Raby, Dir.

47600 ■ Little River Chamber of Commerce
PO Box 160
Ashdown, AR 71822
Ph:(870)898-2758
Fax:(870)898-6699
Co. E-mail: lrcoc0436@sbcglobal.net
URL: http://www.littlerivercounty.org
Contact: Fonda Hawthorne, Dir.

47601 ■ Little Rock Regional Chamber of Commerce
One Chamber Plz.
Little Rock, AR 72201-1618
Ph:(501)374-2001
Fax:(501)374-6018
Co. E-mail: chamber@littlerockchamber.com
URL: http://www.littlerockchamber.com/cwt/external/wcpages/index.aspx
Contact: Jay Chesshir, Pres./CEO

47602 ■ Magnolia-Columbia County Chamber of Commerce
621 E North St.
Magnolia, AR 71753
Ph:(870)234-4352
Free: 800-206-0889
Fax:(870)234-9291
Co. E-mail: ea@ccalliance.us
URL: http://www.magnoliachamber.com
Contact: Jerry Hubbard, Pres.

47603 ■ Marion Chamber of Commerce
PO Box 652
Marion, AR 72364-0652
Ph:(870)739-6041
Fax:(870)739-5448
Co. E-mail: chamber@marionarkansas.org
URL: http://www.marionarkansas.org
Contact: Paul Brewster, Pres.

47604 ■ Maumelle Area Chamber of Commerce
PO Box 13099
Maumelle, AR 72113-0099
Ph:(501)851-9700
Fax:(501)851-6690
Co. E-mail: execdir@maumellechamber.com
URL: http://www.maumellechamber.com
Contact: Pamela Rantisi, Exec. Dir.

47605 ■ McGehee Chamber of Commerce
PO Box 521
McGehee, AR 71654
Ph:(870)222-4451
Fax:(870)222-5729
Co. E-mail: admin@mcgeheechamber.com
URL: http://www.mcgeheechamber.com
Contact: Jim Daniels, Pres.

47606 ■ Monticello Drew County Chamber of Commerce
335 E Gaines St.
Monticello, AR 71655
Ph:(870)367-6741
Fax:(870)367-6741
Co. E-mail: monticellochamber@sbcglobal.net
URL: http://www.montdrewchamber.com

47607 ■ Morrilton Area Chamber of Commerce
PO Box 589
Morrilton, AR 72110
Ph:(501)354-2393
Fax:(501)354-8642
Co. E-mail: johngibson@suddenlinkmail.com
URL: http://www.morrilton.com
Contact: John Gibson, Pres.

47608 ■ Mount Ida Area Chamber of Commerce
PO Box 6
Mount Ida, AR 71957-0006
Ph:(870)867-2723
Co. E-mail: director@mtidachamber.com
URL: http://www.mtidachamber.com/chamber_page.htm
Contact: Phillip Carr, Pres.

47609 ■ Mountain Home Area Chamber of Commerce
PO Box 488
Mountain Home, AR 72654-0488
Ph:(870)425-5111
Free: 800-822-3536
Fax:(870)425-4446
Co. E-mail: salms@enjoymountainhome.com
URL: http://www.mtnhomechamber.com

47610 ■ North Little Rock Chamber of Commerce
100 Main St.
PO Box 5288
North Little Rock, AR 72114
Ph:(501)372-5959
Fax:(501)372-5955
Co. E-mail: nlrchamber@nlrchamber.org
URL: http://www.nlrchamber.org
Contact: Terry C. Hartwick, Pres./CEO

47611 ■ Osceola-South Mississippi County Chamber of Commerce
PO Box 174
Osceola, AR 72370-0174
Ph:(870)563-2281
Fax:(870)563-5385
Co. E-mail: osceolachamber@sbcglobal.net
URL: http://www.osceolachamber.net
Contact: Eric Golde, Exec. Dir.

47612 ■ Ozark Area Chamber of Commerce
300 W Commercial
Ozark, AR 72949
Ph:(479)667-2525
Fax:(479)667-5750
Co. E-mail: ozarkareacoc@centurytel.net
URL: http://www.ozarkareacoc.org
Contact: Susan McIlroy-Stokes, Dir.

47613 ■ Paragould - Greene County Chamber of Commerce
PO Box 124
Paragould, AR 72451-0124
Ph:(870)236-7684
Fax:(870)236-7142
Co. E-mail: ceo@paragould.org
URL: http://chamber.paragould.org
Contact: Sue McGowan, Dir./CEO

47614 ■ Paris Area Chamber of Commerce
301 W Walnut
Paris, AR 72855-3731
Ph:(479)963-2244
Co. E-mail: parischamber@centurytel.net
URL: http://www.parisaronline.com
Contact: Pat McHughes, Pres.

47615 ■ Prairie Grove Chamber of Commerce
PO Box 23
Prairie Grove, AR 72753
Ph:(479)846-2197
Co. E-mail: info@pgchamber.com
URL: http://www.pgchamber.com
Contact: Casey Copeland, Pres.

47616 ■ Randolph County Chamber of Commerce
PO Box 466
Pocahontas, AR 72455-0466
Ph:(870)892-3956
Fax:(870)892-5399
Co. E-mail: chamber010@centurytel.net
URL: http://www.randolphchamber.com
Contact: Mr. Tim Scott, Exec. Dir.

47617 ■ Rector Chamber of Commerce
PO Box 307
Rector, AR 72461-0307
Ph:(870)595-3549
Fax:(870)595-3611
Co. E-mail: ccd@rectorarkansas.com
URL: http://asccreg.weknowarkansas.org/chamber-execs
Contact: Ms. Nancy J. Kemp, Pres.

47618 ■ Rogers Lowell Area Chamber of Commerce
317 W Walnut
Rogers, AR 72756-4566
Ph:(479)636-1240
Fax:(479)636-5485
Co. E-mail: info@rogerslowell.com
URL: http://www.rogerslowell.com
Contact: Mr. Raymond M. Burns CCE, Pres./CEO

47619 ■ Russellville Chamber of Commerce
708 W Main St.
Russellville, AR 72801-3617
Ph:(479)968-2530
Fax:(479)968-5894
Co. E-mail: chamber@russellville.org
URL: http://www.russellvillechamber.org
Contact: Jeff Pipkin, Pres./CEO

47620 ■ Sherwood Chamber of Commerce
2303 E Lee St.
Sherwood, AR 72120
Ph:(501)835-7600
Fax:(501)835-2326
Co. E-mail: shwdchamber@cityofsherwood.net
URL: http://www.cityofsherwood.net
Contact: Herschel Bowman Jr., Pres.

47621 ■ Siloam Springs Chamber of Commerce
PO Box 476
Siloam Springs, AR 72761-0476
Ph:(479)524-6466
Co. E-mail: info@siloamchamber.com
URL: http://siloamchamber.info
Contact: Wayne Mays, Pres./CEO

47622 ■ Spring River Area Chamber of Commerce
2852D Hwy. 62/412
Highland, AR 72542
Ph:(870)856-3210
Fax:(870)856-3320
Co. E-mail: sracc@centurytel.net
URL: http://www.sracc.com
Contact: Charlotte Goodwin, Pres.

47623 ■ Springdale Chamber of Commerce
PO Box 166
Springdale, AR 72765-0166
Ph:(479)872-2222
Free: 800-972-7261
Fax:(479)751-4699
Co. E-mail: info@chamber.springdale.com
URL: http://www.springdale.com
Contact: Perry Webb CCE, Pres./CEO

47624 ■ Stuttgart Chamber of Commerce
507 S Main St.
PO Box 1500
Stuttgart, AR 72160
Ph:(870)673-1602
Fax:(870)673-1604
Co. E-mail: stuttgartchamber@centurytel.net
URL: http://stuttgartarkansas.org
Contact: Mr. Stephen R. Bell, Exec. VP

47625 ■ Van Buren Chamber of Commerce
510 Main St.
Van Buren, AR 72956
Ph:(479)474-2761
Fax:(479)474-6259
Co. E-mail: jackie@vanburenchamber.org
URL: http://www.vanburenchamber.org
Contact: Jackie Krutsch, Exec. Dir.

47626 ■ Waldron Area Chamber of Commerce
PO Box 1985
Waldron, AR 72958
Ph:(479)637-2775
URL: http://www.waldronareachamberofcommerce.com
Contact: Jeff Brewer, Pres.

47627 ■ White Hall Chamber of Commerce
102 Anderson St.
White Hall, AR 71602
Ph:(870)247-5502
Co. E-mail: dburdick@pbjc-lib.state.ar.us
URL: http://www.whitehallarchamber.com
Contact: Dane Reed, Pres.

47628 ■ Yellville Area Chamber of Commerce
PO Box 369
Yellville, AR 72687
Ph:(870)449-4676
Fax:(870)449-4671
Co. E-mail: chamber@yellville.com
URL: http://www.yellville.com
Contact: Nathan Rogers, Pres.

MINORITY BUSINESS ASSISTANCE PROGRAMS

47629 ■ Arkansas Economic Development Commission–Small and Minority Business Division
900 W Capitol
Little Rock, AR 72201
Ph:(501)682-6105
Fax:(501)682-7394
Co. E-mail: info@arkansasedc.com
URL: http://arkansasedc.com/
Contact: Maria Haley, Exec Dir
Description: Provides financial assistance, training seminars, and technical and management assistance to new and expanding minority businesses. Also refers these businesses to other organizations that offer assistance.

FINANCING AND LOAN PROGRAMS

47630 ■ Arkansas Capital Corp.
200 South Commerce, Ste. 400
Little Rock, AR 72201
Ph:(501)374-9247
Free: 800-216-7237
Fax:(501)374-9425
URL: http://www.arcapital.com
Contact: Sam Walls, Chief Executive Officer
E-mail: swalls@arcapital.com
Preferred Investment Size: $50,000 to $500,000.
Investment Types: Start-up, early, and expansion.
Industry Preferences: Communications and media, Internet specific, computer software and services, communications and computer hardware. **Geographic Preferences:** Arkansas. **Principal Exhibits:**

PROCUREMENT ASSISTANCE PROGRAMS

47631 ■ Arkansas Procurement Assistance Center (APAC)
127 W 5th St.
Malvern, AR 72104
Ph:(501)337-5355
Fax:(501)337-5045
Co. E-mail: apac@uaex.edu
URL: http://www.arcommunities.org/APAC.htm
Contact: Sue Coates, Prgm Dir
E-mail: aptan@primenet.com
Description: Provide training and resources that help Arkansas businesses generate revenues and thereby create or retain jobs for Arkansans through effective government contracting.

47632 ■ Arkansas Procurement Assistance Center - Metro Satellite–University of Arkansas - Cooperative Extension Service
2301 S University Ave., Rm. 110
PO Box 391
Little Rock, AR 72203
Ph:(501)671-2390
Fax:(501)671-2394
Co. E-mail: apac@uaex.edu
URL: http://www.arcommunities.org/apac.htm
Contact: Delbert Taylor, Program Asst.
E-mail: dtaylor@uaex.edu
Description: Provide training and resources that help Arkansas businesses generate revenues and thereby create or retain jobs for Arkansans through effective government contracting.

47633 ■ Arkansas Procurement Technical Assistance Center–Satellite Office
2301 S University
PO Box 391
Little Rock, AR 72203
Ph:(501)671-2390
Fax:(501)671-2394
Co. E-mail: apac@uaex.edu
URL: http://www.arcommunities.org
Contact: Delbert Taylor, Counselor
Description: Serves Arkansas businesses in all 75 counties at no charge from the main office in Malvern, supported by a fully staffed satellite office in Little Rock.

INCUBATORS/RESEARCH AND TECHNOLOGY PARKS

47634 ■ Arkansas Biotechnology Incubator–Biomedical Biotechnology Center
4301 W Markham St.
Little Rock, AR 72205
Ph:(501)686-6696
Fax:(501)686-8501
Co. E-mail: biotech@uams.edu
URL: http://www.uamsbiotech.com
Contact: Amanda Stephens, Specialist
Description: The BBC was established to promote Arkansas' biotechnology. The Center seeks to support technology transfer and startup company development as well as forge alliances between industry and research institutions.

47635 ■ BioVentures
University of Arkansas for Medical Sciences
4301 W Markham St.
Little Rock, AR 72205
Ph:(501)686-6696
Fax:(501)686-8501
Co. E-mail: biotech@uams.edu
URL: http://www.uams.edu/bioventures/
Description: A formal outgrowth of the University of Arkansas for Medical Sciences, established to maximize global and industrial interaction with the University of Arkansas faculty, as well as to facilitate technology transfer, the creation of startup companies that are based on UAMS technology, and contributions to Arkansas' economic development.

47636 ■ Genesis Technology Incubator
Engineering Research Center
University of Arkansas
700 Research Center Blvd.
Fayetteville, AR 72701
Ph:(479)575-7227
Fax:(479)575-7446
Co. E-mail: awrc@uark.edu
URL: http://www.genesis.uark.edu/ua/artp/facilities/genesis.html
Contact: Phillip Stafford, Dir
Description: GENESIS provides office space and shared services to technology-based entrepreneurs, enhanced by the resources of the University of Arkansas.

47637 ■ University of Arkansas–Research Support and Sponsored Programs
210 Administration Bldg.
1 University of Arkansas
Fayetteville, AR 72701
Ph:(479)575-3845
Fax:(479)575-3846
Co. E-mail: rsspinfo@uark.edu
URL: http://vpred.uark.edu/242.php
Contact: Dennis Brewer, Dir.
E-mail: rsspinfo@uark.edu
Scope: Administers all contract and grant research and other sponsored programs conducted at the University. Oversees patent and copyright administration and technology transfer. Assists faculty members in preparing proposals for submission to prospective sponsors of research projects and serves as liaison with extramural sponsors. Also provides administrative support to research workers, including reproduction, computer, shop, and special equipment services. The office is also responsible for research compliance. **Publications:** Research frontiers.

LEGISLATIVE ASSISTANCE

47638 ■ Arkansas House and Senate Committees on Insurance and Commerce
State Capitol Bldg., Rm. 315
Little Rock, AR 72201
Ph:(501)682-1937
Fax:(501)682-1936
URL: http://www.arkleg.state.ar.us
Contact: Toni Minicozzi

PUBLICATIONS

47639 ■ *Arkansas Business*
201 E. Markham, Ste. 220
Little Rock, AR 72201-1651
Ph:(501)372-1443
Fax:(501)375-0933
Co. E-mail: abnews@abnews.com
URL: http://abnews.com

47640 ■ *Starting and Operating a Business in Arkansas: A Step-by-Step Guide*
PSI Research
300 N. Valley Dr.
Grants Pass, OR 97526
Ph:(503)479-9464
Free: 800-228-2275

Fax:(503)476-1479
Co. E-mail: psi2@magick.net

Ed: Michael D. Jenkins. **Released:** Revised edition, 1992. **Price:** $29.95 (looseleaf binder); $24.95

(paper). **Description:** Part of the Successful Business Library series.

California

SMALL BUSINESS DEVELOPMENT CENTERS

47641 ■ Alameda Small Business Development Center
475 14th St., Ste. 150
Oakland, CA 94612
Co. E-mail: rohlrich@eastbaysbdc.org
URL: http://www.eastbaysbdc.org
Contact: Rick Ohlrich, Lead Business Advisor

47642 ■ Alliance Small Business Development Center
1010 Eleventh St., Ste. 1013
Modesto, CA 95354
Fax:(209)567-4955
URL: http://www.alliancesbdc.com

47643 ■ Alliance Small Business Development Center - Mariposa
5078 Bullion St.
Mariposa, CA 95338
URL: http://www.alliancesbdc.com

47644 ■ Alliance Small Business Development Center - Merced
PO Box 1029
Merced, CA 95341
Fax:(209)381-6552
URL: http://www.alliancesbdc.com
Contact: William Anderson, Mgr.

47645 ■ Alpine County Small Business Development Center
PO Box 265
Markleeville, CA 96120
Fax:(530)694-2478
Co. E-mail: alpcntv@powernet.net
URL: http://www.sbdc.deltacollege.edu

47646 ■ Amador County Small Business Development Center
PO Box 1077
Jackson, CA 95642
Fax:(530)223-2261
Co. E-mail: aedc@cdepot.net
URL: http://www.sbdc.deltacollege.edu

47647 ■ Butte College Small Business Development Center
19 Williamsburg Ln.
Chico, CA 95928
Fax:(530)566-9851
Co. E-mail: konuwaso@butte.edu
URL: http://www.bcsbdc.org
Contact: Sophie Konuwa, Dir.

47648 ■ Calaveras County Small Business Development Center
700 Mountain Ranch Rd., Ste. A
San Andreas, CA 95249
Fax:(209)754-9792
URL: http://www.sbdc.deltacollege.edu

47649 ■ Central California Small Business Development Center - Fresno
Manchester Center
3302 N Blackstone Ave., Ste. 225
Fresno, CA 93726
URL: http://www.ccsbdc.org
Contact: Bryan Moe, Dir.

47650 ■ Central California Small Business Development Center - Visalia
PO Box 787
Visalia, CA 93279
URL: http://www.ccsbdc.org
Contact: Gil Jaramillo, Mgr.

47651 ■ Central Coast Small Business Development Center
Cabrillo College
6500 Soquel Dr.
Aptos, CA 95003
Fax:(831)479-6166
Co. E-mail: sbdc@cabrillo.edu
URL: http://www.cabrillo.edu/services/sbdc

47652 ■ CHARO Small Business Development Center
4301 E Valley Blvd.
Los Angeles, CA 90032
Fax:(323)343-9483
URL: http://www.charosbdc.com

47653 ■ Coachella Valley Small Business Development Center
500 S Palm Canyon Dr., Ste. 222
Palm Springs, CA 92264
Fax:(760)864-1319
Co. E-mail: cvsbdc@dc.rr.com
URL: http://www.leadsbdc.org

47654 ■ College of the Canyons Small Business Development Center
28460 Stanford Ave., Ste. 100
Santa Clarita, CA 91355
Fax:(661)294-5203
Co. E-mail: donna.plummer@canyons.edu
URL: http://www.canyonsecondev.org/content/small-business-dev.-center.html
Contact: Donna Plummer, Interim Assistant Dir.

47655 ■ Contra Costa Small Business Development Center
2425 Bisso Ln., No. 200
Concord, CA 94520
Fax:(925)646-5299
Co. E-mail: info@contracostasbdc.com
URL: http://www.contracostasbdc.com
Contact: Beverly Hamile, Dir.

47656 ■ Cuesta College Small Business Development Center
3211 Broad St., Ste. 109
San Luis Obispo, CA 93401
Co. E-mail: sccsbdc@smallbusinessinfo.org
URL: http://www.smallbusinessinfo.org

47657 ■ East Bay Small Business Development Center
475 14th St., Ste. 150
Oakland, CA 94612
Fax:(510)208-0413
Co. E-mail: sroth@eastbaysbdc.org
URL: http://www.eastbaysbdc.org
Contact: Steve Roth, Dir.

47658 ■ El Camino College Small Business Development Center
13430 Hawthorne Blvd.
Hawthorne, CA 90250
Fax:(310)973-3132
Co. E-mail: avaughan@elcamino.edu
URL: http://www.elcamino.edu/commadv/sbdc
Contact: A. Alex Vaughan, Dir.

47659 ■ Gavilan Small Business Development Center
8351 Church St., Bldg. E
Gilroy, CA 95020
Free: 800-847-0373
URL: http://www.gavilan.edu/catalog/2005_2007/community.html98

47660 ■ Imperial Valley Small Business Development Center at Imperial Valley College
301 N Imperial Ave., Ste. B
El Centro, CA 92243
Fax:(760)312-9838
Co. E-mail: info@ivsbdc.org
URL: http://www.ivsbdc.org

47661 ■ Inland Empire North Small Business Development Center
15490 Civic Dr., Ste. 102
Victorville, CA 92392
Fax:(760)951-8929
Co. E-mail: jthomas@iesbdc.org
URL: http://www.leadsbdc.org

47662 ■ Inland Empire Small Business Development Center
1201 Research Park Dr., Ste. 100
Riverside, CA 92507
Fax:(909)781-2353
Co. E-mail: ahurtado@iesbdc.org
URL: http://www.iesbdc.org
Contact: Vincent McCoy, Exec. Dir.

47663 ■ Lake County Small Business Development Center
55 First St.
Lakeport, CA 95453
URL: http://www.yubasbdc.org/Lake-County-SBDC.asp
Contact: Jim Magliulo

47664 ■ Long Beach City College Small Business Development Center
3447 Atlantic Ave., Ste. 205
Long Beach, CA 90807
Fax:(562)570-4575
URL: http://lbsbdc.lbcc.edu

47665 ■ Los Angeles Small Business Development Center Network
4040 Paramount Blvd., Ste. 107
Lakewood, CA 90712
Fax:(562)938-5030
Co. E-mail: sbdc@lbcc.edu
URL: http://lasbdcnet.lbcc.edu
Contact: Sheneui Sloan, Regional Dir.

47666 ■ Loyola Marymount University Small Business Development Center
1 LMU Dr.
Los Angeles, CA 90045
Fax:(310)338-5187
URL: http://www.lmu.edu/Page27514.aspx

47667 ■ Mendocino Small Business Development Center
760B Stewart St.
Fort Bragg, CA 95437
Fax:(707)964-7576
URL: http://www.westcompany.org
Contact: Pamela Patterson, CEO

47668 ■ Moreno Valley Small Business Development Center
12625 Frederick St., Ste. V-1
Moreno Valley, CA 92553
Fax:(951)781-2353
URL: http://www.leadsbdc.org

47669 ■ Napa Valley College Small Business Development Center
1556 First St., Ste. 103
Napa, CA 94559
Fax:(707)253-3068
Co. E-mail: nvcsbdc@napasbdc.org
URL: http://www.napasbdc.org

47670 ■ North San Diego Small Business Development Center
Mira Costa College
1823 Mission Ave.
Oceanside, CA 92054
Co. E-mail: centerinfo@miracosta.edu
URL: http://www.sandiegosmallbiz.com

47671 ■ Northcoast Small Business Development Center - Del Norte
225 H St.
Crescent City, CA 95531
Fax:(707)464-1349
Co. E-mail: burke@northcoastsbdc.org
URL: http://www.northcoastsbdc.org
Contact: Barbara Burke

47672 ■ Northcoast Small Business Development Center - Humboldt
Prosperity Center
520 E St.
Eureka, CA 95501
Fax:(707)445-9652
Co. E-mail: neal@northcoastsbdc.org
URL: http://www.northcoastsbdc.org
Contact: Sandy Neal

47673 ■ Northern California Small Business Development Center
Humboldt State University
209 Siemens Hall
Arcata, CA 95521
Fax:(707)826-3912
Co. E-mail: kristin.johnson@humboldt.edu
URL: http://www.norcalsbdc.org
Contact: Kristin Johnson, Dir.

47674 ■ Orange County Small Business Development Center
2323 N Broadway, Ste. 201
Santa Ana, CA 92706
Fax:(714)647-1168
Co. E-mail: oc_sbdc@rsccd.org
URL: http://www.ocsbdc.com
Contact: Leila Mozaffari, Dir.

47675 ■ Redwood Empire Small Business Development Center
Santa Rosa Junior College
606 Healdsburg Ave.
Santa Rosa, CA 95401
Free: 888-346-SBDC
Fax:(707)524-1772
Co. E-mail: lduvernay@santarosa.edu
URL: http://www.santarosa.edu/sbdc
Contact: Lorraine DuVernay, Dir.

47676 ■ San Francisco Small Business Development Center
City College of San Francisco
300 Montgomery St., Ste. 789
San Francisco, CA 94104
URL: http://www.sfsbdc.org
Contact: Susie Biehler, Consultant

47677 ■ San Gabriel Valley Small Business Development Center
Mt. San Antonio College
5200 Irwindale Ave., Ste.140
Irwindale, CA 91706
Fax:(626)337-2104
Co. E-mail: info@mtsacsbdc.com
URL: http://www.sangabrielvalleysbdc.com
Contact: Daniel Morales, Dir.

47678 ■ San Joaquin Delta College Small Business Development Center
56 S Lincoln St.
Stockton, CA 95203
Fax:(209)939-0385
Co. E-mail: gmurphy@sjdccd.cc.ca.us
URL: http://www.sbdc.deltacollege.edu
Contact: Gillia Murphy, Dir.

47679 ■ Santa Ana Regional Lead Small Business Development Center
California State University, Fullerton
Langsdorf Hall, Rm. 640
800 N State College Blvd.
Fullerton, CA 92834
Fax:(714)278-7858
Co. E-mail: vpham@fullerton.edu
URL: http://www.leadsbdc.org
Contact: Vi Pham, Dir.

47680 ■ Santa Monica College Small Business Development Center
3400 Airport Ave., Ste. 76
Santa Monica, CA 90405
Fax:(310)434-3891
URL: http://www.smc.edu/sbdc
Contact: Patricia Ramos, Dir.

47681 ■ Sierra College Small Business Development Center
333 Sunrise Ave., Ste. 885
Roseville, CA 95661
Fax:(916)781-6239
Co. E-mail: sbdc@sierracollege.edu
URL: http://www.sbdcsierra.org
Contact: Indria Gillespie, Program Mgr.

47682 ■ Silicon Valley Small Business Development Center at West Valley/Mission College
84 W Santa Clara St., Ste. 100
San Jose, CA 95113
URL: http://www.siliconvalley-sbdc.org

47683 ■ Small Business Development Center - Greater Sacramento
1410 Ethan Way
Sacramento, CA 95825-2205
Fax:(916)563-3266
Co. E-mail: info@sbdc.net
URL: http://www.sbdc.net
Contact: Panda Morgan, Dir.

47684 ■ Small Business Development Center at Shasta College
1420 Butte St.
Redding, CA 96001
Co. E-mail: kanthis@sbdcsc.org
URL: http://www.sbdcsc.org
Contact: Keli Anthis, Dir.

47685 ■ Solano College Small Business Development Center
360 Campus Ln., Ste. 102
Fairfield, CA 94534
Co. E-mail: charles.eason@solano.edu
URL: http://www.solanosbdc.org
Contact: Charles Eason, Dir.

47686 ■ TriTech Small Business Development Center
2 Park Plz., Ste. 100
Irvine, CA 92614
URL: http://www.leadsbdc.org

47687 ■ UC Merced Small Business Development Center Regional Network
550 E Shaw Ave., Ste. 100
Fresno, CA 93710
Free: 877-826-7232
Fax:(559)241-7422
Co. E-mail: casbdc@ucmerced.edu
URL: http://sbdc.ucmerced.edu
Contact: Diane R. Howerton, Dir.

47688 ■ Ventura College Small Business Development Center
71 Day Rd.
Ventura, CA 93003
Fax:(805)648-8965
Co. E-mail: info@vcsbdc.com
URL: http://www.vcsbdc.com

47689 ■ Weill Institute Small Business Development Center at Bakersfield College
2100 Chester Ave.
Bakersfield, CA 93301
Fax:(661)395-4134
Co. E-mail: contact@weill-sbdc.com
URL: http://www.weill-sbdc.com
Contact: Cope Norcross

47690 ■ Woodland Small Business Development Center
307 First St.
Woodland, CA 95695
URL: http://www.yubasbdc.org/Woodland-SBDC.asp
Contact: David Flory Sr.

47691 ■ Yuba Community College District Small Business Development Center
1227 Bridge St., Ste. C
Yuba City, CA 95991
Fax:(530)822-0163
URL: http://www.yubasbdc.org
Contact: Ken Freeman, Dir.

SCORE OFFICES

47692 ■ Bakersfield SCORE
Path: www.scorebakersfield.com

47693 ■ Central Coast SCORE
Path:

47694 ■ Central Valley SCORE
Path: www.fresnoscore.org

47695 ■ Chico SCORE
Path: www.chico.scorechapter.org/about_chapter.html

47696 ■ Coachella Valley SCORE
Path: www.scorecv.org

47697 ■ Redding SCORE
Path: www.chico.scorechapter.org/about_redding.html

47698 ■ Santa Cruz County SCORE
Path: www.santacruzscore.org

BETTER BUSINESS BUREAUS

47699 ■ Better Business Bureau
1000 Broadway, Ste. 625
Oakland, CA 94607-4042
Ph:(510)844-2000
Free: (866)411-2221
Fax:(510)844-2100
Co. E-mail: info@bbbemail.org
URL: http://www.oakland.bbb.org
Contact: Gene O'Neil, Pres.

47700 ■ Better Business Bureau of Central California
4201 W Shaw Ave., Ste. 107
Fresno, CA 93722
Ph:(559)222-8111
Fax:(559)228-6518
Co. E-mail: info@bbbcencal.org
URL: http://cencal.bbb.org
Contact: Doug Broten, CEO

47701 ■ Better Business Bureau of Northeast California
3075 Beacon Blvd.
West Sacramento, CA 95691
Ph:(916)443-6843
Fax:(916)443-0376
Co. E-mail: info@necal.bbb.org
URL: http://necal.bbb.org
Contact: Barry Goggin, Pres./CEO

47702 ■ Better Business Bureau of San Diego
5050 Murphy Canyon Rd., Ste. 110
San Diego, CA 92123
Ph:(858)496-2131
Fax:(858)496-2141
Co. E-mail: info@sandiego.bbb.org
URL: http://sandiego.bbb.org
Contact: Sheryl Bilbrey, Pres./CEO

47703 ■ Better Business Bureau of San Mateo County
1000 Broadway, Ste. 625
Millbrae, CA 94030-1966
Ph:(510)844-2000
Free: (866)411-2221
Fax:(510)844-2100
URL: http://goldengate.bbb.org

47704 ■ Better Business Bureau of Silicon Valley
1112 S Bascom Ave.
San Jose, CA 95128-4705
Ph:(408)278-7400
Fax:(408)278-7444
Co. E-mail: info@bbbsilicon.org
URL: http://www.bbbsilicon.org

47705 ■ Better Business Bureau of the Southland
315 N La Cadena Dr.
Colton, CA 92324
Ph:(909)835-6064
Fax:(909)825-6246
Co. E-mail: info@labbb.org
URL: http://www.la.bbb.org
Contact: William G. Mitchell, Pres.

47706 ■ Better Business Bureau of Tri-Counties
PO Box 129
Santa Barbara, CA 93102
Ph:(805)963-8657
Fax:(805)962-8557
URL: http://www.santabarbara.bbb.org
Contact: Rick Copelan, Pres.

CHAMBERS OF COMMERCE

47707 ■ Acton Chamber of Commerce
32039 N Crown Valley Rd.
Acton, CA 93510
Ph:(661)269-5785

Fax:(661)269-4121
Co. E-mail: actoncoc@antelecom.net
URL: http://cityofacton.org
Contact: Jim Schutte, Pres.

47708 ■ Agoura - Oak Park - Las Virgenes Chamber of Commerce
30101 Agoura Ct., Ste. 207
Agoura Hills, CA 91301
Ph:(818)889-3150
Fax:(818)889-3366
Co. E-mail: info@agourachamber.org
URL: http://www.agourachamber.org
Contact: Louis Masry, Pres.

47709 ■ Alameda Chamber of Commerce
1416 Park Ave.
Alameda, CA 94501-4579
Ph:(510)522-0414
Fax:(510)522-7677
Co. E-mail: connect@alamedachamber.com
URL: http://www.alamedachamber.com
Contact: Ms. Melody Marr, CEO

47710 ■ Albany Chamber of Commerce
1108 Solano Ave.
Albany, CA 94706
Ph:(510)525-1771
Fax:(510)525-6068
URL: http://www.albanychamber.org
Contact: Tod Abbott, Pres.

47711 ■ Alhambra Chamber of Commerce
104 S 1st St.
Alhambra, CA 91801
Ph:(626)282-8481
Fax:(626)282-5596
Co. E-mail: alhambrachamber@sbcglobal.net
URL: http://www.alhambrachamber.org
Contact: Walter Tang, Pres.

47712 ■ Alpine County Chamber of Commerce
PO Box 265
Markleeville, CA 96120
Ph:(530)694-2475
Fax:(530)694-2478
Co. E-mail: info@alpinecounty.com
URL: http://www.alpinecounty.com
Contact: Teresa Burkhauser, Exec. Dir.

47713 ■ Alpine and Mountain Empire Chamber of Commerce
2707 Alpine Blvd.
Alpine, CA 91901
Ph:(619)445-2722
Fax:(619)445-2871
Co. E-mail: info@alpinechamber.com
URL: http://www.alpinechamber.com

47714 ■ Altadena Chamber of Commerce
Altadena Community Center Bldg.
730 E Altadena Dr.
Altadena, CA 91001
Ph:(626)794-3988
Fax:(626)794-6015
Co. E-mail: altadenachamber@yahoo.com
URL: http://www.abacus-es.com/altadena
Contact: Doug Colliflower, Pres.

47715 ■ Alturas Chamber of Commerce
522 S Main St.
Alturas, CA 96101-4115
Ph:(530)233-4434
Co. E-mail: contactus@alturaschamber.org
URL: http://www.alturaschamber.org

47716 ■ Amador County Chamber of Commerce and Visitors Bureau
125 Peek St., Ste. B
PO Box 596
Jackson, CA 95642-0596
Ph:(209)223-0350
Free: 800-649-4988
Fax:(209)223-4425
Co. E-mail: gold49@amadorcountychamber.com
URL: http://www.amadorcountychamber.com
Contact: Jacqueline Lucido, Exec. Dir.

47717 ■ Anaheim Chamber of Commerce
201 E Center St.
Anaheim, CA 92805
Ph:(714)758-0222
Fax:(714)758-0468
Co. E-mail: info@anaheimchamber.org
URL: http://www.anaheimchamber.org
Contact: Bruce Solari, Chm.

47718 ■ Anderson Valley Chamber of Commerce
PO Box 275
Boonville, CA 95415
Ph:(707)895-2379
Co. E-mail: info@andersonvalleychamber.com
URL: http://www.andersonvalleychamber.com

47719 ■ Angwin Community Council
PO Box 747
Angwin, CA 94508
Ph:(707)965-2867
Co. E-mail: president@angwincouncil.org
URL: http://www.angwincouncil.org
Contact: Barbara Spelletich, Pres.

47720 ■ Antelope Highlands Chamber of Commerce
PO Box 20
North Highlands, CA 95660
Ph:(916)725-5652
URL: http://www.antelopehighlandschamber.com
Contact: Keith Weber, Pres.

47721 ■ Antelope Valley Board of Trade
548 W Lancaster Blvd., Ste. 103
Lancaster, CA 93534-2534
Ph:(661)942-9581
Fax:(661)723-9279
Co. E-mail: josh@avbot.org
URL: http://www.avbot.org
Contact: Josh Mann, Exec. Dir.

47722 ■ Antelope Valley Chambers of Commerce - Rosamond
2861 Diamond St.
Rosamond, CA 93560
Ph:(661)256-3248
Fax:(661)256-3249
Co. E-mail: mark_troth@trothgmac.com
URL: http://www.avchambers.com
Contact: Mark Troth, Chm.

47723 ■ Antioch Chamber of Commerce
324 G St.
Antioch, CA 94509-1255
Ph:(925)757-1800
Fax:(925)757-5286
Co. E-mail: info@antiochamber.com
URL: http://www.antiochchamber.com
Contact: Devi Lanphere, Pres./CEO

47724 ■ Anza Valley Chamber of Commerce
PO Box 391460
Anza, CA 92539
Ph:(951)763-0141
Free: 888-930-0222
URL: http://www.anzavalleychamber.com
Contact: Robyn Garrison, Pres.

47725 ■ Apple Valley Chamber of Commerce
16010 Apple Valley Rd.
Apple Valley, CA 92307
Ph:(760)242-2753
Fax:(760)242-0303
Co. E-mail: info@avchamber.org
URL: http://www.avchamber.org
Contact: Janice Moore, Pres./CEO

47726 ■ Aptos Chamber of Commerce
7605A Old Dominion Ct.
Aptos, CA 95003
Ph:(831)688-1467
Fax:(831)688-6961
Co. E-mail: info@aptos.com
URL: http://www.aptoschamber.com
Contact: Karen Hibble, Dir.

47727 ■ Arcadia Chamber of Commerce
388 W Huntington Dr.
Arcadia, CA 91007-3402
Ph:(626)447-2159
Fax:(626)445-0273
Co. E-mail: arcadiac@pacbell.net
URL: http://www.arcadiachamber.com
Contact: Judy R. Pons, Pres.

47728 ■ Arcata Chamber of Commerce
1635 Heindon Rd.
Arcata, CA 95521
Ph:(707)822-3619
Fax:(707)822-3515
Co. E-mail: contactus@arcatachamber.com
URL: http://www.arcatachamber.com
Contact: Julie Vaissade-Elcock, Pres.

47729 ■ Arroyo Grande Chamber of Commerce
800 W Branch St.
Arroyo Grande, CA 93420-1999
Ph:(805)489-1488
Co. E-mail: info@agchamber.com
URL: http://www.arroyograndecc.com
Contact: Iris Swisher, Chair

47730 ■ Arvin Chamber of Commerce
PO Box 645
Arvin, CA 93203
Ph:(661)854-2265
Fax:(661)854-2265
Co. E-mail: arvinchamberofcommerce@yahoo.com
URL: http://www.arvinchamberofcommerce.com
Contact: Chris Krauter, Pres.

47731 ■ Atascadero Chamber of Commerce
6904 El Camino Real
Atascadero, CA 93422
Ph:(805)466-2044
Fax:(805)466-9218
Co. E-mail: info@atascaderochamber.org
URL: http://www.atascaderochamber.org
Contact: Joanne Main, Pres./CEO

47732 ■ Atwater Chamber of Commerce
1181 Third St.
Atwater, CA 95301
Ph:(209)358-4251
Fax:(209)358-0934
Co. E-mail: chamber@atwaterchamberofcommerce.
 org
URL: http://www.atwaterchamberofcommerce.org
Contact: Connie Hunter, Pres.

47733 ■ Auburn Area Chamber of Commerce
601 Lincoln Way
Auburn, CA 95603
Ph:(530)885-5616
Free: 800-971-1888
Fax:(530)885-5854
Co. E-mail: info@auburnchamber.net
URL: http://www.auburnchamber.net
Contact: Bruce L. Cosgrove, Dir.

47734 ■ Azusa Chamber of Commerce
240 W Foothill Blvd.
Azusa, CA 91702
Ph:(626)334-1507
Fax:(626)334-5217
Co. E-mail: info@azusachamber.org
URL: http://www.azusachamber.org
Contact: Irene Villapania, CEO

47735 ■ Baldwin Park Chamber of Commerce
3942 Maine Ave.
Baldwin Park, CA 91706
Ph:(626)960-4848
Fax:(626)960-2990
Co. E-mail: dluevano@bpchamber.com
URL: http://www.bpchamber.com
Contact: Jose Barrera, Pres.

47736 ■ Banning Chamber of Commerce
PO Box 665
Banning, CA 92220
Ph:(951)849-4695
Fax:(951)849-9395
Co. E-mail: info@banningchamber.org
URL: http://www.banningchamber.org
Contact: Jack Holden, Exec. Dir.

47737 ■ Barstow Area Chamber of Commerce
PO Box 698
Barstow, CA 92312-0698
Ph:(760)256-8617
Free: 888-4-BARSTOW
Fax:(760)256-7675
Co. E-mail: bacc@barstowchamber.com
URL: http://www.barstowchamber.com
Contact: Jeri Justus, Exec. Dir.

47738 ■ Bass Lake Chamber of Commerce
PO Box 126
Bass Lake, CA 93604
Ph:(559)642-3676
Co. E-mail: chamber@basslakechamber.com
URL: http://www.basslakechamber.com

47739 ■ Beaumont Chamber of Commerce
726 Beaumont Ave.
Beaumont, CA 92223
Ph:(951)845-9541
Fax:(951)769-9080
Co. E-mail: info@beaumontcachamber.com
URL: http://www.beaumontcachamber.com
Contact: Jim Walling, Pres.

47740 ■ Bell Gardens Association of Merchants and Commerce
7535 Pery Rd.
Bell Gardens, CA 90201-4502
Ph:(562)806-2355
Fax:(568)806-1585
Co. E-mail: bellgardens1@earthlink.net
URL: http://www.bellgardenschamber.org
Contact: Dennis Grizzle, Exec. Dir.

47741 ■ Belmont Chamber of Commerce
1059A Alameda de las Pulgas
Belmont, CA 94002
Ph:(650)595-8696
Fax:(650)595-8731
Co. E-mail: execdirector@belmontchamber.org
URL: http://www.belmontchamber.org
Contact: Ben Cardenas, Pres.

47742 ■ Benicia Chamber of Commerce and Visitors' Center
601 1st St., Ste. 100
Benicia, CA 94510-3211
Ph:(707)745-2120
Free: 800-559-7377
Fax:(707)745-2275
Co. E-mail: beniciachamber@aol.com
URL: http://www.beniciachamber.com
Contact: Stephanie Christiansen, CEO/Pres.

47743 ■ Berkeley Chamber of Commerce
1834 University Ave.
Berkeley, CA 94703-1516
Ph:(510)549-7000
Fax:(510)549-1789
Co. E-mail: info@berkeleychamber.com
URL: http://www.berkeleychamber.com
Contact: Kevin Allen, Interim CEO

47744 ■ Bethel Island Chamber of Commerce
PO Box 263
Bethel Island, CA 94511
Ph:(925)684-3220
Fax:(925)684-9025
Co. E-mail: bicc@cctrap.com
URL: http://www.bethelisland-chamber.com
Contact: Linda Nowak, Office Mgr.

47745 ■ Beverly Hills Chamber of Commerce
239 S Beverly Dr.
Beverly Hills, CA 90212
Ph:(310)248-1000
Fax:(310)248-1020
Co. E-mail: walsh@beverlyhillschamber.com
URL: http://www.beverlyhillschamber.com
Contact: Dan Walsh, CEO

47746 ■ Big Bear Chamber of Commerce
630 Bartlett Rd.
PO Box 2860
Big Bear Lake, CA 92315-2860
Ph:(909)866-4607
Fax:(909)866-5412
Co. E-mail: info@bigbearchamber.com
URL: http://www.bigbearchamber.com
Contact: Sara Russ, Pres./CEO

47747 ■ Bishop Area Chamber of Commerce and Visitors Bureau
690 N Main St.
Bishop, CA 93514
Ph:(760)873-8405
Free: 888-395-3952
Fax:(760)873-6999
Co. E-mail: info@bishopvisitor.com
URL: http://www.bishopvisitor.com
Contact: Tawni Thomson, Exec. Dir.

47748 ■ Black Business Association of Los Angeles
PO Box 43159
Los Angeles, CA 90043
Ph:(323)291-9334
Fax:(323)291-9234
Co. E-mail: bbala@earthlink.net
URL: http://www.bbala.org
Contact: Earl Cooper II, Pres./CEO

47749 ■ Bonsall Chamber of Commerce
PO Box 1142
Bonsall, CA 92003
Ph:(760)630-1933
Fax:(760)630-7658
Co. E-mail: bonsallchamber@aol.com
URL: http://www.bonsallchamber.com
Contact: Cory Carrier, Pres.

47750 ■ Boron Chamber of Commerce
26922 Twenty Mule Team Rd.
Boron, CA 93516
Ph:(760)762-5810
Co. E-mail: chamber@boronchamber.org
Contact: Randy Smith, Pres.

47751 ■ Borrego Springs Chamber of Commerce
786 Palm Canyon Dr.
PO Box 420
Borrego Springs, CA 92004-0420
Ph:(760)767-5555
Free: 800-559-5524
Fax:(760)767-5976
Co. E-mail: info@borregospringschamber.com
URL: http://www.borregospringschamber.com
Contact: Gwenn Marie, Pres.

47752 ■ Brawley Chamber of Commerce and Economic Development Commission
204 S Imperial Ave.
PO Box 218
Brawley, CA 92227
Ph:(760)344-3160
Fax:(760)344-7611
Co. E-mail: chamber@brawleychamber.com
URL: http://www.brawleychamber.com
Contact: Nicole Nicholas Gilles, CEO

47753 ■ Brea Chamber of Commerce
1 Civic Center Cir.
Brea, CA 92821
Ph:(714)529-4938
Fax:(714)529-6103
Co. E-mail: breachamber@breachamber.com
URL: http://www.breachamber.com
Contact: Cande Avila, Exec. Dir.

47754 ■ Brentwood Chamber of Commerce
240 Oak St.
Brentwood, CA 94513
Ph:(925)634-3344
Fax:(925)634-3731
Co. E-mail: info@brentwoodchamber.com
URL: http://www.brentwoodchamber.com
Contact: Karen Spann, Pres.

47755 ■ Bridgeport Chamber of Commerce
PO Box 541
Bridgeport, CA 93517
Ph:(760)932-7500
Co. E-mail: bridgeportcalifornia@bridgeportcalifornia.com
URL: http://www.bridgeportcalifornia.com

47756 ■ Brisbane Chamber of Commerce
50 Park Pl.
Brisbane, CA 94005
Ph:(415)467-7283
Fax:(415)467-5421
Co. E-mail: info@brisbanechamber.com
URL: http://www.brisbanechamber.com
Contact: Burton H. Alberts, Exec. Dir.

47757 ■ Buena Park Area Chamber of Commerce
6601 Beach Blvd.
Buena Park, CA 90621
Ph:(714)521-0261
Fax:(714)521-1851
Co. E-mail: info@buenaparkchamber.org
URL: http://www.buenaparkchamber.org
Contact: Gail S. Dixon, CEO/Pres.

47758 ■ Burbank Chamber of Commerce
200 W Magnolia Blvd.
Burbank, CA 91502-1724
Ph:(818)846-3111
Fax:(818)846-0109
Co. E-mail: info@burbankchamber.org
URL: http://www.burbankchamber.org
Contact: Gary Olson, Pres.

47759 ■ Burlingame Chamber of Commerce
290 California Dr.
Burlingame, CA 94010
Ph:(650)344-1735
Fax:(650)344-1763
Co. E-mail: info@burlingamechamber.org
URL: http://burlingamechamber.org
Contact: Georgette Naylor, Pres./CEO

47760 ■ Burney Chamber of Commerce
PO Box 36
Burney, CA 96013
Ph:(530)335-2111
Co. E-mail: burneycc@c-zone.net
URL: http://www.burneychamber.com

47761 ■ Buttonwillow Chamber of Commerce
PO Box 251
Buttonwillow, CA 93206
Ph:(661)764-5406
Fax:(661)764-5406
URL: http://www.buttonwillowchamber.com
Contact: Gloria Selvidge, Sec./Office Mgr.

47762 ■ Calabasas Chamber of Commerce
23564 Calabasas Rd., Ste. 101
Calabasas, CA 91302
Ph:(818)222-5680
Fax:(818)222-5690
Co. E-mail: info@calabasaschamber.com
URL: http://www.calabasaschamber.com
Contact: Carol Wasburn, Pres./CEO

47763 ■ Calaveras County Chamber of Commerce
1211 S Main St.
PO Box 1145
Angels Camp, CA 95222
Ph:(209)736-2580
Fax:(209)736-2576
Co. E-mail: chamber@calaveras.org
URL: http://www.calaveras.org
Contact: Diane Gray, Exec. Dir.

47764 ■ Calexico Chamber of Commerce
PO Box 948
Calexico, CA 92232
Ph:(760)357-1166
Fax:(760)357-9043
Co. E-mail: calexicochamber@hotmail.com
URL: http://www.calexicochamber.net
Contact: Eduardo Rivera, Pres.

47765 ■ California Chamber of Commerce
PO Box 1736
Sacramento, CA 95812-1736
Ph:(916)444-6670
Fax:(916)325-1272
URL: http://www.calchamber.com/Pages/Default.aspx
Contact: Allan Zaremberg, Pres./CEO

47766 ■ California Chamber of Commerce, Southern California Office
PO Box 8230
La Verne, CA 91750-8230
Ph:(909)593-0449
Fax:(909)593-0498
Co. E-mail: marlene.carney@calchamber.com
URL: http://www.calchamber.com/Pages/Default.aspx
Contact: Christine Haddon, Deputy Dir.

47767 ■ California Israel Chamber of Commerce
440 N Wolfe Rd.
Sunnyvale, CA 94085
Ph:(408)343-0917
Fax:(408)343-1197
Co. E-mail: info@ca-israelchamber.org
URL: http://www.ca-israelchamber.org
Contact: Shuly Galili, Exec. Dir.

47768 ■ Calistoga Chamber of Commerce
1506 Lincoln Ave.
Calistoga, CA 94515
Ph:(707)942-6333
Free: (866)306-5588
Fax:(707)942-9287
Co. E-mail: office@calistogachamber.com
URL: http://www.calistogachamber.com

47769 ■ Camarillo Chamber of Commerce
2400 E Ventura Blvd.
Camarillo, CA 93010
Ph:(805)484-4383
Fax:(805)484-1395
Co. E-mail: info@camarillochamber.org
URL: http://www.camarillochamber.org
Contact: David M. Smith, Pres./CEO

47770 ■ Cambria Chamber of Commerce
767 Main St.
Cambria, CA 93428
Ph:(805)927-3624
Fax:(805)927-9426
Co. E-mail: info@cambriachamber.org
URL: http://cambriachamber.org
Contact: Mel McColloch, Pres.

47771 ■ Campbell Chamber of Commerce
1628 W Campbell Ave.
Campbell, CA 95008
Ph:(408)378-6252
Fax:(408)378-0192
Co. E-mail: ccoc@pacbell.net
URL: http://www.campbellchamber.com
Contact: Betty C. Deal, Exec. Dir.

47772 ■ Capitola-Soquel Chamber of Commerce
716-G Capitola Ave.
Capitola, CA 95010
Ph:(831)475-6522
Fax:(831)475-6530
Co. E-mail: capcham@capitolachamber.com
URL: http://www.capitolachamber.com
Contact: Richard Ehle, Chm.

47773 ■ Cardiff-by-the-Sea Chamber of Commerce
PO Box 552
Cardiff-by-the-Sea, CA 92007
Ph:(760)436-0431
Fax:(760)753-0144
Co. E-mail: cardiff101chamber@gmail.com
URL: http://www.cardiffbythesea.org
Contact: Brad Maassen, Pres.

47774 ■ Carlsbad Chamber of Commerce
5934 Priestly Dr.
Carlsbad, CA 92008
Ph:(760)931-8400

Fax:(760)931-9153
Co. E-mail: carlsbadchamber@carlsbad.org
URL: http://www.carlsbad.org
Contact: Lou Storrow, Chm.

47775 ■ Carmel Chamber of Commerce
PO Box 4444
Carmel, CA 93921
Ph:(831)624-2522
Free: 800-550-4333
Fax:(831)624-1329
Co. E-mail: info@carmelchamber.org
URL: http://www.carmelcalifornia.org
Contact: Monta Potter, CEO

47776 ■ Carmel Valley Chamber of Commerce
PO Box 288
Carmel Valley, CA 93924
Ph:(831)659-4000
Fax:(831)659-8415
Co. E-mail: info@carmelvalleychamber.com
URL: http://www.carmelvalleychamber.com
Contact: Randi Andrews, Pres.

47777 ■ Carmichael Chamber of Commerce
6825 Fair Oaks Blvd., Ste. 100
Carmichael, CA 95608
Ph:(916)481-1002
Fax:(916)481-1003
Co. E-mail: information@carmichaelchamber.com
URL: http://www.carmichaelchamber.com
Contact: Jim Vargas, Pres.

47778 ■ Carpinteria Valley Chamber of Commerce
1056-B Eugenia Pl.
Carpinteria, CA 93013-2050
Ph:(805)684-5479
Fax:(805)684-3477
Co. E-mail: lynda@carpinteriachamber.org
URL: http://www.carpchamber.org
Contact: Kasey Cronquist, Pres./CEO

47779 ■ Carson Chamber of Commerce
530 E Del Amo Blvd.
Carson, CA 90746
Ph:(310)217-4590
Fax:(310)217-4591
Co. E-mail: carsonchamber@carsonchamber.com
URL: http://www.carsonchamber.com
Contact: Creasie Adams, Chair

47780 ■ Castro Valley Chamber of Commerce
3467 Castro Valley Blvd.
Castro Valley, CA 94546
Ph:(510)537-5300
Fax:(510)537-5335
Co. E-mail: info@castrovalleychamber.com
URL: http://www.castrovalleychamber.com
Contact: Sue Hohl, Pres.

47781 ■ Castroville Chamber of Commerce
PO Box 744
Castroville, CA 95012
Ph:(831)633-6545
Fax:(831)633-0485
Co. E-mail: castrovillechamber@redshift.com
URL: http://www.artichoke-festival.org

47782 ■ Catalina Island Chamber of Commerce and Visitors' Bureau
PO Box 217
Avalon, CA 90704-0217
Ph:(310)510-1520
Fax:(310)510-7606
Co. E-mail: info@catalinachamber.com
URL: http://www.catalinachamber.com
Contact: Wayne G. Griffin ACE, Pres./CEO

47783 ■ Cayucos Chamber of Commerce
PO Box 346
Cayucos, CA 93430
Ph:(805)995-1200
Fax:(805)995-1200
Co. E-mail: info@cayucoschamber.com
URL: http://www.cayucoschamber.com
Contact: Rick Roquet, Pres.

47784 ■ Central California Hispanic Chamber of Commerce
2331 Fresno St.
Fresno, CA 93721
Ph:(559)495-4817
Fax:(559)495-4811
Co. E-mail: info@cchcc.net
URL: http://www.cchcc.net
Contact: John Hernandez, Exec. Dir.

47785 ■ Century City Chamber of Commerce
2029 Century Park E, Concourse Level
Los Angeles, CA 90067
Ph:(310)553-2222
Fax:(310)553-4623
Co. E-mail: contact@centurycitycc.com
URL: http://www.centurycitycc.com
Contact: Susan Bursk, Pres./CEO

47786 ■ Ceres Chamber of Commerce
2491 Lawrence St.
Ceres, CA 95307
Ph:(209)537-2601
Fax:(209)537-2699
Co. E-mail: chamber@cereschamber.org
URL: http://www.cereschamber.org
Contact: Alan Love, Chm.

47787 ■ Cerritos Chamber of Commerce
13259 E South St.
Cerritos, CA 90703
Ph:(562)467-0800
Fax:(562)467-0840
Co. E-mail: chamber@cerritos.org
URL: http://www.cerritos.org
Contact: Ken Kraus, Pres.

47788 ■ Chamber of Commerce of Dana Point
24681 La Plaza, Ste. 115
Dana Point, CA 92629-0012
Ph:(949)496-1555
Free: 800-290-DANA
Fax:(949)496-5321
Co. E-mail: chamber@beach.net
URL: http://www.danapointchamber.com
Contact: Mits Arayama, Exec. Sec.

47789 ■ Chamber of Commerce Mountain View
580 Castro St.
Mountain View, CA 94041
Ph:(650)968-8378
Fax:(650)968-5668
Co. E-mail: info@chambermv.org
URL: http://www.mountainviewchamber.org
Contact: Oscar Garcia, Pres./CEO

47790 ■ Chatsworth - Porter Ranch Chamber of Commerce
10038 Old Depot Plaza Rd.
Chatsworth, CA 91311
Ph:(818)341-2428
Fax:(818)341-4930
Co. E-mail: info@chatsworthchamber.com
URL: http://www.chatsworthchamber.com
Contact: Les Himes, Pres.

47791 ■ Chester/Lake Almanor Chamber of Commerce
PO Box 1198
Chester, CA 96020
Ph:(530)258-2426
Fax:(530)258-2760
Co. E-mail: info@lakealmanorarea.com
URL: http://chester-lakealmanor.com

47792 ■ Chico Chamber of Commerce
300 Salem St.
Chico, CA 95928
Ph:(530)891-5556
Free: 800-852-8570
Fax:(530)891-3613
Co. E-mail: info@chicochamber.com
URL: http://www.chicochamber.com
Contact: Jim Goodwin, Pres./CEO

47793 ■ Chinese Chamber of Commerce
730 Sacramento St.
San Francisco, CA 94108
Ph:(415)982-3000
Fax:(415)982-4720
Contact: Wayne Hu, Pres.

47794 ■ Chino Valley Chamber of Commerce
13150 7th St.
Chino, CA 91710
Ph:(909)627-6177
Fax:(909)627-4180
Co. E-mail: info@chinovalleychamber.com
URL: http://www.chinovalleychamber.com
Contact: Andy Ronquillo, Exec. Dir.

47795 ■ Chula Vista Chamber of Commerce
233 4th Ave.
Chula Vista, CA 91910
Ph:(619)420-6603
Fax:(619)420-1269
Co. E-mail: info@chulavistachamber.org
URL: http://www.chulavistachamber.org
Contact: Chris Boyd, Pres.

47796 ■ Citrus Heights Chamber of Commerce
PO Box 191
Citrus Heights, CA 95611
Ph:(916)722-4545
Fax:(916)722-4543
Co. E-mail: chamber@chchamber.com
URL: http://www.chchamber.com
Contact: Bettie Cosby, CEO

47797 ■ City of Tulelake Chamber of Commerce
436 C St.
Tulelake, CA 96134
Ph:(530)667-5302
Fax:(530)667-5522
URL: http://www.tulelakecalifornia.com
Contact: Mr. Mike Bunch, Pres.

47798 ■ Clear Lake Chamber of Commerce
PO Box 5330
3245 Bowers Ave.
Clearlake, CA 95422
Ph:(707)994-3600
Fax:(707)994-3603
Co. E-mail: clearlakechamber@yahoo.com
URL: http://www.clearlakechamber.com
Contact: Joey Luiz, Pres.

47799 ■ Clements Lockeford Chamber of Commerce
PO Box 971
Lockeford, CA 95237
Ph:(209)727-3142
Fax:(209)727-3365
Co. E-mail: clchamber@sbcglobal.net
URL: http://www.clementslockefordchamber.org
Contact: Cynthia L. Haynes, Pres.

47800 ■ Cloverdale Chamber of Commerce
105 N Cloverdale Blvd.
Cloverdale, CA 95425-0356
Ph:(707)894-4470
Fax:(707)894-9568
Co. E-mail: chamberinfo@cloverdale.com
URL: http://www.cloverdale.net
Contact: Mike Nixon, Chm.

47801 ■ Clovis District Chamber of Commerce
325 Pollasky Ave.
Clovis, CA 93612-1139
Ph:(559)299-7363
Fax:(559)299-2969
Co. E-mail: info@clovischamber.com
URL: http://www.clovischamber.com
Contact: Jim Ware, Pres./CEO

47802 ■ Colfax Area Chamber of Commerce
99 S Railroad Ave.
PO Box 86
Colfax, CA 95713

Ph:(530)346-8888
Co. E-mail: railcar@colfaxarea.com
URL: http://www.colfaxarea.com
Contact: John Potter, Pres.

47803 ■ Colton Chamber of Commerce
655 N La Cadena Dr.
Colton, CA 92324
Ph:(909)825-2222
Fax:(909)824-1650
Co. E-mail: tonypmt@aol.com
URL: http://coltonchamber.org/Home_Page_4M1D.php
Contact: Tony Myrell, Pres.

47804 ■ Commerce Industrial Council Chamber of Commerce
6055 E Washington Blvd., No. 120
Commerce, CA 90040
Ph:(323)728-7222
Fax:(323)728-7565
URL: http://www.industrialcouncil.org
Contact: John Pringle, Pres.

47805 ■ Compton Chamber of Commerce
700 N Bullins Rd., Ste. 6-A
Compton, CA 90221
Ph:(310)631-8611
Co. E-mail: cptchamber@aol.com
URL: http://www.comptonchamberofcommerce.com
Contact: Ms. Lestean M. Johnson, Pres.

47806 ■ Corning District Chamber of Commerce
1110 Solano St.
Corning, CA 96021
Ph:(530)824-5550
Co. E-mail: info@corningchamber.com
URL: http://corningchamber.org
Contact: Linda Tousey, Pres.

47807 ■ Corona Chamber of Commerce
904 E 6th St.
Corona, CA 92879
Ph:(951)737-3350
Fax:(951)737-3531
Co. E-mail: info@coronachamber.org
URL: http://www.coronachamber.org
Contact: Bobby Spiegel, Pres./CEO

47808 ■ Corona Del Mar Chamber of Commerce
2855 E Coast Hwy., Ste. 101
Corona Del Mar, CA 92625
Ph:(949)673-4050
Fax:(949)673-3940
Co. E-mail: info@cdmchamber.com
URL: http://www.cdmchamber.com
Contact: Linda Leonhard, Pres.

47809 ■ Coronado Chamber of Commerce
875 Orange Ave., Ste. No. 102
Coronado, CA 92118
Ph:(619)435-9260
Fax:(619)522-6577
Co. E-mail: info@coronadochamber.com
URL: http://www.coronadochamber.com
Contact: Karen Finch, CEO

47810 ■ Corte Madera Chamber of Commerce
129 Town Ctr.
Corte Madera, CA 94925
Ph:(415)924-0441
Fax:(415)924-1839
Co. E-mail: chamber@cortemadera.org
URL: http://www.cortemadera.org
Contact: Julie Kritzberger, Exec. Dir.

47811 ■ Costa Mesa Chamber of Commerce
1700 Adams Ave., Ste. 101
Costa Mesa, CA 92626
Ph:(714)885-9090
Fax:(714)885-9094
Co. E-mail: info@costamesachamber.com
URL: http://www.costamesachamber.com
Contact: Ed Fawcett, Pres./CEO

47812 ■ Cotati Chamber of Commerce
PO Box 592
Cotati, CA 94931
Ph:(707)795-5508
Fax:(707)795-5868
Co. E-mail: chamber@cotati.org
URL: http://www.cotati.org
Contact: Suzanne Whipple, Exec. Dir.

47813 ■ Cottonwood Chamber of Commerce
PO Box 584
Cottonwood, CA 96022-0584
Ph:(530)347-6800
Fax:(530)347-6800
Co. E-mail: cskudlarek@novb.com
URL: http://www.cottonwoodcofc.org

47814 ■ Covina Chamber of Commerce
935 W Badillo St., Ste. 100
Covina, CA 91722
Ph:(626)967-4191
Fax:(626)966-9660
Co. E-mail: chamber@covina.org
URL: http://www.covina.org
Contact: Dawn Nelson, Pres./CEO

47815 ■ Crescent City-Del Norte County Chamber of Commerce
1001 Front St.
Crescent City, CA 95531
Ph:(707)464-3174
Free: 800-343-8300
URL: http://www.northerncalifornia.net
Contact: Lisa McKeown, Sec.

47816 ■ Crescenta Valley Chamber of Commerce
3131 Foothill Blvd., Ste. D
La Crescenta, CA 91214
Ph:(818)248-4957
Fax:(818)248-9625
Co. E-mail: cvcoc@aol.com
URL: http://www.lacrescenta.org
Contact: Julia Rabago, Exec. Dir.

47817 ■ Crestline Chamber of Commerce
PO Box 926
Crestline, CA 92325
Ph:(909)338-2706
Co. E-mail: info@crestlinechamber.net
URL: http://www.crestlinechamber.net
Contact: Bob Yeomans, Pres.

47818 ■ Crockett Chamber of Commerce
PO Box 191
Crockett, CA 94525
Ph:(510)787-1155
Co. E-mail: crockettchamber@comcast.net
URL: http://www.crockettca-chamber.org
Contact: Aimee Lohr, Pres.

47819 ■ Culver City Chamber of Commerce
4249 Overland Ave.
Culver City, CA 90232-0707
Ph:(310)287-3850
Fax:(310)287-1350
Co. E-mail: ssssteve@culvercitychamber.com
URL: http://www.culvercitychamber.com
Contact: Steven J. Rose, Pres.

47820 ■ Cupertino Chamber of Commerce
20455 Silverado Ave.
Cupertino, CA 95014
Ph:(408)252-7054
Fax:(408)252-0638
Co. E-mail: info@cupertino-chamber.org
URL: http://www.cupertino-chamber.org
Contact: Suzi Blackman, CEO

47821 ■ Cypress Chamber of Commerce
5550 Cerritos Ave., Ste. D
Cypress, CA 90630
Ph:(714)827-2430
Fax:(714)827-1229
Co. E-mail: info@cypresschamber.org
URL: http://www.cypresschamber.org
Contact: Ed Munson, Exec. Dir.

47822 ■ Daly City - Colma Chamber of Commerce
355 Gellert Blvd., No. 138
Daly City, CA 94015-2665
Ph:(650)755-3900
Fax:(650)755-5160
Co. E-mail: gsarles@dalycity-colmachamber.org
URL: http://www.dalycity-colmachamber.org
Contact: Georgette Sales, Pres./CEO

47823 ■ Danville Area Chamber of Commerce
117-E Town and Country Dr.
Danville, CA 94526
Ph:(925)837-4400
Fax:(925)837-5709
URL: http://www.danvilleareachamber.com
Contact: Melony Newman, Pres./CEO

47824 ■ Davis Chamber of Commerce
130 G St., Ste. B
Davis, CA 95616-4630
Ph:(530)756-5160
Fax:(530)756-5190
Co. E-mail: director@davischamber.com
URL: http://www.davischamber.com
Contact: Christi Skibbins, Exec. Dir.

47825 ■ Death Valley Chamber of Commerce
PO Box 157
Shoshone, CA 92384
Ph:(760)852-4524
Fax:(760)852-4354
Co. E-mail: deathvalleych@veawb.coop
URL: http://www.deathvalleychamber.org
Contact: Kari Coughlin, Dir.

47826 ■ Del Mar Regional Chamber of Commerce
1104 Camino Del Mar, Ste. 1
Del Mar, CA 92014
Ph:(858)755-4844
Fax:(858)356-0595
Co. E-mail: info@delmarchamber.org
URL: http://www.delmarchamber.org
Contact: Nancy Wasko, Pres./CEO

47827 ■ Delano Chamber of Commerce
931 High St.
Delano, CA 93215
Ph:(661)725-2518
Co. E-mail: info@chamberofdelano.com
URL: http://www.chamberofdelano.com
Contact: Carla Lapadula

47828 ■ Desert Hot Springs Chamber of Commerce
11711 West Dr.
Desert Hot Springs, CA 92240
Ph:(760)329-6403
Free: 800-346-3347
Fax:(760)329-2833
Co. E-mail: info2@deserthotsprings.com
URL: http://www.deserthotsprings.com
Contact: Carole Farm, CEO

47829 ■ Diamond Bar Chamber of Commerce
21845 E Copley Dr., Ste. 1170
Diamond Bar, CA 91765-6401
Ph:(909)860-1904
Co. E-mail: info@diamondbarchamber.com
URL: http://www.ci.diamond-bar.ca.us/Index.aspx?page=219
Contact: Steve Smith, CEO

47830 ■ Dinuba Chamber of Commerce
210 N L St.
Dinuba, CA 93618
Ph:(559)591-2707
Fax:(559)591-2712
Co. E-mail: info@dinubacommerce.org
URL: http://www.dinubacommerce.org
Contact: Ed Dena, Pres.

47831 ■ Dixon District Chamber of Commerce
PO Box 159
Dixon, CA 95620
Ph:(707)678-2650

Fax:(707)678-3654
Co. E-mail: info@dixonchamber.org
URL: http://www.dixonchamber.org
Contact: Tiffany Wing, Office Mgr.

47832 ■ Downey Chamber of Commerce
11131 Brookshire Ave.
Downey, CA 90241-3860
Ph:(562)923-2191
Fax:(562)869-0461
Co. E-mail: info@downeychamber.com
URL: http://www.downeychamber.com
Contact: Ms. Joan Warner-Plettinck, Exec. Dir.

47833 ■ Duarte Chamber of Commerce
PO Box 1438
Duarte, CA 91009-4438
Ph:(626)357-3333
Fax:(626)357-3645
Co. E-mail: diana@duartechamber.com
URL: http://www.duartechamber.com
Contact: Jan Wight, Pres./CEO

47834 ■ Dublin Chamber of Commerce
7080 Donlon Way, Ste. 110
Dublin, CA 94568
Ph:(925)828-6200
Fax:(925)828-4247
Co. E-mail: info2@dublinchamberofcommerce.org
URL: http://www.dublinchamberofcommerce.org
Contact: Dan Karas, Chm.

47835 ■ Dunsmuir Chamber of Commerce
5915 Dunsmuir Ave., Ste. No. 100
Dunsmuir, CA 96025
Ph:(530)235-2177
Free: 800-386-7684
Fax:(530)235-0911
Co. E-mail: chamber@dunsmuir.com
URL: http://dunsmuir.com/index.php
Contact: Cheryl Petty, Pres.

47836 ■ Eagle Rock Chamber of Commerce
PO Box 41354
Eagle Rock, CA 90041
Ph:(323)257-2197
Fax:(323)257-4245
Co. E-mail: erccwebguy@aol.com
URL: http://www.eaglerockchamberofcommerce.com
Contact: Michael A. Nogueira Jr., Pres.

47837 ■ East Los Angeles Chamber of Commerce
PO Box 63220
Los Angeles, CA 90063-0220
Ph:(323)722-2005
Fax:(323)722-2405
Co. E-mail: elacoc@pacbell.net
URL: http://www.elacoc.com
Contact: Blanca Espinoza, Pres.

47838 ■ Eastern Plumas Chamber of Commerce
PO Box 1043
Blairsden, CA 96103
Ph:(530)836-6811
Free: 800-995-6057
Fax:(530)836-6809
Co. E-mail: epluchmb@psln.com
URL: http://www.easternplumaschamber.com
Contact: Betty J. Heck, Mgr.

47839 ■ El Centro Chamber of Commerce and Visitors Bureau
1095 S 4th St.
PO Box 3006
El Centro, CA 92243
Ph:(760)352-3681
Fax:(760)352-3246
Co. E-mail: generalinfo@elcentrochamber.com
URL: http://www.elcentrochamber.org
Contact: Cathy Kennerson ACE, CEO

47840 ■ El Cerrito Chamber of Commerce
PO Box 538
El Cerrito, CA 94530
Ph:(510)233-7040
Co. E-mail: info@elcerritochamber.org
URL: http://www.elcerritochamber.org
Contact: Sewall Glinternick, Mgr.

47841 ■ El Dorado County Chamber of Commerce
542 Main St.
Placerville, CA 95667-5610
Ph:(530)621-5885
Free: 800-457-6279
Fax:(530)642-1624
Co. E-mail: admin@eldoradocounty.org
URL: http://www.eldoradocounty.org
Contact: Mike Kobus, Pres.

47842 ■ El Dorado Hills Chamber of Commerce
PO Box 5055
El Dorado Hills, CA 95762
Ph:(916)933-1335
Fax:(916)933-5908
Co. E-mail: chamber@eldoradohillschamber.com
URL: http://www.eldoradohillschamber.com
Contact: Debbie Manning, Pres./CEO

47843 ■ El Segundo Chamber of Commerce
427 Main St.
El Segundo, CA 90245
Ph:(310)322-1220
Fax:(310)322-6880
Co. E-mail: elsegundochamber@mail.com
URL: http://www.elsegundochamber.org
Contact: Jim Hart, Pres.

47844 ■ El Sobrante Chamber of Commerce
3769 San Pablo Dam Rd.
El Sobrante, CA 94803
Ph:(510)223-0757
Co. E-mail: michael_frith@mechbank.com
URL: http://elsobrantechamber.com
Contact: Mike Frith, Pres.

47845 ■ Elk Grove Chamber of Commerce
9370 Studio Ct., Ste. 110
Elk Grove, CA 95758
Ph:(916)691-3760
Fax:(916)691-3810
Co. E-mail: chamber@elkgroveca.com
URL: http://www.elkgroveca.com
Contact: Janet Toppenberg, Pres./CEO

47846 ■ Emeryville Chamber of Commerce
3980 Harlan St.
Emeryville, CA 94608-3771
Ph:(510)652-5223
Fax:(510)652-4223
Co. E-mail: info@emeryvillechamber.com
URL: http://www.emeryvillechamber.com
Contact: Bob Canter, Pres./CEO

47847 ■ Encinitas Chamber and Visitors Center
No. 112, 1106 2nd St.
Encinitas, CA 92024
Ph:(760)753-6041
Fax:(760)753-6270
Co. E-mail: info@encinitaschamber.com
URL: http://www.encinitaschamber.com
Contact: Gary Tucker, CEO

47848 ■ Encino Chamber of Commerce
4933 Balboa Blvd.
Encino, CA 91316-3497
Ph:(818)789-4711
Fax:(818)789-2485
Co. E-mail: info@encinochamber.org
URL: http://www.encinochamber.org
Contact: Ms. Diana Donovan, CEO

47849 ■ Escalon Chamber of Commerce
1760 Main St.
Escalon, CA 95320
Ph:(209)838-2793
Co. E-mail: escalonba@yahoo.com
URL: http://www.escalonchambersite.org
Contact: Pat Brown, Pres.

47850 ■ Escondido Chamber of Commerce
720 N Broadway
Escondido, CA 92025-1893
Ph:(760)745-2125
Fax:(760)745-1183
Co. E-mail: info@escondidochamber.org
URL: http://www.escondidochamber.org
Contact: Harvey J. Mitchell, Pres./CEO

47851 ■ Esparto District Chamber of Commerce
PO Box 194
Esparto, CA 95627
Ph:(530)787-3242
Fax:(530)787-3373
Co. E-mail: info@espartochamber.org
URL: http://www.espartochamber.com

47852 ■ Exeter Chamber of Commerce
101 W Pine St.
Exeter, CA 93221
Ph:(559)592-2919
Fax:(559)592-3720
Co. E-mail: chamber@exeterchamber.com
URL: http://www.exeterchamber.com
Contact: Sandy Blankenship, Exec. Dir.

47853 ■ Fair Oaks Chamber of Commerce
10224 Fair Oaks Blvd.
PO Box 352
Fair Oaks, CA 95628
Ph:(916)967-2903
Fax:(916)967-8536
Co. E-mail: info@fairoakschamber.com
URL: http://www.fairoakschamber.com
Contact: Jan Bass Otto, Exec. Dir.

47854 ■ Fallbrook Chamber of Commerce
233 E Mission Rd., Ste. A
Fallbrook, CA 92028-2146
Ph:(760)728-5845
Fax:(760)728-4031
Co. E-mail: info@fallbrookchamber.com
URL: http://fallbrookchamber.com
Contact: Robert K. Leonard, Exec. Dir.

47855 ■ Farmersville Chamber of Commerce
1376 N Farmersville Blvd.
Farmersville, CA 93223
Ph:(559)747-0223
Contact: Don Mason, Pres.

47856 ■ Fillmore Chamber of Commerce
PO Box 815
Fillmore, CA 93016-0815
Ph:(805)524-0351
Fax:(805)524-2551
Co. E-mail: info@fillmorechamber.com
URL: http://www.fillmorechamber.com
Contact: Christie Neal, Pres.

47857 ■ Folsom Chamber of Commerce
200 Wool St.
Folsom, CA 95630
Ph:(916)985-2698
Free: 800-377-1414
Fax:(916)985-4117
Co. E-mail: information@folsomchamber.com
URL: http://www.folsomchamber.com
Contact: Joseph P. Gagliardi, Pres./CEO

47858 ■ Fontana Chamber of Commerce
8491 Sierra Ave.
Fontana, CA 92335-3860
Ph:(909)822-4433
Fax:(909)822-6238
Co. E-mail: info@fontanachamber.com
URL: http://www.fontanachamber.com
Contact: David G. Pulido, Pres.

47859 ■ Foresthill Divide Chamber of Commerce
PO Box 346
Foresthill, CA 95631
Ph:(530)367-2474
Fax:(530)367-2474
Co. E-mail: foresthillchamber@ftcnet.net
URL: http://www.foresthillchamber.org
Contact: Sean Salveson, Pres.

47860 ■ Fort Bragg - Mendocino Coast Chamber of Commerce
PO Box 1141
Fort Bragg, CA 95437
Ph:(707)961-6300
Co. E-mail: chamber@mcn.org
URL: http://www.mendocinocoast.com
Contact: Debra DeGraw, Exec. Dir.

47861 ■ Fortuna Chamber of Commerce
735 14th St.
Fortuna, CA 95540
Ph:(707)725-3959
Free: 800-426-8166
Fax:(707)725-4766
Co. E-mail: chamber@sunnyfortuna.com
URL: http://www.chamber.sunnyfortuna.com
Contact: Cliff Chapman, Exec. Dir.

47862 ■ Foster City Chamber of Commerce
1031 E Hillside Blvd., Ste. F
Foster City, CA 94404
Ph:(650)573-7600
Fax:(650)573-5201
Co. E-mail: info@fostercitychamber.com
URL: http://www.fostercitychamber.com
Contact: Mae Heagerty-Matos, CEO

47863 ■ Fountain Valley Chamber of Commerce
8840 Warner Ave., Ste. 207
Fountain Valley, CA 92708
Ph:(714)841-3822
Fax:(714)841-3877
Co. E-mail: bwhite@fvchamber.com
URL: http://www.fvchamber.com
Contact: Franck Bideau, Pres.

47864 ■ Fremont Chamber of Commerce
39488 Stevenson Pl., Ste. 100
Fremont, CA 94539
Ph:(510)795-2244
Fax:(510)795-2240
Co. E-mail: fmtcc@fremontbusiness.com
URL: http://www.fremontbusiness.com
Contact: Cindy Bonior, Pres./Chief Exec. Dir.

47865 ■ Fullerton Chamber of Commerce
444 N Harbor Blvd., No. 200
Fullerton, CA 92832
Ph:(714)871-3100
Fax:(714)871-2871
Co. E-mail: tharvey@fullertonchamber.com
URL: http://www.fullertonchamber.com
Contact: Theresa Harvey, Exec. Dir.

47866 ■ Galt District Chamber of Commerce
PO Box 1446
Galt, CA 95632
Ph:(209)745-2529
Co. E-mail: info@galtchamber.com
URL: http://www.galtchamber.com
Contact: David Herburger, Sec.

47867 ■ Garberville-Redway Area Chamber of Commerce
PO Box 445
782 Redwood Dr.
Garberville, CA 95542
Ph:(707)923-2613
Free: 800-923-2613
Fax:(707)923-4789
Co. E-mail: chamber@garberville.org
URL: http://www.garberville.org
Contact: Dee Way, Exec. Dir.

47868 ■ Garden Grove Chamber of Commerce
12866 Main St., Ste. 102
Garden Grove, CA 92840-5298
Ph:(714)638-7950
Free: 800-959-5560
Fax:(714)636-6672
Co. E-mail: connie.margolin@gardengrovechamber.org
URL: http://gardengrovechamber.org
Contact: Connie Margolin, CEO/Pres.

47869 ■ Gardena Valley Chamber of Commerce
1204 W Gardena Blvd., Ste. E & F
Gardena, CA 90247
Ph:(310)532-9905
Fax:(310)329-7307
Co. E-mail: gardenavalleycc@aol.com
URL: http://www.gardenachamber.com
Contact: Henry Hoskins, Pres.

47870 ■ Geyserville Chamber of Commerce
PO Box 276
Geyserville, CA 95441
Ph:(707)857-3745
Co. E-mail: moreinfo@geyservillecc.com
URL: http://www.geyservillecc.com
Contact: Rand Derricco, Pres.

47871 ■ Gilroy Chamber of Commerce
7471 Monterey St.
Gilroy, CA 95020
Ph:(408)842-6437
Fax:(408)842-6010
Co. E-mail: chamber@gilroy.org
URL: http://www.gilroy.org
Contact: Susan Valenta ACE, Pres./CEO

47872 ■ Glendale Chamber of Commerce
200 S Louise St.
Glendale, CA 91205
Ph:(818)240-7870
Fax:(818)240-2872
Co. E-mail: info@glendalechamber.com
URL: http://www.glendalechamber.com
Contact: Sharon Beauchamp, Exec. VP

47873 ■ Glendora Chamber of Commerce
131 E Foothill Blvd.
Glendora, CA 91741-3336
Ph:(626)963-4128
Fax:(626)914-4822
Co. E-mail: info@glendora-chamber.org
URL: http://www.glendora-chamber.org
Contact: Miki Carpenter, Pres.

47874 ■ Golden Triangle Chamber of Commerce
6235 Lusk Blvd.
San Diego, CA 92121
Ph:(858)866-0676
Co. E-mail: financialbodyguard@yahoo.com
URL: http://goldentrianglechamber.com
Contact: George Schmall, Pres.

47875 ■ Goleta Valley Chamber of Commerce
PO Box 781
Goleta, CA 93117
Ph:(805)967-2500
Free: 800-646-5382
Fax:(805)967-4615
Co. E-mail: info@goletavalley.com
URL: http://goletavalley.com
Contact: Kristen Miller Amyx, Pres./CEO

47876 ■ Gonzales Chamber of Commerce
PO Box 216
Gonzales, CA 93926
Ph:(831)675-9019
Co. E-mail: email@gonzaleschamber.org
URL: http://www.gonzaleschamber.org
Contact: Frances Muma, Sec.-Treas.

47877 ■ Granada Hills Chamber of Commerce
17723 Chatsworth St.
Granada Hills, CA 91344
Ph:(818)368-3235

Fax:(818)366-7425
Co. E-mail: email@granadachamber.com
URL: http://www.granadachamber.com
Contact: Steve Baker, Treas.

47878 ■ Grand Terrace Area Chamber of Commerce
22365 Barton Rd., Ste. 101
Grand Terrace, CA 92313
Ph:(909)783-3581
Fax:(909)370-2906
Co. E-mail: office@gtchamber.com
URL: http://www.gtchamber.com
Contact: Sally McGuire, Pres.

47879 ■ Greater Bakersfield Chamber of Commerce
PO Box 1947
Bakersfield, CA 93301
Ph:(661)327-4421
Fax:(661)327-8751
Co. E-mail: info@bakersfieldchamber.org
URL: http://www.bakersfieldchamber.org
Contact: Debra L. Moreno, Pres./CEO

47880 ■ Greater Concord Chamber of Commerce
2280 Diamond Blvd., Ste. 200
Concord, CA 94520
Ph:(925)685-1181
Fax:(925)685-5623
Co. E-mail: info@concordchamber.com
URL: http://www.concordchamber.com
Contact: Ellen Williams, Chair

47881 ■ Greater Eureka Chamber of Commerce
2112 Broadway
Eureka, CA 95501
Ph:(707)442-3738
Free: 800-356-6381
Fax:(707)442-0079
Co. E-mail: susan@eurekachamber.com
URL: http://www.eurekachamber.com
Contact: J. Warren Hockaday, Exec. Dir.

47882 ■ Greater Fresno Area Chamber of Commerce
2331 Fresno St.
Fresno, CA 93721
Ph:(559)495-4800
Fax:(559)495-4811
Co. E-mail: info@fresnochamber.com
URL: http://www.fresnochamber.com
Contact: Al Smith, Pres./CEO

47883 ■ Greater Huntington Park Area Chamber of Commerce
6330 Pacific Blvd., Ste. 208
Huntington Park, CA 90255
Ph:(323)585-1155
Fax:(323)585-2176
Co. E-mail: info@hpchamber1.com
URL: http://www.hpchamber1.com
Contact: Dante D'Eramo, Exec. Dir./CEO

47884 ■ Greater Merced Chamber of Commerce
360 E Yosemite Ave., Ste. No. 100
Merced, CA 95340
Ph:(209)384-7092
Free: 800-446-5353
Fax:(209)384-8472
Co. E-mail: info@merced-chamber.com
URL: http://www.merced-chamber.com
Contact: Barbara Hoffman, Chair-Elect

47885 ■ Greater Redding Chamber of Commerce
747 Auditorium Dr.
Redding, CA 96001
Ph:(530)225-4433
Fax:(530)225-4398
Co. E-mail: info@reddingchamber.com
URL: http://www.reddingchamber.com
Contact: Frank J. Strazzarino Jr., Pres./CEO

47886 ■ Greater Riverside Chamber of Commerce
3985 University Ave.
Riverside, CA 92501
Ph:(951)683-7100
Fax:(951)683-2670
Co. E-mail: rchamber@riverside-chamber.com
URL: http://www.riverside-chamber.com
Contact: Cindy Roth, Pres./CEO

47887 ■ Greater Santa Ana Business Alliance
2020 N Broadway, 2nd Fl.
Santa Ana, CA 92702
Ph:(714)541-5353
Fax:(714)541-2238
URL: http://www.santaanachamber.com
Contact: Mr. Michael Metzler, Pres./CEO

47888 ■ Greater Sherman Oaks Chamber of Commerce
14827 Ventura Blvd., Ste. 207
Sherman Oaks, CA 91403-5224
Ph:(818)906-1951
Fax:(818)783-3100
Co. E-mail: chamber@shermanoakschamber.org
URL: http://www.shermanoakschamber.org
Contact: Lisa Clayden, Exec. Dir.

47889 ■ Greater Stockton Chamber of Commerce
445 W Weber Ave., Ste. 220
Stockton, CA 95203
Ph:(209)547-2770
Fax:(209)466-5271
Co. E-mail: schamber@stocktonchamber.org
URL: http://www.stocktonchamber.org
Contact: Douglass W. Wilhoit Jr., CEO

47890 ■ Greater Tehachapi Chamber of Commerce
PO Box 401
798 Tucker Rd., No. 4
Tehachapi, CA 93581
Ph:(661)822-4180
Fax:(661)822-9036
Co. E-mail: chamber@tehachapi.com
URL: http://www.tehachapi.com/chamber
Contact: Ida Perkins, Pres.

47891 ■ Greater Trinidad Chamber of Commerce
PO Box 356
Trinidad, CA 95570
Ph:(707)677-1610
Co. E-mail: info@discovertrinidadca.com
URL: http://www.discovertrinidadca.com

47892 ■ Greater Ukiah Chamber of Commerce
200 S School St.
Ukiah, CA 95482
Ph:(707)462-4705
Fax:(707)462-2088
Co. E-mail: ceo@ukiahchamber.com
URL: http://www.ukiahchamber.com
Contact: Bert Mosier, CEO

47893 ■ Greenfield Chamber of Commerce
PO Box 387
Greenfield, CA 93927
Ph:(831)674-3222
Fax:(831)674-3149
Co. E-mail: postmaster@ci.greenfield.ca.us
URL: http://www.greenfieldchamber.info
Contact: Joe Kolnick, Pres.

47894 ■ Gridley Area Chamber of Commerce
613 Kentucky St.
Gridley, CA 95948
Ph:(530)846-3142
Fax:(530)846-7165
Co. E-mail: gridleychamber@hotmail.com
URL: http://gridleyareachamber.com
Contact: Devona Pace, Sec./Mgr.

47895 ■ Guadalupe Chamber of Commerce and Visitor Center
873 Guadalupe St.
Guadalupe, CA 93434
Ph:(805)343-2236
Fax:(805)343-2246
Co. E-mail: info@guadalupechamber.org
URL: http://www.guadalupechamber.org
Contact: Rhonda Walker, Pres.

47896 ■ Gustine Chamber of Commerce
375 5th St.
Gustine, CA 95322
Ph:(209)854-6975
Fax:(209)854-3511
Co. E-mail: gustinechamber@inreach.com
URL: http://www.gustinechamberofcommerce.com
Contact: Glen Beard, Pres.

47897 ■ Half Moon Bay - Coastside Chamber of Commerce and Visitors' Bureau
235 Main St.
Half Moon Bay, CA 94019
Ph:(650)726-8380
Fax:(650)726-8389
Co. E-mail: info@hmbchamber.com
URL: http://www.halfmoonbaychamber.org
Contact: Charise Hale McHugh, Pres./CEO

47898 ■ Hanford Chamber of Commerce
200 Santa Fe, Ste. D
Hanford, CA 93230
Ph:(559)582-0483
Fax:(559)582-0960
Co. E-mail: hope@hanfordchamber.com
Contact: Hope Williams-Morikawa, CEO

47899 ■ Harbor City - Harbor Gateway Chamber of Commerce
19401 S Vermont Ave., Ste. G104
Torrance, CA 90502
Ph:(310)516-7933
Fax:(310)516-7734
Co. E-mail: hchgchamber@sbcglobal.net
URL: http://www.hchgchamber.com
Contact: Joeann Valle, Exec. Dir.

47900 ■ Hawthorne Chamber of Commerce
4444 El Segundo Blvd.
Hawthorne, CA 90250
Ph:(310)676-1163
Fax:(310)676-7661
Co. E-mail: info@hawthorne-chamber.com
URL: http://www.hawthorne-chamber.com
Contact: Patricia Feldman-Donaldson, Pres.

47901 ■ Healdsburg Chamber of Commerce and Visitors Bureau
217 Healdsburg Ave.
Healdsburg, CA 95448-4103
Ph:(707)433-6935
Free: 800-648-9922
Fax:(707)433-7562
Co. E-mail: info@healdsburg.com
URL: http://www.healdsburg.org
Contact: Craig Schmidt, Pres./CEO

47902 ■ Hemet San Jacinto Valley Chamber of Commerce
615 N San Jacinto St.
Hemet, CA 92543
Ph:(951)658-3211
Free: 800-334-3425
Fax:(951)766-5013
Co. E-mail: info@hemetsanjacintochamber.com
URL: http://hemetsanjacintochamber.com
Contact: Patti Drusky, Pres./CEO

47903 ■ Hercules Chamber of Commerce
PO Box 5283
Hercules, CA 94547
Ph:(510)741-7945
Fax:(510)741-8965
Co. E-mail: office@herculeschamber.com
URL: http://www.herculeschamber.com
Contact: Shirley Gotelli, Exec. Dir.

47904 ■ Hermosa Beach Chamber of Commerce and Visitors Bureau
1007 Hermosa Ave.
Hermosa Beach, CA 90254
Ph:(310)376-0951
Fax:(310)798-2594
Co. E-mail: info@hbchamber.net
URL: http://www.hbchamber.net
Contact: Carla Merriman, Exec. Dir.

47905 ■ High Desert Hispanic Chamber of Commerce
15450 W Sand St., Ste. 108
Victorville, CA 92392
Ph:(760)241-6661
Fax:(760)241-2281
URL: http://www.hdhcc.org
Contact: Vickie Cabriales, Pres./CEO

47906 ■ Highland Area Chamber of Commerce
PO Box 455
Highland, CA 92346
Ph:(909)864-4073
Fax:(909)864-4583
Co. E-mail: hcoc@highlandchamber.org
URL: http://www.highlandchamber.org
Contact: Lindsay Mingee, Exec. Dir.

47907 ■ Hispanic Chamber of Commerce of Orange County
2130 E 4th St., Ste. 160
Santa Ana, CA 92705
Ph:(714)953-4289
Fax:(714)953-0273
Co. E-mail: mail@hcoc.org
URL: http://www.hcoc.org/site
Contact: Priscilla Lopez, Pres./CEO

47908 ■ Hispanic Chamber of Commerce of Sonoma County
PO Box 11392
Santa Rosa, CA 95406
Ph:(707)575-3648
Fax:(707)575-3693
Co. E-mail: hccadmin@hcc-sc.org
URL: http://www.hcc-sc.org
Contact: Juan M. Hernandez, Pres.

47909 ■ Historic Sonora Chamber of Commerce
PO Box 884
Sonora, CA 95370-0251
Ph:(209)588-9625
Co. E-mail: hscc@um.att.com
URL: http://www.sonorachamber.com
Contact: Shirley Sarno, Exec. Dir.

47910 ■ Hollywood Chamber of Commerce
7018 Hollywood Blvd.
Hollywood, CA 90028
Ph:(323)469-8311
Fax:(323)469-2805
Co. E-mail: info@hollywoodchamber.net
URL: http://hollywoodchamber.net
Contact: Mark Panatier, Chm.

47911 ■ Holtville Chamber of Commerce
101 W 5th St.
Holtville, CA 92250
Ph:(760)356-2923
Fax:(760)356-2925
Co. E-mail: info@holtvillechamber.com
URL: http://www.holtvillechamber.com
Contact: Laura Goodsell, Dir.

47912 ■ Huntington Beach Chamber of Commerce
19891 Beach Blvd., Ste. 140
Huntington Beach, CA 92648
Ph:(714)536-8888
Fax:(714)960-7654
Co. E-mail: lpcain@hbcoc.com
URL: http://www.hbchamber.org
Contact: Joyce Riddell CCE, Pres.

47913 ■ Idyllwild Chamber of Commerce
PO Box 304
Idyllwild, CA 92549
Ph:(951)659-3259
Free: 888-659-3259
Fax:(951)659-6216
Co. E-mail: info@idyllwildchamber.com
URL: http://www.idyllwildchamber.com
Contact: Bill Triplett, Pres.

47914 ■ Imperial Beach Chamber of Commerce and Visitor's Bureau
702 Seacoast Dr.
Imperial Beach, CA 91932-1871
Ph:(619)424-3151
Fax:(619)424-3008
URL: http://www.ib-chamber.com
Contact: Cynthia Melcher, Pres.

47915 ■ Imperial Chamber of Commerce
101 E 4th St.
Imperial, CA 92251-1611
Ph:(760)355-1609
Fax:(760)355-3920
URL: http://www.imperialchamber.org
Contact: Meredith Jones, Acting CEO

47916 ■ Indian Valley Chamber of Commerce
PO Box 516
Greenville, CA 95947
Ph:(530)284-6633
Fax:(530)284-6907
Co. E-mail: indianvalleychamber@frontiernet.net
URL: http://www.indianvalley.net
Contact: Alicia Knadler, Pres.

47917 ■ Indio Chamber of Commerce
82-921 Indio Blvd.
Indio, CA 92201
Ph:(760)347-0676
Free: 800-755-8440
Fax:(760)347-6069
Co. E-mail: info@indiochamber.org
URL: http://www.indiochamber.org
Contact: Patrick Swarthout, Chm.

47918 ■ Industry Manufacturers Council
15651 Stafford St.
City of Industry, CA 91744
Ph:(626)968-3737
Fax:(626)330-5060
Co. E-mail: imc@cityofindustry.org
URL: http://www.cityofindustry.org/news.php
Contact: Donald Sachs, Exec. Dir.

47919 ■ Inglewood/Airport Area Chamber of Commerce
330 E Queen St.
Inglewood, CA 90301-1817
Ph:(310)677-1121
Fax:(310)677-1001
Co. E-mail: inglewoodchamber@sbcglobal.net
URL: http://www.inglewoodchamber.com
Contact: Shannon R. Howe, Exec. VP

47920 ■ Irvine Chamber of Commerce
2485 McCabe Way, Ste. 150
Irvine, CA 92614
Ph:(949)660-9112
Fax:(949)660-0829
Co. E-mail: icc@irvinechamber.com
URL: http://www.irvinechamber.com
Contact: Jacquie Warren, Pres./CEO

47921 ■ Irwindale Chamber of Commerce
PO Box 2307
16102 Arrow Hwy.
Irwindale, CA 91706
Ph:(626)960-6606
Fax:(626)960-3868
Co. E-mail: info@irwindalechamber.org
URL: http://www.irwindalechamber.org
Contact: Lisa Bailey, Pres./CEO

47922 ■ Isleton Chamber of Commerce
PO Box 758
Isleton, CA 95641
Ph:(916)777-5880

Fax:(916)777-4330
URL: http://www.isletoncoc.org

47923 ■ Japanese Chamber of Commerce of Southern California
244 San Pedro, Ste. 504
Los Angeles, CA 90012
Ph:(213)626-3067
Fax:(213)626-3070
Co. E-mail: office@jccsc.com
URL: http://www.jccsc.com
Contact: Toshio Handa, Pres.

47924 ■ Joshua Tree Chamber of Commerce
PO Box 600
Joshua Tree, CA 92252
Ph:(760)366-3723
Fax:(760)366-2573
URL: http://joshuatreechamber.org
Contact: George Kopp, Pres.

47925 ■ Julian Chamber of Commerce
PO Box 1866
Julian, CA 92036
Ph:(760)765-1857
URL: http://www.julianca.com

47926 ■ June Lake Chamber of Commerce
PO Box 2
June Lake, CA 93529
Ph:(760)648-7509
URL: http://junelakeloop.org

47927 ■ Kerman District Chamber of Commerce
783 S Madera Ave.
Kerman, CA 93630-1796
Ph:(559)846-6343
Fax:(559)846-6344
Co. E-mail: info@kermanchamber.org
URL: http://www.kermanchamber.org
Contact: Linda Geringer, Exec. Dir.

47928 ■ Kern River Valley Chamber of Commerce
PO Box 567
Lake Isabella, CA 93240
Ph:(760)379-5236
Free: (866)578-4386
Fax:(760)379-5457
Co. E-mail: office@kernrivervalley.com
URL: http://www.kernrivervalley.com
Contact: Ray Thurm, Pres.

47929 ■ Kernville Chamber of Commerce
11447 Kernville Rd.
PO Box 397
Kernville, CA 93238-0397
Ph:(760)376-2629
Free: (866)KERNVILLE
Fax:(760)376-4371
Co. E-mail: office@kernvillechamber.org
URL: http://www.kernvillechamber.org
Contact: Cheryl Borthick, Pres.

47930 ■ Kettleman City Chamber of Commerce
PO Box 179
Kettleman City, CA 93239
Ph:(559)386-5866

47931 ■ King City and Southern Monterey Chamber of Commerce and Agriculture
200 Broadway St., Ste. 40
King City, CA 93930
Ph:(831)385-3814
Fax:(831)386-9462
Co. E-mail: kingcitychamber@sbcglobal.net
URL: http://www.kingcitychamber.com
Contact: Jeremy Burk, Pres.

47932 ■ Kingsburg District Chamber of Commerce
1475 Draper St.
Kingsburg, CA 93631
Ph:(559)897-1111

Fax:(559)897-4621
Co. E-mail: jessatkingsburg@aol.com
URL: http://www.kingsburgchamberofcommerce.com
Contact: Jess Chambers, Exec. Dir.

47933 ■ La Canada - Flintridge Chamber of Commerce
4529 Angeles Crest Hwy., Ste. 102
La Canada, CA 91011
Ph:(818)790-4289
Fax:(818)790-8930
Co. E-mail: exec@lacanadaflintridge.com
URL: http://www.lacanadaflintridge.com
Contact: Pat Anderson, Pres./CEO

47934 ■ La Habra Area Chamber of Commerce
321 E La Habra Blvd.
La Habra, CA 90631
Ph:(562)697-1704
Fax:(562)697-8359
Co. E-mail: info@lahabrachamber.com
URL: http://www.lahabrachamber.com
Contact: Mark Sturdevant, Exec. Dir.

47935 ■ La Mirada Chamber of Commerce
11900 La Mirada Blvd., Ste. 9
La Mirada, CA 90638
Ph:(562)902-1970
Fax:(562)902-1218
Co. E-mail: info@lmchamber.org
URL: http://lmchamber.org
Contact: Demian Ross, Dir.

47936 ■ La Quinta Chamber of Commerce
78-275 Calle Tampico
La Quinta, CA 92253
Ph:(760)564-3199
Fax:(760)564-3111
URL: http://www.lqchamber.com
Contact: David Archer, Pres./CEO

47937 ■ La Verne Chamber of Commerce
2078 Bonita Ave.
La Verne, CA 91750
Ph:(909)593-5265
Fax:(909)596-0579
Co. E-mail: info@lavernechamber.org
URL: http://www.lavernechamber.org
Contact: Brian McNerney, Pres./CEO

47938 ■ Lafayette Chamber of Commerce
100 Lafayette Cir., Ste. 103
Lafayette, CA 94549
Ph:(925)284-7404
Fax:(925)284-3109
Co. E-mail: info@lafayettechamber.org
URL: http://www.lafayettechamber.org
Contact: Jay Lifson, CEO

47939 ■ Laguna Beach Chamber of Commerce
357 Glenneyre Ave.
Laguna Beach, CA 92651
Ph:(949)494-1018
Fax:(949)376-8916
Co. E-mail: info@lagunabeachchamber.org
URL: http://www.lagunabeachchamber.org
Contact: Rose Hancock, Exec. Dir.

47940 ■ Laguna Niguel Chamber of Commerce
28062 Forbes Rd., Ste. C
Laguna Niguel, CA 92677
Ph:(949)363-0136
Fax:(949)363-9026
Co. E-mail: info@lagunaniguelchamber.net
URL: http://lagunaniguelchamber.net
Contact: Debbie Newman, Pres./CEO

47941 ■ Lake Arrowhead Communities Chamber of Commerce
PO Box 219
Lake Arrowhead, CA 92352
Ph:(909)337-3715
Fax:(909)336-1548
Co. E-mail: info@lakearrowhead.net
URL: http://www.lakearrowhead.net
Contact: Lewis Murray, Pres./CEO

47942 ■ Lake Elsinore Valley Chamber of Commerce
132 W Graham Ave.
Lake Elsinore, CA 92530
Ph:(951)245-8848
Fax:(951)245-9127
Co. E-mail: info@lakeelsinorechamber.com
URL: http://www.lakeelsinorechamber.com
Contact: Kim Joseph Cousins, Pres./CEO

47943 ■ Lake Los Angeles Chamber of Commerce
PO Box 500071
Lake Los Angeles, CA 93591-0071
Ph:(661)264-2786
Fax:(661)264-3470
Co. E-mail: risingclouds@sbcglobal.net
URL: http://www.lakelachamber.org
Contact: Paul Bean, Dir.

47944 ■ Lakeport Regional Chamber of Commerce
PO Box 295
Lakeport, CA 95453
Ph:(707)263-5092
Free: (866)525-3767
Fax:(707)263-5104
Co. E-mail: execdirector@pacific.net
URL: http://www.lakeportchamber.com
Contact: Melissa Fulton, Exec. Dir.

47945 ■ Lakeside Chamber of Commerce
9924 Vine St.
Lakeside, CA 92040
Ph:(619)561-1031
Fax:(619)561-7951
Co. E-mail: chamber@lakesideca.com
URL: http://www.lakesideca.com
Contact: Steve Menefee, Pres.

47946 ■ Larkspur Chamber of Commerce
PO Box 998
Larkspur, CA 94977
Ph:(415)686-2062
Fax:(510)868-8550
Co. E-mail: lcc07@comcast.net
URL: http://www.larkspurchamber.org
Contact: Donna Craft, Exec. Sec.

47947 ■ Lassen County Chamber of Commerce
PO Box 338
Susanville, CA 96130-0338
Ph:(530)257-4323
Fax:(530)251-2561
Co. E-mail: director@lassencountychamber.org
URL: http://www.lassencountychamber.org
Contact: Patricia Hagata, Exec. Dir.

47948 ■ Lathrop Chamber of Commerce
PO Box 313
Lathrop, CA 95330
Ph:(209)740-6503
Co. E-mail: mkennedybracken@sbcglobal.net
URL: http://www.lathropchamber.org
Contact: Mary Kennedy Bracken, Pres.

47949 ■ Lee Vining Chamber of Commerce
PO Box 130
Lee Vining, CA 93541
Ph:(760)647-6629
Fax:(760)647-6377
Co. E-mail: info@leevining.com
URL: http://www.leevining.com
Contact: Nancy Boman, Sec.

47950 ■ Lincoln Area Chamber of Commerce
511 5th St.
Lincoln, CA 95648
Ph:(916)645-2035
Fax:(916)645-9455
Co. E-mail: info@lincolnchamber.com
URL: http://www.lincolnchamber.com
Contact: Bob Ramness, CEO

47951 ■ Linden-Peters Chamber of Commerce
PO Box 557
Linden, CA 95236
Ph:(209)547-3046
URL: http://www.lindenchamber.net

47952 ■ Lindsay Chamber of Commerce
PO Box 989
Lindsay, CA 93247
Ph:(559)562-4929
Fax:(559)562-5219
Co. E-mail: lindsaychamber@lindsay.ca.us
URL: http://chamber.lindsay.ca.us
Contact: Juanita C. Hernandez, Exec. Dir.

47953 ■ Littlerock Chamber of Commerce
PO Box 326
Littlerock, CA 93543
Ph:(661)944-6990
Co. E-mail: jackt@qnet.com
URL: http://www.littlerock-ca.us
Contact: Ronni Di Giovanni, Pres.

47954 ■ Live Oak District Chamber of Commerce
PO Box 391
Live Oak, CA 95953
Ph:(530)695-1519
Co. E-mail: liveoakchamber@syix.com
URL: http://www.liveoakchamber.org
Contact: Annette Bertolini, Pres./Treas.

47955 ■ Livermore Chamber of Commerce
2157 1st St.
Livermore, CA 94550
Ph:(925)447-1606
Fax:(925)447-1641
Co. E-mail: lccinfo@livermorechamber.org
URL: http://www.livermorechamber.org
Contact: Dale Kaye, Pres./CEO

47956 ■ Lodi Chamber of Commerce
35 S School St.
Lodi, CA 95240
Ph:(209)367-7840
Co. E-mail: info@lodichamber.com
URL: http://www.lodichamber.com
Contact: Pat Patrick, Pres./CEO

47957 ■ Loma Linda Chamber of Commerce
PO Box 343
Loma Linda, CA 92354-0343
Ph:(909)799-2828
Fax:(909)799-2825
Co. E-mail: info@lomalindachamber.com
URL: http://www.lomalindachamber.com
Contact: Dina Weiss, CEO

47958 ■ Lomita Chamber of Commerce
25332 Narbonne Ave., Ste. 250
Lomita, CA 90717
Ph:(310)326-6378
Fax:(310)326-2904
Co. E-mail: info@lomitacoc.com
URL: http://lomitacoc.com
Contact: Chuck Taylor, Exec. Dir.

47959 ■ Lompoc Valley Chamber of Commerce and Visitors' Bureau
PO Box 626
Lompoc, CA 93438-0626
Ph:(805)736-4567
Free: 800-240-0999
Fax:(805)737-0453
Co. E-mail: chamber@lompoc.com
URL: http://www.lompoc.com
Contact: Kipp Thonack, Chm.

47960 ■ Lone Pine Chamber of Commerce
PO Box 749
Lone Pine, CA 93545
Ph:(760)876-4444
Fax:(760)876-9205
Co. E-mail: info@lonepinechamber.org
URL: http://www.lonepinechamber.org

47961 ■ Long Beach Area Chamber of Commerce
1 World Trade Ctr., Ste. 206
Long Beach, CA 90831-0206
Ph:(562)436-1251
Fax:(562)436-7099
Co. E-mail: info@lbchamber.com
URL: http://www.lbchamber.com
Contact: Randy Gordon, Pres./CEO

47962 ■ Loomis Basin Chamber of Commerce
6090 Horseshoe Bar Rd.
Loomis, CA 95650
Ph:(916)652-7252
Fax:(916)652-7211
Co. E-mail: manager@loomischamber.com
URL: http://www.loomischamber.com
Contact: Carol Voyiatzes, Chamber Mgr.

47963 ■ Los Alamitos Area Chamber of Commerce
3231 Katella Ave.
Los Alamitos, CA 90720
Ph:(562)598-6659
Fax:(562)598-7035
Co. E-mail: info@losalchamber.org
URL: http://www.losalchamber.org
Contact: Chris Barnes, Exec. Off.

47964 ■ Los Altos Chamber of Commerce
321 University Ave.
Los Altos, CA 94022
Ph:(650)948-1455
Fax:(650)948-6238
Co. E-mail: info@losaltoschamber.org
URL: http://www.losaltoschamber.org
Contact: Julie Rose, Pres.

47965 ■ Los Angeles Area Chamber of Commerce
350 S Bixel St.
Los Angeles, CA 90017
Ph:(213)580-7500
Fax:(213)580-7511
Co. E-mail: info@lachamber.com
URL: http://www.lachamber.com
Contact: Gary Toebben, Pres./CEO

47966 ■ Los Banos Chamber of Commerce
PO Box 2117
Los Banos, CA 93635
Ph:(209)826-2495
Fax:(209)826-9689
Co. E-mail: lbcofc@losbanos.com
URL: http://www.losbanos.com
Contact: Geneva M. Brett, Pres.

47967 ■ Los Osos/Baywood Park Chamber of Commerce
PO Box 6282
Los Osos, CA 93412-6282
Ph:(805)528-4884
Fax:(805)528-8401
Co. E-mail: chamber@fix.net
URL: http://www.losososbaywoodpark.org
Contact: Debie Tucker, Exec. Dir.

47968 ■ Lucerne Valley Chamber of Commerce
PO Box 491
Lucerne Valley, CA 92356
Ph:(760)248-7215
Fax:(760)248-2024
Co. E-mail: chamber@lucernevalley.net
URL: http://www.lvcal.org/chamber

47969 ■ Lynwood Chamber of Commerce
3651 E Imperial Hwy.
PO Box 763
Lynwood, CA 90262
Ph:(310)527-1431
Co. E-mail: lynwoodchamber@gmail.com
URL: http://www.lynwoodchamber.org
Contact: Maria Garcia, Pres.

47970 ■ Madera Chamber of Commerce
120 NE St.
Madera, CA 93638
Ph:(559)673-3563
Fax:(559)673-5009
Co. E-mail: dbray@maderachamber.com
URL: http://www.maderachamber.com
Contact: Debi Bray, Pres./CEO

47971 ■ Malibu Chamber of Commerce
23805 Stuart Ranch Rd., Ste. 100
Malibu, CA 90265
Ph:(310)456-9025
Fax:(310)456-0195
Co. E-mail: info@malibu.org
URL: http://malibu.wliinc3.com/index.asp
Contact: Ed Gillespie, Pres.

47972 ■ Manhattan Beach Chamber of Commerce
425 15th St.
PO Box 3007
Manhattan Beach, CA 90266
Ph:(310)545-5313
Fax:(310)545-7203
Co. E-mail: info@manhattanbeachchamber.net
URL: http://www.manhattanbeachchamber.net
Contact: Helen Duncan, Pres./CEO

47973 ■ Manteca Chamber of Commerce
821 W Yosemite Ave.
Manteca, CA 95337
Ph:(209)823-6121
Fax:(209)239-6131
Co. E-mail: chamber@manteca.org
URL: http://www.manteca.org
Contact: Debby Moorhead, CEO

47974 ■ Marina Chamber of Commerce
PO Box 425
Marina, CA 93933
Ph:(831)384-9155
Co. E-mail: info@marinachamber.com
URL: http://www.marinachamber.com
Contact: Joe Sweeney, Pres.

47975 ■ Mariposa County Chamber of Commerce
PO Box 425
Mariposa, CA 95338
Ph:(209)966-2456
Fax:(209)966-4193
Co. E-mail: mariposachamber@sti.net
URL: http://www.mariposachamber.org
Contact: Dorothy Kuhnel, Exec. Dir.

47976 ■ Mark West Area Chamber of Commerce
4787 Old Redwood Hwy., Ste. 101
Santa Rosa, CA 95403
Ph:(707)578-7975
Fax:(707)578-0397
Co. E-mail: markwest@markwest.org
URL: http://www.markwest.org
Contact: James Bajgrowicz, Pres.

47977 ■ Martinez Area Chamber of Commerce and Visitors and Information Center
603 Marina Vista
Martinez, CA 94553
Ph:(925)228-2345
Fax:(925)228-2356
Co. E-mail: director@martinezchamber.com
URL: http://www.martinezchamber.com
Contact: Cynthia Murdough, Exec. Dir.

47978 ■ Maywood Chamber of Commerce
PO Box 645
5720 Heliothrope Ave.
Maywood, CA 90270
Ph:(323)562-3373
Fax:(323)562-2905
Co. E-mail: sjimenez@cityofmaywood.com
URL: http://www.cityofmaywood.com
Contact: Susan Jimenez, Gen. Mgr.

47979 ■ McCloud Chamber of Commerce
PO Box 372
McCloud, CA 96057
Ph:(530)964-3113
Co. E-mail: contact@mccloudchamber.com
URL: http://www.mccloudchamber.com/chamber.html

47980 ■ McKinleyville Chamber of Commerce
1640 Central Ave.
McKinleyville, CA 95519
Ph:(707)839-2449
Fax:(707)839-1205
URL: http://www.mckinleyvillechamber.com

47981 ■ Menifee Valley Chamber of Commerce
27070 Sun City Blvd.
Sun City, CA 92586
Ph:(951)672-1991
Fax:(951)672-4022
Co. E-mail: info@menifeevalleychamber.org
URL: http://www.menifeevalleychamber.com
Contact: Dorothy Wolons, CEO

47982 ■ Menlo Park Chamber of Commerce
1100 Merrill St.
Menlo Park, CA 94025-4386
Ph:(650)325-2818
Fax:(650)325-0920
Co. E-mail: info@menloparkchamber.com
URL: http://www.menloparkchamber.com
Contact: Fran Dehn, Pres./CEO

47983 ■ Merced County Chamber of Commerce
PO Box 1112
Merced, CA 95341-1112
Ph:(209)722-3864
Fax:(209)722-2406
Co. E-mail: info@mercedcountychamber.com
URL: http://www.mercedcountychamber.com
Contact: Nelson Crabb, Pres.

47984 ■ Mid Valley Chamber of Commerce
7120 Hayvenhurst Ave., Ste. 114
Van Nuys, CA 91406-3813
Ph:(818)989-0300
Fax:(818)989-3836
Co. E-mail: info@midvalleychamber.com
URL: http://www.midvalleychamber.com
Contact: Nancy Hoffman Vanyek, CEO

47985 ■ Mill Valley Chamber of Commerce
85 Throckmorton Ave.
Mill Valley, CA 94942
Ph:(415)388-9700
Fax:(415)388-9770
Co. E-mail: info@millvalley.org
URL: http://www.millvalley.org
Contact: Kathy Severson, CEO

47986 ■ Millbrae Chamber of Commerce
50 Victoria Ave., Ste. 103
Millbrae, CA 94030-2622
Ph:(650)697-7324
Fax:(650)259-7918
Co. E-mail: chamber@millbrae.com
URL: http://www.millbrae.com
Contact: John Ford, Pres./CEO

47987 ■ Milpitas Chamber of Commerce
828 N Hillview Dr.
Milpitas, CA 95035-4544
Ph:(408)262-2613
Fax:(408)262-2823
Co. E-mail: info@milpitaschamber.com
URL: http://www.milpitaschamber.com
Contact: Mary Mashburn, VP for Programs

47988 ■ Modesto Chamber of Commerce
1114 J St.
PO Box 844
Modesto, CA 95353-0844
Ph:(209)577-5757
Fax:(209)577-2673
Co. E-mail: info@modchamber.org
URL: http://www.modchamber.org
Contact: Ralph Curtis, Chm.

47989 ■ Modesto Junior Chamber of Commerce
PO Box 76
Modesto, CA 95354
Ph:(209)450-3810
Co. E-mail: mickiemodestojc@yahoo.com
URL: http://www.jayceesmodesto.org
Contact: Vincent Sandoval III, Pres.

47990 ■ Monrovia Chamber of Commerce
620 S Myrtle Ave.
Monrovia, CA 91016-2805
Ph:(626)358-1159
Fax:(626)357-6036
Co. E-mail: chamber@monroviacc.com
URL: http://www.monroviacc.com
Contact: Karin Crehan, Exec. Dir.

47991 ■ Montclair Chamber of Commerce
5222 Benito St.
Montclair, CA 91763
Ph:(909)624-4569
Fax:(909)625-2009
Co. E-mail: info@montclairchamber.com
URL: http://www.montclairchamber.com
Contact: Jeff Fuller, VP

47992 ■ Monte Rio Chamber of Commerce
PO Box 220
Monte Rio, CA 95462-0220
Ph:(707)865-1533
Co. E-mail: mrcc@sonic.net
URL: http://monterio.org
Contact: Mary Baker, Board Sec.

47993 ■ Montebello Chamber of Commerce
817 W Whittier Blvd., Ste. 200
Montebello, CA 90640
Ph:(323)721-1153
Fax:(323)721-7946
Co. E-mail: andrea@montebellochamber.org
URL: http://www.montebellochamber.org
Contact: Andrea Wagg, Pres./CEO

47994 ■ Monterey Peninsula Chamber of Commerce
380 Alvarado St.
Monterey, CA 93940
Ph:(831)648-5360
Fax:(831)649-3502
Co. E-mail: info@mpcc.com
URL: http://www.mpcc.com
Contact: Astrid Coleman, CEO/Pres.

47995 ■ Montrose-Verdugo City Chamber of Commerce
3516 N Verdugo Rd.
Glendale, CA 91208
Ph:(818)249-7171
Fax:(818)249-8919
Co. E-mail: mvcc@montrosechamber.org
URL: http://www.montrosechamber.org
Contact: Marian E. Jocz, Exec. Dir.

47996 ■ Morgan Hill Chamber of Commerce
PO Box 786
Morgan Hill, CA 95038-0786
Ph:(408)779-9444
Fax:(408)779-5405
Co. E-mail: mchh@morganhill.org
URL: http://www.morganhill.org
Contact: Christine Giusiana, Pres./CEO

47997 ■ Morro Bay Chamber of Commerce
845 Embarcadero Rd., Ste. D
Morro Bay, CA 93442
Ph:(805)772-4467
Free: 800-231-0592
Fax:(805)772-6038
Co. E-mail: baywatch@morrobay.org
URL: http://www.morrobay.org/cm/Home.html
Contact: Peter Candela, CEO

47998 ■ Moss Landing Chamber of Commerce
PO Box 41
Moss Landing, CA 95039
Ph:(831)633-4501
URL: http://www.mosslandingchamber.com

47999 ■ Mount Shasta Chamber of Commerce
300 Pine St.
Mount Shasta, CA 96067
Ph:(530)926-4865
Free: 800-926-4865
Fax:(530)926-0976
Co. E-mail: info@mtshastachamber.com
URL: http://mtshastachamber.com/index.php
Contact: Cindy Corrales, Pres.

48000 ■ Napa Chamber of Commerce
1556 1st St.
PO Box 636
Napa, CA 94559-0636
Ph:(707)226-7455
Fax:(707)226-1171
Co. E-mail: info@napachamber.com
URL: http://www.napachamber.com
Contact: Kate King ACE, Pres./CEO

48001 ■ National City Chamber of Commerce
901 National City Blvd.
National City, CA 91950-3203
Ph:(619)477-9339
Free: 800-292-4624
Fax:(619)477-5018
Co. E-mail: thechamber@nationalcitychamber.org
URL: http://www.nationalcitychamber.org
Contact: Ditas Yamane, Pres.

48002 ■ Needles Area Chamber of Commerce
PO Box 705
Needles, CA 92363-0705
Ph:(760)326-2050
Fax:(760)326-2194
Co. E-mail: needlescofc@rraz.net
URL: http://www.needleschamber.com
Contact: Sue Godnick, Exec. Dir.

48003 ■ Networkers of the Costa Mesa Chamber of Commerce
1700 Adams Ave., Ste. 101
Costa Mesa, CA 92626-4865
Ph:(714)885-9090
Fax:(714)885-9094
Co. E-mail: info@costamesachamber.com
URL: http://www.costamesachamber.com
Contact: Ed Fawcett, Pres./CEO

48004 ■ Nevada City Chamber of Commerce
132 Main St.
Nevada City, CA 95959-2520
Ph:(530)265-2692
Free: 800-655-NJOY
Fax:(530)265-3892
Co. E-mail: info@nevadacitychamber.com
URL: http://www.nevadacitychamber.com
Contact: Duane Strawser, Interim Pres.

48005 ■ Newark Chamber of Commerce
6066 Civic Terrace Ave., Ste. 8
Newark, CA 94560
Ph:(510)744-1000
Fax:(510)744-1003
Co. E-mail: info@newark-chamber.com
URL: http://www.newark-chamber.com
Contact: Linda Ashley, Pres./CEO

48006 ■ Newman Chamber of Commerce
PO Box 753
Newman, CA 95360
Ph:(209)862-1000
Fax:(209)862-4133
Contact: Sean McNaughton, Pres.

48007 ■ Newport Harbor Area Chamber of Commerce
1470 Jamboree Rd.
Newport Beach, CA 92660
Ph:(929)729-4400
Fax:(929)729-4417
Co. E-mail: rluehrs@newportbeach.com
URL: http://www.newportbeach.com
Contact: Richard R. Luehrs, Pres./CEO

48008 ■ Nipomo Chamber of Commerce
671 W Tefft St., Ste. 13
Nipomo, CA 93444
Ph:(805)929-1583
Fax:(805)929-5835
Co. E-mail: nipomochamber@yahoo.com
URL: http://www.nipomochamber.org
Contact: Cathy Cachu, Pres.

48009 ■ Norco Chamber of Commerce
2816 Hamner Ave.
Norco, CA 92860
Ph:(951)737-2531
Fax:(951)737-2574
Co. E-mail: staff@norcochamber.com
URL: http://www.norcochamber.com
Contact: Kevin Russell, Pres.

48010 ■ North Fork Chamber of Commerce
PO Box 426
North Fork, CA 93643
Ph:(559)877-2410
Fax:(559)877-2332
Co. E-mail: info@north-fork-chamber.com
URL: http://www.north-fork-chamber.com
Contact: Bob McKee, Pres.

48011 ■ North Monterey County Chamber of Commerce
PO Box 744
Castroville, CA 95012
Ph:(831)633-2465
Fax:(831)633-0485
Co. E-mail: artifest@redshift.com
URL: http://www.northmontereycountychamber.org
Contact: Gary DeAmaral, VP

48012 ■ North Sacramento Chamber of Commerce
PO Box 15468
Sacramento, CA 95851
Ph:(916)925-6773
Co. E-mail: leadership@northsacramentochamber.
  org
URL: http://northsacramentochamber.org
Contact: Rob Kerth, Pres.

48013 ■ North Valley Regional Chamber of Commerce
9401 Reseda Blvd., Ste. 100
Northridge, CA 91324
Ph:(818)349-5676
Fax:(818)349-4343
Co. E-mail: info@nvrcc.com
URL: http://www.nvrcc.com
Contact: Joyce Sipes, Pres./CEO

48014 ■ Norwalk Chamber of Commerce
12040 Foster Rd.
Norwalk, CA 90650
Ph:(562)864-7785
Fax:(562)864-8539
Co. E-mail: ceo@norwalkchamber.com
URL: http://www.norwalkchamber.com
Contact: Susan Arthur, Pres.

48015 ■ Novato Chamber of Commerce
807 DeLong Ave.
Novato, CA 94945
Ph:(415)897-1164
Fax:(415)898-9097
Co. E-mail: info@novatochamber.com
URL: http://www.novatochamber.com
Contact: Coy Smith, CEO

48016 ■ Oakdale District Chamber of Commerce
590 N Yosemite Ave.
Oakdale, CA 95361-2732
Ph:(209)847-2244
Fax:(209)847-0826
Co. E-mail: info@yosemite-gateway.net
URL: http://www.oakdalechamber.com
Contact: Mary Guardiola, CEO

48017 ■ Oakhurst Area Chamber of Commerce
49074 Civic Circle Dr.
Oakhurst, CA 93644-8713
Ph:(559)683-7766
Fax:(559)658-2942
Co. E-mail: chamber@oakhurstchamber.com
URL: http://www.oakhurstchamber.com
Contact: Don DeBernardi, Pres.

48018 ■ Oakland African-American Chamber of Commerce
449 15th St., Ste. 410
Oakland, CA 94612
Ph:(510)268-1600
Fax:(510)268-1602
Co. E-mail: info@oaacc.org
URL: http://www.oaacc.org
Contact: Robert Bobb, Founding Pres.

48019 ■ Oakland Chinatown Chamber of Commerce
Pacific Renaissance Plz.
388 9th St., Ste. 258
Oakland, CA 94607
Ph:(510)893-8979
Fax:(510)893-8988
Co. E-mail: oaklandctchamber@aol.com
URL: http://www.oaklandchinatownstreetfest.com
Contact: Jenny Ong, Exec. Dir.

48020 ■ Oakland Metropolitan Chamber of Commerce
475 14th St.
Oakland, CA 94612-1903
Ph:(510)874-4800
Fax:(510)839-8817
Co. E-mail: jharaburda@oaklandchamber.com
URL: http://www.oaklandchamber.com
Contact: Joseph Haraburda, Pres./CEO

48021 ■ Oakley Chamber of Commerce
PO Box 1340
Oakley, CA 94561
Ph:(925)625-1035
Fax:(925)625-4051
Co. E-mail: oakley@ecis.com
URL: http://www.oakleychamber.com
Contact: Gene Buchholz, Dir.

48022 ■ Oceanside Chamber of Commerce
928 N Coast Hwy.
Oceanside, CA 92054
Ph:(760)722-1534
Free: 800-350-7873
Fax:(760)722-8336
Co. E-mail: info@oceansidechamber.com
URL: http://www.oceansidechamber.com
Contact: David L. Nydegger ACE, CEO

48023 ■ Ojai Valley Chamber of Commerce
PO Box 1134
Ojai, CA 93023
Ph:(805)646-8126
Fax:(805)646-9762
Co. E-mail: info@ojaichamber.com
URL: http://www.ojaichamber.org
Contact: Jeff Haydon, Pres.

48024 ■ Ontario Chamber of Commerce
500 E St., Ste. No. 200
Ontario, CA 91764
Ph:(909)984-2458
Fax:(909)984-6439
Co. E-mail: info@ontario.org
URL: http://www.ontario.org
Contact: Ciriaco Pinedo, Chm.

48025 ■ Orange Chamber of Commerce and Visitor Bureau
439 E Chapman Ave.
Orange, CA 92866
Ph:(714)538-3581
Free: 800-938-0073
Fax:(714)532-1675
Co. E-mail: hlarkin-reed@orangechamber.com
URL: http://www.orangechamber.com
Contact: Heidi Larkin-Reed ACE, Pres./CEO

48026 ■ Orange County Business Council
2 Park Plz., Ste. 100
Irvine, CA 92614-5904
Ph:(949)476-2242
Fax:(949)476-9240
Co. E-mail: ldunn@ocbc.org
URL: http://www.ocbc.org
Contact: Lucy Dunn, Pres./CEO

48027 ■ Orange County Chamber of Commerce Profit Connection
439 E Chapman Ave.
Orange, CA 92866-1509
Ph:(714)538-3581
Fax:(714)532-1675
Co. E-mail: info@orangechamber.com
URL: http://www.orangechamber.com
Contact: Heide Larkin-Reed, Pres./CEO

48028 ■ Orangevale Chamber of Commerce
9267 Greenback Ln., Ste. B91
Orangevale, CA 95662-4864
Ph:(916)988-0175
Fax:(916)988-1049
Co. E-mail: ovchamber@sbcglobal.net
URL: http://www.orangevalechamber.com
Contact: Lorraine Silvera, Pres.

48029 ■ Orinda Chamber of Commerce
PO Box 2271
Orinda, CA 94563
Ph:(925)254-3909
Fax:(925)254-1635
Co. E-mail: info@orindachamber.org
URL: http://www.orindachamber.org
Contact: Candy Kattenburg, Exec. Dir.

48030 ■ Oroville Area Chamber of Commerce
1789 Montgomery St.
Oroville, CA 95965
Ph:(530)538-2542
Free: 800-655-GOLD
Fax:(530)538-2546
Co. E-mail: info@orovillechamber.net
URL: http://www.orovillechamber.net
Contact: Linda Dahlmeier, Pres.

48031 ■ Otay Mesa Chamber of Commerce
9163 Siempre Viva Rd., Ste. I-2
San Diego, CA 92154-7608
Ph:(619)661-6111
Fax:(619)661-6178
Co. E-mail: amieryteran@otaymesa.org
URL: http://www.otaymesa.org
Contact: Alejandra Teran Mier, Exec. Dir.

48032 ■ Oxnard Chamber of Commerce
400 E Esplanade Dr., Ste. 302
Oxnard, CA 93036
Ph:(805)983-6118
Fax:(805)604-7331
Co. E-mail: info@oxnardchamber.org
URL: http://www.oxnardchamber.org
Contact: Nancy Lindholm, Pres./CEO

48033 ■ Pacific Grove Chamber of Commerce
PO Box 167
Pacific Grove, CA 93950
Ph:(831)373-3304
Free: 800-656-6650
Fax:(831)373-3317
Co. E-mail: chamber@pacificgrove.org
URL: http://www.pacificgrove.org
Contact: Moe Ammar, Pres.

48034 ■ Pacific Palisades Chamber of Commerce
15330 Antioch St.
Pacific Palisades, CA 90272
Ph:(310)459-7963
Fax:(310)459-9534
Co. E-mail: info@palisadeschamber.com
URL: http://www.palisadeschamber.com
Contact: Antonia Balfour, Pres.

48035 ■ Pacifica Chamber of Commerce and Visitor Center
225 Rockaway Beach Ave., Ste. 1
Pacifica, CA 94044
Ph:(650)355-4122
Co. E-mail: don@pacificachamber.org
URL: http://www.pacificachamber.com

48036 ■ Pajaro Valley Chamber of Commerce
444 Main St.
PO Box 1748
Watsonville, CA 95077-1748
Ph:(831)724-3900
Fax:(831)728-5300
Co. E-mail: info@pajarovalleychamber.org
URL: http://www.pajarovalleychamber.com
Contact: Luann Lauesen, Chair

48037 ■ Palm Desert Chamber of Commerce
72559 Hwy. 111
Palm Desert, CA 92260
Ph:(760)346-6111
Fax:(760)346-3263
Co. E-mail: info@pdcc.org
URL: http://www.pdcc.org
Contact: Ms. Barbara deBoom, Pres./CEO

48038 ■ Palm Springs Chamber of Commerce
190 W Amado Rd.
Palm Springs, CA 92262
Ph:(760)325-1577
Fax:(760)325-8549
Co. E-mail: info@pschamber.org
URL: http://www.pschamber.org
Contact: Mr. John Pivinski, CEO

48039 ■ Palmdale Chamber of Commerce
817 East Ave., Q-9
Palmdale, CA 93550
Ph:(661)273-3232
Fax:(661)273-8508
Co. E-mail: chamberstaff@palmdalechamber.org
URL: http://www.palmdalechamber.org
Contact: William Hogrefe, Chief Admin. Off.

48040 ■ Palo Alto Chamber of Commerce
122 Hamilton Ave.
Palo Alto, CA 94301
Ph:(650)324-3121
Fax:(650)324-1215
Co. E-mail: info@paloaltochamber.com
URL: http://www.paloaltochamber.com
Contact: Paula Sandas, Pres./CEO

48041 ■ Palos Verdes Peninsula Chamber of Commerce
707 Silver Spur Rd., Ste. 100
Rolling Hills Estates, CA 90274
Ph:(310)377-8111
Fax:(310)377-0614
Co. E-mail: office@palosverdeschamber.com
URL: http://palosverdeschamber.com
Contact: Kay Finer, Pres./CEO

48042 ■ Paradise Ridge Chamber of Commerce
5550 Skyway, No. 1
Paradise, CA 95969
Ph:(530)877-9356
Free: 888-845-2769
Fax:(530)877-1865
Co. E-mail: info@paradisechamber.com
URL: http://www.paradisechamber.com
Contact: Katie Simmons, Exec. Dir.

48043 ■ Paramount Chamber of Commerce
15357 Paramount Blvd.
Paramount, CA 90723-4338
Ph:(562)634-3980
Fax:(562)634-0891
Co. E-mail: plemons@paramountchamber.com
URL: http://www.paramountchamber.org
Contact: Peggy Lemons, Exec. Dir.

48044 ■ Pasadena Chamber of Commerce and Civic Association
865 E Del Mar Blvd.
Pasadena, CA 91101
Ph:(626)795-3355
Fax:(626)795-5603
Co. E-mail: info@pasadena-chamber.org
URL: http://www.pasadena-chamber.org
Contact: Paul Little, Pres./CEO

48045 ■ Paso Robles Chamber of Commerce
1225 Park St.
Paso Robles, CA 93446
Ph:(805)238-0506
Free: 800-406-4040
Fax:(805)238-0527
Co. E-mail: info@pasorobleschamber.com
URL: http://www.pasorobleschamber.com
Contact: Mike Gibson, Pres./CEO

48046 ■ Patterson-Westley Chamber of Commerce
PO Box 365
Patterson, CA 95363
Ph:(209)895-8094
URL: http://www.patterson-westleychamber.com
Contact: George Galloway MacMaster, Pres.

48047 ■ Pearblossom Chamber of Commerce
PO Box 591
Pearblossom, CA 93553
Ph:(661)944-6435
Contact: Cindy Rimmer-Deck, Pres.

48048 ■ Perris Valley Chamber of Commerce
11 S D St.
Perris, CA 92571
Ph:(951)657-3555
Fax:(951)657-3085
Co. E-mail: perrischamber@puhsd.org
URL: http://www.perrischamber.org
Contact: Robert Turner, Pres.

48049 ■ Petaluma Area Chamber of Commerce
6 Petaluma Blvd. N, Ste. A2
Petaluma, CA 94952
Ph:(707)762-2785
Fax:(707)762-4721
Co. E-mail: pacc@petalumachamber.com
URL: http://www.petalumachamber.com
Contact: Ms. Onita Pellegrini, CEO

48050 ■ Phelan Chamber of Commerce
PO Box 290010
Phelan, CA 92329-0010
Ph:(760)868-3291
Fax:(760)868-3291
Co. E-mail: phelanchamber@verizon.net
URL: http://www.phelanchamber.org
Contact: Rosella Bernal, Pres.

48051 ■ Pico Rivera Chamber of Commerce
PO Box 847
Pico Rivera, CA 90660-3647
Ph:(562)949-2473
Fax:(562)949-8320
Co. E-mail: elena@picoriverachamber.org
URL: http://www.picoriverachamber.org
Contact: Bob Tapia, Exec. Dir.

48052 ■ Pinole Chamber of Commerce
PO Box 1
Pinole, CA 94564
Ph:(510)724-4484
Fax:(510)724-4408
Co. E-mail: pinolechamber@msn.com
URL: http://www.pinolechamber.org
Contact: Ivette Ricco, Exec. Dir./Sec.

48053 ■ Pinon Hills Chamber of Commerce
PO Box 720095
Pinon Hills, CA 92372
Ph:(760)868-5801
URL: http://www.ph.qnet.com/lAtmojave/phelan/pin-hill.htm
Contact: Nancy Cosgrove, Pres.

48054 ■ Pismo Beach Chamber of Commerce and Visitors' Information Center
581 Dolliver St.
Pismo Beach, CA 93449
Ph:(805)773-4382
Free: 800-443-7778
Fax:(805)773-6772
Co. E-mail: pbcoc@charter.net
URL: http://www.pismochamber.com
Contact: Rebecca McMurry, Exec. Dir.

48055 ■ Pittsburg Chamber of Commerce
485 Railroad Ave.
Pittsburg, CA 94565
Ph:(925)432-7301
Fax:(925)427-5555
Co. E-mail: mconig@pittsburg.org
URL: http://www.pittsburg.org
Contact: Mary P. Coniglio, Exec. VP/CEO

48056 ■ Placentia Chamber of Commerce
201 E Yorba Linda Blvd., Ste. C
Placentia, CA 92870-3418
Ph:(714)528-1873
Fax:(714)528-1879
Co. E-mail: info@placentiachamber.com
URL: http://www.placentiachamber.com
Contact: Dottie Rogers, Pres.

48057 ■ Pleasant Hill Chamber of Commerce
91 Gregory Ln., Ste. 11
Pleasant Hill, CA 94523-4914
Ph:(925)687-0700
Fax:(925)676-7422
Co. E-mail: info@pleasanthillchamber.com
URL: http://www.pleasanthillchamber.com
Contact: Charley Daly, CEO

48058 ■ Pleasanton Chamber of Commerce
777 Peters Ave.
Pleasanton, CA 94566-6500
Ph:(925)846-5858
Fax:(925)846-9697
Co. E-mail: info@pleasanton.org
URL: http://www.pleasanton.org
Contact: Scott Raty, Pres./CEO

48059 ■ Pomona Chamber of Commerce
PO Box 1457
Pomona, CA 91769-1457
Ph:(909)622-1256
Fax:(909)620-5986
Co. E-mail: info@pomonachamber.org
URL: http://www.pomonachamber.org
Contact: Ricardo Delgado, Pres.

48060 ■ Port Hueneme Chamber of Commerce
220 N Market St.
Port Hueneme, CA 93041-3204
Ph:(805)488-2023
Fax:(805)488-6993
Co. E-mail: phc@huenemechamber.com
URL: http://www.huenemechamber.com
Contact: Kathleen Misewitch, Pres./CEO

48061 ■ Porterville Chamber of Commerce
93 N Main St., Ste. A
Porterville, CA 93257
Ph:(559)784-7502
Fax:(559)784-0770
Co. E-mail: chamber@porterville.com
URL: http://www.chamber.porterville.com
Contact: Donnette Silva Carter, Pres./CEO

48062 ■ Poway Chamber of Commerce
PO Box 868
Poway, CA 92074-0868
Ph:(858)748-0016
Fax:(858)748-1710
Co. E-mail: chamber@poway.com
URL: http://www.poway.com
Contact: Luanne Hulsizer, Chm.

48063 ■ Quartz Hill Chamber of Commerce
42043 50th St. W
Quartz Hill, CA 93536
Ph:(661)722-4811

Fax:(661)722-3235
Co. E-mail: info@quartzhillchamber.org
URL: http://www.quartzhillchamber.org
Contact: Mr. Lee Barron, Pres.

48064 ■ Quincy Chamber of Commerce
464 W Main St.
Quincy, CA 95971
Ph:(530)283-0188
Free: 888-EZW-AY4U
Fax:(530)283-5864
Co. E-mail: office@quincychamber.com
URL: http://www.quincychamber.com
Contact: Dee Dee Driscoll, Pres.

48065 ■ Ramona Chamber of Commerce
960 Main St.
Ramona, CA 92065
Ph:(760)789-1311
Fax:(760)789-1317
Co. E-mail: info@ramonachamber.com
URL: http://www.ramonachamber.com
Contact: Thad Clendenen, Pres.

48066 ■ Rancho Cordova Chamber of Commerce
2729 Prospect Park Dr., Ste. 17
Rancho Cordova, CA 95670
Ph:(916)273-5688
Fax:(916)273-5727
URL: http://www.ranchocordova.org
Contact: Jane Daly, CEO

48067 ■ Rancho Cucamonga Chamber of Commerce
7945 Vineyard Ave., Ste. D-5
Rancho Cucamonga, CA 91730-2314
Ph:(909)987-1012
Fax:(909)987-5917
Co. E-mail: info@ranchochamber.org
URL: http://www.ranchochamber.org
Contact: Michelle Alonzo, Pres./CEO

48068 ■ Rancho Mirage Chamber of Commerce
42-520 Bob Hope Dr., Ste. B
Rancho Mirage, CA 92270
Ph:(760)568-9351
Fax:(760)779-9684
Co. E-mail: info@ranchomirage.org
URL: http://www.ranchomirage.org
Contact: Stuart W. Ackley, Pres./CEO

48069 ■ Red Bluff-Tehama County Chamber of Commerce
PO Box 850
Red Bluff, CA 96080
Ph:(530)527-6220
Free: 800-655-6225
Fax:(530)527-2908
Co. E-mail: rbchamber@att.net
URL: http://www.redbluffchamberofcommerce.com
Contact: Cindy Brown, Pres.

48070 ■ Redlands Chamber of Commerce
1 E Redlands Blvd.
Redlands, CA 92373
Ph:(909)793-2546
Fax:(909)335-6388
Co. E-mail: info@redlandschamber.org
URL: http://www.redlandschamber.org
Contact: Paul Barich, Dir.

48071 ■ Redondo Beach Chamber of Commerce and Visitors Bureau
200 N Pacific Coast Hwy.
Redondo Beach, CA 90277
Ph:(310)376-6911
Free: 800-282-0333
Fax:(310)374-7373
Co. E-mail: customerservice@redondochamber.org
URL: http://www.redondochamber.org
Contact: John Parsons, Chm.

48072 ■ Rialto Chamber of Commerce
120 N Riverside Ave.
Rialto, CA 92376
Ph:(909)875-5364

Fax:(909)875-6790
Co. E-mail: lisa@rialtochamber.com
URL: http://www.rialtochamber.org

48073 ■ Richmond Chamber of Commerce
3925 Macdonald Ave.
Richmond, CA 94805
Ph:(510)234-3512
Fax:(510)234-3540
Co. E-mail: judy@rcoc.com
URL: http://www.rcoc.com
Contact: Ms. Judith Morgan, Pres./CEO

48074 ■ Ridgecrest Chamber of Commerce
128-B E California Ave., Ste. B
Ridgecrest, CA 93555
Ph:(760)375-8331
Fax:(760)375-0365
Co. E-mail: chamber@ridgecrest.ca.us
URL: http://www.ridgecrestchamber.com
Contact: Eric Kauffman, Pres.

48075 ■ Rio Linda-Elverta Chamber of Commerce
PO Box 75
Rio Linda, CA 95673
Ph:(916)991-9344
Fax:(916)922-9074
Co. E-mail: info@rlechamber.com
URL: http://www.rlechamber.com
Contact: Bob Davis, Pres.

48076 ■ Rio Vista Chamber of Commerce
6 N Front St.
Rio Vista, CA 94571
Ph:(707)374-2700
Fax:(707)374-2424
Co. E-mail: volunteer@riovista.org
URL: http://www.riovista.org
Contact: Mary Peinado, Exec. Dir.

48077 ■ Ripon Chamber of Commerce
929 W Main St.
PO Box 327
Ripon, CA 95366
Ph:(209)599-7519
Fax:(209)599-2286
Co. E-mail: boothd@charterinternet.com
URL: http://www.riponchamber.com
Contact: Dorothy Booth, Exec. Dir.

48078 ■ Rocklin Area Chamber of Commerce
3700 Rocklin Rd.
Rocklin, CA 95677
Ph:(916)624-2548
Fax:(916)624-5743
Co. E-mail: info@rocklinchamber.com
URL: http://www.rocklinchamber.com
Contact: Robin Trimble, CEO

48079 ■ Rohnert Park Chamber of Commerce
6050 Commerce Blvd., Ste. 211
Rohnert Park, CA 94928
Ph:(707)584-1415
Fax:(707)584-2945
Co. E-mail: info@rohnertparkchamber.org
URL: http://www.rohnertparkchamber.org
Contact: Roy Gugliotta, Pres./CEO

48080 ■ Rosemead Chamber of Commerce
3953 Muscatel Ave.
PO Box 425
Rosemead, CA 91770
Ph:(626)288-0811
Fax:(626)288-2514
Co. E-mail: office@rosemeadchamber.org
URL: http://www.rosemeadchamber.org
Contact: Nadine Gomez, Pres.

48081 ■ Roseville Chamber of Commerce
650 Douglas Blvd.
Roseville, CA 95678
Ph:(916)783-8136
Fax:(916)783-5261
Co. E-mail: admin@rosevillechamber.com
URL: http://www.rosevillechamber.com
Contact: Wendy A. Gerig, CEO

48082 ■ Rough and Ready Chamber of Commerce
PO Box 801
Rough and Ready, CA 95975
Ph:(530)272-4320
Co. E-mail: evburka@cwnet.com
URL: http://www.roughandreadychamber.com
Contact: Charles Crecilius, Pres.

48083 ■ Running Springs Area Chamber of Commerce
PO Box 96
Running Springs, CA 92382-0096
Ph:(909)867-2411
Co. E-mail: info@runningspringschamber.com
URL: http://www.runningspringschamber.com
Contact: Linda Peabody, Admin. Assist.

48084 ■ Russian River Chamber of Commerce and Visitor Center
16209 1st St.
PO Box 331
Guerneville, CA 95446
Ph:(707)869-9000
Free: 877-644-9001
Fax:(707)869-9009
Co. E-mail: news@russianriver.com
URL: http://www.russianriver.com
Contact: Dawn Bell, Exec. Dir.

48085 ■ Sacramento Black Chamber of Commerce
2655 Del Monte St.
West Sacramento, CA 95691
Ph:(916)374-9355
Fax:(916)374-9366
URL: http://www.sacblackchamber.org
Contact: Clarence Williams, Pres./CEO/Chm.

48086 ■ Sacramento Hispanic Chamber of Commerce
1491 River Park Dr., Ste. No. 101
Sacramento, CA 95825
Ph:(916)486-7700
Fax:(916)486-7728
Co. E-mail: info@sachcc.org
URL: http://www.sachcc.org
Contact: Celia Cortez, Exec. Dir.

48087 ■ Sacramento Metro Chamber of Commerce
1 Capitol Mall, Ste. 300
Sacramento, CA 95814
Ph:(916)552-6800
Fax:(916)443-2672
Co. E-mail: chamber@metrochamber.org
URL: http://www.metrochamber.org
Contact: Matthew R. Mahood, CEO/Pres.

48088 ■ St. Helena Chamber of Commerce
1010 Main St., Ste. A
St. Helena, CA 94574
Ph:(707)963-4456
Free: 800-799-6456
Fax:(707)963-5396
Co. E-mail: info@sthelena.com
URL: http://www.sthelena.com
Contact: Nancy Levenberg, CEO

48089 ■ Salinas Valley Chamber of Commerce
119 E Alisal St.
PO Box 1170
Salinas, CA 93902-1170
Ph:(831)751-7725
Fax:(831)424-8639
Co. E-mail: info@salinaschamber.com
URL: http://www.salinaschamber.com
Contact: Tiffany DiTullio, Pres./CEO

48090 ■ San Anselmo Chamber of Commerce
PO Box 2844
San Anselmo, CA 94979-2844
Ph:(415)454-2510
Fax:(415)258-9458
Co. E-mail: info@sananselmochamber.org
URL: http://www.sananselmochamber.org
Contact: Connie S. Rodgers, Pres./CEO

48091 ■ San Benito County Chamber of Commerce
650 San Benito St., Ste. 130
Hollister, CA 95023-3988
Ph:(831)637-5315
Fax:(831)637-1008
Co. E-mail: info1@sanbenitocountychamber.com
URL: http://www.sanbenitocountychamber.com
Contact: Jessica French, Pres./CEO

48092 ■ San Bernardino Area Chamber of Commerce
PO Box 658
San Bernardino, CA 92402
Ph:(909)885-7515
Fax:(909)384-9979
Co. E-mail: sba.chamber@verizon.net
URL: http://www.sbachamber.org
Contact: Judi Penman, Pres./CEO

48093 ■ San Carlos Chamber of Commerce
1500 Laurel St., Ste. B
San Carlos, CA 94070-5103
Ph:(650)593-1068
Fax:(650)593-9108
Co. E-mail: staff@sancarloschamber.org
URL: http://www.sancarloschamber.org/default.aspx
Contact: Sheryl Pomerenk, CEO

48094 ■ San Clemente Chamber of Commerce
1100 N El Camino Real
San Clemente, CA 92672-4653
Ph:(949)492-1131
Fax:(949)492-3764
Co. E-mail: info@scchamber.com
URL: http://www.scchamber.com
Contact: Lynn Wood, Pres./CEO

48095 ■ San Diego County Hispanic Chamber of Commerce
3443 Camino Del Rio S, Ste. 101
San Diego, CA 92108
Ph:(619)702-0790
Fax:(619)521-6722
Co. E-mail: marcocortes@sdchcc.com
URL: http://www.sdchcc.com
Contact: Marco Polo Cortes, Pres./CEO

48096 ■ San Diego East County Chamber of Commerce
201 S Magnolia Ave.
El Cajon, CA 92020-4525
Ph:(619)440-6161
Fax:(619)440-6164
Co. E-mail: mikec@eastcountychamber.org
URL: http://www.eastcountychamber.org
Contact: Mike Cully, Pres./CEO

48097 ■ San Diego North Chamber of Commerce
11650 Iberia Pl., Ste. 220
San Diego, CA 92128
Ph:(858)487-1767
Fax:(858)487-8051
Co. E-mail: infodesk@sdncc.com
URL: http://www.sdncc.com
Contact: Michael Robinson, Pres./CEO

48098 ■ San Diego Regional Chamber of Commerce
402 W Broadway, Ste. 1000
San Diego, CA 92101-3585
Ph:(619)544-1300
Co. E-mail: webinfo@sdchamber.org
URL: http://www.sdchamber.org
Contact: Ruben Barrales, Pres./CEO

48099 ■ San Dimas Chamber of Commerce
PO Box 175
San Dimas, CA 91773-0175
Ph:(909)592-3818
Fax:(909)592-8178
Co. E-mail: info@sandimaschamber.com
URL: http://www.sandimaschamber.com
Contact: Ted Powl, Pres./CEO

48100 ■ San Francisco Chamber of Commerce
235 Montgomery St., 12th Fl.
San Francisco, CA 94104
Ph:(415)392-4520
Fax:(415)392-0485
Co. E-mail: sfalk@sfchamber.com
URL: http://www.sfchamber.com
Contact: Steve Falk, Pres./CEO

48101 ■ San Gabriel Chamber of Commerce
620 W Santa Anita St.
San Gabriel, CA 91776
Ph:(626)576-2525
Fax:(626)289-2901
Co. E-mail: debsgcofc@yahoo.com
URL: http://www.sangabrielchamber.com/default.
   php?page=main
Contact: Wendy Holten, Pres.

48102 ■ San Jose - Silicon Valley Chamber of Commerce
101 W Santa Clara St.
San Jose, CA 95113
Ph:(408)291-5250
Fax:(408)286-5019
Co. E-mail: info@sjchamber.com
URL: http://www.sjchamber.com
Contact: Pat Dando, Pres./CEO

48103 ■ San Juan Bautista Chamber of Commerce
209 3rd St.
PO Box 1037
San Juan Bautista, CA 95045
Ph:(831)623-2454
Fax:(831)623-0674
Co. E-mail: sjbcc@sbcglobal.net
URL: http://www.sjbchamber.com
Contact: Carolyn Roe-Gargiulo, Pres.

48104 ■ San Juan Capistrano Chamber of Commerce
PO Box 1878
San Juan Capistrano, CA 92675
Ph:(949)493-4700
Fax:(949)489-2695
Co. E-mail: info@sanjuanchamber.com
URL: http://www.sanjuanchamber.com
Contact: Karen Richesin, Office Mgr.

48105 ■ San Leandro Chamber of Commerce
15555 E 14th St., Ste. 100
San Leandro, CA 94578
Ph:(510)317-1400
Fax:(510)317-1404
Co. E-mail: info@sanleandrochamber.com
URL: http://www.sanleandrochamber.com
Contact: David P. Johnson, CEO

48106 ■ San Luis Obispo Chamber of Commerce
1039 Chorro St.
San Luis Obispo, CA 93401
Ph:(805)781-2777
Fax:(805)543-1255
Co. E-mail: slochamber@slochamber.org
URL: http://slochamber.org/cm/Home.html
Contact: Dave Garth, CEO/Pres.

48107 ■ San Marcos Chamber of Commerce
939 Grand Ave.
San Marcos, CA 92078
Ph:(760)744-1270
Fax:(760)744-5230
Co. E-mail: info@sanmarcoschamber.com
URL: http://www.sanmarcoschamber.com
Contact: Sheila Brown, Chair

48108 ■ San Marino Chamber of Commerce
2304 Huntington Dr., Ste. 202
San Marino, CA 91108
Ph:(626)286-1022
Fax:(626)286-7765
Co. E-mail: snmarinocofc@earthlink.net
URL: http://www.sanmarinochamber.org
Contact: Chris Carlos, Pres.

48109 ■ San Mateo Chamber of Commerce
PO Box 936
San Mateo, CA 94403
Ph:(650)401-2440
Fax:(650)401-2446
Co. E-mail: info@sanmateochamber.org
URL: http://www.sanmateoca.org
Contact: Linda Asbury, Pres./CEO

48110 ■ San Pablo Chamber of Commerce
PO Box 6204
San Pablo, CA 94806
Ph:(510)234-2067
Fax:(510)234-0604
Co. E-mail: spchamber39@yahoo.com
URL: http://www.ci.san-pablo.ca.us/main/chamber-
   ofcommerce.htm
Contact: Jerry Sattler, Pres.

48111 ■ San Pedro Peninsula Chamber of Commerce
390 W 7th St.
San Pedro, CA 90731
Ph:(310)832-7272
Fax:(310)832-0685
Co. E-mail: info@sanpedrochamber.com
URL: http://www.sanpedrochamber.com
Contact: Camilla Townsend, CEO

48112 ■ San Rafael Chamber of Commerce
817 Mission Ave.
San Rafael, CA 94901
Ph:(415)454-4163
Fax:(415)454-7039
Co. E-mail: srcc@sanrafaelchamber.com
URL: http://www.sanrafaelchamber.com
Contact: Jay Zlotnick, Interim Pres./CEO

48113 ■ San Ramon Chamber of Commerce
12667 Alcosta Blvd., Ste. 160
Bishop Ranch 15
San Ramon, CA 94583
Ph:(925)242-0600
Fax:(925)242-0603
Co. E-mail: info@sanramon.org
URL: http://www.sanramon.org
Contact: Carolyn Degnan, Pres./CEO

48114 ■ San Simeon Chamber of Commerce
250 San Simeon, Ste. 3A
San Simeon, CA 93452
Ph:(805)927-3500
Free: 800-342-5613
Co. E-mail: sansimeonchamber@yahoo.com
URL: http://www.sansimeonchamber.org

48115 ■ San Ysidro Chamber of Commerce and Visitor Information Center
663 E San Ysidro Blvd.
San Ysidro, CA 92173
Ph:(619)428-1281
Fax:(619)428-1294
Co. E-mail: info@sanysidrochamber.org
URL: http://www.sanysidrochamber.org
Contact: Israel Adato, VP

48116 ■ Sanger District Chamber of Commerce
1789 Jensen Ave., Ste. B
Sanger, CA 93657
Ph:(559)875-4575
Fax:(559)875-0745
Co. E-mail: sanger@psnw.com
URL: http://www.sanger.org
Contact: Nettie Inouye, Pres./CEO

48117 ■ Santa Barbara Hispanic Chamber of Commerce
PO Box 6592
Santa Barbara, CA 93160
Ph:(805)637-3680
Fax:(805)681-1260
Co. E-mail: info@sbhispanicchamber.org
URL: http://www.sbhispanicchamber.org
Contact: Sergio Villa, Chm.

48118 ■ Santa Barbara Region Chamber of Commerce
924 Anacapa St., Ste. 1
Santa Barbara, CA 93101
Ph:(805)965-3023
Free: (866)555-1212
Fax:(805)966-5954
Co. E-mail: info@sbchamber.org
URL: http://www.sbchamber.org
Contact: Steve Cushman, Pres.

48119 ■ Santa Clara Chamber of Commerce and Convention and Visitors Bureau
1850 Warburton Ave.
Santa Clara, CA 95050
Ph:(408)244-9660
Free: 800-272-6822
Fax:(408)244-7830
Co. E-mail: steve.vandorn@santaclara.org
URL: http://www.santaclara.org
Contact: Steve VanDorn, Pres./CEO

48120 ■ Santa Clarita Valley Chamber of Commerce
28460 Stanford Ave., Ste. 100
Santa Clarita, CA 91355
Ph:(661)702-6977
Fax:(661)702-6980
Co. E-mail: info@scvchamber.com
URL: http://www.scvchamber.com
Contact: Larry Mankin, Pres./CEO

48121 ■ Santa Cruz Chamber of Commerce
611 Ocean St., Ste. 1
Santa Cruz, CA 95060
Ph:(831)457-3713
Fax:(831)423-1847
Co. E-mail: info@santacruzchamber.org
URL: http://www.santacruzchamber.org
Contact: Bill Tysseling, Exec. Dir.

48122 ■ Santa Fe Springs Chamber of Commerce and Industrial League
12016 E Telegraph Rd., Ste. 100
Santa Fe Springs, CA 90670
Ph:(562)944-1616
Fax:(562)946-3976
Co. E-mail: mail@sfschamber.com
URL: http://www.sfschamber.com
Contact: Marc Essensa, Pres.-Elect

48123 ■ Santa Maria Valley Chamber of Commerce
614 S Broadway
Santa Maria, CA 93454-5111
Ph:(805)925-2403
Free: 800-331-3779
Fax:(805)928-7559
Co. E-mail: info@santamaria.com
URL: http://www.santamaria.com/cm/Home.html
Contact: Robert P. Hatch, Pres./CEO

48124 ■ Santa Monica Chamber of Commerce
1234 6th St., Ste. 100
Santa Monica, CA 90401
Ph:(310)393-9825
Fax:(310)394-1868
Co. E-mail: info@smchamber.com
URL: http://www.smchamber.com
Contact: Laurel Rosen, Pres./CEO

48125 ■ Santa Paula Chamber of Commerce
PO Box 1
Santa Paula, CA 93060
Ph:(805)525-5561
Fax:(805)525-8950
Co. E-mail: info@santapaulachamber.com
URL: http://www.santapaulachamber.com
Contact: Sam Hishmeh, Chm.

48126 ■ Santa Rosa Chamber of Commerce
637 1st St.
Santa Rosa, CA 95404
Ph:(707)545-1414

Fax:(707)545-6914
Co. E-mail: chamber@santarosachamber.com
URL: http://www.santarosachamber.com
Contact: Michael Hauser, Pres.

48127 ■ Santee Chamber of Commerce
10315 Mission Gorge Rd.
Santee, CA 92071
Ph:(619)449-6572
Fax:(619)562-7906
Co. E-mail: info@santee-chamber.org
URL: http://www.santee-chamber.org
Contact: Warren H. Savage Jr., Exec. Dir.

48128 ■ Saratoga Chamber of Commerce
14485 Big Basin Way
Saratoga, CA 95070
Ph:(408)867-0753
Fax:(408)867-5213
Co. E-mail: info@saratogachamber.org
URL: http://www.saratogachamber.org
Contact: Elizabeth Borbolla, Exec. Dir.

48129 ■ Sausalito Chamber of Commerce
10 Liberty Ship Way, Bay 2, Ste. 250
Sausalito, CA 94965
Ph:(415)331-7262
Fax:(415)332-0323
Co. E-mail: chamber@sausalito.org
URL: http://www.sausalito.org
Contact: Oonagh Kavanagh, CEO

48130 ■ Scotts Valley Chamber of Commerce
360 Kings Village Rd.
Scotts Valley, CA 95066
Ph:(831)438-1010
Fax:(831)438-6544
Co. E-mail: info@scottsvalleychamber.com
URL: http://www.scottsvalleychamber.com
Contact: Sharolynn Ullestad, Exec. Dir.

48131 ■ Seal Beach Chamber of Commerce, California
201 8th St., Ste. 120
Seal Beach, CA 90740
Ph:(562)799-0179
Fax:(562)795-5637
Co. E-mail: info@sealbeachchamber.org
URL: http://www.sealbeachchamber.org
Contact: Jim Klisanin, Pres.

48132 ■ Sebastopol Area Chamber of Commerce and Visitors Center
PO Box 178
Sebastopol, CA 95473-0178
Ph:(707)823-3032
Free: 877-828-4748
Fax:(707)823-8439
Co. E-mail: chamber@sebastopol.org
URL: http://www.sebastopol.org
Contact: Teresa Ramondo, Exec. Dir./CEO

48133 ■ Selma District Chamber of Commerce
1821 Tucker St.
Selma, CA 93662
Ph:(559)891-2235
Fax:(559)896-7075
Co. E-mail: cindyh@cityofselma.com
URL: http://www.cityofselma.com/chamber/index.htm
Contact: Cindy L. Howell, Exec. Dir.

48134 ■ Shafter Chamber of Commerce
336 Pacific Ave.
Shafter, CA 93263
Ph:(661)746-2600
Fax:(661)746-0607
URL: http://www.shafter.com
Contact: Karen Wilkins, Dir.

48135 ■ Shingle Springs/Cameron Park Chamber of Commerce
PO Box 341
Shingle Springs, CA 95682
Ph:(530)677-8000
Fax:(530)676-8313
Co. E-mail: info@sscpchamber.org
URL: http://www.sscpchamber.org
Contact: Carolyn A. Doty

48136 ■ Sierra Madre Chamber of Commerce
37 N Auburn Ave. Ste.1
Sierra Madre, CA 91024
Ph:(626)355-5111
Co. E-mail: info@sierramadrechamber.com
URL: http://www.sierramadrechamber.com
Contact: Karma Bell, Pres.

48137 ■ Signal Hill Chamber of Commerce
2201 E Willow St., Ste. D
Signal Hill, CA 90755
Ph:(562)424-6489
Co. E-mail: info@signalhillchamber.com
URL: http://www.signalhillchamber.com
Contact: Ken Davis, Pres.

48138 ■ Simi Valley Chamber of Commerce
40 W Cochran St., Ste. 100
Simi Valley, CA 93065
Ph:(805)526-3900
Fax:(805)526-6234
Co. E-mail: info@simichamber.org
URL: http://simivalleychamber.org
Contact: Leigh Nixon, Pres./CEO

48139 ■ Solana Beach Chamber of Commerce
PO Box 623
210 W Plaza St.
Solana Beach, CA 92075-0623
Ph:(858)755-4775
Fax:(858)755-4889
Co. E-mail: info@solanabeachchamber.com
URL: http://www.solanabeachchamber.com
Contact: David L. Carroll, Pres.

48140 ■ Solvang Chamber of Commerce
PO Box 465
Solvang, CA 93464
Ph:(805)688-0701
Co. E-mail: linda@solvangcc.org
URL: http://www.solvangcc.org
Contact: Linda Jackson, Pres.

48141 ■ Sonoma Valley Chamber of Commerce
651A Broadway
Sonoma, CA 95476
Ph:(707)996-1033
Fax:(707)996-9402
Co. E-mail: info@sonomachamber.com
URL: http://www.sonomachamber.com
Contact: Jennifer Yankovich, Exec. Dir.

48142 ■ South Gate Chamber of Commerce
3350 Tweedy Blvd.
South Gate, CA 90280
Ph:(323)567-1203
Contact: Jay Flores, Exec. Dir.

48143 ■ South Lake Tahoe Chamber of Commerce
2572 Lake Tahoe Blvd., Ste. 3
South Lake Tahoe, CA 96150
Ph:(530)542-5060
Co. E-mail: southtahoechamberofcommerce@gmail. com
URL: http://www.tahoeinfo.com
Contact: David Kelly, Exec. Dir.

48144 ■ South Orange County Regional Chambers of Commerce
26111 Antonio Pkwy., Ste. 400
Rancho Santa Margarita, CA 92688
Ph:(949)635-5800
Fax:(949)635-1635
Co. E-mail: info@socchambers.com
URL: http://www.socchambers.com

48145 ■ South San Francisco Chamber of Commerce
213 Linden Ave.
South San Francisco, CA 94080
Ph:(650)588-1911
Fax:(650)588-2534
Co. E-mail: info@ssfchamber.com
URL: http://www.ssfchamber.com
Contact: Maria Martinucci, CEO

48146 ■ Spring Valley Chamber of Commerce
PO Box 1211
Spring Valley, CA 91979-1211
Ph:(619)670-9902
Fax:(619)670-9924
URL: http://www.springvalleychamber.org
Contact: Tina Carlson, Exec. Dir.

48147 ■ Springville Chamber of Commerce
PO Box 104
Springville, CA 93265
Ph:(559)539-0100
Co. E-mail: chamber@springville.ca.us
URL: http://springville.ca.us
Contact: Mr. Rick Mitchell, Pres.

48148 ■ Stanton Chamber of Commerce
8381 Katella Ave., Ste. H
Stanton, CA 90680
Ph:(714)995-1485
Fax:(714)995-1184
Co. E-mail: service@stantonchamber.org
URL: http://www.stantonchamber.org
Contact: Don Martinez, Pres.

48149 ■ Studio City Chamber of Commerce
4024 Radford Ave., Ed. 2, Ste. F
Studio City, CA 91604
Ph:(818)655-5916
Fax:(818)655-8392
Co. E-mail: admin@studiocitychamber.com
URL: http://www.studiocitychamber.com
Contact: Esther Walker, Exec. Dir.

48150 ■ Sun Valley Area Chamber of Commerce
PO Box 308
Sun Valley, CA 91353
Ph:(818)768-2014
Fax:(818)767-1947
Co. E-mail: info@svacc.com
Contact: Jessa Dizon, Exec. Dir.

48151 ■ Sunland-Tujunga Chamber of Commerce
8250 Foothill Blvd., No. A
Sunland, CA 91040
Ph:(818)352-4433
Fax:(818)353-7551
Co. E-mail: stchamberofcomm@aol.com
URL: http://www.stchamber.com
Contact: Jim Moore, Pres.

48152 ■ Sunnyvale Chamber of Commerce
260 S Sunnyvale Ave., Ste. 4
Sunnyvale, CA 94086-6193
Ph:(408)736-4971
Fax:(408)736-1919
Co. E-mail: info@svcoc.org
URL: http://www.svcoc.org
Contact: Paul Stewart, CEO

48153 ■ Swedish American Chamber of Commerce of Greater Los Angeles
10940 Wilshire Blvd., No. 700
Los Angeles, CA 90024
Ph:(310)393-9893
Fax:(310)496-1639
Co. E-mail: info@sacc-gla.org
URL: http://www.sacc-gla.org
Contact: Pietro Fallai, Pres.

48154 ■ Swedish-American Chamber of Commerce, San Diego/Tijuana
9625 Black Mountain Rd., Ste. 306
San Diego, CA 92126
Ph:(619)338-4020
Co. E-mail: info@sacc-sandiego.org
URL: http://www.sacc-sandiego.org
Contact: Magnus Gunnarsson, Pres.

48155 ■ Taft District Chamber of Commerce
400 Kern St.
Taft, CA 93268
Ph:(661)765-2165
Fax:(661)765-6639
Co. E-mail: taftchamber@bak.rr.com
URL: http://www.taftchamber.com
Contact: Charmayne Brooks, Exec. Dir.

48156 ■ Tarzana Chamber of Commerce
PO Box 570414
Tarzana, CA 91356
Ph:(818)343-3687
Fax:(818)705-0127
Co. E-mail: info.chamber@sbcglobal.net
URL: http://www.tarzanachamber.com
Contact: Steve Hornstein Esq., Pres.

48157 ■ Temecula Valley Chamber of Commerce
26790 Ynez Ct.
Temecula, CA 92591
Ph:(951)676-5090
Free: (866)676-5090
Fax:(951)694-0201
Co. E-mail: info@temecula.org
URL: http://www.temecula.org
Contact: Alice Sullivan, Pres./CEO

48158 ■ Temple City Chamber of Commerce
9050 Las Tunas Dr.
Temple City, CA 91780
Ph:(626)286-3101
Fax:(626)286-2590
Co. E-mail: info@templecitychamber.org
URL: http://www.templecitychamber.org
Contact: Linda Payne, Pres./CEO

48159 ■ Templeton Chamber of Commerce
PO Box 701
Templeton, CA 93465
Ph:(805)434-2099
Co. E-mail: info@templetonchamber.com
URL: http://www.templetonchamber.com
Contact: Robert Rosales, Pres.

48160 ■ Thousand Oaks - Westlake Village Regional Chamber of Commerce
600 Hampshire Rd., Ste. 200
Westlake Village, CA 91361-2571
Ph:(805)370-0035
Fax:(805)370-1083
Co. E-mail: info@towlvchamber.org
URL: http://www.towlvchamber.org
Contact: Jill Lederer, Pres./CEO

48161 ■ Thousand Palms Chamber of Commerce
PO Box 365
Thousand Palms, CA 92276
Ph:(760)343-1988
Fax:(760)343-1988
Co. E-mail: tp4business@yahoo.com
URL: http://www.thousandpalmscc.com
Contact: Rosemarie Tessier, Exec. Admin.

48162 ■ Tiburon Peninsula Chamber of Commerce
PO Box 563
Tiburon, CA 94920
Ph:(415)435-5633
Fax:(415)435-1132
Co. E-mail: tibcc@sbcglobal.net
URL: http://www.tiburonchamber.org
Contact: Michael Gornet, Pres.

48163 ■ Torrance Area Chamber of Commerce
3400 Torrance Blvd., Ste. 100
Torrance, CA 90503
Ph:(310)540-5858
Fax:(310)540-7662
Co. E-mail: info@torrancechamber.com
URL: http://www.torrancechamber.com
Contact: Ken Brengle, Pres./CEO

48164 ■ Town of Los Gatos Chamber of Commerce
349 N Santa Cruz Ave.
Los Gatos, CA 95030
Ph:(408)354-9300
Fax:(408)399-1594
Co. E-mail: chamber@losgatosweb.com
URL: http://losgatoschamber.com
Contact: Ronee Nassi, Exec. Dir.

48165 ■ Tracy Chamber of Commerce
223 E 10th St.
Tracy, CA 95376
Ph:(209)835-2131
Fax:(209)833-9526
Co. E-mail: info@tracychamber.org
URL: http://www.tracychamber.org
Contact: Art Vallejo, Chm.

48166 ■ Trinity County Chamber of Commerce
211 Trinity Lakes Blvd.
PO Box 517
Weaverville, CA 96093-0517
Ph:(530)623-6101
Free: 800-4-TRINITY
Fax:(530)623-3753
Co. E-mail: chamber@trinitycounty.com
URL: http://www.trinitycounty.com
Contact: Carol Eli, Exec. Dir.

48167 ■ Truckee-Donner Chamber of Commerce
10065 Donner Pass Rd.
Truckee, CA 96161
Ph:(530)587-8808
Fax:(530)587-2439
Co. E-mail: info@truckee.com
URL: http://www.truckee.com
Contact: Lynn Saunders, Pres./CEO

48168 ■ Tuolumne County Chamber of Commerce
222 S Shepherd St.
Sonora, CA 95370
Ph:(209)532-4212
Free: 877-532-4212
Fax:(209)532-8068
Co. E-mail: info@tcchamber.com
URL: http://www.tcchamber.com
Contact: George Segarini, Exec. Dir.

48169 ■ Turlock Chamber of Commerce
115 S Golden State Blvd.
Turlock, CA 95380
Ph:(209)632-2221
Fax:(209)632-5289
Co. E-mail: info@turlockchamber.com
URL: http://www.turlockchamber.com
Contact: Sharon Silva, Pres./CEO

48170 ■ Tustin Chamber of Commerce
399 El Camino Real
Tustin, CA 92780-3605
Ph:(714)544-5341
Fax:(714)544-2083
Co. E-mail: info@tustinchamber.org
URL: http://tustinchamber.org
Contact: Marisa L. Charette, Pres./CEO

48171 ■ Twain Harte Area Chamber of Commerce
PO Box 404
Twain Harte, CA 95383
Ph:(209)586-4482
Fax:(209)586-0360
Co. E-mail: info@twainhartecc.com
URL: http://www.twainhartecc.com
Contact: Rebecca Halvorsen, Pres.

48172 ■ Twentynine Palms Chamber of Commerce
73660 Civic Ctr., Ste. C and D
Twentynine Palms, CA 92277
Ph:(760)367-3445
Fax:(760)367-3366
Co. E-mail: 29coc@29chamber.com
URL: http://www.29chamber.com
Contact: Jessica Wagner-Schultz, Exec. Dir.

48173 ■ Union City Chamber of Commerce
3939 Smith St.
Union City, CA 94587
Ph:(510)952-9637
Fax:(510)952-9647
Co. E-mail: info@unioncitychamber.com
URL: http://www.unioncitychamber.com
Contact: Colin Shutes, Chm.

48174 ■ Universal City-North Hollywood Chamber of Commerce
6369 Bellingham Ave.
North Hollywood, CA 91606
Ph:(818)508-5155
Fax:(818)508-5156
Co. E-mail: info@noho.org
URL: http://www.noho.org
Contact: Victor Viereck, Pres.

48175 ■ Upland Chamber of Commerce
215 N 2nd Ave., Ste. D
Upland, CA 91786
Ph:(909)204-4465
Fax:(909)204-4464
Co. E-mail: realpeople@uplandchamber.org
URL: http://www.uplandchamber.org
Contact: Sonnie S. Faires, Pres./CEO

48176 ■ Vacaville Chamber of Commerce
300 Main St., Ste. A
Vacaville, CA 95688
Ph:(707)448-6424
Fax:(707)448-0424
Co. E-mail: jennifer@vacavillechamber.com
URL: http://www.vacavillechamber.com
Contact: Gary H. Tatum, Pres./CEO

48177 ■ Vallejo Chamber of Commerce
427 York St.
Vallejo, CA 94590
Ph:(707)644-5551
Fax:(707)644-5590
Co. E-mail: info@vallejochamber.com
URL: http://www.vallejochamber.com
Contact: Rick Wells, Pres./CEO

48178 ■ Valley Center Chamber of Commerce
27301 Valley Center Rd.
Valley Center, CA 92082
Ph:(760)749-8472
Fax:(760)749-8483
Co. E-mail: info@vcchamber.com
URL: http://www.vcchamber.com
Contact: Shawneen Burdick, Pres.

48179 ■ Venice Area Chamber of Commerce
PO Box 202
Venice, CA 90294
Ph:(310)822-5425
Fax:(310)664-7938
Co. E-mail: info@venicechamber.net
URL: http://www.venicechamber.net
Contact: Andy Layman, Pres.

48180 ■ Ventura Chamber of Commerce
801 S Victoria Ave., Ste. 200
Ventura, CA 93003
Ph:(805)676-7500
Fax:(805)650-1414
Co. E-mail: info@ventura-chamber.org
URL: http://www.ventura-chamber.org
Contact: Zoe J. Taylor ACE, CEO/Pres.

48181 ■ Vernon Chamber of Commerce
3801 Santa Fe Ave.
Vernon, CA 90058
Ph:(323)583-3313
Co. E-mail: molguin@vernonchamber.org
URL: http://vernonchamber.org
Contact: Marisa Olguin, Exec. Dir.

48182 ■ Victorville Chamber of Commerce
14174 Green Tree Blvd.
Victorville, CA 92395
Ph:(760)245-6506
Fax:(760)245-6505
Co. E-mail: vvchamber@vvchamber.com
URL: http://vvchamber.com
Contact: Michele Spears, Pres./CEO

48183 ■ Vietnamese Chamber of Commerce
9121 Bolsa Ave., Ste. 203
Westminster, CA 92683
Ph:(714)892-6928
Fax:(714)892-6938
Co. E-mail: info@vacoc.com
URL: http://vacoc.com/index_en.php
Contact: Tam Nguyen, Chm.

48184 ■ Visalia Chamber of Commerce
220 N Santa Fe Ave.
Visalia, CA 93292
Ph:(559)734-5876
Free: 877-VIS-ALIA
Fax:(559)734-7479
Co. E-mail: info@visaliachamber.org
URL: http://www.visaliachamber.org
Contact: Michael Cully, Pres./CEO

48185 ■ Vista Chamber of Commerce
201 Washington St.
Vista, CA 92084
Ph:(760)726-1122
Fax:(760)726-8654
Co. E-mail: info@vistachamber.com
URL: http://www.vistachamber.com
Contact: Paul O'Neal, Pres./CEO

48186 ■ Walnut Creek Chamber of Commerce
1777 Botelho Dr., Ste. 103
Walnut Creek, CA 94596-4233
Ph:(925)934-2007
Fax:(925)934-2404
Co. E-mail: chamber@walnut-creek.com
URL: http://www.walnut-creek.com
Contact: Jay Hoyer, Pres./CEO

48187 ■ Wasco Chamber of Commerce and Agriculture
700 G St.
PO Box 783
Wasco, CA 93280
Ph:(661)758-2746
Fax:(661)758-4939
Co. E-mail: vhight@ci.wasco.ca.us
URL: http://www.ci.wasco.ca.us
Contact: Vickie Hight, Office Mgr.

48188 ■ Weed Chamber of Commerce
34 Main St.
Weed, CA 96094-2522
Ph:(530)938-4624
Free: 877-938-4624
Fax:(530)938-1658
Co. E-mail: weedchamber@ncen.org
URL: http://www.weedchamber.com
Contact: Ronda Gubetta, Pres.

48189 ■ West Covina Chamber of Commerce
811 S Sunset Ave.
West Covina, CA 91790-3599
Ph:(626)338-8496
Free: 888-763-3232
Fax:(626)960-0511
Co. E-mail: glawson@westcovinachamber.com
URL: http://www.westcovinachamber.com
Contact: Gary Lawson, Exec. Dir.

48190 ■ West Los Angeles Chamber of Commerce
2990 S Sepulveda Blvd., Ste. 300A
Los Angeles, CA 90064
Ph:(310)481-0600
Fax:(310)478-2068
Co. E-mail: info@westlachamber.org
URL: http://www.westlachamber.org
Contact: Paul Reznik, Pres.

48191 ■ West Marin Chamber of Commerce
PO Box 1045
Point Reyes Station, CA 94956
Ph:(415)663-9232
Co. E-mail: info@pointreyes.org
URL: http://www.pointreyes.org
Contact: Frank Borodic, Pres.

48192 ■ West Sacramento Chamber and Visitors Bureau
PO Box 404
West Sacramento, CA 95691-3209
Ph:(916)371-7042
Fax:(916)371-7007
Co. E-mail: info@westsacramentochamber.com
URL: http://www.westsacramentochamber.com
Contact: W. Kay Fenrich, CEO

48193 ■ West Shores Chamber of Commerce of the Salton Sea
PO Box 5185
Salton City, CA 92275-5185
Ph:(760)394-4112
Fax:(760)394-4112
Co. E-mail: info@westshoreschamber.org
URL: http://www.westshoreschamber.org
Contact: Lavon Jaksch, Pres.

48194 ■ Western Association of Chamber Executives
PO Box 1736
Sacramento, CA 95812-1736
Ph:(916)442-2223
Fax:(916)444-6685
Co. E-mail: info@waceonline.com
URL: http://www.waceonline.com
Contact: Diane Schwenke, Chm.

48195 ■ Westminster Chamber of Commerce
1079 Westminster Mall
Westminster, CA 92683
Ph:(714)898-9648
Fax:(714)373-1499
Co. E-mail: biz@westminsterchamber.org
URL: http://westminsterchamber.org
Contact: Crystal R. Wadsworth, Exec. Dir.

48196 ■ Whittier Area Chamber of Commerce
8158 Painter Ave.
Whittier, CA 90602
Ph:(562)698-9554
Fax:(562)693-2700
Co. E-mail: info@whittierchamber.com
URL: http://www.whittierchamber.com
Contact: Maria Segovia, Pres.

48197 ■ Wildomar Chamber of Commerce
PO Box 885
Wildomar, CA 92595
Ph:(909)245-0437
Co. E-mail: info@wildomarchamber.org
URL: http://www.wildomarchamber.org
Contact: Jeff George, Chm.

48198 ■ Willits Chamber of Commerce
239 S Main St.
Willits, CA 95490
Ph:(707)459-7910
Fax:(707)459-7914
Co. E-mail: info@willits.org
URL: http://www.willits.org
Contact: Lynn R. Kennelly, Exec. Dir.

48199 ■ Willow Creek Chamber of Commerce
PO Box 704
Willow Creek, CA 95573
Ph:(530)629-2693
Free: 800-628-5156
Co. E-mail: info@willowcreekchamber.com
URL: http://www.willowcreekchamber.com
Contact: Tangie Markle, Pres.

48200 ■ Willows Area Chamber of Commerce
118 W Sycamore
Willows, CA 95988
Ph:(530)934-8150
Free: 888-EZW-AY4U
Fax:(530)934-8710
Co. E-mail: info@willowschamber.com
URL: http://www.willowschamber.com
Contact: Jamie Millen, Pres.

48201 ■ Wilmington Chamber of Commerce
PO Box 90
Wilmington, CA 90748
Ph:(310)834-8586
Fax:(310)834-8887
Co. E-mail: info@wilmington-chamber.com
URL: http://www.wilmington-chamber.com
Contact: Dan Hoffman, Exec. Dir.

48202 ■ Windsor Chamber of Commerce and Visitors Center
PO Box 367
Windsor, CA 95492
Ph:(707)838-7285

Fax:(707)838-2778
Co. E-mail: info@windsorchamber.com
URL: http://www.windsorchamber.com
Contact: Kurt Mitchler, Pres.

48203 ■ Winters District Chamber of Commerce
PO Box 423
201 Railroad Ave.
Winters, CA 95694
Ph:(530)795-2329
Fax:(530)795-3202
Co. E-mail: chamberwinters@yahoo.com
URL: http://www.winterschamber.com
Contact: Dan Maguire, Exec. Dir.

48204 ■ Women in Business Roundtable
235 Montgomery St., 12th Fl.
San Francisco, CA 94104
Ph:(415)392-4520
Fax:(415)392-0485
Co. E-mail: nchan@sfchamber.com
URL: http://www.sfchamber.com/eventsprogs/bizdev/ programs_wibr.php
Contact: Nadia Chan

48205 ■ Woodland Area Chamber of Commerce
307 1st St.
Woodland, CA 95695-3412
Ph:(530)662-7327
Free: 888-843-2636
Fax:(530)662-4086
Co. E-mail: staff@woodlandchamber.org
URL: http://www.woodlandchamber.org
Contact: Kristy Wright, CEO

48206 ■ Wrightwood Chamber of Commerce
PO Box 416
Wrightwood, CA 92397
Ph:(760)249-4320
Fax:(760)249-6822
Co. E-mail: info@wrightwoodchamber.org
URL: http://www.wrightwoodchamber.org
Contact: Loretta Thompson, Pres.

48207 ■ Yorba Linda Chamber of Commerce
17670 Yorba Linda Blvd.
Yorba Linda, CA 92886
Ph:(714)993-9537
Co. E-mail: phyllisylcc@sbcglobal.net
URL: http://www.yorbalindachamber.org
Contact: Phyllis A. Coleman, Exec. Dir.

48208 ■ Yountville Chamber of Commerce
6484 Washington St., Ste. F
Yountville, CA 94599
Ph:(707)944-0904
Fax:(707)944-4465
Co. E-mail: info@yountville.com
URL: http://www.yountville.com

48209 ■ Yreka Chamber of Commerce
117 W Miner St.
Yreka, CA 96097
Ph:(530)842-1649
Co. E-mail: yrekachamber@nctv.com
URL: http://www.yrekachamber.com
Contact: Mark Dean, Exec. Dir.

48210 ■ Yuba-Sutter Chamber of Commerce
PO Box 1429
Marysville, CA 95901
Ph:(530)743-6501
Fax:(530)741-8645
Co. E-mail: chamber@yubasutterchamber.com
URL: http://www.yubasutterchamber.com
Contact: Evelyn Cosner, Office Coor.

48211 ■ Yucaipa Valley Chamber of Commerce
PO Box 45
Yucaipa, CA 92399-0045
Ph:(909)790-1841
Fax:(909)363-7373
Co. E-mail: info@yucaipachamber.org
URL: http://www.yucaipachamber.org
Contact: Ms. Pamela Emenger Grigg, Exec. Dir.

MINORITY BUSINESS ASSISTANCE PROGRAMS

48212 ■ Asian, Inc.
1167 Mission St., 4th Fl.
San Francisco, CA 94103
Ph:(415)928-5910
Fax:(415)921-0182
Co. E-mail: supplier@asianinc.org
URL: http://www.asianinc.org
Contact: Michael A. Chan, Pres.
Description: Assisting in the business development and growth of African Americans and other minorities in Northern California.

48213 ■ California Native American Business Center–National Center for American Indian Enterprise
11138 Valley Mall, Ste. 200
El Monte, CA 91731
Ph:(626)442-3701
Fax:(626)442-7115
Co. E-mail: schambers@ncaied.org
URL: http://www.canabec.org
Contact: Sharon Chambers, Dir

48214 ■ East Los Angeles Minority Business Development Center
5271 E Beverly Blvd.
Los Angeles, CA 90022
Ph:(323)726-7734
Fax:(323)721-9794
Co. E-mail: eastlambdc@ibm.net

48215 ■ Inland Empire Minority Business Enterprise Center–CHARO Community Development Corp.
1485 Spruce St., Ste. C-100
Riverside, CA 92507
Ph:(951)320-7020
Fax:(951)320-7023
Co. E-mail: kgutierrez@charo.corp.com
URL: http://www.charocorp.com
Contact: Karla V. Gonzalez-Gutierrez, Proj Mgr
Description: Provides certification, technical assistance, and training services to minority businesses in the Inland Empire, Orange County, and San Diego areas.

48216 ■ Los Angeles Minority Business Enterprise Center
2801 S Hoover St.
Los Angeles, CA 90089
Ph:(213)743-1966
Fax:(213)743-4511
Co. E-mail: info@losangelesmbec.org
URL: http://www.losangelesmbec.org/
Contact: Sergio Gascon, Dir
Description: Provides access to educational and technical resources that foster business expansion and job creation throughout Los Angeles County.

48217 ■ Los Angeles Minority Business Opportunity Center–City of Los Angeles
City Hall
200 N Spring St., 13th Fl.
Los Angeles, CA 90012
Ph:(213)978-0671
Fax:(213)978-0690
Co. E-mail: lamboc@lacity.org
URL: http://www.lamboc.org/
Contact: Linda Smith, Exec Dir
Description: LA MBOC's vision is to achieve entrepreneurial parity for local Minority Business Enterprises by actively promoting their ability to grow and compete in the global economy.

48218 ■ Los Angeles Urban League Entrepreneur Center
3450 Mount Vernon Dr.
Los Angeles, CA 90008
Ph:(323)299-9660

Fax:(323)299-0618
Co. E-mail: info@laul.org
URL: http://www.laul.org
Contact: Blair Taylor, Dir
Description: Provides business development and support to African Americans and other minorities in Los Angeles.

48219 ■ Northern California Minority Business Enterprise Center
111 N Market St., Ste. 920
San Jose, CA 95113
Ph:(408)998-8058
Fax:(408)998-8872
Co. E-mail: aserrudo@norcalmbec.com
URL: http://www.norcalmbec.com
Description: Works to promote the growth and competitiveness of minority businnses in Northern California. Offers access to capital, contracting, and technical assistance.

48220 ■ Small & Minority Business - OSMB–Department of General Services–Office of Small Business and DVBE Services (707 3)
707 3rd St., 1st Fl., Rm. 400
West Sacramento, CA 95605-2811
Ph:(916)375-4940
Fax:(916)375-4950
Co. E-mail: osdchelp@dgs.ca.gov
URL: http://www.pd.dgs.ca.gov/pd/Programs.aspx
Description: Offers technical assistance to small and minority business and promotes their procurement of government contracts for purchases, construction, and services.

48221 ■ Women's Initiative for Self-Employment
1398 Valencia St.
San Francisco, CA 94110
Ph:(415)641-3460
Fax:(415)826-1885
Co. E-mail: jabrams@womensinitiative.org
URL: http://www.womensinitiative.org
Contact: Julie Castro Abrams, CEO
Description: Provides business development services to women-owned businesses in the San Francisco area, with a focus on traditionally underserved groups including low-income and minority women. Maintains seven training sites.

FINANCING AND LOAN PROGRAMS

48222 ■ 5AM Ventures / 5AM Partners
2200 Sand Hill Rd., Ste. 110
Menlo Park, CA 94025
Ph:(650)233-8600
Fax:(650)233-8923
URL: http://www.5amventures.com
Contact: Mark S. Colella, Principal
Investment Policies: Seed and early stage. **Industry Preferences:** Biotechnology. **Geographic Preferences:** East and West Coast. **Principal Exhibits:**

48223 ■ 21st Century Internet Venture Partners
2 South Park, 2nd Fl.
San Francisco, CA 94107
Ph:(415)512-1221
Fax:(415)512-2650
URL: http://www.21vc.com
Contact: J. Neil Weintraut, General Partner
Preferred Investment Size: $3,000,000 minimum. **Investment Types:** Start-up and early stage. **Industry Preferences:** Internet specific, Computer software and services, communications and media, and consumer related. **Geographic Preferences:** U.S. and Canada. **Principal Exhibits:**

48224 ■ Aberdare Ventures
1 Embarcadero Ctr., Ste. 4000
San Francisco, CA 94111
Ph:(415)392-7442

Fax:(415)392-4264
URL: http://www.aberdare.com
Contact: Paul Klingenstein, Managing Partner
Preferred Investment Size: $1,000,000 to $7,000,000. **Investment Types:** Early stage. **Industry Preferences:** Healthcare technology, including biopharmaceutical products, medical devices, and related therapeutic technologies. **Geographic Preferences:** U.S. **Principal Exhibits:**

48225 ■ Acacia Venture Partners
7912 Radnor Rd., Ste. 700
Bethesda, MD 20817
Ph:(301)263-1071
Fax:(301)560-6540
Co. E-mail: jlaubach@acaciavp.com
URL: http://www.acaciavp.com
Contact: David Heer, Managing Director
Preferred Investment Size: $5,000,000 minimum. **Investment Policies:** Seed, start-up, first and second stage, leveraged buyout, and mezzanine. **Industry Preferences:** Internet specific, medical and health, computer software and services, industrial and energy, and communications and media. **Geographic Preferences:** U.S. **Principal Exhibits:**

48226 ■ Accel-KKR, LLC
2500 Sand Hill Rd., Ste. 300
Menlo Park, CA 94025
Ph:(650)289-2460
Fax:(650)289-2461
Co. E-mail: inquires@accel-kkr.com
URL: http://www.accel-kkr.com
Contact: Tom Barnds, Managing Director
Preferred Investment Size: $10,000,000 to $50,000,000. **Investment Types:** Later stage, leveraged buyout, generalist PE, recapitalization, acquisition, and management buyouts. **Industry Preferences:** Communications and media, Internet specific, computer related, and semiconductors and other electronics. **Geographic Preferences:** Canada. **Principal Exhibits:**

48227 ■ Accel Partners
428 University Ave.
Palo Alto, CA 94301
Ph:(650)614-4800
Fax:(650)614-4880
Co. E-mail: siliconvalley@accel.com
URL: http://www.accel.com
Contact: Jim Breyer, Managing Partner
Preferred Investment Size: $1,000,000 minimum. **Investment Policies:** Seed, start-up, and early stage. **Industry Preferences:** Internet specific, computer software and services, communications and media, semiconductors and other electronics, other products, medical and health, computer hardware, biotechnology, industrial and energy, and consumer related. **Geographic Preferences:** U.S. **Principal Exhibits:**

48228 ■ Acorn Campus
3 Results Way
Cupertino, CA 95014-5924
Ph:(408)777-8090
Fax:(408)777-8091
Co. E-mail: info@acorncampus.com
URL: http://www.acorncampus.com
Contact: Wu-fu Chen, Managing Member and Co-founder
Preferred Investment Size: $250,000 to $5,000,000. **Investment Policies:** Seed, start-up, and early stage. **Industry Preferences:** Communications, computer software, semiconductors and other electronics. **Geographic Preferences:** Northern California. **Principal Exhibits:**

48229 ■ Acorn Ventures, Inc.
2635 North First St., Ste. 148
San Jose, CA 95131
Ph:(510)459-6500
Fax:(925)249-1748
Co. E-mail: Partner@Acorn-Ventures.com
URL: http://www.acorn-ventures.com
Contact: Cliff Girard, Chief Executive Officer
Preferred Investment Size: $1,000,000 to $5,000,000. **Investment Types:** Seed, start-up, first, second, and third stage. **Industry Preferences:** Communications and media, Internet specific, com-

puter software and services, semiconductors and other electronics, other products, and computer hardware. **Geographic Preferences:** West Coast. **Principal Exhibits:**

48230 ■ Acuity Ventures LLC
1960 The Alameda, Ste. 200
San Jose, CA 95126-1441
Ph:(408)261-4286
Fax:(408)557-6555
URL: http://www.acuityventures.com
Contact: Eric Hardgrave, Managing Partner
E-mail: eric@acuityventures.com
Investment Policies: Early stage. **Industry Preferences:** Software. **Principal Exhibits:**

48231 ■ Advanced Technology Ventures (Palo Alto)
485 Ramona St.
Palo Alto, CA 94301
Ph:(650)321-8601
Fax:(650)321-0934
Co. E-mail: info@atvcapital.com
URL: http://www.atvcapital.com
Contact: Steve Baloff, General Partner
Preferred Investment Size: $15,000,000 to $35,000,000. **Investment Types:** Seed, first, and second stage, early and later stage, and balanced. **Industry Preferences:** Internet specific, computer software and services, computer hardware, semiconductors and other electronics, communications and media, medical and health, biotechnology, industrial and energy, consumer related, and other products. **Geographic Preferences:** U.S. and Canada. **Principal Exhibits:**

48232 ■ Advent International Corp. (New York)
375 Park Ave.
New York, NY 10152
Ph:(212)813-8300
Fax:(212)451-6503
Co. E-mail: news@adventinternational.com
URL: http://www.adventinternational.com
Contact: Chris Pike, Managing Director
Preferred Investment Size: $1,000,000 minimum. **Investment Types:** Seed, start-up, early, first, second, and later stage, control-block purchases, balanced, mezzanine, leveraged buyout, special situation, recapitalizations, research and development, public companies, industry rollups, generalist PE, and acquisitions. **Industry Preferences:** Communications and media, consumer related, Internet specific, industrial and energy, medical and health, computer software and services, computer hardware, semiconductors and other electronics, and biotechnology, and other products. **Geographic Preferences:** U.S and Canada. **Principal Exhibits:**

48233 ■ Agilent Ventures
395 Page Mill Rd.
Palo Alto, CA 94303-0870
Ph:(650)752-5000
Fax:(650)752-5772
Co. E-mail: agilent_ventures@agilent.com
URL: http://www.agilentventures.com
Contact: Maximilian Schroeck, Managing Director
Preferred Investment Size: $500,000 to $10,000,000. **Investment Types:** Start-up, early, first, and second stage. **Industry Preferences:** Communications and media, semiconductors and other electronics, biotechnology, medical and health, and industrial and energy. **Geographic Preferences:** U.S and Canada. **Principal Exhibits:**

48234 ■ Allegis Capital LLC / Media Technology Ventures
525 University Ave., Ste. 220
Palo Alto, CA 94301
Ph:(650)687-0500
Fax:(650)687-0234
Co. E-mail: vc@allegiscapital.com
URL: http://www.allegiscapital.com
Contact: Barry M. Weinman, Managing Director
Preferred Investment Size: $3,000,000 to $5,000,000. **Investment Policies:** Seed, start-up, early stage, and research and development. **Industry Preferences:** Internet specific, computer software and services, communications and media, semicon-

ductors and other electronics, computer hardware, and other products. **Geographic Preferences:** West Coast. **Principal Exhibits:**

48235 ■ Alloy Ventures, L.P.
400 Hamilton Ave., 4th Fl.
Palo Alto, CA 94301
Ph:(650)687-5000
Fax:(650)687-5010
Co. E-mail: info@alloyventures.com
URL: http://www.alloyventures.com
Contact: David Pidwell, Venture Partner
E-mail: pidwell@alloyventures.com
Investment Types: Start-up, seed, and early stage. **Industry Preferences:** Internet specific, computer software and services, medical and health, biotechnology, communications and media, semiconductors and other electronics, computer hardware, and industrial and energy. **Geographic Preferences:** U.S. **Principal Exhibits:**

48236 ■ Alpine Technology Ventures
20300 Stevens Creek Blvd., Ste. 495
Cupertino, CA 95014
Ph:(408)725-1810
Fax:(408)725-1207
URL: http://www.alpineventures.com
Contact: Chuck Chan, General Partner
Preferred Investment Size: $2,000,000 to $4,000,000. **Investment Types:** Seed, start-up, research and development, first and second stage. **Industry Preferences:** Internet specific, computer software and services, computer hardware, communications and media, semiconductors and other electronics, other products, industrial and energy. **Geographic Preferences:** California. **Principal Exhibits:**

48237 ■ Alta Partners
1 Embarcadero Ctr., 37th Fl.
San Francisco, CA 94111
Ph:(415)362-4022
Fax:(415)362-6178
Co. E-mail: alta@altapartners.com
URL: http://www.altapartners.com
Contact: Alison Kiley, Director
Preferred Investment Size: $2,000,000 to $15,000,000. **Investment Types:** Seed, start-up, first and second stage, early and later stage, mezzanine, and expansion. **Industry Preferences:** Internet specific, computer software and services, industrial and energy, consumer related, communications and media, medical and health, computer hardware, biotechnology, semiconductors and other electronics, and other products. **Geographic Preferences:** West Coast. **Principal Exhibits:**

48238 ■ Alto Tech Ventures LLC
1010 El Camino Real, Ste. 340
Menlo Park, CA 94025
Ph:(650)330-0881
Fax:(650)330-0881
Co. E-mail: info@altotechventures.com
URL: http://www.altotechventures.com
Contact: Gloria Wahl, General Partner
Investment Policies: Early stage. **Industry Preferences:** Communications, computer software, Internet specific, semiconductors and other electronics, and biotechnology. **Geographic Preferences:** U.S. **Principal Exhibits:**

48239 ■ Altos Ventures
2882 Sand Hill Rd., Ste. 100
Menlo Park, CA 94025
Ph:(650)234-9771
Fax:(650)233-9821
Co. E-mail: info@altosventures.com
URL: http://www.altosvc.com
Contact: Anthony Lee, Principal
Preferred Investment Size: $1,000,000 to $3,000,000. **Investment Types:** Start-up, seed, first, second, and later stage. **Industry Preferences:** Internet specific, computer software and services, other products, consumer related, communications and media. **Geographic Preferences:** Northern California and West Coast. **Principal Exhibits:**

48240 ■ American River Ventures
2270 Douglas Blvd., Ste. 212
Roseville, CA 95661
Ph:(916)780-2828
Fax:(916)780-5443
Co. E-mail: info@arventures.com
URL: http://www.arventures.com
Contact: Dr. Barbara Grant, Managing Director
Preferred Investment Size: $500,000 to $2,000,000.
Investment Policies: Start-up, seed, early, first and second stage. **Industry Preferences:** Communications, computer software and hardware, Internet specific, semiconductors and other electronics, and business service. **Geographic Preferences:** Arizona, California, Colorado, Idaho, Nevada, New Mexico, Oregon, Utah, Washington, and West Coast. **Principal Exhibits:** Dr.

48241 ■ Amgen Inc.
1 Amgen Ctr. Dr.
Thousand Oaks, CA 91320-1799
Ph:(805)447-1000
Fax:(805)447-1010
Co. E-mail: amgenventures@amgen.com
URL: http://www.amgen.com
Contact: Kevin Sharer, Chief Executive Officer
Preferred Investment Size: $1,000,000 to $3,000,000. **Investment Policies:** Early stage. **Industry Preferences:** Biotechnology. **Geographic Preferences:** U.S. **Principal Exhibits:**

48242 ■ Amidzad, LLC
370 Convention Way, 3rd Fl.
Redwood City, CA 94063
Ph:(650)678-0123
Fax:(650)323-4044
URL: http://www.amidzad.com
Contact: Pejman Nozad, General Partner
E-mail: pejman@amidzad.com
Investment Policies: Seed and early stage. **Industry Preferences:** Technology and life sciences. **Geographic Preferences:** West Coast. **Principal Exhibits:**

48243 ■ Anthem Venture Partners
225 Arizona Ave., Ste. 200
Santa Monica, CA 90401
Ph:(310)899-6225
Fax:(310)899-6234
Co. E-mail: info@anthemvp.com
URL: http://www.anthemvp.com
Contact: William Woodward, Managing Director
Preferred Investment Size: $500,000 to $400,000,000. **Investment Policies:** Early and later stage. **Industry Preferences:** Communications and media, Internet specific, computer hardware, consumer related, business services, computer software and services, semiconductors and other electronics, other products. **Geographic Preferences:** California. **Principal Exhibits:**

48244 ■ Applied Materials Ventures
1142 Crane St., Ste. 4
Menlo Park, CA 94025
Ph:(650)833-0400
Co. E-mail: info@appliedvc.com
Contact: Julien Nguyen, Managing Partner
Investment Policies: Seed and early stage. **Industry Preferences:** Communications.

48245 ■ Asset Management Company Venture Capital
2100 Geng Rd., Ste. 200
Palo Alto, CA 94303
Ph:(650)494-7400
Fax:(650)856-1826
URL: http://www.assetman.com
Contact: Bennett S. Dubin, Managing Partner
Preferred Investment Size: $500,000 to $2,000,000.
Investment Types: Seed, start-up, early and first stage. **Industry Preferences:** Computer software and services, medical and health, biotechnology, computer hardware, semiconductors and other electronics, Internet specific, communications and media, consumer related, industrial and energy, and other products. **Geographic Preferences:** West Coast. **Principal Exhibits:**

48246 ■ Athena Technology Ventures
100 Hamilton Ave., Ste. 225
Palo Alto, CA 94301
Ph:(650)470-0370
Fax:(650)470-0378
Co. E-mail: info@athenatv.com
URL: http://www.athenatv.com
Contact: Perry Ha, Managing Director
Investment Types: Seed, start-up, early, and first stage. **Industry Preferences:** Internet specific, communications and media, computer software and services, computer hardware, semiconductors and other electronics, and consumer related. **Geographic Preferences:** West Coast. **Principal Exhibits:**

48247 ■ August Capital
2480 Sand Hill Rd., Ste. 101
Menlo Park, CA 94025
Ph:(650)234-9900
Fax:(650)234-9910
URL: http://www.augustcap.com
Contact: Andrew Rappaport, General Partner
Investment Types: Start-up, seed, first stage, early stage, and special situation. **Industry Preferences:** Internet specific, computer software, and services, communications and media, computer hardware, semiconductors and other electronics. **Geographic Preferences:** Northwest, Southwest, Rocky mountains, and West Coast. **Principal Exhibits:**

48248 ■ AVI Capital LP
100 Hamilton Ave., Ste. 250
Palo Alto, CA 94301
Ph:(650)687-0235
Fax:(650)687-0234
URL: http://www.avicapital.com
Contact: Brian J. Grossi, General Partner
E-mail: grossi@avicapital.com
Preferred Investment Size: $1,000,000 to $2,000,000. **Investment Types:** Seed, start-up, first and second stage, and special situation. **Industry Preferences:** Computer software, hardware, and services Internet specific, communications and media, semiconductors and other electronics, industrial and energy, and medical and health. **Geographic Preferences:** West Coast. **Principal Exhibits:**

48249 ■ Band of Angels
535 Middlefield Rd., Ste. 190
Menlo Park, CA 94025
Ph:(650)321-0854
Fax:(650)321-1968
Co. E-mail: contact@bandangels.com
URL: http://www.bandangels.com
Contact: Ian Patrick Sobieski, Managing Director
Preferred Investment Size: $300,000 to $860,000.
Investment Policies: Seed, early stage, and balanced. **Industry Preferences:** Communications, computer software, semiconductors and other electronics, biotechnology, industrial and energy. **Geographic Preferences:** California. **Principal Exhibits:**

48250 ■ Barrington Partners
77 Franklin St., Ste. 802
Boston, MA 02110
Ph:(617)482-3300
Fax:(617)482-3325
URL: http://www.barringtonpartners.com
Contact: James Baker, General Partner
Investment Policies: Seed and early stage. **Industry Preferences:** Internet specific, other products, communications and media. **Principal Exhibits:**

48251 ■ Bay Partners
490 S. California Ave., Ste. 200
Palo Alto, CA 94306
Ph:(650)854-1500
Fax:(650)854-1515
Co. E-mail: partners@baypartners.com
URL: http://www.baypartners.com
Contact: Neal Dempsey, Managing General Partner
E-mail: neal@baypartners.com
Preferred Investment Size: $250,000. **Investment Types:** Seed, start-up and early stage. **Industry Preferences:** Communications and media, Internet specific, computer software and services, computer hardware, semiconductors and other electronics,

consumer related, medical and health, and biotechnology. **Geographic Preferences:** West Coast and Canada. **Principal Exhibits:**

48252 ■ Benchmark Capital
2480 Sand Hill Rd., Ste. 200
Menlo Park, CA 94025
Ph:(650)854-8180
Fax:(650)854-8183
URL: http://www.benchmark.com
Contact: Alex Balkanski, General Partner
E-mail: abalkanski@benchmark.com
Preferred Investment Size: $100,000 to $15,000,000. **Investment Types:** Seed, early stage, research and development, start-up, first and second stage, expansion, leveraged buyout, research and development, and special situation. **Industry Preferences:** Internet specific, communications and media, computer software and services, computer hardware, industrial and energy, semiconductors and other electronics, and consumer related. **Geographic Preferences:** Southwest and West Coast. **Principal Exhibits:**

48253 ■ Berkeley International Capital Corp.
650 California St., 26th Fl.
San Francisco, CA 94108-2607
Ph:(415)249-0450
Co. E-mail: info@berkeleyvc.com
URL: http://www.berkeleyvc.com
Contact: Halsted W. Wheeler, Principal
Preferred Investment Size: $1,000,000 to $50,000,000. **Investment Types:** Second and later stage, mezzanine, leveraged buyout, and special situation. **Industry Preferences:** Semiconductors and other electronics, communications and media, computer software and services, computer hardware, biotechnology, medical and health, other products, Internet specific, industrial and energy. **Geographic Preferences:** U.S. **Principal Exhibits:**

48254 ■ Bessemer Venture Partners (Menlo Park)
535 Middlefield Rd., Ste. 245
Menlo Park, CA 94025
Ph:(650)853-7000
Fax:(650)853-7001
URL: http://www.bessemervp.com
Contact: David Cowan, Partner
Preferred Investment Size: $1,000,000 to $10,000,000. **Investment Types:** Seed, research and development, startup, first, early and second stage, leveraged buyout, special situation, control-block purchases, and expansion. **Industry Preferences:** Communications and media, Internet specific, computer software and services, semiconductors and other electronics, consumer related, medical and health, industrial and energy, and biotechnology, computer hardware, and other products. **Geographic Preferences:** U.S. **Principal Exhibits:**

48255 ■ Blueprint Ventures
The Embaracadero
Pier 33 South, Ste. 201
San Francisco, CA 94111
Ph:(415)901-4000
Fax:(415)901-4035
URL: http://www.blueprintventures.com
Contact: Bart Schachter, Managing Director
E-mail: bart@blueprintventures.com
Preferred Investment Size: $500,000 to $3,000,000.
Investment Types: Seed, Early, first and second stage. **Industry Preferences:** Communications and media, computer related, and semiconductors and other electronics. **Geographic Preferences:** West Coast. **Principal Exhibits:**

48256 ■ Blumberg Capital Ventures
580 Howard St., Ste. 101
San Francisco, CA 94105
Ph:(415)905-5000
Fax:(415)357-5027
Co. E-mail: info@blumbergcapital.com
URL: http://www.blumbergcapital.com
Contact: David J. Blumberg, Managing Partner
Preferred Investment Size: $500,000 to $3,000,000.
Investment Policies: Seed, early and first stage. **Industry Preferences:** Communications, computer software, and Internet specific. **Geographic Preferences:** U.S. **Principal Exhibits:**

48257 ■ Brentwood Venture Capital
11150 Santa Monica Blvd., Ste. 1200
Los Angeles, CA 90025
Ph:(310)477-7678
Fax:(310)312-1868
URL: http://www.brentwoodvc.com
Contact: Brian Atwood, General Partner
Investment Policies: Seed, start-up, and second stage. **Industry Preferences:** Communications and media, computer software, Internet specific, biotechnology, and medical and health. **Geographic Preferences:** West Coast. **Principal Exhibits:**

48258 ■ Burrill & Company
1 Embarcadero Ctr., Ste. 2700
San Francisco, CA 94111-3776
Ph:(415)591-5400
Fax:(415)591-5401
Co. E-mail: burrill@b-c.com
URL: http://www.burrillandco.com
Contact: Ann F. Hanham, Managing Director
Preferred Investment Size: $5,000,000 to $15,000,000. **Investment Types:** Seed, early, first and second stage, and mezzanine. **Industry Preferences:** Biotechnology, medical and health, Internet specific, computer software and services, and consumer related. **Geographic Preferences:** U.S. and Canada. **Principal Exhibits:**

48259 ■ BV Capital / Bertelsmann Ventures, LP (San Francisco)
600 Montgomery St., 43rd Fl.
San Francisco, CA 94111
Ph:(415)869-5200
Fax:(415)869-5200
Co. E-mail: info@bvcapital.biz
URL: http://www.bvcapital.com
Contact: Jan Henric Buettner, Partner
E-mail: jan@bvcapital.com
Preferred Investment Size: $1,000,000 to $5,000,000. **Investment Types:** Early, first and second stage, and expansion. **Industry Preferences:** Communications and media, computer software and services, and Internet specific. **Geographic Preferences:** West Coast. **Principal Exhibits:**

48260 ■ California Technology Ventures, LLC
670 N. Rosemead Blvd., Ste. 201
Pasadena, CA 91107
Ph:(626)351-3700
Fax:(626)351-3702
Co. E-mail: info@ctventures.com
URL: http://www.ctventures.com
Contact: Alexander B. Suh, Managing Director
E-mail: asuh@CTVentures.com
Preferred Investment Size: $250,000 to $2,000,000. **Investment Policies:** Early, first, second and later stage. **Industry Preferences:** Communications, computer software and hardware, Internet specific, semiconductors and other electronics, biotechnology, medical and health, and industrial and energy. **Geographic Preferences:** California, Northern California, and Southern California. **Principal Exhibits:**

48261 ■ The Cambria Group
2055 Woodside Rd., Ste. 195
Redwood City, CA 94061
Ph:(650)241-6400
Fax:(650)241-6401
URL: http://www.cambriagroup.com
Contact: Christopher Sekula, Principal
Preferred Investment Size: $5,000,000 to $25,000,000. **Investment Types:** Second stage, mezzanine, leveraged buyout, special situation, recapitalization and control-block purchases. **Industry Preferences:** Communications and media, semiconductors and other electronics, medical and health, consumer related, industrial and energy, transportation, business service, manufacturing, agriculture, forestry and fishing. **Geographic Preferences:** U.S. **Principal Exhibits:**

48262 ■ Cambrian Ventures, Inc.
444 Castro St., Ste. 109
Mountain View, CA 94041
Ph:(650)938-5900

Fax:(650)938-5959
Co. E-mail: info@cambrianventures.com
URL: http://www.cambrianventures.com
Contact: Anand Rajaraman, Founding Partner
Investment Types: Seed and early stage. **Industry Preferences:** Internet specific. **Geographic Preferences:** U.S. **Principal Exhibits:**

48263 ■ CampVentures
280 2nd St., Ste. 280
Los Altos, CA 94022
Ph:(650)949-0804
Fax:(650)618-1719
URL: http://www.campventures.com
Contact: Jerome Camp, Managing General Partner
E-mail: jerry@campventures.com
Preferred Investment Size: $500,000 to $1,500,000. **Investment Policies:** Seed and early stage. **Industry Preferences:** Communications and media, computer software, and semiconductors and other electronics. **Geographic Preferences:** California. **Principal Exhibits:**

48264 ■ Canaan Partners (Menlo Park)
2765 Sand Hill Rd.
Menlo Park, CA 94025
Ph:(650)854-8092
Fax:(650)854-8127
URL: http://www.canaan.com
Contact: Brent Ahrens, General Partner
Preferred Investment Size: $3,000,000 to $25,000,000. **Investment Types:** Early stage, first stage, and expansion. **Industry Preferences:** Internet specific, computer software and services, computer hardware, medical and health, communications and media, biotechnology, semiconductors and other electronics, consumer related, and industrial and energy. **Geographic Preferences:** Northeast, West Coast, and U.S. **Principal Exhibits:**

48265 ■ Charter Life Sciences
2031 Mission College Blvd., Ste. 210
Santa Clara, CA 94054
Ph:(408)758-4700
Fax:(408)758-4848
URL: http://www.charterls.com
Contact: Andrew K. Klatt, Chief Financial Officer
Preferred Investment Size: $1,000,000 to $5,000,000. **Investment Policies:** Early stage. **Industry Preferences:** Biotechnology, and medical and health. **Geographic Preferences:** Midwest and West Coast. **Principal Exhibits:**

48266 ■ Charter Venture Capital / Charter Ventures
525 University Ave., Ste. 1400
Palo Alto, CA 94301
Ph:(650)325-6953
Fax:(650)325-4762
URL: http://www.charterventures.com
Contact: Bob Kondamoori, Venture Partner
Preferred Investment Size: $500,000 to $10,000,000. **Investment Policies:** Early stage. **Industry Preferences:** Internet specific, biotechnology, medical and health, computer software and services, communications and media, computer hardware, semiconductors and other electronics, other products, and other products. **Geographic Preferences:** U.S. **Principal Exhibits:**

48267 ■ Clearstone Venture Partners / Idealab! Capital Partners
1351 4th St., 4th Fl.
Santa Monica, CA 90401
Ph:(310)460-7900
Fax:(310)460-7901
Co. E-mail: info@clearstone.com
URL: http://www.clearstone.com
Contact: Erik Lassila, Managing Director
Preferred Investment Size: $2,000,000 to $10,000,000. **Investment Types:** Early Stage. **Industry Preferences:** Internet specific, computer software and services, computer hardware, communications and media, industrial and energy, semiconductors and other electronics, and other products. **Geographic Preferences:** Northern and Southern California, California, and West Coast. **Principal Exhibits:**

48268 ■ CMEA Capital / Chemicals & Materials Enterprise Association
1750 Montgomery St.
San Francisco, CA 94111
Ph:(415)352-1520
Fax:(415)352-1524
URL: http://www.cmeaventures.com
Contact: Thomas R. Baruch, Founder and Managing Director
E-mail: tom@cmeaventures.com
Preferred Investment Size: $250,000 to $10,000,000. **Investment Types:** Early, start-up, first, second, and later stage, balanced, and mezzanine. **Industry Preferences:** Medical and health, biotechnology, communications and media, computer software and services, semiconductors and other electronics, Internet specific, industrial and energy, computer hardware, other products. **Geographic Preferences:** Northwest and West Coast. **Principal Exhibits:**

48269 ■ Compass Technology Partners, L.P.
261 Hamilton Ave., Ste. 200
Palo Alto, CA 94301
Ph:(650)322-7595
Fax:(650)322-0588
URL: http://www.compasstechpartners.com
Contact: David G. Arscott, Partner
Preferred Investment Size: $250,000 to $1,250,000. **Investment Types:** Early stage, seed, start-up, first stage, private placement, public companies, and expansion. **Industry Preferences:** Internet specific, medical and health, communications and media, semiconductors and other electronics, computer software and services. **Geographic Preferences:** California and U.S. **Principal Exhibits:**

48270 ■ Convergence Partners
800 W. El Camino Real, Ste. 180
Mountain View, CA 94040
Ph:(650)854-3010
Fax:(650)462-8415
Co. E-mail: info@convergencepartners.com
URL: http://www.convergencepartners.com
Contact: Eric DiBenedetto, Founder and General Partner
Preferred Investment Size: $2,000,000 to $10,000,000. **Investment Types:** Seed, early and first stage. **Industry Preferences:** Internet specific, computer software and services, semiconductors and other electronics, computer hardware, other products, industrial and energy, communications and media. **Geographic Preferences:** U.S. **Principal Exhibits:**

48271 ■ Crocker Capital
1 Post St., Ste. 2515
San Francisco, CA 94104
Ph:(415)956-5250
Fax:(415)956-5710
Co. E-mail: info@crocker-capital.com
URL: http://www.crocker-capital.com
Contact: Charles Crocker, Chairman and CEO
Investment Types: Start-up, second stage, and leveraged buyout. **Industry Preferences:** Communications and media, semiconductors and other electronics, medical and health, consumer related, industrial and energy, manufacturing, and environment. **Geographic Preferences:** West Coast. **Principal Exhibits:**

48272 ■ Crosslink Capital
2 Embarcadero Ctr., Ste. 2200
San Francisco, CA 94111
Ph:(415)617-1800
Fax:(415)617-1801
Co. E-mail: info@crosslinkcapital.com
URL: http://www.crosslinkcapital.com
Contact: Michael Stark, General Partner and Founder
E-mail: mis@crosslinkcapital.com
Preferred Investment Size: $8,000,000 to $20,000,000. **Investment Types:** Seed, early, first, second, and later stage, mezzanine, leveraged buyout, private placement, balanced, and expansion. **Industry Preferences:** Internet specific, computer software and services, semiconductors and other electronics, communications and media, biotechnology, computer hardware, other products, consumer

related, medical and health, industrial and energy. **Geographic Preferences:** California and U.S. **Principal Exhibits:**

48273 ■ De Novo Ventures
2180 Sand Hill Rd., Ste. 200
Menlo Park, CA 94025
Ph:(650)329-1999
Fax:(650)329-1315
URL: http://www.denovovc.com
Contact: Frederick Dotzler, Managing Director
Preferred Investment Size: $1,000,000 to $3,000,000. **Investment Types:** Start-up, seed, first and early stage, and expansion. **Industry Preferences:** Internet specific, biotechnology, and medical and health. **Geographic Preferences:** Northwest, Rocky Mountains, Southwest, and West Coast. **Principal Exhibits:**

48274 ■ Defta Partners
111 Pine St., Ste. 1410
San Francisco, CA 94111-5616
Ph:(415)433-2262
Fax:(415)433-2264
URL: http://www.defta-partners.com
Contact: Masa Isono, Principal
Preferred Investment Size: $500,000 to $3,000,000. **Investment Policies:** Start-up, seed, and early stage. **Industry Preferences:** computer software and services, semiconductors and other electronics, Internet specific, communications and media, medical and health, and computer hardware. **Geographic Preferences:** National. **Principal Exhibits:**

48275 ■ Delphi Ventures
3000 Sand Hill Rd.
Bldg. 1, Ste. 135
Menlo Park, CA 94025
Ph:(650)854-9650
Fax:(650)854-2961
URL: http://www.delphiventures.com
Contact: David L. Douglass, General Partner
Preferred Investment Size: $500,000 to $12,000,000. **Investment Types:** Seed, start-up, first and second stage, early stage, expansion, and balanced. **Industry Preferences:** Medical and health, and biotechnology. **Geographic Preferences:** U.S. **Principal Exhibits:**

48276 ■ DFJ Frontier
800 Anacapa St., Ste. A
Santa Barbara, CA 93101
Ph:(805)963-2277
Co. E-mail: businessplan@dfjfrontier.com
URL: http://www.dfjfrontier.com
Contact: David Cremin, Managing Director
E-mail: david@dfjfrontier.com
Preferred Investment Size: $100,000 to $1,000,000. **Investment Policies:** Seed and early stage. **Industry Preferences:** Communications and media, computer software, Internet specific, semiconductors and other electronics, biotechnology, consumer related, industrial and energy, financial services, agriculture, forestry and fishing. **Geographic Preferences:** California. **Principal Exhibits:**

48277 ■ Diamondhead Ventures, L.P.
c/o Onset Ventures
2400 Sand Hill Rd.
Menlo Park, CA 94025
Ph:(650)529-0700
Fax:(650)529-0777
URL: http://www.dhven.com
Contact: Raman Khanna, Founding Managing Director
Preferred Investment Size: $500,000 to $5,000,000. **Investment Types:** Seed, start-up, early, first and second stage. **Industry Preferences:** Communications and media, computer software, Internet specific, semiconductors and other electronics. **Geographic Preferences:** Northern California and West Coast. **Principal Exhibits:**

48278 ■ Doll Capital Management
2420 Sand Hill Rd., Ste. 200
Menlo Park, CA 94025
Ph:(650)233-1400

Fax:(650)854-9159
URL: http://www.dcmvc.com
Contact: Ruby Lu, Principal
E-mail: rlu@dcm.com
Preferred Investment Size: $3,000,000 to $15,000,000. **Investment Types:** Seed, early, first, second and later stage, and mezzanine. **Industry Preferences:** Internet specific, computer software and services, communications and media, semiconductors and other electronics, computer hardware, other products, and consumer related. **Geographic Preferences:** Midwestern states of Minnesota, Ohio, Iowa, Wisconsin, Michigan, Indiana, Illinois, and Missouri. **Principal Exhibits:**

48279 ■ Dominion Ventures, Inc.
1646 N. California Blvd., Ste. 230
Walnut Creek, CA 94596
Ph:(925)280-6300
Fax:(925)280-6338
Co. E-mail: info@dominion.com
URL: http://www.dominion.com
Contact: Brian Smith, General Partner
E-mail: bsmith@dominion.com
Preferred Investment Size: $2,000,000 to $4,000,000. **Investment Types:** Start-up, first, second, and later stage. **Industry Preferences:** Internet specific, computer software and services, computer hardware, other products, medical and health, semiconductors and other electronics, communications and media, consumer related, biotechnology, industrial and energy. **Geographic Preferences:** U.S. **Principal Exhibits:**

48280 ■ Dorset Capital
343 Sansome St., Ste. 1210
San Francisco, CA 94104
Ph:(415)398-7101
Fax:(415)398-7141
URL: http://www.dorsetcapital.com
Contact: John Berg, Managing Partner
Preferred Investment Size: $5,000,000 to $30,000,000. **Investment Types:** First, second and later stage, expansion, generalist PE, leveraged buy-out, management buyouts, and recapitalizations. **Industry Preferences:** Consumer related, financial services, business service, and manufacturing. **Geographic Preferences:** U.S. **Principal Exhibits:**

48281 ■ Dot Edu Ventures
514 Bryant St., Ste. 101
Palo Alto, CA 94301
Ph:(650)321-3804
Fax:(650)321-3808
Co. E-mail: priya@doteduventures.com
URL: http://www.doteduventures.com
Contact: Asha Jadeja, Founder and Managing Partner
Investment Types: Early stage and seed. **Industry Preferences:** Internet specific. **Geographic Preferences:** U.S. **Principal Exhibits:**

48282 ■ Draper, Fisher, Jurvetson / Draper Associates
2882 Sand Hill Rd., Ste. 150
Menlo Park, CA 94025
Ph:(650)233-9000
Fax:(650)233-9233
Co. E-mail: mail@dfj.com
URL: http://www.dfj.com
Contact: Jennifer Fonstad, Managing Director
Preferred Investment Size: $500,000 to $20,000,000. **Investment Types:** Seed, early, start-up, first and second stage, balanced, and expansion. **Industry Preferences:** Computer software and services, communications and media, semiconductors and other electronics, industrial and energy, consumer related, medical and health, Internet specific, computer hardware, other products, and biotechnology. **Geographic Preferences:** Northeast U.S. and Canada. **Principal Exhibits:**

48283 ■ Draper International
50 California St., Ste. 2925
San Francisco, CA 94111-4779
Ph:(415)616-4050

Fax:(415)616-4060
URL: http://www.draperintl.com
Contact: William Draper, Managing Director
Preferred Investment Size: $250,000 to $1,000,000. **Investment Types:** Early and first stage. **Industry Preferences:** Internet specific, computer hardware, computer software and services, consumer related, communications and media. **Geographic Preferences:** Mid Atlantic, Northeast, Northwest, Southeast and West Coast. **Principal Exhibits:**

48284 ■ Draper Richards L.P.
50 California St., Ste. 2925
San Francisco, CA 94111
Ph:(415)616-4050
Fax:(415)616-4060
URL: http://www.draperrichards.com
Contact: William H. Draper III, General Partner
E-mail: bill@draperrichards.com
Investment Types: Early, first and second stage. **Industry Preferences:** Internet specific, computer software and services, communications and media, consumer related, semiconductors and other electronics, biotechnology, and other products. **Geographic Preferences:** Mid Atlantic, Northeast, Northern California, and West Coast. **Principal Exhibits:**

48285 ■ DynaFund Ventures
21515 Hawthorne Blvd., Ste. 700
Torrance, CA 90503
Ph:(310)543-5477
Fax:(310)543-8733
Co. E-mail: cgray@dynafundventures.com
URL: http://www.dynafundventures.com
Contact: Tony Hung, General Partner
Preferred Investment Size: $1,000,000 to $5,000,000. **Investment Types:** Early, first and second stage. **Industry Preferences:** Semiconductors and other electronics, communications and media, Internet specific, computer software and services, computer hardware, and biotechnology. **Geographic Preferences:** U.S. **Principal Exhibits:**

48286 ■ E*Capital Corporation
1000 Wilshire Blvd., Ste. 830
Los Angeles, CA 90017
Ph:(213)688-8080
Fax:(213)688-8095
URL: http://www.e-cap.com
Contact: Eric Wedbush, Managing Director
Preferred Investment Size: $2,000,000 to $10,000,000. **Investment Types:** Expansion, acquisition, recapitalizations, and management buyouts. **Industry Preferences:** Business and financial services, consumer products and services, and niche manufacturing. **Geographic Preferences:** Western U.S. **Principal Exhibits:**

48287 ■ Ecompanies
2120 Colorado Ave., 3rd Fl.
Santa Monica, CA 90404
Ph:(310)586-4000
Fax:(310)586-4425
URL: http://www.ecompanies.com
Contact: Steve Ledger, Managing General Partner
Investment Types: Early stage. **Industry Preferences:** Internet specific, computer software and services, industrial and energy, and other products. **Principal Exhibits:**

48288 ■ El Dorado Ventures
2440 Sand Hill Rd., Ste. 200
Menlo Park, CA 94025
Ph:(650)854-1200
Fax:(650)854-1202
Co. E-mail: bizplans@eldorado.com
URL: http://www.eldoradoventures.com
Contact: Ray Schuder, Principal
Preferred Investment Size: $250,000 to $1,000,000. **Investment Types:** Seed, start-up, first and early stage. **Industry Preferences:** Internet specific, computer software and services, computer hardware, communications and media, semiconductors and other electronics, medical and health, other products, consumer related, and biotechnology. **Geographic Preferences:** West Coast. **Principal Exhibits:**

48289 ■ Electronics for Imaging / EFI
303 Velocity Way
Foster City, CA 94404
Ph:(650)357-3500
Fax:(650)357-3907
URL: http://www.efi.com
Contact: Guy Gecht, Chief Executive Officer
Investment Types: Early stage. **Principal Exhibits:**

48290 ■ Emergence Capital Partners, L.L.C.
160 Bovet Rd., Ste. 300
San Mateo, CA 94402
Ph:(650)573-3100
Fax:(650)573-3119
Co. E-mail: info@emcap.com
URL: http://www.emergencecap.com
Contact: Kevin Spain, Principal
Preferred Investment Size: $1,000,000 to $10,000,000. **Investment Policies:** Start-up, seed, early stage, and expansion. **Industry Preferences:** Computer software, Internet specific, consumer related, financial services, and business service. **Geographic Preferences:** U.S. **Principal Exhibits:**

48291 ■ Enterprise Partners Venture Capital / EPVC
2223 Avenida de la Playa, Ste. 300
La Jolla, CA 92037-3218
Ph:(858)731-0300
Fax:(858)731-0235
URL: http://www.epvc.com
Contact: Bob Conn, Managing Director
Preferred Investment Size: $3,000,000 to $10,000,000. **Investment Types:** Seed, early and later stage, and acquisition. **Industry Preferences:** Communications and media, computer software and services, Internet specific, computer hardware, other products, medical and health, biotechnology, semiconductors and other electronics, consumer related, industrial and energy. **Geographic Preferences:** Southern California and Southwest. **Principal Exhibits:**

48292 ■ Falcon Fund
100 N. Barranca St., Ste., 920
West Covina, CA 91791
Ph:(626)966-6235
Fax:(626)966-0193
URL: http://www.falconfund.com
Contact: Edward Tuck, Principal
Investment Policies: Seed and early stage. **Industry Preferences:** Communications, computer software, and transportation. **Principal Exhibits:**

48293 ■ Far East Capital Corp.
2 California Plz.
350 S. Grand Ave., Lobby Level
Los Angeles, CA 90071
Ph:(213)687-1260
Fax:(213)626-3884
Co. E-mail: free@fareastnationalbank.com
URL: http://www.fareastnationalbank.com
Contact: Fredrick C. Copeland, Chairman, Chief
   Executive Officer and Pr
Preferred Investment Size: $100,000 to $300,000. **Investment Types:** First and second stage, mezzanine, and special situation. **Industry Preferences:** Communications and media, computer software and hardware, Internet specific, semiconductors and other electronics, medical and health. **Geographic Preferences:** West coast. **Principal Exhibits:**

48294 ■ Finaventures
3340 Ocean Park Blvd., Ste. 1050
Santa Monica, CA 90405
Ph:(310)399-5011
Fax:(310)452-5492
Co. E-mail: contact@finaventures.com
URL: http://www.finaventures.com
Contact: Rachid Sefrioui, Managing Director
Preferred Investment Size: $500,000 to $3,000,000. **Investment Policies:** Early, first, and second stage, balanced, and expansion. **Industry Preferences:** Communications, computer software, and semiconductors and other electronics. **Geographic Preferences:** Northern and Southern California. **Principal Exhibits:**

48295 ■ Flywheel Ventures
341 E. Alameda St.
Santa Fe, NM 87501-2229
Ph:800-750-7870
Fax:800-750-7870
URL: http://www.flywheelventures.com
Contact: Trevor R. Loy, General Partner
E-mail: trevor@flywheelventures.com
Preferred Investment Size: $100,000 to $1,000,000. **Investment Policies:** Seed and early stage. **Industry Preferences:** Communications, computer software, and semiconductors and other electronics. **Geographic Preferences:** New Mexico, Rocky Mountains, and West Coast. **Principal Exhibits:**

48296 ■ Forrest, Binkley & Brown
19800 MacArthur Blvd., Ste. 690
Irvine, CA 92612
Ph:(949)222-1987
Fax:(949)222-1988
Co. E-mail: fbb@fbbvc.com
URL: http://www.fbbvc.com
Contact: Ashish Kaul, Principal
Investment Policies: $2,000,000 to $4,000,000. **Investment Types:** Later stage, expansion, acquisition, generalist PE, leveraged buyout, and management buyouts. **Industry Preferences:** Computer software and services, Internet specific, semiconductors and other electronics, biotechnology, communications and media, other products, computer hardware, medical and health, and consumer related. **Geographic Preferences:** California. **Principal Exhibits:**

48297 ■ Forward Ventures
9393 Towne Centre Dr., Ste. 200
San Diego, CA 92121
Ph:(858)677-6077
Fax:(858)452-8799
Co. E-mail: info@forwardventures.com
URL: http://www.forwardventure.com
Contact: Ivor Royston, Founding Managing Partner
Preferred Investment Size: $1,000,000 to $6,000,000. **Investment Types:** Seed, first and second stage, early and later stage. **Industry Preferences:** Biotechnology, medical and health, and Internet specific. **Geographic Preferences:** U.S. and Canada. **Principal Exhibits:**

48298 ■ Foundation Capital
250 Middlefield Rd.
Menlo Park, CA 94025
Ph:(650)614-0500
Fax:(650)614-0505
Co. E-mail: info@foundationcapital.com
URL: http://www.foundationcapital.com
Contact: Adam Grosser, General Partner
E-mail: agrosser@foundationcapital.com
Preferred Investment Size: $1,000,000 to $10,000,000. **Investment Types:** Start-up, seed, first and second stage, early stage, research and development, and balanced. **Industry Preferences:** Internet specific, communications and media, computer software and services, computer hardware, semiconductors and other electronics, industrial and energy, other products, industrial and energy, medical and health, and consumer related. **Geographic Preferences:** West Coast. **Principal Exhibits:**

48299 ■ Gabriel Venture Partners
350 Marine Pky., Ste. 200
Redwood Shores, CA 94065
Ph:(650)551-5000
Fax:(650)551-5001
Co. E-mail: info@GabrielVP.com
URL: http://www.gabrielvp.com
Contact: Rick Bolander, Managing Director
Preferred Investment Size: $500,000 to $10,000,000. **Investment Types:** Seed, early and first stage. **Industry Preferences:** Internet specific, computer software and services, communications and media, computer hardware, semiconductors and other electronics, medical and health. **Geographic Preferences:** California, Mid Atlantic, Northeast, Northern California, and West Coast. **Principal Exhibits:**

48300 ■ Garage Technology Ventures / Garage.com
502 Waverly St., Ste. 300
Palo Alto, CA 94301
Ph:(650)838-0811
Fax:(650)838-0813
URL: http://www.garage.com
Contact: Bill Reichert, Managing Director
E-mail: reichert@garage.com
Preferred Investment Size: $500,000 to $3,000,000. **Investment Policies:** Seed, early, first and second stage. **Industry Preferences:** Communications, computer software, Internet specific, and semiconductors and other electronics. **Geographic Preferences:** California and West Coast. **Principal Exhibits:**

48301 ■ Glynn Capital Management
3000 Sand Hill Rd.
Bldg. 4, Ste. 230
Menlo Park, CA 94025
Ph:(650)854-2215
Fax:(650)854-8083
URL: http://www.glynncapital.com
Contact: Steven J. Rosston, Managing Director
Preferred Investment Size: $300,000 to 500,000. **Investment Types:** Start-up, first and second stage, leveraged buyout, and mezzanine. **Industry Preferences:** Internet specific, communications and media, medical and health, computer software and services. **Geographic Preferences:** Northeast, Northwest, Southeast and West Coast. **Principal Exhibits:**

48302 ■ Greylock Partners (San Mateo)
2550 Sand Hill Rd., Ste. 200
San Mateo, CA 94025
Ph:(650)493-5525
Fax:(650)493-5575
URL: http://www.greylock.com
Contact: Isaac Fehrenbach, Principal
E-mail: isaac@greylock.com
Preferred Investment Size: $250,000 minimum. **Investment Types:** Seed, start-up, early and first stage, and expansion. **Industry Preferences:** Internet specific, computer hardware, computer software and services, communications and media, semiconductors and other electronics, consumer related, and other products. **Geographic Preferences:** U.S. **Principal Exhibits:**

48303 ■ GRP Partners / Global Retail Partners
2121 Avenue of the Stars, Ste. 1630
Los Angeles, CA 90067
Ph:(310)785-5100
Fax:(310)785-5111
Co. E-mail: la@grpvc.com
URL: http://www.grpvc.com
Contact: Steven Dietz, Managing Partner
Preferred Investment Size: $3,000,000 to $25,000,000. **Investment Types:** First and second stage, early and later stage, expansion, and balanced. **Industry Preferences:** Internet specific, consumer related, business and financial services, computer hardware, computer software and services, communications and media, and other products. **Geographic Preferences:** U.S. **Principal Exhibits:**

48304 ■ Hallador Venture Partners
PO Box 15299
Sacramento, CA 95851
Ph:(916)920-5187
Fax:(916)920-5188
URL: http://www.hallador.com
Contact: Chris L. Branscum, Managing Director
E-mail: chris@shallador.com
Preferred Investment Size: $500,000 to $1,000,000. **Investment Types:** Seed, start-up, first and second stage, and research and development. **Industry Preferences:** Communications and media, computer software, Internet specific, semiconductors and other electronics. **Geographic Preferences:** West Coast. **Principal Exhibits:**

48305 ■ Hamilton Bioventures / Hamilton Apex Technology Ventures
990 Highland Dr., Ste. 314
Solana Beach, CA 92075
Ph:(858)314-2350

Fax:(858)314-2355
Co. E-mail: info@HamiltonBioVenturers.com
URL: http://www.hamiltonbioventures.com
Contact: Richard J. Crosby, Managing Director
E-mail: Richard@hamiltonbioventures.com
Preferred Investment Size: $1,000,000 to $5,000,000. **Investment Policies:** Early, first, second and later stage. **Industry Preferences:** Biotechnology, and medical and health. **Geographic Preferences:** Southern California. **Principal Exhibits:**

48306 ■ Headland Ventures, LP / Sterling Payot Capital
65 Cloudview Rd.
Sausalito, CA 94965
Ph:(415)289-2590
Fax:(415)289-2591
URL: http://www.headlandventures.com
Contact: Larry Stites, Chief Financial Officer
Investment Policies: Early stage. **Industry Preferences:** Computer software, Internet specific, and consumer related. **Geographic Preferences:** U.S. **Principal Exhibits:**

48307 ■ Hewlett Packard / Compaq Computer Corporation
3000 Hanover St.
Palo Alto, CA 94304-1185
Ph:(650)857-1501
Fax:(650)857-5518
URL: http://www.hp.com
Contact: Michael Duggan, Managing Director
Investment Policies: Early stage. **Industry Preferences:** Biotechnology. **Geographic Preferences:** National. **Principal Exhibits:**

48308 ■ HighBAR Ventures
3150 Porter Dr.
Palo Alto, CA 94304
Co. E-mail: info@highbarventures.com
URL: http://www.highbarventures.com
Contact: Roy Thiele-Sardina, Managing Partner
Investment Policies: Seed and early stage. **Industry Preferences:** Technology. **Principal Exhibits:**

48309 ■ Horizon Ventures
4 Main St., Ste. 50
Los Altos, CA 94022
Ph:(650)917-4100
Fax:(650)917-4109
URL: http://www.horizonvc.com
Contact: Doug Tsui, Managing Director
E-mail: doug@horizonvc.com
Preferred Investment Size: $500,000 to $3,500,000. **Investment Types:** Seed, start-up, early, first and second stage. **Industry Preferences:** Internet specific, computer hardware, computer software and services, semiconductors and other electronics, medical and health, communications and media, and other products. **Geographic Preferences:** West Coast. **Principal Exhibits:**

48310 ■ iD Ventures America, LLC
5201 Great America Pky., Ste. 270
Santa Clara, CA 95054
Ph:(408)894-7900
Fax:(408)894-7939
Co. E-mail: info@idsoftcapital.com
URL: http://www.acervc.com
Contact: James C. Lu, Managing Director
Preferred Investment Size: $500,000 to $3,000,000. **Investment Policies:** Start-up, seed, first and second stage. **Industry Preferences:** Communications and media, computer software and hardware, Internet specific, semiconductors and other electronics, consumer related, and financial services. **Geographic Preferences:** U.S. and Canada. **Principal Exhibits:**

48311 ■ Idanta Partners, Ltd. (San Diego)
9255 Towne Centre Dr., Ste. 925
San Diego, CA 92121
Ph:(858)452-9690
Fax:(858)452-2013
URL: http://www.idanta.com
Contact: David Dunn, Managing Partner
Preferred Investment Size: $1,000,000 to $10,000,000. **Investment Types:** Seed, early stage, first and second stage, balanced, acquisition, and management buyouts. **Industry Preferences:** Semiconductors and other electronics, communications and media, computer software, Internet specific, computer hardware, consumer related, medical and health, and other products. **Geographic Preferences:** U.S. **Principal Exhibits:**

48312 ■ Idealab!
130 W. Union St.
Pasadena, CA 91103
Ph:(626)585-6900
Fax:(626)535-2701
Co. E-mail: info@idealab.com
URL: http://www.idealab.com
Contact: Douglas McPherson, Managing Director
Investment Policies: Start-up and early stage. **Industry Preferences:** Internet specific. **Principal Exhibits:**

48313 ■ IDG Ventures (San Francisco)
1 Letterman Dr.
Bldg. D, Ste. 100
San Francisco, CA 94129
Ph:(415)439-4420
Fax:(415)439-4428
Co. E-mail: Plans_sf@idgventures.com
URL: http://www.idgventures.com
Contact: Pat Kenealy, Managing Director
Preferred Investment Size: 1,000,000 to $5,000,000. **Investment Types:** Seed, first stage, early and later stage, mezzanine, and balanced. **Industry Preferences:** Internet specific, computer software and services, computer hardware, communications and media, medical and health, semiconductors and other electronics, biotechnology, consumer related, and other products. **Geographic Preferences:** U.S. **Principal Exhibits:**

48314 ■ The Ignite Group / Ignite Associates, LLC
255 Shoreline Dr., Ste. 510
Redwood City, CA 94065
Ph:(650)622-2000
Fax:(650)622-2015
Co. E-mail: info@ignitegroup.com
URL: http://www.ignitegroup.com
Contact: Nobuo Mii, Managing Partner
E-mail: nmii@ignitegroup.com
Preferred Investment Size: $2,000,000 to $10,000,000. **Investment Types:** Seed, start-up, early, first, and second stage. **Industry Preferences:** Internet specific, communications and media, computer software and services, computer hardware, semiconductors and other electronics, medical and health. **Geographic Preferences:** Northern and Southern California. **Principal Exhibits:**

48315 ■ Infinity Capital, L.L.C.
480 Cowper St., Ste. 200
Palo Alto, CA 94301
Ph:(650)462-8400
Fax:(650)462-8415
URL: http://www.infinityllc.com
Contact: Bruce Graham, Managing Director
E-mail: bruce@infinityllc.com
Preferred Investment Size: $275,000 to $10,000,000. **Investment Types:** Early stage. **Industry Preferences:** Internet specific, communications and media, computer hardware, medical and health, other products, computer software and services, semiconductors and other electronics. **Geographic Preferences:** U.S. **Principal Exhibits:**

48316 ■ Information Technology Ventures
100 Hamilton Ave., Ste. 400
Palo Alto, CA 94301
Ph:(650)462-8400
Fax:(650)462-8415
URL: http://www.itventures.com
Contact: George Kitagawa, Chief Financial Officer
Investment Types: Start-up. **Industry Preferences:** Internet specific, computer software and services, communications and media, semiconductors and other electronics, computer hardware, industrial and energy, and other products. **Geographic Preferences:** Northeast, Northwest, and West Coast. **Principal Exhibits:**

48317 ■ Inglewood Ventures
12526 High Bluff Dr., Ste. 300
San Diego, CA 92130
Ph:(858)792-3579
Fax:(858)792-3417
Co. E-mail: info@inglewoodventures.com
URL: http://www.inglewoodventures.com
Contact: M. Blake Ingle, Principal
E-mail: blake@inglewoodventures.com
Preferred Investment Size: $500,000 to $1,500,000. **Investment Types:** Seed and early stage. **Industry Preferences:** Biotechnology, medical and health. **Geographic Preferences:** Northern and Southern California, and West Coast. **Principal Exhibits:**

48318 ■ Innocal Venture Capital
Center Tower, Ste. 770
650 Town Center Dr.
Costa Mesa, CA 92626
Ph:(714)850-6784
Fax:(714)850-6798
URL: http://www.innocal.com
Contact: Harry Lambert, Managing Director
E-mail: hlambert@innocal.com
Preferred Investment Size: $1,000,000 to $5,000,000. **Investment Types:** Early, first, and second stage, expansion, recapitalizations, and turnaround. **Industry Preferences:** Computer software and services, Internet specific, medical and health, communications and media, industrial and energy, semiconductors and other electronics, and biotechnology. **Geographic Preferences:** Northern and Southern California, and the West Coast. **Principal Exhibits:**

48319 ■ Institutional Venture Partners
3000 Sand Hill Rd.
Bldg. 2, Ste. 250
Menlo Park, CA 94025
Ph:(650)854-0132
Fax:(650)854-2009
URL: http://www.ivp.com
Contact: Dennis Phelps, Partner
Preferred Investment Size: $10,000,000 to $100,000,000. **Investment Types:** Later stage, expansion, public companies, industry rollups, private placement, open market, and mezzanine. **Industry Preferences:** Internet specific, communications and media, computer hardware, computer software and services, semiconductors and other electronics, consumer related, and other products. **Geographic Preferences:** U.S. **Principal Exhibits:**

48320 ■ Interwest Partners (Menlo Park)
2710 Sand Hill Rd., 2nd Fl.
Menlo Park, CA 94025
Ph:(650)854-8585
Fax:(650)854-4706
Co. E-mail: info@interwest.com
URL: http://www.interwest.com
Contact: Doug Pepper, Principal
Preferred Investment Size: $10,000,000 to $15,000,000. **Investment Types:** Seed, research and development, start-up, first and second stage, early and later stage, balanced, and expansion. **Industry Preferences:** Medical and health, Internet specific, consumer related, biotechnology, communications and media, computer hardware, computer software and services, semiconductors and other electronics, industrial and energy, and other products. **Geographic Preferences:** U.S. **Principal Exhibits:**

48321 ■ Invencor, Inc.
PO Box 7355
Menlo Park, CA 94026
Ph:(650)330-1210
Fax:(650)330-1222
Co. E-mail: plans@invencor.com
URL: http://www.invencor.com
Contact: Debra R. Guerin, Principle
E-mail: debra@invencor.com
Preferred Investment Size: $300,000 to $2,000,000. **Investment Types:** Seed, start-up, early, and first stage. **Geographic Preferences:** Primarily in Arizona, California, Hawaii, New Mexico, and Utah. **Principal Exhibits:**

48322 ■ Jafco Ventures
505 Hamilton Ave., Ste. 310
Palto Alto, CA 94301
Ph:(650)463-8800
Fax:(650)463-8801
Co. E-mail: info@jafco.com
URL: http://www.jafco.com
Contact: Joseph Horowitz, Managing General
  Partner
E-mail: joe@jafco.com
Preferred Investment Size: $4,000,000 to
$8,000,000. **Investment Types:** Early, second stage,
and expansion. **Industry Preferences:** Communications and media, computer software and services,
and semiconductors and other electronics. **Geographic Preferences:** U.S. **Principal Exhibits:**

48323 ■ Kaiser Permanente Ventures
1 Kaiser Plz., 22nd Fl.
Oakland, CA 94612
Ph:(510)267-7300
Fax:(510)891-7943
URL: http://www.kpventures.com
Contact: Chris Grant, Senior Vice President and
  Managing Direc
E-mail: chris.m.grant@kp.org
Preferred Investment Size: $500,000 to $2,000,000.
Investment Types: Early, first, and second stage,
balanced, strategic alliances, and expansion. **Industry Preferences:** Biotechnology, and medical and
health. **Geographic Preferences:** Canada. **Principal
Exhibits:**

**48324 ■ Kleiner Perkins Caufield & Byers
(Menlo Park)**
2750 Sand Hill Rd.
Menlo Park, CA 94025
Ph:(650)233-2750
Fax:(650)233-0300
Co. E-mail: plans@kpcb.com
URL: http://www.kpcb.com
Contact: John Denniston, General Partner
E-mail: johnde@kpcb.com
Preferred Investment Size: $500,000 minimum. **Investment Types:** Seed, start-up, first stage, and balanced. **Industry Preferences:** Internet specific,
computer software and services, computer hardware,
communications and media, semiconductors and
other electronics, medical and health, biotechnology,
industrial and energy, consumer related, and other
products. **Geographic Preferences:** West Coast.
Principal Exhibits:

48325 ■ Kline Hawkes & Co.
11726 San Vicente Blvd., Ste. 300
Los Angeles, CA 90049
Ph:(310)442-4700
Fax:(310)442-4707
Co. E-mail: cwood@klinehawkes.com
URL: http://www.klinehawkes.com
Contact: Jay Ferguson, Principle
E-mail: jferg@klinehawkes.com
Preferred Investment Size: $5,000,000 to
$10,000,000. **Investment Types:** Second and later
stage, private placement, expansion, acquisition,
generalist PE, industry rollups, leveraged buyout,
management buyouts, private placement, turnaround,
and recapitalizations. **Industry Preferences:** Communications and media, Internet specific, semiconductors and other electronics, Business services,
computer software, and services, computer hardware,
industrial and energy, and other products. **Geographic Preferences:** Northwest, Southwest, and
West Coast. **Principal Exhibits:**

48326 ■ KLM Capital Group
19925 Stevens Creek Blvd., Ste. 100
Cupertino, CA 95014
Ph:(408)970-8888
Fax:(408)970-8885
Co. E-mail: info@klmcapital.com
URL: http://www.klmtech.com
Contact: Peter Mok, Managing General Partner
E-mail: petermok@klmcapital.com
Preferred Investment Size: $500,000 to $5,000,000.
Investment Types: Seed, expansion, early stage,
and acquisition. **Industry Preferences:** Semiconductors and other electronics, Internet specific, computer

software and services, communications and media,
and consumer related. **Geographic Preferences:**
U.S. **Principal Exhibits:**

48327 ■ KTB Ventures / KTB Venture Capital
203 Redwood Shores Pky., Ste. 610
Redwood City, CA 94065
Ph:(650)324-4681
Fax:(650)324-4682
Co. E-mail: info@ktbvc.com
URL: http://www.ktbvc.com
Contact: Sung Y. Yoon, Managing Partner
Preferred Investment Size: $500,000 to $5,000,000.
Investment Types: Start-up, first and early stage,
and balanced. **Industry Preferences:** Internet
specific, semiconductors and other electronics, communications and media, computer software and
services, computer hardware, and consumer and
business service. **Geographic Preferences:** U.S.
Principal Exhibits:

48328 ■ Kyocera International, Inc.
Corporate Development
8611 Balboa Ave.
San Diego, CA 92123
Ph:(858)576-2600
Fax:(858)492-1456
URL: http://global.kyocera.com
Contact: Makoto Kawamura, President
Preferred Investment Size: $300,000 to $500,000.
Investment Types: Second stage. **Industry Preferences:** Communications and media, computer related, semiconductors and other electronics, biotechnology, medical and health, consumer related,
industrial and energy, business service, agriculture,
forestry and fishing. **Geographic Preferences:** West
Coast. **Principal Exhibits:**

48329 ■ Labrador Ventures
101 University Ave., 4th Fl.
Palo Alto, CA 94301
Ph:(650)366-6000
Fax:(650)366-6430
Co. E-mail: businessplans@labrador.com
URL: http://www.labrador.com
Contact: Larry Kubal, Partner
Preferred Investment Size: $1,000,000 to
$6,000,000. **Investment Policies:** Start-up, seed,
early and first stage. **Industry Preferences:** Communications, computer software, and semiconductors
and other electronics. **Geographic Preferences:**
Northern California and West Coast **Principal Exhibits:**

48330 ■ Latterell Venture Partners
1 Embarcadero Centre, Ste. 4050
San Francisco, CA 94111-4106
Ph:(415)399-9880
Fax:(415)399-9879
Co. E-mail: support@LVPcapital.com
URL: http://www.lvpcapital.com
Contact: Patrick Latterell, Managing Director
E-mail: pat@lvpcapital.com
Preferred Investment Size: $50,000 to $10,000,000.
Investment Policies: Early stage and balanced. **Industry Preferences:** Biotechnology, and medical and
health. **Geographic Preferences:** U.S. **Principal Exhibits:**

48331 ■ Lawrence Financial Group
13320 Westcove Dr.
Box 491773
Los Angeles, CA 90049-2520
Ph:(310)230-1188
Fax:(310)943-2232
Co. E-mail: info@lawrencefinancial.com
URL: http://www.lawrencefinancial.com
Contact: Lawrence Hurwitz, President
E-mail: LNHurwitz@LawrenceFinancial.com
Preferred Investment Size: $500,000 to $1,000,000.
Investment Types: Second stage. **Industry Preferences:** Communications and media, computer related, semiconductors and other electronics, biotechnology, medical and health, consumer related,
industrial and energy, financial services, business
service, agriculture, forestry and fishing. **Geographic
Preferences:** West Coast. **Principal Exhibits:**

48332 ■ Leapfrog Ventures
Ph:(650)926-9900
Fax:(650)233-1301
Co. E-mail: plans@leapfrogventures.com
URL: http://www.leapfrogventures.com
Contact: Pete Sinclair, Managing Director
E-mail: pete@leapfrogventures.com
Preferred Investment Size: $1,000,000 to
$3,000,000. **Investment Policies:** Start-up, seed,
early and first stage. **Industry Preferences:** Communications and media, computer software, and Internet specific. **Geographic Preferences:** Northern
California and West Coast. **Principal Exhibits:**

48333 ■ Legacy Venture
180 Lytton Ave.
Palo Alto, CA 94301
Ph:(650)324-5980
Fax:(650)324-5982
Co. E-mail: info@legacyventure.com
URL: http://www.legacyventure.com
Contact: Chris A. Eyre, Managing Partner
Preferred Investment Size: $3,000,000 to
$10,000,000. **Investment Policies:** Early stage, and
fund of funds. **Industry Preferences:** Communications and media. **Geographic Preferences:** U.S.
Principal Exhibits:

48334 ■ LF USA Investment, Inc.
4 Embarcadero Ctr., Ste. 3400
San Francisco, CA 94111
Ph:(415)315-7440
Co. E-mail: contact.usa@lfvc.com
URL: http://www.lfvc.com
Contact: Michael Hsieh, President
Preferred Investment Size: $1,000,000 to
$10,000,000. **Investment Types:** Early stage, private
placement, later, management buyouts, and expansion. **Industry Preferences:** Consumer related,
technology, software and services. **Geographic Preferences:** U.S. **Principal Exhibits:**

48335 ■ Lighthouse Capital Partners, Inc.
500 Drake's Landing Rd., Ste. 210
Greenbrae, CA 94904-3011
Ph:(415)464-5900
Fax:(415)925-3387
Co. E-mail: info@lcpartners.com
URL: http://www.lcpartners.com
Contact: Rick Stubblefield, Founder and Managing
  Director
Preferred Investment Size: $1,000,000 to
$10,000,000. **Investment Types:** Seed, start-up, first
and second stage, early stage, and expansion. **Industry Preferences:** Internet specific, computer software
and services, other products, semiconductors and
other electronics, communications and media. **Geographic Preferences:** California and Massachusetts.
Principal Exhibits:

**48336 ■ Lightspeed Venture Partners /
Weiss, Peck and Greer**
2200 Sand Hill Rd.
Menlo Park, CA 94025
Ph:(650)234-8300
Fax:(650)234-8333
Co. E-mail: info@lightspeedvp.com
URL: http://www.lightspeedvp.com
Contact: Eric O'Brien, Managing Director
E-mail: eric@lightspeedvp.com
Preferred Investment Size: $500,000 to
$20,000,000. **Investment Types:** Seed, first, second
and later stage. **Industry Preferences:** Communications and media, Internet specific, computer software
and services, computer hardware, semiconductors
and other electronics, medical and health, industrial
and energy, biotechnology, consumer related, and
other products. **Geographic Preferences:** U.S. **Principal Exhibits:**

48337 ■ Magic Venture Capital, LLC
335 Lowell Ave.
Palo Alto, CA 94301
Ph:(650)327-7719
URL: http://www.magicvc.com
Contact: Erin McGurk, Managing Director
Preferred Investment Size: $300,000 to $1,000,000.
Investment Policies: Start-up, seed, and first stage.

Industry Preferences: Medical and health. **Geographic Preferences:** West Coast. **Principal Exhibits:**

48338 ■ Manitou Ventures, LLC
460 Bush St., 2nd Fl.
San Francisco, CA 94108
Ph:(415)288-0727
Fax:(415)627-9079
Co. E-mail: info@maniven.com
URL: http://www.manitouventures.com
Contact: Chris Wadsworth, Partner
Preferred Investment Size: $500,000 to $1,500,000.
Investment Policies: Early stage. **Industry Preferences:** Communications and media, computer hardware, semiconductors and other electronics. **Geographic Preferences:** National. **Principal Exhibits:**

48339 ■ Marwit Capital, LLC
100 Bayview Cir., Ste. 550
Newport Beach, CA 92660
Ph:(949)861-3636
Fax:(949)861-3637
Co. E-mail: info@marwit.com
URL: http://www.marwit.com
Contact: Chris Britt, Managing Partner
Preferred Investment Size: $3,000,000 to $15,000,000. **Investment Types:** Leveraged buyout, management buyouts, acquisition, and recapitalization. **Industry Preferences:** Medical and health, transportation, industrial and energy, business service, and manufacturing. **Geographic Preferences:** Western U.S. **Principal Exhibits:**

48340 ■ Maton Venture
1601 S. De Anza Blvd., Ste. 115
Cupertino, CA 95014
Ph:(408)786-5168
Fax:(408)996-0728
Co. E-mail: info@maton.com
URL: http://www.maton.com
Contact: James Chen, Managing Partner
Preferred Investment Size: $200,000 to $2,000,000.
Investment Types: Seed, start-up, early stage, first and second stage, expansion, private placement, research and development, and turnaround. **Industry Preferences:** Communications and media, computer software and hardware, Internet specific, semiconductors and other electronics. **Geographic Preferences:** Northern California. **Principal Exhibits:**

48341 ■ Matrix Partners (Palo Alto)
260 Homer Ave., Ste. 201
Palo Alto, CA 94025
Ph:(650)798-1600
Fax:(650)798-1601
Co. E-mail: info@matrixpartners.com
URL: http://www.matrixpartners.com
Contact: Bob Lisbonne, General Partner
E-mail: blisbonne@matrixpartners.com
Preferred Investment Size: $2,000,000 to $10,000,000. **Investment Types:** Start-up, early, first and second stage, balanced, and leveraged buyout. **Industry Preferences:** Communications and media, Internet specific, computer software and services, computer hardware, semiconductors and other electronics. **Geographic Preferences:** California and Massachusetts. **Principal Exhibits:**

48342 ■ Mayfield Fund
2800 Sand Hill Rd., Ste. 250
Menlo Park, CA 94025
Ph:(650)854-5560
Fax:(650)854-5712
Co. E-mail: info@mayfield.com
URL: http://www.mayfield.com
Contact: Rajeev Batra, Principal
E-mail: rbatra@mayfield.com
Preferred Investment Size: $1,000,000 to $3,000,000. **Investment Types:** Seed, early, second, and later stage, acquisition, joint ventures, management buyouts, private placement, research and development, and strategic alliances. **Industry Preferences:** Computer software and services, computer hardware, Internet specific, communications and media, semiconductors and other electronics, consumer related, industrial and energy, and other products. **Geographic Preferences:** U.S. **Principal Exhibits:**

48343 ■ McCown De Leeuw and Co.
950 Tower Ln., Ste. 800
Foster City, CA 94025-7111
Ph:(650)854-6000
Fax:(650)854-0853
URL: http://www.mdcpartners.com
Contact: George McCown, Managing Director
Preferred Investment Size: $20,000,000 to $50,000,000. **Investment Types:** Leveraged buyout. **Industry Preferences:** Consumer related, computer software and services, medical and health, Internet specific, communications and media, computer hardware, semiconductors and other electronics, industrial and energy, and other products. **Geographic Preferences:** U.S. **Principal Exhibits:**

48344 ■ Media Technology Ventures
525 University Ave., Ste. 220
Palo Alto, CA 94301
Ph:(650)687-0500
Fax:(650)687-0234
Co. E-mail: vc@allegiscapital.com
URL: http://www.allegiscapital.com
Contact: Robert R. Ackerman, Founder and Managing Director
Preferred Investment Size: $3,000,000 to $5,000,000. **Investment Types:** Start-up, seed, early stage, and research and development. **Industry Preferences:** Communications and media, Internet specific, and computer software and services, other products, computer hardware, semiconductors and other electronics. **Geographic Preferences:** U.S. **Principal Exhibits:**

48345 ■ Media Venture Partners
244 Jackson St., 4th Fl.
San Francisco, CA 94111
Ph:(415)391-4877
Fax:(415)391-4912
URL: http://www.mediaventurepartners.com
Contact: Elliot Evers, Managing Director
E-mail: eevers@mediaventurepartners.com
Preferred Investment Size: $500,000 to $1,000,000.
Investment Types: Seed, start-up, first and second stage, leveraged buyout, control-block purchases, and special situation. **Industry Preferences:** Communications and media, computer software and hardware, consumer related, and manufacturing. **Geographic Preferences:** U.S. and Canada. **Principal Exhibits:**

48346 ■ Medventure Associates
5980 Horton St., Ste. 390
Emeryville, CA 94608
Ph:(510)597-7979
Fax:(510)597-9920
Co. E-mail: medven@medven.com
URL: http://www.medven.com
Contact: Annette Campbell-White, Senior Managing Partner
E-mail: annette.cw@medven.com
Preferred Investment Size: $200,000 to $500,000.
Investment Types: Seed and early stage. **Industry Preferences:** Medical and health, Internet specific, biotechnology, communications and media, computer software and services. **Geographic Preferences:** West Coast. **Principal Exhibits:**

48347 ■ Menlo Ventures
3000 Sand Hill Rd.
Bldg. 4, Ste. 100
Menlo Park, CA 94025
Ph:(650)854-8540
Fax:(650)854-7059
Co. E-mail: info@menloventures.com
URL: http://www.menloventures.com
Contact: H. DuBose Montgomery, Managing Director
E-mail: dubose@menloventures.com
Preferred Investment Size: $5,000,000 to $20,000,000. **Investment Types:** Start-up, early, first, second, and later stage, expansion, and balanced. **Industry Preferences:** Internet specific, communications and media, computer software and services, computer hardware, medical and health, semiconductors and other electronics, biotechnology, consumer related, industrial and energy, and other products. **Geographic Preferences:** U.S. **Principal Exhibits:**

48348 ■ Millennium Hanson
4519 Admiralty Way, Ste. A
Marina del Rey, CA 90292
Ph:(310)550-1995
Fax:(310)482-6944
Co. E-mail: associates@millhanson.com
URL: http://www.millhanson.com
Contact: Jonathan Mork, Investment Committee Officer
Preferred Investment Size: $1,000,000. **Investment Policies:** Early stage, expansion and acquisition. **Industry Preferences:** Internet specific. **Geographic Preferences:** National. **Principal Exhibits:**

48349 ■ Mission Ventures
11455 El Camino Real, Ste. 450
San Diego, CA 92130
Ph:(858)350-2100
Fax:(858)350-2101
URL: http://www.missionventures.com
Contact: David Ryan, Managing Partner
Preferred Investment Size: $2,000,000 to $10,000,000. **Investment Types:** Seed, early, first and second stage, and research and development. **Industry Preferences:** Internet specific, communications and media, computer software and services, consumer related, semiconductors and other electronics, and other products. **Geographic Preferences:** Southern California. **Principal Exhibits:**

48350 ■ Mobius Venture Capital / Softbank Venture Capital
1050 Walnut St., Ste. 210
Boulder, CO 80302
Ph:(303)642-4000
URL: http://www.mobiusvc.com
Contact: Brad Feld, Principal
Preferred Investment Size: $2,000,000 to $100,000,000. **Investment Types:** Seed, start-up, early and first stage. **Industry Preferences:** Internet specific, computer software and services, computer hardware, communications and media, consumer related, semiconductors and other electronics, biotechnology, industrial and energy, and other products. **Geographic Preferences:** California, East and West Coast. **Principal Exhibits:**

48351 ■ Mohr Davidow Ventures (Menlo Park)
3000 Sand Hill Rd.
Bldg. 3, Ste. 290
Menlo Park, CA 94025
Ph:(650)854-7236
Fax:(650)854-7365
Co. E-mail: info@mdv.com
URL: http://www.mdv.com
Contact: Jim Smith, General Partner
E-mail: jsmith@mdv.com
Preferred Investment Size: $500,000 to $10,000,000. **Investment Types:** Seed, early, first and second stage. **Industry Preferences:** Internet specific, computer software and services, computer hardware, semiconductors and other electronics, communications and media, medical and health, consumer related, biotechnology, industrial and energy, and other products. **Geographic Preferences:** Northwest, Mid Atlantic, and West Coast. **Principal Exhibits:**

48352 ■ National Investment Management, Inc.
2601 Airport Dr., Ste. 210
Torrance, CA 90505
Ph:(310)784-7600
Co. E-mail: robins621@aol.com
URL: http://www.wallstreetdex.com
Contact: Richard Robins, President
Preferred Investment Size: $1,000,000 minimum. **Investment Types:** Leveraged buyout. **Industry Preferences:** Internet specific, computer software and services, consumer related, industrial and energy, communications and media, semiconductors and other electronics, computer hardware, and other products. **Geographic Preferences:** U.S. **Principal Exhibits:**

48353 ■ NetFuel Inc.
3 1/2 N. Santa Cruz Ave., Ste. D
Los Gatos, CA 95030
Ph:(408)384-9938
Fax:(408)384-5203
URL: http://www.netfuel.com
Contact: Jim Harlow, Principal
E-mail: jim@netfuel.com
Investment Policies: Seed and start-up. **Industry Preferences:** Internet specific. **Geographic Preferences:** Midwest. **Principal Exhibits:**

48354 ■ New Enterprise Associates (Menlo Park)
2855 Sand Hill Rd.
Menlo Park, CA 94025
Ph:(650)854-9499
Fax:(650)854-9397
URL: http://www.nea.com
Contact: Mohamad Makhzoumi, Principal
E-mail: mmakhzoumi@nea.com
Preferred Investment Size: $200,000 to $20,000,000. **Investment Types:** Seed, early, start-up, first and second stage, and mezzanine. **Industry Preferences:** Communications and media, Internet specific, medical and health, computer software and services, computer hardware, semiconductors and other electronics, biotechnology, consumer related, industrial and energy, and other products. **Geographic Preferences:** U.S. **Principal Exhibits:**

48355 ■ New Vista Capital, LLC
161 E. Evelyn Ave.
Mountain View, CA 94041
Ph:(650)864-2553
Fax:(650)864-2599
URL: http://www.nvcap.com
Contact: Frank S. Greene, Managing Partner
E-mail: fgreene@nvcap.com
Investment Types: Seed, start-up, early, first and second stage. **Industry Preferences:** Internet specific, computer software and services, computer hardware, semiconductors and other electronics, communications and media, consumer related, and other products. **Geographic Preferences:** Northwest, Rocky Mountains, Southwest, and West Coast. **Principal Exhibits:**

48356 ■ Newbury Ventures
255 Shoreline Dr., Ste. 520
Redwood Shores, CA 94065
Ph:(650)486-2444
Fax:(650)595-2442
Co. E-mail: chehrzad@newburyven.com
URL: http://www.newburyven.com
Contact: Bruce Bauer, Senior Managing Director
E-mail: bruce@newburyven.com
Preferred Investment Size: $5,000,000 to $10,000,000. **Investment Types:** First and second stage, later stage, turnaround, and special situation. **Industry Preferences:** Internet specific, semiconductors and other electronics, communications and media, computer software and services, computer hardware, medical and health. **Geographic Preferences:** Northwest U.S. and Eastern Canada. **Principal Exhibits:**

48357 ■ Norwest Venture Partners
525 University Ave., Ste. 800
Palo Alto, CA 94301-1922
Ph:(650)321-8000
Fax:(650)321-8010
Co. E-mail: bizplans@nvp.com
URL: http://www.nvp.com
Contact: Promod Haque, Managing General Partner
Preferred Investment Size: $1,000,000 to $30,000,000. **Investment Types:** Seed, early stage, and expansion. **Industry Preferences:** Internet specific, computer software and services, communications and media, semiconductors and other electronics, consumer related, industrial and energy, medical and health, computer hardware, other products, and biotechnology. **Geographic Preferences:** U.S. **Principal Exhibits:**

48358 ■ Novus Ventures
20111 Stevens Creek Blvd., Ste. 130
Cupertino, CA 95014
Ph:(408)252-3900
Fax:(408)252-1713
Co. E-mail: info@novusventures.com
URL: http://www.novusventures.com
Contact: Daniel Tompkins, General Partner
Preferred Investment Size: $25,000 to $10,000,000. **Investment Types:** First, early and second stage, and expansion. **Industry Preferences:** Communications and media, computer software and services, Internet specific, semiconductors and other electronics, medical and health. **Geographic Preferences:** California and West Coast. **Principal Exhibits:**

48359 ■ Oak Investment Partners (Palo Alto)
525 University Ave., Ste. 1300
Palo Alto, CA 94301
Ph:(650)614-3700
Fax:(650)328-6345
URL: http://www.oakvc.com
Contact: Bandel Carano, Managing Partner
E-mail: bandel@oakvc.com
Preferred Investment Size: $25,000,000 to $150,000,000. **Investment Types:** Later stage, balanced, expansion, management buyouts, private placement, and special situation. **Industry Preferences:** Communications and media, Internet specific, computer software and services, semiconductors and other electronics, computer hardware, consumer related, medical and health, biotechnology, industrial and energy, and other products. **Geographic Preferences:** U.S. **Principal Exhibits:**

48360 ■ Omninet Capital, LLC
9420 Wilshire Blvd., 4th Fl.
Beverly Hills, CA 90212
Ph:(310)300-4100
Fax:(310)300-4101
Co. E-mail: info@omninet.com
URL: http://www.omninet.com
Contact: Benjamin Nazarian, Managing Partner
Investment Policies: Start-up and early stage. **Industry Preferences:** Communications, and Internet specific. **Geographic Preferences:** U.S. **Principal Exhibits:**

48361 ■ Onset Ventures
2400 Sand Hill Rd.
Menlo Park, CA 94025
Ph:(650)529-0700
Fax:(650)529-0777
Co. E-mail: mp@onset.com
URL: http://www.onset.com
Contact: Stephen Bernardez, Principal
Preferred Investment Size: $8,000,000 to $12,000,000. **Investment Types:** Seed and early stage. **Industry Preferences:** Computer software and services, computer hardware, Internet specific, communications and media, semiconductors and other electronics, medical and health, other products, and biotechnology. **Geographic Preferences:** West Coast and U.S. **Principal Exhibits:**

48362 ■ Opportunity Capital Partners
2201 Walnut Ave., Ste. 210
Fremont, CA 94538
Ph:(510)795-7000
Fax:(510)494-5439
URL: http://www.ocpcapital.com
Contact: J. Peter Thompson, Managing Partner
Preferred Investment Size: $2,000,000 to $10,000,000. **Investment Types:** Second and later stage, mezzanine, leveraged buyout, balanced, and industry rollups. **Industry Preferences:** Communications and media, computer software and services, computer hardware, consumer related, Internet specific, medical and health, industrial and energy, other products, and semiconductors and other electronics. **Geographic Preferences:** California and West Coast. **Principal Exhibits:**

48363 ■ Oracle Venture Fund
500 Oracle Pky.
Redwood Shores, CA 94065
Ph:(650)506-7000
Fax:(650)633-0212
URL: http://www.oracle.com
Contact: Laurent Sandrolini, Managing Director
Preferred Investment Size: $2,000,000 to $5,000,000. **Investment Types:** Early and later stage, and balanced. **Industry Preferences:** Internet

specific, computer software and services, medical and health, biotechnology, communications and media, computer hardware, and other products. **Geographic Preferences:** U.S. **Principal Exhibits:**

48364 ■ Osprey Ventures, L.P.
502 Waverley St.
Palo Alto, CA 94065
Ph:(650)620-9450
Fax:(650)620-9458
Co. E-mail: admin@ospreyventures.com
URL: http://www.ospreyventures.com
Contact: David Stastny, Managing Director
Investment Types: Balanced, early stage, and expansion. **Industry Preferences:** Internet specific, semiconductors and other electronics, communications and media, computer software and services, computer hardware, medical and health. **Geographic Preferences:** West Coast. **Principal Exhibits:**

48365 ■ Outlook Ventures / Iminds, Interactive Minds
3000F Danville, Blvd., Ste. 110
Alamo, CA 94105
Ph:(415)547-0000
Fax:(415)547-0010
Co. E-mail: info@outlookventures.com
URL: http://www.outlookventures.com
Contact: Carl Nichols, Managing Director
Preferred Investment Size: $500,000 to $5,000,000. **Investment Policies:** Start-up, seed, early and first stage. **Industry Preferences:** Internet specific, computer software and services, computer hardware, and other products. **Geographic Preferences:** Northern California and West Coast. **Principal Exhibits:**

48366 ■ Pacifica Fund
5150 El Camino Real, Ste. A-32
Los Altos, CA 94022
Ph:(650)318-0063
Fax:(650)318-0290
URL: http://www.pacificafund.com
Contact: Tim Oren, Managing Director
Preferred Investment Size: $1,000,000 to $5,000,000. **Investment Types:** Start-up, early, first and second stage, and expansion. **Industry Preferences:** Communications and media, computer hardware and software, Internet specific, semiconductors and other electronics, and industrial and energy. **Geographic Preferences:** Northern California and West Coast. **Principal Exhibits:**

48367 ■ PacRim Venture Partners
535 Middlefield Rd., Ste. 280
Menlo Park, CA 94025
Ph:(650)330-0880
Fax:(650)330-0785
Co. E-mail: info@pacrimpartners.com
URL: http://www.pacrimpartners.com
Contact: Thomas J. Toy, Managing Director
E-mail: ttoy@pacrimpartners.com
Preferred Investment Size: $100,000 to $2,000,000. **Investment Types:** Seed, start-up, early and first stage. **Industry Preferences:** Communications and media, computer hardware and software, Internet specific, semiconductors and other electronics. **Geographic Preferences:** West Coast. **Principal Exhibits:**

48368 ■ Palo Alto Venture Partners / 21VC Oartners
300 Hamilton Ave., 4th Fl.
Palo Alto, CA 94301
Ph:(650)462-1221
Fax:(650)462-1227
URL: http://www.pavp.com
Contact: Neil Weintraut, Partner
E-mail: nweintraut@pavp.com
Preferred Investment Size: $1,000,000 to $10,000,000. **Investment Policies:** Start-up, seed, early and first stage. **Industry Preferences:** Internet specific, computer software and services, communications and media, other products, and consumer related. **Geographic Preferences:** U.S. **Principal Exhibits:**

48369 ■ Palomar Ventures
100 Wilshire Blvd., Ste. 1700
Santa Monica, CA 90401
Ph:(310)260-6050
Fax:(310)656-4150
URL: http://www.palomarventures.com
Contact: Jim Gauer, Managing Director
E-mail: jgauer@palomarventures.com
Preferred Investment Size: $2,000,000 to $5,000,000. **Investment Types:** Seed, start-up, first and early stage, and expansion. **Industry Preferences:** Communications and media, Internet specific, computer software and services, computer hardware, consumer releated, and other products. **Geographic Preferences:** Northern California, Southwest, West Coast, and U.S. **Principal Exhibits:**

48370 ■ Partech International
50 California St., Ste. 3200
San Francisco, CA 94111
Ph:(415)788-2929
Fax:(415)788-6763
URL: http://www.partechvc.com
Contact: Vincent Worms, Managing Partner
Preferred Investment Size: $1,000,000 to $10,000,000. **Investment Types:** Seed, early and later stage. **Industry Preferences:** Internet specific, computer software, hardware and services, communications and media, semiconductors and other electronics, medical and health, consumer related, biotechnology, industrial and energy. **Geographic Preferences:** U.S. **Principal Exhibits:**

48371 ■ Peninsula Equity Partners
3000 Sand Hill Rd.
Bldg. 2, Ste. 100
Menlo Park, CA 94025
Ph:(650)854-0314
Fax:(650)854-0670
Co. E-mail: info@peninsulaequity.com
URL: http://www.peninsulaequity.com
Contact: Gregory Robinson, Principal
Investment Policies: Early, first and second stage. **Industry Preferences:** Information technology, computer software, hardware and services, semiconductors and other electronics. **Geographic Preferences:** U.S. **Principal Exhibits:**

48372 ■ Phoenix Growth Capital Corp.
2401 Kerner Blvd.
San Rafael, CA 94901
Ph:(415)485-4519
Free: (866)895-5050
Fax:(415)485-4663
Co. E-mail: info@phxa.com
URL: http://www.phxa.com
Contact: Gus Constantin, President and Chief Executive Officer
Preferred Investment Size: $250,000 to $1,000,000. **Investment Types:** First and second stage, and mezzanine. **Industry Preferences:** Communications, computer related, consumer retailing, distribution, electronics, genetic engineering, medical and health related, education, publishing, and transportation. **Geographic Preferences:** U.S. **Principal Exhibits:**

48373 ■ Prescient Capital LLC
2 Harrison St., Ste. 600
San Francisco, CA 94133
Ph:(415)675-6750
Fax:(415)675-6755
URL: http://www.prcap.com
Contact: Eric Mathewson, Managing Director
Investment Types: Early stage. **Industry Preferences:** Communications and media, computer hardware and software, Internet specific, and consumer related. **Geographic Preferences:** Colorado and Northern California. **Principal Exhibits:**

48374 ■ Prospect Venture Partners / Prospect Management LLC
435 Tasso St., Ste. 200
Palo Alto, CA 94301
Ph:(650)327-8800

Fax:(650)324-8838
URL: http://www.prospectventures.com
Contact: Alex Barkas, Managing Director
Preferred Investment Size: $500,000 to $10,000,000. **Investment Types:** Seed, start-up, first and second stage, early and later stage, expansion, and special situation. **Industry Preferences:** Biotechnology, medical and health, computer software and services, semiconductors and other electronics. **Geographic Preferences:** U.S. **Principal Exhibits:**

48375 ■ Putnam Lovell NBF Capital Partners, L.P.
The Plz. at Continental Park
2141 Rosecrans Ave., Ste. 5150
El Segundo, CA 90245
Ph:(310)414-6160
Fax:(310)607-9942
Co. E-mail: Capital@PutnamLovellNBF.com
URL: http://www.putnamlovellcapital.com
Contact: Robert M. Belke, Principal
Preferred Investment Size: $20,000,000 to $100,000,000. **Investment Types:** Seed, start-up, early, first, second and later stage, acquisition, balanced, expansion, leveraged buyout, management buyouts, recapitalizations, and special situation. **Industry Preferences:** Financial services. **Geographic Preferences:** U.S. and Canada. **Principal Exhibits:**

48376 ■ Red Rock Ventures
530 Lytton Ave., 2nd Fl.
Palo Alto, CA 94301
Ph:(650)325-3111
Fax:(650)853-7044
URL: http://www.redrockventures.com
Contact: Laura Gwosden, Chief Financial Officer
Preferred Investment Size: $500,000 to $5,000,000. **Investment Policies:** Seed, early and first stage. **Industry Preferences:** Computer software and services, Internet specific, communications and media, computer hardware, and industrial and energy. **Geographic Preferences:** West Coast. **Principal Exhibits:**

48377 ■ Redleaf Venture Management
14395 Saratoga Ave., Ste. 130
Saratoga, CA 95070
Ph:(408)868-0800
Fax:(408)868-0810
URL: http://www.redleaf.com
Contact: Michael B. Nelson, Managing Director
Preferred Investment Size: $1,000,000 to $20,000,000. **Investment Types:** Seed and first stage. **Industry Preferences:** Computer software and services, Internet specific, medical and health, communications and media, consumer related, and other products. **Geographic Preferences:** California. **Principal Exhibits:**

48378 ■ Rembrandt Venture Partners
2200 Sand Hill Rd., Ste. 100
Menlo Park, CA 94025
Ph:(650)326-7070
Fax:(650)326-3780
Co. E-mail: inquiries@rembrandtvc.com
URL: http://www.rembrandtvc.com
Contact: Douglas Schrier, General Partner
Investment Policies: Early stage. **Industry Preferences:** Communications, and Internet specific. **Geographic Preferences:** U.S. **Principal Exhibits:**

48379 ■ Riordan Lewis & Haden
10900 Wilshire Blvd., Ste. 850
Los Angeles, CA 90024
Ph:(310)405-7200
Fax:(310)405-7222
URL: http://www.rlhinvestors.com
Contact: J. Christopher Lewis, Managing Director
E-mail: clewis@rlhequity.com
Preferred Investment Size: $10,000,000 to $50,000,000. **Investment Types:** First and second stage, start-up, leveraged buyout, and special situation. **Industry Preferences:** Computer software, medical and health, consumer related, industrial and energy, transportation, business service, and manufacturing. **Geographic Preferences:** West Coast. **Principal Exhibits:**

48380 ■ Rocket Ventures
2200 Sand Hill Rd., Ste. 240
Menlo Park, CA 94025
Ph:(650)561-9100
URL: http://www.rocketventures.com
Contact: David Adams, Managing Director
Preferred Investment Size: $1,000,000 to $8,000,000. **Investment Types:** Seed, start-up, and early stage. **Industry Preferences:** Communications and media, computer software, and Internet specific. **Geographic Preferences:** California and West Coast. **Principal Exhibits:**

48381 ■ Rosewood Capital, L.P.
1 Maritime Plz., Ste. 1575
San Francisco, CA 94111
Ph:(415)362-5526
Fax:(415)362-1192
URL: http://www.rosewoodvc.com
Contact: Kevin Reilly, Managing Director
E-mail: kevin@rosewoodvc.com
Preferred Investment Size: $10,000,000 to $40,000,000. **Investment Types:** Second stage, leveraged buyout, special situation and control-block purchases. **Industry Preferences:** Consumer related, Internet specific, Computer software and services, communications and Media, business and financial services, and other products. **Geographic Preferences:** U.S. **Principal Exhibits:**

48382 ■ RWI Ventures
545 Middlefiels Rd., Ste. 220
Menlo Park, CA 94025
Ph:(650)543-3300
Fax:(650)543-3339
URL: http://www.rwigroup.com
Contact: Donald A. Lucas, Managing Director
Preferred Investment Size: $500,000 to $8,000,000. **Investment Types:** Start-up, early, first and second stage. **Industry Preferences:** Internet specific, computer software and services, computer hardware, communications and media, semiconductors and other electronics, medical and health, other products, industrial and energy. **Geographic Preferences:** U.S. **Principal Exhibits:**

48383 ■ Saderling Ventures
400 S. El Camino Real, Ste. 1200
Menlo Park, CA 94402
Ph:(650)401-2000
Fax:(650)375-7077
Co. E-mail: info@sanderling.com
URL: http://www.saderling.com
Contact: Timothy Wollaeger, Managing Director
Preferred Investment Size: $500,000 to $5,000,000. **Investment Types:** Seed, start-up, early stage, and mezzanine. **Industry Preferences:** Biotechnology, medical and health, Internet specific, computer software and services, computer hardware, semiconductors and other electronics, industrial and energy, communications and media, and consumer related. **Geographic Preferences:** U.S. and Canada. **Principal Exhibits:**

48384 ■ Saints Ventures
475 Sansome St., Ste. 1850
San Francisco, CA 94111
Ph:(415)773-2080
Fax:(415)835-5970
Co. E-mail: info@saintsvc.com
URL: http://www.saintsvc.com
Contact: Kenneth B. Sawyer, Managing Director
Preferred Investment Size: $5,000,000 to $100,000,000. **Investment Policies:** Special situation and acquisition. **Industry Preferences:** Consumer related, industrial, computer software, and Internet specific. **Geographic Preferences:** U.S. **Principal Exhibits:**

48385 ■ SBV Venture Partners / Sigefi, Burnette & Vallee
454 Ruthven Ave.
Palo Alto, CA 94301
Ph:(650)522-0085

Fax:(650)522-0087
Co. E-mail: info@sbvpartners.com
URL: http://www.sbvpartners.com
Contact: Jacques F. Vallee, General Partner
Preferred Investment Size: $500,000 to $2,500,000.
Investment Policies: Seed, start-up, research and development, early and first stage. **Industry Preferences:** Communications, computer hardware and software, Internet specific, semiconductors and other electronics, biotechnology, and medical and health.
Geographic Preferences: U.S. and Canada. **Principal Exhibits:**

48386 ■ Selby Venture Partners
3500 Alameda de las Pulgas, Ste. 200
Menlo Park, CA 94025
Ph:(650)854-7399
Fax:(650)854-7039
URL: http://www.selbyventures.com
Contact: Robert Marshall, Managing Director
Preferred Investment Size: $500,000 to $7,000,000.
Investment Types: Seed, early and first stage. **Industry Preferences:** Internet specific, communications and media, consumer related, computer software, and services, computer hardware, semiconductors and other electronics. **Geographic Preferences:** Northern California, Southern California, and West Coast. **Principal Exhibits:**

48387 ■ Semper Ventures
325M Sharon Park Dr., Ste. 460
Menlo Park, CA 94025
Ph:(847)589-4197
URL: http://www.semperventures.com
Contact: Victor J. Lee, Chief Executive Officer
Preferred Investment Size: $500,000 to $2,000,000.
Investment Policies: Early and later stage. **Industry Preferences:** Computer software. **Geographic Preferences:** National. **Principal Exhibits:**

48388 ■ Sequoia Capital
3000 Sand Hill Rd.
Bldg. 4, Ste. 250
Menlo Park, CA 94025
Ph:(650)854-3927
Fax:(650)854-2977
URL: http://www.sequoiacap.com
Contact: Greg McAdoo, Partner
E-mail: mcadoo@sequoiacap.com
Preferred Investment Size: $100,000 to $100,000,000. **Investment Types:** Early, seed, start-up, first and second stage and expansion. **Industry Preferences:** Internet specific, communications and media, computer software and services, computer hardware, other products, semiconductors and other electronics, medical and health, consumer related, biotechnology, industrial and energy. **Geographic Preferences:** West Coast. **Principal Exhibits:**

48389 ■ Shoreline Venture Management, LLC
Mariners Plz.
675 Mariners Island Blvd., Ste. 109
San Mateo, CA 94404
Ph:(650)854-6685
Co. E-mail: info@shorelineventures.com
URL: http://www.shorelineventures.com
Contact: Peter Craddock, Managing Director
Investment Policies: Seed and early stage. **Industry Preferences:** Consumer related, computer software and services, information technology, and medical and health. **Geographic Preferences:** National. **Principal Exhibits:**

48390 ■ Sienna Ventures / Sienna Holdings Inc.
100 Drakes Landing Rd., Ste. 115
Greenbrae, CA 94965
Ph:(415)464-2040
Fax:(415)464-2043
URL: http://www.siennaventures.com
Contact: Daniel L. Skaff, Managing Partner
Preferred Investment Size: $35,000,000 minimum.
Investment Types: Start-up, early, first and second stage, and balanced. **Industry Preferences:** Internet specific, computer software and services, consumer related, computer hardware, communications and media, other products, and semiconductors and other electronics. **Geographic Preferences:** U.S. and Canada. **Principal Exhibits:**

48391 ■ Sierra Ventures
2884 Sand Hill Rd., Ste. 100
Menlo Park, CA 94025
Ph:(650)854-1000
Fax:(650)854-5593
Co. E-mail: info@sierraventures.com
URL: http://www.sierraventures.com
Contact: Mark Fernandes, Managing Director
E-mail: mfernandes@sierraventures.com
Preferred Investment Size: $2,000,000 to $25,000,000. **Investment Types:** Seed, start-up, early, first and second stage. **Industry Preferences:** Internet specific, computer software and services, computer hardware, communications and media, semiconductors and other electronics, industrial and energy, biotechnology, and consumer related. **Geographic Preferences:** U.S. and Canada. **Principal Exhibits:**

48392 ■ Sigma Partners (Menlo Park)
1600 El Camino Real, Ste. 280
Menlo Park, CA 94025
Ph:(650)853-1700
Fax:(650)853-1717
URL: http://www.sigmapartners.com
Contact: Lawrence G. Finch, Managing Director
E-mail: lgf@sigmapartners.com
Preferred Investment Size: $2,000,000 to $8,000,000. **Investment Types:** Start-up, early stage, and expansion. **Industry Preferences:** Internet specific, computer hardware, computer software and services, communications and media, semiconductors and other electronics, consumer related, and other products. **Geographic Preferences:** U.S. **Principal Exhibits:**

48393 ■ Silicon Valley Bancventures / Silicon Valley Bank (Menlo Park)
3000 Sand Hill Rd.
Bldg. 3, Ste. 150
Menlo Park, CA 94025
Ph:(650)233-7420
Fax:(650)233-6611
URL: http://www.svb.com
Contact: Kenneth P. Wilcox, President and Chief Executive Officer
Preferred Investment Size: $500,000 to $1,000,000.
Investment Types: Start-up, first and second stage, fund of funds and mezzanine. **Industry Preferences:** Internet specific, communications and media, semiconductors and other electronics, computer software and services, medical and health, consumer related, computer hardware, other products, biotechnology, and industrial and energy. **Geographic Preferences:** U.S. **Principal Exhibits:**

48394 ■ Skyline Ventures
525 University Ave., Ste. 520
Palo Alto, CA 94301
Ph:(650)462-5800
Fax:(650)329-1090
URL: http://www.skylineventures.com
Contact: John G. Freund, Managing Director
Preferred Investment Size: $15,000,000 to $25,000,000. **Investment Types:** Early stage. **Industry Preferences:** Medical and health, biotechnology, computer software and services, Internet specific, semiconductors and other electronics. **Geographic Preferences:** U.S. **Principal Exhibits:**

48395 ■ Sofinnova Ventures
2800 Sand Hill Rd., Ste. 150
Menlo Park, CA 94025
Ph:(650)681-8420
Fax:(650)322-2037
Co. E-mail: info@sofinnova.com
URL: http://www.sofinnova.com
Contact: Eric Buatois, General Partner
E-mail: eric@sofinnova.com
Preferred Investment Size: $100,000 to $30,000,000. **Investment Types:** Seed, start-up, early, first and second stage, and mezzanine. **Industry Preferences:** Internet specific, computer software and services, computer hardware, communications and media, semiconductors and other electronics, and other products. **Geographic Preferences:** Northeast and West Coast. **Principal Exhibits:**

48396 ■ Sorrento Ventures
12250 El Camino Real, Ste. 100
San Diego, CA 92130
Ph:(858)792-2700
Fax:(858)792-5070
Co. E-mail: investment@sorrentoventures.com
URL: http://www.sorrentoventures.com
Contact: Robert M. Jaffe, President
Preferred Investment Size: $1,000,000 to $10,000,000. **Investment Types:** Early, first and second stage. **Industry Preferences:** Medical and health, computer software and services, Internet specific, biotechnology, communications and media, consumer related, computer hardware, industrial and energy. **Geographic Preferences:** Southern California. **Principal Exhibits:**

48397 ■ Summit Partners (Palo Alto)
499 Hamilton Ave.
Palo Alto, CA 94301
Ph:(650)321-1166
Fax:(650)321-1188
URL: http://www.summitpartners.com
Contact: C.J. Fitzgerald, Managing Director
E-mail: cfitzgerald@summitpartners.com
Preferred Investment Size: $5,000,000 to $500,000,000. **Investment Types:** Second and later stage, balanced, mezzanine, generalist PE, leveraged buyout, special situation, and control-block purchases. **Industry Preferences:** Computer software and services, computer hardware, communications and media, Internet specific, semiconductors and other electronics, medical and health, business services, consumer related, biotechnology, industrial and energy, and other products. **Geographic Preferences:** U.S. and Canada. **Principal Exhibits:**

48398 ■ Sutter Hill Ventures
755 Page Mill Rd., Ste. A-200
Palo Alto, CA 94304-1005
Ph:(650)493-5600
Fax:(650)858-1854
Co. E-mail: shv@shv.com
URL: http://www.shv.com
Contact: David L. Anderson, Managing Director
Preferred Investment Size: $100,000 to $10,000,000. **Investment Types:** Seed, start-up, early, and first stage. **Industry Preferences:** Computer software and services, Internet specific, computer hardware, communications and media, semiconductors and other electronics, consumer related, industrial and energy, and other products. **Geographic Preferences:** U.S. **Principal Exhibits:**

48399 ■ Sybase, Inc.
1 Sybase Dr.
Dublin, CA 94568
Ph:(925)236-5000
Free: 800-792-2735
Fax:(925)236-6815
Co. E-mail: contact_us@anywhere.com
URL: http://www.sybase.com
Contact: John S. Chen, President and Chief Executive Officer
Preferred Investment Size: $500,000 to $5,000,000.
Investment Types: Seed, early stage, and expansion. **Industry Preferences:** Computer software, and Internet specific. **Geographic Preferences:** U.S.
Principal Exhibits:

48400 ■ Synopsys, Inc.
700 E. Middlefield Rd.
Mountain View, CA 94043
Ph:(650)584-5000
Free: 800-541-7737
URL: http://www.synopsys.com
Contact: Brian Beattie, Chief Financial Officer
Preferred Investment Size: $500,000 to $5,000,000.
Investment Types: Seed, start-up, early, first, second, and later stage, and expansion. **Industry Preferences:** Semiconductors and other electronics, computer software and services, manufacturing, and computer hardware. **Principal Exhibits:**

48401 ■ TA Associates, Inc. (Menlo Park)
64 Willow Pl., Ste. 100
Menlo Park, CA 94025
Ph:(650)473-2200

Fax:(650)473-2235
URL: http://www.ta.com
Contact: Michael C. Child, Managing Director
E-mail: mchild@ta.com
Preferred Investment Size: $60,000,000 to $500,000,000. **Investment Types:** Later stage, leveraged buyout, management buyouts, mezzanine, expansion, and recapitalizations. **Industry Preferences:** Computer software and services, other products, communications and media, Internet specific, medical and health, semiconductors and other electronics, consumer related, computer hardware, financial and business services, medical and health.. **Geographic Preferences:** U.S. and Canada. **Principal Exhibits:**

48402 ■ Tallwood Venture Capital
3000 Sand Hill Rd.
Bldg. 3, Ste. 240
Menlo Park, CA 94025-7113
Ph:(650)473-6750
Free: 877-380-6490
Fax:(650)473-6755
Co. E-mail: information@tallwoodvc.com
URL: http://www.tallwoodvc.com
Contact: Dado Banatao, Managing Partner
Investment Policies: start-up, early stage, and balanced. **Industry Preferences:** Communications, and semiconductors and other electronics. **Geographic Preferences:** U.S. **Principal Exhibits:**

48403 ■ Techfarm Ventures / Techfund Capital
1800 Embarcadero Rd.
Palo Alto, CA 94303
Ph:(650)856-8500
Fax:(650)856-8510
URL: http://www.techfarm.com
Contact: Gordon Campbell, Managing Director
E-mail: gordon@techfarm.com
Preferred Investment Size: $1,500,000 to $8,000,000. **Investment Types:** Seed, early, first, and later stage. **Industry Preferences:** Semiconductors and other electronics, computer software and services, Internet specific, communications and media. **Geographic Preferences:** U.S. **Principal Exhibits:**

48404 ■ Technology Crossover Ventures (TCV)
528 Ramona St.
Palo Alto, CA 94301
Ph:(650)614-8200
Fax:(650)614-8222
URL: http://www.tcv.com
Contact: John Rosenberg, Principal
Preferred Investment Size: $20,000 to $200,000,000. **Investment Types:** Start-up, first and second stage, and mezzanine. **Industry Preferences:** Internet specific, computer software, hardware and services, financial services, communications and media, consumer related, semiconductors and other electronics, and biotechnology. **Geographic Preferences:** U.S and Canada. **Principal Exhibits:**

48405 ■ Technology Funding
1107 Investment Blvd., Ste. 180
El Dorado Hills, CA 95762
Ph:(916)941-1400
Fax:(916)941-7551
Co. E-mail: businessplans@technologyfunding.com
URL: http://technologyfunding.com
Contact: Charles R. Kokesh, Managing General Partner
Preferred Investment Size: $500,000 to $2,000,000. **Investment Types:** Early stage, expansion, and joint ventures. **Industry Preferences:** Industrial and energy, biotechnology, medical and health, computer software and services, computer hardware, other products, Internet specific, semiconductors and other electronics, communications and media. **Geographic Preferences:** Northern California. **Principal Exhibits:**

48406 ■ Technology Partners
550 University Ave.
Palo Alto, CA 94301
Ph:(650)289-9000

Fax:(650)289-9001
Co. E-mail: admin@technologypartners.com
URL: http://www.technologypartners.com
Contact: Ira Ehrenpreis, General Partner
E-mail: ira@technologypartners.com
Preferred Investment Size: $1,000,000 to $15,000,000. **Investment Types:** Seed, early and first stage. **Industry Preferences:** Internet specific, medical and health, communications and media, computer software and services, consumer related, biotechnology, semiconductors and other electronics, computer hardware, industrial and energy, and other products. **Geographic Preferences:** West Coast. **Principal Exhibits:**

48407 ■ Telos Venture Partners
835 Page Mill Rd.
Palo Alto, CA 94304
Ph:(650)949-1343
URL: http://www.telosvp.com
Contact: Bruce R. Bourbon, General Partner
E-mail: bourbob@telosvp.com
Preferred Investment Size: $1,000,000 to $3,000,000. **Investment Types:** Early, first and second stage. **Industry Preferences:** Internet specific, computer software and services, computer hardware, semiconductors and other electronics, communications and media, and other products. **Geographic Preferences:** Northern California, Northwest, and West Coast. **Principal Exhibits:**

48408 ■ Ticonderoga Capital Inc.
25 Braintree Hill Park, Ste. 200
Braintree, MA 02184
Ph:(781)416-3409
Fax:(781)416-9868
URL: http://www.ticcap.com
Contact: Craig Jones, Managing Partner
E-mail: craig@ticcap.com
Preferred Investment Size: $2,000,000 to $5,000,000. **Investment Types:** Later stage, acquisition, recapitalizations, and management buyouts. **Industry Preferences:** Computer software, and services, Business services, biotechnology, computer hardware, consumer related, semiconductors and other electronics, medical and health, communications and media, Internet specific, and other products. **Geographic Preferences:** U.S. and Canada. **Principal Exhibits:**

48409 ■ Trinity Ventures
3000 Sand Hill Rd.
Bldg. 4, Ste. 160
Menlo Park, CA 94025
Ph:(650)854-9500
Fax:(650)854-9501
Co. E-mail: info@trinityventures.com
URL: http://www.trinityventures.com
Contact: Jim Tybur, Principal
E-mail: jim@trinityventures.com
Preferred Investment Size: $5,000,000 to $20,000,000. **Investment Types:** Early stage. **Industry Preferences:** Internet specific, computer software and services, computer hardware, communications and media, consumer related, semiconductors and other electronics, medical and health, industrial and energy, and other products. **Geographic Preferences:** U.S. **Principal Exhibits:**

48410 ■ U.S. Venture Partners
2735 Sand Hill Rd.
Menlo Park, CA 94025
Ph:(650)854-9080
Fax:(650)854-3018
URL: http://www.usvp.com
Contact: William K. Bowes Jr., Founding Partner
E-mail: bbowes@usvp.com
Preferred Investment Size: $250,000 to $25,000,000. **Investment Types:** Seed, start-up, first and second stage, early and later stage, and expansion. **Industry Preferences:** Internet specific, computer software and services, computer hardware, communications and media, semiconductors and other electronics, consumer related, medical and health, biotechnology, industrial and energy, and other products. **Geographic Preferences:** U.S. **Principal Exhibits:**

48411 ■ Vanguard Ventures
PO Box 20068
San Jose, CA 95160
Ph:(650)321-2900
Fax:(650)321-2902
URL: http://www.vanguardventures.com
Contact: Donald Wood, Managing Director
Preferred Investment Size: $500,000 to $10,000,000. **Investment Types:** Seed, early, and first stage, research and development. **Industry Preferences:** Communications and media, Internet specific, medical and health, semiconductors and other electronics, computer software and services, biotechnology, computer hardware, semiconductors and other electronics, industrial and energy, and other products. **Geographic Preferences:** U.S. **Principal Exhibits:**

48412 ■ Venrock Associates (Palo Alto)
3340 Hillview Ave.
Palo Alto, CA 94304
Ph:(650)561-9580
Fax:(650)561-9180
URL: http://www.venrock.com
Contact: Brian Ascher, Partner
Preferred Investment Size: $5,000,000 to $15,000,000. **Investment Types:** Seed, start-up, first, early, and later stage. **Industry Preferences:** Biotechnology, Internet specific, computer software and services, computer hardware, communications and media, medical and health, semiconductors and other electronics, industrial and energy, consumer related, and other products. **Geographic Preferences:** U.S. **Principal Exhibits:**

48413 ■ Ventana Capital Management, Inc.
22431 Antonio Pkwy., Ste. B160-1002
Rancho Santa Margarita, CA 92688
Ph:(949)481-4200
Fax:(949)766-4487
URL: http://www.ventanaglobal.com
Contact: Thomas O. Gephart, Managing Partner
Preferred Investment Size: $1,000,000 minimum. **Investment Types:** Early stage. **Industry Preferences:** Communications and media, semiconductors and other electronics, biotechnology, medical and health, and industrial and energy. **Geographic Preferences:** Southern California. **Principal Exhibits:**

48414 ■ Walden International
1 California St., Ste. 2800
San Francisco, CA 94111
Ph:(415)765-7100
Fax:(415)765-7200
Co. E-mail: usa@waldenintl.com
URL: http://www.waldenintl.com
Contact: Mary Coleman, Managing Director
E-mail: mcoleman@waldenintl.com
Preferred Investment Size: $10,000,000 to $25,000,000. **Investment Types:** Seed, start-up, early and first stage. **Industry Preferences:** Communications and media, computer hardware, other products, Internet specific, semiconductors and other electronics, computer Software and services, medical and health, biotechnology, consumer related, industrial and energy. **Geographic Preferences:** U.S. **Principal Exhibits:**

48415 ■ Wedbush Capital Partners
1000 Wilshire Blvd.
Los Angeles, CA 90017
Ph:(213)688-8000
Fax:(213)688-8095
URL: http://www.wedbush.com
Contact: Geoff Bland, Managing Director
Preferred Investment Size: $500,000 minimum. **Investment Types:** Second stage, mezzanine, recapitalizations, and leveraged buyout. **Industry Preferences:** Computer software and hardware, Internet specific, medical and health, consumer related, and business service. **Geographic Preferences:** West Coast. **Principal Exhibits:**

48416 ■ Westar Capital (Costa Mesa)
949 South Coast Dr., Ste. 170
Costa Mesa, CA 92626
Ph:(714)481-5160

Fax:(714)481-5166
Co. E-mail: contact@westarcapital.com
URL: http://www.westarcapital.com
Contact: Sharon Bujacich, Partner
E-mail: sbujacich@westarcapital.com
Preferred Investment Size: $5,000,000 to $25,000,000. **Investment Types:** Leveraged buy-outs, special situation, control-block purchases, turnarounds, and industry rollups. **Industry Preferences:** Communications and media, computer related, semiconductors and other electronics, medical and health, consumer related, industrial and energy, transportation, financial services, and manufacturing. **Geographic Preferences:** Northwest, Southwest, Rocky Mountains, and West Coast. **Principal Exhibits:**

48417 ■ Western States Investment Group
6335 Ferris Sq., Ste. A
San Diego, CA 92121
Ph:(858)678-0800
Fax:(858)678-0900
Co. E-mail: info@wsig.com
URL: http://www.wsig.com
Contact: Scott R. Pancoast, Executive Vice President
Preferred Investment Size: $1,000,000 minimum. **Investment Types:** Seed, start-up, first stage, research and development, and leveraged buyout. **Industry Preferences:** Industrial and energy, medical and health, communications and media, semiconductors and other electronics, computer software and services, and biotechnology. **Geographic Preferences:** Southwest and West Coast. **Principal Exhibits:**

48418 ■ Western Technology Investment
104 La mesa Dr., Ste. 102
Portola Valley, CA 94028
Ph:(650)234-4300
Fax:(650)234-4343
Co. E-mail: info@westerntech.com
URL: http://www.westerntech.com
Contact: Ron Swenson, Investment Partner and Founder
E-mail: rons@westerntech.com
Preferred Investment Size: $250,000 to $30,000,000. **Investment Types:** Seed, research and development, start-up, first and second stage, mezzanine, balanced, and special situation. **Industry Preferences:** Communications and media, semiconductors and other electronics, biotechnology, medical and health. **Geographic Preferences:** U.S. **Principal Exhibits:**

48419 ■ Windward Ventures (Thousand Oaks)
PO Box 7688
Thousand Oaks, CA 91359
Ph:(805)499-7338
Co. E-mail: mailbox@windwardventures.com
URL: http://www.windwardventures.com
Contact: James A. Cole, Managing Partner
E-mail: cole@windwardventures.com
Preferred Investment Size: $1,000,000 to $5,000,000. **Investment Types:** Start-up, early, first, and second stage. **Industry Preferences:** Medical and health, Internet specific, computer software and services, communications and media, semiconductors and other electronics, and other products. **Geographic Preferences:** Southern California. **Principal Exhibits:**

48420 ■ Woodside Fund
350 Marine Pkwy., Ste. 300
Redwood City, CA 94065
Ph:(650)610-8050
Fax:(650)610-8051
Co. E-mail: info@woodsidefund.com
URL: http://www.woodsidefund.com
Contact: Thomas A. Shields, Venture Partner
Preferred Investment Size: $5,000,000 to $10,000,000. **Investment Types:** Seed, start-up, early, first and second stage, and later stage. **Industry Preferences:** Computer software and services, communications and media, Internet specific, consumer related, computer hardware, other products,

semiconductors and other electronics. **Geographic Preferences:** Northern California and West Coast. **Principal Exhibits:**

48421 ■ Worldview Technology Partners
2207 Bridgepointe Pkwy., Ste. 100
San Mateo, CA 94404
Ph:(650)322-3800
Fax:(650)322-3880
URL: http://www.worldview.com
Contact: James Wei, General Partner
Investment Types: Seed, research and development, start-up, first and second stage, balanced, and mezzanine. **Industry Preferences:** Communications and media, Internet specific, semiconductors and other electronics, computer software, and services, computer hardware, and other products. **Geographic Preferences:** U.S. **Principal Exhibits:**

PROCUREMENT ASSISTANCE PROGRAMS

48422 ■ California Procurement Technical Assistance Center–Federal Technology Center Procurement Technical Assistance Center
4600 Roseville Rd., Ste. 100
North Highlands, CA 95660
Ph:(916)334-9388
Fax:(916)334-9078
Co. E-mail: jack@theftc.org
URL: http://www.theftc.org/PTAC
Contact: Jack Toney, Dir.
Description: Promotes economic development by facilitating technology transfer between government and the private sector, and by helping small businesses successfully compete for government contracts.

48423 ■ California Procurement Technical Assistance Center–The Federal Technology Center (The FTC)
4600 Roseville Rd., Ste. 100
North Highlands, CA 95660
Ph:(916)334-9388
Fax:(916)334-9078
Co. E-mail: jack@theftc.org
URL: http://www.theftc.org
Contact: Jack Toney, Dir.
E-mail: Jaxk@TheFTC.org
Description: Promotes economic development by facilitating technology transfer between government and the private sector, and by helping small businesses successfully compete for government contracts.

48424 ■ California Procurement Technical Assistance Center–Los Angeles County Office of Small Business
1100 N Eastern Ave., No. G115
Los Angeles, CA 90063
Ph:(323)881-3964
Fax:(323)881-1871
Co. E-mail: dcabreira@isd.lacounty.gov
URL: http://www.laosb.org
Contact: Debbie Cabreira Johnson, Program Dir.
E-mail: dcabreira@isd.lacounty.gov
Description: Los Angeles County Office of Small Business (OSB) is a source of information on procurement opportunities, certification, financing, and technical assistance. OSB also serves as the County Procurement Technical Assistance Center (PTAC), funded by the U.S. Department of Defense (DoD) to help small businesses get contracts with prime defense contractors.

48425 ■ California Procurement Technical Assistance Center–Pacific American Indian Development (PAID)–Procurement Technical Assistance Center (Bldg.)
Bldg. R1
2000 East El Segundo Blvd.
PO Box 902, Mail Station R01/A501
El Segundo, CA 90245

Ph:(480)545-1298
URL: http://www.ncaied.org/american-indian-procurement-assistance.php
Contact: Oscar Padilla, Dir.
E-mail: oscar.padilla@p-aid.org
Description: Assists Indian owned and tribally owned businesses succeed in government contracting.

48426 ■ California Procurement Technical Assistance Center–Riverside Community College District
14745 Riverside Dr.
Riverside, CA 92518
Ph:(951)571-6475
Free: (866)267-7986
Fax:(951)653-1051
Co. E-mail: susanne.adams@rcc.edu
URL: http://www.rcchelpsbusiness.com
Contact: Julie Ann Padilla, Dir
Description: Helps business firms market their goods and services to federal, state and local government agencies.

48427 ■ California Procurement Technical Assistance Center–San Diego Contracting Opportunities Center
4007 Camino Del Rio S., Ste. 210
San Diego, CA 92108-4189
Ph:(619)285-7020
Fax:(619)285-7030
Co. E-mail: sbdcoc@ptac-sandiego.org
URL: http://www.ptac-sandiego.org
Contact: Gunnar Schalin

INCUBATORS/RESEARCH AND TECHNOLOGY PARKS

48428 ■ Business Technology Center of Los Angeles County
2400 N Lincoln Ave.
Altadena, CA 91001
Ph:(626)296-6300
Fax:(626)296-6301
Co. E-mail: info@labtc.org
URL: http://www.labtc.org
Contact: Mark Loeberman, Manager
Description: The BTC committed to developing high technology firms by providing financial, technical, and business management assistance.

48429 ■ California Institute of Technology–Office of Sponsored Research
1200 E California Blvd., MC 231-15
Pasadena, CA 91125
Ph:(626)395-6219
Fax:(626)795-4571
Co. E-mail: david.mayo@caltech.edu
URL: http://researchadministration.caltech.edu/osr
Contact: David J. Mayo, Dir.
E-mail: david.mayo@caltech.edu
Scope: Responsible for administrative and financial aspects of extramurally sponsored research conducted by faculty members and graduate students of the Institute.

48430 ■ California State University, Fresno–Office of Research and Sponsored Programs
4910 N Chestnut Ave.
Fresno, CA 93726-1852
Ph:(559)278-0840
Fax:(559)278-0992
Co. E-mail: danielg@csufresno.edu
URL: http://www.csufresno.edu/grants/
Contact: Dr. Daniel J. Griffin, Assoc.Dir.
E-mail: danielg@csufresno.edu
Scope: Supports research programs in academic and professional schools in the fields of agriculture, business, engineering, humanities, health and social work, physical and natural sciences, education, and behavioral and social sciences. **Publications:** Brochure; Reports. **Educational Activities:** Research symposium (annually), on current campus and community research.

48431 ■ California State University Fresno Foundation
4910 N Chestnut
Fresno, CA 93726-1852
Ph:(559)278-0850
Fax:(559)278-0992
Co. E-mail: kkompsi@csufresno.edu
URL: http://www.auxiliary.com/Foundation
Contact: Keith Kompsi, Dir.
E-mail: kkompsi@csufresno.edu
Scope: Chemistry, biology, business, and agriculture. Administers grants and contracts for sponsored research performed by faculty members and graduate students of the University and generally promotes the interests of the University.

48432 ■ California State University, Long Beach–Office of University Research
1250 Bellflower Blvd.
Long Beach, CA 90840
Ph:(562)985-4633
Fax:(562)985-8665
Co. E-mail: yih@csulb.edu
URL: http://www.csulb.edu/divisions/aa/research/our
Contact: Dr. T.C. Yih, Assoc.VP
E-mail: yih@csulb.edu
Scope: Responsible for financial administration of extramural grants to the University for research and other sponsored programs. **Publications:** Annual Report; Research Notes (monthly).

48433 ■ California State University, Long Beach Foundation
6300 State University Dr., Ste. 332
Long Beach, CA 90815
Ph:(562)985-5537
Fax:(562)985-7951
Co. E-mail: mestephens@csulb.edu
URL: http://www.foundation.csulb.edu
Contact: Mary Stephens, CEO
E-mail: mestephens@csulb.edu
Scope: Responsible for financial administration of extramural grants to the University for research, campus programs, operations of performing arts center, and other activities.

48434 ■ California State University, Northridge–Office of Research and Sponsored Projects
18111 Nordhoff St.
Northridge, CA 91330-8232
Ph:(818)677-2901
Fax:(818)677-4691
Co. E-mail: scott.perez@csun.edu
URL: http://www.csun.edu/research/research
Contact: Scott Perez, Dir.
E-mail: scott.perez@csun.edu
Scope: Administers and coordinates research at the University and provides support in all fields of scholarly activities for general faculty research projects and application efforts. **Publications:** Research Newsletter. **Awards:** Faculty Research and Creative Activity Awards Competition (annually).

48435 ■ Central Valley Business Incubator
1630 E. Shaw, Ste. 163
Fresno, CA 93710
Ph:(559)292-9033
Fax:(559)294-6537
URL: http://www.cvbi.org/
Contact: Travis Sheridan, Dir.
Description: A public/private partnership, fueled with community resources and helping start-up companies launch successfully by creating an entrepreneurial community where people learn how to balance their passion and ideas with the structure of running a successful business.

48436 ■ Communications Technology Cluster (CTC)
300 Frank H. Ogawa Plaza, Ste. 210
Oakland, CA 94612-1932
Ph:(510)903-1902
Fax:(510)903-1952
Co. E-mail: info@ctcluster.com
URL: http://www.ctcluster.com/main/index.htm
Contact: Joe Gross, Pres & CEO
Description: CTC is a business incubator supporting entrepreneurs and growth-oriented small to mid-sized companies in the fields of business services, consumer products, financial services, healthcare, and technology.

48437 ■ Daly City Business Center
355 Gellert Blvd., Ste. 230
Daly City, CA 94015
Ph:(650)757-2060
Fax:(650)757-2075
Co. E-mail: info@DalyCityBusinessCenter.com
URL: http://www.dalycity.org/services_for_business/Economic_Development/dcbzctr.htm
Description: A small business incubator providing a proven growth environment for small businesses and entrepreneurs.

48438 ■ El Pajaro Community Development Corporation
23 E Beach St., Ste. 209
Watsonville, CA 95076
Ph:(831)722-1224
Fax:(831)722-3128
Co. E-mail: info@elpajarocdc.org/
URL: http://www.elpajarocdc.org/
Contact: Carmen Herrera-Mansir, Exec. Dir.
Description: A small business incubator with more than twenty years of experience in the provision of bilingual/bicultural small business assistance and job creation for primarily minority and low-income entrepreneurs.

48439 ■ The Greater Antelope Valley Economic Alliance
1028 West Ave., L-12, No. 101
Lancaster, CA 93534
Ph:(661)945-2741
Free: 800-888-7483
Fax:(661)945-7711
Co. E-mail: info@aveconomy.org
URL: http://www.aveconomy.org
Contact: Mel Layne, Pres.
Description: Provides a thriving environment for economic growth and offers a wide range of benefits to businesses seeking to relocate or expand into our area.

48440 ■ Humboldt State University Foundation
PO Box 1185
Arcata, CA 95518-1185
Ph:(707)826-4189
Fax:(707)826-4783
Co. E-mail: hsuf@humboldt.edu
URL: http://www.humboldt.edu/hsuf
E-mail: hsuf@humboldt.edu
Scope: Administers extramurally sponsored research and training projects conducted at the University in such areas as education, fisheries, forestry, wildlife management, oceanography, endangered species, mathematics, economics, computer information systems, business management, social welfare, psychology, geology, environmental resources engineering, and native American studies. Also raises funds and makes grants to the University. **Publications:** The Humboldt Stater (quarterly).

48441 ■ Los Angeles Business Owner Outreach Support and Training (LABOOST)
2 Coral Circle
Monterey Park, CA 91755
Ph:(323)890-7110
Free: (866)632-6678
Fax:(323)890-8575
Co. E-mail: Mark.Lieberman@lacdc.org
URL: http://www.lacdc.org/CDCWebsite/la-boost/home.aspx
Contact: Mark Lieberman, Dir.
Description: Provides emerging small businesses with professional training, outreach, counseling, and advisory services. Formerly Athens Westmont Business Center.

48442 ■ San Diego State University Research Foundation
Gateway Ctr.
5250 Campanile Dr.
San Diego, CA 92182
Ph:(619)594-5410
Fax:(619)582-5374
Co. E-mail: dgilbreath@foundation.sdsu.edu
URL: http://www.foundation.sdsu.edu
Contact: Dan Gilbreath, Exec.Dir.
E-mail: dgilbreath@foundation.sdsu.edu
Scope: Works with faculty and staff to develop and administer grants and contracts and community-service programs; develops and administers major centers, institutes, community partnerships and programs; administers a technology transfer program; administers student scholarship, loan funds and financially manages and invests gifts, trusts and endowments, most on behalf of the University's philanthropic foundation; and acquires, develops, and manages real property to provide space for sponsored programs.

48443 ■ San Francisco State University–Office of Research and Sponsored Programs
Administration 471
1600 Holloway Ave.
San Francisco, CA 94132
Ph:(415)338-7094
Fax:(415)338-2493
Co. E-mail: jturkkan@sfsu.edu
URL: http://research.sfsu.edu
Contact: Dr. Jaylan S. Turkkan, Assoc.VP
E-mail: jturkkan@sfsu.edu
Scope: Facilitates faculty research and scholarly and creative activities and assists faculty members in securing extramural funding by locating potential research sponsors and providing all budget, pre-award services, and post-award grant and contract management. Administers grant development and sponsored research activities funded by foundations and corporations. **Services:** Consultation, regarding the conceptualization, planning, networking, critiquing, and editing of a proposal; National funding searches, by computer. **Publications:** Research News (quarterly). **Educational Activities:** Conferences, on federal and non-federal funding sources for faculty, grant office administrators, and the general public; Workshops, on proposal development and identification of funding sources, open to faculty members, University staff.

48444 ■ San Jose Software Business Cluster
2 N First St., Fourth Fl.
San Jose, CA 95113
Ph:(408)535-2701
Fax:(408)535-2711
Co. E-mail: info@sjsbc.org
URL: http://www.sjsbc.org
Contact: Chuck Erickson, Dir.
Description: Small business incubator with capacity for 20 to 30 emerging software firms.

48445 ■ San Jose State University Research Foundation
210 N 4th St., 4th Fl.
San Jose, CA 95112
Ph:(408)924-1400
Fax:(408)924-1499
Co. E-mail: msidney@foundation.sjsu.edu
URL: http://www.sjsufoundation.org
Contact: Mary Sidney, COO
E-mail: msidney@foundation.sjsu.edu
Scope: Develops, administers, and coordinates extramurally sponsored research and training, special projects, conferences, and short courses. Also administers a faculty research grant, provides seed support to faculty members, and develops campus policy with respect to research and advanced studies of the University with assistance of faculty-administrative research committees.

48446 ■ SARTA CleanStart
3801 Power Inn Rd.
Sacramento, CA 95826

Ph:(916)231-0770
Co. E-mail: gary@cleanstart.org
URL: http://www.sarta.org/go/cs/
Contact: Gary Simon
Description: An initiative of McClellan Technology Incubator (MTI) and Sacramento Area Regional Technology Alliance (SARTA) designed to accelerate the development of clean energy technology ventures within the Greater Sacramento Region.

48447 ■ Stanford University–Office of Technology Licensing
1705 El Camino Real
Palo Alto, CA 94306-1106
Ph:(650)723-0651
Fax:(650)725-7295
Co. E-mail: katharine.ku@stanford.edu
URL: http://otl.stanford.edu
Contact: Katharine Ku, Dir.
E-mail: katharine.ku@stanford.edu
Scope: Licenses technology in the fields of scientific and medical instruments, pharmaceuticals, chemicals, computer software and databases, integrated circuit technology, optics, and microbiology. Evaluates, markets, and negotiates licensing agreements with industry.

48448 ■ Stanford University–Stanford Research Park
Stanford Real Estate Office, Ste. 100
2755 Sand Hill Rd.
Menlo Park, CA 94025
Ph:(650)926-0308
Fax:(650)854-9268
Co. E-mail: tgriego@stanford.edu
URL: http://lbre.stanford.edu/realestate/research_park
Contact: Tiffany Griego
E-mail: tgriego@stanford.edu
Scope: 704-acre site linking research resources of the University with Park tenants, particularly in the areas of electronics, software, space, publishing, pharmaceutics, and biotechnology. Activities between park tenants and the University community include cooperative research ventures, instruction, and consulting.

48449 ■ University Auxiliary Services, Inc.
Golden Eagle Bldg., Rm. 314
5151 State University Dr.
Los Angeles, CA 90032
Ph:(323)343-2531
Fax:(323)343-6821
URL: http://www.universityauxiliaryservices.org/
Contact: Patrick Harris, Pres./Chm.
Scope: Administers research and other grants and contracts for projects conducted at the University.
Educational Activities: Conferences; Workshops, both of noncredit.

48450 ■ University of California–Office of Technology Transfer
1111 Franklin St., 5th Fl.
Oakland, CA 94607-5200
Ph:(510)587-6000
Fax:(510)587-6090
Co. E-mail: william.tucker@ucop.edu
URL: http://www.ucop.edu/ott
Contact: William T. Tucker, Exec.Dir.
E-mail: william.tucker@ucop.edu
Scope: Facilitates technology transfer and research activities in biotechnology, health care, engineering, and chemical materials at the Berkeley, Davis, Irvine, Los Angeles, Merced, Riverside, San Diego, San Francisco, Santa Barbara, and Santa Cruz campuses.

48451 ■ University of California–State Governmental Relations Office
1130 K St., Ste. 340
Sacramento, CA 95814-3968
Ph:(916)445-9924
Fax:(916)445-1426
Co. E-mail: steve.juarez@ucop.edu
URL: http://www.ucop.edu/uer/sgr
Contact: Steve Juarez, Assoc.VP/Dir.
E-mail: steve.juarez@ucop.edu
Scope: Responsible for relations with executive and legislative branches of state government, both with respect to legislation and the University's research response to potential state policy problems.

48452 ■ University of California at Berkeley–Sponsored Projects Office
2150 Shattuck Ave., Ste. 300
Berkeley, CA 94720-5940
Ph:(510)642-0120
Fax:(510)642-8236
Co. E-mail: pgates@berkeley.edu
URL: http://www.spo.berkeley.edu
Contact: Patricia Gates, Assoc.Dir.
E-mail: pgates@berkeley.edu
Scope: Administers extramurally funded research contracts and grants at the University.

48453 ■ University of California, Davis–Office of Research
1850 Research Park Dr., Ste. 300
Davis, CA 95618-6153
Ph:(530)754-7679
Fax:(530)754-7894
Co. E-mail: lewin@ucdavis.edu
URL: http://www.research.ucdavis.edu
Contact: Harris Lewin
E-mail: lewin@ucdavis.edu
Scope: Administers contracts, grants, and sponsored research activities. **Publications:** Supports for Teaching and Research.

48454 ■ University of California, Irvine–Office of Research
160 Aldrich Hall, MC 3175
Irvine, CA 92697
Ph:(949)824-5796
Fax:(949)824-2095
Co. E-mail: or@research.uci.edu
URL: http://www.research.uci.edu
Contact: John Hemminger PhD
E-mail: or@research.uci.edu
Scope: Administers research programs and units at the University; fosters research development; obtains and oversees grants, contracts, and research equipment; and sponsors technology transfer activities and animal and human research projects.

48455 ■ University of California, Irvine–Office of Technology Alliances
5171 California Ave., Ste. 150
Irvine, CA 92697-7700
Ph:(949)824-7295
Fax:(949)824-2899
Co. E-mail: dandriko@uci.edu
URL: http://www.ota.uci.edu
Contact: Demetri Andrikos, Dir.
E-mail: dandriko@uci.edu
Scope: University and industry partnership and cooperative research development, including industrial contract development, review, and approval; science and technology research identification; consortia participation; new consortia initiation; and federal and state science and technology center participation.
Services: Technology transfer services (weekly), on licensed and emerging technologies and other materials.

48456 ■ University of California, San Diego–Office of Contract and Grant Administration
9500 Gilman Dr., MC 0934
La Jolla, CA 92093-0934
Ph:(858)534-3330
Fax:(858)534-0280
Co. E-mail: lcollins@ucsd.edu
URL: http://ocga.ucsd.edu
Contact: Linda P. Collins, Asst. Vice Chancellor
E-mail: lcollins@ucsd.edu
Scope: Coordinates grants and contracts at the University.

48457 ■ University of California, Santa Barbara–Office of Research
3227 Cheadle Hall, MC 2050
Santa Barbara, CA 93106-2050
Ph:(805)893-3925

Fax:(805)893-2611
Co. E-mail: murr@research.ucsb.edu
URL: http://www.research.ucsb.edu
Contact: Meredith Murr PhD, Dir., Res.Devel.
E-mail: murr@research.ucsb.edu
Scope: Responsible for administration of organized research units on Santa Barbara campus of the University, and for planning, developing, and supporting other research activities on campus. Present research plan stresses development of strengths in physical, mathematical and biological sciences and developments in marine biotechnology, ocean engineering and coastal zone, geological sciences, biomedical and neurosciences, remote sensing, special education, polymers, microelectronic, artificial intelligence, advanced materials, and society and culture. **Publications:** Research Newsletter (monthly).

48458 ■ University Corporation, San Francisco State
PO Box 320160
San Francisco, CA 94132-0160
Ph:(415)338-2238
Fax:(415)338-7950
Co. E-mail: avictori@sfsu.edu
URL: http://ucorp.sfsu.edu
Contact: Anthony Victoria
E-mail: avictori@sfsu.edu
Scope: Administers a portion of research done at or in connection with San Francisco State University.

48459 ■ University of Southern California–Office of Technology Licensing
Hughes Ctr., Ste. EEB 131
3740 McClintock Ave.
Los Angeles, CA 90089-2561
Ph:(213)821-5000
Fax:(213)821-5001
Co. E-mail: koepnick@usc.edu
URL: http://www.usc.edu/academe/otl
Contact: Joe Koepnick, Dir.
E-mail: koepnick@usc.edu
Scope: Transfers technology from the University to the private sector, including the areas of medicine, engineering, pharmacy, and gerontology. **Publications:** Newsletter. **Educational Activities:** Seminars, for faculty and students.

48460 ■ US Market Access Center
10 S 3rd St., 3rd Fl.
San Jose, CA 95113-1101
Ph:(408)351-3300
Fax:(408)351-3330
Co. E-mail: info@usmarketaccess.com
URL: http://www.usmarketaccess.com
Contact: Omar Mencin, Pres.
Description: US Market Access Center is a nonprofit business incubator sponsored by a collaboration of business, government, and academic organizations. The Center is a leading business gateway into the United States. Formerly International Business Incubator (IBI).

EDUCATIONAL PROGRAMS

48461 ■ American River College
4700 College Oak Dr.
Sacramento, CA 95841-4286
Ph:(916)484-8011
Fax:(916)484-8673
URL: http://www.arc.losrios.edu
Description: Two-year college offering small business management classes.

48462 ■ Chabot College
25555 Hesperian Blvd.
Hayward, CA 94545
Ph:(510)723-6700
Fax:(510)723-7510
URL: http://www.chabotcollege.edu
Description: Two-year college offering a program in entrepreneurship.

48463 ■ Cypress College
Business Office
9200 Valley View St.
Cypress, CA 90630

Ph:(714)484-7000
Fax:(714)527-4733
URL: http://www.cypress.cc.ca.us
Description: Regular business program includes courses on small business management, human relations, and related topics.

48464 ■ De Anza College
21250 Stevens Creek Blvd.
Cupertino, CA 95014
Ph:(408)864-5678
Fax:(408)864-5433
URL: http://www.deanza.fhda.edu
Description: Two-year college offering a small business management program. Certificate program includes marketing, finance, and management.

48465 ■ Empire College–School of Business
3035 Cleveland Ave.
Santa Rosa, CA 95403
Ph:(707)546-4000
Fax:(707)546-4058
Co. E-mail: rhurd@empcol.com
URL: http://www.empcol.com
E-mail: rhurd@empcol.com
Description: College offering a small business management program.

48466 ■ Lake Tahoe Community College
1 College Dr.
South Lake Tahoe, CA 96150-4524
Ph:(530)541-4660
Fax:(530)541-7852
URL: http://www.ltcc.cc.ca.us
Description: Two-year college offering a small business management program.

48467 ■ Ohlone College
43600 Mission Blvd.
Fremont, CA 94539
Ph:(510)659-6000
Fax:(510)659-7321
URL: http://www.ohlone.cc.ca.us
Description: Two-year college offering a small business management program.

48468 ■ Saddleback College
28000 Marguerite Pky.
Mission Viejo, CA 92692
Ph:(949)582-4500
Fax:(949)347-0438
URL: http://www.saddleback.cc.ca.us
Description: Two-year college offering a small business management program.

48469 ■ Santa Ana College
1530 W 17th St.
Santa Ana, CA 92706
Ph:(714)564-6000
Fax:(714)564-6370
URL: http://www.sac.edu
Description: Two-year college offering a small business management program.

48470 ■ Southwestern College
900 Otay Lakes Rd.
Chula Vista, CA 91910
Ph:(619)421-6700
Fax:(619)482-6402
URL: http://www.swc.cc.ca.us
Description: Two-year college offering a program in small business management.

TRADE PERIODICALS

48471 ■ California Employer Advisor
Pub: Employer Resource Institute Inc.
Ed: Larry J. Shapiro, Esq., Editor, lshapiro@arthcink.net. **Released:** Monthly. **Price:** $177, individuals. **Description:** The award-winning guide to California employment law and employee relations.

48472 ■ California Labor and Employment ALERT Newsletter
Pub: Castle Publications Ltd.
Contact: Richard Simmons, President
Released: Bimonthly. **Price:** $90; $105 includes 3-ring binder. **Description:** Reports on current developments in California and federal laws concerning personnel and employment issues. Recurring features include notices of publications available.

48473 ■ California Labor and Employment Law Quarterly
Pub: State Bar of California
Contact: Marty Fassler, Managing Editor
Released: Quarterly. **Description:** Contains information and news on California's labor and employment laws and regulations.

PUBLICATIONS

48474 ■ The Business Journal Serving San Jose and Silicon Valley
96 N. 3rd St., Ste. 100
San Jose, CA 95112-5560
Ph:(408)295-3800
Fax:(408)295-5028
Co. E-mail: sanjose@amcity.com
URL: http://www.amcity.com

48475 ■ California Corporation Formation Package and Minute Book
Oasis Press
300 N. Valley Dr.
Grants Pass, OR 97526
Ph:(541)479-9464
Free: 800-228-2275
Fax:(541)476-1479
Co. E-mail: psi2@magick.net
Ed: Kevin W. Finck. **Released:** Seventh edition, 1992. **Price:** $29.95 (paper); $39.95 (ringbound).

48476 ■ How to Form Your Own California Corporation
Nolo Press
950 Parker St.
Berkeley, CA 94710
Ph:(510)549-1976
Free: 800-992-6656
Fax:800-645-0895
URL: http://www.nolo.com
Ed: Anthony Mancuso. **Released:** Seventh edition, 1988. **Price:** $29.95 (paper).

48477 ■ Orange County Business Journal
4590 McArthur, Ste. 100
Newport Beach, CA 92660
Ph:(714)833-8373
Fax:(714)833-8751
Co. E-mail: ocbj@ocbj.com
URL: http://ocbj@ocbj.com

48478 ■ Sacramento Business Journal
1401 21st St., Ste. 200
Sacramento, CA 95814-3120
Ph:(916)447-7661
Fax:(916)444-7779
Co. E-mail: tbj@ns.net
URL: http://www.amcity.com/sacramento

48479 ■ San Diego Business Journal
4909 Murphy Canyon Rd., Ste. 200
San Diego, CA 92123-4300
Ph:(619)277-6359
Fax:(619)571-3628
Co. E-mail: sdbj@sdbj.com
URL: http://www.sdbj.com

48480 ■ Small Business Success
Pacific Bell Directory
101 Spear St., Rm. 429
San Francisco, CA 94105
Ph:(415)995-3899
Ed: Andrea Hine, editor. **Price:** Free. **Description:** Contains articles on small business development in California. Includes a resource directory.

48481 ■ Starting and Operating a Business in California: A Step-by-Step Guide
PSI Research
300 N. Valley Dr.
Grants Pass, OR 97526
Ph:(503)479-9464
Free: 800-228-2275
Fax:(503)476-1479
Co. E-mail: psi2@magick.net
Ed: Michael D. Jenkins. **Released:** Revised edition, 1992. **Price:** $29.95 (looseleaf binder); $24.95 (paper). **Description:** Part of the Successful Business Library series.

PUBLISHERS

48482 ■ Adams-Blake Company Inc.
8041 Sierra St., Ste. 102
Fair Oaks, CA 95628-7530
Ph:(916)962-9296
Co. E-mail: info@adams-blake.com
URL: http://www.adams-blake.com
Contact: Sam Lewis, Vice President
Description: Publishes business, career and technology books. Accepts unsolicited manuscripts. Reaches market through direct mail and wholesalers and distributors. **Founded:** 1990.

48483 ■ Advisor Media Inc.
12463 Rancho Bernardo Rd., Ste. 509
PO Box 503350
San Diego, CA 92128-3350
Ph:(858)278-5600
Fax:(858)947-3993
URL: http://advisormedia.com/adv/AdvisorLegal
Contact: John L. Hawkins, CEO & Chm Bd
Description: Publishes business related materials. **Founded:** 1983.

48484 ■ Alliance of Area Business Publications
1970 E Grand Ave., Ste. 330
El Segundo, CA 90245
Ph:(310)364-0193
Fax:(310)364-0196
Co. E-mail: info@bizpubs.org
URL: http://www.bizpubs.org
Contact: Steve Jagler, Director
E-mail: steve.jagler@biztimes.com
Description: Publishes on business. Reaches market through commission representatives, direct mail and advertisements. **Founded:** 1979.

48485 ■ Ashar Press
1002 Elk Hills Dr.
PO Box 524
Galt, CA 95632
Ph:(209)745-2756
Free: 877-266-5117
Fax:(209)745-7538
Co. E-mail: beverly@asharpress.com
URL: http://www.asharpress.com
Contact: Tammy J. Deruyter, Editor
Founded: 1999.

48486 ■ Bay Tree Publishing
1400 Pinnacle Ct., Ste. 406
PO Box 70236
Point Richmond, CA 94801-4178
Ph:(510)236-1475
Fax:(866)552-7329
Co. E-mail: dcole@baytreepublish.com
URL: http://www.baytreepublish.com
Contact: David Cole, Publisher
E-mail: dcole@baytreepublish.com
Description: Publishes nonfiction in the areas of current affairs, business and psychology. **Founded:** 2002.

48487 ■ Bell Springs Publishing
106 State St.
PO Box 1240
Willits, CA 95490-3118
Ph:(707)459-6372
Free: 800-515-8050

Fax:(707)459-8614
Co. E-mail: publisher@bellsprings.com
URL: http://www.bellsprings.com
Contact: Sharon Kamoraff, Owner
Description: Publishes small business guidebooks and pinball machine repair manuals. Reaches market through trade sales and wholesalers. Does not accept unsolicited manuscripts. **Founded:** 1976.

48488 ■ BizBest Media Corp.
860 Via de la Paz, Ste. D-4
Pacific Palisades, CA 90272
Ph:(310)230-6868
Free: 800-873-5205
Fax:(310)454-6130
Co. E-mail: info@bizbest.com
URL: http://www.bizbest.com
Contact: Shara Karasic, Mgr
E-mail: skarasic@work.com
Founded: 1999.

48489 ■ Blueprint Books
7734 Creekside Dr.
PO Box 10757
Pleasanton, CA 94588-3686
Ph:(925)425-9513
Free: 800-605-2913
Fax:800-605-2914
Contact: Bette Daoust, Mgr
Description: Publishes business books.

48490 ■ Business Coach Press
48 Matthews Pl.
PO Box 301
Alamo, CA 94507-2600
Free: (866)500-1183
Co. E-mail: info@businesscoachpress.biz
URL: http://www.businesscoachpress.biz
Contact: Tom Leal, Owner
Description: Publishes books that assist small business owners.

48491 ■ California State University Press
2380 E Keats MS/MB99
Fresno, CA 93740-8024
Ph:(559)278-3056
Fax:(559)278-6758
Co. E-mail: press@csufresno.edu
URL: http://www.csufresno.edu/artshum/press/index.
  shtml
Contact: Virginia Solorzano, Mgr
Description: Publishes books on art, drama, music, film, media, architecture, politics, business and autobiography. Reaches market through southern Illinois University Press. Does not accept unsolicited manuscripts. **Founded:** 1982.

48492 ■ CMP Books
6600 Silacci Way
Gilroy, CA 95020-7005
Ph:(408)848-3854
Free: 800-500-6875
Fax:(408)848-5784
Co. E-mail: cmp@rushorder.com
Contact: Susan Kuchinskas, Editor
Description: Publishes information on computing, design and communications solutions.

48493 ■ Collins Publications
3233 Grand Ave., Ste. N-294C
Chino Hills, CA 91709-1489
Ph:(909)590-2471
Free: 800-795-8999
Fax:(909)628-9330
Co. E-mail: collins@collinspub.com
URL: http://www.collinspub.com
Contact: Ann Collins, Editor
Description: Publishes how-to, business, and self-help products. Offers an array of software training materials, such as videos, books and CD-ROMs. Also offers self publishing services. Reaches market through commission representatives, direct mail, trade sales and wholesalers and distributors, including Baker & Taylor and Brodart. Does not accept unsolicited manuscripts. **Founded:** 1991.

48494 ■ D.M.R. Consulting Group
225 S Lake Ave., Ste. 300
Pasadena, CA 91101-3005
Ph:(626)440-8365
Contact: Mark Dunnet, President
Description: Publishes home-based business success manuals and other specialized information on various subjects. Distributes for premier Publishers. Reaches market throughcommission representatives, direct mail, and telephone and trade sales. **Founded:** 1980.

48495 ■ Frontal Lobe
836 Starlite Ln.
Los Altos, CA 94024
Ph:(650)941-8561
Co. E-mail: masonc2@earthlink.net
Contact: Mason A. Clark, Editor
Description: Publishes small business management, entrepreneurship, religion and how-to books. **Founded:** 1978.

48496 ■ Hunter Arts Publishing
PO Box 66578E
Los Angeles, CA 90066
Ph:(310)842-8864
Fax:(310)842-8868
Co. E-mail: publisher@hunterarts.com
URL: http://www.headhuntersrevealed.com/reviews.
  html
Contact: Darrell W. Gurney, Mgr
Description: Publishes Headhunters Revealed! Career Secrets for Choosing and Using Professional Recruiters -an executive recruiter that exposes the mind and mechanics of the search industry to job-seeking professionals. Does not accept unsolicited manuscripts. **Founded:** 1999.

48497 ■ IBIS/Business Information Services International
PO Box 3271
Tustin, CA 92781-3271
Ph:(949)552-8494
Fax:(501)432-5112
Contact: Ray B. Debby, Mgr
Description: Publishes book, audio-tape and video sets on various business topics for entrepreneurs and enterprising managers, business students, and business groups. Also publishes business manuals on a variety of topics. Reaches market through direct mail, trade sales, and through the distributor. Does not accept unsolicited manuscripts. **Founded:** 1980.

48498 ■ International Business & Management Institute
IBMI Ctr.
PO Box 3271
Tustin, CA 92781-3271
Ph:(949)552-8494
Fax:(501)432-5112
Co. E-mail: ibmi-books@juno.com
Contact: T. R. Balla, Director
Description: Publishes on diverse business and management topics focusing on international trade and finance for entrepreneurs and managers. Also publishes booklets. Offers consulting and in-house educational programs. Distributes IBIS Business Reports. Reaches market through direct mail, internet and trade promotions. Does not accept unsolicited manuscripts. **Founded:** 1970.

48499 ■ Jardin Publishing
2325 Fatjo Pl., Ste. 105
Santa Clara, CA 95050
Ph:(408)454-6650
Free: (866)896-8946
Contact: David T. Riveness, Mgr
Description: Publishes books on business and leadership.

48500 ■ Juice Gallery Multimedia
2042 Big Oak Ave.
PO Box 151
Chino Hills, CA 91709-4710
Ph:(909)597-0791
Free: 800-710-8163

Fax:(909)597-0791
Co. E-mail: info@juicegallery.com
URL: http://www.juicegallery.com
Contact: Shelly Kelly, Mgr
Description: Publishes materials related to staring a restaurant business. Accepts unsolicited manuscripts. Reaches market through direct mail, reviews, listings, telephone sales and wholesalers and Baker & Taylor. **Founded:** 1992.

48501 ■ Monterey Media Inc.
566 St., Charles Dr.
Thousand Oaks, CA 91360-3953
Ph:(805)494-7199
Free: 800-424-2593
Fax:(805)496-6061
Co. E-mail: orderenquiry@montereymedia.com
URL: http://www.montereymedia.com
Contact: Tiffany Mastrovito, Mgr
E-mail: publicity@montereymedia.com
Founded: 1979.

48502 ■ Out of Your Mind. . .and into the Marketplace
13381 White Sand Dr.
Tustin, CA 92780-4565
Ph:(714)544-0248
Free: 800-419-1513
Fax:(714)730-1414
Co. E-mail: lpinson@business-plan.com
URL: http://www.business-plan.com
Contact: Ndaba Mdhlongwa, Dir of Mktg
E-mail: ndaba@business-plan.com
Description: Publishes on small and home-based business concerns, stressing step-by-step, hands-on approach to business start-up, record keeping, marketing and business plan preparation. Offers a business plan software program for windows. Reaches market through commission representatives, direct mail, trade sales and wholesalers. Does not accept unsolicited manuscripts. **Founded:** 1987.

48503 ■ Pleasanton Publishing
55 New Montgomery St.
PO Box 1257
San Francisco, CA 94105-3412
Ph:(925)249-9112
Fax:(925)249-1807
Description: Publishes literary works for holistic and natural healing using a teddy bear metaphor to connect reader. Does not accept unsolicited manuscripts. Reaches market through distributors. **Founded:** 2000.

48504 ■ Power2BE Media
2975 Seahorse
Ventura, CA 93001
Ph:(805)650-1248
Fax:(805)650-1249
Co. E-mail: info@powerselling.com
URL: http://www.powerselling.com
Contact: Steven Power, President
Description: Publishes business books about power selling. Does not accept unsolicited manuscripts. Reaches market through commission representatives, direct mail and via e-mail. **Founded:** 2002.

48505 ■ Puma Publishing Co.
1670 Coral Dr.
Santa Maria, CA 93454
Ph:(805)925-3216
Free: 800-255-5730
Fax:(805)925-2656
Co. E-mail: publications@pumapublishing.com
URL: http://www.pumapublishing.com
Contact: William M. Alarid, President
Description: Publishes how-to books for small business. Distributes for Nolo Press, Upstart, and Bell Springs. Does not accept unsolicited manuscripts. Reaches market through trade sales and wholesalers and distributors, including LPC (login) and Quality Books. **Founded:** 1986.

48506 ■ Rampant Lion Publishers Inc.
c/o L. H. Joseph Jr., 8344 Melrose Ave., Ste. 23
Los Angeles, CA 90069
Ph:(323)651-2322

Fax:(323)651-0624
Contact: Lawrence H. Joseph Jr., President
Description: Publishes management and how-to books for business people. Reaches market through business organizations. **Founded:** 1980.

48507 ■ Rhino's Press
PO Box 3520
Laguna Hills, CA 92654
Free: 800-872-3274
Fax:(714)244-3256
Contact: Scott Alexander, Owner
Description: Publishes motivation, small business books. **Founded:** 1980.

48508 ■ Sun Publications
300 Carlsbad Village Dr., Ste. 108A-78
Carlsbad, CA 92008
Ph:(760)476-0777
Free: 888-786-3777
Fax:(760)462-4752
Co. E-mail: debra@debrapestrak.com
URL: http://www.debrapestrak.com
Contact: Steve Pestrak, President
Description: Publishes business leadership and women's issues books and tapes. They are con-

cerned with helping business people succeed and reach their goals. Does not accept unsolicited manuscripts. Reaches market through direct mail, wholesalers and distributors, seminars and speaking engagements. **Founded:** 2000.

48509 ■ Vince Emery Productions
781 Prague St.
PO Box 460279
San Francisco, CA 94112
Ph:(415)337-6000
Free: 800-888-4741
Fax:(650)697-6048
Co. E-mail: vince@emery.com
URL: http://www.emerybooks.com
Contact: Vince Emery, Mgr
E-mail: vince@emery.com

48510 ■ WBusiness Books
9682 Telstar Ave., Ste. 110
El Monte, CA 91731-3009
Ph:(626)448-3448

Fax:(626)602-3817
Co. E-mail: info@academiclearningcompany.com
URL: http://www.wbusinessbooks.com
Contact: Troy Hazard, Mgr
Description: Publishes business books. Accepts unsolicited manuscripts. Reaches market through commission representatives. **Founded:** 2005.

48511 ■ Women's Yellow Pages
13547 Ventura Blvd., Ste. 374
Sherman Oaks, CA 91423
Ph:(818)995-6646
Fax:(818)995-4515
Co. E-mail: info@referral-guide.com
Contact: Nancy Sardella, President
Description: Publishes an annual directory of women-owned businesses, professional women, and their organizations and services. Reaches market through marketing representatives, direct mail, and telephone sales. Does not accept unsolicited manuscripts. **Founded:** 1977.

SMALL BUSINESS DEVELOPMENT CENTERS

48512 ■ Boulder Small Business Development Center
2440 Pearl St.
Boulder, CO 80302
URL: http://www.bouldersbdc.com
Contact: Sharon King

48513 ■ Boulder Small Business Development Center - Longmont
528 Main St.
Longmont, CO 80501
Co. E-mail: sharon.king@boulderchamber.com
URL: http://www.bouldersbdc.com
Contact: Sharon King

48514 ■ Colorado Springs Small Business Development Center
Citti Bldg.
1420 Austin Bluffs Pkwy.
Colorado Springs, CO 80933
URL: http://cssbdc.org
Contact: Michelle Bracewell, Counselor

48515 ■ Denver Metro Small Business Development Center
1445 Market St.
Denver, CO 80202
Fax:(303)534-2145
Co. E-mail: denver.sbdc@den-chamber.org
URL: http://www.denversbdc.org
Contact: Tameka Montgomery, Exec. Dir.

48516 ■ Fort Morgan Small Business Development Center
300 Main St.
Fort Morgan, CO 80701
Co. E-mail: tim.edgar@morancc.edu
URL: http://www.coloradosbdc.org

48517 ■ Grand Junction Small Business Development Center
2591 B 3/4 Rd.
Grand Junction, CO 81503
Co. E-mail: jmorey@gjincubator.org
URL: http://www.coloradosbdc.org

48518 ■ Greeley/Weld Small Business Development Center
902 7th Ave.
Greeley, CO 80631
Co. E-mail: valeen.thomas@unco.edu
URL: http://mcb.unco.edu/Programs/sbdc
Contact: Valeen Thomas

48519 ■ La Junta Small Business Development Center
Otero Junior College
1802 Colorado Ave.
La Junta, CO 81050
Co. E-mail: bryan.bryant@ojc.edu
URL: http://www.coloradosbdc.org

48520 ■ Lakewood Small Business Development Center
Bldg. 19, Ste. 400
1667 Cole Blvd.
Golden, CO 80401
Co. E-mail: jayne.reiter@denverchamber.org
URL: http://www.coloradosbdc.org

48521 ■ Larimer County Small Business Development Center
125 S Howes St., Ste. 150
Fort Collins, CO 80521
Fax:(970)498-8924
Co. E-mail: sbdc@frii.com
URL: http://www.sbdc-larimer.com

48522 ■ Loveland Small Business Development Center
5400 Stone Creek Cir.
Loveland, CO 80538
Co. E-mail: sbdcloveland@frii.com
URL: http://www.coloradosbdc.org

48523 ■ North Metro Small Business Development Center
Front Range Community College
3645 W 112th Ave., Rm. No. 2014
Westminster, CO 80031
Fax:(303)469-7143
Co. E-mail: wcicpd@frontrange.edu
URL: http://www.frontrange.edu/FRCCTemplates/FRCC7.aspx?id=132
Contact: Chris Luchs, Dir.

48524 ■ Pueblo Small Business Development Center
Pueblo Community College
900 W Orman Ave.
Pueblo, CO 81004
Co. E-mail: caroline.parra@pueblocc.edu
URL: http://www.coloradosbdc.org

48525 ■ San Luis Valley Small Business Development Center
609 Main St., Ste. 108
Alamosa, CO 81102
Co. E-mail: donna@slv-sbdc.com
URL: http://www.coloradosbdc.org

48526 ■ South Metro Denver Small Business Development Center - Aurora
5430 S Biscay Cir.
Aurora, CO 80015
Co. E-mail: lhajek@bestchamber.com
URL: http://www.coloradosbdc.org

48527 ■ South Metro Denver Small Business Development Center - Centennial
6840 S University Blvd.
Centennial, CO 80122
Co. E-mail: lhajek@bestchamber.com
URL: http://www.smallbusinessdenver.com
Contact: Marcia Pessemier, Dir.

48528 ■ Southwest Colorado Small Business Development Center - Durango
2700 Main Ave.
Durango, CO 81301
URL: http://www.coloradosbdc.org

48529 ■ Southwest Colorado Small Business Development Center - Pagosa
402 San Juan Dr.
Pagosa Springs, CO 81147
Co. E-mail: beckelhymer_r@fortlewis.edu
URL: http://www.coloradosbdc.org

48530 ■ Southwestern Colorado Small Business Development Center
1000 Rim Dr., EBH 140
Durango, CO 81301
Co. E-mail: sbdc@fortlewis.edu
URL: http://www.coloradosbdc.org

48531 ■ West Central Small Business Development Center
600 N Adams St.
Gunnison, CO 81231
Co. E-mail: sbdc@western.edu
URL: http://www.coloradosbdc.org

48532 ■ West Central Small Business Development Center - Chaffee and Lake County
104 Crestone Ave.
Salida, CO 81201
Co. E-mail: eolson@chaffeecounty.org
URL: http://www.coloradosbdc.org

SMALL BUSINESS ASSISTANCE PROGRAMS

48533 ■ Colorado Office of Economic Development and International Trade–Colorado International Trade Office
1625 Broadway, Ste. 2700
Denver, CO 80202
Ph:(303)892-3840
Fax:(303)892-3848
Co. E-mail: ito@state.co.us
URL: http://www.state.co.us/oed
Contact: Pam Reichert, Dir.
Description: Promotes the export of Colorado's products and assists businesses in many aspects of exporting.

48534 ■ Colorado Office of Economic Development and International Trade–Small Business Development Center
1625 Broadway, Ste. 2700
Denver, CO 80202
Ph:(303)892-3840
Free: 800-333-7798
Fax:(303)892-3848
Co. E-mail: kelly.manning@state.co.us
URL: http://www.coloradosbdc.org
Contact: Kelly Manning, Dir.
Description: Answers small business inquiries or refers them to an appropriate resource. Provides

information on starting a business, marketing, financing, and other aspects of running a business.

48535 ■ Colorado University Business Advancement Center
UCB 034
Boulder, CO 80309
Ph:(303)492-8395
Fax:(303)492-3620
Co. E-mail: cubac@colorado.edu
URL: http://www.colorado.edu/cubac/
Description: Provides consulting on management, marketing, financing, procuring government contracts, and exporting. Also offers BRAIN, a technology transfer service available through NASA's Industrial Application Center. Holds seminars. Has branches in Grand Junction, Durango, Colorado Springs, Trinidad, and Burlington.

48536 ■ Denver Metro Chamber of Commerce–Small Business Development Center
1445 Market St.
Denver, CO 80202
Ph:(303)620-8076
Fax:(303)534-2145
Co. E-mail: denver.sbdc@den-chamber.org
URL: http://www.denversbdc.org
Contact: Tameka Montgomery, Exec. Dir.
Description: Assists companies with 100 or fewer employees. The Management Education Division provides management education and training; the Information/Networking Division sponsors meetings for small business chief executive officers for the exchange of information; and the Special Services Division is involved in such activities as legislative lobbying and sponsoring group health insurance programs for small businesses.

SCORE OFFICES

48537 ■ Grand Junction SCORE
Path:

BETTER BUSINESS BUREAUS

48538 ■ Better Business Bureau of Denver
1020 Cherokee St.
Denver, CO 80204-4039
Ph:(303)758-2100
Fax:(303)577-8101
Co. E-mail: info@denver.bbb.org
URL: http://denver.bbb.org
Contact: Dale Mingilton, Pres./CEO

48539 ■ Better Business Bureau of the Mountain States
8020 S County Rd. 5, Ste. 100
Fort Collins, CO 80528-8994
Ph:(970)484-1348
Fax:(970)221-1239
Co. E-mail: info@wynco.bbb.org
URL: http://wynco.bbb.org
Contact: Pamela King, Pres./CEO

48540 ■ Better Business Bureau of Southern Colorado
25 N Wahsatch Ave.
Colorado Springs, CO 80903
Ph:(719)636-1155
Free: (866)206-1800
Fax:(719)636-5078
Co. E-mail: info@bbbsc.org
URL: http://www.southerncolorado.bbb.org
Contact: Jane Blume, Information Technology Dir.

CHAMBERS OF COMMERCE

48541 ■ Alamosa County Chamber of Commerce
300 Chamber Dr.
Cole Park
Alamosa, CO 81101-2601
Ph:(719)589-3681
Fax:(719)589-1773
Co. E-mail: office@alamosachamber.com
URL: http://alamosa.com
Contact: Ms. Barbara McGinnis, Office Mgr.

48542 ■ Arvada Chamber of Commerce
7305 Grandview Ave.
Arvada, CO 80002-9960
Ph:(303)424-0313
Fax:(303)424-5370
Co. E-mail: dot@arvadachamber.org
URL: http://www.arvadachamber.org
Contact: Dot Wright, Pres.

48543 ■ Aspen Chamber Resort Association
425 Rio Grande Pl.
Aspen, CO 81611
Ph:(970)925-1940
Free: 800-670-0792
Fax:(970)920-1173
Co. E-mail: info@aspenchamber.org
URL: http://www.aspenchamber.org
Contact: Debbie Contini Braun, Pres./CEO

48544 ■ Aurora Chamber of Commerce
562 Sable Blvd., Ste. 200
Aurora, CO 80011-0809
Ph:(303)344-1500
Fax:(303)344-1564
Co. E-mail: info@aurorachamber.org
URL: http://www.aurorachamber.org
Contact: Kevin Hougen, Pres./CEO

48545 ■ Basalt Chamber of Commerce
PO Box 514
Basalt, CO 81621-0514
Ph:(970)927-4031
Fax:(970)927-2833
Co. E-mail: info@basaltchamber.com
URL: http://www.basaltchamber.org
Contact: Elizabeth Phillips, Exec. Dir.

48546 ■ Berthoud Area Chamber of Commerce
345 Mountain Ave.
PO Box 1709
Berthoud, CO 80513
Ph:(970)532-4200
Fax:(970)532-7690
Co. E-mail: bcc@berthoudcolorado.com
URL: http://www.berthoudcolorado.com
Contact: Don Dana, Exec. Dir.

48547 ■ Boulder Chamber of Commerce
PO Box 73
Boulder, CO 80302
Ph:(303)442-1044
Fax:(303)938-8837
Co. E-mail: info@boulderchamber.com
URL: http://www.boulderchamber.com
Contact: Susan Graf, Pres./CEO

48548 ■ Breckenridge Resort Chamber of Commerce
PO Box 1909
Breckenridge, CO 80424-1909
Ph:(970)453-2913
Fax:(970)453-7238
Co. E-mail: gobreck@gobreck.com
URL: http://www.gobreck.com/members/aboutthe-BRC
Contact: John McMahon, Exec. Dir.

48549 ■ Broomfield Chamber of Commerce
350 Interlocken Blvd., Ste. 250
PO Box 301
Broomfield, CO 80021
Ph:(303)466-1775
Fax:(303)466-4481
Co. E-mail: info@broomfieldchamber.com
URL: http://www.broomfieldchamber.com
Contact: Jennifer Kerr, Pres./CEO

48550 ■ Brush Chamber of Commerce
1215 Edison St.
Brush, CO 80723
Ph:(970)842-2666
Free: 800-354-8659
Fax:(970)842-3828
Co. E-mail: brush@brushchamber.org
URL: http://www.brushchamber.org
Contact: Dr. Ronald Prascher, Exec. Dir.

48551 ■ Buena Vista Area Chamber of Commerce
343 Hwy. 24 S
PO Box 2021
Buena Vista, CO 81211
Ph:(719)395-6612
Co. E-mail: buenavista@vtinet.com
URL: http://www.buenavistacolorado.org
Contact: Judy Hassell, Exec. Dir.

48552 ■ Canon City Chamber of Commerce
403 Royal Gorge Blvd.
Canon City, CO 81212
Ph:(719)275-2331
Free: 800-876-7922
Fax:(719)275-2332
Co. E-mail: chamber@canoncity.com
URL: http://www.canoncity.com/index.php
Contact: Dan Riggs, Pres.

48553 ■ Carbondale Community Chamber of Commerce
PO Box 1645
Carbondale, CO 81623
Ph:(970)963-1890
Fax:(970)963-4719
Co. E-mail: chamber@carbondale.com
URL: http://www.carbondale.com
Contact: Ms. Sherri Harrison, Exec. Dir.

48554 ■ Castle Rock Chamber of Commerce
420 Jerry St.
PO Box 282
Castle Rock, CO 80104
Ph:(303)688-4597
Fax:(303)688-2688
Co. E-mail: info@castlerock.org
URL: http://www.castlerock.org
Contact: Pam Ridler, Pres.

48555 ■ Cedaredge Area Chamber of Commerce
PO Box 278
245 W Main St.
Cedaredge, CO 81413
Ph:(970)856-6961
Fax:(970)856-7292
Co. E-mail: cedaredgech@tds.net
URL: http://www.cedaredgechamber.com
Contact: Derek Kehmeier, Pres.

48556 ■ Conifer Chamber of Commerce
PO Box 127
Conifer, CO 80433
Ph:(303)838-5711
Fax:(303)838-5712
Co. E-mail: info@goconifer.com
URL: http://www.goconifer.com
Contact: Jeannette May, Exec. Dir.

48557 ■ Cortez Area Chamber of Commerce
PO Box 968
Cortez, CO 81321
Ph:(970)565-3414
Fax:(970)565-8373
Co. E-mail: cortezchamber@cityofcortez.com
URL: http://www.cortezchamber.com
Contact: Marcy Cummins, Mgr.

48558 ■ Costilla County Chamber of Commerce
PO Box 428
Fort Garland, CO 81133
Ph:(719)379-3512
Co. E-mail: sanluis2@fone.net
URL: http://www.slvguide.com/Costilla

48559 ■ Craig Chamber of Commerce
360 E Victory Way
Craig, CO 81625
Ph:(970)824-5689
Free: 800-864-4405

Fax:(970)824-0231
Co. E-mail: info@craig-chamber.com
URL: http://www.craig-chamber.com
Contact: Christina Curie, Exec. Dir.

**48560 ■ Crawford Area Chamber of
Commerce**
PO Box 22
Crawford, CO 81415
Ph:(970)921-4000
Co. E-mail: info@crawfordcountry.org
URL: http://www.crawfordcountry.org
Contact: Michael A. Hart

**48561 ■ Creede - Mineral County Chamber of
Commerce**
PO Box 580
Creede, CO 81130-0580
Ph:(719)658-2374
Free: 800-327-2102
Fax:(719)658-2717
Co. E-mail: chamber@creede.com
URL: http://www.creede.com/chamber.htm

**48562 ■ Crested Butte/Mount Crested Butte
Chamber of Commerce**
601 Elk Ave.
PO Box 1288
Crested Butte, CO 81224
Ph:(970)349-6438
Free: 800-545-4505
Fax:(970)349-1023
Co. E-mail: cbinfo@cbchamber.com
URL: http://www.cbchamber.com/page.php
Contact: Jay Jaynes, Dir.

**48563 ■ Cripple Creek Chamber of
Commerce**
PO Box 430
Cripple Creek, CO 80813
Ph:(719)689-3461
Free: 877-858-4653
Fax:(719)689-2774
Co. E-mail: info@cripple-creek.co.us
URL: http://www.cripple-creek.co.us

**48564 ■ Custer County Merchants and
Chamber of Commerce**
PO Box 81
Westcliffe, CO 81252-0081
Ph:(719)783-9163
Free: 877-793-3170
Fax:(719)783-2724
Co. E-mail: info@custercountyco.com
URL: http://www.custercountyco.com
Contact: Christy Veltrie, Pres.

48565 ■ Del Norte Chamber of Commerce
505 Grande Ave.
Del Norte, CO 81132
Ph:(719)657-2845
Free: 888-616-4638
Co. E-mail: mail@delnortechamber.org
URL: http://www.delnortechamber.org

48566 ■ Delta Area Chamber of Commerce
301 Main St.
Delta, CO 81416-1881
Ph:(970)874-8616
Fax:(970)874-8618
Co. E-mail: chamber@deltacolorado.org
URL: http://www.deltacolorado.org

**48567 ■ Denver Hispanic Chamber of
Commerce**
924 W Colfax Ave., Ste. No. 201
Denver, CO 80204
Ph:(303)534-7783
Fax:(303)595-8977
Co. E-mail: info@dhcc.com
URL: http://www.dhcc.com
Contact: Jeffrey Campos, Pres./CEO

**48568 ■ Denver Metro Chamber of
Commerce**
1445 Market St.
Denver, CO 80202
Ph:(303)534-8500

Fax:(303)534-3200
Co. E-mail: info@denverchamber.org
URL: http://www.denverchamber.org
Contact: John Ikard, Pres./CEO

48569 ■ Dolores Chamber of Commerce
201 Railroad Ave.
PO Box 602
Dolores, CO 81323
Ph:(970)882-4018
Free: 800-807-4712
Co. E-mail: doloreschamber@fone.net
URL: http://www.doloreschamber.com
Contact: Edward Merritt, Treas.

48570 ■ Durango Chamber of Commerce
PO Box 2587
111 S Camino Del Rio
Durango, CO 81302
Ph:(970)247-0312
Free: 888-414-0835
Fax:(970)385-7884
Co. E-mail: chamber@durangobusiness.org
URL: http://www.durangobusiness.org
Contact: Jack Llewellyn, Exec. Dir.

48571 ■ Eads Chamber of Commerce
PO Box 163
Eads, CO 81036-0163
Ph:(719)438-5590
Co. E-mail: dennis.pearson@state.co.us
URL: http://www.kiowacountycolo.com/chamber-
ofcommerce.htm
Contact: Dennis Pearson, Pres.

48572 ■ Eagle Valley Chamber of Commerce
PO Box 964
Eagle, CO 81631
Ph:(970)328-5220
Fax:(970)328-1120
URL: http://www.eaglevalley.org

**48573 ■ Elizabeth Area Chamber of
Commerce**
166 Main St., Ste. E
Elizabeth, CO 80107
Ph:(303)646-4287
Co. E-mail: director@elizabethchamber.org
URL: http://www.elizabethchamber.org
Contact: Beverly Durant, Dir.

48574 ■ Erie Chamber of Commerce
PO Box 97
235 Wells St.
Erie, CO 80516
Ph:(303)828-3440
Fax:(303)828-3330
Co. E-mail: info@eriechamber.org
URL: http://www.eriechamber.org
Contact: Elle Cabbage, Exec. Dir.

48575 ■ Estes Park Chamber of Commerce
500 Big Thompson Ave.
PO Box 1200
Estes Park, CO 80517
Ph:(970)577-9900
Free: 800-378-3708
URL: http://www.estesparkresort.com

**48576 ■ Evergreen Area Chamber of
Commerce**
28065 Hwy. 74, Ste. 201
Evergreen, CO 80439
Ph:(303)674-3412
Fax:(303)674-8463
Co. E-mail: admin@evergreenchamber.org
URL: http://www.evergreenchamber.org
Contact: Melanie Nuchols, Pres.

48577 ■ Florence Chamber of Commerce
PO Box 145
Florence, CO 81226
Ph:(719)784-3544
Fax:(719)784-9324
URL: http://www.florencecolorado.net

**48578 ■ Fort Collins Area Chamber of
Commerce**
225 S Meldrum St.
Fort Collins, CO 80521
Ph:(970)482-3746
Fax:(970)482-3774
Co. E-mail: general@fcchamber.org
URL: http://www.fcchamber.org/Default.asp
Contact: David L. May CCE, Pres./CEO

**48579 ■ Fort Morgan Area Chamber of
Commerce**
300 Main St.
PO Box 971
Fort Morgan, CO 80701
Ph:(970)867-6702
Free: 800-354-8660
Fax:(970)867-6121
Co. E-mail: fortmorganchamber@flci.net
URL: http://www.fortmorganchamber.org
Contact: Marti Vocke, Pres.

**48580 ■ Fountain Valley Chamber of
Commerce**
PO Box 201
Fountain, CO 80817-0201
Ph:(719)382-3190
Fax:(719)322-9395
Co. E-mail: fvcc@qwest.net
URL: http://www.fountaincolorado.org/department/
index.asp?fDD=25-0
Contact: Scott Turner, Pres.

48581 ■ Fruita Chamber of Commerce
432 E Aspen Ave.
Fruita, CO 81521
Ph:(970)858-3894
Fax:(970)858-3121
Co. E-mail: info@fruitachamber.org
URL: http://www.fruitachamber.org
Contact: Mary Lou Wilson, Dir.

48582 ■ Granby Chamber of Commerce
PO Box 35
Granby, CO 80446
Ph:(970)887-2311
Free: 800-325-1661
Fax:(970)887-3895
Co. E-mail: grcoc@rkymtnhi.com
URL: http://granbychamber.com
Contact: Patty Peterson, Chair

**48583 ■ Grand Junction Area Chamber of
Commerce**
360 Grand Ave.
Grand Junction, CO 81501
Ph:(970)242-3214
Free: 800-352-5286
Fax:(970)242-3694
Co. E-mail: diane@gjchamber.org
URL: http://www.gjchamber.org/index.asp
Contact: Diane Schwenke, Pres./CEO

**48584 ■ Grand Lake Area Chamber of
Commerce**
PO Box 429
Grand Lake, CO 80447
Ph:(970)627-3402
Free: 800-531-1019
Co. E-mail: glinfo@grandlakechamber.com
URL: http://www.grandlakechamber.com
Contact: Brad Taylor, Exec. Dir.

**48585 ■ Greater Brighton Area Chamber of
Commerce**
36 S Main St.
Brighton, CO 80601
Ph:(303)659-0223
Fax:(303)659-5115
Co. E-mail: info@brightonchamber.com
URL: http://www.brightonchamber.com
Contact: Kevin Kildow, Chm.

**48586 ■ Greater Colorado Springs Chamber
of Commerce**
6 S Tejon St., Ste. 700
Colorado Springs, CO 80903
Ph:(719)635-1551

Fax:(719)635-1571
Co. E-mail: info@cscc.org
URL: http://www.coloradospringschamber.org
Contact: Dave Csintyan, Pres./CEO

48587 ■ Greater Englewood Chamber of Commerce
3501 S Broadway, 2nd Fl.
Englewood, CO 80110-3629
Ph:(303)789-4473
Fax:(303)789-0098
URL: http://www.myenglewoodchamber.com
Contact: Sherryl Brandes, Sec.

48588 ■ Greater Golden Chamber of Commerce
1010 Washington Ave.
Golden, CO 80401
Ph:(303)279-3113
Free: 800-590-3113
Fax:(303)279-0332
Co. E-mail: info@goldencochamber.org
URL: http://www.goldencochamber.org
Contact: Gary L. Wink, Pres./CEO

48589 ■ Greater Pueblo Chamber of Commerce
302 N Santa Fe Ave.
Pueblo, CO 81003-4102
Ph:(719)542-1704
Free: 800-233-3446
URL: http://www.pueblochamber.org

48590 ■ Greater Woodland Park Chamber of Commerce
210 E Midland Ave.
PO Box 9022
Woodland Park, CO 80866-9022
Ph:(719)687-9885
Free: 800-551-7886
Fax:(719)687-8216
Co. E-mail: info@gwpcc.biz
URL: http://www.woodlandparkchamber.com
Contact: Ms. Debbie Miller, Pres.

48591 ■ Greeley/Weld Chamber of Commerce
902 7th Ave.
Greeley, CO 80631-4603
Ph:(970)352-3566
Fax:(970)352-3572
Co. E-mail: info@greeleychamber.com
URL: http://www.greeleychamber.com
Contact: Sarah MacQuiddy, Pres.

48592 ■ Gunnison County Chamber of Commerce
500 E Tomichi Ave.
Gunnison, CO 81230-0036
Ph:(970)641-1501
Fax:(970)641-3467
Co. E-mail: info@gunnisonchamber.com
URL: http://www.gunnison-co.com
Contact: Tammy Scott, Exec. Dir.

48593 ■ Haxtun Chamber of Commerce
145 S Colorado Ave.
Haxtun, CO 80731
Ph:(970)774-6104
Fax:(970)774-5875
URL: http://www.haxtunchamber.com
Contact: Diane Fryrear

48594 ■ Heart of the Rockies Chamber of Commerce
406 W Hwy. 50
Salida, CO 81201
Ph:(719)539-2068
Free: 877-772-5432
Fax:(719)539-7844
Co. E-mail: info@salidachamber.org
URL: http://salidachamber.org
Contact: John Engelbrecht, Exec. Dir.

48595 ■ Holyoke Chamber of Commerce
212 S Interocean
PO Box 134
Holyoke, CO 80734-0134
Ph:(970)854-3517

Fax:(970)854-3514
Co. E-mail: holyokec@pctc.net
URL: http://www.holyokechamber.org
Contact: Mary Tomky, Dir.

48596 ■ Hotchkiss Chamber of Commerce
PO Box 158
Hotchkiss, CO 81419-0158
Ph:(970)872-3226
Co. E-mail: hotchkiss@hotchkisschamber.com
URL: http://www.hotchkisschamber.com
Contact: Nathan Sponseller, Pres.

48597 ■ Johnstown-Milliken Chamber of Commerce
PO Box 501
Johnstown, CO 80534-0501
Ph:(970)587-7042
Co. E-mail: info@johnstownmillikenchamber.com
URL: http://jmchamber.com
Contact: Tanis Roeder, Pres.

48598 ■ Kersey Area Chamber of Commerce
PO Box 397
Kersey, CO 80644-0397
Ph:(970)342-4804
Co. E-mail: kris@kblegacydesigns.com
URL: http://www.kerseycolorado.com/tp40/Default.
   asp?ID=86026
Contact: Steve Kramer, Pres.

48599 ■ Kremmling Area Chamber of Commerce and Economic Development Commission
PO Box 471
Kremmling, CO 80459
Ph:(970)724-3472
Fax:(970)724-0397
URL: http://www.kremmlingchamber.com
Contact: Carrie George, Pres.

48600 ■ La Junta Chamber of Commerce
110 Santa Fe Ave.
La Junta, CO 81050
Ph:(719)384-7411
Fax:(719)384-2217
Co. E-mail: ljcc@centurytel.net
URL: http://www.lajuntachamber.com
Contact: Mike Moreno, Pres.

48601 ■ La Veta/Cuchara Chamber of Commerce
PO Box 32
La Veta, CO 81055
Ph:(719)742-3676
Free: (866)615-3676
Co. E-mail: email@lavetacucharachamber.com
URL: http://www.lavetacucharachamber.com
Contact: Steven Perkins, Pres.

48602 ■ Lafayette Chamber of Commerce
PO Box 1018
Lafayette, CO 80026
Ph:(303)666-9555
Fax:(303)666-4392
Co. E-mail: info@lafayettecolorado.com
URL: http://www.lafayettecolorado.com
Contact: Vicki Trumbo, Exec. Dir.

48603 ■ Lake City - Hinsdale County Chamber of Commerce
800 N Gunnison Ave.
PO Box 430
Lake City, CO 81235
Ph:(970)944-2527
Free: 800-569-1874
Co. E-mail: info@lakecityco.com
URL: http://www.lakecityco.com

48604 ■ Lamar Chamber of Commerce
109A E Beech St.
Lamar, CO 81052
Ph:(719)336-4379
Fax:(719)336-4370
Co. E-mail: lamarchamber@bresnan.net
URL: http://www.lamarchamber.com
Contact: Chana Reed, Office Mgr.

48605 ■ Las Animas - Bent County Chamber of Commerce
332 Ambassador Thompson Blvd.
Las Animas, CO 81054
Ph:(719)456-0453
Fax:(719)456-0455
Co. E-mail: russellatchamber@yahoo.com
URL: http://bentcounty.org
Contact: Russell Smith, Exec. Dir.

48606 ■ Leadville/Lake County Chamber of Commerce
PO Box 861
Leadville, CO 80461-0861
Ph:(719)486-3900
Free: 888-532-3845
Fax:(719)486-8478
Co. E-mail: leadville@leadvilleusa.com
URL: http://www.leadvilleusa.com
Contact: Heather Scanlon, Exec. Dir.

48607 ■ Limon Chamber of Commerce
PO Box 101
Limon, CO 80828
Ph:(719)775-9418
Co. E-mail: tandersen@gordonins.com
URL: http://www.limonchamber.com
Contact: Tim Anderson, Pres.

48608 ■ Logan County Chamber of Commerce
PO Box 1683
Sterling, CO 80751
Ph:(970)522-5070
Free: (866)522-5070
Fax:(970)522-4082
Co. E-mail: loganccc@logancountychamber.com
URL: http://www.logancountychamber.com
Contact: Mr. Timothy Edgar, Exec. Dir.

48609 ■ Longmont Area Chamber of Commerce
528 Main St.
Longmont, CO 80501-5537
Ph:(303)776-5295
Fax:(303)776-5657
Co. E-mail: kharding@longmontchamber.org
URL: http://www.longmontchamber.org
Contact: Kathy Weber-Harding, CEO/Pres.

48610 ■ Louisville Chamber of Commerce
901 Main St.
Louisville, CO 80027
Ph:(303)666-5747
Fax:(303)666-4285
Co. E-mail: chamber@h2net.net
URL: http://www.louisvillechamber.com
Contact: Shelley Angell, Exec. Dir.

48611 ■ Loveland Chamber of Commerce and Visitors Center
5400 Stone Creek Cir.
Loveland, CO 80538-8838
Ph:(970)667-6311
Free: 800-258-1278
Fax:(970)667-5211
Co. E-mail: bwillms@loveland.org
URL: http://www.loveland.org
Contact: Brian Willms, Pres./CEO

48612 ■ Loveland Info Chamber of Commerce
5400 Stone Creek Cir.
Loveland, CO 80538
Ph:(970)667-6311
Fax:(970)667-5211
Co. E-mail: info@loveland.org
URL: http://www.loveland.org
Contact: Mark Weaver, Chm.

48613 ■ Lyons Chamber of Commerce
PO Box 426
Lyons, CO 80540
Ph:(303)823-5215
Free: 877-LYO-NSCO
Co. E-mail: admin@lyons-colorado.com
URL: http://www.lyons-colorado.com
Contact: Laurie Kennedy, Pres.

48614 ■ Manitou Springs Chamber of Commerce
354 Manitou Ave.
Manitou Springs, CO 80829
Ph:(719)685-5089
Free: 800-642-2567
Fax:(719)685-0355
URL: http://www.manitousprings.org
Contact: Leslie Lewis, Exec. Dir.

48615 ■ Meeker Chamber of Commerce
PO Box 869
Meeker, CO 81641-0869
Ph:(970)878-5510
Fax:(970)878-0271
Co. E-mail: info@meekerchamber.com
URL: http://www.meekerchamber.net
Contact: Margie Joy, Pres.

48616 ■ Metro North Chamber of Commerce
2921 W 120th Ave., Ste. 210
Westminster, CO 80234
Ph:(303)288-1000
Fax:(303)227-1050
Co. E-mail: info@metronorthchamber.com
URL: http://www.metronorthchamber.com
Contact: Deborah Obermeyer, Pres./CEO

48617 ■ Monte Vista Chamber of Commerce
947 1st Ave.
Monte Vista, CO 81144
Ph:(719)852-2731
Free: 800-562-7085
Fax:(719)852-9382
Co. E-mail: chamber@monte-vista.org
URL: http://www.monte-vista.org
Contact: Don Van Wormer, Pres.

48618 ■ Montrose Chamber of Commerce
1519 E Main St.
Montrose, CO 81401-3807
Ph:(970)249-5000
Free: 800-923-5515
Fax:(970)249-2907
Co. E-mail: information@montrosechamber.com
URL: http://www.montrosechamber.com
Contact: Terri Leben, Exec. Dir.

48619 ■ Nederland Area Chamber of Commerce
PO Box 85
Nederland, CO 80466
Ph:(303)258-3936
Co. E-mail: info@nederlandchamber.org
URL: http://www.nederlandchamber.org
Contact: Kimba Stefane, Pres.

48620 ■ New Castle Area Chamber of Commerce
PO Box 983
New Castle, CO 81647
Ph:(970)984-2897
Co. E-mail: info@newcastlechamber.org
URL: http://www.newcastlechamber.org
Contact: Bill Pugh, Pres.

48621 ■ Ouray Chamber Resort Association
PO Box 145
Ouray, CO 81427-0145
Ph:(970)325-4746
Free: 800-228-1876
Fax:(970)325-4868
Co. E-mail: ouray@ouraycolorado.com
URL: http://www.ouraycolorado.com
Contact: Ms. Jennifer Loshaw, Exec. Dir.

48622 ■ Pagosa Springs Area Chamber of Commerce
PO Box 787
Pagosa Springs, CO 81147
Free: 800-252-2204
Co. E-mail: info@pagosachamber.com
URL: http://visitpagosasprings.com/colorado/
  chamber-of-commerce
Contact: Mary Jo Coulehan, Exec. Dir.

48623 ■ Palisade Chamber of Commerce
319 S Main St.
PO Box 729
Palisade, CO 81526
Ph:(970)464-7458
Fax:(970)464-4757
Co. E-mail: info@palisadecoc.com
URL: http://www.palisadecoc.com
Contact: Ms. Sandie Cooper, Chair

48624 ■ Paonia Chamber of Commerce
PO Box 366
Paonia, CO 81428-0366
Ph:(970)527-3886
Co. E-mail: chamber@paonia.com
URL: http://www.paoniachamber.com
Contact: Regna Jones, Pres.

48625 ■ Parker Chamber of Commerce
19751 E Main St., R12
Parker, CO 80138
Ph:(303)841-4268
Fax:(303)841-8061
URL: http://www.parkerchamber.com
Contact: Lisa Maurer, Admin. Dir.

48626 ■ Rangely Area Chamber of Commerce
209 E Main St.
Rangely, CO 81648
Ph:(970)675-5290
Fax:(970)675-8471
Co. E-mail: info@rangelychamber.com
URL: http://www.rangelychamber.com
Contact: Rebecca Hahn, Pres.

48627 ■ Rifle Area Chamber of Commerce
200 Lions Park Cir.
Rifle, CO 81650-0809
Ph:(970)625-2085
Free: 800-842-2085
Fax:(970)625-4757
Co. E-mail: mail@riflechamber.com
URL: http://www.riflechamber.com
Contact: Annick Pruett, Pres./CEO

48628 ■ Silverton Chamber of Commerce
PO Box 565
Silverton, CO 81433-0565
Ph:(970)387-5654
Free: 800-752-4494
Fax:(970)387-0282
Co. E-mail: chamber@silvertoncolorado.net
URL: http://www.silvertoncolorado.com

48629 ■ Snowmass Village Resort Association
PO Box 5010
Snowmass Village, CO 81615-5010
Ph:(970)922-2297
Free: 800-598-2006
Fax:(970)922-1139
Co. E-mail: harris.wendy@comcast.net
URL: http://www.snowmassvillage.com
Contact: Harris Wendy, Admin.

48630 ■ South Fork Chamber of Commerce and Visitors Center
PO Box 1030
South Fork, CO 81154
Ph:(719)873-5512
Free: 800-571-0881
Fax:(719)873-5693
Co. E-mail: southfrk@amigo.net
URL: http://www.southfork.org
Contact: Josephine Pierce, Dir.

48631 ■ South Metro Denver Chamber of Commerce
6840 S University Blvd.
Centennial, CO 80122
Ph:(303)795-0142
Fax:(303)795-7520
Co. E-mail: jbrackney@bestchamber.com
URL: http://www.bestchamber.com
Contact: John Brackney, Pres.

48632 ■ Southern Colorado Women's Chamber of Commerce
PO Box 49218
Colorado Springs, CO 80949
Ph:(719)442-2007
Co. E-mail: board@scwcc.com
URL: http://www.scwcc.com/CMS
Contact: Leslie Eldridge, Pres.

48633 ■ Springfield Chamber of Commerce
948 Main St.
Springfield, CO 81073
Ph:(719)523-4061
Co. E-mail: springfieldcochamber@springfieldco.info
URL: http://www.springfieldco.info
Contact: Jodi Ricker, Pres.

48634 ■ Steamboat Springs Chamber Resort Association
PO Box 774408
Steamboat Springs, CO 80477-4408
Ph:(970)879-0882
Fax:(970)879-2543
Co. E-mail: info@steamboatchamber.com
URL: http://www.steamboat-chamber.com
Contact: Sandy Evans Hall, Exec. VP

48635 ■ Summit County Chamber of Commerce
PO Box 5450
Frisco, CO 80443
Ph:(970)668-2051
Free: 800-530-3099
Fax:(970)668-1515
Co. E-mail: srussell@summitchamber.org
URL: http://www.summitchamber.org
Contact: Sharon Russell, Exec. Dir.

48636 ■ Swedish-American Chamber of Commerce, Colorado
4525 S Decatur St.
Englewood, CO 80110
Co. E-mail: saccco@msn.com
URL: http://www.sacc-usa.org/colorado
Contact: Per Karlqvist, Chm.

48637 ■ Tri-Lakes Chamber of Commerce
PO Box 147
Monument, CO 80132
Ph:(719)481-3282
Fax:(719)481-1638
Co. E-mail: info@trilakeschamber.com
URL: http://www.trilakeschamber.com
Contact: Mr. David T. Van Ness, Exec. Dir.

48638 ■ Vallecito Lake Chamber of Commerce
PO Box 804
Bayfield, CO 81122
Ph:(970)247-1573
Co. E-mail: info@vallecitolakechamber.com
URL: http://www.vallecitolakechamber.com
Contact: Burt Armstrong, Pres.

48639 ■ West Chamber of Commerce Serving Jefferson County
1667 Cole Blvd., Bldg. 19, Ste. 400
Lakewood, CO 80401
Ph:(303)233-5555
Fax:(303)237-7633
Co. E-mail: info@westchamber.org
URL: http://www.westchamber.org
Contact: Amy Sherman, Pres.

48640 ■ West Yuma County Chamber of Commerce
14 W 2nd Ave.
Yuma, CO 80759
Ph:(970)848-2704
Fax:(970)848-5700
Co. E-mail: director@westyumachamber.com
URL: http://www.seeyuma.com

48641 ■ Windsor Chamber of Commerce
421 Main St.
Windsor, CO 80550
Ph:(970)686-7189

Fax:(970)686-0352
Co. E-mail: michal@windsorchamber.net
URL: http://www.windsorchamber.net
Contact: Erich E. Ehrlich, Pres.

48642 ■ Winter Park-Fraser Valley Chamber of Commerce
PO Box 3236
Winter Park, CO 80482-3236
Ph:(970)726-4118
Free: 800-903-7275
Fax:(970)726-9449
Co. E-mail: visitorcenter@winterpark.com
URL: http://www.winterpark-info.com
Contact: Catherine Ross, Exec. Dir.

48643 ■ Wray Chamber of Commerce
PO Box 101
110 E 3rd St.
Wray, CO 80758
Ph:(970)332-3484
Co. E-mail: director@wraychamber.net
URL: http://www.wraychamber.net
Contact: Kyle Hansen, Exec. Dir.

MINORITY BUSINESS ASSISTANCE PROGRAMS

48644 ■ Colorado Office of Economic Development and International Trade–Minority Business Office
1625 Broadway, Ste. 2700
Denver, CO 80202
Ph:(303)892-3840
Fax:(303)892-3848
Co. E-mail: lromero@state.co.us
URL: http://www.state.co.us
Contact: LeRoy Romero, Dir
Description: Provides information and assistance to minority- and women-owned businesses in Colorado.

FINANCING AND LOAN PROGRAMS

48645 ■ 5280 Partners
360 S. Monroe St., Ste. 600
Denver, CO 80209
Ph:(303)333-1215
Fax:(303)322-3553
URL: http://www.5280partners.com
Contact: Jeffrey D. Bennis, Principal
Preferred Investment Size: $500,000 to $2,500,000. **Investment Policies:** Early, first and second stage. **Industry Preferences:** Communications, computer software, and Internet specific. **Geographic Preferences:** Western United States, primarily in the Rocky Mountain region. **Principal Exhibits:**

48646 ■ Access Venture Partners
8787 Turnpike Dr., Ste. 260
Westminster, CO 80031
Ph:(303)426-8899
Fax:(303)426-8828
Co. E-mail: mail@accessvp.com
URL: http://www.accessventurepartners.com
Contact: Jay Campion, Managing Director
Preferred Investment Size: $250,000 to $2,000,000. **Investment Types:** Seed and early stage. **Industry Preferences:** Internet specific, communications and media, biotechnology, computer software and services, semiconductors and other electronics, and industrial and energy. **Geographic Preferences:** U.S. **Principal Exhibits:**

48647 ■ Altira Group LLC
1675 Broadway, Ste. 2400
Denver, CO 80202
Ph:(303)592-5500
Fax:(303)592-5519
Co. E-mail: info@altiragroup.com
URL: http://www.altiragroup.com
Contact: Dick McDermott, Managing Partner
Preferred Investment Size: $5,000,000 to $10,000,000. **Investment Types:** Early stage. **Industry Preferences:** Industrial and energy, and environment. **Geographic Preferences:** U.S. and Canada. **Principal Exhibits:**

48648 ■ Appian Ventures
1512 Larimer St., Ste. 200
Denver, CO 80202
Ph:(303)830-2450
Fax:(303)830-2449
Co. E-mail: admin@appianvc.com
URL: http://www.appianvc.com
Contact: Chris Onan, Managing Director
Preferred Investment Size: $1,000,000 to $2,000,000. **Investment Policies:** Seed, early and later stage. **Industry Preferences:** Communications, and computer software. **Geographic Preferences:** Colorado, Rocky Mountains, and West Coast. **Principal Exhibits:**

48649 ■ Aweida Venture Partners
500 Discovery Pky., Ste. 300
Superior, CO 80027
Ph:(303)664-9520
Fax:(303)664-9530
Co. E-mail: info@aweida.com
URL: http://www.aweida.com
Contact: Daniel Aweida, Managing Partner
Preferred Investment Size: $500,000 to $1,000,000. **Investment Types:** Seed through mezzanine. **Industry Preferences:** Computer software and hardware, Internet specific, biotechnology, and medical and health. **Geographic Preferences:** Rocky Mountains. **Principal Exhibits:**

48650 ■ Centennial Ventures
1125 17th St., Ste. 740
Denver, CO 80202
Ph:(303)405-7500
Fax:(303)405-7575
URL: http://www.centennial.com
Contact: Duncan Butler, Managing Director
Preferred Investment Size: $100,000 minimum. **Investment Types:** Seed, start-up, early, later, first stage, and balanced. **Industry Preferences:** Communications and media, Internet specific, computer hardware, computer software and services, semiconductors and other electronics, medical and health, biotechnology, consumer related, other products, and industrial and energy. **Geographic Preferences:** U.S. **Principal Exhibits:**

48651 ■ Meritage Private Equity Funds
1675 Larimer St., Ste. 400
Denver, CO 80202
Ph:(303)352-2040
Fax:(303)352-2050
URL: http://www.meritagefunds.com
Contact: Laura Beller, Managing Director
Preferred Investment Size: $5,000,000 to $15,000,000. **Investment Types:** Seed, early and later stage, balanced, expansion, industry rollups, public companies, recapitalizations, special situation, and turnaround. **Industry Preferences:** Internet specific, communications and media, computer hardware, and computer software and services. **Geographic Preferences:** U.S. **Principal Exhibits:**

48652 ■ Roser Ventures LLC
1105 Spruce St.
Boulder, CO 80302
Ph:(303)443-7924
Fax:(303)443-1885
URL: http://www.roserventures.com
Contact: Christopher W. Roser, Partner
E-mail: croser@roseventures.com
Preferred Investment Size: $100,000 to $3,000,000. **Investment Types:** Early stage and expansion. **Industry Preferences:** Internet specific, communications and media, industrial and energy, semiconductors and other electronics, computer software and services, medical and health, computer hardware, other products, biotechnology, and consumer related. **Geographic Preferences:** Colorado and the Rocky Mountains. **Principal Exhibits:**

48653 ■ Sequel Venture Partners
4430 Arapahoe Ave., Ste. 220
Boulder, CO 80303
Ph:(303)546-0400

Fax:(303)546-9728
Co. E-mail: info@sequelvc.com
URL: http://www.sequelvc.com
Contact: Ron Bernal, Partner
Preferred Investment Size: $2,000,000 to $12,000,000. **Investment Types:** Seed, early, and first stage. **Industry Preferences:** Internet specific, computer software and services, medical and health, semiconductors and other electronics, biotechnology, communications and media, computer hardware, and other products. **Geographic Preferences:** Colorado and Rocky Mountains. **Principal Exhibits:**

PROCUREMENT ASSISTANCE PROGRAMS

48654 ■ Colorado Procurement Technical Assistance Center–Denver Small Business Development Procurement Center
1445 Market St.
Denver, CO 80202
Ph:(303)620-8076
Fax:(303)534-2145
URL: http://www.denversbdc.org/
Contact: Tameka Montgomery, Dir.

INCUBATORS/RESEARCH AND TECHNOLOGY PARKS

48655 ■ Colorado Springs Technology Incubator
3595 E Fountain Blvd., Ste. B2
Colorado Springs, CO 80910
Ph:(719)685-7877
Fax:(719)685-7878
Co. E-mail: info@cstionline.org
URL: http://www.cstionline.org/
Contact: Duncan Stewart
Description: A small incubator assisting in the launch of high-technology companies in the greater Colorado Springs area, through business advice, office facilities and access to educational resources.

48656 ■ Colorado State University–Office of Vice President for Research
203 Administration Bldg.
Fort Collins, CO 80523-2001
Ph:(970)491-7194
Fax:(970)491-5541
Co. E-mail: william.farland@colostate.edu
URL: http://www.vpr.colostate.edu
Contact: William H. Farland PhD, VP, Res.
E-mail: william.farland@colostate.edu
Scope: Administers and coordinates research activities in the various colleges, departments, and special research units at the University. **Publications:** Research at Colorado State University. **Educational Activities:** Conference services; Research colloquia.

48657 ■ Colorado State University Research Foundation
PO Box 483
Fort Collins, CO 80522
Ph:(970)482-2916
Fax:(970)484-0354
Co. E-mail: kathleen@csurf.org
URL: http://www.csurf.org
Contact: Kathleen Henry, Pres./CEO
E-mail: kathleen@csurf.org
Scope: Assists Colorado State University and the other universities governed by the Colorado Board of Governors through the management of patents and licenses, acquisition of research equipment and facilities, and the acquisition and management of land. Acts as a support organization in tax-exempt debt financing, which takes the form of municipal bonds, notes, mortgages, revolving lines of credit, and equipment leasing.

48658 ■ The Denver Enterprise Center
3003 Arapahoe St.
Denver, CO 80205
Ph:(303)296-9400

Fax:(303)296-5542
Co. E-mail: decinfo@thedec.org
URL: http://www.thedec.org/
Contact: Pat Durand, Exec Dir
Description: A small business incubator that assists entrepreneurs in the business start-up process and gives aid to new businesses to help ensure their survival.

48659 ■ Fitzsimons BioBusiness Partners
12635 E Montview Blvd.
Aurora, CO 80045
Ph:(720)859-4107
Fax:(720)859-4110
Co. E-mail: ddrake@colobio.com
URL: http://www.fbbp.org
Description: An incubator dedicated to promoting the growth and success of bioscience businesses in Colorado, with a special emphasis on forming a bioscience cluster at Fitzsimons. Connects ideas, technology and people to deliver targeted assistance to start-up companies and entrepreneurs; unites industry experts, venture capitalists, private investors, and the researchers the move discoveries from the lab to the commercial marketplace.

48660 ■ Fitzsimons Life Science District
12635 E. Montview Blvd.
Aurora, CO 80045-7336
Ph:(720)859-4107
Fax:(720)859-4110
URL: http://www.fitzscience.com
Description: A development facility stimulating economic growth by creating a word-class scientific community at Fitzsimons which includes, but is not limited to, entrepreneurial life science organizations, related support services and high-quality amenities.

48661 ■ Fremont County Business Development Corporation
402 Valley Rd.
Canon City, CO 81212
Ph:(719)275-8601
Free: 800-426-4794
Fax:(719)275-4400
Co. E-mail: Edie@qwestoffice.net
URL: http://www.fremontedc.org
Description: A small business incubator that assists entrepreneurs in the business start-up process and gives aid to new businesses to help ensure their survival.

48662 ■ Longmont Entrepreneurial Network
2400 Trade Center Ave.
Longmont, CO 80305
Ph:(303)678-8000
Fax:(303)678-8505
Co. E-mail: alex.sammoury@ctek.biz
URL: http://www.ctek.biz
Contact: Alex Sammoury, Exec Dir
Description: Provides housing and laboratory space for young technology companies. A CTek venture center.

48663 ■ Pueblo Business and Technology Center
301 N Main St.
Pueblo, CO 81003
Ph:(719)546-1133
Free: 800-522-1120
Fax:(719)546-1942
Co. E-mail: btc@pedco.org
URL: http://www.btc-pueblo.com
Description: A small business incubator that assists entrepreneurs in the business start-up process and gives aid to new businesses to help ensure their survival.

48664 ■ Rocky Mountain Innosphere
320 E Vine Dr., Ste. 101
Fort Collins, CO 80524
Ph:(970)221-1301
Fax:(970)221-9423
URL: http://www.rmi2.org/
Description: A business incubator assisting startup companies and rapidly growing young firms. Formerly the Fort Collins Technology Incubator.

48665 ■ University of Colorado at Boulder–Technology Transfer Office
4740 Walnut St., Ste. 100, CB 588
Boulder, CO 80309-0588
Ph:(303)492-5647
Fax:(303)492-2128
Co. E-mail: kate.tallman@cu.edu
URL: http://www.cu.edu/techtransfer
Contact: Kate Tallman, Dir.
E-mail: kate.tallman@cu.edu
Scope: Administers and coordinates sponsored research proposals and post-award administrative activities of the University, provides administrative and accounting services, assists faculty members conducting research, and serves as liaison and negotiator with extramural sponsors of research conducted at the University and with governmental auditors. **Publications:** Technology Transfer Office Annual Report; TTO Newsletter (monthly). **Awards:** Proof-of-Concept Grants (semiannually), to CU researchers working to develop the commercial potential of CU inventions.

48666 ■ Western Colorado Business Development Corp.–Business Incubator Center
2591B 3/4 Rd.
Grand Junction, CO 81503
Ph:(970)243-5242
Fax:(970)241-0771
Co. E-mail: administrative@gjincubator.org
URL: http://www.gjincubator.org
Contact: Chris Reddin, Exec Dir
Description: Assists entrepreneurs in the business start-up process and in managing new businesses.

EDUCATIONAL PROGRAMS

48667 ■ Aims Community College
PO Box 69
Greeley, CO 80632
Ph:(970)330-8008
Free: 800-745-0650
Fax:(970)330-5705
URL: http://www.aims.edu
Description: Two-year college offering a small business management program.

48668 ■ Colorado Northwestern Community College (Craig)
50 College Dr.
Craig, CO 81625
Ph:(970)824-7071
Fax:(970)824-1134
URL: http://www.cncc.edu
Description: Two-year college offering a small business management program.

48669 ■ Emily Griffith Opportunity School
1250 Welton St.
Denver, CO 80204
Ph:(720)423-4700
Fax:(720)575-4840
URL: http://www.egos-school.com
Description: Trade and technical school offering classes in entrepreneurship.

48670 ■ Lamar Community College
2401 S Main St.
Lamar, CO 81052
Ph:(719)336-2248
Free: 800-968-6920
Fax:(719)336-2448
Co. E-mail: angela.woodward@lcc.cccoes.edu
URL: http://www.lcc.cccoes.edu
Description: Two-year college offering a small business management program.

TRADE PERIODICALS

48671 ■ Colorado Job Finder
Pub: Colorado Municipal League
Released: Semimonthly, 1st and 3rd Wednesday of each month. **Price:** individuals; $30 for 6 months.
Description: Consists of local government employment opportunities in Colorado and surrounding area.

PUBLICATIONS

48672 ■ The Denver Business Journal
1700 Broadway, Ste. 515
Denver, CO 80290
Ph:(303)837-3500
Fax:(303)837-3535
URL: http://www.amcity.com/denver

48673 ■ Smart Start your Colorado Business
PSI Research
300 N. Valley Dr.
Grants Pass, OR 97526
Ph:(503)479-9464
Free: 800-228-2275
Fax:(503)476-1479
Co. E-mail: info@psi-research.com
URL: http://www.psi-research.com
Ed: Michael D. Jenkins. **Released:** Revised edition, 1992. **Price:** $29.95 (looseleaf binder); $24.95 (paper). **Description:** Part of the Successful Business Library series.

48674 ■ Starting and Operating a Business in Colorado: A Step-by-Step Guide
PSI Research
300 N. Valley Dr.
Grants Pass, OR 97526
Ph:(503)479-9464
Free: 800-228-2275
Fax:(503)476-1479
Co. E-mail: psi2@magick.net
Ed: Michael D. Jenkins. **Released:** Revised edition, 1992. **Price:** $29.95 (looseleaf binder); $24.95 (paper). **Description:** Part of the Successful Business Library series.

PUBLISHERS

48675 ■ Center for Self-Sufficiency–Publishing Div.
1001 Logan St., Apt. 108
PO Box 416
Denver, CO 80203-3081
Ph:(303)575-5676
Fax:(303)575-1187
Co. E-mail: mail@gumbomedia.com
Contact: A. C. Doyle, Owner
Description: Publishes how-to, consumer, recycling, and small business titles. Does not accept unsolicited manuscripts. Reaches market through direct mail. **Founded:** 1982.

48676 ■ Restaurant Publishing
c/o Prosperity & Profit Unlimited, Distribution Services
PO Box 416
Denver, CO 80201-0416
Ph:(303)575-5676
Fax:(303)575-1187
Co. E-mail: street@gmail.com
Contact: A. Doyle, President
Description: Publishes and distributes cook books, food how-to book and newsletters for restaurants, cafes and catering services. Distributes *Recipe Greetings, Recipe Multiplication Forms*, and *Herbal Verbal* cassettes. Reaches market through direct mail, trade sales and Prosperity and Profits Unlimited. Does not accept unsolicited manuscripts. **Founded:** 1989.

48677 ■ Rollaway Bay Publications Inc.
6334 S Racine Cir., Ste. 100
Centennial, CO 80111-6405
Ph:(303)799-8320
Fax:(303)799-4220
Co. E-mail: publisher@rollawaybay.com
URL: http://www.rollawaybay.com
Contact: Marsha Haigh Arend, Mgr
Description: Publishes business titles. **Founded:** 2003.

48678 ■ Update Publicare Co.
c/o Prosperity & Profits Unlimited
PO Box 416
Denver, CO 80201-0416
Ph:(303)575-5676

Fax:(303)575-1187
Co. E-mail: mail@breadpudding.net
Description: Publishes for consumers and businesses. Offers newsletters on recycling, self employment, publishing, and small business. Does not accept unsolicited manuscripts. **Founded:** 1989.

48679 ■ World Economic Processing Zones Association
3 Bullet Hill Rd.

PO Box 3808
Danbury, CT 06811-2906
Ph:(203)798-9394
Fax:(203)798-9394
Co. E-mail: director@wepza.org
URL: http://www.wepza.org
Contact: Robert Haywood, Director
E-mail: bolinflag@aol.com
Description: Publishes materials on free zones, export processing zones, economic development

zones, research parks, multinational manufacturing and international development agencies. Does not accept unsolicited manuscripts. **Founded:** 1978.

SMALL BUSINESS DEVELOPMENT CENTERS

48680 ■ Connecticut Small Business Development Center - Eastern Connecticut State University
Beckert Hall
83 Windham St.
Willimantic, CT 06226
Fax:(860)832-0656
Co. E-mail: twissdec@ccsu.edu
URL: http://www.ccsu.edu/sbdc
Contact: Milena Stankova Erwin, Business Development Advisor

48681 ■ Connecticut Small Business Development Center - Southern Connecticut State University
Old Student Ctr., Rm. 104
501 Crescent St.
New Haven, CT 06515
Fax:(860)832-0656
Co. E-mail: cruz_ma@ccsu.edu
URL: http://www.ccsu.edu/sbdc
Contact: Maryann Cruz, Counselor

48682 ■ Connecticut Small Business Development Center - Western Connecticut State University
Ancell School of Business
181 White St.
Danbury, CT 06810
Fax:(860)832-0656
Co. E-mail: cilleychj@ccsu.edu
URL: http://www.ccsu.edu/sbdc
Contact: Charlotte Cilley, Business Development Advisor

SMALL BUSINESS ASSISTANCE PROGRAMS

48683 ■ Connecticut Economic Resource Center
805 Brook St., Bldg. 4
Rocky Hill, CT 06067-3405
Ph:(860)571-7136
Free: 800-392-2122
Fax:(860)571-7150
Co. E-mail: solutions@cerc.com
URL: http://www.cerc.com
Contact: Connie Maffeo, Dir
Description: Provides managerial assistance and assists in preparing applications for financing.

48684 ■ Department of Economic & Community Development–Office of Business and Industry Development
505 Hudson St.
Hartford, CT 06106-7106
Ph:(860)270-8000
Free: 800-392-2122
Fax:(860)270-8070
Co. E-mail: DECD@po.state.ct.us
URL: http://www.ct.gov/ecd
Contact: Tricia Paesani
Description: Promotes trade; publishes a brochure on licensing and joint ventures; and administers the Exporters Revolving Loan Fund for small and medium-sized businesses.

SCORE OFFICES

48685 ■ Northwest Connecticut SCORE
Path: www.nwctscore.org

48686 ■ Southeastern Connecticut SCORE
Path: www.southeasternctscore.org

BETTER BUSINESS BUREAUS

48687 ■ Better Business Bureau, Connecticut
94 S Turnpike Rd.
Wallingford, CT 06492
Ph:(203)269-2700
Fax:(203)269-3124
Co. E-mail: info@ctbbb.org
URL: http://www.connecticut.bbb.org
Contact: Paulette N. Hotton, Pres./CEO

CHAMBERS OF COMMERCE

48688 ■ Avon Chamber of Commerce
412 W Avon Rd.
Avon, CT 06001
Ph:(860)675-4832
Fax:(860)675-0469
Co. E-mail: avonchamber@sbcglobal.net
URL: http://www.avonchamber.com
Contact: Lisa Bohman, Exec. Dir.

48689 ■ Berlin Chamber of Commerce
40 Chamberlain Hwy., Ferndale Ctr.
Kensington, CT 06037
Ph:(860)829-1033
Fax:(860)829-1243
Co. E-mail: director@berlinctchamber.org
URL: http://www.berlinctchamber.org
Contact: Katherine A. Fuechsel, Exec. Dir.

48690 ■ Bethel Chamber of Commerce
16 P. T. Barnum Sq.
Bethel, CT 06801
Ph:(203)743-6500
Co. E-mail: info@bethelchamber.com
URL: http://www.bethelchamber.com
Contact: Violet Mattone, Exec. Dir.

48691 ■ Bloomfield Chamber of Commerce
PO Box 938
Bloomfield, CT 06002
Ph:(860)242-3710
Co. E-mail: webmail@bloomfieldchamber.org
URL: http://www.bloomfieldchamber.org
Contact: Vera Smith-Winfree MEd, Exec. Dir.

48692 ■ Branford Chamber of Commerce
PO Box 375
Branford, CT 06405
Ph:(203)488-5500
Fax:(203)488-5046
Co. E-mail: info@branfordct.com
URL: http://www.branfordct.com
Contact: Edward Lazarus, Pres.

48693 ■ Bridgeport Regional Business Council
10 Middle St., 14th Fl.
Bridgeport, CT 06604
Ph:(203)335-3800
Fax:(203)366-0105
Co. E-mail: info@brbc.org
URL: http://www.brbc.org
Contact: Paul S. Timpanelli, Pres./CEO

48694 ■ Canton Chamber of Commerce
PO Box 704
Canton, CT 06019
Ph:(860)693-0405
Fax:(860)693-9105
Co. E-mail: info@cantonchamberofcommerce.com
URL: http://www.cantonchamberofcommerce.com
Contact: Phil Worley, Exec. Dir.

48695 ■ Chamber of Commerce of Eastern Connecticut
PO Box 726
Gales Ferry, CT 06335
Ph:(860)464-7373
Free: (866)274-5587
Fax:(860)464-7374
Co. E-mail: tsheridan@chamberect.com
URL: http://www.chamberect.com
Contact: Thomas A. Sheridan, Pres.

48696 ■ Chamber of Commerce of Newtown
PO Box 314
Newtown, CT 06470
Ph:(203)426-2695
Fax:(203)426-2695
Co. E-mail: chamber@newtown-ct.com
URL: http://www.newtown-ct.com
Contact: Pat Linnell, Pres.

48697 ■ Chamber of Commerce of Northwest Connecticut
PO Box 59
Torrington, CT 06790
Ph:(860)482-6586
Fax:(860)489-8851
Co. E-mail: info@nwctchamberofcommerce.org
URL: http://www.nwctchamberofcommerce.org
Contact: JoAnn Ryan, Pres.

48698 ■ Chamber of Commerce, Windham Region
PO Box 43
Willimantic, CT 06226-0043
Ph:(860)423-6389

Fax:(860)423-8235
Co. E-mail: info@windhamchamber.com
URL: http://www.windhamchamber.com
Contact: Roger Adams, Exec. Dir.

48699 ■ Cheshire Chamber of Commerce
195 S Main St.
Cheshire, CT 06410
Ph:(203)272-2345
Fax:(203)271-3044
Co. E-mail: info@cheshirechamber.com
URL: http://www.cheshirechamber.com
Contact: Sheldon Dill, Pres.

48700 ■ Clinton Chamber of Commerce
PO Box 334
Clinton, CT 06413
Ph:(860)669-3889
Fax:(860)669-3889
Co. E-mail: chamber@clintonct.com
URL: http://clintonct.com
Contact: Tom Pare, Chm.

48701 ■ Connecticut Business and Industry Association
350 Church St.
Hartford, CT 06103-1126
Ph:(860)244-1900
Fax:(860)278-8562
Co. E-mail: joe.dias@cbia.com
URL: http://www.cbia.com/home.php
Contact: Joe Dias, Membership Dir.

48702 ■ Darien Chamber of Commerce
10 Corbin Dr.
Darien, CT 06820
Ph:(203)655-3600
Fax:(203)655-2074
Co. E-mail: darienchamber@optonline.net
URL: http://www.darienchamberonline.com
Contact: Carol Wilder-Tamme, Pres./CEO

48703 ■ East Granby Chamber of Commerce
PO Box 1335
East Granby, CT 06026
Ph:(860)653-3833
Fax:(860)653-3855
Co. E-mail: admin@eastgranbycoc.org
URL: http://www.eastgranbycoc.org
Contact: Bob Sproat, Pres.

48704 ■ East Hartford Chamber of Commerce
1137 Main St.
East Hartford, CT 06108
Ph:(860)289-0239
Co. E-mail: ehchamber@sbcglobal.net
URL: http://www.ehcoc.com
Contact: Guy LaBella, Pres.

48705 ■ East Haven Chamber of Commerce
PO Box 120055
East Haven, CT 06512
Ph:(203)467-4305
Fax:(203)469-2299
Co. E-mail: generalinfo@easthavenchamber.com
URL: http://ehchamber.org
Contact: Mary W. Cacace, Exec. Dir.

48706 ■ Fairfield Chamber of Commerce
1597 Post Rd.
Fairfield, CT 06824
Ph:(203)255-1011
Fax:(203)256-9990
Co. E-mail: info@fairfieldctchamber.com
URL: http://www.fairfieldctchamber.com/online/home/index.asp
Contact: Patricia L. Ritchie, Pres./CEO

48707 ■ Farmington Chamber of Commerce
827 Farmington Ave.
Farmington, CT 06032
Ph:(860)676-8490
Fax:(860)677-8332
Co. E-mail: raygagnon@farmingtonchamber.com
URL: http://www.farmingtonchamber.com
Contact: Ray Gagnon, Membership Dir.

48708 ■ Glastonbury Chamber of Commerce
2400 Main St.
Glastonbury, CT 06033
Ph:(860)659-3587
Fax:(860)659-0102
Co. E-mail: maryellen@glastonburychamber.com
URL: http://www.glastonburychamber.net
Contact: Mary Ellen Dombrowski, Pres.

48709 ■ Granby Chamber of Commerce
PO Box 211
Granby, CT 06035
Ph:(860)653-5085
Co. E-mail: gcoc@granbycoc.org
URL: http://www.granbycoc.org
Contact: Roger Voyer, Admin.

48710 ■ Greater Danbury Chamber of Commerce
39 West St.
Danbury, CT 06810
Ph:(203)743-5565
Fax:(203)794-1439
Co. E-mail: info@danburychamber.com
URL: http://www.danburychamber.com
Contact: Stephen A. Bull, Pres.

48711 ■ Greater Manchester Chamber of Commerce
20 Hartford Rd.
Manchester, CT 06040
Ph:(860)646-2223
Fax:(860)646-5871
Co. E-mail: staffgmcc@manchesterchamber.com
URL: http://www.manchesterchamber.com
Contact: Sue O'Connor, Pres.

48712 ■ Greater Meriden Chamber of Commerce
3 Colony St., Ste. 301
Meriden, CT 06450
Ph:(203)235-7901
Fax:(203)686-0172
Co. E-mail: info@meridenchamber.com
URL: http://www.meridenchamber.com
Contact: Sean W. Moore, Pres.

48713 ■ Greater New Haven Chamber of Commerce
900 Chapel St., 10th Fl.
New Haven, CT 06510
Ph:(203)787-6735
Fax:(203)782-4329
Co. E-mail: info@gnhcc.com
URL: http://www.gnhcc.com
Contact: Anthony P. Rescigno, Pres.

48714 ■ Greater New Milford Chamber of Commerce
11 Railroad St.
New Milford, CT 06776-2717
Ph:(860)354-6080
Fax:(860)354-8526
Co. E-mail: nmcc@newmilford-chamber.com
URL: http://www.newmilford-chamber.com
Contact: Denise Del Mastro, Exec. Dir.

48715 ■ Greater Norwalk Chamber of Commerce
PO Box 668
Norwalk, CT 06852-0668
Ph:(203)866-2521
Fax:(203)852-0583
Co. E-mail: info@norwalkchamberofcommerce.com
URL: http://www.norwalkchamberofcommerce.com
Contact: Edward J. Musante Jr., Pres.

48716 ■ Greater Southington Chamber of Commerce
1 Factory Sq.
Southington, CT 06489
Ph:(860)628-8036
Fax:(860)276-9696
Co. E-mail: info@southingtoncoc.com
URL: http://www.southingtoncoc.com
Contact: Art Secondo, Pres.

48717 ■ Greater Valley Chamber of Commerce
900 Bridgeport Ave., 2nd Fl.
Shelton, CT 06484
Ph:(203)925-4981
Fax:(203)925-4984
Co. E-mail: info@greatervalleychamber.com
URL: http://greatervalleychamber.com
Contact: Win Oppel, Pres.

48718 ■ Greenwich Chamber of Commerce
45 E Putnam Ave., Ste. 121
Greenwich, CT 06830
Ph:(203)869-3500
Fax:(203)869-3502
Co. E-mail: info@greenwichchamber.com
URL: http://www.greenwichchamber.com
Contact: Mary Ann Morrison, Pres./CEO

48719 ■ Guilford Chamber of Commerce
51 Whitfield St.
Guilford, CT 06437
Ph:(203)453-9677
Fax:(203)453-6022
Co. E-mail: chamber@guilfordct.com
URL: http://www.guilfordct.com
Contact: Dale Lehman, Exec. Dir.

48720 ■ Hamden Chamber of Commerce
2969 Whitney Ave.
Hamden, CT 06518
Ph:(203)288-6431
Fax:(203)288-4499
Co. E-mail: hcc@hamdenchamber.com
URL: http://www.hamdenchamber.com
Contact: Meegia Wojcik, Admin. Asst.

48721 ■ Kent Chamber of Commerce
PO Box 124
Kent, CT 06757-0124
Ph:(860)927-1463
Co. E-mail: president@kentct.com
URL: http://www.kentct.com
Contact: Elissa Potts, Pres.

48722 ■ Madison Chamber of Commerce
PO Box 706
Madison, CT 06443
Ph:(203)245-7394
Fax:(203)245-4279
Co. E-mail: chamber@madisonct.com
URL: http://www.madisonct.com
Contact: Eileen Speed, Exec. Dir.

48723 ■ MetroHartford Chamber of Commerce
31 Pratt St., 5th Fl.
Hartford, CT 06103
Ph:(860)525-4451
Fax:(860)293-2592
Co. E-mail: oz@metrohartford.com
URL: http://www.metrohartford.com
Contact: Oz Griebel, Pres./CEO

48724 ■ Middlesex County Chamber of Commerce
393 Main St.
Middletown, CT 06457
Ph:(860)347-6924
Fax:(860)346-1043
Co. E-mail: info@middlesexchamber.com
URL: http://www.middlesexchamber.com
Contact: Larry McHugh, Pres.

48725 ■ Milford Chamber of Commerce
5 Broad St.
Milford, CT 06460
Ph:(203)878-0681
Fax:(203)876-8517
Co. E-mail: chamber@milfordct.com
URL: http://www.milfordct.com
Contact: Kathleen Alagno, Pres./CEO

48726 ■ Monroe Chamber of Commerce
641 Main St.
Monroe, CT 06468
Ph:(203)268-6518

Fax:(203)268-3337
Co. E-mail: info@monroe-chamber.com
URL: http://www.monroe-chamber.com
Contact: Jo-Ellen Stipak, Exec. Dir.

48727 ■ Mystic Chamber of Commerce
14 Holmes St.
PO Box 143
Mystic, CT 06355
Ph:(860)572-9578
Free: (866)572-9578
Fax:(860)572-9273
Co. E-mail: tricia@mysticchamber.org
URL: http://www.mysticchamber.org
Contact: Tricia Cunningham, Pres.

48728 ■ New Britain Chamber of Commerce
1 Court St.
New Britain, CT 06051
Ph:(860)229-1665
Fax:(860)223-8341
Co. E-mail: bill@newbritainchamber.com
URL: http://www.newbritainchamber.com
Contact: William F. Millerick, Pres.

48729 ■ New Canaan Chamber of Commerce
111 Elm St.
New Canaan, CT 06840
Ph:(203)966-2004
Fax:(203)966-3810
Co. E-mail: ncchamber@earthlink.net
URL: http://www.newcanaanchamber.com
Contact: Pamela B. Ogilvie, Exec. Dir.

48730 ■ Newington Chamber of Commerce
1046 Main St.
Newington, CT 06111
Ph:(860)666-2089
Fax:(860)665-7551
Co. E-mail: office@newingtonchamber.com
URL: http://www.newingtonchamber.com
Contact: Dr. Michael P. Crouchley, Pres.

48731 ■ North Central Connecticut Chamber of Commerce
PO Box 294
Enfield, CT 06083
Ph:(860)741-3838
Fax:(860)741-3512
Co. E-mail: chamber@ncccc.org
URL: http://www.ncccc.org
Contact: Mr. Fran Walenta, Pres.

48732 ■ Northeastern Connecticut Chamber of Commerce
3 Central St.
Danielson, CT 06239
Ph:(860)774-8001
Fax:(860)774-4299
Co. E-mail: info@nectchamber.com
URL: http://www.nectchamber.com
Contact: Elizabeth Kuszaj, Exec. Dir.

48733 ■ Old Saybrook Chamber of Commerce
PO Box 625
Old Saybrook, CT 06475-0625
Ph:(860)388-3266
Fax:(860)388-9433
Co. E-mail: info@oldsaybrookchamber.com
URL: http://oldsaybrookchamber.com/cms/welcome.
  htm
Contact: Linanne Lee, Exec. Dir.

48734 ■ Orange Chamber of Commerce
605A Orange Center Rd.
Orange, CT 06477
Ph:(203)795-3328
Fax:(203)795-5926
Co. E-mail: info@orangectchamber.com
URL: http://www.orangectchamber.com
Contact: Ms. Carol Smullen, Exec. Dir.

48735 ■ Quinnipiac Chamber of Commerce
100 S Turnpike Rd.
Wallingford, CT 06492
Ph:(203)269-9891

Fax:(203)269-1358
Co. E-mail: robin@quinncham.com
URL: http://www.quinncham.com
Contact: Robin Wilson, Pres./CEO

48736 ■ Ridgefield Chamber of Commerce
9 Bailey Ave.
Ridgefield, CT 06877
Ph:(203)438-5992
Fax:(203)438-9175
Co. E-mail: jkouroupas@ridgefieldchamber.org
Contact: Marion Roth, Exec. Dir.

48737 ■ Rocky Hill Chamber of Commerce
2264 Silas Deane Hwy.
Rocky Hill, CT 06067
Ph:(860)258-7633
Fax:(860)258-7637
Co. E-mail: cbaio@baiolaw.com
URL: http://www.rhchamber.org
Contact: Claudia Baio, Pres.

48738 ■ Simsbury Chamber of Commerce
PO Box 224
Simsbury, CT 06070
Ph:(860)651-7307
Fax:(860)651-1933
Co. E-mail: info@simsburycoc.org
URL: http://www.simsburycoc.org
Contact: Pamela M. Bowman, Pres.

48739 ■ Stamford Chamber of Commerce
733 Summer St.
Stamford, CT 06901-1019
Ph:(203)359-4761
Fax:(203)363-5069
Co. E-mail: jcondlin@stamfordchamber.com
URL: http://www.stamfordchamber.com
Contact: Jack Condlin, Pres.

48740 ■ Suffield Chamber of Commerce
PO Box 741
Suffield, CT 06078
Ph:(860)668-4848
Fax:(860)668-4848
Co. E-mail: info@suffieldchamber.com
URL: http://www.suffieldchamber.com
Contact: Greg Heinemen, Pres.

48741 ■ Tolland County Chamber of Commerce
30 Lafayette Sq.
Vernon, CT 06066-4527
Ph:(860)872-0587
Fax:(860)872-0588
Co. E-mail: tccc@tollandcountychamber.org
URL: http://www.tollandcountychamber.org
Contact: Candice Corcione, Exec. Dir.

48742 ■ Tri-State Chamber of Commerce
PO Box 386
Lakeville, CT 06039
Ph:(860)435-0740
Co. E-mail: info@tristatechamber.com
URL: http://www.tristatechamber.com
Contact: Mona Staaf-Hoffman, Pres.

48743 ■ West Hartford Chamber of Commerce
948 Farmington Ave.
West Hartford, CT 06107
Ph:(860)521-2300
Fax:(860)521-1996
Co. E-mail: info@whchamber.com
URL: http://www.whchamber.com
Contact: Marjorie Luke, Pres.

48744 ■ West Haven Chamber of Commerce
263 Centre St.
West Haven, CT 06516
Ph:(203)933-1500
Co. E-mail: info@westhavenchamber.com
URL: http://www.westhavenchamber.com
Contact: Nicholas DeMatties, Exec. Dir.

48745 ■ Westport/Weston Chamber of Commerce
215 Main St.
Westport, CT 06880
Ph:(203)227-9234
Fax:(203)454-4019
Co. E-mail: info@westportchamber.com
URL: http://westportchamber.com
Contact: Richard Gordon, Chm.

48746 ■ Wethersfield Chamber of Commerce
860B Silas Deane Hwy.
Wethersfield, CT 06109
Ph:(860)721-6200
Fax:(860)721-8703
Co. E-mail: ceo@capitolregionfcu.org
URL: http://www.wethersfieldchamber.com
Contact: Jeanne Kelly, Pres.

48747 ■ Wilton Chamber of Commerce
PO Box 7094
Wilton, CT 06897-7094
Ph:(203)762-0567
Fax:(203)762-9096
Co. E-mail: wiltoncoc@snet.net
URL: http://www.wiltonchamber.com
Contact: Ms. Stephanie R. Barksdale, Exec. Dir.

48748 ■ Windsor Chamber of Commerce
261 Broad St.
Windsor, CT 06095
Ph:(860)688-5165
Fax:(860)688-0809
Co. E-mail: mcswim@cox.net
URL: http://www.windsorcc.org
Contact: Paula M. Pierce, Pres.

48749 ■ Windsor Locks Chamber of Commerce
PO Box 257
Windsor Locks, CT 06096
Ph:(860)623-9319
Free: (866)WIN-LOCKS
Fax:(860)831-1036
Co. E-mail: info@windsorlockschamber.com
URL: http://www.windsorlockschamber.org
Contact: Michele Monk, Pres.

MINORITY BUSINESS ASSISTANCE PROGRAMS

48750 ■ University of Hartford Entrepreneurial Center–Women's Business Center
50 Elizabeth St.
Hartford, CT 06105-2280
Ph:(860)768-5681
Co. E-mail: entrectr@hartford.edu
Contact: Sandra Cahill, Assoc Dir
Description: Provides business counseling, business workshops and resources, and referrals to SBA programs for start-up and established businesses. Serves both men and women, but emphasis is on women-owned enterprises.

FINANCING AND LOAN PROGRAMS

48751 ■ Advanced Materials Partners, Inc.
45 Pine St.
New Canaan, CT 06840
Ph:(203)966-6415
Fax:(203)966-8448
Co. E-mail: wkb@amplink.com
URL: http://amplink.com
Contact: Warner K. Babcock, Chairman and CEO
E-mail: wkb@amplink
Investment Types: Seed, start-up, first and second stage, early and late stage, generalist PE, joint ventures, mezzanine, leveraged buyout, research and development, and private placement. **Industry Preferences:** Semiconductors and other electronics, biotechnology, medical and health, consumer related, industrial and energy, transportation, business

service, manufacturing, utilities, and other products. **Geographic Preferences:** U.S. and Canada. **Principal Exhibits:**

48752 ■ Axiom Venture Partners, L.P.
CityPlace II, 17th Fl.
185 Asylum St.
Hartford, CT 06103
Ph:(860)548-7799
Fax:(860)548-7797
URL: http://www.axiomventures.com
Contact: Alan Mendelson, Partner
Preferred Investment Size: $1,000,000 to $5,000,000. **Investment Types:** Early and later stage, and expansion. **Industry Preferences:** Communications and media, biotechnology, computer software and services, medical and health, Internet specific, consumer related, semiconductors and other electronics, computer hardware, other products, industrial and energy. **Geographic Preferences:** U.S. and Canada. **Principal Exhibits:**

48753 ■ Beacon Partners Inc.
97 Libbey Pky., Ste. 310
Weymouth, MA 02189
Ph:(781)982-8400
Fax:(781)337-8469
URL: http://www.beaconpartners.com
Contact: Ralph P. Fargnoli Jr., President and CEO
Preferred Investment Size: $300,000 to $1,000,000. **Investment Types:** Second stage, turnaround, mezzanine, recapitalizations, and leveraged buyout. **Industry Preferences:** Consumer related, industrial and energy, Internet specific, other products, medical and health, semiconductors and other electronics, communications and media, computer software and services. **Geographic Preferences:** Northeast. **Principal Exhibits:**

48754 ■ BEV Capital / Brand Equity Ventures
8 Maher Ave.
Greenwich, CT 06830
Ph:(203)724-1101
Fax:(203)724-1155
URL: http://www.bevcapital.com
Contact: Christopher P. Kirchen, Managing General Partner
Preferred Investment Size: $1,000,000 to $5,000,000. **Investment Types:** Early, second and later stage, expansion, balanced, and private placement. **Industry Preferences:** Internet specific, consumer related, semiconductors and other electronics, computer software and services, and other products. **Geographic Preferences:** Mid Atlantic and Northeast. **Principal Exhibits:**

48755 ■ Canaan Partners (Westport)
285 Riverside Ave., Ste. 250
Westport, CT 06880
Ph:(203)855-0400
Fax:(203)854-9117
URL: http://www.canaan.com
Contact: Mickey Kim, Principal
Preferred Investment Size: $3,000,000 to $25,000,000. **Investment Types:** Seed, first and early stage. **Industry Preferences:** Internet specific, computer software and services, medical and health, communications and media, biotechnology, other products, computer hardware, semiconductors and other electronics, consumer related, industrial and energy. **Geographic Preferences:** Northeast, West Coast, and U.S. **Principal Exhibits:**

48756 ■ Catterton Partners
599 W. Putnam Ave.
Greenwich, CT 06830
Ph:(203)629-4901
Fax:(203)629-4903
Co. E-mail: info@cpequity.com
URL: http://www.cpequity.com
Contact: Neda Daneshzadeh, Principal
Preferred Investment Size: $5,000,000 minimum. **Investment Types:** Acquisition, expansion, leveraged buyout, recapitalizations, management buyouts, and turnaround. **Industry Preferences:** Consumer related, communications and media, other products. **Geographic Preferences:** U.S. and Canada. **Principal Exhibits:**

48757 ■ CHL Medical Partners / Collinson, Howe, and Lennox
1055 Washington Blvd., 6th Fl.
Stamford, CT 06901
Ph:(203)324-7700
Fax:(203)324-3636
Co. E-mail: info@chlmedical.com
URL: http://www.chlmedical.com
Contact: Jeffrey J. Collinson, Principal
E-mail: jcollinson@chlmedical.com
Preferred Investment Size: $250,000 to $6,000,000. **Investment Types:** Seed, start-up and early stage. **Industry Preferences:** Medical and health, biotechnology, and Internet specific. **Geographic Preferences:** U.S. **Principal Exhibits:**

48758 ■ Connecticut Innovations, Inc.
865 Brook St.
Rocky Hill, CT 06067
Ph:(860)563-5851
Fax:(860)563-4877
URL: http://www.ctinnovations.com
Contact: Pauline M. Murphy, Managing Director
E-mail: pauline.murphy@ctinnovations.com
Preferred Investment Size: $100,000 to $2,000,000. **Investment Types:** Seed, first, second and early stage. **Industry Preferences:** Internet specific, computer software and services, semiconductors and other electronics, biotechnology, medical and health, industrial and energy, communications and media, other products, computer hardware, and consumer related. **Geographic Preferences:** Connecticut. **Principal Exhibits:**

48759 ■ Endeavor Capital Management
49 Richmondville Ave., Ste. 215
Westport, CT 06880
Ph:(203)341-7788
Fax:(203)341-7799
Co. E-mail: contactus@endeavorcap.com
URL: http://www.endeavor.com
Contact: Anthony Buffa, Managing General Partner
Preferred Investment Size: $50,000 to $5,000,000. **Investment Types:** Early stage and expansion. **Industry Preferences:** Other products, communications and media, Internet specific, consumer related, medical and health, computer hardware, computer software and services, and industrial and energy. **Geographic Preferences:** U.S. and Canada. **Principal Exhibits:**

48760 ■ First New England Capital, L.P.
100 Pearl St.
Hartford, CT 06103
Ph:(860)293-3333
Fax:(860)293-3338
Co. E-mail: info@fnec.com
URL: http://www.firstnewenglandcapital.com
Contact: Richard C. Klaffky, Managing Principal
E-mail: rklaffky@fnec.com
Preferred Investment Size: $2,000,000 to $7,000,000. **Investment Types:** Mezzanine, leveraged buyout, management buyouts, private placement, recapitalizations, later stage, industry rollups, and acquisition. **Industry Preferences:** Consumer related, industrial and energy, transportation, business service, manufacturing, and other products. **Geographic Preferences:** U.S. **Principal Exhibits:**

48761 ■ Generation Partners
1 Greenwich Office Park
Greenwich, CT 06831
Ph:(203)422-8200
Fax:(203)422-8250
URL: http://www.generation.com
Contact: Mark Jennings, Managing Partner
Preferred Investment Size: $10,000,000 to $40,000,000. **Investment Types:** Start-up, first and second stage, and leveraged buyout. **Industry Preferences:** Computer software and services, Internet specific, business services, communications and media, consumer related, healthcare services and technology. **Geographic Preferences:** U.S. and Canada. **Principal Exhibits:**

48762 ■ Landmark Partners, Inc.
10 Mill Pond Ln.
Simsbury, CT 06070
Ph:(860)651-9760
Fax:(860)651-8890
Co. E-mail: info@landmarkpartners.com
URL: http://www.landmarkpartners.com
Contact: Paul G. Giovacchini, Principal
E-mail: Paul.Giovacchini@landmarkpartners.com
Preferred Investment Size: $500,000 minimum. **Investment Types:** Fund of funds, fund of funds of second, mezzanine, management buyouts. **Industry Preferences:** Other products, computer software and services, computer hardware, semiconductors and other electronics, Internet specific, biotechnology, medical and health, consumer related, industrial and energy. **Geographic Preferences:** U.S. and Canada. **Principal Exhibits:**

48763 ■ LTI Ventures Leasing Corp. / Leasing Technologies International, Inc.
221 Danbury Rd.
Wilton, CT 06897
Ph:(203)563-1100
Fax:(203)563-1112
URL: http://www.ltileasing.com
Contact: Jerry Sprole, President and Chief Executive Officer
E-mail: jsprole@ltileasing.com
Preferred Investment Size: $500,000 to $2,000,000. **Investment Types:** Early, first, second, and later stage, mezzanine, and special situation. **Industry Preferences:** Communications and media, computer hardware and software, Internet specific, semiconductors and other electronics, biotechnology, medical and health, consumer related, industrial and energy. **Geographic Preferences:** U.S. **Principal Exhibits:**

48764 ■ The NTC Group
3 Pickwick Plz., Ste. 200
Greenwich, CT 06830
Ph:(203)862-2850
Fax:(203)622-6538
URL: http://www.ntcgroupinc.com
Contact: Thomas C. Foley, Chairman
Preferred Investment Size: $1,000,000 minimum. **Investment Types:** Seed, first stage, control-block purchases, and leveraged buyout. **Industry Preferences:** Semiconductors and other electronics, and industrial and energy. **Geographic Preferences:** U.S. **Principal Exhibits:**

48765 ■ Oak Investment Partners
901 Main Ave., Ste. 600
Norwalk, CT 06851
Ph:(203)226-8346
Fax:(203)846-0282
URL: http://www.oakvc.com
Contact: Bandel Carano, Managing Partner
E-mail: bandel@oakvc.com
Preferred Investment Size: $25,000,000 to $150,000,000. **Investment Types:** Balanced, expansion, later stage, management buyouts, private placement, and special situation. **Industry Preferences:** Communications and media, Internet specific, computer software and services, semiconductors and other electronics, consumer related, medical and health, computer hardware, other products, biotechnology, industrial and energy. **Geographic Preferences:** U.S. **Principal Exhibits:**

48766 ■ Oxford Bioscience Partners (Monroe)
PO Box 573
Monroe, CT 06880
Ph:(203)261-3182
Co. E-mail: bizplan@oxbio.com
URL: http://www.oxbio.com
Contact: Alan G. Walton, Senior General Partner
Preferred Investment Size: $1,000,000 to $10,000,000. **Investment Types:** Start-up, early and first stage, and research and development. **Industry Preferences:** Biotechnology, medical and health, Internet specific, computer software and services, consumer related, and semiconductors and other electronics. **Geographic Preferences:** U.S. and Canada. **Principal Exhibits:**

48767 ■ RFE Investment Partners
195 Oenoke Ridge
New Canaan, CT 06840
Ph:(203)966-2800

Fax:(203)966-3109
Co. E-mail: info@rfeip.com
URL: http://www.rfeip.com
Contact: James A. Parsons, General Partner
E-mail: jparsons@rfeip.com
Preferred Investment Size: $10,000,000 to $25,000,000. **Investment Types:** Later stage, acquisition, leveraged buyout, management buyouts, and recapitalizations. **Industry Preferences:** Other products, business services, medical and health, industrial and energy, consumer related, computer software and services, computer hardware, semiconductors and other electronics, and biotechnology. **Geographic Preferences:** U.S. and Canada. **Principal Exhibits:**

48768 ■ Saugatuck Capital Company
187 Danbury Rd.
Wilton, CT 06897
Ph:(203)348-6669
Fax:(203)324-6995
Co. E-mail: saugatuck@saugatuckcapital.com
URL: http://www.saugatuckcapital.com
Contact: Frank J. Hawley Jr., Managing Director
E-mail: fhawley@saugatuckcapital.com
Preferred Investment Size: $4,000,000 to $7,000,000. **Investment Types:** Leveraged buyout, recapitalizations, management buyouts, and later stage. **Industry Preferences:** Other products, medical and health, consumer related, communications and media, industrial and energy, computer hardware, semiconductors and other electronics, computer software and services, and Internet specific. **Geographic Preferences:** U.S. **Principal Exhibits:**

48769 ■ Signal Lake Management LLC
606 Post Rd. E., Ste. 667
Westport, CT 06880-4549
Ph:(203)454-1133
Fax:(203)454-7142
Co. E-mail: info@signallake.com
URL: http://www.signallake.com
Contact: Bart Stuck, Managing Director
E-mail: BartStuck@signallake.com
Preferred Investment Size: $100,000 to $100,000,000. **Investment Types:** Early stage and balanced. **Industry Preferences:** Internet specific, semiconductors and other electronics, communications and media, computer hardware, computer software and services. **Geographic Preferences:** Northeast and U.S. **Principal Exhibits:**

PROCUREMENT ASSISTANCE PROGRAMS

48770 ■ Connecticut Procurement Technical Assistance Center–Outreach Office
10 Middle St., 6th Fl.
Bridgeport, CT 06604-4223
Ph:(203)333-3338
Fax:(860)437-4662
Co. E-mail: ptap@ctptap.org
URL: http://www.ctptap.org
Contact: Bernie Todisco, Specialist
E-mail: skoos@sector.org
Description: Provides marketing and procurement assistance to Connecticut businesses interested in selling their goods or services to federal, state, or local governments.

48771 ■ Connecticut Procurement Technical Assistance Center–Small Business Development Procurement Center
190 Governor Winthrop Blvd., 4th Fl.
New London, CT 06320-6633
Ph:(860)437-4659
Fax:(860)437-4662
Co. E-mail: brobertson@secter.org
URL: http://www.ctptap.org
Contact: Brien Robertson, Dir
Description: Covers activities for the VA Medical Center (West Haven, CT), Naval Submarine base (Groton, CT), and the U.S. Coast Guard Academy (New London, CT).

48772 ■ SouthEastern Connecticut Enterprise Region (seCTer)–Connecticut Procurement Center
190 Governor Winthrop Blvd.
New London, CT 06320
Ph:(860)437-4659
Fax:(860)437-4662
Co. E-mail: secter@secter.org
URL: http://www.secter.org
Contact: Brien Robertson, Dir
E-mail: lawrence.steele@sba.gov
Description: Covers activities for the VA Medical Center (West Haven, CT), Naval Submarine base (Groton, CT), and the U.S. Coast Guard Academy (New London, CT).

48773 ■ State of Connecticut Procurement Services–Purchasing Services Division
165 Capitol Ave.
Hartford, CT 06106
Ph:(860)713-5093
Fax:(860)622-2904
Co. E-mail: carol.wilson@po.state.ct.us
URL: http://www.das.state.ct.us/Purchase/New_PurchHome/Busopp.asp
Contact: Carol Wilson, Dir

INCUBATORS/RESEARCH AND TECHNOLOGY PARKS

48774 ■ Bridgeport Innovation Center
955 Connecticut Ave., Ste 5103
Bridgeport, CT 06607
Ph:(203)333-9000
Fax:(203)333-9008
Co. E-mail: reneesand@hotmail.com
URL: http://www.bridgeportinnovationcenter.com
Contact: Carleton Pierpont, Gen Mgr
Description: Bridgeport Innovation Center provides an entrepreneurial environment for small to mid-sized growth businesses. As a Bridgeport business your company may qualify for the city's liberal tax incentives and/or for Connecticut State tax abatements, personnel job training, and/or financial assistance programs.

48775 ■ Ceebraid Signal Corp.
112 Hoyt St.
Stamford, CT 06905
Ph:(203)406-1300
Fax:(203)406-1305
URL: http://www.ceebraidsignal.com
Contact: Jason Schiesinger

48776 ■ Connecticut Center for Advanced Technology
222 Pitkin St., Ste. 101
East Hartford, CT 06108
Ph:(860)291-8832
Fax:(860)291-8874
Co. E-mail: info@ccat.us
URL: http://www.ccat.us/incubator/index.php
Contact: Elliot Ginsberg, Pres. & CEO
Description: A non-profit corporation funded under federal and state sponsored grants to develop a national center that addresses military and civilian industrial manufacturing needs; promotes energy planning and policy initiatives; stimulates innovation; and enhances workforce development issues concerning technology competitiveness.

48777 ■ Connecticut Enterprise Center
200 Myrtle St.
New Britain, CT 06053
Ph:(860)229-7700
Fax:(860)229-6847
URL: http://www.cwresources.org/cec.htm
Description: A facility in which a variety of new and growing businesses operate; sharing services, equipment and experiences with other startup entrepreneurs. CEC has admission criteria, support services and encourages graduation from incubator.

48778 ■ Fairfield University–Office of Grants and Sponsored Programs
1073 N Benson Rd.
Fairfield, CT 06824-5195
Ph:(203)254-4000
Fax:(203)254-4291
Co. E-mail: slafrance@fairfield.edu
Contact: Susan LaFrance, Dir. of Sponsored Prog.
E-mail: slafrance@fairfield.edu
Scope: Encourages, facilitates, sponsors, and coordinates sponsored research at the university in all branches of the sciences, engineering, nursing, business, arts, humanities, education, and allied fields.

48779 ■ Institute of Technology and Business Development
Central Connecticut State University
185 Main St.
New Britain, CT 06051
Ph:(860)832-0700
Fax:(860)832-0701
Co. E-mail: mullinsr@ccsu.edu
URL: http://www.ccsu.edu/itbd/
Contact: Richard Mullins, Exec. Assistant
Description: A small business incubator that assists entrepreneurs in the business start-up process and gives aid to new businesses to help ensure their survival.

48780 ■ University of Connecticut–Research Foundation
438 Whitney Rd., Unit 106
Storrs, CT 06269-1006
Ph:(860)486-0987
Fax:(860)486-5381
Co. E-mail: ilze.krisst@uconn.edu
URL: http://www.rac.uconn.edu/
Contact: Ilze Krisst PhD
E-mail: ilze.krisst@uconn.edu
Scope: Reviews and approves research program in all departments of the University, including physical, life, and social sciences, engineering, agriculture, fine arts, and the humanities. Offers advisory service on externally sponsored research opportunities. Manages intellectual properties of the University, including licensing and patenting. Serves as a liaison for faculty with industry.

48781 ■ University of Connecticut Technology Incubation Program
1392 Storrs Rd., U4213
Storrs, CT 06269-4213
Ph:(860)486-3010
Fax:(860)486-3536
Co. E-mail: rita.zangari@uconn.edu
URL: http://www.tip.uconn.edu/
Description: A program that aims to accelerate the successful establishment and development of entrepreneurial companies by providing laboratory/office space and an array of support resources and services which are available through the various departments and functions at the University.

48782 ■ Yale University–Office of Cooperative Research
433 Temple St.
New Haven, CT 06511
Ph:(203)436-8096
Fax:(203)436-8086
Co. E-mail: ocr@yale.edu
URL: http://www.yale.edu/ocr
Contact: E. Jonathan Soderstrom PhD, Mng.Dir.
E-mail: ocr@yale.edu
Scope: Facilitates the transfer of technology from the University to business and industry. Patents and licenses University inventions in the areas of physical sciences and engineering, medicine and biotechnology, and computer sciences. Administers industrial liaison programs in computer science.

EDUCATIONAL PROGRAMS

48783 ■ Housatonic Community College
900 Lafayette Blvd.
Bridgeport, CT 06604
Ph:(203)332-5000

Fax:(203)332-5123
URL: http://www.hcc.commnet.edu
Description: Two-year college offering a small business management program.

PUBLICATIONS

48784 ■ *Starting and Operating a Business in Connecticut: A Step-by-Step Guide*
PSI Research
300 N. Valley Dr.
Grants Pass, OR 97526
Ph:(503)479-9464
Free: 800-228-2275
Fax:(503)476-1479
Co. E-mail: psi2@magick.net
Ed: Michael D. Jenkins. **Released:** Revised edition, 1992. **Price:** $29.95 (looseleaf binder); $24.95 (paper). **Description:** Part of the Successful Business Library series.

PUBLISHERS

48785 ■ Business Books International
194 Putnam Rd.
New Canaan, CT 06840

Ph:(203)966-9645
Fax:(203)966-6018
Co. E-mail: editor@businessbooksusa.com
URL: http://www.businessbooksusa.com
Contact: Ruth D. Villiers, Treasurer
Description: Publishes reference books for business and library use on regions of the world. Reaches market through advertising, direct mail, trade sales and wholesalers. Does not accept unsolicited manuscripts. **Founded:** 1982.

48786 ■ Hannacroix Creek Books Inc.
1127 High Ridge Rd., Ste. 110B
Stamford, CT 06905-1203
Ph:(203)968-8098
Fax:(203)968-0193
Co. E-mail: hannacroix@aol.com
URL: http://www.hannacroixcreekbooks.com
Contact: Peggy Stautberg, Mgr
Description: Publishes books and audio cassettes in the areas of deafness, friendship, business, time management and relationships. **Founded:** 1996.

48787 ■ Hunt-Scanlon Publishing
1037 E Putnam Ave.
Riverside, CT 06878

Ph:(203)344-9281
Free: 800-477-1199
Fax:(203)344-9282
Contact: Scott Scanlon, CEO

Description: Publishes business directories for business-to-business applications. Also publishes CD-ROMs and software, as well as a newsletter. Reaches market through direct mail. **Founded:** 1989.

48788 ■ RDS Associates Inc.
41 Brainerd Rd.
Niantic, CT 06357-1722
Ph:(860)691-0081
Free: 800-363-8867
Fax:(860)691-1145
Co. E-mail: rds@businessbookpress.com
URL: http://www.businessbookpress.com
Contact: Sam Cantor, President

Description: Publishes reference and business books relating to buying, selling, valuing, starting or improving a business. Accepts unsolicited manuscripts. Direct mail and Book World Services. **Founded:** 1996.

SMALL BUSINESS DEVELOPMENT CENTERS

48789 ■ Delaware Small Business Development Center
Delaware Technology Park
One Innovation Way, Ste. 301
Newark, DE 19711
Fax:(302)831-1423
Co. E-mail: necarb@udel.edu
URL: http://www.delawaresbdc.org
Contact: Clinton Tymes, State Dir.

48790 ■ Dover Small Business Development Center
1200 N DuPont Hwy., Ste. 108
Dover, DE 19901
Co. E-mail: apaoli@udel.edu
URL: http://www.delawaresbdc.org

48791 ■ Georgetown Small Business Development Center
103 W Pine St.
Georgetown, DE 19947
Co. E-mail: wpfaff@udel.edu
URL: http://www.delawaresbdc.org

48792 ■ Newark Small Business Development Center
1 Innovation Way, Ste. 301
Newark, DE 19711
Co. E-mail: mdd@udel.edu
URL: http://www.delawaresbdc.org

48793 ■ Wilmington Small Business Development Center
100 W 10th St., Ste. 812
Wilmington, DE 19801
Co. E-mail: mdd@udel.edu
URL: http://www.delawaresbdc.org

SMALL BUSINESS ASSISTANCE PROGRAMS

48794 ■ Delaware Economic Development Office–Business Finance Section
99 Kings Hwy.
Dover, DE 19901
Ph:(302)739-4271
Fax:(302)739-5749
URL: http://dedo.delaware.gov
Contact: Gary Smith, Dir. Finance

Description: Promotes the development and growth of new and existing businesses; trains workers, assists employers with recruiting, and develops training programs; conducts research on the state's business and economic climate; and provides publications entitled *Small Business Start-Up Guide, Selling to the State, Solutions for Delaware Small Business,* and *The Workforce Resource.* The Small Business Advocate acts as a liaison between small businesses and local, state, and federal agencies; helps businesses get into state programs; and provides information on permits, regulations, financing, and procurement programs.

48795 ■ Delaware Economic Development Office–International Trade and Development
820 N. French St.
Wilmington, DE 19801
Ph:(302)577-8464
Fax:(302)577-1176
Co. E-mail: john.pastor@state.de.us
URL: http://itc.omb.delaware.gov
Contact: John Pastor, Dir.

Description: Provides counseling, seminars, and contacts for businesses seeking to engage in international trade.

BETTER BUSINESS BUREAUS

48796 ■ Better Business Bureau of Delaware
60 Reads Way
New Castle, DE 19720
Ph:(302)230-0108
Fax:(302)230-0116
Co. E-mail: info@delaware.bbb.org
URL: http://delaware.bbb.org
Contact: Christine R. Sauers, Pres.

CHAMBERS OF COMMERCE

48797 ■ Bethany-Fenwick Area Chamber of Commerce
36913 Coastal Hwy.
Fenwick Island, DE 19944
Ph:(302)539-2100
Free: 800-962-7873
Fax:(302)539-9434
Co. E-mail: info@bethany-fenwick.org
URL: http://www.bethany-fenwick.org
Contact: Andrew Cripps, Exec. Dir.

48798 ■ Central Delaware Chamber of Commerce
435 N DuPont Hwy.
Dover, DE 19901
Ph:(302)678-0892
Fax:(302)678-0189
Co. E-mail: info@cdcc.net
URL: http://www.cdcc.net
Contact: Judy Diogo, Pres.

48799 ■ Chamber of Commerce for Greater Milford
PO Box 805
Milford, DE 19963
Ph:(302)422-3344
Fax:(302)422-7503
Co. E-mail: milford@milfordchamber.com
URL: http://www.milfordchamber.com
Contact: Ruth Abbate, Pres.

48800 ■ Delaware State Chamber of Commerce
PO Box 671
Wilmington, DE 19899-0671
Ph:(302)655-7221
Free: 800-292-9507
Fax:(302)654-0691
Co. E-mail: dscc@dscc.com
URL: http://www.dscc.com
Contact: James A. Wolfe, Pres./CEO

48801 ■ Greater Seaford Chamber of Commerce
PO Box 26
Seaford, DE 19973
Ph:(302)629-9690
Free: 800-416-GSCC
Fax:(302)629-0281
Co. E-mail: admin@seafordchamber.com
URL: http://www.seafordchamber.com
Contact: Paula K. Gunson, Exec. Dir.

48802 ■ Lewes Chamber of Commerce
120 Kings Hwy.
Lewes, DE 19958
Ph:(302)645-8073
Free: 877-465-3937
Fax:(302)645-8412
Co. E-mail: inquiry@leweschamber.com
URL: http://www.leweschamber.com
Contact: Betsy Reamer, Exec. Dir.

48803 ■ New Castle County Chamber of Commerce
12 Penns Way
New Castle, DE 19720
Ph:(302)737-4343
Co. E-mail: info@ncccc.com
URL: http://www.ncccc.com/cwt/external/wcpages/index.aspx
Contact: Mark Kleinschmidt, Pres.

48804 ■ Rehoboth Beach-Dewey Beach Chamber of Commerce
501 Rehoboth Ave.
PO Box 216
Rehoboth Beach, DE 19971-0216
Ph:(302)227-2233
Free: 800-441-1329
Fax:(302)227-8351
Co. E-mail: rehoboth@beach-fun.com
URL: http://www.beach-fun.com
Contact: Bill Klemkowski, Dir.

MINORITY BUSINESS ASSISTANCE PROGRAMS

48805 ■ Wilmington Minority Business Enterprise Office
Louis L. Redding City/County Bldg.
800 N. French St.
Wilmington, DE 19801
Ph:(302)576-2121

Fax:(302)573-5557
URL: http://www.ci.wilmington.de.us/dbe.htm
Contact: Larraine P. Watson, Dir
Description: Allows the solicitation and assistance to disadvantage businesses to participate in the procurement process and performance of City contracts.

FINANCING AND LOAN PROGRAMS

48806 ■ Blue Rock Capital
PO Box 4513
Wilmington, DE 19807-1312
Ph:(302)426-0981
Fax:(302)426-0982
URL: http://www.bluerockcapital.com
Contact: Virginia Breen, Partner
E-mail: virginia@bluerockcapital.com
Preferred Investment Size: $250,000 to $2,000,000.
Investment Types: Seed, start-up, early and second stage. **Industry Preferences:** Internet specific, semiconductors and other electronics, communications and media, consumer related, computer software and services, and computer hardware. **Geographic Preferences:** Mid Atlantic. **Principal Exhibits:**

PROCUREMENT ASSISTANCE PROGRAMS

48807 ■ Delaware Procurement Technical Assistance Center–Delaware Small Business Development Center Network
1 Innovation Way, Ste. 301
Newark, DE 19711
Ph:(302)831-0783
Fax:(302)831-0771
Co. E-mail: info@delawarecontracts.com
URL: http://www.delawarecontracts.com
Contact: Diane Seymour, Support Specialist
E-mail: jbeau@udel.edu
Description: Offers free resources to small Delaware businesses wanting to grow their sales in the public sector with federal, state and local government entities.

INCUBATORS/RESEARCH AND TECHNOLOGY PARKS

48808 ■ DE Micro Enterprise Program–Retail Incubator Program
Louis L. Redding City/County Bldg
800 French St.
Wilmington, DE 19801-3537
Ph:(302)576-2120
URL: http://www.wilmingtonde.gov/microloan_incubator.htm
Description: A facility that has been re-established to assist early-stage development businesses. Its mission is to provide emerging and new businesses opportunities to start-up operations in a shared service environment that will enable them to receive technical assistance, business and financial management, and retail salesmanship training to help sustain their respective operations.

48809 ■ Delaware Technology Park
15 Innovation Way, Ste. 300
Newark, DE 19711
Ph:(302)452-1100
Fax:(302)452-1101
Co. E-mail: info@deltechpark.org
URL: http://www.deltechpark.org/
Contact: Jane Crouch, Admin.
Description: A business research park devoted to attracting established industries and providing an incubation and acceleration for start-ups in high-technology fields, specifically those in biotechnology, information technology and advanced materials.

48810 ■ University of Delaware–Research Office
209 Hullihen Hall
Newark, DE 19716
Ph:(302)831-4007
Fax:(302)831-2828
Co. E-mail: barteau@udel.edu
URL: http://www.udel.edu/research
Contact: Dr. Mark A. Barteau
E-mail: barteau@udel.edu
Scope: Reviews proposals from university units to external agencies and manages the resulting grants and contracts for the life of the research projects. Also manages the university's intellectual property

holdings, including licensing. research, colloidal studies, climatic research, historic architecture and engineering, and disaster research. **Publications:** University of Delaware Research Magazine (semiannually).

48811 ■ University of Delaware Research Foundation
209 Hullihen Hall
University of Delaware
Newark, DE 19716
Ph:(302)831-4007
Fax:(302)831-2828
Co. E-mail: barteau@udel.edu
URL: http://www.udel.edu/research/about/udrf.html
Contact: Dr. Mark Barteau, Sen. Vice Provost
E-mail: barteau@udel.edu
Scope: Supports University research in science and engineering by awarding grants to faculty members.

LEGISLATIVE ASSISTANCE

48812 ■ Delaware Senate Committee on Small Business
Legislative Hall
Dover, DE 19901
Ph:(302)744-4298
Free: 800-282-8545
Fax:(302)739-6890
Co. E-mail: LIS.Webmaster@state.de.us
URL: http://www.delaware.gov/
Contact: Robert Venables, Chair

PUBLICATIONS

48813 ■ *Starting and Operating a Business in Delaware: A Step-by-Step Guide*
PSI Research
300 N. Valley Dr.
Grants Pass, OR 97526
Ph:(503)479-9464
Free: 800-228-2275
Fax:(503)476-1479
Co. E-mail: psi2@magick.net
Ed: Michael D. Jenkins. **Released:** Revised edition, 1992. **Price:** $29.95 (looseleaf binder); $24.95 (paper). **Description:** Part of the Successful Business Library series.

SMALL BUSINESS DEVELOPMENT CENTERS

48814 ■ District of Columbia Small Business Development Center at University of District of Columbia
4340 Connecticut Ave. NW
Washington, DC 20008
URL: http://www.dcsbdc.org

48815 ■ Washington, D.C. Small Business Development Center at Howard University
Services School of Business, Rm. 128
2600 6th St. NW
Washington, DC 20059
URL: http://www.dcsbdc.org

SMALL BUSINESS ASSISTANCE PROGRAMS

48816 ■ District of Columbia Office of the Deputy Mayor–Planning and Economic Development
John A. Wilson Bldg.
1350 Pennsylvania Ave., NW, Ste. 317
Washington, DC 20004
Ph:(202)727-6365
Fax:(202)727-6703
Co. E-mail: dmped.eom@dc.gov
URL: http://www.dcbiz.dc.gov
Contact: Mary Margaret Plumridge, Dir.
Description: Works to attract new businesses and retain existing ones. The Financial Services Division offers SBA 503/504 loans and other loan programs. The Small Business Incubator Facility Program provides affordable facilities and management assistance to new and small businesses. The Neighborhood Commercial Services Division provides loans and technical assistance to encourage the revitalization of neighborhood commercial districts.

BETTER BUSINESS BUREAUS

48817 ■ Better Business Bureau Serving Metropolitan Washington, DC and Eastern Pennsylvania
1411 K St. NW, Ste. 1000
Washington, DC 20005
Ph:(202)393-8000
Fax:(202)393-1198
Co. E-mail: info@mybbb.org
URL: http://dc-easternpa.bbb.org
Contact: Edward J. Johnson III, Pres./CEO

CHAMBERS OF COMMERCE

48818 ■ District of Columbia Chamber of Commerce
1213 K St., NW
Washington, DC 20005
Ph:(202)347-7201

Fax:(202)638-6762
Co. E-mail: dedwards@dcchamber.org
URL: http://www.dcchamber.org
Contact: Barbara Lang, Pres./CEO

48819 ■ Swedish-American Chamber of Commerce - Washington, DC
2900 K St. NW
Washington, DC 20007
Ph:(202)536-1570
Fax:(202)536-1501
Co. E-mail: sacc@sacc-dc.org
URL: http://www.sacc-dc.org
Contact: Chris Wall, Vice-Chm.

MINORITY BUSINESS ASSISTANCE PROGRAMS

48820 ■ Government of the District of Columbia–Department of Small and Local Business Development
441 4th St. NW, Ste. 970N
Washington, DC 20001
Ph:(202)727-3900
Fax:(202)724-3786
Co. E-mail: dslbd@dc.gov
URL: http://dslbd.dc.gov/DC/DSLBD/
Contact: Lee Smith, Interim Dir
Description: The mission of the Department of Small and Local Business Development is to foster economic growth and the development of local, small, and disadvantaged business enterprises through supportive legislation, business development programs, and agency and public/private contract compliance.

48821 ■ Washington DC Women's Business Center
727 15th St. NW, 10th Fl.
Washington, DC 20005
Ph:(202)393-8307
Co. E-mail: info@dcwbc.org
URL: http://www.dcwbc.org
Contact: Samira B. Cook, Dir
Description: Provides business development and support for women-owned businesses in the field of federal procurements.

48822 ■ Washngton DC Minority Business Enterprise Center
64 New York Ave., NE, Ste. 3152
Washington, DC 20002
Ph:(202)671-1552
Fax:(202)671-3073
Co. E-mail: info@dcmbec.org
URL: http://www.dcmbec.org/home.html
Contact: Eric Rice, Dir
Description: Offers business consulting and development services.

FINANCING AND LOAN PROGRAMS

48823 ■ Core Capital Partners
1401 I St., NW, Ste. 1000
Washington, DC 20005

Ph:(202)589-0090
Fax:(202)589-0091
Co. E-mail: info@core-capital.com
URL: http://www.core-capital.com
Contact: Pascal Luck, Managing Director
E-mail: pluck@core-capital.com
Preferred Investment Size: $2,000,000 to $5,000,000. **Investment Types:** Start-up, early, first, second, and later stage, and expansion. **Industry Preferences:** Communications and media, computer software and computer related. **Geographic Preferences:** East Coast and Washington, D.C. metropolitan area. **Principal Exhibits:**

48824 ■ The Grosvenor Funds
1776 Eye St. NW, Ste. 890
Washington, DC 20006
Ph:(202)861-5650
Fax:(202)861-5653
Co. E-mail: anna@grosvenorfund.com
URL: http://www.grosvenorfund.com
Contact: Bruce B. Dunnan, Managing Partner
Preferred Investment Size: $1,000,000 to $3,000,000. **Investment Types:** Early and expansion stage. **Industry Preferences:** Communications, Internet specific, semiconductors and other electronics, and biotechnology. **Principal Exhibits:**

48825 ■ Next Point Partners, L.P.
701 Pennsylvania Ave. NW, Ste. 900
Washington, DC 20004
Ph:(202)434-7319
Fax:(202)434-7400
Co. E-mail: mf@nextpoingvc.com
URL: http://www.nextpointvc.com
Contact: Michael Faber, Managing General Partner
Preferred Investment Size: $250,000 to $4,000,000. **Investment Types:** Seed, start-up, early stage, and research and development. **Industry Preferences:** Communications and media, computer software, computer related, Internet specific, semiconductors and other electronics, industrial and energy, and other. **Geographic Preferences:** Mid Atlantic, Midwest, Northeast, and Southeast. **Principal Exhibits:**

48826 ■ Telecommunications Development Fund (TDF)
2 Wisconsin Cir., Ste. 920
Chevy Chase, MD 20815
Ph:(240)483-4286
Fax:(301)907-8850
URL: http://www.tdfund.com
Contact: James Pastoriza, Managing Partner
Preferred Investment Size: $500,000 to $5,000,000. **Investment Types:** First, second, and early stage. **Industry Preferences:** Computer software and services, Internet specific, computer hardware, communications and media, semiconductors and other electronics. **Geographic Preferences:** U.S. **Principal Exhibits:**

48827 ■ Women's Growth Capital Fund
Canal Sq., Ste. 110
1054 31st St., NW
Washington, DC 20007
Ph:(202)342-1431

Fax:(202)342-1203
Co. E-mail: info@wgcf.com
URL: http://www.wgcf.com
Contact: Patty Abramson, Managing Director
Preferred Investment Size: $100,000 to $1,800,000.
Investment Types: First, second, and later stage.
Industry Preferences: Internet specific, computer software and services, communications and media, consumer related, biotechnology, medical and health.
Geographic Preferences: Mid Atlantic, Northeast, and Southeast. **Principal Exhibits:**

PROCUREMENT ASSISTANCE PROGRAMS

48828 ■ Procurement Center Representative
Department of Health & Human Services
200 Independence Ave. SW, Rm. 517D
Washington, DC 20201
Ph:(202)690-8330
Fax:(202)827-7228
Co. E-mail: malda.brown@hhs.gov
URL: http://www.sba.gov
Contact: Malda Brown, SBA Representative
E-mail: rlewis@os.dhhs.gov
Description: Covers activities for Department of Health and Human Services (Washington, DC), Army Corps of Engineers (Baltimore, MD), Social Security Administration (Baltimore, MD).

48829 ■ Washington, DC, Metropolitan Area Procurement Center–Department of Transportation
1200 New Jersey Ave, SW
Washington, DC 20590
Ph:(202)366-9142
Fax:(202)366-7228
Co. E-mail: annette.merrion@dot.gov
URL: http://www.sba.gov
Contact: Annette Johnson-Merrion, SBA Representative
Description: Covers activities for Department of Transportation (Washington, DC), Department of Commerce (Washington, DC), Department of Veterans Affairs (Washington, DC), Small Business Administration (Washington, DC), GSA/Regional Office (Washington, DC), Department of Housing and Urban Development (Washington, DC).

INCUBATORS/RESEARCH AND TECHNOLOGY PARKS

48830 ■ American University–Office of Sponsored Programs
Sports Center Annex, Ste. 121
4400 Massachusetts Ave. NW
Washington, DC 20016-8066
Ph:(202)885-3440
Fax:(202)885-3453
Co. E-mail: ckirby@american.edu
URL: http://www.american.edu/provost/osp/
Contact: Catherine E. Kirby, Dir.
E-mail: ckirby@american.edu
Scope: Coordinates and facilitates externally sponsored research and other special educational activities of the University.

48831 ■ Consortium for Ocean Leadership
1201 New York Ave. NW, 4th Fl.
Washington, DC 20005
Ph:(202)232-3900
Fax:(202)332-8887
Co. E-mail: rgagosian@oceanleadership.org
URL: http://www.oceanleadership.org
Contact: Dr. Bob Gagosian, Pres./CEO
E-mail: rgagosian@oceanleadership.org
Scope: Ocean drilling, observing, exploration. **Publications:** Ocean Leadership Newsletter (weekly).

48832 ■ Howard University–Office of University Research and Planning
1400 Shepard NE
Washington, DC 20017
Ph:(202)806-0977

Fax:(202)806-5467
Co. E-mail: rmanning@research.howard.edu
Contact: Ranimor A. Manning III, Interim Dir.
E-mail: rmanning@research.howard.edu
Scope: Primarily responsible for examining the university from an institutional perspective relative to efficient utilization of available resources. Provides analytical services to facilitate formulation of university policy and management decisions. Continuously studies, analyzes, and evaluates existing programs, administrative divisions, units or departments, and all university administrative procedures. Responds to information and data requests from internal and external sources. **Publications:** Facts; Service (annually); Howard University Factbook (annually); Howard University Service (annually). **Educational Activities:** Conference (annually); University Data Conference (quarterly).

LEGISLATIVE ASSISTANCE

48833 ■ Council of the District of Columbia
John A. Wilson Bldg., Ste. 5
1350 Pennsylvania Ave., NW
Washington, DC 20004
Ph:(202)724-8000
Fax:(202)347-3070
Co. E-mail: dccouncil@dccouncil.us
URL: http://www.dccouncil.us
Contact: Vincent C. Gray, Council Chairman

TRADE PERIODICALS

48834 ■ *DMAW Marketing Advents*
Pub: Direct Marketing Association of Washington, DC
Ed: Nancy Scott, Editor. **Released:** Monthly. **Price:** $165, Included in membership. **Description:** Spotlights direct marketing topics for members in the Washington, DC area. Recurring features include interviews, a calendar of events, news of educational opportunities, and job listings.

PUBLICATIONS

48835 ■ *Starting and Operating a Business in District of Columbia: A Step-by-Step Guide*
PSI Research
300 N. Valley Dr.
Grants Pass, OR 97526
Ph:(503)479-9464
Free: 800-228-2275
Fax:(503)476-1479
Co. E-mail: psi2@magick.net
Ed: Michael D. Jenkins. **Released:** Revised edition, 1992. **Price:** $29.95 (looseleaf binder); $24.95 (paper). **Description:** Part of the Successful Business Library series.

PUBLISHERS

48836 ■ Friends of the Earth (Washington, District of Columbia)
1100 15th St. NW, 11th Fl.
Washington, DC 20005
Ph:(202)783-7400
Free: 877-843-8687
Fax:(202)783-0444
Co. E-mail: foe@foe.org
URL: http://www.foe.org
Contact: Michelle Chan, Director
E-mail: mchan@foe.org
Description: Publishes quarterly and annual reports on environmental degradation and studies. **Founded:** 1969.

48837 ■ Gallaudet University Press
800 Florida Ave. NE
Washington, DC 20002-1205
Ph:(202)651-5488

Fax:(202)651-5489
Co. E-mail: gupress@gallaudet.edu
URL: http://gupress.gallaudet.edu
Contact: Dr. John Van Cleve, Director
E-mail: ivey.wallace@gallaudet.edu
Description: Publishes reference books, biographies for and about deaf and hard of hearing people, deaf culture and deaf studies. Accepts unsolicited manuscripts. Reaches market through direct mail, reviews, listings, wholesalers and distributors. **Founded:** 1980.

48838 ■ International Council for Small Business
The George Washington University, School of Business
2201 G St. NW, Funger Hall, Ste. 315
Washington, DC 20052
Ph:(202)994-0704
Fax:(202)994-4930
Co. E-mail: icsb@gwu.edu
URL: http://www.icsb.org
Contact: Sylvio Rosa, President
Description: Publishes periodicals and proceedings for members and other persons interested in helping small businesses. **Founded:** 1955.

48839 ■ International Franchise Association
1501 K St. NW, Ste. 350
Washington, DC 20005
Ph:(202)628-8000
Free: 800-543-1038
Fax:(202)628-0812
Co. E-mail: ifa@franchise.org
URL: http://www.franchise.org
Contact: Virgie Sison
E-mail: vsison@franchise.org
Description: Publishes educational tools for members, public, press and governments to describe the workings and advantages of franchising as a method of doing business. Offers audio cassettes, video tapes, computer diskettes. Distributes for Commerce Clearing House. **Founded:** 1960.

48840 ■ Kiplinger Washington Editors Inc.
1729 H St. NW
Washington, DC 20006
Ph:(202)887-6400
Free: 800-544-0155
Fax:(202)223-8990
Co. E-mail: sub.services@kiplinger.com
URL: http://www.kiplinger.com
Contact: Robert H. Kelly, Publisher
E-mail: bkelly@kiplinger.com
Description: Publishes personal finance and business forecasting books for both professionals and the public. Reaches market through distributors. Does not accept unsolicited manuscripts. **Founded:** 1920.

48841 ■ National Association for Business Economics
1233 20th St. NW, Ste. 505
Washington, DC 20036
Ph:(202)463-6223
Fax:(202)463-6239
Co. E-mail: nabe@nabe.com
URL: http://www.nabe.com
Contact: Tom Beers, Director
E-mail: tbeers@nabe.com
Description: Publishes journals and newsletters on careers, business and economics. Offers placement assistance, economic surveys, annual meetings, seminars and training programs. Reaches market through direct mail. Does not accept unsolicited manuscripts. **Founded:** 1959.

48842 ■ National Small Business Association
1156 15th St. NW, Ste. 1100
Washington, DC 20005
Ph:(202)293-8830
Free: 800-345-6728

Fax:(202)872-8543
Co. E-mail: nsbu@nsbu.org
URL: http://www.nsba.biz
Contact: Todd O. McCracken, President
E-mail: tmccracken@nsbu.org
Description: Publishes information pertinent to small business. Also operates an Export Opportunity Hot

line providing trade information to small firms. Reaches market through direct mail. **Founded:** 1937.

48843 ■ U.S. Small Business Administration
409 3rd St. SW
Washington, DC 20416
Ph:(202)205-8885
Free: 800-827-5722

Fax:(202)481-5881
Co. E-mail: answerdesk@sba.gov
URL: http://www.sba.gov
Contact: Dr. Winslow Sargeant, Mgr
Description: Publishes books and videotapes on starting and financing your own business and on international trade. **Founded:** 1953.

SMALL BUSINESS DEVELOPMENT CENTERS

48844 ■ Florida Small Business Development Center at Daytona State College
Daytona State College
Bldg. 110, Rm. 222
1200 W International Speedway Blvd.
Daytona Beach, FL 32114
Fax:(386)506-4602
Co. E-mail: sbdc@daytonastate.edu
URL: http://www.sbdcdaytona.com
Contact: Ned Harper, Dir.

48845 ■ Florida Small Business Development Center Network
401 E Chase St., Ste. 100
Pensacola, FL 32502
Free: (866)737-7232
Fax:(850)473-7813
Co. E-mail: fsbdc@uwf.edu
URL: http://www.floridasbdc.com
Contact: Jerry Cartwright, Dir.

48846 ■ Florida Small Business Development Center at Seminole Community College
1445 Dolgner Pl.
Sanford, FL 32771
Fax:(407)321-4184
Co. E-mail: goetzr@scc-fl.edu
URL: http://sbdc.scc-fl.edu
Contact: Renee D. Templeton, Admin. Asst.

48847 ■ Small Business Development Center Broward County
Reubin O'D. Askew Tower, Rm. 530
111 E Las Olas Blvd.
Fort Lauderdale, FL 33301
URL: http://www.floridasbdc.org/broward

48848 ■ Small Business Development Center at Central Florida Development Council of Polk County
3433 Winter Lake Rd.
Modular-LMC
Lakeland, FL 33803-9807
Fax:(863)667-7911
Co. E-mail: info@polksbdc.org
URL: http://www.polksbdc.org
Contact: Doretha Brooks, Dir.

48849 ■ Small Business Development Center at Florida A & M University - Perry
Taylor County Chamber of Commerce
428 N Jefferson St.
Perry, FL 32347-2510
URL: http://floridasbdc.org
Contact: Dawn Taylor

48850 ■ Small Business Development Center at Florida A & M University - Tallahassee
Innovation Park
The Morgan Bldg., Ste. 130
2035 E Paul Dirac Dr.
Tallahassee, FL 32310-3700
Co. E-mail: robert.nixon@famu.edu
URL: http://www.sbdcatfamu.org
Contact: Robert Nixon, Exec. Dir.

48851 ■ Small Business Development Center at Florida Atlantic University - Boca Raton
777 Glades Rd., Bldg. T-11
Boca Raton, FL 33431-0991
Fax:(561)297-1141
Co. E-mail: sbdc@fau.edu
URL: http://www.fausbdc.com
Contact: Nancy Young, Dir.

48852 ■ Small Business Development Center at Florida Atlantic University Downtown Campus
Downtown Ft. Lauderdale Campus
Reubin O'D Askew Tower, Rm. 530
111 E Las Olas Blvd.
Fort Lauderdale, FL 33301
URL: http://www.fausbdc.com
Contact: Rafael Cruz, Associate Dir.

48853 ■ Small Business Development Center at Florida Atlantic University - Florida Keys Community College
5901 College Rd., Ste. No. C-226
Key West, FL 33040
Fax:(305)292-2397
Co. E-mail: gbaumann@fau.edu
URL: http://www.fausbdc.com
Contact: Greg Baumann

48854 ■ Small Business Development Center at Florida Atlantic University Miami-Dade County
Festival Plaza-Miami
8500 SW 8th St., No. 224
Miami, FL 33144
Fax:(786)388-9060
Co. E-mail: cardenas@fau.edu
URL: http://www.fausbdc.com
Contact: Carlos Cardenas, Associate Dir.

48855 ■ Small Business Development Center at Florida Atlantic University Okeechobee
Okeechobee One-Stop Career Center
209 SW Park St.
Okeechobee, FL 34972-4160
Fax:(863)462-5355
Co. E-mail: jlilly2@fau.edu
URL: http://www.fausbdc.com
Contact: Jim Lilly

48856 ■ Small Business Development Center at Florida Atlantic University - Port St. Lucie
Bldg. SL, Rm. 125A
500 NW California Blvd.
Port St. Lucie, FL 34986-2601
Co. E-mail: kstepha2@fau.edu
URL: http://www.fausbdc.com
Contact: Ken R. Stephanz

48857 ■ Small Business Development Center at Florida Atlantic University Treasure Coast
SR Bldg., Rm. 221
5353 Parkside Dr.
Jupiter, FL 33458
Co. E-mail: ekramer@fau.edu
URL: http://www.fausbdc.com
Contact: Ted Kramer, Asst. Dir.

48858 ■ Small Business Development Center at Florida Gulf Coast University - Cape Coral
1020 Cultural Park Blvd.
Cape Coral, FL 33990-1229
Fax:(239)573-2797
Co. E-mail: jpultro@fgcu.edu
URL: http://cli.fgcu.edu/sbdc
Contact: Judith Pultro

48859 ■ Small Business Development Center at Florida Gulf Coast University Clewiston
College of Business, Career and Service Center
215 S Franscisco St.
Clewiston, FL 33440-4002
URL: http://www.floridasbdc.com
Contact: Sean Moore

48860 ■ Small Business Development Center at Florida Gulf Coast University - Fort Myers
Florida Gulf Coast University
Lutgert Hall, Rm. 2320
Fort Myers, FL 33965-6565
Co. E-mail: dregelsk@fgcu.edu
URL: http://cli.fgcu.edu/sbdc
Contact: Dan Regelski, Dir.

48861 ■ Small Business Development Center at Florida Gulf Coast University Immokalee
Florida Gulf Coast University
Lutgert Hall, Rm. 2317
Fort Myers, FL 33965-6565
Co. E-mail: jestreme@fgcu.edu
URL: http://cli.fgcu.edu/sbdc
Contact: Julio Estremera, Program Facilitator

48862 ■ Small Business Development Center at Florida Gulf Coast University - Port Charlotte
2702 Tamiami Trail
Port Charlotte, FL 33952-5129
URL: http://www.floridasbdc.com
Contact: Peter Keating

48863 ■ Small Business Development Center at Gulf Coast Community College
2500 Minnesota Ave.
Lynn Haven, FL 32444-4815
Free: 800-542-7232
Fax:(850)271-1109
Co. E-mail: info@northfloridabiz.com
URL: http://www.northfloridabiz.com
Contact: Joe Chavarria, Dir.

48864 ■ Small Business Development Center of the Heartland at South Florida Community College
600 W College Dr.
Avon Park, FL 33825
Fax:(863)784-7355
Co. E-mail: bmckown@coba.usf.edu
URL: http://www.southflorida.edu/sbdc
Contact: Bill McKown

48865 ■ Small Business Development Center at Indian River State College - Fort Pierce
Bldg. E, Rm. 123
3209 Virginia Ave.
Fort Pierce, FL 34981
Free: 888-283-1177
URL: http://floridasbdc.org

48866 ■ Small Business Development Center at Indian River State College - Stuart
924 SE Central Pkwy.
Stuart, FL 34994
URL: http://floridasbdc.org

48867 ■ Small Business Development Center at Manatee Community College - Sarasota
Lakewood Ranch
7131 Professional Pkwy. E
Sarasota, FL 34240
URL: http://floridasbdc.org

48868 ■ Small Business Development Center at Manatee Community College - Venice
8000 S Tamiami Trail, Rm. 809
Venice, FL 34293
Co. E-mail: baxterl@mccfl.edu
URL: http://www.mccfl.edu/pages/324.asp
Contact: Art Mahoney

48869 ■ Small Business Development Center Miami-Dade - Hialeah Gardens
The Church in the Gardens
13090 NW 107th Ave.
Hialeah Gardens, FL 33018
URL: http://floridasbdc.org

48870 ■ Small Business Development Center at North Florida Community College
Business Education Bldg. No.7, Rm. 107
325 NW Turner Davis Dr.
Madison, FL 32340-1602
URL: http://www.nfcc.edu/community-programs/sbdc
Contact: Devona Sewell

48871 ■ Small Business Development Center at Palm Beach Community College - Boca Raton
3000 St. Lucie Ave., Ste. AD408
Boca Raton, FL 33431
URL: http://floridasbdc.org

48872 ■ Small Business Development Center at University of Central Florida Clermont
Lake-Sumter Community College
Bldg. 1, Rm. 106
1250 N Hancock Rd.
Clermont, FL 34711
Co. E-mail: gromagna@bus.ucf.edu
URL: http://www.bus.ucf.edu/sbdc
Contact: Gene Romagna, Area Mgr.

48873 ■ Small Business Development Center at University of Central Florida Kissimmee
1425 E Vine St.
Kissimmee, FL 34744
Co. E-mail: nperez@bus.ucf.edu
URL: http://www.bus.ucf.edu/sbdc
Contact: Janice Lopez, Area Mgr.

48874 ■ Small Business Development Center at University of Central Florida Melbourne
Brevard Community College
3865 N Wickam Rd.
Melbourne, FL 32935
Co. E-mail: pfrimmers@brevardcc.edu
URL: http://www.bus.ucf.edu/sbdc
Contact: Vicky Peake, Dir.

48875 ■ Small Business Development Center at University of Central Florida Orlando
315 E Robinson St., Ste. 100
Orlando, FL 32801
Fax:(407)420-4862
Co. E-mail: sbdc@bus.ucf.edu
URL: http://www.bus.ucf.edu/sbdc
Contact: Eunice Choi, Dir.

48876 ■ Small Business Development Center at University of North Florida Gainesville
Gainesville Technology Enterprise Center
2153 SE Hawthorne Rd., Ste. 126
Gainesville, FL 32641
Co. E-mail: sbdcgnv@atlantic.net
URL: http://www.sbdc.unf.edu
Contact: Dominic Orsini

48877 ■ Small Business Development Center at University of North Florida Jacksonville
UNF University Center
1 2000 Alumni Dr.
Jacksonville, FL 32224
Free: 800-450-4624
Fax:(904)620-2567
Co. E-mail: smallbiz@unf.edu
URL: http://www.sbdc.unf.edu
Contact: Janice William Donaldson, Dir.

48878 ■ Small Business Development Center at University of North Florida Ocala/Marion County
110 E Silver Springs Blvd.
Ocala, FL 34470
Co. E-mail: sbdcoca@atlantic.net
URL: http://www.sbdc.unf.edu
Contact: Dr. Philip Geist, Area Dir.

48879 ■ Small Business Development Center at University of South Florida Hillsborough County
Bldg. 400, Ste. 425
7402 N 56th St.
Temple Terrace, FL 33617-7743
Fax:(813)914-4027
URL: http://sbdc.usf.edu
Contact: Vandita Trivedi, Gen. Business Asst.

48880 ■ Small Business Development Center at University of South Florida - St. Petersburg
College of Business
263 13th Ave. S
St. Petersburg, FL 33701-5511
URL: http://sbdc.usf.edu
Contact: Wayne Brass, Area Mgr.

48881 ■ Small Business Development Center at University of South Florida - Tampa
1101 Channelside Dr., Ste. 210
Tampa, FL 33602
Fax:(813)905-5801
Co. E-mail: sbdc@coba.usf.edu
URL: http://sbdc.usf.edu
Contact: Eileen Rodriguez, Interim Dir.

48882 ■ Small Business Development Center at University of West Florida - Fort Walton Beach
922 Mar Walt Dr., Ste. 203
Fort Walton Beach, FL 32547-6703
Co. E-mail: fwbsbdc@uwf.edu
URL: http://www.sbdc.uwf.edu
Contact: Jane Briere, Mgr.

48883 ■ Small Business Development Center at University of West Florida - Pensacola
401 E Chase St., Ste. 100
Pensacola, FL 32502-6160
Co. E-mail: sbdc@uwf.edu
URL: http://www.sbdc.uwf.edu
Contact: Larry Strain, Exec. Dir.

SMALL BUSINESS ASSISTANCE PROGRAMS

48884 ■ Enterprise Florida, Inc.–Marketing And Development Division
800 N. Magnolia Ave., Ste. 1100
Orlando, FL 32803
Ph:(407)956-5600
Fax:(407)956-5599
URL: http://www.eflorida.com/
Description: Administers the Business Supplier Program, which helps businesses locate suppliers of goods and services in Florida.

48885 ■ NASA/Southern Technology Applications Center
75 5th St. NW, Ste. 100
Atlanta, GA 30308-0390
Ph:800-472-6785
Fax:(404)894-4545
Co. E-mail: nasa@edi.gatech.edu
URL: http://www.edi.gatech.edu/nasa
Description: Provides information on technology, science, industry, management, marketing, economics, and business.

SCORE OFFICES

48886 ■ Bay County SCORE
Path:

48887 ■ Charlotte-Desoto County SCORE
Path: www.charlottedesotoscore.org

48888 ■ Hollywood SCORE
Path: www.scorehollywoodfl.org

48889 ■ Ocala/The Villages SCORE
Path: www.score440.org

48890 ■ Pasco-Hernando County SCORE - Chapter 439
Bank of America Bldg.
6014 US Hwy. 19, Ste. 302
New Port Richey, FL 34652
Ph:(727)842-4638
Fax:(727)841-7266
Co. E-mail: score439@verizon.net
URL: http://www.score439.org
Description: Represents businessmen and women, small business owners, senior corporate executives and experienced professionals. Provides professional guidance and information to maximize the success of existing and emerging small businesses.

48891 ■ SCORE Citrus County
3810 S Lecanto Hwy., Bldg. P1-101
Lecanto, FL 34461
Ph:(352)249-1236
Fax:(352)249-1217
Co. E-mail: citruschapter@scorecitrus.org
URL: http://citrusscore.easycgi.com/ccs
Contact: Norm Mangano, Chm.
Description: Provides professional guidance and information to maximize the success of existing and emerging small businesses. Promotes entrepreneur education in Citrus County area, FL.

48892 ■ SCORE Dade
100 S Biscayne Blvd., 7th Fl.
Miami, FL 33131-2011
Ph:(786)425-9119
Co. E-mail: scoremiami@gmail.com
URL: http://www.scoremiami.org/home.html
Description: Provides professional guidance and information to maximize the success of existing and emerging small businesses. Offers business counseling and workshops.

48893 ■ SCORE Hillsborough
7402 N 56th St., Bldg. 400, Ste. 425
Tampa, FL 33617
Ph:(813)988-1435
Co. E-mail: counselor@tampascore.org
URL: http://www.tampascore.org
Contact: Bill Harkell
Description: Provides resources and expertise to maximize the success of existing and emerging small businesses. Offers business counseling and workshops.

48894 ■ SCORE Manasota
2801 Fruitville Rd., Ste. 280
Sarasota, FL 34237
Ph:(941)955-1029
Fax:(941)955-5581
Co. E-mail: scorech116@verizon.net
URL: http://www.score-suncoast.org
Contact: Mr. Ed Piekarz
Description: Works for the formation, growth, and success of small businesses. Provides on-line business counseling and business improvement activities.

48895 ■ SCORE Naples of Collier
900 Goodlette Rd. N
Naples, FL 34102
Ph:(239)430-0081
Fax:(239)430-0082
Co. E-mail: score@scorenaples.org
URL: http://www.scorenaples.org
Contact: Ekkehard Grampp, Chm.
Description: Creates opportunities for small business owners and potential small business owners to achieve success. Provides entrepreneur education in Naples area, in Florida. Offers individual counseling, workshops, seminars and literature.

48896 ■ SCORE Orlando
One Landmark Center Bldg.
315 E Robinson St., Ste. 100
Orlando, FL 32801
Ph:(407)420-4844
Fax:(407)420-4849
Co. E-mail: score@floridanec.org
URL: http://www.scoreorlando.org
Description: All-volunteer resource partner of the Small Business Administration. Provides business management counselors for present and future small business owners in need of expert advice. Offers free and confidential one-on-one and email counseling, in addition to numerous educational seminars appropriate for entrepreneurs.

48897 ■ SCORE Palm Beach
500 Australian Ave. S, Ste. 115
West Palm Beach, FL 33401
Ph:(561)833-1672
Fax:(561)833-1470
Co. E-mail: wpbscore@us-it.net
URL: http://www.wpbscore.org
Description: Represents retired entrepreneurs and corporate executives. Provides free business counseling to start-ups and small businesses. Includes primary counseling areas such as; business planning, business structure, marketing, distribution, home businesses, accounting, budgeting, personnel, operation issues, etc.

48898 ■ SCORE Space Coast
Melbourne Professional Complex
1600 Sarno, Ste. 205
Melbourne, FL 32935
Ph:(321)254-2288
Fax:(321)254-2288
Co. E-mail: scorechapter400@bellsouth.net
URL: http://www.spacecoastscore.org
Contact: Carol Wheatley, Chm.
Description: Strives for the formation, growth, and success of small businesses. Offers educational seminars and business counseling.

48899 ■ SCORE of Suwannee Valley
Path: scoreofsuwanneevalley.org

BETTER BUSINESS BUREAUS

48900 ■ Better Business Bureau of Central Florida
1600 S Grant St.
Longwood, FL 32750
Ph:(407)621-3300
Fax:(407)786-2625
Co. E-mail: info@centralflorida.bbb.org
URL: http://www.orlando.bbb.org
Contact: Judy Pepper, Pres./CEO

48901 ■ Better Business Bureau of Northeast Florida
4417 Beach Blvd., Ste. 202
Jacksonville, FL 32207
Ph:(904)721-2288
Free: 800-940-1315
Fax:(904)721-7373
Co. E-mail: info@bbbnefla.org
URL: http://northeastflorida.bbb.org
Contact: Tom Stephens, Pres./CEO

48902 ■ Better Business Bureau of Northwest Florida
912 E Gadsden St.
Pensacola, FL 32501
Ph:(850)429-0002
Free: 800-729-9226
Fax:(850)429-0006
Co. E-mail: info@nwfl.bbb.org
URL: http://nwfl.bbb.org
Contact: Norman Wright, Pres.

48903 ■ Better Business Bureau of West Florida
PO Box 7950
Clearwater, FL 33758-7950
Ph:(727)535-5522
Free: 800-525-1447
Fax:(727)539-6301
Co. E-mail: info@bbbwestflorida.org
URL: http://www.clearwater.bbb.org
Contact: Karen Nalven, Pres.

CHAMBERS OF COMMERCE

48904 ■ Alachua Chamber of Commerce
PO Box 387
Alachua, FL 32616-0387
Ph:(386)462-3333
Fax:(386)454-7376
Co. E-mail: info@alachua.com
URL: http://www.alachua.com/about.asp?page_id=3&n=1
Contact: Linda Rice Chapman, Pres.

48905 ■ Anna Maria Island Chamber of Commerce
5313 Gulf Dr.
Holmes Beach, FL 34217
Ph:(941)778-1541
Fax:(941)778-9679
Co. E-mail: info@annamariaislandchamber.org
URL: http://www.annamariaislandchamber.org
Contact: Mary Ann Brockman, Exec. Dir.

48906 ■ Apalachicola Bay Chamber of Commerce
122 Commerce St.
Apalachicola, FL 32320
Ph:(850)653-9419
Fax:(850)653-8219
Co. E-mail: info@apalachicolabay.org
URL: http://www.apalachicolabay.org
Contact: Anita Gregory-Grove, Exec. Dir.

48907 ■ Apollo Beach Chamber of Commerce
PO Box 3686
Apollo Beach, FL 33572
Ph:(813)645-1366
Fax:(813)641-2612
Co. E-mail: abeachcham@verizon.net
URL: http://www.apollobeachchamber.com
Contact: Joanne C. Gadek, Exec. Dir.

48908 ■ Apopka Area Chamber of Commerce
180 E Main St.
Apopka, FL 32703
Ph:(407)886-1441
Fax:(407)886-1131
Co. E-mail: staff@apopkachamber.org
URL: http://www.apopkachamber.org
Contact: Karen Ross, Chair

48909 ■ Auburndale-Mainstreet Chamber of Commerce
109 Main St.
Auburndale, FL 33823
Ph:(863)967-3400
Fax:(863)967-0880
Co. E-mail: information@auburndalechamber.com
URL: http://www.auburndalefl.com
Contact: Joy Pruitt, Exec. Dir.

48910 ■ Avon Park Chamber of Commerce
28 E Main St.
Avon Park, FL 33825
Ph:(863)453-3350

Fax:(863)453-0973
Co. E-mail: apcc@apfla.com
URL: http://www.apfla.com
Contact: David Greenslade, Exec. Dir.

48911 ■ Baker County Chamber of Commerce
20 E Macclenny Ave.
Macclenny, FL 32063
Ph:(904)259-6433
Co. E-mail: dregister@bakerchamberfl.com
URL: http://www.bakerchamberfl.com
Contact: Darryl Register, Exec. Dir.

48912 ■ Bay County Chamber of Commerce
PO Box 1850
Panama City, FL 32402-1850
Ph:(850)785-5206
Fax:(850)763-6229
Co. E-mail: reception2@baychamberfl.com
URL: http://www.panamacity.org
Contact: Ms. Carol Roberts, Pres./CEO

48913 ■ Belle Glade Chamber of Commerce
540 S Main St.
Belle Glade, FL 33430
Ph:(561)996-2745
Fax:(561)996-2252
Co. E-mail: bgchamber@aol.com
URL: http://www.bellegladechamber.com
Contact: Brenda Bunting, Exec. Dir.

48914 ■ Belleview-South Marion Chamber of Commerce
5301 SE Abshier Blvd.
Belleview, FL 34420
Ph:(352)245-2178
Fax:(352)245-7673
Co. E-mail: info@bsmcc.org
URL: http://bsmcc.org
Contact: Sheila Lister, Exec. Dir.

48915 ■ Boca Grande Area Chamber of Commerce
PO Box 704
Boca Grande, FL 33921
Ph:(941)964-0568
Fax:(941)964-0620
Co. E-mail: info@bocagrandechamber.com
URL: http://www.bocagrandechamber.com
Contact: Craig Lutz, Exec. Dir.

48916 ■ Bonita Springs Area Chamber of Commerce
25071 Chamber of Commerce Dr.
Bonita Springs, FL 34135
Ph:(239)992-2943
Free: 800-226-2943
Fax:(239)992-5011
Co. E-mail: info@bonitaspringschamber.com
URL: http://www.bonitaspringschamber.com
Contact: Christine A. Ross, Pres.

48917 ■ British American Chamber of Commerce of Central Florida
Landmark One Center
315 E Robinson St., Ste. 100
Orlando, FL 32801
Ph:(407)226-7251
Fax:(321)540-9700
Co. E-mail: info@britishamericanchamberorlando.com
URL: http://www.britishamericanchamberorlando.com
Contact: Justine Assal, Pres.

48918 ■ British-American Chamber of Commerce, South Florida
PO Box 348237
Miami, FL 33234
Ph:(786)228-8676
Fax:(786)243-1965
Co. E-mail: mpa@myrtlepalexander.com
URL: http://www.baccsouthflorida.org/index.php
Contact: Myrtle P. Alexander, Exec. Dir.

48919 ■ Calhoun County Chamber of Commerce
20816 Central Ave. E, Ste. 2
Blountstown, FL 32424
Ph:(850)674-4519
Fax:(850)674-4962
Co. E-mail: chamber@calhounco.org
URL: http://www.calhounco.org
Contact: Marti Vickery, Exec. Dir.

48920 ■ Cedar Key Chamber of Commerce
PO Box 610
Cedar Key, FL 32625
Ph:(352)543-5600
Fax:(352)543-5600
Co. E-mail: info@cedarkey.org
URL: http://www.cedarkey.org
Contact: Paul Rimavicus, Pres.

48921 ■ Central Pasco Chamber of Commerce
2810 Land O'Lakes Blvd.
PO Box 98
Land O' Lakes, FL 34639-0098
Ph:(813)909-2722
Fax:(813)909-0827
Co. E-mail: office@centralpascochamber.com
URL: http://centralpascochamber.com
Contact: Kathy Dunkley, Exec. Dir.

48922 ■ Chamber of Commerce of Cape Coral
2051 Cape Coral Pkwy. E
Cape Coral, FL 33904
Ph:(239)549-6900
Free: 800-226-9609
Fax:(239)549-9609
Co. E-mail: info@capecoralchamber.com
URL: http://www.capecoralchamber.com
Contact: Michael Quaintance, Pres.

48923 ■ Chamber of Commerce of the Palm Beaches
401 N Flagler Dr.
West Palm Beach, FL 33401
Ph:(561)833-3711
Fax:(561)833-5582
Co. E-mail: chamber@palmbeaches.org
URL: http://www.palmbeaches.org
Contact: Dennis Grady, Pres.

48924 ■ Chamber of Commerce of West Volusia
1656 S Volusia Ave.
Orange City, FL 32763-4802
Ph:(386)775-2793
Fax:(386)775-4575
Co. E-mail: info@chamberofcommerceofwestvolusia.com
URL: http://www.delandchamber.org
Contact: Linda White, Pres./CEO

48925 ■ Chamber South
6410 SW 80th St.
South Miami, FL 33143
Ph:(305)661-1621
Fax:(305)666-0508
Co. E-mail: info@chambersouth.com
URL: http://www.chambersouth.com
Contact: Mary Scott Russell, Pres.

48926 ■ Charlotte County Chamber of Commerce
2702 Tamiami Trail
Port Charlotte, FL 33952
Ph:(941)627-2222
Fax:(941)627-9730
Co. E-mail: askus@charlottecountychamber.org
URL: http://www.charlottecountychamber.org
Contact: Thomas Rice, Pres.

48927 ■ Citrus County Chamber of Commerce
3495 S Suncoast Blvd.
PO Box 709
Homosassa, FL 34448
Ph:(352)628-2666

Fax:(352)621-0920
Co. E-mail: dixie@hollinswoodranch.com
URL: http://www.citruscountychamber.com
Contact: Dixie Hollins, Chair

48928 ■ Citrus County Chamber of Commerce - Crystal River Office
28 NW Hwy. 19
Crystal River, FL 34429-3900
Ph:(352)795-3149
Fax:(352)795-1921
Co. E-mail: deb@hollinswoodranch.com
URL: http://www.citruscountychamber.com
Contact: Dixie Hollins, Pres.

48929 ■ Clay County Chamber of Commerce
1734 Kingsley Ave.
Orange Park, FL 32073
Ph:(904)264-2651
Fax:(904)264-0070
Co. E-mail: kjkilberg@claychamber.com
URL: http://www.claychamber.org
Contact: Kellie Jo Kilberg, Pres./CEO

48930 ■ Clearwater Regional Chamber of Commerce
1130 Cleveland St.
Clearwater, FL 33755
Ph:(727)461-0011
Fax:(727)449-2889
Co. E-mail: info@clearwaterflorida.org
URL: http://www.clearwaterflorida.org
Contact: Douglas Linder, Pres./CEO

48931 ■ Clewiston Chamber of Commerce
109 Central Ave.
Clewiston, FL 33440
Ph:(863)983-7979
Fax:(863)983-7108
Co. E-mail: clewistonchamber@embarqmail.com
URL: http://www.clewiston.org
Contact: Cathy Garrels, Exec. Dir.

48932 ■ Cocoa Beach Area Chamber of Commerce
400 Fortenberry Rd.
Merritt Island, FL 32952
Ph:(321)459-2200
Fax:(321)459-2232
Co. E-mail: mstains@cocoabeachchamber.com
URL: http://www.cocoabeachchamber.com
Contact: Melissa Stains, Pres./CEO

48933 ■ Coconut Grove Chamber of Commerce
2829 McFarlane Rd.
Coconut Grove, FL 33133
Ph:(305)444-7270
Fax:(305)444-2498
Co. E-mail: info@coconutgrove.com
URL: http://cgcc.coconutgrove.com
Contact: Liliana Dones, Pres.

48934 ■ Coral Gables Chamber of Commerce
224 Catalonia Ave.
Coral Gables, FL 33134
Ph:(305)446-1657
Fax:(305)446-9900
Co. E-mail: info@coralgableschamber.org
URL: http://www.coralgableschamber.org
Contact: Mark A. Trowbridge, Pres./CEO

48935 ■ Coral Springs Chamber of Commerce
11805 Heron Bay Blvd.
Coral Springs, FL 33076
Ph:(954)752-4242
Fax:(954)827-0543
Co. E-mail: mona@cschamber.com
URL: http://www.cschamber.com
Contact: Cindy Brief, Pres.

48936 ■ Crestview Area Chamber of Commerce
1447 Commerce Dr.
Crestview, FL 32539
Ph:(850)682-3212

Fax:(850)682-7413
Co. E-mail: info@crestviewchamber.com
URL: http://www.crestviewchamber.com/crestview-chamber.htm
Contact: Wayne Harris, Exec. Dir.

48937 ■ Davie-Cooper City Chamber of Commerce
4185 Davie Rd.
Davie, FL 33314
Ph:(954)581-0790
Fax:(954)581-9684
Co. E-mail: dcch@davie-coopercity.org
URL: http://www.davie-coopercity.org
Contact: Alice Harrington, Pres.

48938 ■ Daytona Beach - Halifax Area Chamber of Commerce
126 E Orange Ave.
Daytona Beach, FL 32115
Ph:(386)255-0981
Fax:(386)258-5104
Co. E-mail: info@daytonachamber.com
URL: http://www.daytonachamber.com
Contact: Larry McKinney, Pres./CEO

48939 ■ DeLand Area Chamber of Commerce
336 N Woodland Blvd.
DeLand, FL 32720
Ph:(386)734-4331
Fax:(386)734-4333
Co. E-mail: contact@delandchamber.org
URL: http://www.delandchamber.org
Contact: Jenny Stumbras, Exec. Dir.

48940 ■ DeSoto County Chamber of Commerce
16 S Volusia Ave.
Arcadia, FL 34266
Ph:(863)494-4033
Fax:(863)494-3312
Co. E-mail: desotochamber@earthlink.net
URL: http://www.desotochamber.net
Contact: Linda Williams, Pres.

48941 ■ Destin Area Chamber of Commerce
4484 Legendary Dr., Ste. A
Destin, FL 32541
Ph:(850)837-6241
Fax:(850)654-5612
Co. E-mail: mail@destinchamber.com
URL: http://www.destinchamber.com
Contact: Shane Moody, Pres./CEO

48942 ■ Dixie County Chamber of Commerce
PO Box 547
Cross City, FL 32628
Ph:(352)498-5454
Fax:(352)498-2601
Co. E-mail: dixiechamber@usa.net
URL: http://www.dixiecounty.org
Contact: Gary Poore, VP

48943 ■ Dunedin Chamber of Commerce
301 Main St.
Dunedin, FL 34698
Ph:(727)733-3197
Fax:(727)734-8942
Co. E-mail: chamber@dunedin-fl.com
URL: http://www.dunedin-fl.com
Contact: Lynn Wargo, Pres./CEO

48944 ■ Dunnellon Area Chamber of Commerce
20500 E Pennsylvania Ave.
Dunnellon, FL 34432
Ph:(352)489-2320
Fax:(352)489-6846
Co. E-mail: dunnellonchamber@bellsouth.net
URL: http://www.dunnellonchamber.org
Contact: Lisa Sheffield, Pres.

48945 ■ East Lake County Chamber of Commerce
PO Box 774
Sorrento, FL 32776-0774
Ph:(352)383-8801

Fax:(352)383-9343
Co. E-mail: chamber@elcchamber.com
URL: http://www.elcchamber.com
Contact: Pam Jennelle, Exec. Dir.

48946 ■ East Orlando Chamber of Commerce
2860 S Alafaya Trail, Ste. 130
Orlando, FL 32828
Ph:(407)277-5951
Fax:(407)381-1720
Co. E-mail: info@eocc.org
URL: http://www.eocc.org
Contact: Annie Winterbottom, Pres.

48947 ■ Englewood-Cape Haze Area Chamber of Commerce
601 S Indiana Ave.
Englewood, FL 34223-3788
Ph:(941)474-5511
Free: 800-603-7198
Co. E-mail: info@englewoodchamber.com
URL: http://www.englewoodchamber.com
Contact: Jon C. Bednerik CAE, Exec. Dir.

48948 ■ Estero Chamber of Commerce
PO Box 588
Estero, FL 33929
Ph:(239)948-7990
Fax:(239)947-9968
Co. E-mail: info@esterochamber.com
URL: http://www.esterochamber.org
Contact: Meg Judge, CEO

48949 ■ Eustis Area Chamber of Commerce
1 W Orange Ave.
PO Box 1210
Eustis, FL 32727-1210
Ph:(352)357-3434
Fax:(352)357-1392
Co. E-mail: info@eustischamber.org
URL: http://www.eustischamber.org
Contact: John R. Buxman, Pres.

48950 ■ Everglades Area Chamber of Commerce
PO Box 130
Everglades City, FL 34139-0130
Ph:(239)695-3941
Co. E-mail: info@evergladeschamber.org
URL: http://www.florida-everglades.com

48951 ■ Flagler Beach Chamber of Commerce
PO Box 5
Flagler Beach, FL 32136-0005
Ph:(386)439-0995
Free: 800-298-0995
Fax:(386)439-0998
Co. E-mail: info@flaglerbeachchamber.com
URL: http://www.flaglerbeachchamber.com
Contact: Mary Stetler, Pres.

48952 ■ Flagler County Palm Coast Chamber of Commerce
20 Airport Rd.
Palm Coast, FL 32164
Ph:(386)437-0106
Free: 800-881-1022
Fax:(386)437-5700
Co. E-mail: info@flaglerchamber.org
URL: http://www.flaglerchamber.org
Contact: Doug Baxter, Pres.

48953 ■ Florida Chamber of Commerce
136 S Bronough St.
PO Box 11309
Tallahassee, FL 32302-3309
Ph:(850)521-1200
Fax:(850)521-1219
Co. E-mail: info@flchamber.com
Contact: Frank M. Ryll Jr., Pres.

48954 ■ Frostproof Chamber of Commerce
118 E Wall St.
Frostproof, FL 33843-0968
Ph:(863)635-9112
Fax:(863)635-6582
Co. E-mail: info@frostproofchamber.com
URL: http://frostproofchamber.com

48955 ■ Gadsden County Chamber of Commerce
PO Box 389
Quincy, FL 32353-0389
Ph:(850)627-9231
Free: 800-627-9231
Fax:(850)875-3299
Co. E-mail: gadsdencc@tds.net
URL: http://www.gadsdencc.com
Contact: David A. Gardner, Exec. Dir.

48956 ■ Gainesville Area Chamber of Commerce
300 E University Ave., Ste. 100
Gainesville, FL 32601
Ph:(352)334-7100
Fax:(352)334-7141
URL: http://www.gainesvillechamber.com
Contact: Brent Christensen, Pres./CEO

48957 ■ Gilchrist County Chamber of Commerce
220 S Main St.
Trenton, FL 32693
Ph:(352)463-3467
Fax:(352)463-3469
Co. E-mail: chamber@gilchristcounty.com
URL: http://www.gilchristcounty.com
Contact: Tammy Beauchamp, Pres.

48958 ■ Goldenrod Area Chamber of Commerce
PO Box 61
4755 Palmetto Ave.
Goldenrod, FL 32733
Ph:(407)667-5980
Fax:(407)667-4928
Co. E-mail: director@goldenrodchamber.com
URL: http://www.goldenrodchamber.com
Contact: Darlene Dangel, Exec. Dir.

48959 ■ Greater Bartow Chamber of Commerce
510 N Broadway Ave.
Bartow, FL 33830-3918
Ph:(863)533-7125
Fax:(863)533-3793
Co. E-mail: discoverbartow@bartowchamber.com
URL: http://www.bartowchamber.com
Contact: Jeff Clark, Exec. Dir.

48960 ■ Greater Boca Raton Chamber of Commerce
1800 N Dixie Hwy.
Boca Raton, FL 33432
Ph:(561)395-4433
Fax:(561)392-3780
Co. E-mail: info@bocaratonchamber.com
URL: http://www.bocaratonchamber.com
Contact: Troy M. Mclellan, Pres./CEO

48961 ■ Greater Boynton Beach Chamber of Commerce
1880 N Congress Ave., Ste. 106
Boynton Beach, FL 33425
Ph:(561)732-9501
Fax:(561)734-4304
Co. E-mail: chamber@boyntonbeach.org
URL: http://www.boyntonbeach.org/index.
    php?sid=349cc8ac080f2b4081fffe8198df83b9
Contact: Glenn Jergensen, Pres./CEO

48962 ■ Greater Brandon Chamber of Commerce
330 Pauls Dr., Ste. 100
Brandon, FL 33511
Ph:(813)689-1221
Fax:(813)689-9440
Co. E-mail: info@brandonchamber.com
URL: http://www.brandonchamber.com
Contact: Tammy C. Bracewell, Pres.

48963 ■ Greater Chiefland Area Chamber of Commerce
PO Box 1397
Chiefland, FL 32644
Ph:(352)493-1849

Fax:(352)493-1849
Co. E-mail: info@chieflandchamber.com
URL: http://www.chieflandchamber.com
Contact: Ben Lott, Pres.

48964 ■ Greater Dade City Chamber of Commerce
14112 8th St.
Dade City, FL 33525
Ph:(352)567-3769
Fax:(352)567-3770
Co. E-mail: info@dadecitychamber.org
URL: http://www.dadecitychamber.org
Contact: Nita Beckwith, Exec. Dir.

48965 ■ Greater Dania Beach Chamber of Commerce
102 W Dania Beach Blvd.
Dania Beach, FL 33004
Ph:(954)926-2323
Fax:(954)926-2384
Co. E-mail: info@greaterdania.org
URL: http://www.greaterdania.org
Contact: Victoria Payne, Exec. Dir.

48966 ■ Greater Deerfield Beach Chamber of Commerce
1601 E Hillsboro Blvd.
Deerfield Beach, FL 33441-4389
Ph:(954)427-1050
Fax:(954)427-1056
Co. E-mail: info@deerfieldchamber.com
URL: http://www.deerfieldchamber.com
Contact: Janyce Becker, Exec. Dir.

48967 ■ Greater Delray Beach Chamber of Commerce
64-A SE 5th Ave.
Delray Beach, FL 33483
Ph:(561)278-0424
Fax:(561)278-0555
Co. E-mail: bwood@delraybeach.com
URL: http://www.delraybeach.com
Contact: William Wood, Pres./CEO

48968 ■ Greater Fort Lauderdale Chamber of Commerce
512 NE 3rd Ave.
Fort Lauderdale, FL 33301-3236
Ph:(954)462-6000
Fax:(954)527-8766
Co. E-mail: carolyn@ftlchamber.com
URL: http://www.ftlchamber.com
Contact: Carolyn Michaels, Exec. VP

48969 ■ Greater Fort Myers Chamber of Commerce
PO Box 9289
Fort Myers, FL 33902
Ph:(239)332-3624
Free: 800-366-3622
Fax:(239)332-7276
Co. E-mail: info@fortmyers.org
URL: http://www.fortmyers.org
Contact: Marietta Mudgett, Exec. Dir.

48970 ■ Greater Fort Walton Beach Chamber of Commerce
PO Box 640
Fort Walton Beach, FL 32549
Ph:(850)244-8191
Fax:(850)244-1935
Co. E-mail: info@fwbchamber.org
URL: http://www.fwbchamber.org
Contact: Ted Corcoran, Pres./CEO

48971 ■ Greater Hernando County Chamber of Commerce
101 E Ft. Dade Ave.
Brooksville, FL 34601
Ph:(352)796-0697
Fax:(352)796-3704
Co. E-mail: info@hernandochamber.com
URL: http://www.hernandochamber.com
Contact: Pat Crowley, Pres./CEO

48972 ■ Greater Hollywood Chamber of Commerce
330 N Federal Hwy.
Hollywood, FL 33020
Ph:(954)923-4000
Free: 800-231-5562
Fax:(954)923-8737
Co. E-mail: information@hollywoodchamber.org
URL: http://www.hollywoodchamber.org
Contact: Laura Gambino, Exec. Dir.

48973 ■ Greater Homestead/Florida City Chamber of Commerce
212 NW 1st Ave.
Homestead, FL 33030
Ph:(305)247-2332
Free: 888-352-4891
Co. E-mail: info@chamberinaction.com
URL: http://www.chamberinaction.com
Contact: Jerome Williams, Chm.

48974 ■ Greater Lake Worth Chamber of Commerce
501 Lake Ave.
Lake Worth, FL 33460
Ph:(561)582-4401
Fax:(561)547-8300
Co. E-mail: lwchamber@lwchamber.com
URL: http://www.lwchamber.com
Contact: Thomas Ramiccio, Pres./CEO

48975 ■ Greater Marathon Chamber of Commerce
12222 Overseas Hwy.
Marathon, FL 33050
Ph:(305)743-5417
Free: 800-262-7284
Fax:(305)289-0183
Co. E-mail: visitus@floridakeysmarathon.com
URL: http://www.floridakeysmarathon.com
Contact: Britt Myers, Pres.

48976 ■ Greater Miami Chamber of Commerce
1601 Biscayne Blvd.
Ballroom Level
Miami, FL 33132-1260
Ph:(305)350-7700
Free: 888-660-5955
Fax:(305)374-6902
Co. E-mail: reception@miamichamber.com
URL: http://www.greatermiami.com
Contact: Barry E. Johnson, Pres./CEO

48977 ■ Greater Miami Chamber of Commerce, Women in Business Group
Omni International Complex
1601 Biscayne Blvd.
Miami, FL 33132-1260
Ph:(305)577-5427
Fax:(305)374-6902
Co. E-mail: reception@miamichamber.com
URL: http://www.greatermiami.com
Contact: Lisa Showers, Exec. Asst.

48978 ■ Greater Miami Shores Chamber of Commerce
9701 NE 2nd Ave.
Miami Shores, FL 33138-2310
Ph:(305)754-5466
Fax:(305)759-8872
Co. E-mail: shoreschamber@bellsouth.net
URL: http://www.miamishores.com
Contact: Lew Soli, Exec. Dir.

48979 ■ Greater Mulberry Chamber of Commerce
PO Box 254
Mulberry, FL 33860
Ph:(863)425-4414
Fax:(863)425-3837
URL: http://www.mulberrychamber.org
Contact: Sharron Jones, Exec. Dir.

48980 ■ Greater Naples Chamber of Commerce
2390 Tamiami Trail N, Ste. 210
Naples, FL 34103
Ph:(239)262-6376
Fax:(239)262-8374
Co. E-mail: info@napleschamber.org
URL: http://www.napleschamber.org
Contact: Mike Reagen PhD, Pres./CEO

48981 ■ Greater Nassau County Chamber of Commerce
PO Box 98
Callahan, FL 32011
Ph:(904)879-1441
Fax:(904)879-4033
Co. E-mail: gncc@juno.com
URL: http://www.greaternassaucounty.com/gn/ frontpage
Contact: Louise Banks, Exec. Dir.

48982 ■ Greater North Miami Beach Chamber of Commerce
1870 NE 171st St.
North Miami Beach, FL 33162
Ph:(305)944-8500
Fax:(305)944-8191
Co. E-mail: chamber@nmbchamber.com
URL: http://www.nmbchamber.com
Contact: Lourdes Perez, Office Mgr.

48983 ■ Greater Palm Harbor Area Chamber of Commerce
1151 Nebraska Ave.
Palm Harbor, FL 34683
Ph:(727)784-4287
Fax:(727)786-2336
Co. E-mail: phcc@palmharborcc.org
URL: http://www.palmharborcc.org
Contact: Connie Davis, Pres./CEO

48984 ■ Greater Panama City Beaches Chamber of Commerce
309 Beckrich Rd.
Panama City Beach, FL 32407
Ph:(850)234-3193
Fax:(850)235-2301
Co. E-mail: chamber@pcbeach.org
URL: http://www.pcbeach.org
Contact: Debi Knight, Pres.

48985 ■ Greater Pine Island Chamber of Commerce
PO Box 525
Matlacha, FL 33993
Ph:(239)283-0888
Fax:(239)283-0336
Co. E-mail: info@pineislandchamber.org
URL: http://www.pineislandchamber.org
Contact: Cynthia Welch, Pres.

48986 ■ Greater Plant City Chamber of Commerce
106 N Evers St.
Plant City, FL 33563-3330
Ph:(813)754-3707
Free: 800-760-2315
Fax:(813)752-8793
Co. E-mail: info@plantcity.org
URL: http://www.plantcity.org
Contact: Marion M. Smith, Pres.

48987 ■ Greater Plantation Chamber of Commerce
7401 NW 4th St.
Plantation, FL 33317
Ph:(954)587-1410
Fax:(954)587-1886
Co. E-mail: info@plantationchamber.org
URL: http://www.plantationchamber.org
Contact: Siobhan Edwards, Pres.

48988 ■ Greater Pompano Beach Chamber of Commerce
2200 E Atlantic Blvd.
Pompano Beach, FL 33062
Ph:(954)941-2940
URL: http://www.pompanobeachchamber.com
Contact: Ric green, CEO/Pres.

48989 ■ Greater Riverview Chamber of Commerce
10520 Riverview Dr.
Riverview, FL 33568
Ph:(813)234-5944
Fax:(813)234-5945
Co. E-mail: riverviewchamber@tampabay.rr.com
URL: http://www.riverviewchamber.com
Contact: Tanya Doran, Exec. Dir.

48990 ■ Greater Sarasota Chamber of Commerce
1945 Fruitville Rd.
Sarasota, FL 34236
Ph:(941)955-8187
Fax:(941)366-5621
Co. E-mail: squeior@sarasotachamber.com
URL: http://www.sarasotachamber.com
Contact: Steve Queior CCE, Pres./CEO

48991 ■ Greater Sebring Chamber of Commerce
227 US Hwy. N
Sebring, FL 33870
Ph:(863)385-8448
Fax:(863)385-8810
Co. E-mail: information@sebring.org
URL: http://www.greatersebringchamberofcommerce. org
Contact: Sarah Pallone, Pres./CEO

48992 ■ Greater Seffner Area Chamber of Commerce
11816 US Hwy. 92 E
PO Box 1920
Seffner, FL 33583-1920
Ph:(813)627-8686
Co. E-mail: info@seffnerchamber.com
URL: http://www.seffnerchamber.com
Contact: Mr. Barrett Smith, Pres.

48993 ■ Greater Seminole Area Chamber of Commerce
8400 113th St. N
Seminole, FL 33772
Ph:(727)392-3245
Fax:(727)397-7753
Co. E-mail: jimmyj@myseminolechamber.com
URL: http://seminolechamber.net
Contact: James Johnson, Exec. Dir.

48994 ■ Greater Sunrise Chamber of Commerce
12801 W Sunrise Blvd.
Sunrise, FL 33323-4020
Ph:(954)835-2428
Co. E-mail: director@greatersunrisechamber.org
URL: http://lovemyzip.com/cityhome. php?city=SUNRISE&state=FL
Contact: Kitty McGowan, Exec. Dir.

48995 ■ Greater Tallahassee Chamber of Commerce
PO Box 1639
100 N Duval St.
Tallahassee, FL 32302
Ph:(850)224-8116
Fax:(850)561-3860
Co. E-mail: info@talchamber.com
URL: http://www.talchamber.com/index.asp
Contact: Sue Dick, Pres.

48996 ■ Greater Tampa Chamber of Commerce
PO Box 420
Tampa, FL 33601
Ph:(813)228-7777
Free: 800-298-2672

Fax:(813)223-7899
Co. E-mail: info@tampachamber.com
URL: http://www.tampachamber.com
Contact: Joe House, Pres./CEO

48997 ■ Greater Temple Terrace Chamber of Commerce
9385 N 56th St.
Temple Terrace, FL 33617
Ph:(813)989-7004
Fax:(813)989-7005
Co. E-mail: cdonohue@templeterracechamber.com
URL: http://www.templeterracechamber.com
Contact: Cheri Donohue, Exec. Dir.

48998 ■ Greater Winter Haven Chamber of Commerce
PO Box 1420
Winter Haven, FL 33882
Ph:(863)293-2138
Fax:(863)297-5818
Co. E-mail: chamber1@winterhavenfl.com
URL: http://winterhavenfl.com
Contact: Bob Gernert Jr., Exec. Dir.

48999 ■ Gulf Breeze Area Chamber of Commerce
409 Gulf Breeze Pkwy.
Gulf Breeze, FL 32561
Ph:(850)932-7888
Fax:(850)934-4601
Co. E-mail: reception@gulfbreezechamber.com
URL: http://www.gulfbreezechamber.com
Contact: Ms. Meg Peltier, Pres./CEO

49000 ■ Gulf County Chamber of Commerce
1014 Reid Ave., Ste. 101
Port St. Joe, FL 32456
Ph:(850)227-1223
Fax:(850)227-9684
Co. E-mail: info@gulfchamber.org
URL: http://www.gulfchamber.org
Contact: Sandra B. Chafin, Exec. Dir.

49001 ■ Haines City Chamber of Commerce
35610 US Hwy. 27
Haines City, FL 33844
Ph:(863)422-3751
Co. E-mail: info@hainescity.com
URL: http://www.hainescity.com
Contact: Lisa Weathersbee, Chair

49002 ■ Hamilton County Chamber of Commerce
PO Box 366
Jasper, FL 32052
Ph:(386)792-1300
Fax:(386)792-0559
Co. E-mail: hamcoc@windstream.net
URL: http://www.hamiltoncountycoc.com
Contact: Joy Howell, Pres.

49003 ■ Hardee County Chamber of Commerce
225 E Main St.
PO Box 683
Wauchula, FL 33873
Ph:(863)773-6967
Fax:(863)773-0229
Co. E-mail: hardeecc@strato.net
URL: http://www.hardeecc.com
Contact: Ms. Casey Prescott, Exec. Dir.

49004 ■ Hawthorne Area Chamber of Commerce
PO Box 125
Hawthorne, FL 32640-0125
Ph:(352)481-4818
Co. E-mail: chamber@hawthorneflorida.org
URL: http://www.hawthorneflorida.org
Contact: Stan Kitching, Pres.

49005 ■ Hialeah Chamber of Commerce and Industry
240 E 1st Ave., Ste. 217
Hialeah, FL 33010
Ph:(305)888-7780

Fax:(305)888-7804
Co. E-mail: info@hialeahchamber.org
URL: http://www.hialeahchamber.org
Contact: Daniel Hernandez, Pres.

49006 ■ High Springs Chamber of Commerce
PO Box 863
High Springs, FL 32655-0863
Ph:(386)454-3120
Fax:(386)454-5848
Co. E-mail: chamber@highsprings.com
URL: http://www.highsprings.com/home/index.php
Contact: Thomas R. Weller, Pres.

49007 ■ Hobe Sound Chamber of Commerce
11954 SE Bridge Rd.
PO Box 1507
Hobe Sound, FL 33475
Ph:(772)546-4724
Fax:(772)546-9969
Co. E-mail: info@hobesound.org
URL: http://hobesound.org
Contact: Jennifer Ferrari, Exec. Dir.

49008 ■ Holly Hill Chamber of Commerce
1056 Ridgewood Ave.
Holly Hill, FL 32117
Ph:(386)255-7311
Fax:(386)267-0485
Co. E-mail: info@hollyhillchamber.com
URL: http://www.hollyhillchamber.com
Contact: Rose Schuhmacher, Exec. Dir.

49009 ■ Immokalee Chamber of Commerce
1300 N 15th St., Ste. 2
Immokalee, FL 34142
Ph:(239)657-3237
Co. E-mail: ecoc@comcast.net
URL: http://www.immokaleechamber.com
Contact: Dick Rice, Exec. Dir.

49010 ■ Indian River County Chamber of Commerce
1146 21st St., Ste. B
Vero Beach, FL 32960
Ph:(772)567-3491
Fax:(772)778-3181
Co. E-mail: info@indianriverchamber.com
URL: http://www.indianriverchamber.com
Contact: Penny Chandler, Pres.

49011 ■ Indiantown Western Martin County Chamber of Commerce
PO Box 602
15935 SW Warfield Blvd.
Indiantown, FL 34956-0602
Ph:(772)597-2184
Fax:(772)597-6063
Co. E-mail: itownccc@onearrow.net
URL: http://indiantownfl.org
Contact: Allon R. Fish, Pres./CEO

49012 ■ Islamorada Chamber of Commerce
PO Box 915
Islamorada, FL 33036-0915
Ph:(305)664-4503
Free: 800-322-5397
Fax:(305)664-4289
Co. E-mail: info@islamoradachamber.com
URL: http://www.islamoradachamber.com
Contact: Judy Hall, Exec. Dir.

49013 ■ Jackson County Chamber of Commerce
PO Box 130
Marianna, FL 32447
Ph:(850)482-8060
Fax:(850)482-8002
Co. E-mail: info@jacksoncounty.com
URL: http://www.jacksoncounty.com
Contact: Art Kimbrough, Pres./CEO

49014 ■ Jacksonville Regional Chamber of Commerce
3 Independent Dr.
Jacksonville, FL 32202
Ph:(904)366-6600

Fax:(904)632-0617
Co. E-mail: info@jacksonvillechamber.com
URL: http://www.myjaxchamber.com/general.as-p?id=2
Contact: Walter M. Lee III, Pres.

49015 ■ Jensen Beach Chamber of Commerce
PO Box 1536
Jensen Beach, FL 34958
Ph:(772)334-3444
Fax:(772)334-0817
Co. E-mail: info@jensenbeachchamber.biz
URL: http://www.jensenbeachchamber.biz
Contact: Ed Griffiths, Pres.

49016 ■ Key Largo Chamber of Commerce
106000 Overseas Hwy.
Key Largo, FL 33037
Ph:(305)451-4747
Free: 800-822-1088
Fax:(305)451-4726
Co. E-mail: info@keylargochamber.org
URL: http://www.keylargochamber.org
Contact: Jackie Harder, Pres.

49017 ■ Key West Chamber of Commerce
402 Wall St.
Key West, FL 33040
Ph:(305)294-2587
Fax:(305)294-2898
Co. E-mail: info@keywestchamber.org
URL: http://www.keywestchamber.org
Contact: Michael Knowles, Pres.

49018 ■ Kissimmee - Osceola County Chamber of Commerce
1425 E Vine St.
Kissimmee, FL 34744
Ph:(407)847-3174
Fax:(407)870-8607
Co. E-mail: mhorner@kissimmeechamber.com
URL: http://www.kissimmeechamber.com
Contact: Mike Horner, Pres.

49019 ■ Lady Lake Area Chamber of Commerce
PO Box 1430
Lady Lake, FL 32158-1430
Ph:(352)753-6029
Fax:(352)753-8029
URL: http://www.ladylakechamber.com
Contact: Betty Bernard, Exec. Dir.

49020 ■ Lafayette County Chamber of Commerce
PO Box 416
Mayo, FL 32066
Ph:(386)294-2705
Co. E-mail: lafayettecnty@aol.com
URL: http://www.lafayettecountychamber.com

49021 ■ Lake Alfred Chamber of Commerce
210 N Seminole Ave.
PO Box 956
Lake Alfred, FL 33850
Ph:(863)291-5380
Co. E-mail: lachamber@lake-alfred.com
URL: http://www.lake-alfred.com
Contact: Jennifer Cone, Pres.

49022 ■ Lake City - Columbia County Chamber of Commerce
162 S Marion Ave.
Lake City, FL 32025-4354
Ph:(386)752-3690
Fax:(386)755-7744
Co. E-mail: jim@lakecitychamber.com
URL: http://www.lakecitychamber.com
Contact: Jim Poole, Exec. Dir.

49023 ■ Lake Placid Chamber of Commerce
18 N Oak St.
Lake Placid, FL 33852
Ph:(863)465-4331
Fax:(863)465-2588
Co. E-mail: chamber@lpfla.com
URL: http://www.lpfla.com
Contact: Eileen M. May, Exec. Dir.

49024 ■ Lake Wales Area Chamber of Commerce
340 W Central Ave.
PO Box 191
Lake Wales, FL 33859-0191
Ph:(863)676-3445
Fax:(863)676-3446
Co. E-mail: info@lakewaleschamber.com
URL: http://www.lakewaleschamber.com
Contact: Betty Wojcik, Exec. Dir.

49025 ■ Lakeland Area Chamber of Commerce
PO Box 3607
Lakeland, FL 33802-3607
Ph:(863)688-8551
Co. E-mail: info@lakelandchamber.com
URL: http://lakelandchamber.com
Contact: Kathleen L. Munson, Pres.

49026 ■ Lauderdale By The Sea Chamber of Commerce
4201 Ocean Dr.
Lauderdale by the Sea, FL 33308
Ph:(954)776-1000
Fax:(954)776-6203
Co. E-mail: info@lbts.com
URL: http://www.lbts.com
Contact: Paul Novak, Pres.

49027 ■ Leesburg Area Chamber of Commerce
103 S 6th St.
Leesburg, FL 34748
Ph:(352)787-2131
Fax:(352)787-3985
Co. E-mail: info@leesburgchamber.com
URL: http://www.leesburgchamber.com
Contact: Jan Zacharchuk, Exec. Dir./Publisher

49028 ■ Lehigh Acres Chamber of Commerce
PO Box 757
Lehigh Acres, FL 33970-0757
Ph:(239)369-3322
Fax:(239)368-0500
Co. E-mail: lehighchamber@comcast.net
URL: http://www.lehighacreschamber.org
Contact: Oliver B. Conover, Exec. Dir.

49029 ■ Longboat Key Chamber of Commerce
5570 Gulf of Mexico Dr.
Longboat Key, FL 34228
Ph:(941)383-2466
Fax:(941)383-8217
Co. E-mail: m@agentmarnie.com
URL: http://longboatkeychamber.com
Contact: Marnie Matarese, Chair

49030 ■ Lower Keys Chamber of Commerce
31020 Overseas Hwy.
Big Pine Key, FL 33043-0511
Ph:(305)872-2411
Fax:(305)872-0752
Co. E-mail: info@lowerkeyschamber.com
URL: http://www.lowerkeyschamber.com
Contact: Carole Stevens, Mgr.

49031 ■ Madison County Chamber of Commerce
177 SW Horry Ave.
Madison, FL 32340
Ph:(850)973-2788
Free: 877-272-3642
Fax:(850)973-8864
Co. E-mail: chamber@madisonfl.org
URL: http://www.madisonfl.org
Contact: Terri Schefbuch, Office Mgr.

49032 ■ Maitland Area Chamber of Commerce
110 N Maitland Ave.
Maitland, FL 32751
Ph:(407)644-0741
Fax:(407)539-2529
Co. E-mail: info@maitlandchamber.com
URL: http://www.maitlandchamber.com
Contact: Mary F. Hodge, Exec. Dir.

49033 ■ Manatee Chamber of Commerce
PO Box 321
Bradenton, FL 34206-0321
Ph:(941)748-3411
Fax:(941)745-1877
Co. E-mail: info@manateechamber.com
URL: http://www.manateechamber.com
Contact: Robert P. Bartz, Pres.

49034 ■ Marco Island Area Chamber of Commerce
1102 N Collier Blvd.
Marco Island, FL 34145
Ph:(239)394-7549
Free: 800-788-6272
Fax:(239)394-3061
Co. E-mail: info@marcoislandchamber.org
URL: http://www.marcoislandchamber.org
Contact: Sandi Riedemann, Exec. Dir.

49035 ■ Melbourne-Palm Bay Area Chamber of Commerce
1005 E Strawbridge Ave.
Melbourne, FL 32901-4782
Ph:(321)724-5400
Fax:(321)725-2093
Co. E-mail: christine@melpb-chamber.org
URL: http://www.melpb-chamber.org
Contact: Christine Michaels, Pres.

49036 ■ Miami Beach Chamber of Commerce
1920 Meridian Ave.
Miami Beach, FL 33139-1818
Ph:(305)674-1300
Co. E-mail: info@miamibeachchamber.com
URL: http://www.miamibeachchamber.com
Contact: Wendy Kallergis, Pres./CEO

49037 ■ Miami-Dade County Chamber of Commerce
11380 NW 27th Ave., Bldg. 1, Ste. 1328
Miami, FL 33167
Ph:(305)751-8648
Fax:(305)758-3839
Co. E-mail: mdcc@m-dcc.org
URL: http://www.m-dcc.org
Contact: Bill Diggs, Pres./CEO

49038 ■ Miramar-Pembroke Pines Regional Chamber of Commerce
10100 Pines Blvd., 4th Fl.
Pembroke Pines, FL 33026-3900
Ph:(954)432-9808
Fax:(954)432-9193
Co. E-mail: info@miramarpembrokepines.org
URL: http://www.miramarpembrokepines.org
Contact: Stella J. Tokar, Pres./CEO

49039 ■ Monticello-Jefferson County Chamber of Commerce
420 W Washington St.
Monticello, FL 32344
Ph:(850)997-5552
Fax:(850)997-1020
Co. E-mail: info@monticellojeffersonfl.com
URL: http://www.monticellojeffersonfl.com
Contact: Mary Frances Drawdy, Dir.

49040 ■ Mount Dora Area Chamber of Commerce
PO Box 196
Mount Dora, FL 32756-0196
Ph:(352)383-2165
Fax:(352)383-1668
Co. E-mail: chamber@mountdora.com
URL: http://www.mountdora.com

49041 ■ Navarre Beach Area Chamber of Commerce
PO Drawer 5430
Navarre, FL 32566
Ph:(850)939-3267
Free: 800-480-7263
Fax:(850)939-0085
Co. E-mail: info@navarrechamber.com
URL: http://www.navarrechamber.com
Contact: Sandi Kemp, Chair

49042 ■ Newberry Area Chamber of Commerce
PO Box 495
Newberry, FL 32669
Ph:(352)472-6611
Co. E-mail: info@newberrychamber.com
URL: http://www.newberrychamber.com
Contact: Michelle Pickett, Pres.

49043 ■ Niceville-Valparaiso Bay Area Chamber of Commerce
1055 E John Sims Pkwy.
Niceville, FL 32578
Ph:(850)678-2323
Fax:(850)678-2602
Co. E-mail: info@nicevillechamber.com
URL: http://www.nicevillechamber.com
Contact: Tricia Brunson, Pres./CEO

49044 ■ North Dade Regional Chamber of Commerce
1300 NW 167th St., Ste. 1
Miami, FL 33169
Ph:(305)690-9123
Fax:(305)690-9124
Co. E-mail: thechamber@thechamber.cc
URL: http://www.thechamber.cc

49045 ■ North Florida Regional Chamber of Commerce
100 E Call St. Starke
Starke, FL 32091
Ph:(904)964-5278
Fax:(904)964-2863
Co. E-mail: commerce@atlantic.net
URL: http://www.northfloridachamber.com
Contact: Ron Lilly, Pres./CEO

49046 ■ North Fort Myers Chamber of Commerce
2787 N Tamiami Trail, No. 10
North Fort Myers, FL 33918-3739
Ph:(239)997-9111
Fax:(239)997-4026
Co. E-mail: nfmchamber@yahoo.com
URL: http://nfmchamber.org
Contact: Morgan Halle, Pres.

49047 ■ North Miami Beach Chamber of Commerce
1870 NE 171 St.
North Miami Beach, FL 33162
Ph:(305)944-8500
Fax:(305)944-8191
Co. E-mail: chamber@nmbchamber.com
URL: http://www.nmbchamber.com
Contact: Paul Lemay, Pres.

49048 ■ North Palm Beach County Chamber of Commerce
3970 RCA Blvd., Ste. 7010
Palm Beach Gardens, FL 33410-4231
Ph:(561)694-2300
Fax:(561)694-0126
Co. E-mail: info@npbchamber.com
URL: http://www.npbchamber.com/splash.php
Contact: Casey Steinbacher, Pres./CEO

49049 ■ North Port Area Chamber of Commerce
15141 Tamiami Trail
North Port, FL 34287-2711
Ph:(941)423-5040
Fax:(941)423-5042
Co. E-mail: info@northportareachamber.com
URL: http://www.northportareachamber.com
Contact: Mindy Tew, Exec. Dir.

49050 ■ North Tampa Chamber of Commerce
PO Box 82043
Tampa, FL 33682
Ph:(813)961-2420
Fax:(813)961-2903
Co. E-mail: info@northtampachamber.com
URL: http://www.northtampachamber.com
Contact: Elaine Kaufman, Pres.

49051 ■ Ocala-Marion County Chamber of Commerce
110 E Silver Springs Blvd.
Ocala, FL 34470-6613
Ph:(352)629-8051
Fax:(352)629-7651
Co. E-mail: jaye@ocalacc.com
URL: http://www.ocalacc.com
Contact: Jaye Baillie APR, Pres./CEO

49052 ■ Okeechobee Chamber of Commerce
55 S Parrott Ave.
Okeechobee, FL 34972
Ph:(863)763-6464
Fax:(863)763-3467
Co. E-mail: commerce@okeechobeechamberofcom-
merce.com
URL: http://okeechobeechamberofcommerce.com
Contact: Candace Burke, Exec. Dir.

49053 ■ Oldsmar/Upper Tampa Bay Regional Chamber of Commerce
163 State Rd. 580 W
Oldsmar, FL 34677
Ph:(813)855-4233
Fax:(813)854-1237
Co. E-mail: jcustin@utbchamber.com
URL: http://www.oldsmarchamber.com
Contact: Jerry Custin, Pres./CEO

49054 ■ Orlando Regional Chamber of Commerce
PO Box 1234
75 S Ivanhoe Blvd.
Orlando, FL 32802-1234
Ph:(407)425-1234
Fax:(407)835-2500
Co. E-mail: info@orlando.org
URL: http://www.orlando.org
Contact: Jacob V. Stuart, Pres./CEO

49055 ■ Ormond Beach Chamber of Commerce
165 W Granada Blvd.
Ormond Beach, FL 32174
Ph:(386)677-3454
Fax:(386)677-4363
Co. E-mail: obchamber@ormondchamber.com
URL: http://www.ormondchamber.com
Contact: Tony Capozzi, Pres.

49056 ■ Oviedo-Winter Springs Regional Chamber of Commerce
PO Box 621236
Oviedo, FL 32762
Ph:(407)365-6500
Fax:(407)650-2712
Co. E-mail: intern@oviedowintersprings.org
URL: http://www.oviedowintersprings.org/pages/
home/default.aspx
Contact: Corydon G. Skeates JD, Exec. Dir.

49057 ■ Pahokee Chamber of Commerce
115 E Main St.
Pahokee, FL 33476
Ph:(561)924-5579
Fax:(561)924-8116
Co. E-mail: info@pahokee.com
URL: http://www.pahokee.com
Contact: Lewis Pope III, Pres.

49058 ■ Palm Beach Chamber of Commerce
400 Royal Palm Way, Ste. 106
Palm Beach, FL 33480
Ph:(561)655-3282
Fax:(561)655-7191
Co. E-mail: info@palmbeachchamber.com
URL: http://www.palmbeachchamber.com
Contact: Laurel Baker, Exec. Dir.

49059 ■ Palm City Chamber of Commerce
880 SW Martin Downs Blvd.
Palm City, FL 34990
Ph:(772)286-8121
Fax:(772)286-3331
Co. E-mail: info@palmcitychamber.com
URL: http://www.palmcitychamber.com
Contact: Carolyn Davi, Exec. Dir.

49060 ■ Palms West Chamber of Commerce
13901 Southern Blvd.
PO Box 1062
Loxahatchee, FL 33470-1062
Ph:(561)790-6200
Free: 800-790-2364
Fax:(561)791-2069
Co. E-mail: info@palmswest.com
URL: http://www.palmswest.com
Contact: Jaene Miranda, CEO

49061 ■ Pensacola Area Chamber of Commerce
117 W Garden St.
Pensacola, FL 32502
Ph:(850)438-4081
Fax:(850)438-6369
Co. E-mail: eemerson@pensacolachamber.com
URL: http://www.pensacolachamber.com
Contact: Evon Emerson, Pres./CEO

49062 ■ Pinellas Park/Mid-County Chamber of Commerce
Park Sta.
5851 Park Blvd.
Pinellas Park, FL 33781
Ph:(727)544-4777
Fax:(727)209-0837
Co. E-mail: info@pinellasparkchamber.com
URL: http://www.pinellasparkchamber.com
Contact: Kenn Brown, Pres./CEO

49063 ■ Port Orange/South Daytona Chamber of Commerce
3431 Ridgewood Ave.
Port Orange, FL 32129
Ph:(386)761-1601
Fax:(386)788-9165
Co. E-mail: info@pschamber.com
URL: http://www.pschamber.com
Contact: Debbie Connors, Exec. Dir.

49064 ■ Putnam County Chamber of Commerce
PO Box 550
1100 Reid St.
Palatka, FL 32178-0550
Ph:(386)328-1503
Fax:(386)328-7076
Co. E-mail: president@putnamcountychamber.org
URL: http://www.putnamcountychamber.org
Contact: Mr. C.W. Larson II, Pres.

49065 ■ Ruskin Chamber of Commerce
315 S Tamiami Trail
Ruskin, FL 33570-4660
Ph:(813)645-3808
Fax:(813)645-2099
Co. E-mail: info@ruskinchamber.org
URL: http://www.ruskinchamber.org
Contact: Melanie D. Morrison, Exec. Dir.

49066 ■ Safety Harbor Chamber of Commerce
200 Main St.
Safety Harbor, FL 34695
Ph:(727)726-2890
Fax:(727)726-2733
Co. E-mail: info@safetyharborchamber.com
URL: http://www.safetyharborchamber.com
Contact: John Schaefer, Chm.

49067 ■ St. Cloud Greater Osceola County Chamber of Commerce
1200 New York Ave.
St. Cloud, FL 34769-3742
Ph:(407)892-3671
Fax:(407)892-5289
Co. E-mail: info@stcloudflchamber.com
URL: http://stcloudflchamber.com/Content/index.aspx
Contact: David C. Lane, Pres./CEO

49068 ■ St. Lucie County Chamber of Commerce
1850 SW Fountainview Blvd., Ste. 201
Port St. Lucie, FL 34986
Ph:(772)340-1333

Fax:(772)785-7021
Co. E-mail: info@stluciechamber.org
URL: http://www.stluciechamber.org
Contact: Linda W. Cox, Exec. VP/Exec. Dir.

49069 ■ St. Petersburg Area Chamber of Commerce
The Chamber Building
100 Second Ave. N, Ste. 150
St. Petersburg, FL 33701-3351
Ph:(727)821-4069
Fax:(727)895-6326
Co. E-mail: jtlong@stpete.com
URL: http://www.stpete.com
Contact: John T. Long III, Pres./CEO

49070 ■ Sanford - Seminole County Chamber of Commerce
400 E First St.
Sanford, FL 32771-1408
Ph:(407)322-2212
Fax:(407)322-8160
Co. E-mail: info@sanfordchamber.com
URL: http://www.sanfordchamber.com
Contact: Pam Czopp, Exec. Dir.

49071 ■ Sanibel-Captiva Islands Chamber of Commerce
1159 Causeway Rd.
Sanibel, FL 33957
Ph:(239)472-1080
Fax:(239)472-1070
Co. E-mail: island@sanibel-captiva.org
URL: http://www.sanibel-captiva.org
Contact: Mr. Ric Base, Pres.

49072 ■ Santa Rosa County Chamber of Commerce
5247 Stewart St.
Milton, FL 32570-4737
Ph:(850)623-2339
Fax:(850)623-4413
Co. E-mail: director@srcchamber.com
URL: http://www.srcchamber.com
Contact: Donna Tucker, Exec. Dir.

49073 ■ Sebastian River Area Chamber of Commerce
700 Main St.
Sebastian, FL 32958
Ph:(772)589-5969
Free: 888-881-7568
Fax:(772)589-5993
Co. E-mail: info@sebastianchamber.com
URL: http://www.sebastianchamber.com
Contact: Beth L. Mitchell, Exec. Dir.

49074 ■ Seminole County Regional Chamber of Commerce
1055 AAA Dr., Ste. 153
Heathrow, FL 32746
Ph:(407)333-4748
Fax:(407)708-4615
Co. E-mail: info@seminolebusiness.org
URL: http://www.seminolebusiness.org
Contact: John Ashworth, Pres.

49075 ■ Siesta Key Chamber of Commerce
5118 Ocean Blvd.
Siesta Key, FL 34242
Ph:(941)349-3800
Free: (866)831-7778
Co. E-mail: info@siestakeychamber.com
URL: http://www.siestakeychamber.com
Contact: Aimee Holmes, Chair

49076 ■ South Lake Chamber of Commerce
691 W Montrose St.
Clermont, FL 34711
Ph:(352)394-4191
Fax:(352)394-5799
Co. E-mail: office@southlakechamber-fl.com
URL: http://www.southlakechamber-fl.com/home
Contact: Ray San Fratello, Pres.

49077 ■ South Tampa Chamber of Commerce
3715 W Horatio St.
Tampa, FL 33609
Ph:(813)637-0156

Fax:(813)514-1885
Co. E-mail: executivedirector@southtampachamber.
   org
URL: http://www.southtampachamber.org
Contact: Ms. Judy Y. Gay, Exec. Dir.

**49078 ■ Southeast Volusia Chamber of
Commerce**
115 Canal St.
New Smyrna Beach, FL 32168-7003
Ph:(386)428-2449
Free: 877-460-8410
Fax:(386)423-3512
Co. E-mail: info@sevchamber.com
URL: http://www.sevchamber.com
Contact: Steve Dennis, Exec. VP

**49079 ■ Sun City Center Area Chamber of
Commerce**
1651 Sun City Center Plz.
Sun City Center, FL 33573
Ph:(813)634-5111
Co. E-mail: sccchamber@aol.com
URL: http://www.suncitycenterchamber.org
Contact: Elaine Brad, Pres.

**49080 ■ Suwannee County Chamber of
Commerce**
816 S Ohio Ave.
Live Oak, FL 32064
Ph:(386)362-3071
Fax:(386)362-4758
URL: http://www.suwanneechamber.com
Contact: Dennis Cason, Pres.

**49081 ■ Swedish American Chamber of
Commerce, Florida**
260 Crandon Blvd., Ste. 32
PMB 192
Key Biscayne, FL 33149
Ph:(305)767-1662
Fax:(305)675-0244
Co. E-mail: sacc@sacc-florida.com
URL: http://www.sacc-florida.com
Contact: Jonas Haeger, Chm.

**49082 ■ Tampa Bay Beaches Chamber of
Commerce**
6990 Gulf Blvd.
St. Pete Beach, FL 33706
Ph:(727)360-6957
Co. E-mail: info@tampabaybeaches.com
URL: http://www.tampabaybeaches.com/cwt/external/
   wcpages/index.aspx
Contact: Robin A. Grabowski, Pres.

**49083 ■ Tarpon Springs Chamber of
Commerce**
11 E Orange St.
Tarpon Springs, FL 34689-3439
Ph:(727)937-6100
Fax:(727)937-2879
Co. E-mail: chamber@tarponsprings.com
URL: http://www.querimax.com
Contact: Sue Thomas, Pres.

**49084 ■ Titusville Area Chamber of
Commerce**
2000 S Washington Ave.
Titusville, FL 32780
Ph:(321)267-3036
Fax:(321)264-0127
Co. E-mail: gaedcke@titusville.org
URL: http://www.titusville.org
Contact: Marcia Gaedcke, Pres.

49085 ■ Umatilla Chamber of Commerce
PO Box 300
Umatilla, FL 32784
Ph:(352)669-3511
Fax:(352)669-8900
Co. E-mail: umatilla@umatillachamber.org
URL: http://www.umatillachamber.org
Contact: C.A. Vossberg, Pres.

**49086 ■ Upper Tampa Bay Regional Chamber
of Commerce**
163 State Rd., 580 W
Oldsmar, FL 34677
Ph:(813)855-4233
Fax:(813)854-1237
Co. E-mail: jcustin@utbchamber.com
URL: http://www.oldsmarchamber.org
Contact: Jerry Custin, Pres./CEO

49087 ■ Venice Area Chamber of Commerce
597 Tamiami Trail S
Venice, FL 34285
Ph:(941)488-2236
Co. E-mail: vchamber@venicechamber.com
URL: http://www.venicechamber.com
Contact: John G. Ryan, Pres./CEO

49088 ■ Villages Chamber of Commerce
1000 Lake Sumter Landing
The Villages, FL 32162
Ph:(352)753-2270
Free: 800-245-1081
Co. E-mail: info@thevillages.com
URL: http://www.thevillages.com

**49089 ■ Wakulla County Chamber of
Commerce**
PO Box 598
Crawfordville, FL 32326
Ph:(850)926-1848
Fax:(850)926-2050
Co. E-mail: wakullacochamber@earthlink.net
URL: http://www.wakullacountychamber.com
Contact: Paul Johnson, Pres.

49090 ■ Walton Area Chamber of Commerce
63 S Centre Trail
Santa Rosa Beach, FL 32459
Ph:(850)267-0683
Fax:(850)267-0603
Co. E-mail: info@waltoncountychamber.com
URL: http://www.waltoncountychamber.com
Contact: Dawn Moliterno, Pres./CEO/Sec.

**49091 ■ Walton County Chamber of
Commerce**
95 Circle Dr.
Defuniak Springs, FL 32435
Ph:(850)892-3191
Fax:(850)892-9688
Co. E-mail: info@waltoncountychamber.com
URL: http://www.waltoncountychamber.com
Contact: Dawn Moliterno, Pres./CEO

**49092 ■ Washington County Chamber of
Commerce**
PO Box 457
Chipley, FL 32428
Ph:(850)638-4157
Fax:(850)638-8770
Co. E-mail: wcchamber@wfeca.net
URL: http://www.washcomall.com
Contact: Kelly Brock, Pres.

49093 ■ Wellington Chamber of Commerce
12230 Forest Hill Blvd., Ste. 183
Wellington, FL 33414
Ph:(561)792-6525
Fax:(561)792-6200
Co. E-mail: info@wellingtonchamber.com
URL: http://www.wellingtonchamber.com
Contact: Ms. Michela Perillo-Green, Exec. Dir.

49094 ■ West Orange Chamber of Commerce
12184 W Colonial Dr.
Winter Garden, FL 34787
Ph:(407)656-1304
Fax:(407)656-0221
Co. E-mail: info@wochamber.com
URL: http://www.wochamber.com
Contact: Stina D'Uva, Pres.

49095 ■ West Pasco Chamber of Commerce
5443 Main St.
New Port Richey, FL 34652
Ph:(727)842-7651

Fax:(727)848-0202
Co. E-mail: info@westpasco.com
URL: http://www.westpasco.com
Contact: Joe Alpine, Pres.

49096 ■ Weston Area Chamber of Commerce
1290 Weston Rd., Ste. 200
Weston, FL 33326-1909
Ph:(954)389-0600
Fax:(954)384-6133
Co. E-mail: jack@westonchamber.com
URL: http://www.westonchamber.com
Contact: Jack Miller, Pres./CEO

**49097 ■ Williston Area Chamber of
Commerce**
33 S Main St.
Williston, FL 32696
Ph:(352)528-5552
Fax:(352)528-4342
Co. E-mail: wcoc@willistonfl.com
URL: http://www.willistonfl.com
Contact: Justin Head, Pres.

49098 ■ Winter Park Chamber of Commerce
151 W Lyman Ave.
Winter Park, FL 32789
Ph:(407)644-8281
Fax:(407)644-7826
Co. E-mail: wpcc@winterpark.org
URL: http://www.winterpark.org
Contact: Sam Stark, Pres./CEO

49099 ■ Ybor City Chamber of Commerce
1800 E 9th Ave.
Tampa, FL 33605-9998
Ph:(813)248-3712
Fax:(813)242-0398
Co. E-mail: info@ybor.org
URL: http://www.ybor.org/index.cfm?section=mb
Contact: Thomas P. Keating, Pres./CEO

49100 ■ Zephyrhills Chamber of Commerce
38550 5th Ave.
Zephyrhills, FL 33542
Ph:(813)782-1913
Fax:(813)783-6060
Co. E-mail: info@zephyrhillschamber.org
URL: http://zephyrhillschamber.org
Contact: Tim Mitchell, Pres.

MINORITY BUSINESS
ASSISTANCE PROGRAMS

**49101 ■ Florida Black Business Investment
Board**
1030-9 E Lafayette St.
Tallahassee, FL 32302
Ph:(850)878-0826
Fax:(850)878-4578
Co. E-mail: info@fbbib.com
URL: http://www.fbbib.com
Contact: Paula Duncan, Interim Pres
Description: Obtains and provides loans for Black-
owned and -operated businesses.

**49102 ■ Florida Minority Supplier
Development Council**
7453 Brokerage Dr.
Orlando, FL 32809
Ph:(407)404-8700
Fax:(407)857-8647
Co. E-mail: malik@fmsdc.org
URL: http://fmsdc.org
Contact: Malik Ali, Pres
Description: The purpose of the FMSDC is to
provide major corporations and government agencies
with easy access to minority owned and operated
businesses.

49103 ■ Minority Business Enterprise Center
970 SW 1st St., Ste. 405 and 406
Miami, FL 33130
Ph:(786)316-0888

Fax:(786)316-0090
Co. E-mail: info@mbdcsouthflorida.org
URL: http://www.mbecflorida.org
Contact: Marie Gill, Dir.
Description: Providing general and specific business assistance, counseling and training to help establish, maintain and grow eligible minority business enterprises.

49104 ■ Palm Beach County Resource Center, Inc.
2001 Broadway, Ste. 250
Riviera Beach, FL 33404
Ph:(561)863-0895
Fax:(561)863-0897
Co. E-mail: p_skyers@pbcrc.org
URL: http://www.pbcrc.org
Contact: Paul Skyers, Dir

49105 ■ Southern Florida Minority Supplier Development Counsel
9499 NE 2nd Ave., Ste. 201
Miami, FL 33138
Ph:(305)762-6151
Free: 800-79F-RMPC
Fax:(305)762-6158
Co. E-mail: info@frmbc.org
URL: http://www.frmbc.org
Contact: Beatrice Louissaint, Pres & CEO
Description: Private-sector corporation that promotes the procurement of goods and services from minority businesses. Provides technical assistance and referral services to minority businesses.

FINANCING AND LOAN PROGRAMS

49106 ■ CEO Advisors
848 Brickel Ave., Ste. 603
Miami, FL 33131
Ph:(305)371-8560
Fax:(305)371-8563
URL: http://www.ceoadvisors.com
Contact: Robert J. Arguello, President
E-mail: rjarguello@ceoadvisors.com
Preferred Investment Size: $300,000 to $500,000. **Investment Types:** Seed, start-up, first stage, and research and development. **Industry Preferences:** Communications and media, computer hardware and software, semiconductors and other electronics, biotechnology, medical and health, consumer related. **Geographic Preferences:** Southeast. **Principal Exhibits:**

49107 ■ Florida Capital Partners
500 N. Westshore Blvd., Ste. 605
Tampa, FL 33609
Ph:(813)222-8000
Fax:(813)222-8001
Co. E-mail: bhc@fcinvestors.com
URL: http://www.fcpinvestors.com
Contact: Peter B. Franz, Managing Director
E-mail: Franz@fcpinvestors.com
Preferred Investment Size: $500,000 minimum. **Investment Types:** Start-up, first and second stage, management buyout, recapitalization, acquisition, and special situation. **Industry Preferences:** Communications and media, semiconductors and other electronics, medical and health, consumer related, industrial and energy, transportation, business service, manufacturing, agriculture, forestry and fishing. **Geographic Preferences:** U.S. **Principal Exhibits:**

49108 ■ Grace Venture Partners
SunTrust Ctr., Ste. 1850
200 S. Orange Ave.
Orlando, FL 32801
Ph:(407)835-7900
Fax:(407)835-7901
URL: http://www.graceventure.com
Contact: Edward P. Grace III, Managing Director
E-mail: ngrace@graceventure.com
Preferred Investment Size: $2,000,000 to $10,000,000. **Investment Policies:** Early and later stage, and mezzanine rounds. **Industry Preferences:** Communications, computer software, semi-

conductors and other electronics, and consumer related. **Geographic Preferences:** East Coast, Northeast, and Southeast. **Principal Exhibits:**

49109 ■ LM Capital Securities, Inc.
619 Datura St.
West Palm Beach, FL 33401-5309
Ph:(561)623-1700
Co. E-mail: info@LMCapitalSecurities.com
URL: http://www.lmcapitalsecurities.com
Contact: Leslie Corley, President
E-mail: LeslieCorley@LMCapitalSecurities.com
Preferred Investment Size: $5,000,000 minimum. **Investment Types:** Leveraged buyout. **Industry Preferences:** Computer hardware, semiconductors and other electronics, medical and health, consumer related, industrial and energy, and financial services. **Principal Exhibits:**

49110 ■ Lovett Miller & Co. Incorporated
1 Independent Sq., Ste. 1600
Jacksonville, FL 32202
Ph:(813)222-1471
Fax:(813)222-1478
Co. E-mail: info@lovettmiller.com
URL: http://www.lovettmiller.com
Contact: W. Radford Lovett II, Co-founder and Managing Partner
E-mail: rad@lovettmiller.com
Preferred Investment Size: $3,000,000 to $10,000,000. **Investment Types:** Seed, start-up, early and later stage, leveraged buyout, expansion, and mezzanine. **Industry Preferences:** Computer software and services, Internet specific, communications and media, consumer related, business services, financial services, medical and health, and other products. **Geographic Preferences:** Southeastern U.S. and Texas. **Principal Exhibits:**

49111 ■ North American Business Development Co., L.L.C.
135 S. LaSalle St., Ste. 3225
Chicago, IL 60603
Ph:(312)332-4950
Fax:(312)332-1540
Co. E-mail: information@northamericanfund.com
URL: http://www.northamericanfund.com
Contact: Robert L. Underwood, Managing Partner
Preferred Investment Size: $500,000 minimum. **Investment Types:** Leveraged buyout, special situation, control-block purchases, and industry rollups. **Industry Preferences:** Manufacturing and service. **Principal Exhibits:**

49112 ■ SI Ventures
12600 Gateway Blvd.
Ft. Myers, FL 33913
Ph:(239)561-4760
Fax:(239)561-4916
Co. E-mail: info@siventures.com
URL: http://www.siventures.com
Contact: Brian C. Beach, Managing Director
Preferred Investment Size: $2,000,000 to $5,000,000. **Investment Types:** Early stage and expansion. **Industry Preferences:** Internet specific, computer software, hardware and services, communications and media, medical and health, semiconductors and other electronics. **Geographic Preferences:** Southeastern U.S. **Principal Exhibits:**

49113 ■ South Atlantic Venture Funds, L.P.
614 W. Bay St.
Tampa, FL 33606-2704
Ph:(813)253-2500
Fax:(813)253-2360
URL: http://www.southatlantic.com
Contact: Sandra P. Barber, Managing Director
E-mail: spbarber@southatlantic.com
Preferred Investment Size: $1,500,000 to $7,500,000. **Investment Types:** First and second stage, acquisition, expansion, later stage, recapitalizations, and management buyouts. **Industry Preferences:** Communications and media, medical and health, Other products, Internet specific, consumer related, semiconductors and other electronics, computer software and services, computer hardware, industrial and energy. **Geographic Preferences:** Southeast, as far as Baltimore, MD and Washington, DC and Texas. **Principal Exhibits:**

PROCUREMENT ASSISTANCE PROGRAMS

49114 ■ Florida Department of Management Services–Division of Purchasing
4050 Esplanade Way
Tallahassee, FL 32399-0950
Ph:(850)488-2786
Fax:(850)922-6149
URL: http://dms.myflorida.com/support/contact_dms
Contact: Russ Rothman, Dir
Description: Publishes *Doing Business with the State of Florida.* Potential vendors should contact each state agency's purchasing office, since the Department of General Services does not make purchases for all agencies.

49115 ■ Florida Procurement Center Representatives
Naval Air Warfare Center
Training Systems Division
12350 Research Blvd.
Orlando, FL 32826-3224
Ph:(407)380-8252
Fax:(407)380-8232
Co. E-mail: walter.wallace@sba.gov
URL: http://www.sba.gov
Contact: Walter Wallace, PCR Rep
E-mail: walter.wallace@sba.gov
Description: Covers activities for Naval Training Systems Center (Orlando, FL). McDill Air Force Base (Tampa, FL), Patrick Air Force Base (Cocoa Beach, FL), and NASA, Kennedy Space Flight Center (Cape Canaveral, FL).

49116 ■ Florida Procurement Technical Assistance Center–Florida Gulf Coast University
Lutgert College of Business, Unit 2313
10501 FGCU Blvd. S.
Ft. Myers, FL 33965-6565
Ph:(239)745-3708
Co. E-mail: dtelep@fgcu.edu
URL: http://www.fptac.org
Contact: Dan Telep, Specialist
E-mail: dtelep@fgcu.edu
Description: Helps Florida businesses interested in obtaining contracts with the Department of Defense, other federal agencies, and state/local government agencies and participating prime contractors covering Lee, Collier, Charlotte, Glades, and Hendry counties.

49117 ■ Florida Procurement Technical Assistance Center–Jacksonville Chamber of Commerce–Small Business Center (SBC) (3 Ind)
3 Independent Dr.
Jacksonville, FL 32302
Ph:(904)366-6650
Fax:(904)632-0617
Co. E-mail: info@jacksonvillechamber.org
URL: http://www.myjaxchamber.com
Contact: Barbara English, Dir.
E-mail: paul.arrington@myjaxchamber.com
Description: Assists the growth and development of Jacksonville's small businesses community by constantly assessing their needs, collaborating with service providers and offering technical assistance, mentoring and access to capital.

49118 ■ Florida Procurement Technical Assistance Center–Palm Beach Community PTAC
3000 St. Lucie Ave., Rm. CB 221
Boca Raton, FL 33431-6490
Ph:(561)862-4782
Co. E-mail: carole.hart@floridaptac.org
URL: http://www.fptac.org
Contact: Carole Hart, Specialist
E-mail: chart@fau.edu
Description: Helps Florida businesses interested in obtaining contracts with the Department of Defense, other federal agencies, and state/local government agencies and participating prime contractors covering Boca Raton area, Palm Beach, and Martin County.

49119 ■ Florida Procurement Technical Assistance Center–Pinellas Park Office–University of South Florida (Techn)
Technical Services Bldg.
6051 78th Ave.
Pinellas Park, FL 33780
Ph:(727)541-0805
URL: http://www.fptac.org
Description: Helps Florida businesses interested in obtaining contracts with the Department of Defense, other federal agencies, and state/local government agencies and participating prime contractors covering St. Petersburg, Sarasota, and Pasco Counties.

49120 ■ Florida Procurement Technical Assistance Center–Tampa Office–University of South Florida (1101)
1101 Channelside Dr., Ste. 210
Tampa, FL 33602-3613
Ph:(813)905-5800
Co. E-mail: cbostic@coba.usf.edu
URL: http://www.fptac.org
Contact: Charlene Bostic, Specialist
E-mail: cbostic@coba.usf.edu
Description: Helps Florida businesses interested in obtaining contracts with the Department of Defense, other federal agencies, and state/local government agencies and participating prime contractors covering Tampa, Bartow, Ocala, and Melbourne areas.

49121 ■ Florida Procurement Technical Assistance Center–University of Central Florida
315 E Robinson St., Ste. 100
Orlando, FL 32805
Ph:(407)420-4850
Co. E-mail: tespinosa@bus.ucf.edu
URL: http://www.fptac.org
Contact: Tony Espinosa, Specialist
E-mail: tespinosa@bus.ucf.edu
Description: Helps Florida businesses interested in obtaining contracts with the Department of Defense, other federal agencies, and state/local government agencies and participating prime contractors covering the Orlando area.

49122 ■ Florida Procurement Technical Assistance Center–University of West Florida
401 E Chase St., Ste 100
Pensacola, FL 32502-6160
Ph:(850)473-7806
Fax:(850)473-7813
Co. E-mail: lsubel@uwf.edu
URL: http://www.fptac.org
Contact: Laura Subel, Prgm Mgr
E-mail: lsubel@uwf.edu
Description: Helps Florida businesses interested in obtaining contracts with the Department of Defense, other federal agencies, and state/local government agencies and participating prime contractors covering the Pensacola area.

49123 ■ Florida Procurement Technical Assistance Center–University of West Florida–FWB Branch Office (409 R)
409 Racetrack Rd.
Ft. Walton Beach, FL 32547
Ph:(850)301-3514
Co. E-mail: pbriere@uwf.edu
URL: http://www.fptac.org
Contact: Paul Briere, Specialist
E-mail: pbriere@uwf.edu
Description: Helps Florida businesses interested in obtaining contracts with the Department of Defense, other federal agencies, and state/local government agencies and participating prime contractors covering Ft. Walton Beach and Crestview areas.

INCUBATORS/RESEARCH AND TECHNOLOGY PARKS

49124 ■ Bay County Small Business Incubator
2500 Minnesota Ave.
Lynn Haven, FL 32444

Ph:(850)271-1107
Co. E-mail: info@nfci.org
URL: http://www.nfci.org/
Contact: Joe Chavarria, Dir.
Description: A non-profit small business incubator program established with a mission to give new and existing service and light manufacturing businesses the training and tools to become successful.

49125 ■ Beaver Street Enterprise Center
1225 W. Beaver St.
Jacksonville, FL 32204
Ph:(904)265-4700
Fax:(904)265-4740
Co. E-mail: info@bsecenter.net
URL: http://www.bsecenter.net/
Description: A small business incubator established to launch new businesses, to assist existing business through growing pains, to create jobs, and enhance economic development in Jacksonville.

49126 ■ Center for Technology, Enterprise & Development Business Incubator
401 W Atlantic Ave., Ste. 09
Delray Beach, FL 33444
Ph:(561)265-3790
Free: (866)353-3790
Fax:(561)265-0806
Co. E-mail: tedcenter@tedcenter.org
URL: http://www.tedcenter.org/BusinessIncubator.html
Contact: Seaborn A. Smith, Exec. Dir.
Description: A business incubator helping businesses grow in order to employ more people from the community in the services industry (janitorial, lawn service, etc.), professional services (accountants, consultants, legal, etc.), food preparation, and the construction industry.

49127 ■ Central Florida Research Park
12424 Research Pky., Ste. 100
Orlando, FL 32826
Ph:(407)282-3944
Fax:(407)282-1988
Co. E-mail: cindyelavsky@yahoo.com
URL: http://www.cfrp.org
Contact: Joe Wallace, Exec.Dir.
E-mail: cindyelavsky@yahoo.com
Scope: 1,027-acre site zoned for commercial and light manufacturing adjacent to the University. Established to create an environment which promotes and fosters relationships between industry and the University. **Publications:** Central Florida Research Park Update.

49128 ■ Enterprise Development Corporation of South Florida
3701 FAU Blvd., Ste. 210
Boca Raton, FL 33431
Ph:(561)620-8494
Fax:(561)620-8493
Co. E-mail: edcinfo@edc-tech.org
URL: http://www.edc-tech.org/
Description: A non profit organization that assists emerging science and technology companies.

49129 ■ Enterprise North Florida Corporation, Inc. (ENFC)
4905 Belfort Rd. Ste.110
Jacksonville, FL 32256
Ph:(904)730-4700
Fax:(904)730-4711
Co. E-mail: admin@enfc.org
URL: http://www.enfc.org
Contact: Alan Rossiter, Pres & CEO
Description: ENFC is a non-profit corporation that assists emerging high technology firms in northern Florida.

49130 ■ Florida Atlantic Research and Development Authority
3701 FAU Blvd., Ste. 210
Boca Raton, FL 33431
Ph:(561)416-6092

Fax:(561)620-8493
Co. E-mail: aduffell@research-park.org
URL: http://www.research-park.org/
Description: Research and development facility offering applied research directed at the industry partners' specific needs.

49131 ■ Florida Atlantic Research and Development Park
3701 FAU Blvd., Ste. 208
Boca Raton, FL 33431
Ph:(561)416-6092
Fax:(561)620-8493
URL: http://www.research-park.org
Contact: Jeffrey Siniawsky, Interim CEO
Scope: Serves as a bridge between the research interests of the tenant companies and research activities of the university community. The park features an innovation center and incubator to aid in transferring technology. There are Seed, Angel and Venture funding sources located within the Incubator and Research Park. The University is now operating Harbor Branch Ocean Institute and a medical school.
Awards: Research awards, $25,000, for faculty projects.

49132 ■ Florida/NASA Business Incubation Center–Technology Research and Development Authority
TRDA
1050 W NASA Blvd., Ste. 125
Melbourne, FL 32901
Ph:(321)872-1050
Fax:(321)872-1051
Co. E-mail: admin@trda.org
URL: http://www.trda.org/incubation-programs/
Description: The goal of this incubator is to increase the number of successful technology-based small companies in Brevard County, Florida. Tenants must be producing a technology-intensive product or be commercializing a NASA technology.

49133 ■ Florida State University–Center for Arts Administration Program
301 Francis Eppes Bldg.
Tallahassee, FL 32306
Ph:(850)644-5473
Fax:(850)644-5067
Co. E-mail: pvilleneuve@fsu.edu
URL: http://arted.fsu.edu/Programs/Arts-Administration
Contact: Pat Villeneuve PhD, Dir.
E-mail: pvilleneuve@fsu.edu
Scope: Serves as an administrative and resource base for the development of research, service, and education in arts administration. Provides psychological, social, business, governance, and art related information to private and public arts agencies. Administers research capabilities at the University in arts, business, and public administration. **Services:** Consultation, to local arts agencies and organizations specializing in rural and minority groups. **Educational Activities:** Conferences; Technical assistance workshops, for small arts organizations; Workshops.

49134 ■ Florida State University–Institute of Science and Public Affairs
296 Champions Way, Rm. C2200 UCC
PO Box 3062641
Tallahassee, FL 32306-2641
Ph:(850)644-2007
Fax:(850)644-7360
Co. E-mail: rbradley@admin.fsu.edu
URL: http://www.ispa.fsu.edu
Contact: Dr. Robert B. (Bob) Bradley, Dir.
E-mail: rbradley@admin.fsu.edu
Scope: Education and training, environment, geography, government, human trafficking, maternal and child health, planning, public administration, physics, economics, law, and social issues. **Services:** Consulting; Data processing; Geographic information system application; Library marketing and citing analysis; Software development. **Publications:** Atlases; Curricula; Maps. **Educational Activities:** Teacher training and workshops; Test assessment and evaluation.

49135 ■ Florida State University–Office of Research
3012 Westcott N
Tallahassee, FL 32306-1330
Ph:(850)644-9694
Fax:(850)645-0108
Co. E-mail: kkemper@research.fsu.edu
URL: http://www.research.fsu.edu
Contact: Dr. Kirby W. Kemper, VP, Res.
E-mail: kkemper@research.fsu.edu
Scope: Administers and coordinates extramurally sponsored research in natural sciences, social sciences, the humanities, and professional schools conducted by faculty members and graduate students of the University. Also administers the University's patenting, copyrighting, and technology transfer functions. **Publications:** Office of Research Newsletter (monthly); Research in Review (3/year). **Educational Activities:** Cornerstone Research Program.

49136 ■ Gainesville Technology Enterprise Center
2153 SE Hawthorne Rd., Ste. 101
Gainesville, FL 32641-7553
Ph:(352)393-6000
Fax:(352)393-6015
Co. E-mail: contact@gtecflorida.com
URL: http://www.gtecflorida.com/
Description: A community organization providing early stage technology startup companies with the tools, training, and infrastructure to become self-sufficient, financially-viable technology enterprises.

49137 ■ Innovation Park
1736 W Paul Dirac Dr.
Tallahassee, FL 32310-3673
Ph:(850)575-0343
Fax:(850)575-0355
Co. E-mail: innpark@embarqmail.com
URL: http://www.innovation-park.com
Contact: Catherine Kunst PhD, Exec.Dir.
E-mail: innpark@embarqmail.com
Scope: Fosters research partnerships between the Universities and industry tenants.

49138 ■ Progress Corporate Park
13709 Progress Blvd., Box 10
Alachua, FL 32615
Ph:(386)462-4040
Free: 877—457-6489
Fax:(386)462-3932
Co. E-mail: sandy@progresscorporatepark.com
URL: http://www.progresscorporatepark.com
Contact: Sandra Burgess
E-mail: sandy@progresscorporatepark.com
Scope: 200-acre research and technology park open to both public and private research and manufacturing organizations emphasizing high-technology development, including electronics, biotechnology, advanced materials, pharmacology, and agriculture. Center provides a link between University researchers and industry and transfers new technologies from the laboratory to the marketplace. **Services:** Assistance, in entrepreneurial development, commercialization of scientific and technological innovations, and international marketing.

49139 ■ Seminole Technology Business Incubation Center
1445 Dolgner Pl.
Sanford, FL 32771
Ph:(407)321-3495
Fax:(407)321-4184
Co. E-mail: hardyw@scc-fl.edu
URL: http://www.seminoleinc.com/
Description: A joint venture of Seminole County, Seminole County Port Authority, and Seminole Community College providing a nurturing environment for technology-based companies in the early stages of development.

49140 ■ University of Central Florida–Office of Research and Commercialization
12201 Research Pky., Ste. 501
Orlando, FL 32826-3246
Ph:(407)823-3778
Fax:(407)823-3299
Co. E-mail: oneal@mail.ucf.edu
URL: http://www.research.ucf.edu
Contact: Dr. Thomas O'Neal, Assoc.VP/Dir.
E-mail: oneal@mail.ucf.edu
Scope: Administers and coordinates contract and grant research conducted at the departmental level and in University research centers and institutes. Specializations include simulation and training, fiber optics, laser electronics, computer hardware and software development, solar energy, alternative energy development, and human factors. **Publications:** Annual report. **Educational Activities:** Seminars, in grant writing and contract/grant administration.

49141 ■ University of Florida–Division of Sponsored Research
219 Grinter Hall
PO Box 115500
Gainesville, FL 32611-5500
Ph:(352)392-3516
Fax:(352)846-1839
Co. E-mail: wphil@ufl.edu
URL: http://www.research.ufl.edu/research
Contact: Dr. Winfred M. Phillips, VP, Res.
E-mail: wphil@ufl.edu
Scope: Administers and stimulates the growth of research and graduate education; creates significant relationships between government, industry, and other research sponsors and the university; promotes economic development in Alachua County, the State of Florida and the nation through technology transfer opportunities. **Publications:** Explore Research Magazine (semiannually); Graduate Catalog (annually); RGP Annual Report. **Awards:** Supplemental Retention Awards.

49142 ■ University of Florida–Sid Martin Biotechnology Incubator
12085 Research Dr.
Alachua, FL 32615
Ph:(386)462-0880
Fax:(386)462-0875
Co. E-mail: pbreedlove@biotech.org
URL: http://www.biotech.ufl.org
Contact: Patti Breedlove, Assoc.Dir.
E-mail: pbreedlove@biotech.org
Scope: Biotechnology development. **Educational Activities:** Biotechnological techniques training, in cooperation with the Interdisciplinary Center for Biotechnology Research.

49143 ■ University of Miami–Office of Research
Dominion Towers, Rm. 1200
1475 NW 12th Ave.
Miami, FL 33136
Ph:(305)243-6415
Co. E-mail: rbookman@miami.edu
URL: http://uresearch.miami.edu
Contact: Dr. Richard J. Bookman
E-mail: rbookman@miami.edu
Scope: Promotes and encourages research at the University and assists and coordinates research programs carried out in individual departments and divisions of the University.

49144 ■ University of South Florida–Office of Research
3702 Spectrum Blvd., Ste. 175
Tampa, FL 33612-9444
Ph:(813)974-5570
Fax:(813)974-3348
Co. E-mail: kholbrook@research.usf.edu
URL: http://www3.research.usf.edu
Contact: Prof. Karen A. Holbrook PhD, Sen.VP for Res. and Innovation
E-mail: kholbrook@research.usf.edu
Scope: Administers activities involving both sponsored and non-sponsored research conducted at the university, including research compliance, intellectual property, and research park development. **Services:** Technical assistance. **Publications:** Annual report. **Awards:** Internal awards program.

49145 ■ University of West Florida–Research and Sponsored Programs
Bldg. 11, Rm. 110
11000 University Pky.
Pensacola, FL 32514-5732
Ph:(850)474-2824
Fax:(850)474-2082
Co. E-mail: rpodemski@uwf.edu
URL: http://research.uwf.edu
Contact: Richard S. Podemski PhD, Assoc.VP
E-mail: rpodemski@uwf.edu
Scope: Administers and coordinates sponsored research programs at the University, including software engineering, behavioral medicine, and bioremediation. **Publications:** Guide to Graduate Student Funding; Perspectives on Research and Creative Activity; Research: Guide to Fellowships. **Educational Activities:** Grant writing workshops; Intellectual property forums.

EDUCATIONAL PROGRAMS

49146 ■ Florida Keys Community College
5901 College Rd.
Key West, FL 33040
Ph:(305)296-9081
Fax:(305)292-5155
URL: http://www.fkcc.edu
Description: Two-year college offering degree and certificate programs in small business management program.

49147 ■ St. Johns River Community College
5001 St. Johns Ave.
Palatka, FL 32177
Ph:(386)312-4200
Fax:(386)312-4292
URL: http://www.sjrcc.cc.fl.us
Description: Two-year college offering a small business management program.

49148 ■ Santa Fe Community College
3000 NW 83rd St., Rm. 112
Gainesville, FL 32606
Ph:(352)395-5443
Fax:(352)395-5922
Co. E-mail: information@sfcc.edu
URL: http://www.santafe.cc.fl.us
Description: Two-year college offering a program in small business management.

49149 ■ Seminole Community College
100 Weldon Blvd.
Sanford, FL 32773-6199
Ph:(407)328-4722
Fax:(407)328-2029
URL: http://www.scc-fl.com
Description: Two-year college offering a small business administration program.

PUBLICATIONS

49150 ■ *Business in Broward*
PO Box 460669
Ft. Lauderdale, FL 33346-0669
Ph:(954)763-3338
Co. E-mail: sfbiz@mindspring.com

49151 ■ *Daily Business Review*
1 SE 3rd Ave., Ste. 900
Miami, FL 33131-1820
Ph:(305)377-3721
Fax:(305)347-6678

49152 ■ *How to Form Your Own Florida Corporation*
Nolo Press
950 Parker St.
Berkeley, CA 94710
Ph:(510)549-1976
Free: 800-992-6656
Fax:(510)548-5902
URL: http://www.nolo.com
Ed: Anthony Mancuso. **Released:** Third edition, 1990. **Price:** $24.95.

49153 ■ *Incorporation and Business Guide for Florida*
Self-Counsel Press, Inc.
1704 N. State St.
Bellingham, WA 98225
Ph:(360)676-4530
Free: 800-663-3007
Fax:(360)676-4549

Ed: Robert C. Waters. **Released:** 1992. **Price:** $21.95. **Description:** Includes forms to help entrepreneurs incorporate in Florida.

49154 ■ *Silver River Marine Institute*
1519 NE 22nd Ave.
Ocala, FL 34470
Ph:(352)620-3601
Fax:(352)620-3604

49155 ■ *Starting and Operating a Business in Florida: A Step-by-Step Guide*
PSI Research
300 N. Valley Dr.
Grants Pass, OR 97526
Ph:(503)479-9464
Free: 800-228-2275

Fax:(503)476-1479
Co. E-mail: psi2@magick.net
Ed: Michael D. Jenkins. **Released:** Revised edition, 1992. **Price:** $29.95 (looseleaf binder); $24.95 (paper). **Description:** Part of the Successful Business Library series.

PUBLISHERS

49156 ■ DC Press
2445 River Tree Cir.
Sanford, FL 32771-8334
Ph:(407)688-1156
Free: (866)602-1476
Fax:(407)688-1135
Co. E-mail: info@focusonethics.com
URL: http://www.focusonethics.com
Contact: Dennis McClellan, President
Founded: 2001.

49157 ■ Donald Wade Johnson
7911 Old Kings Rd. S
Jacksonville, FL 32217-4107
Ph:(904)737-4901
Fax:(904)737-4901
Co. E-mail: dowajo41@cs.com
Contact: Donald Wade Johnson, Publisher
Description: Publishes a manual on piano care.
Founded: 1999.

49158 ■ Famaco Publishers L.L.C.
6001-21 Argyle Forest Blvd., Ste. 323
PO Box 440665
Jacksonville, FL 32244-0665
Ph:(904)434-5901
Fax:(904)777-5901
Co. E-mail: famapub@aol.com
Contact: Steve Forester, Mgr
Description: Publishes scholarly non-fiction works on religion, politics and social commentary. Does not accept unsolicited manuscripts. Reaches market through commission representatives, direct mail, telephone sales, wholesalers and distributors and broadcast Internet. **Founded:** 1996.

49159 ■ Financial Research Associates Inc.
203 A Ave., NW, Ste. 202
Winter Haven, FL 33881-4540
Ph:(863)299-3969
Fax:(863)299-2131
Co. E-mail: sales@frafssb.com
Contact: Karen E. Klein, Mgr
Description: Publishes financial ratio analysis for small business, which is useful for bank loan officers, CPA's, business consultants, leasing companies, and individual business owners. Reaches market through direct mail and wholesalers. **Founded:** 1976.

SMALL BUSINESS DEVELOPMENT CENTERS

49160 ■ Clayton State University Small Business Development Center
Center for Continuing Education
2000 Clayton State Blvd.
Morrow, GA 30260
Fax:(678)466-5109
URL: http://www.sbdc.uga.edu/newsite

49161 ■ Georgia Small Business Development Center
University of Georgia
Chicopee Complex
1180 E Broad St.
Athens, GA 30606-3050
Fax:(706)542-6803
URL: http://www.sbdc.uga.edu/newsite/index.
  aspx?page_name=index
Contact: Allan Adams, State Dir.

49162 ■ Georgia Southern University Small Business Development Center
1100 Brampton Ave., Ste. C
Statesboro, GA 30458
Fax:(912)478-0648
URL: http://www.sbdc.uga.edu/newsite

49163 ■ Georgia State University Small Business Development Center
10 Park Pl. S, Ste. 450
Atlanta, GA 30303
Fax:(404)413-7832
URL: http://www.sbdc.uga.edu/newsite

49164 ■ Kennesaw State University Small Business Development Center
KSU Center, Ste. 500
3333 Busbee Dr.
Kennesaw, GA 30144
Fax:(770)423-6564
URL: http://www.sbdc.uga.edu/newsite

49165 ■ University of Georgia Small Business Development Center - Albany
125 Pine Ave., Ste. 222
Albany, GA 31701
Fax:(229)430-3933
URL: http://www.sbdc.uga.edu/newsite

49166 ■ University of Georgia Small Business Development Center - Athens
Chicopee Complex
1180 E Broad St.
Athens, GA 30602
Fax:(706)542-6803
URL: http://www.sbdc.uga.edu/newsite

49167 ■ University of Georgia Small Business Development Center - Augusta
1450 Greene St., Ste. 3500
Augusta, GA 30901
Fax:(706)721-4554
URL: http://www.sbdc.uga.edu/newsite

49168 ■ University of Georgia Small Business Development Center - Brunswick
501 Gloucester St., Ste. 200
Brunswick, GA 31520
Fax:(912)262-3095
URL: http://www.sbdc.uga.edu/newsite

49169 ■ University of Georgia Small Business Development Center - Columbus
Columbus State University
Cunningham Conference Ctr., Ste. 119
3100 Gentian Blvd.
Columbus, GA 31907
Fax:(706)569-2657
URL: http://www.sbdc.uga.edu/newsite

49170 ■ University of Georgia Small Business Development Center - Dalton
Continuing Education Bldg., Rm. 309
550 N College Dr.
Dalton, GA 30720
Fax:(706)272-2701
URL: http://www.sbdc.uga.edu/newsite

49171 ■ University of Georgia Small Business Development Center - Dekalb
2296 Henderson Mill Rd., Ste. 404B
Atlanta, GA 30345
Fax:(770)414-3109
URL: http://www.sbdc.uga.edu/newsite

49172 ■ University of Georgia Small Business Development Center - Gainesville
The Featherbone Center
999 Chestnut St.
Gainesville, GA 30501
Fax:(770)531-5684
URL: http://www.sbdc.uga.edu/newsite

49173 ■ University of Georgia Small Business Development Center - Gwinnett
2530 Sever Rd., Ste. 202
Lawrenceville, GA 30043
Fax:(678)985-6819
URL: http://www.sbdc.uga.edu/newsite

49174 ■ University of Georgia Small Business Development Center - Macon
Colonial Annex, Ste. 201
111 3rd St.
Macon, GA 31201
Fax:(478)751-6607
URL: http://www.sbdc.uga.edu/newsite

49175 ■ University of Georgia Small Business Development Center - Savannah
111 E Liberty St., Ste. 200
Savannah, GA 31401
Fax:(912)651-3209
URL: http://www.sbdc.uga.edu/newsite

49176 ■ University of West Georgia Small Business Development Center
153 Richards College of Business
Carrollton, GA 30118
Fax:(678)839-5083
URL: http://www.sbdc.uga.edu/newsite

49177 ■ Valdosta State University Small Business Development Center
Harley Langdale, Jr. College of Business Administration
Thaxton Hall, Rm. 100
Valdosta, GA 31698
Fax:(229)245-3741
URL: http://www.sbdc.uga.edu/newsite

SMALL BUSINESS ASSISTANCE PROGRAMS

49178 ■ Georgia Department of Community Affairs–Business and Financial Assistance Division
60 Executive Park South, NE
Atlanta, GA 30329
Ph:(404)679-4940
Free: 800-359-4663
Fax:(404)679-0572
Co. E-mail: jthompso@dca.state.ga.us
URL: http://www.dca.state.ga.us
Contact: James L. Thompson, Mgr.
Description: Coordinates technical and financial assistance programs for rural development.

49179 ■ Georgia Department of Economic Development–Entrepreneur and Small Business Office
75 5th St. NW, Ste. 1200
Atlanta, GA 30308
Ph:(404)962-4000
Fax:(404)962-4829
Co. E-mail: smallbusiness@georgia.org
URL: http://www.georgia.org
Contact: Mary Ellen McClanahan, Dir.
Description: Promotes the interests of small businesses at trade fairs and through a network of resources.

SCORE OFFICES

49180 ■ Dalton-Whitfield SCORE
Path:

49181 ■ SCORE Alpharetta
Path: www.scoreatlanta.org/officelocations.htmalpharetta

49182 ■ SCORE Atlanta
Harris Tower
233 Peachtree St., Ste. 1900
Atlanta, GA 30303
Ph:(404)331-0121

Fax:(404)331-0108
Co. E-mail: scoreatlanta@joimail.com
URL: http://www.scoreatlanta.org
Contact: Al Torpie, Dir.
Description: Works to provide free counseling to small business community.

49183 ■ SCORE Augusta
Path: www.scoreaugusta.org

49184 ■ SCORE Blue Ridge
Path: www.scoreatlanta.org/officelocations.htmfannin

49185 ■ SCORE Buford
Path: www.scoreatlanta.org/officelocations.htmbuford

49186 ■ SCORE Columbus
Path: www.scorecolumbusga.org

49187 ■ SCORE Conyers
Path: www.scoreatlanta.org/officelocations.htmconyers

49188 ■ SCORE Cumming
Path: www.scoreatlanta.org/officelocations.htmcumming

49189 ■ SCORE Fayetteville
Path: www.scoreatlanta.org/officelocations.htmfayette

49190 ■ SCORE Griffin
Path: www.scoreatlanta.org/officelocations.htmgriffin

49191 ■ SCORE Macon
Path: www.scoreatlanta.org/officelocations.htmmacon

49192 ■ SCORE Marietta
Path: www.scoreatlanta.org/officelocations.htmmarietta

49193 ■ SCORE McDonough
Path: www.scoreatlanta.org/officelocations.htmmcdonough

49194 ■ SCORE Newnan
Path: www.scoreatlanta.org/officelocations.htmnewnan

49195 ■ SCORE Savannah
111 E Liberty St.
Savannah, GA 31401
Ph:(912)652-4335
Fax:(912)652-4184
Co. E-mail: info@scoresav.org
URL: http://www.scoresav.org
Contact: Jules Homans, Chm.
Description: Provides professional guidance and information to maximize the success of existing and emerging small businesses. Develops business plans and evaluates financial projections. Identifies problems and potential solutions.

BETTER BUSINESS BUREAUS

49196 ■ Better Business Bureau of Central Georgia
277 Martin Luther King Jr. Blvd., Ste. 102
Macon, GA 31201
Ph:(478)742-7999
Fax:(478)742-8191
Co. E-mail: info@centralgeorgia.bbb.org
URL: http://centralgeorgia.bbb.org
Contact: Kelvin Collins, CEO

49197 ■ Better Business Bureau of Metro Atlanta, Athens and Northeast Georgia
503 Oak Pl., Ste. 590
Atlanta, GA 30349
Ph:(404)766-0875
Fax:(404)768-1085
Co. E-mail: info@atlanta.bbb.org
URL: http://atlanta.bbb.org
Contact: Dottie Callina

49198 ■ Better Business Bureau Southeast Atlantic
6606 Abercorn St., Ste. 108C
Savannah, GA 31405
Ph:(912)354-7521

Fax:(912)354-5068
Co. E-mail: bbbsea@bellsouth.net
URL: http://savannah.bbb.org

49199 ■ Better Business Bureau of West Georgia - East Alabama
PO Box 2587
Columbus, GA 31902
Ph:(706)324-0712
Fax:(706)324-2181
Co. E-mail: info@columbus-ga.bbb.org
URL: http://columbus-ga.bbb.org
Contact: Leonard Crain, Pres.

CHAMBERS OF COMMERCE

49200 ■ Adel-Cook County Chamber of Commerce
100 S Hutchinson Ave.
Adel, GA 31620
Ph:(229)896-2281
Fax:(229)869-8201
Co. E-mail: cookcochamber@alltel.net
URL: http://adelcookchamber.org
Contact: Marietta Brown, Chair

49201 ■ Airport Area Chamber of Commerce
600 S Central Ave., Ste. 100
Atlanta, GA 30354
Ph:(404)209-0910
Fax:(404)389-0271
URL: http://airportchamber.myfive10.com
Contact: Kevin Moss, Pres.

49202 ■ Albany Area Chamber of Commerce, Georgia
225 W Broad Ave.
Albany, GA 31701
Ph:(229)434-8700
Free: 800-475-8700
Fax:(229)434-8716
Co. E-mail: info@albanyga.com
URL: http://www.albanyga.com
Contact: Catherine Glover, Pres./CEO

49203 ■ Alma/Bacon County Chamber of Commerce
1120 W 12th St.
PO Box 450
Alma, GA 31510
Ph:(912)632-5859
Fax:(912)632-7710
Co. E-mail: abcchamber@accessatc.net
URL: http://www.almachamberdevelopment.com
Contact: Mr. John Tanner, Exec. Dir.

49204 ■ American Israel Chamber of Commerce - Southeast Region
1150 Lake Hearn Dr., Ste. 130
Atlanta, GA 30342
Ph:(404)843-9426
Fax:(404)843-1416
Co. E-mail: aiccse@aiccse.org
URL: http://www.aiccse.org
Contact: Tom Glaser, Pres.

49205 ■ Americus-Sumter County Chamber of Commerce
409 Elm Ave. Ste. A
Americus, GA 31709
Ph:(229)924-2646
Fax:(229)924-8784
Co. E-mail: info@americus-sumterchamber.com
URL: http://www.americus-sumterchamber.com
Contact: Rachael Gresham, Membership Dir.

49206 ■ Ashburn - Turner County Chamber of Commerce
238 E Coll. Ave.
Ashburn, GA 31714
Ph:(229)567-9696
Free: 800-471-9696
Fax:(229)567-2541
Co. E-mail: szorn@alltel.net
URL: http://www.turnerchamber.com
Contact: Shelly Zorn, Pres./Economic Developer

49207 ■ Athens Area Chamber of Commerce
246 W Hancock Ave.
Athens, GA 30601
Ph:(706)549-6800
Fax:(706)549-5636
Co. E-mail: info@athenschamber.net
URL: http://www.athenschamber.net
Contact: Doc Eldridge, Pres./CEO

49208 ■ Augusta Metro Chamber of Commerce
PO Box 1837
Augusta, GA 30903
Ph:(706)821-1300
Free: 888-639-8188
Fax:(706)821-1330
Co. E-mail: info@augustausa.com
URL: http://augustachamber.net
Contact: Mrs. Susan E. Parr, Pres./CEO

49209 ■ Bainbridge-Decatur County Chamber of Commerce
PO Box 755
Bainbridge, GA 39818
Ph:(229)246-4774
Free: 800-243-4774
Fax:(229)243-7633
Co. E-mail: info@bainbridgechamber.org
URL: http://www.bainbridgegachamber.com
Contact: Evelyn Clay, Pres.

49210 ■ Banks County Chamber of Commerce
PO Box 57
105 US Hwy. N
Homer, GA 30547-0057
Ph:(706)677-2108
Free: 800-638-5004
Fax:(706)677-2109
Co. E-mail: bankscountychamber@alltel.net
URL: http://www.bankscountyga.org
Contact: Tara Fulcher, Exec. Dir.

49211 ■ Barnesville-Lamar County Chamber of Commerce
PO Box 506
100 Commerce Pl.
Barnesville, GA 30204
Ph:(770)358-5884
Fax:(770)358-5886
Co. E-mail: lchamber5884@charterinternet.com
URL: http://www.barnesville.org
Contact: Amanda Rose, Pres.

49212 ■ Barrow County Chamber of Commerce
6 Porter St.
PO Box 456
Winder, GA 30680-1731
Ph:(770)867-9444
Fax:(770)867-6366
Co. E-mail: mmilner@barrowchamber.com
URL: http://www.barrowchamber.com
Contact: Thomas R. Jennings, Pres.

49213 ■ Baxley-Appling County Chamber of Commerce
PO Box 413
305 W Parker St.
Baxley, GA 31515
Ph:(912)367-7731
Fax:(912)367-2073
Co. E-mail: glennkk@bellsouth.net
URL: http://www.baxley.org/site
Contact: Karen Glenn, Exec. Dir.

49214 ■ Blairsville - Union County Chamber of Commerce
PO Box 789
Blairsville, GA 30514
Ph:(706)745-5789
Free: 877-745-5789
Fax:(706)745-1382
Co. E-mail: admin@blairsvillechamber.com
URL: http://www.blairsvillechamber.com
Contact: Cindy Williams, Pres.

49215 ■ Blakely-Early County Chamber of Commerce
PO Box 189
214 Court Sq.
Blakely, GA 39823
Ph:(229)723-3741
Fax:(229)723-6876
Co. E-mail: info@blakelyearlychamber.com
URL: http://www.blakelyearlycountychamber.com
Contact: Hilary Halford, Pres.

49216 ■ Brunswick-Golden Isles Chamber of Commerce
4 Glynn Ave.
Brunswick, GA 31520
Ph:(912)265-0620
Fax:(912)265-0629
Co. E-mail: chamber@bgicoc.com
URL: http://www.brunswick-georgia.com
Contact: Pat Cooper, Chm.

49217 ■ Camden County Chamber of Commerce
2603 Osborne Rd., Ste. R
St. Marys, GA 31558
Ph:(912)729-5840
Fax:(912)576-7924
Co. E-mail: information@camdenchamber.com
URL: http://www.camdenchamber.com
Contact: Jim Lomis, Chm.

49218 ■ Camilla Chamber of Commerce
PO Box 226
212 E Broad St.
Camilla, GA 31730
Ph:(229)336-5255
Fax:(229)336-5256
Co. E-mail: eric@camillageorgia.com
URL: http://www.camillageorgia.com
Contact: C. Eric Brooks, Exec. Dir.

49219 ■ Carroll County Chamber of Commerce
200 Northside Dr.
Carrollton, GA 30117
Ph:(770)832-2446
Fax:(770)832-1300
Co. E-mail: info@carroll-ga.org
URL: http://www.carroll-ga.org
Contact: Mr. Daniel Jackson, Pres.

49220 ■ Cartersville-Bartow County Chamber of Commerce
PO Box 307
122 W Main St.
Cartersville, GA 30120
Ph:(770)382-1466
Fax:(770)382-2704
Co. E-mail: reception@cartersvillechamber.com
URL: http://www.cartersvillechamber.com
Contact: Kay Read, Pres./CEO

49221 ■ Catoosa County Chamber of Commerce
264 Catoosa Cir.
Ringgold, GA 30736
Ph:(706)965-5201
Free: 877-965-5201
Fax:(706)965-8224
Co. E-mail: meaker@catoosachamberofcommerce.
com
URL: http://www.catoosachamberofcommerce.com
Contact: Martha Eaker, Pres.

49222 ■ Chamber of Commerce for the City of Loganville
PO Box 2390
Loganville, GA 30052
Ph:(770)466-1601
Fax:(770)466-1668
Co. E-mail: info@loganvillechamber.com
URL: http://loganvillechamber.com
Contact: Betty McCullers, Pres.

49223 ■ Chatsworth-Murray County Chamber of Commerce
126 N 3rd Ave.
Chatsworth, GA 30705
Ph:(706)695-6060
Free: 800-969-9490
Fax:(706)517-0198
Co. E-mail: murraychamber@windstream.net
URL: http://www.murraycountychamber.org
Contact: Dinah Rowe, Pres.

49224 ■ Chattooga County Chamber of Commerce
PO Box 217
Summerville, GA 30747
Ph:(706)857-4033
Fax:(706)857-6963
Co. E-mail: chattooga_chamber@windstream.net
URL: http://www.chattooga-chamber.org
Contact: Mr. David Tidmore, Exec. Dir./Pres.

49225 ■ Cherokee County Chamber of Commerce
PO Box 4998
3605 Marietta Hwy.
Canton, GA 30114
Ph:(770)345-0400
Fax:(770)345-0030
Co. E-mail: pam@cherokeechamber.com
URL: http://www.cherokeechamber.com
Contact: Nathan Brandon, Chm.

49226 ■ Claxton-Evans County Chamber of Commerce - Welcome Center
4 N Duval St.
Claxton, GA 30417
Ph:(912)739-1391
Fax:(912)739-3827
Co. E-mail: info@claxtonevanschamber.com
URL: http://www.claxtonevanschamber.com
Contact: Tammi Rogers Hall, Exec. Dir.

49227 ■ Clayton County Chamber of Commerce
2270 Mt. Zion Rd.
Jonesboro, GA 30236
Ph:(678)610-4021
Fax:(678)610-4025
Co. E-mail: info@claytonchamber.org
URL: http://www.claytonchamber.org
Contact: Yulonda Darden Beauford, Pres./CEO

49228 ■ Cobb Chamber of Commerce
PO Box 671868
Marietta, GA 30006
Ph:(770)980-2000
Fax:(770)980-9510
Co. E-mail: info@cobbchamber.org
URL: http://www.cobbchamber.org
Contact: Bill Cooper, Pres./CEO

49229 ■ Colquitt - Miller County Chamber of Commerce
302 E College St.
Colquitt, GA 39837
Ph:(229)758-2400
Fax:(229)758-8140
Co. E-mail: cmccoc@bellsouth.net
URL: http://www.colquitt-georgia.com/site

49230 ■ Conyers-Rockdale Chamber of Commerce
1186 Scott St.
Conyers, GA 30012
Ph:(770)483-7049
Fax:(770)922-8415
Co. E-mail: info@conyers-rockdale.com
URL: http://www.conyers-rockdale.com
Contact: Fred Boscarino, Pres.

49231 ■ Cordele-Crisp Chamber of Commerce
PO Box 158
302 E 16th Ave.
Cordele, GA 31015
Ph:(229)273-3526

Fax:(229)273-5132
Co. E-mail: info@cordele-crisp-chamber.com
URL: http://www.cordele-crisp-chamber.com
Contact: Monica G. Simmons, Pres.

49232 ■ Cumming-Forsyth County Chamber of Commerce
212 Kelly Mill Rd.
Cumming, GA 30040
Ph:(770)887-6461
Fax:(770)781-8800
Co. E-mail: jmccoy@cummingforsythchamber.org
URL: http://wwws.cummingforsythchamber.org
Contact: James McCoy, Pres./CEO

49233 ■ Dade County Chamber of Commerce
111 Railway Ln.
Trenton, GA 30752
Ph:(706)657-4488
Fax:(706)657-7513
Co. E-mail: dcoc@tvn.net
URL: http://www.dadechamber.com
Contact: Debbie Tinker, Exec. Dir.

49234 ■ Dahlonega Lumpkin County Chamber of Commerce
13 S Park St.
Dahlonega, GA 30533-2082
Ph:(706)864-3711
Fax:(706)864-7917
Co. E-mail: amy@dahlonega.org
URL: http://thechamber.dahlonega.org
Contact: Amy Booker, Interim Pres.

49235 ■ Dalton-Whitfield Chamber of Commerce
890 College Dr.
Dalton, GA 30720
Ph:(706)278-7373
Fax:(706)226-8739
Co. E-mail: info@daltonchamber.org
URL: http://www.daltonchamber.org
Contact: Brian Anderson, Pres./CEO

49236 ■ Darien-McIntosh Chamber of Commerce
1111 Magnolia Bluff Way SW, Ste. 255
Darien, GA 31305
Ph:(912)437-6684
Fax:(912)437-5251
Co. E-mail: info@mcintoshchamber.com
URL: http://www.mcintoshcounty.com
Contact: Fred Stregles, Dir.

49237 ■ Dawson County Chamber of Commerce
PO Box 299
Dawsonville, GA 30534
Ph:(706)265-6278
Free: 877-302-9271
Fax:(706)265-6279
Co. E-mail: info@dawson.org
URL: http://www.dawson.org
Contact: Linda Williams, Pres.

49238 ■ Donalsonville-Seminole County Chamber of Commerce
PO Box 713
Donalsonville, GA 39845
Ph:(229)524-2588
Fax:(229)524-8406
Co. E-mail: staff@donalsonvillega.com
URL: http://www.donalsonvillega.com
Contact: Raymond Wilson, Chm.

49239 ■ Dooly County Chamber of Commerce
117 E Union St.
PO Box 308
Vienna, GA 31092
Ph:(229)268-8275
Fax:(229)268-8200
Co. E-mail: dccofc@sowega.net
URL: http://www.doolychamber.com
Contact: Judy Ledford, CEO/Pres.

49240 ■ Douglas - Coffee County Chamber of Commerce
PO Box 2470
Douglas, GA 31534-2470
Ph:(912)384-1873
Fax:(912)383-6304
Co. E-mail: chamber@douglasga.org
URL: http://www.douglasga.org
Contact: JoAnne Lewis, Pres.

49241 ■ Douglas County Chamber of Commerce
6658 Church St.
Douglasville, GA 30134
Ph:(770)942-5022
Fax:(770)942-5876
Co. E-mail: info@douglascountygeorgia.com
URL: http://www.douglascountygeorgia.com
Contact: Kali Boatright, Pres./CEO

49242 ■ Dublin - Laurens County Chamber of Commerce
PO Box 818
Dublin, GA 31040-0818
Ph:(478)272-5546
Fax:(478)275-0811
Co. E-mail: chamber@dublin-georgia.com
URL: http://www.dublin-georgia.com
Contact: Willie Paulk, Pres.

49243 ■ Eastman - Dodge County Chamber of Commerce
PO Box 550
Eastman, GA 31023
Ph:(478)374-4723
Fax:(478)374-4626
URL: http://www.eastman-georgia.com

49244 ■ Eatonton-Putnam County Chamber of Commerce
PO Box 4088
Eatonton, GA 31024
Ph:(706)485-7701
Fax:(706)485-3277
Co. E-mail: epchamber@eatonton.com
URL: http://www.eatonton.com
Contact: Roddie Anne Blackwell, Pres.

49245 ■ Effingham County Chamber of Commerce
520 W 3rd St.
Springfield, GA 31329
Ph:(912)754-3301
Fax:(912)754-1236
Co. E-mail: effingham@windstream.net
URL: http://www.effinghamcounty.com
Contact: John Henry, Exec. Dir.

49246 ■ Fannin County Chamber of Commerce
3990 Appalachian Hwy.
Blue Ridge, GA 30513
Ph:(706)632-5680
Free: 800-899-MTNS
Fax:(706)632-2241
Co. E-mail: chamber@blueridgemountains.com
URL: http://blueridgemountains.com/chamber_info.html
Contact: Jan Hackett, Pres.

49247 ■ Fayette County Chamber of Commerce
200 Courthouse Sq.
Fayetteville, GA 30214
Ph:(770)461-9983
Fax:(770)461-9622
Co. E-mail: info@fayettechamber.org
URL: http://www.fayettechamber.org
Contact: Virginia Gibbs, Pres.

49248 ■ Forsyth-Monroe County Chamber of Commerce
68 N Lee St.
Forsyth, GA 31029
Ph:(478)994-9239
Free: 888-642-4628
Fax:(478)994-9240
Co. E-mail: tiffany@forsyth-monroechamber.com
URL: http://www.forsyth-monroechamber.com
Contact: Tiffany G. Andrews, Pres./CEO

49249 ■ Georgia Association of Chamber of Commerce Executives
PO Box 888401
Atlanta, GA 30356-0401
Ph:(404)531-6988
Fax:(404)459-0403
Co. E-mail: tfulmer@gacce.org
URL: http://www.gacce.org
Contact: Tiffany Fulmer, Admin.

49250 ■ Georgia Chamber of Commerce
235 Peachtree St. NE, Ste. 2000
Atlanta, GA 30303-1564
Ph:(404)233-2264
Free: 800-241-2286
Fax:(404)233-2290
Co. E-mail: lga@gachamber.com
URL: http://www.gachamber.com
Contact: Michael D. Garrett III, Pres./CEO

49251 ■ Georgia Hispanic Chamber of Commerce
2801 Buford Hwy., Ste. 500
Atlanta, GA 30329
Ph:(404)929-9998
Fax:(404)929-9908
Co. E-mail: rinfante@ghcc.org
URL: http://www.ghcc.org
Contact: Tisha Tallman, Pres./CEO

49252 ■ Gilmer County Chamber of Commerce
PO Box 505
368 Craig St., Ste. 4
Ellijay, GA 30540
Ph:(706)635-7400
Fax:(706)635-7410
Co. E-mail: chamber@ellijay.com
URL: http://www.gilmerchamber.com
Contact: Alan May, Pres.

49253 ■ Gordon County Chamber of Commerce
300 S Wall St.
Calhoun, GA 30701
Ph:(706)625-3200
Fax:(706)625-5062
Co. E-mail: contact@gordonchamber.org
URL: http://www.gordonchamber.org
Contact: Jimmy Phillips, Pres.

49254 ■ Greater Columbus Chamber of Commerce
1200 6th Ave.
Columbus, GA 31902-1200
Ph:(706)327-1566
Free: 800-360-8552
Fax:(706)327-7512
Co. E-mail: mgaymon@columbusgachamber.com
URL: http://www.columbusgachamber.com
Contact: Mike Gaymon, Pres./CEO

49255 ■ Greater Hall Chamber of Commerce
230 EE Butler Pkwy.
Gainesville, GA 30501
Ph:(770)532-6206
Fax:(770)535-8419
Co. E-mail: info@ghcc.com
URL: http://www.ghcc.com
Contact: Kit Dunlap, Pres./CEO

49256 ■ Greater Helen Area Chamber of Commerce
PO Box 192
Helen, GA 30545
Ph:(706)878-1619
Co. E-mail: office@helenchamber.com
URL: http://www.helenchamber.com

49257 ■ Greater Macon Chamber of Commerce
PO Box 169
Macon, GA 31202-0169
Ph:(478)621-2000
Fax:(478)621-2021
Co. E-mail: info@maconchamber.com
URL: http://www.maconchamber.com
Contact: Chip Cherry, Pres./CEO

49258 ■ Greater North Fulton Chamber of Commerce
11605 Haynes Bridge Rd., Ste. 100
Alpharetta, GA 30009
Ph:(770)993-8806
Free: (866)840-5770
Fax:(770)594-1059
Co. E-mail: info@gnfcc.com
URL: http://www.gnfcc.com
Contact: Brandon L. Beach, Pres./CEO

49259 ■ Greater Tattnall Chamber of Commerce
PO Box 759
Reidsville, GA 30453
Ph:(912)557-6323
Fax:(912)557-3046
Co. E-mail: avery582@hotmail.com
URL: http://www.tattnall.com
Contact: David Avery, Exec. Dir.

49260 ■ Greene County Chamber of Commerce
PO Box 741
111 N Main St.
Greensboro, GA 30642
Ph:(706)453-7592
Free: 800-886-5253
Fax:(706)453-1430
Co. E-mail: chamber@greeneccoc.org
URL: http://www.greeneccoc.org
Contact: Natasha Strother, Dir.

49261 ■ Griffin-Spalding Chamber of Commerce
143 N Hill St.
Griffin, GA 30223
Ph:(770)228-8200
Fax:(770)228-8031
Co. E-mail: griffinchamber@cityofgriffin.com
URL: http://www.griffinchamber.com
Contact: Stephanie Windham, Chm.

49262 ■ Gwinnett Chamber of Commerce
6500 Sugarloaf Pkwy.
Duluth, GA 30097
Ph:(770)232-3000
Fax:(770)232-8807
Co. E-mail: info@gwinnettchamber.org
URL: http://www.gwinnettchamber.org
Contact: James J. Maran, Pres./CEO

49263 ■ Habersham County Chamber of Commerce
668 Historic Hwy. 441
Cornelia, GA 30531
Ph:(706)778-4654
Free: 800-835-2559
Fax:(706)776-1416
Co. E-mail: taylorjudy@windstream.net
URL: http://www.habershamchamber.com
Contact: Judy Taylor PhD, Exec. Dir.

49264 ■ Haralson County Chamber of Commerce
70 Murphy Campus Blvd.
Waco, GA 30182
Ph:(770)537-5594
Fax:(770)537-5873
Co. E-mail: hccoc@haralson.org
URL: http://www.haralson.org
Contact: Jennie English, Pres.

49265 ■ Harris County Chamber of Commerce
PO Box 426
Hamilton, GA 31811
Ph:(706)628-4381
Free: 800-381-4381
Fax:(706)628-4388
Co. E-mail: info@harriscountychamber.org
URL: http://www.harriscountychamber.org
Contact: Lynda Dawson, Pres.

49266 ■ Hart County Chamber of Commerce
PO Box 793
31 E Howell St.
Hartwell, GA 30643
Ph:(706)376-8590
Fax:(706)376-5177
Co. E-mail: hartchamber@hartcom.net
URL: http://www.hart-chamber.org
Contact: Ginger Johnson, Exec. Dir.

49267 ■ Hawkinsville-Pulaski County Chamber of Commerce
PO Box 300
Hawkinsville, GA 31036
Ph:(478)783-1717
Fax:(478)783-1700
Co. E-mail: kimberly@hawkinsvillechamber.org
URL: http://www.hawkinsvillechamber.org
Contact: Kimberly Brown, Exec. Dir.

49268 ■ Henry County Chamber of Commerce
1709 Hwy. 20 W
McDonough, GA 30253
Ph:(770)957-5786
Fax:(770)957-8030
Co. E-mail: memberservices@henrycounty.com
URL: http://www.henrycounty.com
Contact: Kay Pippin, Exec. Dir.

49269 ■ Homerville - Clinch County Chamber of Commerce
23 W Plant Ave.
Homerville, GA 31634
Ph:(912)487-2360
Fax:(912)487-2384
Co. E-mail: clinchcountychamberofcommerce@windstream.net
URL: http://www.clinchcountychamber.org
Contact: Brent James, Pres.

49270 ■ Jackson County Area Chamber of Commerce
PO Box 629
Jefferson, GA 30549
Ph:(706)387-0300
Fax:(706)387-0304
Co. E-mail: info@jacksoncountyga.com
URL: http://www.jacksoncountyga.com
Contact: Shane Short, Pres./CEO

49271 ■ Jefferson County Chamber of Commerce
PO Box 630
302 E Broad St.
Louisville, GA 30434
Ph:(478)625-8134
Free: (866)527-2642
Fax:(478)625-9060
Co. E-mail: info@jeffersoncounty.org
URL: http://www.jeffersoncounty.org
Contact: Lil Easterlin, Exec. Dir.

49272 ■ LaGrange - Troup County Chamber of Commerce
PO Box 636
LaGrange, GA 30241
Ph:(706)884-8671
Fax:(706)882-8012
Co. E-mail: assistant@lagrangechamber.com
URL: http://www.lagrangechamber.com
Contact: Page Estes, Pres.

49273 ■ Lake Park Area Chamber of Commerce and Visitors Center
5208 Jewel Futch Rd.
Lake Park, GA 31636
Ph:(229)559-5302
Co. E-mail: info@lakeparkga.com
URL: http://www.lakeparkga.com
Contact: Shae Humphries, Exec. Dir.

49274 ■ Lavonia Chamber of Commerce
PO Box 564
Lavonia, GA 30553
Ph:(706)356-8202
Fax:(706)356-4694
Co. E-mail: lavoniacofc@alltel.net
URL: http://www.lavonia-ga.com
Contact: Vivian Young, Exec. Sec.

49275 ■ Liberty County Chamber of Commerce
425 W Oglethorpe Hwy.
Hinesville, GA 31313
Ph:(912)368-4445
Fax:(912)368-4677
Co. E-mail: debbie@libertycounty.org
URL: http://www.libertycounty.org
Contact: R. Kenneth Smiley, Exec. Dir.

49276 ■ Lincolnton - Lincoln County Chamber of Commerce and Development Authority
112 N Washington St.
PO Box 810
Lincolnton, GA 30817
Ph:(706)359-7970
Fax:(706)359-5477
Co. E-mail: lincolncham@nu-z.net
URL: http://www.lincolncountyga.org
Contact: Susan Banks, Exec. Dir.

49277 ■ Madison County Chamber of Commerce and Industrial Authority
PO Box 381
Danielsville, GA 30633-5961
Ph:(706)795-3473
Fax:(706)795-3262
Co. E-mail: mccc@madisoncountyga.org
URL: http://www.madisoncountyga.org
Contact: Marvin White, Exec. Dir.

49278 ■ Madison-Morgan County Chamber of Commerce
115 E Jefferson St.
Madison, GA 30650-0826
Ph:(706)342-4454
Free: 800-709-7406
Fax:(706)342-4455
Co. E-mail: marguerite@madisonga.org
URL: http://www.madisonga.org
Contact: Marguerite Copelan, Pres.

49279 ■ Meriwether County Chamber of Commerce
PO Box 9
Warm Springs, GA 31830
Ph:(706)655-2558
Fax:(706)655-2812
Co. E-mail: meriwetherchamber@windstream.net
URL: http://www.meriwethercountychamberofcommerce.com
Contact: Carolyn McKinley, Exec. Dir.

49280 ■ Metro Atlanta Chamber of Commerce
235 Andrew Young International Blvd. NW
Atlanta, GA 30303-2718
Ph:(404)880-9000
Co. E-mail: rblumenthal@macoc.com
URL: http://www.metroatlantachamber.com/default.aspx?AspxAutoDetectCookieSupport=1
Contact: Sam A. Williams, Pres.

49281 ■ Metter-Candler Chamber of Commerce
Metter I-16 Welcome Ctr.
PO Box 497
Metter, GA 30439-0497
Ph:(912)685-2159
Fax:(912)685-2108
Co. E-mail: ebim@pineland.net
URL: http://www.metter-candler.com
Contact: Mrs. Eddy Jones, Chm.

49282 ■ Milledgeville-Baldwin County Chamber of Commerce
130 S Jefferson St.
Milledgeville, GA 31061
Ph:(478)453-9311
Fax:(478)453-0051
Co. E-mail: mbcchamber@alltel.net
URL: http://www.milledgevillega.com
Contact: Tara Peters, Pres./CEO

49283 ■ Monticello-Jasper County Chamber of Commerce
PO Box 133
Monticello, GA 31064
Ph:(706)468-8994
URL: http://www.monticelloga.org/site

49284 ■ Moultrie-Colquitt County Chamber of Commerce
116 1st Ave. SE
PO Box 487
Moultrie, GA 31776-0487
Ph:(229)985-2131
Fax:(229)890-2638
Co. E-mail: contact@moultriechamber.com
URL: http://www.moultriechamber.com
Contact: Darrell Moore, Pres.

49285 ■ Nashville-Berrien Chamber of Commerce
PO Box 217
201 N Jefferson St.
Nashville, GA 31639
Ph:(229)686-5123
Fax:(229)686-1905
URL: http://www.berrienchamber.com
Contact: Crissy Staley, Exec. Dir.

49286 ■ Ocilla - Irwin Chamber of Commerce
PO Box 104
Ocilla, GA 31774
Ph:(229)468-9114
Fax:(229)468-4452
URL: http://www.ocillachamber.net
Contact: Hazel McCranie, Pres.

49287 ■ Oconee County Chamber of Commerce
PO Box 348
Watkinsville, GA 30677
Ph:(706)769-7947
Fax:(706)769-7948
Co. E-mail: cgrimes@occoc.org
URL: http://www.occoc.org
Contact: Charles Grimes, Pres.

49288 ■ Okefenokee Chamber of Commerce and Folkston and Charlton County Development Authority
PO Box 756
202 W Main St.
Folkston, GA 31537
Ph:(912)496-2536
Fax:(912)496-4601
Co. E-mail: okechamber@alltel.net
URL: http://www.folkston.com
Contact: Claudia Burkhart, Exec. Dir.

49289 ■ Paulding Chamber of Commerce
455 Jimmy Campbell Pkwy.
Dallas, GA 30132
Ph:(770)445-6016
Fax:(770)445-3050
Co. E-mail: bwillingham@pauldingchamber.org
URL: http://www.pauldingcountychamber.org
Contact: Mr. Carolyn Delamont, Pres./CEO

49290 ■ Peach County Chamber of Commerce
201 Oakland Heights Pkwy.
Fort Valley, GA 31030
Ph:(478)825-3733
Fax:(478)825-2501
Co. E-mail: pswanson@peachchamber.com
URL: http://www.peachchamber.com
Contact: Perry Swanson, Pres./CEO

49291 ■ Perry Area Chamber of Commerce
101 Gen. Courtney Hodges Blvd.
Perry, GA 31069
Ph:(478)987-1234

Fax:(478)988-1234
Co. E-mail: megansmith@perrygachamber.com
URL: http://www.perrygachamber.com
Contact: Megan Smith, Pres./CEO

49292 ■ Pine Mountain Chamber of Commerce
PO Box 483
Pine Mountain, GA 31822
Ph:(706)663-8850
Co. E-mail: support@pinemountainchamber.com
URL: http://www.pinemountainchamber.com
Contact: Lee Hale, Pres.

49293 ■ Quitman-Brooks County Chamber of Commerce
900 E Screven St.
Quitman, GA 31643
Ph:(229)263-4841
Fax:(229)263-4822
Co. E-mail: bcchamber@quitmangeorgia.org
URL: http://quitmangeorgia.org/2005/index.php
Contact: John Cox, Pres.

49294 ■ Rabun County Chamber of Commerce
PO Box 750
323 Hwy. 441
Clayton, GA 30525-0019
Ph:(706)782-4812
Fax:(706)782-4810
Co. E-mail: rabunchamber@gamountains.com
URL: http://www.gamountains.com/index.php
Contact: Rhonda Lunsford, Pres.

49295 ■ Roberta - Crawford County Chamber of Commerce
PO Box 417
Roberta, GA 31078
Ph:(478)836-3825
Fax:(478)836-4509
Co. E-mail: rcccoc@pstel.net
URL: http://www.robertacrawfordchamber.org
Contact: Angelia Butler, Exec. Dir.

49296 ■ Savannah Area Chamber of Commerce, Georgia
101 E Bay St.
Savannah, GA 31401
Ph:(912)644-6400
Fax:(912)644-6499
Co. E-mail: bhubbard@savannahchamber.com
URL: http://www.savannahchamber.com
Contact: William W. Hubbard, Pres./CEO

49297 ■ Screven County Chamber of Commerce
101 S Main St.
Sylvania, GA 30467
Ph:(912)564-7878
Free: 800-972-7887
Fax:(912)564-7245
Co. E-mail: scrcoc@planters.net
URL: http://www.screvencounty.com
Contact: Nancy Edenfield, Exec. Dir.

49298 ■ Soperton - Treutlen Chamber of Commerce
402 2nd St.
Soperton, GA 30457
Ph:(912)529-4496
Co. E-mail: johnlee@millionpines.com
URL: http://www.soperton.org
Contact: John Lee, Exec. Dir.

49299 ■ South Fulton Chamber of Commerce
6400 Shannon Pkwy.
Union City, GA 30291
Ph:(770)964-1984
Fax:(770)969-1969
Co. E-mail: info@sfcoc.org
URL: http://www.sfcoc.org
Contact: LaVonne Deavers, Chair

49300 ■ Statesboro-Bulloch Chamber of Commerce
PO Box 303
Statesboro, GA 30459
Ph:(912)764-6111

Fax:(912)489-3108
Co. E-mail: peggychapman@statesboro-chamber.org
URL: http://www.statesboro-chamber.org
Contact: Peggy Chapman, Pres.

49301 ■ Swainsboro-Emanuel County Chamber of Commerce
102 S Main St.
Swainsboro, GA 30401
Ph:(478)237-6426
Fax:(478)237-7460
Co. E-mail: swainsborochambr@bellsouth.net
URL: http://www.emanuelchamber.org
Contact: Bill Rogers Jr., Exec. Dir.

49302 ■ Swedish-American Chamber of Commerce in Atlanta
4775 Peachtree Industrial Blvd., Bldg. 300, Ste. 300
Norcross, GA 30092
Ph:(770)670-2480
Fax:(770)670-2500
Co. E-mail: sacc@sacc-atlanta.org
Contact: Mee Linden, Chair

49303 ■ Telfair County Chamber of Commerce
120 E Oak St.
McRae, GA 31055
Ph:(229)868-6365
Fax:(229)868-7970
Co. E-mail: info@telfairco.com
Contact: Deanna Jones, Chair

49304 ■ Terrell County Chamber of Commerce
PO Box 405
Dawson, GA 39842-0405
Ph:(229)995-2011
Fax:(229)995-3971
Co. E-mail: tccc@windstream.net
URL: http://www.terrellcountygeorgia.org
Contact: Ms. Gina H. Webb, Exec. Dir.

49305 ■ Thomaston - Upson Chamber of Commerce
213 E Gordon St.
PO Box 827
Thomaston, GA 30286
Ph:(706)647-9686
Fax:(706)647-1703
Co. E-mail: lorishowalter@windstream.net
URL: http://www.thomastonchamber.com
Contact: Lory Showalter Smith, Pres.

49306 ■ Thomasville-Thomas County Chamber of Commerce
PO Box 560
Thomasville, GA 31799
Ph:(229)226-9600
Fax:(229)226-9603
Co. E-mail: chamber@rose.net
URL: http://www.thomasvillechamber.com
Contact: Donald P. Sims, Pres.

49307 ■ Toombs-Montgomery Chamber of Commerce
2805 E 1st St.
Vidalia, GA 30474
Ph:(912)537-4466
Fax:(912)537-1805
Co. E-mail: information@toombschamber.com
URL: http://www.toombsmontgomerychamber.com/cwt/external/wcpages/index.aspx
Contact: Bill Mitchell, Pres.

49308 ■ Towns County Chamber of Commerce
1411 Jack Dayton Cir.
Young Harris, GA 30582
Ph:(706)896-4966
Free: 800-984-1543
Fax:(706)896-5441
Co. E-mail: info@mountaintopga.com
URL: http://www.mountaintopga.com
Contact: Ms. Jane Holland

49309 ■ Valdosta-Lowndes County Chamber of Commerce
PO Box 790
Valdosta, GA 31603
Ph:(229)247-8100
Fax:(229)245-0071
Co. E-mail: chamberinfo@valdostachamber.com
URL: http://www.valdostachamber.com
Contact: Myrna Ballard, Pres.

49310 ■ Walker County Chamber of Commerce
PO Box 430
10052 Hwy. 27 N
Rock Spring, GA 30739
Ph:(706)375-7702
Fax:(706)375-7797
Co. E-mail: info@walkercochamber.com
URL: http://www.walkercochamber.com
Contact: Glenda Jones, Dir. of Programs and Events

49311 ■ Walton County Chamber of Commerce
PO Box 89
Monroe, GA 30655
Ph:(770)267-6594
Fax:(770)267-0961
Co. E-mail: teri@waltonchamber.org
URL: http://www.waltonchamber.org
Contact: Teri H. Wommack, Pres.

49312 ■ Warner Robins Area Chamber of Commerce
1228 Watson Blvd.
Warner Robins, GA 31093
Ph:(478)922-8585
Fax:(478)328-7745
Co. E-mail: info@warner-robins.com
URL: http://www.warner-robins.com
Contact: Edward M. Rodriguez, Pres.

49313 ■ Warren County Chamber of Commerce
PO Box 27
Warrenton, GA 30828
Ph:(706)465-9604
Fax:(706)465-1789
Co. E-mail: chamber@warrencountyga.com
URL: http://www.warrencountyga.com/docs/chamber/chamber_home.htm
Contact: O.B. McCorkle, Pres.

49314 ■ Washington County Chamber of Commerce
PO Box 582
131 W Haynes St., Ste. B
Sandersville, GA 31082-0582
Ph:(478)552-3288
Fax:(478)552-1449
Co. E-mail: wacocofc@bellsouth.net
URL: http://www.washingtoncounty-ga.com
Contact: Theo McDonald, Pres.

49315 ■ Washington-Wilkes Chamber of Commerce
PO Box 661
Washington, GA 30673
Ph:(706)678-2013
Fax:(706)678-3033
Co. E-mail: tourism@washingtonwilkes.org
URL: http://www.washingtonwilkes.org
Contact: Alla Soto, Pres.

49316 ■ Wayne County Chamber of Commerce
124 NW Broad St.
Jesup, GA 31545-2708
Ph:(912)427-2028
Free: 888-224-5983
Fax:(912)427-2778
Co. E-mail: jriddle@waynechamber.com
URL: http://www.waynechamber.com
Contact: John Riddle, Pres.

49317 ■ Wheeler County Chamber of Commerce
PO Box 654
Alamo, GA 30411
Ph:(912)568-7808
Fax:(912)568-7808
Co. E-mail: wchamber1@alltel.net
URL: http://www.wheelercounty.org

49318 ■ White County Chamber of Commerce and Development Authority
122 N Main St.
Cleveland, GA 30528
Ph:(706)865-5356
Free: 800-392-8279
Fax:(706)865-0758
Co. E-mail: whitecountychamber@whitecountychamber.org
URL: http://www.whitecountychamber.org
Contact: Judy Walker, Pres.

49319 ■ Wrightsville - Johnson County Chamber of Commerce
PO Box 94
Wrightsville, GA 31096
Ph:(478)864-7200
Fax:(478)864-7200
Co. E-mail: commerce@wrightsville-johnsoncounty.com
URL: http://www.wrightsville-johnsoncounty.com
Contact: Charlene K. Milligan, Exec. Sec.

MINORITY BUSINESS ASSISTANCE PROGRAMS

49320 ■ Atlanta Urban League–Entrepreneurship Center
100 Edgewood Ave. NE, No. 600
Atlanta, GA 30303-3070
Ph:(404)523-0131
Contact: Nancy Flake-Johnson, CEO
Description: Provides business mentoring and networking services to minority business owners in Atlanta.

49321 ■ Georgia Minority Business Enterprise Center–Georgia Tech Enterprise Innovation Institute
75 5th St., Ste. 700
Atlanta, GA 30308-0640
Ph:(404)894-2096
Fax:(404)894-8194
Co. E-mail: donna.ennis@innovate.gatech.edu
URL: http://www.georgiambec.org
Description: Provides emerging and existing minority businesses with business development and technical assistance.

49322 ■ Governor's Small Business Center
State Bldg.
1102 West Tower
200 Piedmont Ave.
1306 West Tower
Atlanta, GA 30334
Ph:(404)656-6315
Free: 800-495-0053
Fax:(404)657-4681
Co. E-mail: gsbc@doas.ga.gov
URL: http://www.doas.ga.gov
Contact: Charlet Taylor
Description: Assists the development of small and minority-owned businesses.

FINANCING AND LOAN PROGRAMS

49323 ■ Accuitive Medical Ventures LLC / AMV Partners
2905 Premiere Pky., Ste. 150
Duluth, GA 30097
Ph:(678)812-1101

Fax:(678)417-7325
Co. E-mail: albert@amvpartners.com
URL: http://www.amvpartners.com
Contact: Charles E. Larsen, Managing Director
Investment Policies: Early stage and expansion. **Industry Preferences:** Medical and health. **Geographic Preferences:** Southeast. **Principal Exhibits:**

49324 ■ Alliance Technology Ventures
1990 Main St., Ste. 750
Sarasota, FL 34236
Ph:(678)336-2000
Fax:(678)336-2001
URL: http://www.alliancetechventures.com
Contact: Michael A. Henos, Managing General Partner
Preferred Investment Size: $500,000 to $5,000,000. **Investment Types:** Seed and first stage. **Industry Preferences:** Internet specific, semiconductors and other electronics, biotechnology, communications and media, computer software and services, computer hardware, medical and health. **Geographic Preferences:** U.S. **Principal Exhibits:**

49325 ■ C & B Capital LP
4200 Northside Pky., NW, Bldg. 1, Ste., 100
Atlanta, GA 30327
Ph:(404)841-3131
Fax:(404)841-3135
Co. E-mail: info@croft-bender.com
URL: http://www.croft-bender.com
Contact: Edward S. Croft III, Managing Director
Investment Types: Early stage, acquisition, expansion, buyouts, and recapitalizations. **Industry Preferences:** Internet specific, computer software and services, medical and health, industrial, communications and media. **Geographic Preferences:** Southeast. **Principal Exhibits:**

49326 ■ CGW Southeast Partners / Cravey, Green & Wahlen Inc.
1 Buckhead Plz.
3060 Peachtree Rd., Ste. 895
Atlanta, GA 30305
Ph:(404)841-3255
Fax:(678)705-9940
URL: http://www.cgwlp.com
Contact: Edwin Wahlen Jr., Managing Partner
Preferred Investment Size: $25,000,000 to $200,000,000. **Investment Types:** Management buyouts, acquisition and recapitalizations. **Industry Preferences:** Other products, industrial and energy, consumer related, medical and health, and communications and media. **Geographic Preferences:** U.S. **Principal Exhibits:**

49327 ■ Cordova Ventures
4080 McGinnis Ferry Rd., Ste. 1201
Alpharetta, GA 30005
Ph:(678)942-0300
Fax:(678)942-0301
URL: http://www.cordovaventures.com
Contact: Gerald F. Schmidt, Co-Founder and Managing Partner
E-mail: js@cordovaventures.com
Preferred Investment Size: $1,000,000 to $5,000,000. **Investment Types:** Seed, start-up, early, first, second and later stage, and expansion. **Industry Preferences:** Computer software and services, medical and health, Internet specific, communications and media, other products, industrial and health, biotechnology, consumer related, semiconductors and other electronics. **Geographic Preferences:** Southeast. **Principal Exhibits:**

49328 ■ EGL Ventures
11 Piedmont Ctr., Ste. 412
3495 Piedmont Rd.
Atlanta, GA 30305
Ph:(404)949-8300
Fax:(404)949-8311
Co. E-mail: info@eglventures.com
URL: http://www.eglventures.com
Contact: Salvatore Massaro, Managing Partner
E-mail: samassaro@eglholdings.com
Preferred Investment Size: $500,000 to $6,000,000. **Investment Types:** Early and later stage, balanced, and expansion. **Industry Preferences:** Communica-

tions, computer hardware and software, Internet specific, semiconductors and other electronics, medical and health, industrial and energy, and manufacturing. **Geographic Preferences:** Mid Atlantic, Midwest, Northeast, Midwest, and Southeast. **Principal Exhibits:**

49329 ■ Equity-South Advisors, LLC / Grubb & Williams Ltd.
6 Piedmont Ctr., Ste. 130
PO Box 191606
Atlanta, GA 31119-1606
Ph:(404)237-6222
Fax:(404)261-1578
URL: http://www.equity-south.com
Contact: Douglas L. Diamond, Managing Director
Preferred Investment Size: $1,000,000 to $6,000,000. **Investment Types:** Acquisition, expansion, leveraged buyout, management buyouts, recapitalizations, generalist PE, later stage, and special situation. **Industry Preferences:** Communications, computer software, semiconductors and other electronics, medical and health, consumer related, industrial and energy, business service, and manufacturing. **Geographic Preferences:** Mid Atlantic, Midwest, and Southeast. **Principal Exhibits:**

49330 ■ First Growth Capital, Inc.
Best Western Plaza, Ste. 105
PO Box 815
Forsyth, GA 31029
Ph:(478)994-9260
Fax:(478)994-1280
Contact: Vijay K. Patel, President
Preferred Investment Size: $100,000 to $300,000. **Investment Types:** Second stage and special situation.

49331 ■ Healthcare Capital Partners
6065 Roswell Rd., Ste. 800
Atlanta, GA 30328
Ph:(678)244-5874
Fax:(404)250-9431
Co. E-mail: bplans@healthcarecp.com
URL: http://www.healthcarecp.com
Contact: Thomas Brooks, Founding Partner
Preferred Investment Size: $100,000 to $1,500,000. **Investment Policies:** Seed and early stage. **Industry Preferences:** Medical and health. **Geographic Preferences:** Southeast. **Principal Exhibits:**

49332 ■ Liveoak Equity Partners
1266 Park Vista Dr.
Atlanta, GA 30319
Ph:(404)790-2666
Fax:(404)842-1502
URL: http://www.liveoakequity.com
Contact: James Gilbert, Managing Partner
Preferred Investment Size: $500,000 to $6,000,000. **Investment Types:** Seed, first and second stage, early and later stage. **Industry Preferences:** Computer software and services, Internet specific, communications and media, medical and health, biotechnology, semiconductors and other electronics. **Geographic Preferences:** Southeast. **Principal Exhibits:**

49333 ■ Noro-Moseley Partners
9 N. Pky. Sq.
4200 Northside Pky., NW
Atlanta, GA 30327-3054
Ph:(404)233-1966
Fax:(404)239-9280
Co. E-mail: info@noro-moseley.com
URL: http://www.noro-moseley.com
Contact: George Mackie, Venture Partner
Preferred Investment Size: $3,000,000 to $10,000,000. **Investment Types:** Start-up, seed, early stage, leveraged buyout, management buyouts, expansion, acquisition, generalist PE, and recapitalizations. **Industry Preferences:** Internet specific, computer software and services, medical and health, consumer related, other products, communications and media, computer hardware, semiconductors and other electronics, industrial and energy, and biotechnology. **Geographic Preferences:** Southeast. **Principal Exhibits:**

49334 ■ River Capital
2 Midtown Plz.
4200 Northside Pky., Bldg. 14, Ste. 250
Atlanta, GA 30327
Ph:(404)873-2166
Fax:(404)873-2158
Co. E-mail: info@river-capital.com
URL: http://www.river-capital.com
Contact: Jerry D. Wethington, Managing Principal
E-mail: jwethington@river-capital.com
Preferred Investment Size: $3,000,000 to $50,000,000 **Investment Types:** Mezzanine, recapitalizations, and leveraged buyout. **Industry Preferences:** Semiconductors and other electronics, medical and health, consumer related, industrial and energy, transportation, and manufacturing. **Geographic Preferences:** U.S. **Principal Exhibits:**

49335 ■ UPS Strategic Enterprise Fund
55 Glenlake Pky., NE
Bldg. 1, 4th Fl.
Atlanta, GA 30328
Ph:(404)828-8814
Fax:(404)828-8088
Co. E-mail: sef@ups.com
URL: http://www.ups.com/sef/sef_home.html
Preferred Investment Size: $250,000 to $1,500,000. **Investment Types:** Start-up, first stage, and expansion. **Industry Preferences:** Internet specific, computer software and services, other products, computer hardware, communications and media, semiconductors and other electronics. **Geographic Preferences:** U.S. and Canada. **Principal Exhibits:**

49336 ■ Wachovia Capital Associates, Inc. (WCA)
191 Peachtree St., NE, 26th Fl.
Atlanta, GA 30303
Ph:(404)332-5000
Fax:(404)332-1392
URL: http://www.wachovia.com/wca
Contact: Andy Rose, Vice President
Preferred Investment Size: $5,000,000 to $15,000,000. **Investment Types:** Expansion, leveraged buyout, later stage, and recapitalizations. **Industry Preferences:** Communications and media, industrial and energy, consumer related, other products, medical and health, Internet specific, computer software and services, semiconductors and other electronics, and computer hardware. **Geographic Preferences:** Southeast. **Principal Exhibits:**

PROCUREMENT ASSISTANCE PROGRAMS

49337 ■ Department of Administrative Services–Office of Small and Minority Business Division
200 Piedmont Ave. SE, Ste. 1804, W Tower
Atlanta, GA 30334-9010
Ph:(404)656-5514
Free: 800-495-0053
Fax:(404)651-9595
Co. E-mail: customerservice@doas.ga.gov
URL: http://doas.georgia.gov
Contact: Brad Douglas, Commissioner
Description: Helps small and minority businesses secure government procurement contracts.

49338 ■ Georgia Procurement Technical Assistance Center–Georgia Institute of Technology–Enterprise Innovation Institute (151 O)
151 Osigian Blvd., Ste. 157
Warner Robins, GA 31088-7810
Ph:(478)953-1460
Fax:(478)953-3169
Co. E-mail: larry.selman@innovate.gatech.edu
URL: http://www.gtpac.org
Contact: Larry O. Selman, Counselor
E-mail: zack.osborne@edi.gatech.edu
Description: Provides marketing and procurement technical assistance to Georgia businesses, large and small, operating in the government procurement markets at the federal, state, and local levels as a prime contractor or subcontractor.

49339 ■ Georgia Procurement Technical Assistance Center–Outreach Center
Featherstone Center
999 Chestnut St. SE, Ste. 7
Gainesville, GA 30501
Ph:(770)535-5844
Fax:(770)535-5847
Co. E-mail: joe.beaulieu@innovate.gatech.edu
URL: http://www.gtpac.org
Contact: Joe Beaulieu, Counselor
E-mail: joe.beaulieu@innovate.gatech.edu
Description: Provides marketing and procurement technical assistance to Georgia businesses, large and small, operating in the government procurement markets at the federal, state, and local levels as a prime contractor or subcontractor.

49340 ■ Georgia Procurement Technical Assistance Center–UIDA Business Services
86 S. Cobb Dr.
MZ0510
Marietta, GA 30063
Ph:(770)494-0431
Fax:(770)494-1236
Co. E-mail: georgew@uida.org
URL: http://www.uida.org
Contact: George Williams, Program Manager
E-mail: georgew@uida.org
Description: Helps establish business relationships between Indian enterprises and private industry.

49341 ■ US Small Business Administration
PO Box 611
Warner Robins, GA 31099-0611
Ph:(478)926-7446
Fax:(478)926-3832
Co. E-mail: thomas.hollingsworth@robins.af.mil
URL: http://www.sba.gov/
Contact: T.C. Hollingsworth, PCR
E-mail: tholling@wrdisol.robins.af.mil
Description: Covers activities for Warner Robins ALC (Warner Robins, GA) and the Marine Corps Logistics Command (Albany, GA).

INCUBATORS/RESEARCH AND TECHNOLOGY PARKS

49342 ■ Advanced Technology Development Center
Georgia Institute of Technology
Enterprise Innovation Institute
75 5th St. NW, Ste. 202
Atlanta, GA 30308
Ph:(404)894-3575
Fax:(404)894-4545
URL: http://www.atdc.org
Contact: Barbara Miller, Admin. Coord.
Description: A start-up accelerator helping technology entrepreneurs in Georgia.

49343 ■ Columbus State University Regional Technology Incubator
Cunningham Center for Leadership Development
3100 Gentian Blvd.
Columbus, GA 31907
Ph:(706)568-8339
Fax:(706)562-8447
Co. E-mail: Miller_Susan@colstate.edu
URL: http://www.columbusincubator.org/
Description: A non-profit organization dedicated to housing and nurturing new companies by providing the space and the support needed to grow technology-related jobs in the Chattahoochee Valley area.

49344 ■ Computer Link Professional Services and Software Training Center
3140 Augusta Tech Dr.
Augusta, GA 30906
Ph:(706)792-0900
Fax:(706)792-9905
Co. E-mail: info@ComputerLinkAugusta.com
URL: http://www.computerlinkaugusta.com
Description:

49345 ■ Georgia BioBusiness Center
University of Georgia
220 Riverbend Rd.
Athens, GA 30602-7411
Ph:(706)583-8209
Fax:(706)542-3804
Co. E-mail: gbbc@uga.edu
URL: http://www.ovpr.uga.edu/gbbc/
Contact: Margaret Wagner Dahl, Dir.
Description: A small business incubator affiliated with several established and startup bioscience companies with research and technology ties to UGA. The program enables bioscience startup companies to accelerate their early growth through access to management expertise and state-of-the-art instrumentation.

49346 ■ Georgia Institute of Technology–Advanced Technology Development Center
75 5th St. NW, Ste. 202
Atlanta, GA 30308
Ph:(404)894-3575
Fax:(404)894-4545
URL: http://atdc.org
Contact: Stephen Fleming, Actg.Dir.
Scope: Promotes the development of advanced technology-based companies throughout Georgia. including firms involved in advanced structural materials, electronic equipment, biotechnology, health and medical products, artificial intelligence, environmental sciences, telecommunications, aerospace systems, instrumentation and test equipment, robotics, and related technologies. **Services:** Business assistance, to start-up technology companies; General management consulting; Technical and business management services, to entrepreneurs. **Publications:** Technology Partners (quarterly).

49347 ■ Georgia Tech Research Corp.
505 10th St.
Atlanta, GA 30332-0415
Ph:(404)894-4819
Fax:(404)385-2078
Co. E-mail: jilda.garton@gtrc.gatech.edu
URL: http://www.gtrc.gatech.edu/
Contact: Jilda D. Garton, Gen.Mgr.
E-mail: jilda.garton@gtrc.gatech.edu
Scope: Serves as contracting agency for extramurally sponsored projects conducted by Georgia Institute of Technology; also as a corporate depository for patents on discoveries and inventions developed in the course of such research.

49348 ■ Gwinnett Innovation Park
4355 Shackleford Rd.
Norcross, GA 30093
Ph:(770)564-5666
Co. E-mail: info@gwinnettinnovationpark.com
URL: http://gwinnettinnovationpark.com/
Contact: Bonnie Herron, Dir.
Description: A small business incubator that supports entrepreneurs and their companies though its Launch Pad for small and fast-growing businesses.

49349 ■ Hispanic American Center for Economic Development
Georgia Hispanic Chamber of Commerce
99 W Paces Ferry, Ste. 200
Atlanta, GA 30305
Ph:(770)457-6770
Fax:(770)457-6944
Co. E-mail: info@haced.org
URL: http://www.ghcc.org/haced.asp
Description: A small business incubator founded in 2001 by the Georgia Hispanic Chamber of Commerce in order to advance the formation and growth of Hispanic Businesses in the state of Georgia.

49350 ■ MicroBusiness Enterprise Center
230 S. Jackson St., Ste. 315
Albany, GA 31701
Ph:(229)483-7650

Fax:(229)430-3989
Co. E-mail: jcraft@albany.ga.us
URL: http://www.albany.ga.us/ced/ced_enterprise_ctr.
  htm
Description: A community resource providing assistance and facilities to create an environment that will stimulate small business formation, growth and survival.

49351 ■ South DeKalb Business Incubator
1599-A Memorial Dr., SE
Atlanta, GA 30317
Ph:(404)329-4508
Fax:(404)378-0768
URL: http://www.sdbusinc.net
Contact: Tonya Weaver, Office Mgr

49352 ■ Southwest Georgia Business Development Center
1150 Industrial Dr.
Vienna, GA 31092
Ph:(229)268-8944
Co. E-mail: foster2@sowega.net
URL: http://www.crispdooly.org/
Description: A small business incubator established to create an environment for the development, growth, and success of emerging service and light manufacturing businesses in the southwest region of Georgia.

49353 ■ University of Georgia–Office of Vice President for Research
Boyd Graduate Studies Research Ctr., Ste. 609
Athens, GA 30602-7411
Ph:(706)542-5969
Fax:(706)542-5978
Co. E-mail: dclee@uga.edu
URL: http://www.ovpr.uga.edu
Contact: David C. Lee PhD, VP,Res.
E-mail: dclee@uga.edu
Scope: Administers and coordinates externally sponsored research in all University academic disciplines. **Publications:** Research Reporter Magazine (semiannually).

EDUCATIONAL PROGRAMS

49354 ■ East Georgia College
131 College Cir.
Swainsboro, GA 30401
Ph:(478)289-2017
Fax:(478)289-2038
URL: http://www.ega.edu
Description: Two-year college offering a program in small business management.

49355 ■ Emory University–Center for Lifelong Learning
Center For Longlife Learning Mailstop 1256/001/1AD
Atlanta, GA 30322-1790
Ph:(404)727-6000
Fax:(404)727-6001
Co. E-mail: evening@emory.edu
URL: http://www.cll.emory.edu
Description: Offers courses for owners—or potential owners—of small business enterprises. Also offers courses through the School of Business Administration.

49356 ■ Georgia Highlands College–Floyd Campus
3175 Cedartown Hwy.
Rome, GA 30162-1864
Ph:(706)802-5000
Free: 800-332-2406
Fax:(706)295-6341
URL: http://www.highlands.edu
Description: Two-year college offering a small business management program.

49357 ■ University of West Georgia–Richards College of Business
1601 Maple St.
Carrollton, GA 30118
Ph:(678)839-6467
Fax:(678)839-6774
Co. E-mail: busn@westga.edu
URL: http://www.westga.edu
E-mail: dhovey@westga.edu
Description: Presents business-related courses, seminars, and workshops to persons interested in professional and staff development. Also provides counseling, databases, and case studies to those interested in starting or building a small business.

LEGISLATIVE ASSISTANCE

49358 ■ Georgia House of Representatives
State Capitol
Atlanta, GA 30334
Ph:(404)656-0305
Fax:(404)656-6897
Co. E-mail: riley.lowry@house.ga.us
URL: http://www.legis.state.ga.us
Contact: Riley Lowry, Dir

PUBLICATIONS

49359 ■ *Atlanta Magazine*
1330 West Peachtree St., Ste. 450
Atlanta, GA 30309-3214

Ph:(404)872-3100
Fax:(404)870-6230
Co. E-mail: atlmag@atlanta.com
URL: http://atlantamag.atlanta.com

49360 ■ *The Atlanta Small Business Monthly*
6129 Oakbrook Pkwy.
Norcross, GA 30093
Ph:(770)446-5434
Fax:(770)446-3970
Co. E-mail: asbm@bellsouth.net

49361 ■ *Starting and Operating a Business in Georgia: A Step-by-Step Guide*
PSI Research
300 N. Valley Dr.
Grants Pass, OR 97526
Ph:(503)479-9464
Free: 800-228-2275
Fax:(503)476-1479
Co. E-mail: psi2@magick.net
Ed: Michael D. Jenkins. **Released:** Revised edition, 1992. **Price:** $29.95 (looseleaf binder); $24.95 (paper). **Description:** Part of the Successful Business Library series.

PUBLISHERS

49362 ■ Franklin-Sarrett Publishers L.L.C.
3761 Vineyard Trace NE
Marietta, GA 30062-5227
Ph:(770)578-9410
Free: 800-346-0656
Fax:(770)973-2222
Co. E-mail: info@franklin-sarrett.com
URL: http://www.franklin-sarrett.com
Contact: Rick Barnes, Vice President
Description: Publishes material for small business. Accepts unsolicited manuscripts. Reaches market through reviews and listings and wholesalers. **Founded:** 1992.

49363 ■ Toca Family Publishing
245 N Highland Ave., Ste. 230-230
Atlanta, GA 30307-1919
Ph:(404)348-4065
Fax:(404)348-4469
Contact: Tiffany Wright, Mgr
Description: Publishes books on small business financing.

SMALL BUSINESS DEVELOPMENT CENTERS

49364 ■ Hawaii Small Business Development Center
308 Kamehameha Ave., Ste. 201
Hilo, HI 96720
Fax:(808)974-7683
URL: http://www.hawaii-sbdc.org
Contact: Bill Carter, Dir.

49365 ■ Honolulu Small Business Development Center
1833 Kalakaua Ave., Ste. 400
Honolulu, HI 96815
Fax:(808)945-1432
URL: http://www.hawaii-sbdc.org/honolulucenter.htm
Contact: Caroline Kim, Dir.

49366 ■ Kaua'i Small Business Development Center
Kaua'i Community College
3-1901 Kaumuali'i Hwy.
Lihue, HI 96766
Fax:(808)241-3229
URL: http://www.hawaii-sbdc.org/kauaicenter.htm
Contact: Diana Shaw, Dir.

49367 ■ Maui Small Business Development Center
590 Lipoa Pkwy., Ste. 130
Kihei, HI 96753
Fax:(808)875-2406
URL: http://www.hawaii-sbdc.org/mauicenter.htm
Contact: David Fisher, Dir.

SMALL BUSINESS ASSISTANCE PROGRAMS

49368 ■ Chamber of Commerce of Hawaii–Small Business Council
1132 Bishop St., Ste. 402
Honolulu, HI 96813
Ph:(808)545-4300
Fax:(808)545-4369
Co. E-mail: info@cochawaii.org
URL: http://www.cochawaii.org
Contact: Jim Tollefson, Pres & CEO

Description: Offers business referrals, financial planning, loan packaging, and business, marketing, and entrepreneurship counseling.

49369 ■ Hawaii Department of Business, Economic Development, and Tourism–Strategic Marketing & Support
PO Box 2359
Honolulu, HI 96804
Ph:(808)586-2423

Fax:(808)587-2790
Co. E-mail: library@dbedt.hawaii.gov
URL: http://www.hawaii.gov/dbedt
Contact: Theodore E. Liu, Dir
Description: Promotes new enterprise development in Hawaii from the U.S. mainland and international business centers.

49370 ■ University of Hawaii–Pacific Business Center Program
College of Business Administration
2404 Maile Way, A413
Honolulu, HI 96822
Ph:(808)956-6286
Fax:(808)956-6278
Co. E-mail: pbcp@hawaii.edu
URL: http://pbcphawaii.com/Default.asp
Description: Provides counseling and referral services to businesses. Conduct some research for program clients.

SCORE OFFICES

49371 ■ SCORE of Hawaii
300 Ala Moana Blvd., Rm. 2-235
Honolulu, HI 96850
Ph:(808)547-2700
Fax:(808)541-2950
Co. E-mail: hawaiiscore@hawaiiscore.org
URL: http://www.hawaiiscore.org
Contact: Dennis P. Bunda, Chm.
Description: Creates opportunities for small business owners and potential business owners to achieve success. Provides business assistance to develop business plans, stimulate business growth and identify problems and potential solutions. Promotes entrepreneur education in Hawaii.

BETTER BUSINESS BUREAUS

49372 ■ Better Business Bureau of Hawaii
1132 Bishop St., Ste. 615
Honolulu, HI 96813-2813
Ph:(808)536-6956
Free: 877-222-6551
Fax:(808)628-3970
Co. E-mail: info@hawaii.bbb.org
URL: http://hawaii.bbb.org
Contact: Bonnie Horibata, VP

CHAMBERS OF COMMERCE

49373 ■ Australian/American Chamber of Commerce - Hawaii
1000 Bishop St., Penthouse
Honolulu, HI 96813
Ph:(808)526-2242
Fax:(808)534-0475
Co. E-mail: info@aacchawaii.org
URL: http://www.aacchawaii.org
Contact: John Fyfe, Pres.

49374 ■ Chamber of Commerce of Hawaii
1132 Bishop St., Ste. 402
Honolulu, HI 96813
Ph:(808)545-4300
Fax:(808)545-4369
Co. E-mail: jtollefson@cochawaii.org
URL: http://cochawaii.com/Default.asp
Contact: Jim Tollefson, Pres./CEO

49375 ■ Chinese Chamber of Commerce of Hawaii
8 S King St., Ste. 201
Honolulu, HI 96813
Ph:(808)533-3181
Fax:(808)537-6767
Co. E-mail: info@chinesechamber.com
URL: http://www.chinesechamber.com
Contact: Ted CT Li, Pres.

49376 ■ Hawaii Island Chamber of Commerce
106 Kamehameha Ave.
Hilo, HI 96720
Ph:(808)935-7178
Fax:(808)961-4435
Co. E-mail: admin@hicc.biz
URL: http://www.hicc.biz
Contact: Barbara Hastings, Pres.

49377 ■ Hawaii Island Portuguese Chamber of Commerce
PO Box 1839
Hilo, HI 96721
Ph:(808)961-3112
Co. E-mail: phoebel@msn.com
URL: http://www.hipcc.org
Contact: Phoebe Lambeth, Pres.

49378 ■ Hawaii Korean Chamber of Commerce
PO Box 2296
Honolulu, HI 96804
Ph:(808)524-7441
Fax:(808)528-0470
URL: http://www.hkccweb.org/en
Contact: Gina Nakamura, Pres.

49379 ■ Honolulu Japanese Chamber of Commerce
2454 S Beretania St., Ste. 201
Honolulu, HI 96826
Ph:(808)949-5531
Fax:(808)949-3020
Co. E-mail: info@honolulujapanesechamber.org
URL: http://www.honolulujapanesechamber.org
Contact: Wayne Ishihara, Pres.

49380 ■ Honolulu Japanese Junior Chamber of Commerce
2454 S Beretania St., Ste. 201
Honolulu, HI 96826
Ph:(808)949-5531

Fax:(808)949-3020
Co. E-mail: info@honolulujapanesechamber.org
URL: http://www.honolulujapanesechamber.org
Contact: Wayne Ishihara, Pres.

49381 ■ Kailua Chamber of Commerce
PO Box 1496
Kailua, HI 96734
Ph:(808)261-2727
Free: 888-261-7997
Co. E-mail: kcoc@kailuachamber.com
URL: http://www.kailuachamber.com
Contact: Evan Scherman, Pres.

49382 ■ Kauai Chamber of Commerce
PO Box 1969
Lihue, HI 96766
Ph:(808)245-7363
Fax:(808)245-8815
Co. E-mail: info@kauaichamber.org
URL: http://www.kauaichamber.org
Contact: Randall Francisco, Pres.

49383 ■ Kona Kohala Chamber of Commerce
75-5737 Kaukini Hwy., Ste. 208
Kailua Kona, HI 96740-1725
Ph:(808)329-1758
Fax:(808)329-8564
Co. E-mail: info@kona-kohala.com
URL: http://www.kona-kohala.com
Contact: Christie Dermengian, Pres.

49384 ■ Maui Chamber of Commerce
313 Ano St.
Kahului, HI 96732
Ph:(808)871-7711
Fax:(808)871-0706
Co. E-mail: rossel@mauichamber.com
URL: http://www.mauichamber.com
Contact: Pamela Tumpap, Pres.

49385 ■ Moloka'i Chamber of Commerce
PO Box 515
Kaunakakai, HI 96748-0515
Ph:(808)553-4482
Fax:(808)553-4482
Co. E-mail: molokaichamber@hawaiiantel.biz
URL: http://www.molokaichamber.org
Contact: Barbara Haliniak, Pres.

49386 ■ Native Hawaiian Chamber of Commerce
PO Box 597
Honolulu, HI 96809
Ph:(808)531-3744
Fax:(808)732-7059
Co. E-mail: robson@hawaii.rr.com
URL: http://www.nativehawaiian.cc
Contact: Linda Paik-Matsura

MINORITY BUSINESS ASSISTANCE PROGRAMS

49387 ■ Honolulu Minority Business Enterprise Center
University of Hawaii at Manoa
Shidler College of Business
2404 Maile Way, D-307
Honolulu, HI 96822
Ph:(808)956-0850
Fax:(808)956-0851
Co. E-mail: info@honolulu-mbdc.org
URL: http://www.honolulu-mbdc.org
Contact: Dana Hauanio, Dir
Description: Established to increase the number of minority-owned businesses and strengthen existing ones.

FINANCING AND LOAN PROGRAMS

49388 ■ HMS Hawaii Management Partners
Davies Pacific Ctr.
841 Bishop St., Ste. 860
Honolulu, HI 96813
Ph:(808)545-3755
Fax:(808)531-2611
Co. E-mail: info@hmshawaii.com
URL: http://www.hmshawaii.com
Contact: Richard G. Grey, General Partner
Preferred Investment Size: $500,000 to $1,500,000.
Investment Types: Seed, start-up, early stage, and joint ventures. **Industry Preferences:** Communications and media, Internet specific, medical and health, other products, and industrial and energy. **Geographic Preferences:** Hawaii and West Coast. **Principal Exhibits:**

INCUBATORS/RESEARCH AND TECHNOLOGY PARKS

49389 ■ Agribusiness Incubator Program
University of Hawaii
3050 Maile Way, Gilmore 115
Honolulu, HI 96822
Ph:(808)956-3530
Fax:(808)956-3547
Co. E-mail: agincubator@ctahr.hawaii.edu
URL: http://aip.hawaii.edu/default.aspx
Contact: Steven Chiang, Dir.
Description: A small business incubator providing business consulting services to agriculture-related businesses throughout the State of Hawaii, maximizing their chance of business viability and success, in order to grow the State's diversified agriculture industry.

49390 ■ Manoa Innovation Center (MIC)
2800 Woodlawn Dr.
Honolulu, HI 96822
Ph:(808)539-3806
Fax:(808)539-3795
Co. E-mail: htdc@htdc.org
URL: http://www.htdc.org
Contact: Philip Bossert, Exec Dir
Description: The MIC is a high technology small business incubator that forges ties between entrepreneurs and university-oriented research and development.

49391 ■ Research Corporation of the University of Hawaii
2800 Woodlawn Dr., Ste. 200
Honolulu, HI 96822
Ph:(808)988-8300
Fax:(808)988-8349
Co. E-mail: rcuhed@rcuh.com
URL: http://www.rcuh.com
Contact: Michael P. Hamnett, Exec.Dir.
E-mail: rcuhed@rcuh.com
Scope: Provides administrative support services for university, state, and private sector research. Assist in promoting and implementing scientific, educational, and economic development activities in the state, Pacific Island areas, and other countries. Administer grants, contracts, and bequests. **Services:** Accounting, fiscal, personnel and purchasing support. **Publications:** Annual report (annually). **Awards:** Awards for Excellence in Research (annually), provided to the University of Hawaii.

LEGISLATIVE ASSISTANCE

49392 ■ Hawaii House Labor and Public Employment Committee
Hawaii State Capital, Rm 326
415 S. Beretania St.
Honolulu, HI 96813

Ph:(808)586-6180
Fax:(808)586-6189
Co. E-mail: reprhoads@capitol.hawaii.gov
URL: http://www.capitol.hawaii.gov
Contact: Karl Rhoads, Chair

49393 ■ Hawaii Senate Consumer Protection Committee
Hawaii State Capitol, Rm. 320
415 S Beretania St.
Honolulu, HI 96813
Ph:(808)586-8400
Fax:(808)586-8404
Co. E-mail: repherkes@capitol.hawaii.gov
URL: http://www.capitol.hawaii.gov
Contact: Robert N. Herkes, Chair

49394 ■ Hawaii Senate Water and Land Use Planning Committee
State Capitol Bldg., Rm. 201
415 S. Beretania St.
Honolulu, HI 96813
Ph:(808)586-7335
Fax:(808)586-7339
Co. E-mail: seninouye@capital.hawaii.gov
URL: http://www.capitol.hawaii.gov
Contact: Sen. Lorraine Inoye

PUBLICATIONS

49395 ■ *Business Basics in Hawaii: Secrets of Starting Your Own Business in Our State*
University of Hawaii Press (Editorial Department)
2840 Kolowalu St.
Honolulu, HI 96822
Ph:(808)956-8694
Fax:(808)988-6052
Co. E-mail: uhpbook@hawaii.edu
Ed: Dennis K. Kondo. **Released:** 1988. **Price:** $14.95.

49396 ■ *Hawaii Business*
825 Keeaumoku
PO Box 913
Honolulu, HI 96808
Ph:(808)537-9500
Fax:(808)537-6455
Co. E-mail: hawbus@pixi.com
URL: http://www.hawaiibusinessmagazine.com

49397 ■ *Pacific Business News*
P.O. Box 833
Honolulu, HI 96808-0833
Ph:(808)596-2021
Fax:(808)591-2321
URL: http://www.amcity.com

49398 ■ *Smart Start your Hawaii Business*
PSI Research
300 N. Valley Dr.
Grants Pass, OR 97526
Ph:(503)479-9464
Free: 800-228-2275
Fax:(503)476-1479
Co. E-mail: info@psi-research.com
URL: http://www.psi-research.com
Ed: Michael D. Jenkins and Franklin Forbes. **Released:** Revised edition, 1992. **Price:** $29.95 (looseleaf binder); $24.95 (paper). **Description:** Part of the Successful Business Library series.

49399 ■ *Starting and Operating a Business in Hawaii: A Step-by-Step Guide*
PSI Research
300 N. Valley Dr.
Grants Pass, OR 97526
Ph:(503)479-9464
Free: 800-228-2275
Fax:(503)476-1479
Co. E-mail: psi2@magick.net
Ed: Michael D. Jenkins. **Released:** Revised edition, 1992. **Price:** $29.95 (looseleaf binder); $24.95 (paper). **Description:** Part of the Successful Business Library series.

SMALL BUSINESS DEVELOPMENT CENTERS

49400 ■ Boise State University Small Business Development Center, Region III
1910 University Dr.
Boise, ID 83725-1655
Fax:(208)426-3877
Co. E-mail: klabrum@boisestate.edu
URL: http://www.idahosbdc.org/index.cfm?fuseaction=content.region&id=4
Contact: Rick Vycital, Dir.

49401 ■ College of Southern Idaho Small Business Development Center
PO Box 1238
Twin Falls, ID 83303-1238
Fax:(208)445-1492
Co. E-mail: isbdc@csi.edu
URL: http://www.csi.edu/support/isbdc/SBDC.html
Contact: Bryan J. Matsuoka, Dir.

49402 ■ Idaho Small Business Development Center
Boise State University
1910 University Dr.
Boise, ID 83725-1655
Free: 800-225-3815
Fax:(208)426-3877
Co. E-mail: info@idahosbdc.org
URL: http://www.idahosbdc.org
Contact: James E. Hogge, State Dir.

49403 ■ Idaho State University Small Business Development Center, Region V
1651 Alvin Ricken Dr.
Pocatello, ID 83201
Fax:(208)282-4813
Co. E-mail: dittmike@isu.edu
URL: http://www.idahosbdc.org/index.cfm?fuseaction=content.region&id=6
Contact: Matthew Creamer, Dir.

49404 ■ Idaho State University Small Business Development Center, Region VI
2300 N Yellowstone Hwy.
Idaho Falls, ID 83401
Fax:(208)528-7127
Co. E-mail: wilsfros@isu.edu
URL: http://www.idahosbdc.org/index.cfm?fuseaction=content.region&id=7
Contact: David Noack, Dir.

49405 ■ Lewis-Clark State College Small Business Development Center, Region II
500 8th Ave.
Lewiston, ID 83501
Fax:(208)792-2878
Co. E-mail: adanttila@lcsc.edu
Contact: Jill Thomas-Jorgenson, Dir.

49406 ■ North Idaho College Small Business Development Center, Region I
525 W Clearwater Loop
Post Falls, ID 83854-9400
Fax:(208)769-3223
Co. E-mail: idaho_sbdc@nic.edu
URL: http://www.idahosbdc.org/index.cfm?fuseaction=content.region&id=2
Contact: William Jhung, Dir.

SMALL BUSINESS ASSISTANCE PROGRAMS

49407 ■ Idaho Department of Commerce–Department of Economic Development
700 W State St.
Boise, ID 83720
Ph:(208)334-2470
Free: 800-842-5858
Fax:(208)334-2631
URL: http://commerce.idaho.gov/business
Contact: Lane Packwood, Admin.
Description: Provides information on regulations, permits, and licenses. Sponsors the Idaho Business Network. Offers international trade assistance, and travel and tourism promotion.

SCORE OFFICES

49408 ■ SCORE Eastern Idaho
c/o Charles M. Rice
2300 N Yellowstone Hwy., Ste. 119
Idaho Falls, ID 83401
Ph:(208)523-1022
Fax:(208)528-7127
Co. E-mail: score295@iictr.com
URL: http://www.score.org/index.html
Contact: Charles M. Rice
Description:

49409 ■ SCORE Treasure Valley
380 E Parkcenter Blvd., Ste. 330
Boise, ID 83706
Ph:(208)334-1696
Co. E-mail: tvscore240@yahoo.com
URL: http://www.idahotvscore.org
Contact: Jeff Weeks, Chm.
Description: Provides professional guidance and information to maximize the success of existing and merging small businesses. Promotes entrepreneur education in Treasure Valley area, Idaho.

BETTER BUSINESS BUREAUS

49410 ■ Better Business Bureau of Eastern Idaho and Western Wyoming
453 River Pkwy.
Idaho Falls, ID 83402-3615
Ph:(208)523-9754

Fax:(208)227-1603
Co. E-mail: info@idahofalls.bbb.org
URL: http://idahofalls.bbb.org
Contact: Donna Oe, Pres./CEO

49411 ■ Better Business Bureau of Southwest Idaho and Eastern Oregon
4355 Emerald St., Ste. 290
Boise, ID 83706
Ph:(208)342-4649
Fax:(208)342-5116
Co. E-mail: info@boise.bbb.org
URL: http://boise.bbb.org
Contact: Nora Carpenter, Exec. Dir.

CHAMBERS OF COMMERCE

49412 ■ Bayview Chamber of Commerce
PO Box 121
Bayview, ID 83803-0121
Ph:(208)683-3293
Co. E-mail: bobobprince@roadrunner.com
URL: http://www.bayviewidaho.org
Contact: Bob Prince, Pres.

49413 ■ Boise Metro Chamber of Commerce
PO Box 2368
Boise, ID 83701
Ph:(208)472-5200
Fax:(208)472-5201
Co. E-mail: info@boisechamber.org
URL: http://www.boisechamber.org
Contact: Paul Hiller, Exec. Dir.

49414 ■ Buhl Chamber of Commerce
716 U.S. Hwy. 30 E
Buhl, ID 83316
Ph:(208)543-6682
Fax:(208)543-2185
Co. E-mail: janet@buhlchamber.org
URL: http://www.buhlchamber.org
Contact: Janet Franklin

49415 ■ Caldwell Chamber of Commerce
PO Box 819
Caldwell, ID 83606
Ph:(208)459-7493
Free: (866)206-6944
Fax:(208)454-1284
Co. E-mail: chamber@ci.caldwell.id.us
URL: http://chamber.cityofcaldwell.com
Contact: Diana Brown, Exec. Dir.

49416 ■ Cascade Chamber of Commerce
PO Box 571
Cascade, ID 83611
Ph:(208)382-3833
Fax:(208)382-3833
Co. E-mail: info@cascadechamber.com
URL: http://www.cascadechamber.com
Contact: Kathy Hull

49417 ■ Coeur d'Alene Area Chamber of Commerce
PO Box 850
Coeur d'Alene, ID 83816
Ph:(208)664-3194
Free: 877-782-9232
Fax:(208)667-9338
Co. E-mail: info@cdachamber.com
URL: http://www.cdachamber.com/default.aspx
Contact: Jonathan S. Coe, Pres./Gen. Mgr.

49418 ■ Council Chamber of Commerce
PO Box 527
Council, ID 83612
Ph:(208)253-6830
Co. E-mail: councilchamber@ctcweb.net
URL: http://www.councilchamberofcommerce.com
Contact: Ken Bell, Pres.

49419 ■ Donnelly Area Chamber of Commerce
PO Box 83
Donnelly, ID 83615-0083
Ph:(208)325-3545
Co. E-mail: donnellychamber@frontiernet.net
URL: http://www.donnellychamber.org
Contact: Monty Ivey, Exec. Dir.

49420 ■ Fruitland Chamber of Commerce
PO Box 408
Fruitland, ID 83619
Ph:(208)452-4350
Fax:(208)452-5028
Co. E-mail: chamber@fmtc.com
URL: http://www.fruitlandidaho.org
Contact: Judy Cordezia, Board Member

49421 ■ Gem County Chamber of Commerce
PO Box 592
Emmett, ID 83617
Ph:(208)365-3485
Fax:(208)365-3220
Co. E-mail: chamber@emmettidaho.com
URL: http://www.emmettidaho.com
Contact: Chuck Rolland, Pres.

49422 ■ Glenns Ferry Chamber of Commerce
PO Box 317
Glenns Ferry, ID 83623
Ph:(208)366-7345
Fax:(208)366-2238
URL: http://www.glennsferryidaho.org

49423 ■ Grangeville Chamber of Commerce
PO Box 212
Grangeville, ID 83530
Ph:(208)983-0460
Fax:(208)983-1429
Co. E-mail: chamber@grangevilleidaho.com
URL: http://www.grangevilleidaho.com
Contact: Melinda Hall, Pres.

49424 ■ Greater Bear Lake Valley Chamber of Commerce
PO Box 265
915 Washington St.
Montpelier, ID 83254
Ph:(208)847-0067
Co. E-mail: lori@bearlakechamber.org
URL: http://www.bearlakechamber.org
Contact: Ms. Amy Bishop, Exec. Dir.

49425 ■ Greater Blackfoot Area Chamber of Commerce
PO Box 801
Blackfoot, ID 83221-0801
Ph:(208)785-0510
Fax:(208)785-7974
Co. E-mail: chamber@blackfootchamber.org
URL: http://www.blackfootchamber.org
Contact: Stephanie Govatos, Exec. Dir.

49426 ■ Greater Bonners Ferry Chamber of Commerce
PO Box X
Bonners Ferry, ID 83805
Ph:(208)267-5277

Fax:(208)267-5922
Co. E-mail: info@bonnersferrychamber.com
URL: http://www.bonnersferrychamber.com
Contact: Brett Brown, Pres.

49427 ■ Greater Pocatello Chamber of Commerce
324 S Main St.
Pocatello, ID 83204
Ph:(208)233-1525
Fax:(208)233-1527
Co. E-mail: amiles@pocatelloidaho.com
URL: http://www.pocatelloidaho.com
Contact: Mr. Matt Hunter, Exec. Dir.

49428 ■ Greater Sandpoint Chamber of Commerce
PO Box 928
Sandpoint, ID 83864
Ph:(208)263-0887
Free: 800-800-2106
Fax:(208)265-5289
Co. E-mail: info@sandpointchamber.com
URL: http://sandpointchamber.org
Contact: Amy Little, Exec. Dir.

49429 ■ Greater Weiser Area Chamber of Commerce
309 State St.
Weiser, ID 83672-2530
Ph:(208)414-0452
Fax:(208)414-0451
Co. E-mail: info@weiserchamber.com
URL: http://www.weiserchamber.com
Contact: Laurel Adams, Dir.

49430 ■ Hagerman Valley Chamber of Commerce
PO Box 599
Hagerman, ID 83332-0599
Ph:(208)837-9131
Co. E-mail: info@hagermanchamber.com
URL: http://www.hagermanchamber.com
Contact: Mark Bolduc, Pres.

49431 ■ Hailey Chamber of Commerce
PO Box 100
Hailey, ID 83333
Ph:(208)788-3484
Fax:(208)578-1595
Co. E-mail: info@haileyidaho.com
URL: http://www.haileyidaho.com
Contact: Jim Spinelli, Exec. Dir.

49432 ■ Historic Silver Valley Chamber of Commerce
10 Station Ave.
Kellogg, ID 83837
Ph:(208)784-0821
Fax:(208)783-4343
Co. E-mail: rachelhopper@minershatrealty.com
URL: http://www.silvervalleychamber.com
Contact: Jeff Waechter, Pres.

49433 ■ Jerome Chamber of Commerce
104 W Main St., Ste. 101
Jerome, ID 83338
Ph:(208)324-2711
Fax:(208)324-6881
Co. E-mail: chamber@visitjerome.com
URL: http://www.visitjerome.com

49434 ■ Kamiah Chamber of Commerce
PO Box 1124
Kamiah, ID 83536-1124
Ph:(208)935-2290
Fax:(208)935-2290
Co. E-mail: info@kamiahchamber.com
URL: http://www.kamiahchamber.com
Contact: Robert Simmons, Pres.

49435 ■ Kuna Chamber of Commerce
PO Box 123
Kuna, ID 83634
Ph:(208)922-9254
Co. E-mail: admin@kunachamber.com
URL: http://kunachamber.com
Contact: Vicki Smith, Exec. Dir.

49436 ■ Lava Hot Springs Chamber of Commerce
PO Box 238
Lava Hot Springs, ID 83246
Ph:(208)776-5500
Co. E-mail: findout@lavahotsprings.org
URL: http://www.lavahotsprings.org
Contact: Scott Pearhill, Pres.

49437 ■ Lewiston Chamber of Commerce
111 Main St., Ste. 120
Lewiston, ID 83501
Ph:(208)743-3531
Free: 800-473-3543
Fax:(208)743-2176
Co. E-mail: info@lewistonchamber.org
URL: http://www.lewistonchamber.org
Contact: Keith Havens, Pres./CEO

49438 ■ Meridian Chamber of Commerce
PO Box 7
Meridian, ID 83680-0007
Ph:(208)888-2817
Fax:(208)888-2682
Co. E-mail: info@meridianchamber.org
URL: http://www.meridianchamber.org
Contact: Teri Sackman, Exec. Dir.

49439 ■ Mini-Cassia Chamber of Commerce
1177 7th St.
PO Box 640
Heyburn, ID 83336
Ph:(208)679-4793
Fax:(208)679-4794
Co. E-mail: visitorinfo@pmt.org
URL: http://www.minicassiachamber.com
Contact: Kae Cameron, Exec. Dir.

49440 ■ Moscow Chamber of Commerce
PO Box 8936
Moscow, ID 83843-0180
Ph:(208)882-1800
Free: 800-380-1801
Fax:(208)882-6186
Co. E-mail: staff@moscowchamber.com
URL: http://www.moscowchamber.com
Contact: Steven Hacker, Exec. Dir.

49441 ■ Mountain Home Chamber of Commerce
205 N 3rd St. E
Mountain Home, ID 83647
Ph:(208)587-4334
Fax:(208)587-0042
Co. E-mail: web@mountainhomechamber.com
URL: http://www.mountainhomechamber.com
Contact: Linda Kettering, Pres.

49442 ■ Nampa Chamber of Commerce
312 13th Ave. S
Nampa, ID 83651
Ph:(208)466-4641
Free: 877-20-NAMPA
Fax:(208)466-4677
Co. E-mail: info@nampa.com
URL: http://www.nampa.com
Contact: Georgia Bowman-Gunstream, Pres./CEO

49443 ■ Post Falls Chamber of Commerce
PO Box 908
Post Falls, ID 83877
Ph:(208)773-5016
Free: 800-292-2553
Fax:(208)773-3843
Co. E-mail: info@postfallschamber.com
URL: http://www.postfallschamber.com
Contact: Ms. Pam Houser, Pres./CEO

49444 ■ Preston Chamber of Commerce
49 N State, Ste. A
Preston, ID 83263
Ph:(208)852-2703
Co. E-mail: pacc@ida.net
URL: http://www.prestonidaho.org
Contact: Pennie Christensen, Exec. Dir.

49445 ■ Priest Lake Chamber of Commerce
PO Box 174
Coolin, ID 83821
Ph:(208)443-3191
Free: 888-774-3785
Fax:(208)443-4061
Co. E-mail: info@priestlake.org
URL: http://www.priestlake.org
Contact: Kathleen Martin, Pres.

49446 ■ Priest River Chamber of Commerce
PO Box 929
Priest River, ID 83856
Ph:(208)448-2721
Co. E-mail: prchamber@povn.com
URL: http://www.priestriver.org
Contact: Ray Roberts, Pres.

49447 ■ Rexburg Chamber of Commerce
127 E Main St.
Rexburg, ID 83440
Ph:(208)356-5700
Free: 888-INF-O880
Fax:(208)356-5799
Co. E-mail: info@rexcc.com
URL: http://www.rexcc.com
Contact: Donna Benfield, Exec. Dir.

49448 ■ St. Maries Chamber of Commerce
PO Box 162
St. Maries, ID 83861
Ph:(208)245-3563
Fax:(208)245-3477
Co. E-mail: manager@stmarieschamber.org
URL: http://www.stmarieschamber.org
Contact: Shirley Ackerman, Pres.

49449 ■ Salmon River Chamber of Commerce
PO Box 289
Riggins, ID 83549
Ph:(208)628-3778
Free: (866)221-3901
Co. E-mail: cfriend@frontiernet.net
URL: http://www.rigginsidaho.com

49450 ■ Salmon Valley Chamber of Commerce
200 Main St., Ste. 1
Salmon, ID 83467
Ph:(208)756-2100
Free: 800-727-2540
Co. E-mail: info@salmonchamber.com
URL: http://www.salmonchamber.com
Contact: Cori Allen, Pres.

49451 ■ Soda Springs Chamber of Commerce
PO Box 697
Soda Springs, ID 83276
Ph:(208)547-4964
Fax:(208)547-2601
Co. E-mail: sodacoc@sodachamber.com
URL: http://www.sodachamber.com
Contact: Bob Ward, Pres.

49452 ■ Stanley - Sawtooth Chamber of Commerce
PO Box 8
Stanley, ID 83278-0008
Ph:(208)774-3411
Free: 800-878-7950
Co. E-mail: info@stanleycc.org
URL: http://www.stanleycc.org

49453 ■ Sun Valley-Ketchum Chamber and Visitors Bureau
PO Box 2420
Sun Valley, ID 83353
Free: (866)305-0408
Co. E-mail: chamberinfo@visitsunvalley.com
URL: http://www.visitsunvalley.com
Contact: Carol Waller, Exec. Dir.

49454 ■ Teton Valley Chamber of Commerce
PO Box 250
Driggs, ID 83422
Ph:(208)354-2500

Fax:(208)354-2517
Co. E-mail: tvcc@tetonvalleychamber.com
URL: http://www.tetonvalleychamber.com
Contact: C. Reid Rogers, Pres.

49455 ■ Twin Falls Area Chamber of Commerce
858 Blue Lakes Blvd. N
Twin Falls, ID 83301
Ph:(208)733-3974
Free: (866)TWIN-FALLS
Fax:(208)733-9216
Co. E-mail: info@twinfallschamber.com
URL: http://www.twinfallschamber.com
Contact: Shawn Barigar, Pres./CEO

49456 ■ Wallace Chamber of Commerce
10 River St., Exit 61
Wallace, ID 83873
Ph:(208)753-7151
Free: 800-434-4204
Fax:(208)753-7151
Co. E-mail: director@wallaceidahochamber.com
URL: http://www.wallaceidahochamber.com
Contact: Rene Gilbert, Coor.

FINANCING AND LOAN PROGRAMS

49457 ■ Akers Capital, LLC
5207 Sunrise Blvd., Ste. 220
Fair Oaks, CA 95628
Ph:(916)966-2236
Fax:(916)966-2239
URL: http://www.akerscapital.com
Contact: Roger Akers, Managing Partner
Preferred Investment Size: $500,000 to $3,000,000.
Investment Policies: Early, first, and second stage.
Industry Preferences: Communications, software, and Internet specific. **Geographic Preferences:** Northern California and Northwest. **Principal Exhibits:**

PROCUREMENT ASSISTANCE PROGRAMS

49458 ■ Idaho Procurement Technical Assistance Center–Idaho Department of Commerce
700 W State St.
PO Box 83720
Boise, ID 83720-0093
Ph:(208)334-2650
Fax:(208)334-2631
Co. E-mail: sundi.smith@commerce.idaho.gov
URL: http://idahoworks.com
Contact: Sundi Smith, Prgm Mgr

INCUBATORS/RESEARCH AND TECHNOLOGY PARKS

49459 ■ Bonner Business Center (BBC)
804 Airport Way
Sandpoint, ID 83864
Ph:(208)263-4073
Fax:(208)263-4609
Co. E-mail: info@bonnerbusinesscenter.com
URL: http://www.bonnerbusinesscenter.com/
Contact: Wally Schmidt, Mgr
Description: A small business incubator assisting the development of new firms in northern Idaho. The BBC is also equipped with a fully licensed shared-use food production facility.

49460 ■ College of Southern Idaho–Small Business Incubator
Evergreen Bldg. C77
315 Falls Ave.
PO Box 1238
Twin Falls, ID 83303-1238
Ph:(208)732-6451

Fax:(208)455-1492
Co. E-mail: bmatsuoka@csi.edu
URL: http://www.csi.edu/support/isbdc/incubator/bus-inc.htm
Contact: Brian J. Matsuoka, Incubator Mgr.
Description: Using the resources of the College of Southern Idaho, this small business incubator offers emerging firms affordable office space, business consulting, and a variety of other services.

49461 ■ CSI Business Incubator
College of Southern Idaho
315 Falls Ave., Evergreen Bldg. C77
PO Box 1238
Twin Falls, ID 83303-1238
Ph:(208)732-6450
Fax:(208)733-9316
Co. E-mail: bMatsuoka@csi.edu
URL: http://www.csi.edu/support/isbdc/incubator/bus-inc.htm
Description: A small business incubator providing entrepreneurs with adequate facilities and resources needed to develop new businesses; expanding the economic base of South-Central Idaho by assisting value-added, non-competing new businesses; creating jobs in the Magic Valley area; and improving new businesses' chances for success.

49462 ■ East Central Idaho Planning Development Association–Upper Snake River Valley Incubator
310 N 2nd E
Rexburg, ID 83440
Ph:(208)356-4524
Fax:(208)356-4544
URL: http://www.ecipda.org
Contact: Ted Hendricks, Mgr

49463 ■ Idaho Innovation Center, Inc.
2300 N Yellowstone Hwy.
Idaho Falls, ID 83401
Ph:(208)523-1026
Fax:(208)528-7127
URL: http://www.iictr.com
Contact: Jeff Krantz, Exec Dir
Description: A small business incubator.

49464 ■ Idaho State University Research and Business Park
1651 Alvin Ricken Dr.
Pocatello, ID 83201
Ph:(208)282-3600
Fax:(208)282-5960
Co. E-mail: blicphil@isu.edu
URL: http://www.isu.edu/departments/respark
Contact: Philip Blick, Dir.
E-mail: blicphil@isu.edu
Scope: Facilitates the interaction of University research community with Park tenants and other professional organizations, particularly in the areas of health professions, biological and physical sciences, pharmacy, nuclear engineering, hazardous waste management, and state of the art decision support systems. Collaborates on technology transfer programs with the Idaho National Engineering Laboratory. **Services:** Technical assistance, to early state companies. **Publications:** An Environment for Innovation.

49465 ■ North Central Idaho Business Technology Incubator
121 W Sweet Ave.
Moscow, ID 83843
Ph:(208)885-3800
Fax:(208)885-3803
Co. E-mail: edc@moscow.com
URL: http://www.bti.uro.uidaho.edu
Contact: Barbara Crouch, Dir
Description: A small business incubator offering affordable space for emerging technology-based firms. Space can be configured to suit the needs of tenants.

49466 ■ Panhandle Area Council–Business Center for Innovation and Development
11100 N Airport Dr.
Hayden, ID 83835-9798
Ph:(208)772-0584

Fax:(208)772-6196
URL: http://www.pacni.org/incubator.html
Contact: Jeff Deffenbaugh, Exec Dir
Description: A small business incubator that assists entrepreneurs in the business start-up process and gives aid to new businesses to help ensure their survival.

49467 ■ Salmon Valley Business Innovation Center
803 Monroe St.
Salmon, ID 83467
Ph:(208)756-1505
Fax:(208)756-1506
Co. E-mail: wayne@centurytel.net
URL: http://www.svbic.com/
Contact: Rene Toman, Exec. Dir.
Description: A project developed to encourage new business growth in the community while creating greater employment opportunities for residents of the Salmon Valley. Its objective is to help new and relocating businesses become successful by providing capital cost reductions during their start up phase, in the form of lease rate discounts, shared office equipment and resources, and business development assistance.

49468 ■ University of Idaho–Office of Technology Transfer
Morrill Hall, 414
PO Box 443003
Moscow, ID 83844-3003
Ph:(208)885-4550
Fax:(208)885-4551
Co. E-mail: ott@uidaho.edu
URL: http://www.uidaho.edu/ott
Contact: Gene A. Merrell PhD, Dir.
E-mail: ott@uidaho.edu
Scope: Technology transfer/commercialization agent for the University of Idaho.

49469 ■ University of Idaho–University Research Office
PO Box 443010
Moscow, ID 83844-3010
Ph:(208)885-4989
Fax:(208)885-6198
Co. E-mail: vpresearch@uidaho.edu
URL: http://www.uidaho.edu/research.aspx
Contact: John K. McIver, VP
E-mail: vpresearch@uidaho.edu
Scope: Coordinates research in various fields at the University, including agriculture, anthropology, education, chemical, civil, electrical, mechanical, transportation and general engineering, forestry, geology, humanities, law, life sciences, physical sciences, social sciences, water resources, materials, aquaculture, microelectronics, metallurgy, mining, computer science, wildlife and wilderness. **Publications:** Idaho Research. **Educational Activities:** Grant seeking workshops; K-12 teacher/student research experiences.

EDUCATIONAL PROGRAMS

49470 ■ BYU Idaho
525 S Center St.
Rexburg, ID 83460-0800
Ph:(208)496-2411
Fax:(208)356-1185
Co. E-mail: infodesk@byui.edu
URL: http://www.byui.edu
Description: General studies associates degrees.

49471 ■ College of Southern Idaho–School of Vo-Tech Education
PO Box 1238
Twin Falls, ID 83303
Ph:(208)733-9554
Free: 800-680-0274
Fax:(208)736-3015
Co. E-mail: info@csi.edu
URL: http://www.csi.edu
Description: Vocation-technical school offering customized training; industry-specific upgrade training; independent business and agribusiness management training; entry/re-entry training; and retraining for displaced workers.

49472 ■ Eastern Idaho Technical College
1600 South 25th East
Idaho Falls, ID 83404
Ph:(208)524-3000
Free: 800-662-0261
Fax:(208)524-3007
URL: http://www.eitc.edu
Description: Vocation-technical school offering customized training; industry-specific upgrade training; independent business and agribusiness management training; entry/re-entry training; and retraining for displaced workers.

49473 ■ Idaho State University–College of Technology
Campus Box 8380
Pocatello, ID 83209
Ph:(208)282-2622
Fax:(208)282-5195
Co. E-mail: ctech@isu.edu
URL: http://www.isu.edu/ctech
Description: Vocation-technical school offering customized training; industry-specific upgrade training; independent business and agribusiness management training; entry/re-entry training; and retraining for displaced workers.

49474 ■ Lewis-Clark State College–School of Technology
500 8th Ave.
Lewiston, ID 83501
Ph:(208)792-5272
Free: 800-933-5272

Fax:(208)792-2816
URL: http://www.lcsc.edu
Description: Vocation-technical school offering customized training; industry-specific upgrade training; independent business and agribusiness management training; entry/re-entry training; and retraining for displaced workers.

49475 ■ North Idaho College–Professional - Technical Education
1000 W Garden Ave.
Coeur D'Alene, ID 83814
Ph:(208)769-3300
Free: 877-404-4536
Fax:(208)769-3459
URL: http://www.nic.edu
Description: Vocation-technical school offering customized training; industry-specific upgrade training; independent business and agribusiness management training; entry/re-entry training; and retraining for displaced workers.

LEGISLATIVE ASSISTANCE

49476 ■ Idaho Department of Commerce
700 W State St.
PO Box 83720
Boise, ID 83720-0093
Ph:(208)334-2470
Free: 800-842-5858
Fax:(208)334-2631
URL: http://commerce.idaho.gov/

PUBLICATIONS

49477 ■ *The Idaho Business Review*
PO Box 8866
Boise, ID 83707
Ph:(208)336-3768
Fax:(208)336-5534

49478 ■ *North Idaho Business Journal*
201 N., Second St.
Coeur D'Alene, ID 83814
Ph:(208)664-8176
Fax:(208)664-0212
Co. E-mail: editor@cbapress.com

49479 ■ *Starting and Operating a Business in Idaho: A Step-by-Step Guide*
PSI Research
300 N. Valley Dr.
Grants Pass, OR 97526
Ph:(503)479-9464
Free: 800-228-2275
Fax:(503)476-1479
Co. E-mail: psi2@magick.net
Ed: Michael D. Jenkins. **Released:** Revised edition, 1992. **Price:** $29.95 (looseleaf binder); $24.95 (paper). **Description:** Part of the Successful Business Library series.

SMALL BUSINESS DEVELOPMENT CENTERS

49480 ■ Illinois Small Business Development Center at Black Hawk College
4703 16th St., Ste. G
Moline, IL 61265-7066
Fax:(309)797-9344
Co. E-mail: scalfd@bhc.edu
URL: http://www.ilsbdc.biz
Contact: Donna Scalf

49481 ■ Illinois Small Business Development Center at Bradley University
141 Jobst Hall
1501 W Bradley Ave.
Peoria, IL 61606-1048
Fax:(309)677-3386
Co. E-mail: sbdc@bradley.edu
URL: http://www.ilsbdc.biz
Contact: Ken Klotz

49482 ■ Illinois Small Business Development Center at Chicago Community Ventures
700 N Sacramento Blvd., Ste. 130
Chicago, IL 60612
Co. E-mail: sbdc@chiventures.org
URL: http://www.ilsbdc.biz
Contact: Tom Cassell

49483 ■ Illinois Small Business Development Center at Chicago State University/Greater Southside
9501 S King Dr.
BHS 601
Chicago, IL 60628-1598
Fax:(773)821-2841
Co. E-mail: i-conda@csu.edu
URL: http://www.ilsbdc.biz
Contact: Isabelle Conda

49484 ■ Illinois Small Business Development Center at College of DuPage
2525 Cabot Dr.
Lisle, IL 60532
Fax:(630)942-3789
Co. E-mail: gaydav@cod.edu
URL: http://www.ilsbdc.biz
Contact: David Gay

49485 ■ Illinois Small Business Development Center at College of Lake County
19351 W Washington St., Rm. T-302
Grayslake, IL 60030-1198
Fax:(847)223-9371
Co. E-mail: clcsbdc@clcillinois.edu
URL: http://www.ilsbdc.biz
Contact: Jan Bauer

49486 ■ Illinois Small Business Development Center at Danville Area Community College
2917 N Vermillion St.
Danville, IL 61832
Fax:(217)442-1897
Co. E-mail: sbdc@dacc.edu
URL: http://www.ilsbdc.biz
Contact: Michael O'Brian

49487 ■ Illinois Small Business Development Center at Duman Microenteprise Center
216 W Jackson Blvd., Ste. 700
Chicago, IL 60606
URL: http://www.ildceo.net

49488 ■ Illinois Small Business Development Center at Elgin Community College
1700 Spartan Dr.
Elgin, IL 60123-7193
Fax:(847)931-3911
Co. E-mail: kknowles@elgin.edu
URL: http://www.ilsbdc.biz
Contact: Kriss Knowles

49489 ■ Illinois Small Business Development Center at Evanston Technology Innovation Center
820 Davis St., Ste. 137
Evanston, IL 60201
Fax:(847)866-1808
Co. E-mail: tjw@evanstonsbdc.com
URL: http://www.ilsbdc.biz
Contact: TJ Weber

49490 ■ Illinois Small Business Development Center at Greater Northwest Chicago Development Corporation
6600 W Armitage Ave.
Chicago, IL 60707-3908
Fax:(773)637-2698
Co. E-mail: sbdc@gncdc.org
URL: http://www.ilsbdc.biz
Contact: Reid Mackin

49491 ■ Illinois Small Business Development Center at Harper College
Harper Professional Bldg., Ste. 106
650 E Higgins Rd.
Schaumburg, IL 60173
Fax:(847)925-6109
Co. E-mail: brichter@harper.edu
URL: http://www.ilsbdc.biz
Contact: Bonita Richter

49492 ■ Illinois Small Business Development Center at Highland Community College
Bldg. H, Rm. 205
2998 W Pearl City Rd.
Freeport, IL 61032
URL: http://www.ildceo.net

49493 ■ Illinois Small Business Development Center at Hull House
Jane Addams Hull House - Parkway Community House
500 E 67th St.
Chicago, IL 60637-4097
Fax:(773)955-8028
Co. E-mail: krobbins@hullhouse.org
URL: http://www.ilsbdc.biz
Contact: Kathleen Robbins

49494 ■ Illinois Small Business Development Center at Illinois Eastern Community College
702 High St.
Olney, IL 62450
URL: http://www.ildceo.net

49495 ■ Illinois Small Business Development Center at Illinois State University
214 College of Business Bldg.
Mail Code 5580
Normal, IL 61761-5580
Fax:(309)438-2114
Co. E-mail: ejbinni@ilstu.edu
URL: http://www.ilsbdc.biz
Contact: Elizabeth Binning

49496 ■ Illinois Small Business Development Center at Illinois Valley Community College
815 N Orlando Smith Ave., Bldg. 11
Oglesby, IL 61348-9692
Fax:(815)223-1780
Co. E-mail: bev_malooley@ivcc.edu
URL: http://www.ilsbdc.biz
Contact: Bev Malooley

49497 ■ Illinois Small Business Development Center at Industrial Council of Nearwest Chicago
2010 W Fulton St., Ste. 280
Chicago, IL 60612
Fax:(312)421-1871
Co. E-mail: sbdc@industrialcouncil.com
URL: http://www.ilsbdc.biz
Contact: Andrew Fogarty

49498 ■ Illinois Small Business Development Center at Joliet Jr. College
City Center Campus, Rm. 400
Joliet, IL 60432-4077
Fax:(708)488-2290
Co. E-mail: bhansen@jjc.edu
URL: http://www.ilsbdc.biz
Contact: Bob Hansen

49499 ■ Illinois Small Business Development Center at Joseph Center
7600 W Roosevelt Rd.
Forest Park, IL 60130
Fax:(708)488-2290
Co. E-mail: sbdc@josephcenter.com
URL: http://www.ilsbdc.biz
Contact: Edna Chapman

49500 ■ Illinois Small Business Development Center at Kankakee Community College
100 College Dr.
Kankakee, IL 60901
Fax:(815)802-8101
Co. E-mail: kcrite@kcc.edu
URL: http://www.ilsbdc.biz
Contact: Ken Crite

49501 ■ Illinois Small Business Development Center at Kaskaskia College
Institute for Entrepreneurial Success
325 S Poplar St.
Centralia, IL 62801
Fax:(618)545-3258
Co. E-mail: ttracy@kaskaskia.edu
URL: http://www.ilsbdc.biz
Contact: Todd Tracy

49502 ■ Illinois Small Business Development Center at Lincoln Land Community College
3 S Old State Capitol Plz.
Springfield, IL 62701
Fax:(217)522-3512
Co. E-mail: sbdc@llcc.edu
URL: http://www.ilsbdc.biz
Contact: Kevin Lust

49503 ■ Illinois Small Business Development Center at McHenry County College
4100 W Shamrock Ln.
McHenry, IL 60050
Fax:(815)578-9684
Co. E-mail: sbdc@mchenry.edu
URL: http://www.ilsbdc.biz
Contact: Mary Margaret Maule

49504 ■ Illinois Small Business Development Center at North Business and Industrial Council
5353 W Armstrong Ave.
Chicago, IL 60646
URL: http://www.ildceo.net

49505 ■ Illinois Small Business Development Center at Rend Lake College
327 Potomac Blvd., Ste. A
Mount Vernon, IL 62864
Fax:(618)242-8220
Co. E-mail: mowrer@rlc.edu
URL: http://www.ilsbdc.biz
Contact: Curt Mowrer

49506 ■ Illinois Small Business Development Center at Rock Valley College
EIGER Lab
605 Fulton Ave., Rm. E109
Rockford, IL 61103
Fax:(815)921-2089
Co. E-mail: sbdc-rvc@rockvalleycollege.edu
URL: http://www.ilsbdc.biz
Contact: Pam Schallhorn

49507 ■ Illinois Small Business Development Center at Sauk Valley Community College
173 Illinois Rte. No. 2
Dixon, IL 61021-9188
Fax:(815)288-5958
Co. E-mail: millerm@svcc.edu
URL: http://www.ilsbdc.biz
Contact: Michelle Miller

49508 ■ Illinois Small Business Development Center at Shawnee Community College
8364 Shawnee College Rd.
Ullin, IL 62992-2206
Fax:(618)634-2347
Co. E-mail: sccsbdc@shawneecc.edu
URL: http://www.ilsbdc.biz
Contact: Candy Eastwood

49509 ■ Illinois Small Business Development Center at SIU-E/East St. Louis
Bldg. D, Rm. 1017
601 James R. Thompson Blvd.
East St. Louis, IL 62201
Fax:(618)482-8341
Co. E-mail: kmister@siue.edu
URL: http://www.ilsbdc.biz
Contact: Kwa Mister

49510 ■ Illinois Small Business Development Center at Southeastern Illinois College
2 E Locust St., Ste. 200
Harrisburg, IL 62946
Fax:(618)252-0210
Co. E-mail: lori.cox@sic.edu
URL: http://www.ilsbdc.biz
Contact: Lori Cox

49511 ■ Illinois Small Business Development Center at Southern Illinois University - Edwardsville
Campus Box 1107
Alumni Hall 2126
Edwardsville, IL 62026
Fax:(618)650-2647
Co. E-mail: kmister@siue.edu
URL: http://www.ilsbdc.biz
Contact: Kwa Mister

49512 ■ Illinois Small Business Development Center at University of Illinois at Chicago
College of Business Administration
Rice Bldg., Ste. 320
815 W Van Buren St.
Chicago, IL 60607
URL: http://www.ildceo.net

49513 ■ Illinois Small Business Development Center at Waubonsee Community College
Aurora Campus
5 E Galena Blvd.
Aurora, IL 60506-4178
Fax:(630)892-4668
Co. E-mail: hparker@waubonsee.edu
URL: http://www.ilsbdc.biz
Contact: Harriet Parker

49514 ■ Illinois Small Business Development Center at Western Illinois University
510 N Pearl St., Ste. 1400
Macomb, IL 61455
Co. E-mail: sb-center@wiu.edu
URL: http://www.ilsbdc.biz
Contact: Dan Voorhis

SMALL BUSINESS ASSISTANCE PROGRAMS

49515 ■ Illinois Department of Commerce and Community Affairs–Entrepreneurship and Small Business Office
620 E Adams St.
Springfield, IL 62701
Ph:800-252-2923
Free: 800-252-3998
URL: http://www.commerce.state.il.us/dceo
Description: Provides management, technical, and financial assistance through its Advocacy, Program Evaluation, Business Development, and Business Finance and Energy Assistance Division.

49516 ■ Illinois Department of Commerce and Economic Opportunity–Energy and Recycling
620 E Adams St.
Chicago, IL 62701
Ph:(217)785-3416
Co. E-mail: Illinois.energy@illinois.gov
URL: http://www.commerce.state.il.us/dceo
Contact: Jack Lavin, Dir
Description: Intervenes in the utility rate-setting process and in disputes between small businesses and utility companies. Assists in financing energy conservation measures.

SCORE OFFICES

49517 ■ Chicago SCORES
222 S Morgan St., No. 4C
Chicago, IL 60607
Ph:(312)666-0496

Fax:(312)850-4951
Co. E-mail: avondrastark@americascores.org
URL: http://www.americascores.org
Contact: Amy Vondra-Stark, Exec. Dir.
Description: Aims to empower students in urban communities using soccer, writing and creative expression, and service-learning.

49518 ■ E. Central Illinois (ECI) SCORE
Path: www.eciscore.org

49519 ■ Peoria SCORE
Path: www.scorepeoria.org

49520 ■ SCORE Central Illinois
402 N Hershey Rd.
Bloomington, IL 61704
Ph:(309)664-0549
Fax:(309)661-1177
Co. E-mail: webmaster@central-illinois-score.org
URL: http://www.central-illinois-score.org
Contact: Dorothy Kennett, Chair
Description: Provides free consulting services to both start-up and existing small businesses in Central Illinois service area.

49521 ■ SCORE Chicago
500 W Madison St., Ste. 1250
Chicago, IL 60661-2511
Ph:(312)353-7724
Fax:(312)886-4879
Co. E-mail: info@scorechicago.org
Description: Works to strengthen the formation, growth and success of small businesses nationwide.

49522 ■ SCORE Decatur
Millikin University
1184 W Main St.
Decatur, IL 62522
Ph:(217)424-6296
Fax:(217)424-3523
Co. E-mail: score@millikin.edu
URL: http://www.decatur.scorechapter.org
Contact: Carroll Moma
Description: Works to strengthen the formation, growth and success of small businesses nationwide.

49523 ■ SCORE Fox Valley
1444 N Farnsworth Ave., Rm. 504
Aurora, IL 60505
Ph:(630)692-1162
Fax:(630)852-3127
Co. E-mail: leemcf@wideonpenwest.com
URL: http://www.scorefoxvalley.org
Contact: Lee McFadden, Chm.
Description: Strives for the formation, growth and success of small businesses. Provides professional guidance and information to maximize the success of existing and emerging small businesses. Promotes entrepreneur education in Fox Valley area, Illinois.

49524 ■ SCORE Kankakee
Path: www.score-kankakee.com

49525 ■ SCORE Northern Illinois
605 Fulton Ave.
Eiger Lab
Rockford, IL 61103
Ph:(815)962-0122
Fax:(815)962-0806
Co. E-mail: info@northernillinoisscore.org
URL: http://www.northernillinoisscore.org
Contact: Jim Dehler, Chm.
Description: Counsels small businesses on start-up, writing a business plan, addressing problems with cash flow, inventory control, and other business-related issues.

49526 ■ SCORE Quad Cities
622 19th St.
Moline, IL 61265
Ph:(309)797-0082
Fax:(309)757-5435
Co. E-mail: info@quadcitiesscore.org
URL: http://www.quadcitiesscore.org
Contact: Mr. Robert Radkiewicz, Chm.
Description: Provides professional guidance and information to maximize the success of existing and emerging small businesses. Develops business plans and evaluate financial projections. Promotes entre-

preneur education in the western Illinois/eastern Iowa Quad Cities area including Moline and Rock Island IL and Davenport and Bettendorf, IA.

49527 ■ SCORE Quincy Tri-State
c/o Quincy Area Chamber of Commerce
300 Civic Center Plz., Ste. 245
Quincy, IL 62301
Ph:(217)222-8093
Co. E-mail: score@adams.net
URL: http://www.score-tristate.org
Contact: Ralph Mortimore, Chm.
Description: Provides counseling to persons wanting to go into business as well as those already in the business. Sponsors seminars and workshops.

49528 ■ SCORE Springfield
3330 Ginger Creek Dr., Ste. B, S
Springfield, IL 62711
Ph:(217)793-5020
Fax:(217)793-5025
Co. E-mail: score571@aol.com
URL: http://www.scorespi.org
Description:

49529 ■ Southeastern Illinois SCORE
Path: castle.eiu.edu/score

49530 ■ Southern Illinois SCORE
Path: silscore.org

49531 ■ Southwestern Illinois SCORE
Path: www2.lc.edu/score/swis.htm

BETTER BUSINESS BUREAUS

49532 ■ Better Business Bureau of Central Illinois
112 Harrison
Peoria, IL 61602
Ph:(309)688-3741
Co. E-mail: bbb@heart.net
URL: http://www.peoria.bbb.org

49533 ■ Better Business Bureau of Chicago and Northern Illinois
330 N Wabash Ave., Ste. 2006
Chicago, IL 60611
Ph:(312)832-0500
Fax:(312)832-9985
Co. E-mail: info@chicago.bbb.org
URL: http://chicago.bbb.org

CHAMBERS OF COMMERCE

49534 ■ Addison Chamber of Commerce and Industry
777 Army Trail Rd., Ste. D
Addison, IL 60101
Ph:(630)543-4300
Fax:(630)543-4355
Co. E-mail: addisonchamber@sbcglobal.net
URL: http://www.addisonchamber.org
Contact: Bernadette Hanrahan, Exec. Dir.

49535 ■ Albany Park Chamber of Commerce
3403 W Lawrence Ave., Ste. 201
Chicago, IL 60625
Ph:(773)478-0202
Fax:(773)478-0282
Co. E-mail: mmcdaniel@northrivercommission.org
URL: http://www.albanyparkchamber.org
Contact: Melissa McDaniel, Exec. Dir.

49536 ■ Aledo Area Chamber of Commerce
PO Box 261
Aledo, IL 61231
Ph:(309)582-5373
Fax:(866)555-1112
Co. E-mail: aledochamber@frontiernet.net
URL: http://www.aledochamber.org
Contact: Lance Meyer, Pres.

49537 ■ Algonquin - Lake in the Hills Chamber of Commerce
2114 W Algonquin Rd.
Lake in the Hills, IL 60156
Ph:(847)658-5300
Co. E-mail: info@algonquin-lith-chamber.com
URL: http://www.algonquin-lith-chamber.com
Contact: Sandy Oslance, Exec. Dir.

49538 ■ Alsip Chamber of Commerce and Economic Development
12159 S Pulaski Rd.
Alsip, IL 60803
Ph:(708)597-2668
Free: 800-INA-LSIP
Fax:(708)597-5962
Co. E-mail: alsipcc@hotmail.com
URL: http://www.alsipchamber.org
Contact: Mary Schmidt, Exec. Dir.

49539 ■ Altamont Chamber of Commerce
PO Box 141
Altamont, IL 62411
Ph:(618)483-6119
Free: (866)483-6119
Co. E-mail: info@altamontchamber.com
URL: http://www.altamontil.net
Contact: Butch Roedl, Pres.

49540 ■ Antioch Chamber of Commerce and Industry
882 Main St.
Antioch, IL 60002
Ph:(847)395-2233
Fax:(847)395-8954
Co. E-mail: info@antiochchamber.org
URL: http://www.antiochchamber.org
Contact: Barbara Porch, Exec. Dir.

49541 ■ Arcola Chamber of Commerce
PO Box 274
Arcola, IL 61910
Ph:(217)268-4530
Co. E-mail: arcolachamber@consolidated.net
URL: http://www.arcolachamber.com
Contact: Lisa Boyer, Pres.

49542 ■ Arlington Heights Chamber of Commerce
311 S Arlington Heights Rd., Ste. 20
Arlington Heights, IL 60005
Ph:(847)253-1703
Fax:(847)253-9133
Co. E-mail: info@arlingtonhtschamber.com
URL: http://www.arlingtonhtschamber.com/web06.nsf
Contact: Jon S. Ridler, Exec. Dir.

49543 ■ ATHENA International
70 E Lake St., Ste. 1220
Chicago, IL 60601-5939
Ph:(312)580-0111
Fax:(312)580-0110
Co. E-mail: athena@athenainternational.org
URL: http://www.athenafoundation.org
Contact: Lynn Myers, Pres.

49544 ■ Barrington Area Chamber of Commerce
325 N Hough St.
Barrington, IL 60010
Ph:(847)381-2525
Co. E-mail: janet@barringtonchamber.com
URL: http://www.barringtonchamber.com
Contact: Janet Meyer, Pres.

49545 ■ Bartlett Chamber of Commerce
138 S Oak Ave.
Bartlett, IL 60103
Ph:(630)830-0324
Fax:(630)830-9724
Co. E-mail: info@bartlettchamber.com
URL: http://www.bartlettchamber.com
Contact: Diane Hubberts IOM, Pres./CEO

49546 ■ Batavia Chamber of Commerce
106 W Wilson St.
Batavia, IL 60510
Ph:(630)879-7134

Fax:(630)879-7215
Co. E-mail: info@bataviachamber.org
URL: http://www.bataviachamber.org
Contact: Mr. Roger Breisch, Exec. Dir.

49547 ■ Beardstown Chamber of Commerce
101 W 3rd St.
Beardstown, IL 62618
Ph:(217)323-3271
Fax:(217)323-3271
Co. E-mail: info@beardstownil.org
URL: http://www.beardstownil.org

49548 ■ Beecher Chamber of Commerce
PO Box 292
Beecher, IL 60401
Ph:(708)946-6803
Co. E-mail: bchamber@villageofbeecher.org
URL: http://www.beecherchamber.com
Contact: Chuck Hoehn, Pres.

49549 ■ Belmont-Central Chamber of Commerce
3250 N Central Ave., 2nd Fl.
Chicago, IL 60634
Ph:(773)202-9923
Fax:(773)205-8986
Co. E-mail: belmontcentralcc@sbcglobal.net
URL: http://www.belmontcentral.org
Contact: Larry Lynch, Pres.

49550 ■ Belvidere Area Chamber of Commerce
200 S State St.
Belvidere, IL 61008
Ph:(815)544-4357
Fax:(815)547-7654
Co. E-mail: tlassandro@belviderechamber.com
URL: http://www.belviderechamber.com
Contact: Thomas Lassandro, Exec. Dir.

49551 ■ Benton-West City Area Chamber of Commerce
211 N Main St.
PO Box 574
Benton, IL 62812
Ph:(618)438-2121
Free: (866)536-8423
Fax:(618)438-8011
Co. E-mail: chamber@bentonwestcity.com
URL: http://www.bentonwestcity.com
Contact: Gloria Atchison, Exec. Sec.

49552 ■ Bloomingdale Chamber of Commerce
108 W Lake St.
Bloomingdale, IL 60108
Ph:(630)980-9082
Fax:(630)980-9092
Co. E-mail: bloomcham@sbcglobal.net
URL: http://www.bloomingdalechamber.com
Contact: Ms. Jane Hove, Exec. Dir.

49553 ■ Blue Island Area Chamber of Commerce and Industry
2434 Vermont St.
Blue Island, IL 60406
Ph:(708)388-1000
Fax:(708)388-1062
Co. E-mail: blueislandchamber@sbcglobal.net
URL: http://www.blueislandchamber.org
Contact: Karen Warrick, Chair

49554 ■ Bolingbrook Area Chamber of Commerce
201-B Canterbury Ln.
Bolingbrook, IL 60440
Ph:(630)226-8420
Fax:(630)226-8426
Co. E-mail: info@bolingbrookchamber.org
URL: http://www.bolingbrookchamber.org
Contact: Mike Evans, Exec. Dir.

49555 ■ Bradley-Bourbonnais Chamber of Commerce
1690 Newtowne Dr.
Bourbonnais, IL 60914
Ph:(815)932-2222

Fax:(815)932-3294
Co. E-mail: bbcc@bbchamber.com
URL: http://bbchamber.com
Contact: Jaclyn Dugan-Roof, Pres./CEO

49556 ■ Breese Chamber of Commerce
PO Box 132
Breese, IL 62230
Co. E-mail: bjwade@cbnstl.com
URL: http://www.breesechamber.org
Contact: Brandon Wade, Pres.

49557 ■ Bridgeview Chamber of Commerce
7300 W 87th St.
Bridgeview, IL 60455
Ph:(708)598-1700
Co. E-mail: bvchamber@aol.com
URL: http://www.bridgeviewchamber.com
Contact: Roseann Bautista, Exec. Dir.

49558 ■ Brookfield Chamber of Commerce
PO Box 38
Brookfield, IL 60513
Ph:(708)485-3893
Co. E-mail: info@brookfieldchamber.net
URL: http://www.brookfieldchamber.net
Contact: Betty LeClere, Pres.

49559 ■ Buffalo Grove Area Chamber of Commerce
50 1/2 Raupp Blvd.
PO Box 7124
Buffalo Grove, IL 60089
Ph:(847)541-7799
Fax:(847)541-7819
Co. E-mail: info@bgacc.org
URL: http://www.bgacc.org/Welcome.asp
Contact: Lynne Schneider, Exec. Dir.

49560 ■ Bushnell Chamber of Commerce
PO Box 111
Bushnell, IL 61422
Ph:(309)772-2171
Fax:(309)772-3616
Co. E-mail: chamber@bushnellchamber.com
URL: http://www.bushnellchamber.com
Contact: Don Swartzbaugh, Pres.

49561 ■ Byron Area Chamber of Commerce
PO Box 405
Byron, IL 61010
Ph:(815)234-5500
Fax:(815)234-7114
Co. E-mail: byronchamber@byronil.net
URL: http://www.byronchamber.org
Contact: Caryn Huber, Exec. Dir.

49562 ■ Cahokia Area Chamber of Commerce
103 Main St.
Cahokia, IL 62206
Ph:(618)332-1900
Co. E-mail: business@cahokiachamber.com
URL: http://www.cahokiachamber.com
Contact: Debbie Craig, Pres.

49563 ■ Canton Area Chamber of Commerce
45 E Side Sq., Ste. 303
Canton, IL 61520
Ph:(309)647-2677
Fax:(309)647-2712
Co. E-mail: cantonareacc@sbcglobal.net
URL: http://www.cantonillinois.org
Contact: Missy Towery, Exec. Dir.

49564 ■ Carbondale Chamber of Commerce
PO Box 877
Carbondale, IL 62903
Ph:(618)549-2146
Fax:(618)529-5063
Co. E-mail: carbondalechamberofcommerce@gmail.
 com
URL: http://www.carbondalechamber.com
Contact: Woody Thorne, Pres.

49565 ■ Carlinville Community Chamber of Commerce
112 N Side Sq.
Carlinville, IL 62626
Ph:(217)854-2141
Fax:(217)854-8548
Co. E-mail: info@carlinvillechamber.com
URL: http://www.carlinvillechamber.com

49566 ■ Carmi Chamber of Commerce
225 E Main St.
Carmi, IL 62821
Ph:(618)382-7606
Co. E-mail: ccc@cityofcarmi.com
URL: http://www.cityofcarmi.com
Contact: Sandra Irvine, Dir.

49567 ■ Carol Stream Chamber of Commerce
150 S Gary Ave.
Carol Stream, IL 60188
Ph:(630)665-3325
Fax:(630)665-6965
Co. E-mail: info@carolstreamchamber.com
URL: http://www.carolstreamchamber.com
Contact: Ms. Luanne Triolo, Exec. Dir.

49568 ■ Carterville Chamber of Commerce
120 N Greenbriar
PO Box 262
Carterville, IL 62918
Ph:(618)985-6942
Fax:(618)985-6942
Co. E-mail: chamber@cartervillechamber.com
URL: http://www.cartervillechamber.com
Contact: Mike Williams, Exec. Dir.

49569 ■ Carthage Area Chamber of Commerce
PO Box 247
Carthage, IL 62321
Ph:(217)357-3024
Fax:(217)357-3024
Co. E-mail: chamber@carthage-il.com
URL: http://www.carthage-il.com/business/chamber1.
 htm
Contact: Nina Boyer, Pres.

49570 ■ Cary/Grove Area Chamber of Commerce
27 E Main St.
PO Box 302
Cary, IL 60013
Ph:(847)639-2800
Fax:(847)639-2168
Co. E-mail: info@carygrovechamber.com
URL: http://www.carygrovechamber.com
Contact: Suzanne Corr, Exec. Dir.

49571 ■ Champaign County Chamber of Commerce
1817 S Neil St., Ste. 201
Champaign, IL 61820-7269
Ph:(217)359-1791
Fax:(217)359-1809
Co. E-mail: info@champaigncounty.org
URL: http://www.ccchamber.org
Contact: Laura E. Weis IOM, Pres./CEO

49572 ■ Charleston Area Chamber of Commerce
501 Jackson Ave.
PO Box 77
Charleston, IL 61920
Ph:(217)345-7041
Fax:(217)345-7042
Co. E-mail: cacc@charlestonchamber.com
URL: http://www.charlestonchamber.com
Contact: Cindy Titus, Exec. Dir.

49573 ■ Chester Chamber of Commerce
PO Box 585
Chester, IL 62233
Ph:(618)826-2721
Co. E-mail: chesterc@egyptian.net
URL: http://www.chesterill.com/chamber
Contact: Linda Sympson, Exec. Dir.

49574 ■ Chicago Area Gay and Lesbian Chamber of Commerce
3656 N Halsted St.
Chicago, IL 60613
Ph:(773)303-0167
Fax:(773)303-0168
Co. E-mail: info@glchamber.org
URL: http://www.glchamber.org
Contact: Christina Pinson, Exec. Dir.

49575 ■ Chicago Chinatown Chamber of Commerce
2169B S China Pl.
Chicago, IL 60616
Ph:(312)326-5320
Fax:(312)326-5668
Co. E-mail: info@chicagochinatown.org
URL: http://www.chicagochinatown.org/cccorg/home.
 jsp
Contact: Susan Ng-Harroun, Exec. Dir.

49576 ■ Chicagoland Chamber of Commerce
Aon Center
200 E Randolph St., Ste. 2200
Chicago, IL 60601-6436
Ph:(312)494-6700
Fax:(312)861-0660
Co. E-mail: staff@chicagolandchamber.org
URL: http://www.chicagolandchamber.org/Pages/
 default.aspx
Contact: Jerry Roper, Pres./CEO

49577 ■ Chillicothe Chamber of Commerce
1028 N 2nd St.
Chillicothe, IL 61523
Ph:(309)274-4556
Fax:(309)274-3303
Co. E-mail: info@chillicothechamber.com
URL: http://www.chillicothechamber.com
Contact: Irvin Latta, Pres.

49578 ■ Cicero Chamber of Commerce and Industry
5801 W Cermak Rd., 2nd Fl.
Cicero, IL 60804
Ph:(708)863-6000
Fax:(708)863-8981
Co. E-mail: cicerocc@cicerochamber.org
URL: http://www.cicerochamber.org
Contact: Mary Esther Hernandez, Exec. Dir.

49579 ■ Clinton Area Chamber of Commerce
100 S Center St., Ste. 101
Clinton, IL 61727-1945
Ph:(217)935-3364
Free: (866)4DE-WITT
Fax:(217)935-0064
Co. E-mail: info@clintonilchamber.com
URL: http://www.clintonilchamber.com
Contact: Marian Brisard, Office Mgr.

49580 ■ Collinsville Chamber of Commerce
221 W Main St.
Collinsville, IL 62234
Ph:(618)344-2884
Fax:(618)344-7499
Co. E-mail: info@discovercollinsville.com
URL: http://www.discovercollinsville.com
Contact: Wendi Valenti, Exec. Dir.

49581 ■ Cosmopolitan Chamber of Commerce
203 N Wabash Ave., Ste. 518
Chicago, IL 60601
Ph:(312)499-0611
Fax:(312)701-0095
Co. E-mail: info@cosmococ.org
URL: http://cosmococ.org
Contact: Carnice Carey, Exec. Dir.

49582 ■ Crete Area Chamber of Commerce
PO Box 263
Crete, IL 60417-0263
Ph:(708)672-9216
Fax:(708)672-7640
Co. E-mail: cretechamber@sbcglobal.net
URL: http://www.cretechamber.com
Contact: Pat Herbert, Exec. Dir.

49583 ■ Crystal Lake Chamber of Commerce
427 W Virginia St.
Crystal Lake, IL 60014
Ph:(815)459-1300
Fax:(815)459-0243
Co. E-mail: info@clchamber.com
URL: http://www.clchamber.com
Contact: Gary Reece, Pres.

49584 ■ Darien Chamber of Commerce
1702 Plainfield Rd.
Darien, IL 60561-5080
Ph:(630)968-0004
Fax:(630)968-2474
Co. E-mail: info@darienchamber.com
URL: http://www.darienchamber.com
Contact: Bill Carpenter, Pres.

49585 ■ Deerfield, Bannockburn, Riverwoods Chamber of Commerce
601 Deerfield Rd., Ste. 200
Deerfield, IL 60015
Ph:(847)945-4660
Fax:(847)940-0381
Co. E-mail: info@dbrchamber.com
URL: http://www.dbrchamber.com
Contact: Victoria Case, Exec. Dir.

49586 ■ DeKalb Chamber of Commerce
164 E Lincoln Hwy.
DeKalb, IL 60115
Ph:(815)756-6306
Fax:(815)756-5164
Co. E-mail: info@dekalbchamber.org
URL: http://www.dekalb.org
Contact: Mr. Jim Allen, Exec. Dir.

49587 ■ Des Plaines Chamber of Commerce and Industry
1401 E Oakton St.
Des Plaines, IL 60018
Ph:(847)824-4200
Fax:(847)824-7932
Co. E-mail: info@dpchamber.com
URL: http://www.dpchamber.com
Contact: Alan Czarnik, Pres.

49588 ■ Dixon Area Chamber of Commerce and Industry
101 W 2nd St., Ste. 301
Dixon, IL 61021
Ph:(815)284-3361
Fax:(815)284-3675
Co. E-mail: dchamber@essex1.com
URL: http://www.dixonillinoischamber.com
Contact: John R. Thompson, Pres./CEO

49589 ■ Downers Grove Area Chamber of Commerce and Industry
The Esplanade at Locust Point
2001 Butterfield Rd., Ste. 105
Downers Grove, IL 60515
Ph:(630)968-4050
Fax:(630)968-8368
Co. E-mail: chamber@downersgrove.org
URL: http://www.downersgrove.org
Contact: Laura Crawford, Pres./CEO

49590 ■ Du Quoin Chamber of Commerce
PO Box 57
Du Quoin, IL 62832
Ph:(618)542-9570
Co. E-mail: dqchamber@comcast.net
URL: http://www.duquoin.org
Contact: Frank Deaton, Pres.

49591 ■ East Peoria Chamber of Commerce and Tourism
111 W Washington St., Ste. 290
East Peoria, IL 61611-2532
Ph:(309)699-6212
Fax:(309)699-6220
Co. E-mail: epcc@epcc.org
URL: http://www.epcc.org/index.php
Contact: Barb Filipiak, Exec. Dir.

49592 ■ Edgebrook Chamber of Commerce
6440 N Central Ave.
Chicago, IL 60646
Ph:(773)775-0378
Fax:(773)775-0371
URL: http://www.edgebrookchamber.com

49593 ■ Edwardsville - Glen Carbon Chamber of Commerce
200 University Park Dr., Ste. 260
Edwardsville, IL 62025
Ph:(618)656-7600
Fax:(618)656-7611
Co. E-mail: cforeman@edglenchamber.com
URL: http://www.edglenchamber.com
Contact: Carol Foreman, Exec. Dir.

49594 ■ El Paso Chamber of Commerce
475 W Front St.
El Paso, IL 61738
Ph:(309)527-4005
Fax:(309)527-4717
Co. E-mail: lbarhum@hbtbank.com
URL: http://www.elpasoil.org/chamber
Contact: Lisa Barhum, Sec.

49595 ■ Elgin Area Chamber of Commerce
31 S Grove Ave.
PO Box 648
Elgin, IL 60120
Ph:(847)741-5660
Fax:(847)741-5677
Co. E-mail: info@elginchamber.com
URL: http://www.elginchamber.com
Contact: Leo Nelson, Pres.

49596 ■ Elizabeth Chamber of Commerce
PO Box 371
Elizabeth, IL 61028
Ph:(815)858-2221
Fax:(815)858-3881
Co. E-mail: info@elizabeth-il.com
URL: http://www.elizabeth-il.com

49597 ■ Elmhurst Chamber of Commerce and Industry
113 Adell Pl.
PO Box 752
Elmhurst, IL 60126-3301
Ph:(630)834-6060
Fax:(630)834-6002
Co. E-mail: info@elmhurstchamber.org
URL: http://www.elmhurstchamber.org
Contact: John R. Quigley, Pres./CEO

49598 ■ Evanston Chamber of Commerce
1 Rotary Ctr.
1560 Sherman Ave., Ste. 860
Evanston, IL 60201
Ph:(847)328-1500
Fax:(847)328-1510
Co. E-mail: info@evchamber.com
URL: http://www.evchamber.com
Contact: Jonathan D. Perman, Exec. Dir.

49599 ■ Evergreen Park Chamber of Commerce
3960 W 95th St., 3rd Fl.
Evergreen Park, IL 60805
Ph:(708)423-1118
Fax:(708)423-1859
Co. E-mail: epchamber@sbcglobal.net
URL: http://www.evergreenparkchamber.com
Contact: Mr. Daniel McKeown, Pres.

49600 ■ Fairbury Chamber of Commerce
101 E Locust
PO Box 86
Fairbury, IL 61739
Ph:(815)692-3899
Co. E-mail: fac@fairburyil.org
URL: http://www.fairburyil.org

49601 ■ Fairview Heights Chamber of Commerce
10003 Bunkum Rd.
Fairview Heights, IL 62208
Ph:(618)397-3127

Fax:(618)397-5563
Co. E-mail: director@fairviewheightschamber.org
URL: http://www.fairviewheightschamber.org
Contact: Scott Leas, Exec. Dir.

49602 ■ Forest Park Chamber of Commerce
7344 W Madison St.
Forest Park, IL 60130
Ph:(708)366-2543
Fax:(708)366-3373
Co. E-mail: info@exploreforestpark.com
URL: http://www.forestparkchamberofcommerce.org
Contact: Laurie Kokenes, Exec. Dir.

49603 ■ Fox Lake Area Chamber of Commerce and Industry
PO Box 203
Fox Lake, IL 60020
Ph:(847)587-7474
Fax:(847)587-1725
Co. E-mail: foxlakechamber@yahoo.com
URL: http://www.discoverfoxlake.com
Contact: Linnea Pioro, Office Mgr.

49604 ■ Frankfort Chamber of Commerce
123 Kansas St.
Frankfort, IL 60423
Ph:(815)469-3356
Free: 877-469-3356
Fax:(815)469-4352
Co. E-mail: info@frankfortchamber.com
URL: http://www.frankfortchamber.com
Contact: John C. Clavio, Pres.

49605 ■ Franklin Park/Schiller Park Chamber of Commerce
PO Box 186
Franklin Park, IL 60131
Ph:(708)865-9510
Co. E-mail: info@chamberbyohare.org
URL: http://www.chamberbyohare.org
Contact: Kenneth Kollar, Pres.

49606 ■ Freeport Area Chamber of Commerce
27 W Stephenson St.
Freeport, IL 61032
Ph:(815)233-1350
Fax:(815)233-3226
Co. E-mail: kim.grimes@aeroinc.net
URL: http://www.freeportilchamber.com
Contact: Mr. Kim Grimes, Pres./CEO

49607 ■ French - American Chamber of Commerce - Chicago
35 E Wacker Dr., Ste. 670
Chicago, IL 60601
Ph:(312)578-0444
Fax:(312)578-0445
Co. E-mail: information@facc-chicago.com
URL: http://www.facc-chicago.com/presentation-of-the-chamber
Contact: Genevieve Gandal, Exec. Dir.

49608 ■ Fulton Chamber of Commerce
415 11th Ave.
PO Box 253
Fulton, IL 61252
Ph:(815)589-4545
Fax:(815)589-4421
Co. E-mail: chamber@cityoffulton.us
URL: http://www.cityoffulton.us
Contact: Heather Bennett, Exec. Dir.

49609 ■ Galena Area Chamber of Commerce
101 Bouthillier St.
Galena, IL 61036
Ph:(815)777-9050
Fax:(815)777-8465
Co. E-mail: office@galenachamber.com
URL: http://www.galenachamber.com
Contact: Ed Schmit, Exec. Dir.

49610 ■ Galesburg Area Chamber of Commerce
PO Box 749
Galesburg, IL 61401
Ph:(309)343-1194
Co. E-mail: chamber@galesburg.org
URL: http://www.galesburg.org
Contact: Robert C. Maus, Pres./CEO

49611 ■ Geneva Chamber of Commerce
8 S 3rd St.
PO Box 481
Geneva, IL 60134-0481
Ph:(630)232-6060
Free: (866)4-GENEVA
Fax:(630)232-6083
Co. E-mail: chamberinfo@genevachamber.com
URL: http://www.genevachamber.com
Contact: Jean Gaines, Pres.

49612 ■ Gibson Area Chamber of Commerce
126 N Sangamon Ave.
Gibson City, IL 60936
Ph:(217)784-5217
Fax:(217)784-4119
Co. E-mail: chamber@gibsoncityillinois.com
Contact: Pam Bradbury, Sec.

49613 ■ Glen Ellyn Chamber of Commerce
800 Roosevelt Rd., Bldg. D, Ste. 108
Glen Ellyn, IL 60137
Ph:(630)469-0907
Fax:(630)469-0426
Co. E-mail: chamber@glenellynchamber.com
URL: http://www.glenellynchamber.com
Contact: Georgia Koch, Exec. Dir.

49614 ■ Glencoe Chamber of Commerce
PO Box 575
Glencoe, IL 60022
Ph:(847)835-3333
Fax:(847)242-0861
Co. E-mail: glencoechamber@yahoo.com
URL: http://www.glencoechamber.org
Contact: Sally Kelly, Exec. Dir.

49615 ■ Glenview Chamber of Commerce
2320 Glenview Rd.
Glenview, IL 60025-2711
Ph:(847)724-0900
Fax:(847)724-0202
Co. E-mail: gcstaff@glenviewchamber.com
URL: http://glenviewchamber.com
Contact: Kathleen Miles, Pres.

49616 ■ GLMV Area Chamber of Commerce
1123 S Milwaukee Ave.
Libertyville, IL 60048
Ph:(847)680-0750
Fax:(847)680-0760
Co. E-mail: info@glmvchamber.org
URL: http://glmvchamber.org
Contact: Mark Foley, Exec. Dir.

49617 ■ Grayslake Area Chamber of Commerce
10 S Seymour Ave.
PO Box 167
Grayslake, IL 60030
Ph:(847)223-6888
Fax:(847)223-6895
Co. E-mail: business@grayslakechamber.com
URL: http://www.grayslakechamber.com
Contact: Karen Christian-Smith, Exec. Dir.

49618 ■ Grayville Chamber of Commerce
618 W North St.
Grayville, IL 62844-1336
Ph:(618)375-7518
URL: http://www.cityofgrayville.com/info.htm

49619 ■ Greater Aurora Chamber of Commerce
43 W Galena Blvd.
Aurora, IL 60506
Ph:(630)897-9214

Fax:(630)897-7002
Co. E-mail: jhenning@aurora-il.org
URL: http://www.aurorachamber.com
Contact: Joseph Henning, Pres./CEO

49620 ■ Greater Belleville Chamber of Commerce
216 E A St.
Belleville, IL 62220
Ph:(618)233-2015
Fax:(618)233-2077
Co. E-mail: info@bellevillechamber.org
URL: http://www.bellevillechamber.org
Contact: John Lengerman, Exec. Dir.

49621 ■ Greater Centralia Chamber of Commerce
130 S Locust St.
Centralia, IL 62801
Ph:(618)532-6789
Free: 888-533-2600
Fax:(618)533-7305
URL: http://www.centraliail.com
Contact: Bob Kelsheimer, Exec. Dir.

49622 ■ Greater Channahon-Minooka Area Chamber of Commerce
505 Bob Blair Rd.
Minooka, IL 60447
Ph:(815)521-9999
Fax:(815)521-0903
Co. E-mail: cmchamber@att.net
URL: http://www.cmchamber.org
Contact: Mandy McGann, Pres.

49623 ■ Greater Decatur Chamber of Commerce
111 E Main St., Ste. 110
Decatur, IL 62523
Ph:(217)422-2200
Fax:(217)422-4576
Co. E-mail: helpdesk@decaturchamber.com
URL: http://www.decaturchamber.com
Contact: Randy Prince, Pres.

49624 ■ Greater Effingham Chamber of Commerce and Industry
PO Box 643
Effingham, IL 62401
Ph:(217)342-4147
Fax:(217)342-4228
Co. E-mail: chamber@effinghamchamber.org
URL: http://www.effinghamchamber.org
Contact: Norma Lansing, Pres.

49625 ■ Greater Fairfield Area Chamber of Commerce
121 E Main St.
Fairfield, IL 62837
Ph:(618)842-6116
Co. E-mail: chamber@fairfieldwireless.net
URL: http://server.cityamerica.net/suspended.page
Contact: Ann Ayers, Exec. Sec.

49626 ■ Greater Harvard Area Chamber of Commerce
62 N Ayer St., Ste. B
Harvard, IL 60033
Ph:(815)943-4404
Fax:(815)943-4410
Co. E-mail: info@harvcc.net
URL: http://www.harvcc.net
Contact: Crystal Musgrove, Exec. Dir.

49627 ■ Greater Lincolnshire Chamber of Commerce
175 Olde Half Day Rd., Ste. 125
Lincolnshire, IL 60069-3061
Ph:(847)793-2409
Fax:(847)793-2405
Co. E-mail: tglcc@aol.com
URL: http://www.lincolnshirechamber.org
Contact: Lenna Scott, Exec. Dir.

49628 ■ Greater Salem Chamber of Commerce
615 W Main St.
Salem, IL 62881
Ph:(618)548-3010

Fax:(618)548-3014
Co. E-mail: visitus@salemilchamber.com
URL: http://www.salemilchamber.com
Contact: Jon Ashby, Pres.

49629 ■ Greater Springfield Chamber of Commerce
3 S Old State Capitol Plz.
Springfield, IL 62701
Ph:(217)525-1173
Fax:(217)525-8768
Co. E-mail: swolin@gscc.org
URL: http://www.gscc.org
Contact: Gary Plummer, Pres./CEO

49630 ■ Greenville Chamber of Commerce
PO Box 283
Greenville, IL 62246
Ph:(618)664-9272
Free: 888-862-8201
Co. E-mail: greenville@newwavecomm.net
URL: http://www.greenvilleusa.org
Contact: Ms. Julia Jenner, Exec. Dir.

49631 ■ Hamilton County Chamber of Commerce and Economic Development Commission
PO Box 64
McLeansboro, IL 62859
Ph:(618)643-3971
URL: http://www.mcleansboro.com
Contact: Mark Becker, Chm.

49632 ■ Hampshire Area Chamber of Commerce
PO Box 157
Hampshire, IL 60140
Ph:(847)683-1122
Fax:(847)683-1146
Co. E-mail: hampshirecc@fvi.net
URL: http://www.hampshireillinois.com
Contact: Art Zwemke, Pres.

49633 ■ Havana Area Chamber of Commerce
PO Box 116
Havana, IL 62644
Ph:(309)543-3528
Co. E-mail: havana@scenichavana.com
URL: http://www.scenichavana.com/CoCofficDetail.
php

49634 ■ Henry Area Chamber of Commerce
PO Box 211
Henry, IL 61537-0211
Ph:(309)364-3261
Co. E-mail: henrychamber@henrychamber.org
URL: http://www.henrychamber.org
Contact: Chris Laible, Pres.

49635 ■ Herrin Chamber of Commerce
3 S Park Ave.
Herrin, IL 62948
Ph:(618)942-5163
Co. E-mail: herrincc@herrinillinois.com
URL: http://www.herrinillinois.com
Contact: Sue Douglas, Exec. Dir.

49636 ■ Herscher Chamber of Commerce
PO Box 437
Herscher, IL 60941
Ph:(815)426-2131
Co. E-mail: hdwhank@sbcglobal.net
URL: http://www.herscher.net/churchorgs/herscher-
ChamberOfCommerce.asp
Contact: Adam Wagner, Pres.

49637 ■ Highland Chamber of Commerce
907 Main St.
Highland, IL 62249
Ph:(618)654-3721
Co. E-mail: jami@highlandillinois.com
URL: http://www.highlandillinois.com
Contact: Jami Jansen, Pres.

49638 ■ Highland Park Chamber of Commerce
508 Central Ave., Ste. 206
Highland Park, IL 60035
Ph:(847)432-0284

Fax:(847)432-2802
Co. E-mail: chamber@ehighlandpark.com
URL: http://www.ehighlandpark.com/default2.asp
Contact: Virginia Anzelmo Glasner, Exec. Dir.

49639 ■ Hills Chamber of Commerce
PO Box 1164
Bridgeview, IL 60455-0164
Ph:(708)364-7739
Fax:(708)364-7735
Co. E-mail: info@thehillschamber.com
URL: http://www.thehillschamber.com
Contact: Phyllis Majka, Pres.

49640 ■ Hinsdale Chamber of Commerce
22 E 1st St.
Hinsdale, IL 60521
Ph:(630)323-3952
Fax:(630)323-3953
Co. E-mail: hinsdalechamber@earthlink.net
URL: http://www.hinsdalechamber.com
Contact: Michael T. Field, Pres.

49641 ■ Hoffman Estates Chamber of Commerce
2200 W Higgins Rd., Ste. 201
Hoffman Estates, IL 60169
Ph:(847)781-9100
Fax:(847)781-9172
Co. E-mail: info@hechamber.com
URL: http://www.hechamber.com
Contact: Cheri Sisson, Exec. Dir.

49642 ■ Homewood Area Chamber of Commerce
2023 Ridge Rd., Ste. 2 NE B
Homewood, IL 60430
Ph:(708)206-3384
Fax:(708)206-3605
Co. E-mail: toddbeele@homewoodareachamber.com
URL: http://www.homewoodareachamber.com
Contact: Todd Belle, Dir.

49643 ■ Huntley Area Chamber of Commerce and Industry
11419 State Rt. 47
Huntley, IL 60142
Ph:(847)669-0166
Fax:(847)669-0170
Co. E-mail: info@huntleychamber.org
URL: http://www.huntleychamber.org
Contact: Rita Slawek, Exec. Dir.

49644 ■ Illinois Association of Chamber of Commerce Executives
215 E Adams St.
Springfield, IL 62701
Ph:(217)522-5512
Fax:(217)522-5518
Co. E-mail: info@iacce.org
URL: http://www.iacce.org
Contact: Elizabeth D. Fiala, Pres.

49645 ■ Illinois Quad City Chamber of Commerce
622 19th St.
Moline, IL 61265-2142
Ph:(309)757-5416
Fax:(309)757-5435
Co. E-mail: rbaker@quadcitychamber.com
URL: http://www.quadcitychamber.com
Contact: Rick L. Baker, Pres./CEO

49646 ■ Illinois State Chamber of Commerce
Chicago Office
311 S Wacker Dr., Ste. 1500
Chicago, IL 60606-6619
Ph:(312)983-7100
Fax:(312)983-7101
Co. E-mail: info@ilchamber.org
URL: http://www.ilchamber.org
Contact: Douglas L. Whitley, Pres./CEO

49647 ■ Illinois Valley Area Chamber of Commerce and Economic Development
300 Bucklin
PO Box 445
La Salle, IL 61301-0446
Ph:(815)223-0227

Fax:(815)223-4827
Co. E-mail: ivaced@ivaced.org
URL: http://www.ivaced.org
Contact: Ms. Barb Koch, Exec. Dir./CEO

49648 ■ Jacksonville Area Chamber of Commerce
155 W Morton
Jacksonville, IL 62650
Ph:(217)245-2174
Fax:(217)245-0661
Co. E-mail: chamber@jacksonvilleareachamber.org
URL: http://www.jacksonvilleareachamber.org
Contact: Ginny Fanning, Pres.

49649 ■ Jasper County Chamber of Commerce
207 1/2 Jourdan St.
Newton, IL 62448
Ph:(618)783-3399
Free: 877-223-0074
Co. E-mail: jasperchamber@psbnewton.com
URL: http://www.newtonillinois.com
Contact: Lisa Meyer, Exec. Dir.

49650 ■ Jefferson County Chamber of Commerce
200 Potomac Blvd.
Mount Vernon, IL 62864
Ph:(618)242-5725
Fax:(618)242-5130
Co. E-mail: chambermarketing@mvn.net
URL: http://www.southernillinois.com
Contact: Floyd Brookman, Exec. Dir.

49651 ■ Jefferson Park Chamber of Commerce
4849 N Milwaukee Ave., Ste. 305
Chicago, IL 60630-2171
Ph:(773)736-6697
Fax:(773)685-3316
Co. E-mail: info@jeffersonpark.net
URL: http://www.jeffersonpark.net
Contact: Carol Gawron, Exec. Dir.

49652 ■ Jersey County Business Association
209 N State St.
Jerseyville, IL 62052-1755
Ph:(618)639-5222
Co. E-mail: brent@jcba-il.us
URL: http://www.jerseycounty.org
Contact: Brent Thompson, Pres.

49653 ■ Joliet Region Chamber of Commerce and Industry
63 N Chicago St.
PO Box 752
Joliet, IL 60434-0752
Ph:(815)727-5371
Fax:(815)727-5374
Co. E-mail: info@jolietchamber.com
URL: http://www.jolietchamber.com
Contact: Russ Slinkard, Pres./CEO

49654 ■ Kankakee Regional Chamber of Commerce
1137 E 5000N Rd.
Bourbonnais, IL 60914
Ph:(815)933-7721
Fax:(815)933-7675
Co. E-mail: david@kankakee.org
URL: http://www.kankakee.org/cwt/external/wcpages/index.aspx
Contact: David Hinderliter, Sec.

49655 ■ Kewanee Chamber of Commerce
113 E 2nd St.
Kewanee, IL 61443
Ph:(309)852-2175
Fax:(309)852-2176
Co. E-mail: chamber@kewanee-il.com
URL: http://www.kewanee-il.com
Contact: Robert Whitmer, Pres.

49656 ■ Lake County Chamber of Commerce
5221 W Grand Ave.
Gurnee, IL 60031
Ph:(847)249-3800

Fax:(847)249-3892
Co. E-mail: info@lakecountychamber.com
URL: http://www.lakecountychamber.com
Contact: B. Dwight Houchins, Pres.

49657 ■ Lake Forest - Lake Bluff Chamber of Commerce
695 N Western Ave.
Lake Forest, IL 60045
Ph:(847)234-4282
Co. E-mail: info@lflbchamber.com
URL: http://www.lflbchamber.com/build1/index.cfm
Contact: Joanna Rolek, Exec. Dir.

49658 ■ Lake Zurich Area Chamber of Commerce
1st Bank Plz., Ste. 308
Lake Zurich, IL 60047
Ph:(847)438-5572
Fax:(847)438-5574
Co. E-mail: info@lzacc.com
URL: http://www.lzacc.com
Contact: Dale Perrin, Exec. Dir.

49659 ■ Lakeview East Chamber of Commerce
3138 N Broadway
Chicago, IL 60657
Ph:(773)348-8608
Fax:(773)348-7409
Co. E-mail: info@lakevieweast.com
URL: http://www.lakevieweast.com

49660 ■ Lawrence County Chamber of Commerce
619 12th St.
Lawrenceville, IL 62439
Ph:(618)943-3516
Fax:(618)943-4748
Co. E-mail: lccc2@verizon.net
URL: http://www.lawrencecountyillinois.com/chamber.html

49661 ■ Lebanon Chamber of Commerce
221 W St. Louis St.
Lebanon, IL 62254
Ph:(618)537-8420
Co. E-mail: lebanonchamber@gmail.com
URL: http://www.lebanonil.org

49662 ■ Lemont Area Chamber of Commerce
101 Main St.
Lemont, IL 60439-3675
Ph:(630)257-5997
Fax:(630)257-3238
Co. E-mail: info@lemontchamber.com
URL: http://www.lemontchamber.com
Contact: Dawn M. Dentzman, Exec. Dir.

49663 ■ Limestone Area Chamber of Commerce
PO Box 4043
Bartonville, IL 61607
Ph:(309)697-1031
Co. E-mail: email@limestonechamber.com
URL: http://www.limestonechamber.com
Contact: Diana Kelly, Pres.

49664 ■ Lincoln - Logan County Chamber of Commerce
1555 5th St.
Lincoln, IL 62656
Ph:(217)735-2385
Fax:(217)735-9205
Co. E-mail: chamber@lincolnillinois.com
URL: http://lincolnillinois.com/ABF.aspx
Contact: Andi Hake, Exec. Dir.

49665 ■ Lincoln Park Chamber of Commerce
1925 N Clybourn Ave., Ste. 301
Chicago, IL 60614-7396
Ph:(773)880-5200
Fax:(773)880-0266
Co. E-mail: info@lincolnparkchamber.com
URL: http://www.lincolnparkchamber.com
Contact: Kim Schilf, Pres./CEO

49666 ■ Lincolnwood Chamber of Commerce and Industry
7001 N Lawndale Ave.
Lincolnwood, IL 60712
Ph:(847)679-5760
Fax:(847)679-5790
Co. E-mail: dlass@lincolnwoodchamber.org
URL: http://www.lincolnwoodchamber.org
Contact: Diana Lass, Exec. Dir.

49667 ■ Lindenhurst - Lake Villa Chamber of Commerce
500 Grand Ave.
PO Box 6075
Lindenhurst, IL 60046-6075
Ph:(847)356-8446
Fax:(847)356-8561
Co. E-mail: llvchamber@sbcglobal.net
URL: http://www.llvchamber.com/page1.aspx
Contact: Connie Meadie, Exec. Dir.

49668 ■ Lisle Chamber of Commerce
4733 Main St.
Lisle, IL 60532
Ph:(630)964-0052
Fax:(630)964-2726
Co. E-mail: info@lislechamber.com
URL: http://www.lislechamber.com
Contact: Tom Althoff, Pres./CEO

49669 ■ Litchfield Chamber of Commerce
311 N Madison
PO Box 334
Litchfield, IL 62056
Ph:(217)324-2533
Co. E-mail: chamber@litchfieldil.com
URL: http://www.litchfieldchamber.com
Contact: Susan Griffin, Pres.

49670 ■ Lockport Chamber of Commerce
921 S State St.
Lockport, IL 60441-3435
Ph:(815)838-3357
Fax:(815)838-2653
Co. E-mail: office@lockportchamber.com
URL: http://www.lockportchamber.com
Contact: Denny Reiter, Pres.

49671 ■ Lombard Area Chamber of Commerce and Industry
10 Lilac Ln.
Lombard, IL 60148
Ph:(630)627-5040
Fax:(630)627-5519
Co. E-mail: info@lombardchamber.com
URL: http://www.lombardchamber.com
Contact: Yvonne Invergo, Exec. Dir.

49672 ■ Loves Park - Machesney Park Chamber of Commerce
100 Heart Blvd.
Loves Park, IL 61111
Ph:(815)633-3999
Fax:(815)633-4057
Co. E-mail: diana@parkschamber.com
URL: http://www.parkschamber.com
Contact: Diana Johnson, Exec. Dir.

49673 ■ Mahomet Chamber of Commerce
PO Box 1031
Mahomet, IL 61853-1031
Ph:(217)586-3165
Fax:(217)586-3774
Co. E-mail: office@mahometchamberofcommerce.com
URL: http://www.mahometchamberofcommerce.com
Contact: Theresa A. Berry, Admin. Sec.

49674 ■ Manhattan Chamber of Commerce
PO Box 357
Manhattan, IL 60442
Ph:(815)478-3811
Fax:(815)478-7611
Co. E-mail: chamber@manhattan-il.com
URL: http://www.manhattan-il.com
Contact: Dr. Jeff Pietrzyk, Pres.

49675 ■ Marengo-Union Chamber of Commerce
116 S State St.
Marengo, IL 60152
Ph:(815)568-6680
Fax:(815)568-6879
Co. E-mail: info@marengo-union.com
URL: http://www.marengo-union.com
Contact: Pat Lawlor

49676 ■ Marion Chamber of Commerce
PO Box 307
Marion, IL 62959
Ph:(618)997-6311
Free: 800-699-1760
Fax:(618)997-4665
Co. E-mail: marionchamber@marionillinois.com
URL: http://www.marionillinois.com
Contact: Rose Mary Crear, Exec. Sec.

49677 ■ Marshall Area Chamber of Commerce
PO Box 263
Marshall, IL 62441
Ph:(217)826-2034
Fax:(217)826-2034
Co. E-mail: marshall.chamber@abcs.com
URL: http://www.marshall-il.com
Contact: George Dallmier, Pres.

49678 ■ Matteson Area Chamber of Commerce
298 Main St.
Park Forest, IL 60466
Ph:(708)747-6000
Fax:(708)747-6054
Co. E-mail: lauren@mattesonareachamber.com
URL: http://www.macclink.com
Contact: Lauren Alspaugh, Exec. Dir.

49679 ■ Mattoon Chamber of Commerce
500 Broadway Ave.
Mattoon, IL 61938
Ph:(217)235-5661
Fax:(217)234-6544
Co. E-mail: matchamber@consolidated.net
URL: http://www.mattoonchamber.com
Contact: Mike Pinnell, Pres.

49680 ■ Maywood Chamber of Commerce
PO Box 172
Maywood, IL 60153
Ph:(708)345-7077
Fax:(708)345-9455
Co. E-mail: info@maywoodchamber.org
URL: http://maywoodchamber.com
Contact: Edwin H. Walker IV, Pres.

49681 ■ McHenry Area Chamber of Commerce
1257 N Green St.
McHenry, IL 60050
Ph:(815)385-4300
Fax:(815)385-9142
Co. E-mail: info@mchenrychamber.com
URL: http://www.mchenrychamber.com
Contact: Kay Rial Bates, Pres.

49682 ■ McLean County Chamber of Commerce
210 S East St.
Bloomington, IL 61701
Ph:(309)829-6344
Fax:(309)827-3940
Co. E-mail: info@mcleancochamber.org
URL: http://www.mcleancochamber.org
Contact: Mike Holzworth, Interim Exec. Dir.

49683 ■ Melrose Park Chamber of Commerce
1718 W Lake St.
Melrose Park, IL 60160-3819
Ph:(708)338-1007
Fax:(708)338-9924
Co. E-mail: info@melroseparkchamber.org
URL: http://www.melroseparkchamber.org
Contact: Mrs. Cathy K. Stenberg, Exec. Dir.

49684 ■ Mendota Area Chamber of Commerce
800 Washington St.
PO Box 620
Mendota, IL 61342-0620
Ph:(815)539-6507
Fax:(815)539-6025
Co. E-mail: mendotachamber@yahoo.com
URL: http://mendotachamber.com
Contact: Alison Wasmer, Exec. Dir.

49685 ■ Metropolis Chamber of Commerce
607 Market St.
Metropolis, IL 62960
Ph:(618)524-2714
Free: 800-949-5740
Fax:(618)524-4780
Co. E-mail: metrochamber@hcis.net
URL: http://www.metropolischamber.com
Contact: Robbin McDaniel, Pres.

49686 ■ Mokena Chamber of Commerce
19820 S Wolf Rd.
Mokena, IL 60448-1545
Ph:(708)479-2468
Fax:(708)479-7144
Co. E-mail: mokena@mokena.com
URL: http://www.mokena.com
Contact: Sharon Filkins Jenrich, Pres.

49687 ■ Momence Chamber of Commerce
203 E River St.
Momence, IL 60954
Ph:(815)472-4620
Fax:(815)472-6453
Co. E-mail: quest4health@sbcglobal.net
URL: http://www.momence.net
Contact: Jennifer Workman, Pres.

49688 ■ Monmouth Area Chamber of Commerce
90 Public Sq.
PO Box 857
Monmouth, IL 61462-0857
Ph:(309)734-3181
Co. E-mail: macc@maplecity.com
URL: http://www.monmouthilchamber.com
Contact: Angela McElwee, Exec. Dir.

49689 ■ Mont Clare - Elmwood Park Chamber of Commerce
11 Conti Pkwy.
Elmwood Park, IL 60707
Ph:(708)456-8000
Fax:(708)456-8680
Co. E-mail: info@mcepchamber.org
URL: http://www.mcepchamber.org
Contact: Ms. Barbara Melnyk, Exec. Dir.

49690 ■ Monticello Chamber of Commerce
PO Box 313
Monticello, IL 61856-0313
Ph:(217)762-7921
Free: 800-952-3396
Fax:(217)762-2711
Co. E-mail: info@monticellochamber.org
URL: http://www.monticellochamber.org
Contact: Sue Gortner, Exec. Dir.

49691 ■ Morrison Chamber of Commerce
PO Box 8
Morrison, IL 61270
Ph:(815)772-3757
Fax:(815)772-3757
URL: http://www.morrisonchamber.com
Contact: Norma Nelson, Pres.

49692 ■ Morton Chamber of Commerce
415 W Jefferson
Morton, IL 61550-1817
Ph:(309)263-2491
Free: 888-765-6588
Fax:(309)263-2401
Co. E-mail: pnknman@mtco.com
URL: http://mortonchamber.org/index.php?section=1
Contact: B. Michael Badgerow, Exec. Dir.

49693 ■ **Morton Grove Chamber of Commerce and Industry**
6101 Capulina Ave., Lower Level
Morton Grove, IL 60053
Ph:(847)965-0330
Fax:(847)965-0349
Co. E-mail: info@mgcci.org
URL: http://www.mgcci.org
Contact: Mark Pendergrass, Exec. Dir.

49694 ■ **Mount Carroll Chamber of Commerce**
PO Box 94
Mount Carroll, IL 61053
Ph:(815)244-2255
Co. E-mail: info@mtcarrollil.org
URL: http://www.mtcarrollil.org
Contact: Mike Lenz, VP

49695 ■ **Mount Greenwood Chamber of Commerce**
3052 W 111th St.
Chicago, IL 60655
Ph:(773)238-6103
Co. E-mail: info@mgcofc.org
URL: http://www.mgcofc.org
Contact: Darlene Myers, Exec. Dir.

49696 ■ **Mount Prospect Chamber of Commerce**
107 S Main St.
Mount Prospect, IL 60056
Ph:(847)398-6616
Fax:(847)398-6780
Co. E-mail: jim@mountprospect.com
URL: http://www.mountprospectchamber.org
Contact: James Uszler, Exec. Dir.

49697 ■ **Mount Zion Chamber of Commerce**
PO Box 84
Mount Zion, IL 62549
Ph:(217)864-2526
Fax:(217)864-6115
Co. E-mail: askjudy4@aol.com
Contact: Judy Kaiser, Admin.

49698 ■ **Murphysboro Chamber of Commerce**
PO Box 606
Murphysboro, IL 62966
Ph:(618)684-6421
Free: 800-406-8774
Fax:(618)684-2010
Co. E-mail: chamber4@verizon.net
URL: http://www.murphysboro.com
Contact: Kaye Carr, Exec. Dir.

49699 ■ **Naperville Area Chamber of Commerce**
55 S Main St., Ste. 351
Naperville, IL 60540
Ph:(630)355-4141
Fax:(630)355-8335
Co. E-mail: chamber@naperville.net
URL: http://www.naperville.net/cwt/external/wcpages/
    index.aspx
Contact: Richard Greene, Pres./CEO

49700 ■ **National Black Chamber of Commerce, Champaign County**
PO Box 8014
Champaign, IL 61826
Ph:(224)356-1987
Co. E-mail: info@theccbcc.com
URL: http://www.theccbcc.com
Contact: Zernial M. Bogan, Pres.

49701 ■ **National Black Chamber of Commerce, Decatur**
132 S Water St., Ste. 430
Decatur, IL 62523
Ph:(217)428-9679
Co. E-mail: info@decaturbcc.org
URL: http://www.decaturbcc.org
Contact: Corey Walker, Pres./CEO

49702 ■ **National Black Chamber of Commerce, Englewood**
PO Box 21453
Chicago, IL 60621
Ph:(773)503-6067
Fax:(773)602-4510
Co. E-mail: info@englewoodbcc.org
Contact: Arness Dancy, Pres./CEO

49703 ■ **National Black Chamber of Commerce, Illinois State**
331 Fulton St., Ste. 530
Peoria, IL 61602
Ph:(309)740-4430
Fax:(309)672-1379
Co. E-mail: info@ilbcc.org
URL: http://www.ilbcc.org
Contact: Larry D. Ivory, Pres.

49704 ■ **National Black Chamber of Commerce, Lake County**
1020 W Glen Flora Ave., Ste. 104
Waukegan, IL 60085
Ph:(847)599-9510
Fax:(847)599-9534
Co. E-mail: gass@bccoflakecounty.com
URL: http://www.bccoflakecounty.com
Contact: Arthur J. Gass Sr., Pres./Chm.

49705 ■ **Nauvoo Chamber of Commerce**
PO Box 41
Nauvoo, IL 62354
Ph:(217)453-6648
Free: 877-NAUVOO-1
Fax:(217)453-2032
Co. E-mail: chamber@nauvoo.net
URL: http://www.nauvoochamber.org
Contact: David C. Miller, Pres.

49706 ■ **New Lenox Chamber of Commerce**
PO Box 42
New Lenox, IL 60451-0042
Ph:(815)485-4241
Fax:(815)485-5001
Co. E-mail: info@newlenoxchamber.com
URL: http://www.newlenoxchamber.com
Contact: Debbera Hyrke, CEO

49707 ■ **Niles Chamber of Chamber of Commerce and Industry**
8060 Oakton St.
Niles, IL 60714
Ph:(847)268-8180
Fax:(847)268-8186
Co. E-mail: contactus@nileschamber.com
URL: http://nileschamber.com
Contact: Katie DiMaria, Exec. Dir.

49708 ■ **Northbrook Chamber of Commerce and Industry**
2002 Walters Ave.
Northbrook, IL 60062
Ph:(847)498-5555
Co. E-mail: info@northbrookchamber.org
URL: http://www.northbrookchamber.org
Contact: Tensley Garris, Pres.

49709 ■ **Norwood Park Chamber of Commerce and Industry**
6097 N Northwest Hwy.
Chicago, IL 60631
Ph:(773)763-3606
Fax:(773)763-3620
Co. E-mail: info@norwoodpark.org
URL: http://www.norwoodpark.org

49710 ■ **Oak Forest Chamber of Commerce**
15440 S Central Ave.
Oak Forest, IL 60452
Ph:(708)687-4600
Fax:(708)687-7878
Co. E-mail: info@oakforestchamber.org
URL: http://www.oakforestchamber.org
Contact: Ms. Tamara Kostecki, Exec. Dir.

49711 ■ **Oak Lawn Chamber of Commerce**
5314 W 95th St.
Oak Lawn, IL 60453
Ph:(708)424-8300

Fax:(708)229-2236
Co. E-mail: olchamber@oaklawnchamber.com
URL: http://www.oaklawnchamber.com
Contact: Jackie Truty, Pres.

49712 ■ **Oak Park-River Forest Chamber of Commerce**
1110 North Blvd.
Oak Park, IL 60301
Ph:(708)848-8151
Fax:(708)848-8182
Co. E-mail: info@oprfchamber.org
URL: http://www.oprfchamber.org
Contact: Jim Doss, Exec. Dir.

49713 ■ **O'Fallon Chamber of Commerce**
116 E 1st St.
PO Box 371
O'Fallon, IL 62269
Ph:(618)632-3377
Fax:(618)632-8162
Co. E-mail: chamber@ofallonchamber.com
URL: http://www.ofallonchamber.com
Contact: Debbie Arell-Martinez, Pres.

49714 ■ **Okawville Chamber of Commerce**
PO Box 345
Okawville, IL 62271
Ph:(618)243-5694
Co. E-mail: tourokaw@htc.net
URL: http://www.okawvillecc.com

49715 ■ **Oregon Area Chamber of Commerce**
PO Box 69
303 W Washington
Oregon, IL 61061
Ph:(815)732-2100
Co. E-mail: ococ@comcast.net
URL: http://www.oregonil.com/chamber.html
Contact: Dr. Michael Nelson

49716 ■ **Orland Park Area Chamber of Commerce**
8799 W 151st St.
Orland Park, IL 60462
Ph:(708)349-2972
Fax:(708)349-7454
Co. E-mail: info@orlandparkchamber.org
URL: http://www.orlandparkchamber.org
Contact: Keloryn Putnam, Exec. Dir.

49717 ■ **Oswego Chamber of Commerce**
22 W VanBuren
Oswego, IL 60543-0863
Ph:(630)554-3505
Fax:(630)554-0050
Co. E-mail: info@oswegochamber.org
URL: http://www.oswegochamber.org
Contact: Cory Poris-Warren, Pres.

49718 ■ **Ottawa Area Chamber of Commerce and Industry**
100 W Lafayette St.
Ottawa, IL 61350
Ph:(815)433-0084
Fax:(815)433-2405
Co. E-mail: info@ottawachamberillinois.com
URL: http://www.ottawachamberillinois.com/
    chamber_services.htm
Contact: Boyd Palmer, Exec. Dir.

49719 ■ **Palatine Area Chamber of Commerce**
625 North Ct., Ste. 320
Palatine, IL 60067
Ph:(847)359-7200
Fax:(847)359-7246
Co. E-mail: info@palatinechamber.com
URL: http://www.palatinechamber.com
Contact: Mindy Phillips, Dir.

49720 ■ **Palestine Chamber of Commerce**
PO Box 155
Palestine, IL 62451
Ph:(618)586-2222
Fax:(618)586-9477
Co. E-mail: palestinecofc@verizon.net
URL: http://www.pioneercity.com/chamberofcom-
    merce
Contact: Jim Clark, Pres.

49721 ■ Palos Hills Chamber of Commerce
10335 S Roberts Rd.
Palos Hills, IL 60465
Ph:(708)598-3400
URL: http://www.paloshillsweb.org
Contact: Phyllis Majka, Pres.

49722 ■ Pana Chamber of Commerce
City Hall
120 E 3rd St.
Pana, IL 62557
Ph:(217)562-4240
Fax:(217)562-3823
Co. E-mail: panail@consolidated.net
URL: http://www.panachamber.com
Contact: Jim Deere, Sec.-Treas.

49723 ■ Paris Area Chamber of Commerce and Tourism
105 N Central Ave.
Paris, IL 61944
Ph:(217)465-4179
URL: http://www.parisilchamber.com
Contact: Brenda Buckley, Exec. Dir.

49724 ■ Pekin Area Chamber of Commerce
402 Court St.
PO Box 636
Pekin, IL 61555-0636
Ph:(309)346-2106
Fax:(309)346-2104
Co. E-mail: chamber@pekin.net
URL: http://www.pekin.net
Contact: Bill Fleming, Exec. Dir.

49725 ■ Peoria Area Chamber of Commerce
100 SW Water St.
Peoria, IL 61602
Ph:(309)676-0755
Fax:(309)676-7534
Co. E-mail: chamber@mail.h-p.org
URL: http://www.peoriachamber.org
Contact: Jim McConoughey, Pres./CEO

49726 ■ Petersburg Chamber of Commerce
125 S 7th St.
PO Box 452
Petersburg, IL 62675
Ph:(217)632-7363
Fax:(217)632-7363
Co. E-mail: dsk@petersburgil.com
URL: http://petersburgilchamber.com
Contact: Betty Winchester, Pres.

49727 ■ Pike County Chamber of Commerce
224 W Washington St.
Pittsfield, IL 62363
Ph:(217)285-2971
Fax:(217)285-5251
Co. E-mail: info@pikeil.org
URL: http://www.pikeil.org
Contact: David Fuhler, Pres.

49728 ■ Pinckneyville Chamber of Commerce
4 S Walnut St.
Pinckneyville, IL 62274
Ph:(618)357-3243
Co. E-mail: pinckneyvillechamber@verizon.net
URL: http://www.pinckneyville.com
Contact: Mr. Chuck Dobrinick, Pres.

49729 ■ Plainfield Area Chamber of Commerce
24047 W Lockport St., No. 109
Plainfield, IL 60544
Ph:(815)436-4431
Fax:(815)436-0520
Co. E-mail: etcollins@plainfieldchamber.com
URL: http://www.plainfieldchamber.com
Contact: Liz Collins, Pres./CEO

49730 ■ Polo Chamber of Commerce
115 S Franklin Ave.
Polo, IL 61064
Ph:(815)946-3131
Fax:(815)946-2004
Co. E-mail: webmaster@poloil.net
URL: http://www.poloil.net
Contact: Judy Estes, Sec.

49731 ■ Pontiac Area Chamber of Commerce
PO Box 534
Pontiac, IL 61764
Ph:(815)844-5131
Fax:(815)844-2600
Co. E-mail: clambert@pontiacchamber.org
URL: http://www.pontiacchamber.org
Contact: Cheri Lambert, Pres./CEO

49732 ■ Portage Park Chamber of Commerce
5758 W Irving Park Rd.
Chicago, IL 60634
Ph:(773)777-2020
Fax:(773)777-0202
Co. E-mail: info@portageparkchamber.org
URL: http://www.portageparkchamber.org
Contact: Tivadar Szabo, Pres.

49733 ■ Princeton Area Chamber of Commerce and Main Street
Prouty Community Bldg.
435 S Main St.
Princeton, IL 61356
Ph:(815)875-2616
Free: 877-730-4306
Fax:(815)875-1156
URL: http://www.visitprinceton-il.com
Contact: Erika Robbins, Exec. Dir.

49734 ■ Prophetstown-Lyndon Area Chamber of Commerce
335 Washington St.
Prophetstown, IL 61277
Ph:(815)437-5139
Fax:(815)437-5139
Co. E-mail: bbmainstreet@thewisp.net
URL: http://www.prophetstownil.com
Contact: Barb Ballew, Exec. Dir.

49735 ■ Quincy Area Chamber of Commerce
300 Civic Center Plz., Ste. 245
Quincy, IL 62301
Ph:(217)222-7980
Fax:(217)222-3033
Co. E-mail: amy@quincychamber.org
URL: http://www.quincychamber.org
Contact: Amy Looten, Exec. Dir.

49736 ■ Rantoul Area Chamber of Commerce
100 W Sangamon Ave., Ste. 101
Rantoul, IL 61866
Ph:(217)893-3323
Co. E-mail: dir@pdnt.com
Contact: Joe Bolser, Exec. Dir.

49737 ■ Richmond/Spring Grove Area Chamber of Commerce
10906 Main St.
PO Box 475
Richmond, IL 60071
Ph:(815)678-7742
Fax:(815)678-2070
Co. E-mail: info@rsgchamber.com
URL: http://www.rsgchamber.com
Contact: Loretta Podeszwa, Exec. Dir.

49738 ■ Riverdale Chamber of Commerce
208 W 144th St.
Riverdale, IL 60827
Ph:(708)841-3311
Fax:(708)841-1805
Co. E-mail: rdpl2@earthlink.net
URL: http://www.district148.net/rcoc
Contact: John Strauss, Pres.

49739 ■ Riverside Chamber of Commerce
PO Box 7
Riverside, IL 60546
Ph:(708)447-8510
Co. E-mail: business@riversidechamberofcommerce.com
URL: http://www.riversidechamberofcommerce.com
Contact: David Moravecek, Pres.

49740 ■ Rochelle Area Chamber of Commerce
350 May Mart Dr.
Rochelle, IL 61068-0220
Ph:(815)562-4189

Fax:(815)562-4180
Co. E-mail: chamber@rochelle.net
URL: http://www.rochellechamber.org
Contact: Jeana Abbott, Exec. Dir.

49741 ■ Rock Falls Chamber of Commerce
601 W 10th St.
Rock Falls, IL 61071-1576
Ph:(815)625-4500
Fax:(815)625-4558
Co. E-mail: doug@rockfallschamber.com
URL: http://www.rockfallschamber.com/index.html
Contact: Doug Wiersema, Pres./CEO

49742 ■ Rockford Chamber of Commerce
308 W State St., Ste. 190
Rockford, IL 61101
Ph:(815)987-8100
Fax:(815)987-8122
Co. E-mail: info@rockfordchamber.com
URL: http://www.rockfordchamber.com
Contact: Einar Forsman, Pres./CEO

49743 ■ Rockford Regional Chamber of Commerce Business Women's Council
308 W State St., Ste. 190
Rockford, IL 61101
Ph:(815)987-8100
Fax:(815)987-8122
Co. E-mail: info@rockfordchamber.com
URL: http://www.rockfordchamber.com
Contact: Stacy Mullins

49744 ■ Rockton Chamber of Commerce
PO Box 237
Rockton, IL 61072
Ph:(815)624-7625
Fax:(815)624-7385
Co. E-mail: info@rocktonchamber.com
URL: http://www.rocktonchamber.com
Contact: Ms. Carol Lamb, Exec. Dir.

49745 ■ Rolling Meadows Chamber of Commerce
2775 Algonquin Rd., Ste. 310
Rolling Meadows, IL 60008
Ph:(847)398-3730
Fax:(847)398-3745
Co. E-mail: office@rmchamber.org
URL: http://www.rmchamber.org
Contact: Linda Liles Ballantine, Exec. Dir.

49746 ■ Romeoville Chamber of Commerce
27 Montrose Dr.
Romeoville, IL 60446-1329
Ph:(815)886-2076
Fax:(815)886-2096
Co. E-mail: info@romeovillechamber.org
URL: http://www.romeovillechamber.org
Contact: Christine Morgan, Chm.

49747 ■ Roselle Chamber of Commerce and Industry
1350 W Lake St., Ste. A
Roselle, IL 60172
Ph:(630)894-3010
Fax:(630)894-3042
Co. E-mail: executivedirector@rosellechamber.com
URL: http://www.rosellechamber.com
Contact: Gail Croson, Exec. Dir.

49748 ■ Round Lake Area Chamber of Commerce and Industry
2007 Civic Center Way
Round Lake Beach, IL 60073
Ph:(847)546-2002
Fax:(847)546-2254
Co. E-mail: info@rlchamber.org
URL: http://www.rlchamber.org
Contact: Shanna Coakley, Exec. Dir.

49749 ■ Rushville Area Chamber of Commerce and Main Street
215 E Adams St.
Springfield, IL 62701
Ph:(217)522-5512

Fax:(217)522-5518
Co. E-mail: dwhitley@ilchamber.org
URL: http://www.ilchamber.org
Contact: Doug Whitley, Pres./CEO

49750 ■ St. Charles Chamber of Commerce
3755 E Main St., Ste. 140
St. Charles, IL 60174
Ph:(630)584-8384
Fax:(630)584-6065
Co. E-mail: info@stcharleschamber.com
URL: http://www.stcharleschamber.com
Contact: Lori G. Hewitt, Pres./CEO

49751 ■ Sandwich Chamber of Commerce
128 E Railroad St.
PO Box 214
Sandwich, IL 60548
Ph:(815)786-9075
Fax:(815)786-2505
Co. E-mail: info@sandwich-il.org
URL: http://www.sandwich-il.org
Contact: Pat Voga, Admin.

49752 ■ Sauk Valley Area Chamber of Commerce
211 Locust St.
Sterling, IL 61081-3536
Ph:(815)625-2400
Fax:(815)625-9361
Co. E-mail: kjanssen@saukvalleyareachamber.com
URL: http://www.saukvalleyareachamber.com
Contact: Kimberly Janssen, Exec. Dir.

49753 ■ Savanna Chamber of Commerce
PO Box 315
Savanna, IL 61074
Ph:(815)273-2722
Fax:(815)273-2754
Co. E-mail: savchamber@grics.net
URL: http://www.savanna-il.com
Contact: Pam Brown, Exec. Dir.

49754 ■ Shelbyville Area Chamber of Commerce
124 N Morgan St.
Shelbyville, IL 62565
Ph:(217)774-2221
Fax:(217)774-2221
Co. E-mail: chamber01@consolidated.net
URL: http://www.shelbyvillechamberofcommerce.com
Contact: Jesse Helton, Pres.

49755 ■ Skokie Chamber of Commerce
5002 Oakton St.
Skokie, IL 60077
Ph:(847)673-0240
Fax:(847)673-0249
Co. E-mail: info@skokiechamber.org
URL: http://www.skokiechamber.org
Contact: Howard Meyer, Exec. Dir.

49756 ■ Southwestern Madison County Chamber of Commerce
PO Box 370
Granite City, IL 62040-0370
Ph:(618)876-6400
Fax:(618)876-6448
Co. E-mail: chamber@chamberswmadisoncounty.com
URL: http://www.chamberswmadisoncounty.com
Contact: Rosemarie Brown, Exec. Dir.

49757 ■ Staunton Chamber of Commerce
PO Box 248
Staunton, IL 62088
Ph:(618)635-8356
Co. E-mail: chamber@stauntonil.com
URL: http://www.stauntonil.com/Home.aspx
Contact: Cindy Feldmann, Pres.

49758 ■ Streamwood Chamber of Commerce
22 W Streamwood Blvd.
Streamwood, IL 60107
Ph:(630)837-5200
Fax:(630)837-5251
Co. E-mail: staff@streamwoodchamber.com
URL: http://www.streamwoodchamber.com
Contact: Susan Berg, Exec. Dir.

49759 ■ Streator Area Chamber of Commerce and Industry
PO Box 360
Streator, IL 61364
Ph:(815)672-2921
Fax:(815)672-1768
Co. E-mail: sacci@mchsi.com
URL: http://www.streatorchamber.com
Contact: Jack Dzuris, Exec. Dir.

49760 ■ Sullivan Chamber and Economic Development
112 W Harrison St.
Sullivan, IL 61951
Ph:(217)728-4223
Co. E-mail: info@sullivanchamber.com
URL: http://www.sullivanchamber.com
Contact: Kathy Woodworth

49761 ■ Swansea Chamber of Commerce
1501 Caseyville Ave.
Swansea, IL 62226
Ph:(618)233-3938
Fax:(618)233-3936
Co. E-mail: swansea@swanseachamber.org
URL: http://www.swanseachamber.org
Contact: Colleen Newlin, Exec. Dir.

49762 ■ Swedish-American Chamber of Commerce, Chicago
150 N Michigan Ave., Ste. 2800
Chicago, IL 60601
Ph:(312)863-8592
Fax:(312)624-7701
Co. E-mail: sacc-chi@sacc-usa.org
URL: http://www.sacc-chicago.org/home
Contact: Mark Podemski, Pres.

49763 ■ Sycamore Chamber of Commerce
407 W State St., Ste. 10
Sycamore, IL 60178
Ph:(815)895-3456
Fax:(815)895-0125
Co. E-mail: info@sycamorechamber.com
URL: http://www.sycamorechamber.com
Contact: Rose Treml, Exec. Dir.

49764 ■ Tinley Park Chamber of Commerce
17316 S Oak Park Ave.
Tinley Park, IL 60477
Ph:(708)532-5700
Fax:(708)532-1475
Co. E-mail: info@tinleychamber.org
URL: http://www.tinleychamber.org
Contact: Ms. Bernadette Shanahan-Haas, Pres./CEO

49765 ■ Troy Area Chamber of Commerce
647 E US Hwy. 40
Troy, IL 62294
Ph:(618)667-8769
Free: 888-667-8769
Fax:(618)667-8759
Co. E-mail: info@troymaryvillecoc.com
URL: http://www.troycoc.com
Contact: Dawn Mushill, Exec. Dir.

49766 ■ Tuscola Chamber of Commerce
PO Box 434
Tuscola, IL 61953
Ph:(217)253-5013
Co. E-mail: khiggins@tuscolaffb.com
URL: http://www.tuscola.org
Contact: Kim Higgins, Pres.

49767 ■ Union County Chamber of Commerce
330 S Main St.
Anna, IL 62906
Ph:(618)833-6311
Fax:(618)833-1903
Co. E-mail: uccc@ajinternet.net
URL: http://www.shawneeheartland.com
Contact: Jeannie Landis, Exec. Dir.

49768 ■ Uptown Chamber of Commerce
4753 N Broadway St., Ste. 822
Chicago, IL 60640-4992
Ph:(773)878-1184

Fax:(773)878-3678
Co. E-mail: info@uptownbusinesspartners.com
URL: http://www.uptownbusinesspartners.com
Contact: Christie Hahn, Exec. Dir.

49769 ■ Vandalia Chamber of Commerce
PO Box 238
Vandalia, IL 62471
Ph:(618)283-2728
Fax:(618)283-4439
Co. E-mail: vandaliachamber@swetlandcom.com
URL: http://www.vandaliachamber.org
Contact: Joanna Helm, Pres.

49770 ■ Vermilion Advantage-Chamber of Commerce Division
28 W North St.
Danville, IL 61832-5729
Ph:(217)442-6201
Fax:(217)442-6228
Co. E-mail: vhaugen@vermilionadvantage.com
URL: http://www.vermilionadvantage.com
Contact: Vicki Haugen, Pres./CEO

49771 ■ Villa Park Chamber of Commerce
10 W Park Blvd.
Villa Park, IL 60181
Ph:(630)941-9133
Fax:(630)941-9134
Co. E-mail: info@villaparkchamber.org
URL: http://www.villaparkchamber.org
Contact: Alesia Bailey, Exec. Dir.

49772 ■ Village of Itasca Chamber of Commerce
550 W Irving Park Rd.
Itasca, IL 60143
Ph:(630)773-0835
Fax:(630)773-2505
Co. E-mail: mayor@itasca.com
URL: http://www.itasca.com
Contact: Claudia Gruber

49773 ■ Walnut Chamber of Commerce
105 N Main St.
Walnut, IL 61376
Ph:(815)379-2141
Co. E-mail: director@villageofwalnut.com
URL: http://www.villageofwalnut.com
Contact: Ms. Nicole Blessing, Exec. Dir.

49774 ■ Waterloo Chamber of Commerce
PO Box 1
Waterloo, IL 62298
Ph:(618)939-5300
Fax:(618)939-1805
Co. E-mail: chamber@htc.com
URL: http://www.enjoywaterloo.com
Contact: Debbie Ruggeri, Exec. Dir.

49775 ■ Watseka Area Chamber of Commerce
110 S 3rd St.
Watseka, IL 60970
Ph:(815)432-2416
Fax:(815)432-2762
Co. E-mail: office@watsekachamber.org
URL: http://www.watsekachamber.org
Contact: Darcey Smith, Exec. Dir.

49776 ■ Wauconda Chamber of Commerce
100 N Main St.
Wauconda, IL 60084
Ph:(847)526-5580
Fax:(847)526-3059
Co. E-mail: info@waucondachamber.org
URL: http://www.waucondachamber.org
Contact: Debra Ogorzaly, Exec. Dir.

49777 ■ West Chicago Chamber of Commerce and Industry
306 Main St.
West Chicago, IL 60185
Ph:(630)231-3003
Fax:(630)231-3009
Co. E-mail: info@westchicagochamber.com
Contact: David J. Sabathne, Pres./CEO

49778 ■ West Lawn Chamber of Commerce
4425 W 63rd St., Ste. 208
Chicago, IL 60629
Ph:(773)735-7690
Fax:(773)284-8110
Co. E-mail: westlawnchamber@sbcglobal.net
URL: http://www.westlawnchamber.org
Contact: Mrs. Edie Cavanaugh, Exec. Dir.

49779 ■ West Suburban Chamber of Commerce and Industry
9440 Joliet Rd., Ste. B
Hodgkins, IL 60525
Ph:(708)387-7550
Fax:(708)387-7556
Co. E-mail: info@wscci.org
URL: http://www.westsuburbanchamber.org
Contact: Bob Ware, Exec. Dir.

49780 ■ Westchester Chamber of Commerce
PO Box 7309
Westchester, IL 60154
Ph:(708)240-8400
Fax:(708)240-8400
Co. E-mail: bakasb@comcast.net
URL: http://www.westchesterchamber.org
Contact: Mr. Bob Bakas, Pres.

49781 ■ Westmont Chamber of Commerce and Tourism Bureau
1 S Cass Ave.
Westmont, IL 60559
Ph:(630)960-5553
Co. E-mail: information@westmontchamber.com
URL: http://www.westmontchamber.com
Contact: Larry Forssberg, Exec. Dir.

49782 ■ Westridge Chamber of Commerce
2720 W Devon, Ste. B
Chicago, IL 60659
Ph:(773)743-6022
Fax:(773)743-2893
Co. E-mail: westridgechamber@sbcglobal.net
URL: http://westridgechamber.org
Contact: Vimal Prajapati, Pres.

49783 ■ Wheaton Chamber of Commerce
108 E Wesley St.
Wheaton, IL 60187
Ph:(630)668-6464
Fax:(630)668-2744
URL: http://www.wheatonchamber.com
Contact: Vickie Austin, Chair

49784 ■ Wheeling - Prospect Heights Area Chamber of Commerce and Industry
395 E Dundee Rd., Ste. 300
Wheeling, IL 60090
Ph:(847)541-0170
Fax:(847)541-0296
Co. E-mail: info@wphchamber.com
URL: http://www.wphchamber.com
Contact: Catherine Powers, Exec. Dir.

49785 ■ Will County Center for Economic Development
116 N Chicago St.
Two Rialto Sq., Ste. 101
Joliet, IL 60432-4204
Ph:(815)723-1800
Fax:(815)723-6972
Co. E-mail: john.greuling@willcountyced.com
URL: http://www.willcountyced.com
Contact: Mr. John E. Greuling, Pres./CEO

49786 ■ Willowbrook - Burr Ridge Chamber of Commerce and Industry
8300 S Madison St.
Burr Ridge, IL 60527
Ph:(630)654-0909
Fax:(630)654-0922
Co. E-mail: info@wbbrchamber.org
URL: http://www.wbbrchamber.org
Contact: Cheryl Collins, Exec. Dir.

49787 ■ Wilmette Chamber of Commerce
1150 Wilmette Ave., Ste. A
Wilmette, IL 60091
Ph:(847)251-3800

Fax:(847)251-6321
Co. E-mail: info@wilmettechamber.org
URL: http://www.wilmettechamber.org
Contact: Julie Yusim, Exec. Dir.

49788 ■ Wilmington Chamber of Commerce
111 S Water St.
Wilmington, IL 60481
Ph:(815)476-7966
Fax:(815)476-7002
Co. E-mail: eric.fisher@cbcast.com
URL: http://www.wilmingtonchamberofcommerce.org
Contact: Eric Fisher, Pres.

49789 ■ Winfield Chamber of Commerce
PO Box 209
Winfield, IL 60190
Ph:(630)682-3712
Fax:(630)682-3726
Co. E-mail: winfieldchamber@sbcglobal.net
URL: http://www.winfieldchamber.biz
Contact: Rich Bysina, Exec. Dir.

49790 ■ Winnetka Chamber of Commerce
841 Spruce St., Ste. 204
Winnetka, IL 60093
Ph:(847)446-4451
Co. E-mail: wcc@winnetkachamber.com
URL: http://www.winnetkachamber.com
Contact: Cicely Clarke Michalak, Exec. Dir.

49791 ■ Wood Dale Chamber of Commerce
PO Box 353
Wood Dale, IL 60191-0353
Ph:(630)595-0505
Fax:(630)595-0677
Co. E-mail: info@wooddalechamber.com
URL: http://www.wooddalechamber.com
Contact: Lorrie Heggaton, Pres.

49792 ■ Woodridge Area Chamber of Commerce
5 Plaza Dr., Ste. 212
Woodridge, IL 60517-5014
Ph:(630)960-7080
Fax:(630)852-2316
Co. E-mail: chamber@woodridgechamber.org
URL: http://www.woodridgechamber.org
Contact: Amy Melinder, Pres./CEO

49793 ■ Woodstock Chamber of Commerce and Industry
136 Cass St.
Woodstock, IL 60098
Ph:(815)338-2436
Fax:(815)338-2927
Co. E-mail: chamber@woodstockilchamber.com
URL: http://www.woodstockilchamber.com
Contact: Susan Schmieding, Pres.

49794 ■ Yorkville Area Chamber of Commerce
26 W Countryside Pkwy.
Yorkville, IL 60560
Ph:(630)553-6853
Fax:(630)553-0702
Co. E-mail: sherri@yorkvillechamber.org
URL: http://www.yorkvillechamber.org
Contact: Sherri Farley, Interim Exec. Dir.

49795 ■ Zion Area Chamber of Commerce
2730 Sheridan Rd., Ste. 1
Zion, IL 60099
Ph:(847)872-5405
Fax:(847)872-9309
Co. E-mail: info@zionchamber.com
URL: http://www.zionchamber.com
Contact: Diana Gornik, Exec. Dir.

MINORITY BUSINESS ASSISTANCE PROGRAMS

49796 ■ Chicago Minority Business Opportunity Center
105 W Adams St., Ste. 2300
Chicago, IL 60603
Ph:(312)755-8888

Fax:(312)755-8891
Co. E-mail: business@cmboc.org
URL: http://www.cmboc.org
Contact: Dave Thomas, Exec Dir
Description: Works to foster and promote the growth of minority-owned businesses in the Chicago area.

49797 ■ Chicago Minority Supplier Development Council
105 West Adams Ste. 2300
Chicago, IL 60603
Ph:(312)755-8880
Fax:(312)755-8890
Co. E-mail: info@chicagomsdc.org
URL: http://msdc.adaptone.com/cmbdc/
Contact: Shelia C. Hill Morgan, Pres.

49798 ■ Latin American Chamber of Commerce
3512 W Fullerton Ave.
Chicago, IL 60647
Ph:(773)252-5211
Fax:(773)252-7065
Co. E-mail: bsantana@latinamericachamberofcommerce.com
URL: http://www.latinamericanchamberofcommerce.com
Contact: Antonio Guillen, Pres

FINANCING AND LOAN PROGRAMS

49799 ■ ABN AMRO Private Equity
208 S. La Salle St., 10th Fl.
Chicago, IL 60604
Ph:(312)855-7292
Fax:(312)553-6648
URL: http://www.abnequity.com
Contact: Daniel Foreman, Managing Director
Preferred Investment Size: $1,000,000 to $10,000,000. **Investment Types:** Expansion. **Industry Preferences:** Consumer related, computer software and services, other products, communications and media, Internet specific, medical and health, semiconductors and other electronics, and biotechnology. **Geographic Preferences:** U.S. and Canada. **Principal Exhibits:**

49800 ■ Allstate Private Equity
3075 Sanders Rd., Ste. G5D
Northbrook, IL 60062
Ph:(847)402-6709
Fax:(866)695-0483
URL: http://www.allstateinvestments.com
Contact: Ross Posner, Chief Financial Advisor
E-mail: rposner@allstate.com
Preferred Investment Size: $15,000,000-$20,000,000. **Investment Types:** Start-up, first and second stage, mezzanine, leveraged buyout, and special situation. **Industry Preferences:** Communications and media, computer hardware and software, semiconductors and other electronics, biotechnology, medical and health, consumer related, industrial and energy, financial services, and manufacturing. **Geographic Preferences:** U.S. **Principal Exhibits:**

49801 ■ Alpha Capital Partners, Ltd.
122 S. Michigan Ave., Ste. 1700
Chicago, IL 60603
Ph:(312)322-9800
Fax:(312)322-9808
Co. E-mail: info@alphacapital.com
URL: http://www.alphacapital.com
Contact: Andrew H. Kalnow, President
E-mail: ahkalnow@alphacapital.com
Preferred Investment Size: $500,000 to $5,000,000. **Investment Types:** First, second, and later stage, leveraged buyout, expansion, and special situation. **Industry Preferences:** Computer software and services, consumer related, other products, communications and media, medical and health, biotechnology, semiconductors and other electronics, Internet specific, industrial and energy, and computer hardware. **Geographic Preferences:** Midwest. **Principal Exhibits:**

49802 ■ Apex Venture Partners
225 W. Washington, Ste. 1500
Chicago, IL 60606
Ph:(312)857-2800
Fax:(312)857-1800
Co. E-mail: apex@apexvc.com
URL: http://www.apexvc.com
Contact: Amando Pauker, General Partner
Preferred Investment Size: $200,000 to $6,000,000.
Investment Types: Seed, start-up, and early stage.
Industry Preferences: Internet specific, computer software and services, other products, communications and media, semiconductors and other electronics, consumer related, medical and health, industrial and energy, and biotechnology. **Geographic Preferences:** U.S. **Principal Exhibits:**

49803 ■ Arch Venture Partners
8725 W. Higgins Rd., Ste. 290
Chicago, IL 60631
Ph:(773)380-6600
Fax:(773)380-6606
URL: http://www.archventure.com
Contact: Steven Lazarus, Managing Director
Preferred Investment Size: $500,000 to $10,000,000.
Investment Types: Seed, start-up, and early stage.
Industry Preferences: Internet specific, semiconductors and other electronics, computer software and services, medical and health, biotechnology, communications and media, computer hardware, industrial and energy, consumer related, and other products. **Geographic Preferences:** Midwest, Mid Atlantic, Northeast, Northern and Southern California, Northwest, Rocky Mountains, Southwest, and West Coast. **Principal Exhibits:**

49804 ■ Batterson Cross Zakin, LLC (BCZ)
303 W. Madison St., Ste. 1625
Chicago, IL 60606
Ph:(312)269-0300
Fax:(312)269-0021
URL: http://www.battersonvp.com
Contact: Leonard A. Batterson, Chief Executive Officer and Managing Pri
Preferred Investment Size: $500,000 to $3,000,000.
Investment Types: Seed, start-up, early and later stage.
Industry Preferences: Computer software and services, medical and health, Internet specific, communications and media, biotechnology, industrial and energy, computer hardware, other products, semiconductors and other electronics, and consumer related. **Geographic Preferences:** U.S. **Principal Exhibits:**

49805 ■ Beecken Petty O'Keefe & Company
131 S Dearborn St., Ste. 2800
Chicago, IL 60603
Ph:(312)435-0300
Fax:(312)435-0371
Co. E-mail: partners@bpoc.com
URL: http://www.beeckenpetty.com
Contact: Dave K. Beecken, Partner
Preferred Investment Size: $5,000,000 to $500,000,000.
Investment Types: Early and later stage, leveraged buyout, management buyouts, expansion, and recapitalizations. **Industry Preferences:** Medical and health, computer software and services, Internet specific, other products, communications and media. **Geographic Preferences:** U.S. and Canada. **Principal Exhibits:**

49806 ■ Bluestar Ventures LP
200 W. Madison St., 37th Fl.
Chicago, IL 60606
Ph:(312)384-5000
Fax:(312)384-5005
Co. E-mail: info@bluestarventures.com
URL: http://www.bluestarventures.com
Contact: Patrick Pollard, Managing Director and President
E-mail: pat@bluestarventures.com
Preferred Investment Size: $500,000 to $3,000,000.
Investment Types: Start-up, early, first, and second stage. **Industry Preferences:** Communications, computer software, and Internet specific. **Geographic Preferences:** Mid Atlantic, Midwest, Northwest, Southeast, and Southwest. **Principal Exhibits:**

49807 ■ The Capital Strategy Management Co.
233 S. Wacker Dr.
Box 06334
Chicago, IL 60606-0334
Ph:(312)444-1170
URL: http://capitalstrategymanagement.com
Contact: Eric E. von Bauer, President
E-mail: evb@capitalstrategymanagement.com
Preferred Investment Size: $200,000 to $50,000,000.
Investment Types: Start-up, first, second, early and later stage, acquisition, balanced, distressed debt, control-block purchases, industry rollups, leveraged buyout, private placement, public companies, strategic alliance, management buyouts, expansion, generalist PE, joint ventures, mezzanine, recapitalizations, turnaround, and special situation.
Industry Preferences: Communications, computer hardware and software, Internet specific, semiconductors and other electronics, biotechnology, medical and health, consumer related, industrial and energy, transportation, business service, manufacturing, agriculture, forestry and fishing, environment, and utilities. **Geographic Preferences:** Mid Atlantic, Midwest, Rocky Mountains, Southwest, and Southeast. **Principal Exhibits:**

49808 ■ DN Partners LLC
180 N. LaSalle St., Ste. 3001
Chicago, IL 60601
Ph:(312)332-7960
Fax:(312)332-0856
URL: http://www.dnpartners.com
Contact: Maury J. Bell, Managing Partner
Preferred Investment Size: $3,000,000 to $15,000,000.
Investment Types: Control-block purchases, generalist PE, industry rollups, later stage, leveraged buyout, management buyouts, and recapitalizations. **Industry Preferences:** Communications, computer hardware, Internet specific, semiconductors and other electronics, medical and health, consumer related, industrial and energy, transportation, financial services, business service, manufacturing, agriculture, forestry and fishing. **Geographic Preferences:** Midwest and U.S. **Principal Exhibits:**

49809 ■ Dresner Capital Resources, Inc.
20 N. Clark St., Ste. 3550
Chicago, IL 60602
Ph:(312)726-3600
Fax:(312)726-7448
Co. E-mail: info@dresnerco.com
URL: http://www.dresnerpartners.com
Contact: Steven M. Dresner, President
E-mail: sdresner@dresnerco.com
Preferred Investment Size: $500,000 to $1,000,000.
Investment Types: Leveraged buyout, mezzanine, and second stage. **Industry Preferences:** Communications, computer hardware and software, Internet specific, semiconductors and other electronics, medical and health, consumer related, industrial and energy, financial services, business service, and manufacturing. **Principal Exhibits:**

49810 ■ Duchossois Technology Partners LLC (DTEC)
845 Larch Ave.
Elmhurst, IL 60126-1196
Ph:(630)993-6105
Fax:(630)993-8644
Co. E-mail: duchtec@duch.com
URL: http://www.duchtec.com
Contact: Robert L. Fealy, Managing Director
E-mail: rfealy@duch.com
Preferred Investment Size: $2,000,000 to $7,000,000.
Investment Types: Early, first, and second stage. **Industry Preferences:** Communications, computer software, semiconductors and other electronics. **Geographic Preferences:** U.S. **Principal Exhibits:**

49811 ■ First Analysis Corp.
1 S. Wacker Dr., Ste. 3900
Chicago, IL 60606
Ph:(312)258-1400

Fax:(312)258-0334
URL: http://www.firstanalysis.com
Contact: Michael Siemplenski, Managing Director
Preferred Investment Size: $3,000,000 to $10,000,000.
Investment Types: Early and later stage, expansion, and balanced. **Industry Preferences:** Industrial and energy, Internet specific, other products, computer software and services, communications and media, consumer related, medical and health, computer hardware, semiconductors and other electronics, and biotechnology. **Geographic Preferences:** U.S. **Principal Exhibits:**

49812 ■ Frontenac Company
135 S. LaSalle St., Ste. 3800
Chicago, IL 60603
Ph:(312)368-0044
Fax:(312)368-9520
Co. E-mail: info@frontenac.com
URL: http://www.frontenac.com
Contact: Paul D. Carbery, Managing Director
Preferred Investment Size: $10,000,000 to $50,000,000.
Investment Types: Leveraged buyout, expansion, acquisition, later stage, management buyouts, and recapitalizations. **Industry Preferences:** Consumer related, other products, Internet specific, computer software and services, medical and health, communications and media, industrial and energy, computer hardware, semiconductors and other electronics, and biotechnology. **Geographic Preferences:** U.S. **Principal Exhibits:**

49813 ■ GTCR Golder Rauner LLC
300 N. LaSalle St., Ste. 5600
Chicago, IL 60654
Ph:(312)382-2200
Fax:(312)382-2201
Co. E-mail: info@gtcr.com
URL: http://www.gtcr.com
Contact: Barry R. Dunn, Principal
E-mail: barry.dunn@gtcr.com
Preferred Investment Size: $10,000,000 to $300,000,000.
Investment Types: Acquisition, expansion, leveraged buyout, management buyouts, industry rollups, generalist PE, and recapitalizations. **Industry Preferences:** Communications, other products, computer software and services, consumer related, semiconductors and other electronics, medical and health, Internet specific, computer hardware. **Geographic Preferences:** U.S. **Principal Exhibits:**

49814 ■ High Street Capital
11 S. LaSalle St., 5th Fl.
Chicago, IL 60603
Ph:(312)423-2650
Fax:(312)267-2861
Co. E-mail: info@HighStreetCapital.com
URL: http://www.highstr.com
Contact: Joseph Katcha, Principal
E-mail: Joe@highstreetcapital.com
Preferred Investment Size: $2,000,000 to $8,000,000.
Investment Types: Acquisition, control-block purchases, expansion, generalist PE, leveraged buyout, industry rollups, management buyouts, mezzanine, strategic alliances, recapitalizations, and special situation. **Industry Preferences:** Communications, computer software, semiconductors and other electronics, medical and health, industrial and energy, business service, and manufacturing. **Geographic Preferences:** U.S. **Principal Exhibits:**

49815 ■ IEG Venture Management, Inc.
70 West Madison St., 14th Fl.
Chicago, IL 60602
Ph:(312)644-0890
Fax:(312)454-0369
URL: http://www.iegventure.com
Contact: Frank Blair, President
E-mail: frankblair@iegventure.com
Investment Types: Seed, start-up, first and second stage. **Industry Preferences:** Communications, computer hardware and software, Internet specific, semiconductors and other electronics, biotechnology, medical and health, industrial and energy, transportation, manufacturing, agriculture, forestry and fishing. **Geographic Preferences:** Midwest. **Principal Exhibits:**

49816 ■ JK&B Capital
2 Prudential PLz.
180 N. Stetson Ave., Ste. 4500
Chicago, IL 60601
Ph:(312)946-1200
Fax:(312)946-1103
URL: http://www.jkbcapital.com
Contact: Albert DaValle Jr., Partner
Preferred Investment Size: $5,000,000 to $30,000,000. **Investment Types:** Early, first, second, and later stage, and expansion. **Industry Preferences:** Internet specific, communications and media, computer software and services, semiconductors and other electronics, industrial and energy, and consumer related. **Geographic Preferences:** U.S. **Principal Exhibits:**

49817 ■ KB Partners LLC
1780 Green Bay Rd., Ste. 202
Highland Park, IL 60035
Ph:(847)681-1270
Fax:(847)681-1370
Co. E-mail: ideas@kbpartners.com
URL: http://www.kbpartners.com
Contact: Keith Bank, Managing Director
E-mail: keith@kbpartners.com
Preferred Investment Size: $1,000,000 to $5,000,000. **Investment Types:** Early stage and expansion. **Industry Preferences:** Internet specific, computer software and services, industrial and energy, communications and media, semiconductors and other electronics, medical and health, and other products. **Geographic Preferences:** Midwest and Rocky Mountains. **Principal Exhibits:**

49818 ■ Lake Capital Partners, Inc.
676 N. Michigan Ave., Ste. 3900
Chicago, IL 60611-2896
Ph:(312)640-7050
Fax:(312)640-7051
Co. E-mail: info@lakecapital.com
URL: http://www.lakecapital.com
Contact: Terence M. Graunke, Principal
Preferred Investment Size: $50,000,000 to $100,000,000. **Investment Types:** Start-up, expansion, acquisition, and leveraged buyout. **Industry Preferences:** Technology, financial services, healthcare and business services. **Geographic Preferences:** U.S. **Principal Exhibits:**

49819 ■ LaSalle Capital Group, Inc.
5710 Three First National Plz.
70 W. Madison St.
Chicago, IL 60602
Ph:(312)236-7041
Fax:(312)236-0720
Co. E-mail: contact@lasallecapitalgroup.com
URL: http://www.lasallecapitalgroup.com
Contact: Jeffrey M. Walters, Principal
E-mail: jwalters@lasallecapitalgroup.com
Preferred Investment Size: $5,000,000 to $15,000,000. **Investment Types:** Leveraged buyout, acquisition, turnaround, management buyouts, industry rollups, and recapitalizations. **Industry Preferences:** Communications, consumer related, semiconductors and other electronics, medical and health, industrial and energy, business service, manufacturing, and agriculture, forestry and fishing. **Geographic Preferences:** U.S. **Principal Exhibits:**

49820 ■ Madison Dearborn Partners LLC
3 First National Plz., Ste. 4600
Chicago, IL 60602
Ph:(312)895-1000
Fax:(312)895-1001
Co. E-mail: info@mdcp.com
URL: http://www.mdcp.com
Contact: Benjamin Chereskin, Managing Director
Preferred Investment Size: $100,000,000 to $600,000,000. **Investment Types:** Leveraged buyout, management buyouts, expansion, acquisition, and recapitalizations. **Industry Preferences:** Communications and media, Internet specific, consumer related, semiconductors and other electronics, medical and health, industrial and energy, computer software and services, computer hardware, and other products. **Geographic Preferences:** U.S. and Canada. **Principal Exhibits:**

49821 ■ Marquette Venture Partners
PO Box 1609
Vail, CO 81658
Free: 877-215-3400
Fax:(970)476-2316
URL: http://www.marquetteventures.com
Contact: Lloyd D. Ruth, General Partner
E-mail: cruth@marquetteventures.com
Preferred Investment Size: $1,000,000 to $5,000,000. **Investment Types:** Start-up, first and second stage. **Industry Preferences:** Medical and health, consumer related, computer software and services, communications and media, biotechnology, Internet specific, semiconductors and other electronics, industrial and energy, and computer hardware. **Geographic Preferences:** Mid Atlantic, Midwest, Rocky Mountains, and West Coast. **Principal Exhibits:**

49822 ■ Mesirow Private Equity Investments, Inc.
353 N. Clark St.
Chicago, IL 60654
Ph:(312)595-6000
Free: 800-453-0600
Fax:(312)595-4246
URL: http://www.meisirowfinancial.com
Contact: Thomas E. Galuhn, Senior Managing Director
E-mail: tgaluhn@mesirowfinancial.com
Preferred Investment Size: $2,000,000 to $10,000,000. **Investment Types:** Later stage, mezzanine, generalist PE, leveraged buyout, management buyouts, fund of funds, acquisition, expansion, and recapitalizations. **Industry Preferences:** Computer software and services, other products, computer hardware, consumer related, Internet specific, communications and media, industrial and energy, semiconductors and other electronics, medical and health. **Geographic Preferences:** U.S. and Canada. **Principal Exhibits:**

49823 ■ Mosaix Ventures
1822 N. Mohawk St.
Chicago, IL 60614
Ph:(312)274-0988
Fax:(773)913-2792
URL: http://www.mosaixventures.com
Contact: Ranjan Lal, Managing Partner
E-mail: rlal@mosaixventures.com
Preferred Investment Size: $1,000,000 to $4,000,000. **Investment Types:** Balanced. **Industry Preferences:** Medical and health, and biotechnology. **Geographic Preferences:** U.S. and Canada. **Principal Exhibits:**

49824 ■ Motorola Ventures
1303 E. Algonquin Rd., 6th Fl.
Schaumburg, IL 60196
Ph:(847)576-0278
Fax:(847)576-2569
URL: http://www.motorola.com/ventures
Contact: Reese Schroeder, Managing Director
Preferred Investment Size: $3,000,000 to $5,000,000. **Investment Types:** Startup, growth, and expansion. **Industry Preferences:** Communications and media, Internet specific, computer software and services, semiconductors and other electronics, Internet specific, computer hardware, biotechnology, consumer related, and other products. **Geographic Preferences:** U.S. **Principal Exhibits:**

49825 ■ New World Ventures
111 South Wacker Dr., Ste. 4000
Chicago, IL 60606
Ph:(312)447-6000
Fax:(312)447-6006
Co. E-mail: info@newworldvc.com
URL: http://www.newworldvc.com
Contact: Christopher E. Girgenti, Managing Director
Preferred Investment Size: $5,000,000 to $12,000,000. **Investment Types:** Early stage. **Industry Preferences:** Internet specific, communications and media, medical and health, and computer software and services. **Geographic Preferences:** U.S. **Principal Exhibits:**

49826 ■ Open Prairie Ventures
400 E. Jefferson
Effingham, IL 62401
Ph:(217)347-1000
Fax:(217)347-1001
Co. E-mail: info@openprairie.com
URL: http://www.openprairie.com
Contact: Dennis Beard, Chief Financial Officer
Preferred Investment Size: $250,000 to $2,500,000. **Investment Types:** Early stage. **Industry Preferences:** Communications and media, computer hardware and software, Internet specific, computer related, semiconductors and other electronics, biotechnology, medical and health, industrial and energy. **Geographic Preferences:** Midwest. **Principal Exhibits:**

49827 ■ Polestar Capital, Inc.
180 N. Michigan Ave., Ste. 1905
Chicago, IL 60601
Ph:(312)984-9090
Fax:(312)984-9877
Co. E-mail: info@polestarvc.com
URL: http://www.polestarvc.com
Contact: Derrick K. Collins, General Partner
E-mail: dkcollins@polestarvc.com
Investment Types: Early stage. **Industry Preferences:** Communications and media, computer software, computer related, and manufacturing. **Geographic Preferences:** U.S. **Principal Exhibits:**

49828 ■ Portage Venture Partners / Graystone Venture Partners
1 Northfield Plz., Ste. 530
Northfield, IL 60093
Ph:(847)446-9460
Fax:(847)446-9470
URL: http://www.portageventures.com
Contact: Mathew McCall, Managing Director
Preferred Investment Size: $500,000 to $20,000,000. **Investment Types:** Seed and early stage. **Industry Preferences:** Internet specific, computer software and services, biotechnology, communications and media, medical and health, other products, semiconductors and other electronics, and consumer related. **Geographic Preferences:** Midwest. **Principal Exhibits:**

49829 ■ Prism Capital
444 N. Michigan Ave., Ste. 1910
Chicago, IL 60611
Ph:(312)464-7900
Fax:(312)464-7915
URL: http://www.prismfund.com
Contact: John Hoesley, Partner
E-mail: john@prismfund.com
Preferred Investment Size: $2,000,000 to $15,000,000. **Investment Types:** Later stage, mezzanine, leveraged buyout, acquisition, and expansion. **Industry Preferences:** Computer software and services, Internet specific, and consumer related, medical and health, semiconductors and other electronics, computer hardware, and other products. **Geographic Preferences:** U.S. **Principal Exhibits:**

49830 ■ Third Coast Capital
1 N. Franklin St., Ste. 2700
Chicago, IL 60610
Ph:(312)332-6484
Fax:(312)337-2567
URL: http://www.thirdcoastcapital.com
Contact: Kathleen Wilkerson, Managing Director
Preferred Investment Size: $1,000,000 to $5,000,000. **Investment Types:** Start-up, early and second stage. **Industry Preferences:** Communications, computer software, Internet specific, biotechnology, medical and health, and consumer related. **Geographic Preferences:** U.S. **Principal Exhibits:**

49831 ■ Thoma Cressey Equity Partners
9200 Sears Tower
233 S. Wacker Dr.
Chicago, IL 60606
Ph:(312)777-4444

Fax:(312)777-4445
URL: http://www.thomacressey.com
Contact: Merrick J. Axel, Principal
E-mail: maxel@cresseyco.com
Preferred Investment Size: $10,000,000 to $100,000,000. **Investment Types:** Later stage, leveraged buyout, and recapitalizations. **Industry Preferences:** Other products, medical and health, computer software and services, Internet specific, consumer related, computer hardware, and biotechnology. **Geographic Preferences:** U.S. and Canada. **Principal Exhibits:**

49832 ■ Transcap Associates Inc.
900 Skokie Blvd., Ste. 210
Northbrook, IL 60062
Ph:(847)753-9600
Fax:(847)753-9090
Co. E-mail: admin@transcaptrade.com
URL: http://www.transcaptrade.com
Preferred Investment Size: $500,000 to $50,000,000. **Investment Types:** Mezzanine, second stage, and special situation. **Industry Preferences:** Communications, computer hardware, semiconductors and other electronics, medical and health, consumer related, industrial and energy. **Geographic Preferences:** U.S.

49833 ■ Tribune Ventures
435 N. Michigan Ave.
Chicago, IL 60611
Ph:(312)222-9100
Fax:(312)222-5993
Co. E-mail: gweitman@tribune.com
URL: http://www.tribuneventures.com
Contact: Andy Oleszczuk, President
Preferred Investment Size: $2,000,000 to $10,000,000. **Investment Types:** Early, first and second stage, and expansion. **Industry Preferences:** Internet specific, computer software and services, communications and media, and other products. **Geographic Preferences:** Midwest, Northeast, an West Coast. **Principal Exhibits:**

49834 ■ William Blair Capital Partners
222 W. Adams St.
Chicago, IL 60606
Ph:(312)236-1600
Fax:(312)621-0687
Co. E-mail: info@wmblair.com
URL: http://www.williamblair.com
Contact: Mio Stojkovich, Vice President
Preferred Investment Size: $7,000,000 to $35,000,000. **Investment Types:** Early and later stage, expansion, generalist PE, management and leveraged buyouts, recapitalizations, and special situation. **Industry Preferences:** Consumer related, medical and health, computer software, hardware and services, biotechnology, industrial and energy, communications and media, semiconductors and other electronics. **Geographic Preferences:** U.S. **Principal Exhibits:**

49835 ■ Wind Point Partners (Chicago)
676 N. Michigan Ave., Ste. 3700
Chicago, IL 60611
Ph:(312)255-4800
Fax:(312)255-4820
URL: http://www.wppartners.com
Contact: Nathan Brown, Managing Director
Preferred Investment Size: $30,000,000 to $150,000,000. **Investment Types:** Later stage, leveraged buyout, and management buyouts, balanced, generalist PE, acquisition, expansion, and recapitalizations. **Industry Preferences:** Industrial and energy, consumer related, other products, communications and media, medical and health, Internet specific, biotechnology, computer software and services, computer hardware, semiconductors and other electronics. **Geographic Preferences:** U.S. **Principal Exhibits:**

PROCUREMENT ASSISTANCE PROGRAMS

49836 ■ Disa Conus–Defense Information Systems Agency
c/o DITCO/DO4DT
Small Business Administration/PCR
2300 East Dr., Bldg. 3189, R
Scott Air Force B, IL 62225-5406

Ph:(618)220-8840
Co. E-mail: chut@scott.disa.mil
Contact: Tung Shing Chu, TPCR Supervisor
Description: Covers activities for Defense Information & Technological Contracting (Scott Air Force Base, IL), 375th Airlift Wing (Scott Air Force Base, IL), and USAF AMC Contracting Flight (Scott Air Force Base, IL).

49837 ■ Illinois Procurement Technical Assistance Center–Black Hawk Community College
4703 16th St., Ste. G
Moline, IL 61265
Ph:(309)797-2806
Co. E-mail: millerv@bhc.edu
URL: http://www.bhc.edu
Contact: Vicky Miller, Dir.
E-mail: millerv@bhc.edu
Description: Assists entrepreneurs start a new business or expand existing business.

49838 ■ Illinois Procurement Technical Assistance Center–College of DuPage
425 Fawell Blvd.
Glen Ellyn, IL 60137-6599
Ph:(630)942-2184
Fax:(630)942-2771
Co. E-mail: haaker@cod.edu
URL: http://www.cod.edu
Contact: Rita Haake, Dir.
E-mail: hatcher@cdnet.cod.edu
Description: Assists with doing business with the government, or to improve your current level of government contracting.

49839 ■ Illinois Procurement Technical Assistance Center–College of Lake County
19351 W Washington St.
Grayslake, IL 60030-1198
Ph:(847)543-2580
Fax:(847)223-9371
Co. E-mail: illinoisptac@clcillinois.edu
URL: http://www.clcillinois.edu
Contact: Marc N. Violante, Dir.
E-mail: mviolante@clcillinois.edu
Description: Assists businesses in competing for contracts with the municipal, state, and federal government.

49840 ■ Illinois Procurement Technical Assistance Center–Illinois Central College
Arbor Hall, Ste. 126
5407 N University
Peoria, IL 61602-1388
Ph:(309)690-6818
Fax:(309)690-6810
Co. E-mail: Linda.krendick@icc.edu
URL: http://www.icc.edu
Contact: Linda Krendick, Dir.
E-mail: sgorman@icc.edu
Description: Provides government contracting services for small and medium-sized existing businesses in Central Illinois. The Center assists regional companies in doing business with federal, state, and local government agencies, private sector prime contractors, and second-tier suppliers.

49841 ■ Illinois Procurement Technical Assistance Center–Illinois Hispanic Chamber of Commerce
111 W. Washington, Ste. 1660
Chicago, IL 60602
Ph:(312)425-9500
Fax:(312)425-9510
Co. E-mail: ptac@ihccbusiness.net
URL: http://www.ihccbusiness.net
Contact: Gerardo Rodriguez, Dir.
Description: Promotes the growth and success of Hispanic firms and serves as a strong advocate for business issues.

49842 ■ Illinois Procurement Technical Assistance Center–John A. Logan Community College–Center for Business & Industry (700 L)
700 Logan College Rd.
Carterville, IL 62918-9802
Ph:(618)985-3741
Fax:(618)985-2867
Co. E-mail: ccrr@jal.cc.il.us
URL: http://www.jal.cc.il.us
Contact: Christopher Barr, Dir.
E-mail: chrisbarr@jalc.edu
Description: Helps familiarize firms with the government procurement process and provides them the specific marketing and technical assistance required to do business with the government or government prime contractors. Assistance may be in the form of contract preparation, acquisition, or administration.

49843 ■ Illinois Procurement Technical Assistance Center–North Business & Industrial Council (NORBIC)
Pyramid Mouldings Bldg.
5353 W Armstrong Ave., 2nd Fl.
Chicago, IL 60646-6509
Ph:(773)594-9562
Fax:(773)594-9416
Co. E-mail: info@norbic.org
URL: http://www.norbic.org
Contact: James Peters, Dir.
Description: Advises Illinois companies on procurement opportunities and keeps them abreast of changes in the procurement process at the federal, State of Illinois, and local municipal levels. Technical expertise and assistance are offered in proposal preparation, the procurement process, and contract administration. NORBIC also offers assistance with small business preference programs, including Small Women Owned Businesses, Small Disadvantaged Businesses, Veteran, and 8(a) Certification Assistance.

49844 ■ Illinois Procurement Technical Assistance Center–Rock Valley College
EIGERlab
605 Fulton Ave., Rm. E-108
Rockford, IL 61103
Ph:(815)921-2091
Fax:(815)921-2089
Co. E-mail: j.digiacomo@rockvalleycollege.edu
URL: http://www.rockvalleycollege.com
Contact: John DiGiacomo, Dir.
E-mail: j.digiacomo@rvc.cc.il.us
Description: Provides such services as trade/export assistance through international trade centers, access to financial and energy management assistance, and job training help.

49845 ■ Illinois Procurement Technical Assistance Center–South Suburban College
15800 S State St.
South Holland, IL 60473
Ph:(708)596-2000
Fax:(708)210-5703
Co. E-mail: procurement@southsuburbancollege.edu
URL: http://www.southsuburbancollege.edu
Contact: David Talbot, Dir.
E-mail: dtalbot@southsuburbancollege.edu
Description: Provides free counseling and technical assistance to Illinois firms pursuing government contracts.

49846 ■ Illinois Procurement Technical Assistance Center–U.S. General Services Administration (GSA)–Great Lakes (Region 5) (230 S)
230 S Dearborn St.
Chicago, IL 60604
Ph:(312)353-5395
Fax:(312)886-5595
Co. E-mail: david.hood@gsa.gov
URL: http://www.gsa.gov
Contact: David J. Hood, Regional Administrator
E-mail: james.handley@gsa.gov
Description: Serve its federal agency customers in Illinois, Indiana, Michigan, Minnesota, Ohio, and Wisconsin.

49847 ■ Illinois Procurement Technical Assistance Center–University Entrepreneurship Center
100 N Locust St.
Centralia, IL 62801
Ph:(618)532-1086
Fax:(618)532-2736
Co. E-mail: kimsand@siu.edu
URL: http://www.universityec.com
Contact: Kim Sanders, Dir.
Description: Provides one-on-one counseling, technical information, marketing assistance and training to existing businesses that are interested in selling their products and/or services to local, state, or federal government agencies.

49848 ■ Illinois Procurement Technical Assistance Center–Women's Business Development Center
8 South Michigan, Ste. 400
Chicago, IL 60603-3306
Ph:(312)853-3477
Fax:(312)853-0145
Co. E-mail: wbdc@wbdc.org
URL: http://www.wbdc.org
Contact: Freida Curry, Dir.
E-mail: mangledc.org
Description: Works with women to launch new businesses and strengthen existing businesses in the Chicago area.

49849 ■ Illinois Procurement Technical Assistance Center at Western Illinois–Quincy Business & Technology Center
301 Oak St., Rm. 2-27
Quincy, IL 62301
Ph:(217)223-5636
Fax:(217)223-5672
Co. E-mail: qbtc@adams.net
URL: http://www.qbtc.org
Contact: Mary Turner, Dir.
E-mail: mturner@imec1.org
Description: Nurtures the development of entrepreneurial companies helping them to service and grow during their start up period.

49850 ■ Latin American Chamber of Commerce
3512 W Fullerton Ave.
Chicago, IL 60647
Ph:(773)252-5211
Fax:(773)252-7065
Co. E-mail: lacc@latinamericanchamberofcommerce.com
URL: http://www.latinamericanchamberofcommerce.com
Contact: Jorge Sanchez-Ferrer, Small Bus Dir

INCUBATORS/RESEARCH AND TECHNOLOGY PARKS

49851 ■ Argonne National Laboratory–Office of Technology Transfer
9700 S Cass Ave.
Argonne, IL 60439
Ph:(630)252-8111
Free: 800—627-2596
Fax:(630)252-5230
Co. E-mail: sdban@anl.gov
URL: http://www.anl.gov/techtransfer
Contact: Stephen Ban, Dir.
E-mail: sdban@anl.gov
Scope: Facilitates the exchange of Argonne research resources and inventions with U.S. industry and develops partnerships with industry. **Publications:** Argonne News (biweekly); Resources for Technology-Based Small Businesses in the Midwest Region (annually); TransForum (quarterly). **Educational Activities:** Community roundtable.

49852 ■ Bradley University–Office for Teaching Excellence and Faculty Development
1501 W Bradley Ave.
Peoria, IL 61625
Ph:(309)677-4118
Co. E-mail: goblue@bradley.edu
URL: http://www.bradley.edu/otefd/
Contact: Kim Willis, Interim Dir.
E-mail: goblue@bradley.edu
Scope: Internal research mechanisms are coordinated by the Teaching Excellence Committee and Research Excellence Committee. Development activities of foundational nature are coordinated under the direction of Vice President for Development and University Relations. **Services:** Business Technology Incubator; International Trade Center; Small Business Development Center. **Publications:** Catalyst. **Educational Activities:** Proposal Development Workshop (annually), open to University staff and faculty; Student Research/Creative Production Exhibition and Competition (annually), open to students and faculty involved in collaborative research and creative production activity.

49853 ■ Business Center of Decatur
2121 S Imboden Ct.
Decatur, IL 62521
Ph:(217)423-2832
Fax:(217)423-7214
Co. E-mail: bcd@decaturcenter.com
URL: http://www.decaturcenter.com/2home.htm
Contact: Jim Seaberg, Gen Mgr
Description: The Business Center of Decatur is a business incubator for new and growing businesses.

49854 ■ Business and Technology Center (Champaign)
701 Devonshire Dr., C-2
Champaign, IL 61820
Ph:(217)398-5759
Fax:(217)398-0413
Co. E-mail: information@btcservices.net
URL: http://www.btcservices.net
Contact: Cindy Somers, Owner
Description: We are committed to the provision of an affordable, flexible and professional environment in which startup and existing businesses can prosper. We will consistently provide the best possible support services to our clients and will strive to make the latest in business technology available at an affordable price.

49855 ■ Chicago Southland Enterprise Center
1655 Union St
Chicago Heights, IL 60411
Ph:(708)754-6960
Fax:(708)754-8779
Description: Owned by a not-for-profit corporation, this small business incubator fosters collaboration among its tenants, businesses ranging from service to light manufacturing.

49856 ■ Chicago Technology Park
2201 W Campbell Park Dr., Ste. 2
Chicago, IL 60612-3547
Ph:(312)829-7252
Fax:(312)829-4069
Co. E-mail: mjanghor@hotmail.com
URL: http://www.techpark.com
Contact: Mort Janghorbani PhD, Pres.
E-mail: mjanghor@hotmail.com
Scope: Seeks to coordinate industry, university, and government partnerships to stimulate the formation of science-based companies and economic development in the Chicago area. Provides access to university and hospital resources, offers assistance in the creation of new venture companies, and provides space in an incubator building.

49857 ■ Chicago Technology Park Corp.
2201 W Campbell Park Dr., Ste. 1
Chicago, IL 60612-3547
Ph:(312)633-3434
Fax:(312)633-3438
Co. E-mail: info@techpark.com
URL: http://www.techpark.com
Description: A small business incubator serving as a ground for technology companies in early development, as well as expansion facilities for those companies that are growing their operations.

49858 ■ Foundation for Agronomic Research
107 S State St., Ste. 300
Monticello, IL 61856-1968
Ph:(217)762-2074
Fax:(217)762-8655
Co. E-mail: hreetz@farmresearch.com
URL: http://www.farmresearch.com/
Contact: Dr. Harold F. Reetz Jr., Dir.
E-mail: hreetz@farmresearch.com
Scope: Encourages multidisciplinary crop production research by developing funding strategies to capitalize on research opportunities at existing institutions. **Publications:** FAR Letter (quarterly). **Educational Activities:** Research workshops (periodically).

49859 ■ Fulton Carroll Center Incubator
Industrial Council of Northwest Chicago
320 N Damen Ave., Ste. D-100
Chicago, IL 60612
Ph:(312)421-3941
Fax:(312)421-1871
Co. E-mail: info@industrialcouncil.com
URL: http://www.industrialcouncil.com
Contact: Joyce Shanahan, Exec. Dir.
Description: A small business incubator providing no-cost business development services and resources.

49860 ■ Galesburg Business and Technology Center
2051 Tom L. Wilson Blvd.
Galesburg, IL 61401
Ph:(309)345-3501
Fax:(309)345-3526
Co. E-mail: info@galesburgbtc.org
URL: http://www.galesburgbtc.org
Description: A small business incubator is designed to accelerate the growth of entrepreneurial companies through an array of support services.

49861 ■ Greater Sterling Development Corporation
1741 Industrial Dr.
Sterling, IL 61081
Ph:(815)625-5255
Fax:(815)625-5094
Co. E-mail: hsotelo@sterlingdevelopment.org
URL: http://www.sterlingdevelopment.org
Contact: Heather Sotelo, Exec. Dir.
Description: Provides a variety of business development and relocation assistance services.

49862 ■ Macomb Area Economic Development Corporation
Western Illinois University
510 N Pearl St., Ste. 300
Macomb, IL 61455
Ph:(309)837-4684
Fax:(309)837-4688
Co. E-mail: maedco@wiu.edu
URL: http://www.maedco.org
Description: The Macomb Area Economic Development Corporation (MAEDCO) is a not-for-profit corporation dedicated to the economic growth of the Macomb region. We have crafted an environment that can foster long-term growth, success, and profits for your business. We are capable of arranging a business package tailored to meet your individual requirements.

49863 ■ Maple City Business and Technology Center Incubator–Technology Center Incubator
620 S Main St.
Monmouth, IL 61462
Ph:(309)734-8544
Fax:(309)734-8579

49864 ■ Michael Reese Hospital and Medical Center–Research and Education Foundation
2240 W Ogden, 2nd Fl.
Chicago, IL 60612-4220
Ph:(312)768-6095

Fax:(312)348-1998
Co. E-mail: waclark@michaelreesefoundation.org
URL: http://www.michaelreesefoundation.org
Contact: William A. Clark PhD, Dir.
E-mail: waclark@michaelreesefoundation.org
Scope: Administers and coordinates contracts and grants for biomedical research conducted in the various departments of the Michael Reese Hospital and Medical Center. Research projects are funded by the government, private philanthropy, and outside sources and include studies on cancer, heart disease, stroke, neurological disorders, arthritis, birth defects, schizophrenia, and other afflictions.

49865 ■ Northern Illinois University–Technology Transfer Office
Division of Research & Graduate Studies
301 Lowden Hall
DeKalb, IL 60115
Ph:(815)753-2117
Fax:(815)753-1631
Co. E-mail: ryusko@niu.edu
URL: http://www.tto.niu.edu/tto/
Contact: Rita I. Yusko, Mgr.
E-mail: ryusko@niu.edu
Scope: Assists faculty at NIU with technical and commercial assessments, patent applications and licensing. **Publications:** Newsletter for faculty (semiannually). **Educational Activities:** Seminars on commercialization process, intellectual property matters.

49866 ■ Northwestern University–Office for Research
633 Clark St.
Evanston, IL 60208-1108
Ph:(847)491-3485
Fax:(847)467-4620
Co. E-mail: vp-research@northwestern.edu
URL: http://www.research.northwestern.edu/
Contact: Joseph Walsh, VP
E-mail: vp-research@northwestern.edu
Scope: Provides support for interdisciplinary research centers. Oversees Center for Comparative Medicine, the Office of Research Safety, Office of Sponsored Research, Office for the Protection of Research Subjects, Office for Research Integrity, Office for Research Planning, Finance and Communications, and the Office for Research Information Systems. Administers interdisciplinary research service centers of the University. **Publications:** Annual report; CenterPiece magazine (quarterly).

49867 ■ Northwestern University–Technology Innovation Center
820 Davis St.
Evanston, IL 60201
Ph:(847)864-0800
Fax:(847)866-1808
Co. E-mail: t-lavengood@theincubator.com
URL: http://www.theincubator.com/dojo/32/index.html
Contact: Tim Lavengood, Dir.
E-mail: t-lavengood@theincubator.com
Scope: Matches University resources with the needs of businesses, including assisting faculty entrepreneurs to commercialize their new technologies. The Center maintains three administrative offices: the incubator component leases space to technology-based small companies; the Small Business Development Center provides technical and business assistance companies in the Research Park and northern Cook County, manages the Evanston Business Investment Corporation (a seed capital fund) and links companies to campus expertise; and the Minority Business Development Office administers special training projects. **Publications:** Park Facts.

49868 ■ Peoria NEXT Innovation Center
801 W Main St.
Peoria, IL 61606
Ph:(309)495-7238
Fax:(309)676-7534
URL: http://www.peorianext.org/index.php
Description: A small business incubator designed to enable leadership in discovery, innovation, and commercialization.

49869 ■ Performance Improvement Institute
Chicago, IL 60606
URL: http://www.zyworld.com/lisandro/IMD1English.htm
Description: A small business incubator focusing on developing and graduating new companies through an incubation process under the leadership of PhD candidates and the supervision of an international faculty.

49870 ■ Quincy Business and Technology Center
301 Oak St.
Quincy, IL 62301
Ph:(217)228-5500
Fax:(217)228-5501
Co. E-mail: qbtc@adams.net
URL: http://www.qbtc.org/
Contact: Les McKenzie, Exec. Dir.
Description: A not-for-profit business incubator encouraging economic development in the Quincy Area by providing a business environment tailored primarily to business start-ups, home-based businesses ready for their first expansion, and businesses requiring assistance in the various management phases of successful entrepreneurship.

49871 ■ Research Park & Enterprise Works
University of Illinois
60 Hazelwood Dr.
Champaign, IL 61820
Ph:(217)333-8324
Co. E-mail: lfrerich@illinois.edu
URL: http://researchpark.illinois.edu/
Contact: Laura A. Frerichs, Assoc. Dir.
Description: A small business incubator providing an environment where technology-based businesses can work with the research faculty and students at UIUC to take advantage of opportunities for collaborative research and easy access to University labs, equipment, and services.

49872 ■ Shetland Properties Limited Partnership
5400 W Roosevelt Rd.
Chicago, IL 60644
Ph:(773)921-5400
Fax:(773)921-6680
Co. E-mail: slate@shetland.com
URL: http://www.shetland.com
Contact: Andrew Lappin, Pres
Description: Creates research parks out of second-generation industrial facilities.

49873 ■ Southern Illinois Research Park Inc.
150 E Pleasant Hill Rd.
Carbondale, IL 62903
Ph:(618)453-3427
Fax:(618)453-5040
Co. E-mail: info@sirpark.com
URL: http://researchpark.siuc.edu
Contact: Dr. Kyle L. Harfst, Exec.Dir.
E-mail: info@sirpark.com
Scope: Facilitates the retention, expansion, and creation of businesses in research park to diversify the southern Illinois region. Serves as a catalyst for economic, community, and regional development in Southern Illinois. **Services:** Grant writing assistance, to incubator tenants and clients within Illinois; Grant writing assistance, to incubator tenants and clients within Illinois. **Publications:** Carbondale Forum (monthly); Connections (quarterly). **Educational Activities:** Conferences, forums; Seminars; Workshops, both on business startup and applications.

49874 ■ Southern Illinois University at Carbondale–Office of Research Development and Administration
Woody Hall C-206, MC 4709
900 S Normal Ave.
Carbondale, IL 62901
Ph:(618)453-4540

Fax:(618)453-8038
Co. E-mail: pmrice@siu.edu
URL: http://orda.siu.edu
Contact: Dr. Prudence M. Rice, Dir.
E-mail: pmrice@siu.edu
Scope: Serves as central administrative coordinating agency for organized research; supports a variety of research facilities, and administers special internal grants programs conducted by the University; acts as a comprehensive information source about grant programs, and provides logistical support and service to faculty and staff seeking and administering grants. **Publications:** Perspectives Research Magazine (semiannually); Research Matters (monthly); Sponsored Project Guide.

49875 ■ Southern Illinois University at Edwardsville–Office of Research and Projects
Rendleman Hall, Rm. 2202, CB 1046
Graduate School
Edwardsville, IL 62026-2202
Ph:(618)650-3010
Fax:(618)650-3523
Co. E-mail: jbarnes@siue.edu
URL: http://www.siue.edu/research
Contact: Dr. Josephine Barnes, Dir.
E-mail: jbarnes@siue.edu
Scope: Serves as coordinating unit between the University and agencies and foundations that provide support for research, training, and other programs at the University. Functions as a service facility to assist faculty members in obtaining outside support for their projects. **Publications:** Research and Creative Activities (biennially); Research Highlights (quarterly). **Educational Activities:** Proposal Development (daily), assist faculty in proposal development; Seminars and workshops, on grant development. **Awards:** Award Management (daily), assist faculty with management of grants and contracts.

49876 ■ Turner Center for Entrepreneurship
1501 W. Bradley Ave.
141 Jobst Hall
Peoria, IL 61625
Ph:(309)677-4321
Fax:(309)677-3386
Co. E-mail: tce@bradley.edu
URL: http://www.bradley.edu/turnercenter/
Contact: James F. Foley, Dir.
Description: A not-for-profit program located at Bradley University providing business counseling, technical assistance, training, and educational activities for individuals interested in owning their own businesses. It also helps existing entrepreneurs and businesses who want to expand or take advantage of new opportunities and technologies, are interested in marketing their products and services internationally, or are seeking to commercialize new products and technologies.

49877 ■ University of Illinois at Chicago–Office of Research Services
310 Administrative Office Bldg., MC 672
1737 W Polk St.
Chicago, IL 60612
Ph:(312)996-2862
Fax:(312)996-9005
Co. E-mail: lrvargas@uic.edu
URL: http://tigger.uic.edu/depts/ovcr/research/proposals
Contact: Luis R. Vargas, Exec.Dir.
E-mail: lrvargas@uic.edu
Scope: Administers and coordinates extramurally supported research conducted by faculty members of various departments of the University.

49878 ■ University of Illinois at Chicago–Office of Technology Management
1853 W Polk St., Ste. 446, MC 682
Chicago, IL 60612
Ph:(312)996-7018
Fax:(312)996-1995
Co. E-mail: nansulli@uic.edu
URL: http://www.otm.uic.edu
Contact: Nancy Sullivan, Dir.
E-mail: nansulli@uic.edu
Scope: Assists in the support, development, and commercialization of University inventions and discoveries, and coordinates campus-developed

intellectual property, including copyrights, patents, and licensing. **Publications:** Technology Transfer (annually). **Educational Activities:** Workshops.

49879 ■ University of Illinois at Urbana-Champaign–Office of Technology Management
319 Ceramics Bldg.
105 S Goodwin Ave.
Urbana, IL 61801
Ph:(217)333-7862
Fax:(217)265-5530
Co. E-mail: millar@illinois.edu
URL: http://www.otm.illinois.edu
Contact: Lesley Millar, Dir.
E-mail: millar@illinois.edu
Scope: Transfers technology from the university to business and industry, particularly in the areas of engineering, agriculture and computing.

49880 ■ University Technology Park–Incubator and ITT Tower
3440 S Dearborn St.
Chicago, IL 60616
Ph:(312)567-3900
Fax:(312)567-3911
Co. E-mail: marselle@utp.iit.edu
URL: http://www.universitytechnologypark.com/
  incubator/index.html
Contact: Daniel F. Marselle, Dir.
Description: A technology park established to serve technology-based companies in the early product- and customer-development stages that require lab and/or office space as well as convenient access to business development and university-based services.

49881 ■ Western Illinois University–Office of Sponsored Projects
Sherman Hall 320
1 University Cir.
Macomb, IL 61455
Ph:(309)298-1191
Fax:(309)298-2091
Co. E-mail: b-seaton@wiu.edu
URL: http://www.wiu.edu/SponsoredProjects
Contact: Beth Seaton, Dir.
E-mail: b-seaton@wiu.edu
Scope: Serves as a coordinating agency for sponsored projects at the University in life, physical, and social sciences, agriculture, and education. Coordinates all sources of external funds for research, institutes, workshops, and other extramurally supported activities at the University. **Publications:** Sponsored Projects News & Notes (5/year).

EDUCATIONAL PROGRAMS

49882 ■ Black Hawk College–Quad-Cities Campus
6600 34th Ave.
Moline, IL 61265
Ph:(309)796-5000
Free: 800-334-1311
Fax:(309)792-5976
URL: http://www.bhc.edu
Description: Two-year college offering a small business management program.

49883 ■ Chicago State University–Office of Continuing Education
9501 S King Dr.
Robinson University Center Rm 200
Chicago, IL 60628-1598
Ph:(773)995-2545
Fax:(773)995-2941
Co. E-mail: conted@csu.edu
URL: http://www.csu.edu/
Description: Offers mature students career-updating and business-related courses, seminars, and workshops for degree, nondegree, credit, or noncredit status. Conducts course work in advanced business, management, human relations, and small business management. Also provides on-site training and development for employees of small businesses involved in computer operation, budgeting, marketing, and personnel management. Additional courses are presented through the College of Business Administration.

49884 ■ Loyola University Chicago–School of Professional Studies
820 N Michigan Ave., Ste. 401
Chicago, IL 60611
Ph:(312)915-6501
Fax:(312)915-6508
Co. E-mail: sps@luc.edu
URL: http://www.luc.edu
Description: Sponsors several programs of interest to small business professionals: The Weekend College is a concentrated program for men and women who wish to attend college while working full time. The program offers 11 majors, with residence opportunity. The Continuing Education Program serves women interested in beginning or continuing their college careers through day classes. Other courses of study are offered through the Business Administration Department.

49885 ■ Rend Lake College
468 N Ken Gray Pky.
Ina, IL 62846
Ph:(618)437-5321
Fax:(618)437-5677
URL: http://www.rlc.edu/
Description: Two-year college offering a small business management program.

49886 ■ Rock Valley College
3301 N Mulford Rd.
Rockford, IL 61114
Ph:(815)921-7821
Free: 800-973-7821
Fax:(815)636-4074
URL: http://www.rockvalleycollege.edu
Description: Two-year college offering a small business management program.

49887 ■ Sauk Valley Community College
173 IL., Rte. 2
Dixon, IL 61021
Ph:(815)288-5511
Fax:(815)288-1880
URL: http://www.svcc.edu
Description: Two-year college offering small business management classes.

PUBLICATIONS

49888 ■ *How to Form Your Own Illinois Corporation Before the Inc. Dries!: A Step by Step Guide, With Forms*
P. Gaines Publishing Co.
333 S. Taylor Ave.
PO Box 2253
Oak Park, IL 60302
Ph:(708)524-9033
Fax:(708)524-9038
Ed: Phillip Williams. **Released:** Fourth edition, 1994. **Price:** $26.95. **Description:** Volume 1 of the Small Business Incorporation series. Explains the advantages and disadvantages of incorporation and shows, step-by-step, how the small business owners can incorporate at low cost. Covers Illinois profit and nonprofit corporations, Illinois professional service corporations, subchapter S corporations, and Delaware corporations. Includes forms necessary for incorporation.

49889 ■ *Smart Start your Illinois Business*
PSI Research
300 N. Valley Dr.
Grants Pass, OR 97526
Ph:(503)479-9464
Free: 800-228-2275
Fax:(503)476-1479
Co. E-mail: info@psi-research.com
URL: http://www.psi-research.com
Ed: Michael D. Jenkins. **Released:** Revised edition, 1992. **Price:** $29.95 (looseleaf binder); $24.95 (paper). **Description:** Part of the Successful Business Library series.

49890 ■ *Starting and Operating a Business in Illinois: A Step-by-Step Guide*
PSI Research
300 N. Valley Dr.
Grants Pass, OR 97526

Ph:(503)479-9464
Free: 800-228-2275
Fax:(503)476-1479
Co. E-mail: psi2@magick.net
Ed: Michael D. Jenkins. **Released:** Revised edition, 1992. **Price:** $29.95 (looseleaf binder); $24.95 (paper). **Description:** Part of the Successful Business Library series.

PUBLISHERS

49891 ■ Blackman Kallick Bartelstein L.L.P.
10 S Riverside Plz., 9th Fl.
Chicago, IL 60606-3770
Ph:(312)207-1040
Fax:(312)207-1066
Co. E-mail: info@blackmankallick.com
URL: http://www.blackmankallick.com
Contact: Paul Oetter, Mgr
E-mail: poetter@bkadvice.com
Description: Publishes on personal taxes and tax information for closely held businesses. Also produces cassettes. Reaches market through direct mail. **Founded:** 1962.

49892 ■ Dearborn Trade Publishing Inc.
30 S Wacker Dr., Ste. 2500
Chicago, IL 60606-7481
Ph:(312)836-4400
Free: 800-621-9621
Fax:(312)836-1146
Co. E-mail: trade@dearborn.com
URL: http://www.kaplanfinancial.com
Contact: Roy Lipner, President
Description: Publishes books for consumers and professionals on finance, business, real estate, and marketing sales. Accepts proposals for new books. Reaches market through commission representatives, direct mail, and telephone sales. Accepts unsolicited manuscripts. **Founded:** 1959.

49893 ■ Institute of Real Estate Management
430 N Michigan Ave.
Chicago, IL 60611
Ph:(312)329-6000
Free: 800-837-0706
Fax:800-338-4736
Co. E-mail: custserv@irem.org
URL: http://www.irem.org
Contact: Victoria Parmentier, Senior VP
Description: Publishes an array of publications, software and a journal geared toward real estate professionals.

49894 ■ McGraw-Hill/Irwin
1333 Burr Ridge Pky.
Burr Ridge, IL 60527-6423
Ph:(630)789-5401
Free: 800-338-3987
Fax:(630)789-6944
Co. E-mail: jim_kelly@mcgraw-hill.com
URL: http://www.mhhe.com
Contact: Robert J. Bahash, CFO
Founded: 1933.

49895 ■ PivotPoint Press
5315 N Clark St., Ste. 124
PO Box 577468
Chicago, IL 60640-1121
Ph:(773)561-1512
Free: (866)323-9865
Co. E-mail: amedea@pivotpointpress.com
URL: http://www.pivotpointpress.com
Contact: Andra Medea, Mgr
Founded: 2005.

49896 ■ Productivity Press (University Park, Illinois)
2427 Bond St.
University Park, IL 60466-3101
Ph:(708)587-4152
Free: 888-319-5852
Fax:(708)534-7803
Co. E-mail: info@productivitypress.com
URL: http://www.productivitypress.com
Contact: Ralph Bernstein, Editor
E-mail: Ralph.bernstein@taylorandfrancis.com

49897 ■ Sourcebooks Inc.
1935 Brookdale Rd., Ste. 139
Naperville, IL 60563
Ph:(630)961-3900
Free: 800-432-7444
Fax:(630)961-2168

URL: http://www.sourcebooks.com
Contact: Todd Stocke, Editor
E-mail: todd.stocke@sourcebooks.com
Description: Publishes on small business, childcare, parenting, self-help, women's issues, history, sports, gift, fiction, family, gifts, entertainment, health and business. Accepts unsolicited manuscripts; query first with a chapter outline and sample chapters. Reaches market through direct mail, trade sales, and wholesalers and distributors, including Baker & Taylor Books, Ingram Book Co., and Quality Books. **Founded:** 1987.

SMALL BUSINESS DEVELOPMENT CENTERS

49898 ■ Central Indiana Small Business Development Center
Ivy Tech Lawrence Campus
9301 E 59th St., Rm. 147
Indianapolis, IN 46216
Fax:(317)917-7101
Co. E-mail: centralindiana@isbdc.org
URL: http://www.isbdc.org

49899 ■ East Central Indiana Small Business Development Center
PO Box 1912
Muncie, IN 47308
Free: (866)596-7232
Fax:(765)254-1450
Co. E-mail: eastcentral@isbdc.org
URL: http://www.isbdc.org

49900 ■ Hoosier Heartland Small Business Development Center
Burton D. Morgan Center for Entrepreneurship
1201 W State St.
West Lafayette, IN 47907
Free: 877-882-7273
Fax:(765)496-9676
Co. E-mail: hoosierheartland@isbdc.org
URL: http://www.hhsbdc.org
Contact: Jenna Wargo

49901 ■ Indiana Small Business Development Center
1 N Capitol, Ste. 900
Indianapolis, IN 46204
Free: 888-472-3244
Fax:(317)232-8872
Co. E-mail: leadcenter@isbdc.org
URL: http://www.isbdc.org
Contact: Jeff Heinzmann, Dir.

49902 ■ Indiana Small Business Development Center Network
One N Capitol, Ste. 900
Indianapolis, IN 46204
Free: 888-472-3244
Fax:(317)232-8872
Co. E-mail: leadcenter@isbdc.org
URL: http://www.isbdc.org
Contact: Jeff Heinzmann, Dir.

49903 ■ Northeast Indiana Small Business Development Center
2101 E Coliseum Blvd.
Fort Wayne, IN 46805
Fax:(260)481-0499
Co. E-mail: northeast@isbdc.org
URL: http://www.isbdc.org

49904 ■ Northwest Indiana Small Business Development Center
9800 Connecticut Dr.
Crown Point, IN 46307
Fax:(219)644-3514
Co. E-mail: northwest@isbdc.org
URL: http://www.nwisbdc.org
Contact: Joshua Lybolt, Dir.

49905 ■ South Bend Small Business Development Center
Commerce Center Bldg.
401 E Colfax Ave., Ste. 120
South Bend, IN 46617
URL: http://www.southbendbcg.com
Contact: Janet A. Fye, Dir.

49906 ■ South Central Indiana Small Business Development Center
501 N Morton St., Ste. 100
Bloomington, IN 47404
Fax:(812)335-7352
Co. E-mail: southcentral@isbdc.org
URL: http://www.isbdc.org

49907 ■ Southeastern Indiana Small Business Development Center
975 Industrial Dr., Ste. 2
Madison, IN 47250
Free: 800-595-3127
Fax:(812)265-5544
Co. E-mail: southeastern@isbdc.org
URL: http://www.seisbdc.org
Contact: Lynda Knoebel, Admin. Asst.

49908 ■ Southwestern Indiana Small Business Development Center
100 NW 2nd St., Ste. 100
Evansville, IN 47708
Fax:(812)421-5883
Co. E-mail: dalbin@isbdc.org
URL: http://www.ccswin.com
Contact: Debbie Albin, Training Coor.

49909 ■ West Central Indiana Small Business Development Center
Indiana State University
College of Business, Rm. 510
800 Sycamore St.
Terre Haute, IN 47809
Free: 800-227-7232
Fax:(812)237-7675
Co. E-mail: westcentral@isbdc.org
URL: http://www.westcentralindianasbdc.com
Contact: Heather Penney, Dir.

SMALL BUSINESS ASSISTANCE PROGRAMS

49910 ■ Indiana Department of Commerce–Energy Policy Division
1 N Capitol Ave., Ste. 700
Indianapolis, IN 46204-2288
Ph:(317)232-8940
Free: 800-382-4631
Fax:(317)232-8995
URL: http://www.indianacommerce.com
Description: Provides information on energy conservation. Gives free energy audits for small businesses. Provides some loan subsidies for energy conservation measures.

49911 ■ Indiana Department of Commerce–International Development
1 N Capitol Ave., Ste. 700
Indianapolis, IN 46204
Ph:(317)234-2083
Fax:(317)232-4146
URL: http://www.in.gov/iedc
Contact: Stephen Akard, Dir
Description: Helps businesses interested in foreign trade to establish contacts and leads. Organizes trade missions.

49912 ■ Indiana Economic Development Corporation
1 N Capitol Ave., Ste. 700
Indianapolis, IN 46204-2288
Ph:(317)232-8800
Free: 800-463-8081
Fax:(317)232-4146
Co. E-mail: sakard@iedc.in.gov
URL: http://www.in.gov/iedc
Contact: Stephen Akard, Dir.
Description: Coordinates business services offered by the Department of Commerce and other agencies. Serves as a switchboard for access to those services, such as export promotion, defense procurement, minority business development, and regulatory assistance.

49913 ■ Indiana Institute of Technology–McMillen Productivity and Design Center
1600 E Washington Blvd.
Ft. Wayne, IN 46803
Ph:(260)422-5561
Free: 800-937-2448
Fax:(260)422-7696
URL: http://www.indianatech.edu
Description: Offers industrial-quality production-level hardware and software, and staff expertise. Provides consulting and seminars in computer-aided design.

49914 ■ Indiana State University–Small Business Development Center
800 Sycamore St., Rm. 510
Terre Haute, IN 47809
Ph:(812)237-7676
Free: 800-227-7232
Fax:(812)237-7675
Co. E-mail: westcentral@isbdc.org
URL: http://www.isbdc.org/home.aspx
Description: Provides consulting, seminars, training, and access to economic databases.

49915 ■ Indiana University–Indiana Business Research Center
100 S College Ave., Ste. 240
777 Indiana Ave., Ste. 210
Bloomington, IN 47404
Ph:(812)855-5507
Fax:(812)855-7763
Co. E-mail: ibrc@iupui.edu
URL: http://www.ibrc.indiana.edu
Contact: Jerry N. Conover, Dir
Description: Collects and analyses business and economic data in the state. Information is accessible through the Indiana Information Retrieval System at libraries, universities, and public agencies. Puts out two bimonthly publications. Presents a Business Outlook Panel annually in several cities.

49916 ■ Indiana University–Indiana Molecular Biology Institute
915 E 3rd St.
Bloomington, IN 47405
Ph:(812)855-4183
Fax:(812)855-6082
Co. E-mail: freemanr@indiana.edu
URL: http://imbi.bio.indiana.edu
Contact: Rhea Freeman, Admin Asst
Description: Offers expertise and use of its facilities for industrial research in molecular and cellular biology.

49917 ■ Purdue University–Technical Assistance Program
Vistech 1, Ste. 205
1435 Win Hentschel Blvd., Ste. 205
West Lafayette, IN 47906-4154
Ph:(765)494-9189
Fax:(765)494-9187
Co. E-mail: mckinnis@purdue.edu
URL: http://www.tap.purdue.edu
Contact: David R. McKinnis, Ph.D., Dir
Description: Provides technology transfers to businesses free of charge.

SCORE OFFICES

49918 ■ Greater Madison SCORE
Path: www.madisonchamber.org

49919 ■ Greater Wabash Valley SCORE
301 Home Ave.
Terre Haute, IN 47803
Ph:(812)231-6763
Fax:(812)231-6777
Co. E-mail: scorechapter661@aol.com
URL: http://www.scorechapter661.org
Description: Promotes business and community development in the Terre Haute, IN area. Conducts business education seminars and workshops to those wanting to start a business.

49920 ■ Logansport SCORE
Path:

49921 ■ Northwest Indiana SCORE
Path: www.scorenorthwestindiana.com

49922 ■ SCORE Anderson
c/o Anderson Chamber of Commerce
700 Meridian St.
Anderson, IN 46016
Ph:(765)642-0264
Co. E-mail: postmaster@scoreanderson.org
URL: http://www.scoreanderson.org
Contact: Jim Alexander
Description: Provides counseling to persons wanting to go into business as well as those already in the business. Sponsors seminars and workshops.

49923 ■ SCORE Bloomington
216 W Allen St., Ste. 133
Bloomington, IN 47403
Ph:(812)334-2392
Co. E-mail: score527@sbcglobal.net
URL: http://www.bloomingtonscore.org
Contact: James Rusie
Description: Serves a wide range of clients from the central Indiana area. Conducts business education seminars and workshops to those wanting to start a business.

49924 ■ SCORE Chapter 50
National City bank Bldg.
100 W Berry St., Ste. LL101
Fort Wayne, IN 46802
Ph:(260)422-2601
Fax:(260)422-2601
Co. E-mail: scorefw50@verizon.net
URL: http://www.score-fortwayne.org
Contact: Les Baggett, Chair
Description: Represents volunteer businessmen and women. Provides free small business management assistance to individuals in Northeast Indiana.

49925 ■ SCORE Dearborn County
Path: www.scoreworks.org/contact.htm

49926 ■ SCORE Elkhart
Elkhart Chamber Plz.
418 S Main St.
Elkhart, IN 46515
Ph:(574)293-1531
Fax:(574)294-1859
Co. E-mail: score@elkhart.org
Description: Provides professional guidance and information to America's small businesses.

49927 ■ SCORE Evansville
c/o Carmen Mazick, Chair
318 Main St., Ste. 223
Evansville, IN 47708-1146
Ph:(812)426-6144
Fax:(812)426-6138
Co. E-mail: scoreevv@aol.com
URL: http://www.scoreevansville.com
Contact: Carmen Mazick, Chair
Description: Provides general business advice to existing small business.

49928 ■ SCORE Kokomo/Howard Counties
325 N Main St.
Kokomo, IN 46901
Ph:(765)457-5301
Fax:(765)452-4564
Co. E-mail: counselors543@kokomoscore.org
URL: http://www.kokomoscore.org
Contact: Mr. Bob Straub, Chm.
Description: Represents business professionals and counselors. Seeks to provide assistant and counsel to existing and newly opened small businesses.

49929 ■ SCORE Marion/Grant Co
215 S Adams St.
Marion, IN 46952
Ph:(765)664-5107
Co. E-mail: score550@nxco.com
URL: http://www.bloomington.in.us/lAtmscore
Description: Provides free business counseling and management training programs for small business owners/managers, and for those who plan to start a new business.

49930 ■ SCORE South Bend
401 E Colfax Ave., Ste. 120
South Bend, IN 46601
Ph:(574)282-4350
Fax:(574)236-1056
Co. E-mail: chair@southbend-score.org
URL: http://www.southbend-score.org
Contact: George Stump, Vice Chair
Description: Provides counseling to persons wanting to go into business as well as those already in the business. Sponsors seminars and workshops.

49931 ■ SCORE South Central Indiana
719 E 8th St.
New Albany, IN 47150-3215
Ph:(812)944-9178
Co. E-mail: 522score@netpointe.com
URL: http://www.score.socentind.com/content/anm-viewer.asp?a=1&z=2
Description: Provides counseling to persons wanting to go into business as well as those already in the business. Sponsors seminars and workshops.

49932 ■ SCORE South East Indiana
500 Franklin St.
Columbus, IN 47201
Ph:(812)379-4457

Fax:(812)378-7308
Co. E-mail: vchowning@columbusareachamber.com
URL: http://www.score419.org
Contact: Valerie Chowning, Membership Dir.
Description:

49933 ■ Service Corps of Retired Executives-Chapter 6
8500 Keystone Crossing, Ste. 401
Indianapolis, IN 46240
Ph:(317)226-7264
Co. E-mail: score@indyscore.org
URL: http://www.indyscore.org
Contact: Bob Miramonti, Chm.
Description: Consults those who want to start a new business or grow an existing business.

BETTER BUSINESS BUREAUS

49934 ■ Better Business Bureau of Central Indiana
22 E Washington St., Ste. 200
Indianapolis, IN 46204
Ph:(317)488-2222
Free: (866)463-9222
Fax:(317)488-2224
Co. E-mail: info@indybbb.org
URL: http://indy.bbb.org
Contact: Linda R. Carmody, Pres./CEO

49935 ■ Better Business Bureau of Northeastern Indiana
4011 Parnell Ave.
Fort Wayne, IN 46805
Ph:(260)423-4433
Free: 800-552-4631
Fax:(260)423-3301
Co. E-mail: info@neindianabbb.org
URL: http://neindiana.bbb.org
Contact: Michael D. Coil, Pres./CEO

49936 ■ Central Indiana Better Business Bureau
22 E Washington St., Ste. 200
Indianapolis, IN 46204
Ph:(317)488-2222
Free: (866)463-9222
Fax:(317)488-2224
Co. E-mail: info@indybbb.org
URL: http://indy.bbb.org
Contact: Linda Carmody, Pres./CEO

49937 ■ Tri-State Better Business Bureau
5401 Vogel Rd., Ste. 410
Evansville, IN 47715-7837
Ph:(812)473-0202
Free: 800-359-0979
Fax:(812)473-3080
Co. E-mail: info@evansville.bbb.org
URL: http://evansville.bbb.org

CHAMBERS OF COMMERCE

49938 ■ Alexandria - Monroe Chamber of Commerce
110 E Church St.
Alexandria, IN 46001
Ph:(765)724-2131
Co. E-mail: info@alexandriachamber.com
URL: http://alexandriachamber.com
Contact: Jim Mollette, Chm.

49939 ■ Angola Area Chamber of Commerce
211 E Maumee St., Ste. B
Angola, IN 46703
Ph:(260)665-3512
Fax:(260)665-7418
Co. E-mail: info@angolachamber.org
URL: http://www.angolachamber.org
Contact: Patti Anderson, Exec. Dir.

49940 ■ Auburn Chamber of Commerce
PO Box 168
208 S Jackson St.
Auburn, IN 46706-0168
Ph:(260)925-2100

Fax:(260)925-2199
Co. E-mail: kelly@chamberinauburn.com
URL: http://www.chamberinauburn.com
Contact: Kelly Knox, Exec. Dir.

49941 ■ Batesville Area Chamber of Commerce
132 S Main St.
Batesville, IN 47006
Ph:(812)934-3101
Fax:(812)932-0202
Co. E-mail: chamber@batesvillein.com
URL: http://www.batesvillein.com
Contact: Melissa Tucker, Exec. Dir.

49942 ■ Bedford Area Chamber of Commerce
1116 16th St.
Bedford, IN 47421
Ph:(812)275-4493
Co. E-mail: bedford@bedfordchamber.com
URL: http://www.bedfordchamber.com

49943 ■ Berne Chamber of Commerce
205 Main St.
Berne, IN 46711
Ph:(260)589-8080
Fax:(260)589-8384
Co. E-mail: tourism@bernein.com
URL: http://www.bernein.com

49944 ■ Boone County Chamber of Commerce
221 N Lebanon St.
Lebanon, IN 46052
Ph:(765)482-1320
Fax:(765)482-3114
Co. E-mail: info@boonechamber.org
URL: http://www.boonechamber.org
Contact: Curtis Wood, Pres.

49945 ■ Brown County Chamber of Commerce
PO Box 164
Nashville, IN 47448-0164
Ph:(812)988-6647
Fax:(812)988-1547
Co. E-mail: commerce@browncounty.org
URL: http://www.browncounty.org
Contact: Paul Schultheis, Dir.

49946 ■ Brownsburg Chamber of Commerce
PO Box 82
Brownsburg, IN 46112-0082
Ph:(317)852-7885
Fax:(317)852-8688
Co. E-mail: chamber@brownsburg.com
URL: http://www.brownsburg.com
Contact: Walter Duncan, Exec. Dir.

49947 ■ Carmel Clay Chamber of Commerce
37 E Main St., Ste. 300
Carmel, IN 46032
Ph:(317)846-1049
Fax:(317)844-6843
Co. E-mail: chamberinfo@carmelchamber.com
URL: http://www.carmelchamber.com
Contact: Mo Merhoff, Pres.

49948 ■ Chamber of Commerce for Anderson and Madison County
2701 Enterprise Dr., Ste. 109
Anderson, IN 46013
Ph:(765)642-0264
Fax:(765)642-0266
Co. E-mail: andersonchamber@ameritech.net
URL: http://www.andersoninchamber.com
Contact: Keith J. Pitcher, Pres./CEO

49949 ■ Chamber of Commerce of St. Joseph County
401 E Colfax Ave., Ste. 310
South Bend, IN 46617
Ph:(574)234-0051
Fax:(574)289-0358
Co. E-mail: info@sjchamber.org
URL: http://www.sjchamber.org
Contact: Gregory S. Downes, Pres./CEO

49950 ■ Chesterton and Duneland Chamber of Commerce
220 Broadway
Chesterton, IN 46304
Ph:(219)926-5513
Fax:(219)926-7593
Co. E-mail: info@chestertonchamber.org
URL: http://www.chestertonchamber.org
Contact: Ms. Bonnie Trout, Exec. Dir.

49951 ■ Cicero Area Chamber of Commerce
70 N Byron St.
PO Box 466
Cicero, IN 46034
Ph:(317)984-4079
Fax:(317)984-4079
Co. E-mail: jane@hamiltonnorthchamber.com
Contact: Jane Hunter, Exec. Dir.

49952 ■ Clinton County Chamber of Commerce
259 E Walnut St.
Frankfort, IN 46041
Ph:(765)654-5507
Co. E-mail: chamber@ccinchamber.org
URL: http://ccinchamber.org
Contact: Gina L. Sheets, CEO

49953 ■ Cloverdale Area Chamber of Commerce
PO Box 83
Cloverdale, IN 46120
Ph:(765)795-3993
Co. E-mail: chamber@ccrtc.com
URL: http://www.cloverdale.in.us/chamber/index.htm
Contact: Steve Walters

49954 ■ Columbia City Area Chamber of Commerce
201 N Line St.
PO Box 166
Columbia City, IN 46725-0166
Ph:(260)248-8131
Fax:(260)248-8162
Co. E-mail: office@columbiacity.org
URL: http://www.columbiacity.org
Contact: Jack Moore, Pres.

49955 ■ Columbus Area Chamber of Commerce
500 Franklin St.
Columbus, IN 47201-6214
Ph:(812)379-4457
Fax:(812)378-7308
Co. E-mail: info@columbusareachamber.com
URL: http://www.columbusareachamber.com
Contact: Jack Hess, Pres.

49956 ■ Crawfordsville - Montgomery County Chamber of Commerce
309 N Green St.
Crawfordsville, IN 47933
Ph:(765)362-6800
Fax:(765)362-6900
URL: http://www.crawfordsvillechamber.com
Contact: S. Dave Long, Exec. VP

49957 ■ Culver Chamber of Commerce
PO Box 129
Culver, IN 46511-0129
Ph:(574)842-5253
Co. E-mail: m.stallings@sbc.global.net
URL: http://www.culverchamber.com
Contact: Mike Stallings, Pres.

49958 ■ Dearborn County Chamber of Commerce
320 Walnut St.
Lawrenceburg, IN 47025
Ph:(812)537-0814
Free: 800-322-8198
Fax:(812)537-0845
Co. E-mail: maryc@seidata.com
URL: http://www.dearborncountychamber.org
Contact: Debbie Smith, Dir., Visitor Center

49959 ■ Decatur Chamber of Commerce
125 E Monroe St.
Decatur, IN 46733-1732
Ph:(260)724-2604
Co. E-mail: wkuntzman@decaturchamber.org
URL: http://www.decaturchamber.org
Contact: Wes Kuntzman, Exec. Dir.

49960 ■ Demotte Chamber of Commerce
PO Box 721
Demotte, IN 46310
Ph:(219)987-5800
Co. E-mail: demottechamber@netnitco.net
URL: http://www.townofdemotte.com
Contact: Rodney Urbano, Pres.

49961 ■ Ferdinand Chamber of Commerce
PO Box 7
Ferdinand, IN 47532-0101
Ph:(812)367-2280
Co. E-mail: btretter@buildingvalue.net
URL: http://www.ferdinandchamber.org
Contact: Brian Tretter, Exec. Dir.

49962 ■ Fishers Chamber of Commerce
11601 Municipal Dr.
PO Box 353
Fishers, IN 46038
Ph:(317)578-0700
Fax:(317)578-1097
Co. E-mail: info@fisherschamber.com
URL: http://www.fisherschamber.com
Contact: Christi J. Wolf, Pres./CEO

49963 ■ Franklin Chamber of Commerce
370 E Jefferson St.
Franklin, IN 46131
Ph:(317)736-6334
Fax:(317)736-9553
Co. E-mail: franklincoc@franklincoc.org
URL: http://www.franklincoc.org/cwt/external/wcpages/index.aspx
Contact: Tricia E. Bechman, Exec. Dir.

49964 ■ Fremont Area Chamber of Commerce
PO Box 462
Fremont, IN 46737
Ph:(260)495-9010
Fax:(260)495-2070
Co. E-mail: fremontc@locl.net
URL: http://www.fremontchamber.org
Contact: Chris Snyder, Exec. Dir.

49965 ■ French Lick - West Baden Chamber of Commerce
PO Box 347
French Lick, IN 47432
Ph:(812)936-2405
Co. E-mail: trichardson@flwbcc.com
URL: http://www.frenchlick-westbadencc.org
Contact: Teresa Richardson

49966 ■ Gary Chamber of Commerce
839 Broadway, Ste. S103
Gary, IN 46402
Ph:(219)885-7407
Fax:(219)885-7408
Co. E-mail: info@garychamber.com
URL: http://www.garychamber.com
Contact: Charles Hughes, Exec. Dir.

49967 ■ Goshen Chamber of Commerce
232 S Main St.
Goshen, IN 46526-3723
Ph:(574)533-2102
Free: 800-307-4204
Fax:(574)533-2103
Co. E-mail: brandall@goshen.org
URL: http://www.goshen.org
Contact: Brent Randall, VP

49968 ■ Greater Avon Chamber of Commerce
8244 E Hwy. 36, Ste. 140
Avon, IN 46123
Ph:(317)272-4333

Fax:(317)272-7217
Co. E-mail: info@avonchamber.org
URL: http://www.avonchamber.org
Contact: Tom Downard, Exec. Dir.

49969 ■ Greater Bloomington Chamber of Commerce
PO Box 1302
Bloomington, IN 47402
Ph:(812)336-6381
Fax:(812)336-0651
Co. E-mail: info@chamberbloomington.org
URL: http://www.chamberbloomington.org/cwt/
  external/wcpages/index.aspx
Contact: Christy Gillenwater, Pres./CEO

49970 ■ Greater Danville Chamber of Commerce
17 W Marion St.
PO Box 273
Danville, IN 46122
Ph:(317)745-0670
Fax:(317)745-0682
URL: http://www.danville-chamber.org
Contact: Greg VanLaere, Pres.

49971 ■ Greater Elkhart County Chamber of Commerce
418 S Main St.
Elkhart, IN 46515-0428
Ph:(574)293-1531
Fax:(574)294-1859
Co. E-mail: info@elkhart.org
URL: http://www.elkhart.org
Contact: Philip Penn, Pres./CEO

49972 ■ Greater Fort Wayne Chamber of Commerce
826 Ewing St.
Fort Wayne, IN 46802
Ph:(260)424-1435
Fax:(260)426-7232
Co. E-mail: kfoate@fwchamber.org
URL: http://www.fwchamber.org
Contact: Kristine Foate, Pres./CEO

49973 ■ Greater Greencastle Chamber of Commerce
16 S Jackson St.
PO Box 389
Greencastle, IN 46135
Ph:(765)653-4517
Fax:(765)848-1015
Co. E-mail: gchamber@gogreencastle.com
URL: http://www.gogreencastle.com
Contact: Tammy Amor, Exec. Dir.

49974 ■ Greater Greenfield Chamber of Commerce
1 Courthouse Plz.
Greenfield, IN 46140
Ph:(317)477-4188
Fax:(317)477-4189
Co. E-mail: info@greenfieldcc.org
URL: http://www.greenfieldcc.org
Contact: Retta Livengood, Pres.

49975 ■ Greater Greenwood Chamber of Commerce
550 U.S. 31 S
Greenwood, IN 46142
Ph:(317)888-4856
Fax:(317)865-2609
Co. E-mail: info@greenwood-chamber.com
URL: http://www.greenwood-chamber.com
Contact: Christian Maslowski, Exec. Dir.

49976 ■ Greater Indianapolis Chamber of Commerce
Chase Tower
111 Monument Cir., Ste. 1950
Indianapolis, IN 46204
Ph:(317)464-2200
Fax:(317)464-2217
Co. E-mail: rdorson@indylink.com
URL: http://www.indychamber.com
Contact: Roland M. Dorson, Pres.

49977 ■ Greater La Porte Chamber of Commerce
414 Lincolnway
PO Box 486
La Porte, IN 46352-0486
Ph:(219)362-3178
Fax:(219)324-7349
Co. E-mail: info@lpchamber.com
URL: http://www.lpchamber.com
Contact: Michael B. Seitz, Pres.

49978 ■ Greater Martinsville Chamber of Commerce
109 E Morgan St.
PO Box 1378
Martinsville, IN 46151
Ph:(765)342-8110
Fax:(765)342-5713
Co. E-mail: gmcoc@sbcglobal.net
URL: http://www.martinsvillechamber.com
Contact: Jamie Thompson, Exec. Dir.

49979 ■ Greater Monticello Chamber of Commerce and Visitors Bureau
116 N Main St.
Monticello, IN 47960
Ph:(574)583-7220
Co. E-mail: janeto@sugardog.com
URL: http://www.monticelloin.com
Contact: Janet Dold, Exec. Dir.

49980 ■ Greater Scott County Chamber of Commerce
PO Box 404
Scottsburg, IN 47170
Ph:(812)752-4080
Fax:(812)752-4307
Co. E-mail: scottcom@c3bb.com
URL: http://www.greatscottindiana.org/Scott_County/
  chamber/chamber.htm
Contact: Keith Colbert, Exec. Dir.

49981 ■ Greater Seymour Chamber of Commerce
105 S Chestnut St.
Seymour, IN 47274
Ph:(812)522-3681
Fax:(812)524-1800
Co. E-mail: seycoc@broadreach.net
URL: http://www.seymourchamber.org
Contact: Bill Bailey, Pres.

49982 ■ Greater Terre Haute Chamber of Commerce
630 Wabash Ave., Ste. 105
PO Box 689
Terre Haute, IN 47808-0689
Ph:(812)232-2391
Fax:(812)232-2905
Co. E-mail: rleslie@terrehautechamber.com
URL: http://www.terrehautechamber.com/cwt/
  external/wcpages/index.aspx
Contact: G. Roderick Henry, Pres.

49983 ■ Greater Valparaiso Chamber of Commerce
PO Box 330
Valparaiso, IN 46384-0330
Ph:(219)462-1105
Fax:(219)462-5710
Co. E-mail: info@valparaisochamber.org
URL: http://www.valparaisochamber.org
Contact: Rex G. Richards, Pres.

49984 ■ Greater Zionsville Chamber of Commerce
135 S Elm St.
PO Box 148
Zionsville, IN 46077
Ph:(317)873-3836
Co. E-mail: info@zionsvillechamber.org
URL: http://www.zionsvillechamber.org
Contact: Debbie Cranfill, Exec. Dir.

49985 ■ Greensburg Decatur County Chamber of Commerce
115 E North St.
Greensburg, IN 47240
Ph:(812)663-2832
Fax:(812)663-4275
Co. E-mail: info@greensburgchamber.com
URL: http://www.greensburgchamber.com
Contact: Jennifer Sturges, Exec. Dir.

49986 ■ Griffith Chamber of Commerce
PO Box 204
Griffith, IN 46319
Ph:(219)838-2661
Fax:(219)838-2401
Co. E-mail: griffithchamber@dopplerexpress.net
URL: http://griffithchamber.org
Contact: Mike Loughmiller

49987 ■ Harrison County Chamber of Commerce
310 N Elm St.
Corydon, IN 47112
Ph:(812)738-2137
Fax:(812)738-6438
Co. E-mail: dvoelker@harrisonchamber.org
URL: http://www.harrisonchamber.org
Contact: Darrell R. Voelker, Economic
  Developmental Dir.

49988 ■ Highland Chamber of Commerce
8536 Kennedy Ave.
Highland, IN 46322
Ph:(219)923-3666
Co. E-mail: mary@highlandchamber.com
URL: http://www.highlandchamber.com/pages/index.
  php
Contact: Mary Luptak, Exec. Dir.

49989 ■ Hobart Chamber of Commerce
1001 Lillian St.
Hobart, IN 46342
Ph:(219)942-5774
Fax:(219)942-4928
Co. E-mail: info@hobartchamber.com
URL: http://www.hobartchamber.com
Contact: Brenda Clemmons, Exec. Dir.

49990 ■ Huntingburg Chamber of Commerce
309 N Geiger St.
Huntingburg, IN 47542
Ph:(812)683-5699
Free: (866)586-8494
Fax:(812)683-3524
Co. E-mail: info@huntingburgchamber.org
URL: http://www.huntingburgchamber.org
Contact: Christine Prior, Exec. Dir.

49991 ■ Huntington County Chamber of Commerce
305 Warren St.
Huntington, IN 46750-2854
Ph:(260)356-5300
Fax:(260)356-5434
Co. E-mail: info@huntington-chamber.com
URL: http://www.huntington-chamber.com
Contact: Mr. Robert Brown Jr., Pres./CEO

49992 ■ Indiana Chamber of Commerce
115 W Washington St., Ste. 850 S
Indianapolis, IN 46204-3420
Ph:(317)264-3110
Fax:(317)264-6855
Co. E-mail: kbrinegar@indianachamber.com
URL: http://www.indianachamber.com
Contact: Kevin M. Brinegar, Pres.

49993 ■ Indiana State Hispanic Chamber of Commerce
2511 E 46th St.
Indianapolis, IN 46205
Ph:(317)547-0200
Fax:(317)547-0210
Co. E-mail: mjgm@ishcc.com

49994 ■ Jasper Chamber of Commerce
302 W 6th St.
PO Box 307
Jasper, IN 47547-0307

Ph:(812)482-6866
Fax:(812)482-1883
Co. E-mail: chamber@jasperin.org
URL: http://www.jasperin.org
Contact: Mrs. Nancy Eckerle, Dir.

49995 ■ Jennings County Chamber of Commerce
PO Box 340
North Vernon, IN 47265
Ph:(812)346-2339
Fax:(812)346-2065
Co. E-mail: mgauger@jenningscountychamber.com
URL: http://www.jenningscountychamber.com/php/index.php
Contact: Mandy Gauger, Pres.

49996 ■ Kendallville Area Chamber of Commerce
122 S Main St.
Kendallville, IN 46755-1716
Ph:(260)347-1554
Free: 877-347-1554
Fax:(260)347-1575
Co. E-mail: kchamber@locl.net
URL: http://www.kendallvillechamber.com
Contact: Anita Shephard, Exec. Dir.

49997 ■ Kentland Area Chamber of Commerce
PO Box 273
Kentland, IN 47951-0273
Ph:(219)474-6665
Co. E-mail: knochel@kentlandbank.com
Contact: Sue Knochel, Membership/Welcoming Committee Off.

49998 ■ Knightstown Indiana Chamber of Commerce
PO Box 44
Knightstown, IN 46148-0044
Ph:(765)345-5290
Free: 800-668-1895
Co. E-mail: suehood@hotmail.com
URL: http://www.knightstownchamber.org
Contact: Sue Hood, Pres.

49999 ■ Knox County Chamber of Commerce
102 N 3rd St.
PO Box 553
Vincennes, IN 47591-0553
Ph:(812)882-6440
Free: 888-895-6622
Fax:(812)882-6441
Co. E-mail: info@knoxcountychamber.com
URL: http://www.knoxcountychamber.com
Contact: Mark A. McNeece, Pres./CEO

50000 ■ Kokomo - Howard County Chamber of Commerce
325 N Main St.
Kokomo, IN 46901-4621
Ph:(765)457-5301
Fax:(765)452-4564
Co. E-mail: reastman@kokomochamber.com
URL: http://www.kokomochamber.com
Contact: Cathy Weidler, Admin. Asst.

50001 ■ Kouts Chamber of Commerce
PO Box 330
Kouts, IN 46347
Ph:(219)766-2867
Fax:(219)766-3152
Co. E-mail: koutschamber@verizon.net
URL: http://www.kouts.org
Contact: Julie Jones, Exec. Dir.

50002 ■ Lafayette - West Lafayette Chamber of Commerce
337 Columbia St.
PO Box 348
Lafayette, IN 47902-0348
Ph:(765)742-4041
Fax:(765)742-6276
Co. E-mail: information@lafayettechamber.com
URL: http://www.lafayettechamber.com
Contact: . Joseph Seaman, Pres./CEO

50003 ■ Lagrange County Chamber of Commerce
901 S Detroit St., Ste. A
Lagrange, IN 46761
Ph:(260)463-2443
Free: 877-735-0340
Fax:(260)463-2683
Co. E-mail: info@lagrangechamber.org
URL: http://www.lagrangechamber.org
Contact: Jack Dold, Exec. Dir.

50004 ■ Lake Station Chamber of Commerce
2400 Central Ave.
Lake Station, IN 46405
Ph:(219)963-1565
Fax:(219)963-4030
Co. E-mail: questions@lakestationchamber.com
URL: http://www.lakestationchamber.com/hc3.asp
Contact: Jim Bradford, Sec.

50005 ■ Lakeshore Chamber of Commerce
5246 Hohman Ave., Ste. 100
Hammond, IN 46320
Ph:(219)931-1000
Fax:(219)937-8778
Co. E-mail: info@lakeshorechamber.com
URL: http://www.lakeshorechamber.com
Contact: Dave Ryan, Exec. Dir.

50006 ■ Ligonier Chamber of Commerce
PO Box 121
Ligonier, IN 46767-0121
Ph:(260)894-9909
URL: http://www.ligonierindianachamber.org
Contact: Margarita White, Pres.

50007 ■ Linton-Stockton Chamber of Commerce
PO Box 208
Linton, IN 47441
Ph:(812)847-4846
Fax:(812)847-0246
Co. E-mail: chamber@joink.com
URL: http://www.lintonchamber.org
Contact: Cheryl Hamilton, Exec. Dir.

50008 ■ Logansport - Cass County Chamber of Commerce
300 E Broadway, Ste. 103
Logansport, IN 46947-3185
Ph:(574)753-6388
Fax:(574)735-0909
Co. E-mail: info@logan-casschamber.com
URL: http://www.logan-casschamber.com
Contact: Brain Shafer, Pres./CEO

50009 ■ Madison Area Chamber of Commerce
975 Industrial Dr., Ste. 1
Madison, IN 47250
Ph:(812)265-3135
Fax:(812)265-9784
Co. E-mail: info@madisonchamber.org
URL: http://www.madisonchamber.org
Contact: Mr. Galen L. Bremmer, Exec. VP

50010 ■ Marion-Grant County Chamber of Commerce
215 S Adams St.
Marion, IN 46952-3895
Ph:(765)664-5107
Fax:(765)668-5443
Co. E-mail: info@marionchamber.org
URL: http://www.marionchamber.org
Contact: Aaron DeWeese, Pres.

50011 ■ Martin County Chamber of Commerce
PO Box 257
Loogootee, IN 47553
Ph:(812)295-4093
Co. E-mail: mccc@martincountyindianachamberof-commerce.org
URL: http://www.martincountyindianachamberof-commerce.org
Contact: Jim Stoughton, Pres.

50012 ■ Mentone Chamber of Commerce
PO Box 366
Mentone, IN 46539
Ph:(574)353-7417
Co. E-mail: valley@medt.com
URL: http://www.mentoneeggcity.com
Contact: Rita Simpson, Pres.

50013 ■ Merrillville Chamber of Commerce
255 W 80th Pl.
Merrillville, IN 46410
Ph:(219)769-8180
Fax:(219)736-6223
Co. E-mail: geninq@merrillvillecoc.com
URL: http://www.merrillvillecoc.com
Contact: Edward C. Dernulc, Exec. Dir.

50014 ■ Michigan City Area Chamber of Commerce
200 E Michigan Blvd.
Michigan City, IN 46360-3270
Ph:(219)874-6221
Fax:(219)873-1204
Co. E-mail: info@mcachamber.com
URL: http://www.michigancitychamber.com
Contact: Tim Bietry, Pres.

50015 ■ Muncie-Delaware County Chamber of Commerce
PO Box 842
Muncie, IN 47308-0842
Ph:(765)288-6681
Free: 800-336-1373
Fax:(765)751-9151
Co. E-mail: chamber@muncie.com
URL: http://www.muncie.com
Contact: Dan Allen, Pres.

50016 ■ Munster Chamber of Commerce
1040 Ridge Rd.
Munster, IN 46321
Ph:(219)836-5549
Fax:(219)836-5551
Co. E-mail: rhonda@chambermunster.org
URL: http://www.chambermunster.org
Contact: Rhonda Damjanovich, Pres./CEO

50017 ■ Nappanee Area Chamber of Commerce
302 W Market St.
Nappanee, IN 46550
Ph:(574)773-7812
Fax:(574)773-4961
Co. E-mail: info@nappaneechamber.com
URL: http://www.nappaneechamber.com
Contact: Larry Andrews, Exec. Dir.

50018 ■ New Castle-Henry County Chamber of Commerce
100 S Main St., Ste. 108
New Castle, IN 47362
Ph:(765)529-5210
Fax:(765)521-7408
Co. E-mail: info@nchcchamber.com
URL: http://www.nchcchamber.com
Contact: Mike McIntosh, Exec. Dir.

50019 ■ New Palestine Area Chamber of Commerce
PO Box 541
New Palestine, IN 46163
Ph:(317)861-2345
Fax:(317)861-4201
Co. E-mail: info@newpalchamber.com
URL: http://www.newpalchamber.com
Contact: Rebecca Gaines, Sec.

50020 ■ Noblesville Chamber of Commerce
601 E Conner St.
Noblesville, IN 46060
Ph:(317)773-0086
Fax:(317)773-1966
Co. E-mail: info@noblesvillechamber.com
URL: http://www.noblesvillechamber.com
Contact: Sharon McMahon, Pres.

50021 ■ North Manchester Chamber of Commerce
109 N Market St.
North Manchester, IN 46962-1518
Ph:(260)982-7644
Fax:(260)982-8718
Co. E-mail: nmcc@kconline.com
URL: http://www.northmanchesterchamber.com
Contact: Kathy Roberts, Exec. Dir.

50022 ■ North Webster Tippecanoe Township Chamber of Commerce
301 N Main St., Ste. F
North Webster, IN 46555
Ph:(574)834-1600
Co. E-mail: nwttchamber@earthlink.net
Contact: Tonya Bowser, Pres.

50023 ■ Orleans Chamber of Commerce
PO Box 9
Orleans, IN 47452-0009
Ph:(812)865-9930
Co. E-mail: orleanstownhall@netsurfusa.net
URL: http://www.historicorleans.com
Contact: Dr. Kelly Kirk, Pres.

50024 ■ Owen County Chamber of Commerce and Economic Development Corporation
205 E Morgan St., Ste. D
PO Box 87
Spencer, IN 47460
Ph:(812)829-3245
Fax:(812)829-0936
Co. E-mail: occcedc@sbcglobal.net
URL: http://www.owencountyindiana.org
Contact: Denise Shaw, Exec. Dir.

50025 ■ Paoli Chamber of Commerce
210 SW Court St.
Paoli, IN 47454
Ph:(812)723-4769
URL: http://www.paoliindiana.info/pcoc/pcoc.htm

50026 ■ Parke County Chamber of Commerce
105 N Market St., Ste. A
Rockville, IN 47872
Ph:(765)569-5565
Co. E-mail: info@parkecountychamber.com
URL: http://www.parkecountychamber.com
Contact: Alan Ader, Exec. Dir.

50027 ■ Perry County Chamber of Commerce
645 Main St., Ste. A
PO Box 82
Tell City, IN 47586-0082
Ph:(812)547-2385
Fax:(812)547-8378
Co. E-mail: perrychamber@psci.net
URL: http://www.perrycountychamber.com
Contact: Cheri Cronin, Admin. Asst.

50028 ■ Peru - Miami County Chamber of Commerce
13 E Main St.
Peru, IN 46970
Ph:(765)472-1923
Fax:(765)472-7099
Co. E-mail: info@miamicochamber.com
URL: http://www.miamicochamber.com
Contact: Sandy Chittum, Pres.

50029 ■ Pike County Chamber of Commerce
PO Box 291
Petersburg, IN 47567-0291
Ph:(812)354-8155
Fax:(812)354-2335
Co. E-mail: chamber@verizon.net
URL: http://pikecountyin.org
Contact: Alycia Church, Exec. Dir.

50030 ■ Plainfield Chamber of Commerce
210 W Main St.
PO Box 14
Plainfield, IN 46168-0014
Ph:(317)839-3800
Free: 877-597-4763
Fax:(317)839-9670
Co. E-mail: chamber@town.plainfield.in.us
URL: http://www.plainfield-in.com
Contact: Kent McPhail, Exec. Dir.

50031 ■ Plymouth Area Chamber of Commerce
120 N Michigan St.
Plymouth, IN 46563
Ph:(574)936-2323
Fax:(574)936-6584
Co. E-mail: plychamber@plychamber.org
URL: http://www.plychamber.org
Contact: Doug Anspach, Exec. Dir.

50032 ■ Richmond-Wayne County Chamber of Commerce
33 S 7th St., Ste. 2
Richmond, IN 47374
Ph:(765)962-1511
Fax:(765)966-0882
Co. E-mail: info@rwchamber.org
URL: http://www.rwchamber.org
Contact: Dennis Andrews, Pres./CEO

50033 ■ Ripley County Chamber of Commerce
102 N Main St.
PO Box 576
Versailles, IN 47042
Ph:(812)689-6654
Fax:(812)689-3934
Co. E-mail: ripleycc@ripleycountychamber.org
URL: http://ripleycountychamber.org
Contact: Barry Lauber, Pres.

50034 ■ Rush County Chamber of Commerce
315 N Main St.
Rushville, IN 46173-1635
Ph:(765)932-2880
Fax:(765)932-4191
Co. E-mail: rccc@rushdsl.net
URL: http://www.rushcounty.com/chamber
Contact: Pamela C. Leisure, Exec. Dir.

50035 ■ St. John Chamber of Commerce
9495 Keilman St.
St. John, IN 46373
Ph:(219)365-4686
Fax:(219)365-4602
Co. E-mail: info@stjohnchamber.com
URL: http://www.stjohnchamber.com
Contact: Al Konieczka, Pres.

50036 ■ Schererville Chamber of Commerce
13 W Joliet St.
Schererville, IN 46375
Ph:(219)322-5412
Fax:(219)322-0598
Co. E-mail: info@46375.com
URL: http://www.46375.org
Contact: Lisa Williams, Pres.

50037 ■ Shakamak Area Chamber of Commerce
PO Box 101
Jasonville, IN 47438
Ph:(812)847-4047
URL: http://www.shakamakchamber.org/home/main.php
Contact: Andrea Pierce, Pres.

50038 ■ Shelby County Chamber of Commerce
501 N Harrison St.
Shelbyville, IN 46176
Ph:(317)398-6647
Free: 800-318-4083
Fax:(317)392-3901
Co. E-mail: chamberinfo@shelbychamber.net
URL: http://www.shelbychamber.net/cwt/external/wcpages/index.aspx
Contact: Scott Carmony, Pres.

50039 ■ Southern Indiana Chamber of Commerce
4100 Charlestown Rd.
New Albany, IN 47150-9538
Ph:(812)945-0266
Fax:(812)948-4664
Co. E-mail: info@1si.org
URL: http://www.1si.org
Contact: Michael Dalby, Pres./CEO

50040 ■ Spencer County Regional Chamber of Commerce
2792 N U.S. Hwy. 231, Ste. 100
Rockport, IN 47635
Ph:(812)649-2186
Fax:(812)649-2246
Co. E-mail: scrcc@psci.net
URL: http://www.spencercoin.org
Contact: Barbie Brown, Exec. Dir.

50041 ■ Starke County Chamber of Commerce
400 N Heaton St.
Knox, IN 46534
Ph:(574)772-5548
Fax:(574)772-0867
Co. E-mail: info@starkechamber.com
URL: http://www.starkechamber.com
Contact: Anthony Manning, Dir.

50042 ■ Syracuse-Wawasee Chamber of Commerce
101 E Main St.
Syracuse, IN 46567
Ph:(574)457-5637
Fax:(574)528-6040
Co. E-mail: info@swchamber.com
URL: http://www.swchamber.com
Contact: Tammy Cotton, Exec. Dir.

50043 ■ Tipton County Chamber of Commerce
136 E Jefferson St.
Tipton, IN 46072
Ph:(765)675-7533
Fax:(765)675-8917
Co. E-mail: jservies@tds.net
URL: http://www.tiptonchamber.com
Contact: Jennifer Servies

50044 ■ Wabash County Chamber of Commerce
210 S Wabash St.
Wabash, IN 46992
Ph:(260)563-1168
Fax:(260)563-6920
Co. E-mail: info@wabashchamber.org
URL: http://www.wabashchamber.org
Contact: Ms. Kimberly A. Pinkerton, Pres.

50045 ■ Wakarusa Chamber of Commerce
100 W Waterford St.
PO Box 291
Wakarusa, IN 46573
Ph:(574)862-4344
Fax:(574)862-2245
Co. E-mail: chamber@wakarusachamber.com
URL: http://www.wakarusachamber.com
Contact: Doris Biller, Exec. Sec.

50046 ■ Walkerton Area Chamber of Commerce
612 Roosevelt Rd.
Walkerton, IN 46574-1218
Ph:(574)586-3100
Fax:(574)586-3469
Co. E-mail: chamber@walkerton.org
URL: http://www.walkerton.org
Contact: Phil Buckmaster, Pres.

50047 ■ Warrick County Chamber of Commerce
224 W Main St.
PO Box 377
Boonville, IN 47601-0377
Ph:(812)897-2340
Fax:(812)897-2360
Co. E-mail: warco@sigecom.net
URL: http://www.warrickcounty.us
Contact: Tracy Holder, Exec. Dir.

50048 ■ Warsaw - Kosciusko County Chamber of Commerce
313 S Buffalo St.
Warsaw, IN 46580-4304
Ph:(574)267-6311
Free: 800-776-6311
Fax:(574)267-7762
Co. E-mail: jmccarthy-sessing@wkchamber.com
URL: http://www.wkchamber.com
Contact: Joy McCarthy-Sessing, Pres.

50049 ■ Wells County Chamber of Commerce
211 W Water St.
Bluffton, IN 46714
Ph:(260)824-0510
Fax:(260)824-5871
Co. E-mail: shuffman@blufftonwellschamber.com
URL: http://www.blufftonwellschamber.com
Contact: Suzanne Huffman, Dir.

50050 ■ Westfield Washington Chamber of Commerce
PO Box 534
Westfield, IN 46074
Ph:(317)804-3030
Fax:(317)804-3035
Co. E-mail: info@westfield-chamber.org
URL: http://www.westfield-chamber.org
Contact: Julieann Sole, Exec. Dir.

50051 ■ Whiting - Robertsdale Chamber of Commerce
1442 119th St.
Whiting, IN 46394
Ph:(219)659-0292
Fax:(219)659-5851
Co. E-mail: marylu.chamber@sbcglobal.net
URL: http://www.whitingindiana.com
Contact: Darlene Beerling, Pres.

50052 ■ Winchester Area Chamber of Commerce
112 W Washington St.
Winchester, IN 47394
Ph:(765)584-3731
Fax:(765)584-5544
Co. E-mail: chamber@globalsite.net
URL: http://www.winchesterareachamber.org/page/
page/5454056.htm
Contact: Janis Sarver, Office Mgr.

MINORITY BUSINESS ASSISTANCE PROGRAMS

50053 ■ Fort Wayne's Woman's Bureau–Women's Enterprise
3521 Lake Ave., Ste. 1
Fort Wayne, IN 46805
Ph:(260)424-7977
Fax:(260)426-7576
Co. E-mail: info@womensenterprise.org
URL: http://womensbureau.com/we
Description: Provides business counseling, mentoring, training, and other assistance to promote the growth of women-owned businesses.

50054 ■ Gary Minority Business Opportunity Center
21 Buffington Harbor Dr., Ste. 182
Gary, IN 46406
Ph:(219)977-7071
Fax:(219)977-9668
Co. E-mail: hpuckett@cmbdc.org
Description:

50055 ■ Indiana Department of Administration–Minority & Women's Business Enterprises Division
Indiana Government Center S
402 W Washington St., Rm. W479
Indianapolis, IN 46204
Ph:(317)232-3061
Fax:(317)233-6921
Co. E-mail: isoadisparitystudy@idoa.gov
URL: http://www.in.gov/idoa/2352.htm
Description: Supports minority and women's businesses in Indiana.

50056 ■ Indiana Department of Transportation–Economic Opportunity Division–Disadvantaged Business Enterprise Program (State)
State Office Bldg.
100 N Senate Ave.
Rm. IGCN 755
Indianapolis, IN 46204
Ph:(317)232-5089
Fax:(317)233-0891
Co. E-mail: indot@indot.in.gov
URL: http://www.in.gov/indot/2576.htm
Contact: Tiffany Mulligan, Dir
Description: Promotes the securing of Department of Highways contracts by minority and women-owned businesses. Provides certification for these companies.

50057 ■ Indiana Minority Supplier Development Council
2126 N Meridian St.
Indianapolis, IN 46202
Ph:(317)921-2680
Fax:(317)923-2204
Co. E-mail: jarode@imsdc.org
URL: http://www.imsdc.org
Contact: Michele R. Howell, Pres and CEO
Description: Promotes purchases by corporations from minority businesses through training programs, a Business Opportunity Fair, meetings, and supplier and purchaser directories.

50058 ■ Indiana Small Business Development Center
1 N Capitol Ave., Ste. 900
Indianapolis, IN 46204-2026
Ph:(317)234-2082
Fax:(317)232-8872
Co. E-mail: leadcenter@isdc.org
URL: http://www.isbdc.org
Contact: Jeff Heinzmann, Dir
Description: Providing entrepreneurs with the education, information and tools necessary to build successful businesses.

50059 ■ Indianapolis Minority Business Economic Center
402 W Washington St., W69
Indianapolis, IN 46204
Ph:(317)234-5223
Fax:(317)233-6921
Co. E-mail: rhorne@mbec.in.gov
Description:

FINANCING AND LOAN PROGRAMS

50060 ■ 1st Source Capital Corp.
100 N Michigan St.
PO Box 1602
South Bend, IN 46634
Ph:(574)235-2000
Free: 800-513-2360
Fax:(574)235-2227
URL: http://www.1stsource.com
Contact: Eugene L. Cavanaugh, Vice President
Preferred Investment Size: $200,000 to $750,000.
Investment Types: Acquisition and management buyout and special situation. **Industry Preferences:** Communications and media, computer hardware and software, semiconductors and other electronics, medical and health, consumer related, industrial and energy, and transportation. **Geographic Preferences:** Indiana and Midwestern states. **Principal Exhibits:**

50061 ■ Cambridge Ventures, L.P.
4181 E. 96th St., Ste. 200
Indianapolis, IN 46240
Ph:(317)843-9704
Fax:(317)844-9815
URL: http://www.cambridgecapitalmgmt.com
Contact: Jean Wojtowicz, President
Preferred Investment Size: $100,000 to $1,000,000.
Investment Types: Mezzanine, later stage, acquisition, and recapitalizations. **Geographic Preferences:** Midwest. **Principal Exhibits:**

50062 ■ Gazelle Techventures
11611 N. Meridian St., Ste. 310
Carmel, IN 46032
Ph:(317)275-6800
Fax:(317)275-1100
URL: http://www.gazellevc.com
Contact: Don N. Aquilano, Managing Director
Preferred Investment Size: $1,000,000 to $3,000,000. **Investment Types:** Early and later stage, and expansion. **Industry Preferences:** Communications and media, computer hardware and software, biotechnology, medical and health, consumer related, industrial and energy, agriculture, forestry, and fishing. **Geographic Preferences:** Indiana, Illinois, Kentucky, Michigan, Midwest, and Ohio. **Principal Exhibits:**

50063 ■ Irwin Ventures LLC / Irwin Ventures Incorporated
500 Washington St.
PO Box 929
Columbus, IN 47202
Ph:(812)376-1909
Fax:(812)376-1709
Co. E-mail: info@IrwinFinancial.com
URL: http://www.irwinventures.com
Contact: Will Miller, Chief Executive Officer
Investment Types: Seed, early and first stage, start-up, and joint ventures. **Industry Preferences:** Communications, computer related, financial services, and business service. **Geographic Preferences:** Mid Atlantic, Northeast, Northern California, Northwest, and West Coast. **Principal Exhibits:**

50064 ■ Monument Advisors, Inc.
Chase Tower, Ste. 4500
111 Monument Circle
Indianapolis, IN 46204-5172
Ph:(317)656-5065
Fax:(317)656-5060
Co. E-mail: request@monumentadv.com
URL: http://www.monumentadv.com
Contact: Larry S. Wechter, Chief Executive Officer and Managing Dir
Preferred Investment Size: $1,000,000 to $3,000,000. **Investment Types:** Leveraged buyout, later stage, management buyouts, expansion, acquisition, mezzanine, recapitalizations, generalist PE. **Industry Preferences:** Computer software and services, other products, industrial and energy, communications and media, consumer related, medical and health. **Geographic Preferences:** Indiana and Midwest. **Principal Exhibits:**

PROCUREMENT ASSISTANCE PROGRAMS

50065 ■ Partners in Contracting Corporation
5217 Hohman Ave., 4th Fl.
Hammond, IN 46320
Ph:(219)931-7561
Fax:(219)931-7594
Co. E-mail: picc@piccorp.org
URL: http://www.piccorp.org
Contact: Mary K. Kaczka, Exec. Dir.
E-mail: kdfox@netnitco.net
Description: Provides marketing and technical assistance and workshop training assisting with all aspects of marketing to the federal, state and local governments.

INCUBATORS/RESEARCH AND TECHNOLOGY PARKS

50066 ■ Ball State University–Office of Academic Research and Sponsored Programs
2100 W Riverside
Muncie, IN 47306
Ph:(765)285-1600

Fax:(285)285-1624
Co. E-mail: kkoriath@bsu.edu
URL: http://www.bsu.edu/research
Contact: Kristi Koriath, Dir.
E-mail: kkoriath@bsu.edu

Scope: Encourages and facilitates research at the University by assisting individual investigators in developing research proposals, obtaining outside support for their research projects, and providing assistance in research design. **Services:** Consulting with Indiana nonprofit organizations. **Publications:** Bene Facta (annually); Information Newsletter (monthly). **Educational Activities:** Benefacta Day; Focus on Excellence; Seminars; Student symposium; Workshops.

50067 ■ Chamber of Commerce of Southwestern Indiana–Small Business Development Center (SBDC)
318 Main St., Ste. 401
Evansville, IN 47708
Ph:(812)425-7232
Fax:(812)421-5883
Co. E-mail: chamberinfo@ccswin.com
URL: http://www.ccswin.com/busndev/swsbdc.asp
Contact: Greg Wathen, Exec. Dir.

Description: A small business incubator providing affordable office space, shared services, and business support necessary to create an atmosphere to greatly increase an emerging company's chances for success. Formerly Evansville Small Business Center.

50068 ■ Flagship Enterprise Center
2701 Enterprise Dr.
Anderson, IN 46013
Ph:(765)622-0100
Fax:(765)622-0211
Co. E-mail: ceo@flagshipenterprise.org
URL: http://www.flagshipenterprise.org/
Contact: DeWayne Landwehr, Exec. Dir.

Description: A facility supporting the needs of incubator graduates and qualified early stage companies that are transitioning to a permanent location within Anderson and Madison County.

50069 ■ Innovation Connector
1208 W White River Blvd.
Muncie, IN 47303
Ph:(765)285-4900
Fax:(765)286-0565
Co. E-mail: kfrederick@bsu.edu
URL: http://www.innovationconnector.com/
Contact: Katie Frederick, Exec. Dir.

Description: A small business incubator committed to start-up and spin-off businesses through the nurturing and supportive efforts of its extensive advisory business leaders, Ball State University, and additional experts from across the business spectrum.

50070 ■ Inventrek Technology Park
Greater Kokomo Economic Development Alliance
700 E Firmin St., Ste. 200
Kokomo, IN 46902
Ph:(765)457-2000
Fax:(765)854-0481
Co. E-mail: info@inventrek.org
URL: http://www.inventrek.org/

Description: A small business incubator focusing on long-term economic growth for Kokomo and Howard counties by creating new high-tech companies and supporting the development of new technologies for our existing companies.

50071 ■ Lexington Business Centre
530 E. Lexington Ave.
Elkhart, IN 46516
Ph:(574)522-0390
Fax:(574)295-1711
Co. E-mail: info@thetiedemanngroup.com
URL: http://www.lexingtonbizctr.com/

Description: A small business incubator offering affordable space in a prime location and providing crucial support to new and developing businesses.

50072 ■ Northeast Indiana Innovation Center
3211 Stellhorn Rd.
Fort Wayne, IN 46815
Ph:(260)402-8576
Co. E-mail: dryost@niic.net
URL: http://www.niic.net/
Contact: Daryl Yost

Description: A small business incubator dedicated to developing ideas and growing businesses by fostering an environment of innovation and providing a wealth of essential business resources to accelerate growth.

50073 ■ Purdue Research Foundation
Kurz Purdue Technology Center
1281 Win Hentschel Blvd.
West Lafayette, IN 47906
Ph:(765)588-3470
Fax:(765)463-3501
Co. E-mail: humanresources@prf.org
URL: http://www.purdueresearchfoundation.org
Contact: Joseph B. Hornett, Sen.VP/Treas./COO
E-mail: humanresources@prf.org

Scope: Serves as contracting agency for the University in acceptance of research grants and contracts from government, industry, and other foundations. Its Division of Sponsored Programs, established in 1966, serves the University and the Foundation in review, approval, and submission of proposals for research, instructional, and other externally sponsored programs. The Foundation acts as the University's agency in processing and managing patents and copyrights which grow out of research projects and provides research grants and fellowships from its own funds to faculty members and graduate students of the University.

50074 ■ Purdue Research Park
Kurz Purdue Technology Center
1281 Win Hentschel Blvd.
West Lafayette, IN 47906
Ph:(765)588-3470
Fax:(765)463-3217
Co. E-mail: gwdeason@prf.org
URL: http://www.purdueresearchpark.com
Contact: Gregory W. Deason, VP/Exec.Dir.
E-mail: gwdeason@prf.org

Scope: Provides facilities and University research and technical support services to research and development tenants. **Services:** Own and manage an incubator. **Publications:** Purdue Research Park Newsletter (quarterly).

50075 ■ Purdue University–Office of the Vice President for Research
610 Purdue Mall
West Lafayette, IN 47907-2040
Ph:(765)494-9806
Fax:(765)496-7474
Co. E-mail: rbuckius@purdue.edu
URL: http://www.purdue.edu/research/vpr
Contact: Richard O. Buckius, VP, Res.
E-mail: rbuckius@purdue.edu

Scope: Assists faculty in contacting potential research sponsors, negotiates research agreements with industrial sponsors, and communicates university interests to the Indiana Congressional delegation. Acts for the Purdue Research Foundation and University regarding research proposals and projects. Serves the instructional programs at the University with grant assistance for fellowships, training, institutes, curriculum development, equipment, and institutional development.

50076 ■ St. Joseph Station
Business Center
300 N Michigan St.
South Bend, IN 46601
Ph:(574)289-5471
Fax:(574)289-7105

50077 ■ University of Notre Dame–Office of Research
317 Main Bldg.
Notre Dame, IN 46556
Ph:(574)631-1862

Fax:(574)631-6630
Co. E-mail: rbernhar@nd.edu
URL: http://or.nd.edu
Contact: Prof. Robert J. Bernhard, VP for Res.
E-mail: rbernhar@nd.edu

Scope: Responsible for coordination and administration of sponsored research in all academic departments of the University and for awards received from U.S. government agencies, industrial and business organizations, philanthropic foundations, nonprofit organizations, professional societies, and individuals.

50078 ■ Uptown Innovation Center
814 E. Main St.
Richmond, IN 47374
Ph:(765)962-8151
Fax:(765)936-6197
Co. E-mail: uptown@uptownrichmond.com
URL: http://www.rwcstartup.com/
Contact: Renee Oldham, Exec. Dir.

Description: A ten-suite business incubator designed to create an environment which would foster entrepreneurship, allowing not only young companies to grow and develop, but strengthen existing local companies as well, ultimately resulting in a stronger local economy.

50079 ■ Venture Out Business Center
Madison Area Chamber of Commerce
975 Industrial Dr., Ste. 1
Madison, IN 47250
Ph:(812)265-3135
Fax:(812)265-9784
Co. E-mail: info@madisonchamber.org
URL: http://www.madisonchamber.org/business_center/
Contact: David Collier, Exec. Dir.

Description: A business incubator that offers rental space as well as assistance to new and expanding businesses.

EDUCATIONAL PROGRAMS

50080 ■ Ball State University–Small Business Entrepreneurship Program
2000 W University Ave
Department of Management
Muncie, IN 47306
Ph:(765)289-1241
Free: 800-382-8540
Fax:(765)285-8024
URL: http://www.bsu.edu

Description: Offers a degree program, courses, seminars, and conferences for entrepreneurs and small business professionals. Covers financial and legal aspects of business ownership as well as small business assistance. Includes courses on business plan preparation and microcomputer use. 1-800-382-8540

50081 ■ Ivy Tech State College of Indiana–Columbus
4475 Central Ave.
Columbus, IN 47203
Ph:(812)372-9925
Free: 800-922-4838
Fax:(812)372-0311
URL: http://www.ivytech.edu/columbus

Description: Trade and technical college offering a business administration program, and a small business management program.

50082 ■ Ivy Tech State College of Indiana–Fort Wayne
3800 N Anthony Blvd.
Ft. Wayne, IN 46805
Ph:(260)482-9171
Fax:(260)480-4177
URL: http://www.ivytech.edu/fortwayne

Description: Trade and technical school offering a program in small business management. 1-888-489-5463

50083 ■ Ivy Tech State College of Indiana–Gary
1440 E 35th Ave.
Gary, IN 46409
Ph:(219)981-1111

Free: 800-843-4882
Fax:(219)981-4415
URL: http://www.gary.ivytech.edu
Description: Trade and technical school offering a program in small business management.

LEGISLATIVE ASSISTANCE

50084 ▪ Indiana Chamber of Commerce–Indiana Small Business Council–Small Business Legislative Network (115 W)
115 W Washington St., Ste. 850S
Indianapolis, IN 46204
Ph:(317)264-3110
Fax:(317)264-6855
URL: http://www.indianachamber.com/

50085 ▪ Indiana Senate Committee on Agriculture and Small Business
920 Pribble Cir.
Lawrenceburg, IN 47025

Ph:(812)537-0628
Fax:(812)537-0636
Co. E-mail: nugentts@one.net
URL: http://www.in.gov/legislative/
Contact: Johnny Nejent, Chair

PUBLICATIONS

50086 ▪ *How to Form Your Own Indiana Corporation Before the Inc. Dries!: A Step by Step Guide, With Forms*
P. Gaines Publishing Company
333 S. Taylor Ave.
PO Box 2253
Oak Park, IL 60302
Ph:(708)524-9033
Fax:(708)524-9038
Ed: Phillip Williams. **Released:** 1992. **Price:** $19.95 (paper). **Description:** Volume 4 of the Small Business Incorporation series. Explains the advantages

and disadvantages of incorporation and shows, step-by-step, how the small business owners can incorporate at low cost. Covers Indiana profit and nonprofit corporations, Indiana professional service corporations, subchapter S corporations, and Delaware corporations. Includes forms necessary for incorporation.

50087 ▪ *Smart Start your Indiana Business*
PSI Research
300 N. Valley Dr.
Grants Pass, OR 97526
Ph:(503)479-9464
Free: 800-228-2275
Fax:(503)476-1479
Co. E-mail: info@psi-research.com
URL: http://www.psi-research.com
Ed: Michael D. Jenkins. **Released:** Revised edition, 1992. **Price:** $29.95 (looseleaf binder); $24.95 (paper). **Description:** Part of the Successful Business Library series.

SMALL BUSINESS DEVELOPMENT CENTERS

50088 ■ Eastern Iowa Small Business Development Center - Davenport
331 W 3rd St., Ste. 100
Davenport, IA 52801
Free: 800-462-3255
Fax:(563)336-3479
Co. E-mail: ahutchinson@eicc.edu
URL: http://www.iowasbdc.org/Categories/Davenport/tabid/1752/Default.aspx
Contact: Ann Hutchinson, Dir.

50089 ■ Indian Hills Small Business Development Center - Ottumwa
651 Indian Hills Dr., Bldg. 17
Ottumwa, IA 52501
Free: 800-726-2585
Fax:(641)683-5296
Co. E-mail: bziegler@indianhills.edu
URL: http://www.iowasbdc.org/Categories/Ottumwa/tabid/1766/Default.aspx
Contact: Brian Ziegler, Dir.

50090 ■ Iowa Small Business Development Center
Iowa State University
340 Gerdin Business Bldg.
Ames, IA 50011
Fax:(515)294-6522
Co. E-mail: iowasbdc@iastate.edu
URL: http://www.iowasbdc.org
Contact: Jim Heckmann, Dir.

50091 ■ Iowa State University Small Business Development Center - Ames
2501 N Loop Dr., Ste. 1615
Ames, IA 50010-8283
Fax:(515)296-6714
Co. E-mail: mjupah@iastate.edu
URL: http://www.iowasbdc.org/Categories/Ames/tabid/1108/Default.aspx
Contact: Mike Upah, Dir.

50092 ■ Iowa Western Small Business Development Center - Council Bluffs
21915 Cessna Ave.
Council Bluffs, IA 51503
Fax:(712)256-6555
Co. E-mail: spitts@iwcc.edu
URL: http://www.iowasbdc.org/Categories/Council-Bluffs/tabid/1750/Default.aspx
Contact: Sue Pitts, Dir.

50093 ■ Kirkwood Small Business Development Center - Marion
Kirkwood Community College
3375 Armar Dr.
Marion, IA 52302
Fax:(319)398-5698
Co. E-mail: al.beach@kirkwood.edu
URL: http://www.iowasbdc.org/Categories/MarionCedarRapids/tabid/1765/Default.aspx
Contact: Al Beach, Dir.

50094 ■ Mid Iowa Small Business Development Center - Urbandale
10861 Douglas Ave., Ste. B
Urbandale, IA 50322
Co. E-mail: sshafer@iastate.edu
URL: http://www.iowasbdc.org/Categories/Urbandale/tabid/1771/Default.aspx
Contact: Sherry Shafer, Dir.

50095 ■ North Central Iowa Small Business Development Center - Fort Dodge
217 S 25th St., Ste. C12
Fort Dodge, IA 50501
Fax:(515)576-6447
Co. E-mail: ncibusinesscenter@gmail.com
URL: http://www.iowasbdc.org/Categories/Fort-Dodge/tabid/1764/Default.aspx
Contact: Lisa Shimkat, Dir.

50096 ■ North Iowa Area Small Business Development Center - Mason City
500 College Dr.
Mason City, IA 50401
Free: 888-466-4222
Fax:(641)422-4129
Co. E-mail: bairted@niacc.edu
URL: http://www.iowasbdc.org/Categories/Mason-City/tabid/1768/Default.aspx
Contact: Ted Bair, Dir.

50097 ■ Northeast Iowa Small Business Development Center - Dubuque
680 Main St.
Dubuque, IA 52001
Fax:(563)557-0319
Co. E-mail: sullivant@nicc.edu
URL: http://www.iowasbdc.org/Categories/Dubuque/tabid/1762/Default.aspx
Contact: Terry Sullivan, Dir.

50098 ■ Northwest Iowa Small Business Development Center - Spencer
Iowa Lakes Community College
1900 N Grand Ave., Ste. 8
Spencer, IA 51301
Fax:(712)262-4047
URL: http://www.iowasbdc.org/tabid/1770/Default.aspx
Contact: Kelly McCarty, Dir.

50099 ■ South Central Iowa Small Business Development Center - Creston
1501 W Townline St.
Creston, IA 50801
Fax:(641)782-1334
Co. E-mail: mclaren@swcciowa.edu
URL: http://www.iowasbdc.org/Categories/Creston/tabid/1751/Default.aspx
Contact: Dave McLaren, Dir.

50100 ■ Southeastern Iowa Small Business Development Center - Burlington
River Park Pl.
610 N 4th St., Ste. 201
Burlington, IA 52601
Fax:(319)752-3407
Co. E-mail: jclover@scciowa.edu
URL: http://www.iowasbdc.org/Categories/Burlington/tabid/1749/Default.aspx
Contact: Janine Clover, Dir.

50101 ■ University of Iowa Small Business Development Center - Iowa City
2663 University Capitol Ctr.
Iowa City, IA 52242
Co. E-mail: paul-heath@uiowa.edu
URL: http://www.iowasbdc.org/Categories/IowaCity/tabid/1763/Default.aspx
Contact: Paul Heath, Dir.

50102 ■ University of Northern Iowa Small Business Development Center - Waterloo
212 E 4th St.
Waterloo, IA 50703
Fax:(319)236-8240
Co. E-mail: maureen.collins-williams@uni.edu
URL: http://www.iowasbdc.org/Categories/Waterloo/tabid/1772/Default.aspx
Contact: Maureen Collins-Williams, Dir.

50103 ■ Western Iowa Tech Small Business Development Center - Sioux City
Box 5199
Sioux City, IA 51102-5199
Co. E-mail: wubbend@witcc.edu
URL: http://www.iowasbdc.org/Categories/SiouxCity/tabid/1769/Default.aspx
Contact: Dan Wubbena, Dir.

SMALL BUSINESS ASSISTANCE PROGRAMS

50104 ■ Iowa Department of Economic Development–Business Development
200 E Grand Ave.
Des Moines, IA 50309
Ph:(515)725-3000
Free: 800-532-1216
Fax:(515)725-3010
Co. E-mail: info@iowalifechanging.com
URL: http://www.iowalifechanging.com
Contact: Bret Mills
Description: Works with the private sector to promote policies and implement programs that will expand the economy and increase job opportunities for Iowans.

50105 ■ Iowa Department of Economic Development–International Division
200 E Grand Ave.
Des Moines, IA 50309
Ph:(515)725-3000
Free: 800-532-1216

Fax:(515)725-3010
Co. E-mail: international@iowalifechanging.com
URL: http://www.iowalifechanging.com
Contact: Bret Mills, Dir.
Description: Provides information and consulting to companies interested in international trade. Organizes booth space at international trade shows; publishes directories of products to be exported from Iowa.

50106 ■ Iowa Department of Economic Development–Targeted Small Business Assistance
200 E Grand Ave.
Des Moines, IA 50309
Ph:(515)725-3000
Free: 800-532-1216
Fax:(515)725-3010
Co. E-mail: businessfinance@iowalifechanging.com
URL: http://www.iowalifechanging.com
Description: Strives to further the economic well being of Iowa small business and to provide them with growth opportunities by offering services and coordinating efforts with existing programs.

SCORE OFFICES

50107 ■ Burlington SCORE
Path:

50108 ■ Central Iowa SCORE
Path: www.marshalltown.org

50109 ■ Council Bluffs SCORE
IWCC Aviation and Entrepreneurial Center
21915 Cessna Ave.
Council Bluffs, IA 51503
Ph:(712)256-6552
Co. E-mail: jmierau@iwcc.edu
Description: Represents retired businesspeople in southwestern Iowa. Provides consulting services to individuals wishing to start a new business or who have problems with established businesses. Conducts business education seminars. Publications: none.

50110 ■ Dubuque Area SCORE
Path: www.scoredbq.org

50111 ■ Muscatine SCORE
Chamber of Commerce
319 E 2nd St., Ste. 102
Muscatine, IA 52761
Ph:(563)263-8895
Free: 800-25-PEARL
Fax:(563)263-7662
Co. E-mail: chamber@muscatine.com
URL: http://www.muscatine.com
Contact: Mr. Mel McMains, Chapter Chm.
Description:

50112 ■ River City SCORE
Path: www.scorecr.org/contact-info.php

50113 ■ SCORE Cedar Rapids
2750 1st Ave. NE, Ste. 350
Cedar Rapids, IA 52402-4831
Ph:(319)362-6405
Fax:(319)362-7861
URL: http://www.scorecr.org
Description: Provides professional guidance and information to maximize the success of existing and emerging small businesses. Offers business assistance to develop business idea or plan and identify problems and potential solutions. Promotes entrepreneur education in Cedar Rapids area.

50114 ■ SCORE Des Moines
Path: scoredm.org

50115 ■ SCORE Fort Dodge
217 S 25th St., Ste. C12
Fort Dodge, IA 50501
Ph:(515)955-2622
Co. E-mail: fortdodgescore@frontiernet.net
Description: Provides professional guidance and information to maximize the success of existing and emerging small businesses. Promotes entrepreneur education in Fort Dodge area, Iowa.

50116 ■ SCORE Illowa
721 S 2nd St.
Clinton, IA 52732
Ph:(563)242-5702
Co. E-mail: illowascoreclinton0541@yahoo.com
Description: Provides professional guidance and information to maximize the success of existing and emerging small businesses. Promotes entrepreneur education in Illowa area.

50117 ■ SCORE Iowa City
PO Box 1853
Iowa City, IA 52240-1853
Ph:(319)338-1662
URL: http://www.scorecr.org
Description:

50118 ■ SCORE Iowa Lakes
122 W 5th St.
Spencer, IA 51301
Ph:(712)262-3059
Co. E-mail: scoreil@smunet.net
Description: Provides professional guidance and information to maximize the success of existing and emerging small businesses. Promotes entrepreneur education in Spencer area, Iowa.

50119 ■ SCORE Northeast Iowa
Decorah Chamber of Commerce
507 W Water St.
Decorah, IA 52101
Ph:(563)382-3990
URL: http://www.neiowascore.org
Description: Provides professional guidance and information to maximize the success of existing and emerging small businesses. Promotes entrepreneur education in Northeast Iowa.

50120 ■ SCORE Sioux City
320 6th St.
Federal Bldg., Rm. 186
Sioux City, IA 51101
Ph:(712)277-2324
Fax:(712)277-2325
Co. E-mail: score104@iw.net
URL: http://knology.net/webmigrate
Description: Provides professional guidance and information to maximize the success of existing and emerging small businesses. Promotes entrepreneur education in Sioux area, Iowa.

50121 ■ SCORE South Central
121 Richland Ave. E
Ottumwa, IA 52501
Ph:(641)683-5127
Co. E-mail: bziegler@indianhills.edu
Description: Provides professional guidance and information to maximize the success of existing and emerging small businesses. Promotes entrepreneur education in Ottumwa area, Iowa.

50122 ■ SCORE Waterloo
Regional Business Center
212 E 4th St.
Waterloo, IA 50703
Ph:(319)236-9878
Fax:(319)236-8240
Co. E-mail: score247@consultant.com
Description: Provides professional guidance and information to maximize the success of existing and emerging small businesses. Promotes entrepreneur education in Waterloo area, Iowa.

50123 ■ Vista SCORE
Path: www.vistascore0617.com

BETTER BUSINESS BUREAUS

50124 ■ Better Business Bureau of Central and Eastern Iowa
505 5th Ave., Ste. 950
Des Moines, IA 50309-2375
Ph:(515)243-8137
Free: 800-222-1600
Fax:(515)243-2227
Co. E-mail: info@dm.bbb.org
URL: http://iowa.bbb.org
Contact: Chris Coleman, Pres.

CHAMBERS OF COMMERCE

50125 ■ Adel Partners Chamber of Commerce
301 S 10th St.
Adel, IA 50003
Ph:(515)993-4525
Fax:(515)993-4527
Co. E-mail: adel@netins.net
URL: http://www.adeliowa.org/default.page
Contact: John Standley

50126 ■ Algona Area Chamber of Commerce
123 E State St.
Algona, IA 50511
Ph:(515)295-7201
Fax:(515)295-5920
Co. E-mail: info@algona.org
URL: http://www.algona.org
Contact: Vicki Mallory, Exec. Dir.

50127 ■ Alta Chamber of Commerce
106 W Railroad St.
Storm Lake, IA 50588
Ph:(712)732-7594
Co. E-mail: chamber@altaiowa.com
Contact: Joe Aube, Pres.

50128 ■ Altoona Area Chamber of Commerce
119 2nd St.
Altoona, IA 50009
Ph:(515)967-3366
Fax:(515)967-3346
Co. E-mail: altoona@netins.net
URL: http://www.altoonachamber.org
Contact: Paulette Franklin, Exec. VP

50129 ■ Ames Chamber of Commerce
1601 Golden Aspen Dr., Ste. 110
Ames, IA 50010
Ph:(515)232-2310
Fax:(515)232-6716
Co. E-mail: dan@ameschamber.com
URL: http://www.ameschamber.com
Contact: Daniel A. Culhane, Pres./CEO

50130 ■ Anamosa Area Chamber of Commerce
124 E Main St.
Anamosa, IA 52205
Ph:(319)462-4879
Co. E-mail: director@anamosachamber.org
URL: http://www.anamosachamber.org

50131 ■ Ankeny Area Chamber of Commerce
210 S Ankeny Blvd.
PO Box 488
Ankeny, IA 50023
Ph:(515)964-0685
Fax:(515)964-0487
Co. E-mail: chamber@ankeny.org
URL: http://www.ankeny.org/cwt/external/wcpages/index.aspx
Contact: Julie Cooper, Exec. Dir.

50132 ■ Atlantic Area Chamber of Commerce
102 Chestnut St.
Atlantic, IA 50022-1451
Ph:(712)243-3017
Free: 877-283-2124
Fax:(712)243-4404
Co. E-mail: atlanticchamber@a-m-u.net
URL: http://www.atlanticiowa.com
Contact: Ronda Harry, Office Coor.

50133 ■ Bedford Chamber of Commerce
601 Madison Ave.
Bedford, IA 50833
Ph:(712)523-3637
Fax:(712)523-3384
Co. E-mail: bedfordareadc@frontiernet.net
URL: http://www.bedford-iowa.com
Contact: Mitch Green, Pres.

50134 ■ Bellevue Area Chamber of Commerce
210 N Riverview St.
Bellevue, IA 52031
Ph:(563)872-5830
Fax:(563)872-3611
Co. E-mail: chamber@bellevueia.com
URL: http://www.bellevueia.com

50135 ■ Belmond Area Chamber of Commerce
235 E Main St.
Belmond, IA 50421
Ph:(641)444-3937
Fax:(641)444-3944
URL: http://www.belmond.com
Contact: Gary Berkland

50136 ■ Bettendorf Chamber of Commerce
2117 State St.
Bettendorf, IA 52722
Ph:(563)355-4753
Fax:(563)344-4203
Co. E-mail: mitzi.hook@bettendorfchamber.com
URL: http://www.bettendorfchamber.com
Contact: Paul Neuharth, Chm.

50137 ■ Boone Area Chamber of Commerce
903 Story St.
Boone, IA 50036
Ph:(515)432-3342
Free: 800-BOO-NE12
Fax:(515)432-3343
Co. E-mail: boonechamber@iowatelecom.net
URL: http://booneiowa.homestead.com/index_1.html
Contact: Richard Baker, Exec. Dir.

50138 ■ Britt Chamber of Commerce
PO Box 63
Britt, IA 50423
Ph:(641)843-3867
Co. E-mail: brittcoc@wctatel.net
URL: http://www.brittiowa.com/chamber/index.htm
Contact: Bill Eckells

50139 ■ Burlington/West Burlington Area Chamber of Commerce
River Park Pl.
610 N 4th St., Ste. 200
Burlington, IA 52601-5069
Ph:(319)752-6365
Free: 800-827-4837
Fax:(319)752-6454
Co. E-mail: info@growburlington.com
URL: http://www.growburlington.com
Contact: Dennis Hinkle, Pres./CEO

50140 ■ Carroll Chamber of Commerce
407 W 5th St.
PO Box 307
Carroll, IA 51401
Ph:(712)792-4383
Free: (866)586-4383
Fax:(712)792-4384
Co. E-mail: chamber@carrolliowa.com
URL: http://www.carrolliowa.com
Contact: Howie Drees, Pres.

50141 ■ Cedar Falls Chamber of Commerce
PO Box 367
10 Main St.
Cedar Falls, IA 50613-0367
Ph:(319)266-3593
Fax:(319)277-4325
Co. E-mail: kassey@greatercedarvalleychamber.com
URL: http://www.cedarfalls.org
Contact: Sherry Padavich, Chair

50142 ■ Cedar Rapids Area Chamber of Commerce
424 1st Ave. NE
Cedar Rapids, IA 52401-1196
Ph:(319)398-5317
Fax:(319)398-5228
Co. E-mail: chamber@cedarrapids.org
URL: http://www.cedarrapids.org
Contact: Shannon Meyer, Pres.

50143 ■ Centerville Area Chamber of Commerce
128 N 12th St.
Centerville, IA 52544-1703
Ph:(641)437-4102
Free: 800-611-3800
Fax:(641)437-0527
Co. E-mail: chamber@centervilleia.com
URL: http://www.centervilleia.com
Contact: Joyce Bieber, Exec. Dir.

50144 ■ Chamber-Main Street Sac City
615 W Main St.
Sac City, IA 50583-1701
Ph:(712)662-7316
Fax:(712)662-7399
Co. E-mail: saccitymainstreet@prairieinet.net
URL: http://www.saccity.org
Contact: Laura Zimmerman, Program Dir.

50145 ■ Chariton Chamber and Development Corp.
104 N Grand St.
Chariton, IA 50049
Ph:(641)774-4059
Co. E-mail: ccdc@iowatelecom.net
URL: http://www.charitonchamber.com
Contact: Betty Pepping, Pres.

50146 ■ Cherokee Chamber of Commerce
416 W Main St.
Cherokee, IA 51012
Ph:(712)225-6414
Fax:(712)225-2803
Co. E-mail: cofccherokee@ncn.net
URL: http://www.cherokeeiowachamber.com
Contact: Julie Hering Kent, Exec. Dir.

50147 ■ Clarinda Chamber of Commerce
115 E Main St.
Clarinda, IA 51632
Ph:(712)542-2166
Fax:(712)542-4113
Co. E-mail: chamber@clarinda.org
URL: http://www.clarinda.org
Contact: Elaine Farwell, Exec. Dir.

50148 ■ Clear Lake Area Chamber of Commerce
205 Main Ave.
PO Box 188
Clear Lake, IA 50428
Ph:(641)357-2159
Free: 800-285-5338
Fax:(641)357-8141
Co. E-mail: info@clearlakeiowa.com
URL: http://www.clearlakeiowa.com
Contact: Mikke Finnegan, Pres.

50149 ■ Clinton Area Chamber of Commerce
721 S 2nd St.
Clinton, IA 52732
Ph:(563)242-5702
Co. E-mail: chamber@clintonia.com
URL: http://www.clintonia.com
Contact: Kent Campbell, Pres.

50150 ■ Colfax Chamber of Commerce
PO Box 62
Colfax, IA 50054
Ph:(515)674-4033
Co. E-mail: info@colfaxiowachamber.com
URL: http://www.colfaxiowachamber.com
Contact: J.D. Smith, Pres.

50151 ■ Conrad Chamber of Commerce
PO Box 10
Conrad, IA 50621
Ph:(515)366-2165
Fax:(515)366-3505
Co. E-mail: jamjar@netins.net
Contact: Julie McNair

50152 ■ Council Bluffs Area Chamber of Commerce
7 N 6th St.
Council Bluffs, IA 51502
Ph:(712)325-1000
Free: 800-228-6878

Fax:(712)322-5698
Co. E-mail: bmundt@councilbluffsiowa.com
URL: http://www.councilbluffsiowa.com
Contact: Bob Mundt, Pres./CEO

50153 ■ Cresco Area Chamber of Commerce
PO Box 403
Cresco, IA 52136
Ph:(563)547-3434
Fax:(563)547-2056
Co. E-mail: crescochamber@yahoo.com
URL: http://www.crescochamber.com
Contact: Laura Ollendick, Exec. Dir.

50154 ■ Creston Chamber of Commerce
208 W Taylor St.
PO Box 471
Creston, IA 50801
Ph:(641)782-7021
Fax:(641)782-9927
Co. E-mail: chamber@crestoniowachamber.com
URL: http://www.crestoniowachamber.com
Contact: Ellen Gerharz, Exec. Dir.

50155 ■ DavenportOne
130 W 2nd St.
Davenport, IA 52801
Ph:(563)322-1706
Co. E-mail: tbarney@davenportone.com
URL: http://www.davenportone.com
Contact: Tara Barney, Pres./CEO

50156 ■ De Witt Chamber of Commerce
524 10th St.
De Witt, IA 52742
Ph:(563)659-8500
Fax:(563)659-2410
Co. E-mail: info@dewitt.org
URL: http://www.dewitt.org
Contact: JoElla O'Connell, Exec. Dir.

50157 ■ Decorah Area Chamber of Commerce
507 W Water St.
Decorah, IA 52101
Ph:(563)382-3990
Free: 800-463-4692
Fax:(563)382-5515
Co. E-mail: director@decorah-iowa.com
URL: http://www.decoraharea.com
Contact: Nikki Brevig, Exec. Dir.

50158 ■ Dubuque Area Chamber of Commerce
300 Main St., Ste. 200
PO Box 705
Dubuque, IA 52001
Ph:(563)557-9200
Free: 800-798-4748
Fax:(563)557-1591
Co. E-mail: office@dubuquechamber.com
URL: http://www.dubuquechamber.com
Contact: Molly Grover, Pres./CEO

50159 ■ Dyersville Area Chamber of Commerce
1100 16th Ave. Ct. SE
Dyersville, IA 52040
Ph:(563)875-2311
Fax:(563)875-8391
Co. E-mail: dyersvillechamber@dyersville.org
URL: http://www.dyersville.org
Contact: Karla Thompson, Exec. Dir.

50160 ■ Eagle Grove Area Chamber of Commerce
120 N Lucas
PO Box 2
Eagle Grove, IA 50533
Ph:(515)448-4821
Fax:(515)448-4821
Co. E-mail: egchambr@goldfieldaccess.net
URL: http://www.eaglegrove.com
Contact: Lindsay Nevins, Exec. Dir.

50161 ■ Eldora Area Chamber and Development Council
1442 Washington St.
Eldora, IA 50627
Ph:(641)939-3241
Fax:(641)939-7555
Co. E-mail: eldoraecondev@heartofiowa.net
URL: http://www.eldoraiowa.com
Contact: Deb Crosser, Exec. Dir.

50162 ■ Elkader Area Chamber of Commerce
207 N Main St.
PO Box 599
Elkader, IA 52043-0599
Ph:(563)245-2857
Free: (866)334-2857
Fax:(563)245-2857
Co. E-mail: elkader@alpinecom.net
URL: http://www.elkader-iowa.com
Contact: Diane Akin, Exec. Sec.

50163 ■ Emmetsburg Chamber of Commerce
1121 Broadway
Emmetsburg, IA 50536
Ph:(712)852-2283
Fax:(712)852-2156
Co. E-mail: eburgwelcome@kemb.org
URL: http://www.emmetsburg.com
Contact: Cecilia Miller, Exec. Dir.

50164 ■ Estherville Area Chamber of Commerce
620 First Ave. S
Estherville, IA 51334
Ph:(712)362-3541
Fax:(712)362-7742
Co. E-mail: echamber@ncn.net
URL: http://www.estherville.org
Contact: Dustin Embree, Exec. Dir.

50165 ■ Fairfield Area Chamber of Commerce
204 W Broadway
Fairfield, IA 52556
Ph:(641)472-2111
Fax:(641)472-6510
Co. E-mail: chamber@fairfieldiowa.com
URL: http://fairfieldiowa.com
Contact: Brent M. Willett, Exec. Dir.

50166 ■ Fayette Chamber of Commerce
PO Box 28
Fayette, IA 52142-0028
Ph:(563)425-4316
Co. E-mail: fayettecity@iowatelecom.net
URL: http://www.fayetteia.com

50167 ■ Fort Dodge Area Chamber of Commerce
1406 Central Ave.
PO Box T
Fort Dodge, IA 50501
Ph:(515)955-5500
Fax:(515)955-3245
Co. E-mail: info@fortdodgechamber.com
URL: http://www.fortdodgechamber.com
Contact: Amy Bruno, Exec. Dir.

50168 ■ Fort Madison Area Chamber of Commerce
614 9th St.
Fort Madison, IA 52627
Ph:(319)372-5471
Fax:(319)372-6404
Co. E-mail: chamber@fortmadison.com
URL: http://www.fortmadison.com
Contact: Kirk Butler, Pres.

50169 ■ Garner Chamber of Commerce
211 State St.
Garner, IA 50438
Ph:(641)923-3993
Fax:(641)923-3993
Co. E-mail: chamberoffice@qwestoffice.net
URL: http://www.garneriachamber.com
Contact: Verne Brunsen, Pres.

50170 ■ Greater Cedar Valley Chamber of Commerce - Waterloo
315 E 5th St.
Waterloo, IA 50703
Ph:(319)233-8431
Fax:(319)233-4580
Co. E-mail: jstodd2000@aol.com
URL: http://www.waterloochamber.org
Contact: Jay Stoddard, Dir.

50171 ■ Greater Des Moines Partnership
700 Locust St., Ste. 100
Des Moines, IA 50309
Ph:(515)286-4950
Free: 800-451-2625
Fax:(515)286-4974
Co. E-mail: info@desmoinesmetro.com
URL: http://www.desmoinesmetro.com
Contact: Martha A. Willits, Pres./CEO

50172 ■ Greater Eldora Chamber of Commerce
PO Box 303
Eldora, IA 50627
Ph:(641)939-3000
Co. E-mail: president@eldorachamber.com
URL: http://www.eldorachamber.com

50173 ■ Greater Muscatine Chamber of Commerce and Industry
319 E 2nd St., Ste. 102
Muscatine, IA 52761-4100
Ph:(563)263-8895
Fax:(563)263-8896
Co. E-mail: chamber@muscatine.com
URL: http://www.muscatine.com
Contact: Jane L. Daufeldt, Exec. Dir.

50174 ■ Greenfield Chamber/Main Street and Community Development Corporation
201 S 1st St.
PO Box 61
Greenfield, IA 50849
Ph:(641)743-8444
Fax:(641)743-8205
Co. E-mail: grfld_cc_ms_dev@iowatelecom.net
URL: http://www.greenfieldiowa.com
Contact: Ginny Kuhfus

50175 ■ Grinnell Area Chamber of Commerce
833 4th Ave.
PO Box 538
Grinnell, IA 50112
Ph:(641)236-6555
Fax:(641)236-3499
Co. E-mail: gcrec@grinnellchamber.org
URL: http://www.grinnellchamber.org
Contact: Melissa West, Admin. Asst.

50176 ■ Grundy Center Chamber of Commerce and Development
705 F Ave.
Grundy Center, IA 50638
Ph:(319)825-3838
Fax:(319)825-6471
Co. E-mail: chamber@gcmuni.net
URL: http://www.grundycenter.com
Contact: Ms. Melanie Kirkpatrick, Co-Dir.

50177 ■ Guthrie Center Chamber of Commerce
102 N 1st St.
Guthrie Center, IA 50115
Ph:(641)332-2191
URL: http://www.guthriecenter.com
Contact: Eric Rinehart, Pres.

50178 ■ Hampton Area Chamber of Commerce
5 1st St. SW
Hampton, IA 50441
Ph:(641)456-5668
Fax:(641)456-5660
Co. E-mail: hacc@hamptoniowa.org
URL: http://www.hamptoniowa.org
Contact: Jennifer Gruelke, Exec. Dir.

50179 ■ Hartley Chamber of Commerce
PO Box 146
Hartley, IA 51346
Ph:(712)928-4278
Co. E-mail: hart2020@tcaexpress.net
URL: http://www.hartleyiowa.com
Contact: Pam Lux, Sec.-Treas.

50180 ■ Hawarden Area Partnership for Progress
1150 Central Ave.
PO Box 266
Hawarden, IA 51023
Ph:(712)551-4433
Co. E-mail: happ@cityofhawarden.com
URL: http://www.cityofhawarden.com
Contact: Patty Anderson, Pres.

50181 ■ Humboldt/Dakota City Chamber of Commerce
PO Box 247
Humboldt, IA 50548
Ph:(515)332-1481
Fax:(515)332-1496
Co. E-mail: chamber@goldfieldaccess.net
URL: http://www.ci.humboldt.ia.us
Contact: Tonya Harklau, Exec. Dir.

50182 ■ Independence Area Chamber of Commerce
PO Box 104
Independence, IA 50644
Ph:(319)334-7178
Fax:(319)334-7394
Co. E-mail: indycommerce@indytel.com
URL: http://www.indycommerce.com
Contact: Tammy Shaffer, Exec. Dir.

50183 ■ Indianola Chamber of Commerce
515 N Jefferson, Ste. D
Indianola, IA 50125
Ph:(515)961-6269
Co. E-mail: chamber@indianolachamber.com
URL: http://www.indianolachamber.com
Contact: Denise Day, Exec. Dir.

50184 ■ Iowa City Area Chamber of Commerce
325 E Washington St.
Iowa City, IA 52240
Ph:(319)337-9637
Fax:(319)338-9958
Co. E-mail: nancy@iowacityarea.com
URL: http://www.iowacityarea.com
Contact: Nancy Quellhorst, Pres./CEO

50185 ■ Iowa Falls Chamber of Commerce - Main Street
520 Rocksylvania
Iowa Falls, IA 50126-2313
Ph:(641)648-5549
Co. E-mail: chamber@iafalls.com
URL: http://www.iowafallsdevelopment.com/iowafalls-chamber

50186 ■ Iowa Great Lakes Area Chamber of Commerce
243 W Broadway
PO Box 9
Arnolds Park, IA 51331-0009
Ph:(712)332-2107
Free: 800-839-9987
Fax:(712)332-7714
Co. E-mail: tom@okobojichamber.com
URL: http://www.iowachamber.net
Contact: Tom Kuhlman, Exec. VP

50187 ■ Jefferson Area Chamber of Commerce
220 N Chestnut St.
Jefferson, IA 50129
Ph:(515)386-2155
Fax:(515)386-2156
Co. E-mail: chamber@jeffersoniowa.com
URL: http://www.gojacc.com
Contact: Amy Milligan, Exec. Dir.

50188 ■ Jesup Chamber of Commerce
PO Box 592
Jesup, IA 50648-0592
Ph:(319)827-1522
Fax:(319)827-3510
Co. E-mail: todd.rohlfsen@fsb1879.com
URL: http://www.jesupiowa.com
Contact: Rodney Duroe, Pres.

50189 ■ Kalona Area Chamber of Commerce
514 B Ave.
PO Box 615
Kalona, IA 52247
Ph:(319)656-2660
Co. E-mail: chamber@kctc.net
URL: http://www.kalonachamber.com

50190 ■ Keokuk Area Chamber of Commerce
329 Main St.
Keokuk, IA 52632
Ph:(319)524-5055
Fax:(319)524-5016
Co. E-mail: keokukcc@iowatelecom.net
URL: http://www.keokukchamber.com
Contact: Katie O'Brien, Exec. Dir.

50191 ■ Knoxville Chamber of Commerce and Economic Development
309 E Main St.
PO Box 71
Knoxville, IA 50138
Ph:(641)828-7555
Fax:(641)828-7978
Co. E-mail: rxjohnson@iowatelecom.net
URL: http://www.discoverknoxville.com
Contact: Roxanne Johnson, Exec. Dir.

50192 ■ Lake City Betterment Association
113 E Main St.
Lake City, IA 51449
Ph:(712)464-7611
Co. E-mail: lakecitybett@iowatelecom.net
URL: http://www.lakecityiowa.com
Contact: Jenifer Villhauer, Coor.

50193 ■ Madison County Chamber of Commerce
73 Jefferson St.
Winterset, IA 50273
Ph:(515)462-1185
Free: 800-298-6119
Fax:(515)462-1393
Co. E-mail: chamber@madisoncounty.com
URL: http://www.madisoncounty.com

50194 ■ Main Street Chamber of Commerce - Adel Partners
PO Box 73
Adel, IA 50003
Ph:(515)993-5472
Fax:(515)993-3384
Co. E-mail: adel@netins.net
URL: http://www.adelpartners.org
Contact: Julie Bailey, Program Dir.

50195 ■ Manchester Area Chamber of Commerce
200 E Main St.
Manchester, IA 52057
Ph:(563)927-4141
Fax:(563)927-2958
Co. E-mail: macc@manchesteriowa.org
URL: http://www.manchesteriowa.org
Contact: Jack Klaus, Exec. Dir.

50196 ■ Manning Chamber of Commerce
PO Box 345
Manning, IA 51455-0354
Ph:(712)655-3541
Fax:(712)655-2478
Co. E-mail: ddoyel@iowatelecom.net
URL: http://www.manningia.com
Contact: Jodi Hiatt AGP, VP

50197 ■ Maquoketa Area Chamber of Commerce
117 S Main St.
Maquoketa, IA 52060
Ph:(563)652-4602
Free: 800-989-4602
Fax:(563)652-3020
Co. E-mail: maqchamber@qwestoffice.net
URL: http://www.maquoketachamber.com
Contact: Stacy Driscoll, Exec. Dir.

50198 ■ Marshalltown Area Chamber of Commerce
709 S Center St.
PO Box 1000
Marshalltown, IA 50158
Ph:(641)753-6645
Fax:(641)752-8373
Co. E-mail: info@marshalltown.org
URL: http://www.marshalltown.org
Contact: Ken Anderson, Pres.

50199 ■ Mason City Area Chamber of Commerce
25 W State St.
Mason City, IA 50401
Ph:(641)423-5724
Fax:(641)423-5725
Co. E-mail: chamber@masoncityia.com
URL: http://www.masoncityia.com
Contact: Robin Anderson, Exec. Dir.

50200 ■ McGregor/Marquette Chamber of Commerce
146 Main St.
PO Box 105
McGregor, IA 52157
Ph:(563)873-2186
Free: 800-896-0910
Fax:(563)873-2847
Co. E-mail: mac-marq@alpinecom.net
URL: http://www.mcgreg-marq.org

50201 ■ Missouri Valley Chamber of Commerce
100 S 4th St.
Missouri Valley, IA 51555
Ph:(712)642-2553
Fax:(712)642-3771
Co. E-mail: chamberofcommerce1@juno.com
URL: http://www.missourivalleychamber.com
Contact: Mr. Steve Keller, Pres.

50202 ■ Monticello Area Chamber of Commerce
204 E First St.
Monticello, IA 52310
Ph:(319)465-5626
Fax:(319)465-3537
Co. E-mail: chamber@macc-ia.us
URL: http://www.macc-ia.us/Monticello.shtml
Contact: Suzan Ehlers, Pres.

50203 ■ Mount Pleasant Area Chamber of Commerce
124 S Main St.
PO Box 109
Mount Pleasant, IA 52641
Ph:(319)385-3101
Free: 877-385-3103
Fax:(319)385-3012
Co. E-mail: mpaca@mountpleasantiowa.org
URL: http://www.mountpleasantiowa.org/alliance
Contact: Kiley Miller, Exec. VP

50204 ■ Mount Vernon Area Chamber of Commerce
213 1st St. NW
Mount Vernon, IA 52314
Ph:(319)895-8742
Fax:(319)895-6108
Co. E-mail: cmv@cityofmtvernon-ia.gov
URL: http://www.cityofmtvernon-ia.gov
Contact: Lisa White

50205 ■ Nevada Chamber of Commerce
1015 6th St.
Nevada, IA 50201
Ph:(515)382-6538
Fax:(515)382-3803
Co. E-mail: chamber@midiowa.net
URL: http://www.nevadaiowa.org
Contact: Sara Clausen, Exec. Dir.

50206 ■ Northwood Area Chamber of Commerce
PO Box 71
Northwood, IA 50459
Ph:(641)324-1042
Co. E-mail: info@northwoodchamber.org
URL: http://www.northwoodchamber.org

50207 ■ Norwalk Area Chamber of Commerce
1017 Main St.
Norwalk, IA 50211
Ph:(515)981-0619
Fax:(515)981-1890
Co. E-mail: norwalkchamber@smsn.com
URL: http://www.norwalkchamber.org
Contact: Dr. Denny Wulf, Pres.

50208 ■ Oelwein Chamber and Area Development
25 W Charles St.
Oelwein, IA 50662
Ph:(319)283-1105
Fax:(319)283-2890
Co. E-mail: ocad@oelwein.com
URL: http://www.oelwein.com
Contact: Sally Falb, Exec. Dir.

50209 ■ Onawa Chamber of Commerce
707 Iowa Ave.
Onawa, IA 51040
Ph:(712)423-1801
Fax:(712)423-4622
Co. E-mail: chamber@onawa.com
URL: http://www.onawa.com
Contact: Mike Goslin, Pres.

50210 ■ Orange City Chamber of Commerce
PO Box 36
Orange City, IA 51041
Ph:(712)707-4510
Fax:(712)707-4523
Co. E-mail: chamberwindmill@frontiernet.net
URL: http://www.orangecityiowa.com
Contact: Mike Hofman, Exec. Dir.

50211 ■ Osage Chamber of Commerce
808 Main St.
Osage, IA 50461
Ph:(641)732-3163
Fax:(641)732-3163
Co. E-mail: chamber@osage.net
URL: http://www.osage.net/IAtchamber
Contact: Wendy Heuton, Exec. Dir.

50212 ■ Osceola Chamber of Commerce
PO Box 425
Osceola, IA 50213
Ph:(641)342-4200
Fax:(641)342-6353
Co. E-mail: ocms@iowatelecom.net
URL: http://www.osceolachamber.com
Contact: Dave Walkup, Pres.

50213 ■ Oskaloosa Area Chamber and Development Group
124 N Market St.
Oskaloosa, IA 52577-2827
Ph:(641)672-2591
Free: 888-562-6759
Fax:(641)672-2047
Co. E-mail: oskycofc@oacdg.org
URL: http://www.oacdg.org
Contact: Connie Bryan, Mgr.

50214 ■ Ottumwa Area Chamber of Commerce
217 E Main St.
PO Box 308
Ottumwa, IA 52501
Ph:(641)682-3465
Co. E-mail: info@ottumwaiowa.com
URL: http://www.ottumwaiowa.com/chamber/index.html
Contact: Terry McNitt, Exec. Dir.

50215 ■ Pella Chamber of Commerce
518 Franklin St.
Pella, IA 50219-1636
Ph:(641)628-2626
Free: 888-746-3882
Fax:(641)628-9697
Co. E-mail: pellacoc@pella.org
URL: http://www.pella.org
Contact: Karen Eischen, Exec. Dir.

50216 ■ Perry Chamber of Commerce
1102 Willis Ave.
Perry, IA 50220-1556
Ph:(515)465-4601
Fax:(515)465-2256
Co. E-mail: perrychmbr@aol.com
URL: http://www.perryia.org
Contact: Julie Schieb, Office Asst.

50217 ■ Pocahontas Chamber of Commerce
PO Box 125
Pocahontas, IA 50574
Co. E-mail: chamber@pocahontasiowa.com
URL: http://www.pocahontasiowa.com/chamber.htm.
  html
Contact: Kelly Otto, Pres.

50218 ■ Red Oak Chamber of Commerce
307 E Reed St.
Red Oak, IA 51566
Ph:(712)623-4821
Fax:(712)623-4822
Co. E-mail: adminasst@redoakiowa.com
URL: http://www.redoakiowa.com
Contact: Jodie Smith, Admin. Asst.

**50219 ■ Rock Rapids Community Affairs
Corporation**
206 1st Ave.
PO Box 403
Rock Rapids, IA 51246
Ph:(712)472-3456
Fax:(712)472-3456
Co. E-mail: chamber@rockrapids.com
URL: http://www.rockrapids.com
Contact: Angie Jager, Exec. Dir.

50220 ■ Rock Valley Chamber of Commerce
PO Box 89
Rock Valley, IA 51247
Ph:(712)476-9300
Fax:(712)476-9116
Co. E-mail: curt@cityofrockvalley.com
URL: http://www.cityofrockvalley.com
Contact: Curt Strouth, Community Activities Dir.

**50221 ■ Rockwell City Chamber and
Development**
3012 270th St.
Rockwell City, IA 50579
Ph:(712)297-8874
Co. E-mail: rcdev@iowatelecom.net
URL: http://www.rockwellcity.com

50222 ■ St. Ansgar Chamber of Commerce
PO Box 133
St. Ansgar, IA 50472-0133
Ph:(641)736-4444
Co. E-mail: stagreenhouse@iowatelecom.net
URL: http://www.stansgar.org

**50223 ■ Shelby County Chamber of
Commerce**
1101 7th St.
Harlan, IA 51537
Ph:(712)755-2114
Free: 888-876-1774
Fax:(712)755-2115
Co. E-mail: info@exploreshelbycounty.com
URL: http://www.exploreshelbycounty.com
Contact: Dawn Cundiff, Dir.

**50224 ■ Sheldon Chamber and Development
Corp.**
416 9th St.
PO Box 276
Sheldon, IA 51201-0276
Ph:(712)324-2813

Fax:(712)324-4602
Co. E-mail: rachelk@sheldoniowa.com
URL: http://www.sheldoniowa.com
Contact: Shanelle Matus, Dir.

**50225 ■ Shenandoah Chamber and Industry
Association**
100 Maple St.
PO Box 38
Shenandoah, IA 51601
Ph:(712)246-3455
Fax:(712)246-3456
Co. E-mail: chamber@simplyshenandoah.com
URL: http://shenandoahiowa.net
Contact: Shelly Smith, Marketing Dir.

50226 ■ Sibley Chamber of Commerce
838 3rd Ave.
Sibley, IA 51249
Ph:(712)754-3212
Fax:(712)754-3212
Co. E-mail: chamber@hickorytech.net
URL: http://www.sibleyiowa.net
Contact: Carissa Janssen, Exec. Dir.

50227 ■ Sidney Chamber of Commerce
PO Box 401
Sidney, IA 51652
Ph:(712)374-2023
URL: http://www.sidneyia.net
Contact: Randy Moreland, Pres.

50228 ■ Sioux Center Chamber of Commerce
303 N Main Ave.
Sioux Center, IA 51250
Ph:(712)722-3457
Free: 800-SXC-ENTR
Fax:(712)722-3465
Co. E-mail: scchambr@mtcnet.net
URL: http://www.siouxcenterchamber.com
Contact: Ardith Lein, Exec. Dir.

50229 ■ Siouxland Chamber of Commerce
101 Pierce St.
Sioux City, IA 51101
Ph:(712)255-7903
Free: 800-228-7903
Fax:(712)258-7578
Co. E-mail: chamber@siouxlandchamber.com
URL: http://www.siouxlandchamber.com
Contact: Debi Durham, Pres.

50230 ■ Spencer Chamber of Commerce
122 W 5th St.
PO Box 7937
Spencer, IA 51301-7937
Ph:(712)262-5680
Fax:(712)262-5747
Co. E-mail: spencerchamber@smunet.net
URL: http://www.spenceriowachamber.org
Contact: Robert Rose, Exec. Dir.

50231 ■ Storm Lake Chamber of Commerce
119 W 6th St.
PO Box 584
Storm Lake, IA 50588
Ph:(712)732-3780
Free: 888-752-4692
Fax:(712)732-1511
Co. E-mail: slc@stormlake.org
URL: http://www.stormlakechamber.com
Contact: Gary Lalone, Exec. Dir.

50232 ■ Story City Chamber of Commerce
602 Broad St.
Story City, IA 50248
Ph:(515)733-4214
Fax:(515)733-4504
Co. E-mail: chamber@storycity.net
URL: http://www.storycity.net
Contact: Carolyn Honeycutt, Dir.

**50233 ■ Tama/Toledo Area Chamber of
Commerce**
PO Box 367
Toledo, IA 52342
Ph:(641)484-6661

Fax:(641)484-6540
Co. E-mail: tama.toledochamber@yahoo.com
URL: http://www.tamatoledo.com
Contact: Carolyn Dolezal, Coor.

50234 ■ Urbandale Chamber of Commerce
3600 8th St.
Urbandale, IA 50322
Ph:(515)331-6855
Fax:(515)278-3927
Co. E-mail: info@urbandalechamber.com
URL: http://www.uniquelyurbandale.com
Contact: Tiffany Menke IOM, Exec. Dir.

50235 ■ Walcott Chamber of Commerce
128 W Lincoln St.
Walcott, IA 52773
Ph:(563)386-4566
Co. E-mail: walcottclerk@mchsi.com
URL: http://www.cityofwalcott.com
Contact: Wendy Minnick, Chair

50236 ■ Washington Chamber of Commerce
205 W Main St.
Washington, IA 52353
Ph:(319)653-3272
Fax:(319)653-5805
Co. E-mail: washcofc@iowatelecom.net
URL: http://www.washingtoniowachamber.com
Contact: Lil Perry, Pres.

50237 ■ Waukon Chamber of Commerce
101 W Main St.
Waukon, IA 52172
Ph:(563)568-4110
Fax:(563)568-6990
Co. E-mail: waukoncc@mchsi.com
URL: http://www.waukon.org
Contact: Danny Schlitter, Exec. Dir.

50238 ■ Waverly Area Development Group
112 W Bremer Ave., Ste. A
Waverly, IA 50677
Ph:(319)352-4526
Fax:(319)352-0136
Co. E-mail: waverly@wl-p.net
URL: http://wadg.waverlyia.com/index.asp
Contact: Kelly Engelken, Exec. Dir.

50239 ■ West Bend Chamber of Commerce
PO Box 366
West Bend, IA 50597
Ph:(515)887-2181
Co. E-mail: chamber@westbendiowa.com
URL: http://www.westbendiowa.com
Contact: Karen Schwartzkopf, Publisher

**50240 ■ West Des Moines Chamber of
Commerce**
PO Box 65320
West Des Moines, IA 50265
Ph:(515)225-6009
Fax:(515)225-7129
Co. E-mail: info@wdmchamber.org
URL: http://www.wdmchamber.org
Contact: Linda Hulleman, Exec. Dir.

50241 ■ West Union Chamber of Commerce
101 N Vine St.
West Union, IA 52175-0071
Ph:(563)422-3070
Free: 800-477-5073
Co. E-mail: wuchamber@alpinecom.net
URL: http://www.westunion.com
Contact: Robin Bostrom, Exec. Dir.

50242 ■ Williamsburg Chamber of Commerce
PO Box 982
Williamsburg, IA 52361
Ph:(319)668-1500
Co. E-mail: jonesweb@iowatelecom.net
URL: http://www.williamsburgiowa.org
Contact: Barbara Hopp

50243 ■ Wilton Chamber of Commerce
118 W 4th St.
PO Box 280
Wilton, IA 52778-0005
Ph:(563)732-2330

Fax:(563)732-2332
Co. E-mail: wiltoncc@netins.net
Contact: Mrs. Eva Belitz, Exec. VP

MINORITY BUSINESS ASSISTANCE PROGRAMS

50244 ■ Iowans for Social and Economic Development–Iowa Women's Enterprise Center
United Way Human Service Bldg.
1111 9th St., Ste. 380
Des Moines, IA 50314
Ph:(515)283-0940
Co. E-mail: info@isediowa.org
URL: http://www.isedventures.org
Contact: Linda Firkins, Interim Pres
Description: Offers female entrepreneurs business financing, technical assistance, and training to start a small business.

FINANCING AND LOAN PROGRAMS

50245 ■ Aavin Equity Partners, LLC
118 3rd Ave. SE, Ste. 630
Cedar Rapids, IA 52401
Ph:(319)247-1072
Fax:(319)363-9519
URL: http://www.aavin.com
Contact: James D. Thorp, Managing Partner
E-mail: jthorp@aavin.com
Preferred Investment Size: $500,000 to $3,000,000. **Investment Policies:** Early, first, second, and third stage, buyouts, recapitalization, and late stage. **Industry Preferences:** Medical devices and services, telecommunications, financial services, manufacturing and distribution, industrial products and services, and computer and software. **Geographic Preferences:** Middle America: the states located between the two major mountain ranges. **Principal Exhibits:**

50246 ■ Allsop Venture Partners / AAVIN
118 3rd Ave. SE, Ste. 630
Cedar Rapids, IA 52401
Ph:(319)247-1072
Fax:(319)363-9519
URL: http://www.aavin.com
Contact: James D. Thorp, Managing Partner
E-mail: jthorp@aavin.com
Preferred Investment Size: $500,000 to $3,000,000. **Investment Types:** Early, first, second, and later stage, buyout, and recapitalization. **Industry Preferences:** communications and media, computer hardware and software, semiconductors and other electronics, medical and health, consumer related, industrial and energy, transportation, financial services, business service, and manufacturing. **Geographic Preferences:** Middle America: the states located between the two major mountain ranges. **Principal Exhibits:**

50247 ■ Berthel Fisher & Company Planning, Inc.
701 Tama St., Bldg. B
PO Box 609
Marion, IA 52302-0609
Ph:(319)447-5700
Free: 800-356-5234
Fax:(319)447-4250
URL: http://www.berthel.com
Contact: Thomas J. Berthel, Chief Executive Officer and President
E-mail: tberthel@berthel.com
Investment Types: Later stage. **Geographic Preferences:** Midwest. **Principal Exhibits:**

50248 ■ InvestAmerica Venture Group, Inc.
101 2nd St. SE, Ste. 800
Cedar Rapids, IA 52401
Ph:(319)363-8249

Fax:(319)363-9683
URL: http://www.investamericaventuregroup.com
Contact: David R. Schroder, President
Preferred Investment Size: $1,000,000 to $2,000,000. **Investment Types:** First and second stage, leveraged buyout, and special situation. **Industry Preferences:** Other products, industrial and energy, Internet specific, communications and media, consumer related, computer hardware, computer software and services, semiconductors and other electronics, biotechnology, medical and health. **Geographic Preferences:** U.S. **Principal Exhibits:**

PROCUREMENT ASSISTANCE PROGRAMS

50249 ■ Iowa Procurement Outreach Center
2701 SE Convenience Blvd., Ste. 13
2272 Howe Hall, CIRAS, Ste. 2620
Ankeny, IA 50021
Ph:(515)289-0281
Fax:(515)294-4483
Co. E-mail: bconey@ciras.iastate.edu
URL: http://www.ciras.iastate.edu
Description: Helps small businesses secure federal government contracts.

50250 ■ Iowa Procurement Technical Assistance Center–Iowa State University Extension Office–Center for Industrial Research and Service (CIRAS) (2272)
2272 Howe Hall, Ste. 2620
Ames, IA 50011
Ph:(515)294-3420
Fax:(515)294-4925
Co. E-mail: ciras.info@iastate.edu
URL: http://www.ciras.iastate.edu
E-mail: stevev@iastate.edu
Description: Provides assistance to business in marketing products and services to the Federal, state and local governments.

50251 ■ Iowa Procurement Technical Assistance Center–Iowa State University of Science & Technology–Center For Industrial Research & Service (CIRAS) (2272)
2272 Howe Hall, Ste. 2620
Ames, IA 50011-2272
Ph:(515)294-3420
Fax:(515)294-4925
Co. E-mail: ciras.info@iastate.edu
URL: http://www.ciras.iastate.edu/procurement
Contact: Ronald A. Cox, Dir.
E-mail: bogaczyk@iastate.edu
Description: Provide assistance to business in marketing products and services to the federal, state and local governments.

50252 ■ Iowa Procurement Technical Assistance Center–Outreach Center
2701 SE Convenience Blvd., Ste. 13
Ankeny, IA 50021
Ph:(515)289-0281
Fax:(515)294-4483
Co. E-mail: bconey@ciras.iastate.edu
URL: http://www.ciras.iastate.edu
Contact: Kathleen Bryan, Dir
Description: Helps small businesses secure federal government contracts.

INCUBATORS/RESEARCH AND TECHNOLOGY PARKS

50253 ■ Iowa State University Research Park
2711 S. Loop Dr., Ste. 4050
Ames, IA 50010-8648
Ph:(515)296-PARK
Fax:(515)296-9924
URL: http://www.isupark.org/
Description: A small business incubator which identifies technology-based concepts and businesses at early stages of development and provides an environment for their growth.

50254 ■ Iowa State University of Science and Technology–ISU Foundation
2505 University Blvd.
Ames, IA 50010-2230
Ph:(515)294-4607
Free: (866)-419-6768
Fax:(515)294-4648
Co. E-mail: dansaftig@foundation.iastate.edu
URL: http://www.foundation.iastate.edu
Contact: Dan Saftig, Pres.
E-mail: dansaftig@foundation.iastate.edu
Scope: Supports research and educational activities at the University through the administration of grants, gifts, and bequests to the University. **Publications:** Partners.

50255 ■ John Pappajohn Entrepreneurial Center
North Iowa Area Community College
500 College Dr.
Mason City, IA 50401
Ph:(641)422-4111
Free: 888-466-4222
Co. E-mail: zaniojam@niacc.edu
URL: http://www.niacc.edu/pappajohn/
Contact: Mark Olchefske, Dir.
Description: Provides business consulting, access to capital, networking events, business acceleration services, and a variety of educational opportunities.

50256 ■ New Ventures Initiative
331 W. Third St., Ste. 100
Davenport, IA 52801
Ph:(563)327-0160
Co. E-mail: info@newventuresinc.com
URL: http://www.newventuresinc.com/
Contact: Chad Stamper, Dir.
Description: A small business incubator providing professionals with real world business experience to help develop businesses, commercialize technologies, and prepare new companies for the investment community.

50257 ■ University of Iowa–Division of Sponsored Programs
2 Gilmore Hall
Iowa City, IA 52242-1320
Ph:(319)335-2123
Fax:(319)335-2130
Co. E-mail: twila-reighley@uiowa.edu
URL: http://research.uiowa.edu/dsp
Contact: Twila Fisher Reighley, Asst.VP for Res.
E-mail: twila-reighley@uiowa.edu
Scope: Serves as coordinating agency and institutional representative for external funding of educational and scientific research and development at the University. Maintains a reference center on funding resources and government policy on research.

50258 ■ University of Iowa–Technology Innovation Center
100 Oakdale Campus, Rm. 109 TIC
Iowa City, IA 52242-5000
Ph:(319)335-4063
Fax:(319)335-4489
Co. E-mail: thomas_bauer@uiowa.edu
URL: http://research.uiowa.edu/techtransfer/tic_main.htm
Contact: Thomas K. Bauer, Assoc.Dir.
E-mail: thomas_bauer@uiowa.edu
Scope: Fosters collaborative applied research involving faculty and corporate investigators in developing new business ventures in technological areas. Provides referral to research capabilities of University faculty, access to equipment, instruments, and computing facilities, office help, grant and contract assistance, and capital and business advice to new business. Leases space to new and existing research-oriented firms.

50259 ■ University of Iowa Research Park–Business Incubation Program
2500 Crosspark Rd.
100 Oakdale Campus, Rm. 109 TIC
Coralville, IA 52241
Ph:(319)335-4063

Fax:(319)335-4550
Co. E-mail: diane-gallagher@uiowa.edu
URL: http://enterprise.uiowa.edu/researchpark/index.
php
Description: A small business incubator fostering the development of new business ventures that make use of advanced technology, offering services and facilities to start-up businesses and established companies eager to initiate new endeavors. Comprised of the BioVentures Center Facility and the Technology Innovation Center.

EDUCATIONAL PROGRAMS

50260 ■ Des Moines Area Community College–Urban Campus
1100 7th St.
Des Moines, IA 50314
Ph:(515)244-4226
Free: 800-362-2127
Fax:(515)248-7253
URL: http://www.dmacc.org
Description: A wide variety of courses and workshops are offered to the working student wishing to develop or update specific occupational skills. Programs emphasize both fundamental concepts and practical experience to assure thorough competence in the chosen field. The Small Business Management Education Program offers a number of courses for credit and noncredit status—designed to meet the educational needs of the small business owner.

50261 ■ Iowa Lakes Community College (Estherville)
300 S 18th St.
Estherville, IA 51334
Ph:(712)362-2604
Free: 800-242-5106
Fax:(712)362-8363
Co. E-mail: info@iowalakes.edu
URL: http://www.ilcc.cc.ia.us
Description: Two-year college offering a small business management program.

50262 ■ Marshalltown Community College
3700 S Center St.
Marshalltown, IA 50158
Ph:(641)752-7106
Fax:(641)752-8149
Co. E-mail: mccinfo@iavalley.edu
URL: http://www.iavalley.cc.ia.us/mcc
Description: Two-year college offering a small business course through the continuing education program.

LEGISLATIVE ASSISTANCE

50263 ■ Iowa Senate Committee on Small Business, Economic Development and Tourism
State Capitol Bldg.
E 12th and Grand
Des Moines, IA 50319
Ph:(515)281-5381
Fax:(319)938-2659
URL: http://www.legis.state.ia.us
Contact: Sen. Kitty Rehberg

PUBLICATIONS

50264 ■ *Business Record*
100 4th St.
Des Moines, IA 50309
Ph:(515)288-3336
Fax:(515)288-0309

50265 ■ *Innovation in Iowa*
Iowa State University
Small Business Development Center
137 Lynn Ave.
Ames, IA 50014-7198
Free: 800-373-7232

Fax:(515)292-0020
URL: http://www.Iowsbe.org/
Ed: Bryan Ziegler. **Price:** $7.00. **Description:** Offers information on developing and marketing products.

50266 ■ *Smart Start your Iowa Business*
PSI Research
300 N. Valley Dr.
Grants Pass, OR 97526
Ph:(503)479-9464
Free: 800-228-2275
Fax:(503)476-1479
Co. E-mail: info@psi-research.com
URL: http://www.psi-research.com
Ed: Michael D. Jenkins. **Released:** Revised edition, 1992. **Price:** $29.95 (looseleaf binder); $24.95 (paper). **Description:** Part of the Successful Business Library series.

50267 ■ *Starting and Operating a Business in Iowa: A Step-by-Step Guide*
PSI Research
300 N. Valley Dr.
Grants Pass, OR 97526
Ph:(503)479-9464
Free: 800-228-2275
Fax:(503)476-1479
Co. E-mail: psi2@magick.net
Ed: Michael D. Jenkins. **Released:** Revised edition, 1992. **Price:** $29.95 (looseleaf binder); $24.95 (paper). **Description:** Part of the Successful Business Library series.

50268 ■ *Starting a Small Business in Iowa*
Iowa State University
Small Business Development Center
137 Lynn Ave.
Ames, IA 50014-7198
Free: 800-373-7232
Fax:(515)292-0020
Ed: Bryan Ziegler. **Price:** $10.00. **Description:** Provides details on Iowa resources and requirements, from marketing surveys to insurance needs and licensing permits.

SMALL BUSINESS DEVELOPMENT CENTERS

50269 ■ Kansas Small Business Development Center
214 SW 6th St., Ste. 301
Topeka, KS 66603-3719
Free: 877-625-7232
Fax:(785)291-3261
Co. E-mail: ksbdcs@fhsu.edu
URL: http://www.kansas.gov/ksbdc
Contact: Wally Kearns, Dir.

50270 ■ Kansas Small Business Development Center at Fort Hays State University
Fort Hays State University
Custer Hall 105
600 Park St.
Hays, KS 67601
Fax:(785)628-4163
Co. E-mail: ksbdc@fhsu.edu
URL: http://www.fhsu.edu/ksbdc

SMALL BUSINESS ASSISTANCE PROGRAMS

50271 ■ Business and Technology Institute–Small Business Development Center
Pittsburg State University
1501 S. Joplin St.
Pittsburg, KS 66762
Ph:(620)235-4920
Fax:(620)235-4919
Co. E-mail: ksbdc@pittstate.edu
URL: http://www.pittstate.edu/bti/sbdc/
Contact: Kathryn Richard, Dir.

Description: Provides one-stop managerial, financial, and technical assistance to new and expanding businesses in Southeast Kansas, Missouri, Oklahoma, and Arkansas.

50272 ■ Kansas Department of Commerce–Agriculture Marketing
1000 SW Jackson St., Ste. 100
Topeka, KS 66612
Ph:(785)296-3737
Fax:(785)296-3776
Co. E-mail: ruraldev@kansascommerce.com
URL: http://www.kansascommerce.com
Contact: Carole Jordan

Description: Provides marketing assistance through food shows, seminars, and media promotions.

50273 ■ Kansas Department of Commerce–Business Development Division
1000 SW Jackson St., Ste. 100
Topeka, KS 66612
Ph:(785)296-5298

Fax:(785)296-3490
Co. E-mail: busdev@kansascommerce.com
URL: http://www.kansascommerce.com/
Contact: Edwyn Bryan

Description: Promotes the growth, diversification, and retention of business and industry in Kansas. Advocates on behalf of small businesses. Act as a clearinghouse for information on permits and licenses. Maintains six regional offices to provide assistance to small businesses.

50274 ■ Kansas Department of Commerce–Trade Development Division
Curtis State Office Bldg., Ste. 100
1000 SW Jackson St.
Topeka, KS 66612
Ph:(785)296-1866
Fax:(785)296-5263
Co. E-mail: jwatson@kansascommerce.com
URL: http://www.kansascommerce.com
Contact: John Watson, Dir

Description: Provides information and assistance to businesses interested in international trade. Services offered include identifying agents and distributors worldwide, assisting in market development, providing technical information, offering world trade statistical data, and trade lead information services.

50275 ■ Kansas Technology Enterprise Corporation
214 SW 6th St., 1st Fl.
Topeka, KS 66603
Ph:(785)296-5272
Fax:(785)296-1160
Co. E-mail: info@ktec.com
URL: http://www.ktec.com
Contact: Kevin Carr, CEO

Description: Provides technical information and referral services. Provides funds for technology-based research.

50276 ■ Wichita State University–College of Education Technology Center
104 Corbin Education Ctr.
Campus Box 131
1845 Fairmount
Wichita, KS 67260-0131
Ph:(316)978-3301
Fax:(316)978-3302
Co. E-mail: day.radenbaugh@wichita.edu
URL: http://webs.wichita.edu/?u=coetech&p=/index/
Contact: Day Radenbaugh

Description: Provides training, seminars, and technical information to engineers, managers, and other employees.

SCORE OFFICES

50277 ■ Emporia SCORE
Path: www.emporiakschamber.org

50278 ■ Golden Belt SCORE
Path:

50279 ■ McPherson SCORE
Path: www.mcphersonks.org/chamber

50280 ■ North Central Kansas SCORE
Path: concordiakansaschamber.com

50281 ■ SCORE Ark Valley
205 E Ninth St.
Winfield, KS 67156
Ph:(316)221-1617
Co. E-mail: arkvalleyscore317@yahoo.com
URL: http://www.geocities.com/arkvalleyscore317/home.html
Contact: Wally Bell, Chm.

Description: Provides free business counseling and management training programs for small business owners/managers, and for those who plan to start a new business.

50282 ■ SCORE Hutchinson
One E 9th Ave.
Hutchinson, KS 67501
Ph:(620)665-8468
Fax:(620)665-7619

Description: Provides professional guidance and information to America's small businesses.

50283 ■ SCORE Topeka
120 SE 6th, Ste. 110
Topeka, KS 66603
Ph:(785)234-3049
Co. E-mail: score@topekachamber.org
URL: http://www.scoretopeka.org

Description: Helps people in planning small business operations.

50284 ■ SCORE Wichita
271 W 3rd St. N, Ste. 2500
Wichita, KS 67202
Ph:(316)269-6273
Fax:(316)269-6499
Co. E-mail: score143@sbcglobal.net

Description: Provides professional guidance and information to America's small businesses.

50285 ■ Southwest Kansas SCORE
Path:

BETTER BUSINESS BUREAUS

50286 ■ Better Business Bureau of Northeast Kansas
501 SE Jefferson, Ste. 24
Topeka, KS 66607-1190
Ph:(785)232-0454
Fax:(785)232-9677
Co. E-mail: bbbinfo@kansas.net
URL: http://topeka.bbb.org
Contact: H. Art Taylor, Pres./CEO

50287 ■ Better Business Bureau, Wichita
345 N Riverview St., Ste. 720
Wichita, KS 67203
Ph:(316)263-3146

Fax:(316)263-3063
Co. E-mail: info@wichita.bbb.org
URL: http://wichita.bbb.org
Contact: Mac Carter, Pres./CEO

CHAMBERS OF COMMERCE

50288 ■ Abilene Area Chamber of Commerce
500 N Buckeye
Abilene, KS 67410
Ph:(785)263-1770
Free: (866)224-5357
Fax:(785)263-1536
Co. E-mail: visitus1@sbcglobal.net
URL: http://www.abileneks.com
Contact: Lynda Lowry, Dir.

50289 ■ Alma Chamber of Commerce
PO Box 234
Alma, KS 66401
Ph:(785)765-3327
Fax:(785)765-3384
URL: http://www.kansaschamber.org/mx/hm.
asp?id=home

50290 ■ Andover Area Chamber of Commerce and Convention and Visitors' Bureau
1607 E Central Ave.
PO Box 339
Andover, KS 67002
Ph:(316)733-0648
Fax:(316)733-8808
Co. E-mail: chamber@andoverinformation.com
Contact: Dave Tingley, Pres.

50291 ■ Anthony Chamber of Commerce
PO Box 354
Anthony, KS 67003
Ph:(620)842-5456
Co. E-mail: info@anthonychamber.com
URL: http://www.anthonychamber.com
Contact: Gwen Warner, Exec. Dir.

50292 ■ Arkansas City Area Chamber of Commerce
106 S Summit
PO Box 795
Arkansas City, KS 67005
Ph:(620)442-0230
Co. E-mail: ac-aa@arkcitychamber.org
URL: http://www.arkcity.org/portal/portal.aspx
Contact: Janet Siebert, Pres./CEO

50293 ■ Ashland Chamber of Commerce
PO Box 37
Ashland, KS 67831
Ph:(620)635-0427
Co. E-mail: aac@ashlandks.com
URL: http://www.ashlandks.com

50294 ■ Atchison Area Chamber of Commerce
PO Box 126
Atchison, KS 66002
Ph:(913)367-2427
Free: 800-234-1854
Fax:(913)367-2485
Co. E-mail: president@atchisonkansas.net
URL: http://www.atchisonkansas.net
Contact: Jacque Pregont, Pres./CEO

50295 ■ Atwood Chamber of Commerce
PO Box 152
Atwood, KS 67730-0152
Ph:(785)626-9630
Fax:(785)626-9630
Co. E-mail: ripper@ruraltel.net
URL: http://www.atwoodkansas.com
Contact: Richard Rippe, Exec. Dir.

50296 ■ Baldwin City Chamber of Commerce
720 High St.
PO Box 501
Baldwin City, KS 66006-0501
Ph:(785)594-3200
Co. E-mail: info@baldwin-city.com
URL: http://baldwincitychamber.com

50297 ■ Baxter Springs Chamber of Commerce
1004 Military Ave.
Baxter Springs, KS 66713-1547
Ph:(620)856-3131
Fax:(620)856-3182
Co. E-mail: info@baxtersprings.us
URL: http://www.baxtersprings.org
Contact: Steve Minor

50298 ■ Belle Plaine Area Chamber of Commerce
PO Box 721
Belle Plaine, KS 67013-0721
Co. E-mail: joanderson_98@yahoo.com
URL: http://www.belleplainechamber.com
Contact: Julie Gooch, Pres.

50299 ■ Belleville Chamber of Commerce
1309 18th St.
PO Box 280
Belleville, KS 66935-0280
Ph:(785)527-5524
Co. E-mail: bellevcham@nckcn.com
URL: http://www.skyways.org/towns/Belleville/index.html

50300 ■ Beloit Area Chamber of Commerce
123 N Mill
PO Box 582
Beloit, KS 67420-0582
Ph:(785)738-2717
Co. E-mail: beloitchamber@nckcn.com
URL: http://skyways.lib.ks.us/towns/Beloit

50301 ■ Bonner Springs/Edwardsville Area Chamber of Commerce
111 Oak St., Ste. C
Box 403
Bonner Springs, KS 66012-0403
Ph:(913)422-5044
Fax:(913)441-1366
Co. E-mail: bilesc@hotmail.com
URL: http://www.lifeisbetter.org
Contact: Charlene A. Biles, Exec. Sec.

50302 ■ Caldwell Area Chamber of Commerce
PO Box 42
Caldwell, KS 67022
Ph:(620)845-6666
Co. E-mail: caldwell@kanokla.net
URL: http://caldwellkansas.com
Contact: LuAnn Jamison, Sec.

50303 ■ Caney Chamber of Commerce
PO Box 211
Caney, KS 67333
Ph:(620)879-5131
URL: http://www.caney.com/chamber.htm
Contact: Barbara Bush, Sec.

50304 ■ Chanute Area Chamber of Commerce and Office of Tourism
21 N Lincoln Ave.
PO Box 747
Chanute, KS 66720
Ph:(620)431-3350
Free: 877-431-3350
Fax:(620)431-7770
Co. E-mail: information@chanutechamber.com
URL: http://www.chanutechamber.com
Contact: Jane Brophy, Exec. Dir.

50305 ■ Cheney Chamber of Commerce
PO Box 716
Cheney, KS 67025
Ph:(316)540-3151
URL: http://www.cheneychamber.com
Contact: Jeff Albers, Pres.

50306 ■ Chetopa Chamber of Commerce
PO Box 203
Chetopa, KS 67336
Ph:(620)236-7511
Fax:(620)236-7025
Co. E-mail: chetopacity@kans.com
URL: http://www.chetopacity.org
Contact: Toni Crumrine, City Clerk

50307 ■ Cimarron Chamber of Commerce
102 East Ave. A
Cimarron, KS 67835
Ph:(620)855-2507
URL: http://skyways.lib.ks.us/towns/Cimarron

50308 ■ Clay Center Area Chamber of Commerce
426 Lincoln Ave.
Clay Center, KS 67432-2908
Ph:(785)632-5674
Fax:(785)632-5674
Co. E-mail: ccchamber@eaglecom.net
URL: http://www.claycenterkschamber.org
Contact: Andy Contreras, Pres.

50309 ■ Coffey County Chamber of Commerce
110 N 4th St.
Burlington, KS 66839-1602
Ph:(620)364-2002
Free: 877-364-2002
Co. E-mail: executivedirector@coffeycountychamber.com
URL: http://www.coffeycountychamber.com
Contact: Jennifer Anderson, Exec. Dir.

50310 ■ Coffeyville Chamber of Commerce
PO Box 457
Coffeyville, KS 67337-0457
Ph:(620)251-2550
Free: 800-626-3357
Fax:(620)251-5448
Co. E-mail: chamber@coffeyville.com
URL: http://www.coffeyville.com
Contact: Chuck Goad, Dir.

50311 ■ Colby - Thomas County Chamber of Commerce
350 S Range, Ste. 10
Colby, KS 67701
Ph:(785)460-3401
Fax:(785)460-4509
Co. E-mail: colbychamber@thomascounty.com
URL: http://oasisontheplains.com
Contact: Holly Stephens, Exec. Dir.

50312 ■ Coldwater Chamber of Commerce
PO Box 333
Coldwater, KS 67029-0333
Ph:(620)582-2859
Co. E-mail: stalcup@carrollsweb.com
URL: http://www.coldwaterkansas.com/bd.html
Contact: Phyllis Sherman, Pres.

50313 ■ Columbus Chamber of Commerce
320 E Maple
Columbus, KS 66725
Ph:(620)429-1492
Fax:(620)429-1674
Co. E-mail: columbuschamber@columbus-ks.com
URL: http://www.columbus-kansas.com/chamber
Contact: Jean Pritchett

50314 ■ Decatur County Area Chamber of Commerce
104 S Penn
Oberlin, KS 67749
Ph:(785)475-3441
Co. E-mail: dcacc@kans.com
URL: http://www.oberlinkansas.org
Contact: Glenva Nichols, Office Mgr.

50315 ■ Derby Chamber of Commerce
330 E Madison St., Ste. 150
Derby, KS 67037
Ph:(316)788-3421
Fax:(316)788-6861
Co. E-mail: chamber@derbychamber.com
URL: http://www.derbychamber.com
Contact: Rhonda Cott, Pres.

50316 ■ Dodge City Area Chamber of Commerce
311 W Spruce
PO Box 939
Dodge City, KS 67801-0939
Ph:(620)227-3119

Fax:(620)227-2957
Co. E-mail: info@dodgechamber.com
URL: http://www.dodgechamber.com
Contact: Cindy Malek, Pres.

50317 ■ Doniphan County Chamber of Commerce and Economic Development Commission
209 Roseport Rd.
PO Box 325
Elwood, KS 66024-0325
Ph:(913)365-2604
Fax:(913)365-0203
Co. E-mail: gweiland@highlandcc.edu
URL: http://www.dpcountyks.com/ChamberofCommerce/tabid/2343/Default.aspx
Contact: Galen Weiland, Exec. Dir.

50318 ■ Douglass Chamber of Commerce
PO Box 401
Douglass, KS 67039
Ph:(316)746-3135
URL: http://www.kansaschamber.org/mx/hm.asp?id=home
Contact: Brenda Davis, Sec.

50319 ■ Edwards County Chamber of Commerce
PO Box 161
Kinsley, KS 67547
Ph:(620)659-2711
Fax:(620)659-2711
Co. E-mail: ecedcweb@sbcglobal.net
URL: http://www.edwardscounty.org
Contact: Fred Burgess, Dir.

50320 ■ El Dorado Chamber of Commerce
201 E Central
PO Box 509
El Dorado, KS 67042
Ph:(316)321-3150
Fax:(316)321-5419
Co. E-mail: eldoradochamber@powwwer.net
URL: http://www.eldoradochamber.com
Contact: Jeffrey Black, Exec. VP

50321 ■ Ellinwood Area Chamber of Commerce
PO Box 482
Ellinwood, KS 67526-0482
Ph:(620)564-3300
Co. E-mail: ellinwoodchamber@hotmail.com
URL: http://www.ellinwoodchamber.com
Contact: Sharon Schartz, Pres.

50322 ■ Ellsworth-Kanopolis Area Chamber of Commerce
114-1/2 N Douglas
PO Box 315
Ellsworth, KS 67439
Ph:(785)472-4071
Fax:(785)472-5668
Co. E-mail: ecofc@eaglecom.net
URL: http://ellsworthkschamber.net
Contact: Mr. Nick V. Slechta, Dir.

50323 ■ Emporia Chamber of Commerce and Convention and Visitors Bureau
719 Commercial St.
PO Box 703
Emporia, KS 66801-0703
Ph:(620)342-1600
Free: 800-279-3730
Fax:(620)342-3223
Co. E-mail: chamber@emporiakschamber.org
URL: http://www.emporiakschamber.org
Contact: Jeanine McKenna, Pres./CEO

50324 ■ Fort Scott Area Chamber of Commerce
231 E Wall St.
PO Box 205
Fort Scott, KS 66701-0205
Ph:(620)223-3566
Free: 800-245-3678

Fax:(620)223-3574
Co. E-mail: fschamber@fortscott.com
URL: http://www.fortscott.com
Contact: Vicki Pritchett, Pres./CEO

50325 ■ Fredonia Chamber of Commerce
PO Box 449
Fredonia, KS 66736-0449
Ph:(620)378-3221
Free: 800-788-3500
Fax:(620)378-4833
Co. E-mail: fredoniakschamber@twinmounds.com
URL: http://www.fredoniaks.org/index.asp?NID=168

50326 ■ Garden City Area Chamber of Commerce
1511 E Fulton Terr.
Garden City, KS 67846-6165
Ph:(620)276-3264
Fax:(620)276-3290
Co. E-mail: chamber@gcnet.com
URL: http://www.gardencitychamber.net
Contact: Neil Hawley, Chm.

50327 ■ Gardner Area Chamber of Commerce
PO Box 402
Gardner, KS 66030
Ph:(913)856-6464
Fax:(913)856-5274
Co. E-mail: solie@gardnerchamber.com
URL: http://www.gardnerchamber.com
Contact: Carol Lehman, Pres.

50328 ■ Garnett Area Chamber of Commerce
419 S Oak St.
Garnett, KS 66032
Ph:(785)448-6767
Fax:(785)448-6767
Co. E-mail: garnettchamber@earthlink.net
URL: http://www.garnettchamber.org
Contact: Kimberly Spencer, Pres.

50329 ■ Glasco Chamber Pride
PO Box 572
Glasco, KS 67445-0572
Ph:(785)568-2515
Co. E-mail: jnothern334@usd334.org
URL: http://skyways.lib.ks.us/kansas/towns/Glasco
Contact: Joan Nothern

50330 ■ Goodland Area Chamber of Commerce
PO Box 568
Goodland, KS 67735
Ph:(785)899-7130
Co. E-mail: gdlchmbr@eaglecom.net
URL: http://www.goodlandchamber.com
Contact: Jordie Mann

50331 ■ Grant County Chamber of Commerce
113B S Main St.
Ulysses, KS 67880
Ph:(620)356-4700
Fax:(620)424-2437
Co. E-mail: uchamber@pld.com
URL: http://www.ulysseschamber.org/home
Contact: Larry Altis, Dir.

50332 ■ Great Bend Chamber of Commerce
1125 Williams
Great Bend, KS 67530
Ph:(620)792-2401
Co. E-mail: gbcc@greatbend.org
URL: http://www.greatbend.org
Contact: Jan Peters, Pres./CEO

50333 ■ Greater Topeka Chamber of Commerce
120 SE 6th St., Ste. 110
Topeka, KS 66603-3515
Ph:(785)234-2644
Fax:(785)234-8656
Co. E-mail: topekainfo@topekachamber.org
URL: http://www.topekachamber.org
Contact: Douglas S. Kinsinger, Pres./CEO

50334 ■ Greensburg Chamber of Commerce
315 S Sycamore St.
Greensburg, KS 67054
Ph:(620)723-2400
Free: 800-207-7369
Co. E-mail: dea@corns.us
URL: http://www.bigwell.org

50335 ■ Halstead Chamber of Commerce
PO Box 328
Halstead, KS 67056
Ph:(316)835-2662
Co. E-mail: coc@halsteadkansas.com
URL: http://chamberofcommerce.halsteadkansas.com
Contact: Stacey Weesner, Sec.-Treas.

50336 ■ Hays Area Chamber of Commerce
1301 Pine St.
Hays, KS 67601
Ph:(785)628-8201
Fax:(785)628-1471
Co. E-mail: hayscc@discoverhays.com
URL: http://www.discoverhays.com
Contact: Ericka Gillespie-Weintz, Exec. Dir.

50337 ■ Haysville Chamber of Commerce
PO Box 372
Haysville, KS 67060
Ph:(316)529-2461
Fax:(316)524-0091
Co. E-mail: haysvillechamber@gmail.com
URL: http://www.haysville-ks.com/chamber
Contact: Barbara Walters, Admin. Sec.

50338 ■ Hesston Community Chamber of Commerce
PO Box 100
Hesston, KS 67062
Ph:(620)327-4412
Free: 800-442-1563
Fax:(620)327-4595
Co. E-mail: chamber@hesstonks.org
URL: http://www.hesstonks.org
Contact: Shana Smith, Exec. Dir.

50339 ■ Hillsboro Chamber of Commerce
109 S Main
Hillsboro, KS 67063-1525
Ph:(620)947-3506
Fax:(620)947-2585
Co. E-mail: hillsborochamber@hillsboro-kansas.com
URL: http://www.hillsboro-kansas.com
Contact: Davis Baker, Pres.

50340 ■ Hoisington Chamber of Commerce
123 N Main St.
Hoisington, KS 67544
Ph:(620)653-4311
URL: http://www.hoisingtonkansas.com
Contact: Nancy Farmner, Pres.

50341 ■ Holton/Jackson County Chamber of Commerce
416 Pennsylvania Ave.
Holton, KS 66436
Ph:(785)364-3963
Co. E-mail: chamber@holtonks.net
URL: http://www.holtonks.net/chamber/index.html
Contact: Katie Ingles, Exec. Dir.

50342 ■ Horton Chamber of Commerce
PO Box 30
Horton, KS 66439-0030
Ph:(785)486-2681
Fax:(785)486-2381
Co. E-mail: cityofhorton@hortonkansas.net
URL: http://www.hortonkansas.net

50343 ■ Hutchinson/Reno County Chamber of Commerce
117 N Walnut
PO Box 519
Hutchinson, KS 67504-0519
Ph:(620)662-3391
Co. E-mail: davek@hutchchamber.com
URL: http://www.hutchchamber.com
Contact: Dave Kerr, Pres./CEO

50344 ■ Independence Chamber of Commerce
322 N Penn
PO Box 386
Independence, KS 67301
Ph:(620)331-1890
Free: 800-882-3606
Fax:(620)331-1899
Co. E-mail: chamber@indkschamber.org
URL: http://www.indkschamber.org
Contact: Gwen Wilburn, Pres./CEO

50345 ■ Iola Area Chamber of Commerce
208 W Madison Ave.
Iola, KS 66749
Ph:(620)365-5252
Fax:(620)365-8078
Co. E-mail: chamber@iolaks.com
URL: http://www.iolachamber.org
Contact: Duane McGraw, Pres.

50346 ■ Jewell Chamber of Commerce
PO Box 235
Jewell, KS 66949
Ph:(785)428-3549
Co. E-mail: tshelton@nckcn.com
URL: http://www.kansaschamber.org/mx/hm.
    asp?id=home
Contact: Thelma Shelton, Sec.-Treas.

50347 ■ Junction City Area Chamber of Commerce
814 N Washington Ave.
PO Box 26
Junction City, KS 66441
Ph:(785)762-2632
Fax:(785)762-3353
Co. E-mail: jcchamber@junctionchamber.org
URL: http://www.junctioncitychamber.org
Contact: Ms. Wendy King-Luttman, Chair

50348 ■ Kansas Chamber of Commerce and Industry
835 SW Topeka Blvd.
Topeka, KS 66612-1671
Ph:(785)357-6321
Fax:(785)357-4732
Co. E-mail: info@kansaschamber.org
URL: http://www.kansaschamber.org/mx/hm.
    asp?id=home
Contact: Amy J. Blankenbiller, Pres./CEO

50349 ■ Kansas City, Kansas Area Chamber of Commerce
727 Minnesota Ave.
PO Box 171337
Kansas City, KS 66117
Ph:(913)371-3070
Fax:(913)371-3732
Co. E-mail: chamber@kckchamber.com
URL: http://www.kckchamber.com
Contact: Cindy Cash, Pres./CEO

50350 ■ Kingman Area Chamber of Commerce
322 N Main St.
Kingman, KS 67068
Ph:(620)532-1853
Co. E-mail: kingmanchamber@copper.net
URL: http://www.skyways.org/towns/Kingman/
    chamber.html
Contact: Tom Archer, Pres.

50351 ■ Larned Area Chamber of Commerce
502 Broadway St.
Larned, KS 67550
Ph:(620)285-6916
Free: 800-747-6919
Co. E-mail: larnedcofc@gbta.net
URL: http://larned.org/chamber/show.html?id=161
Contact: Linda Henderson, Exec. Dir.

50352 ■ Lawrence Chamber of Commerce
734 Vermont St., Ste. 101
Lawrence, KS 66044-0586
Ph:(785)865-4411
Co. E-mail: tkern@lawrencechamber.com
URL: http://www.lawrencechamber.com/cwt/external/
    wcpages/index.aspx
Contact: Tom Kern, Pres./CEO

50353 ■ Leavenworth-Lansing Area Chamber of Commerce
518 Shawnee
PO Box 44
Leavenworth, KS 66048
Ph:(913)682-4112
Fax:(913)682-8170
Co. E-mail: lloffice.chamber@sbcglobal.net
URL: http://www.llchamber.com
Contact: Tim Holverson, Exec. VP

50354 ■ Leawood Chamber of Commerce
4707 W 135 St., Ste. 270
Leawood, KS 66224
Ph:(913)498-1514
Fax:(913)491-0134
Co. E-mail: chamber@leawoodchamber.org
URL: http://www.leawoodchamber.org
Contact: Kevin Jeffries, Pres./CEO

50355 ■ Lenexa Chamber of Commerce
11180 Lackman Rd.
Lenexa, KS 66219
Ph:(913)888-1414
Fax:(913)888-3770
Co. E-mail: staff@lenexa.org
URL: http://www.lenexa.org
Contact: Blake Schreck CED, Pres.

50356 ■ Liberal Area Chamber of Commerce
4 Rock Island Rd.
PO Box 676
Liberal, KS 67905
Ph:(620)624-3855
Fax:(620)624-8851
Co. E-mail: liberalcoc@adelphia.net
URL: http://www.liberalkschamber.com
Contact: Rozelle Webb, Exec. Dir.

50357 ■ Lincoln Area Chamber of Commerce
144 E Lincoln Ave.
Lincoln, KS 67455
Ph:(785)524-4934
Fax:(785)524-4934
Co. E-mail: lcoc137@sbcglobal.net
URL: http://www.lincolnkansaschamber.com
Contact: Lori Obermuelller, Pres.

50358 ■ Lindsborg Chamber of Commerce
104 E Lincoln
Lindsborg, KS 67456-2416
Ph:(785)227-3706
Free: 888-227-2227
Fax:(785)227-4128
Co. E-mail: chamber@lindsborg.org
URL: http://www.lindsborg.org
Contact: Bryan Katchay, Pres.

50359 ■ Louisburg Chamber of Commerce
PO Box 245
Louisburg, KS 66053
Ph:(913)837-2826
Co. E-mail: chamber@louisburgkansas.com
URL: http://louisburgkansas.com
Contact: Patsey Bortner, Exec. Dir.

50360 ■ Lucas Area Chamber of Commerce
201 S Main
PO Box 186
Lucas, KS 67648
Ph:(785)525-6288
Co. E-mail: lucascoc@wtciweb.com
URL: http://skyways.lib.ks.us/towns/Lucas/index.html
Contact: Connie Dougherty, Dir.

50361 ■ Lyndon Chamber of Commerce
PO Box 523
Lyndon, KS 66451
URL: http://www.kansaschamber.org/mx/hm.
    asp?id=home
Contact: Steve Niemack, Pres.

50362 ■ Madison Area Chamber of Commerce
PO Box 58
Madison, KS 66860-0058
Ph:(620)437-3463
URL: http://www.madisonkschamber.org

50363 ■ Manhattan Area Chamber of Commerce
501 Poyntz Ave.
Manhattan, KS 66502-6005
Ph:(785)776-8829
Fax:(785)776-0679
Co. E-mail: lyle@manhattan.org
URL: http://www.manhattan.org
Contact: Lyle Butler III, Pres./CEO

50364 ■ Mankato Chamber of Commerce
202 E Jefferson St.
Mankato, KS 66956
Ph:(785)378-3141
Co. E-mail: mankato@nckcn.com
URL: http://www.kansaschamber.org/mx/hm.
    asp?id=home
Contact: Lori Carter, Sec.-Treas.

50365 ■ Marysville Chamber of Commerce
101 N 10th Hwy. 77 and 36
Marysville, KS 66508
Ph:(785)562-3101
Free: 800-752-3965
Co. E-mail: marysvillechamber@sbcglobal.net
URL: http://skyways.lib.ks.us/towns/Marysville
Contact: Paula Landoll-Smith, Pres.

50366 ■ McPherson Chamber of Commerce
306 N Main
PO Box 616
McPherson, KS 67460-0616
Ph:(620)241-3303
Fax:(620)241-8708
Co. E-mail: saraphin@mcphersonks.org
URL: http://www.mcphersonks.org/chamber
Contact: Ms. Jennifer Burch, Exec. Dir.

50367 ■ Meade Chamber of Commerce
PO Box 576
Meade, KS 67864-0576
Ph:(620)873-2979
Co. E-mail: lpodrebarac@sbcglobal.net
URL: http://www.meadechamber.com
Contact: Louis Podrebarac, Sec.

50368 ■ Medicine Lodge Area Chamber of Commerce
108 W 1st St.
Medicine Lodge, KS 67104
Ph:(316)886-3417
Co. E-mail: mlchamber@cyberlodg.com
URL: http://www.barbercounty.net/medicinelodge.
    html
Contact: Karen Larson, Pres.

50369 ■ Minneapolis Area Chamber of Commerce
200 W 2nd St.
Minneapolis, KS 67467
Ph:(785)392-3068
Co. E-mail: mplschamber@sbcglobal.net
URL: http://www.minneapolisksorg.org

50370 ■ Mound City Area Chamber of Commerce
PO Box 10
Mound City, KS 66056
Ph:(913)795-2074
Fax:(913)795-3089
URL: http://www.kansaschamber.org/mx/hm.
    asp?id=home
Contact: Naomi Childress, Dir./Sec.

50371 ■ Moundridge Community Chamber of Commerce
225 S Christian Ave.
Moundridge, KS 67107
Ph:(620)345-6300
Co. E-mail: images@mtelco.net
URL: http://www.moundridge.com
Contact: Rosemary Fisher, Coor.

50372 ■ Mulvane Chamber of Commerce
PO Box 67
Mulvane, KS 67110-0067
Ph:(316)777-4850
URL: http://www.mulvanekansas.com

50373 ■ Ness City Chamber of Commerce
102 W Main
PO Box 262
Ness City, KS 67560-0262
Ph:(785)798-2413
Co. E-mail: nccofc@gbta.net
URL: http://skyways.lib.ks.us/towns/NessCity/
  chamber.html
Contact: Yvette Schlegel, Exec. Dir.

50374 ■ Newton Area Chamber of Commerce and Visitors Bureau
500 N Main, Ste. 101
Newton, KS 67114
Ph:(316)283-2560
Free: 800-868-2560
Fax:(316)283-8732
Co. E-mail: info@thenewtonchamber.org
URL: http://www.thenewtonchamber.org
Contact: Virgil Penner, Staff Liaison

50375 ■ Northeast Johnson County Chamber of Commerce
5800 Foxridge Dr., Ste. 100
Mission, KS 66202
Ph:(913)262-2141
Fax:(913)262-2146
Co. E-mail: rjohnson@nejcchamber.com
URL: http://www.nejcchamber.com
Contact: Rob Johnson, Pres./CEO

50376 ■ Norton Area Chamber of Commerce
PO Box 97
Norton, KS 67654
Ph:(785)877-2501
Co. E-mail: nortoncc@ruraltel.net
URL: http://us36.net/nortonkansas
Contact: Karla Reed, Exec. Dir.

50377 ■ Oakley Area Chamber of Commerce
216 Center Ave.
Oakley, KS 67748-1714
Ph:(785)672-4862
Fax:(785)672-3838
Co. E-mail: oakleycc@st-tel.net
URL: http://www.discoveroakley.com
Contact: Dave Nelson, Pres.

50378 ■ Olathe Chamber of Commerce
18001 W 106 St., Ste. 160
PO Box 98
Olathe, KS 66051-0098
Ph:(913)764-1050
Fax:(913)782-4636
Co. E-mail: chamber@olathe.org
URL: http://www.olathe.org/default.asp
Contact: L. Franklin Taylor, Pres.

50379 ■ Osage City Chamber of Commerce
PO Box 250
201 S 5th St.
Osage City, KS 66523
Ph:(785)528-3714
Co. E-mail: robyn.williams@edwardjones.com
URL: http://www.osagecity.com
Contact: Robyn Williams, Pres.

50380 ■ Osawatomie Chamber of Commerce
PO Box 63
Osawatomie, KS 66064
Ph:(913)755-4114
Fax:(913)755-4114
URL: http://www.osawatomiechamber.org

50381 ■ Osborne Area Chamber of Commerce
130 N 1st St.
Osborne, KS 67473-2002
Ph:(785)346-2670
Free: (866)346-2670
Fax:(785)346-2522
Co. E-mail: osborneed@ruraltel.net
URL: http://www.discoverosborne.com
Contact: Brian Befort, Pres.

50382 ■ Ottawa Area Chamber of Commerce
PO Box 580
Ottawa, KS 66067
Ph:(785)242-1000
Fax:(785)242-4792
Co. E-mail: chamber@ottawakansas.org
URL: http://www.ottawakansas.org
Contact: Tom Weigand, Pres./CEO

50383 ■ Overland Park Chamber of Commerce
9001 W 110th, Ste. 150
Overland Park, KS 66210
Ph:(913)491-3600
Fax:(913)491-0393
Co. E-mail: opcc@opks.org
URL: http://www.opks.org
Contact: Tracey Osborne, Pres.

50384 ■ Paola Chamber of Commerce
3 W Wea St.
Paola, KS 66071-1403
Ph:(913)294-4335
Fax:(913)294-4336
Co. E-mail: mgr@paolachamber.org
URL: http://www.paolachamber.org
Contact: Carol Everhart, Exec. Dir.

50385 ■ Parsons Chamber of Commerce
1715 Corning
Parsons, KS 67357
Ph:(620)421-6500
Free: 800-280-6401
Fax:(620)421-6501
Co. E-mail: rikki@parsonschamber.org
URL: http://www.parsonschamber.org
Contact: Rikki Hess, Exec. VP/Dir.

50386 ■ Phillipsburg Area Chamber of Commerce
270 State St.
PO Box 326
Phillipsburg, KS 67661-0326
Ph:(785)543-2321
Fax:(785)543-0038
Co. E-mail: cvbcham@ruraltel.net
URL: http://www.phillipsburgks.us/development/
  chamber
Contact: Jackie L. Swatzell, Office Dir.

50387 ■ Pittsburg Area Chamber of Commerce
117 W 4th St.
PO Box 1115
Pittsburg, KS 66762
Ph:(620)231-1000
Fax:(620)231-3178
Co. E-mail: bbenson@pittsburgareachamber.com
URL: http://pittsburgareachamber.com
Contact: Blake Benson, Pres.

50388 ■ Pratt Area Chamber of Commerce
114 N Main
Pratt, KS 67124
Ph:(620)672-5501
Free: 888-886-1164
Co. E-mail: info@prattkan.com
URL: http://www.prattkan.com
Contact: Brian Hoffman, Exec. Dir.

50389 ■ Russell Area Chamber of Commerce
610 N Main
Russell, KS 67665
Ph:(785)483-6960
Co. E-mail: chamber@russellks.org
URL: http://www.russellks.org
Contact: Peggy Chrisler, Chair

50390 ■ Sabetha Chamber of Commerce
808 Main St.
Sabetha, KS 66534
Ph:(785)284-2158
Co. E-mail: chamber@mewlan.com
URL: http://skyways.lib.ks.us/towns/Sabetha/
  chamber.htm
Contact: Judy Elliot, Exec. Sec.

50391 ■ St. Francis Area Chamber of Commerce
212 E Washington St.
St. Francis, KS 67756
Ph:(785)332-2961
Co. E-mail: coc@cityofstfrancis.net
Contact: Gloria Bracelin, Sec.

50392 ■ Salina Area Chamber of Commerce
120 W Ash St.
PO Box 586
Salina, KS 67402-0586
Ph:(785)827-9301
Fax:(785)827-9758
Co. E-mail: info@salinakansas.org
URL: http://salinakansas.org/index.html
Contact: Mr. Dennis Lauver, Pres./CEO

50393 ■ Satanta Chamber of Commerce
PO Box 98
Satanta, KS 67870-0098
Ph:(620)649-3602
Co. E-mail: chamber@satanta.org
URL: http://skyways.lib.ks.us/towns/Satanta/index.
  html
Contact: Brent Howie, Pres.

50394 ■ Sedan Area Chamber of Commerce
108 N Sherman
Sedan, KS 67361
Ph:(620)725-4033
Fax:(620)725-4023
Co. E-mail: sedanchamber@yahoo.com
URL: http://www.kansaschamber.org/mx/hm.
  asp?id=home
Contact: Lisa Hudson, Pres.

50395 ■ Seneca Chamber of Commerce
PO Box 135
Seneca, KS 66538-0135
Ph:(785)336-2294
Fax:(785)336-6344
Co. E-mail: seneca_chamber@yahoo.com
URL: http://www.kansaschamber.org/mx/hm.
  asp?id=home
Contact: Harry Leem, Exec. Dir.

50396 ■ Shawnee Area Chamber of Commerce
15100 W 67th St., Ste. 202
Shawnee, KS 66217-9344
Ph:(913)631-6545
Free: 888-550-7252
Fax:(913)631-9628
Co. E-mail: mtaylor@shawneekschamber.com
URL: http://shawneekschamber.com
Contact: Linda Leeper, Pres.

50397 ■ Smith Center Chamber of Commerce
219 S Main
Smith Center, KS 66967
Ph:(785)282-3895
Fax:(785)282-3895
Co. E-mail: ckirkendall@smithcenter.net
URL: http://www.smithcenterks.com
Contact: Karen Cole, Pres.

50398 ■ Sterling Chamber of Commerce
PO Box 56
Sterling, KS 67579
Ph:(620)278-3727
Co. E-mail: lcbuckman@cm.kscoxmail.com
URL: http://www.sterling-kansas.org
Contact: Josh Gilmore, Pres.

50399 ■ Tri-County Area Chamber of Commerce
106 N Broadway
Herington, KS 67449
Ph:(785)258-2115
URL: http://www.tricountycofc.com

50400 ■ Wamego Area Chamber of Commerce
529 Lincoln Ave.
Wamego, KS 66547
Ph:(785)456-7849
Fax:(785)456-7427
Co. E-mail: wchamber@wamego.net
URL: http://www.wamegochamber.com
Contact: Kourtney Nrase, Exec. Dir.

50401 ■ Waterville Chamber of Commerce
PO Box 7
Waterville, KS 66548
Ph:(785)363-2515
URL: http://watervillekansas.com
Contact: Sandy Harding

50402 ■ Wellsville Area Chamber of Commerce
PO Box 472
Wellsville, KS 66092
Ph:(785)883-2296
URL: http://www.wellsvillechamber.com

50403 ■ Wichita Area Chamber of Commerce
350 W Douglas Ave.
Wichita, KS 67202-2970
Ph:(316)265-7771
Fax:(316)265-7502
Co. E-mail: info@wichitachamber.org
URL: http://www.wichitakansas.org
Contact: Bryan S. Derreberry, Pres./CEO

50404 ■ Winfield Area Chamber of Commerce
PO Box 640
Winfield, KS 67156
Ph:(620)221-2420
Fax:(620)221-2958
Co. E-mail: win@winfieldchamber.org
URL: http://www.winfieldks.org/index.aspx?NID=11
Contact: Mike Niederee, Chm.

50405 ■ Women's Chamber of Commerce of Kansas City, Kansas
PO Box 171337
Kansas City, KS 66117
Ph:(913)371-3165
Fax:(913)233-3350
Co. E-mail: deason_a@wmhci.org
URL: http://www.womenschamberkck.org
Contact: Ardith Deason, Corresponding Sec.

50406 ■ Woodson County Chamber of Commerce
108 S Main
PO Box 233
Yates Center, KS 66783
Ph:(620)625-3235
Fax:(620)625-2416
Co. E-mail: chamber@wccc.kscoxmail.com
URL: http://www.woodsoncountychamber.com
Contact: Hollie Yoho, Exec. Dir.

MINORITY BUSINESS ASSISTANCE PROGRAMS

50407 ■ Kansas Department of Commerce–Office of Minority and Women Business Development
1000 SW Jackson St., Ste. 100
Topeka, KS 66612-1354
Ph:(785)296-3425

Fax:(785)296-3490
Co. E-mail: rharris@kansascommerce.com
URL: http://www.kansascommerce.com
Contact: Rhonda F. Harris, Dir
Description: Provides counseling, technical assistance, and procurement counseling. Conducts low-cost business seminars, workshops, and conferences. Offers business reference materials.

FINANCING AND LOAN PROGRAMS

50408 ■ Child Health Investment Company, LLC
6803 W. 64th St.
Shawnee Mission, KS 66202
Ph:(913)262-1436
Fax:(913)262-1575
Co. E-mail: info@chca.com
URL: http://www.chca.com
Contact: Don Black, President
Investment Types: Balanced, early stage, first stage, seed, and start-up. **Industry Preferences:** Medical and health, biotechnology, other products, Internet specific, computer software and services, computer hardware, and semiconductors and other electronics. **Geographic Preferences:** U.S. **Principal Exhibits:**

50409 ■ Kansas Technology Enterprise Corporation
214 SW 6th, 1st Fl.
Topeka, KS 66603-3719
Ph:(785)296-5272
Fax:(785)296-1160
Co. E-mail: info@ktec.com
URL: http://www.ktec.com
Contact: Kevin Carr, Chief Executive Officer
E-mail: kcarr@ktec.com
Preferred Investment Size: $250,000 to $500,000. **Investment Types:** Seed, start-up, first and early stage. **Industry Preferences:** Communications, computer hardware and software, Internet specifics, semiconductors and other electronics, biotechnology, transportation, medical and health, consumer related, industrial and energy, and business service, and manufacturing. **Geographic Preferences:** Midwest. **Principal Exhibits:**

50410 ■ Kansas Venture Capital, Inc.
10601 Mission Rd., Ste. 250
Leawood, KS 66211
Ph:(913)262-7117
Fax:(913)262-3509
URL: http://www.kvci.com
Contact: Marshall D. Parker, President and CEO
E-mail: mparker@kvci.com
Preferred Investment Size: $500,000 to $260,000,000. **Investment Types:** Later stage, mezzanine, leveraged buyout, management buyouts, acquisition, expansion, turnaround, and recapitalizations. **Industry Preferences:** Communications and media, computer related, semiconductors and other electronics, medical and health, consumer related, industrial and energy, business service, and manufacturing. **Geographic Preferences:** Midwest. **Principal Exhibits:**

PROCUREMENT ASSISTANCE PROGRAMS

50411 ■ Kansas Department of Administration–Division of Purchases
102 N Landon State Office Bldg.
900 SW Jackson St., Rm. 102N
Topeka, KS 66612-1286
Ph:(785)296-2376
Fax:(785)296-7240
Co. E-mail: purchweb@da.state.ks.us
URL: http://www.da.state.ks.us/purch
Contact: Christopher Howe, Purchasing Dir
Description: In cooperation with the Division of Existing Industry Development, provides assistance to businesses seeking procurement opportunities with the state.

INCUBATORS/RESEARCH AND TECHNOLOGY PARKS

50412 ■ Enterprise Center of Johnson County
8527 Bluejacket St.
Lenexa, KS 66214
Ph:(913)438-2282
Fax:(913)888-6928
Co. E-mail: rvaughn@ecjc.com
URL: http://www.ecjc.com/
Description: A small business incubator providing high-growth potential companies with office space, consulting and advisory services, and financing resources in order to help them grow and succeed.

50413 ■ Johnson County Community College–Office of Institutional Research
12345 College Blvd.
Overland Park, KS 66210
Ph:(913)469-8500
Fax:(913)469-4481
Co. E-mail: jseybert@jccc.net
Contact: Dr. Jeffrey A. Seybert, Dir.
E-mail: jseybert@jccc.net
Scope: Conducts assessments of student learning outcomes and institutional effectiveness, program evaluation for instructional programs, student services, and support services. Provides decision support and assistance to College planning processes through analysis of management information. Conducts market research for enrollment management and program development. Offers information resource services and consulting services. Provides research and technical support services to public and private agencies and various consortia, including Kansas Association of Community Colleges and the League for Innovation in the Community College. **Educational Activities:** National Community College Benchmark Conference.

50414 ■ Kansas State University–Office of the Vice Provost for Research
Anderson Hall, Rm. 108
Manhattan, KS 66506
Ph:(785)532-5110
Fax:(785)532-6507
Co. E-mail: trewyn@ksu.edu
URL: http://www.k-state.edu/research/provost.htm
Contact: Prof. Ronald W. Trewyn PhD
E-mail: trewyn@ksu.edu
Scope: Administers all University related research projects and intellectual property activities at Kansas State University. Also administers research projects supported by extramural agencies in all units of the University, including the physical, biological, behavioral sciences, agriculture, engineering, and humanities. Monitors university compliance with federal regulations. **Publications:** Funding Bulletin (weekly); Proposal Manual; Research Notes (bimonthly). **Educational Activities:** Seminars (periodically); Training workshops, open to the general public; Workshops, for faculty and graduate students. **Awards:** Distinguished Graduate Faculty Award; Travel awards.

50415 ■ Kansas State University Research Foundation
2005 Research Park Cir., Ste. 105
Manhattan, KS 66502-5020
Ph:(785)532-5720
Fax:(785)532-3920
Co. E-mail: tech.transfer@k-state.edu
URL: http://www.k-state.edu/tech.transfer
Contact: Marcia Molina, VP
E-mail: tech.transfer@k-state.edu
Scope: Provides patenting and licensing assistance to Kansas State University researchers. **Educational Activities:** Seminars, on patent and technology transfer.

50416 ■ Kansas Technology Enterprise Corporation
109 SW 9th St., Ste. 508
Topeka, KS 66603
Ph:(785)296-5272

Fax:(785)296-1160
Co. E-mail: info@ktec.co
URL: http://www.ktec.com/index_Flash.htm
Description: A private/public partnership established by the state of Kansas to promote technology-based economic development. It serves as a partner to companies bringing economic growth to Kansas.

50417 ■ Lawrence Regional Technology Center
2029 Becker Dr.
Lawrence, KS 66047
Ph:(785)832-2110
Fax:(785)832-8234
Co. E-mail: info@lrtc.biz
URL: http://www.lrtc.biz/
Description: A not-for-profit small business incubator offering resources and services to support the formation and growth of high-technology start-up companies in Lawrence and the surrounding. Its mission is to provide business development assistance to early-stage businesses that have spun off from the University of Kansas, as well as to local entrepreneurs who would like to create their own high-technology firms.

50418 ■ Pittsburg State University–Kansas Polymer Research Center–Business and Technology Institute
Shirk Hall
1501 S Joplin St.
Pittsburg, KS 66762-7560
Ph:(620)235-4920
Fax:(620)235-4919
Co. E-mail: bti@pittstate.edu
URL: http://www.btikansas.com
Contact: R. Steve Robb, Exec.Dir.
E-mail: bti@pittstate.edu
Scope: Conducts applied research, transfers technology, and provides assistance to industry through its research associates, staff, and through the School of Technology. Emphasis in polymer/plastics, secondary wood processing, and rapid prototyping. **Educational**

Activities: Training programs, in advanced technology in manufacturing, production problem solving, product design, and prototype development.

50419 ■ Wichita Technology Corporation
7829 E. Rockhill Rd., Ste. 307
Wichita, KS 67206
Ph:(316)651-5900
Fax:(866)810-6671
Co. E-mail: wtc@wichitatechnology.com
URL: http://www.wichitatechnology.com/
Description: A private commercialization corporation established to create and sustain a formal innovation network that will support technology advancement, transfer, and commercialization in Kansas in order to maintain and facilitate business formation and growth by enhancing research and development activity, providing business assistance at critical phases of a technology start-up life cycle, and providing access to capital.

EDUCATIONAL PROGRAMS

50420 ■ Coffeyville Community College
400 W 11th St.
Coffeyville, KS 67337
Ph:(620)251-7700
Fax:(620)252-7098
URL: http://www.ccc.cc.ks.us
Description: Two-year college offering a small business management program.

50421 ■ Labette Community College
200 S 14th St.
Parsons, KS 67357
Ph:(620)421-6700
Free: 888-522-3883
Fax:(620)421-0180
Co. E-mail: juliusg@labette.edu
URL: http://www.labette.cc.ks.us
Description: Two-year college offering a small business management program.

50422 ■ Wichita State University–Center for Entrepreneurship
Devlin Hall, 2nd Fl.
1845 N Fairmount
Wichita, KS 67260-0147
Ph:(316)978-3000
Fax:(316)978-3687
URL: http://www.cfe.wichita.edu
Description: Offers degreed courses for entrepreneurs and small business management.

LEGISLATIVE ASSISTANCE

50423 ■ Kansas House Standing Committee on Economic Development and Tourism
Statehouse, Rm. 545 N
Kansas Legis. Research Department
300 SW 10th St.
Topeka, KS 66612
Ph:(785)296-2149
Fax:(785)296-3824
URL: http://www.kslegislature.org
Contact: April Holman

PUBLICATIONS

50424 ■ *Smart Start your Washington D.C. Business*
PSI Research
300 N. Valley Dr.
Grants Pass, OR 97526
Ph:(503)479-9464
Free: 800-228-2275
Fax:(503)476-1479
Co. E-mail: info@psi-research.com
URL: http://www.psi-research.com
Ed: Michael D. Jenkins. **Released:** Revised edition, 1992. **Price:** $29.95 (looseleaf binder); $24.95 (paper). **Description:** Part of the Successful Business Library series.

SMALL BUSINESS DEVELOPMENT CENTERS

50425 ■ Ashland Small Business Development Center - Kentucky
1645 Winchester Ave., 2nd Fl.
Ashland, KY 41101
Fax:(606)324-4570
Co. E-mail: k.jenkins@moreheadstate.edu
URL: http://www.ksbdc.org/locations/ashland
Contact: Kimberly Jenkins, Dir.

50426 ■ Bluegrass Small Business Development Center
330 E Main St., Ste. 210
Lexington, KY 40507
Free: 888-475-SBDC
Fax:(859)257-1751
Co. E-mail: smack3@uky.edu
URL: http://www.ksbdc.org/locations/lexington
Contact: Shirie Mack, Dir./Management Consultant

50427 ■ Greater Louisville Small Business Development Center
614 W Main St.
Louisville, KY 40202
Fax:(502)625-1181
Co. E-mail: tcardell@louisvillesmallbiz.org
URL: http://www.ksbdc.org/locations/louisville
Contact: Toni Cardell, Asst. Dir.

50428 ■ Hopkinsville Small Business Development Center
2800 Ft. Campbell Blvd.
Hopkinsville, KY 42240
Fax:(270)881-9366
Co. E-mail: roy.keller@murraystate.edu
URL: http://www.ksbdc.org/locations/hopkinsville
Contact: Roy Keller, Dir./Management Consultant

50429 ■ Kentucky Small Business Development Center
University of Kentucky
225 Gatton College of Business and Economics
Lexington, KY 40506-0034
Fax:(859)323-1907
URL: http://www.ksbdc.org
Contact: Becky Naugle, Dir.

50430 ■ Kentucky Small Business Development Center at Eastern Kentucky University - Richmond
Eastern Kentucky University
College of Business & Technology
Hall Dr., Rm. 145
Richmond, KY 40475
Free: 877-358-7232
Fax:(859)622-1413
Co. E-mail: kevin.norvell@eku.edu
URL: http://ekubiz.com
Contact: Kevin Norvell, Dir.

50431 ■ Kentucky Small Business Development Center at Eastern Kentucky University - Somerset
675 Monticello St., Ste. A
Somerset, KY 42501
Free: 877-EKU-SBDC
Fax:(606)678-3065
Co. E-mail: johnpreston@alltel.net
URL: http://ekubiz.com
Contact: John Preston, Business Coor.

50432 ■ Maysville Small Business Development Center
201 E Third St.
Maysville, KY 41056
Co. E-mail: m.jackson@moreheadstate.edu
URL: http://www.ksbdc.org/locations/maysville
Contact: Mike Jackson, Management Consultant

50433 ■ Morehead Small Business Development Center
150 E First St.
Morehead, KY 40351
Fax:(606)783-5020
Co. E-mail: d.barber@moreheadstate.edu
URL: http://www.ksbdc.org/locations/morehead
Contact: David Barber, Dir./Management Consultant

50434 ■ Murray Small Business Development Center
Murray State University
Business Bldg. S, Rm. 253
Murray, KY 42071
Fax:(270)809-3049
Co. E-mail: chris.wooldridge@murraystate.edu
URL: http://www.ksbdc.org/locations/murray
Contact: Chris Wooldridge, Dir.

50435 ■ Northern Kentucky University Small Business Development Center
305 Johns Hill Rd.
Highland Heights, KY 41076-1412
Fax:(859)442-4285
Co. E-mail: cornellc1@nku.edu
URL: http://www.ksbdc.org/locations/highland-heights
Contact: Carol Cornell, Dir.

50436 ■ Owensboro Small Business Development Center
200 E 3rd St., Ste. 302
Owensboro, KY 42303
Fax:(270)684-0714
Co. E-mail: mickey.johnson@murraystate.edu
URL: http://www.ksbdc.org/locations/owensboro
Contact: Mickey Johnson, Dir./Management Consultant

50437 ■ Paducah Small Business Development Center
401 Kentucky Ave.
Paducah, KY 42003-1551
Fax:(270)442-9152
Co. E-mail: khalsell@kyinnovation.com
URL: http://www.ksbdc.org/locations/paducah
Contact: Kirby Halsell, Admin. Asst.

50438 ■ Paintsville Small Business Development Center
120 Scott Perry Dr.
Teays Branch Rd.
Paintsville, KY 41240-9000
Fax:(606)789-5623
Co. E-mail: sk.jude@moreheadstate.edu
URL: http://www.ksbdc.org/locations/paintsville
Contact: Sabrina Jude, Data Entry Specialist

50439 ■ Pikeville Small Business Development Center
3455 N Mayo Trail, No. 4
Pikeville, KY 41501-3298
Fax:(606)432-8924
Co. E-mail: m.morley@moreheadstate.edu
URL: http://www.ksbdc.org/locations/pikeville
Contact: Mike Morley, Dir./Management Consultant

50440 ■ Small Business Development Center at Western Kentucky University
Garrett Conference Ctr.
1906 College Heights Blvd., No. 61086
Bowling Green, KY 42101
Fax:(270)745-1931
Co. E-mail: adam.brownlee@wku.edu
URL: http://wkusbdc.com
Contact: Adam Brownlee, Dir.

50441 ■ Southeast Small Business Development Center
Bell County Campus
1300 Chichester Ave.
Middlesboro, KY 40965-2265
Fax:(606)248-3267
Co. E-mail: samuel.coleman@kctcs.edu
URL: http://www.ksbdc.org/locations/middlesboro
Contact: Sam Coleman, Dir./Management Consultant

50442 ■ University of Kentucky Small Business Development Center - Elizabethtown
1105 Juliana Ct., No. 6
Elizabethtown, KY 42701-7937
Fax:(270)769-5095
Co. E-mail: patricia.krausman@uky.edu
URL: http://www.ksbdc.org/locations/elizabethtown
Contact: Patricia Krausman, Dir./Management Consultant

50443 ■ West Liberty Small Business Development Center
Morehead State University Regional Enterprise Ctr.
151 University Dr.
West Liberty, KY 41472
Fax:(606)743-4002
Co. E-mail: m.rodriguez@moreheadstate.edu
URL: http://www.ksbdc.org/locations/west-liberty
Contact: Michael Rodriguez, Management Consultant

SMALL BUSINESS ASSISTANCE PROGRAMS

50444 ■ Kentucky Cabinet for Economic Development–International Trade Division
Old Capital Annex
300 W Broadway
Frankfort, KY 40601
Ph:(502)564-7140
Free: 800-626-2930
Fax:(502)564-3256
Co. E-mail: econdev@ky.gov
URL: http://www.thinkkentucky.com/kyedc/internationaltrade.aspx
Contact: Mark Peachey, Dir
Description: Preserves and increases employment opportunities through foreign investment within the state, and increased export of Kentucky's manufactured products. Operates a Far East office in Japan and a European office in England.

50445 ■ Kentucky Cabinet for Economic Development–New Business Development Division
Old Capital Annex
300 W Broadway
Frankfort, KY 40601
Ph:(502)564-7140
Fax:(502)564-3256
Co. E-mail: econdev@ky.gov
URL: http://www.thinkkentucky.com
Contact: Jum Navolio, Commissioner
Description: Provides site selection assistance and information. Focuses on new job creation and job retention through an Existing Industries Branch, an Industrial Marketing Branch, an Enterprise Zone Program, and a Site Evaluation Branch.

50446 ■ Kentucky Cabinet for Economic Development–Office of Business Technology
2200 Capitol Plaza Tower, 22nd Fl., Rm. 2224
500 Mero St.
Frankfort, KY 40601
Ph:(502)564-4252
Fax:(502)564-5932
URL: http://www.thinkkentucky.com
Description: Serves as a link between businesses and the technological resources and research capabilities of the state universities. Provides coordination of technology transfer to the private sector and works with the federal Small Business Innovation Research program.

50447 ■ Kentucky Cabinet for Economic Development–Small Business Services Division
Old Capital Annex Building
300 W Broadway
Frankfort, KY 40601
Ph:(502)564-2064
Fax:(502)564-9758
Co. E-mail: cedsbsd@ky.gov
URL: http://www.thinkkentucky.com/kyedc/busstart.aspx
Contact: John E. Cole III, Dir
Description: Serves as an advocate and ombudsman for small business. Works with the Legislative Small Business Task Force, provides information on programs of interest, and provides information on specialized resource assistance.

50448 ■ Kentucky Cabinet for Economic Development–Small and Minority Business Division–Office of Export Development (Old C)
Old Capital Annex Building
300 W Broadway
Frankfort, KY 40601
Ph:(502)564-2064
Fax:(502)564-9758
URL: http://www.thinkkentucky.com
Description: Provides exporting assistance to small manufacturers.

SCORE OFFICES

50449 ■ London SCORE
Path: www.score-kentucky.org/london.html

50450 ■ Louisville SCORE
Federal Bldg., Rm. 188
600 Dr. Martin Luther King Jr. Pl.
Louisville, KY 40202
Ph:(502)582-5976
Fax:(502)582-5819
Co. E-mail: score75@score-louisville.org
URL: http://www.score-louisville.org
Contact: Joe Hatfield, Chm.
Description: Provides professional guidance, mentoring services and financial assistance to maximize the success of existing and emerging small businesses.

50451 ■ SCORE Ashland
Path: www.score-kentucky.org/ashland.html

50452 ■ SCORE Bardstown
Path: www.score-kentucky.org/bardstown.html

50453 ■ SCORE Bowling Green
Path: www.score-kentucky.org/bowling_green.html

50454 ■ SCORE Elizabethtown
Path: www.score-kentucky.org/elizabethtown.html

50455 ■ SCORE Fort Mitchell
Path: www.score-kentucky.org/fortmitchell.html

50456 ■ SCORE LaGrange
Path: www.score-kentucky.org/LaGrange.html

50457 ■ SCORE Lexington
389 Waller Ave., Ste. 130
Lexington, KY 40504-2900
Ph:(859)231-9902
Fax:(859)253-3190
Co. E-mail: score@pdqweb.com
URL: http://www.score-kentucky.org/lexington.html
Contact: Billy Kelley, Chm.
Description: Provides professional guidance and information to America's small businesses.

50458 ■ SCORE Owensboro
Path: www.score-kentucky.org/owensboro.html

50459 ■ SCORE Pikeville
Path: www.score-kentucky.org/pikeville.html

50460 ■ SCORE Purchase Area
Path: www.score-kentucky.org/mayfield.html

BETTER BUSINESS BUREAUS

50461 ■ Better Business Bureau of Central and Eastern Kentucky
1460 Newtown Pike
Lexington, KY 40511
Ph:(859)259-1008
Free: 800-866-6668
Fax:(859)259-1639
Co. E-mail: info@ky.bbb.org
URL: http://bluegrass.bbb.org

50462 ■ Better Business Bureau - Louisville, Southern Indiana and Western Kentucky
844 S 4th St.
Louisville, KY 40203-2186
Ph:(502)583-6546
Free: 800-388-2222
Fax:(502)589-9940
Co. E-mail: info@bbbkyin.org
URL: http://www.ky-in.bbb.org
Contact: Charlie Mattingly, Pres./CEO

CHAMBERS OF COMMERCE

50463 ■ Anderson County Chamber of Commerce
100 N Main St., Ste. 213
Lawrenceburg, KY 40342-0543
Ph:(502)839-5564
Fax:(502)839-5106
Co. E-mail: chamber@lawrenceburgky.org
URL: http://www.lawrenceburgky.org
Contact: Catherine Myers, Exec. Dir.

50464 ■ Ashland Alliance
1733 Winchester Ave.
PO Box 830
Ashland, KY 41105-0830
Ph:(606)324-5111
Fax:(606)325-4607
Co. E-mail: bhammond@inicity.net
URL: http://www.ashlandalliance.com
Contact: Bob Hammond, Dir. of Business Development

50465 ■ Bell County Chamber of Commerce
PO Box 788
Middlesboro, KY 40965
Ph:(606)248-1075
Fax:(606)248-8851
Co. E-mail: chamber@bellcountychamber.com
URL: http://www.bellcountychamber.com
Contact: Nioma Lawson, Exec. Dir.

50466 ■ Bowling Green Area Chamber of Commerce
710 Coll. St.
PO Box 51
Bowling Green, KY 42102
Ph:(270)781-3200
Free: (866)330-2422
Fax:(270)843-0458
Co. E-mail: info@bgchamber.com
URL: http://www.bgchamber.com
Contact: James N. Hizer CEcD, Pres./CEO

50467 ■ Bullitt County Chamber of Commerce
PO Box 1656
Shepherdsville, KY 40165
Ph:(502)543-6727
Fax:(502)543-1765
Co. E-mail: bcchamber@alltel.net
URL: http://www.travelbullitt.org
Contact: Kristie Walls, Exec. Dir.

50468 ■ Burkesville Cumberland County Chamber of Commerce
PO Box 312
Burkesville, KY 42717
Ph:(270)864-5890
Co. E-mail: chamber@burkesville.com
URL: http://www.burkesville.com/chamber
Contact: Jeremy White, Pres.

50469 ■ Cadiz-Trigg County Chamber of Commerce
PO Box 647
Cadiz, KY 42211
Ph:(270)522-3892
Fax:(270)522-6343
Co. E-mail: cadizky@apex.net
URL: http://www.cadizchamber.com
Contact: John Durden, Pres.

50470 ■ Campbellsville - Taylor County Chamber of Commerce
107 W Broadway
Campbellsville, KY 42718
Ph:(270)465-8601
Fax:(270)465-0607
Co. E-mail: chamber@teamtaylorcounty.com
URL: http://www.campbellsvillechamber.com
Contact: Mike Judd, Pres.

50471 ■ Carroll County Chamber of Commerce
511 Highland Ave.
Carrollton, KY 41008
Ph:(502)732-7034
Fax:(502)732-7028
Co. E-mail: chamber@carrollcountyky.com
URL: http://www.carrollcountyky.com
Contact: Lonie Sundermeyer, Pres.

50472 ■ Crittenden County Chamber of Commerce
PO Box 164
Marion, KY 42064
Ph:(270)965-5015
Co. E-mail: chamber@marionkentucky.us
URL: http://www.marionkentucky.us/chamber
Contact: Ron Padget, Pres.

50473 ■ Cynthiana-Harrison County Chamber of Commerce
203 W Pike St.
Cynthiana, KY 41031
Ph:(859)234-5236
Fax:(859)234-6647
Co. E-mail: cynchamber@setel.com
URL: http://www.cynthianaky.com/chamber
Contact: Pat Grenier, Exec. Dir.

50474 ■ Danville-Boyle County Chamber of Commerce
304 S Fourth St.
Danville, KY 40422-2005
Ph:(859)236-2361
Fax:(859)236-3197
Co. E-mail: info@danvilleboylechamber.com
URL: http://www.danvilleboylechamber.com
Contact: Paula Fowler Kilby, Exec. Dir.

50475 ■ Dawson Springs Chamber of Commerce
PO Box 403
Dawson Springs, KY 42408
Ph:(270)797-2781
Fax:(270)797-2221
Co. E-mail: whi@dawsonspringsky.com
URL: http://www.dawsonspringsky.com/default.aspx
Contact: Rick Hendrickson, Pres.

50476 ■ Edmonton - Metcalfe County Chamber of Commerce
PO Box 42
Edmonton, KY 42129
Ph:(270)432-3222
Fax:(270)432-3222
Co. E-mail: metchamb@scrtc.com
URL: http://www.metcalfechamber.com
Contact: Gaye Shaw, Exec. Dir.

50477 ■ Elizabethtown-Hardin County Chamber of Commerce
111 W Dixie Ave.
Elizabethtown, KY 42701
Ph:(270)765-4334
Fax:(270)737-0690
Co. E-mail: etownchamber@kvnet.org
URL: http://www.etownchamber.org
Contact: Tim Asher, Pres.

50478 ■ Estill Development Alliance
PO Box 421
Irvine, KY 40336
Ph:(606)723-2450
Co. E-mail: info@estillcountyky.net
Contact: Joseph A. Crawford, Exec. Dir.

50479 ■ Fleming County Chamber of Commerce
PO Box 24
Flemingsburg, KY 41041
Ph:(606)845-1223
Fax:(606)845-1223
Co. E-mail: crystal@flemingkychamber.com
URL: http://www.flemingkychamber.com
Contact: Crystal L. Ruark, Exec. Dir.

50480 ■ Floyd County Chamber of Commerce
113 S Central Ave.
PO Box 1508
Prestonsburg, KY 41653
Ph:(606)886-0364
Fax:(606)886-0422
Co. E-mail: floydchamber@setel.com
URL: http://www.floydcountykentucky.com
Contact: Mandy Stumbo, Exec. Dir.

50481 ■ Frankfort Area Chamber of Commerce
100 Capital Ave.
Frankfort, KY 40601
Ph:(502)223-8261
Fax:(502)223-5942
Co. E-mail: chamber@frankfortky.info
URL: http://www.frankfortky.info
Contact: Carmen Inman, Exec. Dir.

50482 ■ Franklin-Simpson County Chamber of Commerce
201 S Main St.
PO Box 513
Franklin, KY 42135-0513
Ph:(270)586-7609
Fax:(270)586-5438
Co. E-mail: cfreese@f-schamber.com
URL: http://www.f-schamber.com
Contact: Cristi Freese

50483 ■ Garrard County Chamber of Commerce
656 Stanford Rd.
Lancaster, KY 40444
Ph:(859)792-2282
Fax:(859)792-2282
Co. E-mail: garrardchamber@gmail.com
URL: http://www.garrardcounty.ky.gov/Chamber-ofCommerce
Contact: Susan Ledford, Sec.-Treas.

50484 ■ Georgetown-Scott County Chamber of Commerce
160 E Main St.
Georgetown, KY 40324
Ph:(502)863-5424
Fax:(502)863-5756
Co. E-mail: info@gtown.org
URL: http://www.gtown.org
Contact: Jack Conner, Exec. Dir.

50485 ■ Glasgow-Barren County Chamber of Commerce
118 E Public Sq.
Glasgow, KY 42141
Ph:(270)651-3161
Fax:(270)651-3122
Co. E-mail: chamber@glasgow-ky.com
URL: http://www.glasgowbarrenchamber.com
Contact: Ernie Myers, Exec. VP

50486 ■ Grand Rivers Tourism Commission
PO Box 181
Grand Rivers, KY 42045
Ph:(270)362-0152
Free: 888-493-0152
Co. E-mail: info@grandrivers.com
URL: http://www.grandrivers.com
Contact: Ms. Kim Kraemer, Exec. Dir.

50487 ■ Grant County Chamber of Commerce
PO Box 365
Williamstown, KY 41097-0365
Ph:(859)824-3322
Free: 800-824-2858
Fax:(859)824-7082
Co. E-mail: wgutman@grantcommerce.com
URL: http://www.grantcommerce.com
Contact: Wade Gutman, Exec. Dir.

50488 ■ Grayson Area Chamber of Commerce
PO Box 612
Grayson, KY 41143
Ph:(606)474-4401
Co. E-mail: don.combs@graysonrecc.com
URL: http://www.graysonchamber.org
Contact: Don Combs, Pres.

50489 ■ Greater Breckinridge County Chamber of Commerce
PO Box 725
Hardinsburg, KY 40143-0725
Ph:(270)756-0268
Co. E-mail: chamber@breckinridgecountychamberky.com
URL: http://www.breckinridgecountychamberky.com
Contact: Sherry D. Stith, Exec. Dir.

50490 ■ Greater Corbin Chamber of Commerce
805 S Main St.
Corbin, KY 40701
Ph:(606)528-6390
Fax:(606)528-1583
Co. E-mail: chamberofcommerce@corbinkentucky.us
URL: http://www.corbinkentucky.us
Contact: Joe House, Pres.

50491 ■ Greater Louisville Inc. - The Metro Chamber of Commerce
614 W Main St., Ste. 6000
Louisville, KY 40202
Ph:(502)625-0000
Fax:(502)625-0010
Co. E-mail: sfarnsworth@greaterlouisville.com
URL: http://www.greaterlouisville.com
Contact: Joseph F. Reagan, Pres./CEO

50492 ■ Hancock County Chamber of Commerce
PO Box 404
Hawesville, KY 42348
Ph:(270)927-8223
Fax:(270)927-8223
Co. E-mail: erice@hancockky.us
URL: http://www.hancockky.us/Commerce/chamber.htm
Contact: Edna Rice, Exec. Dir.

50493 ■ Hart County Chamber of Commerce
PO Box 688
Munfordville, KY 42765
Ph:(270)524-2892
Fax:(270)524-1127
Co. E-mail: hart_co@scrtc.com
URL: http://www.hartcountyky.org

50494 ■ Henderson - Henderson County Chamber of Commerce
201 N Main St.
Henderson, KY 42420
Ph:(270)826-9531
Fax:(270)827-4461
Co. E-mail: info@hendersonchamber.org
URL: http://www.hendersonky.com
Contact: Brad Schneider, Pres.

50495 ■ Henry County Chamber of Commerce
PO Box 355
New Castle, KY 40050
Ph:(502)845-0806
Fax:(502)845-5313
Co. E-mail: henrychamber@insightbb.com
URL: http://chamber.henrycountyky.com/index.html
Contact: Ms. Pat Wallace, Exec. Dir.

50496 ■ Hickman Chamber of Commerce
808 Moscow Ave.
PO Box 166
Hickman, KY 42050
Ph:(270)236-2902
Co. E-mail: hickmanchamber@mygalaxyexpress.com
URL: http://www.hickmankychamber.org
Contact: Velva Yarbro, Exec. Dir.

50497 ■ Hopkinsville-Christian County Chamber of Commerce
2800 Ft. Campbell Blvd.
Hopkinsville, KY 42240
Ph:(270)885-9096
Free: 800-842-9959

Fax:(270)886-2059
Co. E-mail: chamber@hopkinsvillechamber.com
URL: http://www.hopkinsville.info/QCMS
Contact: Betsy Shelton, Pres./CEO

50498 ■ Jeffersontown Chamber of Commerce
10434 Watterson Trail
Jeffersontown, KY 40299
Ph:(502)267-1674
Fax:(502)267-2070
Co. E-mail: beth@jtownchamber.com
URL: http://www.jtownchamber.com
Contact: Beth Cassity, Pres.

50499 ■ Jessamine County Chamber of Commerce
508 N Main St.
Nicholasville, KY 40356
Ph:(859)887-4351
Fax:(859)887-1211
Co. E-mail: jessaminechamber@windstream.com
URL: http://www.jessaminechamber.com
Contact: Christopher Horne, Pres.

50500 ■ Kentucky Chamber of Commerce
464 Chenault Rd.
Frankfort, KY 40601
Ph:(502)695-4700
Fax:(502)695-6824
Co. E-mail: info@kychamber.com
URL: http://www.kychamber.com/mx/hm.
    asp?id=home
Contact: Dave Adkisson, Pres./CEO

50501 ■ Knox County Chamber of Commerce
196 Daniel Boone Dr., Ste. 205
Barbourville, KY 40906
Ph:(606)546-4300
Co. E-mail: chamber@barbourville.com
URL: http://www.knoxcochamber.com
Contact: Janet Jones, Sec./Office Mgr.

50502 ■ LaRue County Chamber of Commerce
60 Lincoln Sq.
PO Box 176
Hodgenville, KY 42748-0176
Ph:(270)358-3411
Co. E-mail: info@laruecounty.org
URL: http://www.laruecounty.org
Contact: Robin Terry, Exec. Dir.

50503 ■ Lebanon-Marion County Chamber of Commerce
239 N Spalding Ave., Ste. 201
Lebanon, KY 40033-1518
Ph:(270)692-9594
Fax:(270)692-2661
Co. E-mail: chamber@hamdays.com
URL: http://www.hamdays.com
Contact: Kandice Engle-Gray, Pres.

50504 ■ Liberty-Casey County Chamber of Commerce
PO Box 278
Liberty, KY 42539
Ph:(606)787-6463
Fax:(606)787-7992
Co. E-mail: chamber@libertykentucky.org
URL: http://www.libertykentucky.org/chamber.html
Contact: Jonathan Wilkerson, Pres.

50505 ■ Lincoln County Chamber of Commerce
201 E Main St., No. 5
Stanford, KY 40484
Ph:(606)365-4118
Fax:(606)365-4118
Co. E-mail: director@lincolncountychamber.com
URL: http://www.lincolncountychamber.com
Contact: Andrea E. Miller, Exec. Dir.

50506 ■ Logan County Chamber of Commerce
116 S Main St.
Russellville, KY 42276
Ph:(270)726-2206

Fax:(270)726-2237
Co. E-mail: logancounty@logantele.com
URL: http://www.loganchamber.com/QCMS_
    Chamber
Contact: Lisa Browning, Exec. Dir.

50507 ■ London-Laurel County Chamber of Commerce
409 S Main St.
London, KY 40741
Ph:(606)864-4789
Fax:(606)864-7300
Co. E-mail: bengefarm@windstream.net
URL: http://www.londonlaurelchamber.com
Contact: Randy L. Smith, Exec. Dir.

50508 ■ Madisonville-Hopkins County Chamber of Commerce
15 E Center St.
Madisonville, KY 42431
Ph:(270)821-3435
Fax:(270)821-9190
Co. E-mail: c.commerce@charter.net
URL: http://www.hopkinschamber.com
Contact: Hannah Myers, Chair

50509 ■ Marshall County Chamber of Commerce
17 U.S. Hwy. 68 W
Benton, KY 42025
Ph:(270)527-7665
Co. E-mail: info@marshallcounty.net
URL: http://www.marshallcounty.net
Contact: William J. Butler, Pres./CEO

50510 ■ Mayfield-Graves County Chamber of Commerce
201 E College St.
Mayfield, KY 42066
Ph:(270)247-6101
Fax:(270)247-6110
Co. E-mail: chamber@mayfieldchamber.com
URL: http://www.mayfieldchamber.com
Contact: Wendy Hunter, Exec. Dir.

50511 ■ Maysville-Mason County Area Chamber of Commerce
201 E 3rd St.
Maysville, KY 41056
Ph:(606)564-5534
Free: 888-875-6297
Fax:(606)564-5535
Co. E-mail: chamber@maysvilleky.net
URL: http://www.maysvillekentucky.com/articles/
    home.asp
Contact: Vicki Steigleder, Exec. Dir.

50512 ■ McCreary County Chamber of Commerce
PO Box 548
Whitley City, KY 42653
Ph:(606)376-5004
Co. E-mail: chamber7@highland.net
URL: http://mccrearychamber.com
Contact: Patricia Greene, Pres.

50513 ■ McLean County Chamber of Commerce
PO Box 303
170 E 2nd St.
Calhoun, KY 42327
Ph:(270)273-9760
Fax:(270)273-9760
Co. E-mail: chamfond@owensboro.net
Contact: Ms. Kathy Gish, Pres.

50514 ■ Mercer County Chamber of Commerce
488 Price Ave.
Harrodsburg, KY 40330
Ph:(859)734-2365
Co. E-mail: info@mercerchamber.com
URL: http://www.mercerchamber.com
Contact: Brenda Sexton, Exec. Dir.

50515 ■ Middletown Chamber of Commerce
12906 Shelbyville Rd.
Louisville, KY 40243
Ph:(502)244-8086

Fax:(502)244-0185
Co. E-mail: judy@middletownchamber.com
URL: http://www.middletownchamber.com
Contact: Judy Francis, Pres./CEO

50516 ■ Monticello/Wayne County Chamber of Commerce
PO Box 566
157 S Main St.
Monticello, KY 42633
Ph:(606)348-3064
Free: (866)348-3064
Co. E-mail: info@monticellokychamber.com
URL: http://www.monticellokychamber.com
Contact: Don Bethel, Pres.

50517 ■ Morehead-Rowan County Chamber of Commerce
150 E 1st St.
Morehead, KY 40351
Ph:(606)784-6221
Fax:(606)783-1373
Co. E-mail: tcwilliam@moreheadchamber.com
URL: http://www.moreheadchamber.com/cwt/
    external/wcpages/index.aspx
Contact: Tracy C. Williams, Exec. Dir.

50518 ■ Morgantown-Butler County Chamber of Commerce
PO Box 408
Morgantown, KY 42261
Ph:(270)526-6827
Co. E-mail: bcchamber07@bellsouth.net
Contact: James Runion, Pres.

50519 ■ Mount Sterling-Montgomery County Chamber of Commerce
126 W Main St.
Mount Sterling, KY 40353
Ph:(859)498-5343
Fax:(859)498-3947
Co. E-mail: contact@mtsterlingchamber.com
URL: http://www.mtsterlingchamber.com
Contact: Ellen P. Morgan, Pres.

50520 ■ Murray-Calloway County Chamber of Commerce
805 N 12th St.
PO Box 190
Murray, KY 42071-0190
Ph:(270)753-5171
Free: 800-900-5171
Fax:(270)753-0948
Co. E-mail: chamber@mymurray.com
URL: http://www.mymurray.com
Contact: Don Fraher, Pres.

50521 ■ Northern Kentucky Chamber of Commerce
PO Box 17416
300 Buttermilk Pike, Ste. 330
Fort Mitchell, KY 41017-0416
Ph:(859)578-8800
Fax:(859)578-8802
Co. E-mail: info@nkychamber.com
URL: http://www.nkychamber.com
Contact: Steve Stevens CCE, Pres.

50522 ■ Oldham County Chamber of Commerce
412 E Main St.
La Grange, KY 40031-0366
Ph:(502)222-1635
Fax:(502)222-3159
Co. E-mail: dekarem@oldhamcountychamber.com
URL: http://www.oldhamcountychamber.com
Contact: Deana Epperly Karem, Exec. Dir.

50523 ■ Owensboro-Daviess County Chamber of Commerce
200 E 3rd St.
PO Box 825
Owensboro, KY 42302-0825
Ph:(270)926-1860
Fax:(270)926-3364
Co. E-mail: chamber@owensboro.com
URL: http://www.owensboro.com
Contact: Jody Wassmer, Pres.

50524 ■ Owingsville-Bath County Chamber of Commerce
PO Box 360
Owingsville, KY 40360
Ph:(606)674-2531
Co. E-mail: info@owingsville.com
URL: http://www.owingsville.com
Contact: Mike Ray, Pres.

50525 ■ Paducah Area Chamber of Commerce
PO Box 810
Paducah, KY 42002-0810
Ph:(270)443-1746
Fax:(270)442-9152
Co. E-mail: info@paducahchamber.org
URL: http://www.paducahchamber.org
Contact: Elaine Spalding, Pres.

50526 ■ Paris-Bourbon County Chamber of Commerce
720 High St.
Paris, KY 40361
Ph:(859)987-3205
Co. E-mail: lcooper@parisky.com
URL: http://www.parisky.com
Contact: Lucy Cooper, Exec. Dir.

50527 ■ Pike County Chamber of Commerce
787 Hambley Blvd.
Pikeville, KY 41501
Ph:(606)432-5504
Fax:(606)432-7295
Co. E-mail: info@pikecountychamber.org
URL: http://www.pikecountychamber.org
Contact: Brad N. Hall, Pres.

50528 ■ Prospect Chamber of Commerce
9219-D US Hwy. 42, No. 283
Prospect, KY 40059
Ph:(502)228-7493
Co. E-mail: prospectchmbrcom@sbcglobal.net
URL: http://www.prospectareachamber.org
Contact: Kim Buckler, Pres.

50529 ■ Radcliff-Hardin County Chamber of Commerce
306 N Wilson Rd.
Radcliff, KY 40160
Ph:(270)351-4450
Fax:(270)352-4449
Co. E-mail: jo@radcliffchamber.org
URL: http://www.radcliffchamber.org
Contact: Jo Emary, Exec. Dir.

50530 ■ Richmond Chamber of Commerce
201 E Main St.
Richmond, KY 40475
Ph:(859)623-1720
Fax:(859)623-0839
Co. E-mail: rchamber@richmondchamber.com
URL: http://www.richmondchamber.com
Contact: Stuart K. Olds, Pres.

50531 ■ Russell County Chamber of Commerce
PO Box 64
Russell Springs, KY 42642-0064
Ph:(270)866-4333
Fax:(270)866-4304
Co. E-mail: info@russellcountyky.com
URL: http://www.russellcountyky.com
Contact: Cory Stearns, Pres.

50532 ■ Scottsville-Allen County Chamber of Commerce
102 Public Sq.
PO Box 416
Scottsville, KY 42164-0416
Ph:(270)237-4782
Fax:(270)237-5498
Co. E-mail: chamber@scottsvilleky.info
URL: http://painfreewebdev.com/mbr/PortalsWeb-
  sites/tabid/213/Default.aspx/drt/sac
Contact: Sue Shaver, Exec. Dir.

50533 ■ Somerset-Pulaski County Chamber of Commerce
445 S Hwy. 27, Ste. 101
Somerset, KY 42501
Ph:(606)679-7323
Fax:(606)679-1744
Co. E-mail: info@spcchamber.com
URL: http://www.spcchamber.com
Contact: Jack Keeney, Dir.

50534 ■ Sturgis Chamber of Commerce
513 N Main St.
Sturgis, KY 42459
Ph:(270)333-9316
Fax:(270)333-9319
Co. E-mail: sturgisrally@bellsouth.net
URL: http://www.littlesturgisrally.net
Contact: Paul Hart, Pres.

50535 ■ Tompkinsville - Monroe County Chamber of Commerce
PO Box 433
Tompkinsville, KY 42167
Ph:(270)487-1314
Fax:(270)487-0975
Co. E-mail: monroemoney@centernetwork.net
URL: http://www.monroeky.com
Contact: Susan Turner, Pres.

50536 ■ Winchester-Clark County Chamber of Commerce
2 S Maple St.
Winchester, KY 40391
Ph:(859)744-6420
Fax:(859)744-9229
Co. E-mail: chamber@winchesterky.com
URL: http://www.winchesterky.com
Contact: Karen Haley, Pres.

50537 ■ Woodford County Chamber of Commerce
141 N Main St.
Versailles, KY 40383
Ph:(859)873-5122
Fax:(859)873-4576
Co. E-mail: info@woodfordcountyinfo.com
URL: http://woodfordcountyinfo.com
Contact: Tami Vater, Exec. Dir.

MINORITY BUSINESS ASSISTANCE PROGRAMS

50538 ■ Kentucky Cabinet for Economic Development–Community Development Department–Small and Minority Business Division (Old C)
Old Capital Annex
300 W Broadway
Frankfort, KY 40601
Ph:(502)564-7140
Free: 800-626-2930
Fax:(502)564-3256
Co. E-mail: MarkL.Johnson@ky.gov
URL: http://www.thinkkentucky.com
Contact: Mark L. Johnson, Branch Mgr.
Description: Coordinates minority enterprise activities throughout the state's administrative structure. Acts as an advocate. Mobilizes resources and information. Develops marketing resources and provides individual guidance. Also administers a public-sector purchasing assistance program.

50539 ■ Tri-State Minority Supplier Development Council
614 W Main St., Ste. 5500
Louisville, KY 40202
Ph:(502)625-0159
Fax:(502)625-0082
Co. E-mail: info@tsmsdc.com
URL: http://www.tsmsdc.com
Contact: Ty Gettis, Pres & CEO
Description: Provides a variety of business development and referral services to minority business owners in Kentucky, West Virginia, and parts of Indiana.

FINANCING AND LOAN PROGRAMS

50540 ■ Chrysalis Ventures
101 S. Fifth St., Ste., 1650
Louisville, KY 40202-3122
Ph:(502)583-7644
Fax:(502)583-7648
Co. E-mail: info@chrysalisventures.com
URL: http://www.chrysalisventures.com
Contact: David A. Jones Jr., Chairman and Managing Director
Preferred Investment Size: $2,000,000 to $15,000,000. **Investment Types:** First and second stage, early and later stage, and expansion. **Industry Preferences:** Internet specific, medical and health, computer software and services, other products, communications and media, consumer related, and biotechnology. **Geographic Preferences:** South regions and Midwest. **Principal Exhibits:**

50541 ■ Iceberg Ventures
124 N. 1st St.
Louisville, KY 40202
Ph:(502)583-6810
Fax:(502)583-5606
Co. E-mail: info@icebergventures.com
URL: http://www.icebergventures.com
Contact: Keith Williams, Co-founder and Chief Operating Officer
Investment Policies: Early stage. **Geographic Preferences:** U.S. **Principal Exhibits:**

50542 ■ K–Kentucky Highlands Investment Corporation
362 Old Whitley Rd.
PO Box 1738
London, KY 40741
Ph:(606)864-5175
Fax:(606)864-5194
Co. E-mail: khicnet@khic.org
URL: http://www.khic.org
Contact: Brenda McDaniel, Executive Vice President and Chief Finan
Preferred Investment Size: $500 to $10,000,000. **Investment Policies:** Start-up, second stage, and special situation. **Industry Preferences:** Manufacturing. **Geographic Preferences:** Kentucky. **Principal Exhibits:**

PROCUREMENT ASSISTANCE PROGRAMS

50543 ■ Kentucky Procurement Assistance Program
Old Capitol Annex
300 W. Broadway
Frankfort, KY 40601
Ph:(502)564-2064
Free: 800-626-2930
Fax:(502)564-3256
Co. E-mail: ced.kpap@ky.gov
URL: http://www.thinkkentucky.com
Contact: Debbie McKnight, Branch Mgr
Description: Helps Kentucky businesses tap the federal procurement market.

50544 ■ Kentucky & Tennessee Procurement Center
PO Box 59, Rm. 173M
Louisville, KY 40202
Ph:(502)582-6662
Fax:(502)582-5547
Co. E-mail: kathleen.hyatt@sba.gov
URL: http://www.sba.gov
Contact: Kathleen Hyatt, PCR
E-mail: kathleen.hyatt@sba.gov
Description: Covers activities for Army Corps of Engineers (Louisville, KY), Fort Knox (Fort Knox, KY), Fort Campbell (Fort Campbell, KY), and Army Corps of Engineers (Nashville, TN).

INCUBATORS/RESEARCH AND TECHNOLOGY PARKS

50545 ■ Center for Economic Development, Entrepreneurship and Technology
Eastern Kentucky University
BTC 147
521 Lancaster Ave.
Richmond, KY 40475
Ph:(859)622-2334
Fax:(859)622-6274
Co. E-mail: Ian.Mooers@eku.edu
URL: http://www.cedet.eku.edu/
Description: A small business incubator providing assistance to businesses, organizations, industries, and communities to aid in their development.

50546 ■ Morgan County Regional Technology Center
151 University Dr.
West Liberty, KY 41472
Free: 877-743-4005
URL: http://www.mcrtc.com/
Description: A small business incubator designed to create a dynamic environment where businesses can focus on product and technology development, sales, and marketing. The Technology Center provides facilities and equipment when available, management assistance, administrative assistance and back office support to its tenants.

50547 ■ Northern Kentucky University Foundation Inc.
Lucas Administrative Ctr., Ste. 221
Highland Heights, KY 41099
Ph:(859)572-5126
Fax:(859)572-6005
Co. E-mail: zerhusenkk1@nku.edu
URL: http://foundation.nku.edu
Contact: Karen Zerhusen Kruer, Exec.Dir.
E-mail: zerhusenkk1@nku.edu
Scope: Solicits, records, and administers gifts in support of research and educational activities at the University.

50548 ■ University of Kentucky Office of Commercialization and Development–Advanced Science and Technology Commercialization Center
152 ASTeCC Bldg.
Lexington, KY 40503-0286
Ph:(859)218-6563
Fax:(859)257-2489
Co. E-mail: astecc@uky.edu
URL: http://www.econdev.uky.edu/about-astecc.aspx
Description: A faculty research facility and commercialization center established for multidisciplinary research, technology transfer, and new business startups.

50549 ■ University of Louisville–Sponsored Programs Development
Belknap Campus
Louisville, KY 40292
Ph:(502)852-6512
Fax:(502)852-8361
Co. E-mail: sponprog@louisville.edu
Contact: Kim Lalley, Dir.
E-mail: sponprog@louisville.edu
Scope: Coordinates research grants and contracting for the University in the following schools both on the main campus and at the Health Sciences Center: Medicine; Dentistry; Nursing; Health and Social Services; Arts and Sciences; Engineering; Business and Public Administration; Law; Music; Education; and Graduate Schools. **Publications:** Impact.

EDUCATIONAL PROGRAMS

50550 ■ Bowling Green Community College of Western Kentucky University
2355 Nashville Rd., Ste. B
Bowling Green, KY 42101
Ph:(270)780-2550
Fax:(270)745-2011
URL: http://www.wku.edu/Dept/Academic/BGCC
Description: Two-year college offering a small business management program.

50551 ■ Morehead State University
Small Business Development Center
College of Business
150 E First St.
Morehead, KY 40351
Ph:(606)783-2895
Fax:(606)783-5020
URL: http://www.morehead-st.edu
E-mail: k.moore@morehead-st.edu
Description: Provides training programs that benefit the small business community.

50552 ■ National College of Business and Technology
7627 Ewing Blvd.
Florence, KY 41042
Ph:(859)525-6510
Fax:(859)525-8961
URL: http://www.ncbt.edu
Description: Business college offering a small business management program.

LEGISLATIVE ASSISTANCE

50553 ■ Office of the Governor–Legislative Liaison Office
700 Capitol Ave., Ste. 100
Frankfort, KY 40601
Ph:(502)564-2611

Fax:(502)564-2517
URL: http://www.governor.ky.gov/
Description: Assists the governor in formulating small business policies.

PUBLICATIONS

50554 ■ *Business Bulletin*
464 Chenault Rd.
PO Box 817
Frankfort, KY 40602
Ph:(502)695-4700
Fax:(502)695-6824
Co. E-mail: kccmis.net
URL: http://www.kychamber.com

50555 ■ *Business First*
111 W. Washington St.
P.O. Box 249
Louisville, KY 40202
Ph:(502)583-1731
Fax:(502)587-1703
URL: http://www.ancity.com-louiseville

50556 ■ *Smart Start your Kentucky Business*
PSI Research
300 N. Valley Dr.
Grants Pass, OR 97526
Ph:(503)479-9464
Free: 800-228-2275
Fax:(503)476-1479
Co. E-mail: info@psi-research.com
URL: http://www.psi-research.com
Ed: Michael D. Jenkins. **Released:** Revised edition, 1992. **Price:** $29.95 (looseleaf binder); $24.95 (paper). **Description:** Part of the Successful Business Library series.

PUBLISHERS

50557 ■ Hatfield House Books
7710 Commonwealth Dr.
Crestwood, KY 40014
Ph:(502)241-5950
Contact: Kenneth F. Hatfield, President
E-mail: kenhat@yahoo.com
Description: Publishes books for small business owners. Reviews books on business related topics and acts as a literary agent. Reaches market through commission representatives and direct mail. Does not accept unsolicited manuscripts. **Founded:** 1984.

50558 ■ Kentucky Cabinet for Economic Development–Small & Minority Business Div.
Old Capitol Annex
300 W Broadway
Frankfort, KY 40601
Ph:(502)564-7140
Free: 800-626-2930
Fax:(502)564-3256
Co. E-mail: econdev@ky.gov
URL: http://www.thinkkentucky.com/smbd
Contact: Steven Vest, Director
E-mail: steven.vest@ky.gov
Description: Publishes on Kentucky-based small, minority and women-owned businesses. **Founded:** 1972.

SMALL BUSINESS DEVELOPMENT CENTERS

50559 ■ Louisiana Small Business Development Center
University of Louisiana at Monroe
700 University Ave., Administration 2-123
Monroe, LA 71209-6530
Co. E-mail: lsbdc.ulm@lsbdc.org
URL: http://www.lsbdc.org

50560 ■ Louisiana Small Business Development Center - Greater New Orleans Region
UNO Jefferson Center
3330 N Causeway Blvd., Ste. 422
Metairie, LA 70002
Co. E-mail: lsbdc.gnor@lsbdc.org
URL: http://www.lsbdc.org

50561 ■ Louisiana Small Business Development Center at Louisiana State University in Shreveport
LSUS Technology Ctr., Rm. 209
One University Pl.
Shreveport, LA 71115
Co. E-mail: lsbdc.lsus@lsbdc.org
URL: http://www.lsbdc.org

50562 ■ Louisiana Small Business Development Center - LSU South Campus
LBTC Bldg. 3000
8000 GSRI Ave.
Baton Rouge, LA 70820
Fax:(225)578-3975
Co. E-mail: lbtc@lsu.edu
URL: http://www.bus.lsu.edu/sbdc

50563 ■ Louisiana Small Business Development Center at McNeese State University
Burton Business Center
4450 Ryan St.
Lake Charles, LA 70605
Co. E-mail: lsbdc.msu@lsbdc.org
URL: http://www.lsbdc.org

50564 ■ Louisiana Small Business Development Center - New Orleans and the Bayou Region
Nicholls State University
310 Ardoyne Ave.
Thibodaux, LA 70301
Co. E-mail: lsbdc.slec@lsbdc.org
URL: http://www.lsbdc.org

50565 ■ Louisiana Small Business Development Center at Northwestern State University
Dunbar Plz., Ste. 114C
3600 Jackson St.
Alexandria, LA 71303-3064
Co. E-mail: lsbdc.nsu@lsbdc.org
URL: http://www.lsbdc.org

50566 ■ Louisiana Small Business Development Center at Southeastern Louisiana University
Southeast Louisiana Business Center
1514 Martens Dr.
Hammond, LA 70402-0001
Co. E-mail: lsbdc.slu@lsbdc.org
URL: http://www.lsbdc.org

50567 ■ Louisiana Small Business Development Center at Southern University
4826 Jamestown Ave., Ste. 1
Baton Rouge, LA 70808-3224
Co. E-mail: lsbdc.subr@lsbdc.org
URL: http://www.lsbdc.org

50568 ■ Louisiana Small Business Development Center at University of Louisiana at Lafayette
220 E St. Mary Blvd.
Lafayette, LA 70503-2036
Co. E-mail: lsbdc.ull@lsbdc.org
URL: http://www.lsbdc.org

50569 ■ Louisiana Small Business Development Center at University of Louisiana Monroe
Administration Bldg.
700 University Ave., Bldg. 2-123
Monroe, LA 71209
Co. E-mail: lsbdc.ulm@lsbdc.org
URL: http://www.lsbdc.org

SCORE OFFICES

50570 ■ Northshore SCORE
Path: www.scorens.org

50571 ■ SCORE Baton Rouge
c/o William H. Brown, Chm.
Louisiana Technology Park
7117 Florida Blvd.
Baton Rouge, LA 70806
Ph:(225)381-7130
Fax:(225)215-0080
Co. E-mail: scorebr@scorebr.org
URL: http://www.scorebr.org
Contact: William H. Brown, Chm.

Description: Assists new businesses or businesses facing challenges in the greater Baton Rouge area or in the Northshore area. Provides free and confidential business counseling tailored to meet the needs of small business and their personal objectives.

50572 ■ SCORE Lafayette
Travis Technology Center
110 Travis, Rm. 89
Lafayette, LA 70503
Ph:(337)889-0214
Fax:(337)889-0212
Co. E-mail: cajun_score@yahoo.com
URL: http://www.lafayettescore.org
Description: Provides public service to America by offering small business advice and training.

50573 ■ SCORE New Orleans
Path: www.neworleans.scorechapter.org

50574 ■ SCORE Northeast Louisiana
1810 Auburn Ave., Ste. 102
Monroe, LA 71201
Ph:(318)323-0878
Fax:(318)323-9492
Co. E-mail: score644@comcast.net
URL: http://www.monroe.scorechapter.org
Contact: Miles K. Luke, Chm.

Description: Serves as volunteer program in which working and retired business management professionals provide free business counseling to men and women who are considering starting a small business, encountering problems with their business, or expanding their business. Offers free one-on-one counseling, online counseling and low cost workshops on a variety of business topics.

50575 ■ SCORE Shreveport
400 Edwards St.
Shreveport, LA 71101
Ph:(318)677-2536
Fax:(318)677-2548
Co. E-mail: shelia@nledf.org
URL: http://www.shreveport.scorechapter.org
Description: Provides professional guidance and information to America's small businesses.

50576 ■ Southwest Louisiana SCORE
Path:

BETTER BUSINESS BUREAUS

50577 ■ Better Business Bureau of Acadiana
4007 W Congress St., Ste. B
Lafayette, LA 70506
Ph:(337)981-3497
Fax:(337)981-7559
Co. E-mail: info@acadiana.bbb.org
URL: http://lafayette.bbb.org
Contact: Sharane A. Gott, Pres./CEO

50578 ■ Better Business Bureau of Central Louisiana
5220-C Rue Verdun, Ste. 135
Alexandria, LA 71303
Ph:(318)473-4494
Fax:(318)473-8906
URL: http://www.alexandria-la.bbb.org
Contact: Ellis Isom, Office Mgr.

50579 ■ Better Business Bureau of Northeast Louisiana
212 Walnut St., Ste. 210
Monroe, LA 71201
Ph:(318)387-4600
Free: 800-960-7756
Co. E-mail: info@bbbnela.org
URL: http://nela.bbb.org
Contact: Amy Lawson, Pres.

50580 ■ Better Business Bureau, Shreveport
401 Edwards St., Ste. 135
Shreveport, LA 71101
Ph:(318)222-7575
Fax:(318)222-7576
Co. E-mail: info@shreveport.bbb.org
URL: http://shreveport.bbb.org
Contact: Andrew Fisher, Pres./CEO

50581 ■ Better Business Bureau of South Central Louisiana
748 Main St.
Baton Rouge, LA 70802-5526
Ph:(225)346-5222
Fax:(225)346-1029
Co. E-mail: info@batonrouge.bbb.org
URL: http://batonrouge.bbb.org

50582 ■ Better Business Bureau of Southwest Louisiana
PO Box 7314
Lake Charles, LA 70606
Ph:(337)478-6253
Free: 800-542-7085
Fax:(337)474-8981
Co. E-mail: swlabbb@suddenlinkmail.com
URL: http://lakecharles.bbb.org
Contact: Mrs. Carmen Million, Pres.

CHAMBERS OF COMMERCE

50583 ■ Ascension Chamber of Commerce
1006 W Hwy. 30
PO Box 1204
Gonzales, LA 70707-1204
Ph:(225)647-7487
Fax:(225)647-5124
Co. E-mail: info@ascensionchamber.com
URL: http://www.ascensionchamber.com
Contact: Sherrie Despino, Pres.

50584 ■ Assumption Area Chamber of Commerce
PO Box 718
4751 Hwy. 1
Napoleonville, LA 70390
Ph:(985)369-2816
Fax:(985)369-2811
Co. E-mail: assumption@bellsouth.net
URL: http://www.assumptionchamber.org
Contact: Ella Metrejean, Exec. Dir.

50585 ■ Bogalusa Chamber of Commerce
608 Willis Ave.
Bogalusa, LA 70427-3002
Ph:(985)735-5731
Fax:(985)735-6707
Co. E-mail: bogalusachamber@bellsouth.net
URL: http://www.bogalusachamber.org
Contact: Marilyn G. Bateman

50586 ■ Bossier Chamber of Commerce
710 Benton Rd.
Bossier City, LA 71111-3797
Ph:(318)746-0252
Fax:(318)746-0357
Co. E-mail: info@bossierchamber.com
URL: http://www.bossierchamber.com
Contact: Gary Hubbard, Pres.

50587 ■ Breaux Bridge Area Chamber of Commerce
314 E Bridge St.
Breaux Bridge, LA 70517
Ph:(337)332-5406
Fax:(337)332-5424
Co. E-mail: bbcc@centurytel.net
URL: http://www.breauxbridgelive.com
Contact: Tina Begnaud, Exec. Dir.

50588 ■ Central Louisiana Chamber of Commerce
PO Box 992
Alexandria, LA 71309
Ph:(318)442-6671

Fax:(318)442-6734
Co. E-mail: eltonpody@cenlachamber.org
URL: http://www.cenlachamber.org
Contact: Elton Pody, Pres.

50589 ■ Chamber of Commerce of Lafourche and the Bayou Region
PO Box 1462
LaRose, LA 70373
Ph:(985)693-6700
Fax:(985)693-6702
URL: http://www.lafourchechamber.com
Contact: Lin Kiger, Pres./CEO

50590 ■ Chamber - Southwest Louisiana
120 W Pujo St.
PO Box 3110
Lake Charles, LA 70602-3110
Ph:(337)433-3632
Fax:(337)436-3727
Co. E-mail: gswift@allianceswla.org
URL: http://www.chamberswla.org
Contact: George Swift, Pres./CEO

50591 ■ Claiborne Chamber of Commerce
519 S Main St.
Homer, LA 71040
Ph:(318)927-3271
Fax:(318)927-3271
Co. E-mail: claibornecoc@claiborneone.org
URL: http://www.claiborneone.org/homer/coc/index.html
Contact: Mr. John Watson, Exec. Dir.

50592 ■ Coushatta-Red River Chamber of Commerce
PO Box 333
Coushatta, LA 71019
Ph:(318)932-3289
Fax:(318)932-6919
Co. E-mail: redriverchamber@bellsouth.net
URL: http://coushattaredriverchamberofcommerce.com/default.aspx
Contact: Martha Gates, Exec. Asst.

50593 ■ Donaldsonville Area Chamber of Commerce
714 Railroad Ave.
PO Box 646
Donaldsonville, LA 70346
Ph:(225)473-4814
Fax:(225)473-4817
Co. E-mail: dvillecoc@bellsouth.net
URL: http://www.donaldsonvillecoc.org
Contact: Becky Katz, Exec. Dir.

50594 ■ Eunice Chamber of Commerce
200 S CC Duson
PO Box 508
Eunice, LA 70535
Ph:(337)457-2565
Fax:(337)546-0278
Co. E-mail: eunicecc@charterinternet.com
URL: http://www.eunicechamber.com
Contact: Robin McGee

50595 ■ French - American Chamber of Commerce - Louisiana Chapter
2 Canal St., Ste. 2426
New Orleans, LA 70130
Ph:(504)561-0070
Fax:(504)592-9999
Co. E-mail: info@faccmi.org
URL: http://www.facc-la.com
Contact: Jennifer Weinhart, Exec. Dir.

50596 ■ Greater Abbeville-Vermilion Chamber of Commerce
1907 Veterans Memorial Dr.
Abbeville, LA 70510
Ph:(337)893-2491
Fax:(337)893-1807
Co. E-mail: abbevillechamber@abbevillechamber.com
URL: http://www.abbevillechamber.com
Contact: Lynn Guillory, Exec. Dir.

50597 ■ Greater Denham Springs Chamber of Commerce
PO Box 591
Denham Springs, LA 70727
Ph:(225)665-8155
Fax:(225)665-2411
Co. E-mail: info@livingstonparishchamber.org
Contact: Ms. Sherry Mely, Chair

50598 ■ Greater Jennings Chamber of Commerce
246 N Main St.
PO Box 1209
Jennings, LA 70546
Ph:(337)824-0933
Fax:(337)824-0934
Co. E-mail: info@jdbusinessalliance.com
Contact: Cynthia Hoffpauir, Pres./CEO

50599 ■ Greater Lafayette Chamber of Commerce
804 E Saint Mary Blvd.
PO Box 51307
Lafayette, LA 70503-1307
Ph:(337)233-2705
Fax:(337)234-8671
Co. E-mail: rob@lafchamber.org
URL: http://www.lafchamber.org
Contact: Robert M. Guidry, Pres./CEO

50600 ■ Greater Pointe Coupee Chamber of Commerce
PO Box 555
New Roads, LA 70760
Ph:(225)638-3500
Fax:(225)638-9858
Co. E-mail: pointecoupeechamber@yahoo.com
URL: http://www.pcchamber.org
Contact: Brian Adams, Pres.

50601 ■ Greater Shreveport Chamber of Commerce
400 Edwards St.
Shreveport, LA 71101
Ph:(318)677-2500
Free: 800-448-5432
Fax:(318)677-2541
Co. E-mail: info@shreveportchamber.org
URL: http://www.shreveportchamber.org
Contact: Mr. Richard H. Bremer, Pres.

50602 ■ Greater Slidell Area Chamber of Commerce
118 W Hall Ave.
Slidell, LA 70458
Ph:(985)643-5678
Free: 800-471-3758
Fax:(985)649-2460
Co. E-mail: info@slidellchamber.com
URL: http://www.slidellchamber.com
Contact: Dawn Sharpe, CEO

50603 ■ Greater Vernon Chamber of Commerce
PO Box 1228
Leesville, LA 71496-1228
Ph:(337)238-0349
Free: 877-234-0349
Fax:(337)238-0340
Co. E-mail: cofcvernonparish@bellsouth.net
URL: http://www.chambervernonparish.com
Contact: Eddie Wise, Exec. Dir.

50604 ■ Hammond Chamber of Commerce
400 NW Railroad Ave.
PO Box 1455
Hammond, LA 70401
Ph:(985)345-4457
Fax:(985)345-4749
URL: http://www.moveuptohammond.com
Contact: Charlotte Lenoir, Exec. Dir.

50605 ■ Houma-Terrebonne Chamber of Commerce
6133 Hwy. 311
Houma, LA 70364
Ph:(985)876-5600

Fax:(985)876-5611
Co. E-mail: info@houmachamber.com
URL: http://www.houmachamber.com
Contact: Drake Pothier, Pres./CEO

50606 ■ Iberville Chamber of Commerce
23675 Church St.
PO Box 248
Plaquemine, LA 70764
Ph:(225)687-3560
Fax:(225)687-3575
Co. E-mail: hgrace@ibervillechamber.com
URL: http://www.ibervillechamber.com
Contact: Hank Grace, Exec. Dir.

50607 ■ Jefferson Chamber of Commerce
3421 N Causeway Blvd., Ste. 203
Metairie, LA 70002
Ph:(504)835-3880
Fax:(504)835-3828
Co. E-mail: glenn@jeffersonchamber.org
URL: http://www.jeffersonchamber.org
Contact: Glenn W. Hayes, Pres./CEO

50608 ■ Kentwood Chamber of Commerce
PO Box 685
Kentwood, LA 70444
Ph:(985)229-4656
Fax:(985)230-0841
Co. E-mail: kcd@kentwoodla.org
URL: http://www.kentwoodla.org

50609 ■ Marksville Chamber of Commerce
PO Box 767
Marksville, LA 71351
Ph:(318)253-9222
Co. E-mail: carrollsanders@bellsouth.net
URL: http://www.marksvillechamberofcommerce.com
Contact: Eleanor Gremillion, Sec.-Treas.

50610 ■ Minden/South Webster Chamber of Commerce
110 Sibley Rd.
PO Box 819
Minden, LA 71058-0819
Ph:(318)377-4240
Free: 800-264-6336
Fax:(318)377-4215
Co. E-mail: ebey@mindenchamber.com
URL: http://www.mindenchamber.com
Contact: Jason E. Ebey, Pres.

50611 ■ Monroe Chamber of Commerce
212 Walnut St., Ste. 100
Monroe, LA 71201-6707
Ph:(318)323-3461
Free: 888-531-9535
Fax:(318)322-7594
Co. E-mail: sedmunds@monroe.org
URL: http://www.monroe.org
Contact: Sue Edmunds, Pres./CEO

50612 ■ Natchitoches Area Chamber of Commerce
562 2nd St.
PO Box 3
Natchitoches, LA 71457
Ph:(318)352-6894
Fax:(318)352-5385
Co. E-mail: chamber@natchitoches.net
URL: http://www.natchitocheschamber.com
Contact: Nick Pollacia Jr., Pres.

50613 ■ National Black Chamber of Commerce, Baton Rouge
263 3rd St., Ste. 704
Baton Rouge, LA 70801
Ph:(225)381-8480
Fax:(225)343-4247
Co. E-mail: info@brblackchamber.org
URL: http://www.nbrcc.org
Contact: Eric B. Lewis, Pres.

50614 ■ Opelousas-St. Landry Chamber of Commerce
109 W Vine St.
Opelousas, LA 70570
Ph:(337)942-2683

Fax:(337)942-2684
Co. E-mail: chamberdesk@charter.net
URL: http://www.opelousaschamber.org
Contact: Ms. Frankie Bertrand, Pres./CEO

50615 ■ Ponchatoula Chamber of Commerce
109 W Pine St.
PO Box 306
Ponchatoula, LA 70454
Ph:(985)386-2536
Co. E-mail: info@ponchatoulachamber.com
URL: http://www.ponchatoulachamber.com
Contact: Tessa Beckler, Pres.

50616 ■ Rayne Chamber of Commerce
PO Box 383
Rayne, LA 70578
Ph:(337)334-2332
Fax:(337)334-8341
Co. E-mail: raynechamber1@bellsouth.net
URL: http://www.rayne.org/chamber.html
Contact: Louis Nugent

50617 ■ Ruston - Lincoln Chamber of Commerce
PO Box 1383
Ruston, LA 71273-1383
Ph:(318)255-2031
Free: 800-392-9032
Fax:(318)255-3481
Co. E-mail: sterry@rustonlincoln.org
URL: http://www.rustonlincoln.org
Contact: Scott Terry, Pres.

50618 ■ Sabine Parish Chamber of Commerce
1601 Texas Hwy.
Many, LA 71449
Ph:(318)256-3523
Fax:(318)256-4137
URL: http://www.sabineparish.com
Contact: John Godfrey, Pres.

50619 ■ St. Martinville Chamber of Commerce
PO Box 436
St. Martinville, LA 70582
Ph:(337)394-7578
Fax:(337)394-4497
URL: http://www.stmartinvillechamber.com
Contact: Michelle V. Broussard

50620 ■ St. Tammany West Chamber of Commerce
610 Hollycrest Blvd.
Covington, LA 70433
Ph:(985)892-3216
Fax:(985)893-4244
Co. E-mail: info@sttammanychamber.org
URL: http://www.sttammanychamber.org
Contact: Lacey Toledano, Pres./CEO

50621 ■ Springhill - North Webster Chamber of Commerce
400 N Giles St.
Springhill, LA 71075
Ph:(318)539-4717
Fax:(318)539-2500
Co. E-mail: chamberc@cmaaccess.com
URL: http://www.springhilllouisiana.net
Contact: Robert Bryan, Pres.

50622 ■ Thibodaux Chamber of Commerce
318 E Bayou Rd.
Thibodaux, LA 70301
Ph:(985)446-1187
Fax:(985)446-1191
Co. E-mail: info@thibodauxchamber.com
URL: http://www.thibodauxchamber.com
Contact: Kathy Benoit, Pres./CEO

50623 ■ Union Parish Chamber of Commerce
303 E Water St.
Farmerville, LA 71241-3031
Ph:(318)368-3947
Fax:(318)368-3945
Co. E-mail: upcoc@bayou.com
URL: http://unionparishchamber.org
Contact: Stan Elkins, Pres.

50624 ■ Vidalia Chamber of Commerce
1401 Carter St.
Vidalia, LA 71373
Ph:(318)336-8223
Co. E-mail: chamber@vidaliala.com
URL: http://www.vidaliala.com

50625 ■ West Baton Rouge Chamber of Commerce
PO Box 448
Addis, LA 70710
Ph:(225)383-3140
Fax:(225)685-1044
Co. E-mail: info@wbrchamber.org
URL: http://www.wbrchamber.org
Contact: Deborah L. Biggs, Exec. Dir.

50626 ■ West Monroe-West Ouachita Chamber of Commerce
112 Professional Dr.
West Monroe, LA 71291
Ph:(318)325-1961
Fax:(318)325-4296
Co. E-mail: info@westmonroechamber.org
Contact: Mary Ann Newton, Pres.

50627 ■ Winn Chamber of Commerce
PO Box 565
Winnfield, LA 71483-0565
Ph:(318)628-4461
Fax:(318)628-2551
Co. E-mail: info@winnchamberofcommerce.com
URL: http://www.winnchamberofcommerce.com

50628 ■ Winnsboro - Franklin Parish Chamber of Commerce
3830 Front St.
PO Box 1574
Winnsboro, LA 71295
Ph:(318)435-4488
Co. E-mail: info@winnsborochamber.com
URL: http://www.winnsborochamber.com
Contact: Kevin Cobb, Pres.

50629 ■ Zachary Chamber of Commerce
4633 Main St.
Zachary, LA 70791
Ph:(225)654-6777
Fax:(225)654-3957
Co. E-mail: bfuselier@aol.com
URL: http://www.zacharyla.com
Contact: Brent Fuselier, Pres.

MINORITY BUSINESS ASSISTANCE PROGRAMS

50630 ■ Louisiana Minority Business Opportunity Center
400 Poydras St., Ste. 1350
New Orleans, LA 70130
Ph:(504)229-2960
Fax:(514)299-2961
Co. E-mail: Rfrederick@lamsdc.org
URL: http://www.mbclouisiana.biz
Contact: Rivers Frederick, Dir
Description: Provides free developmental services to strategic-growth minority business enterprises in Louisiana.

50631 ■ Louisina MBEC
2714 Canal St., Ste. 300
New Orleans, LA 70119
Ph:(504)821-4811
Fax:(504)324-0217
Co. E-mail: norman@capitalaccessproject.org
Description:

50632 ■ Louisina Minority Supplier Development Council
400 Poydras St., Ste. 1960
New Orleans, LA 70130
Ph:(504)293-0400

Fax:(504)293-0401
Co. E-mail: info@lamsdc.org
URL: http://msdc.adaptone.com/lamsdc/
Contact: Phala Kimbrough Mire, Pres
Description: Assists corporations in developing and expanding minority vendor programs.

50633 ■ **Urban League of Greater New Orleans–Women's Business Resource Center**
3308 Tulane Ave., Ste. 301
New Orleans, LA 70119
Ph:(504)620-9647
Fax:(504)620-9564
Contact: Angela S. VonDerPool, Dir
Description: Provides women business owners with formalized business planning for business expansion.

PROCUREMENT ASSISTANCE PROGRAMS

50634 ■ **Louisiana Procurement Technical Assistance Center–University of Louisiana–LAPTAC State Administrative Office (241 E)**
241 E Lewis St., Rm. 110
PO Box 44172
Lafayette, LA 70504-4172
Ph:(337)482-6422
Free: 800-206-3545
Fax:(337)482-5837
Co. E-mail: la-ptac@louisiana.edu
URL: http://www.la-ptac.org
Contact: Sherrie Mullins, Program Mgr.
E-mail: sherlm@louisiana.edu
Description: Generates employment and improve the general economy of Louisiana by assisting business firms in obtaining and performing under the U.S. Department of Defense, other federal agencies, state and local government contracts.

50635 ■ **Louisiana Procurement Technical Assistance Center at Kisatchie-Delta**
3516 Parliament Ct.
Alexandria, LA 71303
Ph:(318)487-5454
Fax:(318)487-5451
Co. E-mail: kdptac@kricket.net
URL: http://www.la-ptac.org
Contact: Shelia Wallace, Counselor
E-mail: kdptac@kricket.net
Description: Businesses and individuals interested in learning about government contracting and subcontracting, and/or are actively seeking or currently performing under government contracts and subcontracts with the Department of Defense, federal state and local governments, contact the procurement specialists below covering Allen, Avoyelles, Beauregard, Catahoula, Concordia, Grant, LaSalle, Rapides, Vermon, and Winn Parishes.

50636 ■ **Louisiana Procurement Technical Assistance Center at LEDA**
211 E Devalcourt St.
Lafayette, LA 70506
Ph:(337)593-1400
Fax:(337)234-3009
Co. E-mail: information@lafayette.org
URL: http://www.lafayette.org
Contact: Billy Lawson, Counselor
E-mail: billy1@lafayette.org
Description: Businesses and individuals interested in learning about government contracting and subcontracting, and/or are actively seeking or currently performing under government contracts and subcontracts with the Department of Defense, federal state and local governments, contact the procurement specialists below covering Acadia, Evangeline, Iberia, Lafayette, St. Landry, St. Martin, St. Mary and Vermilion Parishes.

50637 ■ **Louisiana Procurement Technical Assistance Center at New Orleans**
PO Box 44172
Lafayette, LA 70504-4172
Ph:800-206-3545

Free: 800-206-3545
Co. E-mail: noptac@bellsouth.net
URL: http://www.la-ptac.org
Contact: Robert Dempsey, Counselor
E-mail: noptac@bellsouth.net
Description: Businesses and individuals interested in learning about government contracting and subcontracting, and/or are actively seeking or currently performing under government contracts and subcontracts with the Department of Defense, federal state and local governments, contact the procurement specialists below covering Jefferson, Orleans, Plaquemines and St. Bernard Parishes.

50638 ■ **Louisiana Procurement Technical Assistance Center at SLEC**
PO Box 44172
Lafayette, LA 70504
Ph:800-206-3545
Free: 800-206-3545
Co. E-mail: noptac@bellsouth.net
URL: http://www.la-ptac.org
Contact: Robert Dempsey, Counselor
E-mail: jan.labat@nicholls.edu
Description: Businesses and individuals interested in learning about government contracting and subcontracting, and/or are actively seeking or currently performing under government contracts and subcontracts with the Department of Defense, federal state and local governments, contact the procurement specialists below covering Assumption, LaFourche, St. Charles, St. James, St. John the Baptist and Terrebonne Parishes.

50639 ■ **Northwest Louisiana Government Procurement Center–Greater Shreveport Chamber of Commerce**
400 Edward St.
Shreveport, LA 71101
Ph:(318)677-2530
Fax:(318)677-2534
Co. E-mail: gpc@shreveportchamber.org
URL: http://shreveportla.usachamber.com
Contact: Kelly Ford, Dir.
E-mail: kellyford@shreveportchamber.org
Description: Increases the number of federal, state, and local government contract award dollars being awarded to businesses thus creating and retaining jobs.

50640 ■ **Southeast Louisiana Procurement Technical Assistance Center**
PO Box 1771
Denham Springs, LA 70727-1771
Ph:(225)664-2600
Fax:(225)664-0050
Co. E-mail: ccarrier@cox.net
URL: http://www.la-ptac.org
Contact: Cindy Carrier, Counselor
E-mail: ccarrier@cox.net
Description: Businesses and individuals interested in learning about government contracting and subcontracting, and/or are actively seeking or currently performing under government contracts and subcontracts with the Department of Defense, federal state and local governments, contact the procurement specialists below covering Ascension, East Baton Rouge, East Feliciana, Iberville, Livingston, Point Coupee, St. Helena, St. Tammany, Tangipahoa, Washington, West Baton Rouge and West Feliciana Parishes.

50641 ■ **Southwest Louisiana Procurement Technical Assistance Center**
120 West Pujo St.
Lake Charles, LA 70601
Ph:(337)433-3632
Fax:(337)436-3727
Co. E-mail: la-ptac@louisiana.edu
URL: http://www.la-ptac.org
Contact: Roy Paul, Counselor
E-mail: kmm1928@louisiana.edu
Description: Businesses and individuals interested in learning about government contracting and subcontracting, and/or are actively seeking or currently performing under government contracts and subcontracts with the Department of Defense, federal state

and local governments, contact the procurement specialists below covering Allen, Beauregard, Calcasieu, Cameron, and Jefferson Davis Parishes.

INCUBATORS/RESEARCH AND TECHNOLOGY PARKS

50642 ■ **Arts Business Program**
Arts Council of New Orleans
818 Howard Ave., Ste. 300
New Orleans, LA 70113
Ph:(504)523-1465
Fax:(504)529-2430
Co. E-mail: gmeneray@artscouncilofneworleans.org
URL: http://www.artscouncilofneworleans.org/
Contact: Dolita Brown, Coord.
Description: A small business incubator created as an arts management resource center and a professional business environment, serving the creative and administrative growth of individuals and organizations in the arts community; it is a place where individuals and organizations can learn and where they can come together for an exchange of ideas and creative energy.

50643 ■ **Central Louisiana Business Incubator**
1501-A Wimbledon Dr.
Alexandria, LA 71301
Ph:(318)561-2299
Fax:(318)561-2249
Co. E-mail: info@clbi.org
URL: http://www.clbi.org/
Description: A not-for-profit corporation created as an economic tool designed to accelerate the growth and success of entrepreneurial companies through an array of business support resources and services.

50644 ■ **Dixie Business Center**
1810 S. Range Ave.
Denham Springs, LA 70726
Ph:(225)665-0809
Fax:(225)665-8171
Co. E-mail: info@dixiebusinesscenter.org
URL: http://www.dixiebusinesscenter.org/
Contact: John Ware, Exec. Dir.
Description: A nonprofit business incubator program dedicated to helping new and emerging businesses develop, grow, and succeed.

50645 ■ **Enterprise Center of Louisiana**
3419 NW Evangeline Thruway
Carencro, LA 70520
Ph:(337)896-9115
Fax:(337)896-8736
Co. E-mail: rholleman@ecol.org
URL: http://www.ecol.org/
Description: A small business incubator providing an environment in which a new or small emerging business can learn effective business practices while actually engaging in business operations with the end result of creating jobs and diversifying the economy in Acadiana.

50646 ■ **InterTech Science Park**
2031 Kings Hwy.
Shreveport, LA 71103
Ph:(318)213-0200
Fax:(318)213-0205
Co. E-mail: info@intertechsciencepark.org
URL: http://www.intertechsciencepark.com/
Contact: Sue Doughty, Coord.
Description: An 800-acre urban science and technology park created to develop the region's human, financial and physical infrastructure required for technology companies to flourish. It provides its tenants with access to academic facilities, researchers, core equipment laboratories, animal care, multitenant wet lab and office space, land for building, venture capital, business planning assistance. and financial incentives.

50647 ■ **Jefferson Parish Economic Development Commission–Business Innovation Center and Technology Incubator**
700 Churchill Blvd.
Avondale, LA 70092
Ph:(504)833-1881

Fax:(504)833-7676
Co. E-mail: srojas@jedco.org
URL: http://www.jedco.org/business-incubator/
Description: A small business incubator offering affordable services designed to help new businesses grow and thrive.

50648 ■ Louisiana Business & Technology Center
Louisiana State University
E.J. Ourso College of Business
8000 GSRI Ave., Bldg. 3000
Baton Rouge, LA 70820
Ph:(225)578-7555
Fax:(225)578-3975
Co. E-mail: lbtc@lsu.edu
URL: http://www.bus.lsu.edu/lbtc/
Description: A small business incubator located on the campus of Louisiana State University providing space for new business start-ups within its 25,000 square-foot incubator. Companies located in the incubator can concentrate on production and marketing, which directly affects success and profits, while leaving the day-to-day administrative details and overhead problems to the LBTC staff.

50649 ■ Louisiana Emerging Technology Center
PO Box 25128
Baton Rouge, LA 70894
Ph:(225)615-8901
Fax:(225)615-8910
Co. E-mail: acooper@laetc.com
URL: http://www.laetc.com
Contact: Arthur R. Cooper, Exec. Dir.
Description: designed specifically as an incubator for companies with wet-lab needs, serves small and start-up businesses developing and commercializing university technologies.

50650 ■ Louisiana Tech Enterprise Center
509 W Alabama
Ruston, LA 71270
Ph:(318)257-4343
Fax:(318)257-4442
Co. E-mail: dnorris@latech.edu
URL: http://www.lbia.org/members/la_tech_incubator.htm
Contact: Dave N. Norris, Exec. Dir.
Description: A small business incubator established to create successful businesses by providing assistance and facilities to stimulate small business formation, growth and development. It provides administrative assistance and overhead facilities to start-up companies, allowing them to concentrate on research, marketing, and production.

50651 ■ Louisiana Technology Park
7117 Florida Blvd.
Baton Rouge, LA 70806
Ph:(225)218-1100
Fax:(225)218-0101
Co. E-mail: info@latechpark.com
URL: http://www.latechpark.com/
Description: A business incubator formed to create an active and innovative atmosphere for e-business, high-technology and biotechnology. The Park is a comprehensive catalyst for the Internet, e-commerce and biotech economies, focused on growing startup companies; providing high-speed, high-volume commercial data storage and transmission; and offering swift, direct Internet connectivity.

50652 ■ Metro/Regional Business Incubator
Ark-La-Tex Export & Technology Center
7100 W. Park Rd.
Shreveport, LA 71129
Ph:(318)671-1050
Fax:(318)671-9032
Co. E-mail: dsimek@shreve.net
URL: http://www.cdconline.org
Description: A business development project of The Coordinating & Development Corporation providing subsidized rental space for tenants primarily engaged in manufacturing and warehousing/distribution. In addition to the leased space, tenants have access to conference rooms, a training center, shared office equipment, an employee break room, and full access to the staff for any counseling and technical assistance they may need.

50653 ■ New Orleans BioInnovation Center
134 LaSalle St.
New Orleans, LA 70112
Ph:(504)680-2973
Fax:(504)680-2977
Co. E-mail: aaronm@neworleansbio.com
URL: http://www.neworleansbio.com/
Contact: Aaron Miscenich, Exec. Dir.
Description: A technology business incubator created to foster entrepreneurship within the New Orleans bioscience community by assisting companies commercializing biotechnologies from New Orleans-based universities.

50654 ■ Southeast Louisiana Business Center
1514 Martens Dr.
Hammond, LA 70401
Ph:(985)549-3199
Co. E-mail: wjoubert@selu.edu
URL: http://www.selu.edu/admin/slbc/
Description: A small business incubator whose goal is to extend a nurturing environment to start-up and expanding small businesses in the area. The Center

houses area economic development agencies, business counseling resources, and incubator space.

50655 ■ Southwest Louisiana Economic Development Alliance
120 W Pujo St.
Lake Charles, LA 70601
Ph:(337)433-3632
Fax:(337)436-3727
Co. E-mail: gswift@allianceswla.org
URL: http://www.allianceswla.org/
Contact: George Swift, Pres. & CEO
Description: An alliance established to strengthen the business recruiting and retention efforts for Allen, Beauregard, Calcasieu, Cameron, and Jeff Davis parishes.

50656 ■ Student Business Incubator
Bossier Parish Community College
6220 E. Texas St.
Bossier City, LA 71112
Ph:(318)678-6427
Co. E-mail: tlogan@bpcc.edu
URL: http://www.lbia.org/members/bpcc_incubator.htm
Contact: Tamika Logan, Dir.
Description: A supportive environment where students' new entrepreneurial start-up businesses are nurtured. Students receive use of fully-equipped office space and office equipment, on-going training and coaching, technical assistance, access to capital, use of meeting rooms, and professional help in launching their own business.

PUBLICATIONS

50657 ■ *Smart Start your Connecticut Business*
PSI Research
300 N. Valley Dr.
Grants Pass, OR 97526
Ph:(503)479-9464
Free: 800-228-2275
Fax:(503)476-1479
Co. E-mail: info@psi-research.com
URL: http://www.psi-research.com
Ed: Michael D. Jenkins. **Released:** Revised edition, 1992. **Price:** $29.95 (looseleaf binder); $24.95 (paper). **Description:** Part of the Successful Business Library series.

PUBLISHERS

50658 ■ Trost Publishing
400 Poydras St., Ste. 1850
New Orleans, LA 70130
Ph:(504)680-6754
Contact: Tripp Friedler, Mgr
Description: Publishes nonfiction books on business and economics. **Founded:** 2004.

SMALL BUSINESS ASSISTANCE PROGRAMS

50659 ■ Maine Department of Economic and Community Development
59 State House Station
Augusta, ME 04333-0059
Ph:(207)624-9800
Fax:(207)287-5701
Co. E-mail: biz.growth@maine.gov
URL: http://www.econdevmaine.com
Contact: Mike Baran, Dir.
Description: Provides business planning, financing, information, and networking assistance to existing Maine businesses that need financing for expansion purposes. Utilizes programs offered through the Maine WEET and JTPA offices. Assists in identifying funding sources, including federal, state, and private. Also runs the Job Opportunity Zone Program which focuses attention on four designated depressed areas.

50660 ■ Maine Department of Economic and Community Development–Office of Business Development
59 State House Station
Augusta, ME 04333
Ph:(207)624-9804
Fax:(207)287-5701
Co. E-mail: biz.growth@maine.gov
URL: http://www.mainebiz.org
Contact: Mark Ouellette, Dir.
Description: Encourages investment in new Maine businesses and provides technical assistance to businesses in labor training, financing, site selection, and state licenses, and permits. Includes Maine Products Marketing Program which promotes regional and national awareness of Maine's products.

50661 ■ Maine Development Foundation
295 Water St., Ste. 5
Augusta, ME 04330
Ph:(207)622-6345
Fax:(207)622-6346
Co. E-mail: mdf@mdf.org
URL: http://www.mdf.org
Contact: Kristen Cady, Dir
Description: Nonprofit corporation that assists Maine businesses. Services include coordination of joint public-private projects; research and long-range planning for future economic development; and economic education.

50662 ■ Maine International Trade Center
511 Congress St., Ste. 100
Portland, ME 04101-3428
Ph:(207)541-7400
Fax:(207)541-7420
Co. E-mail: info@mitc.com
URL: http://www.mitc.com
Contact: Janine Bisaillon-Cary, Pres. and State Dir
Description: A private, nonprofit organization offering extensive export services to Maine businesses. Also includes a library of information on world trade.

SCORE OFFICES

50663 ■ Bangor SCORE
Path: www.scorebangor.org

50664 ■ Downeast Maine SCORE
Path: www.scoredowneastmaine.org

50665 ■ Lewiston-Auburn SCORE
Path: www.scoremaine.org/pages/augusta.htm

50666 ■ SCORE Augusta
68 Sewall St., Rm. 512
Augusta, ME 04330
Ph:(207)622-8509
URL: http://www.scoremaine.org
Description: Provides entrepreneur education and the formation, growth and success of small business nationwide. Provides free counseling and low-cost workshops.

50667 ■ SCORE Belfast
Path: www.scoremaine.org/pages/augusta.htm

50668 ■ SCORE Camden
Path: www.scoremaine.org/pages/augusta.htm

50669 ■ SCORE Damariscotta
Path: www.scoremaine.org/pages/augusta.htm

50670 ■ SCORE Oxford Hills
2 Market Sq.
South Paris, ME 04281
Ph:(207)743-0499
Co. E-mail: oxscore@megalink.net
URL: http://www.scoremaine.org
Description: Serves as volunteer program in which working and retired business management professionals provide free business counseling to men and women who are considering starting a small business, encountering problems with their business, or expanding their business. Offers free one-on-one counseling, online counseling and low cost workshops on a variety of business topics.

50671 ■ SCORE Portland
100 Middle St.
East Tower, 2nd Fl.
Portland, ME 04101
Ph:(207)772-1147
Co. E-mail: info@scoremaine.com
URL: http://www.scoremaine.com
Description: Delivers expertise and resources to maximize the success of existing and emerging small businesses. Offers 3-hour workshops in how to start own business, writing a business plan, marketing and sales, face to face or email counseling at no cost.

50672 ■ SCORE Rockford
Path: www.scoremaine.org/pages/augusta.htm

50673 ■ SCORE Western Mountains
c/o Oxford Federal Credit Union
Box 8
60 Lowell St.
Rumford, ME 04276

Ph:(207)364-3123
Co. E-mail: lkimball@megalink.net
URL: http://www.scoremaine.org
Description: Serves as volunteer program in which working and retired business management professionals provide free business counseling to men and women who are considering starting a small business, encountering problems with their business, or expanding their business. Offers free one-on-one counseling, online counseling and low cost workshops on a variety of business topics.

CHAMBERS OF COMMERCE

50674 ■ Androscoggin County Chamber of Commerce
PO Box 59
415 Lisbon St.
Lewiston, ME 04243-0059
Ph:(207)783-2249
Fax:(207)783-4481
Co. E-mail: cmorrison@androscoggincounty.com
URL: http://www2.androscoggincounty.com/public
Contact: Charles Morrison, Pres.

50675 ■ Bangor Regional Chamber of Commerce
519 Main St.
PO Box 1443
Bangor, ME 04401
Ph:(207)947-0307
Fax:(207)990-1427
Co. E-mail: chamber@bangorregion.com
URL: http://www.bangorregion.com
Contact: Ken Huhn, Chm.

50676 ■ Bar Harbor Chamber of Commerce
1201 Bar Harbor Rd.
Trenton, ME 04605
Ph:(207)288-5103
Free: 800-245-4619
Fax:(207)667-9080
Co. E-mail: visitors@barharborinfo.com
URL: http://www.barharbormaine.com
Contact: Chris Fogg, Exec. Dir.

50677 ■ Belfast Area Chamber of Commerce
PO Box 58
Belfast, ME 04915
Ph:(207)338-5900
Fax:(207)338-3808
Co. E-mail: info@belfastmaine.org
URL: http://www.belfastmaine.org
Contact: Jayne Crosby-Giles, Pres.

50678 ■ Bethel Area Chamber of Commerce
PO Box 1247
Bethel, ME 04217-1247
Ph:(207)824-2282
Free: 800-442-5826
Fax:(207)824-7123
Co. E-mail: info@bethelmaine.com
URL: http://www.bethelmaine.com
Contact: Ms. Robin Zinchuk

50679 ■ Biddeford-Saco Chamber of Commerce and Industry
138 Main St., Ste. 101
Saco, ME 04072
Ph:(207)282-1567
Fax:(207)282-3149
Co. E-mail: info@biddefordsacochamber.org
URL: http://www.biddefordsacochamber.org
Contact: Linda Houy, Office Mgr.

50680 ■ Blue Hill Peninsula Chamber of Commerce
PO Box 520
28 Water St.
Blue Hill, ME 04614
Ph:(207)374-3242
Fax:(207)374-3242
Co. E-mail: chamber@bluehillpeninsula.org
URL: http://www.bluehillpeninsula.org
Contact: Sue Walsh, Exec. Dir.

50681 ■ Boothbay Harbor Region Chamber of Commerce
PO Box 356
Boothbay Harbor, ME 04538-0356
Ph:(207)633-2353
Co. E-mail: seamaine@boothbayharbor.com
URL: http://www.boothbayharbor.com
Contact: Jaimie K. Logan, Exec. Dir.

50682 ■ Bucksport Bay Area Chamber of Commerce
PO Box 1880
Bucksport, ME 04416
Ph:(207)469-6818
Free: 888-678-6746
Fax:(207)469-2078
Co. E-mail: director@bucksportbaychamber.com
URL: http://www.bucksportchamber.org
Contact: Cindy Kimball, Dir.

50683 ■ Caribou Chamber of Commerce and Industry
24 Sweden St., Ste. 101
Caribou, ME 04736-2132
Ph:(207)498-6156
Fax:(207)492-1362
Co. E-mail: info@cariboumaine.net
URL: http://www.cariboumaine.net
Contact: Wendy Landes, Exec. Dir.

50684 ■ Cobscook Bay Area Chamber of Commerce
PO Box 42
Whiting, ME 04691-0042
Ph:(207)733-2201
Co. E-mail: info@cobscookbay.com
URL: http://www.cobscookbay.com

50685 ■ Damariscotta Region Chamber of Commerce
PO Box 13
Damariscotta, ME 04543
Ph:(207)563-8340
Fax:(207)563-8348
Co. E-mail: info@damariscottaregion.com
URL: http://www.damariscottaregion.com
Contact: Cerina Leeman, Exec. Dir.

50686 ■ Deer Isle - Stonington Chamber of Commerce
PO Box 490
Deer Isle, ME 04627
Ph:(207)348-6124
Co. E-mail: deerisle-stoningtonchamber@verizon.net
URL: http://www.deerislemaine.com
Contact: Darwin Davidson

50687 ■ Eastport Area Chamber of Commerce
PO Box 254
Eastport, ME 04631
Ph:(207)853-4644
Co. E-mail: chamber@eastport.net
URL: http://www.eastport.net
Contact: Roland Lavelle, Pres.

50688 ■ Ellsworth Area Chamber of Commerce
163 High St.
PO Box 267
Ellsworth, ME 04605
Ph:(207)667-5584
Co. E-mail: info@ellsworthchamber.org
URL: http://www.ellsworthchamber.org
Contact: Micki Sumpter, Exec. Dir.

50689 ■ Fort Fairfield Chamber of Commerce
18 Community Center Dr.
Fort Fairfield, ME 04742
Ph:(207)472-3802
Fax:(207)472-3810
Co. E-mail: jkelle@fortfairfield.org
URL: http://fortcc.org
Contact: Janet Kelle, Exec. Dir.

50690 ■ Franklin County Chamber of Commerce
407 Wilton Rd.
Farmington, ME 04938
Ph:(207)778-4215
Fax:(207)778-2438
Co. E-mail: info@franklincountymaine.org
URL: http://www.franklincountymaine.org
Contact: Matt Wotton, Pres.

50691 ■ Freeport Merchants Association
23 Depot St.
PO Box 452
Freeport, ME 04032-0452
Ph:(207)865-1212
Free: 800-865-1994
Co. E-mail: info@freeportusa.com
URL: http://www.freeportusa.com
Contact: Myra Hopkins, Exec. Dir.

50692 ■ Greater Bridgton-Lakes Region Chamber of Commerce
PO Box 236
Bridgton, ME 04009-0236
Ph:(207)647-3472
Co. E-mail: info@mainelakeschamber.com
URL: http://www.mainelakeschamber.com
Contact: Michael McClellan, Exec. Dir.

50693 ■ Greater Fort Kent Area Chamber of Commerce
PO Box 430
291 W Main St.
Fort Kent, ME 04743
Ph:(207)834-5354
Co. E-mail: info@fortkentchamber.com
URL: http://www.fortkentchamber.com
Contact: Cheryl Harvey, Pres.

50694 ■ Greater Houlton Chamber of Commerce
109 Main St.
Houlton, ME 04730
Ph:(207)532-4216
Fax:(207)532-4961
Co. E-mail: chamber@greaterhoulton.com
URL: http://www.greaterhoulton.com
Contact: Chris Batby, Admin.

50695 ■ Greater Madawaska Chamber of Commerce
PO Box 144
356 Main St.
Madawaska, ME 04756
Ph:(207)728-7000
Fax:(207)728-4696
Co. E-mail: valleyvisit@pwless.net
URL: http://www.greatermadawaskachamber.com
Contact: Stephen Hughes, Exec. Dir.

50696 ■ Greater Portland Chamber of Commerce
60 Pearl St.
Portland, ME 04101
Ph:(207)772-2811

Fax:(207)772-1179
Co. E-mail: chamber@portlandregion.com
URL: http://www.portlandregion.com/index.
  php?sec=1
Contact: W. Godfrey Wood, CEO

50697 ■ Greater Van Buren Chamber of Commerce
51 Main St., Ste. 101
Van Buren, ME 04785
Ph:(207)868-5059
Fax:(207)868-2222
Co. E-mail: vbchamber@pwless.net
URL: http://www.greatervanburenchamber.com
Contact: Sheila Cannon, Exec. Dir./Sec.

50698 ■ Katahdin Area Chamber of Commerce
PO Box 426
Millinocket, ME 04462
Ph:(207)723-4443
Fax:(207)723-4459
Co. E-mail: info@katahdinmaine.com
URL: http://www.katahdinmaine.com
Contact: Brian G. Wiley, Pres.

50699 ■ Kennebec Valley Chamber of Commerce
PO Box 676
Augusta, ME 04332-0676
Ph:(207)623-4559
Fax:(207)626-9342
Co. E-mail: info@augustamaine.com
URL: http://www.augustamaine.com
Contact: Peter G. Thompson, Pres./CEO

50700 ■ Kennebunk-Kennebunkport Chamber of Commerce
PO Box 740
Kennebunk, ME 04043
Ph:(207)967-0857
Fax:(207)967-2867
Co. E-mail: info@visitthekennebunks.com
URL: http://www.visitthekennebunks.com
Contact: Brian Strack, Chm.

50701 ■ Maine State Chamber of Commerce
125 Community Dr., Ste. 101
Augusta, ME 04330
Ph:(207)623-4568
Fax:(207)622-7723
Co. E-mail: dana.f.connors@mainechamber.org
URL: http://www.mainechamber.org/mx/hm.
  asp?id=home
Contact: Dana F. Connors, Pres.

50702 ■ Mid-Maine Chamber of Commerce
1 Post Office Sq.
Waterville, ME 04901-6651
Ph:(207)873-3315
Fax:(207)877-0087
Co. E-mail: info@midmainechamber.com
URL: http://www.midmainechamber.com
Contact: Kimberly Lindlof, Pres./CEO

50703 ■ Moosehead Lake Region Chamber of Commerce
PO Box 581
Greenville, ME 04441-0581
Ph:(207)695-2702
Free: 888-876-2778
Fax:(207)695-3440
Co. E-mail: info@mooseheadlake.org
URL: http://www.mooseheadlake.org
Contact: Bob Hamer, Exec. Dir.

50704 ■ Mount Desert Chamber of Commerce
PO Box 675
Northeast Harbor, ME 04662-0675
Ph:(207)276-5040
Co. E-mail: info@mountdesertchamber.org
URL: http://www.mountdesertchamber.org

50705 ■ Northern Kathadin Valley Region Chamber of Commerce
PO Box 374
Island Falls, ME 04747
Ph:(207)463-4634
Co. E-mail: nkvrcc1@fairpoint.net
URL: http://www.northernmainechamber.com

50706 ■ Ogunquit Chamber of Commerce
PO Box 2289
Ogunquit, ME 03907
Ph:(207)646-1279
Fax:(207)641-0856
Co. E-mail: director@ogunquit.org
URL: http://www.ogunquit.org
Contact: Karen Marie Arel, Exec. Dir.

50707 ■ Old Orchard Beach Chamber of Commerce
PO Box 600
Old Orchard Beach, ME 04064
Ph:(207)934-2500
Co. E-mail: info@oldorchardbeachmaine.com
URL: http://www.oldorchardbeachmaine.com
Contact: James Harmon, Exec. Dir.

50708 ■ Oxford Hills Chamber of Commerce
4 Western Ave.
South Paris, ME 04281
Ph:(207)743-2281
Fax:(207)743-0687
Co. E-mail: info@oxfordhillsmaine.com
URL: http://www.oxfordhillsmaine.com
Contact: Steve Wallace, Exec. Dir.

50709 ■ Penobscot Bay Regional Chamber of Commerce
PO Box 508
1 Park Dr.
Rockland, ME 04841-0508
Ph:(207)596-0376
Free: 800-562-2529
Fax:(207)596-6549
Co. E-mail: info@therealmaine.com
URL: http://www.therealmaine.com
Contact: Shari Closter, Interim Exec. Dir.

50710 ■ Rangeley Lakes Region Chamber of Commerce
PO Box 317
Rangeley, ME 04970
Ph:(207)864-5364
Free: 800-MT-LAKES
Co. E-mail: info@rangeleymaine.com
URL: http://www.rangeleymaine.com

50711 ■ River Valley Chamber of Commerce
10 Bridge St.
Rumford, ME 04276
Ph:(207)364-3241
Fax:(207)369-0356
Co. E-mail: info@rivervalleychamber.com
URL: http://www.rivervalleychamber.com
Contact: Cherri L. Crockett, Admin.

50712 ■ Rockport-Camden-Lincolnville Chamber of Commerce
PO Box 919
Camden, ME 04843
Ph:(207)236-4404
Free: 800-223-5459
Fax:(207)236-4315
Co. E-mail: chamber@camdenme.org
URL: http://www.visitcamden.com
Contact: Claire Adams, Pres.

50713 ■ St. Croix Valley Chamber of Commerce
Downeast Heritage Museum Bldg.
39 Union St.
Calais, ME 04619
Ph:(207)454-2308
Free: 888-422-3112
Fax:(207)454-2308
Co. E-mail: visitstcroixvalley@myfairpoint.net
URL: http://www.visitcalais.com

50714 ■ Schoodic Area Chamber of Commerce
PO Box 381
Winter Harbor, ME 04693
Ph:(207)963-7658
Co. E-mail: lelliott@mainesavings.com
URL: http://www.acadia-schoodic.org
Contact: Ed Brackett, Pres.

50715 ■ Sebago Lakes Region Chamber of Commerce
PO Box 1015
Windham, ME 04062
Ph:(207)892-8265
Fax:(207)893-0110
Co. E-mail: info@sebagolakeschamber.com
URL: http://www.sebagolakeschamber.com
Contact: Barbara Clark, Exec. Dir.

50716 ■ Skowhegan Area Chamber of Commerce
23 Commercial St.
Skowhegan, ME 04976
Ph:(207)474-3621
Free: 888-772-4392
Fax:(207)474-3306
Co. E-mail: info@skowheganchamber.com
URL: http://www.skowheganchamber.com
Contact: Dan Plante, Pres.

50717 ■ Southern Midcoast Maine Chamber
Border Trust Business Center
2 Main St.
Topsham, ME 04086
Ph:(207)725-8797
Free: 877-725-8797
Fax:(207)725-9787
Co. E-mail: chamber@midcoastmaine.com
URL: http://www.midcoastmaine.com
Contact: Heather Collins, Pres./Exec. Dir.

50718 ■ Southern Piscataquis County Chamber of Commerce
PO Box 376
Dover Foxcroft, ME 04426
Ph:(207)564-7533
Fax:(207)564-7573
Co. E-mail: exdir@piscataquischamber.com
URL: http://www.piscataquischamber.com
Contact: Russ Page, Exec. Dir.

50719 ■ Upper Kennebec Valley Chamber of Commerce
PO Box 491
Bingham, ME 04920
Ph:(207)672-4100
Co. E-mail: info@upperkennebecvalley.com
URL: http://www.upperkennebecvalleychamber.me
Contact: Erin Marden, Pres.

50720 ■ Wells Chamber of Commerce
PO Box 356
Wells, ME 04090-0356
Ph:(207)646-2451
Fax:(207)646-8104
Co. E-mail: wellschamber@wellschamber.org
URL: http://www.wellschamber.org
Contact: Sandee Mariner, Exec. Sec.

50721 ■ Yarmouth Chamber of Commerce
162 Main St.
Yarmouth, ME 04096
Ph:(207)846-3984
Fax:(207)846-5419
Co. E-mail: info@yarmouthmaine.org
URL: http://www.yarmouthmaine.org
Contact: Carolyn Schuster, Managing Dir.

MINORITY BUSINESS ASSISTANCE PROGRAMS

50722 ■ The Maine Women's Business Center at CEI–Coastal Enterprises Inc.
36 Water St.
Wiscasset, ME 04578
Ph:(207)882-7552

Fax:(207)882-7308
Co. E-mail: cei@ceimaine.org
URL: http://www.ceimaine.org/women
Contact: Gretchen Henn, Dir
Description: Provides counseling and training services for new and existing women business owners in Maine.

FINANCING AND LOAN PROGRAMS

50723 ■ CEI Ventures, Inc. / CVI
2 Portland Fish Pier, Ste. 206
Portland, ME 04101
Ph:(207)772-5356
Fax:(207)772-5503
URL: http://www.ceiventures.com
Contact: Nathaniel V. Henshaw, Managing Director
E-mail: nvh@ceimaine.org
Preferred Investment Size: $1,000,000 to $4,000,000. **Investment Types:** Balanced. **Geographic Preferences:** Northeast. **Principal Exhibits:**

50724 ■ North Atlantic Capital Corporation
2 City Ctr., 5th Fl.
Portland, ME 04101
Ph:(207)772-4470
Fax:(207)772-3257
Co. E-mail: ccoyne@northatlanticcapital.com
URL: http://www.northatlanticcapital.com
Contact: David Coit, Managing Director
Preferred Investment Size: $4,000,000 $8,000,000. **Investment Types:** Later stage, acquisition, expansion, leveraged buyout, mezzanine, management buyouts, and recapitalizations. **Industry Preferences:** Internet specific, computer hardware, other products, consumer related, industrial and energy, computer software and services, communications and media, medical and health, semiconductors and other electronics, and biotechnology. **Geographic Preferences:** East Coast. **Principal Exhibits:**

PROCUREMENT ASSISTANCE PROGRAMS

50725 ■ Maine Procurement Technical Assistance Center–Eastern Maine Development Corporation–Market Development Center (40 Ha)
40 Harlow St.
Bangor, ME 04401
Ph:(207)942-6389
Free: 800-339-6389
Fax:(207)942-3548
Co. E-mail: info@emdc.org
URL: http://www.emdc.org
Contact: Patricia Rice, Dir
E-mail: ralexander@emdc.org

50726 ■ Maine Procurement Technical Assistance Center–Outreach Center
403 Hallowell Rd.
Pownal, ME 04069
Ph:(207)653-8625
URL: http://www.maineptac.org
Contact: Ernest Gray, Dir.
E-mail: egray1@maine.rr.com
Description: Helps Maine small businesses obtain government contracts with the Department of Defense, other federal agencies, state/local governments, and prime contractors.

50727 ■ Maine Procurement Technical Assistance Center–Service Center
17 Main St.
Fairfield, ME 04937-1119
Ph:(207)453-4258
Fax:(207)453-4264
Co. E-mail: jmr@ceimaine.org
URL: http://www.mainesbdc.org
Contact: Janet Roderick, Specialist
E-mail: edahl@emdc.org
Description: Helps Maine small businesses obtain government contracts with the Department of Defense, other federal agencies, state/local governments, and prime contractors.

50728 ■ U.S. SBA Office of Government Contracting for Maine and New Hampshire
68 Sewall St., Rm. 512
Augusta, ME 04330
Ph:(207)622-8379
Fax:(207)481-5513
Co. E-mail: sean.crean@sba.gov
URL: http://www.sba.gov
Contact: Sean F. Crean, SBA Representative
E-mail: sean.crean@sba.gov
Description: Covers activities for the VA Hospital (Togus, ME), the Portsmouth Naval Shipyard (Portsmouth, NH), and the Naval Air Station (Brunswick, ME).

INCUBATORS/RESEARCH AND TECHNOLOGY PARKS

50729 ■ Maine Center for Enterprise Development
University of S Maine
70 Falmouth St.
Portland, ME 04103
Ph:(207)228-8524
Fax:(207)228-8526
Co. E-mail: info@mced.biz
URL: http://www.mced.biz/
Contact: Steven N. Bazinet, Exec. Dir.
Description: A small business incubator providing business incubation services for innovative start-ups.

50730 ■ River Valley Technology Center
60 Lowell St.
Rumford, ME 04276

Ph:(207)369-0396
URL: http://www.rvgc.org/rvtc/home.cfm
Description: A public/private partnership dedicated to nurturing small technology and precision manufacturing businesses during the start-up stage. It provides a variety of business development assistance including low cost space, shared office services, onsite training and managerial and technical assistance in an environment conducive to new small businesses.

50731 ■ Target Technology Center
University of Maine
20 Godfrey Dr.
Orono, ME 04473
Ph:(207)866-6500
Fax:(207)866-6501
URL: http://www.targetincubator.umaine.edu/
Contact: Debbie Neuman, Dir.
Description: A small business incubator providing information technology companies expertise, tools, resources, and networks.

50732 ■ University of Maine–Office of the Vice President for Research
5703 Alumni Hall, Rm. 209
Orono, ME 04469-5703
Ph:(207)581-1506
Fax:(207)581-1300
Co. E-mail: michael.eckardt@umit.maine.edu
URL: http://www.umaine.edu/research/vice-president-for-research/
Contact: Michael J. Eckardt PhD, VP,Res.
E-mail: michael.eckardt@umit.maine.edu
Scope: Responsible for research at the university and for administration and coordination of research

activities of various departments, colleges, and specialized research units, including extramurally supported projects.

EDUCATIONAL PROGRAMS

50733 ■ University of Maine at Machias
9 O'Brien Ave.
Machias, ME 04654-1397
Ph:(207)255-1200
Free: 888-468-6866
Fax:(207)255-4864
Co. E-mail: ummwebmaster@maine.edu
URL: http://www.umm.maine.edu
Description: Offers programs in small business management.

PUBLICATIONS

50734 ■ *Smart Start your Arizona Business*
PSI Research
300 N. Valley Dr.
Grants Pass, OR 97526
Ph:(503)479-9464
Free: 800-228-2275
Fax:(503)476-1479
Co. E-mail: info@psi-research.com
URL: http://www.psi-research.com
Ed: Michael D. Jenkins. **Released:** Revised edition, 1992. **Price:** $29.95 (looseleaf binder); $24.95 (paper). **Description:** Part of the Successful Business Library series.

SMALL BUSINESS DEVELOPMENT CENTERS

50735 ■ Anne Arundel Small Business Development Center
Anne Arundel Economic Development Corporation
2660 Riva Rd., Ste. 200
Annapolis, MD 21401
Fax:(410)222-7415
Co. E-mail: tfrancovitch@aaedc.org
URL: http://www.centralmdsbdc.org/counseling/an-nearundelcounty.php
Contact: Thomas Francovitch

50736 ■ Baltimore County Small Business Development Center
Towson University
7400 York Rd.
Towson, MD 21204
Fax:(410)296-6142
Co. E-mail: cpanos@towson.edu
URL: http://www.centralmdsbdc.org/counseling/balti-morecounty.php
Contact: Craig Panos

50737 ■ Harford County Maryland Small Business Development Center
Harford Community College
Edgewood Hall
401 Thomas Run Rd.
Bel Air, MD 21015
Fax:(410)836-4353
Co. E-mail: sbdc@harford.edu
URL: http://www.harford.edu/sbdc/Index.asp
Contact: Russell Teter, Dir.

50738 ■ Howard County Small Business Development Center
Howard County Center for Business and Technology Development
9250 Bendix Rd.
Columbia, MD 21045
Fax:(410)313-7515
Co. E-mail: mredmond@towson.edu
URL: http://www.centralmdsbdc.org/counseling/howardcounty.php
Contact: Mary Redmond

50739 ■ Maryland Small Business Development Center - Central Region
8000 York Rd.
Towson, MD 21252
Free: 877-421-0830
Fax:(410)296-6142
Co. E-mail: sstockton@towson.edu
URL: http://www.centralmdsbdc.org
Contact: Sonia Stockton, Dir.

50740 ■ Maryland Small Business Development Center - Eastern Region
Perdue School of Business - Salisbury University
215 E Campus Complex
Salisbury, MD 21801
Free: 800-999-7232

Fax:(410)548-5389
Co. E-mail: sbdctraining@salisbury.edu
URL: http://www.salisbury.edu/sbdc
Contact: John Hickman, Dir.

50741 ■ Maryland Small Business Development Center - Southern Region
PO Box 910
La Plata, MD 20646
Co. E-mail: bduboff@csmd.edu
URL: http://www.sbdchelp.com
Contact: Brian DuBoff, Dir.

50742 ■ Western Region Maryland Small Business Development Center
14701 National Hwy., Ste. 1
LaVale, MD 21502
Fax:(301)687-1008
URL: http://www.sbdc-wmd.com

SMALL BUSINESS ASSISTANCE PROGRAMS

50743 ■ Maryland Department of Business and Economic Development–Business Development Division
401 E Pratt St.
Baltimore, MD 21202-3316
Ph:(410)767-6300
Free: 800-811-0051
Fax:(410)333-4302
Co. E-mail: communications@choosemaryland.org
URL: http://www.choosemaryland.org
Contact: Jayson Knott, Dir.
Description: attracts new businesses to the state, expands global commerce, cultivates important industry clusters and raises awareness of Maryland as a leader in technology and innovation

50744 ■ Maryland Economic Development Corp.
100 N Charles St., 6th Fl.
Baltimore, MD 21201
Ph:(410)625-0051
Fax:(410)625-1848
URL: http://www.medco-corp.com
Contact: Robert C. Brennan, Exec Dir
Description: Develops vacant or under-utilized industrial sites and other facilities and economic resources that would serve the public interest. Assists in the expansion, modernization, and retention of existing Maryland businesses. Provides marketing, financing, and networking information.

SCORE OFFICES

50745 ■ Frederick County SCORE
Path: www.scorefrederick.org

50746 ■ Mid-Shore SCORE
Path: www.easternshorescore.org

50747 ■ SCORE Greater Baltimore
10 S Howard St.
Baltimore, MD 21201
Ph:(410)962-2233
Co. E-mail: baltimorescore@verizon.net
URL: http://www.scorebaltimore.org
Description: Serves as volunteer program in which working and retired business management professionals provide free business counseling to men and women who are considering starting a small business, encountering problems with their business, or expanding their business. Offers free one-on-one counseling, online counseling and low cost workshops on a variety of business topics.

50748 ■ SCORE Hagerstown
28 W Washington St., Ste. 200
Hagerstown, MD 21740
Ph:(301)739-2015
Fax:(301)739-1278
Co. E-mail: info@scorehagerstown.org
URL: http://www.scorehagerstown.org
Contact: David Peters, Chm.
Description: Aims to help emerging businesses succeed and stay active in the local and national small business marketplace.

50749 ■ SCORE Salisbury
Salisbury Area Chamber of Commerce Bldg.
144 E Main St.
Salisbury, MD 21801
Ph:(410)749-0185
Fax:(410)860-9925
Co. E-mail: score@salisburyarea.com
URL: http://www.salisburyarea.com/score.htm
Contact: Chuck Lemak, Chm.
Description: Serves as volunteer program in which working and retired business management professionals provide free business counseling to men and women who are considering starting a small business, encountering problems with their business, or expanding their business. Offers free one-on-one counseling, online counseling and low cost workshops on a variety of business topics.

50750 ■ SCORE Southern Maryland
49 Old Solomons Island Rd., Ste. 204
Annapolis, MD 21401
Ph:(410)266-9553
Co. E-mail: info@score390.org
URL: http://www.score390.org
Contact: Mr. Julian Bigden, Chm.
Description: Provides no cost business counseling and workshops on starting and growing small businesses to entrepreneurs and individuals interested to start a small business in Anne Arundel, Calvert, Charles, and St. Mary's Counties in Maryland.

50751 ■ SCORE Upper Shore
122 N Cross St.
Chestertown, MD 21620-1547

Ph:(410)810-0021
Co. E-mail: chapter670@easternshorescore.org
URL: http://www.easternshorescore.org/chapter670.
php
Description: Serves as volunteer program in which working and retired business management professionals provide free business counseling to men and women who are considering starting a small business, encountering problems with their business, or expanding their business. Offers free one-on-one counseling, online counseling and low cost workshops on a variety of business topics.

BETTER BUSINESS BUREAUS

50752 ■ Better Business Bureau of Greater Maryland
1414 Key Hwy., Ste. 100
Baltimore, MD 21230
Ph:(410)347-3990
Fax:(410)347-3936
Co. E-mail: info@greatermd.bbb.org
URL: http://www.baltimore.bbb.org
Contact: Angie Barnett, Pres./CEO

CHAMBERS OF COMMERCE

50753 ■ Aberdeen Chamber of Commerce
214 W Bel Air Ave.
PO Box 292
Aberdeen, MD 21001
Ph:(410)272-2580
Fax:(410)272-9357
Co. E-mail: aberdeenchamber@verizon.net
URL: http://www.aberdeencc.com
Contact: Janet Emmons, Dir.

50754 ■ Allegany County Chamber of Commerce
Bell Tower Bldg.
24 Frederick St.
Cumberland, MD 21502
Ph:(301)722-2820
Fax:(301)722-5995
Co. E-mail: info@alleganycountychamber.com
URL: http://www.alleganycountychamber.com
Contact: Kolin M. Jan, Pres.

50755 ■ Annapolis and Anne Arundel County Chamber of Commerce
49 Old Solomons Island Rd., Ste. 204
Annapolis, MD 21401
Ph:(410)266-3960
Fax:(410)266-8270
Co. E-mail: rburdon@aaaccc.org
URL: http://www.annapolischamber.com
Contact: Bob Burdon, Pres./CEO

50756 ■ Baltimore City Chamber of Commerce
312 N Martin Luther King Jr. Blvd.
Baltimore, MD 21201-1211
Ph:(410)837-7101
Fax:(410)837-7104
Co. E-mail: baltcham@aol.com
URL: http://www.baltimorecitychamber.com
Contact: John Walters, Chm.

50757 ■ Baltimore County Chamber of Commerce
102 W Pennsylvania Ave., Ste. 101
Towson, MD 21204-4526
Ph:(410)825-6200
Fax:(410)821-9901
Co. E-mail: kscott@baltcountychamber.com
URL: http://www.baltcountycc.com
Contact: Keith Scott, Pres./CEO

50758 ■ Baltimore - Washington Corridor Chamber of Commerce
312 Marshall Ave., Ste. 104
Laurel, MD 20707-4824
Ph:(410)792-9714
Fax:(301)725-0776
Co. E-mail: bwcc@baltwashchamber.org
URL: http://www.baltwashchamber.org
Contact: H. Walter Townshend III, Pres./CEO

50759 ■ Calvert County Chamber of Commerce
120 Dares Beach Rd.
PO Box 9
Prince Frederick, MD 20678-0009
Ph:(410)535-2577
Fax:(410)257-3140
Co. E-mail: calvertchamber@calvertchamber.org
URL: http://www.calvertchamber.org
Contact: Carolyn McHugh, Pres./CEO

50760 ■ Carroll County Chamber of Commerce
700 Corporate Center Ct., Ste. L
PO Box 871
Westminster, MD 21158-0871
Ph:(410)848-9050
Fax:(410)876-1023
Co. E-mail: info@carrollcountychamber.org
URL: http://www.carrollcountychamber.org
Contact: Richard Haddad, Pres.

50761 ■ Cecil County Chamber of Commerce
233 E Main St.
Elkton, MD 21921
Ph:(410)392-3833
Fax:(410)392-6225
Co. E-mail: info@cecilchamber.org
URL: http://www.cecilchamber.org
Contact: Laura Mayse, Exec. Dir.

50762 ■ Chamber of Commerce of Frederick County
8420-B Gas House Pike
Frederick, MD 21701-4972
Ph:(301)662-4164
Fax:(301)846-4427
Co. E-mail: info@frederickchamber.org
URL: http://www.frederickchamber.org/cwt/external/
wcpages/index.aspx
Contact: Richard Adams, Pres./CEO

50763 ■ Charles County Chamber of Commerce
101 Centennial Ave., Ste. A
La Plata, MD 20646-4208
Ph:(301)932-6500
Fax:(301)932-3945
Co. E-mail: info@charlescountychamber.org
URL: http://www.charlescountychamber.org
Contact: Ken Gould Jr., Exec. Dir.

50764 ■ Crisfield Area Chamber of Commerce
PO Box 292
Crisfield, MD 21817-0292
Ph:(410)968-2500
Free: 800-782-3913
Fax:(410)968-0524
Co. E-mail: info@crisfieldchamber.com
URL: http://www.crisfieldchamber.com
Contact: Chris Sterling, Pres.

50765 ■ Dorchester Chamber of Commerce
528 Poplar St.
Cambridge, MD 21613
Ph:(410)228-3575
Fax:(410)228-6848
Co. E-mail: allen@dorchesterchamber.org
URL: http://www.dorchesterchamber.org
Contact: Allen Nelson, Exec. Dir.

50766 ■ Elkton Chamber and Alliance
101 E Main St.
Elkton, MD 21921-6109
Ph:(410)398-5076
Fax:(410)398-4971
Co. E-mail: info@elktonalliance.org
URL: http://www.elktonalliance.org
Contact: Ms. Mary Jo Jablonski, Exec. Dir.

50767 ■ Essex - Middle River - White Marsh Chamber of Commerce
405 Williams Ct., Ste. 108
Middle River, MD 21220
Ph:(410)686-2233

Fax:(410)687-9081
Co. E-mail: info@emrchamber.org
URL: http://www.emrchamber.org
Contact: Nick Nichols, Admin. Dir.

50768 ■ Gaithersburg-Germantown Chamber of Commerce
4 Professional Dr., Ste. 132
Gaithersburg, MD 20879-3426
Ph:(301)840-1400
Fax:(301)963-3918
Co. E-mail: info@ggchamber.org
URL: http://www.ggchamber.org
Contact: Marilyn Balcombe PhD, Pres./CEO

50769 ■ Garrett County Chamber of Commerce
15 Visitors Center Dr.
McHenry, MD 21541
Ph:(301)387-4386
Fax:(301)387-2080
Co. E-mail: charlie@garrettchamber.com
URL: http://www.garrettchamber.com
Contact: Charlie Ross, Pres./CEO

50770 ■ Greater Bethesda-Chevy Chase Chamber of Commerce
7910 Woodmont Ave., Ste. 1204
Bethesda, MD 20814-3015
Ph:(301)652-4900
Fax:(301)657-1973
Co. E-mail: staff@bccchamber.org
URL: http://www.bccchamber.org
Contact: Jerry Morenoff, Pres.

50771 ■ Greater Bowie Chamber of Commerce
6911 Laurel Bowie Rd., Ste. 302
Bowie, MD 20715
Ph:(301)262-0920
Fax:(301)262-0921
Co. E-mail: info@bowiechamber.org
URL: http://www.bowiechamber.org
Contact: Cathy Woods, Pres.

50772 ■ Greater Crofton Chamber of Commerce
PO Box 4146
Crofton, MD 21114-4146
Ph:(410)721-9131
Fax:(410)721-0785
Co. E-mail: coachops@aol.com
URL: http://www.croftonchamber.com
Contact: Bob Carr, Pres.

50773 ■ Greater Severna Park Chamber of Commerce
1 Holly Ave.
Severna Park, MD 21146
Ph:(410)647-3900
Fax:(410)647-3999
Co. E-mail: info@severnaparkchamber.com
URL: http://www.severnaparkchamber.com
Contact: Linda S. Zahn, Exec. Dir.

50774 ■ Greater Silver Spring Chamber of Commerce
8601 Georgia Ave., Ste. 203
Silver Spring, MD 20910-3458
Ph:(301)565-3777
Fax:(301)565-3377
Co. E-mail: info@gsscc.org
URL: http://www.silverspringchamber.com
Contact: Jane Redicker, Pres.

50775 ■ Hagerstown-Washington County Chamber of Commerce
28 W Washington St., Ste. 200
Hagerstown, MD 21740
Ph:(301)739-2015
Fax:(301)739-1278
Co. E-mail: chamber@hagerstown.org
URL: http://www.hagerstown.org
Contact: Brien J. Poffenberger, Pres.

50776 ■ Harford County Chamber of Commerce
108 S Bond St.
Bel Air, MD 21014
Ph:(410)838-2020
Free: 800-682-8536
Fax:(410)893-4715
Co. E-mail: info@harfordchamber.org
URL: http://www.harfordchamber.org
Contact: William B. Seccurro, Pres./CEO

50777 ■ Havre de Grace Chamber of Commerce
450 Pennington Ave.
Havre de Grace, MD 21078
Ph:(410)939-3303
Fax:(410)939-3490
Co. E-mail: hdegchamber1@comcast.net
URL: http://www.hdgchamber.com
Contact: Cathy L. Vincenti, Exec. Dir.

50778 ■ Howard County Chamber of Commerce
5560 Sterrett Pl., Ste. 105
Columbia, MD 21044-2616
Ph:(410)730-4111
Fax:(410)730-4584
Co. E-mail: info@howardchamber.com
URL: http://www.howardchamber.com
Contact: Pamela J. Klahr CCE, Pres./CEO

50779 ■ Kent County Chamber of Commerce
122 N Cross St.
PO Box 146
Chestertown, MD 21620
Ph:(410)810-2968
Fax:(410)778-1406
Co. E-mail: kentchamber@verizon.net
URL: http://www.kentchamber.org
Contact: Cindy Genther, Exec. Dir.

50780 ■ Maryland Chamber of Commerce
60 West St., Ste. 100
Annapolis, MD 21401
Ph:(410)269-0642
Fax:(410)269-5247
Co. E-mail: ksnyder@mdchamber.org
URL: http://www.mdchamber.org
Contact: Kathleen T. Snyder CCE, Pres./CEO

50781 ■ Montgomery County Chamber of Commerce
51 Monroe St., Ste. 1800
Rockville, MD 20850
Ph:(301)738-0015
Fax:(301)738-8792
Co. E-mail: ggodwin@montgomerycountychamber.com
URL: http://www.montgomerycountychamber.com
Contact: Georgette Godwin, Pres./CEO

50782 ■ North East Chamber of Commerce
PO Box 787
North East, MD 21901
Ph:(410)287-5252
Co. E-mail: info@northeastchamber.org
URL: http://www.northeastchamber.org
Contact: Carolyn Crouch, Pres.

50783 ■ Northern Anne Arundel County Chamber of Commerce
7477 Baltimore-Annapolis Blvd., Ste. 204
Glen Burnie, MD 21061
Ph:(410)766-8282
Fax:(410)766-5722
Co. E-mail: info@naaccc.com
URL: http://www.naaccc.com
Contact: Wayne Shipley, Pres.

50784 ■ Ocean City Chamber of Commerce
12320 Ocean Gateway
Ocean City, MD 21842
Ph:(410)213-0552
Fax:(410)213-7521
Co. E-mail: info@oceancity.org
URL: http://www.oceancity.org
Contact: Melanie Pursel, Exec. Dir.

50785 ■ Ocean Pines Area Chamber of Commerce
10514G Racetrack Rd.
Ocean Pines, MD 21811
Ph:(410)641-5306
Fax:(410)641-6176
Co. E-mail: info@oceanpineschamber.org
URL: http://www.oceanpineschamber.org
Contact: Carol Ludwig, Exec. Dir.

50786 ■ Olney Chamber of Commerce
PO Box 550
Olney, MD 20830
Ph:(301)774-7117
Fax:(301)774-4944
Co. E-mail: olneycoc@aol.com
URL: http://www.olneymd.org
Contact: Ellen Coleman, Pres.

50787 ■ Pikesville Chamber of Commerce
7 Church Ln., Ste. 14
Pikesville, MD 21208
Ph:(410)484-2337
Fax:(410)484-4151
URL: http://www.pikesvillechamber.org
Contact: Todd Brown, Pres.

50788 ■ Pocomoke City Chamber of Commerce
144 Market St.
PO Box 356
Pocomoke City, MD 21851-0356
Ph:(410)957-1919
Fax:(410)957-4784
Co. E-mail: pocomokechamber@gmail.com
URL: http://www.pocomoke.com
Contact: Jill Marsh, Sec./Dir.

50789 ■ Poolesville Area Chamber of Commerce
PO Box 256
Poolesville, MD 20837-0256
Ph:(301)349-5753
URL: http://www.pacc.cc
Contact: Maggie Nightingale, Exec. Sec.

50790 ■ Potomac Chamber of Commerce
9812 Falls Rd., Ste. 114
Box 321
Potomac, MD 20854
Ph:(301)299-2170
Fax:(301)299-4650
Co. E-mail: pcc@potomacchamber.org
URL: http://potomacchamber.org
Contact: Ms. Adam Greenberg, Pres.

50791 ■ Prince George's Chamber of Commerce
4640 Forbes Blvd., Ste. 130
Lanham, MD 20706
Ph:(301)731-5000
Fax:(301)731-5011
Co. E-mail: info@pgcoc.org
URL: http://www.pgcoc.org
Contact: Craig M. Muckle, Chm.

50792 ■ Queen Anne's County Chamber of Commerce
PO Box 511
Chester, MD 21619-0511
Ph:(410)643-8530
Fax:(410)643-8477
Co. E-mail: business@qacchamber.com
URL: http://www.qacchamber.com
Contact: Linda W. Friday, Pres.

50793 ■ Reisterstown - Owings Mills - Glyndon Chamber of Commerce
100 Owings Ct., Ste. 9
Reisterstown, MD 21136
Ph:(410)356-2888
Fax:(410)356-5112
Co. E-mail: romg@romgchamber.org
URL: http://www.romgchamber.org
Contact: Brian A. Ditto, Exec. Dir.

50794 ■ Rockville Chamber of Commerce
1 Research Ct., Ste. 450
Rockville, MD 20850-4165
Ph:(301)424-9300
Fax:(301)762-7599
Co. E-mail: rockville@rockvillechamber.org
URL: http://rockvillechamber.org
Contact: Jeff Miller, Pres.

50795 ■ St. Mary's County Chamber of Commerce
44200 Airport Rd.
California, MD 20619
Ph:(301)737-3001
Fax:(301)737-0089
Co. E-mail: info@smcchamber.com
URL: http://www.smcchamber.com
Contact: William Scarafia, Pres./CEO

50796 ■ Salisbury Area Chamber of Commerce
144 E Main St.
PO Box 510
Salisbury, MD 21801
Ph:(410)749-0144
Fax:(410)860-9925
Co. E-mail: chamber@salisburyarea.com
URL: http://www.salisburyarea.com
Contact: Bradley A. Bellacicco, Exec. Dir.

50797 ■ Snow Hill Chamber of Commerce
PO Box 176
Snow Hill, MD 21863
Ph:(410)632-0809
URL: http://www.atbeach.com/cities/snowhill/snow-comm.asp

50798 ■ West Anne Arundel County Chamber of Commerce
8373 Piney Orchard Pkwy., Ste. 200
Odenton, MD 21113
Ph:(410)672-3422
Fax:(410)672-3475
Co. E-mail: info@waaccc.org
URL: http://www.waaccc.org
Contact: Ms. Claire Louder, Exec. Dir.

MINORITY BUSINESS ASSISTANCE PROGRAMS

50799 ■ The Center for Minority Business Development–Prince George's Community College
301 Largo Rd., CAT-135
Largo, MD 20774-2199
Ph:(301)583-5205
URL: http://www.cmbd.biz
Contact: Carl E. Brown, Exec Dir
Description: Provides business development, educational programs, assessment tools, counseling, and mentoring programs to local minority businesses.

50800 ■ Mayor's Office of Baltimore–Minority & Women-Owned Business Development
City Hall, Rm. 334
Baltimore, MD 21202
Ph:(410)396-3818
Fax:(410)528-1671
Co. E-mail: mombd@baltimorecity.gov
URL: http://www.baltimorecity.gov
Description: Works to improve the opportunites for minority and women-owned businesses to do business with the city of Baltimore.

50801 ■ Women Entrepreneurs of Baltimore Inc.
1118 Light St., Ste. 101
Baltimore, MD 21230
Ph:(410)727-4921
Co. E-mail: jsaltzberg@webinc.org
URL: http://www.webinc.org
Contact: Joanne Saltzberg, CEO
Description: Offers business training and support programs to help women start their own businesses. Primarily serves lower-income women and the unemployed.

FINANCING AND LOAN PROGRAMS

50802 ■ Abell Venture Fund
111 S. Calvert St., Ste. 2300
Baltimore, MD 21202-6164
Ph:(410)547-1300
Fax:(410)539-6579
Co. E-mail: abell@abell.org
URL: http://www.abell.org/abellinvestments
Contact: Robert C. Embry Jr., President
E-mail: embry@abell.org
Preferred Investment Size: $200,000 to $3,000,000. **Investment Policies:** Early stage and expansion. **Industry Preferences:** Internet specific, semiconductors and other electronics, communications and media, computer software and services, industrial and energy and medical and health. **Geographic Preferences:** Maryland. **Principal Exhibits:**

50803 ■ ABS Ventures
950 Winter St., Ste. 2600
Waltham, MA 02451
Ph:(781)250-0400
Fax:(781)250-0345
Co. E-mail: abs@absventures.com
URL: http://www.absventures.com
Contact: Scott Yaphe, General Partner
Preferred Investment Size: $5,000,000 to $15,000,000. **Investment Policies:** Early and later stage, fund of funds, expansion, recapitalization, and special situation. **Industry Preferences:** Computer software and services, medical and health, communications and media, Internet specific, computer hardware, biotechnology, other products, industrial and energy, consumer related, semiconductors and other electronics. **Geographic Preferences:** U.S. **Principal Exhibits:**

50804 ■ Anthem Capital Management LLC
1448 South Rolling Rd., Ste. 200
Baltimore, MD 21227
Ph:(410)625-1510
Fax:(410)625-1735
URL: http://www.anthemcapital.com
Contact: Bill Gust, Managing General Partner
E-mail: wgust@anthemcapital.com
Preferred Investment Size: $1,000,000 to $2,000,000. **Investment Types:** Seed, early and first stage. **Industry Preferences:** Computer software and services, Internet specific, biotechnology, industrial and energy, medical and health, communications and media, and other products. **Geographic Preferences:** Mid Atlantic. **Principal Exhibits:**

50805 ■ Boulder Ventures, Ltd.
5425 Wisconsin Ave., Ste. 704
Chevy Chase, MD 20815
Ph:(301)913-0213
Fax:(301)913-0434
URL: http://www.boulderventures.com
Contact: Andrew Jones, General Partner
E-mail: andy@boulderventures.com
Preferred Investment Size: $5,000,000 to $10,000,000. **Investment Types:** Start-up, early, first and second stage. **Industry Preferences:** Communications and media, Internet specific, computer software and services, consumer related, semiconductors and other electronics, other products, consumer related, biotechnology, and medical and health. **Geographic Preferences:** Colorado and Mid Atlantic. **Principal Exhibits:**

50806 ■ Catalyst Ventures
1119 St. Paul St.
Baltimore, MD 21202
Ph:(410)244-0123
Fax:(410)752-7721
Co. E-mail: info@catalystventures.com
URL: http://www.catalystventures.com
Preferred Investment Size: $500,000 maximum. **Investment Policies:** Equity. **Investment Types:** Research and development, and early stage. **Industry Preferences:** Data communications, biotechnology, and medical related. **Geographic Preferences:** Middle Atlantic. **Principal Exhibits:**

50807 ■ Grotech Capital Group
230 Schilling Cir., Ste. 362
Hunt Valley, MD 21031
Ph:(703)637-9555
Fax:(410)527-1307
URL: http://www.grotech.com
Contact: Frank Adams, Managing General Partner
E-mail: fadams@grotech.com
Preferred Investment Size: $500,000 to $5,000,000. **Investment Types:** Early, first, second and later stage, mezzanine, management buyouts, leveraged buyout, private placement, industry rollups, acquisition, expansion, turnaround, recapitalizations, and special situation. **Industry Preferences:** Internet specific, consumer related, communications and media, other products, computer software, and services, and semiconductors and other electronics, and other products. **Geographic Preferences:** Southeast and Mid Atlantic. **Principal Exhibits:**

50808 ■ Kinetic Ventures LLC
2 Wisconsin Cir., Ste. 620
Chevy Chase, MD 20815-7046
Ph:(301)652-8066
Fax:(301)652-8310
Co. E-mail: kinetic@kineticventures.com
URL: http://www.kineticventures.com
Contact: Nelson Chu, Principal
Preferred Investment Size: $2,000,000 to $7,000,000. **Investment Types:** Seed, early and first stage, and special situation. **Industry Preferences:** Internet specific, communications and media, computer software and services, industrial and energy, semiconductors and other electronics, and computer hardware. **Geographic Preferences:** U.S. **Principal Exhibits:**

50809 ■ Maryland Venture Capital Trust
401 E. Pratt St.
Baltimore, MD 21202
Ph:(410)767-6300
Free: 888-ChooseMD
URL: http://www.choosemaryland.org
Contact: Elizabeth Good, Managing Director
Investment Types: Fund of funds. **Industry Preferences:** Medical and health, computer software and services, other products, industrial and energy, semiconductors and other electronics, consumer related, biotechnology, and computer hardware. **Geographic Preferences:** Maryland. **Principal Exhibits:**

50810 ■ New Enterprise Associates (Chevy Chase)
5425 Wisconsin Ave., Ste. 800
Chevy Chase, MD 20815
Ph:(301)272-2300
Fax:(301)272-1700
URL: http://www.nea.com
Contact: Peter Barris, Managing General Partner
E-mail: pbarris@nea.com
Preferred Investment Size: $200,000 to $20,000,000. **Investment Types:** Seed, early, start-up, first and second stage, and mezzanine. **Industry Preferences:** Communications and media, Internet specific, medical and health, computer software and services, semiconductors and other electronics, biotechnology, computer hardware, other products, consumer related, industrial and energy. **Geographic Preferences:** U.S. **Principal Exhibits:**

50811 ■ Novak Biddle Venture Partners, L.P.
7501 Wisconsin Ave., Ste. 1380-E
Bethesda, MD 20814
Ph:(240)497-1910
Fax:(240)223-0255
Co. E-mail: info@novakbiddle.com
URL: http://www.novakbiddle.com
Contact: E. Rogers Novak Jr., General Partner
Preferred Investment Size: $100,000 to $10,000,000. **Investment Types:** Seed and early stage. **Industry Preferences:** Internet specific, communications and media, computer software and services, semiconductors and other electronics, computer hardware, other products, and medical and health. **Geographic Preferences:** Mid Atlantic, Northeast, and Southeast. **Principal Exhibits:**

50812 ■ Spring Capital Partners, L.P.
Latrobe Bldg., 5th Fl.
2 E. Read St.
Baltimore, MD 21202
Ph:(410)685-8000
Fax:(410)545-0015
Co. E-mail: mailbox@springcap.com
URL: http://www.springcap.com
Contact: Michael F. Donoghue, General Partner
E-mail: mfd@springcap.com
Preferred Investment Size: $2,000,000 to $7,000,000. **Investment Types:** Second and later stage, acquisition, industry rollups, balanced, mezzanine, recapitalization, and management or leveraged buyouts. **Industry Preferences:** Communications and media, computer related, semiconductors and other electronics, medical and health, consumer related, industrial and energy, transportation, and manufacturing. **Geographic Preferences:** Eastern half of U.S. **Principal Exhibits:**

50813 ■ Sterling Partners
650 S. Exeter St., Ste. 1000
Baltimore, MD 21202
Ph:(443)703-1700
Fax:(443)703-1750
URL: http://www.sterlingcap.com
Contact: Eric D. Becker, Senior Managing Director
Preferred Investment Size: Up to $200,000,000. **Investment Types:** Early stage and leveraged buyout. **Industry Preferences:** Communications and media, computer software, medical and health, consumer related, business service, and manufacturing. **Geographic Preferences:** Mid Atlantic and Midwest. **Principal Exhibits:**

50814 ■ T. Rowe Price Threshold Partnerships
100 E. Pratt St.
Baltimore, MD 21202
Ph:(410)345-2000
Free: 800-638-7890
Fax:(410)345-2349
Co. E-mail: usintitinquiries@troweprice.com
URL: http://www.troweprice.com
Preferred Investment Size: $3,000,000 to $5,000,000. **Investment Types:** Mezzanine, turnaround, leveraged buyout, later stage, expansion, and special situation. **Industry Preferences:** Computer software and services, Internet specific, consumer related, medical and health, other products, semiconductors and other electronics, communications and media, industrial and energy, biotechnology, and other products. **Geographic Preferences:** U.S. **Principal Exhibits:**

50815 ■ Toucan Capital
4800 Montgomery Ln., Ste. 801
Bethesda, MD 20814
Ph:(240)497-4060
Fax:(240)497-4065
Co. E-mail: info@toucancapital.com
URL: http://www.toucancapital.com
Contact: Linda Powers, Managing Director
Preferred Investment Size: $100,000 to $5,000,000. **Investment Types:** Early stage, seed, and start-up. **Industry Preferences:** Biotechnology, industrial and energy. **Geographic Preferences:** Mid Atlantic and Northeast. **Principal Exhibits:**

50816 ■ Walker Ventures SBIC / Walker Ventures
3060 Washington Rd., Ste. 200
Glenwood, MD 21738
Ph:(301)854-6850
Fax:(301)854-6235
Co. E-mail: plans@walkerventures.com
URL: http://www.walkerventures.com
Contact: Rusty Griffith, Principal
Preferred Investment Size: $250,000 to $3,000,000. **Investment Types:** Early stage. **Industry Preferences:** Internet specific, computer software and services, communications and media, other products, and semiconductors and other electronics. **Geographic Preferences:** Mid Atlantic. **Principal Exhibits:**

PROCUREMENT ASSISTANCE PROGRAMS

50817 ■ Maryland Department of Business and Economic Development Center–Administration Division–Contracts and Procurement Office (401 E)
401 E Pratt St.
Baltimore, MD 21202
Ph:(410)767-2211
Fax:(410)767-2216
Co. E-mail: dchronister@mdchoosemaryland.org
URL: http://www.choosemaryland.org
Contact: Debi Chronister, Dir.

50818 ■ Maryland Procurement Technical Assistance Center
7100 Baltimore Ave., Ste. 402
College Park, MD 20740
Ph:(301)403-2740
Fax:(301)403-2743
Co. E-mail: admin@mdptap.umd.edu
URL: http://www.mdptap.umd.edu
Contact: Mary Lee Kolich, Program Dir.
E-mail: mkolich@mdptap.umd.edu
Description: Provides marketing, contractual and technical assistance to Maryland small business owners who are interested in marketing their products and services to federal, state and local government agencies.

50819 ■ Office of Government Contacting
National Aeronautics and Space Administration
Goddard Space Flight Center
Bldg. 8, Code 210
Greenbelt, MD 20771
Ph:(301)286-4378
Fax:(202)481-0427
Co. E-mail: bernard.a.durham.1@gfsc.nasa.gov
URL: http://www.sba.gov
Contact: Bernard Durham, SBA Representative
E-mail: bkilyk@pop200.gsfc.nasa.gov
Description: Covers activities for NASA, Goddard Space Flight Center (Greenbelt, MD), NASA Headquarters (Washington, DC), LABCOM Adelphi Lab Center (Adelphi, MD), and Navy Surface Warfare Center (Indian Head, MD).

50820 ■ Regional Contracting Assistance Center–Ranson
322 W Washington St., Ste. 3
Charles Town, WV 25414
Ph:(304)724-7547
Fax:(304)724-7547
Co. E-mail: ctodd@rcacwv.com
URL: http://www.rcacwv.com
Contact: Christine Todd, Marketing Assistance Specialist
Description: Serves as a clearinghouse for information on contracting/subcontracting opportunities, and as a source for technical resources, information, and training. Offers an electronic bid match, access to government and industry regulations and standards, past procurement histories, technical assistance in understanding bid and contract requirements, assistance in bid proposal preparation, training in various aspects of contracting, and assistance in understanding contract pricing, packaging, and administration.

INCUBATORS/RESEARCH AND TECHNOLOGY PARKS

50821 ■ bwTech@UMBC Research and Technology Park
5523 Research Park Dr., Ste. 310
Baltimore, MD 21228
Ph:(410)455-5900
Fax:(410)455-5901
Co. E-mail: bwtech@umbc.edu
URL: http://www.bwtechumbc.com
Description: A small business incubator supportng technology by providing business development mentoring and assistance, as well as introductions to UMBC researchers and students for early-stage, start-up companies.

50822 ■ Emerging Technology Centers
Factory Bldg., 3rd Fl.
2400 Boston St.
Baltimore, MD 21224
Ph:(410)327-9150
Fax:(410)327-4086
URL: http://www.etcbaltimore.com/contact.html
Description: A non-profit business incubator program focused on growing early-stage technology and biotechnology companies in Baltimore City. It offers fully wired offices and space for participating companies at below market rates, with flexible leases, shared basic services and equipment, tech support, and onsite management.

50823 ■ Frederick Innovative Technology Center
4539 Metropolitan Ct.
Frederick, MD 21704
Ph:(301)694-2999
Fax:(301)360-3554
Co. E-mail: info@fitci.org
URL: http://www.fitci.org/
Description: A small business incubator offering local entrepreneurs facilities, services, and an environment in which they can prosper.

50824 ■ Garrett Information Enterprise Center
685 Mosser Rd., Ste. 1
McHenry, MD 21541
Ph:(301)387-3167
Fax:(301)387-3140
Co. E-mail: Lydia.reiser@garrettcollege.edu
URL: http://www.giecworks.com/
Contact: Lydia G. Reiser, Dir.
Description: A small business incubator whose goal it is to increase new firms' chances of survival during the early, risky years by providing a low-cost, supportive environment, and a network of assistance that will enable young firms to grow.

50825 ■ Maryland Advanced Development Laboratory
University Research Foundation
6411 Ivy Ln., Ste. 110
Greenbelt, MD 20770
Ph:(301)345-8664
Fax:(301)345-7305
Co. E-mail: krone@urf.com
URL: http://www.urf.com/madl/index.html
Contact: Dr. Norris J. Krone Jr., Pres.
E-mail: krone@urf.com
Scope: Science, engineering, and business. Research and development activities focus on advanced aircraft avionics, optics, lasers, and advanced computer systems such as high speed parallel processing. Performs contract research and development involving classified or proprietary research, complex program management, and quick reaction contracting.

50826 ■ Maryland Technology Enterprise Institute
University of Maryland
2120 Potomac Bldg. 092
College Park, MD 20742
Ph:(301)405-3906
Free: 800-245-5810
Fax:(301)403-4105
URL: http://www.mtech.umd.edu
Contact: Robert Barazotto
Description: Assists in problem identification, provides support, and formulates solutions. Also performs information searches. Reviews and critiques new ideas, products, and designs.

50827 ■ Montgomery County Department of Economic Development–Business Innovation Network
101 Monroe St., 2nd Fl.
Rockville, MD 20850
Ph:(240)777-2000

Fax:(240)777-2046
Co. E-mail: ded.info@montgomerycountymd.gov
URL: http://www.mcinnovationnetwork.com
Description: A small business incubator and accelerator offering fertile ground for innovations in bioscience, information technology, education, and the arts. Its goal is to nurture and grow young, enterprising businesses into smart and successful companies through its Business Innovation Network.

50828 ■ Mtech Technology Advancement Program
387 Technology Dr., Ste. 1105
College Park, MD 20742
Ph:(301)405-3809
Fax:(301)226-5378
Co. E-mail: smagids@umd.edu
URL: http://www.tap.umd.edu/
Contact: Dean Chang, Dir
Description: Mtech TAP is a program of the Engineering Research Center utilizing the extensive resources of the University of Maryland at College Park.

50829 ■ R&D Village
Montgomery County Department of Economic Development
111 Rockville Pike, Ste. 800
Rockville, MD 20850
Ph:(240)777-2000
Fax:(240)777-2001
Co. E-mail: ded.info@montgomerycountymd.gov
URL: http://www.montgomerycountymd.gov/mcgtmpl.
asp?url=/Content/DED/BRD/biotech.asprd
Contact: Steven A. Silverman, Dir.
E-mail: ded.info@montgomerycountymd.gov
Scope: 1,200-acre site linking biomedical research and development activities between government, park tenants, and academia. Houses the Center for Advanced Research in Biotechnology, a joint research venture between the National Institute of Standards and Technology, University of Maryland, and Montgomery county government; also houses a Johns Hopkins University facility focusing on advanced study programs in computer science, electrical engineering, and technical management, and the University's campus at Shady Grove. The Village also includes the Shady Grove Life Sciences Center, Shady Grove Executive Center, Decoverly, and The Washingtonian. **Services:** Site location assistance. **Publications:** Newsletter (biweekly). **Educational Activities:** Conferences; Meetings (monthly), of Biotechnology Network and Telecommunications Network; Workshops.

50830 ■ Rockville Innovation Center
95 Monroe St.
Rockville, MD 20850
Ph:(301)315-8096
Fax:(301)315-8097
Co. E-mail: Info@RockvilleREDI.org
URL: http://www.rockvilleredi.org/business/incubator.
html
Description: A small business incubator providing space and support for approximately 30 start-up technology companies to grow.

50831 ■ The Rural Development Center
University of Maryland, Eastern Shore
Richard E. Henson Center, Rm. 2147
Princess Anne, MD 21853
Ph:(410)651-6186
Fax:(410)651-6207
Co. E-mail: dskuennen@mail.umes.edu
URL: http://www.skipjack.net/le_shore/rural/
Contact: Daniel Kuennen, Dir.
Description: The RDC is a community-based incubator serving the needs of people in rural communities. It is located on the campus of the University of Maryland Eastern Shore.

50832 ■ Technical Innovation Center
Hagerstown Community College
11400 Robinwood Dr., Ste. 321
Hagerstown, MD 21742
Ph:(301)790-2800

Fax:(301)797-4808
Co. E-mail: marschnerc@hagerstowncc.edu
URL: http://www.technicalinnovationcenter.com/
Description: A self-sustaining economic develop-ment effort fostering the growth of new and expand-ing businesses by providing access to advanced technologies, business development resources, and collaborative opportunities.

50833 ■ Towson University–Office of University Research Services
7800 York Rd., Rms. 225-220
Towson, MD 21252-0001
Ph:(410)704-2236
Fax:(410)704-4494
Co. E-mail: ours@towson.edu
URL: http://www2.towson.edu/research/ours.asp
Contact: Mary Louise Healy, Asst.VP, Res.
E-mail: ours@towson.edu
Scope: Identifies funding agencies, collaborates with faculty on proposal submissions, administers exter-nally funded grants and contracts, negotiates re-search contracts, advises University administration on federal regulations affecting research, and devel-ops university policies and procedures for sponsored research. **Educational Activities:** Proposal-writing workshops.

50834 ■ TowsonGlobal - International Incubator
Townson University Business Globalization Center
7801 York Rd., Ste. 342
Towson, MD 21204
Ph:(410)769-6449
Fax:(410)769-6477
Co. E-mail: info@twonsonglobal.com
URL: http://www.townsonglobal.com/dotnetnuke/
Description: An international incubator for early-stage serving as a gateway to international markets for product-oriented Maryland companies and as a magnet for foreign companies looking to market their products in the mid-Atlantic region. It will offer workshops and resources to companies in the greater business community to help them compete in a global marketplace.

50835 ■ University of Maryland–Biotechnology Institute
9600 Gudelsky Dr.
Rockville, MD 20850
Ph:(240)314-6277

Fax:(240)314-6250
Co. E-mail: eisenste@umbi.umd.edu
URL: http://www.umbi.umd.edu
Contact: Prof. Edward Eisenstein PhD, Actg.Pres.
E-mail: eisenste@umbi.umd.edu
Scope: Coordinates basic biotechnology research in the following areas: protein engineering, structure, and function; molecular biology of plant and animal protection; bioprocess engineering; legal, and ethical issues raised by biotechnology and its applications; marine molecular biology and molecular genetics; human virology; and medical biotechnology. **Publica-tions:** Annual Report; mMBI; Scientific Proceedings. **Educational Activities:** Research seminars; Science and technology courses, for middle school students; Short courses; Specialized workshops; Symposium; Tours for local industry.

50836 ■ Wheaton Business Innovation Center
Montgomery County Business Incubator Network
Wheaton South Bldg.
11002 Veirs Mill Rd., 7th Fl.
Wheaton, MD 20902
Ph:(301)942-4005
Fax:(301)942-4493
Co. E-mail: john.korpela@montgomerycountymd.gov
URL: http://www.montgomerycountymd.gov/content/ded/incub/pdf/wbic.pdf
Contact: John Korpela, Mgr.
Description: A small business incubator created for current, locally-based business service, government contracting, and/or professional trade businesses looking to grow.

EDUCATIONAL PROGRAMS

50837 ■ University of Baltimore–Merrick School of Business
1420 N Charles St.
Baltimore, MD 21201
Ph:(410)837-4200
Fax:(410)837-5652
URL: http://www.ubalt.edu
Description: Undergraduate and graduate business courses, institutes, and conferences are offered in flexible evening and weekend schedules. Programs are designed for persons already in positions of executive responsibility, as well as for those about to enter into managerial positions.

PUBLICATIONS

50838 ■ *Baltimore Business Journal*
111 Market Place, Ste. 720
Baltimore, MD 21202
Ph:(410)576-1161
Fax:(410)752-3112
URL: http://www.amcity.com/baltimore

50839 ■ *Smart Start your Maryland Business*
PSI Research
300 N. Valley Dr.
Grants Pass, OR 97526
Ph:(503)479-9464
Free: 800-228-2275
Fax:(503)476-1479
Co. E-mail: info@psi-research.com
URL: http://www.psi-research.com
Ed: Michael D. Jenkins. **Released:** Revised edition, 1992. **Price:** $29.95 (looseleaf binder); $24.95 (paper). **Description:** Part of the Successful Busi-ness Library series.

PUBLISHERS

50840 ■ Rolling Hills Publishing
242 Eagle Flight
PO Box 724
Ozark, MO 65721
Ph:(410)635-3233
Free: 800-918-7323
Fax:888-329-2747
Co. E-mail: info@rollinghillspublishing.com
URL: http://www.rollinghillspublishing.com
Contact: Michael E. Gray, Publisher
Description: Publishes educational, automobiles. **Founded:** 2003.

50841 ■ Schreiber Publishing Inc.
51 Monroe St., Ste. 101
PO Box 4193
Rockville, MD 20850-2420
Ph:(301)424-7737
Free: 800-822-3213
Fax:(301)424-2336
Co. E-mail: books@schreiberpublishing.com
URL: http://www.schreiberpublishing.com
Contact: Yohanan Manor, Editor
Description: Publishes language and translation books and books relating to art, the Holocaust, his-tory and children. Publishes reference books and fic-tion books. Accepts unsolicited manuscripts. Reaches market through commission reps, direct mail, reviews, listings, telephone sales as well as distributors. **Founded:** 1994.

SMALL BUSINESS DEVELOPMENT CENTER LEAD OFFICE

50842 ■ University of Massachusetts–Small Business Development Center
227 Isenberg School of Management
121 President's Dr.
Amherst, MA 01003-4935
Ph:(413)545-6301
Fax:(413)545-1273
Co. E-mail: gep@msbdc.umass.edu
URL: http://www.msbdc.org/
Contact: Georgianna Parkin, State Director
Description: Provides one-to-one free comprehensive and confidential services focusing on, business growth and strategies, financing and loan assistance as well as strategic, marketing and operational analysis.

SMALL BUSINESS DEVELOPMENT CENTERS

50843 ■ Central Massachusetts Small Business Development Center
950 Main St.
Worcester, MA 01610
Co. E-mail: sbdc@clarku.edu
URL: http://www.clarku.edu/offices/sbdc
Contact: Larry Marsh, Dir

50844 ■ Massachusetts Small Business Development Center - Berkshire
75 North St., Ste. 360
Pittsfield, MA 01201
Fax:(413)499-3005
Co. E-mail: kgirouard@msbdc.umass.edu
URL: http://www.msbdc.org/berkshire
Contact: Keith Girouard

50845 ■ Massachusetts Small Business Development Center Network - Western
Scibelli Enterprise Center
1 Federal St.
Springfield, MA 01105
Fax:(413)737-2312
Co. E-mail: ddoherty@msbdc.umass.edu
URL: http://www.msbdc.org/wmass
Contact: Dianne Fuller Doherty, Dir.

50846 ■ Massachusetts Small Business Development Center - Northeast
Enterprise Center
121 Loring Ave., Ste. 310
Salem, MA 01970
Fax:(978)542-6345
Co. E-mail: msomer@salemstate.edu
URL: http://www.salemstate.edu/sbdc
Contact: Margaret Somer, Dir.

50847 ■ Southeastern Massachusetts Regional Small Business Development Center
200 Pocasset St.
Fall River, MA 02721
Fax:(508)674-1929
Co. E-mail: mlailes@msbdc.umass.edu
URL: http://www.msbdc.org/semass
Contact: Melinda Ailes

50848 ■ Springfield Business Development Corporation
1441 Main St., Ste. 111
Springfield, MA 01103
Fax:(413)781-1595
Co. E-mail: information@developspringfield.com
URL: http://developspringfield.com
Contact: Maureen Hayes, Pres.

SMALL BUSINESS ASSISTANCE PROGRAMS

50849 ■ Massachusetts Export Center
State Transportation Bldg.
10 Park Plaza, Ste. 4510
Boston, MA 02116
Ph:(617)973-8664
Fax:(617)973-8681
Co. E-mail: pmurphy@state.ma.us
URL: http://www.mass.gov/export
Contact: Paula Murphy, Dir
Description: Provides assistance in market analysis, training, advice on export practices and financing for participation in foreign trade missions, export counseling, and market research. Also identifies foreign contacts for exporting firms and organizes and conducts trade events.

50850 ■ Massachusetts Office of Housing and Economic Development
1 Ashburton Pl., Ste. 2101
Boston, MA 02108
Ph:(617)788-3610
Free: 800-CAP-ITAL
Fax:(617)788-3605
URL: http://www.mass.gov
Contact: Tina Brooks, Chief
Description: Provides assistance and information on relocating and expanding businesses in Massachusetts.

50851 ■ Massachusetts Office of International Trade and Investment
Boston Fish Pier
East Bldg. 1, Ste. 300
212 Northern Ave.
Boston, MA 02210
Ph:(617)973-8650
Fax:(617)227-3488
Co. E-mail: ted.carr@state.ma.us
URL: http://www.mass.gov/moiti
Contact: Ted Carr, Exec Dir
Description: Oversees the state's international trade activities. Also monitors the degree of foreign investment in Massachusetts.

SCORE OFFICES

50852 ■ SCORE Agawam
Path: www.scorewesternmass.org

50853 ■ SCORE Amherst
Path: www.scorewesternmass.org

50854 ■ SCORE Boston
Thomas P. O'Neill Federal Bldg.
10 Causeway St., Rm. 265
Boston, MA 02222-1093
Ph:(617)565-5591
Co. E-mail: boston-score-20@verizon.net
URL: http://www.scoreboston.org
Description: Serves as volunteer program in which working and retired business management professionals provide free business counseling to men and women who are considering starting a small business, encountering problems with their business, or expanding their business. Offers free one-on-one counseling, online counseling and low cost workshops on a variety of business topics.

50855 ■ SCORE Cape Cod
270 Communications Way, Ste. 5-B
Hyannis, MA 02601
Ph:(508)775-4884
Fax:(508)790-2540
Co. E-mail: capecodscore@verizon.net
URL: http://www.scorecapecod.com
Description: Serves as volunteer program in which working and retired business management professionals provide free business counseling to men and women who are considering starting a small business, encountering problems with their business, or expanding their business. Offers free one-on-one counseling, online counseling and low cost workshops on a variety of business topics.

50856 ■ SCORE Greenfield
Path: www.scorewesternmass.org

50857 ■ SCORE Northampton
Path: www.scorewesternmass.org

50858 ■ SCORE Northeast Massachusetts
Danvers Savings Bank
100 Cummings Ctr., Ste. 101 K
Beverly, MA 01915
Ph:(978)922-9441
Co. E-mail: info@scorenemass.org
URL: http://www.scorenemass.org
Description: Serves as volunteer program in which working and retired business management professionals provide free business counseling to men and women who are considering starting a small business, encountering problems with their business, or expanding their business. Offers free one-on-one counseling, online counseling and low cost workshops on a variety of business topics.

50859 ■ SCORE Pittsfield
Path: www.scorewesternmass.org

50860 ■ SCORE Southeastern Massachusetts
60 School St.
Brockton, MA 02301
Ph:(508)587-2673
URL: http://www.scoresema.org
Description: Serves as volunteer program in which working and retired business management professionals provide free business counseling to men and women who are considering starting a small business, encountering problems with their business, or expanding their business. Offers free one-on-one counseling, online counseling and low cost workshops on a variety of business topics.

50861 ■ SCORE Springfield
Path: www.scorewesternmass.org

50862 ■ SCORE Westfield
Path: www.scorewesternmass.org

50863 ■ SCORE Worcester
c/o Worcester Regional Chamber of Commerce
446 Main St.
Worcester, MA 01608
Ph:(508)753-2929
Co. E-mail: info@scoreworcester.org
URL: http://www.scoreworcester.org
Description: Works to facilitate the formation, success and growth of small business. Provides free, confidential business counseling to individuals just starting a business and to existing small businesses. Offers low cost educational workshops on business topics.

BETTER BUSINESS BUREAUS

50864 ■ Better Business Bureau of Central New England
340 Main St., Ste. 802
Worcester, MA 01608
Free: (866)566-9222
Fax:(508)754-4158
Co. E-mail: worcester@cne.bbb.org
URL: http://central-westernma.bbb.org
Contact: Nancy B. Cahalen, Pres./CEO

50865 ■ Better Business Bureau Serving Eastern Massachusetts, Maine and Vermont
235 W Central St., Ste. 1
Natick, MA 01760-3767
Ph:(508)652-4800
Fax:(508)652-4820
Co. E-mail: info@bosbbb.org
URL: http://boston.bbb.org
Contact: Mr. Kevin J. Sanders, Pres./CEO

CHAMBERS OF COMMERCE

50866 ■ Affiliated Chambers of Commerce of Greater Springfield
1441 Main St., Ste. 136
Springfield, MA 01103-1449
Ph:(413)787-1555
Fax:(413)731-8530
Co. E-mail: denver@myonlinechamber.com
URL: http://www.myonlinechamber.com
Contact: Russell F. Denver, Pres.

50867 ■ Alliance for Amesbury
5 Market Sq.
Amesbury, MA 01913
Ph:(978)388-3178
Fax:(978)388-4952
Co. E-mail: steffiemccowan@verizon.net
URL: http://www.amesburychamber.com
Contact: Stefanie McCowan, Exec. Dir.

50868 ■ Amherst Area Chamber of Commerce
28 Amity St.
Amherst, MA 01002
Ph:(413)253-0700
Fax:(413)256-0771
Co. E-mail: info@amherstarea.com
URL: http://www.amherstarea.com
Contact: Tony Maroulis, Exec. Dir.

50869 ■ Arlington Chamber of Commerce
1 Whittemore Park
Arlington, MA 02474
Ph:(781)643-4600
Fax:(781)646-5581
Co. E-mail: info@arlcc.org
URL: http://www.arlcc.org
Contact: Michele M. Meagher, Exec. Dir.

50870 ■ Assabet Valley Chamber of Commerce
18 Church St.
PO Box 578
Hudson, MA 01749
Ph:(978)568-0360
Fax:(978)562-4118
Co. E-mail: info@assabetvalleychamber.org
URL: http://www.assabetvalleychamber.org
Contact: Sarah B. Cressy, Pres./CEO

50871 ■ Bedford Chamber of Commerce
Town Center Bldg.
12 Mudge Way (2-2)
Bedford, MA 01730-2138
Ph:(781)275-8503
Co. E-mail: bcoc@bedfordchamber.org
URL: http://www.bedfordchamber.org
Contact: Maureen McAulifee Sullivan, Exec. Dir.

50872 ■ Berkshire Chamber of Commerce
6 W Main St.
North Adams, MA 01247
Ph:(413)449-4000
Fax:(413)664-1049
Co. E-mail: info@berkshirechamber.com
URL: http://www.berkshirechamber.com
Contact: Michael Supranowicz, Pres./CEO

50873 ■ Berkshires Chamber of Commerce
75 North St., Ste. 360
Pittsfield, MA 01201
Ph:(413)499-4000
Fax:(413)447-9641
Co. E-mail: info@berkshirechamber.com
URL: http://www.berkshirechamber.com
Contact: Ms. Christina Barrett, Dir. of Marketing and Communications

50874 ■ Beverly Chamber of Commerce
28 Cabot St.
Beverly, MA 01915
Ph:(978)232-9559
Fax:(978)232-9372
Co. E-mail: info@beverlychamber.com
URL: http://www.beverlychamber.com/board.html
Contact: Sheila Field, Exec. Dir.

50875 ■ Billerica Chamber of Commerce
574 Boston Rd., Unit 1
Billerica, MA 01821
Ph:(978)663-0036
Fax:(978)670-1020
Co. E-mail: info@billericachamberofcommerce.com
Contact: Edna M. Chalmers, Pres.

50876 ■ Blackstone Valley Chamber of Commerce
110 Church St.
Whitinsville, MA 01588-1442
Ph:(508)234-9090
Fax:(508)234-5152
Co. E-mail: achamberlain@blackstonevalley.org
URL: http://www.blackstonevalley.org
Contact: Jeannie Hebert, Pres./CEO

50877 ■ Brookline Chamber of Commerce
251 Harvard St., Ste. 1
Brookline, MA 02446-3202
Ph:(617)739-1330
Fax:(617)739-1200
Co. E-mail: info@brooklinechamber.com
URL: http://www.brooklinechamber.com
Contact: Harry R. Robinson, Exec. Dir.

50878 ■ Cambridge Chamber of Commerce
859 Massachusetts Ave.
Cambridge, MA 02139
Ph:(617)876-4100
Fax:(617)354-9874
Co. E-mail: ccinfo@cambridgechamber.org
URL: http://www.cambridgechamber.org
Contact: Kelly Thompson Clark, Pres./CEO

50879 ■ Cape Ann Chamber of Commerce
33 Commercial St.
Gloucester, MA 01930-5087
Ph:(978)283-1601
Fax:(978)283-4740
Co. E-mail: info@capeannchamber.com
URL: http://www.capeannchamber.com
Contact: Todd Tanger, Pres.

50880 ■ Cape Cod Canal Regional Chamber of Commerce
70 Main St.
Buzzards Bay, MA 02532
Ph:(508)759-6000
Fax:(508)759-6965
Co. E-mail: info@capecodcanalchamber.org
URL: http://www.capecodcanalchamber.org/cwt/
external/wcpages/index.aspx
Contact: Marie Oliva, Pres./CEO

50881 ■ Chamber of Commerce of the Attleboro Area
42 Union St.
Attleboro, MA 02703-2911
Ph:(508)222-0801
Fax:(508)222-1498
URL: http://www.attleborochamber.com
Contact: Jack Lank, Pres.

50882 ■ Chatham Chamber of Commerce
PO Box 793
Chatham, MA 02633-0793
Ph:(508)945-5199
Free: 800-715-5567
Fax:(508)430-7919
Co. E-mail: chamber@chathaminfo.com
URL: http://www.chathaminfo.com
Contact: Scott Hamilton, Pres.

50883 ■ Chicopee Chamber of Commerce
264 Exchange St.
Chicopee, MA 01013
Ph:(413)594-2101
Fax:(413)594-2103
Co. E-mail: gailsherman@chicopeechamber.org
URL: http://www.chicopeechamber.org
Contact: Gail Sherman, Pres.

50884 ■ Cohasset Chamber of Commerce
PO Box 336
Cohasset, MA 02025-0336
Ph:(781)383-1010
Co. E-mail: info@cohassetchamber.com
URL: http://www.cohassetchamber.org
Contact: Frank Campbell, Pres.

50885 ■ Concord Chamber of Commerce
15 Walden St., Ste. 7
Concord, MA 01742-2504
Ph:(978)369-3120
Fax:(978)369-1515
Co. E-mail: info@concordchamberofcommerce.org
URL: http://www.concordchamberofcommerce.org
Contact: Stephanie Stillman, Exec. Dir.

50886 ■ Cranberry Country Chamber of Commerce
PO Box 409
Middleboro, MA 02346-0409
Ph:(508)947-1499
Fax:(508)947-1446
Co. E-mail: info@cranberrycountry.org
URL: http://www.cranberrycountry.org
Contact: Jean Scarborough, Pres.

50887 ■ East Boston Chamber of Commerce
296 Bennington St., 2nd Fl.
East Boston, MA 02128
Ph:(617)569-5000
Fax:(617)569-1945
Co. E-mail: eastboston.chamber@verizon.net
URL: http://www.eastbostonchamber.com
Contact: John Dudley, Exec. Dir.

50888 ■ Eastham Chamber of Commerce
PO Box 1329
Eastham, MA 02642
Ph:(508)240-7211
Co. E-mail: info@easthamchamber.com
URL: http://www.easthamchamber.com
Contact: Janet Demetri, Pres.

50889 ■ Fall River Area Chamber of Commerce and Industry
200 Pocasset St.
Fall River, MA 02721-1533
Ph:(508)676-8226
Fax:(508)675-5932
Co. E-mail: info@fallriverchamber.com
URL: http://www.fallriverchamber.com
Contact: Robert Mellion Esq., Pres./CEO

50890 ■ Falmouth Chamber of Commerce
20 Academy Ln.
Falmouth, MA 02540
Ph:(508)548-8500
Free: 800-526-8532
Fax:(508)548-8521
Co. E-mail: info@falmouthchamber.com
URL: http://www.falmouthchamber.com
Contact: Jay Zavala, Pres.

50891 ■ Franklin County Chamber of Commerce
PO Box 898
Greenfield, MA 01302-0898
Ph:(413)773-5463
Fax:(413)773-7008
Co. E-mail: fccc@crocker.com
URL: http://www.franlincc.org
Contact: Ann L. Hamilton, Pres.

50892 ■ Greater Boston Chamber of Commerce
265 Franklin St., 12th Fl.
Boston, MA 02110
Ph:(617)227-4500
Fax:(617)227-7505
Co. E-mail: info@bostonchamber.com
URL: http://www.bostonchamber.com
Contact: Paul Guzzi, Pres./CEO

50893 ■ Greater Gardner Chamber of Commerce
210 Main St.
Gardner, MA 01440
Ph:(978)632-1780
Fax:(978)630-1767
Co. E-mail: mellis@gardnerma.com
URL: http://www.gardnerma.com
Contact: Michael F. Ellis, Pres./CEO

50894 ■ Greater Haverhill Chamber of Commerce
87 Winter St.
Haverhill, MA 01830
Ph:(978)373-5663
Fax:(978)373-8060
Co. E-mail: info@haverhillchamber.com
URL: http://www.haverhillchamber.com
Contact: James P. Jajuga, Pres./CEO

50895 ■ Greater Holyoke Chamber of Commerce
177 High St.
Holyoke, MA 01040-6504
Ph:(413)534-3376
Fax:(413)534-3385
Co. E-mail: ransford@holycham.com
URL: http://www.holyokechamber.com
Contact: Doris M. Ransford, Pres.

50896 ■ Greater Lowell Chamber of Commerce
131 Merrimack St.
Lowell, MA 01852
Ph:(978)459-8154
Fax:(978)452-4145
Co. E-mail: info@greaterlowellchamber.org
URL: http://www.glcc.biz
Contact: Jeanne Osborn, Pres./CEO

50897 ■ Greater Newburyport Chamber of Commerce and Industry
38R Merrimac St.
Newburyport, MA 01950
Ph:(978)462-6680
Fax:(978)465-4145
Co. E-mail: info@newburyportchamber.org
URL: http://www.newburyportchamber.org
Contact: Ann Ormond, Pres.

50898 ■ Greater Northampton Chamber of Commerce
99 Pleasant St.
Northampton, MA 01060
Ph:(413)584-1900
Fax:(413)584-1934
Co. E-mail: info@explorenorthampton.com
URL: http://www.explorenorthampton.com/chamber/about.htm
Contact: Suzanne Beck, Exec. Dir.

50899 ■ Hanover Chamber of Commerce
PO Box 68
Hanover, MA 02339-0068
Ph:(781)826-8865
Fax:(781)826-7721
Co. E-mail: chamber@hanovermachamber.com
URL: http://www.hanovermachamber.com
Contact: Tom Burke, Pres.

50900 ■ Harwich Chamber of Commerce
One Schoolhouse Rd.
Harwich Port, MA 02646
Ph:(508)430-1165
Free: 800-4-HARWICH
Fax:(508)430-2105
Co. E-mail: info@harwichcc.com
URL: http://www.harwichcc.com
Contact: Jeremy Gingras, Pres.

50901 ■ Holden Area Chamber of Commerce
1174 Main St.
Holden, MA 01520-0377
Ph:(508)829-9220
Fax:(508)829-9220
Co. E-mail: info@holdenareachamber.org
URL: http://www.holdenareachamber.org
Contact: Caron Dooley, Pres.

50902 ■ Hyannis Area Chamber of Commerce
PO Box 100
Hyannis, MA 02601
Ph:(508)775-2201
Free: 877-492-6647
Fax:(508)775-7131
Co. E-mail: chamber@hyannis.com
URL: http://www.hyannis.com
Contact: Deborah Converse, CEO

50903 ■ Lenox Chamber of Commerce
14 Housatonic St.
Lenox, MA 01240
Ph:(413)637-3646
Fax:(413)637-3626
Co. E-mail: info@lenox.org
URL: http://www.lenox.org
Contact: Ralph Petillo, Dir.

50904 ■ Lexington Chamber of Commerce
1875 Massachusetts Ave.
Lexington, MA 02420
Ph:(781)862-2480
Fax:(781)862-5995
Co. E-mail: jterhune@lexingtonchamber.org
URL: http://www.lexingtonchamber.org
Contact: Mary Jo Bohart, Exec. Dir.

50905 ■ Lynn Area Chamber of Commerce
100 Oxford St.
Lynn, MA 01901
Ph:(781)592-2900
Fax:(781)592-2903
Co. E-mail: info@lynnareachamber.com
URL: http://www.lynnareachamber.com
Contact: Leslie Gould, Exec. Dir.

50906 ■ Malden Chamber of Commerce
200 Pleasant St., Ste. 416
Malden, MA 02148-4884
Ph:(781)322-4500
Fax:(781)322-4866
Co. E-mail: info@maldenchamber.org
URL: http://www.maldenchamber.org
Contact: Maurene J. Campbell, Exec. Dir.

50907 ■ Marblehead Chamber of Commerce
62 Pleasant St.
Marblehead, MA 01945
Ph:(781)631-2868
Fax:(781)639-8582
Co. E-mail: info@marbleheadchamber.org
URL: http://www.marbleheadchamber.org
Contact: Ann Marie Casey, Exec. Dir.

50908 ■ Marlborough Regional Chamber of Commerce
11 Florence St.
Marlborough, MA 01752-2822
Ph:(508)485-7746
Fax:(508)481-1819
Co. E-mail: marlcham@marlboroughchamber.org
URL: http://www.marlboroughchamber.org
Contact: Susanne Morreale-Leeber, Pres./CEO

50909 ■ Martha's Vineyard Chamber of Commerce
PO Box 1698
Vineyard Haven, MA 02568
Ph:(508)693-0085
Free: 800-505-4815
Co. E-mail: info@mvy.com
URL: http://www.mvy.com/cwt/external/wcpages/index.aspx
Contact: Nancy Gardella, Exec. Dir.

50910 ■ Medford Chamber of Commerce
1 Shipyard Way
Medford, MA 02155
Ph:(781)396-1277
Fax:(781)396-1278
Co. E-mail: director@medfordchamberma.com
URL: http://www.medfordchamberma.com
Contact: Cheryl White, Exec. Dir.

50911 ■ Melrose Chamber of Commerce
1 W Foster St.
Melrose, MA 02176
Ph:(781)665-3033
Fax:(781)665-5595
Co. E-mail: info@melrosechamber.org
URL: http://www.melrosechamber.org
Contact: Joan Ford Mongeau, Exec. Dir.

50912 ■ Merrimack Valley Chamber of Commerce
264 Essex St.
Lawrence, MA 01840-1496
Ph:(978)686-0900
Fax:(978)794-9953
Co. E-mail: thechamber@merrimackvalleychamber.com
URL: http://www.merrimackvalleychamber.com
Contact: Joseph J. Bevilacqua, Pres./CEO

50913 ■ Metro South Chamber of Commerce
60 School St.
Brockton, MA 02301
Ph:(508)586-0500
Fax:(508)587-1340
Co. E-mail: info@metrosouthchamber.com
URL: http://www.metrosouthchamber.com
Contact: Christopher Cooney, Pres./CEO

50914 ■ MetroWest Chamber of Commerce
1671 Worcester Rd., Ste. 201
Framingham, MA 01701-5400
Ph:(508)879-5600
Fax:(508)875-9325
Co. E-mail: chamber@metrowest.org
URL: http://www.metrowest.org
Contact: A. Theodore Welte CCE, Pres./CEO

50915 ■ Middlesex West Chamber of Commerce
77 Great Rd., Ste. 214
Acton, MA 01720-0212
Ph:(978)263-0010
Fax:(978)264-0303
Co. E-mail: info@mwcoc.com
URL: http://www.mwcoc.com
Contact: Sarah Fletcher, Exec. Dir.

50916 ■ Milford Area Chamber of Commerce
258 Main St., Ste. 306
PO Box 621
Milford, MA 01757
Ph:(508)473-6700
Fax:(508)473-8467
Co. E-mail: chamber@milfordchamber.org
URL: http://www.milfordchamber.org
Contact: Barry Feingold, Pres./CEO

50917 ■ Nantucket Island Chamber of Commerce
Zero Main St., 2nd Fl.
Nantucket, MA 02554-3595
Ph:(508)228-1700
Fax:(508)325-4925
Co. E-mail: info@nantucketchamber.org
URL: http://www.nantucketchamber.org
Contact: Ms. Tracy Bakalar, Exec. Dir.

50918 ■ Nashoba Valley Chamber of Commerce
100 Sherman Ave., Ste. 3
Devens, MA 01434
Ph:(978)772-6976
Fax:(978)772-3503
Co. E-mail: director@nvcoc.com
URL: http://www.nvcoc.com
Contact: Scott Lathrop, Pres.

50919 ■ National Black Chamber of Commerce, New England
1127 Main St., 2nd Fl.
Springfield, MA 01103
Ph:(413)731-6444
Fax:(413)731-1011
Co. E-mail: yebyam@neblackchamber.org
URL: http://www.neblackchamber.org
Contact: Yvonne E. Byam

50920 ■ Neponset Valley Chamber of Commerce
190 Vanderbilt Ave., Ste. 1
Norwood, MA 02062-5047
Ph:(781)769-1126
Fax:(781)769-0808
Co. E-mail: kathleen@nvcc.com
URL: http://www.nvcc.com
Contact: Sue McQuaid, Pres./CEO

50921 ■ New Bedford Area Chamber of Commerce
794 Purchase St.
New Bedford, MA 02740
Ph:(508)999-5231
Fax:(508)999-5237
Co. E-mail: info@newbedfordchamber.com
URL: http://www.newbedfordchamber.com
Contact: Roy Nascimento, Pres.

50922 ■ Newton - Needham Chamber of Commerce
281 Needham St.
Newton, MA 02464
Ph:(617)244-5300
Fax:(617)244-5302
Co. E-mail: info@nnchamber.com
URL: http://www.nnchamber.com/cwt/external/
wcpages/index.aspx
Contact: Thomas J. O'Rourke CCE, Pres.

50923 ■ North Attleboro and Plainville Chamber of Commerce
PO Box 1071
North Attleboro, MA 02761
Ph:(508)695-6011

Fax:(508)695-6096
Co. E-mail: info@napcc.org
URL: http://www.napcc.org
Contact: Oreste D'Arconte, Chm.

50924 ■ North Central Massachusetts Chamber of Commerce
860 South St.
Fitchburg, MA 01420
Ph:(978)353-7600
Fax:(978)353-4896
Co. E-mail: chamber@massweb.org
URL: http://northcentralmass.com
Contact: David L. McKeehan, Pres.

50925 ■ North Quabbin Chamber of Commerce
PO Box 157
Athol, MA 01331
Ph:(978)249-3849
Fax:(978)249-7151
Co. E-mail: nqcc1@verizon.net
URL: http://www.northquabbinchamber.com
Contact: Steve Raymond, Exec. Dir.

50926 ■ North Shore Chamber of Commerce
5 Cherry Hill Dr., Ste. 100
Danvers, MA 01923-4395
Ph:(978)774-8565
Fax:(978)774-3418
Co. E-mail: info@northshorechamber.org
URL: http://www.northshorechamber.org
Contact: Robert G. Bradford, Pres.

50927 ■ North Suburban Chamber of Commerce
76R Winn St., Ste. 3D
Woburn, MA 01801
Ph:(781)933-3499
Fax:(781)933-1071
Co. E-mail: info@northsuburbanchamber.com
URL: http://www.northsuburbanchamber.com
Contact: Maureen A. Rogers, Pres.

50928 ■ Peabody Chamber of Commerce
24 Main St.
Peabody, MA 01960-5593
Ph:(978)531-0384
Fax:(978)532-7227
Co. E-mail: pcc@peabodychamber.com
URL: http://www.peabodychamber.com
Contact: Deanne Healey, Pres./CEO

50929 ■ Plymouth Area Chamber of Commerce
10 Cordage Park Cir., Ste. 231
Plymouth, MA 02360
Ph:(508)830-1620
Fax:(508)830-1621
Co. E-mail: info@plymouthchamber.com
URL: http://www.plymouthchamber.com
Contact: Denis Hanks, Exec. Dir.

50930 ■ Provincetown Chamber of Commerce
PO Box 1017
Provincetown, MA 02657-1017
Ph:(508)487-3424
Co. E-mail: info@ptownchamber.com
URL: http://www.ptownchamber.com
Contact: Candice Collins-Boden, Exec. Dir.

50931 ■ Quaboag Valley Chamber of Commerce
3 Converse St., Ste. 103
Palmer, MA 01069-0269
Ph:(413)283-2418
Fax:(413)289-1355
Co. E-mail: lenny@qvcc.org
URL: http://www.quaboagvalley.org
Contact: Leonard N. Weake, Pres.

50932 ■ Reading-North Reading Chamber of Commerce
PO Box 771
Reading, MA 01867
Ph:(781)944-8824

Fax:(781)944-6125
Co. E-mail: rnrchambercom@aol.com
URL: http://www.readingnreadingchamber.org
Contact: Irene Collins, Exec. Dir.

50933 ■ Revere Chamber of Commerce
270 Broadway
Revere, MA 02151
Ph:(781)289-8009
Fax:(781)289-2166
Co. E-mail: reverechamber@verizon.net
URL: http://www.reverechamber.org
Contact: Jeff Howe, Pres.

50934 ■ Salem Chamber of Commerce
265 Essex St., Ste. 101
Salem, MA 01970
Ph:(978)744-0004
Fax:(978)745-3855
Co. E-mail: scc@salem-chamber.org
URL: http://www.salem-chamber.org
Contact: Rinus Oosthoek, Exec. Dir.

50935 ■ Saugus Chamber of Commerce
394 Lincoln Ave.
Saugus, MA 01906
Ph:(781)233-8407
Fax:(781)231-1145
Co. E-mail: sauguschamber@verizon.net
URL: http://www.sauguschamber.org
Contact: Jim Morin, Pres.

50936 ■ Scituate Chamber of Commerce
PO Box 401
Scituate, MA 02066-0401
Ph:(781)545-4000
Co. E-mail: info@scituatechamber.org
URL: http://www.scituatechamber.org
Contact: Elaine Bongarzone, Pres.

50937 ■ Somerville Chamber of Commerce
PO Box 440343
Somerville, MA 02144
Ph:(617)776-4100
Fax:(617)776-1157
Co. E-mail: info@somervillechamber.org
URL: http://www.somervillechamber.org
Contact: Stephen Mackey, Pres./CEO

50938 ■ South Hadley Chamber of Commerce
116 Main St., Ste. 4
South Hadley, MA 01075
Ph:(413)532-6451
Co. E-mail: mail@shchamber.com
URL: http://www.southhadleygranbychamber.com
Contact: Susan Stockman, Exec. Dir.

50939 ■ South Shore Chamber of Commerce
36 Miller Stile Rd.
PO Box 690625
Quincy, MA 02269
Ph:(617)479-1111
Fax:(617)479-9274
Co. E-mail: info@southshorechamber.org
URL: http://www.southshorechamber.org
Contact: Peter Forman, Pres./CEO

50940 ■ Southern Berkshire Chamber of Commerce
PO Box 810
Great Barrington, MA 01230
Ph:(413)528-4284
Free: 800-269-4825
Fax:(413)528-2200
Co. E-mail: info@southernberkshirechamber.com
URL: http://www.southernberkshirechamber.com
Contact: Christine B. Ludwiszewski, Interim Exec. Dir.

50941 ■ Stockbridge Chamber of Commerce
50 Main St.
PO Box 224
Stockbridge, MA 01262-0224
Ph:(413)298-5200
Free: (866)626-5327
Co. E-mail: info@stockbridgechamber.org
URL: http://www.stockbridgechamber.org
Contact: Barbara Zanetti, Exec. Dir.

50942 ■ Stoneham Chamber of Commerce
269 Main St.
Stoneham, MA 02180
Ph:(781)438-0001
Fax:(781)438-0007
Co. E-mail: info@stonehamchamber.org
URL: http://www.stonehamchamber.org
Contact: Sharon A. Iovanni, Exec. Dir.

50943 ■ Stoughton Chamber of Commerce
PO Box 41
Stoughton, MA 02072
Ph:(781)297-7450
Fax:(781)344-1747
Co. E-mail: chamber@stoughtonma.com
URL: http://www.stoughtonma.com
Contact: Terry Schneider, Exec. Dir.

50944 ■ Swedish American Chamber of Commerce, New England
41 Kimlo Rd.
Wellesley, MA 02481
Ph:(617)395-8534
Co. E-mail: info@sacc-ne.org
URL: http://www.sacc-ne.org
Contact: Per Baverstam, Chm.

50945 ■ Taunton Area Chamber of Commerce
12 Taunton Green, Ste. 201
Taunton, MA 02780
Ph:(508)824-4068
Fax:(508)884-8222
Co. E-mail: info@tauntonareachamber.org
URL: http://www.tauntonareachamber.org
Contact: Kerrie Babin, Pres./CEO

50946 ■ Three Rivers Chamber of Commerce
PO Box 233
Three Rivers, MA 01080
Ph:(413)283-8321
Contact: Roger Duguay Jr., Sec.-Treas.

50947 ■ Tri-Town Chamber of Commerce, Massachusetts
15 West St.
Mansfield, MA 02048
Ph:(508)339-5655
Fax:(508)339-8333
Co. E-mail: edirector@tri-townchamber.org
URL: http://www.tri-townchamber.org
Contact: Kara Griffin, Exec. Dir.

50948 ■ United Chamber of Commerce
620 Old W Central St., Ste. 202
Franklin, MA 02038
Ph:(508)528-2800
Fax:(508)520-7864
Co. E-mail: claire@unitedchamber.org
URL: http://www.unitedchamber.org
Contact: Paul Cheli, Chm.

50949 ■ Wachusett Chamber of Commerce
PO Box 703
Clinton, MA 01510
Ph:(978)368-7687
Fax:(978)368-7689
Co. E-mail: maegen@wachusettchamber.com
URL: http://www.wachusettchamber.com
Contact: Maegen McCaffrey, Exec. Dir.

50950 ■ Wakefield Chamber of Commerce
PO Box 585
Wakefield, MA 01880
Ph:(781)245-0741
Co. E-mail: chamber@wakefieldma.org
URL: http://www.wakefieldma.org
Contact: Larry Andrews, Pres.

50951 ■ Walpole Chamber of Commerce
PO Box 361
Walpole, MA 02081
Ph:(508)668-0081
Co. E-mail: office@walpolechamber.com
URL: http://walpolechamber.com
Contact: Virginia Griffin, Pres.

50952 ■ Waltham West Suburban Chamber of Commerce
84 South St.
Waltham, MA 02453
Ph:(781)894-4700
Fax:(781)894-1708
Co. E-mail: info@walthamchamber.com
URL: http://www.walthamchamber.com
Contact: John C. Peacock, Exec. Dir.

50953 ■ Watertown - Belmont Chamber of Commerce
182 Main St.
Watertown, MA 02471
Ph:(617)926-1017
Fax:(617)926-2322
Co. E-mail: info@wbcc.org
URL: http://www.wbcc.org/home/index.html
Contact: Brenda Fanara, Exec. Dir.

50954 ■ Wellesley Chamber of Commerce
1 Hollis St., Ste. 232
Wellesley, MA 02482-4685
Ph:(781)235-2446
Co. E-mail: mobrien@wellesleychamber.org
URL: http://www.wellesleychamber.org
Contact: Maura M. O'Brien, Pres./CEO

50955 ■ Wellfleet Chamber of Commerce
PO Box 571
Wellfleet, MA 02667-0571
Ph:(508)349-2510
Fax:(508)349-3740
Co. E-mail: info@wellfleetchamber.com
URL: http://www.wellfleetchamber.com
Contact: Maureen Schraut, Exec. Sec.

50956 ■ Williamstown Chamber of Commerce
PO Box 357
Williamstown, MA 01267
Ph:(413)458-9077
Free: 800-214-3799
Fax:(413)458-2666
Co. E-mail: info@williamstownchamber.com
URL: http://williamstownchamber.com
Contact: Bonnie Clark, Co-Pres.

50957 ■ Wilmington Chamber of Commerce
PO Box 463
Wilmington, MA 01887-0463
Ph:(978)657-7211
Fax:(978)657-0139
Co. E-mail: wilmingtonchamber@verizon.net
URL: http://www.wilmingtonbusiness.com
Contact: Arthur Hayden, Pres.

50958 ■ Winchester Chamber of Commerce
25 Waterfield St.
Winchester, MA 01890
Ph:(781)729-8870
Fax:(781)729-8884
URL: http://www.winchesterchamber.com
Contact: Catherine S. Alexander, Dir.

50959 ■ Winthrop Chamber of Commerce
207 Hagman Rd.
Winthrop, MA 02152-0005
Ph:(617)846-9898
Fax:(617)846-9922
Co. E-mail: info@winthropchamber.com
URL: http://www.winthropchamber.com
Contact: Eric Gaynor, Exec. Dir.

50960 ■ Worcester Regional Chamber of Commerce
446 Main St., Ste. 200
Worcester, MA 01608
Ph:(508)753-2924
Fax:(508)754-8560
URL: http://www.worcesterchamber.org
Contact: Richard B. Kennedy, Pres./CEO

MINORITY BUSINESS ASSISTANCE PROGRAMS

50961 ■ Center for Women and Enterprise
24 School St., Ste. 700
Boston, MA 02108
Ph:(617)536-0700
Fax:(617)536-7373
Co. E-mail: info@cweonline.org
URL: http://www.cweonline.org
Contact: Susan Rittscher, CEO
Description: Encourages the creation and growth of women-owned businesses through business training, technical assistance, certification, and access to capital.

50962 ■ MSBDC Boston Regional Office
University of Massachusetts, Boston
McCormack Bldg., 5th Fl., Rm. 403
100 Morresy Blvd.
Boston, MA 02125-3393
Ph:(617)287-7750
Fax:(617)287-7767
Co. E-mail: mark.allio@umb.edu
URL: http://www.sbdc.umb.edu
Contact: Mark Allio, Dir
Description: Committed to helping your business succeed in Massachusetts.

FINANCING AND LOAN PROGRAMS

50963 ■ Abry Partners, LLC
111 Huntington Ave.
Boston, MA 02199
Ph:(617)859-2959
Fax:(617)859-8797
Co. E-mail: information@abry.com
URL: http://www.abry.com
Contact: Erik Brooks, Managing Partner
E-mail: ebrooks@abry.com
Preferred Investment Size: $25,000,000 to $150,000,000. **Investment Policies:** Leveraged buy-out, expansion, acquisition, recapitalization, roll-ups, and mezzanine. **Industry Preferences:** Communications and media, medical and health, and other products. **Geographic Preferences:** U.S. **Principal Exhibits:**

50964 ■ Advanced Technology Ventures (ATV)
500 Boylston St., Ste. 1380
Boston, MA 02116
Ph:(617)850-9700
Co. E-mail: info@atvcapital.com
URL: http://www.atvcapital.com
Contact: Steve Baloff, General Partner
E-mail: sbaloff@atvcapital.com
Preferred Investment Size: $15,000,000 to $35,000,000. **Investment Types:** Start-up, seed, first and second stage, early and later stage, and balanced. **Industry Preferences:** Internet specific, computer software and services, computer hardware, other products, semiconductors and other electronics, communications and media, medical and health, biotechnology, industrial and energy, and consumer related. **Geographic Preferences:** U.S. and Canada. **Principal Exhibits:**

50965 ■ Advent International Corp.
75 State St.
Boston, MA 02109
Ph:(617)951-9400
Fax:(617)951-0566
Co. E-mail: news@adventinternational.com
URL: http://www.adventinternational.com
Contact: Chris Pike, Managing Director
Preferred Investment Size: $1,000,000 minimum. **Investment Types:** Seed, early, later, first and second stage, balanced, control-block purchases, expansion, generalist PE, industry rollups, leveraged buyout, mezzanine, public companies, recapitalizations, research and development, and special situation. **Industry Preferences:** Other products, consumer related, communications and media, Internet specific, industrial and energy, medical and health,

computer software and services, computer hardware, semiconductors and other electronics, and biotechnology. **Geographic Preferences:** U.S. and Canada. **Principal Exhibits:**

50966 ■ Ampersand Ventures
55 William St., Ste. 240
Wellesley, MA 02481
Ph:(781)239-0700
Fax:(781)239-0824
Co. E-mail: info@ampersandventures.com
URL: http://www.ampersandventures.com
Contact: Richard A. Charpie, Managing General Partner
Preferred Investment Size: $5,000,000 to $10,000,000. **Investment Types:** Early and later stage, first and second stage, expansion, generalist PE, industry rollups, management buyouts, mezzanine, private placement, recapitalizations, special situation, and turnaround. **Industry Preferences:** Healthcare and industrial. **Geographic Preferences:** U.S. **Principal Exhibits:**

50967 ■ Ascent Venture Partners
255 State St., 5th Fl.
Boston, MA 02109
Ph:(617)720-9400
Fax:(617)720-9401
Co. E-mail: info@ascentvp.com
URL: http://www.ascentvp.com
Contact: Matt Fates, Partner
Preferred Investment Size: $2,000,000 to $8,000,000. **Investment Types:** Early. **Industry Preferences:** Internet specific, medical and health, computer software and services, communications and media, medical and health, computer hardware, consumer related, industrial and energy, semiconductors and other electronics. **Geographic Preferences:** Eastern U.S. **Principal Exhibits:**

50968 ■ Atlantic Capital Corporation
87 Cambridge St.
Burlington, MA 01803-4115
Ph:(781)272-0088
Free: 800-381-5944
Fax:(781)272-4744
Co. E-mail: scire@atlanticcap.com
URL: http://www.atlanticcap.com
Contact: Peter H. Sprayregen, President
Preferred Investment Size: $300,000 to $500,000. **Investment Types:** Start-up and first stage. **Industry Preferences:** Diversified. **Geographic Preferences:** National. **Principal Exhibits:**

50969 ■ Atlas Venture
25 First St., Ste. 303
Cambridge, MA 02141
Ph:(617)588-2600
Co. E-mail: boston@atlasventure.com
URL: http://www.atlasventure.com
Contact: Peter Shannon, Principal
Preferred Investment Size: $500,000 to $5,000,000. **Investment Types:** Seed, start-up, research and development, first and second stage, mezzanine, and balanced. **Industry Preferences:** Internet specific, computer software, hardware and services, biotechnology, communications and media, medical and health, semiconductors and other electronics, industrial and energy. **Geographic Preferences:** U.S. **Principal Exhibits:**

50970 ■ Axxon Capital
28 State St., 37th Fl.
Boston, MA 02109
Ph:(617)722-0980
Fax:(617)557-6014
Co. E-mail: info@axxoncapital.com
URL: http://www.axxoncapital.com
Contact: Paula Groves, Founding Partner
Preferred Investment Size: $500,000 to $3,500,000. **Investment Types:** Early later, first, and second stage, and expansion. **Industry Preferences:** Communications, and business service. **Geographic Preferences:** Northeast. **Principal Exhibits:**

50971 ■ Battery Ventures, L.P.
2884 Sand Hill Rd., Ste. 101
Menlo Park, CA 94025
Ph:(650)372-3939
Fax:(650)372-3930
URL: http://www.battery.com
Contact: Ken Lawler, General Partner
E-mail: ken@battery.com
Preferred Investment Size: $300,000 to $50,000,000. **Investment Types:** Seed, start-up, first stage, balanced, mezzanine, and leveraged buyout. **Industry Preferences:** Internet specific, computer software and services, communications and media, other products, semiconductors and other electronics, computer hardware, industrial and energy. **Geographic Preferences:** U.S. and Canada. **Principal Exhibits:**

50972 ■ Beacon Technology Ventures
8 Saint Mary's St., Ste. 914
Boston, MA 02215
Ph:(617)358-1600
Fax:(617)358-1536
Co. E-mail: info@btehventures.com
URL: http://www.btechventures.com
Contact: Alok Prasad, President
Preferred Investment Size: $250,000 to $3,000,000. **Investment Policies:** Start-up, seed, early, first and second stage. **Industry Preferences:** Communications and media, computer related, semiconductors and other electronics, biotechnology, medical and health. **Geographic Preferences:** Northeast. **Principal Exhibits:**

50973 ■ Berkshires Capital Investors
430 Main St., Ste. 4
Williamstown, MA 01267
Ph:(413)458-9683
Fax:(413)458-5603
Co. E-mail: info@berkshirescap.com
URL: http://www.berkshirescap.com
Contact: Russell Howard, Managing Director
Preferred Investment Size: $250,000 to $1,500,000. **Investment Policies:** Seed and early stage. **Industry Preferences:** Communications, computer software, Internet specific, and business service. **Geographic Preferences:** Western Massachusetts. **Principal Exhibits:**

50974 ■ Bessemer Venture Partners (Cambridge)
196 Broadway, 2nd Fl.
Cambridge, MA 02139
Ph:(617)588-1700
Fax:(617)588-1701
URL: http://www.bessemervp.com
Contact: Christopher Gabrieli, Partner
Preferred Investment Size: $1,000,000 to $10,000,000. **Investment Types:** Seed, start-up, early, first and second stage, research and development, expansion, control-block purchases, leveraged buyout, and special situation. **Industry Preferences:** Internet specific, communications and media, computer software and services, semiconductors and other electronics, consumer related, medical and health, industrial and energy, other products, and biotechnology. **Geographic Preferences:** U.S. **Principal Exhibits:**

50975 ■ BioVentures Investors
70 Walnut St., Ste. 302
Cambridge, MA 02481
Ph:(617)252-3443
Fax:(617)621-7993
Co. E-mail: info@bioventuresinvestors.com
URL: http://www.bioventuresinvestors.com
Contact: Anthony Coia, Principal
Preferred Investment Size: $3,000,000 to $7,000,000. **Investment Policies:** Seed, early, first and second stage, balanced, special situation, and private placement. **Industry Preferences:** Biotechnology, and medical and health. **Geographic Preferences:** East Coast U.S. and Canada. **Principal Exhibits:**

50976 ■ Boston Capital Ventures
84 State St., Ste. 320
Boston, MA 02109-2221
Ph:(617)227-6550
Fax:(617)227-3847
Co. E-mail: info@bcv.com
URL: http://www.bcv.com
Contact: Jack Shields, General Partner
E-mail: jshields@bcv.com
Preferred Investment Size: $500,000 to $3,000,000. **Investment Types:** Start-up, first and second stage, recapitalizations, expansion, and leveraged buyout. **Industry Preferences:** Internet specific, communications and media, other products, medical and health, computer software and services, consumer related, industrial and energy, semiconductors and other electronics, industrial and energy, biotechnology, and computer hardware. **Geographic Preferences:** Northeast and Canada. **Principal Exhibits:**

50977 ■ Boston Financial & Equity Corporation
1260 Boylston St.
Boston, MA 02215
Ph:(617)267-2900
Fax:(617)437-7601
Co. E-mail: debbie@bfec.com
URL: http://www.bfec.com
Contact: Deborah J. Monosson, Senior Vice President
Preferred Investment Size: $500,000 to $1,000,000. **Investment Types:** Seed, start-up, first and second stage, leveraged buyout, mezzanine, and research and development. **Industry Preferences:** Diversified. **Geographic Preferences:** National. **Principal Exhibits:**

50978 ■ Boston Millennia Partners
30 Rowes Wharf, Ste. 400
Boston, MA 02110
Ph:(617)428-5150
Co. E-mail: info@millenniapartners.com
URL: http://www.millenniapartners.com
Contact: Dana Callow, Managing General Partner
E-mail: dana@milleniapartners.com
Preferred Investment Size: $3,000,000 to $10,000,000. **Investment Types:** First and second stage, start-up, later stage, and expansion. **Industry Preferences:** Internet specific, computer software and services, biotechnology, communications and media, semiconductors and other electronics, other products, computer hardware, consumer related, medical and health. **Geographic Preferences:** All U.S., East Coast, and Canada. **Principal Exhibits:**

50979 ■ Brook Venture Partners
301 Edgewater Pl., 4th Fl.
Wakefield, MA 01880
Ph:(781)295-4000
Fax:(781)295-4007
URL: http://www.brookventure.com
Contact: Edward C. Williams, Partner
E-mail: ewilliams@brookventure.com
Preferred Investment Size: $2,000,000 to $5,000,000. **Investment Types:** Early, first, and second stage, and expansion. **Industry Preferences:** Communications, computer software, Internet specific, semiconductors and other electronics, medical and health, other products. **Geographic Preferences:** Northeast and Mid Atlantic states. **Principal Exhibits:**

50980 ■ Cambridge Samsung Partners LLC
1 Exeter Plz., 9th Fl.
Boston, MA 02116
Ph:(617)638-0100
Fax:(617)262-5562
URL: http://www.cspartners.com
Contact: Sundar Subramaniam, Managing Director
Investment Types: First stage. **Geographic Preferences:** U.S. **Principal Exhibits:**

50981 ■ CambridgeLight Partners
c/o Cambridge Light & Power
1 Broadway, 14th Fl.
Cambridge, MA 02142
Ph:(617)497-6310
Co. E-mail: info@cambridgelight.com
URL: http://www.cambridgelight.com
Contact: Daniel Alexander, Co-Founder
Preferred Investment Size: $50,000 to $1,000,000. **Investment Policies:** Seed and early stage. **Industry Preferences:** Communications, computer software,

Internet specific, and semiconductors and other electronics. **Geographic Preferences:** Greater Boston. **Principal Exhibits:**

50982 ■ Castile Ventures
930 Winter St., Ste. 500
Waltham, MA 02451-1540
Ph:(781)890-0060
Fax:(781)890-0065
Co. E-mail: plans@castileventures.com
URL: http://www.castileventures.com
Contact: Roger Walton, General Partner
Preferred Investment Size: $1,000,000 to $10,000,000. **Investment Types:** Seed and early stage. **Industry Preferences:** Communications and media, and Internet specific. **Geographic Preferences:** Mid Atlantic and Northeast. **Principal Exhibits:**

50983 ■ Charles River Ventures
1000 Winter St., Ste. 3300
Waltham, MA 02451
Ph:(781)768-6000
Fax:(781)768-6100
URL: http://www.crv.com
Contact: Austin Westerling, Principal
Preferred Investment Size: $25,000 to $5,000,000. **Investment Types:** Seed, Start-up and first stage. **Industry Preferences:** Internet specific, communications and media, computer software and services, computer hardware, other products, industrial and energy, semiconductors and other electronics, medical and health, consumer related, and biotechnology. **Geographic Preferences:** U.S. **Principal Exhibits:**

50984 ■ Commonwealth Capital Ventures
Bay Colony Corporate Ctr.
950 Winter St., Ste. 4100
Waltham, MA 02451
Ph:(781)890-5554
Fax:(781)890-3414
URL: http://www.commonwealthvc.com
Contact: Jeffrey M. Hurst, General Partner
Preferred Investment Size: $2,000,000 to $8,000,000. **Investment Types:** Early, first and second stage. **Industry Preferences:** Computer software and services, Internet specific, communications and media, industrial and energy, medical and health, consumer related, semiconductors and other electronics, biotechnology, and other products. **Geographic Preferences:** Northeast U.S. **Principal Exhibits:**

50985 ■ DFJ New England / Draper Fisher Jurvetson
1 Broadway, 14th Fl.
Cambridge, MA 02142
Ph:(617)758-4275
Free: (758)-4234
Fax:(617)758-4101
Co. E-mail: info@dfjne.com
URL: http://www.dfjne.com
Contact: Scott M. Johnson, Managing Director
E-mail: scott1@dfjne.com
Preferred Investment Size: $500,000 to $5,000,000. **Investment Policies:** Start-up, seed, second, early and later stage. **Industry Preferences:** Communications, computer hardware and software, Internet specific, semiconductors and other electronics, consumer related, industrial and energy, and business service. **Geographic Preferences:** Northeast. **Principal Exhibits:**

50986 ■ Downer & Company
60 State St.
Boston, MA 02109
Ph:(617)482-6200
Fax:(617)482-6201
Co. E-mail: info@downer.com
URL: http://www.downer.com
Contact: Charles Downer, Chief Executive Officer
E-mail: cdowner@cwdowner.com
Preferred Investment Size: $300,000 to $500,000. **Investment Types:** Start-up, first and second stage, and mezzanine. **Industry Preferences:** Computer hardware and software, semiconductors and other electronics, medical and health, consumer related,

industrial and energy, and manufacturing. **Geographic Preferences:** Northeast and Canada. **Principal Exhibits:**

50987 ■ Echelon Ventures LLC
303 Wyman St., Ste. 300
Waltham, MA 02451
Ph:(781)530-3707
Fax:(781)530-3717
Co. E-mail: info@echelonventures.com
URL: http://www.echelonventures.com
Contact: Alfred S. Woodworth, Managing Director
Preferred Investment Size: $1,000,000 to $5,000,000. **Investment Policies:** Early, first, and second stage, and expansion. **Industry Preferences:** Computer software, semiconductors and other electronics, biotechnology, and medical and health. **Geographic Preferences:** New England-based. **Principal Exhibits:**

50988 ■ Egan-Managed Capital
30 Federal St.
Boston, MA 02110-2508
Ph:(617)695-2600
Fax:(617)695-2699
Co. E-mail: businessplans@egancapital.com
URL: http://www.egancapital.com
Contact: John R. Egan, Managing Partner
Preferred Investment Size: $2,000,000 to $3,000,000. **Investment Types:** Seed, start-up, Early, and first stage. **Industry Preferences:** Computer software and services, Internet specific, semiconductors and other electronics, communications and media, and computer hardware. **Geographic Preferences:** New England. **Principal Exhibits:**

50989 ■ Fidelity Ventures
1 Federal St., 27th Fl.
Boston, MA 02110
Ph:(617)830-2100
URL: http://www.fidelityventures.com
Contact: Larry Cheng, Partner
E-mail: lcheng@fidelityventures.com
Preferred Investment Size: $1,000,000 to $10,000,000. **Investment Types:** Seed, start-up, early, first and second stage, and expansion. **Industry Preferences:** Internet specific, computer software, and services, communications and media, medical and health, financial services, computer hardware, consumer related, semiconductors and other electronics, and other products. **Geographic Preferences:** U.S. and Canada. **Principal Exhibits:**

50990 ■ Flagship Ventures
1 Memorial Dr., 7th Fl.
Cambridge, MA 02142
Ph:(617)868-1888
Fax:(617)868-1115
URL: http://www.flagshipventures.com
Contact: Noubar Afeyan, Managing Partner and Chief Executive Off
Preferred Investment Size: $500,000 to $5,000,000. **Investment Policies:** Start-up, seed, research and development, early and first stage, and balanced. **Industry Preferences:** Computer software and services, communications and media, biotechnology, Internet specific, medical and health, semiconductors and other electronics, other products, computer hardware, and industrial and energy. **Geographic Preferences:** Mid Atlantic, Northeast, and West Coast. **Principal Exhibits:**

50991 ■ Fletcher Spaght Ventures
222 Berkeley St., 20th Fl.
Boston, MA 02116-3761
Ph:(617)247-6700
Fax:(617)247-7757
Co. E-mail: info@fletcherspaght.com
URL: http://www.fletcherspaght.com
Contact: Pearson Spaght, President
E-mail: ps@fletcherspaght.com
Investment Policies: Early stage. **Industry Preferences:** Communications, computer hardware and software, Internet specific, semiconductors and other electronics, medical and health, industrial and energy, transportation, and financial services. **Geographic Preferences:** U.S. **Principal Exhibits:**

50992 ■ Gemini Investors / GMN Investors
20 William St., Ste. 250
Wellesley, MA 02481
Ph:(781)237-7001
Fax:(781)237-7233
URL: http://www.gemini-investors.com
Contact: James Goodman, President
E-mail: jgoodman@gemini-investors.com
Preferred Investment Size: $3,000 to $8,000. **Investment Types:** Expansion, generalist PE, later stage, private placement, management buyouts, and recapitalizations. **Industry Preferences:** Communications and media, medical and health, computer software and services, Internet specific, other products, computer hardware, industrial and energy, manufacturing, and consumer related. **Geographic Preferences:** U.S. **Principal Exhibits:**

50993 ■ General Catalyst Partners / General Catalyst Group LLC
20 University Rd., 4th Fl.
Cambridge, MA 02138
Ph:(617)234-7000
Fax:(617)234-7040
Co. E-mail: info@generalcatalyst.com
URL: http://www.generalcatalyst.com
Contact: William Fitzgerald, Managing Director and Chief Financial Of
Preferred Investment Size: $1,000,000 to $25,000,000. **Investment Types:** Seed, start-up, early, and first stage. **Industry Preferences:** Internet specific, computer software and services, communications and media, other products, industrial and energy, semiconductors and other electronics, and consumer related. **Geographic Preferences:** Northeast. **Principal Exhibits:**

50994 ■ Great Hill Equity Partners, LLC
1 Liberty Sq.
Boston, MA 02109
Ph:(617)790-9400
Fax:(617)790-9401
URL: http://www.greathillpartners.com
Contact: Christopher S. Gaffney, Managing Partner
E-mail: cgaffney@greathillpartners.com
Preferred Investment Size: $50,000,000 to $150,000,000. **Investment Types:** Balanced, recapitalization, acquisition. **Industry Preferences:** Internet specific, communications and media, computer hardware, software and services, semiconductors and other electronics, and other products. **Geographic Preferences:** U.S. **Principal Exhibits:**

50995 ■ Greylock Management Corp. (Boston)
880 Winter St., Ste. 300
Waltham, MA 02451
Ph:(781)622-2300
Fax:(781)622-2300
Co. E-mail: bostongreylock.com
URL: http://www.greylock.com
Contact: Tom Bogan, Partner
Preferred Investment Size: $250,000 minimum. **Investment Types:** Seed, start-up, first and early stage, and expansion. **Industry Preferences:** Diversified. **Geographic Preferences:** No preference. **Principal Exhibits:**

50996 ■ Grove Street Advisors, LLC
20 William St., Ste. 230
Wellesley, MA 02481
Ph:(781)263-6100
Fax:(781)263-6101
Co. E-mail: info@grovestreetadvisors.com
URL: http://www.grovestreetadvisors.com
Contact: Clinton Harris, Founder and Managing Partner
Preferred Investment Size: $1,000,000 to $7,500,000. **Investment Types:** Early and later stage, mezzanine, special situation, fund of funds, expansion, and other. **Industry Preferences:** Communications and media, computer software and hardware, Internet specific, semiconductors and other electronics, consumer related, industrial and energy, and business service. **Principal Exhibits:**

50997 ■ Halpern, Denny & Co.
100 City Hall Plz., Ste. 305
Boston, MA 02108
Ph:(617)536-6602
Fax:(617)536-8535
Co. E-mail: info@HalpernDenny.com
URL: http://www.halperndenny.com
Contact: John D. Halpern, Partner
E-mail: jhalpern@halperndenny.com
Preferred Investment Size: $5,000,000 to $50,000,000. **Investment Types:** Seed, early, first, second, and later stage, acquisition, balanced, control-block purchases, management buyouts, leveraged buyout, expansion, generalist PE, joint ventures, mezzanine, recapitalizations, and turnaround. **Industry Preferences:** Consumer related, Internet specific, other products, communications and media, computer software and services, industrial and energy, medical and health, and computer hardware. **Geographic Preferences:** U.S. **Principal Exhibits:**

50998 ■ Harbourvest Partners, LLC
1 Financial Ctr., 44th Fl.
Boston, MA 02111
Ph:(617)348-3707
Fax:(617)350-0305
Co. E-mail: usinfo@barnourvest.com
URL: http://www.harbourvest.com
Contact: Edward W. Kane, Senior Managing Director
Preferred Investment Size: $10,000,000 to $100,000,000. **Investment Types:** Later stage, balanced, fund of funds, fund of funds of second, generalist PE, and leveraged buyout, recapitalizations, mezzanine, and acquisition. **Industry Preferences:** Other products, Internet specific, communications and media, computer software and services, consumer related, computer hardware, semiconductors and other electronics, industrial and energy, biotechnology, medical and health. **Geographic Preferences:** U.S. **Principal Exhibits:**

50999 ■ High Peaks Venture Partners, LLC / Berkshires Capital Invest
10 2nd St.
Troy, NY 12180
Ph:(518)720-3090
Fax:(518)720-3091
Co. E-mail: info@hpvp.com
URL: http://www.hpvp.com
Contact: Russell Howard, Managing Director
Preferred Investment Size: $100,000 to $2,000,000. **Investment Types:** Seed and early stage. **Industry Preferences:** Communications and media, computer hardware, Internet specific, consumer related, semiconductors and other electronics. **Geographic Preferences:** New York and Northeast. **Principal Exhibits:**

51000 ■ Highland Capital Partners
92 Hayden Ave.
Cambridge, MA 02142
Ph:(617)401-4500
Fax:(781)861-5499
Co. E-mail: info@hcp.com
URL: http://www.hcp.com
Contact: Corey Mulloy, General Partner
E-mail: cmulloy@hcp.com
Preferred Investment Size: $100,000 to $20,000,000. **Investment Types:** Seed, early, and later stage. **Industry Preferences:** Internet specific, computer software and services, communications and media, medical and health, other products, biotechnology, semiconductors and other electronics, computer hardware, and industrial and energy. **Geographic Preferences:** U.S. and Canada. **Principal Exhibits:**

51001 ■ Industry Ventures
750 Battery St., 7th Fl.
San Francisco, CA 94111
Ph:(415)273-4201
Fax:(415)391-7262
Co. E-mail: info@industryventures.com
URL: http://www.industryventures.com
Contact: Hans Swildens, Founder and Principal
Preferred Investment Size: $250,000 to $250,000,000. **Investment Types:** Seed, start-up, early, first, and second stage, and acquisition. **Indus-**try **Preferences:** Communications and media, computer software, Internet specific, consumer related, and business service. **Geographic Preferences:** Mid Atlantic, Northeast, Northern California, and West Coast. **Principal Exhibits:**

51002 ■ Kestrel Venture Management / Corning Venture Management
1 Boston Pl., Ste. 1650
Boston, MA 02108
Ph:(617)451-6722
Fax:(617)451-3322
Co. E-mail: msilva@kestrelvm.com
URL: http://www.kestrelvm.com
Contact: R. Gregg Stone, Principal
Preferred Investment Size: $250,000 minimum. **Investment Policies:** Early stage. **Industry Preferences:** Internet specific, biotechnology, Computer software and services, semiconductors and other electronics, other products, consumer related, computer hardware, communications and media, medical and health, and industrial and energy. **Geographic Preferences:** Northeast. **Principal Exhibits:**

51003 ■ Lee Munder Venture Partners, LLC
John Hancock Tower
200 Clarendon St., 28th Fl.
Boston, MA 02116
Ph:(617)380-5600
Free: 877-241-5191
Fax:(617)380-5601
URL: http://www.leemunder.com
Contact: Lee P. Munder, Founder and Chairman
Preferred Investment Size: $500,000 to $3,000,000. **Investment Types:** Early, first stage, and expansion. **Industry Preferences:** Communications, computer software, industrial and energy, semiconductors and other electronics, and financial services. **Geographic Preferences:** Mid Atlantic, Northeast, and Southeast. **Principal Exhibits:**

51004 ■ Longworth Venture Partners, L.P.
1050 Winter St., Ste. 2600
Waltham, MA 02451
Ph:(781)663-3600
Fax:(781)663-3691
Co. E-mail: businessplans@longworth.com
URL: http://www.longworth.com
Contact: John Lawrence, Partner and Chief Financial Officer
Preferred Investment Size: $2,000,000 to $3,000,000. **Investment Types:** Seed, start-up, first, and second stage. **Industry Preferences:** Computer software, Internet specific, financial services, and business service. **Geographic Preferences:** Mid Atlantic, New England, West Coast and elsewhere. **Principal Exhibits:**

51005 ■ M/C Venture Partners
75 State St., Ste. 2500
Boston, MA 02109
Ph:(617)345-7200
Fax:(617)345-7201
Co. E-mail: mcp@mcpartners.com
URL: http://www.mcventurepartners.com
Contact: Edward J. Keefe, Chief Financial Officer
Preferred Investment Size: $5,000,000 to $50,000,000. **Investment Types:** Early stage and leveraged buyout. **Industry Preferences:** Communications and media, Internet specific, semiconductors and other electronics, computer software and services, and consumer related. **Geographic Preferences:** U.S. and Canada. **Principal Exhibits:**

51006 ■ Manulife Capital Corporation
200 Bloor St. E.
North Tower 4
Toronto, ON, Canada M4W 1E5
Ph:(416)926-5727
Fax:(416)926-5737
URL: http://www.manulife.com
Contact: William Euewes, Vice President
Preferred Investment Size: $5,000,000 to $25,000,000. **Investment Policies:** Early stage, mezzanine, buyouts, expansion, and recapitalization. **Industry Preferences:** Biotechnology. **Geographic Preferences:** National. **Principal Exhibits:**

51007 ■ Massachusetts Capital Resource Company
420 Boylston St.
Boston, MA 02116
Ph:(617)536-3900
Fax:(617)536-7930
URL: http://www.masscapital.com
Contact: Richard W. Anderson, President
E-mail: randerson@masscapital.com
Preferred Investment Size: $750,000 to $5,000,000. **Investment Types:** Second stage, leveraged buyout, mezzanine, and recapitalizations. **Industry Preferences:** Industrial and energy, semiconductors and other electronics, computer software, hardware and services, consumer related, communications and media, medical and health, and Internet specific. **Geographic Preferences:** Massachusetts. **Principal Exhibits:**

51008 ■ Massachusetts Technology Development Corp. (MTDC)
40 Board St., Ste. 230
Boston, MA 02109
Ph:(617)723-4920
Fax:(617)723-5983
Co. E-mail: jhodgman@mtdc.com
URL: http://www.mtdc.com
Contact: Robert J. Crowley, President
E-mail: rcrowley@mtdc.com
Preferred Investment Size: $350,000 to $500,000. **Investment Types:** Early, seed, and start-up. **Industry Preferences:** Computer software, hardware and services, semiconductors and other electronics, Internet specific, biotechnology, medical and health, industrial and energy, communications and media. **Geographic Preferences:** Massachusetts. **Principal Exhibits:**

51009 ■ Masthead Venture
55 Cambridge Pky., Ste. 103
Cambridge, MA 02142-1234
Ph:(617)621-3000
Fax:(617)621-3055
Co. E-mail: info@mvpartners.com
URL: http://www.mvpartners.com
Contact: Timothy P. Agnew, Principal
Preferred Investment Size: $500,000 to $5,000,000. **Investment Policies:** Seed and early stage. **Industry Preferences:** Communications, computer software, semiconductors and other electronics, biotechnology, and medical and health. **Geographic Preferences:** Northeast. **Principal Exhibits:**

51010 ■ Matrix Partners
Bay Colony Corporate Ctr.
1000 Winter St., Ste. 4500
Waltham, MA 02451
Ph:(781)890-2244
Fax:(781)890-2288
Co. E-mail: info@matrixpartners.com
URL: http://www.matrixpartners.com
Contact: Nicholas F. Beim, General Partner
E-mail: nbeim@matrixpartners.com
Preferred Investment Size: $2,000,000 to $10,000,000. **Investment Types:** Start-up, early, first and second stage, balanced, and leveraged buyout. **Industry Preferences:** Communications and media, Internet specific, computer software and services, computer hardware, semiconductors and other electronics. **Geographic Preferences:** California and Massachusetts. **Principal Exhibits:**

51011 ■ MDT Advisers, Inc.
Oliver Street Tower, 21st Fl.
125 High St.
Boston, MA 02110
Ph:(617)235-7100
Fax:(617)235-7199
URL: http://www.mdtai.com
Contact: John B. Fisher, President and Chief Executive Officer
Preferred Investment Size: $500,000 to $5,000,000. **Investment Types:** Early stage and expansion. **Industry Preferences:** Consumer related, other products, Internet specific, communications and media, computer software and services, semiconductors and other electronics, industrial and energy,

medical and health, computer hardware, and biotechnology. **Geographic Preferences:** Northeast. **Principal Exhibits:**

51012 ■ Mediphase Venture Partners / EHealth Technology Fund
2223 Washington St., Ste. 102
Newton, MA 02462
Ph:(617)332-3408
Fax:(617)332-8463
Co. E-mail: info@mediphaseventure.com
URL: http://www.mediphaseventure.com
Contact: Lawrence G. Miller M.D., Partner and Founder
Investment Types: Early stage. **Industry Preferences:** Biotechnology, medical and health. **Geographic Preferences:** U.S. **Principal Exhibits:**

51013 ■ Megunticook Management, Inc.
143 Newbury St., 6th Fl.
Boston, MA 02116
Ph:(617)986-3000
Fax:(617)986-3100
Co. E-mail: cvaughan@megunticook.com
URL: http://www.megunticook.com
Contact: Tom Matlack, Managing Partner
Preferred Investment Size: $500,000 to $3,000,000. **Investment Types:** Early and second stage stage. **Industry Preferences:** Internet specific, communications and media, computer software and services, semiconductors and other electronics, consumer related, computer hardware, and other products. **Geographic Preferences:** Northeast. **Principal Exhibits:**

51014 ■ MPM Capital / MPM Asset Management LLC
The John Hancock Tower
200 Clarendon St., 54th Fl.
Boston, MA 02116
Ph:(617)425-9200
Fax:(617)425-9201
Co. E-mail: info@mpmcapital.com
URL: http://www.mpmcapital.com
Contact: Ken Greenberg, Principal
Preferred Investment Size: $5,000,000 to $50,000,000. **Investment Types:** Start-up, first and early stage, balanced, expansion, other, and mezzanine. **Industry Preferences:** Biotechnology, medical and health, computer software and services, and Internet specific. **Geographic Preferences:** U.S. **Principal Exhibits:**

51015 ■ Navigator Technology Ventures / NTV
1 Broadway, Ste. 1300
Cambridge, MA 02142
Ph:(617)494-0111
Fax:(617)497-1600
Co. E-mail: info@ntven.com
URL: http://www.ntven.com
Contact: Alan Hanover, Chief Executive Officer and Managing Dir
E-mail: alain@ntven.com
Preferred Investment Size: $500,000 to $750,000,000. **Investment Policies:** Early and later stage. **Industry Preferences:** Communications, technology, semiconductors and other electronics, and biotechnology. **Geographic Preferences:** U.S. . **Principal Exhibits:**

51016 ■ Neocarta Ventures, Inc.
396 Washington St., Ste. 278
Wellesley Hills, MA 02481
Ph:(781)591-0303
Co. E-mail: info@neocarta.com
URL: http://www.neocarta.com
Contact: D. Jarrett Collins, Managing Director
Preferred Investment Size: $1,000,000 to $5,000,000. **Investment Types:** Start-up, early, second, and later stage. **Industry Preferences:** Internet specific, communications and media, computer software and services, semiconductors and other electronics, computer hardware, and other products. **Geographic Preferences:** U.S. **Principal Exhibits:**

51017 ■ North Bridge Venture Partners
950 Winter St. Ste. 4600
Waltham, MA 02451
Ph:(781)290-0004

Fax:(781)290-0999
Co. E-mail: info@northbridge.com
URL: http://www.nbvp.com
Contact: Edward T. Anderson, Managing General Partner
Preferred Investment Size: $1,000,000 to $10,000,000. **Investment Types:** Seed and early stage. **Industry Preferences:** Communications and media, Internet specific, computer software and services, computer hardware, semiconductors and other electronics, medical and health, other products, and biotechnology. **Geographic Preferences:** Northeast and Southeast. **Principal Exhibits:**

51018 ■ North Hill Ventures
10 Post Office Sq., 11th Fl.
Boston, MA 02109
Ph:(617)788-2150
Fax:(617)788-2152
URL: http://www.northhillventures.com
Contact: Benjamin Malka, Principal
E-mail: ben.malka@northhillventures.com
Preferred Investment Size: $2,000,000 to $5,000,000. **Investment Types:** Early stage, and expansion. **Industry Preferences:** Consumer related, financial services, and business service. **Geographic Preferences:** U.S. **Principal Exhibits:**

51019 ■ One Liberty Ventures
150 Cambridge Park Dr., 10th Fl.
Cambridge, MA 02140
Ph:(617)492-7280
Fax:(617)492-7290
Co. E-mail: info@oneliberty.com
URL: http://www.oneliberty.com
Contact: Edwin Kania, Senior Managing Director
Preferred Investment Size: $1,000,000 to $10,000,000. **Investment Types:** Early stage. **Industry Preferences:** Communications and media, computer software, hardware and services, Internet specific, biotechnology, medical and health, semiconductors and other electronics, industrial and energy. **Geographic Preferences:** Northeast and Southeast. **Principal Exhibits:**

51020 ■ Osborn Capital LLC
171 Grove St.
Lexington, MA 02420
Ph:(781)402-1790
Fax:(781)402-1793
Co. E-mail: info@osborncapital.com
URL: http://www.osborncapital.com
Contact: Eric Janszen, Managing Director
E-mail: eric@osborncapital.com
Investment Types: Seed and start-up. **Principal Exhibits:**

51021 ■ Polaris Venture Partners
1000 Winter St., Ste. 3550
Waltham, MA 02451
Ph:(781)290-0770
Fax:(781)290-0880
URL: http://www.polarisventures.com
Contact: Alan G. Spoon, Managing Partner
E-mail: aspoon@polarisventures.com
Preferred Investment Size: $250,000 to $15,000,000. **Investment Types:** Seed, start-up, early, first and second stage, expansion, research and development, and balanced. **Industry Preferences:** Internet specific, computer software services, computer hardware, biotechnology, communications and media, business services, manufacturing, medical and health, and other products. **Geographic Preferences:** U.S. **Principal Exhibits:**

51022 ■ Prism Venture Partners
117 Kendrick St., Ste. 200
Needham, MA 02494
Ph:(781)302-4000
Fax:(781)302-4040
URL: http://www.prismventure.com
Contact: Steve D. Weintein, Principal
Preferred Investment Size: $5,000,000 to $15,000,000. **Investment Types:** Early stage. **Industry Preferences:** Internet specific, medical and health, communications and media, computer software and services, biotechnology, semiconductors

and other electronics, and computer hardware. **Geographic Preferences:** Mid Atlantic, Northeast, and West Coast U.S.; and Canada. **Principal Exhibits:**

51023 ■ Rockport capital Partners
160 Federal St., 18th Fl.
Boston, MA 02110-1700
Ph:(617)912-1420
Fax:(617)912-1449
URL: http://www.rockportcap.com
Contact: David J. Prend, Managing General Partner
Preferred Investment Size: $500,000 to $25,000,000. **Investment Policies:** Seed, early, first, second, and later stage. **Industry Preferences:** Semiconductors and other electronics, industrial and energy, utilities, transportation, and environmental. **Geographic Preferences:** U.S. **Principal Exhibits:**

51024 ■ RSA Capital
174 Middlesex Tpke.
Bedford, MA 01730
Ph:(781)515-5000
Free: 877-RSA-4900
Fax:(781)515-5010
URL: http://www.rsasecurity.com
Contact: Arthur W. Coviello Jr., President
Preferred Investment Size: $2,000,000 to $5,000,000. **Investment Types:** Seed, expansion and early stage. **Industry Preferences:** Communications, computer software, and Internet specific. **Geographic Preferences:** U.S. **Principal Exhibits:**

51025 ■ Seacoast Capital
55 Ferncroft Rd., Ste. 110
Danvers, MA 01923
Ph:(978)750-1300
Fax:(978)750-1301
URL: http://www.seacoastcapital.com
Contact: Eben S. Moulton, Managing Director
Preferred Investment Size: $2,000,000 to $10,000,000. **Investment Types:** Mezzanine. **Industry Preferences:** Other products, Internet specific, consumer related, semiconductors and other electronics, medical and health, industrial and energy, computer software and services. **Geographic Preferences:** U.S. **Principal Exhibits:**

51026 ■ Seaflower Ventures
Bay Colony Corporate Ctr.
1000 Winter St., Ste. 1000
Waltham, MA 02451
Ph:(781)466-9552
Fax:(781)466-9553
URL: http://www.seaflower.com
Contact: James Sherblom, Managing General Partner
Preferred Investment Size: $1,000,000 to $3,000,000. **Investment Types:** Seed, start-up, early, first and second stage. **Industry Preferences:** Medical and health, biotechnology, Internet specific, computer hardware, industrial and energy, and other products. **Geographic Preferences:** New England, the Mid Atlantic, the Great Lakes region (Michigan, Wisconsin, Illinois), Easter Canada (Montreal & Toronto), and the Southeast. **Principal Exhibits:**

51027 ■ Shawmut Capital Partners
75 Federal St., 18th Fl.
Boston, MA 02110
Ph:(617)368-4900
Fax:(617)368-4910
URL: http://www.shawmutcapital.com
Contact: Daniel K. Doyle, Managing Director
Preferred Investment Size: $3,000,000 to $10,000,000. **Investment Types:** Start-up, first and second stage, mezzanine, leveraged buyout, industry rollups, control-block purchases, and special situation. **Industry Preferences:** Financial services. **Geographic Preferences:** U.S. and Canada. **Principal Exhibits:**

51028 ■ Softbank Capital Partners
1188 Centre St.
Newton Center, MA 02459
Ph:(617)928-9300

Fax:(617)928-9304
Co. E-mail: ContactSBCCapital@softbank.com
URL: http://www.sbcap.com
Contact: Ronald D. Fisher, Managing Partner
Investment Types: Seed, start-up, first and second stage, early and later stage, mezzanine, leveraged buyout, and special situation. **Industry Preferences:** Internet specific, consumer related, computer software and services, communications and media, computer hardware, semiconductors and other electronics, and industrial and energy. **Geographic Preferences:** U.S. and Canada. **Principal Exhibits:**

51029 ■ Solstice Capital
81 Washington St., Ste. 303
Salem, MA 02109-4216
Ph:(617)523-7733
Fax:(617)523-5827
URL: http://www.solcap.com
Contact: Harry George, Managing General Partner
Preferred Investment Size: $500,000 to $1,000,000. **Investment Types:** Seed, early, and first stage. **Industry Preferences:** Computer software and services, industrial and energy, Internet specific, biotechnology, medical and health, semiconductors and other electronics, computer hardware, communications and media, consumer related, and other products. **Geographic Preferences:** Northeast and Southwest. **Principal Exhibits:**

51030 ■ Spectrum Equity Investors
333 Middlefield Rd., Ste. 200
Menlo Park, CA 94025
Ph:(415)464-4600
Fax:(415)464-4601
URL: http://www.spectrumequity.com
Contact: Benjamin M. Coughlin, Managing Director
E-mail: ben@spectrumequity.com
Preferred Investment Size: $25,000,000 to $100,000,000. **Investment Types:** Start-up, seed, first, second, early and later stage, balanced, acquisition, expansion, leveraged buyout, mezzanine, and recapitalizations. **Industry Preferences:** Communications and media, Internet specific, computer software and services, business services, other products, semiconductors and other electronics, and consumer related. **Geographic Preferences:** U.S. and Canada. **Principal Exhibits:**

51031 ■ Spray Venture Partners
2330 Washington St.
Newton, MA 02462
Ph:(617)332-6060
Fax:(617)332-6070
Co. E-mail: info@spraypartners.com
URL: http://www.spraypartners.com
Contact: Kevin G. Connors, General Partner
Preferred Investment Size: $50,000 to $6,000,000. **Investment Types:** Seed, start-up, first, and second stage. **Industry Preferences:** Medical and health, biotechnology, and Internet specific. **Geographic Preferences:** U.S. **Principal Exhibits:**

51032 ■ The Still River Fund
Reservoir Pl.
1601 Trapelo Rd., Ste. 182
Waltham, MA 02451
Ph:(781)290-5363
Fax:(781)290-0606
URL: http://www.stillriverfund.com
Contact: James A. Saalfield, Managing General Partner
E-mail: jim.saalfield@stillriverfund.com
Preferred Investment Size: $500,000 to $5,000,000. **Investment Types:** Seed and early stage. **Industry Preferences:** Other products, communications and media, Internet specific, semiconductors and other electronics, computer software and services, biotechnology, and consumer related. **Geographic Preferences:** Northeast. **Principal Exhibits:**

51033 ■ Summit Partners (Boston)
222 Berkeley, 18th Fl.
Boston, MA 02116
Ph:(617)824-1000

Fax:(617)824-1100
URL: http://www.summitpartners.com
Contact: John R. Carroll, Managing Director
E-mail: john@summitpartners.com
Preferred Investment Size: $5,000,000 to $500,000,000. **Investment Types:** Second and later stage, mezzanine, leveraged buyout, special situation, control-block purchases, balanced, generalist PE. **Industry Preferences:** Other products, computer software and other services, communications and media, Internet specific, computer hardware, semiconductors and other electronics, medical and health, consumer related, biotechnology, business services, industrial and energy. **Geographic Preferences:** U.S. and Canada. **Principal Exhibits:**

51034 ■ TA Associates, Inc. (Boston)
John Hancock Tower, 56th Fl.
200 Clarendon St.
Boston, MA 02116
Ph:(617)574-6700
Fax:(617)574-6728
URL: http://www.ta.com
Contact: Brian J. Conway, Managing Director
E-mail: bconway@ta.com
Preferred Investment Size: $60,000,000 to $500,000,000. **Investment Types:** Later stage, leveraged buyout, management buyouts, expansion, mezzanine, and recapitalizations. **Industry Preferences:** Computer software and services, other products, communications and media, Internet specific, medical and health, semiconductors and other electronics, consumer related, computer hardware, financial and business services, medical and health. **Geographic Preferences:** U.S. and Canada. **Principal Exhibits:**

51035 ■ TTC Ventures
1 Main St., 6th Fl.
Cambridge, CT 02142
Ph:(617)528-3137
Fax:(617)577-1715
URL: http://www.ttcventures.com
Investment Types: Seed, start-up, first and second stage, and mezzanine. **Industry Preferences:** Internet specific, computer software and services, communications and media, and computer hardware. **Geographic Preferences:** U.S. **Principal Exhibits:**

51036 ■ The Venture Capital Fund of New England
30 Washington St.
Wellesley Hills, MA 02481
Ph:(781)431-8400
Fax:(781)237-6578
Co. E-mail: inquiries@vcfne.com
URL: http://www.vcfne.com
Contact: Kevin J. Dougherty, Managing Director
Preferred Investment Size: $500,000 to $1,500,000. **Investment Types:** Early stage. **Industry Preferences:** Computer software and services, communications and media, medical and health, industrial and energy, semiconductors and other electronics, computer hardware, other products, Internet specific, biotechnology, and consumer related. **Geographic Preferences:** Northeast. **Principal Exhibits:**

51037 ■ Venture Investment Management Company LLC (VIMAC)
177 Milk St.
Boston, MA 02190-3410
Ph:(617)350-9800
Fax:(617)350-9899
Co. E-mail: info@vimac.com
URL: http://www.vimac.com
Contact: Robert C. Roeper, Director
E-mail: rroeper@vimac.com
Preferred Investment Size: $5,000,000 to $15,000,000. **Investment Types:** Seed and early stage. **Industry Preferences:** Internet specific, computer software, hardware and services, communications and media, semiconductors and other electronics, medical and health, and consumer related. **Geographic Preferences:** Ontario and Quebec, Canada. **Principal Exhibits:**

51038 ■ Ventures
1601 TrapeloRoad, Ste. 170
Waltham, MA 02451
Ph:(978)658-8980
Co. E-mail: info@ventures.com
URL: http://www.ventures.com
Contact: Peter H. Mills, Managing Director
Preferred Investment Size: $1,000,000 to $20,000,000. **Investment Policies:** Early and later stage, expansion, generalist PE, industry rollups, recapitalizations, and special situation. **Industry Preferences:** Internet specific, information technology, consumer related, and industrial and energy. **Geographic Preferences:** U.S. and Canada. **Principal Exhibits:**

51039 ■ Yankee Tek Ventures
1 Memorial Dr., 12th Fl.
Cambridge, MA 01242
Ph:(617)250-0500
Fax:(617)250-0501
Co. E-mail: info@yankeetek.com
URL: http://www.yankeetek.com
Contact: Howard Anderson, Senior Managing Director
Preferred Investment Size: $500,000 to $6,000,000. **Investment Types:** Seed and first stage. **Industry Preferences:** Communications, computer software, Internet specific, semiconductors and other electronics, and business service. **Geographic Preferences:** Northeast. **Principal Exhibits:**

51040 ■ Zero Stage Capital Co., Inc.
265 Franklin St.
Boston, MA 02110
Ph:(617)876-5355
Fax:(617)876-1248
Co. E-mail: info@zerostage.com
URL: http://www.zerostage.com
Contact: Ben R. Bronstein, Managing Director
Preferred Investment Size: $2,000 to $10,000,000. **Investment Types:** Seed, start-up, first and second stage, early and later stage, and fund of funds. **Industry Preferences:** Computer software and services, Internet specific, communications and media, medical and health, biotechnology, semiconductors and other electronics, industrial and energy, consumer related, and other products. **Geographic Preferences:** East Coast and Northeast. **Principal Exhibits:**

PROCUREMENT ASSISTANCE PROGRAMS

51041 ■ Massachusetts Procurement Technical Assistance Center–University of Massachusetts–Small Business Development Center (SBDC) (121 P)
121 President's Dr., Rm. 227
Amherst, MA 01003
Ph:(413)545-6303
Fax:(413)545-1273
Co. E-mail: ptachelp@msbdc.umass.edu
URL: http://www.msbdc.org/ptac
Contact: Grace Otta, Program Mgr.
Description: Helps to guide you through the government procurement process and provide you with information on how to become more competitive in the government marketplace.

51042 ■ Small Business Administration
Electronic Systems Center
Hanscom AFB
275 Randolf Rd., Bldg. 1101
Bedford, MA 01731-2818
Ph:(781)377-2737
Fax:(202)481-0340
Co. E-mail: arvind.patel@sba.gov
URL: http://www.sba.gov
Contact: Arvind Patel
E-mail: keith.hubbard@sba.gov
Description: Covers activities for Hanscom Air Force Base (Bedford, MA), Army Corps of Engineers (Waltham, MA), Army Soldiers Systems Command (Natick, MA), Transportation Systems Control (Cambridge, MA).

INCUBATORS/RESEARCH AND TECHNOLOGY PARKS

51043 ■ Biogen Idec Innovation Incubator
14 Cambridge Center
Cambridge, MA 02142
Ph:(858)401-8242
Co. E-mail: bi3@biogenidec.com
URL: http://www.bi3.biogenidec.com
Description: A biotech incubator offering a comprehensive set of resources and services to ensure rapid startup and quick progression by supplying all the business and administrative support required to manage day-to-day company operations.

51044 ■ Boston College–Office for Sponsored Programs
140 Commonwealth Ave.
Chestnut Hill, MA 02467
Ph:(617)552-3344
Fax:(617)552-0747
Co. E-mail: joanne.scibilia@bc.edu
URL: http://www.bc.edu/research/osp.html
Contact: Joanne Scibilia, Dir.
E-mail: joanne.scibilia@bc.edu
Scope: Administers and coordinates extramurally sponsored research in biology, business, chemistry, economics, education, English, geology, geophysics, law, mathematics, nursing, physics, psychology, social work, and sociology conducted in various academic and research units of the College. **Publications:** OSP Newsletter.

51045 ■ Boston University–Office of Sponsored Programs
25 Buick St.
Boston, MA 02215
Ph:(617)353-4365
Fax:(617)353-6660
Co. E-mail: joank@bu.edu
URL: http://www.bu.edu/osp
Contact: Joan Kirkendall, Dir.
E-mail: joank@bu.edu
Scope: Responsible for coordination of University funding efforts with government and foundation sources and for administration of all grant/contract awards received at the University's Charles River Campus.

51046 ■ Economic Development & Industrial Corporation of Lynn, Massachusetts–Office of Economic Development
Lynn City Hall
3 City Hall Sq., Rm. 307
Lynn, MA 01901
Ph:(781)581-9399
Fax:(781)581-9731
Co. E-mail: info@ediclynn.org
URL: http://www.ediclynn.org
Contact: James Marsh, Dir.
Description: The Economic Development & Industrial Corporation of Lynn (EDIC/Lynn) is a non-profit corporation established under a state mandate in 1977 that functions as the City of Lynn's development bank.

51047 ■ Enterprise Center at Salem State College
121 Loring Ave.
Salem, MA 01970
Ph:(978)542-7528
Fax:(978)542-7061
Co. E-mail: sgibney@enterprisectr.org
URL: http://www.enterprisectr.org/
Description: A business incubator and virtual center for entrepreneurs throughout the North Shore of Boston at every stage of business development. The Center leases office space to start up companies, offers free skill-building workshops to the public, and hosts numerous other programs including one hundred twenty-eight Venture North Networking Breakfasts and an annual Business Plan Competition.

51048 ■ Harvard University–Office for Sponsored Programs
Holyoke Center, 6th Fl., Ste. 600
1350 Massachusetts Ave.
Cambridge, MA 02138
Ph:(617)495-5501
Fax:(617)496-2524
URL: http://vpf-web.harvard.edu/osp
Contact: Deloris Pettis
Scope: Administers and coordinates all extramurally sponsored research conducted at the University.

51049 ■ Harvard University–Office of Technology Development
Holyoke Ctr., Ste. 727E
1350 Massachusetts Ave.
Cambridge, MA 02138
Ph:(617)495-3067
Fax:(617)495-9568
Co. E-mail: otd@harvard.edu
URL: http://www.otd.harvard.edu
Contact: Isaac T. Kohlberg, Ch.
E-mail: otd@harvard.edu
Scope: Facilitates University-industry relations through technology licensing in the areas of applied sciences, recombinant DNA, hybridoma technology, software and courseware, chemistry, therapeutics, vaccines, bioprocesses, and medical, veterinary, and agricultural diagnostics.

51050 ■ Martin Luther King Jr. Business Empowerment Center
237 Chandler St.
Worcester, MA 01609
Ph:(508)756-6330
Fax:(508)751-8591
Co. E-mail: mlkj-bec@rcn.com
URL: http://www.mlkj-bec.org/
Description: A community-based operation focusing on business development, business incubation, and job placement and training; clients are provided technical support and business training skills in the areas of accounting, cash management, employee relations, technology, and business planning. The Center offers quality office space, office equipment, supplies and furniture, conference rooms, internet access, and secretarial staff resources to small, and start-up businesses.

51051 ■ Massachusetts Biomedical Initiatives
Gateway Park
60 Prescott St.
Worcester, MA 01605
Ph:(508)797-4200
Fax:(508)799-4039
Co. E-mail: info@massbiomed.org
URL: http://www.massbiomed.org/
Description: An independent, tax-exempt corporation created to support the growth and expansion of biotechnology and medical device companies throughout the region, enhancing the status of Massachusetts as a world leader in the medical industry.

51052 ■ Massachusetts Institute of Technology–Office of Sponsored Programs
Bldg. E19-750
77 Massachusetts Ave.
Cambridge, MA 02139
Ph:(617)324-9022
Fax:(617)253-4734
Co. E-mail: mchristy@mit.edu
URL: http://osp.mit.edu
Contact: Michelle D. Christy, Dir.
E-mail: mchristy@mit.edu
Scope: Administers sponsored research program of the Institute, negotiating research contracts, taking care of business and contractual obligations, and serving as liaison with research sponsors.

51053 ■ Massachusetts Institute of Technology–Technology Licensing Office
1 Cambridge Center, Kendall Sq., Rm. NE18-501
Cambridge, MA 02142-1601
Ph:(617)253-6966

Fax:(617)258-6790
Co. E-mail: tlo-www@mit.edu
URL: http://web.mit.edu/tlo/www/
Contact: Lita Nelsen, Dir.
E-mail: tlo-www@mit.edu
Scope: Commercializes technology from the Institute in the areas of biotechnology, biomedicine, ceramics, chemistry, computers, electrooptics, integrated circuits, and polymers. Markets inventions and software developed at Lincoln Laboratory.

51054 ■ MassInnovation, LLC
360 Merrimack St., Bldg. 5
Lawrence, MA 01843
Ph:(978)683-2901
Fax:(978)683-2837
Co. E-mail: info@massinnovation.com
URL: http://www.massinnovation.com
Contact: Robert Ansin, Pres & CEO
Description: The MIC supports entrepreneurs with facilities for offices, laboratories, and light manufacturing as well as access to venture capital.

51055 ■ Smith College–Office of Institutional Research
305 College Hall
Elm St.
Northampton, MA 01063
Ph:(413)585-3021
Fax:(413)585-3026
Co. E-mail: crowen@smith.edu
URL: http://www.smith.edu/ir
Contact: Cate Rowen, Dir.
E-mail: crowen@smith.edu
Scope: Institutional planning.

51056 ■ Springfield Business Incubator
Springfield Technical Community College
Andrew M. Scibelli Enterprise Center
1 Federal St., Bldg. 101
Springfield, MA 01105
Ph:(413)755-6109
Co. E-mail: marla@admin.umass.edu
URL: http://www.stcc.edu/sbi/
Description: A small business incubator striving to enhance the economic development of the Pioneer Valley by providing entrepreneurs with the opportunity to experience being in business for themselves, while still having a team of advisors guiding them.

51057 ■ University of Massachusetts at Amherst–Office of Research Affairs
Research Administration Bldg.
70 Butterfield Terrace
Amherst, MA 01003-9242
Ph:(413)545-3428
Fax:(413)577-1728
Co. E-mail: mccandless@ora.umass.edu
URL: http://www.umass.edu/research/research-affairs
Contact: Bruce McCandless, Dir.
E-mail: mccandless@ora.umass.edu
Scope: Provides coordination, funds, and information for research efforts of the University. Serves as faculty liaison on research grant proposals.

51058 ■ Worcester Polytechnic Institute–Division of Academic Affairs
100 Institute Rd.
Worcester, MA 01609-2280
Ph:(508)831-5222
Fax:(508)831-5774
Co. E-mail: ewo@wpi.edu
URL: http://www.wpi.edu/Admin/Provost
Contact: Eric W. Overstrom
E-mail: ewo@wpi.edu
Scope: Administers research activities for Intelligent Materials Processing Multidisciplinary Research Center, Center for Image Understanding, Center for Inorganic Membrane Studies, Artificial Intelligence Research Group, Center for Holographic Studies and Laser Technology, Aluminum Casting Research Laboratory, Applied Bioengineering Multidisciplinary Research Center, Carl Gunnard Johnson Powder Metallurgy Research Center, Center for Wireless Information Network Studies, and Magnetic Resonance Imaging Center, Metal Processing Institute. **Services:** Consulting; Technical assistance.

EDUCATIONAL PROGRAMS

51059 ■ Becker College
61 Sever St.
Worcester, MA 1609
Ph:(508)791-9241
Free: 877-5-BECKER
Fax:(508)831-7505
URL: http://www.beckercollege.edu
Description: Four and two year college offering a small business management programs.

51060 ■ Bunker Hill Community College
250 New Rutherford Ave.
Boston, MA 02129-2925
Ph:(617)228-2000
Fax:(617)228-2082
URL: http://www.bhcc.mass.edu
Description: Two-year college offering a small business management course.

51061 ■ Dean College
99 Main St.
Franklin, MA 02038
Ph:(508)541-1508
Free: 800-852-7702
Fax:(508)541-8726
Co. E-mail: admissions@dean.edu
URL: http://www.dean.edu
Description: Two-year college offering a small business management program.

51062 ■ MassBay Community College
50 Oakland St.
Wellesley Hills, MA 02481
Ph:(781)239-3000
Fax:(781)239-1047
URL: http://www.massbay.edu
Description: College offering a two-year small business management program.

51063 ■ Mt. Ida College–Division of Continuing Education
777 Dedham St.
Newton Centre, MA 02459
Ph:(617)928-4500
Fax:(617)928-4760
URL: http://www.mountida.edu
Description: Offers certificate and/or associate degree programs in business administration and paralegal studies. Also provides noncredit professional development programs to small business owners.

PUBLICATIONS

51064 ■ Boston Business Journal
200 High St.
Boston, MA 02110
Ph:(617)330-1000
Fax:(617)330-1016
URL: http://www.amcity.com/boston

51065 ■ New England Economic Review
PO Box 2076
Boston, MA 02106-2076
Ph:(617)973-3403

Fax:(617)973-3957

51066 ■ Smart Start your Massachusetts Business
PSI Research
300 N. Valley Dr.
Grants Pass, OR 97526
Ph:(503)479-9464
Free: 800-228-2275
Fax:(503)476-1479
Co. E-mail: info@psi-research.com
URL: http://www.psi-research.com
Ed: Michael D. Jenkins. **Released:** Revised edition, 1992. **Price:** $29.95 (looseleaf binder); $24.95 (paper). **Description:** Part of the Successful Business Library series.

51067 ■ Worcester Business Journal
172 Shrewsbury St.
Worcester, MA 01604
Ph:(508)755-8004
Free: 800-925-8004
Fax:(508)755-8860
URL: http://www.wbjournal.com

PUBLISHERS

51068 ■ Charles River Media
25 Thomson Pl.
Boston, MA 02210
Ph:(617)757-7900
Free: 800-347-7707
Fax:(617)757-7969
Co. E-mail: info@charlesriver.com
URL: http://www.courseptr.com/crm/
Contact: Riccard Linde, Mgr
Founded: 1994.

51069 ■ DBA Books
291 Beacon St., Ste. 8
Boston, MA 02116
Ph:(617)262-0411
Contact: Diane Bellavance, Owner
E-mail: dbellava@lynx.neu.edu
Description: Publishes books for small business owners. Reaches market through direct mail and internet bookstores. Does not accept unsolicited manuscripts. **Founded:** 1979.

51070 ■ HRD Press
22 Amherst Rd.
Amherst, MA 01002-9709
Ph:(413)253-3488
Free: 800-822-2801
Fax:(413)253-3490
Co. E-mail: info@hrdpress.com
URL: http://www.hrdpress.com
Contact: Mark Snow, VP of Sales
E-mail: marksnow@hrdpress.com
Description: Publishes textbooks and workshops on human resources development, management and training. Reaches market through direct mail and telephone sales. **Founded:** 1972.

51071 ■ Jeffrey Lant Associates Inc.
50 Follen St., Ste. 507
PO Box 38-2767
Cambridge, MA 02138-3509
Fax:(617)547-0061
URL: http://www.jeffreylant.com
Contact: Jeffrey Lant, President
E-mail: drjlant@worldprofit.com
Description: Publishes technical assistance books for nonprofit organizations, consultants, independent professionals and small and home-based businesses. Offers audio cassettes, workshops and consultation services. Also publishes twice monthly Worlgram newsletter. Reaches market through commission representatives, direct mail, telephone sales and the Internet. Accepts unsolicited manuscripts. **Founded:** 1979.

51072 ■ JLA Publications
50 Follen St., Ste. 507
PO Box 38-2767
Cambridge, MA 02138
Ph:(617)547-6372
Fax:(617)547-0061
Co. E-mail: drjlant@worldprofit.com
Contact: Dr. Jeffrey L. Lant, President
E-mail: drjlant@worldprofit.com
Description: Publishes guides and books on small business topics. Accepts unsolicited manuscripts. **Founded:** 1979.

51073 ■ Nicholas Brealey Publishing
20 Park Plz., Ste. 115A
Boston, MA 02108
Ph:(617)523-3801
Free: 888-273-2539
Fax:(617)523-3708
Co. E-mail: info@nicholasbrealey.com
URL: http://www.nicholasbrealey.com
Contact: Vanessa Descalzi, Editor
E-mail: vdescalzi@nicholasbrealey.com
Description: Publishes trade and professional books in business, intelligent self-help and popular psychology. Accepts unsolicited manuscripts. Reaches market through commission representatives, direct mail, reviews, listings and distributors. **Founded:** 1992.

51074 ■ Standish Press
105 Standish St.
Duxbury, MA 02332
Ph:(781)934-9570
Fax:(781)934-9570
Co. E-mail: standish@verizon.net
Contact: Olga L. Rothschild, Editor
Description: Publishes health and fitness for self-help, medical care, writing, home improvement, humor, business, travel and fiction for an adult audience. Does not accept unsolicited manuscripts. Reaches market through reviews and listings as well as wholesalers and distributors. **Founded:** 1999.

SMALL BUSINESS ASSISTANCE PROGRAMS

51075 ■ Michigan Economic Development Corp.
300 N Washington Sq.
Lansing, MI 48913
Ph:(517)373-9808
Free: 888-522-0103
Fax:(517)335-0198
Co. E-mail: MEDCservices@michigan.org
URL: http://www.themedc.org
Contact: Greg Maine, Pres and CEO
Description: Advocate for businesses in Michigan that have a conflict with state agencies or that need assistance in getting attention from state agencies.

51076 ■ Michigan Economic Development Corporation–International Development
300 N Washington Sq.
Lansing, MI 48913
Ph:(517)335-5975
Free: 888-522-0103
Fax:(517)241-3689
Co. E-mail: internationaldevinfo@michigan.org
URL: http://www.michigan.org/medc/
Contact: Greg Maine, Pres and CEO
Description: Assists firms in developing foreign markets.

51077 ■ Michigan Economic Development Corp.–Small Business Outreach
300 N Washington Sq.
Lansing, MI 48913
Ph:(517)373-9808
Fax:(517)335-0198
URL: http://www.michigan.org/medc
Contact: Greg Maine, Pres and CEO
Description: Assists firms in developing foreign markets.

51078 ■ Midland Tomorrow
300 Rodd St., Ste. 201
Midland, MI 48640-6596
Ph:(989)839-0340
Fax:(989)839-7372
Co. E-mail: info@midlandtomorrow.org
URL: http://www.midlandtomorrow.org/
Contact: Scott Walker, CEO

SCORE OFFICES

51079 ■ SCORE Ann Arbor Area Chapter
115 W Huron St., 3rd Fl.
Ann Arbor, MI 48104
Ph:(734)665-4433
Fax:(734)665-4191
Co. E-mail: info@annarborchamber.org
URL: http://annarborscore.org
Contact: Henry D. Kopicko, Chm.
Description: Provides public service by offering small business advice and training.

51080 ■ SCORE Barry County
Path: www.mibarry.com/chamber/index.htm

51081 ■ SCORE Cadillac
222 N Lake St.
Cadillac, MI 49601
Ph:(231)775-9776
Fax:(231)775-1440
Co. E-mail: score@cadillac.org
Description: Serves as volunteer program in which working and retired business management professionals provide free business counseling to men and women who are considering starting a small business, encountering problems with their business, or expanding their business. Offers free one-on-one counseling, online counseling and low cost workshops on a variety of business topics.

51082 ■ SCORE Cornerstone Alliance
Path: www.cornerstonechamber.com

51083 ■ SCORE Detroit
477 Michigan Ave., Rm. 515
Detroit, MI 48226
Ph:(313)226-7947
Fax:(313)226-3448
Co. E-mail: detscore@sbcglobal.net
URL: http://scoredetroit.org
Contact: Mr. Jay Stark, Chm.
Description: Seeks to provide counseling for new and small business.

51084 ■ SCORE Grand Rapids
111 Pearl St. NW
Grand Rapids, MI 49503
Ph:(616)771-0305
Co. E-mail: score@grandrapids.org
URL: http://www.scoregr.org
Contact: Bill Leete, Chm.
Description: Dedicated to entrepreneur education and the formation, growth and success of small businesses nationwide.

51085 ■ SCORE Greenville
Path: greenvillechamber.net

51086 ■ SCORE Holland
Path: www.scoreholland.org

51087 ■ SCORE Kalamazoo
Path: www.scorekazoo.org

51088 ■ SCORE Ludington & Scottville
Path: www.ludington.org

51089 ■ SCORE Muskegon
c/o Muskegon Chamber of Commerce
900 3rd St., Ste. 200
Muskegon, MI 49443-1087
Ph:(231)722-3751
Fax:(231)728-7251
Co. E-mail: score@muskegon.org
URL: http://www.scoremuskegon.org
Description: Serves as volunteer program in which working and retired business management professionals provide free business counseling to men and women who are considering starting a small busi-

ness, encountering problems with their business, or expanding their business. Offers free one-on-one counseling, online counseling and low cost workshops on a variety of business topics.

51090 ■ SCORE Traverse City
202 E Grandview Pkwy.
Traverse City, MI 49684-0387
Ph:(231)947-5075
Co. E-mail: score@tcchamber.org
URL: http://score-tvc.org/contact.html
Contact: Pat Hobson
Description: Provides entrepreneurs with free, confidential, face-to-face and email business counseling.

51091 ■ Tip of the Mitt SCORE
Path: www.tipofthemittscore.org

BETTER BUSINESS BUREAUS

51092 ■ Better Business Bureau of Detroit and Eastern Michigan
30555 Southfield Rd., Ste. 200
Southfield, MI 48076-7751
Ph:(248)644-9100
Fax:(248)644-5026
Co. E-mail: info@easternmichiganbbb.org
URL: http://www.easternmichigan.bbb.org
Contact: Vicki Galpin, Pres./CEO

51093 ■ Better Business Bureau of Western Michigan
Trust Bldg.
40 Pearl St. NW, Ste. 354
Grand Rapids, MI 49503
Ph:(616)774-8236
Free: 800-684-3222
Fax:(616)774-2014
Co. E-mail: bbbinfo@iserv.net
URL: http://westernmichigan.bbb.org
Contact: Kenneth J. Vander Meeden, Pres./CEO

CHAMBERS OF COMMERCE

51094 ■ Alger Chamber of Commerce
114 W Superior St.
PO Box 405
Munising, MI 49862
Ph:(906)387-2138
Co. E-mail: chamber@algercounty.org
URL: http://www.algercounty.org
Contact: Denise Hansen, Exec. Dir.

51095 ■ Allegan Area Chamber of Commerce
221 Trowbridge St., Ste. B
Allegan, MI 49010
Ph:(269)673-2479
Co. E-mail: info@alleganchamber.com
URL: http://www.alleganchamber.com
Contact: Grace Grant, Pres.

51096 ■ Anchor Bay Chamber of Commerce
36341 Front St., Ste. 2
New Baltimore, MI 48047
Ph:(586)725-5148
Fax:(586)725-5369
Co. E-mail: info@anchorbaychamber.com
URL: http://www.anchorbaychamber.com
Contact: Lisa M. Edwards, Pres.

51097 ■ Ann Arbor Area Chamber of Commerce
115 W Huron St., 3rd Fl.
Ann Arbor, MI 48104
Ph:(734)665-4433
Fax:(734)665-4191
Co. E-mail: info@annarborchamber.org
URL: http://www.annarborchamber.org
Contact: Jesse Bernstein, Pres./CEO

51098 ■ Atlanta Area Chamber of Commerce
PO Box 410
Atlanta, MI 49709
Ph:(989)785-3400
Fax:(989)785-3400
Co. E-mail: memberships@atlanta-mi-chamber.com
URL: http://www.atlantamichigan.com
Contact: Betty Comoford, Pres.

51099 ■ Au Gres Chamber of Commerce
PO Box 455
Au Gres, MI 48703
Ph:(989)876-6688
Co. E-mail: staff@augreschamber.com
URL: http://www.augreschamber.com

51100 ■ Auburn Area Chamber of Commerce
PO Box 215
Auburn, MI 48611
Ph:(989)662-4001
Co. E-mail: cornfest@auburnmichigan.org

51101 ■ Barry County Area Chamber of Commerce
221 W State St.
Hastings, MI 49058
Ph:(269)945-2454
Free: 800-510-2922
Fax:(269)945-3839
Co. E-mail: valerie@barrychamber.com
URL: http://www.barrychamber.com
Contact: Valerie Byrnes, Exec. Dir.

51102 ■ Battle Creek Area Chamber of Commerce
Commerce Pointe
77 E Michigan Ave., Ste. 80
Battle Creek, MI 49017
Ph:(269)962-4076
Fax:(269)962-6309
Co. E-mail: kmechem@battlecreek.org
URL: http://www.battlecreek.org
Contact: Kathleen L. Mechem, Pres./CEO

51103 ■ Bay Area Chamber of Commerce
901 Saginaw St.
Bay City, MI 48708
Ph:(989)893-4567
Free: 877-770-4438
Fax:(989)995-5594
Co. E-mail: chamber@baycityarea.com
URL: http://www.baycityarea.com
Contact: Michael D. Seward CCE, Pres./CEO

51104 ■ Bellaire Area Chamber of Commerce
PO Box 205
Bellaire, MI 49615
Ph:(231)533-6023
Fax:(231)533-8764
Co. E-mail: info@bellairechamber.org
URL: http://www.bellairechamber.org
Contact: Patricia W. Savant, Exec. Dir.

51105 ■ Belleville Area Chamber of Commerce
248 Main St.
Belleville, MI 48111
Ph:(734)697-7151
Fax:(734)697-1415
Co. E-mail: bellechamber@bellevillech.org
URL: http://www.bellevillech.org
Contact: Kelly Boelter, Exec. Dir.

51106 ■ Benzie County Chamber of Commerce
826 Michigan Ave.
PO Box 204
Benzonia, MI 49616
Ph:(231)882-5801
Free: 800-882-5801
Fax:(231)882-9249
Co. E-mail: chamber@benzie.org
URL: http://www.benzie.org
Contact: Mary Carroll, Exec. Dir.

51107 ■ Birch Run Area Chamber of Commerce
11600 N Beyer Rd., Ste. 100
Birch Run, MI 48415
Ph:(989)624-9193
Free: 888-624-9193
Fax:(989)624-5337
Co. E-mail: inman@birchrunchamber.com
URL: http://www.birchrunchamber.com
Contact: Marianne Nelson, Sec.

51108 ■ Birmingham-Bloomfield Chamber of Commerce
124 W Maple Rd.
Birmingham, MI 48009-3322
Ph:(248)644-1700
Fax:(248)644-0286
Co. E-mail: thechamber@bbcc.com
URL: http://www.bbcc.com/home
Contact: Carrie Zarotney, Pres.

51109 ■ Blissfield Area Chamber of Commerce
PO Box 25
Blissfield, MI 49228-0025
Ph:(517)486-3642
Fax:(517)486-4328
Co. E-mail: info@blissfieldchamber.org
URL: http://www.blissfieldchamber.org
Contact: Zola Farrar, VP

51110 ■ Boyne Area City Chamber of Commerce
28 S Lake St.
Boyne City, MI 49712
Ph:(231)582-6222
Fax:(231)582-6963
Co. E-mail: bcbooks@freeway.net
URL: http://www.boynecity.com
Contact: Kathy Anderson, Pres.

51111 ■ Branch County Area Chamber of Commerce
20 Division St.
Coldwater, MI 49036-1966
Ph:(517)278-5985
Fax:(517)278-8369
Co. E-mail: info@branchareachamber.com
URL: http://www.branchareachamber.com
Contact: Hillary Eley, Pres.

51112 ■ Brooklyn - Irish Hills Chamber of Commerce
221 N Main St.
Brooklyn, MI 49230-8999
Ph:(517)592-8907
Fax:(517)592-8907
Co. E-mail: cindy@brooklynmi.com
URL: http://www.brooklynmi.com
Contact: Cindy Hubbells, Exec. Dir.

51113 ■ Buchanan Area Chamber of Commerce
103 W Front St.
Buchanan, MI 49107-1410
Ph:(269)695-3291
Fax:(269)695-3813
Co. E-mail: bacc@buchanan.mi.us
URL: http://www.buchanan.mi.us
Contact: Monroe Lemay, Exec. Dir.

51114 ■ Cadillac Area Chamber of Commerce
222 Lake St.
Cadillac, MI 49601-1874
Ph:(231)775-9776
Fax:(231)775-1440
Co. E-mail: info@cadillac.org
URL: http://www.cadillac.org
Contact: Bill Tencza, Pres.

51115 ■ Canton Chamber of Commerce
45525 Hanford Rd.
Canton, MI 48187
Ph:(734)453-4040
Fax:(734)453-4503
Co. E-mail: info@cantonchamber.com
URL: http://www.cantonchamber.com
Contact: Dianne Cojei, Pres.

51116 ■ Caro Chamber of Commerce
157 N State St.
Caro, MI 48723
Ph:(989)673-5211
Fax:(989)672-4098
Co. E-mail: executivedirector@carochamber.org
URL: http://www.carochamber.org
Contact: Brenda Caruthers, Exec. Dir.

51117 ■ Cass City Chamber of Commerce
6506 Main St.
Cass City, MI 48726
Ph:(989)872-4618
Free: (866)266-3822
Fax:(989)276-3822
Co. E-mail: chamber@cass-city.net
URL: http://main.casscitychamber.com
Contact: Dee Mulligan, Admin.

51118 ■ Central Lake Chamber of Commerce
2587 N M-88 Hwy.
Central Lake, MI 49622
Ph:(231)544-3322
Co. E-mail: clcc@torchlake.com
URL: http://www.central-lake.com
Contact: Jackie White, Pres.

51119 ■ Central Macomb County Chamber of Commerce
28 First St., Ste. B
Mount Clemens, MI 48043
Ph:(586)493-7600
Fax:(586)493-7602
Co. E-mail: info@macombcountychamber.com
URL: http://www.macombcountychamber.com
Contact: Grace Shore, CEO/COO

51120 ■ Chamber - Grand Haven, Spring Lake, Ferrysburg
1 S Harbor Dr.
Grand Haven, MI 49417
Ph:(616)842-4910
Fax:(616)842-0379
Co. E-mail: areainfo@grandhavenchamber.org
URL: http://www.grandhavenchamber.org
Contact: Joy A. Gaasch, Pres.

51121 ■ Charlevoix Area Chamber of Commerce
109 Mason St.
Charlevoix, MI 49720-1417
Ph:(231)547-2101
Free: 800-951-2101
Fax:(231)547-6633
Co. E-mail: info@charlevoix.org
URL: http://www.charlevoix.org
Contact: Tom Conlan, Chm.

51122 ■ Cheboygan Area Chamber of Commerce
124 N Main St.
Cheboygan, MI 49721
Ph:(231)627-7183
Free: 800-968-3302
Fax:(231)627-2770
Co. E-mail: info@cheboygan.com
URL: http://www.cheboygan.com

51123 ■ Chelsea Area Chamber of Commerce
310 N Main St., Ste. 120
Chelsea, MI 48118
Ph:(734)475-1145
Fax:(734)475-6102
Co. E-mail: info@chelseamichamber.org
URL: http://www.chelseamichamber.org
Contact: Bob Pierce, Exec. Dir.

51124 ■ Chesaning Chamber of Commerce
PO Box 83
Chesaning, MI 48616
Ph:(989)845-3055
Free: 800-255-3055
Fax:(989)845-6006
Co. E-mail: info@chesaningchamber.org
URL: http://www.chesaningchamber.org
Contact: Steve Keck, Pres.

51125 ■ Clare Area Chamber of Commerce
429 N McEwan St.
Clare, MI 48617
Ph:(989)386-2442
Free: 888-ATC-LARE
Fax:(989)386-3173
URL: http://www.claremichigan.com

51126 ■ Clarkston Area Chamber of Commerce
5856 S Main St.
Clarkston, MI 48346
Ph:(248)625-8055
Fax:(248)625-8041
Co. E-mail: info@clarkston.org
URL: http://www.clarkston.org
Contact: Penny Shanks, Pres.

51127 ■ Coloma-Watervliet Area Chamber of Commerce
PO Box 418
Coloma, MI 49038
Ph:(269)468-9160
Fax:(269)468-7088
Co. E-mail: info@coloma-watervliet.org
URL: http://www.coloma-watervliet.org
Contact: Sandy Kraemer, Pres.

51128 ■ Coopersville Area Chamber of Commerce
289 Danforth St.
Coopersville, MI 49404
Ph:(616)997-5164
Fax:(616)997-6679
Co. E-mail: ctimmerman@cityofcoopersville.com
URL: http://www.coopersville.com
Contact: Cindy Timmerman, Exec. Dir.

51129 ■ Dearborn Chamber of Commerce
15544 Michigan Ave.
Dearborn, MI 48126
Ph:(313)584-6100
Fax:(313)584-9818
Co. E-mail: info@dearbornchamber.org
URL: http://www.dearbornchamber.org
Contact: Jennifer Giering, Pres.

51130 ■ Delta County Area Chamber of Commerce
230 Ludington St.
Escanaba, MI 49829
Ph:(906)786-2192
Free: 800-DEL-TAMI
Fax:(906)786-8830
Co. E-mail: info@deltami.org
URL: http://www.deltami.org
Contact: Vickie Micheau, Exec. Dir.

51131 ■ Detroit Regional Chamber
PO Box 33840
Detroit, MI 48232-0840
Ph:(313)596-0320
Free: (866)627-5463
Fax:(313)964-0183
Co. E-mail: members@detroitchamber.com
URL: http://www.detroitchamber.com
Contact: Richard E. Blouse Jr., Pres./CEO

51132 ■ East Jordan Area Chamber of Commerce
PO Box 137
100 Main St., Ste. B
East Jordan, MI 49727
Ph:(231)536-7351
Fax:(231)536-0966
Co. E-mail: info@ejchamber.org
URL: http://www.ejchamber.org
Contact: Mary H. Faculak, Pres.

51133 ■ Eastpointe Area Chamber of Commerce
24840 Gratiot Ave., Ste. B
Eastpointe, MI 48021
Ph:(586)776-5520
Fax:(586)776-7808
URL: http://epchamber.com
Contact: Catherine Green, Exec. Dir.

51134 ■ Edwardsburg Area Chamber of Commerce
PO Box 575
Edwardsburg, MI 49112
Ph:(269)663-6344
Free: 800-942-8413
Fax:(269)663-5344
Co. E-mail: administration@edwardsburg.biz
URL: http://www.edwardsburg.biz
Contact: David Ball, Pres.

51135 ■ Elk Rapids Area Chamber of Commerce
305 U.S. 31 N
PO Box 854
Elk Rapids, MI 49629
Ph:(231)264-8202
Free: 800-626-7328
Fax:(231)264-6591
Co. E-mail: info@elkrapidschamber.org
URL: http://www.elkrapidschamber.org
Contact: Sheila Marker, Interim Exec. Dir.

51136 ■ Evart Area Chamber of Commerce
PO Box 688
Evart, MI 49631-0668
Ph:(231)734-9799
Fax:(231)734-9799
URL: http://www.evartchamberofcommerce.com
Contact: Herb Phelps, Pres.

51137 ■ Farmington/Farmington Hills Chamber of Commerce
27555 Executive Dr., Ste. No. 145
Farmington Hills, MI 48331
Ph:(248)474-3440
Fax:(248)474-9235
Co. E-mail: mary@ffhchamber.com
URL: http://ffhchamber.com
Contact: Mary Engelman, Pres./CEO

51138 ■ Farwell Area Chamber of Commerce
PO Box 771
Farwell, MI 48622
Ph:(989)588-0580
Co. E-mail: facc@farewellareachamber.com
URL: http://www.farwellareachamber.com
Contact: Mike Fetzer, Chm.

51139 ■ Fenton Area Chamber of Commerce
114 N Leroy St.
Fenton, MI 48430
Ph:(810)629-5447
Fax:(810)629-6608
Co. E-mail: info@fentonchamber.com
URL: http://www.fentonchamber.com
Contact: Mrs. Shelly Day, Pres.

51140 ■ Flushing Area Chamber of Commerce
PO Box 44
Flushing, MI 48433-0044
Ph:(810)659-4141
Fax:(810)659-6964
Co. E-mail: flushingchamber@sbcglobal.net
URL: http://www.flushingchamber.com
Contact: Susan Little, Exec. Dir.

51141 ■ Four Flags Area Chamber of Commerce
321 E Main St.
Niles, MI 49120-0010
Ph:(269)683-3720
Fax:(269)683-3722
Co. E-mail: nileschamber@qtm.net
URL: http://www.nilesmi.com
Contact: Ronald J. Sather, Pres./CEO

51142 ■ Frankenmuth Chamber of Commerce and Convention and Visitors Bureau
635 S Main St.
Frankenmuth, MI 48734
Ph:(989)652-6106
Free: 800-FUN-TOWN
Fax:(989)652-3841
Co. E-mail: ceo@frankenmuth.org
URL: http://www.frankenmuth.org
Contact: Jamie Furbush, Pres./CEO

51143 ■ Frankfort - Elberta Area Chamber of Commerce
PO Box 566
Frankfort, MI 49635
Ph:(231)352-7251
Fax:(231)352-6750
Co. E-mail: fcofc@frankfort-elberta.com
URL: http://www.frankfort-elberta.com
Contact: Joanne Bartley, Exec. Dir.

51144 ■ Fremont Area Chamber of Commerce
7 E Main St.
Fremont, MI 49412
Ph:(231)924-0770
Fax:(231)924-9248
Co. E-mail: info@fremontcommerce.com
URL: http://www.fremontcommerce.com
Contact: Ron Vliem, Exec. Dir.

51145 ■ French - American Chamber of Commerce - Michigan Chapter
2000 Town Ctr., Ste. 1800
Southfield, MI 48075
Ph:(248)936-9473
Fax:(248)208-9115
Co. E-mail: info@faccmi.org
URL: http://www.faccmi.org
Contact: Emmanuelle Lavergne, Exec. Dir.

51146 ■ Garden City Chamber of Commerce
30120 Ford Rd., Ste. D
Garden City, MI 48135
Ph:(734)422-4448
Fax:(734)422-1601
Co. E-mail: chamberoffice@gardencity.org
URL: http://www.gardencity.org
Contact: Bob Hunt, Pres.

51147 ■ Gaylord - Otsego County Chamber of Commerce
101 W Main St.
PO Box 513
Gaylord, MI 49734
Ph:(989)732-6333
Free: 800-345-8621
Fax:(989)732-7990
Co. E-mail: info@gaylordchamber.com
URL: http://www.gaylordchamber.com
Contact: Matt Rooyakker, Chm.

51148 ■ Grand Blanc Chamber of Commerce
512 E Grand Blanc Rd.
Grand Blanc, MI 48439
Ph:(810)695-4222
Fax:(810)695-0053
Co. E-mail: jet@grandblancchamber.org
Contact: Jet Kilmer, Pres.

51149 ■ Grand Ledge Area Chamber of Commerce
121 S Bridge St.
Grand Ledge, MI 48837
Ph:(517)627-2383

Fax:(517)627-5006
Co. E-mail: glacc@grandledgemi.com
URL: http://www.grandledgemi.com
Contact: Norman Snyder, Exec. Dir.

51150 ■ Grand Rapids Area Chamber of Commerce
111 Pearl St. NW
Grand Rapids, MI 49503-2831
Ph:(616)771-0300
Fax:(616)771-0318
Co. E-mail: info@grandrapids.org
URL: http://grandrapids.org
Contact: Ms. Jeanne Englehart, Pres.

51151 ■ Grandville Chamber of Commerce
2905 Wilson Ave., Ste. 202-A
Grandville, MI 49418
Ph:(616)531-8890
Co. E-mail: gcc@grandvillechamber.org
URL: http://www.jenison.com
Contact: Sandy LeBlanc, Exec. Dir.

51152 ■ Gratiot Area Chamber of Commerce
110 W Superior St.
PO Box 516
Alma, MI 48801
Ph:(989)463-5525
Fax:(989)463-6588
Co. E-mail: chamber@gratiot.org
URL: http://www.gratiot.org/chamber
Contact: Patricia F. Nelson, Exec. Dir.

51153 ■ Grayling Regional Chamber of Commerce
213 N James St.
PO Box 406
Grayling, MI 49738
Ph:(989)348-2921
Fax:(989)348-7315
Co. E-mail: board@graylingchamber.com
URL: http://graylingchamber.com
Contact: Jeddy Hood, Chair

51154 ■ Greater Albion Chamber of Commerce
416 S Superior St.
PO Box 238
Albion, MI 49224
Ph:(517)629-5533
Fax:(517)629-4284
Co. E-mail: gacoc@forks.org
URL: http://www.greateralbionchamber.org
Contact: Sue Marcos, Pres.

51155 ■ Greater Algonac Chamber of Commerce
1396 St. Clair River Dr.
PO Box 375
Algonac, MI 48001
Ph:(810)794-5511
Fax:(866)794-0023
Co. E-mail: execdirector@algonacchamber.com
URL: http://www.algonacchamber.com

51156 ■ Greater Berkley Chamber of Commerce
PO Box 72-1253
Berkley, MI 48072
Ph:(248)414-9157
Co. E-mail: membership@berkleychamber.com
URL: http://berkleychamber.com
Contact: Kees Hiatt, Pres.

51157 ■ Greater Brighton Area Chamber of Commerce
131 Hyne St.
Brighton, MI 48116
Ph:(810)227-5086
Fax:(810)227-5940
URL: http://www.brightoncoc.org
Contact: Pam McConeghy, Pres./CEO

51158 ■ Greater Croswell - Lexington Chamber of Commerce
PO Box 142
Lexington, MI 48450
Ph:(810)359-2262
Co. E-mail: croslex@greatlakes.net
URL: http://www.cros-lex-chamber.com
Contact: Marcy Bartniczak, Pres.

51159 ■ Greater Decatur Chamber of Commerce
PO Box 211
Decatur, MI 49045
Ph:(269)423-2411
Fax:(269)423-9047
Co. E-mail: villageofdecatur@comcast.net
URL: http://www.decaturmi.org
Contact: Dave Moormann, Pres.

51160 ■ Greater Dowagiac Area Chamber of Commerce
200 Depot Dr.
Dowagiac, MI 49047
Ph:(269)782-8212
Fax:(269)782-6701
Co. E-mail: vickie@dowagiacchamber.com
URL: http://www.dowagiacchamber.com
Contact: Vickie Phillipson, Chair

51161 ■ Greater Durand Area Chamber of Commerce
100 W Clinton St.
Durand, MI 48429
Ph:(989)288-3715
Fax:(989)288-5177
Co. E-mail: office@durandchamber.com
URL: http://www.durandchamber.com
Contact: Pat Post, Exec. Dir.

51162 ■ Greater Jackson Chamber of Commerce
141 S Jackson St.
Jackson, MI 49201
Ph:(517)782-8221
Fax:(517)780-3688
Co. E-mail: mindy@gjcc.org
URL: http://www.jacksonchamber.org
Contact: Minda Bradish APR, Pres./Exec. Dir.

51163 ■ Greater Paw Paw Chamber of Commerce
129 S Kalamazoo St.
Paw Paw, MI 49079
Fax:(269)655-8755
Co. E-mail: ppccdda@btc-bci.com
URL: http://www.pawpawmi.com
Contact: Mary Springer, Community Relations Rep.

51164 ■ Greater Romulus Chamber of Commerce
11189 Shook, Ste. C
Romulus, MI 48174
Ph:(734)893-0694
Fax:(734)893-0596
Co. E-mail: info@romuluschamber.org
URL: http://www.romuluschamber.org
Contact: Keith L. Johnston, Pres.

51165 ■ Greater Royal Oak Chamber of Commerce
200 S Washington Ave.
Royal Oak, MI 48067-3821
Ph:(248)547-4000
Fax:(248)547-0504
Co. E-mail: coc@royaloakchamber.com
URL: http://www.royaloakchamber.com
Contact: Mr. Bill Allen, Exec. Dir.

51166 ■ Greater South Haven Area Chamber of Commerce
606 Phillips St.
South Haven, MI 49090
Ph:(616)637-5171
Fax:(616)639-1570
Co. E-mail: cofc@southhavenmi.com
URL: http://www.southhavenmi.com
Contact: Rachel Vochaska, Exec. Dir.

51167 ■ Greater West Bloomfield Chamber of Commerce
6668 Orchard Lake Rd., Ste. 207
West Bloomfield, MI 48322
Ph:(248)626-3636
Fax:(248)626-4218
Co. E-mail: wbcc@sbcglobal.net
URL: http://www.westbloomfieldchamber.com
Contact: Ann Corwell, Exec. Dir.

51168 ■ Greenville Area Chamber of Commerce
108 N Lafayette St., Ste. C
Greenville, MI 48838
Ph:(616)754-5697
Fax:(616)754-4710
Co. E-mail: info@greenvillechamber.net
URL: http://www.greenvillechamber.net
Contact: Mike Knapp, Chm.

51169 ■ Harbor Beach Chamber of Commerce
PO Box 113
Harbor Beach, MI 48441
Ph:(989)479-6477
Free: 800-HBM-ICH5
Co. E-mail: visitor@harborbeachchamber.com
URL: http://www.harborbeachchamber.com
Contact: Bob Montana, Pres.

51170 ■ Harbor Country Chamber of Commerce
530 S Whittaker, Ste. F
New Buffalo, MI 49117
Ph:(269)469-5409
Fax:(269)469-2257
Co. E-mail: info@harborcounty.org
URL: http://www.harborcountry.org
Contact: Greg Bubb, Pres.

51171 ■ Harbor Springs Chamber of Commerce
368 E Main St.
Harbor Springs, MI 49740-0037
Ph:(231)526-7999
Fax:(231)526-5593
Co. E-mail: jody@staffords.com
URL: http://www.harborspringschamber.com
Contact: Jody Ewbank, Pres.

51172 ■ Harrison Chamber of Commerce
809 N 1st St.
PO Box 682
Harrison, MI 48625-0682
Ph:(989)539-6011
Fax:(989)539-6099
Co. E-mail: harrisonchamber@sbcglobal.net
URL: http://harrisonchamber.com
Contact: Debbie Gadberry, Pres.

51173 ■ Hart - Silver Lake Mears Chamber of Commerce
2388 N Comfort Dr.
Hart, MI 49420
Ph:(231)873-2247
Free: 800-870-9786
Co. E-mail: info@hartsilverlakemears.com
URL: http://www.thinkdunes.com
Contact: Linda Foster, Exec. Dir.

51174 ■ Hillman Area Chamber of Commerce
PO Box 506
Hillman, MI 49746
Ph:(989)742-3739
Fax:(989)742-4757
URL: http://www.hillmanmichigan.org/chamber.html

51175 ■ Hillsdale County Chamber of Commerce
22 N Manning St.
Hillsdale, MI 49242
Ph:(517)437-6401
Fax:(517)437-6408
Co. E-mail: info@hillsdalecountychamber.com
URL: http://www.hillsdalecountychamber.com
Contact: Karri Doty, Exec. Dir./Pres.

51176 ■ Holland Area Chamber of Commerce
272 E 8th St.
Holland, MI 49423
Ph:(616)392-2389
Fax:(616)392-7379
Co. E-mail: info@hollandchamber.org
URL: http://www.hollandchamber.org
Contact: Jane Clark, Pres.

51177 ■ Holly Area Chamber of Commerce
202 S Saginaw St.
Holly, MI 48442
Ph:(248)215-7099
Fax:(248)215-7106
Co. E-mail: staffhollychamber@yahoo.com
URL: http://www.hollychamber.com
Contact: Sandra Kleven, Pres.

51178 ■ Houghton Lake Chamber of Commerce
1625 W Houghton Lake Dr.
Houghton Lake, MI 48629
Ph:(989)366-5644
Free: 800-248-5253
Fax:(989)366-9472
Co. E-mail: hlcc@houghtonlakemichigan.net
URL: http://cms.houghtonlakechamber.org
Contact: Kim Rathbun

51179 ■ Howell Area Chamber of Commerce
123 E Washington St.
Howell, MI 48843
Ph:(517)546-3920
Fax:(517)546-4115
Co. E-mail: pconvery@howell.org
URL: http://www.howell.org
Contact: Ms. Pat Convery, Pres.

51180 ■ Hudson Area Chamber of Commerce
121 N Church St.
Hudson, MI 49247
Ph:(517)448-8983
Fax:(517)448-7339
Co. E-mail: matt@hartmanbooks.com
URL: http://www.hudsonmich.com
Contact: Matt Hartman, Pres.

51181 ■ Hudsonville Area Chamber of Commerce
5340 Plaza Ave.
PO Box 216
Hudsonville, MI 49426
Ph:(616)662-0900
Fax:(616)662-4557
Co. E-mail: support@hudsonvillechamber.com
URL: http://hudsonvillechamber.com
Contact: Laurie Van Haitsma, Dir.

51182 ■ Huron Shores Chamber of Commerce
PO Box 581
Harrisville, MI 48740
Ph:(989)724-5107
Free: 800-432-2823
Fax:(989)724-6656
Co. E-mail: info@huronshorescc.com
URL: http://www.huronshoreschamber.com
Contact: Cheryl Peterson, Pres.

51183 ■ Huron Township Chamber of Commerce
19132 Huron River Dr.
PO Box 247
New Boston, MI 48164
Ph:(734)753-4220
Fax:(734)753-4602
Co. E-mail: hurontwpchmbrcomm@yahoo.com
URL: http://www.members.tripod.com/htcc48164
Contact: Teresa A. Shearrer-Lewis-Trosin, Exec. Office Sec.

51184 ■ Huron Valley Chamber of Commerce
317 Union St.
Milford, MI 48381
Ph:(248)685-7129

Fax:(248)685-9047
Co. E-mail: info@huronvcc.com
URL: http://www.huronvcc.com/1/HVCC/index.asp
Contact: Joell Beether, Exec. Dir.

51185 ■ Indian River Resort Region Chamber of Commerce
3435 S Straits Hwy.
PO Box 57
Indian River, MI 49749
Ph:(231)238-9325
Free: 800-394-8310
Fax:(231)238-0949
Co. E-mail: info@irchamber.com
URL: http://www.irchamber.com
Contact: Mary Jo Dismang, Pres.

51186 ■ Inkster Chamber of Commerce
29150 Carlysle St.
Inkster, MI 48141-2807
Ph:(734)552-1391
Fax:(734)722-2527
Co. E-mail: info@inksterchamber.org
URL: http://www.inksterchamber.org
Contact: Ernestine Williams, Pres.

51187 ■ Interlochen Area Chamber of Commerce
PO Box 13
Interlochen, MI 49643
Ph:(231)276-7141
Co. E-mail: interlochenchamber@juno.com
URL: http://www.interlochenchamber.org
Contact: Laura M. Franke, Dir.

51188 ■ Ionia Area Chamber of Commerce
439 W Main St.
Ionia, MI 48846
Ph:(616)527-2560
Co. E-mail: info@ioniachamber.net
URL: http://www.ioniachamber.org
Contact: Dave Cook, Pres.

51189 ■ Iron County Chamber of Commerce
50 E Genesee St.
Iron River, MI 49935
Ph:(906)265-3822
Fax:(906)265-5605
Co. E-mail: info@iron.org
URL: http://www.iron.org
Contact: Bill Leonoff, Exec. Dir.

51190 ■ Ironwood Area Chamber of Commerce
PO Box 45
Ironwood, MI 49938
Ph:(906)932-1122
Fax:(906)932-2756
Co. E-mail: chamber@ironwoodmi.org
URL: http://www.ironwoodmi.org
Contact: Kim Kolesar, Exec. Dir.

51191 ■ Ishpeming Office of Lake Superior Community Partnership
119 W Division St.
Ishpeming, MI 49849
Ph:(906)486-4841
Free: 888-578-6489
Fax:(906)486-4850
Co. E-mail: lscp@marquette.org
URL: http://www.marquette.org
Contact: Amy Clickner, Dir. of Chamber Operations

51192 ■ Kalamazoo Regional Chamber of Commerce
346 W Michigan Ave.
Kalamazoo, MI 49007
Ph:(269)381-4000
Fax:(269)343-0430
Co. E-mail: editor@kazoochamber.com
URL: http://www.kazoochamber.com
Contact: Steward Sandstrom CCE, Pres./CEO

51193 ■ Kalkaska Area Chamber of Commerce
353 S Cedar St.
PO Box 291
Kalkaska, MI 49646
Ph:(231)258-9103

Fax:(231)258-6155
Co. E-mail: kalkaska@tcchamber.org
URL: http://www.kalkaskami.com
Contact: Annie Shelter, Pres.

51194 ■ Keweenaw Peninsula Chamber of Commerce
902 College Ave.
PO Box 336
Houghton, MI 49931-0336
Ph:(906)482-5240
Free: (866)304-5722
Fax:(906)482-5241
Co. E-mail: info@keweenaw.org
URL: http://www.keweenaw.org
Contact: Dallas Bond, Exec. Dir.

51195 ■ Lake City Area Chamber of Commerce
PO Drawer H
Lake City, MI 49651-0908
Ph:(231)839-4969
Fax:(231)839-5991
Co. E-mail: info@lakecitymich.com
URL: http://www.lakecitymich.com/michigan
Contact: Kim Mosher, Admin. Asst.

51196 ■ Lake Gogebic Area Chamber of Commerce
PO Box 114
Bergland, MI 49910-0114
Ph:(906)842-3611
Free: 888-464-3242
Fax:(906)842-3653
Co. E-mail: info@lakegogebicarea.com
URL: http://www.lakegogebicarea.com
Contact: Carol Peterson, Sec.

51197 ■ Lakes Area Chamber of Commerce
305 N Pontiac Trail, Ste. B
Walled Lake, MI 48390-3479
Ph:(248)624-2826
Fax:(248)624-2892
Co. E-mail: info@lakesareachamber.com
URL: http://www.lakesareachamber.com
Contact: Jo Louise Alley, Exec. Dir.

51198 ■ Lakeshore Chamber of Commerce
PO Box 93
Stevensville, MI 49127-0093
Ph:(269)429-1170
Fax:(269)429-8882
Co. E-mail: information@lakeshorechamber.org
URL: http://www.lakeshorechamber.org
Contact: Griffin Ott, Pres.

51199 ■ Lakeview Area Chamber of Commerce
PO Box 57
Lakeview, MI 48850
Ph:(989)352-1200
Fax:(989)352-6435
Co. E-mail: brian.brasser@spectrum-health.org
URL: http://lakeviewmichigan.com
Contact: Brian Brasser, Pres.

51200 ■ Lansing Regional Chamber of Commerce
PO Box 14030
Lansing, MI 48901
Ph:(517)487-6340
Fax:(517)484-6910
Co. E-mail: wsepic@lansingchamber.org
URL: http://www.lansingchamber.org
Contact: William Sepic, Pres.

51201 ■ Lapeer Area Chamber of Commerce
108 W Park St.
Lapeer, MI 48446
Ph:(810)664-6641
Fax:(810)664-4349
Co. E-mail: staff@lapeerareachamber.org
URL: http://www.lapeerareachamber.org
Contact: Neda Payne, Exec. Dir.

51202 ■ Leelanau Peninsula Chamber of Commerce
5046 SW Bayshore Dr., Ste. G
Suttons Bay, MI 49682-9709
Ph:(231)271-9895
Free: 800-980-9895
Fax:(231)271-9896
Co. E-mail: info@leelanauchamber.com
URL: http://www.leelanauchamber.com
Contact: Terry Ely, Pres.

51203 ■ Lewiston Area Chamber of Commerce
PO Box 656
Lewiston, MI 49756
Ph:(989)786-2293
Fax:(989)786-4515
Co. E-mail: lewistonchamber@i2k.com
Contact: Marcia Andrews, Exec. Dir.

51204 ■ Litchfield Chamber of Commerce
PO Box 343
Litchfield, MI 49252
Ph:(517)542-2921
Co. E-mail: manager@cityoflitchfield.org
URL: http://www.ci.litchfield.mi.us
Contact: Doug Terry, Mgr.

51205 ■ Livonia Chamber of Commerce
33233 Five Mile Rd.
Livonia, MI 48154
Ph:(734)427-2122
Fax:(734)427-6055
Co. E-mail: chamber@livonia.org
URL: http://www.livonia.org
Contact: Dan West, Pres.

51206 ■ Lowell Area Chamber of Commerce
113 Riverwalk Plz.
PO Box 224
Lowell, MI 49331
Ph:(616)897-9161
Fax:(616)897-9101
Co. E-mail: info@lowellchamber.org
URL: http://www.lowellchamber.org
Contact: Liz Baker, Exec. Dir.

51207 ■ Ludington Area Chamber of Commerce
5300 W U.S. 10
Ludington, MI 49431
Ph:(231)845-0324
Free: 877-420-6618
Fax:(231)845-6857
Co. E-mail: chamberinfo@ludington.org
URL: http://www.ludington.org
Contact: Kathy Maclean, Pres./CEO

51208 ■ Mackinac Island Tourism Bureau
PO Box 451
Mackinac Island, MI 49757
Free: 877-847-0086
Co. E-mail: info@mackinacisland.org
URL: http://www.mackinacisland.org
Contact: Mrs. Mary McGuire Slevin, Exec. Dir.

51209 ■ Mackinaw City Chamber of Commerce
216 E Central Ave.
PO Box 856
Mackinaw City, MI 49701
Ph:(231)436-5574
Free: 888-455-8100
Co. E-mail: dedwards@mackinawchamber.com
URL: http://www.mackinawchamber.com
Contact: Dawn Edwards, Exec. Dir.

51210 ■ Macomb County Chamber
32101 Chicago Rd., Ste. A-103
Chicago Plz.
Warren, MI 48093
Ph:(586)268-6430
Fax:(586)493-7602
Co. E-mail: info@macombcountychamber.com
URL: http://www.macombcountychamber.com
Contact: Grace Shore, CEO/COO

51211 ■ Madison Heights - Hazel Park Chamber of Commerce
724 W 11 Mile Rd.
Madison Heights, MI 48071
Ph:(248)542-5010
Fax:(248)542-6821
Co. E-mail: mary@mhhpchamlber.org
URL: http://www.mhhpchamber.org
Contact: Mary Sames, Exec. Dir.

51212 ■ Mancelona Area Chamber of Commerce
PO Box 558
Mancelona, MI 49659
Ph:(231)587-5500
Fax:(231)587-5500
Co. E-mail: info@mancelonachamber.org
URL: http://www.mancelonachamber.org
Contact: Joanie Moore, Exec. Dir.

51213 ■ Manchester Area Chamber of Commerce
PO Box 521
Manchester, MI 48158
Ph:(734)428-6222
Co. E-mail: president@manchestermi.org
URL: http://www.manchestermi.org
Contact: Ray Berg, Pres.

51214 ■ Manistee Area Chamber of Commerce
11 Cypress St.
Manistee, MI 49660
Ph:(231)723-2575
Free: 800-288-2286
Co. E-mail: contact@manisteechamber.com
URL: http://www.manisteecountychamber.com
Contact: Dianna Wall, Admin. Sec.

51215 ■ Marine City Chamber of Commerce
226 S Water St.
Marine City, MI 48039
Ph:(810)765-4501
Co. E-mail: chamberoffice@marinecitychamber.net
URL: http://www.marinecitychamber.net

51216 ■ Marquette Area Chamber of Commerce- Lake Superior Community Partnership
501 S Front St.
Marquette, MI 49855
Ph:(906)226-6591
Free: 888-578-6489
Fax:(906)226-2099
Co. E-mail: lscp@marquette.org
URL: http://www.marquette.org
Contact: Amy Clickner, Exec. Dir.

51217 ■ Marshall Area Chamber of Commerce
424 E Michigan Ave.
Marshall, MI 49068
Ph:(269)781-5163
Free: 800-877-5163
Co. E-mail: mcoc@voyager.net
URL: http://www.marshallmi.org/index.taf
Contact: Monica Anderson, Pres.

51218 ■ Marysville Chamber of Commerce
2055 Gratiot Blvd., Ste. D
Marysville, MI 48040
Ph:(810)364-6180
Fax:(810)364-9388
Co. E-mail: chamber@marysvillechamber.com
URL: http://www.marysvillechamber.com
Contact: Laura J. Crawford, Exec. Dir.

51219 ■ Mason Area Chamber of Commerce
148 E Ash St.
Mason, MI 48854-1646
Ph:(517)676-1046
Fax:(517)676-8504
Co. E-mail: masonchamber@masonchamber.org
URL: http://www.masonchamber.org
Contact: Douglas J. Klein APR, Exec. Dir.

51220 ■ Mecosta County Area Chamber of Commerce
246 N State St.
Big Rapids, MI 49307
Ph:(231)796-7649
Fax:(231)796-1625
Co. E-mail: info@mecostacounty.com
URL: http://www.mecostacounty.com
Contact: Anja J. Wing, Exec. Dir.

51221 ■ Metro East Chamber of Commerce
27601 Jefferson Ave.
St. Clair Shores, MI 48081
Ph:(586)777-2741
Fax:(586)777-4811
Co. E-mail: info@metroeastchamber.org
URL: http://www.metroeastchamber.org
Contact: Heather Lynn, Exec. Dir./Admin.

51222 ■ Michigan Chamber of Commerce
600 S Walnut St.
Lansing, MI 48933
Ph:(517)371-2100
Free: 800-748-0266
Fax:(517)371-7224
Co. E-mail: info@michamber.com
URL: http://www.michamber.com
Contact: Jim Barrett, Pres./CEO

51223 ■ Midland Area Chamber of Commerce
300 Rodd St., Ste. 101
Midland, MI 48640
Ph:(989)839-9901
Fax:(989)835-3701
Co. E-mail: chamber@macc.org
URL: http://www.macc.org
Contact: Mr. Sid Allen, Pres./CEO

51224 ■ Milan Area Chamber of Commerce
PO Box 164
Milan, MI 48160
Ph:(734)439-7932
Fax:(734)241-3520
Co. E-mail: info@milanchamber.org
URL: http://www.milanchamber.org
Contact: Christine Mann, Pres.

51225 ■ Monroe County Chamber of Commerce
1645 N Dixie Hwy., Ste. 2
Monroe, MI 48162
Ph:(734)242-3366
Fax:(734)289-2505
Co. E-mail: chamber@monroecountychamber.com
URL: http://monroemi.usachamber.com
Contact: Michelle Dugan, Exec. Dir.

51226 ■ Mount Pleasant Area Chamber of Commerce
114 E Broadway
Mount Pleasant, MI 48858
Ph:(989)772-2396
Fax:(989)773-2656
Co. E-mail: lhadden@mt-pleasant.net
URL: http://www.mt-pleasant.net
Contact: Lisa Hadden, Pres./CEO

51227 ■ Muskegon Area Chamber of Commerce
380 W Western Ave., Ste. 202
Muskegon, MI 49440
Ph:(231)722-3751
Fax:(231)728-7251
Co. E-mail: macc@muskegon.org
URL: http://www.muskegon.org
Contact: Cindy Larsen, Pres.

51228 ■ Northville Chamber of Commerce
195 S Main St.
Northville, MI 48167
Ph:(248)349-7640
Fax:(248)349-8730
Co. E-mail: chamber@northville.org
URL: http://www.northville.org
Contact: Jody Humphries, Pres.

51229 ■ Novi Chamber of Commerce
41875 W 11 Mile Rd., Ste. 201
Novi, MI 48375
Ph:(248)349-3743
Fax:(248)349-9719
Co. E-mail: info@novichamber.com
URL: http://www.novichamber.com
Contact: Bob Thorne, Chm.

51230 ■ Ontonagon County Chamber of Commerce
PO Box 266
Ontonagon, MI 49953
Ph:(906)884-4735
Co. E-mail: ontcofc@up.net
URL: http://www.ontonagonmi.com
Contact: Edith Basile, Corresponding Sec.

51231 ■ Orion Area Chamber of Commerce
PO Box 484
Lake Orion, MI 48361-0484
Ph:(248)693-6300
Fax:(248)693-9227
Co. E-mail: oacc@msn.com
URL: http://www.orion.lib.mi.us/orion
Contact: Donna Heyniger, Managing Dir.

51232 ■ Otsego Chamber of Commerce
135 E Allegan St.
Otsego, MI 49078
Ph:(269)694-6880
Co. E-mail: director@otsegochamber.org
URL: http://otsegochamber.org
Contact: Steven Lick, Exec. Dir.

51233 ■ Oxford Area Chamber of Commerce
PO Box 142
Oxford, MI 48371-0142
Ph:(248)628-0410
Fax:(248)628-0430
Co. E-mail: info@oxfordchamberofcommerce.com
URL: http://www.oxfordchamberofcommerce.com
Contact: Lynette Johnson, Pres.

51234 ■ Pentwater Chamber of Commerce
PO Box 614
Pentwater, MI 49449
Ph:(231)869-4150
Free: (866)869-4150
Co. E-mail: travelinfo@pentwater.org
URL: http://www.pentwater.org
Contact: Julie Shaw, Exec. Dir.

51235 ■ Petoskey Regional Chamber of Commerce
401 E Mitchell St.
Petoskey, MI 49770-2623
Ph:(231)347-4150
Fax:(231)348-1810
Co. E-mail: chamber@petoskey.com
URL: http://www.petoskey.com
Contact: Carlin Smith, Pres.

51236 ■ Pigeon Chamber of Commerce
29 S Main St.
Pigeon, MI 48755
Ph:(989)453-7400
Co. E-mail: pgncofc@avci.net
URL: http://www.pigeonchamber.com
Contact: Deanne Murdoch, Pres.

51237 ■ Plainwell Chamber of Commerce
798 E Bridge St., Ste. A
Plainwell, MI 49080
Ph:(269)685-8877
Co. E-mail: info@plainwellchamber.com
URL: http://www.plainwellchamber.com
Contact: Katie Bell Moore, Pres.

51238 ■ Plymouth Community Chamber of Commerce
850 W Ann Arbor Trail
Plymouth, MI 48170
Ph:(734)453-1540
Fax:(734)453-1724
Co. E-mail: chamber@plymouthmi.org
Contact: Wes Graff, Exec. Dir.

51239 ■ Pontiac Regional Chamber
402 N Telegraph Rd.
Pontiac, MI 48341
Ph:(248)335-9600
Fax:(248)335-9601
Co. E-mail: info@pontiaccchamber.com
URL: http://www.pontiacchamber.com
Contact: Greg Cavanaugh, Chm.

51240 ■ Redford Township Chamber of Commerce
26050 5 Mile Rd.
Redford, MI 48239-3289
Ph:(313)535-0960
Fax:(313)535-6356
Co. E-mail: rtcc@wanemail.com
URL: http://redfordchamber.org
Contact: Rick Brown, Pres.

51241 ■ Reed City Area Chamber of Commerce
211 W Upton Ave., Ste. A
Reed City, MI 49677
Ph:(231)832-5431
Free: 877-832-7332
Fax:(231)832-5431
Co. E-mail: chamberdirector@reedcitycrossroads.com
URL: http://www.reedcitycrossroads.com
Contact: Mr. Gary Brower, Pres.-Elect

51242 ■ Richmond Area Chamber of Commerce
68371 Oak St.
Richmond, MI 48062
Ph:(586)727-3266
Fax:(586)727-3635
Co. E-mail: info@robn.org
URL: http://www.robn.org
Contact: Kim Galante, Exec. Dir.

51243 ■ Rockford Area Chamber of Commerce
PO Box 520
598 Byrne Industrial Dr.
Rockford, MI 49341
Ph:(616)866-2000
Fax:(616)866-2141
Co. E-mail: info@rockfordmichamber.com
URL: http://www.rockfordmichamber.com
Contact: Brenda Davis, Exec. Dir.

51244 ■ Rogers City Chamber of Commerce
292 S Bradley Hwy.
Rogers City, MI 49779
Ph:(989)734-2535
Free: 800-622-4148
Fax:(989)734-7767
Co. E-mail: rcchamber@lhi.net
URL: http://www.rogerscity.com
Contact: David M. Snow, Exec. Dir.

51245 ■ Romeo-Washington Chamber of Commerce
PO Box 175
Romeo, MI 48065-0175
Ph:(586)752-4436
Fax:(586)752-2835
Co. E-mail: contact@rwchamber.com
URL: http://www.rwchamber.com
Contact: Shaun Whitehead, Pres.

51246 ■ Saginaw County Chamber of Commerce
515 N Washington Ave., 2nd Fl.
Saginaw, MI 48607-1370
Ph:(989)752-7161
Fax:(989)752-9055
Co. E-mail: info@saginawchamber.org
URL: http://www.saginawchamber.org
Contact: Bob Van Deventer, Pres./CEO

51247 ■ St. Ignace Chamber of Commerce
560 N State St.
St. Ignace, MI 49781-1429
Ph:(906)643-8717

Free: 800-970-8717
Co. E-mail: sichamber@lighthouse.net
URL: http://www.saintignace.org
Contact: Janet Peterson, Exec. Dir.

51248 ■ St. Johns Area Chamber of Commerce
PO Box 61
St. Johns, MI 48879
Ph:(989)224-7248
Fax:(989)224-7667
Co. E-mail: ccchamber@power-net.net
URL: http://www.clintoncountychamber.org
Contact: Brenda Tarpening, Exec. Dir.

51249 ■ Saline Area Chamber of Commerce
141 E Michigan Ave.
Saline, MI 48176-1552
Ph:(734)429-4494
Fax:(734)944-6835
Co. E-mail: salinechamber@aol.com
URL: http://www.salinechamber.com
Contact: Brian Lott, Pres.

51250 ■ Sault Area Chamber of Commerce
2581 I-75 Business Spur
Sault Ste. Marie, MI 49783
Ph:(906)632-3301
Fax:(906)632-2331
Co. E-mail: info@saultstemarie.org
URL: http://www.saultstemarie.org
Contact: Leisa Mansfield, Exec. Dir.

51251 ■ Schoolcraft County Chamber of Commerce
1000 W Lakeshore Dr.
Manistique, MI 49854
Ph:(906)341-5010
Free: 888-819-7420
Fax:(906)341-1549
Co. E-mail: chamber@reiters.net
URL: http://www.schoolcraftcountychamber.com
Contact: Ms. Lenore Heminger, Exec. Dir.

51252 ■ Shiawassee Regional Chamber of Commerce
215 N Water St.
Owosso, MI 48867-2875
Ph:(989)723-5149
Fax:(989)723-8353
Co. E-mail: customerservice@shiawasseechamber.org
URL: http://www.shiawasseechamber.org
Contact: Renita Mikolajczyk, Pres.

51253 ■ South Lyon Area Chamber of Commerce
125 N Lafayette (Pontiac Trail)
South Lyon, MI 48178
Ph:(248)437-3257
Fax:(248)437-4116
Co. E-mail: tamra@southlyonchamber.com
URL: http://www.southlyonchamber.com/1/123/index.asp
Contact: Gene Bobic

51254 ■ Southern Wayne County Regional Chamber
20600 Eureka Rd.
Taylor, MI 48180-5306
Ph:(734)284-6000
Fax:(734)284-0198
Co. E-mail: info@swccc.org
URL: http://www.lacdc.org/CDCWebsite/SWCRC/Home.aspx
Contact: Joe Vig, Chm.

51255 ■ Southfield Area Chamber of Commerce
17515 W 9 Mile Rd., No. 190
Southfield, MI 48075
Ph:(248)557-6661
Fax:(248)557-3931
Co. E-mail: southfieldchamber@yahoo.com
URL: http://www.southfieldchamber.com
Contact: Ed Powers, Pres./Exec. Dir.

51256 ■ Sterling Heights Area Chamber of Commerce
12900 Hall Rd., Ste. 190
Sterling Heights, MI 48313
Ph:(586)731-5400
Fax:(586)731-3521
Co. E-mail: ladams@suscc.com
URL: http://www.suscc.com
Contact: Lil Adams, Exec. Dir.

51257 ■ Sturgis Area Chamber of Commerce
200 W Main
PO Box 189
Sturgis, MI 49091-0189
Ph:(269)651-5758
Fax:(269)651-4124
Co. E-mail: sturgischamber@charter.net
URL: http://www.sturgischamber.com
Contact: Cathi Garn Abbs, Exec. Dir.

51258 ■ Suttons Bay Chamber of Commerce
PO Box 46
Suttons Bay, MI 49682-0046
Ph:(231)271-5077
URL: http://www.suttonsbayarea.com
Contact: Jim Munro, Pres.

51259 ■ Tawas Area Chamber of Commerce
402 E Lake St.
PO Box 608
Tawas City, MI 48764-0608
Free: 800-55-TAWAS
Co. E-mail: info@tawas.com
URL: http://www.tawas.com

51260 ■ Three Rivers Area Chamber of Commerce
57 N Main St.
Three Rivers, MI 49093
Ph:(269)278-8193
Co. E-mail: info@trchamber.com
URL: http://www.trchamber.com
Contact: Christy Trammell, Pres./CEO

51261 ■ Traverse City Area Chamber of Commerce
202 E Grandview Pkwy.
Traverse City, MI 49684
Ph:(231)947-5075
Fax:(231)946-2565
Co. E-mail: info@tcchamber.org
URL: http://www.tcchamber.org
Contact: Douglas R. Luciani, Pres./CEO

51262 ■ Troy Chamber of Commerce
4555 Investment Dr., 3rd Fl., Ste. 300
Troy, MI 48098-6338
Ph:(248)641-8151
Fax:(248)641-0545
Co. E-mail: theteam@troychamber.com
URL: http://www.troychamber.com/index.aspx?Aspx-
    AutoDetectCookieSupport=1
Contact: Michele Hodges, Pres.

51263 ■ Wayne Chamber of Commerce
34844 W Michigan Ave.
Wayne, MI 48184
Ph:(734)721-0100
Fax:(734)721-3070
Co. E-mail: jill@waynechamber.net
URL: http://waynechamber.net
Contact: Jill Gaudet, Exec. Dir.

51264 ■ West Branch Area Chamber of Commerce
422 W Houghton Ave.
West Branch, MI 48661
Ph:(989)345-2821
Free: 800-755-9091
URL: http://www.wbacc.com

51265 ■ Westland Chamber of Commerce
36900 Ford Rd.
Westland, MI 48185-2231
Ph:(734)326-7222
Fax:(734)326-6040
Co. E-mail: info@westlandchamber.com
URL: http://www.westlandchamber.com
Contact: Brookellen Swope, Pres./CEO

51266 ■ White Cloud Area Chamber of Commerce
12 N Charles
White Cloud, MI 49349
Ph:(231)689-6607
Co. E-mail: kb8ife@ncats.net
URL: http://www.whitecloudchamber.org
Contact: Ms. Sherry Adams, Sec.

51267 ■ White Lake Area Chamber of Commerce
124 W Hanson St.
Whitehall, MI 49461
Ph:(231)893-4585
Free: 800-879-9702
Fax:(231)893-0914
Co. E-mail: info@whitelake.org
URL: http://www.whitelake.org

51268 ■ Williamston Area Chamber of Commerce
369 W Grand River
PO Box 53
Williamston, MI 48895
Ph:(517)655-1549
Fax:(517)655-8859
Co. E-mail: info@williamston.org
URL: http://www.williamston.org

51269 ■ Wyoming Kentwood Area Chamber of Commerce
590 32nd St. SE
Wyoming, MI 49548-2345
Ph:(616)531-5990
Fax:(616)531-0252
Co. E-mail: john@southkent.org
URL: http://www.southkent.org
Contact: John J. Crawford, Pres./CEO

51270 ■ Ypsilanti Area Chamber of Commerce
301 W Michigan Ave., Ste. 101
Ypsilanti, MI 48197-5450
Ph:(734)482-4920
Fax:(734)482-2021
Co. E-mail: trish@ypsichamber.org
URL: http://www.ypsichamber.org
Contact: Keith Peters, Pres.

51271 ■ Zeeland Chamber of Commerce
149 Main Pl.
Zeeland, MI 49464-1735
Ph:(616)772-2494
Fax:(616)772-0065
Co. E-mail: zchamber@zeelandcofc.org
URL: http://www.zeelandcofc.org
Contact: Ann L. Query, Pres.

MINORITY BUSINESS ASSISTANCE PROGRAMS

51272 ■ GROW - Grand Rapids Opportunities for Women
25 Sheldon Blvd. SE, Ste. 210
Grand Rapids, MI 49503
Ph:(616)458-3404
URL: http://www.growbusiness.org
Contact: Bonnie Nawara, CEO
Description: Offers connections, education, and resources to create and grow women-owned businesses in the Grand Rapids area.

51273 ■ Michigan Economic Development Corporation–Office of Small Business Group
300 N Washington Sq.
Lansing, MI 48913
Ph:(517)373-8431
Free: 888-522-0103
Fax:(517)373-9143
Co. E-mail: medcservices@michigan.org
URL: http://www.michiganadvantage.org/
Contact: James Epolito, Pres & CEO
Description: Encourages greater minority enterprise development by providing financial and business education programs. Assists in state certification processes, reviews the impact of legislation, and increases awareness of minority businesses.

51274 ■ Michigan Economic Development Corp.–Office of Women Business Owners Services
300 N Washington Sq., 4th Fl.
Lansing, MI 48913
Ph:(517)335-2877
Fax:(517)335-0198
URL: http://www.michigan.org
Contact: James Epolito, Pres and CEO
Description: Provides advocacy, technical assistance, and references to outside sources for financial counseling for women entrepreneurs.

51275 ■ Michigan Minority Supplier Development Council
3011 W Grand Blvd., Ste. 230
Detroit, MI 48202-3011
Ph:(313)873-3200
Fax:(313)873-4783
Co. E-mail: ceo@mmbdc.org
URL: http://www.mmbdc.com
Contact: Louis Green, Pres & CEO

51276 ■ Michigan Small Business and Technology Development Center
Grand Valley State University
510 West Foltan
Grand Rapids, MI 49504
Ph:(616)331-7480
Fax:(616)331-7485
Co. E-mail: sbtdchq@gvsu.edu
URL: http://misbtdc.org
Contact: Carol Lopucki, Dir
Description: Provides a full-range of services for a variety of small businesses including: counseling; training; programs for a variety of needs, from how to get started, to financing; effective selling and e-commerce as well as how to develop business plans. Also provides research help and advocacy.

FINANCING AND LOAN PROGRAMS

51277 ■ Arbor Partners, LLC
130 S. First St.
Ann Arbor, MI 48104
Ph:(734)668-9000
Fax:(734)669-4195
Co. E-mail: info@arborpartners.com
URL: http://www.arborpartners.com
Contact: Donald Walker, Managing Director
Preferred Investment Size: $500,000 to $2,000,000. **Investment Types:** Early and expansion. **Industry Preferences:** Internet specific, computer software and services, consumer related, communications and media. **Geographic Preferences:** Michigan and Midwest. **Principal Exhibits:**

51278 ■ Arboretum Ventures
Market Place Bldg.
303 Detroit St., Ste. 301
Ann Arbor, MI 48104
Ph:(734)998-3688
Fax:(734)988-3689
Co. E-mail: info@arboretumvc.com
URL: http://www.arboretumvc.com
Contact: Jan Garfinkle, Founder and Managing Director
Preferred Investment Size: $1,000,000 to $3,000,000. **Investment Policies:** Seed, early and later stage. **Industry Preferences:** Biotechnology, medical and health. **Geographic Preferences:** Illinois, Indiana, Michigan, Midwest, and Ohio. **Principal Exhibits:**

51279 ■ Camelot Venture Group
27725 Stansbury, Ste. 175
Farmington Hills, MI 48334
Ph:(248)741-5100
URL: http://www.camelotventures.com
Contact: David B. Katzman, Managing Partner
Preferred Investment Size: $5,000,000 to $150,000,000. **Investment Types:** Balanced, early, second and later stage, expansion, generalist PE, mezzanine, and private placement. **Industry Preferences:** Communications and media, computer software and hardware, Internet specific, semiconductors

and other electronics, consumer related, financial services, and business service. **Geographic Preferences:** U.S. and Canada. **Principal Exhibits:**

51280 ■ EDF Ventures / Enterprise Development Fund
425 N. Main St.
Ann Arbor, MI 48104-1147
Ph:(734)663-3213
Fax:(734)663-7358
Co. E-mail: bizplans@edfvc.com
URL: http://www.edfvc.com
Contact: Mary Campbell, Founder and Managing Director

Preferred Investment Size: $1,500,000 to $5,000,000. **Investment Types:** Seed, start-up, first, second and early stage, and research and development. **Industry Preferences:** Internet specific, computer software and services, medical and health, biotechnology, semiconductors and other electronics, communications and media, consumer and related, other products, and computer hardware. **Geographic Preferences:** Midwest. **Principal Exhibits:**

PROCUREMENT ASSISTANCE PROGRAMS

51281 ■ Genesee County Metropolitan Planning Commission
1101 Beach St., Rm. 223
Flint, MI 48502-1420
Ph:(810)257-3010
Fax:(810)257-3185
Co. E-mail: gcmpc@co.genesee.mi.us
URL: http://www.gcmpc.org
Contact: Julie Hinterman, Dir.

51282 ■ Haworth College of Business–Western Michigan University
3110 Schneider Hall
Kalamazoo, MI 49008-5416
Ph:(269)387-6004
Fax:(269)387-5710
Co. E-mail: sbtdc-kzoo@wmich.edu
URL: http://www.gvsu.edu/misbtdc/region11/
Contact: Tamara Davis, Regional Dir.
E-mail: sledbett@sabien.net

Description: Provides businesses with marketing know-how and technical tools they need to obtain and perform successfully under federal, state and local government contracts

51283 ■ Michigan Procurement Technical Assistance Center–Business Development Center
Schoolcraft College
18600 Haggerty Rd.
Livonia, MI 48152-2696
Ph:(734)462-4438
Fax:(734)462-4673
Co. E-mail: inforeq@schoolcraft.edu
URL: http://www.schoolcraft.edu
Contact: Tammy Thomson, Counselor

Description: Provides businesses with marketing know-how and technical tools they need to obtain and perform successfully under federal, state and local government contracts

51284 ■ Michigan Procurement Technical Assistance Center–Downriver Community Conference
15100 Northline Rd., Ste. 179
Southgate, MI 48195
Ph:(734)362-7070
Fax:(734)281-0265
Co. E-mail: paulaa@dccwf.org
URL: http://www.dccwf.org
Contact: Paula Boase, Dir

Description: Provides businesses with marketing know-how and technical tools they need to obtain and perform successfully under federal, state and local government contracts

51285 ■ Michigan Procurement Technical Assistance Center–Economic Development Alliance of St. Clair County
735 Erie St., Ste. 250
Port Huron, MI 48060
Ph:(810)982-9511
Fax:(810)982-9531
Co. E-mail: adeprez@edascc.com
URL: http://www.edascc.com
Contact: Doug Alexander, Dir.

Description: Provides businesses with marketing know-how and technical tools they need to obtain and perform successfully under federal, state and local government contracts

51286 ■ Michigan Procurement Technical Assistance Center–Genesee Regional Chamber of Commerce (Region 6)–Satellite Office (519 S)
519 S Saginaw St., Ste. 200
Flint, MI 48502
Ph:(810)600-1432
URL: http://www.michigantac.org
Contact: Dustin Frigy
E-mail: dfrigy@thegrcc.org

Description: Serves as an administrative agent for state and federal employment programs, provides economic development and technical assistance to regional businesses, and coordinates and supports regional planning activities.

51287 ■ Michigan Procurement Technical Assistance Center–Kalamazoo Regional Chamber of Commerce
Chamber Bldg.
346 W Michigan Ave.
Kalamazoo, MI 49007-3737
Ph:(269)381-2977
Fax:(269)381-0430
Co. E-mail: Editor@KazooChamber.com
URL: http://www.kazoochamber.com
Contact: Janice Campbell, Dir.
E-mail: jcampbell@kazoochamber.com

Description: Assists businesses in their growth and development.

51288 ■ Michigan Procurement Technical Assistance Center–Macomb Community College PTAC
7900 Tank Ave.
Warren, MI 48092
Ph:(586)498-4122
Fax:(586)498-4165
Co. E-mail: oliverr@macomb.edu
URL: http://www.macomb.edu/
Contact: Rosanne Oliver
E-mail: janet_masi@chambercom.com

Description: Provides businesses with marketing know-how and technical tools they need to obtain and perform successfully under federal, state and local government contracts

51289 ■ Michigan Procurement Technical Assistance Center–Macomb Community College (Region 4)–Satellite Office (3270)
3270 Wilson St.
Marlette, MI 48453
Ph:(989)635-0063
Fax:(989)635-2230
Co. E-mail: cryderman-mossb@macomb.edu
URL: http://www.michigantac.org
Contact: Beth Cryderman Moss, Program Mgr.
E-mail: mossb@thumbworks.org

Description: Michigan Works! Agency provides job training assistance for Huron, Lapeer, Sanilac and Tuscola County residents.

51290 ■ Michigan Procurement Technical Assistance Center–Muskegon Area First
380 West Ave., Ste. 202
Muskegon, MI 49440
Ph:(231)722-7700
Free: 800-528-8776

Fax:(231)722-6182
Co. E-mail: pport@muskegon.org
URL: http://www.muskegonareafirst.org
Contact: Pamela Vanderlaan-Poort, Program Mgr.
E-mail: psvander@gte.net

Description: Provides businesses with marketing know-how and technical tools they need to obtain and perform successfully under federal, state and local government contracts

51291 ■ Michigan Procurement Technical Assistance Center–Northeast Michigan Consortium (Presque Isle Region)
20709 State St.
PO Box 711
Onaway, MI 49765
Ph:(989)733-8548
Fax:(989)733-8069
Co. E-mail: general@miworks-nemc.gen.mi.us
URL: http://www.michigantac.org
Contact: Denise Hoffmeyer, Program Mgr.
E-mail: denise@miworks-nemc.gen.mi.us

Description: Offers services including job training, welfare reform, employment service (including America's Talent Bank/Job Bank automated resume system), TAA/NAFTA programs, assistance in securing federal and state procurement contracts and a variety of youth programs.

51292 ■ Michigan Procurement Technical Assistance Center–Northwest Michigan Council of Governments
1209 S Garfield Ave., Ste. C
Traverse City, MI 49685-0506
Ph:(231)929-5036
Free: 800-692-7774
Fax:(231)929-5042
Co. E-mail: toddolson@nwm.cog.mi.us
URL: http://www.michigantac.org/region1.html
Contact: Todd Olson, Dir.
E-mail: jhasling@nwm.cog.mi.us

Description: Provides businesses with marketing know-how and technical tools they need to obtain and perform successfully under federal, state and local government contracts

51293 ■ Michigan Procurement Technical Assistance Center–Saginaw Future Inc. (Region 5)–Satellite Office (515 N)
515 N Washington, Ste. 300
Saginaw, MI 48607
Ph:(989)754-8222
Fax:(989)754-1715
Co. E-mail: dsallen@saginawfuture.com
URL: http://www.michigantac.org
Contact: Delena Spates Allen, Dir.
E-mail: dsallen@saginawfuture.com

Description: Private, non-profit one stop economic development agency helps accomplish business moves and provide a wide array of business services to existing businesses in Saginaw County.

51294 ■ Michigan Procurement Technical Assistance Center–West Central Michigan Employment & Training Consortium
380 W Western Ave., Ste. 202
Big Rapids, MI 49440
Ph:(231)722-7700
Fax:(231)722-6182
Co. E-mail: spolacco@charter.net
URL: http://www.michworkswc.org
Contact: Shelia Polacco, Tech Spec

Description: Provides businesses with marketing know-how and technical tools they need to obtain and perform successfully under federal, state and local government contracts

51295 ■ Michigan Procurement Technical Assistant Center–Schoolcraft College
18600 Haggerty Rd.
Livonia, MI 48152-3932
Ph:(734)462-4438

Fax:(734)462-4673
Co. E-mail: bdc@schoolcraft.edu
URL: http://www.schoolcraft.edu/bdc
Contact: Jann Deane, Program Mgr.
E-mail: tthomson@schoolcraft.edu
Description: Help to locate bidding opportunities for companies and explore what it takes to sell their products and services to the government.

51296 ■ Procurement Technical Assistance Center of South Central Michigan–Enterprise Group of Jackson, Inc.

1 Jackson Sq., Ste. 1100
Jackson, MI 49204
Ph:(517)788-4680
Fax:(517)782-0061
Co. E-mail: pennie@enterprisegroup.org
URL: http://www.enterprisegroup.org/ptac
Contact: Pennie Kay Southwell, Program Mgr.
E-mail: pennie@enterprisegroup.org
Description: Enhances national defense and economic development of the State of Michigan by assisting Michigan businesses in obtaining and performing on federal, state and local government contracts.

INCUBATORS/RESEARCH AND TECHNOLOGY PARKS

51297 ■ Albion Economic Development Corp.

309 N Superior
PO Box 725
Albion, MI 49224
Ph:(517)629-3926
Free: 877-696-8682
Fax:(517)629-3929
Co. E-mail: psindt@albionedc.org
URL: http://www.albionedc.org
Contact: Peggy Sindt, Pres & CEO
Description: Works to improve the economic health of the Albion area. Offers an incubator for new businesses with access to equipment and advice.

51298 ■ Altarum Institute

3520 Green Ct., Ste. 300
Ann Arbor, MI 48105
Ph:(734)302-4600
Fax:(734)302-4991
Co. E-mail: jeff.moore@altarum.org
URL: http://www.altarum.org
Contact: Ken Baker, Pres & CEO
Description: Research and development facility emphasizing electronics, computer sciences, and optics and their applications. Provides analytical and experimental investigations and technical assistance.

51299 ■ Andrews University–Office of Scholarly Research

Administration 210
Berrien Springs, MI 49104-0355
Ph:(269)471-6361
Fax:(269)471-6246
Co. E-mail: stout@andrews.edu
URL: http://www.andrews.edu/GRAD/OSR/
Contact: Dr. John Stout
E-mail: stout@andrews.edu
Scope: Administers research grants and contracts for the University. Oversees human subject involvement in research. **Publications:** Brief Guidelines for Human Subjects Research; Grants Guidebook.

51300 ■ Ann Arbor SPARK Regional Incubator Network

201 S Davison St., Ste. 430
Ann Arbor, MI 48104
Ph:(734)761-9317
Fax:(734)761-9062
Co. E-mail: Lori@AnnArborUSA.org
URL: http://www.annarborspark.org/
Description: A small business incubator committed to advancing the economic development of innovation-based businesses in the Ann Arbor region by offering programs, resources, and proactive support to business at every stage, from start-ups to large organizations looking for expansion opportunities.

51301 ■ Ann Arbor/Ypsilanti Regional Chamber

115 W Huron St., 3rd Fl.
Ann Arbor, MI 48104
Ph:(734)665-4433
Fax:(734)665-4191
Co. E-mail: info@annarborchamber.org
URL: http://www.annarborchamber.org
Contact: Administrative Ass.
Description: Promotes commerce in the Ann Arbor/Ypsilanti region.

51302 ■ Battle Creek Chamber of Commerce Self-Employment Program

77 E. Michigan Ave., Ste. 80
Commerce Pointe Bldg.
Battle Creek, MI 49017
Ph:(269)962-4076
Fax:(269)962-6309
URL: http://www.battlecreek.org/chamber/index2.html
Description: A business assistance center providing existing firms and entrepreneurs with professional assistance in developing business ventures in greater Battle Creek. It combines the resources of various professional and volunteer organizations, enabling it to offer a variety of services at no or a very nominal charge.

51303 ■ Central Michigan University Research Corporation

2625 Denison Dr.
Mount Pleasant, MI 48858
Ph:(989)774-2424
Fax:(989)774-2416
Co. E-mail: cmurc@cmich.edu
URL: http://www.cmurc.com/
Description: A not-for-profit organization established to facilitate innovative research and development opportunities between the university and high technology companies and dedicated to establishing and operating a national center of excellence in the research fields of business intelligence and nanoscale sciences.

51304 ■ Delta Properties

401 Hall St. SW
Box 95
Grand Rapids, MI 49503
Ph:(616)243-9000
Fax:(616)243-1013
Co. E-mail: rick@delta-space.com
URL: http://www.deltapropertiesinc.com
Contact: Rick Ford, Lease Agent
Description: Provides low-cost industrial space to encourage economic development.

51305 ■ Eastern Michigan University–Office of Research Development

Starkweather Hall, 2nd Fl.
Ypsilanti, MI 48197
Ph:(734)487-3090
Fax:(734)481-0650
Co. E-mail: caryn.charter@emich.edu
URL: http://ord.emich.edu
Contact: Caryn Charter, Interim Dir.
E-mail: caryn.charter@emich.edu
Scope: Administers sponsored activities at a comprehensive university, specific research capabilities include geographic information systems, remote sensing, coatings and paint research, advanced materials, surface science and nanotribology, entrepreneurship, statistical process control, inventory management, computer-assisted instruction, child and family research, bilingual education, immunology, environmental biology, microbiology, exercise physiology, instructional effectiveness, teacher education, STEM education, economic development, environmental assessment, information systems, orthotics and prosthetics, textiles, information security. **Services:** Outreach and liaison services, to business and government agencies for matches with University resources; Technology Transfer; manages and licenses portfolio of technologies available for commercialization to business and industry. **Publications:** Annual report. **Educational Activities:** Proposal development services to faculty (daily); Workshops (monthly), on proposal development.

51306 ■ Institute for Food Laws and Regulations–Michigan State University

140 G.M. Trout Bldg. (Food Science and Human Nutrition)
East Lansing, MI 48824
Ph:(517)355-8295
Fax:(517)432-1492
Co. E-mail: vhegarty@msu.edu
URL: http://www.iflr.msu.edu
Contact: Dr. Vincent Hegarty, Dir
Description: Provides workshops/seminars.

51307 ■ Kettering University–SBDC

1700 University Ave
Flint, MI 48504
Ph:(810)762-9660
Fax:(810)762-9678
Co. E-mail: mlyttle@kettering.edu
Contact: Marsha Lyttle, Dir.

51308 ■ Lakeshore Business Garden

201. W. Washington Ave., Ste. 410
Zeeland, MI 49464
Ph:(616)772-5226
Co. E-mail: info@lakeshoreadvantage.com
URL: http://www.lakeshoreadvantage.com/garden.asp
Description: A business accelerator facility which acts as a launch pad for early stage companies by supporting entrepreneurs during the creation, start up and early growth stages of development; and by linking entrepreneurs to affordable office space, community resources, expert advice and capital to help increase their chances of success.

51309 ■ Michigan Biotechnology Institute International

3815 Technology Blvd.
Lansing, MI 48910-8596
Ph:(517)337-3181
Fax:(517)337-2122
Co. E-mail: info@mbi.org
URL: http://www.mbi.org
Contact: Bobby Bringi, Pres & CEO
Description: Coordinates the development of biotechnology research and technology transfer to businesses; provides in-house research and development; and provides technology transfer to biotechnology businesses.

51310 ■ Michigan Molecular Institute & Impact Analytical

1910 W St Andrews Rd.
Midland, MI 48640
Ph:(989)832-5555
Fax:(989)832-5560
Co. E-mail: mmiinfo@mmi.org
URL: http://mmi.org
Contact: Dr. Robert Nowak, Pres & CEO
E-mail: wood@impactanalytical.org
Description: Performs advanced research and development, and graduate-level education in polymer science and composite technology. Provides technical assistance and consulting services. Develops new information on the molecular structure and behavior of non-metallic materials. Also performs proprietary research.

51311 ■ Michigan Tech Enterprise SmartZone

PO Box 395
Houghton, MI 49931
Ph:(906)487-7000
Fax:(906)487-9523
Co. E-mail: jleinonen@mtecsmart.com
URL: http://www.mtecsz.com/default.aspx
Contact: Jonathan Leinonen, Mgr.
Description: A private, non-profit corporation fostering high-tech business incubation and growth by offering programs and services that encourage entrepreneurial development and that help ensure the success of start-ups and small companies.

51312 ■ Michigan Technological University–Office of the Vice President for Research

Lakeshore Ctr., 3rd Fl.
1400 Townsend Dr.
Houghton, MI 49931-1295

Ph:(906)487-3043
Fax:(906)487-2245
Co. E-mail: ddreed@mtu.edu
URL: http://www.mtu.edu/research/administration/
  vpr-office
Contact: Dr. David D. Reed, VP, Res.
E-mail: ddreed@mtu.edu
Scope: Administers and develops University research programs; manages grants and contracts; and administers intellectual property trademark, and licensing program. Serves as a clearing and coordinating agency for interdepartmental research at the University and for other assistance to faculty members engaged in research and graduate education. **Publications:** Michigan Tech Research Magazine (annually); Office of Research and Graduate School Annual Report. **Educational Activities:** Grant workshops, open to all faculty and staff members of the University.

51313 ■ Michigan Technological University–Research and Sponsored Programs
Lakeshore Ctr., 3rd Fl.
1400 Townsend Dr.
Houghton, MI 49931-1295
Ph:(906)487-2225
Fax:(906)487-2245
Co. E-mail: jhseppal@mtu.edu
URL: http://www.mtu.edu/research/administration/
  sponsored-programs
Contact: Julie Seppala, Dir.
E-mail: jhseppal@mtu.edu
Scope: Administers and coordinates research conducted by academic programs at the University. Manages all grants and contracts for externally funded programs. Negotiates research contracts, acts as a clearing house for all proposal submission and provides budget preparation and review. **Publications:** Research Magazine (annually).

51314 ■ MidMichigan Innovation Center
4520 E. Ashman Rd., Ste. M
Midland, MI 48642
Ph:(989)839-2333
Fax:(989)923-1572
Co. E-mail: moultrop@midmichiganinnovationcenter.
  org
URL: http://www.midmichiganinnovationcenter.org/
Contact: Chris Moultrup, Dir.
Description: A private, non-profit organization created to provide entrepreneurs and start-up companies with a supportive and collaborative environment, connecting companies with critical resources, valuable services, flexible facilities, and entrepreneurial training and education that will help develop their business ventures.

51315 ■ Southwest Michigan Innovation Center
4717 Campus Dr.
Kalamazoo, MI 49008
Ph:(269)353-1823
Fax:(269)372-3397
Co. E-mail: info@kazoosmic.com
URL: http://www.kazoosmic.com/
Description: A multi-tenant incubator/accelerator providing space and intensive support for life science startup firms in their early stages. There is also space available for graduates of the incubator and for firms that are at a later stage and no longer need the intensive support services of an incubator.

51316 ■ Southwestern Michigan Economic Growth Alliance, Inc.
1950 Industrial Dr.
Niles, MI 49120
Ph:(269)683-1833
Fax:(269)683-7515
Co. E-mail: smega1@sbcglobal.net
URL: http://www.southwesternalliance.org
Contact: Sharon Witt, Exec Dir
Description: Works to retain and expand businesses in southwestern Michigan. Formerly the Greater Niles Economic Growth Alliance.

51317 ■ TechTown
440 Burroughs St.
Detroit, MI 48202
Ph:(313)897-5250
Fax:(313)875-5850
Co. E-mail: contact@techtownwsu.org
URL: http://www.techtownwsu.org/
Description: A small business incubator providing the support and access to capital needed to build high tech companies in Detroit. It is a community of entrepreneurs, investors, mentors, service providers, and corporate partners committed to empowering entrepreneurs to build successful technology businesses to improve the quality of life for people across the country and around the world.

51318 ■ University of Detroit Mercy–Sponsored Research Administration
4001 W McNichols Rd.
Detroit, MI 48221-3038
Ph:(313)993-1544
Fax:(313)993-1534
Co. E-mail: caldwecr@udmercy.edu
URL: http://www.udmercy.edu/academicaffairs/ospra
Contact: Cate Caldwell PhD, Dir.
E-mail: caldwecr@udmercy.edu
Scope: Serves as a central bureau of information for sources of funds for supporting research projects at the University and assists faculty members and administration in preparation and submission of proposals for such support.

51319 ■ University of Michigan–Division of Research Development and Administration
Wolverine Tower, 1st Fl., Rm. 1002
3003 S State St.
Ann Arbor, MI 48109-1274
Ph:(734)764-5500
Fax:(734)764-8510
Co. E-mail: mgparnes@umich.edu
URL: http://www.drda.umich.edu
Contact: Marvin G. Parnes, Dir.
E-mail: mgparnes@umich.edu
Scope: Administers and coordinates extramurally sponsored research and other scholarly activities conducted in all departments and special research units of the University. **Publications:** Administration of Sponsored Programs; The DRDA Reporter; Nongovernmental Research Grant and Fellowship Opportunities in the Health Sciences; Project Director's Guide; Proposal Writer's Guide; Research News; Research Opportunities for Minorities and Women; University of Michigan Research Resources.

51320 ■ University of Michigan Tech Transfer–College of Engineering–Office of Technology Transfer (1600)–Industrial Development Division (Huron Pky.)
1600 Huron Pky., 2nd Fl., Bldg. 520
Wolverine Tower, Rm. 2071
Ann Arbor, MI 48109-2590
Ph:(734)763-0614
Fax:(734)936-1330
Co. E-mail: techtransfer@umich.edu
URL: http://www.techtransfer.umich.edu
Contact: Ken Nisbet, Exec Dir
Description: Involved with industry liaison and direct assistance, conferences, workshops, and economic development. Service programs are designed to retain and create employment by expanding and strengthening industry. Supports the Michigan Industrial Developers Association with practitioners training, community economic profiles, and target industry research using national databases.

51321 ■ Wayne State University–Sponsored Program Administration
Office of the VP for Research, 13th Fl., Ste. 13202
5057 Woodward Ave.
Detroit, MI 48202
Ph:(313)577-3726
Fax:(313)577-3626
Co. E-mail: cbach@med.wayne.edu
URL: http://www.spa.wayne.edu
Contact: Carole Bach, Dir.
E-mail: cbach@med.wayne.edu
Scope: Administers and coordinates extramurally sponsored research conducted at the University. Serves as liaison between research faculty and

research-funding organizations. Under the general administrative direction of the Vice President for Research, the office oversees fulfillment of contractual obligations by individual investigators. **Publications:** New Science (annually).

51322 ■ West Michigan Science & Technology Initiative
301 Michigan St. NE, Ste. 537
Grand Rapids, MI 49503
Ph:(616)331-5840
Fax:(616)331-5869
Co. E-mail: wmsti@gvsu.edu
URL: http://www.wmsti.org/
Description: A small business incubator dedicating time, product development tools, amenities, and community assets that innovators, entrepreneurs, or small science and technology entrepreneurs need to commercialize their discoveries.

51323 ■ Western Michigan University–Office of the Vice President for Research
210W Walwood Hall
Kalamazoo, MI 49008-5456
Ph:(269)387-8298
Fax:(269)387-8276
Co. E-mail: paula.kohler@wmich.edu
URL: http://www.wmich.edu/research
Contact: Paula Kohler PhD, Assoc.VP
E-mail: paula.kohler@wmich.edu
Scope: Coordinates proposal submission and grant and contract administration for all individual research projects conducted throughout the University in such areas as health and human services, education, engineering, applied sciences, humanities, social sciences, and business. Research venues exist in the areas of educational evaluation, school reform, biological sciences, geology, physics, math and science education, aviation, paper and printing science and engineering, medieval studies, and rehabilitation/intervention science in health and human services. The University fosters research initiatives in nanotechnology enabling technology, geographic information systems, and the body's response to envi. **Publications:** Annual report; Newsletter. **Educational Activities:** Grantmanship workshops. **Awards:** Research Development Award Program.

EDUCATIONAL PROGRAMS

51324 ■ Alpena Community College
666 Johnson St.
Alpena, MI 49707-1495
Ph:(989)356-9021
Free: 888-468-6222
Fax:(989)358-7561
URL: http://www.alpenacc.org
Description: Two-year college offering a small business management program.

51325 ■ Baker College–Owosso Campus
1020 S Washington St.
Owosso, MI 48867
Ph:(989)729-3300
Free: 800-879-3797
Fax:(989)729-3330
URL: http://www.baker.edu
Description: Vocational school offering a small business management program.

51326 ■ Mid Michigan Community College
1375 S Clare Ave.
Harrison, MI 48625
Ph:(989)386-6622
Fax:(989)386-9088
Co. E-mail: bmather@midmich.cc.mi.us
URL: http://www.midmich.cc.mi.us
Description: Two-year college offering a small business management program.

51327 ■ Montcalm Community College
2800 College Dr. SW
Sidney, MI 48885-0300
Ph:(989)328-2111
Fax:(989)328-2950
URL: http://www.montcalm.cc.mi.us
Description: Two-year college offering a small business management program.

51328 ■ North Central Michigan College
1515 Howard St.
Petoskey, MI 49770
Ph:(231)348-6600
Free: 888-298-6605
Fax:(231)348-6628
URL: http://www.ncmich.edu/
Description: Two-year college offering a program in small business management.

51329 ■ Southwestern Michigan College–Business Development and Corporate Services
2229 U.S. 12 E
Niles, MI 49120
Ph:(269)782-1000
Free: 800-456-8675
Fax:(269)687-5655
Co. E-mail: info@swmich.edu
URL: http://www.smc.cc.mi.us
Description: Offers programs/classes in small business/small business management.

51330 ■ Wayne State University–School of Business Administration
Business Management Office
5201 Cass Ave.
Detroit, MI 48202
Ph:(313)577-4515
Fax:(313)993-7664
URL: http://www.wayne.edu
Description: Schedules business and management courses. Also provides free management consulting to small business managers in the metropolitan Detroit area.

TRADE PERIODICALS

51331 ■ *Leader's Edge*
Pub: Michigan Association of CPAs
Contact: Corinne F. Duluk, Asst. Mgr. of Mktg.
Ed: Marla Janness, Editor, mjanness@ix.netcom.com. **Released:** Bimonthly, 6/year. **Price:** $20. **Description:** Contains professional and technical information for certified public accountants.

51332 ■ *MIOSHA News*
Pub: Michigan Department of Consumer and Industry Services
Contact: Judith M. Shaine, Communications Dir.
E-mail: judith.simons@cis.state.mi.us
Released: Quarterly. **Price:** Free. **Description:** Contains information relevant to occupational safety and health in relation to Michigan's employers and employees.

PUBLICATIONS

51333 ■ *How to Form Your Own Michigan Corporation Before the Inc. Dries!: A Step by Step Guide, With Forms*
P. Gaines Publishing Company
333 S. Taylor Ave.
PO Box 2253
Oak Park, IL 60302
Ph:(708)524-9033
Fax:(708)524-9038
Ed: Phillip Williams. **Released:** Second edition, 1993. **Price:** $24.95. **Description:** Volume 3 of the Small Business Incorporation series. Explains the advantages and disadvantages of incorporation and shows, step-by-step, how the small business owners can incorporate at low cost. Covers Michigan profit and nonprofit corporations, Michigan professional service corporations, subchapter S corporations, and Delaware corporations. Includes forms necessary for incorporation.

51334 ■ *Smart Start your Michigan Business*
PSI Research
300 N. Valley Dr.
Grants Pass, OR 97526
Ph:(503)479-9464
Free: 800-228-2275
Fax:(503)476-1479
Co. E-mail: info@psi-research.com
URL: http://www.psi-research.com
Ed: Michael D. Jenkins. **Released:** Revised edition, 1992. **Price:** $29.95 (looseleaf binder); $24.95 (paper). **Description:** Part of the Successful Business Library series.

PUBLISHERS

51335 ■ Agnes Press
6160 Brambleberry Dr.
Howell, MI 48855
Fax:(517)546-9565
Co. E-mail: pete@marelco.com
Contact: Peter H. Burgher, Owner
E-mail: pete@marelco.com
Description: Publishes business books. offers seminars and consulting. Does not accept unsolicited manuscripts. Reaches market through direct mail. **Founded:** 1986.

51336 ■ Delta Alpha Publishing Ltd.
c/o Port City Fulfillment Services
35 Ash Dr.
Kimball, MI 48074
Ph:(810)985-1165
Free: 800-292-5544
Fax:(810)985-1168
Co. E-mail: dap@deltaalpha.com
URL: http://www.deltaalpha.com
Contact: Damien Abbott, Editor
E-mail: abbott@deltaalpha.com
Founded: 1997.

51337 ■ Humanergy Inc.
213 W Mansion St.
Marshall, MI 49068
Ph:(269)789-0446
Fax:(269)789-0057
Co. E-mail: info@humanergy.com
URL: http://www.humanergy.com
Contact: Paula Bokoch, Mgr
Description: Publishes books on business and leadership.

51338 ■ Jenkins Group Inc.
1129 Woodmere Ave., Ste. B
Traverse City, MI 49686
Ph:(231)933-0445
Fax:(231)933-0448
Co. E-mail: publish@jenkinsgroupinc.com
URL: http://www.jenkinsgroupinc.com/
Contact: Rachel Jones, Mktg Mgr
Description: Publishes on business, motivational and professional improvement, health, fitness, nonfiction and children's titles. **Founded:** 1988.

SMALL BUSINESS DEVELOPMENT CENTERS

51339 ■ Central Lakes College Small Business Development Center
501 W College Dr.
Brainerd, MN 56401
Fax:(218)855-8141
Co. E-mail: gbergman@clcmn.edu
URL: http://www.clcmn.edu/smallbusiness
Contact: Greg Bergman, Dir.

51340 ■ Central Minnesota Small Business Development Center
St. Cloud State University
616 Roosevelt Rd.
St. Cloud, MN 56301
Fax:(320)255-4957
Co. E-mail: klross@stcloudstate.edu
URL: http://www.stcloudstate.edu/sbdc
Contact: LaRae Ross

51341 ■ Minnesota Small Business Development Center - Northeast
University of Minnesota Duluth
Center for Economic Development
Duluth Technology Village
11 E Superior St., Ste. 210
Duluth, MN 55802
Fax:(218)726-6338
Co. E-mail: ehansen@umdced.com
URL: http://www.mnsbdc.com
Contact: Elaine Hansen, Dir.

51342 ■ Minnesota Small Business Development Center - Northwest
Bemidji State University
Center for Research and Innovation
3801 Bemidji Ave. N
Bemidji, MN 56601
Fax:(218)755-4903
Co. E-mail: saugustine@bemidjistate.edu
URL: http://www.mnsbdc.com
Contact: Shari Augustine, Coor.

51343 ■ Minnesota Small Business Development Center - South Central
Region Nine Development Commission
1961 Premier Dr., Ste. 268
Mankato, MN 56001
Fax:(507)389-8868
Co. E-mail: robertk@rndc.mankato.mn.us
URL: http://www.mnsbdc.com
Contact: Bob Klanderud, Dir.

51344 ■ Minnesota Small Business Development Center - Southeast
Rochester Community and Technical College
Heintz Center
1926 Collegeview Rd. E
Rochester, MN 55904

Fax:(507)280-5502
Co. E-mail: kay.wiegert@roch.edu
URL: http://www.mnsbdc.com
Contact: Kay Wiegert, Coor.

51345 ■ Minnesota Small Business Development Center - West Central
Minnesota State University - Moorhead
1104 7th Ave. S
Moorhead, MN 56563
Fax:(218)477-2280
Co. E-mail: sliwoski@mnstate.edu
URL: http://www.mnsbdc.com
Contact: Leonard Sliwoski, Dir.

51346 ■ St. Thomas (Metro) Small Business Development Center
Schulze Hall 103
46 S 11th St.
Minneapolis, MN 55403
Co. E-mail: mpryan@stthomas.edu
URL: http://www.stthomas.edu/sbdc

51347 ■ Southwest Small Business Development Center - Minnesota
Southwest Minnesota State University
1501 State St., Ste. 105
Marshall, MN 56258
Free: 800-642-0684
Fax:(507)537-6094
Co. E-mail: sbdc@southwestmsu.edu
URL: http://www.southwestmsu.edu/sbdc
Contact: Liz Struve, Dir.

51348 ■ Twin Cities Small Business Development Center
University of St. Thomas
Opus College of Business
Schulze Hall 103
46 S 11th St.
Minneapolis, MN 55403
Fax:(651)962-4508
Co. E-mail: mpryan@stthomas.edu
URL: http://www.stthomas.edu/business/centers/sbdc
Contact: Michael Ryan, Dir.

SMALL BUSINESS ASSISTANCE PROGRAMS

51349 ■ Minnesota Department of Employment and Economic Development
First National Bank Bldg.
332 Minnesota St., Ste. E200
St. Paul, MN 55101-1351
Ph:(651)259-7114
Free: 800-657-3858
Fax:(651)296-1290
URL: http://www.deed.state.mn.us
Contact: Mark Lofthus, Dir.
Description: Coordinates state government information and resources available to small businesses. Provides information relating to start-up, operation, and expansion of businesses. Offers several free publications.

51350 ■ Minnesota Department of Employment and Economic Development–Business and Community Development Division and Trade
First National Bank Bldg.
332 Minnesota St., Ste. E-200
St. Paul, MN 55101-1351
Ph:(651)259-7114
Free: 800-657-3858
Fax:(651)296-1290
URL: http://www.deed.state.mn.us
Contact: Dan McElroy, Commissioner
Description: Provides grants to cities, townships and counties.

51351 ■ Minnesota Department of Employment and Economic Development–Minnesota Trade Office
First National Bank Bldg.
332 Minnesota St., Ste. E200
St. Paul, MN 55101-1351
Ph:(651)259-7499
Free: 800-657-3858
Fax:(651)296-3555
Co. E-mail: mto@state.mn.us
URL: http://www.exportminnesota.com
Contact: Tony Lorusso, Dir
Description: Promotes Minnesota goods and services through export and attraction of foreign investors. Efforts concentrate on small business through several divisions, including Export Development Division, International Marketing and Investment Division, and Export Finance Division.

SCORE OFFICES

51352 ■ SCORE Albert Lea
Path: www.score-rochester.org/meet_albert_lea.html

51353 ■ SCORE Alexandria
Path: www.stcloudscore.org/alexandria_branch_office.html

51354 ■ SCORE Austin
Path: score-rochester.org/austin2.html

51355 ■ SCORE Brainerd
Path: www.stcloudscore.org/brainerd_lakes.html

51356 ■ SCORE Cannon Falls
Path: www.cannonfalls.org

51357 ■ SCORE Central Area (St. Cloud)
616 Roosevelt Rd., Ste. 100
St. Cloud, MN 56301-1332
Ph:(320)240-1332
Co. E-mail: info@stcloudscore.org
URL: http://www.stcloudscore.org
Contact: Don Schiffler, Chm.
Description: Provides one-on-one confidential business consultation, at no cost. Offers low-cost workshops to current and potential entrepreneurs on business planning, finance, marketing, and similar topics.

51358 ■ SCORE Counselors to America's Small Business
c/o Rochester Area Chamber of Commerce
220 S Broadway, Ste. 100
Rochester, MN 55904
Ph:(507)288-8103
Fax:(507)282-8960
Co. E-mail: info@score-rochester.org
URL: http://www.score-rochester.org
Contact: Dean L. Swanson, Chm.

Description: Volunteer businessmen and women. Provides free small business management assistance to individuals in the Rochester, MN area. Sponsors workshops.

51359 ■ SCORE Detroit Lakes
Path: www.stcloudscore.org/contacting_dl.html

51360 ■ SCORE Lake Superior Region
Path: www.score-lsr.org

51361 ■ SCORE Minneapolis
Bremer Bank Bldg., Ste. 103
8800 Hwy. 7
Minneapolis, MN 55426
Ph:(952)938-4570
Fax:(952)938-2651
Co. E-mail: minneapolis@score-mn.org
URL: http://www.score-minneapolis.org
Contact: Ed Hennen, Chm.

Description: Serves as volunteer program in which working and retired business management professionals provide free business counseling to men and women who are considering starting a small business, encountering problems with their business, or expanding their business. Offers free one-on-one counseling, online counseling and low cost workshops on a variety of business topics.

51362 ■ SCORE New Ulm Area
c/o New Ulm Chamber of Commerce
1 N Minnesota St.
PO Box 384
New Ulm, MN 56073
Ph:(507)233-4300
Fax:(507)354-1504
URL: http://www.score-newulm.org

Description: Serves as volunteer program in which working and retired business management professionals provide free business counseling to men and women who are considering starting a small business, encountering problems with their business, or expanding their business. Offers free one-on-one counseling, online counseling and low cost workshops on a variety of business topics.

51363 ■ SCORE Park Rapids
Path: www.stcloudscore.org/contacting_parkrapids.html

51364 ■ SCORE Red Wing
Path: www.score-redwing.org

51365 ■ SCORE St. Paul
176 N Snelling Ave., Ste. 300
St. Paul, MN 55104-4707
Ph:(651)632-8937
Fax:(651)632-8938
Co. E-mail: stpaul@score-mn.org
URL: http://www.score-stpaul.org
Contact: Jerry Norsby, Chm.

Description: Serves as volunteer program in which working and retired business management professionals provide free business counseling to men and women who are considering starting a small business, encountering problems with their business, or expanding their business. Offers free one-on-one counseling, online counseling and low cost workshops on a variety of business topics.

51366 ■ SCORE South Metro
101 W Burnsville Pkwy., Ste. 152
Burnsville, MN 55337
Ph:(952)890-7020

Fax:(952)890-7019
Co. E-mail: southmetro@score-mn.org
URL: http://www.score-southmetro.org
Contact: Ken Ahlgren, Chm.

Description: Serves as volunteer program in which working and retired business management professionals provide free business counseling to men and women who are considering starting a small business, encountering problems with their business, or expanding their business.

51367 ■ SCORE Willmar
Path: www.score-minneapolis.com

51368 ■ SCORE Worthington
Path: www.worthingtonmnchamber.com

BETTER BUSINESS BUREAUS

51369 ■ Better Business Bureau Serving Minnesota and North Dakota
2706 Gannon Rd.
St. Paul, MN 55116-2600
Ph:(651)699-1111
Free: 800-646-6222
Fax:(651)699-7665
Co. E-mail: ask@bbbmnd.org
URL: http://minnesota.bbb.org

CHAMBERS OF COMMERCE

51370 ■ Aitkin Area Chamber of Commerce
PO Box 127
Aitkin, MN 56431-0127
Ph:(218)927-2316
Free: 800-526-8342
Fax:(218)927-4494
Co. E-mail: upnorth@aitkin.com
URL: http://www.aitkin.com
Contact: Sue Marxen, Exec. Dir.

51371 ■ Albany Chamber of Commerce
PO Box 634
Albany, MN 56307
Ph:(320)845-7777
Fax:(320)845-2346
Co. E-mail: albanycc@albanytel.com
URL: http://www.albanymnchamber.com
Contact: Melissa Sand, Pres.

51372 ■ Albert Lea - Freeborn County Chamber of Commerce
701 Marshall St.
Albert Lea, MN 56007
Ph:(507)373-3938
Fax:(507)373-0344
Co. E-mail: alfccoc@albertlea.org
URL: http://www.albertlea.org
Contact: Randy Kehr, Exec. Dir.

51373 ■ Alexandria Lakes Area Chamber of Commerce
206 Broadway
Alexandria, MN 56308
Ph:(320)763-3161
Free: 800-235-9441
Co. E-mail: info@alexandriamn.org
URL: http://www.alexandriamn.org
Contact: Coni McKay, Exec. Dir.

51374 ■ Anoka Area Chamber of Commerce
12 Bridge Sq.
Anoka, MN 55303
Ph:(763)421-7130
Fax:(763)421-0577
Co. E-mail: mail@anokaareachamber.com
URL: http://www.anokaareachamber.com
Contact: Peter Turok, Pres.

51375 ■ Apple Valley Chamber of Commerce
14800 Galaxie Ave., Ste. 301
Apple Valley, MN 55124
Ph:(952)432-8422
Free: 800-301-9435
Fax:(952)432-7964
Co. E-mail: info@applevalleychamber.com
URL: http://www.applevalleychamber.com
Contact: Edward Kearney, Pres.

51376 ■ Austin Area Chamber of Commerce
329 N Main St., Ste. 102
Austin, MN 55912
Ph:(507)437-4561
Free: 888-319-5655
Fax:(507)437-4869
Co. E-mail: execdir@austincoc.com
URL: http://www.austincoc.com
Contact: Sandy Forstner, Exec. Dir.

51377 ■ Baudette-Lake of the Woods Chamber of Commerce
PO Box 659
Baudette, MN 56623-0659
Ph:(218)634-1174
Free: 800-382-3474
Fax:(218)634-2915
Co. E-mail: lakwoods@wiktel.com
URL: http://www.lakeofthewoodsmn.com
Contact: Jane Sindelir, Office Mgr.

51378 ■ Bemidji Area Chamber of Commerce
300 Bemidji Ave.
PO Box 850
Bemidji, MN 56601
Ph:(218)444-3541
Free: 800-458-2223
Fax:(218)444-4276
Co. E-mail: chamber@paulbunyan.net
URL: http://www.bemidji.org
Contact: Lori Paris, Pres.

51379 ■ Big Stone Lake Area Chamber of Commerce
987 US Hwy. 12
Ortonville, MN 56278
Ph:(320)839-3284
Free: 800-568-5722
Co. E-mail: chamber@bigstonelake.com
URL: http://www.bigstonelake.com
Contact: Sue Kaercher-Blake, Dir.

51380 ■ Brainerd Lakes Area Chambers of Commerce
124 N 6th St.
PO Box 356
Brainerd, MN 56401-0356
Ph:(218)829-2838
Free: 800-450-2838
Fax:(218)829-8199
Co. E-mail: info@explorebrainerdlakes.com
URL: http://www.explorebrainerdlakes.com
Contact: Lisa Paxton, CEO

51381 ■ Buffalo Area Chamber of Commerce
9 Central Ave.
Buffalo, MN 55313
Ph:(763)682-4902
Fax:(763)682-5677
Co. E-mail: info@buffalochamber.org
URL: http://www.buffalochamber.org
Contact: Sally Custer, Pres.

51382 ■ Burnsville Chamber of Commerce
101 W Burnsville Pkwy., Ste. 150
Burnsville, MN 55337
Ph:(952)435-6000
Fax:(952)435-6972
Co. E-mail: chamber@burnsvillechamber.com
URL: http://www.burnsvillechamber.com
Contact: Daron Van Helden, Pres.

51383 ■ Cambridge Area Chamber of Commerce
PO Box 343
Cambridge, MN 55008
Ph:(763)689-2505
Fax:(763)552-2505
Co. E-mail: info@cambridge-chamber.com
URL: http://www.cambridge-chamber.com
Contact: Nicki Klanderud, Pres.

51384 ■ Canby Area Chamber of Commerce
123 1st St. E
Canby, MN 56220
Ph:(507)223-7775
Co. E-mail: amy.szumal.sp13@statefarm.com
Contact: Amy Szumal, Sec.

51385 ■ Cannon Falls Area Chamber of Commerce
PO Box 2
Cannon Falls, MN 55009
Ph:(507)263-2289
Co. E-mail: tourism@cannonfalls.org
URL: http://www.cannonfalls.org
Contact: Patricia A. Anderson, Pres.

51386 ■ Chisholm Area Chamber of Commerce
223 W Lake St.
Chisholm, MN 55719
Ph:(218)254-7930
Free: 800-422-0806
Co. E-mail: info@chisholmchamber.com
URL: http://www.chisholmchamber.com
Contact: Shannon Kishel Roche, Exec. Dir.

51387 ■ Cloquet Carlton Area Chamber of Commerce
225 Sunnyside Dr.
Cloquet, MN 55720
Ph:(218)879-1551
Free: 800-554-4350
Fax:(218)878-0223
Co. E-mail: chamber@cloquet.com
URL: http://www.cloquet.com
Contact: Dave Manderfeld, Chm.

51388 ■ Cokato Chamber of Commerce
PO Box 819
Cokato, MN 55321
Ph:(320)286-5505
Fax:(320)286-5876
URL: http://www.cokato.mn.us
Contact: Louann Worden, Exec. Sec.

51389 ■ Cook Area Chamber of Commerce
PO Box 296
Cook, MN 55723
Ph:(218)666-5850
Free: 800-648-5897
URL: http://www.cookminnesota.com
Contact: Lee Phillips, Pres.

51390 ■ Cottage Grove Area Chamber of Commerce
PO Box 16
Cottage Grove, MN 55016-0016
Ph:(651)458-8334
Fax:(651)458-8383
Co. E-mail: office@cottagegrovechamber.org
URL: http://www.cottagegrovechamber.org
Contact: Rhonda Mann, Pres.

51391 ■ Crookston Convention and Visitors Bureau
107 2nd St. W
Crookston, MN 56716
Ph:(218)281-4320
Free: 800-809-5997
Fax:(218)281-4349
Co. E-mail: chamber@visitcrookston.com
URL: http://www.visitcrookston.com
Contact: Lori A. Wagner, CEO/Pres.

51392 ■ Delano Area Chamber of Commerce
PO Box 27
Delano, MN 55328-0027
Ph:(763)972-6756
Fax:(763)972-9326
Co. E-mail: info@delanochamber.com
URL: http://www.delanochamber.com
Contact: Lisa Koenecke, Exec. Dir.

51393 ■ Detroit Lakes Regional Chamber of Commerce
PO Box 348
Detroit Lakes, MN 56502-0348
Ph:(218)847-9202
Free: 800-542-3992
Fax:(218)847-9082
Co. E-mail: dlchamber@visitdetroitlakes.com
URL: http://www.visitdetroitlakes.com
Contact: Kris Tovson, Pres.

51394 ■ Duluth Area Chamber of Commerce
5 W First St., Ste. 101
Duluth, MN 55802
Ph:(218)722-5501
Fax:(218)722-3223
Co. E-mail: inquiry@duluthchamber.com
URL: http://www.duluthchamber.com
Contact: David M. Ross, Pres./CEO

51395 ■ Eden Prairie Chamber of Commerce
11455 Viking Dr., Ste. 270
Eden Prairie, MN 55344
Ph:(952)944-2830
Fax:(952)944-0229
Co. E-mail: adminj@epchamber.org
URL: http://www.epchamber.org
Contact: Pat MulQueeny, Pres.

51396 ■ Elk River Area Chamber of Commerce
509 Hwy. 10
Elk River, MN 55330-1415
Ph:(763)441-3110
Fax:(763)441-3409
Co. E-mail: eracc@elkriverchamber.org
URL: http://www.elkriverchamber.org
Contact: Debbi Rydberg, Pres.

51397 ■ Ely Chamber of Commerce
1600 E Sheridan St.
Ely, MN 55731
Ph:(218)365-6123
Free: 800-777-7281
Fax:(218)365-5929
Co. E-mail: fun@ely.org
URL: http://www.ely.org
Contact: Linda Fryer, Admin. Dir.

51398 ■ Fairmont Area Chamber of Commerce
PO Box 826
Fairmont, MN 56031
Ph:(507)235-5547
Fax:(507)235-8411
Co. E-mail: info@fairmontchamber.org
URL: http://www.fairmont.org
Contact: Bob Wallace, Pres.

51399 ■ Faribault Area Chamber of Commerce and Tourism
PO Box 434
Faribault, MN 55021-0434
Ph:(507)334-4381
Free: 800-658-2354
Fax:(507)334-1003
Co. E-mail: chamber@faribaultmn.org
URL: http://www.faribaultmn.org
Contact: Kymn Anderson, Pres.

51400 ■ Fergus Falls Area Chamber of Commerce
202 S Court St.
Fergus Falls, MN 56537
Ph:(218)736-6951
Fax:(218)736-6952
Co. E-mail: chamber@prtel.com
URL: http://www.fergusfalls.com
Contact: Lisa Workman, Exec. Dir.

51401 ■ Forest Lake Area Chamber of Commerce
PO Box 474
Forest Lake, MN 55025
Ph:(651)464-3200
Fax:(651)464-3201
Co. E-mail: chamber@flacc.org
URL: http://www.flacc.org
Contact: Colleen Eddy, Pres.

51402 ■ Glencoe Area Chamber of Commerce
630 E 10th St.
Glencoe, MN 55336
Ph:(320)864-3650
Co. E-mail: chamber@glencoechamber.com
URL: http://www.glencoechamber.com
Contact: Chip Anderson, Chm.

51403 ■ Glenwood Area Chamber of Commerce
2 E Minnesota Ave., Ste. 100
Glenwood, MN 56334
Ph:(320)634-3636
Free: (866)634-3636
Fax:(320)634-3637
Co. E-mail: chamber@glenwood-lakes-area.info
URL: http://glenwoodlakesarea.org/index.cfm?pageid=1
Contact: Brenda Baumler, Office Mgr.

51404 ■ Grand Marais Chamber of Commerce
PO Box 805
Grand Marais, MN 55604-0805
Ph:(218)387-9112
Co. E-mail: gmcc@boreal.org
URL: http://www.grandmaraismn.com
Contact: Bev Wolke, Exec. Dir.

51405 ■ Grand Rapids Area Chamber of Commerce
1 NW 3rd St.
Grand Rapids, MN 55744
Ph:(218)326-6619
Free: 800-472-6366
Co. E-mail: info@grandmn.com
URL: http://www.grandmn.com
Contact: Bud Stone, Pres./CEO

51406 ■ Granite Falls Area Chamber of Commerce
646 Prentice St.
Granite Falls, MN 56241
Ph:(320)564-4039
Fax:(320)564-3843
Co. E-mail: gfchamber@mvtvwireless.com
URL: http://www.granitefalls.com
Contact: Nicole Richter, Exec. Dir.

51407 ■ Greater Stillwater Chamber of Commerce
106 S Main St.
PO Box 516
Stillwater, MN 55082
Ph:(651)439-4001
Fax:(651)439-4035
Co. E-mail: info@ilovestillwater.com
URL: http://www.ilovestillwater.com
Contact: Curt Geissler, Pres.

51408 ■ Greater Wayzata Area Chamber of Commerce
402 E Lake St.
Wayzata, MN 55391-1651
Ph:(952)473-9595
Fax:(952)473-6266
Co. E-mail: info@wayzatachamber.com
URL: http://www.wayzatachamber.com
Contact: Peggy Douglas, Pres.

51409 ■ Hastings Area Chamber of Commerce and Tourism Bureau
111 E 3rd St.
Hastings, MN 55033-1211
Ph:(651)437-6775
Free: 888-612-6122
Fax:(651)437-2697
Co. E-mail: info@hastingsmn.org
URL: http://www.hastingsmn.org
Contact: Michelle Jacobs, Pres.

51410 ■ Hermantown Chamber of Commerce
4940 Lightning Dr.
Hermantown, MN 55811-1447
Ph:(218)729-6843
Fax:(218)729-7132
Co. E-mail: info@hermantownchamber.com
URL: http://www.hermantownchamber.com
Contact: Mike Lundstrom, Exec. Dir.

51411 ■ Hibbing Area Chamber of Commerce
PO Box 727
Hibbing, MN 55746-1763
Ph:(218)262-3895

Fax:(218)262-3897
Co. E-mail: hibbcofc@hibbing.org
URL: http://www.hibbing.org
Contact: Lory Fedo, Pres./CEO

51412 ■ Hutchinson Area Chamber of Commerce, Convention and Visitors Bureau
2 Main St. S
Hutchinson, MN 55350
Ph:(320)587-5252
Free: 800-572-6689
Fax:(320)587-4752
Co. E-mail: info@explorehutchinson.com
URL: http://www.explorehutchinson.com
Contact: Megan Peterson, Marketing Specialist

51413 ■ I-94 West Chamber of Commerce
PO Box 95
Rogers, MN 55374
Ph:(763)428-2921
Co. E-mail: requests@i94westchamber.org
URL: http://www.i94westchamber.org
Contact: Kathleen Poate, Pres.

51414 ■ International Falls Area Chamber of Commerce
301 2nd Ave.
International Falls, MN 56649
Ph:(218)283-9400
Free: 800-325-5766
Fax:(218)283-3572
Co. E-mail: chamber@intlfalls.org
URL: http://www.internationalfallsmn.us
Contact: Betsy Jensen, Pres.

51415 ■ Jackson Area Chamber of Commerce
82 W Ashley St.
Jackson, MN 56143-1669
Ph:(507)847-3867
Fax:(507)847-3869
Co. E-mail: chamber@cityofjacksonmn.com
URL: http://jacksonmn.com
Contact: Marilyn Reese, Exec. Dir.

51416 ■ Kanabec Area Chamber of Commerce
200 S Hwy. 65
Mora, MN 55051
Ph:(320)679-5792
Free: 800-291-5792
Co. E-mail: karen@kanabecchamber.org
URL: http://www.kanabecchamber.org
Contact: Karen Onan Amundson, Exec. Dir.

51417 ■ La Crescent Chamber of Commerce
109 S Walnut St., Ste. B
La Crescent, MN 55947
Ph:(507)895-2800
Free: 800-926-9480
Fax:(507)895-2619
Co. E-mail: lacrescent.chamber@acegroup.com
URL: http://lacrescentmn.com
Contact: Eileen Krenz, Exec. Sec.

51418 ■ Lake Benton Area Chamber of Commerce and Convention and Visitors Bureau
110 S Center St.
PO Box 205
Lake Benton, MN 56149
Ph:(507)368-9577
Co. E-mail: lbenton@itctel.com
URL: http://www.itctel.com/lbenton

51419 ■ Lake City Area Chamber of Commerce
101 W Center St.
Lake City, MN 55041
Ph:(651)345-4123
Free: 800-369-4123
Fax:(651)345-4195
Co. E-mail: lcchamber@lakecity.org
URL: http://www.lakecity.org
Contact: Mary Huselid, Exec. Dir.

51420 ■ Lake Crystal Area Chamber of Commerce
PO Box 27
Lake Crystal, MN 56055
Ph:(507)726-6088
Co. E-mail: lcchambr@hickorytech.net
URL: http://www.lakecrystalchamber.com
Contact: Karen Ahrenstorff, Pres.

51421 ■ Lake Minnetonka Chamber of Commerce
2323 Commerce Blvd.
Mound, MN 55364
Ph:(952)472-5622
Fax:(952)472-5624
Co. E-mail: chamber@lakeminnetonkachamber.com
URL: http://www.lakeminnetonkachamber.com
Contact: John B. Waldron, Pres.

51422 ■ Lake Vermilion Area Chamber of Commerce
PO Box 776
Tower, MN 55790
Ph:(218)753-8909
Free: 800-869-3766
Co. E-mail: troy@lakevermilioncommerce.com
URL: http://www.lakevermilioncommerce.com
Contact: Troy Swanson

51423 ■ Laurentian Chamber of Commerce
403 1st St. N
Virginia, MN 55792
Ph:(218)741-2717
Fax:(218)749-4913
Co. E-mail: admin@laurentianchamber.org
URL: http://laurentianchamber.org
Contact: James Currie, Pres./CEO

51424 ■ Le Sueur Area Chamber of Commerce
500 N Main St.
Le Sueur, MN 56058
Ph:(507)665-2501
Fax:(507)665-4372
Co. E-mail: julieb@lesueurchamber.org
URL: http://www.lesueurchamber.org
Contact: Julie Boyland, Exec. Dir.

51425 ■ Leech Lake Area Chamber of Commerce
PO Box 1089
Walker, MN 56484-1089
Ph:(218)547-1313
Free: 800-833-1118
Fax:(218)547-1338
Co. E-mail: walker@eot.com
URL: http://www.leech-lake.com
Contact: Cindy Wannarka, Exec. Dir.

51426 ■ Litchfield Chamber of Commerce
219 N Sibley Ave.
PO Box 820
Litchfield, MN 55355-0820
Ph:(320)693-8184
Fax:(320)593-8184
Co. E-mail: litch@litch.com
URL: http://www.litch.com/lit_chamber.php
Contact: Dee Schutte, Exec. Dir.

51427 ■ Little Falls Area Chamber of Commerce
200 NW 1st St.
Little Falls, MN 56345
Ph:(320)632-5155
Fax:(320)632-2122
Co. E-mail: assistance@littlefallsmnchamber.com
URL: http://littlefallsmnchamber.com
Contact: Debora K. Boelz, Pres./CEO

51428 ■ Long Prairie Area Chamber of Commerce
42 N 3rd St.
Long Prairie, MN 56347
Ph:(320)732-2514
Fax:(320)732-2514
Co. E-mail: info@longprairie.org
URL: http://www.longprairie.org/chamber/index.html
Contact: Toni Tebben, Pres.

51429 ■ Luverne Area Chamber of Commerce
211 E Main St., Ste. 103
Luverne, MN 56156
Ph:(507)283-4061
Free: 888-283-4061
Fax:(507)283-4061
Co. E-mail: luvernechamber@iw.net
URL: http://www.luvernechamber.org
Contact: Jeff Strauss, Pres.

51430 ■ Madelia Area Chamber of Commerce
PO Box 171
Madelia, MN 56062
Ph:(507)642-8822
Free: 888-941-7283
Fax:(507)642-8832
Co. E-mail: chamber@madeliamn.com
URL: http://www.visitmadelia.com
Contact: Brent Christensen, Pres.

51431 ■ Madison Area Chamber of Commerce
PO Box 70
Madison, MN 56256-0070
Ph:(320)598-7301
Fax:(320)598-7955
Co. E-mail: loutfisk@yahoo.com
URL: http://www.madisonmn.info
Contact: Maynard R. Meyer, Coor.

51432 ■ Marshall Area Chamber of Commerce
317 W Main St.
PO Box 352B
Marshall, MN 56258
Ph:(507)532-4484
Fax:(507)532-4485
Co. E-mail: chamber@starpoint.net
URL: http://www.marshall-mn.org
Contact: Dan Schenkein, Pres./CEO

51433 ■ Melrose Chamber of Commerce
PO Box 214
Melrose, MN 56352
Ph:(320)256-7174
Fax:(320)256-7177
Co. E-mail: chamber@meltel.net
URL: http://www.melrosemn.org
Contact: Marlene Blommel, Pres.

51434 ■ MetroNorth Chamber of Commerce
21st Century Bank Bldg.
9380 Central Ave. NE, Ste. 320
Blaine, MN 55434
Ph:(763)783-3553
Fax:(763)783-3557
Co. E-mail: chamber@metronorthchamber.org
URL: http://www.metronorthchamber.org
Contact: Thomas Snell, Exec. Dir.

51435 ■ Milaca Area Chamber of Commerce
PO Box 155
255 1st St. E
Milaca, MN 56353
Ph:(320)983-3140
Co. E-mail: chamber@milacacity.com
URL: http://www.cityofmilaca.org

51436 ■ Minneapolis Regional Chamber of Commerce
81 S 9th St., Ste. 200
Minneapolis, MN 55402-3223
Ph:(612)370-9100
Fax:(612)370-9195
Co. E-mail: info@minneapolischamber.org
URL: http://www.minneapolischamber.org
Contact: Todd Klingel, Pres./CEO

51437 ■ Minnesota Chamber of Commerce
400 N Robert St., Ste. 1500
St. Paul, MN 55101
Ph:(651)292-4650
Free: 800-821-2230
Fax:(651)292-4656
Co. E-mail: dolson@mnchamber.com
URL: http://www.mnchamber.com
Contact: David Olson, Pres.

51438 ■ Montevideo Area Chamber of Commerce
202 N 1st St., Ste. 150
Montevideo, MN 56265
Ph:(320)269-5527
Free: 800-269-5527
Fax:(320)269-5696
Co. E-mail: generalinfo@montechamber.com
URL: http://www.montechamber.com
Contact: Dr. Jennie Gunlogson, Pres.

51439 ■ Monticello Area Chamber of Commerce and Industry
PO Box 192
Monticello, MN 55362
Ph:(763)295-2700
Fax:(763)295-2705
Co. E-mail: info@monticellocci.com
URL: http://www.monticellocci.com
Contact: Dr. Kelly Cripe

51440 ■ Moose Lake Area Chamber of Commerce
PO Box 110
Moose Lake, MN 55767
Ph:(218)485-4145
Free: 800-635-3680
Fax:(218)485-4522
Co. E-mail: mlchamber@moose-tec.com
URL: http://www.mooselake-mn.com
Contact: Dean Paulson, Exec. Dir.

51441 ■ Morris Area Chamber of Commerce and Agriculture
507 Atlantic Ave.
Morris, MN 56267
Ph:(320)589-1242
Co. E-mail: info@morrismnchamber.org
URL: http://www.morrismnchamber.org
Contact: Ben Winchester, Chm.

51442 ■ New Prague Chamber of Commerce
PO Box 191
New Prague, MN 56071
Ph:(952)758-4360
Fax:(952)758-5396
Co. E-mail: info@newprague.com
URL: http://www.newprague.com
Contact: Kristy Mach, Exec. Dir.

51443 ■ New Ulm Area Chamber of Commerce
PO Box 384
New Ulm, MN 56073
Ph:(507)233-4300
Free: 888-463-9856
Fax:(507)354-1504
Co. E-mail: nuchamber@newulmtel.net
URL: http://www.newulm.com
Contact: Sharon Weinkauf, Pres./CEO

51444 ■ Nisswa Chamber of Commerce
PO Box 185
Nisswa, MN 56468
Ph:(218)963-2620
Free: 800-950-9610
Fax:(218)963-1420
Co. E-mail: requests@nisswa.com
URL: http://www.nisswa.com
Contact: Lee Seipp, Pres.

51445 ■ North Branch Area Chamber of Commerce
PO Box 577
North Branch, MN 55056
Ph:(651)674-4077
Co. E-mail: nbachamber@izoom.net
URL: http://www.northbranchchamber.com
Contact: Kathy Lindo, Exec. Dir.

51446 ■ North Hennepin Area Chamber of Commerce
229 1st Ave. NE
Osseo, MN 55369-1201
Ph:(763)424-6744

Fax:(763)424-6927
Co. E-mail: info@nhachamber.com
URL: http://www.nhachamber.com
Contact: Jill Johnson, Pres.

51447 ■ Northern Dakota County Chamber of Commerce
1121 Town Center Dr., Ste. 102
Eagan, MN 55123
Ph:(651)452-9872
Fax:(651)452-8978
Co. E-mail: info@ndcchambers.com
URL: http://dcrchamber.com
Contact: Ruthe Batulis, Pres.

51448 ■ Northfield Area Chamber of Commerce
PO Box 198
Northfield, MN 55057-0198
Ph:(507)645-5604
Free: 800-658-2548
Fax:(507)663-7782
Co. E-mail: info@northfieldchamber.com
URL: http://www.northfieldchamber.com
Contact: Kathy Feldbrugge, Exec. Dir.

51449 ■ Olivia Area Chamber of Commerce
PO Box 37
Olivia, MN 56277
Ph:(320)523-1350
Free: 888-265-CORN
Fax:(320)523-1514
URL: http://www.oliviachamber.org
Contact: Nancy Standfuss, Exec. Dir.

51450 ■ Owatonna Area Chamber of Commerce and Tourism
320 Hoffman Dr.
Owatonna, MN 55060
Ph:(507)451-7970
Free: 800-423-6466
Co. E-mail: oacct@owatonna.org
URL: http://www.owatonna.org
Contact: Brad Meier, Pres./CEO

51451 ■ Park Rapids Area Chamber of Commerce
PO Box 249
Park Rapids, MN 56470
Ph:(218)732-4111
Free: 800-247-0054
Fax:(218)732-4112
Co. E-mail: chamber@parkrapids.com
URL: http://www.parkrapids.com
Contact: Katie Magozzi, Exec. Dir.

51452 ■ Paynesville Area Chamber of Commerce
PO Box 4
Paynesville, MN 56362
Ph:(320)243-3233
Free: 800-547-9034
Co. E-mail: chamber@lakedalelink.net
URL: http://www.paynesvillechamber.org
Contact: DuDonne Andrie, Pres.

51453 ■ Pelican Rapids Area Chamber of Commerce
PO Box 206
Pelican Rapids, MN 56572-0206
Ph:(218)863-1221
Co. E-mail: tourism@loretel.net
URL: http://www.pelicanrapidschamber.com
Contact: Steve Foster, Pres.

51454 ■ Perham Area Chamber of Commerce
185 E Main St.
Perham, MN 56573
Ph:(218)346-7710
Free: 800-634-6112
Fax:(218)346-7712
Co. E-mail: chamber@perham.com
URL: http://www.perham.com
Contact: Nick Theroux, Pres.

51455 ■ Pine City Area Chamber of Commerce
900 4th St. SE, Ste. 85
Pine City, MN 55063
Ph:(320)629-4565
Co. E-mail: info@pinecitychamber.com
URL: http://www.pinecitychamber.com
Contact: Rick Herzog, Pres.

51456 ■ Pipestone Area Chamber of Commerce
PO Box 8
Pipestone, MN 56164
Ph:(507)825-3316
Free: 800-336-6125
Co. E-mail: pipecham@pipestoneminnesota.com
URL: http://www.pipestoneminnesota.com
Contact: Mick Myers, Exec. Dir.

51457 ■ Princeton Area Chamber of Commerce
705 N 2nd St.
Princeton, MN 55371-1550
Ph:(763)389-1764
Fax:(763)631-1764
Co. E-mail: pacc@sherbtel.net
URL: http://www.princetonmnchamber.org
Contact: Cheryl Brindle, Exec. Dir./Coor.

51458 ■ Prior Lake Area Chamber of Commerce
4775 Dakota St.
PO Box 114
Prior Lake, MN 55372
Ph:(952)440-1000
Fax:(952)440-1611
Co. E-mail: sandi@priorlakechamber.com
URL: http://priorlakechamber.com
Contact: Sandi Fleck, Exec. Dir.

51459 ■ Red Wing Area Chamber of Commerce
439 Main St.
Red Wing, MN 55066
Ph:(651)388-4719
Free: 800-762-9516
Co. E-mail: chamber@redwingchamber.com
URL: http://www.redwingchamber.com
Contact: Marie Mikel, Pres.

51460 ■ Redwood Area Chamber and Tourism
200 S Mill St.
PO Box 21
Redwood Falls, MN 56283
Ph:(507)637-2828
Free: 800-657-7070
Fax:(507)637-5202
Co. E-mail: chamber@redwoodfalls.org
URL: http://www.redwoodfalls.org

51461 ■ River Heights Chamber of Commerce
5782 Blackhire Path
Inver Grove Heights, MN 55076
Ph:(651)451-2266
Fax:(651)451-0846
Co. E-mail: info@riverheights.com
URL: http://www.riverheights.com
Contact: Jennifer Gale, Pres.

51462 ■ Robbinsdale Chamber of Commerce
PO Box 22646
Robbinsdale, MN 55422-0646
Ph:(763)531-1279
Co. E-mail: webmaster@ci.robbinsdale.mn.us
Contact: D. Kiser, Sec.

51463 ■ Rochester Area Chamber of Commerce
220 S Broadway, Ste. 100
Rochester, MN 55904
Ph:(507)288-1122
Fax:(507)282-8960
Co. E-mail: chamber@rochestermnchamber.com
URL: http://www.rochestermnchamber.com
Contact: John Wade, Pres.

51464 ■ St. Cloud Area Chamber of Commerce
PO Box 487
St. Cloud, MN 56302-0487
Ph:(320)251-2940
Fax:(320)251-0081
Co. E-mail: information@stcloudareachamber.com
URL: http://www.stcloudareachamber.com
Contact: Teresa Bohnen, Pres.

51465 ■ St. Joseph Chamber of Commerce
PO Box 696
St. Joseph, MN 56374
Ph:(320)363-7721
Co. E-mail: janel@fsbstjoseph.com
URL: http://www.stjosephchamber.com
Contact: Jean Dotzler, Pres.

51466 ■ St. Paul Area Chamber of Commerce
401 N Robert St., Ste. 150
St. Paul, MN 55101
Ph:(651)223-5000
Fax:(651)223-5119
Co. E-mail: kris@saintpaulchamber.com
URL: http://www.saintpaulchamber.com
Contact: Kristofer Johnson, Pres.

51467 ■ St. Peter Area Chamber of Commerce
101 S Front St.
St. Peter, MN 56082
Ph:(507)934-3400
Free: 800-473-3404
Fax:(507)934-8960
Co. E-mail: spchamb@hickorytech.net
URL: http://tourism.st-peter.mn.us

51468 ■ Sandstone Chamber of Commerce
402 N Main
Sandstone, MN 55072
Ph:(320)245-2271
Co. E-mail: info@sandstonechamber.com
URL: http://www.sandstonechamber.com

51469 ■ Sauk Centre Area Chamber of Commerce
PO Box 222
Sauk Centre, MN 56378
Ph:(320)352-5201
Fax:(320)352-5202
Co. E-mail: chamber@saukcentrechamber.com
URL: http://www.saukcentrechamber.com

51470 ■ Savage Chamber of Commerce
First Community Bank Bldg.
14141 Glendale Rd., Ste. 210
Savage, MN 55378
Ph:(952)894-8876
Fax:(952)894-9906
Co. E-mail: mail@savagechamber.com
URL: http://www.savagechamber.com
Contact: Lori Anderson, Exec. Dir.

51471 ■ Shakopee Chamber of Commerce
1801 E County Rd. 101
PO Box 717
Shakopee, MN 55379-0717
Ph:(952)445-1660
Free: 800-574-2150
Fax:(952)445-1669
Co. E-mail: chamber@shakopee.org
URL: http://www.shakopee.org/chamber
Contact: Carol Schultz, Pres.

51472 ■ Slayton Area Chamber of Commerce
2635 Broadway Ave.
Slayton, MN 56172
Ph:(507)836-6902
Fax:(507)836-6650
Co. E-mail: info@slaytonchamber.com
URL: http://www.slaytonchamber.com
Contact: Ms. April Gangestad, Dir.

51473 ■ Sleepy Eye Area Chamber of Commerce
232 E Main St.
Sleepy Eye, MN 56085
Ph:(507)794-4731
Free: 800-290-0588
Fax:(507)794-4732
Co. E-mail: secofc@sleepyeyetel.net
URL: http://sleepyeye-mn.com
Contact: Mrs. Julie Schmitt, Exec. Dir.

51474 ■ Springfield Area Chamber of Commerce
PO Box 134
Springfield, MN 56087
Ph:(507)723-3508
Fax:(507)723-4270
Co. E-mail: spfdchamber@newulmtel.net
URL: http://www.springfieldmnchamber.org
Contact: Alan Fritch, Pres.

51475 ■ Swedish-American Chamber of Commerce, Minnesota
2600 Park Ave.
Minneapolis, MN 55407
Ph:(612)991-3001
Co. E-mail: info@sacc-minnesota.org
URL: http://www.sacc-minnesota.org
Contact: Michael Davis, Chair

51476 ■ Thief River Falls Chamber of Commerce
2017 Hwy. 59 SE
Thief River Falls, MN 56701
Ph:(218)681-3720
Free: 800-827-1629
Fax:(218)681-3739
Co. E-mail: lori.trfchamber@wiktel.com
URL: http://www.visitthiefriverfalls.com
Contact: Nate Dalager, Chm.

51477 ■ Tracy Area Chamber of Commerce
372 Morgan St.
Tracy, MN 56175
Ph:(507)629-4021
Co. E-mail: tracychamber@iw.net
URL: http://www.tracymnchamber.com
Contact: Matt Knakmuhs, Chm.

51478 ■ Twin Cities North Chamber of Commerce
5394 Edgewood Dr., Ste. 100
Mounds View, MN 55112
Ph:(763)571-9781
Fax:(763)572-7950
Co. E-mail: info@twincitiesnorth.org
URL: http://www.twincitiesnorth.org
Contact: Sarah Anderson, Dir.

51479 ■ Twin Cities Quorum
1821 University Ave., Ste. S-306A
St. Paul, MN 55104
Ph:(651)646-1029
Co. E-mail: sam@twincitiesquorum.com
URL: http://www.twincitiesquorum.com
Contact: Sam McClure, Exec. Dir.

51480 ■ TwinWest Chamber of Commerce
10700 Old County Rd. 15, Ste. 170
Plymouth, MN 55441
Ph:(763)450-2220
Fax:(763)450-2221
Co. E-mail: info@twinwest.com
URL: http://www.twinwest.com
Contact: Bruce Nustad, Pres.

51481 ■ Two Harbors Area Chamber of Commerce
1313 Fairgrounds Rd.
Two Harbors, MN 55616-1149
Ph:(218)834-2600
Free: 800-777-7384
Fax:(218)834-4012
Co. E-mail: thchamber@frontiernet.net
URL: http://www.twoharborschamber.com
Contact: Gordy Anderson, Pres./CEO

51482 ■ Waconia Area Chamber of Commerce
209 S Vine St.
Waconia, MN 55387
Ph:(952)442-5812

Fax:(952)856-4476
Co. E-mail: ksites@destinationwaconia.org
URL: http://www.waconiachamber.org
Contact: Kellie Sites, Pres.

51483 ■ Waseca Area Chamber of Commerce
111 N State St.
Waseca, MN 56093
Ph:(507)835-3260
Free: 888-820-1243
Fax:(507)835-3267
Co. E-mail: info@wasecachamber.com
URL: http://www.wasecamncc.com
Contact: Kim Foels, Pres.

51484 ■ Wells Area Chamber of Commerce
28 S Broadway
Wells, MN 56097-1633
Ph:(507)553-6450
Free: (866)553-6450
Co. E-mail: wellscc@bevcomm.net
URL: http://wells.govoffice.com
Contact: Andrea Neubauer, Exec. Dir.

51485 ■ Wheaton Area Chamber of Commerce
PO Box 493
Wheaton, MN 56296-0493
URL: http://www.cityofwheaton.com
Contact: Trista Whaley, Pres.

51486 ■ White Bear Area Chamber of Commerce
4801 Hwy. 61, Ste. 305
White Bear Lake, MN 55110
Ph:(651)429-8593
Fax:(651)429-8592
Co. E-mail: info@whitebearchamber.com
URL: http://www.whitebearchamber.com
Contact: William Dinkel, Exec. Dir.

51487 ■ Willmar Lakes Area Chamber of Commerce
2104 E Hwy. 12
Willmar, MN 56201
Ph:(320)235-0300
Fax:(320)231-1948
Co. E-mail: chamber@willmarareachamber.com
URL: http://www.willmarareachamber.com
Contact: Ken Warner, Pres.

51488 ■ Windom Area Chamber of Commerce and Visitors Bureau
PO Box 8
Windom, MN 56101-0008
Ph:(507)831-2752
Free: 800-7W1-NDOM
Fax:(507)831-2755
Co. E-mail: windomchamber@windomnet.com
URL: http://www.winwacc.com
Contact: Cheryl Hanson, Pres.

51489 ■ Winona Area Chamber of Commerce
PO Box 870
Winona, MN 55987-0870
Ph:(507)452-2272
Fax:(507)454-8814
Co. E-mail: info@winonachamber.com
URL: http://www.winonachamber.com
Contact: Della Schmidt, Pres.

51490 ■ Winthrop Area Chamber of Commerce
PO Box 51
Winthrop, MN 04364
Ph:(207)377-8020
Fax:(207)377-2767
Co. E-mail: info@winthropchamber.org
URL: http://www.winthropchamber.org
Contact: Jeffrey Seguin, Pres.

51491 ■ Woodbury Chamber of Commerce
7650 Currell Blvd., Ste. 360
Woodbury, MN 55125
Ph:(651)578-0722
Fax:(651)578-7276
Co. E-mail: chamber@woodburychamber.org
URL: http://www.woodburychamber.org
Contact: Dan Morrow, Chm.

51492 ■ Worthington Area Chamber of Commerce
1121 Third Ave.
Worthington, MN 56187-2435
Ph:(507)372-2919
Free: 800-279-2919
Fax:(507)372-2827
Co. E-mail: wcofc@frontiernet.net
URL: http://www.worthingtonmnchamber.com

51493 ■ Zumbrota Chamber of Commerce
PO Box 2
Zumbrota, MN 55992-0002
Ph:(507)732-4282
URL: http://www.zumbrota.com

MINORITY BUSINESS ASSISTANCE PROGRAMS

51494 ■ Metropolitan Economic Development Association
250 Second Ave. S, Ste. 106
Minneapolis, MN 55401
Ph:(612)332-6332
Fax:(612)317-1002
Co. E-mail: info@meda.net
URL: http://www.meda.net
Contact: Yvonne Cheung Ho, Pres & CEO
Description: Provides services to entrepreneurs of color in Minnesota.

51495 ■ Minnesota Chippewa Tribe–Native American Business Enterprise Center
PO Box 217
Cass Lake, MN 56633
Ph:(218)335-8583
Fax:(218)335-8496
Co. E-mail: mctvhb@paulbunyan.net
URL: http://www.mnchippewatribe.org/economic_development.htm
Contact: Vernon Barsness Jr.

51496 ■ Women's Business Development Center - Minnesota
250 2nd Ave. S, Ste. 106
Minneapolis, MN 55401
Ph:(612)259-6584
Fax:(612)317-1002
Co. E-mail: wbdc-mn@wbdc.org
URL: http://www.wbdc.org/MN/Defaut.aspx
Description: Offers certification, training, mentoring, networking, and business development services to women's businesses in Minnesota, North Dakota, South Dakota, and Wisconsin.

FINANCING AND LOAN PROGRAMS

51497 ■ Affinity Capital Management
901 Marquette Ave., Ste. 2820
Minneapolis, MN 55402
Ph:(612)252-9900
Fax:(612)252-9911
URL: http://www.affinitycapital.net
Contact: Edson W. Spencer Jr., Managing General Partner
Investment Types: Seed, early, first and second stage. **Industry Preferences:** Internet specific, medical and health, computer software and services, biotechnology, semiconductors and other electronics. **Geographic Preferences:** Midwest. **Principal Exhibits:**

51498 ■ Bluestream Ventures
221 E. Myrtle St.
Stillwater, MN 55082
Ph:(651)967-5040
Fax:(612)967-5055
URL: http://www.bluestreamventures.com
Contact: Steve Sigmond, Venture Partner
E-mail: steve@bluestreamventures.com
Preferred Investment Size: $2,000,000 to $10,000,000. **Investment Types:** Early, second, and later stage, and expansion. **Industry Preferences:**

Communications, computer software, Internet specific, semiconductors and other electronics. **Geographic Preferences:** U.S. **Principal Exhibits:**

51499 ■ Cherry Tree Investments, Inc.
301 Carlson Pky., Ste. 103
Minnetonka, MN 55305
Ph:(952)893-9012
Fax:(952)893-9036
Co. E-mail: info@cherrytree.com
URL: http://www.cherrytree.com
Contact: Tony Christianson, Managing Partner
Preferred Investment Size: $250,000 to $1,000,000. **Investment Types:** Start-up, early, first and second, and later stage, management buyouts, mezzanine, special situation, turnaround, private placement, and recapitalizations. **Industry Preferences:** Communications, computer hardware and software, Internet specific, semiconductors and other electronics, biotechnology, medical and health, consumer related, financial services, business service, agriculture, forestry and fishing. **Geographic Preferences:** Midwest. **Principal Exhibits:**

51500 ■ Coral Ventures
60 S. 6th St., Ste. 2210
Minneapolis, MN 55402
Ph:(612)335-8666
Fax:(612)335-8668
URL: http://www.coralventures.com
Contact: Yuval Almog, Founder and Senior Managing Director
E-mail: yuval@coralgrp.com
Preferred Investment Size: $1,000,000 to $10,000,000. **Investment Types:** Seed, start-up, early, first and second stage, and balanced. **Industry Preferences:** Communications and media, medical and media, computer software, hardware and services, Internet specific, biotechnology, semiconductors and other electronics, industrial and energy, and consumer related. **Geographic Preferences:** U.S. **Principal Exhibits:**

51501 ■ Crescendo Venture Management, LLP
480 Cowper St., Ste. 300
Palo Alto, CA 94301
Ph:(650)470-1200
Fax:(650)470-1201
Co. E-mail: businessplans@crescendoventures.com
URL: http://www.crescendoventures.com
Contact: David Spreng, Managing General Partner
E-mail: dspreng@crescendoventures.com
Preferred Investment Size: $5,000,000 to $30,000,000. **Investment Types:** Start-up, seed, first and early stage. **Industry Preferences:** Internet specific, communications and media, semiconductors and other electronics, other products, computer hardware, computer software and services, medical and health, biotechnology, industrial and energy. **Geographic Preferences:** U.S. **Principal Exhibits:**

51502 ■ Gideon Hixon Fund
800 Anacapa St., Ste. A
Santa Barbara, CA 93101
Ph:(805)963-2277
Fax:(805)565-0929
URL: http://www.gideonhixon.com
Contact: Eric Hixon, General Partner
Preferred Investment Size: $500,000 to $1,500,000. **Investment Policies:** Start-up, seed, first and second stage. **Industry Preferences:** Internet specific, medical and health, computer software and services, other products, and semiconductors and other electronics. **Geographic Preferences:** U.S. **Principal Exhibits:**

51503 ■ Mayo Medical Ventures
200 First St. SW
Rochester, MN 55905
Ph:(507)284-2511
Free: 800-323-2688
Fax:(507)284-5410
Co. E-mail: mca.cme@mayo.edu
URL: http://www.mayo.edu
Preferred Investment Size: $250,000 to $1,000,000. **Investment Types:** Seed and early stage. **Industry Preferences:** Biotechnology, medical and health, Internet specific, industrial and energy. **Geographic Preferences:** U.S. **Principal Exhibits:**

51504 ■ Norwest Equity Partners
80 S. 8th St., Ste. 3600
Minneapolis, MN 55402
Ph:(612)215-1600
Fax:(612)215-1601
URL: http://www.nep.com
Contact: Andrew Cantwell, Principal
E-mail: acantwell@nep.com
Preferred Investment Size: $30,000,000 to $150,000,000. **Investment Types:** Expansion, later stage, acquisition, leveraged buyout, management buyouts, mezzanine, and recapitalizations. **Industry Preferences:** Computer software and services, communications and media, consumer related, agriculture, industrial and energy, medical and health, manufacturing, and business service. **Geographic Preferences:** U.S. **Principal Exhibits:**

51505 ■ Oak Investment Partners (Minneapolis)
4550 Wells Fargo Ctr.
90 S. 7th St.
Minneapolis, MN 55402
Ph:(612)339-9322
Fax:(612)337-8017
URL: http://www.oakvc.com
Contact: Scot Javis, Venture Partner
Preferred Investment Size: $25,000,000 to $150,000,000. **Investment Types:** Balanced, expansion, later stage, management buyouts, private placement, and special situation. **Industry Preferences:** Communications and media, Internet specific, computer software and services, semiconductors and other electronics, consumer related, computer hardware, other products, medical and health, biotechnology, industrial and energy. **Geographic Preferences:** U.S. **Principal Exhibits:**

51506 ■ Sherpa Partners LLC
5775 Wayzata Blvd., Ste. 995
St. Louis Park, MN 55416
Ph:(612)803-3169
Co. E-mail: info@sherpapartners.com
URL: http://www.sherpapartners.com
Contact: Richard A. Brimacomb, Partner
Preferred Investment Size: $250,000 to $1,000,000. **Investment Types:** Seed, start-up, early and first stage, and expansion. **Industry Preferences:** Communications and media, computer software, semiconductors and other electronics. **Geographic Preferences:** Minnesota. **Principal Exhibits:**

51507 ■ U.S. Bancorp Piper Jaffray Private Capital
800 Nicollet Mall, Ste. 800
Minneapolis, MN 55402
Ph:(612)303-6000
Fax:(612)303-1350
URL: http://www.piperjaffrey.com
Contact: Scott Barrington, Managing Partner
Investment Types: Fund of funds, and leveraged buyout. **Industry Preferences:** Diversified. **Geographic Preferences:** U.S. **Principal Exhibits:**

PROCUREMENT ASSISTANCE PROGRAMS

51508 ■ Metropolitan Economic Development Association (MEDA)–Procurement Technical Assistance Center
250 2nd Ave. S, Ste. 106
Minneapolis, MN 55401
Ph:(612)332-6332
Fax:(612)317-1002
Co. E-mail: info@meda.net
URL: http://www.meda.net
Contact: Sherri Komrosky, Dir.
E-mail: gjohnson@mpi.org

51509 ■ Minnesota Procurement Technical Assistance Center–Metropolitan Economic Development Association (MEDA)
St. Cloud State University
616 Roosevelt Rd., Ste. 100
St. Cloud, MN 56301
Ph:(320)202-6496

Fax:(320)654-5412
Co. E-mail: cnebel@meda.net
URL: http://www.ptac-meda.net
Contact: Christina Nebel-Dickerson, Prgm Mgr
E-mail: rmcgee@mpi.org

51510 ■ Minnesota Procurement Technical Assistance Center–Minnesota Project Innovation, Inc.
250 2nd Ave. S, Ste. 106
Minneapolis, MN 55401
Ph:(612)332-6332
Fax:(612)317-1002
Co. E-mail: skomrosky@meda.net
URL: http://www.ptac-meda.net
Contact: Sherri Komrosky, Prog. Dir.

INCUBATORS/RESEARCH AND TECHNOLOGY PARKS

51511 ■ Ceridian Corp.
3311 E. Old Shakopee Rd.
Minneapolis, MN 55425
Ph:(952)853-8100
URL: http://www.ceridian.com
Contact: Lee A. Kennedy, Chairman & CEO

51512 ■ Genesis Business Centers, Ltd.
902 1/2 First St. N
PO Box 5644
Hopkins, MN 55343
Ph:(612)455-2215
Co. E-mail: harlanjacobs@genesiscenters.com
URL: http://www.genesiscenters.com
Contact: Harlan Jacobs, Pres
Description: An incubator specially designed for emerging high-tech businesses.

51513 ■ Greater Mankato Business Accelerator–Chamber of Commerce & Economic Development
1961 Premier Dr., Ste. 100
Mankato, MN 56001
Ph:(507)385-6649
Free: 800-697-0652
Fax:(507)385-3202
Co. E-mail: jklinger@greatermankato.com
URL: http://www.greatermankato.com
Contact: Jonathan G. Zierdt, Pres. & CEO
Description: Provides business acceleration and start-up services.

51514 ■ Owatonna Business Incubator
1065 SW 24th Ave.
Owatonna, MN 55060
Ph:(507)451-0517
Fax:(507)455-2788
Co. E-mail: obi@owatonnaincubator.com
URL: http://www.owatonnaincubator.com/
Description: A small business incubator providing a facility in which small and start-up businesses can grow, prosper, and contribute to the surrounding community's economic base.

51515 ■ Time Share Systems
511 11th Ave., Ste. 402
Minneapolis, MN 55415
Ph:(612)332-2071
Fax:(612)332-2249

51516 ■ University of Minnesota–Center for the Development of Technological Leadership
West Bank Office Bldg., Ste. 510
1300 S 2nd St.
Minneapolis, MN 55454
Ph:(612)624-5747
Fax:(612)624-7510
Co. E-mail: amin@umn.edu
URL: http://tli.umn.edu
Contact: Dr. Massoud Amin, Dir.
E-mail: amin@umn.edu
Scope: Issues in the management of technology and technology forecasting. **Services:** Consulting, in areas of innovation, technology foresight, intellectual property management for technology-intensive companies; Technical services, in global transition dynamics to enhance resilience, security, and ef-

ficiency of national critical infrastructures. **Publications:** Management of Technology follow-up study; Miscellaneous reports; Newsletter. **Educational Activities:** Annual Technology Futures Forum; Short courses and seminars.

51517 ■ University of Minnesota–Office of Sponsored Projects Administration
450 McNamara Alumni Ctr.
200 Oak St. SE
Minneapolis, MN 55455
Ph:(612)624-5599
Fax:(612)624-4843
Co. E-mail: pwebb@umn.edu
URL: http://www.ospa.umn.edu
Contact: Pamela Webb, Assoc.VP for Res.
E-mail: pwebb@umn.edu
Scope: Serves as the research support unit for University of Minnesota faculty members by administering non-programmatic aspects of all research, training, and public service projects funded by external sources. Reviews and processes all proposals and awards for research, training, and public service projects. **Publications:** Research Review Newsletter.

51518 ■ University of Minnesota–Office for Technology Commercialization
160 University Enterprise Laboratories
1000 Westgate Dr.
St. Paul, MN 55114-8658
Ph:(612)624-0550
Fax:(612)624-6554
Co. E-mail: jwschrankler@umn.edu
URL: http://www.research.umn.edu/techcomm
Contact: Jay Schrankler, Exec.Dir.
E-mail: jwschrankler@umn.edu
Scope: Transfers technology from the University to business and industry in the areas of health sciences, engineering, biotechnology, and agriculture. **Educational Activities:** Paid internships in technology evaluation and marketing.

51519 ■ University of Minnesota Duluth Center for Economic Development–Business Incubator
11 E Superior St., Ste. 210
Duluth, MN 55802
Ph:(218)726-7298
Free: 888-387-4594
Fax:(218)726-6338
Co. E-mail: ced@umdced.com
URL: http://www.umdced.com/
Description: An incubator for technology development companies. Offers access to UMD's Center for Economic Development services.

51520 ■ University Technology Enterprise Center (Minneapolis)
1313 5th St. SE
Minneapolis, MN 55414
Ph:(612)379-3800
Fax:(612)379-3875
Co. E-mail: info@utecinc.com
URL: http://utec-center.com
Description: An enterprise center offering office space and support services for entrepreneurs.

EDUCATIONAL PROGRAMS

51521 ■ Alexandria Technical College
1601 Jefferson St.
Alexandria, MN 56308
Ph:(320)762-0221
Free: 888-234-1222
Fax:(320)762-4501
URL: http://www.alextech.org
Description: Trade and technical school offering a program in small business management.

51522 ■ Central Lakes College
501 W College Dr.
Brainerd, MN 56401
Ph:(218)855-8000
Free: 800-933-0346

Fax:(218)855-8220
URL: http://www.clc.mnscu.edu
Description: Trade and technical school offering a program in entrepreneurship and small business management.

51523 ■ Hibbing Community College
1515 E 25th St.
Hibbing, MN 55746
Ph:(218)262-7200
Free: 800-224-4422
Fax:(218)262-6717
Co. E-mail: admissions@hibbing.edu
URL: http://www.hibbing.edu
Description: Vocational school offering a small business management program.

51524 ■ Minneapolis Community and Technical College–Business Management Program
1501 Hennepin Ave. S
Minneapolis, MN 55403-1778
Ph:(612)659-6000
Free: 800-247-0911
Fax:(612)359-1357
URL: http://www.minneapolis.edu/
Description: Offers long-term instruction at an individual's place of business. Conducts seminars and individualized instruction to improve the management skills of prospective and current business owners.

51525 ■ Minnesota State Community and Technical College–Detroit Lakes
900 Hwy. 34 E
Detroit Lakes, MN 56501
Ph:(218)846-3700
Free: 800-492-4836
Fax:(218)846-3710
URL: http://www.minnesota.edu
Description: Trade and technical school offering a program in small business management.

51526 ■ Minnesota State Community and Technical College–Fergus Falls
1414 College Way
Fergus Falls, MN 56537
Ph:(218)736-1500
Free: 877-450-3322
Fax:(218)736-1510
URL: http://www.minnesota.edu
Description: Two-year college offering a small business management program.

51527 ■ Minnesota West Community & Technical College
1314 N Hiawatha Ave.
PO Box 250
Pipestone, MN 56164-0250
Ph:800-658-2330
Free: 800-658-2330
Fax:(507)825-4656
Co. E-mail: info@mnwest.edu
URL: http://www.mnwest.mnscu.edu
Description: Vocational school offering a small business management program.

51528 ■ Normandale Community College
9700 France Ave. S
Bloomington, MN 55431
Ph:(952)487-8200
Free: (886)880-8740
Fax:(612)832-6571
URL: http://www.nr.cc.mn.us
Description: Two-year college offering a business and marketing management program, covering management skills, cash management, and marketing techniques used in business.

LEGISLATIVE ASSISTANCE

51529 ■ Enterprise Minnesota–Minnesota Department of Trade and Economic Development Center
310 4th Ave. S, Ste. 7050
Minneapolis, MN 55415
Ph:(612)373-2900
Free: 800-325-3073

Fax:(612)373-2901
URL: http://www.enterpriseminnesota.org/
Description: Coordinates and develops technology initiatives and policy recommendations. Advises the legislature, the governor, and the commissioner of trade and economic development on the state's science and technology policy.

PUBLICATIONS

51530 ■ *Smart Start your Arkansas Business*
PSI Research
300 N. Valley Dr.
Grants Pass, OR 97526
Ph:(503)479-9464
Free: 800-228-2275
Fax:(503)476-1479
Co. E-mail: info@psi-research.com
URL: http://www.psi-research.com
Ed: Michael D. Jenkins. **Released:** Revised edition, 1992. **Price:** $29.95 (looseleaf binder); $24.95 (paper). **Description:** Part of the Successful Business Library series.

PUBLISHERS

51531 ■ American Institute of Small Business
23075 Hwy. 7, Ste. 200
Shorewood, MN 55331-3168
Ph:(952)545-7001
Free: 800-328-2906
Fax:(952)545-7020
Co. E-mail: info@aisb.biz
URL: http://www.aisb.biz
Contact: Max Fallek, Mgr
Description: Publishes books on setting up a small business and entrepreneurship. Offers a bimonthly newsletter, video cassettes and software packages. Accepts unsolicited manuscripts. Reaches market through direct mail, trade sales, telephone sales, wholesalers and distributors. **Founded:** 1986.

51532 ■ Expert Publishing Inc.
14314 Thrush St. NW
PO Box 679
Andover, MN 55304
Ph:(763)755-4966
Free: 877-755-4966
Fax:(763)757-8202
Co. E-mail: harry@expertpublishinginc.com
URL: http://www.expertpublishinginc.com
Contact: Sharron Stockhausen, CEO
E-mail: sharron@expertpublishinginc.com

51533 ■ Little Leaf Press Inc.
PO Box 187
Milaca, MN 56353
Ph:(651)774-3770
Free: 877-548-2431
Fax:(320)556-3585
Co. E-mail: littleleaf@maxminn.com
Contact: R. Bedford Watkins, Mgr
Description: Publishes children's, history, hobby and academic books. Accepts unsolicited manuscripts. Reaches market through direct mail, telephone sales, wholesalers and distributors. **Founded:** 1998.

51534 ■ Thomson Legal & Regulatory
610 Opperman Dr.
Eagan, MN 55123-1340
Ph:(651)687-7000
Free: 800-328-9378
Fax:(651)687-5642
Co. E-mail: tlrcorporate.communications@thomson.com
URL: http://www.thomsonreuters.com
Contact: Sharon Rowlands, CEO & Pres

51535 ■ Two-Can Publishing
11571 K-Tel Dr.
PO Box 86
Minnetonka, MN 55343
Ph:(952)933-7537
Free: 888-255-9989
Fax:(952)933-3630
Co. E-mail: sales@tnkidsbooks.com
Contact: Robert Nicholson, Mgr
Description: Publishes multimedia products and books. Does not accept unsolicited manuscripts. Reaches market through commission representatives, reviews and listings. **Founded:** 2000.

SMALL BUSINESS DEVELOPMENT CENTERS

51536 ■ East Central Community College Small Business Development Center
52 E 9th St.
Decatur, MS 39327
Fax:(601)635-4031
Co. E-mail: rwestbrook@eccc.edu
URL: http://www.mssbdc.org/center.
aspx?center=47026&subloc=0
Contact: Ronald B. Westbrook, Dir.

51537 ■ Jackson State University Small Business Development Center
Box 500
Jackson, MS 39204
Fax:(601)914-0833
Co. E-mail: henry.thomas@jsums.edu
URL: http://www.jsums.edu/business/sbdc
Contact: Mr. Henry Thomas, Dir.

51538 ■ Jones County Junior College Small Business Development Center
900 S Court St.
Ellisville, MS 39437
Fax:(601)477-4166
Co. E-mail: sbdc@jcjc.edu
URL: http://www.jcjc.edu/depts/sbdc/index.htm
Contact: Greg Butler, Dir.

51539 ■ Mississippi Small Business Development Center, Copiah Lincoln Community College
11 Co Lin Cir.
Natchez, MS 39120
URL: http://www.mssbdc.org

51540 ■ Mississippi Small Business Development Center at Delta State University
PO Box 3235
Cleveland, MS 38733
Co. E-mail: csledge@deltastate.edu
URL: http://www.deltastate.edu/pages/294.asp
Contact: Christie D. Sledge, Dir.

51541 ■ Mississippi Small Business Development Center, Hinds Community College
International Trade Center, 3rd Fl.
1500 Raymond Lake Rd.
Raymond, MS 39154
URL: http://www.mssbdc.org

51542 ■ Mississippi Small Business Development Center State Office
University of Mississippi
B-19 Jeanette Phillips Dr.
PO Box 1848
University, MS 38677-1848
Free: 800-725-7232
Fax:(662)915-5650
Co. E-mail: msbdc@olemiss.edu
URL: http://www.olemiss.edu/depts/mssbdc
Contact: Walter D. Gurley, State Dir.

51543 ■ Mississippi State University Small Business Development Center
PO Box 5288
Mississippi State, MS 39762
Fax:(662)325-4016
Co. E-mail: sfisher@cobilan.msstate.edu
URL: http://www.cbi.msstate.edu/sbdc
Contact: Sonny Fisher, Dir.

51544 ■ University of Mississippi Small Business Development Center
PO Box 1848
University, MS 38677
Free: 800-725-7232
Fax:(662)915-5650
Co. E-mail: umsbdc@olemiss.edu
URL: http://www.olemiss.edu/depts/umsbdc
Contact: Don Fischer, Dir.

SMALL BUSINESS ASSISTANCE PROGRAMS

51545 ■ Mississippi Development Authority
501 N. West St.
PO Box 849
Jackson, MS 39201
Ph:(601)359-3449
Fax:(601)359-2832
URL: http://www.mississippi.org
Contact: Gray Swoope, Dir.

Description: Provides assistance to the state's businesses and industries, including loans and loan guarantees to small businesses, and an outreach program.

51546 ■ Mississippi Enterprise for Technology–Mississippi Technology Transfer Office
John C. Stennis Space Center, Bldg. 1103, Rm. 143
Stennis Space Center, MS 39529-6000
Ph:(228)688-3144
Fax:(228)688-1064
Co. E-mail: Charles.E.Beasley@nasa.gov
URL: http://www.mset.org
Contact: Charles E. Beasley, Pres & CEO

Description: Helps advanced technology companies locate or expand in Mississippi.

51547 ■ Mississippi University for Women–Career Services
1100 College St., W-1624
Columbus, MS 39701
Ph:(662)241-7619
Fax:(662)329-7192
Co. E-mail: twilliams@ss.muw.edu
URL: http://www.muw.edu/career
Contact: Towanda Williams, Asst Dir

Description: Provides employment-related services to students and organizations.

SCORE OFFICES

51548 ■ SCORE Gulfcoast
Hancock Bank Plz.
2510 14th St., Ste. 105
Gulfport, MS 39501
Ph:(228)875-0691
Co. E-mail: philos@cableone.net
URL: http://www.scoregulfport.org
Contact: Dave Philo

Description: Provides public service to America by offering small business advice and training.

BETTER BUSINESS BUREAUS

51549 ■ Better Business Bureau of Mississippi
PO Box 3302
Ridgeland, MS 39158
Ph:(601)707-0960
Free: 800-987-8280
Fax:(601)856-9331
Co. E-mail: info@ms.bbb.org
URL: http://ms.bbb.org
Contact: Bill Moak, Pres./CEO

CHAMBERS OF COMMERCE

51550 ■ Area Development Partnership
1 Convention Center Plz.
Hattiesburg, MS 39401
Ph:(601)296-7500
Free: 800-238-4288
Fax:(601)296-7505
Co. E-mail: adp@theadp.com
URL: http://www.theadp.com
Contact: Dr. Angie Godwin, Pres.

51551 ■ Belzoni - Humphreys Development Foundation
111 Magnolia St.
PO Box 145
Belzoni, MS 39038
Ph:(662)247-4838
Free: 800-408-4838
Fax:(662)247-4805
Co. E-mail: catfish@belzonicable.com
URL: http://www.catfishcapitalonline.com
Contact: Tiffany Greer, Pres.

51552 ■ Biloxi Chamber of Commerce
11975 E Seaway Rd.
Gulfport, MS 39503
Ph:(228)604-0014
Fax:(228)604-0105
Co. E-mail: rachael@mscoastchamber.com
URL: http://biloxi.org
Contact: Kimberly Nastasi Crim, CEO

51553 ■ Booneville Area Chamber of Commerce
100 W Church St.
Booneville, MS 38829
Ph:(662)728-4130

Free: 800-300-9302
Fax:(662)728-4134
Co. E-mail: rgreening@boonevillemississippi.com
URL: http://boonevillemississippi.com
Contact: Rhonda Greening, Exec. Dir.

51554 ■ Brookhaven - Lincoln County Chamber of Commerce
230 S Whitworth Ave.
PO Box 978
Brookhaven, MS 39602-0978
Ph:(601)833-1411
Free: 800-613-4667
Fax:(601)833-1412
Co. E-mail: chb@brookhavenchamber.com
URL: http://www.brookhavenchamber.com/index.php
Contact: Cliff Brumfield, Exec. VP

51555 ■ Calhoun City Chamber of Commerce
102 S Monroe St.
PO Box 161
Calhoun City, MS 38916-0161
Ph:(662)628-6990
Fax:(662)628-8931
Co. E-mail: city1@tds.net
URL: http://www.calhouncity.net
Contact: James Franklin, Pres.

51556 ■ Canton Chamber of Commerce
PO Box 74
Canton, MS 39046-0074
Ph:(601)859-5816
Fax:(601)855-0149
URL: http://www.canton-mississippi.com/index.php
Contact: Deborah Anderson, Exec. Dir.

51557 ■ City of Ridgeland Chamber of Commerce
PO Box 194
Ridgeland, MS 39158-0194
Ph:(601)991-9996
Fax:(601)991-9997
Co. E-mail: admin@ridgelandchamber.com
URL: http://www.ridgelandchamber.com
Contact: Linda T. Bynum, Exec. Dir.

51558 ■ Clarke County Chamber of Commerce
PO Box 172
Quitman, MS 39355
Ph:(601)776-5701
Fax:(601)776-5745
Co. E-mail: clarkechamber@att.net
URL: http://www.visitclarkecounty.com
Contact: Patty Combest, Sec.

51559 ■ Clarksdale - Coahoma County Chamber of Commerce and Industry Foundation
PO Box 160
Clarksdale, MS 38614
Ph:(662)627-7337
Free: 800-626-3764
Fax:(662)627-1313
Co. E-mail: chamberofcommerce@clarksdale-ms.com
URL: http://www.clarksdale.com/chamber
Contact: Ronald E. Hudson, Exec. Dir.

51560 ■ Cleveland-Bolivar County Chamber of Commerce
600 3rd St.
PO Box 490
Cleveland, MS 38732
Ph:(662)843-2712
Fax:(662)843-2718
Co. E-mail: judson@clevelandmschamber.com
URL: http://www.clevelandmschamber.com
Contact: Judson Thigpen, Exec. Dir.

51561 ■ Clinton Chamber of Commerce
100 E Leake
PO Box 143
Clinton, MS 39060-0143
Ph:(601)924-5912
Free: 800-611-9980

Fax:(601)925-4009
Co. E-mail: info@clintonchamber.org
URL: http://www.clintonms.org
Contact: Dianne Newman Carson, Exec. Dir.

51562 ■ Community Development Foundation
300 W Main St.
PO Box A
Tupelo, MS 38804
Ph:(662)842-4521
Free: 800-523-6434
Fax:(662)841-0693
Co. E-mail: info@cdfms.org
URL: http://www.cdfms.org
Contact: David P. Rumbarger, Pres./CEO

51563 ■ Community Development Partnership
256 W Beacon St.
Philadelphia, MS 39350
Ph:(601)656-1000
Co. E-mail: dvowell@bellsouth.net
URL: http://www.neshoba.org/index.php
Contact: David Vowell, Pres.

51564 ■ Covington County Chamber of Commerce
500 Korno St.
Collins, MS 39428-1595
Ph:(601)765-6012
Fax:(601)765-1740
Co. E-mail: contact@covingtonchamber.com
URL: http://www.covingtonchamber.com
Contact: Marie Shoemake, Exec. Dir.

51565 ■ D'Iberville-St. Martin Chamber of Commerce
PO Box 6054
D'Iberville, MS 39540
Ph:(228)392-2293
Fax:(228)396-3216
URL: http://www.dsmchamber.com
Contact: Sharon Seymour, Exec. Dir.

51566 ■ Greater Picayune Area Chamber of Commerce
201 Hwy. 11 N
PO Box 448
Picayune, MS 39466
Ph:(601)798-3122
Fax:(601)798-6984
Co. E-mail: chambercommerce1@bellsouth.net
URL: http://www.picayunechamber.org
Contact: Ted Musgrove, Pres.

51567 ■ Greenwood-Leflore Chamber of Commerce
PO Box 848
Greenwood, MS 38935-0848
Ph:(662)453-4152
Co. E-mail: info@greenwoodms.com
URL: http://www.greenwoodms.com/index.php
Contact: Beth Stevens, Exec. VP

51568 ■ Grenada County Chamber of Commerce
PO Box 628
Grenada, MS 38902-0628
Ph:(662)226-2571
Free: 800-373-2571
Fax:(662)226-9745
Co. E-mail: phillipheard@yahoo.com
URL: http://www.grenadamississippi.com
Contact: Phillip Heard, Exec. Dir.

51569 ■ Hancock County Chamber of Commerce
412 Hwy. 90, Ste. 6
Bay St. Louis, MS 39520
Ph:(228)467-9048
Fax:(228)467-6033
Co. E-mail: lynne@hancockchamber.org
URL: http://www.hancockchamber.org
Contact: Ms. Tish Haas Williams, Exec. Dir.

51570 ■ Hernando Area Chamber of Commerce
2465 Hwy. 51 S
Hernando, MS 38632
Ph:(662)429-9055
Fax:(662)429-2909
Co. E-mail: chamber@hernandoms.org
URL: http://www.hmscoc.com
Contact: Brian K. Goff, Exec. Dir.

51571 ■ Holly Springs Chamber of Commerce
104 E Gholson Ave.
Holly Springs, MS 38635
Ph:(662)252-2943
Co. E-mail: director@hschamber.org
URL: http://www.hschamber.org
Contact: Amy S. Heaton, Exec. Dir.

51572 ■ Horn Lake Chamber of Commerce
3040 Goodman Rd. W, Ste. 2A
Horn Lake, MS 38637
Ph:(662)393-9897
Fax:(662)393-2942
Co. E-mail: info@hornlakechamber.com
URL: http://www.hornlakechamber.com
Contact: Larry Witherspoon, Exec. Dir.

51573 ■ Indianola Chamber of Commerce
PO Box 151
Indianola, MS 38751
Ph:(662)887-4454
Free: 877-816-7581
Fax:(662)887-4454
Co. E-mail: icoc@tecinfo.com
URL: http://www.indianolams.org
Contact: Scott Shafer, Pres.

51574 ■ Itawamba County Development Council
PO Box 577
Fulton, MS 38843
Ph:(662)862-4571
Fax:(662)862-5637
Co. E-mail: icdc@itawamba.com
URL: http://www.itawamba.com
Contact: Greg Deakle, Exec. Dir.

51575 ■ Jones County Chamber of Commerce
PO Box 527
Laurel, MS 39441-0527
Ph:(601)649-3031
Fax:(601)428-2047
Co. E-mail: info@edajones.com
URL: http://www.edajones.com
Contact: Sandy Holifield, Dir.

51576 ■ Kosciusko-Attala Chamber of Commerce
124 N Jackson St.
Kosciusko, MS 39090
Ph:(662)289-2981
Co. E-mail: info@kadcorp.org
URL: http://www.kosciuskotourism.com
Contact: Steve Zea, Pres.

51577 ■ Leake County Chamber of Commerce
103 N Pearl St.
PO Box 209
Carthage, MS 39051-0209
Ph:(601)267-9231
Fax:(601)267-8123
Co. E-mail: director@leakems.com
URL: http://www.leakems.com
Contact: Renodda Dorman, Exec. Dir.

51578 ■ Leland Chamber of Commerce
PO Box 67
Leland, MS 38756
Ph:(662)686-2687
Fax:(662)686-2689
Co. E-mail: lcoc@tecinfo.com
URL: http://www.lelandms.org
Contact: Ashley Zepponi, Exec. Dir.

51579 ■ Louisville-Winston County Chamber of Commerce
PO Box 551
Louisville, MS 39339
Ph:(662)773-3921
Fax:(662)773-8909
Co. E-mail: info@winstoncounty.com
URL: http://www.winstoncounty.com
Contact: Linda Skelton, Mgr.

51580 ■ Madison Chamber of Commerce
1239 Hwy. 51
Madison, MS 39110
Ph:(601)856-7060
Fax:(601)856-4852
Co. E-mail: info@madisonthecitychamber.com
URL: http://www.madisonthecity.com
Contact: Rosie Vassallo, Exec. Dir.

51581 ■ Marion County Development Partnership
PO Box 272
Columbia, MS 39429
Ph:(601)736-6385
Fax:(601)736-6392
Co. E-mail: info@marionpartnership.org
URL: http://www.mcdp.info
Contact: Gerald Frazier, Pres.

51582 ■ MetroJackson Chamber of Commerce
PO Box 22548
Jackson, MS 39225-2548
Ph:(601)948-7575
Fax:(601)352-5539
Co. E-mail: contact@metrochamber.com
URL: http://www.metrochamber.com
Contact: Duane A. O'Neill, Pres.

51583 ■ Mississippi Gulf Coast Chamber of Commerce
11975E Seaway Rd.
Gulfport, MS 39503
Ph:(228)604-0014
Fax:(228)604-0105
Co. E-mail: info@mscoastchamber.com
URL: http://mscoastchamber.com
Contact: Kimberly Nastasi, CEO

51584 ■ Monroe County Chamber of Commerce
124 W Commerce St.
Aberdeen, MS 39730
Ph:(662)369-6488
Fax:(662)369-6489
Co. E-mail: chamber@gomonroe.org
URL: http://www.gomonroe.org
Contact: Tony Green, Pres.

51585 ■ Natchez-Adams County Chamber of Commerce
211 Main St.
Natchez, MS 39120
Ph:(601)445-4611
Fax:(601)445-9361
Co. E-mail: natchezchamber@natchezchamber.com
URL: http://natchezchamber.com
Contact: Cliff Merritt, Chm.

51586 ■ Newton Chamber of Commerce
PO Box 301
Newton, MS 39345
Ph:(601)683-2201
Fax:(601)683-2201
Co. E-mail: chambernewton@bellsouth.net
URL: http://www.ci.newton.ms.us
Contact: Angie Burkes, Exec. Dir.

51587 ■ Ocean Springs Chamber of Commerce
1000 Washington Ave.
Ocean Springs, MS 39564
Ph:(228)875-4424
Fax:(228)875-0332
Co. E-mail: mail@oceanspringschamber.com
URL: http://www.oceanspringschamber.com
Contact: Margaret Miller, Exec. Dir.

51588 ■ Okolona Area Chamber of Commerce-Main Street Program
219 Main St.
PO Box 446
Okolona, MS 38860
Ph:(662)447-5913
Fax:(662)447-0254
URL: http://www.okolona.org
Contact: Linda M. Carnathan, Dir.

51589 ■ Olive Branch Chamber of Commerce
PO Box 608
Olive Branch, MS 38654-0608
Ph:(662)895-2600
Fax:(662)895-2625
Co. E-mail: info@olivebranchms.com
URL: http://www.olivebranchms.com
Contact: Vickie DuPree, Exec. Dir.

51590 ■ Oxford-Lafayette County Chamber of Commerce
299 W Jackson Ave.
PO Box 147
Oxford, MS 38655
Ph:(662)234-4651
Free: 800-880-6967
Fax:(662)234-4655
Co. E-mail: info@oxfordms.com
URL: http://www.oxfordms.com
Contact: Max D. Hipp, Pres./CEO

51591 ■ Pearl Chamber of Commerce
PO Box 54125
Pearl, MS 39288-4125
Ph:(601)939-3338
Fax:(601)936-5717
Co. E-mail: kathy@pearlms.org
URL: http://www.pearlms.org
Contact: Kathy Deer, Exec. Dir.

51592 ■ Pike County Chamber of Commerce and Economic Development District
112 N Railroad Blvd.
McComb, MS 39648
Ph:(601)684-2291
Free: 800-399-4404
Fax:(601)684-4899
Co. E-mail: pcedd@pikeinfo.com
URL: http://www.pikeinfo.com
Contact: J. Britt Herrin, Exec. Dir.

51593 ■ Pontotoc County Chamber of Commerce
109 N Main St.
Pontotoc, MS 38863
Ph:(662)489-5042
Fax:(662)489-5263
Co. E-mail: cecilia@pontotocchamber.com
URL: http://www.pontotocchamber.com
Contact: Cecilia Derrington, Exec. Dir.

51594 ■ Port Gibson-Claiborne County Chamber of Commerce
1601 Church St.
PO Box 491
Port Gibson, MS 39150
Ph:(601)437-4351
Co. E-mail: jcruggs@portgibson.org
URL: http://www.portgibsononthemississippi.com/chamber_of_commerce.html
Contact: Judith M. Scruggs

51595 ■ Rankin County Chamber of Commerce
101 Service Dr.
PO Box 428
Brandon, MS 39043-0428
Ph:(601)825-2268
Fax:(601)825-1977
Co. E-mail: gmartin@rankinchamber.com
URL: http://www.rankinchamber.com/home.aspx
Contact: Gale Martin, Exec. Dir.

51596 ■ Southaven - Horn Lake Area Chamber of Commerce
8700 Northwest Dr.
PO Box 211
Southaven, MS 38671
Ph:(662)342-6114
Free: 800-272-6551
Fax:(662)342-6365
Co. E-mail: info@southavenchamber.com
URL: http://www.southavenchamber.com
Contact: Ford Moore, Pres.

51597 ■ Starkville Area Chamber of Commerce
200 E Main St.
Starkville, MS 39759
Ph:(662)323-3322
Free: 800-649-8687
Fax:(662)323-5815
Co. E-mail: info@starkville.org
URL: http://www.starkville.org
Contact: Jon Maynard, Pres./CEO

51598 ■ Swedish-American Chamber of Commerce, South Central United States
PO Box 248
Madison, MS 39130
Ph:(601)853-2647
Co. E-mail: info@sacc-scus.org
URL: http://www.sacc-scus.org
Contact: Steve Vassallo, Pres.

51599 ■ Tunica County Chamber of Commerce
PO Box 1888
Tunica, MS 38676
Ph:(662)363-2865
Fax:(662)357-0378
Co. E-mail: marketing@tunicachamber.com
URL: http://www.tunicachamber.com
Contact: Lyn Arnold, Pres./CEO

51600 ■ Union Chamber of Commerce
101 Bank St.
Union, MS 39365
Ph:(601)774-9586
Fax:(601)774-9586
Co. E-mail: unioncommerce@bellsouth.net
URL: http://www.unionms.com

51601 ■ Vicksburg-Warren County Chamber of Commerce
2020 Mission 66
Vicksburg, MS 39180
Ph:(601)636-1012
Fax:(601)636-4422
Co. E-mail: info@vicksburgchamber.org
URL: http://www.vicksburgchamber.org
Contact: Christi Kilroy, Exec. Dir.

51602 ■ Walthall County Chamber of Commerce
PO Box 227
Tylertown, MS 39667
Ph:(601)876-2680
Co. E-mail: walthallchamber@bellsouth.net
URL: http://www.walthallcountychamber.org
Contact: Frank Bonner, Pres.

MINORITY BUSINESS ASSISTANCE PROGRAMS

51603 ■ City of Jackson Economic Development Division–Equal Business Opportunity
200 S President St., Rm. 223
Jackson, MS 39201
Ph:(601)960-1055
Fax:(601)960-2403
Co. E-mail: mdavis@city.jackson.ms.us
URL: http://www.jacksonms.gov/government/planning/ebo/
Contact: Mike Davis, Mgr
Description: Provides assistance in the development of minority entrepreneurs.

51604 ■ Crudup-Ward Women's Business Center
PO Box 1113
Forest, MS 39074
Ph:(601)469-3357

Fax:(601)469-3357
Co. E-mail: anniewlowery@gmail.com
URL: http://cwainc.org
Contact: Annie Lowery, Exec Dir
Description: Provides business information, counseling, management, and technical assistance to women looking to create or expand a business.

51605 ■ Mississippi Development Authority–Minority and Small Business Development Division
501 NW St.
PO Box 849
Jackson, MS 39205
Ph:(601)359-3448
Fax:(601)359-5290
Co. E-mail: rcovington@mississippi.org
URL: http://www.mississippi.org
Contact: Bob Covington, Dir
Description: Facilitates networking and industry partnerships for minority and women-owned businesses.

51606 ■ Mississippi Minority Business Enterprise Center
John S. and James L. Knight Nonprofit Center
11975 Seaway Rd., Ste. B231
Gulfport, MS 39503
Ph:(228)896-6868
Fax:(228)896-6870
Co. E-mail: info@msmbec.org
URL: http://www.msmbec.org
Contact: Michael Anderson, Dir
Description: Provides business development services to minority enterprises, focusing on strategic growth businesses.

PROCUREMENT ASSISTANCE PROGRAMS

51607 ■ Mississippi Contract Procurement Center, Inc.–Delta Contract Procurement Center, Inc. (DCPC)
342 Washington Ave., 2nd Fl.
Greenville, MS 38702
Ph:(662)334-1518
Fax:(662)334-1598
Co. E-mail: dcpc2@suddenlinkmail.com
URL: http://www.mscpc.com
Contact: H.L. "Lee" Woodyard, Dir.
E-mail: dcpc@juno.com
Description: Assisting Mississippi businesses in obtaining federal, state, local government and commercial contracts.

51608 ■ Mississippi Contract Procurement Center, Inc.–Northeast Mississippi Contract Procurement Center, Inc. (NMCPC)
PO Box 1805
318 7th St. N
Columbus, MS 39703-1805
Ph:(662)329-1077
Fax:(662)327-6600
Co. E-mail: nmcpc@ebicom.net
URL: http://www.mscpc.com
Contact: Bill Burge, Dir.
Description: Assisting Mississippi businesses in obtaining federal, state, local government and commercial contracts.

51609 ■ Mississippi Contract Procurement Center, Inc.–South Mississippi Contract Procurement Center, Inc. (SMCPC)
1636 Popps Ferry Rd., Ste. 203
Biloxi, MS 39532
Ph:(228)396-1288
Fax:(228)396-2520
Co. E-mail: mcdowell@mscpc.com
URL: http://www.mscpc.com
Contact: Marcia McDowell, Dir.
Description: Provides information and direct assistance to firms wishing to do business with the federal government.

51610 ■ Mississippi Contract Procurement Technical Assistance Center, Inc.–East Central Procurement Center (ECCPC)
c/o Meridian Community College
910 Highway 19 N
Meridian, MS 39307
Ph:(601)482-7445
Fax:(601)482-5803
URL: http://www.mscpc.com
Contact: Bill Mabry, Dir.
Description: Enhances national defense and economic development of the state of Mississippi by assisting Mississippi businesses in obtaining federal, state, local government and commercial contracts serving Clarke, Covington, Jasper, Jones, Kemper, Lauderdale, Leake, Neshoba, Newton, Scott, Smith, and Wayne Counties.

51611 ■ Mississippi Contract Procurement Technical Center, Inc.–Central Mississippi Procurement Center, Inc. (CMPC)
c/o Mississippi Development Authority
501 North West St.
Jackson, MS 39201
Ph:(601)359-3485
Fax:(601)359-5290
Co. E-mail: jhatcher@mississippi.org
URL: http://www.mscpc.com
Contact: Johnithan Hatcher, Dir.
Description: Enhances national defense and economic development of the state of Mississippi by assisting Mississippi businesses in obtaining federal, state, local government and commercial contracts serving Adams, Claiborne, Copiah, Franklin, Hinds, Jefferson, Jefferson Davis, Lawrence, Lincoln, Madison, Rankin, Simpson, and Warren counties.

51612 ■ Mississippi Procurement Technical Assistance Program–Mississippi Development Authority
PO Box 849
Jackson, MS 39205
Ph:(601)359-3349
Fax:(601)359-2832
URL: http://www.mscpc.com
Contact: Carol Harris, Program Mgr.
E-mail: charris@mississippi.org

51613 ■ Mississippi Procurement Technical Assistance Program–Mississippi Development Authority–Minority and Small Business Development Division (MSBDD) (PO Bo)
PO Box 849
Jackson, MS 39205
Ph:(601)359-3449
Fax:(601)359-2832
URL: http://www.mscpc.com
Contact: Robert Covington, Dep. Dir.
Description: To enhance economic development of the state of Mississippi by assisting Mississippi businesses in obtaining federal, state, local government and commercial contracts.

51614 ■ South Mississippi Contract Procurement Center, Inc. (SMCPC)
1636 Popps Ferry Rd., Ste. 203
Biloxi, MS 39532
Ph:(228)396-1288
Fax:(228)396-2520
Co. E-mail: mcdowell@mscpc.com
URL: http://www.mscpc.com
Contact: Marcia McDowell, Dir.
Description: Enhances national defense and economic development of the state of Mississippi by assisting Mississippi businesses in obtaining federal, state, local government and commercial contracts serving Amite, Forrest, George, Greene, Hancock, Harrison, Jackson, Lamar, Marion, Pearl River, Perry, Pike, Stone, Walthall, Wilkinson.

INCUBATORS/RESEARCH AND TECHNOLOGY PARKS

51615 ■ Coahoma County Business Development Center
1540 DeSoto Ave.
PO Box 160
Clarksdale, MS 38614

Ph:(662)627-7337
Fax:(662)627-1313
Co. E-mail: chamberofcommerce@clarksdale-ms.com
URL: http://www.clarksdale-ms.com/
Description: A small business incubator that assists entrepreneurs in the business start-up process and gives aid to new businesses to help ensure their survival.

51616 ■ Gulf Coast Innovation Center
1636 Popps Ferry Rd., Ste. 100
Biloxi, MS 39532
Ph:(228)392-9741
Fax:(228)392-9743
Co. E-mail: contact@innovatems.com
URL: http://www.gcbtc.org/
Contact: Stephen Whitt, Exec. Dir.
Description: A small business incubator providing an atmosphere to encourage the development of small, start-up businesses and enable them to survive.

51617 ■ Jackson Enterprise Center
931 Hwy. 80 W
Jackson, MS 39204
Ph:(601)352-0957
Fax:(601)948-3250
Co. E-mail: leasing@jxnenterprise.com
URL: http://www.jxnenterprise.com
Contact: Fred LaRue, Dir
Description: Provides facilities with shared services and networking opportunties for entrepreneurs.

51618 ■ John C. Stennis Space Center–Institute for Technology Development
Bldg. 1103, Ste. 118
Stennis Space Center, MS 39529
Ph:(228)688-2509
Fax:(228)688-2861
Co. E-mail: dlewis@iftd.org
URL: http://www.iftd.org
Contact: David Lewis PhD, Dir.
E-mail: dlewis@iftd.org
Scope: Identifies national and state technological needs in the areas products and services for older americans, microelectronics, and space remote sensing and coordinates the commercialization of research and development from the state's university, government, small business laboratories, and internal resources. Conducts applied technology development for internal purposes and external sponsors. **Publications:** Innovations.

51619 ■ Mississippi Action for Community Education, Inc. (MACE)
119 S Theobald St.
Greenville, MS 38701
Ph:(662)335-3523
Free: 888-812-5837
Fax:(662)334-2939
Co. E-mail: mace03@deltamace.org
URL: http://www.deltamace.org
Description: A non-profit minority, rural development organization Working to improve the economic situation of minorities and the poor.

51620 ■ Mississippi Enterprise for Technology
Bldg. 1103, Ste. 140
Stennis Space Center, MS 39529
Ph:(228)688-3372
Free: 800-746-4699
Fax:(228)688-1064
Co. E-mail: Charles.E.Beasley@nasa.gov
URL: http://www.mset.org/
Description: A small business incubator whose mission is to create, retain, and attract high-skill, high-wage jobs in Mississippi by assisting with the growth and development of young, technology-based companies.

51621 ■ Mississippi Research and Technology Park
Mississippi Technology Center, Ste. 204
Oktibbeha County Economic Development Authority
1 Research Blvd.
Starkville, MS 39759
Ph:(662)324-7776

Fax:(662)323-3726
URL: http://www.starkville.org/econ_dev/park.html
Contact: John Rucker
Scope: Research laboratories, incubator and multi-tenant facilities, professional and business services, and office space to foster high technology research collaboration between the University and industry tenants. **Educational Activities:** Mississippi State University Graduate Student Internship Program.

51622 ■ Mississippi State University–Office of the Vice President for Research and Economic Development
Campus MS 9722
PO Box 6343
Mississippi State, MS 39762
Ph:(662)325-3570
Fax:(662)325-8028
Co. E-mail: dshaw@research.msstate.edu
URL: http://www.research.msstate.edu
Contact: Dr. David Shaw, VP
E-mail: dshaw@research.msstate.edu
Scope: Coordinates research programs of the University in engineering, business, education, physical and biological sciences, social sciences, water resources, and computer science through specialized research centers and institutes administratively responsible to the Office of the Vice President for Research and Economic Development. **Publications:** Research Magazine (annually).

51623 ■ Mississippi Technology Alliance
134 Market Ridge Dr.
Box 600
Ridgeland, MS 39157
Ph:(601)960-3610

Fax:(601)960-3605
Co. E-mail: tjeff@technologyalliance.ms
URL: http://www.technologyalliance.ms/index.php
Contact: Tony Jeff, Pres. & CEO
Description: A non-profit, public-private partnership whose primary mission is to drive science and technology-based economic development efforts throughout the state, with the end goal being wealth creation through higher paying quality jobs; it focuses on creating wealth by leveraging research capacity and supporting technology business development for Mississippi companies.

51624 ■ North Mississippi Enterprise Initiative, Inc.
9 Industrial Park Dr., Ste. 104
Oxford, MS 38655
Ph:(662)281-0720
Co. E-mail: holly@northmiss.org
URL: http://www.northmiss.org/
Contact: Holly Kelly, Exec. Dir.
Description: A non-profit, public/private regional partnership for entrepreneurial growth. It manages three business incubators - Oxford, Batesville and Grenada - and provides leadership in entrepreneurship within the region.

51625 ■ Renasant Center for IDEAs–Tupelo/ Lee County Regional Business Incubator
300 W Main St.
Tupelo, MS 38804
Ph:(662)842-4521
Free: 800-523-3463
Fax:(662)841-0693
Co. E-mail: info@cdfms.org
URL: http://www.cdfms.org/renasant/?id=189
Description: A business incubator helping small businesses grow into global competitors, utilizing a suite

of productive services and resources to help design, develop and distribute entrepreneurs and their business goals into the community and global economy.

51626 ■ University of Southern Mississippi–Sponsored Programs Administration
118 College Dr., No. 5157
2609 W 4th St.
Hattiesburg, MS 39406-0001
Ph:(601)266-4119
Fax:(601)266-4312
Co. E-mail: connie.wyldmon@usm.edu
URL: http://www.usm.edu/spa
Contact: Constance V. (Connie) Wyldmon, Dir.
E-mail: connie.wyldmon@usm.edu
Scope: Responsible for administration of externally sponsored research and training at the University. **Publications:** Newsletter (monthly). **Educational Activities:** Activities related to proposal development; Workshops, for faculty and staff.

PUBLICATIONS

51627 ■ *Smart Start your Florida Business*
PSI Research
300 N. Valley Dr.
Grants Pass, OR 97526
Ph:(503)479-9464
Free: 800-228-2275
Fax:(503)476-1479
Co. E-mail: info@psi-research.com
URL: http://www.psi-research.com
Ed: Carl R. Sniffen and Michael D. Jenkins. **Released:** Revised edition, 1992. **Price:** $29.95 (looseleaf binder); $24.95 (paper). **Description:** Part of the Successful Business Library series.

SMALL BUSINESS DEVELOPMENT CENTERS

51628 ■ Missouri Small Business Development Centers
200 Engineering N
410 S 6th St.
Columbia, MO 65211
Co. E-mail: summersm@missouri.edu
URL: http://www.missouribusiness.net/sbdc/index.asp
Contact: Max Summers, Dir.

51629 ■ Missouri Small Business Development Centers - Chillicothe
715 Washington St.
Chillicothe, MO 64601
Fax:(660)646-6811
Co. E-mail: sbdchill@greenhills.net
URL: http://www.nwmissouri.edu/sbdc
Contact: Steve Holt, Dir.

51630 ■ Missouri Small Business Development Centers - Northwest Region
423 N Market St.
Maryville, MO 64468
Fax:(660)582-3071
Co. E-mail: fveeman@nwmissouri.edu
URL: http://www.nwmissouri.edu/sbdc
Contact: Frank Veeman, Dir.

51631 ■ Missouri Small Business Development Centers - St. Joseph
3003 Frederick Ave.
St. Joseph, MO 64506
Fax:(816)364-4873
Co. E-mail: evanssbdc@saintjoseph.com
URL: http://www.nwmissouri.edu/sbdc
Contact: Rebecca Evans, Dir.

51632 ■ Small Business Development Center - Southeast Missouri State University
1 University Plz.
MS 0110
Cape Girardeau, MO 63701
Co. E-mail: wrvickery@semo.edu
URL: http://www2.semo.edu/sesbdc/homepage.html
Contact: Bill Vickery

51633 ■ Truman State University's Small Business Development Center
100 E Normal Ave.
Kirksville, MO 63501
Fax:(660)785-4357
Co. E-mail: sbdc@truman.edu
URL: http://sbdc.truman.edu
Contact: Glen Giboney, Dir.

SMALL BUSINESS ASSISTANCE PROGRAMS

51634 ■ Missouri Department of Economic Development–Division of Business and Community Services
301 W. High St., Rms. 720, 770
Jefferson City, MO 65102

Ph:(866)647-3633
Free: 800-523-1434
Fax:(573)751-7384
Co. E-mail: missouridevelopment@ded.mo.gov
URL: http://www.missouridevelopment.org
Contact: Ann Pardalos, Dir
Description: Provides assistance to international firms. Works to stimulate direct foreign investment in the state and develop export possibilities.

51635 ■ University of Central Missouri–Small Business and Technology Development Center
Dockery Ste. 102
Warrensburg, MO 64093
Ph:(660)543-4402
Fax:(660)543-8159
Co. E-mail: sbtdc@ucmo.edu
URL: http://www.ucmo.edu/sbtdc/
Contact: Wes Savage, Dir
Description: Provides assistance to small business owners from start-up to operation processes.

51636 ■ University of Missouri–Missouri Business Development Program
W 1026 Lafferre Hall
410 S. Sixth St.
Columbia, MO 65211
Ph:(573)882-7096
Fax:(573)882-9931
Co. E-mail: wilsonv@missouri.edu
URL: http://www.missouribusiness.net
Description: Provides assistance to company officials and local community leaders in their efforts to retain existing jobs and create additional jobs through business expansion. Provides technical assistance and information. People wanting to start small business.

SCORE OFFICES

51637 ■ Mid-Missouri SCORE
Path: www.midmoscore.org

51638 ■ Ozark-Gateway SCORE
Path: www.sos.mo.gov/business/corporations/score.html

51639 ■ SCORE Kansas City
Business Resource Center
4747 Troost Ave., Ste. 128
Kansas City, MO 64110
Ph:(816)235-6675
Fax:(816)235-6590
Co. E-mail: chapter19@scorekc.org
URL: http://www.scorekc.org
Description: Provides consulting services to individuals wishing to start a new business or who have problems with established businesses.

51640 ■ SCORE Lake Ozark
PO Box 2403
Lake Ozark, MO 65049

Ph:(573)346-5441
Co. E-mail: info@lakeozarkscore.org
URL: http://www.lakeozarkscore.org
Contact: Larry Laminger, Chm.
Description: Serves as volunteer program in which working and retired business management professionals provide free business counseling to men and women who are considering starting a small business, encountering problems with their business, or expanding their business. Offers free one-on-one counseling, online counseling and low cost workshops on a variety of business topics.

51641 ■ SCORE St. Louis
200 N Broadway, Ste. 1500
St. Louis, MO 63102
Ph:(314)539-6600
Fax:(314)539-3785
Co. E-mail: admin@stlscore.org
URL: http://www.stlscore.org
Description: Serves as volunteer program in which working and retired business management professionals provide free business counseling to men and women who are considering starting a small business, encountering problems with their business, or expanding their business. Offers free one-on-one counseling, online counseling and low cost workshops on a variety of business topics.

51642 ■ SCORE Springfield
830 E Primrose, Ste. 101
Springfield, MO 65809
Ph:(417)890-8501
Fax:(417)889-0074
Co. E-mail: office@springfieldscore.org
URL: http://www.springfieldscore.org
Contact: Allan S. Clapp, Sec.
Description: Serves as volunteer program in which working and retired business management professionals provide free business counseling to men and women who are considering starting a small business, encountering problems with their business, or expanding their business. Offers free one-on-one counseling, online counseling and low cost workshops on a variety of business topics.

51643 ■ Southeast Missouri SCORE
Path: www.sos.mo.gov/business/corporations/score.html

BETTER BUSINESS BUREAUS

51644 ■ Better Business Bureau of Eastern Missouri and Southern Illinois
15 Sunnen Dr., Ste. 107
St. Louis, MO 63143-1400
Ph:(314)645-3300
Co. E-mail: bbb@stlouisbbb.org
URL: http://stlouis.bbb.org
Contact: Michelle L. Corey, Pres./CEO

51645 ■ Better Business Bureau of Greater Kansas City
8080 Ward Pkwy., Ste. 401
Kansas City, MO 64114
Ph:(816)421-7800

Fax:(816)472-5442
Co. E-mail: info@kansascity.bbb.org
URL: http://www.kansascity.bbb.org
Contact: David Buckley, Pres.

51646 ■ Better Business Bureau of Southwest Missouri
430 S Glenstone Ave.
Springfield, MO 65802
Ph:(417)862-4222
Fax:(417)869-5544
Co. E-mail: info@southwestmissouri.bbb.org
URL: http://southwestmissouri.bbb.org
Contact: Ms. Judy R. Mills, Pres.

CHAMBERS OF COMMERCE

51647 ■ Affton Chamber of Commerce
10203 Gravois Rd.
Affton, MO 63123-4029
Ph:(314)849-6499
Fax:(314)849-6399
Co. E-mail: info@afftonchamber.com
URL: http://www.afftonchamber.com
Contact: Ms. Joan Edleson, Exec. Dir.

51648 ■ Arnold Chamber of Commerce
PO Box 1156
Arnold, MO 63010
Ph:(636)296-1910
Fax:(636)296-1910
Co. E-mail: contact@arnoldchamber.org
URL: http://www.arnoldchamber.org
Contact: Mr. Bob Gruenewald, Pres.

51649 ■ Aurora Chamber of Commerce
PO Box 257
Aurora, MO 65605-1666
Ph:(417)678-4150
Fax:(417)678-1387
Co. E-mail: auroracoc@mo-net.com
URL: http://www.auroramochamber.com

51650 ■ Ava Area Chamber of Commerce
PO Box 1103
Ava, MO 65608
Ph:(417)683-4594
Fax:(417)683-9464
Co. E-mail: director@avachamber.org
URL: http://avachamber.org
Contact: Mandy Mackey, Dir.

51651 ■ Barton County Chamber of Commerce
PO Box 577
Lamar, MO 64759
Ph:(417)682-3595
Fax:(417)682-9566
Co. E-mail: nancy@bartoncounty.com
URL: http://www.bartoncounty.com
Contact: Nancy Curless, Dir. of Member Services

51652 ■ Belton Chamber of Commerce
512 Main St.
PO Box 350
Belton, MO 64012-0350
Ph:(816)331-2420
Fax:(816)331-8736
Co. E-mail: chamber@beltonmochamber.com
URL: http://www.beltonmochamber.com/joomla/
  index.php
Contact: Renee Kerckhoff, Pres.

51653 ■ Black Chamber of Commerce of Greater Kansas City
1501 E 18th St.
Kansas City, MO 64108
Ph:(816)474-9901
Fax:(816)842-1748
URL: http://www.bcckc.org

51654 ■ Blue Springs Chamber of Commerce
1000 Main St.
Blue Springs, MO 64015
Ph:(816)229-8558

Fax:(816)229-1244
Co. E-mail: bschamberinfo@comcast.net
URL: http://www.bluespringschamber.com
Contact: Kyle Jones, Chair

51655 ■ Bolivar Area Chamber of Commerce
PO Box 202
Bolivar, MO 65613-0202
Ph:(417)326-4118
Fax:(417)777-9080
Co. E-mail: info@bolivarchamber.com
URL: http://bolivarchamber.com/index.html
Contact: Roxy Hudson, Pres.

51656 ■ Bowling Green Chamber of Commerce
PO Box 401
Bowling Green, MO 63334-0401
Ph:(573)324-3733
Fax:(573)324-0152
Co. E-mail: bgmocc@att.net
URL: http://www.bgchamber.org
Contact: Corey Sanborn, Pres.

51657 ■ Branson - Lakes Area Chamber of Commerce
269 State Hwy. 248
PO Box 1897
Branson, MO 65615-1897
Ph:(417)334-4084
Free: 800-214-3661
Fax:(417)334-4139
Co. E-mail: rsummers@bransoncvb.com
URL: http://www.explorebranson.com
Contact: Ross Summers, Pres./CEO

51658 ■ Brookfield Area Chamber of Commerce
101 S Main St.
Brookfield, MO 64628
Ph:(660)258-7255
Fax:(660)258-7255
Co. E-mail: chamber@brookfieldmochamber.com
URL: http://www.brookfieldmochamber.com
Contact: Fran Graff, Dir.

51659 ■ Buckner Chamber of Commerce
PO Box 325
Buckner, MO 64016
Ph:(816)650-5535
Co. E-mail: sibleyorchards@hotmail.com
URL: http://www.discoverynet.com/lAtajsnead/my-
  comm/chamber.html
Contact: Patrick J. Farrell, Pres.

51660 ■ Buffalo Area Chamber of Commerce
101 N Maple St.
PO Box 258
Buffalo, MO 65622
Ph:(417)345-2852
Fax:(417)345-2852
Co. E-mail: chamber@buffalococ.com
URL: http://www.buffalococ.com
Contact: Kathy Kesler, Exec. Dir.

51661 ■ California Chamber of Commerce
500 S Oak St., Ste. A
PO Box 85
California, MO 65018
Ph:(573)796-3040
Fax:(573)796-8309
Co. E-mail: chamber@calmo.com
URL: http://www.calmo.com
Contact: Ruth Ellis, Exec. Sec.

51662 ■ Camdenton Area Chamber of Commerce
PO Box 1375
Camdenton, MO 65020-1375
Ph:(573)346-2227
Free: 800-769-1004
Fax:(573)346-3496
Co. E-mail: cchamber@thelake.net
URL: http://www.camdentonchamber.com
Contact: Bruce Mitchell, Exec. Dir.

51663 ■ Cameron Chamber of Commerce
205 N Main St.
Cameron, MO 64429
Ph:(816)632-2005
Fax:(816)632-2005
Co. E-mail: office@cameronmochamber.com
URL: http://www.cameronmochamber.com/about.htm
Contact: Artis Stoebener, Exec. Dir.

51664 ■ Cape Girardeau Area Chamber of Commerce
1267 N Mt. Auburn Rd.
Cape Girardeau, MO 63701
Ph:(573)335-3312
Fax:(573)335-4686
Co. E-mail: info@capechamber.com
URL: http://www.capechamber.com
Contact: John E. Mehner, Pres./CEO

51665 ■ Carrollton Chamber of Commerce
111 N Mason
Carrollton, MO 64633
Ph:(660)542-0922
Fax:(660)542-3489
Co. E-mail: director@carrolltonareachamber.org
URL: http://carrolltonareachamber.org
Contact: Sharon Metz, Exec. Dir.

51666 ■ Carthage Chamber of Commerce
402 S Garrison Ave.
Carthage, MO 64836
Ph:(417)358-2373
Fax:(417)358-7479
Co. E-mail: info@carthagechamber.com
URL: http://www.carthagechamber.com
Contact: John Bode, Pres.

51667 ■ Cassville Area Chamber of Commerce
504 Main St.
Cassville, MO 65625-1418
Ph:(417)847-2814
Co. E-mail: cassville@mo-net.com
URL: http://www.cassville.com

51668 ■ Centralia Area Chamber of Commerce
PO Box 235
Centralia, MO 65240
Ph:(573)682-2272
Fax:(573)682-1111
Co. E-mail: ginny@midamerica.net
URL: http://www.centraliamochamber.com
Contact: Ginny Zoellers, Exec. Dir.

51669 ■ Chaffee Chamber of Commerce
State Farm Insurance
231 W Yoakum
Chaffee, MO 63740
Ph:(573)887-3691
Fax:(573)887-4049
Co. E-mail: information@chaffeechamber.com
URL: http://spicecat.com/chaffee_chamber
Contact: Pete Dooley, Pres.

51670 ■ Charleston Chamber of Commerce
110 E Commercial St.
Charleston, MO 63834
Ph:(573)683-6509
Fax:(573)683-6799
Co. E-mail: chamber@charlestonmo.org
URL: http://www.charlestonmo.org/Clubs.Orgs/COC/
  index.htm

51671 ■ Chesterfield Chamber of Commerce
101 Chesterfield Business Pkwy.
Chesterfield, MO 63005
Ph:(636)532-3399
Free: 888-242-4262
Fax:(636)532-7446
Co. E-mail: info@chesterfieldmochamber.com
URL: http://www.chesterfieldmotourism.com
Contact: Joan Schmelig, Pres.

51672 ■ Chillicothe Area Chamber of Commerce
514 Washington St.
PO Box 407
Chillicothe, MO 64601

Ph:(660)646-4050
Free: 877-C-CHILLI
Fax:(660)646-3309
Co. E-mail: chamber@chillicothemo.com
URL: http://www.chillicothemo.com
Contact: Kevin Murray, Pres.

51673 ■ Clayton Chamber of Commerce
225 S Meramec Ave., Ste. 300
Clayton, MO 63105
Ph:(314)726-3033
Fax:(314)726-0637
Co. E-mail: ccc@claytoncommerce.com
URL: http://www.claytoncommerce.com
Contact: Ellen M. Gale, Exec. Dir.

51674 ■ Clinton Area Chamber of Commerce
200 S Main
Clinton, MO 64735
Ph:(660)885-8166
Free: 800-222-5251
Fax:(660)885-8168
Co. E-mail: information@clintonmochamber.com
URL: http://www.clintonmochamber.com
Contact: Dennis Sieger, Pres.

51675 ■ Columbia Chamber of Commerce
PO Box 1016
Columbia, MO 65205-1016
Ph:(573)874-1132
Fax:(573)443-3986
Co. E-mail: admin@columbiamochamber.com
URL: http://www.columbiamochamber.com
Contact: Don Laird, Pres.

51676 ■ Concordia Chamber of Commerce
802 S Gordon St.
PO Box 143
Concordia, MO 64020
Ph:(660)463-2454
Co. E-mail: concordiachamber@centurytel.net
URL: http://www.concordiamo.com

51677 ■ Crane Area Chamber of Commerce
PO Box 287
Crane, MO 65633
Ph:(417)669-7294
Co. E-mail: cranechamber@aol.com
URL: http://www.cranemo.com
Contact: Gerald W. Coenen

51678 ■ Creve Coeur - Olivette Chamber of Commerce
677 N New Ballas, No. 214
Creve Coeur, MO 63141
Ph:(314)569-3536
Fax:(314)569-3073
Co. E-mail: info@ccochamber.com
URL: http://www.ccochamber.com
Contact: Nancy Gray, Exec. VP

51679 ■ Cuba Chamber of Commerce and Visitor Center
PO Box 405
Cuba, MO 65453
Ph:(573)885-2531
Free: 877-212-8429
Co. E-mail: cuba@misn.com
URL: http://www.cubamochamber.com/chamber
Contact: Doug Lasley, Pres.

51680 ■ Desloge Chamber of Commerce
207 N Desloge Dr.
Desloge, MO 63601-3533
Ph:(573)431-3006
Fax:(573)431-3006
Co. E-mail: deslogechamber@sbcglobal.net
URL: http://www.deslogechamber.com

51681 ■ Dexter Chamber of Commerce
PO Box 21
Dexter, MO 63841
Ph:(573)624-7458
Free: 800-332-8857
Fax:(573)624-7459
Co. E-mail: info@dexterchamber.com
URL: http://www.dexterchamber.com
Contact: Janet Coleman, Exec. Dir.

51682 ■ East Prairie Chamber of Commerce
106 S Washington
East Prairie, MO 63845
Ph:(573)649-5243
Fax:(573)649-2024
URL: http://www.eastprairiemo.net/chamber.htm
Contact: Keith Grissom, Pres.

51683 ■ El Dorado Springs Chamber of Commerce
1303 S Highway 32
El Dorado Springs, MO 64744-2302
Ph:(417)876-4154
Fax:(417)876-4154
Co. E-mail: info@eldomo-cofc.org
URL: http://www.eldomo-cofc.org
Contact: Deedee Hunter, Exec. Dir.

51684 ■ Eldon Chamber of Commerce
203 E 1st St.
Eldon, MO 65026
Ph:(573)392-3752
Fax:(573)392-0634
Co. E-mail: wayne@eldonchamber.com
URL: http://www.eldonchamber.com
Contact: Brandon Opie, Pres.

51685 ■ Ellington Chamber of Commerce
PO Box 515
Ellington, MO 63638-0515
Ph:(573)663-7997
Fax:(573)663-7873
Co. E-mail: chamber@ellingtonmo.com
URL: http://www.ellingtonmo.com
Contact: David G. Burns, Pres.

51686 ■ Elsberry Chamber of Commerce
PO Box 32
Elsberry, MO 63343
Ph:(573)898-9124
Co. E-mail: chamber.info@elsberrycofc.org
URL: http://elsberrycofc.org
Contact: Michael Short, Pres.

51687 ■ Eureka Chamber of Commerce
208 N Central, Ste. D
Eureka, MO 63025
Ph:(636)938-6062
Fax:(636)938-9983
Co. E-mail: assocdirector@eurekachamber.us
URL: http://www.eurekachamber.com
Contact: Leland S. Kropp Jr., Pres.

51688 ■ Excelsior Springs Area Chamber of Commerce
PO Box 632
461 S Thompson Ave.
Excelsior Springs, MO 64024
Ph:(816)630-6161
Co. E-mail: escoc@sbcglobal.net
URL: http://www.exspgschamber.com
Contact: Mr. Terry Smelcer, Exec. Dir.

51689 ■ Farmington Chamber of Commerce
PO Box 191
Farmington, MO 63640
Ph:(573)756-3615
Fax:(573)756-1003
Co. E-mail: ursalak@farmingtonmo.org
URL: http://www.farmingtonmo.org
Contact: Ursala Kthiri, Exec. Dir.

51690 ■ Fenton Area Chamber of Commerce
1720-F W Park Ctr.
Fenton, MO 63026
Ph:(636)717-0200
Fax:(636)717-0214
Co. E-mail: exdir@fentonmochamber.com
URL: http://www.fentonmochamber.com
Contact: Jeannie Braun, Exec. Dir.

51691 ■ Florissant Valley Chamber of Commerce
420 W Washington St.
Florissant, MO 63031
Ph:(314)831-3500

Fax:(314)831-9682
Co. E-mail: info@florissantvalleycc.com
URL: http://www.florissantvalleycc.com
Contact: Diana Weidinger, Pres.

51692 ■ Forsyth Chamber of Commerce
PO Box 777
16075 Hwy. 160
Forsyth, MO 65653
Ph:(417)546-2741
Co. E-mail: forsyth.chamber@yahoo.com
URL: http://www.forsythmissouri.net
Contact: Donna Bassett, Exec. Dir.

51693 ■ Fredericktown Chamber of Commerce
120 W Main St.
PO Box 505
Fredericktown, MO 63645
Ph:(573)783-2604
Fax:(573)783-2645
Co. E-mail: ftownchamber@sbcglobal.net
URL: http://fredericktownmissouri.net
Contact: Christina Mattingly, Exec. Dir.

51694 ■ Grandview Area Chamber of Commerce
12500 S Hwy. 71
Grandview, MO 64030
Ph:(816)761-6505
Fax:(816)763-8460
Co. E-mail: ksc@grandview.org
Contact: Kim Curtis, Pres.

51695 ■ Greater Kansas City Chamber of Commerce
2600 Commerce Tower
911 Main St.
Kansas City, MO 64105
Ph:(816)221-2424
Fax:(816)221-7440
Co. E-mail: waltz@kcchamber.com
URL: http://www.kcchamber.com
Contact: Peter S. Levi, Pres.

51696 ■ Greater Poplar Bluff Area Chamber of Commerce
1111 W Pine St.
Poplar Bluff, MO 63901
Ph:(573)785-7761
Fax:(573)785-1901
Co. E-mail: info@poplarbluffchamber.org
URL: http://www.poplarbluffchamber.org
Contact: Steve Halter, Pres.

51697 ■ Greater Warrensburg Area Chamber of Commerce
100 S Holden St.
Warrensburg, MO 64093-2331
Ph:(660)747-3168
Free: 877-OLD-DRUM
Fax:(660)429-5490
Co. E-mail: chamber@warrensburg.org
URL: http://www.warrensburg.org
Contact: Tamara Long, Exec. Dir.

51698 ■ Greater West Plains Area Chamber of Commerce
401 Jefferson Ave.
West Plains, MO 65775-2659
Ph:(417)256-4433
Fax:(417)256-8711
Co. E-mail: info@wpchamber.com
URL: http://wpchamber.com

51699 ■ Hannibal Area Chamber of Commerce
PO Box 230
Hannibal, MO 63401
Ph:(573)221-1101
Fax:(573)221-3389
Co. E-mail: info@hannibalchamber.org
URL: http://www.hannibalchamber.org
Contact: Terry R. Sampson, Exec. Dir.

51700 ■ Harrisonville Area Chamber of Commerce
2819 Cantrell Rd.
Harrisonville, MO 64701
Ph:(816)380-5271
Free: (866)380-5271
Fax:(816)884-4291
Co. E-mail: info@harrisonvillechamber.com
URL: http://www.harrisonvillechamber.com
Contact: Ann Britt, Exec. Dir.

51701 ■ Hermann Area Chamber of Commerce
312 Market St.
Hermann, MO 65041
Ph:(573)486-2313
Free: 800-932-8687
Co. E-mail: info@hermannmo.info
URL: http://www.visithermann.com
Contact: Megan Stiers, Pres.

51702 ■ Higginsville Chamber of Commerce
PO Box 164
Higginsville, MO 64037
Ph:(660)584-3030
Fax:(660)584-3033
Co. E-mail: chamber@ctcis.net
URL: http://www.higginsvillechamber.org
Contact: Dan Hawkins, Pres.

51703 ■ Holden Chamber of Commerce
100 E 2nd St.
Holden, MO 64040
Ph:(816)732-6844
Co. E-mail: info@holdenchamber.com
URL: http://www.holdenchamber.com
Contact: Jo Ann Alpert, Pres.

51704 ■ Houston Area Chamber of Commerce
PO Box 374
Houston, MO 65483
Ph:(417)967-2220
Fax:(417)967-2187
Co. E-mail: chamber004@centurytel.net
URL: http://www.houstonmochamber.com
Contact: Kim Scroggins, Exec. Dir.

51705 ■ Independence Chamber of Commerce
210 W Truman Rd.
PO Box 1077
Independence, MO 64051
Ph:(816)252-4745
Fax:(816)252-4917
Co. E-mail: info@independencechamber.org
URL: http://www.independencechamber.com
Contact: Rick Hemmingsen, Pres.

51706 ■ Jackson Chamber of Commerce
PO Box 352
Jackson, MO 63755
Ph:(573)243-8131
Free: 888-501-8827
Fax:(573)243-0725
Co. E-mail: assistant@jacksonmochamber.org
URL: http://www.jacksonmochamber.org
Contact: Brian Gerau, Exec. Dir.

51707 ■ Jefferson City Area Chamber of Commerce
PO Box 776
213 Adams St.
Jefferson City, MO 65101
Ph:(573)634-3616
Fax:(573)634-3805
Co. E-mail: info@jcchamber.org
URL: http://www.jcchamber.org
Contact: David Turner, Chm.

51708 ■ Joplin Area Chamber of Commerce
320 E 4th St.
Joplin, MO 64801
Ph:(417)624-4150
Fax:(417)624-4303
Co. E-mail: robrian@joplincc.com
URL: http://www.joplincc.com
Contact: Rob O'Brian, Pres.

51709 ■ Kahoka - Clark County Chamber of Commerce
659 Vine St.
Kahoka, MO 63445
Ph:(660)727-2179
Fax:(660)727-3601
URL: http://mochamber.com/mx/hm.asp?id=home
Contact: Tim Ayer, Pres.

51710 ■ Kearney Chamber of Commerce
PO Box 242
Kearney, MO 64060
Ph:(816)628-4229
Co. E-mail: kearneychamber@exop.net
URL: http://www.kearneychamber.org
Contact: Ms. Siouxsan Eisen, Exec. Dir.

51711 ■ Kennett Chamber of Commerce
1601 1st St.
PO Box 61
Kennett, MO 63857
Ph:(573)888-5828
Free: (866)848-5828
Fax:(573)888-9802
Co. E-mail: info@kennettmo.com
URL: http://www.kennettmo.com
Contact: Jan McElwrath, Exec. Dir.

51712 ■ Kingdom of Callaway Chamber of Commerce
409 Court St.
Fulton, MO 65251-1724
Ph:(573)642-3055
Free: 800-257-3554
Fax:(573)642-5182
Co. E-mail: nancycoc@sbcglobal.net
URL: http://www.callawaychamber.com/Callaway-Chamber
Contact: Nancy Lewis, Exec. Dir.

51713 ■ Kirksville Area Chamber of Commerce
PO Box 251
Kirksville, MO 63501-3581
Ph:(660)665-3766
Fax:(660)665-3767
Co. E-mail: kvacoc@cableone.net
URL: http://www.kirksvillechamber.com
Contact: Alisa R. Kigar, Exec. Dir.

51714 ■ Kirkwood Area Chamber of Commerce
108 W Adams
Kirkwood, MO 63122
Ph:(314)821-4161
Fax:(314)821-5229
Co. E-mail: jim@thechamber.us
URL: http://www.kirkwooddesperes.com
Contact: Jim Wright, Pres.

51715 ■ Lake of the Ozarks West Chamber of Commerce
PO Box 340
Sunrise Beach, MO 65079-0340
Ph:(573)374-5500
Free: 877-227-4086
Fax:(573)374-8576
Co. E-mail: info@lakewestchamber.com
URL: http://www.lakewestchamber.com
Contact: Mr. Michael Kenagy, Exec. Dir.

51716 ■ Lebanon Area Chamber of Commerce
PO Box 505
Lebanon, MO 65536
Ph:(417)588-3256
Fax:(417)588-3251
Co. E-mail: stephanie@lebanonmissouri.com
URL: http://www.lebanonmissouri.com
Contact: Debbie Wikowsky, Exec. Dir.

51717 ■ Lexington Area Chamber of Commerce
1029 Franklin Ave.
Lexington, MO 64067
Ph:(660)259-3082

Fax:(660)259-7776
Co. E-mail: lexcofc@iland.net
URL: http://www.historiclexington.com
Contact: Carol Baker, Exec. Dir.

51718 ■ Liberty Area Chamber of Commerce
9 S Leonard
Liberty, MO 64068
Ph:(816)781-5200
Co. E-mail: info@libertychamber.com
URL: http://www.libertychamber.com
Contact: Gayle Potter, Pres.

51719 ■ Macon Area Chamber of Commerce
1407 N Missouri St.
Macon, MO 63552
Ph:(660)385-2811
Fax:(660)385-6543
Co. E-mail: director@maconmochamber.com
URL: http://maconmochamber.com
Contact: Sharon Scott, Exec. Dir.

51720 ■ Malden Chamber of Commerce
123 W Main
Malden, MO 63863
Ph:(573)276-4519
Fax:(573)276-4925
Co. E-mail: info@maldenchamber.com
URL: http://www.maldenchamber.com
Contact: Paula Reeder, Dir.

51721 ■ Marceline Chamber of Commerce
PO Box 93
Marceline, MO 64658
Ph:(660)376-3528
Fax:(660)376-3881
Co. E-mail: goddards@cvalley.net
URL: http://www.marceline.com
Contact: Jed Frost, Pres.

51722 ■ Mark Twain Lake Chamber of Commerce
PO Box 182
Monroe City, MO 63456-0182
Ph:(573)565-2228
Co. E-mail: mtlcoc@socket.net
URL: http://www.marktwainlake.com

51723 ■ Marshall Chamber of Commerce
214 N Lafayette Ave.
Marshall, MO 65340-1700
Ph:(660)886-3324
Fax:(660)831-0349
Co. E-mail: jill@marshallchamber.com
URL: http://www.marshallchamber.com
Contact: Mr. Ken Yowell, Exec. Dir.

51724 ■ Maryland Heights Chamber of Commerce
547 Wesport Plz.
St. Louis, MO 63146-3007
Ph:(314)576-6603
Fax:(314)576-6855
Co. E-mail: kim@mhcc.com
URL: http://www.mhcc.com
Contact: Kim Braddy, Exec. Dir.

51725 ■ Maryville Chamber of Commerce
423 N Market
Maryville, MO 64468
Ph:(660)582-8643
Fax:(660)582-3071
Co. E-mail: chamber@asde.net
URL: http://www.maryvillechamber.com
Contact: Lisa Luke, Exec. Dir.

51726 ■ Mexico Area Chamber of Commerce
100 W Jackson St.
Mexico, MO 65265
Ph:(573)581-2765
Free: 800-581-2765
Fax:(573)581-6226
URL: http://www.mexico-chamber.org
Contact: George Huffman, Pres.

51727 ■ Monett Chamber of Commerce
PO Box 47
Monett, MO 65708
Ph:(417)235-7919

Fax:(417)235-4076
Co. E-mail: chamber@monett-mo.com
URL: http://www.kdbsites.com/chamber
Contact: John Bruner, Board Pres.

51728 ■ Monroe City Area Chamber of Commerce
314 S Main
Monroe City, MO 63456
Ph:(573)735-4391
URL: http://www.marktwainlake.com/monroecity/mc-chamber.html

51729 ■ Montgomery City Area Chamber of Commerce
723 N Sturgeon St.
Montgomery City, MO 63361
Ph:(573)564-2712
Free: 800-242-8829
Fax:(573)564-3802
Co. E-mail: byjones@ktis.net
URL: http://www.montgomerycity.org
Contact: Josh Beck, Dir.

51730 ■ Mound City Chamber of Commerce
PO Box 149
428 E Capitol Ave.
Jefferson City, MO 65102
Ph:(573)634-3511
Fax:(573)634-8855
Co. E-mail: kbuschmann@mochamber.com
URL: http://mochamber.com

51731 ■ Mount Vernon Chamber of Commerce
PO Box 373
Mount Vernon, MO 65712
Ph:(417)466-7654
Fax:(417)466-7654
Co. E-mail: mtvchamber@mchsi.com
URL: http://www.mtvernonchamber.com
Contact: Doris McBride, Exec. Sec.

51732 ■ Mountain Grove Chamber of Commerce
PO Box 434
Mountain Grove, MO 65711
Ph:(417)926-4135
Co. E-mail: chamber@mountaingrovechamber.com
URL: http://www.mountaingrovechamber.com
Contact: Mike Williams, Pres.

51733 ■ Nevada-Vernon County Chamber of Commerce
225 W Austin, Ste. 200
Nevada, MO 64772
Ph:(417)667-5300
Fax:(417)667-3492
Co. E-mail: chamber@nevada-mo.com
URL: http://www.nevada-mo.com
Contact: Cat McGrath-Farmer, Dir.

51734 ■ New Madrid Chamber of Commerce
PO Box 96
New Madrid, MO 63869
Ph:(573)748-5300
Free: 877-748-5300
Fax:(573)748-5402
Co. E-mail: chambernm@yahoo.com
URL: http://www.new-madrid.mo.us
Contact: Christina McWaters, Exec. Dir.

51735 ■ Nixa Area Chamber of Commerce
105 Sherman Way, Ste. 108
Nixa, MO 65714
Ph:(417)725-1545
Contact: Sharon Whitehill Gray, Pres./CEO

51736 ■ Northland Regional Chamber of Commerce
634 NW Englewood Rd.
Kansas City, MO 64118
Ph:(816)455-9911
Fax:(816)455-9933
Co. E-mail: northland@northlandchamber.com
URL: http://www.northlandchamber.com
Contact: Sheila Tracy, Pres.

51737 ■ Northwest Chamber of Commerce
11965 St. Charles Rock Rd., Ste. 203
Bridgeton, MO 63044
Ph:(314)291-2131
Fax:(314)291-2153
Co. E-mail: info@nwcommchamber.org
URL: http://www.northwestchamber.com/index.php
Contact: Pat Watson, Sec.

51738 ■ Oak Grove Chamber of Commerce
103 SE 12th St.
Oak Grove, MO 64075
Ph:(816)690-4147
Fax:(816)690-4147
Co. E-mail: oakgrovechamber@yahoo.com
URL: http://ogchamber.org
Contact: Cindy Panza, Exec. Dir.

51739 ■ Odessa Chamber of Commerce
309A Park Ln.
Odessa, MO 64076
Ph:(816)633-4044
Fax:(816)633-4044
URL: http://www.odessamochamber.com
Contact: Doug Turnbough, Pres.

51740 ■ O'Fallon Chamber of Commerce
1299 Bryan Rd.
O'Fallon, MO 63366
Ph:(636)240-1818
Fax:(309)402-7131
Co. E-mail: info@ofallonchamber.org
URL: http://www.ofallonchamber.org
Contact: Rose Mack, Pres./CEO

51741 ■ Owensville Chamber of Commerce
PO Box 77
Owensville, MO 65066
Ph:(573)437-4270
Co. E-mail: office@owensvillemissouri.com
URL: http://www.owensvillemissouri.com/chamber.html
Contact: Mr. Robert Niebruegge, Exec. Dir.

51742 ■ Ozark Chamber of Commerce
PO Box 1450
Ozark, MO 65721
Ph:(417)581-6139
Fax:(417)581-0639
Co. E-mail: ozarkchamber@aol.com
URL: http://www.ozarkchamber.com
Contact: Chris Stone, Exec. Dir.

51743 ■ Pacific Area Chamber of Commerce
333 Chamber Dr.
Pacific, MO 63069
Ph:(636)271-6639
Fax:(636)257-2109
Co. E-mail: a.baldwin@bank-star.com
URL: http://www.pacificchamber.com
Contact: Al Baldwin, Pres.

51744 ■ Paris Area Chamber of Commerce
208 N Main St.
Paris, MO 65275-1397
Ph:(660)327-4450
Fax:(660)327-4280
Co. E-mail: chamber@parismo.net
URL: http://www.parismo.net
Contact: Vanessa Forrest, Exec. Dir.

51745 ■ Park Hills Chamber of Commerce
5 Municipal Dr.
Park Hills, MO 63601-2064
Ph:(573)431-1051
Fax:(573)431-2327
Co. E-mail: phlcoc@sbcglobal.net
URL: http://phlcoc.brick.net
Contact: Mrs. Tamara Burns, Exec. Dir.

51746 ■ Perryville Chamber of Commerce
2 W St. Maries St.
Perryville, MO 63775
Ph:(573)547-6062
Fax:(573)547-6071
Co. E-mail: perryvillemo@sbcglobal.net
URL: http://www.perryvillemo.com
Contact: Melissa Hemmann, Exec. Dir.

51747 ■ Piedmont Area Chamber of Commerce
PO Box 101
Piedmont, MO 63957
Ph:(573)223-4046
Co. E-mail: contact@piedmontchamber.com
URL: http://www.piedmontchamber.com
Contact: Robert Gayle, Pres.

51748 ■ Platte City Chamber of Commerce
PO Box 650
Platte City, MO 64079
Ph:(816)858-5270
Co. E-mail: chamber@plattecitymo.com
URL: http://www.plattecitymo.com
Contact: Karen E. Wagoner, Exec. Dir.

51749 ■ Plattsburg Chamber of Commerce
101 S Main
Plattsburg, MO 64477
Ph:(816)539-2649
Fax:(816)539-3539
Co. E-mail: chamber@plattsburgmo.com
URL: http://www.plattsburgmo.com/chamber/index.htm
Contact: Tonya Sloan, Pres.

51750 ■ Raymore Chamber of Commerce
1907 W Foxwood Dr.
Raymore, MO 64083
Ph:(816)322-0599
Fax:(816)322-7127
Co. E-mail: info@raymorechamber.com
URL: http://www.raymorechamber.com
Contact: Cherie Turney, Office Mgr.

51751 ■ Raytown Area Chamber of Commerce
5909 Raytown Trafficway
Raytown, MO 64133-3860
Ph:(816)353-8500
Fax:(816)353-8525
Co. E-mail: staff@raytownchamber.com
URL: http://www.raytownchamber.com
Contact: Vicki A. Turnbow, Pres.

51752 ■ Republic Area Chamber of Commerce
145 W Highway 174
Republic, MO 65738
Ph:(417)732-5200
Fax:(417)732-2851
Co. E-mail: rchamber@televar.com
URL: http://www.republicchamber.com
Contact: Brad Weaver, Chm.

51753 ■ Richmond Chamber of Commerce
104 W North Main St.
Richmond, MO 64085
Ph:(816)776-6916
Fax:(816)776-6917
Co. E-mail: cofcommerce@mchsi.com
URL: http://www.richmondchamber.org
Contact: Ellen Franklin, Exec. Dir.

51754 ■ Ripley County Chamber of Commerce
101 Washington St.
Doniphan, MO 63935
Ph:(573)996-2212
Fax:(573)351-1441
Co. E-mail: rcchamber@windstream.net
URL: http://www.ripleycountymissouri.org/Ripley-CountyChamberHome.php
Contact: Ms. Tracey Holden, Exec. Dir.

51755 ■ Rolla Area Chamber of Commerce
1301 Kingshighway St.
Rolla, MO 65401
Ph:(573)364-3577
Free: 888-809-3817
Co. E-mail: stevie@rollachamber.org
URL: http://rollachamber.org
Contact: Stevie Kearse, Exec. Dir.

51756 ■ St. Charles Chamber of Commerce
2201 1st Capitol Dr.
St. Charles, MO 63301-5805
Ph:(636)946-0633

Fax:(636)946-0301
Co. E-mail: info@stcharleschamber.org
URL: http://www.stcharleschamber.org/home.php3
Contact: Claire Felder

51757 ■ St. Clair Area Chamber of Commerce
920F St. Clair Plaza Dr.
St. Clair, MO 63077
Ph:(636)629-1889
Fax:(636)629-5510
Co. E-mail: chamber@stclairmo.com
URL: http://www.stclairmo.com
Contact: Terry Triphahn, Exec. Dir.

51758 ■ Ste. Genevieve Chamber of Commerce
251 Market St.
Ste. Genevieve, MO 63670
Ph:(573)883-3686
Fax:(573)883-7092
Co. E-mail: stegenchamber@sbcgobal.net
URL: http://www.saintegenevieve.org
Contact: Ron Armbruster, Pres.

51759 ■ St. James Chamber of Commerce
PO Box 358
St. James, MO 65559
Ph:(573)265-6649
Co. E-mail: stjameschamber@centurytel.net
URL: http://www.stjamesmissouri.org
Contact: Renee Ridling, Pres.

51760 ■ St. Joseph Area Chamber of Commerce
3003 Frederick Ave.
St. Joseph, MO 64506
Ph:(816)232-4461
Free: 800-748-7856
Fax:(816)364-4873
Co. E-mail: chamber@saintjoseph.com
URL: http://www.saintjoseph.com
Contact: Ted Allison, Pres./CEO

51761 ■ St. Peters Chamber of Commerce
1236 Jungermann Rd., Ste. C
St. Peters, MO 63376
Ph:(636)447-3336
Fax:(636)447-9575
Co. E-mail: info@stpeterschamber.com
URL: http://www.stpeterschamber.com/home/index.
   html
Contact: Ed Weeks, Pres./CEO

51762 ■ Salem Area Chamber of Commerce
200 S Main St.
Salem, MO 65560
Ph:(573)729-6900
Fax:(573)729-6741
Co. E-mail: chamber@salemmo.com
URL: http://www.salemmo.com/chamber/AboutCh-
   amber.asp
Contact: Patty Shults, Dir.

51763 ■ Savannah Area Chamber of Commerce
PO Box 101
Savannah, MO 64485
Ph:(816)324-3976
Fax:(816)324-5728
Co. E-mail: sacc@savannahmochamber.com
URL: http://www.savannahmochamber.com
Contact: Christy Sipes, Coor.

51764 ■ Sedalia Area Chamber of Commerce
600 E 3rd St.
Sedalia, MO 65301-4499
Ph:(660)826-2222
Fax:(660)826-2223
Co. E-mail: chamber@visitsedaliamo.com
URL: http://www.sedaliachamber.com
Contact: Deborah L. Biermann, Exec. VP

51765 ■ Sikeston Area Chamber of Commerce
One Industrial Dr.
Sikeston, MO 63801-5216
Ph:(573)471-2498

Fax:(573)471-2499
Co. E-mail: chamber@sikeston.net
URL: http://www.sikeston.net
Contact: Missy Marshall, Exec. Dir.

51766 ■ South Kansas City Chamber of Commerce
5908 E Bannister Rd.
Kansas City, MO 64134-1141
Ph:(816)761-7660
Fax:(816)761-7340
Co. E-mail: vwolgast@southkcchamber.com
URL: http://www.southkcchamber.com
Contact: Vickie Wolgast, Exec. Dir.

51767 ■ Springfield Area Chamber of Commerce
202 S John Q. Hammons Pkwy.
Springfield, MO 65806
Ph:(417)862-5567
Fax:(417)862-1611
Co. E-mail: jim@springfieldchamber.com
URL: http://www.springfieldchamber.com
Contact: Jim Anderson, Pres.

51768 ■ Steelville Chamber of Commerce
PO Box 956
Steelville, MO 65565
Ph:(573)775-5533
Co. E-mail: chamber@misn.com
URL: http://chamberofcommerce.steelville.com
Contact: Liz Bennett, Pres.

51769 ■ Stockton Area Chamber of Commerce
PO Box 410
Stockton, MO 65785
Ph:(417)276-5213
Co. E-mail: stocktonchamber@windstream.net
URL: http://www.stocktonmochamber.com
Contact: Charlotte Haden, Exec. Dir.

51770 ■ Sullivan Area Chamber of Commerce
PO Box 536
Sullivan, MO 63080-0536
Ph:(573)468-3314
Fax:(573)860-2313
Co. E-mail: chamber@sullivanmo.com
URL: http://www.sullivanmo.com
Contact: Debbe Campbell, Exec. Dir.

51771 ■ Summersville Chamber of Commerce
PO Box 251
Summersville, MO 65571
Ph:(417)932-4299
Fax:(417)932-4358
URL: http://mochamber.com/mx/hm.asp?id=home
Contact: Ronald Hayes, Pres.

51772 ■ Table Rock Lake - Kimberling City Area Chamber of Commerce
14226 State Hwy. 13
PO Box 495
Kimberling City, MO 65686
Ph:(417)739-2564
Free: 800-595-0393
Fax:(417)739-2580
Co. E-mail: trlchamber@visittablerocklake.com
URL: http://www.visittablerocklake.org
Contact: Ms. Wyli Barnes, Pres./CEO

51773 ■ Tipton Chamber of Commerce
PO Box 307
Tipton, MO 65081-0307
Ph:(660)433-6377
Co. E-mail: chamber@tiptonmo.com
URL: http://www.tiptonmo.com
Contact: Mark Koechner, Pres.

51774 ■ Trenton Area Chamber of Commerce
617 Main St.
Trenton, MO 64683
Ph:(660)359-4324
Fax:(660)359-4606
Co. E-mail: trentonchamber@grundyec.net
URL: http://www.trentonmochamber.com
Contact: Terri Henderson, Pres.

51775 ■ Troy Area Chamber of Commerce
543 E Cherry St.
Troy, MO 63379
Ph:(636)462-8769
Fax:(636)528-3731
Co. E-mail: info@troyonthemove.com
URL: http://www.troyonthemove.com
Contact: Kerry M. Klump, Exec. Dir.

51776 ■ Union Chamber of Commerce
PO Box 168
Union, MO 63084
Ph:(636)583-8979
Fax:(636)583-4001
Co. E-mail: tammy@unionmochamber.org
URL: http://www.unionmochamber.org/unionchamber
Contact: Tammy Stowe, Exec. Dir.

51777 ■ Van Buren Area Chamber of Commerce
PO Box 693
Van Buren, MO 63965
Ph:(573)323-4117
Co. E-mail: chamber@seevanburen.com
URL: http://www.seevanburen.com
Contact: Wanda Cumins

51778 ■ Versailles Area Chamber of Commerce
PO Box 256
Versailles, MO 65084
Ph:(573)378-4401
Fax:(573)378-2499
Co. E-mail: info@versailleschamber.com
URL: http://versailleschamber.com
Contact: Mary Henderson, Sec.

51779 ■ Warrenton Area Chamber of Commerce
111 Steinhagen
Warrenton, MO 63383
Ph:(636)456-2530
Fax:(636)456-2329
Co. E-mail: info@warrentoncoc.com
URL: http://warrentoncoc.com
Contact: Shelley Rowe, Pres.

51780 ■ Warsaw Area Chamber of Commerce
PO Box 264
Warsaw, MO 65355
Ph:(660)438-5922
Free: 800-WARSAW-4
Co. E-mail: warsawcc@earthlink.net
URL: http://warsawmo.org

51781 ■ Washington Area Chamber of Commerce
323 W Main St.
Washington, MO 63090
Ph:(636)239-2715
Free: 888-7-WASHMO
Fax:(636)239-1381
Co. E-mail: wluther@washmo.org
URL: http://www.washmo.org/cgi-bin/template/
   chamber/chamber.htm
Contact: Mark Wessels, Pres./CEO

51782 ■ Waynesville-St. Robert Area Chamber of Commerce
137 St. Robert Blvd.
St. Robert, MO 65584
Ph:(573)336-5121
Fax:(573)336-5472
Co. E-mail: chamber@wsrchamber.com
URL: http://www.waynesville-strobertchamber.com
Contact: Steve Lynch, Pres.

51783 ■ Webb City Area Chamber of Commerce
555 S Main St.
PO Box 287
Webb City, MO 64870
Ph:(417)673-1154
Fax:(417)673-2856
Co. E-mail: info@webbcitychamber.com
URL: http://www.webbcitychamber.com
Contact: Dixie Meredith, Exec. Dir.

51784 ■ **Webster Groves-Shrewsbury Area Chamber of Commerce**
357 Marshall Ave., Ste. 3
Webster Groves, MO 63119
Ph:(314)962-4142
Fax:(314)962-9398
Co. E-mail: chamberinfo@go-webster.com
URL: http://www.webstershrewsburychamber.com
Contact: Diane Lamboley, Pres./CEO

51785 ■ **Wentzville Chamber of Commerce**
PO Box 11
Wentzville, MO 63385
Ph:(636)327-6914
Co. E-mail: info@wentzvillechamber.com
URL: http://www.wentzvillechamber.com
Contact: Erin Williams, Exec. Dir.

51786 ■ **West St. Louis County Chamber of Commerce**
14811 Manchester Rd., Ste. 100
Ballwin, MO 63011
Ph:(636)230-9900
Fax:(636)230-9912
Co. E-mail: info@westcountychamber.com
URL: http://www.westcountychamber.com
Contact: Lori Kelling, Exec. Dir.

51787 ■ **Windsor Area Chamber of Commerce**
102 N Main
Windsor, MO 65360
Ph:(660)647-2318
Co. E-mail: windsorm@iland.net
URL: http://www.windsormo.org
Contact: Terri Kline, Pres.

51788 ■ **Wright City Area Chamber of Commerce**
PO Box 444
Wright City, MO 63390
Ph:(636)745-7855
Co. E-mail: wcchamber@wrightcitychamber.com
URL: http://www.wrightcitychamber.com
Contact: Phil Cartwright, Pres.

MINORITY BUSINESS ASSISTANCE PROGRAMS

51789 ■ **St. Louis Minority Business Council**
308 N 21st St., Ste. 700
St. Louis, MO 63103
Ph:(314)241-1143
Fax:(314)241-1073
Co. E-mail: info@simbc
URL: http://www.slmbc.org
Contact: James Webb, Pres

Description: Provides ongoing growth opportunities, financial support, and training and education for its corporate members and for Minority Business Enterprises

51790 ■ **University of Missouri—Kansas City–Small Business and Technology Development Center**
4747 Troost, Rm. 104A
Kansas City, MO 64110
Ph:(816)235-6063
Fax:(816)235-2947
Co. E-mail: umkcsbdc@umkc.edu
URL: http://sbtdc.umkc.edu
Contact: Carmen DeHart, Dir.

FINANCING AND LOAN PROGRAMS

51791 ■ **A.G. Edwards & Sons**
1 N. Jefferson
Saint Louis, MO 63103
Ph:(314)955-3000
Fax:(314)955-2890
URL: http://www.agedwards.com
Contact: 866224-5708 Chris Redmond, Managing Director

Investment Policies: Fund of funds. **Industry Preferences:** Agriculture, forestry, and fishing. **Geographic Preferences:** Missouri. **Principal Exhibits:** 866224-5708

51792 ■ **Bankers Capital Corporation**
3100 Gillham Rd.
Kansas City, MO 64109
Ph:(816)531-1600
Fax:(816)531-1334
Contact: Raymond E. Glasnapp, President

Preferred Investment Size: $100,000 minimum. **Investment Types:** Leveraged buyout. **Industry Preferences:** Semiconductors and other electronics, consumer related, industrial and energy. **Geographic Preferences:** Midwest.

51793 ■ **Capital for Business, Inc.**
11 S. Meramac St., Ste. 1430
Clayton, MO 63105
Ph:(314)746-7427
Fax:(314)746-8739
Co. E-mail: info@capitalforbusiness.com
URL: http://www.capitalforbusiness.com
Contact: Stephen B. Broun, Managing Partner
E-mail: steve.broun@capitalforbusiness.com

Preferred Investment Size: $500,000 to $5,000,000. **Investment Types:** Leveraged buyout, management buyouts, mezzanine, expansion, recapitalization, acquisition, and later stage. **Industry Preferences:** Internet specific, medical and health, consumer related, semiconductors and other electronics, computer hardware, communications and media. **Geographic Preferences:** Midwest. **Principal Exhibits:**

51794 ■ **Crown Capital Corporation**
12935 N. Forty Dr., Ste. 212
Saint Louis, MO 63141
Ph:(314)590-5100
Fax:(314)590-5105
URL: http://www.crown-cap.com
Contact: R. William Breece, President and Chief Executive Officer
E-mail: rbreece@crown-cap.com

Preferred Investment Size: $1,000,000 minimum. **Investment Types:** Management buyouts, acquisition, control block purchases, distressed debt, expansion, later stage, leveraged buyout, private placement, and recapitalizations. **Industry Preferences:** Communications, computer software, Internet specific, semiconductors and other electronics, medical and health, consumer related, industrial and energy, financial services, business service, agriculture, forestry and fishing, and other. **Geographic Preferences:** U.S. **Principal Exhibits:**

51795 ■ **InvestAmerica Venture Group, Inc. (Kansas City)**
Commerce Tower
911 Main St., Ste. 2424
Kansas City, MO 64105
Ph:(816)842-0114
Fax:(816)471-7339
URL: http://www.investamericaventuregroup.com
Contact: Kevin F. Mullane, Senior Vice President

Preferred Investment Size: $1,000,000 to $2,000,000. **Investment Types:** First and second stage, leveraged buyout, and special situation. **Industry Preferences:** Other products, industrial and energy, Internet specific, communications and media, consumer related, computer software, and services, semiconductors and other electronics, computer hardware, biotechnology, medical and health. **Geographic Preferences:** U.S. **Principal Exhibits:**

51796 ■ **Kansas City Equity Partners**
233 W. 47th St.
Kansas City, MO 64112
Ph:(816)960-1771
Fax:(816)960-1777
Co. E-mail: info@kcep.com
URL: http://www.kcep.com
Contact: Abel Mojica, Principal

Preferred Investment Size: $2,000,000 to $6,000,000. **Investment Types:** First and second stage, expansion, leveraged buyout, and management buyouts. **Industry Preferences:** Internet specific, communications and media, consumer related, industrial and energy, computer software and services, semiconductors and other electronics. **Geographic Preferences:** Mid Atlantic, Midwest, Northeast, Rocky Mountains, and West Coast. **Principal Exhibits:**

51797 ■ **RiverVest Venture Partners**
7733 Forsyth Blvd., Ste. 1650
Saint Louis, MO 63150
Ph:(314)726-6700
Fax:(314)726-6715
Co. E-mail: info@rivervest.com
URL: http://www.rivervest.com
Contact: Thomas C. Melzer, Managing Director
E-mail: tmelzer@rivervest.com

Preferred Investment Size: $500,000 to $6,000,000. **Investment Types:** Start-up, seed, early and later stage, and expansion. **Industry Preferences:** Biotechnology, medical and health. **Geographic Preferences:** U.S. **Principal Exhibits:**

PROCUREMENT ASSISTANCE PROGRAMS

51798 ■ **Heartland Procurement Technical Assistance Center–Institute for Entrepreneurship and Innovation**
University of Missouri - Kansas City
4747 Troost Bldg., Rm. 106
Kansas City, MO 64110
Ph:(816)235-2891
Fax:(816)235-2947
Co. E-mail: longdew@umkc.edu
URL: http://www.mssu.edu/heartlandptac/
Contact: Dewayne Long, Dir.

Description: Assists viable businesses located in Southwest Missouri and the State of Kansas with potential market expansion through procurement opportunities with the government.

51799 ■ **Heartland Procurement Technical Assistance Center–Missouri Southern State University–Central Office (Plast)**
Plaster Hall, Rm. 111
3950 Newman Rd.
Joplin, MO 64801-1512
Ph:(417)625-9538
Fax:(417)625-3090
Co. E-mail: heartlandptac@mssu.edu
URL: http://www.heartlandptac.org
Contact: Terri Bennett, Program Mgr.
E-mail: Bennett-T@mssu.edu

Description: Mission is to assist viable businesses located in Southwest Missouri and the State of Kansas with potential market expansion through procurement opportunities with the government.

51800 ■ **Missouri Procurement Technical Assistance Center–Central Region PTAC–University of Missouri-Columbia (W1026)**
W1026 Lafferre Hall
Columbia, MO 65211
Ph:(573)882-9398
Fax:(573)882-9931
Co. E-mail: stubyb@missouri.edu
URL: http://www.missouribusiness.net
Contact: Bill Stuby, Dir.
E-mail: stubyb@missouri.edu

Description: Assists businesses including small, disadvantaged and women owned firms in obtaining federal, state and local government contracts.

51801 ■ Missouri Procurement Technical Assistance Center–Eastern Region PTAC–University of Missouri at St. Louis (100 N)
100 N Tucker, Ste. 530
St. Louis, MO 63101
Ph:(314)621-7280
Fax:(314)621-9871
Co. E-mail: frankjo@missouri.edu
URL: http://www.missouribusiness.net
Contact: Joe Frank, Dir.
E-mail: fyker@missouri.edu
Description: Assists businesses including small, disadvantaged and women owned firms in obtaining federal, state and local government contracts.

51802 ■ Missouri Procurement Technical Assistance Center–Mid-South Region PTAC–Howell County Extension Center (217 S)–University of Missouri (Aid Ave.)
217 S Aid Ave.
West Plains, MO 65775
Ph:(417)256-2391
Fax:(417)256-8569
Co. E-mail: mushrushw@missouri.edu
URL: http://www.missouribusiness.net
Contact: Willis Mushrush, Specialist
E-mail: mushrushw@missouri.edu
Description: Assists businesses including small, disadvantaged and women owned firms in obtaining federal, state and local government contracts.

51803 ■ Missouri Procurement Technical Assistance Center–South Central Region PTAC–Center for Entrepreneurship and Outreach (203 C)
203 Centennial Hall
300 W 12th St.
Rolla, MO 65409-1110
Ph:(573)341-4562
Fax:(573)341-6579
Co. E-mail: bwhite@mst.edu
URL: http://ecodevo.mst.edu/
Contact: Barry White
E-mail: bwhite@umr.edu
Description: Assists businesses including small, disadvantaged and women owned firms in obtaining federal, state and local government contracts. Formerly University of Missouri-Rolla.

51804 ■ Missouri Procurement Technical Assistance Center–Western Region PTAC–University of Missouri, Kansas City (4747)
4747 Troost Bldg., Rm. 105
Kansas City, MO 64110
Ph:(816)235-2891
Fax:(816)235-2947
Co. E-mail: leonardd@umkc.edu
URL: http://www.missouribusiness.net/ptac
Contact: Donna Leonard, Dir
Description: Connects small business owners with government agencies in search of products and services at competitive prices.

51805 ■ Missouri Southern State University–Heartland Procurement Technical Assistance Center–Institute for Procurement Assistance (Plast)
Plaster Hall, Rm. 111
3950 Newman Rd.
Joplin, MO 64801-1512
Ph:(417)625-9538
Fax:(417)625-3090
Co. E-mail: heartlandptac@mssu.edu
URL: http://www.heartlandptac.org
Contact: Terrie Bennett, Program Mgr.
Description: Covers activities for Kansas.

51806 ■ St. Louis County Economic Council
121 S Meramec Ave., Ste. 900
St. Louis, MO 63105
Ph:(314)615-7663
Fax:(314)615-7666
Co. E-mail: info@SLCEC.com
URL: http://www.slcec.com
Contact: Denny Coleman, Pres & CEO

INCUBATORS/RESEARCH AND TECHNOLOGY PARKS

51807 ■ Arts Incubator of Kansas City
115 W. 18th St.
Kansas City, MO 64108
Ph:(816)421-2292
Fax:(816)421-2293
Co. E-mail: info@artsincubatorkc.org
URL: http://artsincubatorkc.org/
Description: A nonprofit organization dedicated to working with emerging artists in the development of their careers by providing affordable, quality studio space in the Crossroads Arts District, a community experiencing extraordinary growth and national recognition as one of the top arts communities in the nation, in addition to providing business workshops and consulting.

51808 ■ Growth Opportunity Connection–Center for Business Innovation
4747 Troost Ave.
Kansas City, MO 64110
Ph:(816)235-6146
Fax:(816)235-6586
Co. E-mail: info@goconnection.org
URL: http://www.goconnection.org

51809 ■ Hispanic Economic Development Corporation
2130 Jefferson St.
Kansas City, MO 64108
Ph:(816)221-3442
Fax:(816)221-6458
Co. E-mail: hedc@kchedc.org
URL: http://www.kchedc.org
Contact: Bernardo Ramirez, Exec. Dir.
Description: not-for-profit community development corporation in the State of Missouri. Founded for the purpose of developing and implementing economic development initiatives that would positively contribute to the quality of life for Latinos in Kansas City, HEDC utilizes its designation as a CDC to access various resources and tools that allow the organization to serve as a catalyst for change within the Latino community.

51810 ■ Joseph Newman Innovation Center
407 Pennsylvania
Joplin, MO 64801
Ph:(417)624-4150
Co. E-mail: steve@joplincc.com
URL: http://www.newmaninnovationcenter.com/
Description: An economic development tool designed to accelerate the growth and success of entrepreneurial companies through an array of business support resources and services. The center's main goal is to produce successful firms that will leave the program financially viable and freestanding.

51811 ■ Life Science Business Incubator at Monsanto Place
1601 S Providence Rd.
University of Missouri
Missouri, MO 65211-3460
Ph:(573)884-0496
Fax:(573)884-3600
Co. E-mail: info@MUincubator.com
URL: http://muincubator.com/index.html
Contact: Jake Halliday, Pres. & CEO
Description: A small business incubator promoting comprehensive economic development strategy for mid-Missouri by leveraging research and innovation at the University of Missouri-Columbia in order to attract additional life science enterprises to the region and to create new life science ventures around university technologies.

51812 ■ Missouri Enterprise
900 Innovation Dr.
Rolla, MO 65401
Ph:(573)341-0117
Free: 800-956-2682
Fax:(573)341-0135
URL: http://www.missourienterprise.org
Contact: Mary Dean, Pres
Description: Offers business consulting services to mid-sized manufacturing companies.

51813 ■ Nidus Center for Scientific Enterprise
1005 N Warson rd., Ste. 201
St. Louis, MO 63132
Ph:(314)812-8003
Fax:(314)812-8080
Co. E-mail: susan@niduspartners.com
URL: http://www.niduscenter.com/
Description: An agriculture and energy incubator serving entrepreneur clients who are refining and preparing new technologies for market.

51814 ■ St. Charles County Economic Development Center
5988 Mid Rivers Mall Dr.
St Charles, MO 63304-7195
Ph:(636)441-6880
Free: 877-441-6880
Fax:(636)441-6881
Co. E-mail: info@edcscc.com
URL: http://www.edcscc.com
Description: A small business incubator working in partnership with local governments, community and business leaders, and other regional organizations to offer business financing programs, job creation, and business recruitment and retention.

51815 ■ St. Louis Enterprise Centers
121 S Meramec, Ste. 900
St. Louis, MO 63105
Ph:(314)615-7663
Fax:(314)615-7666
Co. E-mail: Incubators@SLCEC.com
URL: http://www.slcec.com/st-louis-enterprise-centers.html
Description: A small business incubator providing new and growing small businesses with affordable business space, shared support services, access to expert mentors, and valuable networking opportunities. Maintains five state-of-the-art enterprise centers.

51816 ■ St. Louis University–Office of Research Services
Fusz Memorial Hall, 2nd Fl.
3700 W Pine Mall
St. Louis, MO 63108-3306
Ph:(314)977-2241
Fax:(314)977-2026
Co. E-mail: lischwst@slu.ed
URL: http://www.slu.edu/x24192.xml
Contact: Sheila T. Lischwe PhD, Dir.
E-mail: lischwst@slu.ed
Scope: Administers and coordinates research conducted at the University.

51817 ■ Students In Free Enterprise
1959 Kerr St.
900 N. Benton Ave.
Springfield, MO 65803
Ph:(417)575-3509
Free: 800-922-2274
Fax:(417)873-7529
Co. E-mail: dpatterson@sife.org
URL: http://www.sife.org
Description: A global non-profit organization active on more than 1,800 college campuses in more than 43 countries and territories consisting of student teams who develop projects to help create economic opportunity by teaching concepts related to free market economics, business ethics, entrepreneurship, and personal finance and success skills.

51818 ■ Technology Entrepreneur Center
210 N. Tucker Blvd., Ste. 600
St. Louis, MO 63101
Ph:(314)436-3500
Fax:(314)333-0409
Co. E-mail: info@tecstl.org
URL: http://www.tecstl.org/
Description: A small business incubator assisting technology start-up companies in St. Louis to increase their likelihood of success through access to highly qualified mentors, assistance with business planning and strategies, and office services.

51819 ■ The Thomas Hill Enterprise Center
PO Box 276
Macon, MO 63552
Ph:(660)385-6550
URL: http://www.e-center.org
Description: The Center describes itself as an internet/intranet incubator that offers entrepreneurs skills training, government forms, and other services.

51820 ■ University of Central Missouri–Office of Sponsored Programs
Ward Edward 1800
Warrensburg, MO 64093
Ph:(660)543-4264
Fax:(660)543-4778
Co. E-mail: steel@ucmo.edu
URL: http://www.ucmo.edu/osp
Contact: Victoria Steel, Interim Dir.
E-mail: steel@ucmo.edu
Scope: Establishes, administers, and coordinates programs that guide University of Central Missouri's research, scholarly activity, and creative endeavors. **Publications:** Central Research (annually); Newsletter (quarterly). **Educational Activities:** Two workshops, per academic year for faculty and students.

51821 ■ University of Missouri–Missouri Research Park
309 University Hall
Columbia, MO 65211
Ph:(573)882-6756
Fax:(636)777-7881
Co. E-mail: williamsgreg@umsystem.edu
URL: http://www.um-mrp.org
Contact: Greg Williams, Dir.
E-mail: williamsgreg@umsystem.edu
Scope: A 750-acre research park designed to be a link between academia and industry as a center for research and development in such fields as advanced manufacturing, medical technology, and agriculture.

51822 ■ University of Missouri–Office of Research Administration
205 Jesse Hall
Columbia, MO 65211
Ph:(573)882-9500
Fax:(573)884-8371
Co. E-mail: duncanrv@missouri.edu
URL: http://www.research.missouri.edu
Contact: Dr. Robert Duncan, Vice Chancellor for Res.
E-mail: duncanrv@missouri.edu
Scope: Coordinates and administers research, especially extramurally sponsored research, performed in various departments and research units of the University, including Dalton Cardiovascular Research Center, Missouri Resource Assessment Partnership, and Research Reactor Facility. **Publications:** Illumination.

51823 ■ University of Missouri—Kansas City–Office of Research Services
5211 Rockhill Rd.
Kansas City, MO 64110-2499
Ph:(816)235-5600
Fax:(816)235-6532
Co. E-mail: hannounm@umkc.edu
URL: http://www.umkc.edu/ors
Contact: Maureen Hannoun, Dir.
E-mail: hannounm@umkc.edu
Scope: Serves as information and coordinating center for research activities of Kansas City campus of the University. **Publications:** Research Notes (monthly).

51824 ■ University of Missouri—St. Louis–Office of Research Administration
341 Woods Hall
1 University Blvd.
St. Louis, MO 63121
Ph:(314)516-5899
Fax:(314)516-6759
Co. E-mail: arshadi@umsl.edu
URL: http://www.umsl.edu/services/ora
Contact: Nasser Arshadi PhD, Vice Provost, Res.
E-mail: arshadi@umsl.edu
Scope: Responsible for formulation and implementation of research policies at the University of Missouri—St. Louis.

51825 ■ Washington University in St. Louis–Office of Technology Management
660 S Euclid Ave., CB 8013
St. Louis, MO 63110
Ph:(314)747-0920
Fax:(314)362-5872
Co. E-mail: bjcastanho@wustl.edu
URL: http://research.wustl.edu/Offices_Committees/otm/Pages/OTM.aspx
Contact: Bradley Castanho PhD, Dir.
E-mail: bjcastanho@wustl.edu
Scope: Transfers technology from the University to business and industry in the area of biotechnology.

EDUCATIONAL PROGRAMS

51826 ■ Jefferson College–Extended Learning
1000 Viking Dr.
Hillsboro, MO 63050
Ph:(636)789-3000
Fax:(636)789-4012
URL: http://www.jeffco.edu
Description: Offers a program/classes in small business/small business management.

51827 ■ St. Louis Community College–Institute for Continuing Education
300 S Broadway
St. Louis, MO 63102
Ph:(314)539-5000
Fax:(314)539-5170
URL: http://www.stlcc.cc.mo.us
Description: Small Business Program offers courses designed for small business owners.

LEGISLATIVE ASSISTANCE

51828 ■ Missouri Department of Economic Development–Economic Development Office
301 W. High St.
PO Box 1157
Jefferson City, MO 65102
Ph:(573)751-4962
Free: 800-523-1434
Fax:(573)526-7700
Co. E-mail: ecodev@ded.mo.gov
URL: http://www.ded.mo.gov
Description: Works to identify and solve problems specific to small business.

PUBLICATIONS

51829 ■ How to Form Your Own Missouri Corporation Before the Inc. Dries!: A Step by Step Guide, With Forms
P. Gaines Publishing Company
333 S. Taylor Ave.
PO Box 2253
Oak Park, IL 60302

Ph:(708)524-9033
Fax:(708)524-9038
Ed: Phillip Williams. **Released:** 1992. **Price:** $19.95 (paper). **Description:** Volume 5 of the Small Business Incorporation series. Explains the advantages and disadvantages of incorporation and shows, step-by-step, how the small business owners can incorporate at low cost. Covers Missouri profit and nonprofit corporations, Missouri professional service corporations, subchapter S corporations, and Delaware corporations. Includes forms necessary for incorporation.

51830 ■ Ingram's
306 E. 12th St., Ste. 1014
Kansas City, MO 64106
Ph:(816)842-9994
Fax:(816)474-1111

51831 ■ Kansas City Business Journal
1101 Walnut, Ste. 800
Kansas City, MO 64106
Ph:(816)421-5900
Fax:(816)472-4010
Co. E-mail: kcbj@unicom.net
URL: http://www.amcity.com

51832 ■ Missouri Business
65101 E. Capitol
PO Box 149
Jefferson City, MO 65102
Ph:(573)634-3511
Fax:(573)634-8855
Co. E-mail: mchamber@computerland.net
URL: http://mochambar.org

51833 ■ St. Louis Business Journal
One Metropolitan Sq., Ste. 2170
St. Louis, MO 63102
Ph:(314)421-6200
Fax:(314)621-5031
Co. E-mail: stlouis@amcity.com
URL: http://amcity.com/stlouis

51834 ■ Smart Start your Missouri Business
PSI Research
300 N. Valley Dr.
Grants Pass, OR 97526
Ph:(503)479-9464
Free: 800-228-2275
Fax:(503)476-1479
Co. E-mail: info@psi-research.com
URL: http://www.psi-research.com
Ed: Michael D. Jenkins. **Released:** Revised edition, 1992. **Price:** $29.95 (looseleaf binder); $24.95 (paper). **Description:** Part of the Successful Business Library series.

PUBLISHERS

51835 ■ Three House Publishing
490 Hillbrook Dr.
PO Box 6672
Chesterfield, MO 63006-6672
Ph:(314)277-4560
Contact: Ray Goldman, Publisher
Description: Publishes course materials. Also publishes novels and short stories.

SMALL BUSINESS DEVELOPMENT CENTERS

51836 ■ Billings Small Business Development Center
Big Sky Economic Development Authority
222 N 32nd St.
Billings, MT 59101
Fax:(406)256-6877
Co. E-mail: helvik@bigskyeda.org
URL: http://bigskyeda-edc.org/small-business-development.php
Contact: Rebecca Helvik, Business Advisor

51837 ■ Bozeman Small Business Development Center
Northern Rocky Mountain RC&D
502 S 19th Ave., Ste. 105
Bozeman, MT 59718
Fax:(406)582-5855
Co. E-mail: sbdc@nrmrcd.org
URL: http://www.nrmrcd.org/business_assistance.htm
Contact: Gary Slane, Business Advisor

51838 ■ Butte Small Business Development Center
Headwaters RC&D Area, Inc.
305 W Mercury, Ste. 211
Butte, MT 59701
Fax:(406)782-2990
Co. E-mail: djohnson@bigskyhsd.com
URL: http://www.headwatersrcd.org/sbdc.html
Contact: Deanna Johnson, Business Advisor

51839 ■ Great Falls Small Business Development Center
PO Box 949
Great Falls, MT 59403
Fax:(406)454-2995
Co. E-mail: rengum@gfdevelopment.org
URL: http://sbdc.mt.gov
Contact: Rebecca Engum, Business Advisor

51840 ■ Havre Small Business Development Center
PO Box 170
Havre, MT 59501
Fax:(406)265-5602
Co. E-mail: jlaplante@bearpaw.org
URL: http://www.bearpaw.org/services.htmlsbdc
Contact: Joe LaPlante

51841 ■ Helena Small Business Development Center
Montana Business Assistance Connections, Inc.
225 Cruise Ave.
Helena, MT 59601
Fax:(406)447-1514
Co. E-mail: danderson@mbac.biz
URL: http://www.mbac.biz/index.php?pr=Small_Business_Development_Center
Contact: Dan Anderson, Business Advisor

51842 ■ Kalispell Small Business Development Center
Kalispell Area Chamber of Commerce
15 Depot Park
Kalispell, MT 59901
Fax:(406)758-2805
URL: http://sbdc.mt.gov

51843 ■ Missoula Small Business Development Center
Montana Community Development Corporation
110 E Broadway, 2nd Fl.
Missoula, MT 59802
Fax:(406)542-6671
Co. E-mail: lynnd@mtcdc.org
URL: http://sbdc.mt.gov/offices.asp
Contact: Lynn Dankowski, Co-Business Advisor

51844 ■ Southeastern Montana Small Business Development Center
PO Box 1935
Colstrip, MT 59323
Fax:(406)748-2900
Co. E-mail: sbdc@bhwi.net
URL: http://www.semdc.org/sbdc.htm
Contact: Blayr Barnard, Business Advisor

51845 ■ Wolf Point Small Business Development Center
233 Cascade St.
Wolf Point, MT 59201
Fax:(406)653-1840
Co. E-mail: sbdc@gndc.org
URL: http://www.gndc.org/sbdc.htm
Contact: Lorene Hintz, Business Advisor

SMALL BUSINESS ASSISTANCE PROGRAMS

51846 ■ Big Sky Economic Development Authority
222 N 32nd St., Ste. 200
Billings, MT 59101-1911
Ph:(406)256-6871
Fax:(406)256-6877
Co. E-mail: arveschoug@bigskyeda.org
URL: http://www.bigskyeda.org
Contact: Steve Arveschoug, Chair and VP
Description: Offers U.S. Customs services, bonded and general warehouse storage, no inventory tax, and licensing brokerage services to shippers, wholesalers, and manufacturers. Access is provided to international and domestic shippers.

51847 ■ Montana Department of Agriculture–Agriculture Development Division
303 N Roberts St.
PO Box 200201
Helena, MT 59620-0201
Ph:(406)444-3144

Fax:(406)444-5409
Co. E-mail: agr@mt.gov
URL: http://www.agr.state.mt.us
Contact: Ron DeYong, Dir
Description: Provides market research and other assistance to Montana's agricultural producers through identification, analysis, and direction in development of both foreign and domestic markets.

51848 ■ Montana Department of Commerce–Business Resources Division
301 S. Park
PO Box 200501
Helena, MT 59620-0501
Ph:(406)841-2730
Fax:(406)841-2731
URL: http://businessresources.mt.gov/
Contact: Anthony J. Preite, Dir
Description: Publicizes and advertises Montana to firms planning relocations or expansions.

51849 ■ Montana Department of Commerce–Census and Economic Information Center
301 S Park Ave.
PO Box 200505
Helena, MT 59620-0505
Ph:(406)841-2740
Fax:(406)841-2731
Co. E-mail: ceic@mt.gov
URL: http://ceic.mt.gov/
Description: Provides population and economic information to businesses, government agencies, and the general public for research, planning, and decision-making purposes.

51850 ■ Montana Department of Commerce–Community Development Division
301 S Park Ave.
Helena, MT 59601
Ph:(406)841-2770
Fax:(406)841-2771
Co. E-mail: dacole@mt.gov
URL: http://comdev.mt.gov/
Contact: Dave Cole, Administrator
Description: Provides assistance to cities, towns, counties, and tribal governments in planning and carrying out effective economic development programs specifically designed to meet local needs.

51851 ■ Montana Department of Commerce–Economic Development Division–Marketing Assistance and Made in Montana Program (301 S)
301 S Park Ave.
PO Box 200505
Helena, MT 59620-0505
Ph:(406)841-2757
Fax:(406)841-2728
URL: http://www.madeinmontanausa.com/
Contact: Anthony J. Preite, Dir
Description: Works with individual small businesses to develop and expand outlets for products manufactured or processed in Montana.

51852 ■ **Montana Department of Commerce–Montana Science and Technology Alliance Division**
301 S Park Ave.
Helena, MT 59601
Ph:(406)841-2700
Fax:(406)841-2701
Co. E-mail: apreite@state.mt.us
URL: http://www.commerce.state.mt.us
Contact: Anthony J. Preite, Dir
Description: Encourages innovative scientific and technical development within the state. Aids in the creation of new jobs. Assists in financing the establishment of technology-intensive businesses and finances projects that it believes have outstanding technological and commercial potential. Has four complementary investment programs for financial assistance: seed capital investment, applied technology research, technical assistance and technology transfer, and research capability development.

51853 ■ **Montana Department of Commerce–Trade & International Relations Bureau**
301 S Park Ave.
Helena, MT 59601
Ph:(406)841-2757
Fax:(406)841-2731
URL: http://businessresources.mt.gov/BRD_TIR.asp
Contact: Mark Bisom, Chief
Description: Enhances sales of Montana goods and services in international markets and encourages tourism promotion and reverse investment opportunities. Also offers one-stop technical assistance to businesses wishing to enter foreign markets.

51854 ■ **University of Montana–Montana Business Connections**
231 Gallagher Business Bldg.
Missoula, MT 59812-2086
Ph:(406)243-4009
Fax:(406)243-2086
Co. E-mail: mtbc@business.umt.edu
URL: http://www.mbc.umt.edu
Description: Seeks to use the Montana University System to link business owners and entrepreneurs with information, resources, and expertise.

SCORE OFFICES

51855 ■ **Billings SCORE**
Path: www.montanascore.org/?page=billings

51856 ■ **Bitterroot SCORE**
Path: www.montanascore.org/?page=bitterroot

51857 ■ **Butte SCORE**
Path: www.montanascore.org/?page=butte

51858 ■ **Great Falls SCORE**
Path: www.montanascore.org/?page=greatfalls

51859 ■ **Helena SCORE**
Path: www.montanascore.org/?page=helena

51860 ■ **Missoula SCORE**
Path: www.montanascore.org/?page=missoula

51861 ■ **Northwest Montana SCORE**
Path: www.montanascore.org/?page=northwest

51862 ■ **Panhandle SCORE**
Path: www.score-chapter301.org

51863 ■ **SCORE Bozeman**
2000 Commerce Way
Bozeman, MT 59715
Ph:(406)586-5421
Co. E-mail: macd1120@yahoo.com
URL: http://www.scorebozeman.org
Contact: Robert Macdonald
Description: Serves as volunteer program in which working and retired business management professionals provide free business counseling to men and women who are considering starting a small business, encountering problems with their business, or expanding their business. Offers free one-on-one counseling, online counseling and low cost workshops on a variety of business topics.

CHAMBERS OF COMMERCE

51864 ■ **Anaconda Chamber of Commerce**
306 E Park St.
Anaconda, MT 59711
Ph:(406)563-2400
Fax:(406)563-2400
Co. E-mail: anacondachamber@rfwave.net
URL: http://www.anacondamt.org
Contact: Edith Fransen, Exec. Dir.

51865 ■ **Baker Chamber of Commerce and Agriculture**
PO Box 849
Baker, MT 59313-0849
Ph:(406)778-2266
Free: 800-862-2537
Co. E-mail: bakerchamber@bakerahcs.com
URL: http://www.bakermt.com
Contact: Karol Zachmann, Pres.

51866 ■ **Beaverhead Chamber of Commerce**
10 W Reeder
Dillon, MT 59725
Ph:(406)683-5511
Fax:(406)683-9233
Co. E-mail: info@beaverheadchamber.org
URL: http://www.beaverheadchamber.org
Contact: Melissa Hannah, Exec. Dir.

51867 ■ **Belgrade Chamber of Commerce**
10 E Main St.
Belgrade, MT 59714
Ph:(406)388-1616
Fax:(406)388-2090
Co. E-mail: info@belgradechamber.org
URL: http://www.belgradechamber.org
Contact: Debra Youngberg IOM, Exec. Dir.

51868 ■ **Bigfork Area Chamber of Commerce**
PO Box 237
Bigfork, MT 59911
Ph:(406)837-5888
Fax:(406)837-5808
Co. E-mail: chamber@bigfork.org
URL: http://www.bigfork.org
Contact: Bruce Solberg, Exec. Dir.

51869 ■ **Billings Area Chamber of Commerce**
815 S 27th St.
Billings, MT 59107-1177
Ph:(406)245-4111
Co. E-mail: info@billingschamber.com
URL: http://www.billingschamber.com
Contact: John Brewer, Pres./CEO

51870 ■ **Bitter Root Valley Chamber of Commerce**
105 E Main St.
Hamilton, MT 59840
Ph:(406)363-2400
Fax:(406)363-2402
Co. E-mail: localinfo@bvchamber.com
URL: http://www.bitterrootvalleychamber.com
Contact: Richard O'Brien, Exec. Dir.

51871 ■ **Bozeman Area Chamber of Commerce**
2000 Commerce Way
Bozeman, MT 59715
Ph:(406)586-5421
Free: 800-228-4224
Fax:(406)586-8286
Co. E-mail: info@bozemanchamber.com
URL: http://www.bozemanchamber.com
Contact: David R. Smith, Pres./CEO

51872 ■ **Butte-Silver Bow Chamber of Commerce**
1000 George St.
Butte, MT 59701
Ph:(406)723-3177
Free: 800-735-6814
Fax:(406)723-1215
Co. E-mail: chamber@buttechamber.org
URL: http://www.buttechamber.org
Contact: Marko Lucich, Exec. Dir.

51873 ■ **Circle Chamber of Commerce and Agriculture**
PO Box 321
Circle, MT 59215
Ph:(406)485-2741
Co. E-mail: chamber@circle-montana.com
URL: http://circle-montana.com
Contact: Dick Melvin

51874 ■ **Columbia Falls Area Chamber of Commerce**
PO Box 312
Columbia Falls, MT 59912
Ph:(406)892-2072
Fax:(406)892-2725
Co. E-mail: info@columbiafallschamber.com
URL: http://www.columbiafallschamber.com

51875 ■ **Columbia Falls Area Chamber Foundation**
PO Box 312
Columbia Falls, MT 59912-0312
Ph:(406)892-2072
Fax:(406)892-2725
Co. E-mail: info@columbiafallschamber.com
URL: http://www.columbiafallschamber.com
Contact: Carol Pike, Exec. Dir.

51876 ■ **Conrad Area Chamber of Commerce**
7 6th Ave. SW
Conrad, MT 59425
Ph:(406)271-7791
Fax:(406)221-2924
URL: http://www.conradmt.com

51877 ■ **Culbertson Chamber of Commerce**
PO Box 351
Culbertson, MT 59218
Ph:(406)787-5271
Fax:(406)787-5271
Co. E-mail: culbertsonmt@hotmail.com
URL: http://www.culbertsonmt.com
Contact: Bruce Houle

51878 ■ **Cut Bank Area Chamber of Commerce**
PO Box 1243
Cut Bank, MT 59427
Ph:(406)873-4041
Co. E-mail: info@cutbankchamber.com
URL: http://www.cutbankchamber.com
Contact: Jeff Billman, Pres.

51879 ■ **Daniels County Chamber of Commerce and Agriculture**
PO Box 91
Scobey, MT 59263
Ph:(406)487-2061
Co. E-mail: scobey@nemontel.net
URL: http://www.scobeymt.com

51880 ■ **Ennis Area Chamber of Commerce**
PO Box 291
Ennis, MT 59729
Ph:(406)682-4388
Fax:(406)682-4328
Co. E-mail: info@ennischamber.com
URL: http://www.ennischamber.com

51881 ■ **Eureka Area Chamber of Commerce**
PO Box 186
Eureka, MT 59917
Ph:(406)889-4636
Co. E-mail: info@welcome2eureka.com
URL: http://www.welcome2eureka.com
Contact: Randy Wilson, Pres.

51882 ■ **Fort Benton Chamber of Commerce**
PO Box 12
Fort Benton, MT 59442
Ph:(406)622-3864
Co. E-mail: info@fortbenton.com
URL: http://www.fortbentonchamber.org
Contact: Stella Scott, Pres.

51883 ■ **Gardiner Chamber of Commerce**
PO Box 81
Gardiner, MT 59030
Ph:(406)848-7971

Fax:(406)848-2446
Co. E-mail: info@gardinerchamber.com
URL: http://www.gardinerchamber.com
Contact: Mr. Chris Waters

51884 ■ Garfield County Chamber of Commerce
434 Main St.
Jordan, MT 59337
Ph:(406)557-6158
Fax:(406)557-6158
Co. E-mail: chamber@garfieldcounty.com
URL: http://www.garfieldcounty.com
Contact: Rocky Nelson, Pres.

51885 ■ Glasgow Area Chamber of Commerce and Agriculture
PO Box 832
Glasgow, MT 59230-0832
Ph:(406)228-2222
Fax:(406)228-2244
Co. E-mail: chamber@glasgowmt.net
URL: http://www.glasgowmt.net
Contact: Ms. Diane Brandt, Exec. Dir.

51886 ■ Glendive Chamber of Commerce and Agriculture
808 N Merrill Ave.
Glendive, MT 59330
Ph:(406)377-5601
Fax:(406)377-5602
Co. E-mail: chamber@midrivers.com
URL: http://www.glendivechamber.com
Contact: Kim Trangmoe, Exec. Dir.

51887 ■ Great Falls Area Chamber of Commerce
100 1 Ave. N
PO Box 2127
Great Falls, MT 59401
Ph:(406)761-4434
Fax:(406)761-6129
URL: http://www.greatfallschamber.org
Contact: Steve Malicott, Pres./CEO

51888 ■ Greater Stillwater County Chamber of Commerce
PO Box 783
Columbus, MT 59019
Ph:(406)322-4505
Co. E-mail: admin@stillwatercountychamber.com
URL: http://www.stillwatercountychamber.com
Contact: Charles Sangmeister, Pres.

51889 ■ Hardin Area Chamber of Commerce and Agriculture
PO Box 446
Hardin, MT 59034
Ph:(406)665-1672
Free: 888-450-3577
Fax:(406)665-2917
Co. E-mail: hardinchamber@bhwi.net
URL: http://www.custerslaststand.org
Contact: Trina Maurer, Pres.

51890 ■ Havre Area Chamber of Commerce
130 5th Ave.
PO Box 308
Havre, MT 59501-0308
Ph:(406)265-4383
Fax:(406)265-7748
Co. E-mail: chamber@havremt.net
URL: http://www.havremt.net
Contact: Debbie Vandeberg, Exec. Dir.

51891 ■ Helena Area Chamber of Commerce
225 Cruse Ave.
Helena, MT 59601
Ph:(406)442-4120
Free: 800-743-5362
Fax:(406)447-1532
Co. E-mail: info@helenachamber.com
URL: http://www.helenachamber.com
Contact: Cathy Burwell, Pres./CEO

51892 ■ Kalispell Area Chamber of Commerce
15 Depot Park
Kalispell, MT 59901
Ph:(406)758-2800
Fax:(406)758-2805
Co. E-mail: info@kalispellchamber.com
URL: http://kalispellchamber.com
Contact: Joe Unterreiner, Pres./CEO

51893 ■ Lakeside-Somers Chamber of Commerce
PO Box 177
Lakeside, MT 59922
Ph:(406)844-3715
Co. E-mail: info@lakesidesomers.org
URL: http://www.lakesidesomers.org
Contact: Dave Christensen, Pres.

51894 ■ Laurel Chamber of Commerce
108 E Main St.
Laurel, MT 59044-3104
Ph:(406)628-8105
Co. E-mail: lchamber@rbbmt.org
URL: http://www.laurelmontana.org
Contact: Jared Kaiser, Pres.

51895 ■ Lewistown Area Chamber of Commerce
408 NE Main St.
Lewistown, MT 59457-0818
Ph:(406)538-5436
Free: (866)912-3980
Co. E-mail: lewchamb@midrivers.com
URL: http://www.lewistownchamber.com

51896 ■ Libby Area Chamber of Commerce
PO Box 704
905 W 9th
Libby, MT 59923
Ph:(406)293-4167
Fax:(406)293-2197
Co. E-mail: libbyacc@libbychamber.org
URL: http://www.libbychamber.org
Contact: Louise Rice, Exec. Dir.

51897 ■ Lincoln Valley Chamber of Commerce
PO Box 985
Lincoln, MT 59639-0985
Ph:(406)362-4949
Fax:(406)362-4171
Co. E-mail: lincolnmontana@gmail.com
URL: http://www.lincolnmontana.com

51898 ■ Livingston Area Chamber of Commerce
303 E Park St.
Livingston, MT 59047
Ph:(406)222-0850
Co. E-mail: info@livingston-chamber.com
URL: http://www.livingston-chamber.com

51899 ■ Malta Area Chamber of Commerce
PO Box 1420
Malta, MT 59538
Ph:(406)654-1776
Fax:(406)654-1776
Co. E-mail: malta@ttc-cmc.net
URL: http://www.maltachamber.com
Contact: Anne Boothe, Sec.

51900 ■ Manhattan Area Chamber of Commerce
PO Box 606
Manhattan, MT 59741
Ph:(406)284-4162
Co. E-mail: manhattanmontana@yahoo.com
URL: http://www.manhattanmontana.com
Contact: Brad Price, Pres.

51901 ■ Miles City Area Chamber of Commerce
511 Pleasant St.
Miles City, MT 59301
Ph:(406)234-2890

Fax:(406)234-6914
Co. E-mail: mcchamber@mcchamber.com
URL: http://www.mcchamber.com/tiki-index.php
Contact: Dannette Cremer, Pres.

51902 ■ Mineral County Chamber of Commerce
PO Box 483
Superior, MT 59872
Ph:(406)649-6400
Co. E-mail: mccoc@blackfoot.net
URL: http://www.montanarockies.org
Contact: George Bailey, Pres.

51903 ■ Missoula Area Chamber of Commerce
PO Box 7577
Missoula, MT 59807
Ph:(406)543-6623
Fax:(406)543-6625
Co. E-mail: info@missoulachamber.com
URL: http://www.missoulachamber.com
Contact: Kim Latrielle, Pres./CEO

51904 ■ Montana Chamber of Commerce
PO Box 1730
Helena, MT 59624-1730
Ph:(406)442-2405
Fax:(406)442-2409
Co. E-mail: schaefer@3rivers.net
URL: http://www.montanachamber.com
Contact: Webb Scott Brown, Pres.

51905 ■ Philipsburg Chamber of Commerce
PO Box 661
Philipsburg, MT 59858
Ph:(406)859-3388
Co. E-mail: chamber@philipsburgmt.com
URL: http://www.philipsburgmt.com

51906 ■ Plains-Paradise Chamber of Commerce
PO Box 1531
Plains, MT 59859
Ph:(406)826-4700
URL: http://wildhorseplainschamber.com

51907 ■ Polson Chamber of Commerce
418 Main St.
Polson, MT 59860
Ph:(406)883-5969
Fax:(406)883-1716
Co. E-mail: chamber@polsonchamber.com
URL: http://www.polsonchamber.com
Contact: Michelle Cope, Exec. Dir.

51908 ■ Powell County Chamber of Commerce
1109 Main St.
Deer Lodge, MT 59722
Ph:(406)846-2094
Fax:(406)846-2094
Co. E-mail: chamber@powellcountymontana.com
URL: http://www.powellcountymontana.com
Contact: Mrs. Patty Cowan, Exec. Sec.

51909 ■ Red Lodge Area Chamber of Commerce
601 N Broadway
PO Box 988
Red Lodge, MT 59068
Ph:(406)446-1718
Free: 888-281-0625
Fax:(406)446-1718
Co. E-mail: information@redlodge.com
URL: http://www.redlodge.com
Contact: Gwenn Williams, Pres.

51910 ■ Shelby Area Chamber of Commerce
PO Box 865
Shelby, MT 59474-0865
Ph:(406)434-7184
Co. E-mail: shelbycoc@3rivers.net
URL: http://www.shelbymtchamber.org
Contact: Heather Gottfried, Pres.

51911 ■ Sheridan County Chamber of Commerce
PO Box 104
Plentywood, MT 59254-0104
Ph:(406)765-1733
Fax:(406)765-2106
Co. E-mail: chamber59254@yahoo.com
URL: http://sheridancountychamber.org
Contact: Richard Rice, Pres.

51912 ■ Sidney Area Chamber of Commerce and Agriculture
909 S Central Ave.
Sidney, MT 59270
Ph:(406)433-1916
Fax:(406)433-1127
Co. E-mail: schamber@midrivers.com
URL: http://www.sidneymt.com
Contact: Laura Schieber, Exec. Dir.

51913 ■ Sweet Grass County Chamber of Commerce
PO Box 1012
Big Timber, MT 59011
Ph:(406)932-5131
Fax:(406)932-5131
Co. E-mail: info@bigtimber.com
URL: http://www.bigtimber.com
Contact: Tracy Bolstad, Mgr.

51914 ■ Thompson Falls Chamber of Commerce
PO Box 493
Thompson Falls, MT 59873
Ph:(406)827-4930
Fax:(406)827-4430
Co. E-mail: tfchamber@thompsonfallschamber.com
URL: http://www.thompsonfallschamber.com
Contact: Cindy Bronner, Co-Pres.

51915 ■ Three Forks Chamber of Commerce
PO Box 1103
Three Forks, MT 59752-1103
Ph:(406)285-4753
Co. E-mail: tfchamber@gmail.com
URL: http://www.threeforksmontana.com
Contact: Barbara Frost, Pres.

51916 ■ West Yellowstone Chamber of Commerce
PO Box 458
West Yellowstone, MT 59758-0458
Ph:(406)646-7701
Fax:(406)646-9691
Co. E-mail: visitorsservices@westyellowstonechamber.com
URL: http://www.westyellowstonechamber.com
Contact: Marysue Costello, Exec. Dir.

51917 ■ Whitefish Chamber of Commerce
520 E 2nd St.
Whitefish, MT 59937
Ph:(406)862-3501
Free: 877-862-3548
Fax:(406)862-9494
Co. E-mail: visitus@whitefishchamber.org
URL: http://www.whitefishchamber.org
Contact: Sheila Bowen, Pres./CEO

PROCUREMENT ASSISTANCE PROGRAMS

51918 ■ Montana Department of Administration–State Procurement Bureau
Mitchell Bldg., Rm. 165
PO Box 200135
Helena, MT 59620-0135
Ph:(406)444-2575
Fax:(406)444-2529
URL: http://mt.gov/govt/statedir/agency/doa.asp
Contact: Brad Sanders, Bureau Chief
Description: Offers current government procurement information to interested small business bidders. Also provides technical assistance.

51919 ■ Montana Procurement Technical Assistance Center–Government Marketing Assistance Group–Big Sky Economic Development Authority (222 N)
222 N 32nd St., Ste. 200
Billings, MT 59101
Ph:(406)256-6871
Fax:(406)256-6877
Co. E-mail: jewell@bigskyeda.org
URL: http://www.bigskyeda-edc.org
Contact: Maureen Jewell, Pgrm Mgr
E-mail: jewell@bigskyeda.org
Description: Helps to create jobs and grow companies in Montana by helping area businesses win government contracts

51920 ■ Montana Procurement Technical Assistance Center–Great Falls Development Authority
PO Box 949
Great Falls, MT 59403
Ph:(406)771-9020
Fax:(406)454-2995
Co. E-mail: info@greatfallsdevelopment.org
URL: http://www.gfdevelopment.org
Contact: Brett Doney, Pres. & CEO
E-mail: karl@mt.net

51921 ■ Montana Procurement Technical Assistance Center–Kalispell Area Chamber of Commerce
Flathead Business Regional Center
15 Depot Park
Kalispell, MT 59901
Ph:(406)755-4221
Co. E-mail: ptac@kalispellchamber.com
URL: http://www.kalispellchamber.com
Contact: Doug Bolender, Mgr.
Description: Free assistance to help Montana businesses obtain city, county, state, or federal government contracts serving Flathead, Lake, Sanders, and Lincoln Counties.

51922 ■ Montana Procurement Technical Assistance Center–Missoula Area Economic Development Corp. (MAEDC)
1121 E Broadway, Ste. 135
Missoula, MT 59802
Ph:(406)532-3207
Fax:(406)543-2304
Co. E-mail: ptac@maedc.org
URL: http://www.maedc.org
Contact: Doug Bolender, Dir.
Description: The organization helps employers create quality jobs for area residents, diversify the regional economic base, and improve the economy by taking leadership positions and forming partnerships with other organizations on community issues that affect local economic development. MAEDC helps existing companies expand by providing technical assistance and financing.

51923 ■ Montana Procurement Technical Assistance Center–Montana National Center for American Indian Enterprise Development
219 1st St. E
Polson, MT 59860
Ph:(406)883-4833
Co. E-mail: lou.thompson@ncaied.org
URL: http://www.ncaied.org
Contact: Lou Thompson, Counselor
E-mail: lou.thompson@ncaied.org
Description: Develop and expand an American Indian private sector which employs Indian labor, increases the number of viable tribal and individual Indian businesses, and positively impacts and involves reservation communities, by establishing business relationships between Indian enterprises and private industry.

51924 ■ Montana Procurement Technical Assistance Center–Prospera Business Network
222 E Main St., Ste. 102
Bozeman, MT 59715
Ph:(406)587-3113

Fax:(406)587-9565
Co. E-mail: info@prosperabusinessnetwork.com
URL: http://www.bozeman.org/index.html
Contact: Stuart R. Leidner, Exec. Dir.
E-mail: PRenevier@prosperabusinessnetwork.com
Description: Encourages and supports business expansion, retention and relocation by providing access to guidance, capital, professional development, networking and recognition.

INCUBATORS/RESEARCH AND TECHNOLOGY PARKS

51925 ■ Advanced Technology Park
1711 W College
Bozeman, MT 59715
Ph:(406)587-4480
Fax:(406)587-4480
Co. E-mail: info@bozemantechpark.com
URL: http://www.bozemantechpark.com
Contact: Roger N. Flair, Pres.
E-mail: info@bozemantechpark.com
Scope: Provides access for park tenants to the research community and facilities at the University.
Publications: Montana State University Resources Catalog.

51926 ■ College of Forestry and Conservation–Institute for Tourism and Recreation Research
University of Montana
32 Campus Dr., No. 1234
Missoula, MT 59812-1234
Ph:(406)243-5686
Fax:(406)243-4845
Co. E-mail: request@forestry.umt.edu
URL: http://www.forestry.umt.edu/
Contact: Kate Cenis, Dir.
Description: Provides research data needed to support the state's tourism industry.

51927 ■ Lake County Community Development Corporation
407 Main St. SW
Ronan, MT 59864
Ph:(406)676-5901
Co. E-mail: lccd@ronan.net
URL: http://www.lakecountycdc.org/
Contact: Billie Lee, Dir.
Description: A small business incubator working with existing companies to develop and expand their businesses and to structure financial resources appropriate to their situation, and helping recruit new companies which may provide additional and higher wage jobs.

51928 ■ Montana Business Incubator
Montana State University - Billings
100 Poly Dr., Ste. 150
Billings, MT 59101
Ph:(406)657-2138
Fax:(406)657-2006
Co. E-mail: mbinc@mtbiz.org
URL: http://www.mtbiz.org/
Contact: Dave Stoltenberg, Dir.
Description: A small business incubator committed to creating jobs and wealth in the Billings Montana region by supporting entrepreneurship and innovation. It seeks to assist companies involved in many technical areas, however a special emphasis is placed upon agriculture, medical, and energy related businesses.

51929 ■ Montana State University, Bozeman–Office of Vice President for Research, Creativity, and Technology Transfer
207 Montana Hall
PO Box 172460
Bozeman, MT 59717-2460
Ph:(406)994-2891

Fax:(406)994-2893
Co. E-mail: research@montana.edu
URL: http://www.montana.edu/wwwvr
Contact: Thomas J. McCoy PhD, VP
E-mail: research@montana.edu
Scope: Coordinates research and creative activities in all departments and colleges of the University, operating through its subsidiary, Office of Research, Creativity and Technology Transfer, which provides technology transfer management, pre-award services, and coordinates interdisciplinary and multidisciplinary research projects, and its office of Sponsored Programs, which provides fiscal and contract arrangement services. **Publications:** Newsletter. **Awards:** BEST Awards.

51930 ■ Montana Technology Enterprise Center
1121 E. Broadway, Ste. 100
Missoula, MT 59802
Ph:(406)728-3337
Fax:(406)543-2304
Co. E-mail: maedc@maedc.org
URL: http://www.maedc.org/montec
Contact: Dick King, Pres. & CEO
Description: A technology and business incubator conceived to bolster local start-ups and to encourage the commercialization of university research. Col-

laborative enterprise between the University of Montana and the Missoula Area Economic Development Foundation.

51931 ■ TechRanch
910 Technology Blvd., Ste. A
Bozeman, MT 59718
Ph:(406)556-0272
Fax:(406)556-0969
Co. E-mail: gbloomer@techranch.org
URL: http://www.techranch.org/
Contact: Gary Bloomer
Description: A business incubator created to help Montana-based entrepreneurs launch and build companies that will become long term, profitable operating entities in Montana. Its goal is to create more high-paying, intellectually-stimulating, clean jobs in Montana.

PUBLICATIONS

51932 ■ *Big Sky Business Journal*
PO Box 3262
Billings, MT 59103
Ph:(406)259-2309
Fax:(406)259-7040
Co. E-mail: bsbj@imt.net
URL: http://www.montanamarket.com/bsbj

51933 ■ *Livingston Enterprise*
PO Box 665
Livingston, MT 59047
Ph:(406)222-2000
Fax:(406)222-8580
Co. E-mail: enterprise@ycsi.net

51934 ■ *Montana Magazine*
PO Box 5630
Helena, MT 59604
Ph:(406)443-2842
Fax:(406)443-5480
Co. E-mail: magedit@montmang.mt.net
URL: http://www.montanamagazine.com

51935 ■ *Smart Start Your California Business*
PSI Research
300 N. Valley Dr.
Grants Pass, OR 97526
Ph:(503)479-9464
Free: 800-228-2275
Fax:(503)476-1479
Co. E-mail: info@psi-research.com
URL: http://www.psi-research.com
Ed: Michael D. Jenkins. **Released:** Revised edition, 1992. **Price:** $29.95 (looseleaf binder); $24.95 (paper). **Description:** Part of the Successful Business Library series.

SMALL BUSINESS DEVELOPMENT CENTERS

51936 ■ Nebraska Small Business Development Center
University of Nebraska at Omaha
College of Business Administration
Roskens Hall, Rm. 415
Omaha, NE 68182-0248
URL: http://nbdc.unomaha.edu
Contact: Robert E. Bernier, Dir.

51937 ■ Nebraska Small Business Development Center - Chadron State College
1000 Main St.
Chadron, NE 69337
Co. E-mail: jkoehn@csc.edu
URL: http://nbdc.unomaha.edu
Contact: James Koehn, Dir.

51938 ■ Nebraska Small Business Development Center - Kearney
University of Nebraska at Kearney
West Center Bldg., Rm. 127E
1917 W 24th St.
Kearney, NE 68849-4440
Fax:(308)865-8153
Co. E-mail: ingersollo@unk.edu
URL: http://nbdc.unomaha.edu
Contact: Odee Ingersoll, Dir.

51939 ■ Nebraska Small Business Development Center - Lincoln
UNL Office of Technology Development
1320 Q St., Office 109
Lincoln, NE 68588-0467
Fax:(402)472-0398
Co. E-mail: mrodriguez2@unl.edu
URL: http://nbdc.unomaha.edu
Contact: Marisol U. Rodriguez, Dir.

51940 ■ Nebraska Small Business Development Center - Norfolk
Lifelong Learning Center
801 E Benjamin Ave.
Norfolk, NE 68702-0469
Co. E-mail: rheld@mail.unomaha.edu
URL: http://nbdc.unomaha.edu
Contact: Renee Held, Consultant

51941 ■ Nebraska Small Business Development Center - North Platte
300 E 3rd St., Rm. 275
North Platte, NE 69101
Fax:(308)534-5117
Co. E-mail: jtuller@mail.unomaha.edu
URL: http://nbdc.unomaha.edu
Contact: Jason Tuller, Dir.

51942 ■ Nebraska Small Business Development Center - Omaha
13006 W Center Rd.
Omaha, NE 68144
Fax:(402)595-1194
Co. E-mail: nbdcomaha@aol.com
URL: http://www.nbdc.unomaha.edu
Contact: Cliff Mosteller, Dir.

51943 ■ Nebraska Small Business Development Center - Scottsbluff
Panhandle Research and Extension Center
4502 Ave. I
Scottsbluff, NE 69361
Co. E-mail: ibattershell@mail.unomaha.edu
URL: http://nbdc.unomaha.edu
Contact: Ingrid Battershell, Dir.

51944 ■ Nebraska Small Business Development Center - Wayne
Wayne State College
Gardner Hall
1111 Main St.
Wayne, NE 68787
Co. E-mail: lokucer1@wsc.edu
URL: http://nbdc.unomaha.edu
Contact: Loren Kucera, Dir.

SMALL BUSINESS ASSISTANCE PROGRAMS

51945 ■ Nebraska Ombudsman's Office
State Capitol, Rm. 807
PO Box 94604
Lincoln, NE 68509-4604
Ph:(402)471-2035
Free: 800-742-7690
Fax:(402)471-4277
Co. E-mail: ombud@leg.ne.gov
URL: http://www.unicam.state.ne.us/web/public/ombudsman
Contact: Marshall Lux, Ombudsman
Description: Receives complaints against state agencies.

SCORE OFFICES

51946 ■ Norfolk SCORE
Path: norfolk.scorechapter.org

51947 ■ North Platte SCORE
Path: www.nparea.com

51948 ■ SCORE Central Nebraska
PO Box 2288
Kearney, NE 68848-2288
Ph:(308)865-5675
Co. E-mail: rhobbs@scorecentralnebraska.org
URL: http://www.scorecentralnebraska.org
Contact: Mr. Robert E. Hobbs, Assignment Off.
Description: Provides technical assistance and counseling for new and existing business owners.

51949 ■ SCORE Columbus
3014 39th St.
Columbus, NE 68601
Ph:(402)564-2769
Co. E-mail: dlux@cccneb.edu
Description: Promotes business and community development in Columbus, NE area.

51950 ■ SCORE Lincoln
285 S 68th Pl., Ste. 530
Lincoln, NE 68510
Ph:(402)437-2409
Co. E-mail: nescore39@aol.com
URL: http://www.score39.org
Contact: Fred Bailey, Chm.
Description: Provides entrepreneur education for the formation, growth and success of small businesses in the area.

51951 ■ SCORE Omaha
10675 Bedford Ave., Ste. 100
Omaha, NE 68134
Ph:(402)221-3606
Fax:(402)221-7228
Co. E-mail: score@scoreomaha.org
URL: http://www.tandt.com/score
Description: Provides entrepreneur education for the formation, growth and success of small businesses in the area.

BETTER BUSINESS BUREAUS

51952 ■ Cornhusker Better Business Bureau
11811 P St.
Omaha, NE 68137
Ph:(402)391-7612
Free: 800-649-6814
Fax:(402)391-7535
Co. E-mail: info@bbbnebraska.org
URL: http://www.nebraska.bbb.org

CHAMBERS OF COMMERCE

51953 ■ Ainsworth Area Chamber of Commerce and North Central Development Center
335 N Main St.
Ainsworth, NE 69210
Ph:(402)387-2740
Free: (866)387-2740
Fax:(402)387-2740
Co. E-mail: ainsworthchamber@ainsworthlinks.com
URL: http://www.ainsworthlinks.com/aacc.html
Contact: Linda O'Hare, Exec. Sec.

51954 ■ Albion Chamber of Commerce
420 W Market St.
Albion, NE 68620
Ph:(402)395-5012
Fax:(402)395-6723
Co. E-mail: ccalbn@hotmail.com
URL: http://www.cityofalbion-ne.com
Contact: Larry Lambert

51955 ■ Alliance Area Chamber of Commerce
111 W 3rd St.
PO Box 571
Alliance, NE 69301
Ph:(308)762-1520

Free: 800-738-0648
Co. E-mail: chamber@bbc.net
URL: http://www.alliancechamber.com
Contact: Dixie Nelson, Exec. Dir.

51956 ■ Alma Chamber of Commerce
PO Box 52
Alma, NE 68920-0052
Ph:(308)928-2992
URL: http://www.ci.alma.ne.us/ChamberIndex.htm

51957 ■ Arapahoe Chamber of Commerce
PO Box 624
Arapahoe, NE 68922
Ph:(308)962-7777
Co. E-mail: chamber@arapahoe-ne.com
URL: http://www.arapahoe-ne.com
Contact: Tammie Middagh, Sec.-Treas.

51958 ■ Ashland Area Chamber of Commerce
PO Box 5
Ashland, NE 68003
Ph:(402)944-2050
URL: http://www.historicashland.com/chamber-of-commerce

51959 ■ Auburn Chamber of Commerce
1211 J St.
Auburn, NE 68305
Ph:(402)274-3521
Fax:(402)274-4020
URL: http://www.auburnneb.com
Contact: Kendall Neiman, Pres.

51960 ■ Aurora Area Chamber and Development
1604 L St.
PO Box 146
Aurora, NE 68818
Ph:(402)694-6911
Fax:(402)694-5766
Co. E-mail: aacd@hamilton.net
URL: http://www.auroranebraska.com
Contact: Mr. Christian Evans, Exec. Dir.

51961 ■ Beatrice Area Chamber of Commerce
226 S 6th St.
Beatrice, NE 68310
Ph:(402)223-2338
Fax:(402)223-2339
Co. E-mail: info@beatricechamber.com
URL: http://www.beatricechamber.com
Contact: Dave Eskra, Chm.

51962 ■ Blair Area Chamber of Commerce
1646 Washington St.
Blair, NE 68008
Ph:(402)533-4455
Co. E-mail: mail@blairchamber.org
URL: http://www.blairchamber.org
Contact: Harriet Waite, Exec. Dir.

51963 ■ Broken Bow Chamber of Commerce
444 S 8th Ave.
Broken Bow, NE 68822
Ph:(308)872-5691
Fax:(308)872-6137
Co. E-mail: info@brokenbow-ne.com
URL: http://www.brokenbow-ne.com
Contact: Denise Russell, Exec. Dir.

51964 ■ Burwell Chamber of Commerce
PO Box 131
Burwell, NE 68823
Ph:(308)346-5210
Free: 888-328-7935
Fax:(308)346-5121
Co. E-mail: burwellcondev@nctc.net
URL: http://www.burwellnebraska.net
Contact: Lynn Kratky, Dir.

51965 ■ Cambridge Chamber of Commerce
PO Box Q
Cambridge, NE 69022
Ph:(308)697-3711
Fax:(308)697-3253
URL: http://www.cambridgene.org

51966 ■ Central City Area Chamber of Commerce
PO Box 418
Central City, NE 68826
Ph:(308)946-3897
Fax:(308)946-3334
Co. E-mail: cchamber@ccablene.com
URL: http://www.centralcitychamber.com
Contact: Kendra Jefferson, Exec. Dir.

51967 ■ Chadron - Dawes County Area Chamber of Commerce
706 W 3rd St.
PO Box 646
Chadron, NE 69337-0646
Ph:(308)432-4401
Free: 800-603-2937
Co. E-mail: director@chadron.com
URL: http://www.chadron.com
Contact: Colette Fernandez, Exec. Dir.

51968 ■ Chappell Chamber of Commerce
PO Box 121
Chappell, NE 69129-0121
Ph:(308)874-9912
Fax:(308)874-2929
Co. E-mail: chamber69129@yahoo.com
URL: http://www.chappellne.org/chamber.htm
Contact: Cindy Williams, Pres.

51969 ■ Cheyenne County Chamber of Commerce
740 Illinois St.
Sidney, NE 69162-1748
Ph:(308)254-5851
Free: 800-421-4769
Fax:(308)254-3081
Co. E-mail: ccchamber@hamilton.net
URL: http://cheyennecountychamber.com
Contact: Ms. Megan McGown, Exec. Dir.

51970 ■ Columbus Area Chamber of Commerce
764 33rd Ave.
PO Box 515
Columbus, NE 68601-0515
Ph:(402)564-2769
Fax:(402)564-2026
Co. E-mail: chamber@megavision.com
URL: http://www.thecolumbuspage.com
Contact: K.C. Belitz, Pres.

51971 ■ Crete Chamber of Commerce
1341 Main Ave.
Crete, NE 68333
Ph:(402)826-2136
Fax:(402)826-2136
Co. E-mail: cretechamber@neb.rr.com
URL: http://www.crete-ne.com
Contact: Sharlyn Sieck, Dir.

51972 ■ David City Area Chamber of Commerce
457 D St.
David City, NE 68632
Ph:(402)367-4238
Co. E-mail: dcchamber@windstream.net
URL: http://www.davidcityne.com
Contact: Mr. Willow Holoubek, Exec. Dir.

51973 ■ Fairbury Chamber of Commerce
518 E St.
PO Box 274
Fairbury, NE 68352
Ph:(402)729-3000
Fax:(402)729-3076
Co. E-mail: fairburychamber@diodecom.net
URL: http://www.fairburychamber.org
Contact: Sharon Priefert, Exec. Dir.

51974 ■ Falls City Area Chamber of Commerce
1705 Stone St.
Falls City, NE 68355
Ph:(402)245-4228

Fax:(402)245-4228
Co. E-mail: fcchamber@sentco.net
URL: http://www.fallscityonline.com/chamber/chamberindex.html
Contact: Michael Moore, Pres.

51975 ■ Fremont Area Chamber of Commerce
605 N Broad St.
PO Box 182
Fremont, NE 68026-0182
Ph:(402)721-2641
Fax:(402)721-9359
Co. E-mail: info@fremontne.org
URL: http://www.fremontne.org
Contact: Allan Hale, Pres./CEO

51976 ■ Gordon Chamber of Commerce
PO Box 160
Gordon, NE 69343
Ph:(308)282-0730
Co. E-mail: gcc@gordonchamber.com
URL: http://www.gordonchamber.com

51977 ■ Gothenburg Area Chamber of Commerce
PO Box 263
Gothenburg, NE 69138
Ph:(308)537-3505
Co. E-mail: annea@gothenburgdelivers.com
URL: http://www.ci.gothenburg.ne.us/chamber_of_commerce.htm
Contact: Anne Anderson, Exec. Dir.

51978 ■ Grand Island Area Chamber of Commerce
309 W 2nd St.
PO Box 1486
Grand Island, NE 68802-1486
Ph:(308)382-9210
Fax:(308)382-1154
Co. E-mail: cjohnson@gichamber.com
URL: http://www.gichamber.com
Contact: Cindy K. Johnson, Pres.

51979 ■ Greater Omaha Chamber of Commerce
1301 Harney St.
Omaha, NE 68102
Ph:(402)346-5000
Fax:(402)346-7050
Co. E-mail: info@omahachamber.org
URL: http://www.omahachamber.org
Contact: David G. Brown, Pres./CEO

51980 ■ Greater York Area Chamber of Commerce
603 Lincoln Ave.
York, NE 68467
Ph:(402)362-5531
Fax:(402)362-5953
Co. E-mail: yorkcc@yorkchamber.net
Contact: Todd Kirshenbaum, Exec. Dir.

51981 ■ Hartington Area Chamber of Commerce
PO Box 742
Hartington, NE 68739
Ph:(402)254-6357
Fax:(402)254-6391
Co. E-mail: devcoor@hartel.net
URL: http://www.ci.hartington.ne.us/chamber.asp
Contact: Stephanie Scoggan, Pres.

51982 ■ Hastings Area Chamber of Commerce
301 S Burlington
PO Box 1104
Hastings, NE 68902-1104
Ph:(402)461-8400
Fax:(402)461-4400
Co. E-mail: info@hastingschamber.com
URL: http://www.hastingschamber.com
Contact: Tom Hastings, Pres.

51983 ■ Holdrege Area Chamber of Commerce
PO Box 200
Holdrege, NE 68949-0200
Ph:(308)995-4444
Fax:(308)995-4445
Co. E-mail: chamber@justtheplacenebraska.com
URL: http://www.holdrege.org
Contact: Trenna Lawrence, Admin. Asst.

51984 ■ Imperial Chamber of Commerce
PO Box 87
Imperial, NE 69033
Ph:(308)882-5444
URL: http://www.imperialchamber.com

51985 ■ Kearney Area Chamber of Commerce
PO Box 607
1007 2nd Ave.
Kearney, NE 68848
Ph:(308)237-3101
Free: 800-652-9435
Fax:(308)237-3103
Co. E-mail: info@kearneycoc.org
URL: http://www.kearneycoc.org
Contact: Roger Jasnoch, Pres.

51986 ■ Kimball - Banner County Chamber of Commerce
122 S Chestnut St.
Kimball, NE 69145
Ph:(308)235-3782
Fax:(308)235-3825
Co. E-mail: kbccc@megavision.com
URL: http://www.ci.kimball.ne.us
Contact: Kim Baliman, Exec. Dir.

51987 ■ La Vista Area Chamber of Commerce
8040 S 84th St.
La Vista, NE 68128
Ph:(402)339-2078
Fax:(402)339-2026
Co. E-mail: info@lavistachamber.org
URL: http://www.lavistachamber.org
Contact: Mary Harper, Exec. Dir.

51988 ■ Lexington Area Chamber of Commerce
302 E 6th St., Ste. 2
PO Box 97
Lexington, NE 68850
Ph:(308)324-5504
Fax:(308)324-5505
URL: http://www.lexcoc.com
Contact: Susan Bennett, Exec. Dir.

51989 ■ Lincoln Chamber of Commerce
PO Box 83006
Lincoln, NE 68501-3006
Ph:(402)436-2350
Fax:(402)436-2360
Co. E-mail: info@lcoc.com
URL: http://www.lcoc.com
Contact: Wendy Birdsall, Pres.

51990 ■ Loup City Chamber of Commerce
PO Box 24
Loup City, NE 68853-0024
Ph:(308)745-0430
Co. E-mail: lcchamber@cornhusker.net
URL: http://www.loupcity.com
Contact: Mark Eurek, Pres.

51991 ■ McCook Area Chamber of Commerce
107 Norris Ave.
PO Box 337
McCook, NE 69001
Ph:(308)345-3200
Free: 800-657-2179
Fax:(308)345-3201
Co. E-mail: info@aboutmccook.com
URL: http://aboutmccook.com
Contact: Pamela C. Harsh, Exec. Dir.

51992 ■ Minden Chamber of Commerce
PO Box 375
Minden, NE 68959
Ph:(308)832-1811
Fax:(308)832-1811
Co. E-mail: mindenchamber@gtmc.net
URL: http://www.mindenne.org
Contact: Sonya Nelsen, Dir.

51993 ■ Nebraska Chamber of Commerce and Industry
PO Box 95128
1320 Lincoln Mall
Lincoln, NE 68509-5128
Ph:(402)474-4422
Fax:(402)474-5681
Co. E-mail: bkennedy@nechamber.com
URL: http://www.nechamber.com
Contact: Barry L. Kennedy CAE, Pres.

51994 ■ Nebraska City Tourism and Commerce
806 1st Ave.
Nebraska City, NE 68410
Ph:(402)873-6654
Free: 800-514-9113
Fax:(402)873-6701
Co. E-mail: tourism@nebraskacity.com
URL: http://www.nebraskacity.com
Contact: Jim Johnston, Exec. Dir.

51995 ■ Norfolk Area Chamber of Commerce
405 Madison Ave.
Norfolk, NE 68701
Ph:(402)371-4862
Fax:(402)371-0182
Co. E-mail: information@norfolk.ne.us
URL: http://www.norfolk.ne.us
Contact: Dennis Houston, Pres.

51996 ■ North Platte Area Chamber of Commerce
502 S Dewey St.
North Platte, NE 69101
Ph:(308)532-4966
Fax:(308)532-4827
Co. E-mail: devco@grownorthplatte.org
URL: http://www.northplattechamber.com
Contact: Dan Mauk, Pres.

51997 ■ Ogallala - Keith County Chamber of Commerce
PO Box 628
Ogallala, NE 69153
Ph:(308)284-4066
Free: 800-658-4390
Co. E-mail: info@visitogallala.com
URL: http://www.visitogallala.com
Contact: Marion Kroeker, Exec. Dir.

51998 ■ O'Neill Area Chamber of Commerce
125 S 4th St.
O'Neill, NE 68763-1813
Ph:(402)336-2355
Fax:(402)336-4563
Co. E-mail: oneill@morcomm.net
URL: http://www.oneillchamber.org
Contact: Pat Fritz, Exec. Dir.

51999 ■ Ord Area Chamber of Commerce
1514 K St.
Ord, NE 68862
Ph:(308)728-7875
Fax:(308)728-7691
Co. E-mail: valleycountyed@frontiernet.net
URL: http://www.ordnebraska.com/chamber.asp
Contact: Caleb Pollard, Exec. Dir.

52000 ■ Plainview Chamber of Commerce
306 W Park Ave.
Plainview, NE 68769-0813
Ph:(402)582-4433
URL: http://www.plvwtelco.net/chamber-commerce. html
Contact: Audrey Green, Exec. Sec.

52001 ■ Plattsmouth Chamber of Commerce
918 Washington Ave.
Plattsmouth, NE 68048
Ph:(402)296-6021
Fax:(402)296-6974
Co. E-mail: lisad@plattsmouthchamber.com
URL: http://www.plattsmouthchamber.com
Contact: Lisa Davis, Exec. Dir.

52002 ■ Ralston Area Chamber of Commerce
5505 Miller Ave.
Ralston, NE 68127
Ph:(402)339-7737
Fax:(402)339-7954
Co. E-mail: chamber@cityofralston.com
URL: http://www.ralstonareachamber.org
Contact: Marlene Hansen, Pres.

52003 ■ Ravenna Area Chamber of Commerce
PO Box 56
Ravenna, NE 68869
Ph:(308)452-3225
Co. E-mail: ravchamber@towncountrybank.net
URL: http://www.ci.ravenna.ne.us/chamber.htm
Contact: Margaret Treffer, Exec. Dir.

52004 ■ Sarpy County Chamber of Commerce
Shadow Lake Town Center
7775 Olson Dr., Ste. 207
Papillion, NE 68046
Ph:(402)339-3050
Fax:(402)339-9968
Co. E-mail: jane@sarpychamber.org
URL: http://www.sarpychamber.org
Contact: Jane Nielsen, Pres.

52005 ■ Schuyler Area Chamber of Commerce
1107 B St.
Schuyler, NE 68661
Ph:(402)352-5472
Fax:(402)352-5472
Co. E-mail: schuylercc@hotmail.com
URL: http://www.ci.schuyler.ne.us/chamber.asp
Contact: Marie Myrick, Exec. Dir.

52006 ■ Scottsbluff - Gering United Chamber of Commerce
1517 Broadway, Ste. 104
Scottsbluff, NE 69361
Ph:(308)632-2133
Free: 800-788-9475
Fax:(308)632-7128
Co. E-mail: chamber@scottsbluffgering.net
URL: http://www.scottsbluffgering.net
Contact: Max Miller, Chm.

52007 ■ Seward Area Chamber of Commerce
616 Bradford
Seward, NE 68434
Ph:(402)643-4189
Co. E-mail: sewcham@sewardne.com
URL: http://www.sewardne.com
Contact: Sharon Pennington, Admin. Asst.

52008 ■ Superior Area Chamber of Commerce
354 N Commercial Ave.
Superior, NE 68978
Ph:(402)879-3419
Co. E-mail: superiorcc@alltel.net
URL: http://www.ci.superior.ne.us

52009 ■ Tecumseh Chamber of Commerce
PO Box 126
Tecumseh, NE 68450-0126
Ph:(402)335-3400
Co. E-mail: tecumsehchamber@windstream.net
URL: http://www.tecumsehne.com
Contact: Eloise Bartels, Sec.

52010 ■ Tekamah Chamber of Commerce
PO Box 231
Tekamah, NE 68061
Ph:(402)374-2020

Fax:(402)374-1392
Co. E-mail: hshafer@washingtoncountybank.com
URL: http://www.tekamahchamberofcommerce.com
Contact: Harriet Shafer, Sec.

52011 ■ Valentine Chamber of Commerce
PO Box 201
Valentine, NE 69201
Ph:(402)376-2969
Free: 800-658-4024
URL: http://www.heartcity.com

52012 ■ Wahoo Chamber of Commerce and Economic Development
PO Box 154
Wahoo, NE 68066-0154
Ph:(402)443-4001
Fax:(402)443-3077
Co. E-mail: watts@wahoo.ne.us
URL: http://www.wahoo.ne.us/index.asp
Contact: Doug Watts, Exec. Dir.

52013 ■ West Point Chamber of Commerce
PO Box 125
West Point, NE 68788
Ph:(402)372-2981
Fax:(402)372-1105
Co. E-mail: info@westpointchamber.com
URL: http://www.westpointchamber.com
Contact: DJ Weddle, Pres.

52014 ■ Western Douglas County Chamber of Commerce
20801 Elkhorn Dr.
PO Box 202
Elkhorn, NE 68022
Ph:(402)289-9560
Fax:(402)289-9560
Co. E-mail: lilly@wdccc.org
URL: http://www.wdccc.org
Contact: Jim Tomanek, Pres.

FINANCING AND LOAN PROGRAMS

52015 ■ Odin Capital Group, LLC
1625 Farnam St., Ste. 700
Omaha, NE 68102
Ph:(402)827-9900
Fax:(402)408-6354
URL: http://www.odincapital.com
Contact: John Gustafson, Principal
E-mail: jgustafson@odincapital.com
Preferred Investment Size: $1,000,000 to $4,000,000. **Investment Types:** Early, first, and second stage, and expansion. **Industry Preferences:** Communications, computer software, Internet specific, medical and health, industrial and energy, financial services, and business service. **Geographic Preferences:** Midwest, Rocky mountains, and Southwest. **Principal Exhibits:**

PROCUREMENT ASSISTANCE PROGRAMS

52016 ■ Nebraska Procurement Technical Assistance Center–Nebraska Business Development Center–University of Nebraska at Kearney (West)
West Ctr. Bldg., Rm. 127E
1917 W 24th St.
Kearney, NE 68849-4440
Ph:(308)865-8244
Fax:(308)865-8153
Co. E-mail: knappse@unk.edu
URL: http://ptac.unomaha.edu
Contact: Scott Knapp, Counselor
E-mail: knappse@unk.edu
Description: Helps Nebraska businesses grow and generate new business by locating opportunities for business with the government.

52017 ■ Procurement Technical Assistance Center at Lincoln–Nebraska Business Development Center
285 S 68th St. Place, Ste. 550
Lincoln, NE 68510
Ph:(402)472-1177
Fax:(402)472-3363
Co. E-mail: kcarlin@mailunomaha.edu
URL: http://ptac.unomaha.edu
Contact: Kate Carlin, Counselor
E-mail: wrjohnson@mail.unomaha.edu
Description: Helps Nebraska businesses grow and generate new business by locating opportunities for business with the government.

INCUBATORS/RESEARCH AND TECHNOLOGY PARKS

52018 ■ Omaha Small Business Network
2505 N. 24th St.
Omaha, NE 68110
Ph:(402)453-5336
Fax:(402)451-2876
Co. E-mail: info@osbntc.org
URL: http://www.osbnbtc.org/
Description: A small business incubator dedicated to providing the tools needed to have a successful business; helping businesses bridge the gap between survival and independence by offering numerous programs and collaborative relationships with Omaha's leading lenders and support agencies.

52019 ■ University of Nebraska—Lincoln–Office of Sponsored Programs
Alexander Bldg. W
312 N 14th St.
Lincoln, NE 68588-0430
Ph:(402)472-3171

Fax:(402)472-9323
Co. E-mail: jwicks2@unl.edu
URL: http://research.unl.edu/sp1/index.shtml
Contact: Jeanne Wicks, Dir.
E-mail: jwicks2@unl.edu
Scope: Administers and coordinates sponsored research at the University, negotiates research grants and contracts with outside agencies for the University, and serves as liaison between research sponsors, the University administration, individual faculty members, and University of Nebraska Foundation. Maintains files on research in progress at the University, government and foundation sources of research support, and application procedures. **Publications:** Annual report. **Educational Activities:** Workshops, on grantsmanship and patenting.

52020 ■ University of Nebraska Technology Park
4701 Innovation Dr.
Lincoln, NE 68521-5330
Ph:(402)472-4200
Fax:(402)472-4203
Co. E-mail: info@nutechpark.com
URL: http://www.nutechpark.com/
Contact: Stephen Frayser, Pres
Description: The first planned business campus in Nebraska. A business incubator serving new and established technology companies.

EDUCATIONAL PROGRAMS

52021 ■ Nebraska Department of Economic Development–Industrial Training Programs
301 Centennial Mall S
PO Box 94666
Lincoln, NE 68509-4666
Ph:800-426-6505
Free: 800-426-6505
Fax:(402)471-3778
URL: http://www.neded.org
Description: Customized job training programs.

52022 ■ University of Nebraska at Lincoln–Center for Entrepreneurship
Office of Entrepreneurship
University of Nebraska Lincoln CBA 209
Lincoln, NE 68588-0487
Ph:(402)472-3353
Fax:(402)472-5855
Co. E-mail: tsebora1@unl.edu
URL: http://www.cba.unl.edu/outreach/ent
Description: Offers a program/classes in small business/small business management.

PUBLISHERS

52023 ■ GHC Business Books
11202 N Post Rd.
Omaha, NE 68112
Ph:(402)453-1769
Contact: Raymond L. Gustafson, President
Description: Publishes book on small business development. services include a business brokerage. Reaches market through direct mail. **Founded:** 1982.

SMALL BUSINESS DEVELOPMENT CENTERS

52024 ■ Carson City Nevada Small Business Development Center
1900 S Carson St., No. 100
Carson City, NV 89701-4514
Fax:(775)882-4179
URL: http://www.nsbdc.org

52025 ■ Carson Valley Nevada Small Business Development Center
1477 Hwy. 395
Gardnerville, NV 89410
Fax:(775)782-1025
URL: http://www.nsbdc.org

52026 ■ Churchill County Nevada Small Business Development Center
PO Box 1236
Fallon, NV 89407
Fax:(775)623-1664
Co. E-mail: sbdc@ceda-nv.org
URL: http://www.nsbdc.org

52027 ■ Elko Nevada Small Business Development Center
Great Basin College
723 Railroad St.
Elko, NV 89801
Fax:(775)753-2242
Co. E-mail: judye@gwmail.gbcnv.edu
URL: http://www.nsbdc.org
Contact: Judy Emerson, Management Consultant

52028 ■ Ely Nevada Small Business Development Center
1320 E Alultman St.
Ely, NV 89301
Free: (866)404-5204
Fax:(775)289-8214
Co. E-mail: clint@rndcnv.org
URL: http://www.nsbdc.org
Contact: Clint Koble, Business Advisor

52029 ■ Henderson Nevada Small Business Development Center
112 Water St., Ste. 108
Henderson, NV 89015
Fax:(702)992-7245
URL: http://www.nsbdc.org

52030 ■ Las Vegas Nevada Small Business Development Center
PO Box 456011
Las Vegas, NV 89154
Fax:(702)895-4273
Co. E-mail: nsbdc@unlv.edu
URL: http://www.nsbdc.org
Contact: Janis Stevenson, Business Development Advisor

52031 ■ Laughlin Nevada Small Business Development Center
1585 S Casino Dr.
Laughlin, NV 89029
Fax:(702)298-5708
URL: http://www.nsbdc.org

52032 ■ Nevada Small Business Development Center
University of Nevada, Reno
College of Business Administration
Ansari Business Bldg., Rm. 411
Reno, NV 89557-0100
Free: 800-240-7094
Fax:(775)784-4337
Co. E-mail: nsbdc@unr.nevada.edu
URL: http://www.nsbdc.org
Contact: Sam Males, Dir.

52033 ■ Pahrump Nevada Small Business Development Center
Rural Nevada Development Corporation
NSB Bldg., 2nd Fl.
1301 S Hwy. 160
Pahrump, NV 89048
Fax:(775)751-1933
Co. E-mail: alparker@rndcnv.org
URL: http://www.nsbdc.org
Contact: Allan Parker, Business Consultant

52034 ■ Winnemucca Nevada Small Business Development Center
90 W Fourth St.
Winnemucca, NV 89445
Fax:(775)623-1664
Co. E-mail: bills@unr.edu
URL: http://www.nsbdc.org
Contact: Bill Sims

SMALL BUSINESS ASSISTANCE PROGRAMS

52035 ■ Nevada Commission on Economic Development
108 E Proctor St.
Carson City, NV 89701
Ph:(775)687-4325
Free: 800-336-1600
Fax:(775)687-4450
Co. E-mail: mskaggs@bizopp.state.nv.us
URL: http://www.expand2nevada.com
Contact: Michael E. Skaggs, Exec Dir
Description: Provides assistance to small businesses from start-up to operations.

52036 ■ Nevada Department of Business and Industry
555 E Washington Ave., Ste 4900
Las Vegas, NV 89101
Ph:(702)486-2750

Fax:(702)486-2758
Co. E-mail: biinfo@dbi.state.nv.us
URL: http://www.doi.state.nv.us/
objective is to encourage and promote growth, development, and legal operation of business within the State of Nevada.

SCORE OFFICES

52037 ■ SCORE Las Vegas
City Centre Pl.
400 S 4th St., Ste. 250A
Las Vegas, NV 89101
Ph:(702)388-6104
Fax:(702)388-5849
Co. E-mail: scorelv@coam.net
URL: http://www.scorelv.org
Contact: Ross Lagattuta, Chair
Description: Works to help people start and successfully manage their own businesses.

52038 ■ SCORE Northern Nevada
University of Nevada
College of Business Administration
Nevada Small Business Development Center
Reno, NV 89557
Ph:(775)784-4436
Fax:(775)784-4337
Co. E-mail: info@score-reno.org
URL: http://www.score-reno.org/sr
Contact: Bill Boon, Vice Chm.
Description: Offers free and confidential business advice, mentoring and information.

BETTER BUSINESS BUREAUS

52039 ■ Better Business Bureau of Southern Nevada
6040 S Jones Blvd.
Las Vegas, NV 89118-2619
Ph:(702)320-4500
Fax:(702)320-4560
Co. E-mail: info@vegasbbb.org
URL: http://southernnevada.bbb.org

CHAMBERS OF COMMERCE

52040 ■ Beatty Chamber of Commerce
PO Box 956
Beatty, NV 89003
Ph:(775)553-2424
Free: (866)736-3716
Co. E-mail: beattychamber@sbcglobal.net
URL: http://www.beattynevada.org
Contact: Ann Marchand, Pres.

52041 ■ Boulder City Chamber of Commerce
465 Nevada Way
Boulder City, NV 89005-2613
Ph:(702)293-2034
Free: 888-399-2948

Fax:(702)293-0574
Co. E-mail: info@bouldercitychamber.com
URL: http://www.bouldercitychamber.com

52042 ■ Caliente Chamber of Commerce
PO Box 553
Caliente, NV 89008
Ph:(775)726-3129
URL: http://www.lincolncountynevada.com

52043 ■ Carson City Area Chamber of Commerce
1900 S Carson St., Ste. 200
Carson City, NV 89701
Ph:(775)882-1565
Fax:(775)882-4179
Co. E-mail: director@carsoncitychamber.com
URL: http://www.carsoncitychamber.com
Contact: Ronni Hannaman, Exec. Dir.

52044 ■ Carson Valley Chamber of Commerce and Visitors Authority
1477 US Hwy. 395, Ste. A
Gardnerville, NV 89410
Ph:(775)782-8144
Free: 800-727-7677
Fax:(775)782-1025
Co. E-mail: info@carsonvalleynv.org
URL: http://www.carsonvalleynv.org
Contact: Sam Slack, Pres.

52045 ■ Dayton Area Chamber of Commerce
PO Box 2408
Dayton, NV 89403
Ph:(775)246-7909
Fax:(775)246-5838
Co. E-mail: info@daytonnvchamber.org
URL: http://www.daytonnvchamber.org
Contact: Susan Skaggs, Exec. Dir.

52046 ■ Elko Chamber of Commerce
1405 Idaho St.
Elko, NV 89801
Ph:(775)738-7135
Free: 800-428-7143
Fax:(775)738-7136
Co. E-mail: chamber@elkonevada.com
URL: http://www.elkonevada.com
Contact: LaVon Thomsen, CEO

52047 ■ Fernley Chamber of Commerce
70 N West St.
Fernley, NV 89408
Ph:(775)575-4459
Fax:(775)575-2626
Co. E-mail: fernleychamber@sbcglobal.net
URL: http://www.fernleychamber.org
Contact: Chris Beni, Pres.

52048 ■ Greater Austin Chamber of Commerce
PO Box 212
Austin, NV 89310-0212
Ph:(775)964-2200
Fax:(775)964-2447
Co. E-mail: austinnvchamber@yahoo.com
URL: http://www.austinnevada.com
Contact: Phillip Williams, Pres.

52049 ■ Greater Fallon Area Chamber of Commerce
85 N Taylor St.
Fallon, NV 89406
Ph:(775)423-2544
Fax:(775)423-0504
Co. E-mail: info@fallonchamber.com
URL: http://www.fallonchamber.com
Contact: Rick Dentino, Exec. Dir.

52050 ■ Henderson Chamber of Commerce
590 S Boulder Hwy.
Henderson, NV 89015-7512
Ph:(702)565-8951
Fax:(702)565-3115
Co. E-mail: info@hendersonchamber.com
URL: http://www.hendersonchamber.com
Contact: Alice Martz, CEO

52051 ■ Humboldt County Chamber of Commerce
30 W Winnemucca Blvd.
Winnemucca, NV 89445
Ph:(775)623-2225
Free: 877-326-1916
Fax:(775)623-6478
Co. E-mail: chamber@winnemucca.net
URL: http://www.humboldtcountychamber.com
Contact: John Arant, VP

52052 ■ Incline Village - Crystal Bay Chamber of Commerce
969 Tahoe Blvd.
Incline Village, NV 89451
Ph:(775)831-4440
Free: 800-519-1584
Fax:(775)832-1625
Co. E-mail: stevet@puretahoenorth.com
URL: http://www.laketahoechamber.com
Contact: Steve Teshara, Exec. Dir.

52053 ■ Las Vegas Chamber of Commerce
6671 Las Vegas Blvd. S, Ste. 300
Las Vegas, NV 89119
Ph:(702)735-1616
Fax:(702)735-2011
Co. E-mail: info@lvchamber.com
URL: http://www.lvchamber.com
Contact: Kara J. Kelley, Pres./CEO

52054 ■ Latin Chamber of Commerce of Nevada
300 N 13th St.
Las Vegas, NV 89101
Ph:(702)385-7367
Fax:(702)385-2614
Co. E-mail: info@lvlcc.com
URL: http://www.lvlcc.com
Contact: Otto Merida, Pres./CEO

52055 ■ Laughlin Chamber of Commerce
1585 S Casino Dr.
Laughlin, NV 89028
Ph:(702)298-2214
Free: 800-227-5245
Fax:(702)298-5708
Co. E-mail: info@laughlinchamber.com
URL: http://www.laughlinchamber.com
Contact: Janet Medina, Exec. Dir.

52056 ■ Lovelock/Pershing County Chamber of Commerce
PO Box 821
Lovelock, NV 89419-0821
Ph:(775)273-7213
Co. E-mail: info@pershingcountynevada.com
URL: http://www.pershingcountynevada.com
Contact: Lynn Christofferson, Chair

52057 ■ Mesquite Area Chamber of Commerce
12 W Mesquite Blvd., Ste. 107
Mesquite, NV 89027
Ph:(702)346-2902
Fax:(702)346-6138
Co. E-mail: meschamber@cascadeaccess.com
URL: http://www.mesquite-chamber.com
Contact: Deb Parsley, Pres.

52058 ■ Mineral County Chamber of Commerce
314 5th St.
PO Box 2250
Hawthorne, NV 89415
Ph:(775)945-2507
Co. E-mail: info@mineralcountychamber.com
URL: http://www.mineralcountychamber.com
Contact: J.R. Gibson, Pres.

52059 ■ Moapa Valley Chamber of Commerce
PO Box 430
Overton, NV 89040
Ph:(702)397-6246
Co. E-mail: chamber@moapavalley.com
URL: http://www.moapavalley.com
Contact: Vernon Robison, Pres.

52060 ■ Nevada Chamber of Commerce Association
One E First St., No. 1600
PO Box 3499
Reno, NV 89501
Ph:(775)337-3030
Fax:(775)337-3038
Co. E-mail: info@renosparkschamber.org
URL: http://www.reno-sparkschamber.org
Contact: Doug Kurkul, CEO

52061 ■ North Las Vegas Chamber of Commerce
3345 W Craig Rd., Ste. B
North Las Vegas, NV 89032
Ph:(702)642-9595
Fax:(702)642-0439
Co. E-mail: contact@nlvchamber.org
URL: http://www.nlvchamber.org
Contact: Sharon Powers, Pres./CEO

52062 ■ Pahrump Valley Chamber of Commerce
1301 S Hwy. 160, 2nd Fl.
PO Box 42
Pahrump, NV 89041
Ph:(775)727-5800
Free: (866)722-5800
Fax:(775)727-3909
Co. E-mail: info@pahrumpchamber.com
URL: http://www.pahrumpchamber.com
Contact: Michael Selbach, Pres.

52063 ■ Pioche Chamber of Commerce
PO Box 127
Pioche, NV 89043-0127
Ph:(775)962-5544
Co. E-mail: chamber@piocheneveda.com
URL: http://www.piochenevada.com
Contact: Bob Rowe, Pres.

52064 ■ Reno-Sparks Chamber of Commerce
1 E 1st St., Ste. 1600
Reno, NV 89501
Ph:(775)337-3030
Fax:(775)337-3038
Co. E-mail: info@renosparkschamber.org
URL: http://www.renosparkschamber.org
Contact: Jane Gilbert, Exec. Dir.

52065 ■ Sparks Chamber of Commerce
PO Box 1176
Sparks, NV 89432
Ph:(775)358-1976
Fax:(775)358-1992
Co. E-mail: l.stevens@sparkschamber.org
URL: http://www.sparkschamber.org
Contact: Len Stevens, Exec. Dir.

52066 ■ Virginia City/Gold Hill Chamber of Commerce
178 S C St.
Virginia City, NV 89440
Ph:(775)847-4499
Fax:(775)847-4499
Co. E-mail: vccoc@callatg.com
URL: http://www.virginiacity-nv.com

52067 ■ Wells Chamber of Commerce
PO Box 615
Wells, NV 89835
Ph:(775)752-3540
Fax:(775)752-2172
Co. E-mail: coc@californiatrailinterpretivecenter.com
URL: http://wellsnevada.com
Contact: Pat Kelly, Pres.

52068 ■ White Pine Chamber of Commerce
636 Aultman St.
Ely, NV 89301-1555
Ph:(775)289-8877
Fax:(775)289-6144
Co. E-mail: elycc@whitepinechamber.com
URL: http://www.whitepinechamber.com
Contact: Evie Pinneo, Exec. Dir.

MINORITY BUSINESS ASSISTANCE PROGRAMS

52069 ■ **Nevada Minority Business Enterprise Center–New Ventures Capital Development Corp.**
626 S Ninth St.
Las Vegas, NV 89101
Ph:(702)382-9522
Fax:(702)382-0375
Co. E-mail: vershaun_ragland@lvcoxmail.com
URL: http://www.newventurescdc.com
Contact: Vershaun Ragland, Sr Loan Off
Description: Provides business consulting, development, and management services to minority business enterprises in Nevada.

52070 ■ **Nevada Women's Business Resource and Assistance Center**
2770 S Maryland Pky., Ste. 212
Las Vegas, NV 89109
Ph:(702)732-0414
Fax:(702)732-2705
Co. E-mail: nwbrac@aol.com
Description: Helps low to moderate income women in Nevada to start or grow a small business. Provides advocacy, education, and outreach.

FINANCING AND LOAN PROGRAMS

52071 ■ **Benefit Capital Companies Inc.**
3235-3245 N. Pioneer Rd.
PO Box 542
Logandale, NV 89021
Ph:(702)398-3222
Fax:(702)398-3700
Co. E-mail: mail@benefitcapital.com
URL: http://www.benefitcapital.com
Contact: Robert W. Smiley, Chairman and Managing Director
E-mail: rsmiley@benefitcapital.com
Preferred Investment Size: $2,500,000 minimum. **Investment Types:** Leveraged buyout and mezzanine. **Industry Preferences:** Diversified. **Geographic Preferences:** U.S. **Principal Exhibits:**

PROCUREMENT ASSISTANCE PROGRAMS

52072 ■ **Nevada Commission on Economic Development–Procurement Outreach Program–Northern Nevada Regional Office (108 E)**
108 E Proctor St.
Carson City, NV 89701-4240
Ph:(775)687-1813
Free: 800-336-1600
Fax:(775)687-4450
Co. E-mail: tbaldassare@bizopp.state.nv.us
URL: http://www.expand2nevada.com/procurement.html
Contact: Kathy Dow, Counselor
Description: Assists small and disadvantaged businesses in Nevada obtain and complete federal government contracts. Also encourages the expansion of the manufacturing and service sectors into government contracting.

52073 ■ **Nevada Commission on Economic Development–Procurement Outreach Program–Southern Nevada Regional Office (555 E)**
555 E Washington Ave., Ste. 5400
Las Vegas, NV 89101
Ph:(702)486-2700
Fax:(702)486-2701
Co. E-mail: rhorn@bizopp.state.nv.us
URL: http://www.expand2nevada.com/procurement.html
Contact: Rick Horn, Dir.
Description: Assists small and disadvantaged businesses in Nevada obtain and complete federal government contracts. Also encourages the expansion of the manufacturing and service sectors into government contracting.

52074 ■ **Nevada Procurement Technical Assistance Center–Economic Development**
108 E Proctor St.
Carson City, NV 89701-4240
Ph:(775)687-4325
Free: 800-336-1600
Fax:(775)687-4450
Co. E-mail: mskaggs@bizopp.state.nv.us
URL: http://www.expand2nevada.com/procurement.html
Contact: Michael E. Skaggs, Exec. Dir.
Description: Assists small and disadvantaged businesses in Nevada obtain and complete federal government contracts. Also encourages the expansion of the manufacturing and service sectors into government contracting.

INCUBATORS/RESEARCH AND TECHNOLOGY PARKS

52075 ■ **Dandini Research Park**
2215 Raggio Pky.
Reno, NV 89512-1095
Ph:(775)849-3376
Fax:(702)862-5406
Co. E-mail: researchparkinfo@dri.edu
URL: http://researchpark.dri.edu
Contact: Jeff Pickett, Mng.Dir.
E-mail: researchparkinfo@dri.edu
Scope: 470-acre site that links the research and development activities of Park tenants with the Desert Research Institute's technological equipment, personnel, laboratories, and training programs. Instrument design, environmental testing, and research and development services may be done in cooperation with DRI staff.

52076 ■ **Henderson Business Resource Center**
112 Water St.
Henderson, NV 89015
Ph:(702)992-7200
Fax:(702)992-7241
Co. E-mail: hbrc@hendersonchamber.com
URL: http://www.hendersonbizcenter.com/
Description: A small business incubator who develops and supports local businesses and strengthens and diversifies the local economy through entrepreneurship training opportunities, mentoring programs, and introductions to potential capital sources.

EDUCATIONAL PROGRAMS

52077 ■ **Community College of Southern Nevada–Cheyenne Campus**
3200 E Cheyenne Ave.
North Las Vegas, NV 89030

Ph:(702)651-4000
Free: 800-492-5728
Fax:(702)643-1474
URL: http://www.ccsn.nevada.edu
Description: Offers a program/classes in small business/small business management.

52078 ■ **Truckee Meadows Community College–Institute for Business and Industry**
5270 Neil Rd.
4001 S Virginia St.
Reno, NV 89502
Ph:(775)829-9000
Fax:(775)829-9009
URL: http://www.tmcc.edu/
Description: Offers a program designed to bring courses to the workplace; in addition, curriculum can be customized for the particular needs of a company.

PUBLICATIONS

52079 ■ *Smart Start your Georgia Business*
PSI Research
300 N. Valley Dr.
Grants Pass, OR 97526
Ph:(503)479-9464
Free: 800-228-2275
Fax:(503)476-1479
Co. E-mail: info@psi-research.com
URL: http://www.psi-research.com
Ed: Michael D. Jenkins. **Released:** Revised edition, 1992. **Price:** $29.95 (looseleaf binder); $24.95 (paper). **Description:** Part of the Successful Business Library series.

PUBLISHERS

52080 ■ **Everett L. Gracey**
3288 Alum Creek Ct.
PO Box 6000
Reno, NV 89509
Ph:(775)324-3290
Fax:(775)324-3289
Co. E-mail: Ev@EverettGacey.com
URL: http://www.EverettGracey.com
Contact: Everett L. Gracey, Publisher
Description: Publishes business related books. Reaches market through wholesalers Ingram and Baker and Taylor. Does not accept unsolicited manuscripts. **Founded:** 1994.

52081 ■ **GifTech Corp.**
2961 Industrial Rd., Ste. 731
Las Vegas, NV 89109
Free: 800-594-9829
Co. E-mail: taxmama@taxmama.com
URL: http://www.taxmama.com
Contact: Eva Rosenberg, Editor
Description: Publishes information about tax, business, women, networking and e-books. Offers video tapes and calendars. Also offers a weekly newsletter. Does not accept unsolicited manuscripts. Reaches market through reviews, listings and the Internet. **Founded:** 1984.

52082 ■ **Long & Silverman Publishing Inc.**
800 N Rainbow Blvd., Ste. 208
Las Vegas, NV 89107-1103
Ph:(702)948-5073
Free: 888-902-2766
Fax:(702)447-9733
Co. E-mail: sales@lspub.com
URL: http://www.lspub.com
Contact: Rebecca A. Stein
E-mail: rstein@lspub.com
Founded: 2003.

SMALL BUSINESS DEVELOPMENT CENTERS

52083 ■ **New Hampshire Small Business Development Center**
University of NH
The Whittemore School of Business
110 McConnell Hall
Durham, NH 03824
Fax:(603)862-4876
Co. E-mail: mary.collins@unh.edu
URL: http://www.nhsbdc.org
Contact: Mary E. Collins, State Dir.

52084 ■ **Small Business Development Center - Keene**
Keene State College
Mailstop 2101
Keene, NH 03435-2101
Fax:(603)358-2612
Co. E-mail: cflanagan@keene.edu
URL: http://www.nhsbdc.org
Contact: Christina Flanagan, Program Asst.

52085 ■ **Small Business Development Center - Littleton**
120 Main St.
Littleton, NH 03561
Fax:(603)444-5463
Co. E-mail: nh.sbdc@unh.edu
URL: http://www.nhsbdc.org

52086 ■ **Small Business Development Center - Manchester**
33 S Commercial St.
Manchester, NH 03101-1796
Fax:(603)647-4410
Co. E-mail: jason.cannon@unh.edu
URL: http://www.nhsbdc.org

52087 ■ **Small Business Development Center - Nashua**
Daniel Webster College
20 University Dr.
Nashua, NH 03060-5086
Co. E-mail: mcmillan_rosemary@dwc.edu
URL: http://www.nhsbdc.org
Contact: Rosemary McMillan, Program Asst.

52088 ■ **Small Business Development Center - Seacoast**
18 S Main St., Ste. 2A
Rochester, NH 03867
Fax:(603)330-1948
Co. E-mail: krysteen.hopkins@unh.edu
URL: http://www.nhsbdc.org
Contact: Krysteen Hopkins, Program Asst.

SMALL BUSINESS ASSISTANCE PROGRAMS

52089 ■ **New Hampshire Department of Resources and Economic Development–Business Resource Center**
172 Pembroke Rd.
PO Box 1856
Concord, NH 03302-1856
Ph:(603)271-2591
Fax:(603)271-6784
Co. E-mail: info@nheconomy.com
URL: http://www.nheconomy.com/
Contact: Roy Duddy, Dir
Description: Assists companies considering locating in New Hampshire in their review of staffing and facility requirements, marketing considerations, support services, and other services. Also offers complete, current, and reliable information on those sections of the state best able to support a specific project. Also helps existing businesses.

SCORE OFFICES

52090 ■ **Mount Washington Valley SCORE**
53 Technology Ln., Ste. 101
Conway, NH 03818
Ph:(603)447-4388
Fax:(603)447-9947
Co. E-mail: info@score641.org
URL: http://www.score641.org
Contact: Richard Ficke, Chm.
Description: Provides professional guidance and information to America's small business in order to strengthen the local and national economy.

52091 ■ **SCORE Merrimack Valley, NH, Chapter 199**
275 Chestnut St.
Manchester, NH 03101
Ph:(603)666-7561
Co. E-mail: info@score199.mv.com
URL: http://www.score-manchester.org
Description: Represents business people supported by and affiliated with the U.S. Small Business Administration. Provides free, confidential and professional business counseling for small business and those wishing to start their own business.

52092 ■ **SCORE Monadnock**
34 Mechanic St.
Keene, NH 03431-3421
Ph:(603)352-0320
Co. E-mail: info@monadnockscore.org
URL: http://www.monadnockscore.org
Contact: Adele Knight, Chair
Description: Works to provide quality business counseling without charge to residents and business area.

52093 ■ **Seacoast SCORE Chapter 185**
195 Commerce Way, Ste. A
Portsmouth, NH 03801
Ph:(603)433-0575
Fax:(603)433-0576
Co. E-mail: info@scorehelp.org
URL: http://www.scorehelp.org/chapter_185.html
Contact: Ted Papoutsy
Description: Represents the interests of retired business professionals who volunteer their experience and knowledge to help small business owners and potential small business owners achieve success. Provides free business counseling and seminars.

52094 ■ **Upper Valley SCORE**
Citizens Bank Bldg., Rm. 316
20 W Park St.
Lebanon, NH 03766
Ph:(603)448-3491
Fax:(603)448-1908
Co. E-mail: score@valley.net
URL: http://www.uppervalleyscore.org
Description: Provides free and confidential business counseling tailored to meet the needs of small business and personal objectives.

BETTER BUSINESS BUREAUS

52095 ■ **Better Business Bureau of New Hampshire**
25 Hall St., Ste. 102
Concord, NH 03301-3483
Ph:(603)224-1991
Fax:(603)228-9035
Co. E-mail: info@bbbnh.org
URL: http://concord.bbb.org

CHAMBERS OF COMMERCE

52096 ■ **Bethlehem Chamber of Commerce**
2182 Main St., Rte. 302
PO Box 748
Bethlehem, NH 03574-0748
Free: 888-845-1957
Co. E-mail: info@bethlehemwhitemtns.com
URL: http://www.bethlehemwhitemtns.com

52097 ■ **Conway Village Area Chamber of Commerce**
PO Box 1019
Conway, NH 03818
Ph:(603)447-2639
Co. E-mail: info@conwaychamber.com
URL: http://www.conwaychamber.com

52098 ■ **Exeter Area Chamber of Commerce**
PO Box 278
Exeter, NH 03833
Ph:(603)772-2411
Fax:(603)772-9965
Co. E-mail: info@exeterarea.org
URL: http://www.exeterarea.org
Contact: Thomas J. Kraus, Pres.

52099 ■ **Franconia Notch Chamber of Commerce**
PO Box 780
Franconia, NH 03580-0780
Ph:(603)823-5661
Co. E-mail: info@franconianotch.org
URL: http://www.franconianotch.org
Contact: Barbara Ashley, Exec. Dir.

52100 ■ **Greater Claremont Chamber of Commerce**
24 Opera House Sq.
Claremont, NH 03743
Ph:(603)543-1296

Fax:(603)542-1469
Co. E-mail: claremontchamber@verizon.net
URL: http://www.claremontnhchamber.org
Contact: Shelly Hudson, Exec. Dir.

52101 ■ Greater Derry Chamber of Commerce
29 W Broadway
Derry, NH 03038
Ph:(603)432-8205
Fax:(603)432-7938
Co. E-mail: derrychamber@earthlink.net
URL: http://www.derry-chamber.org
Contact: Gina Gulino-Payne, Exec. Dir.

52102 ■ Greater Dover Chamber of Commerce
299 Central Ave.
Dover, NH 03820-4127
Ph:(603)742-2218
Co. E-mail: info@dovernh.org
URL: http://www.dovernh.org
Contact: Jack Story, Pres./CEO

52103 ■ Greater Franklin Chamber of Commerce
PO Box 464
Franklin, NH 03235
Ph:(603)934-6909
Co. E-mail: info@franklinnhchamber.com
URL: http://www.laconia-weirs.org
Contact: Sandy Marshall, Pres.

52104 ■ Greater Hudson Chamber of Commerce
71 Lowell Rd.
Hudson, NH 03051
Ph:(603)889-4731
Fax:(603)889-7939
Co. E-mail: info@hudsonchamber.com
URL: http://www.hudsonchamber.com
Contact: Brenda Collins, Exec. Dir.

52105 ■ Greater Keene Chamber of Commerce
48 Central Sq.
Keene, NH 03431
Ph:(603)352-1303
Fax:(603)358-5341
Co. E-mail: info@keenechamber.com
URL: http://www.keenechamber.com
Contact: Thomas Dowling, Pres.

52106 ■ Greater Laconia-Weirs Beach Chamber of Commerce
383 S Main St.
Laconia, NH 03246
Ph:(603)524-5531
Fax:(603)524-5534
Co. E-mail: dholmes@laconia-weirs.org
URL: http://www.laconia-weirs.org
Contact: Douglas R. Holmes, Exec. Dir.

52107 ■ Greater Manchester Chamber of Commerce
889 Elm St.
Manchester, NH 03101
Ph:(603)666-6600
Fax:(603)626-0910
Co. E-mail: robinc@manchester-chamber.org
URL: http://www.manchester-chamber.org
Contact: Robin Comstock, Pres./CEO

52108 ■ Greater Nashua Chamber of Commerce
151 Main St.
Nashua, NH 03060
Ph:(603)881-8333
Fax:(603)881-7323
Co. E-mail: chamber@nashuachamber.com
URL: http://www.nashuachamber.com
Contact: J. Christopher Williams, Pres./CEO

52109 ■ Greater Ossipee Area Chamber of Commerce
PO Box 323
Center Ossipee, NH 03814
Ph:(603)539-6201

Free: (866)683-6295
Co. E-mail: info@ossipeevalley.org
URL: http://www.ossipeevalley.org
Contact: Bill Grover, Pres.

52110 ■ Greater Peterborough Chamber of Commerce
PO Box 401
10 Wilton Rd., Rte. 101
Peterborough, NH 03458
Ph:(603)924-7234
Fax:(603)924-7235
Co. E-mail: info@peterboroughchamber.com
URL: http://www.greater-peterborough-chamber.com
Contact: Jack Burnett, Exec. Dir.

52111 ■ Greater Portsmouth Chamber of Commerce
PO Box 239
Portsmouth, NH 03802-0239
Ph:(603)436-3988
Fax:(603)436-5118
Co. E-mail: info@portsmouthchamber.org
URL: http://www.portsmouthchamber.org
Contact: Doug Bates, Pres.

52112 ■ Greater Rochester Chamber of Commerce
18 S Main St.
Rochester, NH 03867-2702
Ph:(603)332-5080
Fax:(603)332-5216
Co. E-mail: chamber@rochesternh.org
URL: http://www.rochesternh.org
Contact: Laura A. Ring, Pres.

52113 ■ Greater Salem Chamber of Commerce
224 N Broadway, 1st Fl.
PO Box 304
Salem, NH 03079-0304
Ph:(603)893-3177
Fax:(603)894-5158
Co. E-mail: donna@gschamber.com
URL: http://www.salemnhchamber.com
Contact: Donna Morris, Exec. Dir.

52114 ■ Greater Somersworth Chamber of Commerce
58 High St.
PO Box 615
Somersworth, NH 03878-0615
Ph:(603)692-7175
Fax:(603)692-4501
Co. E-mail: jennifer@somersworthchamber.com
URL: http://www.somersworthchamber.com
Contact: Ms. Jennifer Soldati, Pres.

52115 ■ Hampton Beach Area Chamber of Commerce
PO Box 790
Hampton, NH 03843
Ph:(603)926-8718
Fax:(603)926-9977
Co. E-mail: info@hamptonchamber.com
URL: http://www.hamptonchamber.com
Contact: B.J. Noel, Pres.

52116 ■ Hanover Area Chamber of Commerce
47-53 S Main St.
PO Box 5105
Hanover, NH 03755
Ph:(603)643-3115
Fax:(603)643-5606
Co. E-mail: hacc@hanoverchamber.org
URL: http://www.hanoverchamber.org
Contact: Janet Rebman, Exec. Dir.

52117 ■ Hillsborough Chamber of Commerce
PO Box 541
Hillsborough, NH 03244-0541
Ph:(603)464-5858
Fax:(603)464-9166
Co. E-mail: hcofc@conknet.com
URL: http://www.hillsboroughnhchamber.com
Contact: Mark Belden

52118 ■ Jaffrey Chamber of Commerce
7 Main St.
PO Box 2
Jaffrey, NH 03452-0002
Ph:(603)532-4549
Fax:(603)532-8823
Co. E-mail: info@jaffreychamber.com
URL: http://www.jaffreychamber.com
Contact: Cathy Furze, Pres.

52119 ■ Lebanon Chamber of Commerce
1 School St.
PO Box 97
Lebanon, NH 03766
Ph:(603)448-1203
Fax:(603)448-6489
Co. E-mail: lebanonchamber@lebanonchamber.com
URL: http://www.lebanonchamber.com
Contact: Paul R. Boucher, Pres./CEO

52120 ■ Lincoln-Woodstock Chamber of Commerce
PO Box 1017
Lincoln, NH 03251-0358
Ph:(603)745-6621
Fax:(603)745-4908
Co. E-mail: info@lincolnwoodstock.com
URL: http://www.lincolnwoodstock.com/chamber/index.php
Contact: Mark LaClair, Exec. Dir.

52121 ■ Lisbon Area Chamber of Commerce
46 School St.
Lisbon, NH 03585
Ph:(603)838-6376
Co. E-mail: lisbonnh@roadrunner.com
URL: http://www.lisbonnh.org/public_documents/LisbonNH_WebDocs
Contact: John Northrop, Pres.

52122 ■ Littleton Area Chamber of Commerce
PO Box 105
Littleton, NH 03561
Ph:(603)444-6561
Fax:(603)444-2427
Co. E-mail: info@lacc.mv.com
URL: http://www.littletonareachamber.com
Contact: Chad Stearns, Service Coor.

52123 ■ Meredith Area Chamber of Commerce
PO Box 732
Meredith, NH 03253-0732
Ph:(603)279-6121
Free: 877-279-6121
Fax:(603)279-4525
Co. E-mail: meredith@lr.net
URL: http://www.meredithcc.org
Contact: Susan Cerutti, Exec. Dir.

52124 ■ Merrimack Chamber of Commerce
PO Box 254
Merrimack, NH 03054-0254
Ph:(603)424-3669
Fax:(603)429-4325
Co. E-mail: info@merrimackchamber.org
URL: http://www.merrimackchamber.org
Contact: Bob Ellis, Pres.

52125 ■ New London - Lake Sunapee Region Chamber of Commerce
PO Box 532
New London, NH 03257-0532
Ph:(603)526-6575
Free: 877-526-6575
Co. E-mail: chamberinfo@nhvt.net
URL: http://www.lakesunapeenh.org
Contact: Rob Bryant, Exec. Dir.

52126 ■ Newfound Region Chamber of Commerce
PO Box 454
Bristol, NH 03222
Ph:(603)744-2150
Co. E-mail: newfoundchamber@metrocast.net
URL: http://www.newfoundchamber.com
Contact: Denice DeStefano, Pres.

52127 ■ Newport Area Chamber of Commerce
2 N Main St.
Newport, NH 03773
Ph:(603)863-1510
Fax:(603)863-9486
Co. E-mail: chamber@newportnhchamber.org
URL: http://www.newportnhchamber.org
Contact: Ella M. Casey, Exec. Dir.

52128 ■ North Country Chamber of Commerce
PO Box 1
Colebrook, NH 03576
Ph:(603)237-8939
Free: 800-698-8939
Fax:(603)237-4573
Co. E-mail: nccoc@verizon.net
URL: http://www.northcountrychamber.org
Contact: Luc Lambert, Pres.

52129 ■ Northern Gateway Chamber of Commerce
PO Box 537
Lancaster, NH 03584-0537
Ph:(603)788-2530
Free: 877-788-2530
Co. E-mail: ngchamber@yahoo.com
URL: http://www.northerngatewaychamber.org
Contact: Sally Pratt, Pres.

52130 ■ Plymouth Chamber of Commerce
PO Box 65
Plymouth, NH 03264
Ph:(603)536-1001
Free: 800-386-3678
Fax:(603)536-4017
Co. E-mail: sally@plymouthnh.org
URL: http://www.plymouthnh.org
Contact: Sarah A. Kilfoyle, Exec. Dir.

52131 ■ Souhegan Valley Chamber of Commerce
89 State Rte. 101A
Amherst, NH 03031
Ph:(603)673-4360
Fax:(603)673-5018
URL: http://www.souhegan.net
Contact: May Balsama, Exec. Dir.

52132 ■ Waterville Valley Region Chamber of Commerce
12 Vintinner Rd.
Campton, NH 03223
Ph:(603)726-3804
Free: 800-237-2307
Fax:(603)726-4058
Co. E-mail: info@watervillevalleyregion.com
URL: http://www.watervillevalleyregion.com
Contact: Chris Bolan, Exec. Dir.

MINORITY BUSINESS ASSISTANCE PROGRAMS

52133 ■ WREN - Women's Rural Entrepreneurial Network
2011 Main St.
PO Box 331
Bethlehem, NH 03574
Ph:(603)869-9736
Fax:(603)869-9738
Co. E-mail: wren@wrencommunity.org
URL: http://www.wrencommunity.org
Contact: Marilinne Cooper, Exec Dir
Description: Provides business development and technical assistance to women who would like to start a business.

FINANCING AND LOAN PROGRAMS

52134 ■ Arete Corporation
PO Box 1299
Center Harbor, NH 03226
Ph:(603)253-9797

Fax:(603)253-9799
Co. E-mail: aretecorp@adelphia.net
URL: http://www.arete-microgen.com
Contact: Robert W. Shaw, President
Preferred Investment Size: $500,000 to $3,000,000.
Investment Types: Seed, start-up, early and first stage, and research and development. **Industry Preferences:** Industrial and energy. **Geographic Preferences:** U.S. and Canada. **Principal Exhibits:**

PROCUREMENT ASSISTANCE PROGRAMS

52135 ■ New Hampshire Procurement Technical Assistance Center–State of New Hampshire–Economic Development (172 P)
172 Pembroke Rd.
PO Box 1856
Concord, NH 03302-1856
Ph:(603)271-7581
Fax:(603)271-6784
Co. E-mail: info@nheconomy.com
URL: http://www.nheconomy.com
Contact: Brad Martin, Prgm. Mgr.

52136 ■ New Hampshire Procurement Technical Assistance Center–State of New Hampshire–Office of Business & Industrial Department of Defense (172 P)
172 Pembroke Rd.
PO Box 1856
Concord, NH 03302-1856
Ph:(603)271-7581
Fax:(603)271-6784
Co. E-mail: bmartin@dred.state.nh.us
URL: http://www.nheconomy.com/ptac.html
Contact: Brad Martin, Prgm. Mgr.
E-mail: cway@dred.state.nh.us
Description: The New Hampshire Procurement Technical Assistance Program (NH-PTAP) exists to help New Hampshire client businesses - whether large, small, newly established, minority owned, women-owned, veteran owned, etc obtain information needed to bid competitively on Department of Defense, federal, state and local contracts.

INCUBATORS/RESEARCH AND TECHNOLOGY PARKS

52137 ■ Amoskeag Business Incubator
33 S. Commercial St.
Manchester, NH 03101
Ph:(603)629-9511
Fax:(603)629-9510
Co. E-mail: info@abi-nh.com
URL: http://www.abi-nh.com/
Description: A small business incubator seeking to provide a supportive entrepreneurial environment that stimulates the growth of businesses to ensure economic vitality and encourage job creation by providing affordable office space and technical assistance to early-stage companies.

52138 ■ Dartmouth Regional Technology Center
Centerra Research Park
16 Cavendish Ct.
Lebanon, NH 03766
Ph:(603)676-3300
Fax:(603)646-3670
Co. E-mail: info@thedrtc.com
URL: http://www.thedrtc.com
Contact: Alla Kan, Dir.
Description: A small business incubator focusing on developing businesses with a proven concept and a solid plan. It offers an educational and infrastructure support program aimed at developing promising technology startups by assisting them in refining their business plans, helping them identify and seek sources of investment and expertise, and providing them with basic business infrastructure and support to make them as productive as possible in as short a time as possible.

52139 ■ University of New Hampshire–Office of Vice President for Research and Public Service
Thompson Hall, Rm. 107
105 Main St.
Durham, NH 03824-3547
Ph:(603)862-1948
Fax:(603)862-3617
Co. E-mail: office.vicepresident.rps@unh.edu
URL: http://www.unh.edu/orps/
Contact: T. Taylor Eighmy, Interim VP
E-mail: office.vicepresident.rps@unh.edu
Scope: Promotes research and development relationships between the private sector and the University. Organizes problem solving teams and makes available University instrumentation and computer facilities and research and development laboratories. Assists business and industry with product development, process development, long-range research and planning, modeling, software development, technical troubleshooting, feasibility studies, development of laboratory testing procedures, market analysis, risk analysis, and planning and educational programs. Develops patents and licenses technology and other intellectual property of the University.

EDUCATIONAL PROGRAMS

52140 ■ Hesser College
3 Sundial Ave.
Manchester, NH 03103
Ph:(603)668-6660
Free: 800-526-9231
Fax:(603)666-4722
URL: http://www.hesser.edu
Description: Two-year college offering a small business management program.

PUBLICATIONS

52141 ■ *BNH: The Business of New Hampshire*
404 Chestnut St., Ste. 201
Manchester, NH 03101
Ph:(603)626-6354
Fax:(603)626-6359
Co. E-mail: businessnh@nh.interwebb.com

52142 ■ *New Hampshire Business Review*
150 Dow St.
Manchester, NH 03101-1151
Ph:(603)624-1442
Fax:(603)624-1310
Co. E-mail: nhbr@aol.com
URL: http://www.nhbr.com

52143 ■ *New Hampshire Department of Resources and Economic Development—Agenda*
New Hampshire Division of Economic Development
PO Box 1856
Concord, NH 03302-1856
Ph:(603)271-2341
Fax:(603)271-6784
URL: http://www.dred.state.nh.us/ded/
Ed: Kristi Forrest. **Description:** Presents news on business and industrial development in New Hampshire. Focuses on technology, workers compensation, business awards, legislation, and international trade.

52144 ■ *Smart Start your New Hampshire Business*
PSI Research
300 N. Valley Dr.
Grants Pass, OR 97526
Ph:(503)479-9464
Free: 800-228-2275
Fax:(503)476-1479
Co. E-mail: info@psi-research.com
URL: http://www.psi-research.com
Ed: Michael D. Jenkins. **Released:** Revised edition, 1992. **Price:** $29.95 (looseleaf binder); $24.95 (paper). **Description:** Part of the Successful Business Library series.

PUBLISHERS

52145 ■ New Hampshire Small Business Development Center
The Whittemore School of Business

University of New Hampshire, 110 McConnell Hall
Durham, NH 03824
Ph:(603)862-2200
Fax:(603)862-4876
Co. E-mail: nh.sbdc@unh.edu
URL: http://www.nhsbdc.org

Contact: Tim Dining, Chairman of the Board

Description: Publishes guidebooks of business and marketing data. Reaches market through direct mail. Does not accept unsolicited manuscripts. **Founded:** 1984.

SMALL BUSINESS DEVELOPMENT CENTERS

52146 ■ Bergen Small Business Development Center
Ciarco Learning Center
355 Main St.
Hackensack, NJ 07601
Fax:(201)489-8673
Co. E-mail: sbdc@bergen.edu
URL: http://www.bergen.edu/pages/675.asp
Contact: Vincent A. D'Elia, Dir.

52147 ■ Centenary College Small Business Development Center
400 Jefferson St.
Hackettstown, NJ 07840
Co. E-mail: sbdc@centenarycollege.edu
URL: http://www.centenarycollege.edu/cms/index.php?id=sbdc
Contact: Dolores J. Stammer, Dir.

52148 ■ Kean University Small Business Development Center
301 Morris Ave.
Union, NJ 07083
Co. E-mail: mkostak@kean.edu
Contact: Ms. Mira Kostak, Regional Dir.

52149 ■ Monmouth/Ocean Small Business Development Center
765 Newman Springs Rd.
Lincroft, NJ 07738
URL: http://ux.brookdalecc.edu/staff/sbdc/Default/Default.htm
Contact: Bill Nunnally, Dir.

52150 ■ New Jersey City University Small Business Development Center
20 College St.
Jersey City, NJ 07305-1520
Fax:(201)200-3404
Co. E-mail: boneal@njcu.edu
URL: http://www.njsbdc.com/contact/njcu.php
Contact: Barbara O'Neal, Dir.

52151 ■ New Jersey Small Business Development Center, Rutgers University - Camden
Waterfront Technology Center
200 Federal St., Ste. 435
Camden, NJ 08103
Fax:(856)225-6621
Co. E-mail: rsbdc@camden.rutgers.edu
URL: http://crab.rutgers.edu/lAtrsbdc/index.htm
Contact: Gary Rago, Dir.

52152 ■ Rutgers-Newark Small Business Development Center
43 Bleeker St.
Newark, NJ 07102
Fax:(973)353-1030
Co. E-mail: rnsbdc@newark.rutgers.edu
URL: http://www.rnsbdc.newark.rutgers.edu
Contact: Tendai Ndoro, Dir.

52153 ■ Small Business Development Center at Raritan Valley Community College
PO Box 3300
Somerville, NJ 08876
Co. E-mail: sbdc@raritanval.edu
URL: http://www.sbdcrvcc.com/about.html
Contact: Larry Jenkins, Dir.

52154 ■ Small Business Development Center - The College of New Jersey
Forcina Hall 447
2000 Pennington Ave.
Ewing, NJ 08628
Fax:(609)637-5217
Co. E-mail: sbdc@tcnj.edu
URL: http://www.tcnj.edu/lAtsbdc

52155 ■ William Paterson University Small Business Development Center
131 Ellison St.
Paterson, NJ 07505
Co. E-mail: sbdc@wpunj.edu
URL: http://www.wpunj.edu/sbdc
Contact: Kate Muldoon, Dir.

SMALL BUSINESS ASSISTANCE PROGRAMS

52156 ■ New Jersey Commerce Economic Growth and Tourism Commission–International Trade and Protocol
Mary G. Roebling Bldg.
20 W. State St.
PO Box 820
Trenton, NJ 08625-0820
Ph:(609)292-3860
URL: http://www.state.nj.us/njbusiness/wmb/inc/pro-gin/oitp.shtml
Description: Helps New Jersey companies in export development and expansion. Also encourages foreign investment in the state.

52157 ■ New Jersey Commerce Economic Growth and Tourism Commission–Office of Marketing
Mary G. Roebling Bldg.
20 W State St., 4th Fl.
PO Box 820
Trenton, NJ 08625-0835
Ph:(609)292-0700
Fax:(609)292-9145
URL: http://www.newjerseycommerce.org
Description: Acts as an ombudsman, handling complaints and problems of small business owners. Also serves as an advocate for small businesses and administers the One Stop Permit Identification System.

52158 ■ New Jersey Department of Business and Economic Development
Mary G. Roebling Bldg.
20 W State St.
Trenton, NJ 08625-0990

Ph:(609)292-4431
URL: http://www.newjerseycommerce.org/
Description: Provides complete assistance packages, including financing, site selection, and construction. Package may also include labor recruitment and training.

52159 ■ New Jersey Economic Development Authority–Office of the Business Advocate
36 W. State St
P.O Box 990
Trenton, NJ 08625-0820
Ph:(609)292-3863
URL: http://www.njeda.com/web/default.aspx
Contact: Lauren Moore, Dir
Description: Certify Minority, women- owned and small businesses. Formerly New Jersey Commerce Commission.

52160 ■ New Jersey Economic Growth & Tourism–Business Services & Urban Programs
33 W. State St
P.O Box 026
PO Box 820
Trenton, NJ 08625-0820
Ph:(609)292-2146
Fax:(609)292-9145
URL: http://www.state.nj.us/commerce/about_busserv_urbanpro.shtml
Description: Provides a central resource for small, women-owned, and minority-owned businesses in dealing with federal, state, and local governments. Also provides financial, marketing, procurement, technical, and managerial assistance.

SCORE OFFICES

52161 ■ Central Jersey SCORE
Path: www.scorechapter14.org

52162 ■ Monmouth SCORE
Path: www.score36.org

52163 ■ North West SCORE
Path: www.njscore24.org

52164 ■ Ocean County SCORE
Dover Township Municipal Bldg.
33 Washington St.
Toms River, NJ 08753
Ph:(732)505-6033
Co. E-mail: score150@litenet.net
URL: http://www.oceancountyscore.org
Contact: Mr. Robert Ermatinger, Chapter Chm.
Description: Serves small business community for many years and has a track record of providing small business owners with the advice they need to succeed.

52165 ■ Princeton SCORE
Path: www.scoreprinceton.org

52166 ■ SCORE Bergen
Path: www.scorebergen.org

52167 ■ SCORE Newark
Small Business Administration
2 Gateway Ctr., 15th Fl.
Newark, NJ 07102
Ph:(973)645-3982
Co. E-mail: newarkscore@yahoo.com
URL: http://www.scoremetronj.org
Description: Provides personalized, confidential counseling to help people start and operate a successful small business.

52168 ■ Southern New Jersey SCORE
Path: www.score254.org

52169 ■ Tri-County SCORE
Path: tri-countyscore.org

BETTER BUSINESS BUREAUS

52170 ■ Better Business Bureau of New Jersey
1700 Whitehorse-Hamilton Square Rd., Ste. D-5
Trenton, NJ 08690
Ph:(609)588-0808
Fax:(609)588-0546
Co. E-mail: info@trenton.bbb.org
URL: http://newjersey.bbb.org
Contact: Ms. Melissa Companick, Pres.

CHAMBERS OF COMMERCE

52171 ■ Atlantic City Regional Chamber of Commerce
The Garage at Gordon's Alley
12 S Virginia Ave.
Atlantic City, NJ 08401-4806
Ph:(609)345-4524
Fax:(609)345-1666
Co. E-mail: tthomas@atlanticcitychamber.com
URL: http://www.atlanticcitychamber.com
Contact: Joseph Kelly, Pres.

52172 ■ Avalon Chamber of Commerce
PO Box 22
Avalon, NJ 08202-0022
Ph:(609)967-3936
Co. E-mail: chamber@avalonbeach.com
URL: http://www.avalonbeach.com
Contact: Edward Galante, Pres.

52173 ■ Belmar Chamber of Commerce
1005 1/2 Main St.
Belmar, NJ 07719
Ph:(732)681-2900
Fax:(732)681-8471
Co. E-mail: info@belmarchamber.com
URL: http://www.belmarchamber.com
Contact: Rachel Rogers, Pres.

52174 ■ Bound Brook Area Chamber of Commerce
PO Box 227
Bound Brook, NJ 08805
Ph:(732)356-7273
URL: http://bbareachamber.com
Contact: Dr. Deanne Confalone, Pres.

52175 ■ Brick Township Chamber of Commerce
270 Chambers Bridge Rd., Ste. 6
Brick, NJ 08723
Ph:(732)477-4949
Fax:(732)477-5788
Co. E-mail: info@brickchamber.org
URL: http://www.brickchamber.org
Contact: Michele Eventoff, Exec. Dir.

52176 ■ Bridgeton Area Chamber of Commerce
53 S Laurel St.
PO Box 1063
Bridgeton, NJ 08302
Ph:(856)455-1312
Fax:(856)453-9795
Co. E-mail: bacc@baccnj.com
URL: http://www.baccnj.com
Contact: Anthony Stanzione, Exec. Dir.

52177 ■ Brigantine Beach Chamber of Commerce
PO Box 484
Brigantine, NJ 08203
Ph:(609)266-6111
Co. E-mail: info@brigantinechamber.com
URL: http://www.brigantinechamber.com
Contact: Betty Dillon, Pres.

52178 ■ Burlington County Chamber of Commerce
100 Technology Way, Ste. 110
Mount Laurel, NJ 08054
Ph:(856)439-2520
Fax:(856)439-2523
Co. E-mail: bccoc@bccoc.com
URL: http://bccoc.com
Contact: Kristi M. Howell-Ikeda, Pres.

52179 ■ Cape May County Chamber of Commerce
PO Box 74
Cape May Court House, NJ 08210-0074
Ph:(609)465-7181
Fax:(609)465-5017
Co. E-mail: inquiry@cmccofc.com
URL: http://www.cmccofc.com
Contact: Vickie Clark, Pres.

52180 ■ Central Jersey Chamber of Commerce
PO Box 300
Elizabeth, NJ 07207-0300
Ph:(908)352-0900
Fax:(908)352-0865
Co. E-mail: info@gatewaychamber.com
URL: http://www.gatewaychamber.com
Contact: James R. Coyle, Pres.

52181 ■ Chamber of Commerce of Greater Cape May
609 Lafayette, 2nd Fl.
PO Box 556
Cape May, NJ 08204-0556
Ph:(609)884-5508
Fax:(609)884-2054
Co. E-mail: request@capemaychamber.com
URL: http://www.capemaychamber.com
Contact: Mr. David Ellenberg, Exec. Dir.

52182 ■ Chamber of Commerce Serving Old Bridge, Sayerville and South Amboy
PO Box 5241
Old Bridge, NJ 08857
Ph:(732)607-6340
Fax:(732)607-6341
Co. E-mail: info@obssachamber.com
URL: http://www.obssachamber.org
Contact: Reggie Butler, Pres.

52183 ■ Chamber of Commerce Southern New Jersey
6014 Main St.
Voorhees, NJ 08043-4659
Ph:(856)424-7776
Fax:(856)424-8180
Co. E-mail: info@chambersnj.com
URL: http://www.chambersnj.com
Contact: Debra P. DiLorenzo, Pres./CEO

52184 ■ Chatham Area Chamber of Commerce
PO Box 231
Chatham, NJ 07928-0231
Ph:(973)635-2444
Fax:(973)635-2953
Co. E-mail: chathamchamber@gmail.com
URL: http://www.chathamchambernj.org/page/page/5520500.htm
Contact: Carolyn A. Cherry, Exec. Dir.

52185 ■ Cherry Hill Regional Chamber of Commerce
1060 Kings Hwy. N, Ste. 200
Cherry Hill, NJ 08034
Ph:(856)667-1600

Fax:(856)667-1464
Co. E-mail: chamber@cherryhillregional.com
URL: http://www.cherryhillregional.com
Contact: Arthur C. Campbell, Pres./CEO

52186 ■ Cranford Chamber of Commerce
PO Box 165
Cranford, NJ 07016
Ph:(908)272-6114
Fax:(908)272-3742
Co. E-mail: cranfordchamber@comcast.net
URL: http://www.cranford.com/chamber
Contact: Kurt Petschow, Pres.

52187 ■ Dennis Township Chamber of Commerce
PO Box 85
Ocean View, NJ 08230
Ph:(609)624-0990
Fax:(609)624-9110
Co. E-mail: info@dennistwpchamber.com
URL: http://www.dennistwpchamber.com
Contact: Kimberly Schiela, Pres.

52188 ■ Denville Chamber of Commerce
PO Box 333
Denville, NJ 07834
Ph:(973)625-1171
Fax:(973)575-5795
Co. E-mail: alanverbeke@mail.yukongraphics.com
URL: http://www.denville-nj.com
Contact: Alan Verbeke, Pres.

52189 ■ Dover Area Chamber of Commerce
PO Box 506
Dover, NJ 07802
Ph:(973)989-4000
Fax:(973)673-5828
Co. E-mail: email@doverareachamber.com
URL: http://www.doverareachamber.com
Contact: Susan Konight, Pres.

52190 ■ East Brunswick Regional Chamber of Commerce
PO Box 56
East Brunswick, NJ 08816-0056
Ph:(732)257-3009
Fax:(732)257-0949
Co. E-mail: office@ebchamber.org
URL: http://www.ebchamber.org

52191 ■ East Orange Chamber of Commerce
PO Box 2418
East Orange, NJ 07019-2418
Ph:(973)674-0900
Fax:(973)673-5828
Co. E-mail: info@eastorangechamber.biz
URL: http://www.eastorangechamber.biz
Contact: Raymond L. Scott, Pres.

52192 ■ Eastern Monmouth Area Chamber of Commerce
170 Broad St.
Red Bank, NJ 07701
Ph:(732)741-0055
Fax:(732)741-6778
Co. E-mail: emacc@emacc.org
URL: http://www.emacc.org
Contact: Lynda Rose, Pres./COO

52193 ■ Edison Chamber of Commerce
336 Raritan Ctr. Pkwy.
Campus Plz. 6
Edison, NJ 08837
Ph:(732)738-9482
Fax:(732)738-9485
Co. E-mail: president@edisonchamber.com
URL: http://www.edisonchamber.com
Contact: Barbara C. Roos, Pres./CEO

52194 ■ Egg Harbor City Chamber of Commerce
400 Liverpool Ave.
Egg Harbor City, NJ 08215
Ph:(609)965-0001
Contact: Lloyd Wimberg, Chm.

52195 ■ Englewood Chamber of Commerce
2-10 N Van Brunt St.
Englewood, NJ 07631-3485
Ph:(201)871-6635
Fax:(201)871-4549
URL: http://www.englewood-chamber.com
Contact: Karen L. Rawl, Exec. Dir.

52196 ■ Fair Lawn Chamber of Commerce
18-00 Fair Lawn Ave.
Fair Lawn, NJ 07410
Ph:(201)796-7050
Fax:(201)475-0619
Co. E-mail: info@fairlawnchamber.org
URL: http://www.fairlawnchamber.org
Contact: Hank Pawski, Pres.

52197 ■ Franklin Lakes Chamber of Commerce
PO Box 81
Franklin Lakes, NJ 07417
Ph:(201)560-1289
Co. E-mail: info@flcoc.org
URL: http://www.flcoc.org
Contact: Mina Kozma, Exec. Admin.

52198 ■ Greater Asbury Park Chamber of Commerce
PO Box 649
Asbury Park, NJ 07712
Ph:(732)775-7676
Fax:(732)775-7675
Co. E-mail: info@asburyparkchamber.com
URL: http://www.asburyparkchamber.com
Contact: Cindi D'Onofrio, Exec. Dir.

52199 ■ Greater Elizabeth Chamber of Commerce
456 N Broad St.
Elizabeth, NJ 07208
Ph:(908)355-7600
Fax:(908)436-2054
Co. E-mail: gecc@juno.com
URL: http://www.elizabethchamber.com
Contact: Gordon Haas, Exec. Dir.

52200 ■ Greater Fort Lee Chamber of Commerce
210 Whiteman St.
Fort Lee, NJ 07024
Ph:(201)944-7575
Fax:(201)944-5168
Co. E-mail: gflcoc@verizon.net
URL: http://www.greaterfortleechamber.com

52201 ■ Greater Glassboro Chamber of Commerce
PO Box 651
Glassboro, NJ 08028
Ph:(856)881-7900
Co. E-mail: info@glassborochamber.com
URL: http://www.glassborochamber.com
Contact: Karal Corradetti, Pres.

52202 ■ Greater Hackensack Chamber of Commerce
5 University Plaza Dr.
Hackensack, NJ 07601
Ph:(201)489-3700
Fax:(201)489-1741
Co. E-mail: chamberhacknj@aol.com
URL: http://www.hackensackchamber.org
Contact: Darlene Damstrom, Exec. Dir.

52203 ■ Greater Hammonton Chamber of Commerce
PO Box 554
Hammonton, NJ 08037-0554
Ph:(609)561-9080
Fax:(609)561-9411
URL: http://www.hammontonnj.us
Contact: John Runfolo

52204 ■ Greater Long Branch Chamber of Commerce
PO Box 628
Long Branch, NJ 07740
Ph:(732)222-0400

Fax:(732)571-3385
Co. E-mail: longbranchchamber@verizon.net
URL: http://www.longbranchchamber.org
Contact: Nancy Kleiberg, Exec. Dir.

52205 ■ Greater Mahwah Chamber of Commerce
67 Ramapo Valley Rd., Ste. 211
Mahwah, NJ 07430
Ph:(201)529-5566
Fax:(201)529-8122
Co. E-mail: sharon@mahwah.com
URL: http://www.mahwah.com
Contact: Sharon Rounds, Exec. Dir.

52206 ■ Greater Millville Chamber of Commerce
PO Box 831
Millville, NJ 08332
Ph:(856)825-2600
Fax:(856)825-5333
Co. E-mail: info@millville-nj.com
URL: http://www.millville-nj.com
Contact: Earl Sherrick, Exec. Dir.

52207 ■ Greater Paramus Chamber of Commerce
PO Box 325
Paramus, NJ 07652-0325
Ph:(201)261-3344
Fax:(201)261-3346
Co. E-mail: office2005@paramuschamber.com
URL: http://www.paramuschamber.com
Contact: Dimitri Miaoulis, Chm.

52208 ■ Greater Paterson Chamber of Commerce
100 Hamilton Plz., Ste. 1201
Paterson, NJ 07505
Ph:(973)881-7300
Fax:(973)881-8233
Co. E-mail: gpcc@greaterpatersoncc.org
URL: http://www.greaterpatersoncc.org
Contact: Charles T. Miller, Associate Dir.

52209 ■ Greater Vineland Chamber of Commerce
2115 S Delsea Dr.
Vineland, NJ 08360
Ph:(856)691-7400
Fax:(856)691-2113
Co. E-mail: pdesiere@vinelandchamber.org
URL: http://www.vinelandchamber.org
Contact: Paige Desiere, Exec. Dir.

52210 ■ Greater Wildwood Chamber of Commerce
3306 Pacific Ave.
Wildwood, NJ 08260-4824
Ph:(609)729-4000
Fax:(609)729-4003
Co. E-mail: info@gwcoc.org
URL: http://www.gwcoc.com
Contact: Tracey Dufault, Exec. Dir.

52211 ■ Howell Chamber of Commerce
PO Box 196
Howell, NJ 07731
Ph:(732)363-4114
Fax:(732)363-8747
Co. E-mail: info@howellchamber.com
URL: http://www.howellchamber.com
Contact: Susan Dominguez, Exec. Dir.

52212 ■ Hudson County Chamber of Commerce
660 Newark Ave., Ste. 220
Jersey City, NJ 07306
Ph:(201)386-0699
Fax:(201)386-8480
Co. E-mail: info@hudsonchamber.org
URL: http://www.hudsonchamber.org
Contact: Joanne VanDorn, Pres.

52213 ■ Hunterdon County Chamber of Commerce
2200 Rte. 31, Ste. 15
Lebanon, NJ 08833
Ph:(908)735-5955

Fax:(908)730-6580
Co. E-mail: info@hunterdon-chamber.org
URL: http://www.hunterdon-chamber.org
Contact: Karen Widico, Chair

52214 ■ Irvington Chamber of Commerce
PO Box 323
Irvington, NJ 07111-0323
Ph:(973)372-4100
URL: http://www.irvington-nj.com/ICC.html
Contact: Herb Ramo, Field Coor.

52215 ■ Lakewood Chamber of Commerce
395 Rte. 70 W, Ste. 125
Lakewood, NJ 08701
Ph:(732)363-0012
Fax:(732)367-4453
Co. E-mail: info@mylakewoodchamber.com
URL: http://www.mylakewoodchamber.com
Contact: Ms. Maureen Stankowitz, Exec. Dir.

52216 ■ Lambertville Area Chamber of Commerce
60 Wilson St.
Lambertville, NJ 08530
Ph:(609)397-0055
Fax:(609)397-7423
Co. E-mail: info@lambertville.org
URL: http://www.lambertville.org
Contact: Thomas E. Martin, Pres.

52217 ■ Livingston Area Chamber of Commerce
25 S Livingston Ave., 2nd Fl., Ste. E
Livingston, NJ 07039
Ph:(973)992-4343
Fax:(973)992-8024
Co. E-mail: info@livingstonchambernj.com
URL: http://www.livingstonchambernj.com
Contact: Beth Lippman, Exec. Dir./Admin.

52218 ■ Madison Chamber of Commerce
PO Box 152
Madison, NJ 07940
Ph:(973)377-7830
Fax:(973)822-3336
Co. E-mail: info@madisonnjchamber.org
URL: http://www.spotlitesolutions.com/working-progress
Contact: Susan Marcy, Exec. Dir.

52219 ■ Maplewood Chamber of Commerce
PO Box 423
Maplewood, NJ 07040
Ph:(973)761-4333
Fax:(973)762-9105
Co. E-mail: contact11@mindspring.com
URL: http://www.maplewoodchamber.com
Contact: Rene Conlon, VP/Exec. Sec.

52220 ■ Matawan - Aberdeen Chamber of Commerce
PO Box 522
Matawan, NJ 07747-0522
Ph:(732)290-1125
Co. E-mail: macocnj@macocnj.com
URL: http://www.macocnj.com
Contact: Michael Moyers, Pres.

52221 ■ Meadowlands Regional Chamber of Commerce
201 Rte. 17 N
Rutherford, NJ 07070
Ph:(201)939-0707
Fax:(201)939-0522
Co. E-mail: office@meadowlands.org
URL: http://www.meadowlands.org/mrcc
Contact: Jim Kirkos, Pres./CEO

52222 ■ Mercer Regional Chamber of Commerce
1A Quakerbridge Plaza Dr.
Mercerville, NJ 08619
Ph:(609)689-9960
Fax:(609)586-9989
Co. E-mail: info@mercerchamber.org
URL: http://www.mercerchamber.org
Contact: Michele N. Siekerka Esq., Pres.

52223 ■ Metuchen Area Chamber of Commerce
323 Main St., Ste. B
Metuchen, NJ 08840-2433
Ph:(732)548-2964
Fax:(732)548-4094
Co. E-mail: metuchenchamber@metuchenchamber. com
URL: http://www.metuchenchamber.com
Contact: Caroline Woodruff, Office Admin.

52224 ■ Middle Township Chamber of Commerce
PO Box 6
Cape May Court House, NJ 08210
Ph:(609)463-1655
Co. E-mail: middletownshipchamberofcom@middle-townshipchamberofcommerce.org
URL: http://www.middletownshipchamberofcom-merce.org
Contact: Barbara Peltzer, Pres.

52225 ■ Middlesex County Regional Chamber of Commerce
109 Church St.
New Brunswick, NJ 08901
Ph:(732)745-8090
Fax:(732)745-8098
Co. E-mail: info@mcrcc.org
URL: http://www.mcrcc.org
Contact: Christopher J. Phelan, Pres.

52226 ■ Millburn-Short Hills Chamber of Commerce
PO Box 651
Millburn, NJ 07041
Ph:(973)379-1198
Fax:(973)376-5678
Co. E-mail: info@millburnchamber.com
URL: http://www.millburnchamber.com
Contact: Bert James, Pres.

52227 ■ Montville Township Chamber of Commerce
195 Change Bridge Rd.
Montville, NJ 07045
Ph:(973)263-3310
Fax:(973)263-3453
Co. E-mail: info@montvillechamber.com
URL: http://montvillechamber.com

52228 ■ Morris County Chamber of Commerce
25 Lindsley Dr.
Morristown, NJ 07960-4454
Ph:(973)539-3882
Fax:(973)539-3960
Co. E-mail: paul@morrischamber.org
URL: http://www.morrischamber.org
Contact: Paul Boudreau, Pres.

52229 ■ Mount Olive Area Chamber of Commerce
PO Box 192
Budd Lake, NJ 07828-0192
Ph:(973)691-0109
Fax:(973)691-0110
Co. E-mail: info@mtolivechambernj.com
URL: http://www.mtolivechambernj.com
Contact: Lou Nisivoccia, Pres.

52230 ■ North Essex Chamber of Commerce
3 Fairfield Ave.
West Caldwell, NJ 07006-7692
Ph:(973)226-5500
Fax:(973)403-9335
Co. E-mail: email@northessexchamber.com
URL: http://www.northessexchamber.com
Contact: Meryl Layton, Exec. Dir.

52231 ■ North Jersey Regional Chamber of Commerce
1033 Rte. 46 E, Ste. A103
Clifton, NJ 07013
Ph:(973)470-9300

Fax:(973)470-9245
Co. E-mail: staff@njrcc.org
URL: http://www.njrcc.org
Contact: Gloria Martini, Pres.

52232 ■ Northern Burlington Regional Chamber of Commerce
PO Box 65
Bordentown, NJ 08505
Ph:(609)298-7774
Fax:(609)291-5008
Co. E-mail: info@nbrchamber.org
URL: http://www.nbrchamber.org
Contact: Paul Schwork, Pres.

52233 ■ Northern Monmouth Chamber of Commerce
PO Box 5007
Hazlet, NJ 07730
Ph:(732)203-0340
Fax:(732)203-0341
Co. E-mail: info@northernmonmouthchamber.com
URL: http://www.northernmonmouth.org
Contact: Paul Morris, Exec. Dir.

52234 ■ Nutley Chamber of Commerce
299 Franklin Ave.
Nutley, NJ 07110
Ph:(973)667-5300
Fax:(973)667-5300
Co. E-mail: chamber@nutleychamber.com
URL: http://www.nutleychamber.com
Contact: Dr. Donna Pontoriero DC, Pres.

52235 ■ Oakland Chamber of Commerce
PO Box 8
Oakland, NJ 07436
Ph:(201)337-9282
URL: http://www.oakland-nj.org/chamberofcom-merce.html
Contact: David Mital, Pres.

52236 ■ Ocean City Regional Chamber of Commerce
16 E 9th St.
Ocean City, NJ 08226
Ph:(609)399-1412
Fax:(609)398-3932
Co. E-mail: info@oceancitychamber.com
URL: http://www.oceancityvacation.com
Contact: Michele Gillian, Exec. Dir.

52237 ■ Ocean Grove Chamber of Commerce
PO Box 415
Ocean Grove, NJ 07756
Ph:(732)774-1391
Free: 800-388-4768
Fax:(732)774-3799
Co. E-mail: info@oceangrovenj.com
URL: http://oceangrovenj.com
Contact: Lois Hetfield, Admin.

52238 ■ Parsippany Area Chamber of Commerce
12-14 N Beverwyck Rd.
Lake Hiawatha, NJ 07034
Ph:(973)402-6400
Fax:(973)334-2242
Co. E-mail: njpacc@yahoo.com
URL: http://www.njpacc.org
Contact: Robert J. Peluso, Pres.

52239 ■ Perth Amboy Chamber of Commerce
69A Smith St.
Perth Amboy, NJ 08861
Ph:(732)442-7400
Fax:(732)442-7450
Co. E-mail: pachamerofcommerce@verizon.net
URL: http://www.perthamboychamber.com
Contact: Yvonne Taylor, Pres.

52240 ■ Phillipsburg Area Chamber of Commerce
675 Corliss Ave.
Phillipsburg, NJ 08865-1698
Ph:(908)454-5500
Co. E-mail: info@phillipsburgnj.org
URL: http://www.lehighvalleychamber.org/DetailS-ingle.aspx?id=466
Contact: Deborah N. Russo, Exec. Dir.

52241 ■ Point Pleasant Beach Chamber of Commerce
517A Arnold Ave.
Point Pleasant Beach, NJ 08742-2501
Ph:(732)899-2181
Free: 888-772-3862
Fax:(732)899-0103
Co. E-mail: info@pointpleasantbeachnj.com
URL: http://www.pointpleasantbeachnj.com
Contact: Patrick English, Pres.

52242 ■ Pompton Lakes Chamber of Commerce
PO Box 129
Pompton Lakes, NJ 07442
Ph:(973)839-0187
Fax:(973)839-0187
Co. E-mail: info@pomptonchamber.com
URL: http://www.pomptonlakeschamber.com
Contact: Art Kaffka, Pres.

52243 ■ Princeton Regional Chamber of Commerce
9 Vandeventer Ave.
Princeton, NJ 08542
Ph:(609)924-1776
Fax:(609)924-5776
Co. E-mail: info@princetonchamber.org
URL: http://www.princetonchamber.org
Contact: Herbert K. Ames, Pres./CEO

52244 ■ Randolph Area Chamber of Commerce
PO Box 391
Mount Freedom, NJ 07970-0391
Ph:(973)361-3462
Fax:(973)895-3297
URL: http://www.randolphchamber.org
Contact: William F. Burke Jr., Pres.

52245 ■ Ridgewood Chamber of Commerce
199 Dayton St.
Ridgewood, NJ 07450
Ph:(201)445-2600
Fax:(201)251-1958
Co. E-mail: info@ridgewoodchamber.com
URL: http://www.ridgewoodchamber.com

52246 ■ Ringwood Chamber of Commerce
PO Box 62
Ringwood, NJ 07456
Ph:(973)835-7998
Co. E-mail: info@ringwoodchamber.com
URL: http://www.ringwoodchamber.com
Contact: Kathy Heck, Pres.

52247 ■ Roxbury Area Chamber of Commerce
PO Box 436
Ledgewood, NJ 07852
Ph:(973)770-0740
Co. E-mail: elaineracc@verizon.net
URL: http://www.roxburynjchamber.org
Contact: Elaine Honig, Sec.

52248 ■ Rutherford Chamber of Commerce
PO Box 216
Rutherford, NJ 07070
Ph:(201)933-5230
Fax:(201)507-7077
Co. E-mail: info@rutherfordchamber.com
URL: http://www.rutherfordchamber.com
Contact: Herbert L. Cutter, Exec. Sec. Emeritus

52249 ■ Salem County Chamber of Commerce
91 S Virginia Ave., Ste. A
Carneys Point, NJ 08069
Ph:(856)299-6699

Fax:(856)299-0299
Co. E-mail: sccoc@verizon.net
URL: http://salemnjchamber.homestead.com
Contact: Jennifer A. Jones, Exec. Dir.

52250 ■ South Orange Chamber of Commerce
PO Box 621
South Orange, NJ 07079
Ph:(973)762-4333
Fax:(973)763-0943
Co. E-mail: director@southorangechamber.com
URL: http://www.southorangechamber.com
Contact: Leslie Pogany, Pres.

52251 ■ Southern Monmouth Chamber of Commerce
PO Box 1305
Wall, NJ 07719-1305
Ph:(732)280-8800
Fax:(732)280-8505
Co. E-mail: info@smcconline.org
URL: http://www.southernmonmouthchamber.com
Contact: Ms. Dana Gangemi, Pres.

52252 ■ Southern Ocean County Chamber of Commerce
265 W 9th St.
Ship Bottom, NJ 08008-4614
Ph:(609)494-7211
Free: 800-292-6372
Fax:(609)494-5807
Co. E-mail: info@discoversouthernocean.com
URL: http://www.visitlbiregion.com
Contact: David Taylor, Pres.

52253 ■ Stone Harbor Chamber of Commerce
PO Box 422
Stone Harbor, NJ 08247-0422
Ph:(609)368-6101
Co. E-mail: joe@wjse.com
URL: http://stoneharborbeach.com
Contact: Karl Giulian, Pres.

52254 ■ Suburban Chamber of Commerce
71 Summit Ave.
Summit, NJ 07901
Ph:(908)522-1700
Fax:(908)522-9252
Co. E-mail: info@suburbanchambers.org
URL: http://www.suburbanchambers.org
Contact: Maureen Kelly, Pres.

52255 ■ Suburban Essex Chamber of Commerce
256 Broad St., Rm. 2F
Bloomfield, NJ 07003
Ph:(973)748-2000
Fax:(973)748-2450
Co. E-mail: admin@suburbanessexchamber.com
URL: http://www.suburbanessexchamber.com
Contact: Joseph Sandora, Pres.

52256 ■ Sussex County Chamber of Commerce
120 Hampton House Rd.
Newton, NJ 07860
Ph:(973)579-1811
Fax:(973)579-3031
Co. E-mail: mail@sussexcountychamber.org
URL: http://www.sussexcountychamber.org
Contact: Tammie Horsfield, Pres.

52257 ■ Teaneck Chamber of Commerce
555 Cedar Ln., Ste. 4
Teaneck, NJ 07666
Ph:(201)801-0012
Fax:(201)907-0870
Co. E-mail: teaneckchamber@aol.com
URL: http://www.teaneckchamber.org
Contact: Karen Careccio, Exec. Dir.

52258 ■ Toms River - Ocean County Chamber of Commerce
1200 Hooper Ave.
Toms River, NJ 08753-3324
Ph:(732)349-0220

Fax:(732)349-1252
Co. E-mail: info@oc-chamber.com
URL: http://www.oc-chamber.com
Contact: Lucy Greene, Pres.

52259 ■ Tri-Town Chamber of Commerce
PO Box 496
Boonton, NJ 07005
Ph:(973)334-4117
Fax:(973)402-0719
Co. E-mail: info@tritownchamber.org
URL: http://www.tritownchamber.org
Contact: Gina Ramich, Exec. Dir./Sec.

52260 ■ Union Township Chamber of Commerce
355 Chestnut St., 2nd Fl.
Union, NJ 07083-9405
Ph:(908)688-2777
Fax:(908)688-0338
Co. E-mail: info@unionchamber.com
URL: http://www.unionchamber.com
Contact: Jim Brody, Exec. Dir.

52261 ■ Vernon Chamber of Commerce
PO Box 308
Vernon, NJ 07462
Ph:(973)764-0764
Free: 888-663-9989
Co. E-mail: info@vernonchamber.com
URL: http://www.vernonchamber.com

52262 ■ Warren County Regional Chamber of Commerce
10 Brass Castle Rd.
Washington, NJ 07882
Ph:(908)835-9200
Fax:(908)835-9296
Co. E-mail: info@warrencountychamber.org
URL: http://www.warrencountychamber.org
Contact: Robert L. Goltz, Pres./CEO

52263 ■ West Milford Chamber of Commerce
PO Box 234
West Milford, NJ 07480
Ph:(973)728-3150
URL: http://www.westmilford.com
Contact: Rocky Hazelman, Pres.

52264 ■ Western Monmouth Chamber of Commerce
17 Broad St.
Freehold, NJ 07728-1703
Ph:(732)462-3030
Fax:(732)462-2123
Co. E-mail: info@wmchamber.com
URL: http://www.greatermonmouthchamber.com
Contact: Loretta R. Kuhnert, Pres.

52265 ■ Westfield Area Chamber of Commerce
173 Elm St., 3rd Fl.
Westfield, NJ 07090
Ph:(908)233-3021
Fax:(908)654-8183
Co. E-mail: info@westfieldchamber.com
URL: http://www.westfieldareachamber.com
Contact: Naomi McElynn, Exec. Dir.

52266 ■ Woodbridge Metro Chamber of Commerce
52 Main St.
Woodbridge, NJ 07095-2892
Ph:(732)636-4040
Fax:(732)636-3492
Co. E-mail: help@woodbridgechamber.com
URL: http://www.woodbridgechamber.org
Contact: Carole S. Hila, Pres.

52267 ■ Wyckoff Chamber of Commerce
PO Box 2
Wyckoff, NJ 07481-0002
Ph:(201)891-3616
Co. E-mail: info@wyckoffchamber.com
URL: http://www.wyckoffchamber.com
Contact: Douglas Padla, Pres.

MINORITY BUSINESS ASSISTANCE PROGRAMS

52268 ■ Minority Business Enterprise Center of New Jersey
744 Broad St., Ste. 1812
Newark, NJ 07102
Ph:(973)297-1142
Fax:(973)297-1439
Co. E-mail: njmbdc@newjerseymbec.com
URL: http://www.newjerseymbec.com
Contact: Hilda Rayas, Acting Dir
Description: Assists in the growth and expansion of minority businesses in New Jersey.

52269 ■ New Jersey Department of Commerce and Economic Development–Division of Small, Women, and Minority Business
20 W State St., 4th Fl.
Mary G. Roebling Bldg. 4th Fl.
Trenton, NJ 08625
Ph:(609)292-2146
Free: 888-239-1288
Fax:(609)292-9145
Co. E-mail: cevramb@commerce.state.nj.us
URL: http://www.newjerseycommerce.org/
Description: Assists minority businesses in financing, procurement, and management training.

52270 ■ New Jersey Division of Revenue–Business Action Center–Small Business Set-Aside (PO Bo)
PO Box 455
PO Box 990
Trenton, NJ 08846
Ph:(609)292-2146
Fax:(609)292-9145
Co. E-mail: njedia@njeda.com
URL: http://www.state.nj.us/njbusiness/contracting/sbsa
Contact: Caren Franzini, CEO
Description: Responsible for administering the Set-Aside Act for small, women-, and minority-owned businesses. Also helps these businesses compete for government contracts.

FINANCING AND LOAN PROGRAMS

52271 ■ BaseCamp Ventures
1 Executive Dr., Ste. 8
Moorestown, NJ 08057
Ph:(856)813-1100
Fax:(856)813-1148
Co. E-mail: mel@basecampventures.com
URL: http://www.basecampventures.com
Contact: Mel Baiada, Principal
Preferred Investment Size: $500,000 to $2,500,000. **Investment Policies:** Early and first stage. **Industry Preferences:** Communications, computer software, and Internet specific. **Geographic Preferences:** Mid Atlantic. **Principal Exhibits:**

52272 ■ BD Ventures / Becton, Dickinson and Co.
1 Becton Dr.
Franklin Lakes, NJ 07417
Ph:(201)847-6800
Fax:(201)847-4874
Co. E-mail: BDBioVentureCenter@bd.com
URL: http://www.bd.com
Contact: Peter A. Origenes, President and General Manager
Investment Types: Early stage. **Industry Preferences:** Biotechnology. **Principal Exhibits:**

52273 ■ Cardinal Partners / Cardinal Health Partners
230 Nassau St.
Princeton, NJ 08542
Ph:(609)924-6452

Fax:(609)683-0174
Co. E-mail: info@cardinalpartners.com
URL: http://www.cardinalpartners.com
Contact: John K. Clarke, Managing Partner
Preferred Investment Size: $6,000,000 to $12,000,000. **Investment Types:** Start-up, seed, first, and early stage. **Industry Preferences:** Computer software and services, medical and health, Internet specific, biotechnology, computer hardware, semiconductors and other electronics, communications and media, industrial and energy, other products, and consumer related. **Geographic Preferences:** U.S. **Principal Exhibits:**

52274 ■ CIT Group / Venture Capital
650 CIT Dr.
Livingston, NJ 07039
Ph:(973)740-5181
Fax:(973)740-5555
URL: http://www.citgroup.com
Contact: Colby W. Collier, Manager
Preferred Investment Size: $3,000,000 minimum. **Investment Types:** First and second stage, mezzanine, and leveraged buyout. **Industry Preferences:** Diversified. **Geographic Preferences:** Entire U.S. **Principal Exhibits:**

52275 ■ CS Capital Partners, LLC
328 Second St., Ste. 200
Lakewood, NJ 08701
Ph:(732)901-1111
URL: http://www.cs-capital.com
Contact: Solomon Lax, Partner
Preferred Investment Size: $500,000 to $3,000,000. **Investment Types:** Early, first and second stage, expansion, control-block purchases, generalist PE, distressed debt, recapitalizations, and private placement. **Industry Preferences:** Internet specific, computer software and services, other products, communications and media, medical and health. **Geographic Preferences:** Mid Atlantic, Northeast, and Southeast. **Principal Exhibits:**

52276 ■ DFW Capital Partners / Demuth, Folger & Wetherill
Glenpointe Ctr. E., 5th Fl.
300 Frank W. Burr Blvd.
Teaneck, NJ 07666
Ph:(201)836-6000
Fax:(201)836-5666
Co. E-mail: info@dfwcapital.com
URL: http://www.dfwcapital.com
Contact: Donald F. DeMuth, General Partner
Preferred Investment Size: $5,000,000 to $20,000,000. **Investment Types:** Acquisition, control-block purchases, later stage, expansion, leveraged and management buyouts, recapitalizations, and special situation. **Industry Preferences:** Medical and health, consumer related, communications and media, computer hardware, Internet specific, semiconductors and other electronics, computer software and services, other products, industrial and energy. **Geographic Preferences:** U.S. **Principal Exhibits:**

52277 ■ Domain Associates L.L.C.
1 Palmer Sq., Ste. 515
Princeton, NJ 08542
Ph:(609)683-5656
Fax:(609)683-9789
Co. E-mail: more@domainvc.com
URL: http://www.domainvc.com
Contact: Todd C. Brady, Principal
Preferred Investment Size: $1,000,000 to $20,000,000. **Investment Types:** Seed, start-up, early, first, second, and later stage, balanced, expansion, mezzanine, private placement, research and development, and private placement. **Industry Preferences:** Biotechnology, medical and health, Internet specific, computer software and services, industrial and energy, semiconductors and other electronics, and consumer related. **Geographic Preferences:** U.S. **Principal Exhibits:**

52278 ■ Early Stage Enterprises, L.P.
995 Rte. 518
Skillman, NJ 08558
Ph:(609)921-8896

Fax:(609)921-8703
Co. E-mail: jim@esevc.com
URL: http://www.esevc.com
Contact: Ronald R. Hahn, Partner
E-mail: ron@esevc.com
Preferred Investment Size: $500,000 to $1,000,000. **Investment Types:** Seed, start-up, first and early stage. **Industry Preferences:** Internet specific, computer software and services, other products, communications and media, medical and health, and biotechnology. **Geographic Preferences:** Mid Atlantic. **Principal Exhibits:**

52279 ■ Edelson Technology Partners
300 Tice Blvd.
Woodcliff Lake, NJ 07677
Ph:(201)930-9898
Fax:(201)930-8899
URL: http://www.edelsontech.com
Contact: Harry Edelson, General Partner
E-mail: harry@edelsontech.com
Preferred Investment Size: $1,000,000 to $3,000,000. **Investment Types:** Start-ups, later stage, and mezzanine. **Industry Preferences:** Communications and media, industrial and energy, computer software and services, consumer related, computer hardware, semiconductors and other electronics, other products, medical and health, Internet specific, and biotechnology. **Geographic Preferences:** U.S. and Canada. **Principal Exhibits:**

52280 ■ Edison Venture Fund
1009 Lenox Dr., Ste. 4
Lawrenceville, NJ 08648
Ph:(609)896-1900
Fax:(609)896-0066
URL: http://www.edisonventure.com
Contact: John Martinson, Managing Partner
E-mail: jmartinson@edisonventure.com
Preferred Investment Size: $5,000,000 to $8,000,000. **Investment Types:** Expansion, roll-ups, recapitalization, and management buyouts. **Industry Preferences:** Computer software and services, Internet specific, industrial and energy, communications and media, medical and health, consumer related, other products, computer hardware, semiconductors and other electronics. **Geographic Preferences:** Mid Atlantic, Delaware, Maryland, New Jersey, New York, Virginia, Pennsylvania, New England, and North Carolina. **Principal Exhibits:**

52281 ■ Geocapital Partners, LLC
1 executive Dr., Ste. 160
Fort Lee, NJ 07024
Ph:(201)461-9292
Fax:(201)461-7793
URL: http://www.geocapital.com
Contact: Lawrence W. Lepard, Managing General Partner
E-mail: llepard@geocapital.com
Preferred Investment Size: $2,000,000 to $20,000,000. **Investment Types:** Seed, start-up, early, first and later stage, expansion, and private placement. **Industry Preferences:** Internet specific, computer software and services, communications and media, other products, consumer related, industrial and energy, medical and health. **Geographic Preferences:** U.S. and Canada. **Principal Exhibits:**

52282 ■ Healthcare Ventures LLC / Healthcare Investments
55 Cambridge Pky., Ste. 102
Cambridge, MA 02142-1234
Ph:(617)252-4343
Fax:(617)252-4342
URL: http://www.hcven.com
Contact: Harold R. Werner, Managing Director
Preferred Investment Size: $500,000 to $10,000,000. **Investment Types:** Seed, start-up, early, first, second and later stage, expansion, mezzanine, and public companies. **Industry Preferences:** Biotechnology, medical and health, Internet specific, and consumer related. **Geographic Preferences:** Mid Atlantic and Northeast. **Principal Exhibits:**

52283 ■ Johnston Associates, Inc.
155 Lambert Dr.
Princeton, NJ 08540
Ph:(609)924-2575
Fax:(609)924-3135
Co. E-mail: info@jaivc.com
URL: http://www.jaivc.com
Contact: Robert F. Johnston, President
Preferred Investment Size: $300,000 to $3,000,000. **Investment Types:** Start-up and early stage. **Industry Preferences:** Biotechnology, medical and health. **Geographic Preferences:** Northeast. **Principal Exhibits:**

52284 ■ New Jersey Technology Council / NJTC Venture Fund
1001 Briggs Rd., Ste. 280
Mount Laurel, NJ 08054
Ph:(856)273-6800
Fax:(856)273-0990
Co. E-mail: info@njtcvc.com
URL: http://www.njtcvc.com
Contact: James Gunton, General Partner
E-mail: jim@njtcvc.com
Preferred Investment Size: $1,000,000 to $10,000,000. **Investment Types:** Seed, start-up, early, first and second stage, and expansion. **Industry Preferences:** Communications, computer software, Internet specific, semiconductors and other electronics, biotechnology, medical and health, and financial services. **Geographic Preferences:** New Jersey, New York, and Pennsylvania. **Principal Exhibits:**

52285 ■ New Venture Partners LLC
430 Mountain Ave.
Murray Hill, NJ 07974
Ph:(908)464-0900
Fax:(908)464-8131
Co. E-mail: info@nvpllc.com
URL: http://www.nvpllc.com
Contact: Andrew Garman, Managing Partner
Investment Policies: Seed and early stage. **Industry Preferences:** Communications and media, computer software, and semiconductors and other electronics. **Geographic Preferences:** U.S. **Principal Exhibits:**

52286 ■ Origin Partners
5 Slater Ct.
Hillsborough, NJ 08844
Ph:(908)595-9100
Fax:(908)281-6831
URL: http://www.originpartners.com
Contact: Scott Jones, Managing Director
E-mail: jones@originpartners.com
Preferred Investment Size: $3,000,000 to $5,000,000. **Investment Policies:** Start-up, seed, early and first stage. **Industry Preferences:** Communications and media, computer software, Internet specific, semiconductors and other electronics, and medical and health. **Geographic Preferences:** Northeast and Southwest. **Principal Exhibits:**

52287 ■ Proquest Investments
90 Nassau St., 5th Fl.
Princeton, NJ 08542
Ph:(609)919-3560
Fax:(609)919-3570
URL: http://www.proquestvc.com
Contact: Joyce Tsang, Principal
Preferred Investment Size: $250,000 to $25,000,000. **Investment Types:** Seed, start-up, early, first, second, and later stage, balanced, expansion, mezzanine, research and development, and private placement. **Industry Preferences:** Medical and health, biotechnology, and Internet specific. **Geographic Preferences:** U.S. and Canada. **Principal Exhibits:**

52288 ■ Ridgewood Capital Management, LLC
14 Philips Pkwy.
Montvale, NJ 07645
Ph:(201)447-9000
Free: 800-942-5550

Fax:(201)447-0474
Co. E-mail: businessplan@ridgewoodcapital.com
URL: http://www.ridgewoodcapital.com
Contact: Robert L. Gold, President and Chief Executive Officer
E-mail: bgold@ridgewoodcapital.com
Preferred Investment Size: $2,000,000 to $5,000,000. **Investment Types:** Early and later stage, and expansion. **Industry Preferences:** Internet specific, semiconductors and other electronics, communications and media, computer software and services, computer hardware, other products, industrial and energy, and biotechnology. **Geographic Preferences:** Mid Atlantic, Northeast, and West Coast. **Principal Exhibits:**

52289 ■ The Vertical Group
25 DeForest Ave.
Summit, NJ 07901
Ph:(908)277-3737
Fax:(908)273-9434
Co. E-mail: info@vertical-group.com
URL: http://www.vertical-group.com
Contact: Stephen D. Baksa, General Partner
Preferred Investment Size: $250,000 to $10,000,000. **Investment Types:** Early and later stage, leveraged buyout, mezzanine, and special situation. **Industry Preferences:** Medical and health, biotechnology, Internet specific, semiconductors and other electronics, computer software and services, communications and media, and industrial and energy. **Principal Exhibits:**

PROCUREMENT ASSISTANCE PROGRAMS

52290 ■ Air Services Development Office of New Jersey
Newark Liberty International Airport
Bldg. 80
Newark, NJ 07114-3707
Ph:(973)961-4278
Fax:(973)961-4282
Co. E-mail: njasdo@asdoaonline.com
URL: http://www.asdoonline.com
Contact: Helene M. Gibbs, Prgm Mgr
Description: A procurement facility funded by the Port Authority of New York and New Jersey to assist small firms in Essex, Hudson, and Union counties in obtaining contracts with airlines and other businesses at Newark International Airport.

52291 ■ Defense Procurement Technical Assistance Center–New Jersey Institute of Technology
University Heights
Newark, NJ 07102-1982
Ph:(973)596-3105
Fax:(973)596-5806
Co. E-mail: chaplin@njit.edu
URL: http://www.njit.edu/DPTAC/
Contact: Dolcey E. Chaplin, Dir
E-mail: chaplin@admin.njit.edu
Description: Provides contractual and technical assistance to small-established New Jersey businesses, who are interested in marketing their products, services to federal, state and local government agencies.

52292 ■ Defense Procurement Technical Assistance Center–New Jersey Institute of Technology–Atlantic Cape Community College (1535)–Satellite Office (Bacharach)
1535 Bacharach Blvd., Rm. 211
Atlantic City, NJ 08401
Ph:(609)343-4845
Fax:(609)343-4710
Co. E-mail: rrose@njit.edu
URL: http://www.njit.edu/DPTAC
Contact: Sherry Rose, Mktg. Specialist
Description: Provides contractual and technical assistance to small-established New Jersey businesses, who are interested in marketing their products, services to federal, state and local government agencies.

52293 ■ Defense Procurement Technical Assistance Center–New Jersey Institute of Technology–Business & Career Development Center (1 Hig)–Satellite Office (h St.)
1 High St.
Mount Holly, NJ 08060
Ph:(609)267-5618
Fax:(609)267-5165
Co. E-mail: mirijanian@njit.edu
URL: http://www.njit.edu/DPTAC
Contact: Jan Mirijanian, Mktg. Specialist
Description: Provides contractual and technical assistance to small-established New Jersey businesses, who are interested in marketing their products, services to federal, state and local government agencies.

52294 ■ Defense Procurement Technical Assistance Center–New Jersey Institute of Technology–New Jersey Commerce & Economic Growth Commission (Mary)–Satellite Office (G. Roeblin)
Mary G. Roebling Bldg.
20 W State St.
Trenton, NJ 08650
Ph:(609)292-3861
URL: http://www.njit.edu/DPTAC
Description: Provides contractual and technical assistance to small-established New Jersey businesses, who are interested in marketing their products, services to federal, state and local government agencies.

52295 ■ New Jersey Procurement Technical Assistance Center–Union County Economic Development Corporation (UCEDC)
1085 Morris Ave.
Union, NJ 07083
Ph:(908)527-1166
Fax:(908)527-1207
Co. E-mail: info@ucedc.com
URL: http://www.ucedc.com
Contact: Maryann Williams, Dir
Description: providing financial, technical, and community assistance to new and existing businesses with emphasis on benefiting under-served people and communities.

52296 ■ Rutgers School of Management–New Jersey Small Business Development Centers–New Jersey Procurement Technical Assistance Center (43 Bl)
43 Bleeker St.
Newark, NJ 07102
Ph:(973)353-1927
Fax:(973)353-1110
Co. E-mail: sburroughs@njsbdc.com
URL: http://www.njsbdc.com
Contact: Brenda B. Hopper, Dir
E-mail: britman@andromeda.rutgers.edu

52297 ■ United States Small Business Administration
U.S. Army Electronics and Communications Command
ATTN: SBA-PCR, Bldg. 1208
Ft. Monmouth, NJ 07703-5000
Ph:(732)532-3419
Fax:(732)532-8732
Co. E-mail: larry.hanson@sba.gov
URL: http://www.sba.gov
Contact: Larry Hansen, SBA Representative
E-mail: larry.hansen@sba.gov
Description: Covers activities for Communications & Electronics Command (Fort Monmouth, NJ), Army Training Center (Fort Dix, NJ), McGuire Air Force Base (Wrightstown, NJ), and Naval Air Warfare Center (Lakehurst, NJ).

52298 ■ US Small Business Administration
US Army JM&L-LCMC, Bldg. 323
Picatinny Arsenal, NJ 07806-5000
Ph:(973)724-6574

Fax:(973)724-5704
Co. E-mail: michael.cecere@us.army.mil
URL: http://www.sba.gov
Contact: Michael Cecere, SBA Representative
E-mail: michael.cecere@sba.gov
Description: Covers activities for Research and Development Command (Picatinny Arsenal, NJ), Military Traffic Management Command (Bayonne, NJ), and the Medical Center (East Orange, NJ).

INCUBATORS/RESEARCH AND TECHNOLOGY PARKS

52299 ■ ACIN Camden Center for Entrepreneurship in Technology
Waterfront Technology Center, Ste. 300
200 Federal St.
Camden, NJ 08103
Ph:(856)614-5415
Fax:(856)614-5489
Co. E-mail: info@acincenter.org
URL: http://www.acincenter.org
Description: A full-service technology accelerator program designed to assist small companies trying to exploit opportunities within the military through delivering products and services based on emerging technologies that meet an immediate need.

52300 ■ High Technology Small Business Incubator
Burlington County College
601 Pemberton-Browns Mills Rd.
Pemberton, NJ 08068
Ph:(856)222-9311
Co. E-mail: mgenzano@bcc.edu
URL: http://www.bcc.edu/pages/131.asp
Description: An engine for economic growth in New Jersey, creating new jobs, products and services by offering promising start-up companies a nurturing environment for growth. Each tenant company has access to extensive resources, support in developing business and technology plans, and opportunities to exhibit at conferences and venture capital showcases. Each can tap into a rich network of business resources: legal, venture capital, governmental, scientific, licensing, patent, grant funding, marketing, and e-commerce resources.

52301 ■ The Incubator/The BOSS (Business One Stop Service)
320 Park Ave.
Plainfield, NJ 07060
Ph:(908)757-5155
Fax:(908)757-8398
Co. E-mail: info@thebusinessonestopservice.com
URL: http://www.thebusinessonestopservice.com/main.html
Description: A small business incubator with the resources and solutions to help businesses achieve their short- and long-term goals.

52302 ■ Institute for Entrepreneurial Leadership
211 Warren St.
Newark, NJ 07103
Ph:(973)353-0611
URL: http://www.ifelnj.org/
Description: A small business incubator that takes a holistic, hands-on approach to helping entrepreneurs grow their business. Companies with a strong vision and viable business model can be helped to create wealth for themselves and their community by building a strong foundation for the long-term success of their business.

52303 ■ New Jersey City University Business Development Incubator
285 W. Side Ave.
Jersey City, NJ 07305
Ph:(201)200-2313
Fax:(201)200-2315
Co. E-mail: bdi@njcu.edu
URL: http://web.njcu.edu/sites/profstudies/bdi/Content/default.asp
Description: A small business incubator created to assist young, small companies to commercialize their products, processes and services by providing access to marketing, technical, finance, accounting, sales, legal and management assistance.

52304 ■ NJIT Enterprise Development Center
211 Warren St.
Newark, NJ 07103
Ph:(973)643-4063
Fax:(973)643-4502
Co. E-mail: Jerry.Creighton@njit-edc.org
URL: http://www.njit-edc.org/
Contact: Jerry Creighton, Exec. Dir.

Description: A program committed to the long-term economic vitality and growth of life science and high tech entrepreneurial ventures in the State of New Jersey. The incubator exists to increase the rate of small business formations and to decrease the failure rate of start-ups.

52305 ■ Picatinny Technology Innovation Center
3159 Schrader Rd.
Dover, NJ 07801
Ph:(973)442-6400
Fax:(973)442-6402
Co. E-mail: mmerclean@ccm.edu
URL: http://www.picinnovation.org/

Description: A small business incubator seeking to accelerate the successful commercialization of new products by entrepreneurial technology companies and corporate development teams, by supplying a supportive and resourceful infrastructure and by providing a broad base of support, including business, technical and financing assistance, shared business services to reduce overhead costs, access to the considerable resources and technology of the United States government, and reasonably priced office space.

52306 ■ Princeton University–Office of Research and Project Administration
4 New South Bldg.
PO Box 36
Princeton, NJ 08544
Ph:(609)258-3090
Fax:(609)258-1159
Co. E-mail: jfried@princeton.edu
URL: http://www.princeton.edu/orpa/
Contact: Jeffrey Friedland, Dir.
E-mail: jfried@princeton.edu

Scope: Administers and coordinates all extramurally sponsored research and other projects conducted at the University. Assists faculty members in obtaining financial support for their research or other projects and in fulfilling their contractual obligations to sponsors.

52307 ■ Princeton University–Princeton Forrestal Center
105 College Rd. E
Princeton, NJ 08540
Ph:(609)452-7720
Fax:(609)452-7485
Co. E-mail: picus@picusassociates.com
URL: http://www.princetonforrestalcenter.com
Contact: Susan Intravartola
E-mail: picus@picusassociates.com

Scope: Planned multiuse development area creating an interdependent mix of academic and business enterprise in the Princeton area.

52308 ■ Rutgers Camden Technology Campus
Waterfront Technology Center
200 Federal St., 2nd Fl., Ste. 244
Camden, NJ 08103
Ph:(856)479-9010
Fax:(856)225-6683
Co. E-mail: fskeith@camden.rutgers.edu
URL: http://www.rutgersbiz.com

Description: A non-profit, mixed-use, small business incubator encouraging entrepreneurs to locate their businesses in Camden by assisting them with low-cost office and conference space, technical support services and mentoring for successful startup. The incubator provides the safety net needed during a new company's most critical and vulnerable period.

52309 ■ Rutgers University–Office of Corporate Liaison and Technology Transfer
ASB III
3 Rutgers Plz., 3rd Fl.
New Brunswick, NJ 08901
Ph:(732)932-0115
Fax:(732)932-0146
Co. E-mail: info@ocltt.rutgers.edu
URL: http://ocltt.rutgers.edu
Contact: William Adams, Dir.
E-mail: info@ocltt.rutgers.edu

Scope: Serves as University liaison for corporate and industrial firms supporting graduate and faculty researchers in departments and centers throughout the University. **Educational Activities:** Conferences; Seminars (occasionally), for industrial clients.

52310 ■ Rutgers University–Office of Research and Sponsored Programs
ASB III
3 Rutgers Plz.
New Brunswick, NJ 08901
Ph:(732)932-0150
Fax:(732)932-0162
Co. E-mail: goldberg@orsp.rutgers.edu
URL: http://orsp.rutgers.edu
Contact: Sheryl N. Goldberg, Dir.
E-mail: goldberg@orsp.rutgers.edu

Scope: Coordinates intramural research activities, including programs designed to maximize faculty incentive to seek external funds. Administers programs on protection of human subjects in research, use of animals in research, and pre-award procedures for proposals to external funding agencies. Advises central administration on research policies. Serves as a clearinghouse for information on sources of research support. Administers the Research Council, which awards grants and fellowships to faculty. **Publications:** Annual Report; GrantNet Electronics Newsletter (monthly). **Educational Activities:** Colloquia; Workshops, on grantsmanship.

52311 ■ Technology Centre of New Jersey
Rte. 1 S and Milltown Rd.
North Brunswick, NJ 08902
Ph:(732)729-0022
Co. E-mail: mwiley@njeda.com
URL: http://www.njtechcentre.com/

Description: A small business incubator offering young, growing firms, as well as large established companies, a way to afford modern laboratory and production facilities that are customized to fit their specific research and development needs. Stand-alone facilities from 5,000 to 60,000 square feet can accommodate state-of-the-art clean rooms and wet labs. Individual wet and dry lab modules of 800 square feet, combinable up to 6,600 square feet, are available in the Commercialization Center for Innovative Technologies. Custom build-to-suit facilities are also available for larger companies that require substantial space on an individual basis.

52312 ■ William Paterson University of New Jersey–Office of Institutional Research and Assessment
College Hall
358 Hamburg Tpke.
Wayne, NJ 07470
Ph:(973)720-3115
Fax:(973)720-3624
Co. E-mail: zeffj@wpunj.edu
URL: http://www.wpunj.edu/ira
Contact: Dr. Jane Zeff, Dir.
E-mail: zeffj@wpunj.edu

Scope: Collects and analyzes data on the operation of the University and provides assistance in institutional planning and policy decisions especially those pertaining to the assessment of student learning outcomes.

EDUCATIONAL PROGRAMS

52313 ■ Bergen Community College
400 Paramus Rd.
Paramus, NJ 07652
Ph:(201)447-7100

Fax:(201)670-7973
URL: http://www.bergen.cc.nj.us
Description: Two-year college offering a small business management program.

52314 ■ Brookdale Community College
765 Newman Springs Rd.
Lincroft, NJ 07738-1597
Ph:(732)224-2345
Fax:(732)224-2772
URL: http://www.brookdale.cc.nj.us
Description: Two-year college offering a program in small business management.

52315 ■ Burlington County College
601 Pemberton-Browns Mills Rd.
Pemberton Browns Mills Rd.
Pemberton, NJ 08068
Ph:(609)894-9311
Fax:(609)894-0764
URL: http://www.bcc.edu
Description: Two-year college offering a certificate in small business management.

TRADE PERIODICALS

52316 ■ *Linux Business Week*
Pub: SYS-CON Media
Contact: Lin Goetz, Online Ed.
E-mail: lin@sys-con.com
Ed: Jeremy Geelan, Editor, jeremy@sys-con.com. **Released:** Monthly. **Price:** $129 two years digital edition; $99 digital edition. **Description:** Professional journal covering Linux news and issues.

PUBLICATIONS

52317 ■ *Mercer Business*
2550 Kuser Rd.
P.O. Box 8307
Trenton, NJ 08650
Ph:(609)586-2056
Fax:(609)586-8052
Co. E-mail: WEgraphics@aol.com

52318 ■ *New Jersey Business*
New Jersey Business and Industry Association
310 Passaic Ave.
Fairfield, NJ 07004
Ph:(973)882-5004
Fax:(973)882-4648
Co. E-mail: njbmag@intac.com
URL: http://www.njbmagazine.com

52319 ■ *New Jersey Monthly*
55 Park Pl.
P.O. Box 920
Morristown, NJ 07963-0920
Ph:(973)539-8230
Fax:(973)538-2953
URL: http://www.njmonthly.com

52320 ■ *Smart Start your New Jersey Business*
PSI Research
300 N. Valley Dr.
Grants Pass, OR 97526
Ph:(503)479-9464
Free: 800-228-2275
Fax:(503)476-1479
Co. E-mail: info@psi-research.com
URL: http://www.psi-research.com
Ed: Michael D. Jenkins. **Released:** Revised edition, 1992. **Price:** $29.95 (looseleaf binder); $24.95 (paper). **Description:** Part of the Successful Business Library series.

PUBLISHERS

52321 ■ Factiva Inc.
4300 Rte. 1 N, Bldg. 5, 2nd Fl.
PO Box 300
Princeton, NJ 08543-0300
Ph:(609)627-2000
Free: 800-522-3567

Fax:(609)627-2310
Co. E-mail: moreinfo.americas@factiva.com
URL: http://www.factiva.com
Contact: Stephen Daintith, COO
Description: Publishes databases listing current financial and investment material and general news and information. Also produces software. Databases accessible through personal computers, communicating word processors and terminals, and teletypewriters. Reaches market through direct mail, telephone sales, advertising, and trade sales. **Founded:** 1974.

52322 ■ Fictionwise Inc.
346 Main St.
Chatham, NJ 07928-2137
Ph:(973)701-6771
Fax:(973)701-6774
Co. E-mail: support@fictionwise.com
URL: http://www.fictionwise.com
Contact: Scott Pendergrast, Mgr
Description: Publishes fiction in e-book format and also publishes nonfiction, erotica, humor, horror and romance. **Founded:** 2000.

52323 ■ LexisNexis Matthew Bender (Newark, New Jersey)
744 Broad St.
Newark, NJ 07102-3885
Ph:(973)820-2000
Free: 800-424-4200
Fax:(973)820-2007
Co. E-mail: corpcomm@lexisnexis.com
URL: http://www.lexisnexis.com
Contact: Mario Garnica, Mktg Mgr
Description: Publishes analytical legal information in print, CD-ROM and via the Internet. Works are authored by leading experts in the legal community. **Founded:** 1887.

52324 ■ Passaic County Department of Community and Economic Development
Passaic County Administration Bldg., Freeholder's Office
401 Grand St.
Paterson, NJ 07505-2027
Ph:(973)881-4402
Fax:(973)684-2042
Co. E-mail: pcupdate@passaiccountynj.org
URL: http://www.passaiccountynj.org
Contact: Deborah Hoffman, Director
E-mail: deborahh@passaiccountynj.org
Description: Publishes materials on business, economic development and financing. Offers a newsletter. **Founded:** 1978.

52325 ■ Prentice Hall Business Publishing
1 Lake St.
Upper Saddle River, NJ 07458
Ph:(201)236-7000
Free: 800-227-1816
Fax:(201)236-3400
URL: http://phbusiness.prenhall.com
Contact: Jerome Grant, President
Description: Publishes business books.

52326 ■ Prentice Hall Press
1 Lake St.
Upper Saddle River, NJ 07458-1813
Ph:(201)236-7000
Free: 800-745-8489
Fax:(201)236-3290
URL: http://www.pearsoned.com
Contact: Wendy Spiegel, Mgr
Description: Publishes books on business, education and self-help in publishing. **Founded:** 1913.

52327 ■ PubEasy
630 Central Ave.
New Providence, NJ 07974
Ph:(908)219-0053
Free: 888-269-5372
Fax:(908)219-0191
Co. E-mail: help@pubeasy.com
URL: http://www.pubeasy.com
Contact: John Phillips, Dir of Sales
E-mail: john.phillips@pubeasy.com

SMALL BUSINESS DEVELOPMENT CENTERS

52328 ■ Alamogordo Small Business Development Center
2230 Lawrence Blvd.
Alamogordo, NM 88310
Fax:(575)434-1432
Co. E-mail: kat@nmsua.nmsu.edu
URL: http://www.nmsbdc.org/alamogordo
Contact: G. Dwight Harp, Dir.

52329 ■ Albuquerque Small Business Development Center
2501 Yale Blvd. SE, Ste. 302
Albuquerque, NM 87106
Fax:(505)224-5256
Co. E-mail: sbdc@cnm.edu
URL: http://www.nmsbdc.org/albuquerque
Contact: Ray Garcia, Dir.

52330 ■ Carlsbad Small Business Development Center
221 S Canyon St.
Carlsbad, NM 88220
Fax:(505)885-1515
Co. E-mail: lcoalson@cavern.nmsu.edu
URL: http://www.nmsbdc.org/carlsbad
Contact: Larry Coalson, Dir.

52331 ■ Clovis Small Business Development Center
Clovis Community College
417 Schepps Blvd.
Clovis, NM 88101-8381
Fax:(575)769-4135
Co. E-mail: sbdc@clovis.cc.nm.us
URL: http://www.nmsbdc.org/clovis
Contact: Dr. Sandra Taylor-Sawyer, Dir.

52332 ■ Farmington Small Business Development Center
San Juan College
5101 College Blvd.
Farmington, NM 87402
Fax:(505)566-3698
Co. E-mail: bumbyj@sanjuancollege.edu
URL: http://www.nmsbdc.org/farmington
Contact: Carmen Martinez, Dir.

52333 ■ Las Cruces Small Business Development Center
2345 E Nevada Ave., Ste. 101
Las Cruces, NM 88001-3902
Fax:(575)528-7432
Co. E-mail: fowensby@nmsu.edu
URL: http://www.nmsbdc.org/lascruces/index.html
Contact: Fred K. Owensby, Dir.

52334 ■ Las Vegas Small Business Development Center
Luna Community College
366 Luna Dr.
Las Vegas, NM 87701
Free: 800-588-7232

Fax:(505)454-5326
Co. E-mail: dbustos@luna.edu
URL: http://www.nmsbdc.org/lasvegas
Contact: Don Bustos, Dir.

52335 ■ Los Alamos Small Business Development Center
190 Central Park Sq.
Los Alamos, NM 87544
Fax:(505)662-0099
URL: http://www.nmsbdc.org/losalamos
Contact: Patrick Sullivan, Dir.

52336 ■ Los Lunas Small Business Development Center
University of New Mexico-Valencia
280 La Entrada Rd.
Los Lunas, NM 87031
Fax:(505)925-8981
Co. E-mail: robscott@unm.edu
URL: http://www.nmsbdc.org/loslunas
Contact: Roberta Scott, Dir.

52337 ■ Mesalands Community College Small Business Development Center
911 S 10th St.
Tucumcari, NM 88401
Fax:(575)461-1901
Co. E-mail: sbdc@mesalands.edu
URL: http://www.nmsbdc.org/tucumcari
Contact: Carl Kallansrud, Dir.

52338 ■ New Mexico State University-Grants Small Business Development Center
701 E Roosevelt Ave.
Grants, NM 87020-2113
Fax:(505)287-2125
Co. E-mail: clemente@nmsu.edu
URL: http://www.nmsbdc.org/grants
Contact: Clemente Sanchez, Dir.

52339 ■ Roswell Small Business Development Center
PO Box 6000
Roswell, NM 88202-6000
Fax:(505)624-7132
Co. E-mail: eugene.simmons@roswell.enmu.edu
URL: http://www.nmsbdc.org/roswell
Contact: Eugene Simmons, Dir.

52340 ■ Sandoval County's Small Business Development Center
282 Camino del Pueblo, Ste. 2-A
Bernalillo, NM 87004
Fax:(505)867-3746
Co. E-mail: sandovalsbdc@la.unm.edu
URL: http://www.nmsbdc.org/sandoval
Contact: Ted Trujillo, Dir.

52341 ■ Santa Fe Small Business Development Center
Santa Fe Community College
6401 Richards Ave.
Santa Fe, NM 87508-4887

Fax:(505)428-1469
Co. E-mail: sfccsbdc@sfccnm.edu
URL: http://www.nmsbdc.org/santafe
Contact: Michael Mykris, Dir.

52342 ■ Small Business Development Center at Northern New Mexico College
1027 N Railroad Ave.
Espanola, NM 87532
Fax:(505)747-2234
Co. E-mail: jbarbee@nnmc.edu
URL: http://www.nmsbdc.org/espanola

52343 ■ South Valley Small Business Development Center
1309 4th St., Ste. A SW
Albuquerque, NM 87102
Fax:(505)248-0127
Co. E-mail: svsbdc@abq.com
URL: http://www.nmsbdc.org/southvalley

52344 ■ Southwest Small Business Development Center - New Mexico
PO Box 680
Silver City, NM 88062
Fax:(575)538-6341
Co. E-mail: sbdc@wnmu.edu
URL: http://www.nmsbdc.org/silvercity
Contact: Mary Vigil-Tarazoff, Dir.

52345 ■ University of New Mexico-Gallup Small Business Development Center
103 W Hwy. 66
Gallup, NM 87301
Fax:(505)863-6006
Co. E-mail: esanchez@cia-g.com
URL: http://www.nmsbdc.org/gallup
Contact: Elsie Sanchez, Dir./Business Counselor

SMALL BUSINESS ASSISTANCE PROGRAMS

52346 ■ New Mexico Department of Agriculture–Marketing and Economic Development Division
3190 S. Espina
Las Cruces, NM 88003-8005
Ph:(505)646-3007
Fax:(505)646-8120
Co. E-mail: nmagsec@nmda.nmsu.edu
URL: http://nmdaweb.nmsu.edu/marketing-and-economic-development
Contact: I. Miley Gonzalez, Dir/Secretary
Description: Provides technical assistance to agricultural producers and processors who export both domestically and internationally.

52347 ■ New Mexico Economic Development Department
1100 St. Francis Dr., Ste. 1060
Santa Fe, NM 87505
Ph:(505)827-0300
Free: 800-374-3060

Fax:(505)827-0328
Co. E-mail: edd.info@state.nm.us
URL: http://www.edd.state.nm.us/
Description: Formulates and implements statewide economic development. Also provides assistance to various individuals and groups.

52348 ■ New Mexico Procurement Assistance Program–General Services Department
PO Box 6850
Santa Fe, NM 87502-6850
Ph:(505)827-0472
Fax:(505)827-2484
URL: http://www.generalservices.state.nm.us/spd/spd.html
Contact: Michael C. Vineyard, Dir.
Description: Promotes and assists small, minority-owned, and women-owned businesses in marketing their goods and services to government, especially to the state of New Mexico.

52349 ■ New Mexico State University–Arrowhead Center
MSC 3CR
PO Box 30001
Las Cruces, NM 88003
Ph:(575)646-1434
Fax:(575)646-7037
Co. E-mail: info@arrowheadcenter.org
URL: http://arrowheadcenter.nmsu.edu/
Contact: Dr. Kevin Boberg, Dir
Description: Provides research services and a data bank for economic and business related information. Also provides business and economic research to public and private sectors.

SCORE OFFICES

52350 ■ SCORE Albuquerque
Path: www.abqscore.org

52351 ■ SCORE Las Cruces
Loretto Towne Center
505 S Main St., Ste. 125
Las Cruces, NM 88001
Ph:(505)523-5627
Fax:(505)524-2101
Co. E-mail: score.397@zianet.com
URL: http://www.zianet.com/score.397
Contact: Gabriel Fusco, Chm.
Description: Provides entrepreneur education for the formation, growth and success of small businesses in the area.

52352 ■ SCORE Santa Fe and Northern New Mexico
Montoya Federal Bldg.
120 Federal Pl., Rm. 307
Santa Fe, NM 87501
Ph:(505)988-6302
Fax:(505)988-6300
Co. E-mail: scoresf@yahoo.com
URL: http://www.santafescore.org
Contact: Dick Rogers, Chm.
Description: Provides professional guidance, mentoring services and financial assistance to maximize the success of existing and merging small businesses.

BETTER BUSINESS BUREAUS

52353 ■ Better Business Bureau of New Mexico
2625 Pennsylvania St. NE, Ste. 2050
Albuquerque, NM 87110-3657
Ph:(505)346-0110
Fax:(505)346-0696
Co. E-mail: jerry@bbbsw.org
URL: http://www.bbbnm.com
Contact: Jerry Shipman, Pres.

52354 ■ Better Business Bureau Serving Four Corners and Western Slope
308 N Locke
Farmington, NM 87401-5855
Ph:(505)326-6501

Fax:(505)327-7731
Co. E-mail: jerry@bbbsw.org
URL: http://www.newmexicoandsouthwestcolorado.bbb.org/Home.aspx
Contact: Jerry W. Shipman, Pres.

CHAMBERS OF COMMERCE

52355 ■ Alamogordo Chamber of Commerce
1301 N White Sands Blvd.
Alamogordo, NM 88310
Ph:(505)437-6120
Free: 888-843-3441
Fax:(505)437-6334
Co. E-mail: chamber@alamogordo.com
URL: http://www.alamogordo.com
Contact: Mike Espiritu, Exec. Dir.

52356 ■ Angel Fire Chamber of Commerce
PO Box 547
Angel Fire, NM 87710
Ph:(505)377-6661
Free: 800-446-8117
Fax:(505)377-3034
Co. E-mail: askus@angelfirechamber.org
URL: http://www.angelfirechamber.org
Contact: Tom Bowles, Pres.

52357 ■ Aztec Chamber of Commerce and Visitor Center
110 N Ash St.
Aztec, NM 87410
Ph:(505)334-9551
Free: 888-838-9551
Fax:(505)334-7648
Co. E-mail: info@aztecchamber.com
URL: http://www.aztecchamber.com
Contact: Becki Christensen, Exec. Dir.

52358 ■ Belen Chamber of Commerce
712 Dalies Ave.
Belen, NM 87002-3618
Ph:(505)864-8091
Fax:(505)864-7461
Co. E-mail: belenchamber@belenchamber.com
URL: http://www.belenchamber.com
Contact: Michael Vallejos, Pres.

52359 ■ Bloomfield Chamber of Commerce
224 W Broadway
Bloomfield, NM 87413
Ph:(505)632-0880
Co. E-mail: askme@bloomfieldnm.info
URL: http://www.bloomfieldnm.info
Contact: Janet Mackey, Pres.

52360 ■ Capitan Chamber of Commerce
PO Box 441
Capitan, NM 88316
Ph:(505)354-2273
Co. E-mail: capitannm@villageofcapitan.com
URL: http://www.villageofcapitan.com

52361 ■ Carrizozo Chamber of Commerce
PO Box 567
Carrizozo, NM 88301
Ph:(505)648-2732
Co. E-mail: zozoccc@tularosa.net
URL: http://carrizozochamber.org

52362 ■ Chama Valley Chamber of Commerce
PO Box 306-RB
Chama, NM 87520
Ph:(505)756-2306
Free: 800-477-0149
Fax:(505)756-2892
Co. E-mail: info@chamavalley.com
URL: http://www.chamavalley.com

52363 ■ Cimarron Chamber of Commerce
PO Box 604
Cimarron, NM 87714
Ph:(505)376-2417
Free: 888-376-2417

Fax:(505)376-2417
Co. E-mail: cimarronnm@gmail.com
URL: http://www.cimarronnm.com
Contact: Tracy Boyce, Pres.

52364 ■ Clayton-Union County Chamber of Commerce
PO Box 476
Clayton, NM 88415-0476
Ph:(505)374-9253
Free: 800-390-7858
Co. E-mail: cuchamber@plateautel.net
URL: http://www.claytonnewmexico.net
Contact: Michael Gonzalez, Exec. Dir.

52365 ■ Cloudcroft Chamber of Commerce
PO Box 1290
Cloudcroft, NM 88317
Ph:(505)682-2733
Free: (866)874-4447
Fax:(505)682-6028
Co. E-mail: cloudcroft@cloudcroft.net
URL: http://www.cloudcroft.net
Contact: Marsha Slane, Pres.

52366 ■ Clovis - Curry County Chamber of Commerce
105 E Grand Ave.
Clovis, NM 88101
Ph:(505)763-3435
Free: 800-261-7656
Fax:(505)763-7266
Co. E-mail: ernie@clovisnm.org
URL: http://www.clovisnm.org
Contact: Mrs. Ernie Kos, Exec. Dir.

52367 ■ Deming-Luna County Chamber of Commerce
PO Box 8
Deming, NM 88031-0008
Ph:(505)546-2674
Free: 800-848-4955
Co. E-mail: info@demingchamber.com
URL: http://www.demingchamber.com
Contact: Cyndi Longoria, Exec. Dir.

52368 ■ Eagle Nest Chamber of Commerce
PO Box 322
Eagle Nest, NM 87718
Ph:(505)377-2420
Free: 800-494-9117
Co. E-mail: info@eaglenestchamber.org
URL: http://www.eaglenestchamber.org
Contact: Judy Montague, Pres.

52369 ■ Elephant Butte Chamber of Commerce
PO Box 1355
Elephant Butte, NM 87935
Ph:(505)744-4708
Free: 877-744-4900
Fax:(505)744-0044
Co. E-mail: info@elephantbuttechamberofcommerce.com
URL: http://www.elephantbuttechamberofcommerce.com
Contact: Susan LaFont, Pres.

52370 ■ Espanola Valley Chamber of Commerce
1 Calle de las Espanolas, Ste. F and G
Espanola, NM 87532
Ph:(505)753-2831
Fax:(505)753-1252
Co. E-mail: info@espanolanmchamber.com
URL: http://www.espanolanmchamber.com
Contact: Alice Lucero, Exec. Dir.

52371 ■ Farmington Chamber of Commerce
100 W Broadway
Farmington, NM 87401
Ph:(505)325-0279
Free: 888-325-0279
Fax:(505)327-7556
Co. E-mail: chamber@gofarmington.com
URL: http://www.gofarmington.com
Contact: Melissa Bateman-Lane, Pres./CEO

52372 ■ Fort Sumner Chamber of Commerce
PO Box 28
Fort Sumner, NM 88119-0028
Ph:(505)355-7705
Fax:(505)355-2850
Co. E-mail: ftsumnercoc@plateautel.net
URL: http://www.ftsumnerchamber.com

52373 ■ Greater Albuquerque Chamber of Commerce
PO Box 25100
Albuquerque, NM 87125-0100
Ph:(505)764-3700
Fax:(505)764-3714
Co. E-mail: info@abqchamber.com
URL: http://www.abqchamber.com
Contact: Mrs. Terri L. Cole, Pres./CEO

52374 ■ Greater Artesia Chamber of Commerce
107 N 1st St.
Artesia, NM 88210-2101
Ph:(505)746-2744
Free: 800-658-6251
Fax:(505)746-2745
Co. E-mail: hklein@artesiachamber.com
URL: http://www.artesiachamber.com
Contact: Hayley Klein, Exec. Dir.

52375 ■ Greater Las Cruces Chamber of Commerce
760 W Picacho Ave.
Las Cruces, NM 88005
Ph:(505)524-1968
Fax:(505)527-5546
Co. E-mail: jberry@lascruces.org
URL: http://www.lascruces.org
Contact: Jim Berry, Pres.

52376 ■ Hispano Chamber of Commerce de Las Cruces
308 E Griggs Ave.
Las Cruces, NM 88001
Ph:(505)523-2681
Fax:(505)523-4639
URL: http://www.hispanochamberlc.org

52377 ■ Hobbs Chamber of Commerce
400 N Marland Blvd.
Hobbs, NM 88240-6330
Ph:(505)397-3202
Free: 800-658-6291
Fax:(505)397-1689
Co. E-mail: hobbschamber@leaconet.com
URL: http://www.hobbschamber.org/html_2002/index.htm
Contact: Kent Waldrop, Chm.

52378 ■ Las Vegas-San Miguel Chamber of Commerce
503 6th St.
PO Box 128
Las Vegas, NM 87701
Ph:(505)425-8631
Free: 800-832-5947
Fax:(505)425-3057
Co. E-mail: lvexec@qwestoffice.net
URL: http://www.lasvegasnewmexico.com
Contact: Diana Ortiz, Exec. Dir.

52379 ■ Los Alamos Chamber of Commerce
109 Central Park Sq.
Los Alamos, NM 87544-0460
Ph:(505)662-8105
Fax:(505)662-8399
Co. E-mail: chamber@losalamos.com
URL: http://www.losalamoschamber.com
Contact: Kevin Holsapple, Exec. Dir.

52380 ■ Los Alamos Commerce and Development Corporation
PO Box 1206
Los Alamos, NM 87544
Ph:(505)662-0001
Fax:(505)662-0099
Co. E-mail: lacdc@losalamos.org
URL: http://www.losalamos.org/lacdc
Contact: Kevin Holsapple, Exec. Dir.

52381 ■ Lovington Chamber of Commerce
201 S Main
Lovington, NM 88260-4222
Ph:(505)396-5311
Fax:(505)396-2823
Co. E-mail: lovington-nm-chamber@valornet.com
URL: http://lovington.leaco.net
Contact: Leticia Kanmore, Exec. Dir.

52382 ■ Magdalena Chamber of Commerce
PO Box 281
Magdalena, NM 87825-0281
Free: (866)854-3217
Co. E-mail: info@magdalena-nm.com
URL: http://www.magdalena-nm.com
Contact: Beverley Gallaher, Treas.

52383 ■ Moriarty Chamber of Commerce
PO Box 96
Moriarty, NM 87035
Ph:(505)832-4087
Co. E-mail: info@moriartychamber.com
URL: http://moriartychamber.com

52384 ■ Mountainair Chamber of Commerce
PO Box 595
Mountainair, NM 87036-0595
Ph:(505)847-2795
Fax:(505)847-0907
Co. E-mail: mcc@mountainairchamber.com
URL: http://www.mountainairchamber.com
Contact: Kevin Turner, Pres.

52385 ■ Red River Chamber of Commerce
PO Box 870
Red River, NM 87558
Ph:(505)754-2366
Free: 800-348-6444
Fax:(505)754-3104
Co. E-mail: rrinfo@redriverchamber.org
URL: http://www.redrivernewmex.com

52386 ■ Rio Rancho Chamber of Commerce
4001 Southern Blvd. SE
Rio Rancho, NM 87124-2069
Ph:(505)892-1533
Fax:(505)892-6157
Co. E-mail: info@rrrcc.org
URL: http://www.rrchamber.org
Contact: Debbi Moore, Pres./CEO

52387 ■ Roosevelt County Chamber of Commerce
100 S Ave. A
Portales, NM 88130
Ph:(505)356-8541
Free: 800-635-8036
Fax:(505)356-8542
Co. E-mail: chamber@portales.com
URL: http://www.portales.com
Contact: Sharon King, Exec. Dir.

52388 ■ Roswell Chamber of Commerce
PO Box 70
Roswell, NM 88202-0070
Ph:(505)623-5695
Free: 877-849-7679
Fax:(505)624-6870
Co. E-mail: information@roswellnm.org
URL: http://www.roswellnm.org
Contact: Bernarr Treat, Exec. Dir.

52389 ■ Ruidoso Valley Chamber of Commerce
720 Sudderth Dr.
PO Box 698
Ruidoso, NM 88355-0698
Ph:(505)257-7395
Free: 877-RUI-DOSO
Fax:(505)257-4693
Co. E-mail: info@ruidosonow.com
URL: http://ruidosonow.com
Contact: Brad Treptow, Exec. Dir.

52390 ■ Santa Fe Chamber of Commerce
PO Box 1928
Santa Fe, NM 87507
Ph:(505)988-3279

Fax:(505)984-2205
Co. E-mail: trish@santafechamber.com
URL: http://www.santafechamber.com
Contact: Simon Brackley, Pres./CEO

52391 ■ Silver City-Grant County Chamber of Commerce
201 N Hudson Ave.
Silver City, NM 88061
Ph:(505)538-3785
Free: 800-548-9378
Co. E-mail: info@silvercity.org
URL: http://www.silvercity.org
Contact: Floyd Robertson, Pres.

52392 ■ Taos County Chamber of Commerce
108 Kit Carson Rd., Ste. F
Taos, NM 87571
Ph:(575)751-8800
Fax:(575)751-1801
Co. E-mail: info@taoschamber.com
URL: http://www.taoschamber.com/index.html
Contact: Ralph Lombardi, Chm.

52393 ■ Truth or Consequences/Sierra County Chamber of Commerce
PO Box 31
Truth or Consequences, NM 87901
Ph:(505)894-3536
Fax:(505)894-3536
Co. E-mail: contact@truthorconsequencesnm.net
URL: http://www.truthorconsequencesnm.net
Contact: Jessica Mackenzie, Pres.

52394 ■ Tucumcari-Quay County Chamber of Commerce
404 W Rte. 66
PO Box E
Tucumcari, NM 88401-7005
Ph:(505)461-1694
Fax:(505)461-3884
Co. E-mail: chamber@tucumcarinm.com
URL: http://www.tucumcarinm.com
Contact: Dianne Paris, Exec. Dir.

MINORITY BUSINESS ASSISTANCE PROGRAMS

52395 ■ NEDA Business Consultants Inc.–New Mexico Minority Business Enterprise Center
718 Central Ave. SW
Albuquerque, NM 87102
Ph:(505)843-7114
Fax:(505)242-2030
Co. E-mail: info@nedainc.net
URL: http://www.nm-mbec.com
Contact: Ann Muller, Pres & Project Dir
Description: Provides assistance to small and minority businesses in New Mexico.

52396 ■ New Mexico Native American Business Enterprise Center
2401 12th St. NW, Ste. 5-S
Albequerque, NM 87104
Ph:(505)243-6775
Fax:(505)766-9499
Co. E-mail: tedpedro@nmnabec.org
URL: http://www.nmnabec.org
Contact: Theodore M. Pedro, Exec Dir
Description: Assists Native American businesses with developmental needs both on and off the reservation.

52397 ■ WESST
609 Broadway Blvd. NE
Albuquerque, NM 87102
Ph:(505)246-6900
Fax:(505)243-3035
URL: http://www.wesst.org
Contact: Agnes Noonan, Pres
Description: Provides statewide small business development and training in New Mexico. Serves all people, but focus is on women and minorities.

FINANCING AND LOAN PROGRAMS

52398 ■ Technology Ventures Corp.
1155 University Blvd. SE
Albuquerque, NM 87106
Ph:(505)246-2882
Fax:(505)246-2891
URL: http://www.techventures.org
Contact: Sherman McCorkle, President and CEO
Investment Types: Seed, start-up, first and second stage. **Industry Preferences:** Diversified. **Geographic Preferences:** Southwest. **Principal Exhibits:**

PROCUREMENT ASSISTANCE PROGRAMS

52399 ■ New Mexico Procurement Technical Assistance Center
6401 Richards Ave.
Santa Fe, NM 87508
Ph:(505)428-1622
Fax:(505)428-1469
Co. E-mail: wendy.ederer@sfcc.edu
URL: http://www.dla.mil/db/procurem.htm
Contact: Wendy Ederer, Program Mgr.
E-mail: cmarquez@state.nm.us

INCUBATORS/RESEARCH AND TECHNOLOGY PARKS

52400 ■ Albuquerque SBDC
2501 Yale Blvd. SE, Ste. 302
Albuquerque, NM 87106
Ph:(505)224-5250
Fax:(505)224-5256
Co. E-mail: sbdc@cnm.edu
Contact: Ray Garcia, Dir

52401 ■ Eastern New Mexico University–Office of Grant and Contract Management
ENMU Station 9
1500 S Ave. K
Portales, NM 88130
Ph:(575)562-2677
Fax:(575)562-2578
Co. E-mail: jo.laney@enmu.edu
URL: http://www.enmu.edu/services/grants
Contact: Jo Laney, Dir.
E-mail: jo.laney@enmu.edu
Scope: Administers and coordinates both intramurally and extramurally supported research projects conducted in various units of the University, particularly in environmental sciences, education, and Southwestern archeology. Encourages faculty scholarship in bilingual and multicultural education, archeology, chemistry, fish and game, paleobotany, lipoproteins, and rocket propellents. Performs archeological surveys and excavations for government and private agencies through its subdivision, Agency for Conservation Archaeology. **Publications:** Contributions in Anthropology.

52402 ■ Economic Development Corporation of Lea County
200 E Broadway, Ste. A201
PO Box 1376
Hobbs, NM 88241-1376
Ph:(505)397-2039
Free: 800-443-2236
Fax:(505)392-2300
Co. E-mail: edclea@leaco.net
URL: http://www.edclc.org
Contact: Bethe Cunningham, Exec Dir
Description: Works to improve the economic condition of Lea County through business expansion, relocation, and retention.

52403 ■ Los Alamos Research Park
190 Central Park Sq.
PO Box 1206
Los Alamos, NM 87544
Ph:(505)661-4999

Fax:(505)662-0099
Co. E-mail: lacdc@losalamos.org
URL: http://www.la-rp.org
Description: Provides a research and development focused research park.

52404 ■ New Mexico State University–Office of the Vice President
Anderson Hall, MSC 3RES, Box 30001
Las Cruces, NM 88003-8001
Ph:(505)646-2481
Fax:(505)646-5717
Co. E-mail: vpr@nmsu.edu
URL: http://research.nmsu.edu/ovpr.html
Contact: Vimal Chaitanya, VP
E-mail: vpr@nmsu.edu
Scope: Serves as a coordinating office for all externally supported research at the University.

52405 ■ Quality Center for Business
San Juan College
5101 College Blvd.
Farmington, NM 87402
Ph:(505)566-3700
Co. E-mail: welchj@sanjuancollege.edu
URL: http://www.sjc.cc.nm.us/qcb/
Description: A small business incubator offering an integrated approach to assisting area businesses, industry and organizations with staff or management training; assistance in business planning and technical support; space and office support for growing companies; and the economic development of San Juan County.

52406 ■ Santa Fe Business Incubator
3900 Paseo del Sol
Santa Fe, NM 87507
Ph:(505)424-1140
Fax:(505)424-1144
Co. E-mail: info@sfbi.net
URL: http://www.sfbi.net
Contact: Marie Longserre, Pres & CEO
Description: The SFBI seeks to enhance the quality of life in Santa Fe County by supporting emerging businesses through shared resources. Provides office, lab, and light manufacturing space.

52407 ■ South Valley Economic Development Center
318 Isleta Blvd. SW
Albuquerque, NM 87105-3822
Ph:(505)877-0373
Co. E-mail: admin@svedc.com
URL: http://www.bernco.gov/live/departments.asp-?dept=7147
Description: A small business incubator with processes that accelerate the successful development of start-up and fledgling companies by providing entrepreneurs with an array of targeted resources and services.

52408 ■ University of New Mexico–Office of the Vice President for Research and Economic Development
Scholes Hall, Rm. 327, MSC05 3480
1 University of New Mexico
Albuquerque, NM 87131-0001
Ph:(505)277-6128
Fax:(505)277-5271
Co. E-mail: jfulghum@unm.edu
URL: http://research.unm.edu
Contact: Julia Fulghum PhD, VP for Res.
E-mail: jfulghum@unm.edu
Scope: Provides general administrative support to all sponsored activities at the University for the Colleges of Arts and Sciences, Education, Engineering, Fine Arts, Law, Business Administration, Architecture, and various institutes and divisions. Supplies information on external sources of funds for all types of research, service, and training activities; assists with preparation of proposals; approves proposal budgets; and retains files on all proposals submitted to external sources. Provides general support in the area of inventions/patents/licensing to faculty and staff. **Publications:** Research Notes (monthly).

52409 ■ WESST Enterprise Center
609 Broadway Blvd., NE
Albuquerque, NM 87102
Ph:(505)246-6900
Free: 800-469-3778
Fax:(505)243-3035
Co. E-mail: jmeyer@wesst.org
URL: http://www.wesst.org/enterprise-center/
Contact: Clare Zurawski, Regional Mgr.
Description: A mixed-use small business incubator for up to 20 light manufacturing, service, and technology enterprises.

EDUCATIONAL PROGRAMS

52410 ■ Albuquerque Technical-Vocational Institute
525 Buena Vista SE
Albuquerque, NM 87106
Ph:(505)224-3000
Fax:(505)224-4556
URL: http://www.tvi.cc.nm.us
Description: Trade and technical school offering a program in entrepreneurship.

52411 ■ Eastern New Mexico University—Roswell
PO Box 6000
Roswell, NM 88202-6000
Ph:(505)624-7000
Fax:(505)624-7119
URL: http://www.roswell.enmu.edu
Description: Part of a small business assistance center system that provides a variety of training programs, including self-paced, evening, and business courses. 1800-243-6687

52412 ■ New Mexico Junior College–Business Assistance Center
5317 Lovington Hwy.
Hobbs, NM 88240
Ph:(505)392-4510
Free: 800-657-6260
Fax:(505)392-2526
URL: http://www.nmjc.cc.nm.us
Description: Part of a small business system that provides a variety of training, including self-paced, evening, and business courses. 1-800-657-6260.

52413 ■ Northern New Mexico Community College
921 Paso de Onate
Espanola, NM 87532
Ph:(505)747-2100
Fax:(505)747-2180
URL: http://www.nnmcc.edu
Description: Part of a small business assistance center system that provides a variety of training, including self-paced, evening, and business courses.

52414 ■ Santa Fe Community College
3000 NW 83rd St., Rm. 112
Gainesville, FL 32606
Ph:(352)395-5443
Fax:(352)395-5922
Co. E-mail: information@sfcc.edu
URL: http://www.santafe.cc.fl.us
Description: Two-year college offering a program in small business management.

LEGISLATIVE ASSISTANCE

52415 ■ NM Commission on the Status of Women
300 San Mateo Blvd. NE, Ste. 101
Albuquerque, NM 87108
Ph:(505)222-6600
Free: 800-432-9168
Fax:(505)222-6611
URL: http://www.womenscommission.state.nm.us
Description: Assesses the needs of women in business in the state of New Mexico and formulates plans to meet those needs.

PUBLICATIONS

52416 ■ *Smart Start your New Mexico Business*
PSI Research
300 N. Valley Dr.
Grants Pass, OR 97526
Ph:(503)479-9464
Free: 800-228-2275
Fax:(503)476-1479
Co. E-mail: info@psi-research.com
URL: http://www.psi-research.com
Ed: Michael D. Jenkins. **Released:** Revised edition, 1992. **Price:** $29.95 (looseleaf binder); $24.95 (paper). **Description:** Part of the Successful Business Library series.

PUBLISHERS

52417 ■ Sun Books - Sun Publishing
1274 Calle De Comercio
PO Box 5588
Santa Fe, NM 87502-5588
Ph:(505)471-5177
Free: 877-849-0051
Fax:(505)473-4458
Co. E-mail: info@sunbooks.com
URL: http://www.sunbooks.com
Contact: Skip Whitson, Director
E-mail: info@sunbooks.com
Description: Publishes self-help, motivational, astrology, business, history, art, philosophy and art books.

Distributes for Far West Publishing Co. and Sun-Books. **Founded:** 1973.

52418 ■ Via Media Publishing Co.
941 Calle Mejia, Ste. 822
Santa Fe, NM 87501-1467
Ph:(505)983-1919
Fax:(814)455-2726
Co. E-mail: info@goviamedia.com
URL: http://www.goviamedia.com
Contact: Michael A. Demarco, Mgr
E-mail: md@goviamedia.com
Description: Publishes fiction and nonfiction about martial arts. Accepts unsolicited manuscripts. Reaches market through direct mail, reviews, listings and distributors including Bibliog. **Founded:** 1991.

SMALL BUSINESS DEVELOPMENT CENTERS

52419 ■ Albany Small Business Development Center
7A Harriman Campus Rd.
Albany, NY 12206
Fax:(518)485-8223
Co. E-mail: wbrigham@uamail.albany.edu
URL: http://www.nyssbdc.org
Contact: William Brigham, Dir.

52420 ■ Binghamton Small Business Development Center
Binghamton University
The Artco Bldg., 3rd Fl.
Binghamton, NY 13901-2705
Fax:(607)777-4029
Co. E-mail: sbdc@binghamton.edu
URL: http://www.nyssbdc.org
Contact: Douglas Boyce, Dir.

52421 ■ Brockport Small Business Development Center
350 New Campus Dr.
Brockport, NY 14420
Fax:(585)395-2467
Co. E-mail: sbdc@brockport.edu
URL: http://www.nyssbdc.org
Contact: Jan Pisanczyn, Dir.

52422 ■ Bronx Small Business Development Center
250 Bedford Park Blvd. W
Bronx, NY 10468-1589
Fax:(718)960-7340
Co. E-mail: clarence.stanley@lehman.cuny.edu
URL: http://www.nyssbdc.org
Contact: Clarence Stanley, Dir.

52423 ■ Buffalo State College Small Business Development Center
Buffalo State College
Cleveland Hall 206
1300 Elmwood Ave.
Buffalo, NY 14222
Fax:(716)878-4067
Co. E-mail: smallbus@buffalostate.edu
URL: http://www.buffalostate.edu/sbdc
Contact: Susan A. McCartney, Dir.

52424 ■ Canton Small Business Development Center
PO Box 6069
Massena, NY 13662
Fax:(315)764-0854
Co. E-mail: sbdc@canton.edu
URL: http://www.nyssbdc.org
Contact: Dale Rice, Dir.

52425 ■ College of Staten Island Small Business Development Center
College of Staten Island
2800 Victory Blvd., Bldg. 2A
Staten Island, NY 10314-9806
Fax:(718)982-2323
Co. E-mail: sullivane@mail.csi.cuny.edu
URL: http://www.nyssbdc.org
Contact: Dean Balsamini, Dir.

52426 ■ Farmingdale Small Business Development Center
Farmingdale State College
Campus Commons
2350 Rte. 110
Farmingdale, NY 11735
Fax:(631)370-8895
Co. E-mail: sbdc@farmingdale.edu
URL: http://www.farmingdale.edu/campuspages/
  CAMPUSAFFILIATES/SBDC/homepage.htm
Contact: Lucille Wesnofske, Dir.

52427 ■ Greater Syracuse Business Development Corporation
572 S Salina St.
Syracuse, NY 13202
Fax:(315)471-8545
Co. E-mail: padams@gsbdc.com
URL: http://www.gsbdc.com
Contact: Peggy A. Adams, Exec. Dir.

52428 ■ Jamestown Small Business Development Center
Jamestown Community College
525 Falconer St.
Jamestown, NY 14702-0020
Fax:(716)338-1476
Co. E-mail: irenedobies@mail.sunyjcc.edu
URL: http://www.nyssbdc.org
Contact: Irene Dobies, Dir.

52429 ■ Manhattan Small Business Development Center at Pace University
163 William St., 16th Fl.
New York, NY 10038
Fax:(212)618-6669
Co. E-mail: sbdc@pace.edu
URL: http://www.nyssbdc.org
Contact: Ira Davidson, Dir.

52430 ■ Mid-Hudson Small Business Development Center
Business Resource Center
One Development Ct.
Kingston, NY 12401
Fax:(845)339-1631
Co. E-mail: sbdc@sunyulster.edu
URL: http://www.nyssbdc.org
Contact: Arnaldo Sehwerert, Dir.

52431 ■ Midtown Manhattan Small Business Development Center at Baruch College
Baruch College, Field Ctr.
55 Lexington Ave.
New York, NY 10010-0010
Fax:(646)312-4781
Co. E-mail: sbdc@baruch.cuny.edu
URL: http://www.nyssbdc.org
Contact: Monica Dean, Dir.

52432 ■ Mohawk Valley Small Business Development Center
PO Box 3050
Utica, NY 13504-3050
Fax:(315)792-7554
Co. E-mail: sbdc@sunyit.edu
URL: http://www.sunyit.edu/sbdc

52433 ■ New York State Small Business Development Center
22 Corporate Woods Bldg., 3rd Fl.
Albany, NY 12246
Free: 800-732-SBDC
URL: http://www.nyssbdc.org
Contact: Mr. James King, State Dir./Sec.

52434 ■ Niagara Small Business Development Center
3111 Saunders Settlement Rd.
Sanborn, NY 14132
Fax:(716)433-5155
Co. E-mail: sbdc@niagaracc.suny.edu
URL: http://www.nyssbdc.org
Contact: Richard Gorko, Dir.

52435 ■ North Country Small Business Development Center
State University of New York College at Plattsburgh
194 US Oval
Plattsburgh, NY 12903-3900
Fax:(518)564-2043
Co. E-mail: sbdc@plattsburgh.edu
URL: http://www.nyssbdc.org
Contact: Rick Leibowitz, Dir.

52436 ■ Onondaga Small Business Development Center
Onondaga Community College
Whitney ATC , Ste. 206
Syracuse, NY 13215-4585
Fax:(315)492-3704
Co. E-mail: sbdc@sunyocc.edu
URL: http://www.nyssbdc.org
Contact: Patricia Higgins, Dir.

52437 ■ Stony Brook Small Business Development Center
Stony Brook University
Harriman Hall, Rm. 109
Stony Brook, NY 11794-3777
Fax:(631)632-7176
Co. E-mail: lynne.schmidt@sunysb.edu
URL: http://www.nyssbdc.org
Contact: Jeff Saelens, Dir.

52438 ■ Westchester Small Business Development Center
Rockland Community College
Brucker Hall, No. 6101
Suffern, NY 10901-3699
Fax:(845)356-6117
Co. E-mail: tmorley@sunyrockland.edu
URL: http://www.nyssbdc.org
Contact: Thomas Morley, Dir.

52439 ■ York Small Business Development Center
City University of New York, York College
9450 159th St.
Jamaica, NY 11451
Fax:(718)262-2881
Co. E-mail: sbdc@york.cuny.edu
URL: http://www.nyssbdc.org

SMALL BUSINESS ASSISTANCE PROGRAMS

52440 ■ New Jersey Department of Business and Economic Development
Mary G. Roebling Bldg.
20 W State St.
Trenton, NJ 08625-0990
Ph:(609)292-4431
URL: http://www.newjerseycommerce.org/
Description: Provides complete assistance packages, including financing, site selection, and construction. Package may also include labor recruitment and training.

52441 ■ New York Department of Economic Development–Division of Minority- and Women-owned Business Development
30 S Pearl St.
Albany, NY 12245
Ph:(518)292-5250
Free: 800-STA-TENY
Fax:(518)292-5803
Co. E-mail: esd@empire.state.nv.us
URL: http://www.empire.state.ny.us/Small_and_Growing_Businesses/
Contact: Michael H. Jones-Bey, Exec. Dir.
Description: Certify minority and women owned businesses. Monitor the compliance of state agencies. Meet the goals that the agency sets for the utility of minority and women owned businesses.

52442 ■ New York Department of Economic Development–Division for Small Business–Business Service Ombudsman (30 S)
30 S Pearl St.
Albany, NY 12245
Ph:(518)292-5220
Free: 800-STA-TENY
Fax:(518)292-5884
URL: http://www.empire.state.ny.us
Description: Assists businesses in resolving red tape difficulties with all levels of government.

52443 ■ New York State Foundation for Science, Technology and Innovation
30 S Pearl St., 11th Fl.
Albany, NY 12207
Ph:(518)292-5700
Fax:(518)292-5798
Co. E-mail: contact@nystar.state.ny.us
URL: http://www.nystar.state.ny.us
Contact: Edward Reinfurt, Exec. Dir.
Description: Provides major services, including conducting special training programs, awarding research and development grants for university-based research, encouraging high technology, and providing grants and other services to the Centers for Advanced Technology.

52444 ■ New York State Foundation for Science, Technology and Innovation–Incubators & High Technology Economic Development
30 S Pearl St., 11th Fl.
Albany, NY 12207
Ph:(518)292-5700
Fax:(518)292-5780
URL: http://www.nystar.state.ny.us/incubators.htm
Contact: Jannette Rondo
Description: Provides established small and medium-sized manufacturing businesses with knowledge, attitudes, and skills so they can address issues of technology based productivity improvements. Assistance is provided on an individualized basis.

52445 ■ State University of New York at Plattsburgh–Economic Development and Technical Assistance
Redcay, Rm. 213
101 Broad St.
Plattsburgh, NY 12901
Ph:(518)564-2214
Fax:(518)564-3220
Co. E-mail: tac@plattsburgh.edu
URL: http://www.tacsuny.com
Contact: Howard Lowe, Dir
Description: Provides technical support and data to the business community and develops and promotes new venture capital formation. Specializes in short-term management, marketing, financial packaging, and feasibility analysis services.

SCORE OFFICES

52446 ■ Auburn SCORE
Path: www.cayugacountychamber.com

52447 ■ Brooklyn SCORE
Path:

52448 ■ Chautauqua Region SCORE
Path:

52449 ■ Chemung Valley SCORE
Path: www.chemungvalley.scorechapter.org

52450 ■ Greater Binghamton SCORE
Path: www.greaterbinghamtonscore.org

52451 ■ Orange County SCORE
Path: orangenyscore.com

52452 ■ Putnam SCORE
Path: putnamscore.org

52453 ■ Rochester SCORE
601 Keating Federal Bldg.
100 State St., Rm. 410
Rochester, NY 14614
Ph:(585)263-6473
Fax:(585)263-3146
Co. E-mail: scorerochester@frontiernet.net
URL: http://www.scorerochester.org
Contact: Tony Carlisi, Chapter Chm.
Description: Provides business owners with information, resources and tools vital to their success. Offers business counseling.

52454 ■ Rockland SCORE
Path: www.rocklandscore.org

52455 ■ SCORE Brookhaven
Path: www.brookhaven.org/Committees/SCORE.aspx

52456 ■ SCORE Buffalo - Niagara
130 S Elmwood Ave.
Buffalo, NY 14202
Ph:(716)551-4301
Free: 800-745-0355
Fax:(716)551-4418
Co. E-mail: scorebuffalo@roadrunner.com
URL: http://www.scorebuffalo.org
Description: Aims to assist entrepreneurs in the startup and growth of small businesses. Includes services such as free, confidential counseling and low-cost management workshops. Acts as a resource partner in association with the Small Business Administration.

52457 ■ SCORE Clinton Franklin Essex County
Path: www.scoreplattsburgh.org

52458 ■ SCORE Dutchess
c/o Dutchess County Regional Chamber of Commerce
1 Civic Ctr. Plz.
Poughkeepsie, NY 12601

Ph:(845)454-1700
Co. E-mail: scoredcny@hotmail.com
URL: http://www.scoredutchessny.com
Contact: Nancy Kappler-Foster, Chair
Description: Provides resources and expertise to maximize the success of existing and emerging small businesses. Offers business counseling and workshops.

52459 ■ SCORE Huntington
Path: www.huntingtonchamber.com

52460 ■ SCORE Long Island
Path: scorelongisland.org

52461 ■ SCORE Northeast
1 Computer Dr. S
Albany, NY 12205
Ph:(518)446-1118
Co. E-mail: info@scorealbany.org
URL: http://www.scorealbany.org
Contact: Don Finney, Chm.
Description: Strives for the formation, growth, and success of small businesses. Promotes entrepreneur education in Albany area, New York.

52462 ■ SCORE NYC
Path: www.scorenyc.org

52463 ■ SCORE Queens County
Path:

52464 ■ SCORE Staten Island
Path: scorestatenisland.org

52465 ■ SCORE Syracuse
401 S Salina St., 5th Fl.
Syracuse, NY 13202
Ph:(315)471-9393
Co. E-mail: info@syracusescore.org
URL: http://www.syracusescore.org
Contact: Joe Pagano, Pres.
Description:

52466 ■ SCORE Ulster
Path: www.scoreulster.org

52467 ■ SCORE Watertown
Path: watertown.scorechapter.org

52468 ■ SCORE Westchester
120 Bloomingdale Rd.
White Plains, NY 10605
Ph:(914)948-3907
URL: http://www.scorewestchester.com
Description: Strives for the formation, growth, and success of small businesses. Promotes entrepreneur education in Westchester area, New York.

52469 ■ Suffolk SCORE
200 Howell Ave.
Riverhead, NY 11901
Ph:(631)727-3200
Co. E-mail: webmaster@easternsuffolkscore.org
URL: http://www.easternsuffolkscore.org
Contact: Harold Deutsch
Description: Promotes business and community development in Islip and Eastern Suffolk County. Conducts business education seminars and workshops to those wanting to start a business.

52470 ■ Sullivan SCORE
Path: www.sullivanscore.com

52471 ■ Utica SCORE
Path: www.uticascore.org

BETTER BUSINESS BUREAUS

52472 ■ Better Business Bureau, Buffalo
100 Bryant Woods S
Buffalo, NY 14228
Ph:(716)881-5222
Free: 800-828-5000
Fax:(716)883-5349
Co. E-mail: geninquiries@upstatenybbb.org
URL: http://www.buffalo.bbb.org

52473 ■ Better Business Bureau of Metropolitan New York
257 Park Ave. S
New York, NY 10010-7384
Ph:(212)533-6200
Fax:(212)477-4912
Co. E-mail: inquiry@newyork.bbb.org
URL: http://www.newyork.bbb.org

52474 ■ Better Business Bureau, Rochester
55 St. Paul St.
Rochester, NY 14604
Free: 800-828-5000
Co. E-mail: geninquiries@upstatenybbb.org
URL: http://www.rochester.bbb.org

52475 ■ Long Island Better Business Bureau
399 Conklin St.
Farmingdale, NY 11735
Ph:(516)420-0500
Fax:(516)420-1095
Co. E-mail: longislandbbb@newyork.bbb.org
URL: http://www.newyork.bbb.org

52476 ■ Mid-Hudson Better Business Bureau
150 White Plains Rd., Ste. 107
Tarrytown, NY 10591
Ph:(914)333-0550
Fax:(914)333-7519
Co. E-mail: mhinquiries@newyork.bbb.org
URL: http://www.newyork.bbb.org

CHAMBERS OF COMMERCE

52477 ■ 1000 Islands - Clayton Region Chamber of Commerce
517 Riverside Dr.
Clayton, NY 13624
Ph:(315)686-3771
Free: 800-252-9806
Fax:(315)686-5564
Co. E-mail: info@1000islands-clayton.com
URL: http://www.1000islands-clayton.com
Contact: Karen Goetz, Exec. Dir.

52478 ■ Adirondack Regional Chamber of Commerce
5 Warren St.
Glens Falls, NY 12801
Ph:(518)798-1761
Fax:(518)792-4147
Co. E-mail: frontdesk@adirondackchamber.org
URL: http://www.adirondackchamber.org
Contact: Todd L. Shimkus CCE, Pres.

52479 ■ Adirondacks-Speculator Region Chamber of Commerce
PO Box 184
Speculator, NY 12164
Ph:(518)548-4521
Fax:(518)548-4905
Co. E-mail: info@speculatorchamber.com
URL: http://www.adrkmts.com

52480 ■ African American Chamber of Commerce of Westchester and Rockland Counties
100 Stevens Ave., Ste. 202
Mount Vernon, NY 10550
Ph:(914)699-9050
Fax:(914)699-6279
Co. E-mail: robinlisadouglas@cs.com
URL: http://www.aaccnys.org
Contact: Ms. Robin L. Douglas, Pres./CEO

52481 ■ Albany-Colonie Regional Chamber of Commerce
1 Computer Dr. S
Albany, NY 12205-1631
Ph:(518)431-1400
Fax:(518)431-1402
Co. E-mail: info@acchamber.org
URL: http://acchamber.org
Contact: Mark Eagan, Pres./CEO

52482 ■ Alexandria Bay Chamber of Commerce
PO Box 365
Alexandria Bay, NY 13607
Ph:(315)482-9531
Free: 800-541-2110
Co. E-mail: info@alexbay.org
URL: http://www.alexbay.org

52483 ■ Amherst Chamber of Commerce
350 Essjay Rd., Ste. 200
Williamsville, NY 14221-8214
Ph:(716)632-6905
Fax:(716)632-0548
Co. E-mail: cdipirro@amherst.org
URL: http://www.amherst.org
Contact: Colleen C. DiPirro, Pres./CEO

52484 ■ Arcade Area Chamber of Commerce
278 Main St.
Arcade, NY 14009
Ph:(585)492-2114
Fax:(585)492-5103
Co. E-mail: aacc278@verizon.net
URL: http://www.arcadechamber.org
Contact: Dorie Clinch, Exec. Sec.

52485 ■ Bainbridge Chamber of Commerce
PO Box 2
Bainbridge, NY 13733
Ph:(607)967-8700
Co. E-mail: helen@mkl.com
URL: http://www.bainbridgechamberny.org
Contact: Lincoln Groat, Pres.

52486 ■ Baldwin Chamber of Commerce
PO Box 804
Baldwin, NY 11510
Ph:(516)223-8080
URL: http://www.baldwinchamber.com
Contact: Kathleen Healy Englehart, Sec.

52487 ■ Bedford Hills Chamber of Commerce
PO Box 162
Bedford Hills, NY 10507-0162
Ph:(914)381-3356
URL: http://www.bedfordhills.org
Contact: Dr. Greg Riley, Pres.

52488 ■ Bethlehem Chamber of Commerce
318 Delaware Ave., Main Sq.
Delmar, NY 12054-1911
Ph:(518)439-0512
Fax:(518)475-0910
Co. E-mail: info@bethlehemchamber.com
URL: http://www.bethlehemchamber.com
Contact: Laura Wander, Chair

52489 ■ Blooming Grove - Washingtonville Chamber of Commerce
PO Box 454
Washingtonville, NY 10992
Ph:(845)496-5449

52490 ■ Boonville Area Chamber of Commerce
PO Box 163
Boonville, NY 13309
Ph:(315)942-5112
Fax:(315)942-6823
Co. E-mail: info@boonvillechamber.org
URL: http://www.boonvillechamber.com
Contact: Kim Lynch, Pres.

52491 ■ Brewster Chamber of Commerce
16 Mt. Ebo Rd. S, Ste. 12A
Brewster, NY 10509-1528
Ph:(845)279-2477
Fax:(845)278-8349
Co. E-mail: info@brewsterchamber.com
URL: http://www.brewsterchamber.com
Contact: Beth R. Murtha, Exec. Dir.

52492 ■ Bronx Chamber of Commerce
1200 Waters Pl., Ste. 305
Bronx, NY 10461
Ph:(718)828-3900

Fax:(718)409-3748
Co. E-mail: jkelleher@hutchmetrocenter.com
URL: http://www.bronxchamber.org
Contact: Joseph Kelleher, Pres.

52493 ■ Bronxville Chamber of Commerce
81 Pondfield Rd., Ste. 7
Bronxville, NY 10708
Ph:(914)337-6040
Fax:(914)337-6040
Co. E-mail: broxvillechamber@verizon.net
URL: http://www.bronxvillechamber.com
Contact: Michele MacMillan, Exec. Dir.

52494 ■ Brooklyn Chamber of Commerce
25 Elm Pl., Ste. 200, 2nd Fl.
Brooklyn, NY 11201
Ph:(718)875-1000
Fax:(718)237-4274
Co. E-mail: info@brooklynchamber.com
URL: http://www.ibrooklyn.com
Contact: Carl Hum, Pres./CEO

52495 ■ Buffalo Niagara Partnership
665 Main St., Ste. 200
Buffalo, NY 14203
Ph:(716)852-7100
Free: 800-241-0474
Fax:(716)852-2761
Co. E-mail: membership@thepartnership.org
URL: http://www.thepartnership.org
Contact: Dr. Andrew J. Rudnick, Pres./CEO

52496 ■ Business Council of Westchester
108 Corporate Park Dr., Ste. 101
White Plains, NY 10604
Ph:(914)948-2110
Fax:(914)948-0122
Co. E-mail: mgordon@westchesterny.org
URL: http://www.westchesterny.org
Contact: Dr. Marsha Gordon, Pres./CEO

52497 ■ Cairo Chamber of Commerce
PO Box 515
Cairo, NY 12413-0515
Ph:(518)622-3939
URL: http://www.cairochamberofcommerce.com/page/page/5695726.htm
Contact: Claudia Zucker, Pres.

52498 ■ Camden Area Chamber of Commerce
PO Box 134
Camden, NY 13316
Ph:(315)245-5000
Co. E-mail: contact@camdennychamber.com
URL: http://www.camdennychamber.com
Contact: Ms. Beth Osteen, Exec. Dir.

52499 ■ Canandaigua Chamber of Commerce
113 S Main St.
Canandaigua, NY 14424-1903
Ph:(585)394-4400
Fax:(585)394-4546
Co. E-mail: chamber@canandaiguachamber.com
URL: http://www.canandaiguachamber.com
Contact: Alison Grems, Pres./CEO

52500 ■ Canastota Chamber of Commerce
PO Box 206
Canastota, NY 13032
Ph:(315)697-3677
Co. E-mail: sales@ricksrags.com
URL: http://www.canastota.org
Contact: Rick Stevens, Co-Pres.

52501 ■ Canton Chamber of Commerce
PO Box 369
Canton, NY 13617
Ph:(315)386-8255
Fax:(315)386-8255
Co. E-mail: cantoncc@northnet.org
URL: http://www.cantonnychamber.org
Contact: Sally Hill, Exec. Dir.

52502 ■ Cape Vincent Chamber of Commerce
PO Box 482
Cape Vincent, NY 13618-0482
Ph:(315)654-2481

Fax:(315)654-4141
Co. E-mail: thecape@tds.net
URL: http://www.capevincent.org
Contact: Shelley Higgins, Exec. Dir.

52503 ■ Carthage Area Chamber of Commerce
120 S Mechanic St.
Carthage, NY 13619
Ph:(315)493-3590
Co. E-mail: carthage@gisco.net
URL: http://www.carthageny.com
Contact: Mea Rosner, Pres.

52504 ■ Cayuga County Chamber of Commerce
36 South St.
Auburn, NY 13021-3930
Ph:(315)252-7291
Fax:(315)255-3077
Co. E-mail: contact@cayugacountychamber.com
URL: http://www.cayugacountychamber.com
Contact: Terri Bridenbecker, Exec. Dir.

52505 ■ Chamber of Commerce of the Bellmores
PO Box 861
Bellmore, NY 11710
Ph:(516)679-1875
Fax:(516)409-0544
Co. E-mail: bellmorecc@aol.com
URL: http://www.bellmorechamber.com
Contact: Ms. Joni Caputo, Exec. Dir./Festival Coor.

52506 ■ Chamber of Commerce of the Borough of Queens
75-20 Astoria Blvd., Ste. 140
East Elmhurst, NY 11370-1131
Ph:(718)898-8500
Fax:(718)898-8599
Co. E-mail: info@queenschamber.org
URL: http://www.queenschamber.org
Contact: Albert F. Pennisi, Pres.

52507 ■ Chamber of Commerce of Greater Bay Shore
PO Box 5110
Bay Shore, NY 11706
Ph:(631)665-7003
Co. E-mail: bayshorecofcbi@optonline.net
URL: http://www.bayshorecommerce.com

52508 ■ Chamber of Commerce of the Greater Ronkonkoma
PO Box 2546
Ronkonkoma, NY 11779
Ph:(631)471-0302
Co. E-mail: info@ronkonkomachamber.com
URL: http://www.ronkonkomachamber.com/rcc
Contact: Steve Browne, Pres.

52509 ■ Chamber of Commerce of the Massapequas
674 Broadway
Massapequa, NY 11758
Ph:(516)541-1443
Fax:(516)541-8625
Co. E-mail: masscoc@aol.com
URL: http://www.massapequachamber.com
Contact: Robert R. Barrett, Pres.

52510 ■ Chamber of Commerce of the Mastics and Shirley
PO Box 4
Mastic, NY 11950
Ph:(631)399-2228
Co. E-mail: admin@masticshirleychamber.com
URL: http://www.masticshirleychamber.com
Contact: Mark Smothergill, Pres.

52511 ■ Chamber of Commerce of the Nyacks
PO Box 677
Nyack, NY 10960-0677
Ph:(845)353-2221
Fax:(845)353-4204
Co. E-mail: info@nyack-ny.com
URL: http://www.nyack-ny.com
Contact: Bob Gundersen, Pres.

52512 ■ Chamber of Commerce of Olean and Vicinity
319 N Union St.
Olean, NY 14760
Ph:(716)373-4230
Co. E-mail: margek9061@aol.com
URL: http://oleanny.org
Contact: Margaret Kenney, Pres.

52513 ■ Chamber of Commerce of the Tonawandas
15 Webster St.
North Tonawanda, NY 14120
Ph:(716)692-5120
Fax:(716)692-1867
Co. E-mail: chamber@the-tonawandas.com
URL: http://www.the-tonawandas.com
Contact: Rhonda Ried, Pres.

52514 ■ Chamber of Commerce of Ulster County
55 Albany Ave.
Kingston, NY 12401
Ph:(845)338-5100
Fax:(845)338-0968
Co. E-mail: info@ulsterchamber.org
URL: http://www.ulsterchamber.org
Contact: Ward Todd, Pres.

52515 ■ Chamber of Commerce of the Willistons
PO Box 207
Williston Park, NY 11596
Ph:(516)739-1943
Fax:(516)294-1444
Co. E-mail: rayhaller@hzinsurance.com
URL: http://www.chamberofthewillistons.org
Contact: Raymond J. Haller, Pres.

52516 ■ Chamber of Southern Saratoga County
PO Box 399
Clifton Park, NY 12065
Ph:(518)371-7748
Fax:(518)371-5025
Co. E-mail: info@southernsaratoga.org
URL: http://www.southernsaratoga.org
Contact: Peter L. Aust, Pres./CEO

52517 ■ Chautauqua County Chamber of Commerce
10785 Bennett Rd.
Dunkirk, NY 14048
Ph:(716)366-6200
Fax:(716)366-4276
Co. E-mail: cccc@chautauquachamber.org
URL: http://www.chautauquachamber.org
Contact: Todd Tranum, Pres./CEO

52518 ■ Cheektowaga Chamber of Commerce
Apple Tree Business Park
2875 Union Rd., Ste. 50
Cheektowaga, NY 14227
Ph:(716)684-5838
Fax:(716)684-5571
Co. E-mail: chamber@cheektowaga.org
URL: http://www.cheektowaga.org
Contact: Debra S. Liegl, Pres./CEO

52519 ■ Chemung County Chamber of Commerce
400 E Church St.
Elmira, NY 14901-2803
Ph:(607)734-5137
Free: 800-MARK-TWAIN
Fax:(607)734-4490
Co. E-mail: info@chemungchamber.org
URL: http://www.chemungchamber.org
Contact: Kevin D. Keeley, Pres./CEO

52520 ■ Clarence Chamber of Commerce
8975 Main St.
Clarence, NY 14031
Ph:(716)631-3888

Fax:(716)631-3946
Co. E-mail: info@clarence.org
URL: http://www.clarence.org
Contact: David Hartzel, Pres.

52521 ■ Clifton Springs Area Chamber of Commerce
PO Box 86
Clifton Springs, NY 14432
Ph:(315)462-8200
Co. E-mail: info@cliftonspringschamber.com
URL: http://www.cliftonspringschamber.com
Contact: Brian Morris, Pres.

52522 ■ Clinton - Oneida County Chamber of Commerce
PO Box 142
Clinton, NY 13323-0142
Ph:(315)853-1735
Co. E-mail: info@clintonnychamber.org
URL: http://www.clintonnychamber.org
Contact: Ferris J. Betrus, Exec. VP

52523 ■ Cold Spring - Garrison Area Chamber of Commerce
PO Box 36
Cold Spring, NY 10516
Ph:(845)265-3200
Co. E-mail: chamberdirector@gmail.com
URL: http://www.hvgateway.com/CHAMBER.HTM
Contact: Nat Prentice, Pres.

52524 ■ Colonie Chamber of Commerce
950 New Loudon Rd.
Latham, NY 12110
Ph:(518)785-6995
Fax:(518)785-7173
Co. E-mail: info@coloniechamber.org
URL: http://www.coloniechamber.org
Contact: Tom Nolte, Exec. Dir.

52525 ■ Columbia County Chamber of Commerce
507 Warren St.
Hudson, NY 12534-2801
Ph:(518)828-4417
Co. E-mail: mail@columbiachamber-ny.com
URL: http://www.columbiachamber-ny.com
Contact: David B. Colby, Pres.

52526 ■ Cooperstown Chamber of Commerce
31 Chestnut St.
Cooperstown, NY 13326
Ph:(607)547-9983
Fax:(607)547-6006
Co. E-mail: info1@cooperstownchamber.org
URL: http://www.cooperstownchamber.org
Contact: Susan O'Handley, Exec. Dir.

52527 ■ Corning Area Chamber of Commerce
1 W Market St., Ste. 302
Corning, NY 14830
Ph:(607)936-4686
Free: (866)463-6264
Fax:(607)936-4685
Co. E-mail: info@corningny.com
URL: http://www.corningny.com
Contact: Denise Ackley, Pres.

52528 ■ Cortland County Chamber of Commerce
37 Church St.
Cortland, NY 13045
Ph:(607)756-2814
Fax:(607)756-4698
Co. E-mail: info@cortlandchamber.com
URL: http://www.cortlandchamber.com
Contact: Garry L. VanGorder, Exec. Dir.

52529 ■ Council of Dedicated Merchants Chamber of Commerce
PO Box 512
Miller Place, NY 11764
Ph:(631)821-1313
Fax:(631)928-6504
Co. E-mail: cdmchamber@yahoo.com
URL: http://www.cdmlongisland.com
Contact: Maureen Schneider, Sec./Exec. Dir.

52530 ■ Dansville Chamber of Commerce
PO Box 105
126 Main St.
Dansville, NY 14437-0105
Ph:(585)335-6920
Free: 800-949-0174
Fax:(585)335-6920
Co. E-mail: dansvillechamber@hotmail.com
URL: http://www.dansvilleny.net
Contact: William Bacon, Pres.

52531 ■ Delaware County Chamber of Commerce
5 1/2 Main St.
Delhi, NY 13753
Ph:(607)746-2281
Fax:(607)746-3571
Co. E-mail: info@delawarecounty.org
URL: http://www.delawarecounty.org
Contact: Mary Beth Silano, Exec. Dir.

52532 ■ Deposit Chamber of Commerce
PO Box 222
Deposit, NY 13754
Ph:(607)467-1436
Co. E-mail: jdunham@echoes.net
URL: http://www.depositchamber.com
Contact: Nick Barone, Pres.

52533 ■ East Hampton Chamber of Commerce
42 Gingerbread Ln.
East Hampton, NY 11937
Ph:(631)324-0362
Co. E-mail: info@easthamptonchamber.com
URL: http://easthamptonchamber.com

52534 ■ Eastchester - Tuckahoe Chamber of Commerce
PO Box 66
Eastchester, NY 10709
Ph:(914)779-7344
Co. E-mail: cetcoc@aol.com
URL: http://www.eastchestertuckahoechamberof-
  commerce.com/c
Contact: Kathy Muscat, Co-Pres.

52535 ■ Ellenville - Wawarsing Chamber of Commerce
PO Box 227
Ellenville, NY 12428
Ph:(845)647-4620
Co. E-mail: chamberofcommerce2@hvc.rr.com
URL: http://ewcoc.com/default.aspx
Contact: Red Roudis, Office Sec.

52536 ■ Ellicottville Chamber of Commerce
PO Box 456
Ellicottville, NY 14731
Free: 800-349-9099
Fax:(716)699-5637
Co. E-mail: info@ellicottvilny.com
URL: http://www.ellicottvilleny.com
Contact: Brian McFadden, Exec. Dir.

52537 ■ Fair Haven Area Chamber of Commerce
PO Box 13
Fair Haven, NY 13064
Ph:(315)947-6037
Co. E-mail: fairhaveninfo@fairhavenny.com
URL: http://www.fairhavenny.com
Contact: Alan Avrich, Pres.

52538 ■ Farmington Chamber of Commerce
1000 County Rd. 8
Farmington, NY 14425
Ph:(315)986-8100
Fax:(315)986-4377
Contact: Rose M. Kleman, Pres.

52539 ■ Fort Edward Chamber of Commerce
118 Broadway
Fort Edward, NY 12828-0267
Ph:(518)747-4023
Co. E-mail: info@fortedwardchamber.com
URL: http://www.fortedwardchamber.com
Contact: Darlene DeVoe

52540 ■ Fredonia Chamber of Commerce
5 E Main St.
Fredonia, NY 14063
Ph:(716)679-1565
Fax:(716)672-5240
Co. E-mail: fredcham@netsync.net
URL: http://www.fredoniachamber.org
Contact: Shannon Smith

52541 ■ Fulton County Regional Chamber of Commerce and Industry
2 N Main St.
Gloversville, NY 12078
Ph:(518)725-0641
Free: 800-676-3858
Fax:(518)725-0643
Co. E-mail: info@fultoncountyny.org
URL: http://www.fultoncountyny.org
Contact: Mr. Wally Hart, Pres.

52542 ■ Garden City Chamber of Commerce
230 Seventh St.
Garden City, NY 11530
Ph:(516)746-7724
Fax:(516)746-7725
Co. E-mail: gcchamber@verizon.net
URL: http://www.gardencitychamber.org
Contact: Althea Robinson, Exec. Dir.

52543 ■ Genesee County Chamber of Commerce
210 E Main St.
Batavia, NY 14020
Ph:(585)343-7440
Free: 800-622-2686
Fax:(585)343-7487
Co. E-mail: chamber@geneseeny.com
URL: http://www.geneseeny.com
Contact: Lynn Freeman, Pres.

52544 ■ Geneva Area Chamber of Commerce
PO Box 587
Geneva, NY 14456
Ph:(315)789-1776
Free: 877-543-6382
Fax:(315)789-3993
Co. E-mail: info@genevany.com
URL: http://www.genevany.com
Contact: Rob Gladden, Pres./CEO

52545 ■ Glen Cove Chamber of Commerce
70 Glenn St., 2nd Fl.
Glen Cove, NY 11542
Ph:(516)676-6666
Fax:(516)676-5490
Co. E-mail: info@glencovechamber.org
URL: http://www.glencovechamber.info
Contact: Gabor Karsai, Pres.

52546 ■ Goshen Chamber of Commerce
44 Park Pl.
PO Box 506
Goshen, NY 10924-0506
Ph:(845)294-7741
Fax:(845)294-3998
Co. E-mail: info@goshennychamber.com
URL: http://www.goshennychamber.com
Contact: Lynn A. Cione, Exec. Dir.

52547 ■ Gowanda Area Chamber of Commerce
PO Box 45
Gowanda, NY 14070-0045
Ph:(716)532-2834
URL: http://gowanda-chamber.com

52548 ■ Grand Island Chamber of Commerce
2257 Grand Island Blvd.
Grand Island, NY 14072
Ph:(716)773-3651
Fax:(716)773-3316
Co. E-mail: info@gichamber.org
URL: http://www.gichamber.org
Contact: John Bonora, Pres.

52549 ■ Great Neck Chamber of Commerce
PO Box 220432
Great Neck, NY 11022
Ph:(516)487-2000
Co. E-mail: info@greatneckchamber.org
URL: http://www.greatneckchamber.org
Contact: Valerie A. Link, Pres.

52550 ■ Greater Baldwinsville Chamber of Commerce
12 Oswego St.
Baldwinsville, NY 13027
Ph:(315)638-0550
Co. E-mail: info@baldwinsvillechamber.com
URL: http://www.baldwinsvillechamber.com
Contact: Lori Diver, Pres.

52551 ■ Greater Bath Area Chamber of Commerce
10 Pulteney Sq. W
Bath, NY 14810
Ph:(607)776-7122
Co. E-mail: chamber@bathnychamber.com
URL: http://www.bathnychamber.com
Contact: Bill Caudill, Pres.

52552 ■ Greater Binghamton Chamber of Commerce
PO Box 995
Binghamton, NY 13902-0995
Ph:(607)772-8860
Fax:(607)772-4513
Co. E-mail: chamber@binghamtonchamber.com
URL: http://www.binghamtonchamber.com
Contact: Frank E. Berrish, Pres./CEO

52553 ■ Greater Brockport Chamber of Commerce
PO Box 119
Brockport, NY 14420
Ph:(585)234-1512
URL: http://www.brockportchamber.org
Contact: Nancy Duff, Dir.

52554 ■ Greater Cazenovia Area Chamber of Commerce
59 Albany St.
Cazenovia, NY 13035
Ph:(315)655-9243
Free: 888-218-6305
Co. E-mail: cazchamber@alltel.net
URL: http://www.cazenoviachamber.com
Contact: Bob Barbero, Sec.

52555 ■ Greater East Aurora Chamber of Commerce
431 Main St.
East Aurora, NY 14052-1783
Ph:(716)652-8444
Free: 800-441-2881
Fax:(716)652-8384
Co. E-mail: eanycc@verizon.net
URL: http://www.eanycc.com
Contact: Gary D. Grote, Exec. Dir.

52556 ■ Greater Gouverneur Chamber of Commerce
214 E Main St.
Gouverneur, NY 13642
Ph:(315)287-0331
Fax:(315)287-3694
URL: http://www.gouverneurchamber.net
Contact: Donna M. Lawrence, Exec. Dir.

52557 ■ Greater Greenwich Chamber of Commerce
6 Academy St.
Greenwich, NY 12834-1002
Ph:(518)692-7979
Fax:(518)692-7979
Co. E-mail: info@greenwichchamber.org
URL: http://www.greenwichchamber.org
Contact: Kathy Nichols-Tomkins, Sec.

52558 ■ Greater Harlem Chamber of Commerce
200A W 136th St.
New York, NY 10030
Ph:(212)862-7200
Fax:(212)862-8745
Co. E-mail: info@harlemdiscover.com
URL: http://greaterharlemchamber.com
Contact: Lloyd A. Williams, Pres./CEO

52559 ■ Greater Liverpool Chamber of Commerce
314 2nd St.
Liverpool, NY 13088
Ph:(315)457-3895
Fax:(315)234-3226
Co. E-mail: chamber@liverpoolchamber.com
URL: http://liverpoolchamber.com
Contact: Lucretia M. Hudzinski, Exec. Dir.

52560 ■ Greater Mahopac-Carmel Chamber of Commerce
PO Box 160
Mahopac, NY 10541-0160
Ph:(845)628-5553
Fax:(845)628-5962
Co. E-mail: info@mahopaccarmelchamber.com
URL: http://www.mahopacchamber.com
Contact: Grace Vinciguerra, Pres.

52561 ■ Greater Massena Chamber of Commerce
50 Main St.
Massena, NY 13662
Ph:(315)769-3525
Fax:(315)769-5295
Co. E-mail: chamber@massenachamber.com
URL: http://www.massenachamber.com
Contact: Paul Haggett, Exec. Dir.

52562 ■ Greater New York Chamber of Commerce
20 W 44th St., 4 Fl.
New York, NY 10036
Ph:(212)686-7220
Fax:(212)686-7232
Co. E-mail: info@chamber.com
URL: http://www.chamber.com
Contact: Mark S. Jaffe, Pres./CEO

52563 ■ Greater Ogdensburg Chamber of Commerce
330 Ford St.
Ogdensburg, NY 13669
Ph:(315)393-3620
Fax:(315)393-1380
Co. E-mail: chamber@gisco.net
URL: http://www.ogdensburgny.com
Contact: Melinda McNamara, Pres.

52564 ■ Greater Olean Area Chamber of Commerce
120 N Union St.
Olean, NY 14760
Ph:(716)372-4433
Fax:(716)372-7912
Co. E-mail: info@oleanny.com
URL: http://www.oleanny.com/2
Contact: John Sayegh, COO

52565 ■ Greater Oneida Chamber of Commerce
136 Lenox Ave.
Oneida, NY 13421
Ph:(315)363-4300
Fax:(315)361-4558
Co. E-mail: executivedirector@oneidachamber.com
URL: http://www.oneidachamber.com
Contact: Brett N. Bogardus, Exec. Dir.

52566 ■ Greater Ossining Chamber of Commerce
2 Church St.
Ossining, NY 10562
Ph:(914)941-0009

Fax:(914)941-0812
Co. E-mail: info@ossiningchamber.org
URL: http://www.ossiningchamber.org
Contact: Jerry Gershner, Pres.

52567 ■ Greater Oswego Chamber of Commerce
44 E Bridge St.
Oswego, NY 13126
Ph:(315)343-7681
Fax:(315)342-0831
Co. E-mail: gocc@oswegofultonchamber.com
URL: http://oswegochamber.com
Contact: Nick Canale Jr., Pres.

52568 ■ Greater Patchogue Chamber of Commerce
15 N Ocean Ave.
Patchogue, NY 11772
Ph:(631)475-0121
Co. E-mail: info@patchoguechamber.com
URL: http://www.patchoguechamber.com
Contact: Charles Baker, Pres.

52569 ■ Greater Port Jefferson Chamber of Commerce
118 W Broadway
Port Jefferson, NY 11777
Ph:(631)473-1414
Fax:(631)474-4540
Co. E-mail: info@portjeffchamber.com
URL: http://www.portjeffchamber.com
Contact: Rich DeClemente, Pres.

52570 ■ Greater Smithtown Chamber of Commerce
PO Box 1216
Smithtown, NY 11787
Ph:(631)979-8069
Fax:(631)979-2206
Co. E-mail: info@smithtownchamber.com
URL: http://www.smithtownchamber.org
Contact: Barbara Franco, Exec. Dir.

52571 ■ Greater Southern Dutchess Chamber of Commerce
Nussbickel Bldg.
2582 S Ave., Rte. 9D
Wappingers Falls, NY 12590
Ph:(845)296-0001
Fax:(845)296-0006
Co. E-mail: annm@gsdcc.org
URL: http://www.gsdcc.org
Contact: Ann Meagher, Pres./CEO

52572 ■ Greater Syracuse Chamber of Commerce
572 S Salina St.
Syracuse, NY 13202-3320
Ph:(315)470-1800
Fax:(315)471-8545
Co. E-mail: info@syracusechamber.com
URL: http://www.syracusechamber.com
Contact: Ms. Darlene Kerr, Pres.

52573 ■ Greater Warsaw Chamber of Commerce
PO Box 221
Warsaw, NY 14569
Ph:(585)786-3730
Co. E-mail: info@warsawchamber.com
URL: http://www.warsawchamber.com
Contact: Dolly Pierson, Pres.

52574 ■ Greater Watertown - North Country Chamber of Commerce
1241 Coffeen St.
Watertown, NY 13601
Ph:(315)788-4400
Fax:(315)788-3369
Co. E-mail: chamber@watertownny.com
URL: http://www.watertownny.com
Contact: Karen K. Delmonico, Pres./CEO

52575 ■ Greater Westhampton Chamber of Commerce
PO Box 1228
Westhampton Beach, NY 11978
Ph:(631)288-3337

Fax:(631)288-3322
Co. E-mail: info@whbcc.org
URL: http://www.whbcc.com
Contact: Robert Murray, Pres.

52576 ■ Greene County Chamber of Commerce
1 Bridge St., 2nd Fl.
Catskill, NY 12414
Ph:(518)943-4222
Fax:(518)943-1700
Co. E-mail: tmcnally@greenecounty-chamber.com
URL: http://www.greenecounty-chamber.com
Contact: Tracy McNally, Exec. Dir.

52577 ■ Greenvale Chamber of Commerce
PO Box 123
Greenvale, NY 11548
Ph:(516)484-2550
URL: http://www.greenvalechamber.com
Contact: Michael Lucarelli, Sec.

52578 ■ Greenwich Village-Chelsea Chamber of Commerce
154 Christopher St., Ste. 3A
New York, NY 10014
Ph:(212)337-5912
Fax:(212)924-0714
Co. E-mail: info@villagechamber.com
URL: http://www.villagechelsea.com
Contact: Mr. Tony Juliano, Pres.

52579 ■ Guilderland Chamber of Commerce
2050 Western Ave.
Start Plz., No. 109
Guilderland, NY 12084
Ph:(518)456-6611
Fax:(518)456-6690
Co. E-mail: info@guilderlandchamber.com
URL: http://www.guilderlandchamber.com
Contact: Katherine Burbank, Exec. Dir.

52580 ■ Hamburg Chamber of Commerce
8 S Buffalo St.
Hamburg, NY 14075-6261
Ph:(716)649-7917
Free: 877-322-6890
Fax:(716)649-6362
Co. E-mail: hccmail@hamburg-chamber.org
URL: http://www.hamburg-chamber.org
Contact: Betty B. Newell, Pres./CEO

52581 ■ Hampton Bays Chamber of Commerce
140 W Main St., Ste. 1
Hampton Bays, NY 11946
Ph:(631)728-2211
Fax:(631)728-0308
Co. E-mail: hamptonbayschamber@verizon.net
URL: http://www.hamptonbayschamber.com
Contact: Stan Glinka, Pres.

52582 ■ Harrison Chamber of Commerce
1 Heineman Pl.
Harrison, NY 10528
Ph:(914)835-7039
Fax:(914)835-7039
Co. E-mail: harrisoncc04@yahoo.com
URL: http://www.theharrisoncofc.org
Contact: Ada B. Angarano, Pres./CEO

52583 ■ Heart of Catskill Association - Catskill Chamber of Commerce
PO Box 248
Catskill, NY 12414
Ph:(518)943-0989
Free: 800-603-7737
Co. E-mail: catskillchamber@mhcable.com
URL: http://www.catskillny.org
Contact: Linda Overbaugh, Exec. Dir.

52584 ■ Hempstead Chamber of Commerce
PO Box 4264
1776 Denton Green Park
Hempstead, NY 11550
Ph:(516)483-2000
Fax:(516)483-2000
Co. E-mail: president@hempsteadchamber.com
Contact: Leo Fernandez, Pres.

52585 ■ Hicksville Chamber of Commerce
10 W Marie St.
Hicksville, NY 11801-3804
Ph:(516)931-7170
Fax:(516)931-8546
Co. E-mail: info@hicksvillechamber.com
URL: http://www.hicksvillechamber.com/Pages/L01/
   Home.aspx
Contact: Mr. Lionel Chitty, Pres.

52586 ■ Hudson Valley Gateway Chamber of Commerce
1 S Division St.
Peekskill, NY 10566
Ph:(914)737-3600
Fax:(914)737-0541
URL: http://www.hvgatewaychamber.com
Contact: Ron Forehand, Pres./CEO

52587 ■ Huntington Township Chamber of Commerce
164 Main St.
Huntington, NY 11743-3383
Ph:(631)423-6100
Fax:(631)351-8276
Co. E-mail: ellen@huntingtonchamber.com
URL: http://www.huntingtonchamber.com
Contact: Ellen O'Brien, Exec. Dir.

52588 ■ Hyde Park Chamber of Commerce
PO Box 17
Hyde Park, NY 12538
Ph:(845)229-8612
Fax:(845)229-8638
Co. E-mail: info@hydeparkchamber.org
URL: http://www.hydeparkchamber.org
Contact: Elizabeth L. Roger, Pres.

52589 ■ Inlet Information Office
PO Box 266
Inlet, NY 13360-0266
Free: (866)GOI-NLET
Co. E-mail: inletny@eagle-wireless.com
URL: http://www.inletny.com

52590 ■ Islip Chamber of Commerce
PO Box 112
Islip, NY 11751-0112
Ph:(631)581-2720
Fax:(631)581-2720
Co. E-mail: info@islipchamberofcommerce.com
URL: http://www.islipchamberofcommerce.com
Contact: Tom Cilmi, Pres.

52591 ■ Japanese Chamber of Commerce and Industry of New York
145 W 57th St.
New York, NY 10019
Ph:(212)246-8001
Fax:(212)246-8002
Co. E-mail: info@jcciny.org
URL: http://www.jcciny.org
Contact: Michihisa Shinagawa, Pres./CEO

52592 ■ Kenmore-Town of Tonawanda Chamber of Commerce
3411 Delaware Ave.
Kenmore, NY 14217-1422
Ph:(716)874-1202
Free: 888-281-1680
Fax:(716)874-3151
Co. E-mail: info@ken-ton.org
URL: http://www.ken-ton.org
Contact: Ms. Tracey M. Lukasik, Exec. Dir.

52593 ■ Kings Park Chamber of Commerce
PO Box 322
Kings Park, NY 11754
Ph:(631)269-7678
Fax:(631)269-5575
Co. E-mail: kpcc@kingspark.net
URL: http://www.kingsparkli.com
Contact: Charles Gardner, Pres.

52594 ■ Lackawanna Area Chamber of Commerce
638 Ridge Rd.
Lackawanna, NY 14218
Ph:(716)823-8841

Free: 800-747-8841
Fax:(716)823-8848
Co. E-mail: info@lackawannachamber.com
URL: http://www.lackawannachamber.com
Contact: Edy Molly, Admin.

52595 ■ Lake George Regional Chamber of Commerce
PO Box 272
Lake George, NY 12845-0272
Ph:(518)668-5755
Free: 800-705-0059
Co. E-mail: info@lakegeorgechamber.com
URL: http://www.lakegeorgechamber.com
Contact: Janice Bartkowski, Pres.

52596 ■ Lancaster Area Chamber of Commerce
PO Box 284
Lancaster, NY 14086
Ph:(716)681-9755
Fax:(716)684-3385
Co. E-mail: info@laccny.org
URL: http://www.laccny.org
Contact: Kathy Konst, Pres./CEO

52597 ■ Lewis County Chamber of Commerce
7383-C Utica Blvd.
Lowville, NY 13367
Ph:(315)376-2213
Free: 800-724-0242
Co. E-mail: info@lewiscountychamber.org
URL: http://www.lewiscountychamber.org
Contact: Anne Merrill, Exec. Dir.

52598 ■ Livingston County Chamber of Commerce
4635 Millennium Dr.
Geneseo, NY 14454
Ph:(585)243-2222
Fax:(585)243-4824
Co. E-mail: coswald@frontiernet.net
URL: http://livingstoncountychamber.com
Contact: Cynthia Oswald, Pres.

52599 ■ Long Beach Chamber of Commerce
350 National Blvd.
Long Beach, NY 11561-3312
Ph:(516)432-6000
Fax:(516)432-0273
URL: http://www.lbnewyorkchamber.com
Contact: Michael J. Kerr, Pres.

52600 ■ Long Island Association
300 Broadhollow Rd., Ste. 110W
Melville, NY 11747-4840
Ph:(631)493-3000
Fax:(631)499-2194
Co. E-mail: mcrosson@longislandassociation.org
URL: http://www.longislandassociation.org
Contact: Matthew T. Crosson, Pres.

52601 ■ Lyons Chamber of Commerce
PO Box 39
Lyons, NY 14489
Ph:(315)573-8170
Co. E-mail: videomark@gmail.com
URL: http://www.lyonsny.com
Contact: Mark De Cracker, Pres.

52602 ■ Malone Chamber of Commerce
497 E Main St.
Malone, NY 12953
Ph:(518)483-3760
Free: 877-625-6631
Fax:(518)483-3172
Co. E-mail: info@malonenychamber.com
URL: http://visitmalone.com
Contact: Minique Barnett, Exec. Dir.

52603 ■ Manhasset Chamber of Commerce
PO Box 754
Manhasset, NY 11030
Contact: Nancy Morris, Pres.

52604 ■ Manhattan Chamber of Commerce
1375 Broadway, 3rd Fl.
New York, NY 10018
Ph:(212)479-7772
Fax:(212)473-8074
Co. E-mail: info@manhattancc.org
URL: http://www.manhattancc.org/common/11001/
   default.cfm?clientID=11001
Contact: Nancy Ploeger, Pres.

52605 ■ Mattituck Chamber of Commerce
PO Box 1056
Mattituck, NY 11952
Co. E-mail: info@mattituckchamber.org
URL: http://www.mattituckchamber.org
Contact: Terry McShane, Pres.

52606 ■ Mayville - Chautauqua Area Chamber of Commerce
PO Box 22
Mayville, NY 14757-0022
Ph:(716)753-3113
Fax:(716)753-3113
Co. E-mail: maychautchamb@yahoo.com
URL: http://mayville-chautauquachamber.org

52607 ■ Mineola Chamber of Commerce
PO Box 62
Mineola, NY 11501
Ph:(516)408-3554
Co. E-mail: info@mineolachamber.com
URL: http://www.mineolachamber.com
Contact: Mr. Steven Ford, Pres.

52608 ■ Mohawk Valley Chamber of Commerce
Radisson Hotel
200 Genesee St.
Utica, NY 13502
Ph:(315)724-3151
Fax:(315)724-3177
Co. E-mail: info@mvchamber.org
URL: http://www.mvchamber.org
Contact: Frank Elias, Pres.

52609 ■ Mount Kisco Chamber of Commerce
3 N Moger Ave.
Mount Kisco, NY 10549
Ph:(914)666-7525
Fax:(914)666-7663
Co. E-mail: mtkiscochamber@aol.com
URL: http://www.mtkisco.com
Contact: Janet Deane, Exec. Dir.

52610 ■ Mount Vernon Chamber of Commerce
PO Box 351
Mount Vernon, NY 10550-2009
Ph:(914)667-7500
Fax:(914)699-0139
Co. E-mail: mtvcoc@hotmail.com
URL: http://www.mtvernonchamber.org
Contact: Gerrie Post, Pres.

52611 ■ New Hartford Chamber of Commerce
PO Box 372
New Hartford, NY 13413
Ph:(315)735-1974
Fax:(315)266-1231
Co. E-mail: info@newhartfordchamber.com
URL: http://www.newhartfordchamber.com
Contact: Mark A. Turnbull, Pres.

52612 ■ New Paltz Chamber of Commerce
124 Main St.
New Paltz, NY 12561-1610
Ph:(845)255-0243
Fax:(845)255-5189
Co. E-mail: info@newpaltzchamber.org
URL: http://www.newpaltzchamber.org
Contact: Joyce M. Minard, Pres.

52613 ■ New Rochelle Chamber of Commerce
459 Main St.
New Rochelle, NY 10801-6412
Ph:(914)632-5700

Fax:(914)632-0708
Co. E-mail: chamber@newrochellechamber.org
URL: http://www.newrochellechamber.org
Contact: Denise Lally, Exec. Dir.

52614 ■ New Yorktown Chamber of Commerce
PO Box 632
Yorktown Heights, NY 10598
Ph:(914)245-4599
Fax:(914)734-7171
Co. E-mail: info@yorktownchamber.org
URL: http://www.yorktownchamber.org
Contact: Arlette Rossignol, Dir. of Operations

52615 ■ Newark Chamber of Commerce
199 Van Buren St.
Newark, NY 14513
Ph:(315)331-2705
Co. E-mail: newarkchamber@rochester.rr.com
URL: http://www.newarknychamber.org
Contact: John Tickner, Pres.

52616 ■ Newcomb Chamber of Commerce
PO Box 222
Newcomb, NY 12852
Ph:(518)582-2274
URL: http://www.newcombny.com/newchamber.html

52617 ■ Niagara USA Chamber
Vantage Ctre.
6311 Inducon Corporate Dr.
Sanborn, NY 14132
Ph:(716)285-9141
Fax:(716)285-0941
Co. E-mail: dalteriobrennen@niagarachamber.org
URL: http://www.niagarachamber.org
Contact: Deanna Alterio Brennen, Pres./CEO

52618 ■ Oceanside Chamber of Commerce
PO Box 1
Oceanside, NY 11572
Ph:(516)763-9177
Co. E-mail: info@oceansidechamber.org
URL: http://www.oceansidechamber.org
Contact: Joe Garay, Pres.

52619 ■ Orchard Park Chamber of Commerce
4211 N Buffalo St., Ste. 14
Orchard Park, NY 14127-2401
Ph:(716)662-3366
Fax:(716)662-5946
Co. E-mail: opcc@orchardparkchamber.com
URL: http://www.orchardparkchamber.com
Contact: Nancy L. Conley, Exec. Dir.

52620 ■ Orleans County Chamber of Commerce
121 N Main St., Ste. 1
Albion, NY 14411
Ph:(585)589-7727
Fax:(585)589-7326
Co. E-mail: kkiebala@orleanschamber.com
URL: http://www.orleanschamber.com
Contact: Dr. Kelly Kiebala, Exec. Dir.

52621 ■ Otsego County Chamber of Commerce
189 Main St., Ste. 201
Oneonta, NY 13820
Ph:(607)432-4500
Free: 877-5OT-SEGO
Fax:(607)432-4506
Co. E-mail: tocc@otsegocountychamber.com
URL: http://www.otsegocountychamber.com
Contact: Peter Livshin, Chm.

52622 ■ Partnership for New York City
1 Battery Park Plz., 5th Fl.
New York, NY 10004
Ph:(212)493-7400
Fax:(212)344-3344
Co. E-mail: info@pfnyc.org
URL: http://www.nycp.org
Contact: Kathryn Wylde, Pres./CEO

52623 ■ Patterson Chamber of Commerce
PO Box 316
Patterson, NY 12563-0316
Ph:(845)878-4696
Fax:(845)319-2010
Co. E-mail: info@pcofc.org
URL: http://www.pcofc.org
Contact: Toni LoMeli, Pres.

52624 ■ Pawling Chamber of Commerce
PO Box 19
Pawling, NY 12564
Ph:(845)855-0500
URL: http://www.pawlingchamber.org
Contact: Peter Cris, Pres.

52625 ■ Pittsford Chamber of Commerce
PO Box 576
Pittsford, NY 14534
Ph:(585)234-0308
Co. E-mail: info@pittsfordchamber.org
URL: http://pittsfordchamber.org
Contact: Dr. Shirley Joseph, Pres.

52626 ■ Plank Road Chamber of Commerce
PO Box 324
North Syracuse, NY 13212
Ph:(315)458-4181
Co. E-mail: smay@twcny.rr.com
URL: http://www.northsyracuse.org
Contact: Sharon A. May, Sec.

52627 ■ Plattsburgh - North Country Chamber of Commerce
PO Box 310
Plattsburgh, NY 12901
Ph:(518)563-1000
Fax:(518)563-1028
Co. E-mail: chamber@westelcom.com
URL: http://www.northcountrychamber.com
Contact: Garry Douglas, Pres./CEO

52628 ■ Potsdam Chamber of Commerce
One Market St.
PO Box 717
Potsdam, NY 13676
Ph:(315)274-9000
Fax:(315)274-9222
Co. E-mail: potsdam@slic.com
URL: http://www.potsdamchamber.com
Contact: Pamela Maurer, Pres.

52629 ■ Poughkeepsie Area Chamber of Commerce
1 Civic Center Plz., Ste. 400
Poughkeepsie, NY 12601
Ph:(845)454-1700
Fax:(845)454-1702
Co. E-mail: charlesnorth@dcrcoc.org
URL: http://www.dutchesscountyregionalchamber.org
Contact: Charles S. North, Pres./CEO

52630 ■ Pulaski - Eastern Shore Chamber of Commerce
PO Box 34
Pulaski, NY 13142
Ph:(315)298-2213
URL: http://www.pulaskinychamber.com
Contact: Margaret Clerkin

52631 ■ Red Hook Area Chamber of Commerce
PO Box 254
Red Hook, NY 12571
Ph:(845)758-0824
Co. E-mail: info@redhookchamber.org
URL: http://www.redhookchamber.org
Contact: Ryan McCann, Pres.

52632 ■ Rensselaer County Regional Chamber of Commerce
255 River St.
Troy, NY 12180
Ph:(518)274-7020
Fax:(518)272-7729
Co. E-mail: info@renscochamber.com
URL: http://www.renscochamber.com
Contact: Linda Hillman, Pres.

52633 ■ Rhinebeck Chamber of Commerce
PO Box 42
Rhinebeck, NY 12572
Ph:(845)876-5904
Fax:(845)876-8624
Co. E-mail: info@rhinebeckchamber.com
URL: http://www.rhinebeckchamber.com
Contact: Ms. Nancy Amy, Exec. Dir.

52634 ■ Riverhead Chamber of Commerce
542 E Main St., Ste. 2
Riverhead, NY 11901
Ph:(631)727-7600
Fax:(631)727-7946
Co. E-mail: info@riverheadchamber.com
URL: http://www.riverheadchamber.com
Contact: Angela Reese, Pres.

52635 ■ Rochester Business Alliance, Women's Council
150 State St.
Rochester, NY 14614
Ph:(585)256-4612
Fax:(585)244-4864
Co. E-mail: susan.george@rballiance.com
URL: http://www.grwc.com
Contact: Susan George, Affiliate Mgr.

52636 ■ Rockville Centre Chamber of Commerce
PO Box 226
Rockville Centre, NY 11571
Ph:(516)766-0666
Fax:(516)706-2236
Co. E-mail: mailbox@rvcchamber.org
URL: http://www.rvcchamber.com/index.php
Contact: Lawrence Siegel, Pres.

52637 ■ Rome Area Chamber of Commerce
139 W Dominick St.
Rome, NY 13440-5809
Ph:(315)337-1700
Fax:(315)337-1715
Co. E-mail: info@romechamber.com
URL: http://www.romechamber.com
Contact: William K. Guglielmo, Pres.

52638 ■ Roscoe-Rockland Chamber of Commerce
PO Box 443
Roscoe, NY 12776-0443
Ph:(607)498-5765
URL: http://www.roscoeny.com

52639 ■ Rye Merchants Association
PO Box 256
Rye, NY 10580
Ph:(914)921-5950
Co. E-mail: wineatfive@verizon.net
URL: http://www.ryemerchantsassociation.com

52640 ■ Sag Harbor Chamber of Commerce
PO Box 2810
Sag Harbor, NY 11963
Ph:(631)725-0011
Fax:(631)725-3028
Co. E-mail: sagchamber@peconic.net
URL: http://www.sagharborchamber.com
Contact: Mr. Robert Evjen, Pres.

52641 ■ St. James Chamber of Commerce
PO Box 286
St. James, NY 11780
Ph:(631)584-8510
Fax:(631)584-8784
Co. E-mail: info@stjameschamber.org
URL: http://www.stjameschamber.org
Contact: Lawrence Glazer, Pres.

52642 ■ St. Lawrence County Chamber of Commerce
101 Main St., 1st Fl.
Canton, NY 13617-1248
Free: 877-228-7810
Co. E-mail: slccoc@northnet.org
URL: http://northcountryguide.com/slc-chamber

52643 ■ Salamanca Area Chamber of Commerce
26 Main St.
Salamanca, NY 14779-1516
Ph:(716)945-2034
Fax:(716)945-2034
Co. E-mail: sal.cofc@verizon.net
URL: http://www.salamancachamber.org
Contact: Jayne L. Fenton, Pres.

52644 ■ Saranac Lake Area Chamber of Commerce
39 Main St.
Saranac Lake, NY 12983
Ph:(518)891-1990
Free: 800-347-1992
Fax:(518)891-7042
Co. E-mail: info@saranaclake.com
URL: http://www.saranaclake.com
Contact: Sylvie D. Nelson, Exec. Dir.

52645 ■ Saratoga County Chamber of Commerce
28 Clinton St.
Saratoga Springs, NY 12866-2143
Ph:(518)584-3255
Fax:(518)587-0318
Co. E-mail: info@saratoga.org
URL: http://www.saratoga.org
Contact: Joseph W. Dalton Jr., Pres.

52646 ■ Schenectady County Chamber of Commerce
306 State St.
Schenectady, NY 12305-2302
Ph:(518)372-5656
Free: 800-962-8007
Fax:(518)370-3217
Co. E-mail: info@schenectadychamber.org
URL: http://www.schenectadychamber.org
Contact: Charles P. Steiner, Pres.

52647 ■ Schoharie County Chamber of Commerce
113 Park Pl.
Schoharie, NY 12157-5205
Ph:(518)295-6550
Free: 800-41V-ISIT
Fax:(518)295-7453
Co. E-mail: info@schohariechamber.com
URL: http://www.schohariechamber.com
Contact: Jodie Rutt, Exec. Dir.

52648 ■ Schroon Lake Area Chamber of Commerce
PO Box 726
Schroon Lake, NY 12870-0726
Ph:(518)532-7675
Free: 888-724-7666
Fax:(518)532-7675
Co. E-mail: info@schroonlake.org
URL: http://www.schroonlake.org

52649 ■ Schuyler County Chamber of Commerce
100 N Franklin St., Rte. 14
Watkins Glen, NY 14891
Ph:(607)535-4300
Free: 800-607-4552
Fax:(607)535-6243
Co. E-mail: chamber@schuylerny.com
URL: http://www.watkinsglenchamber.com
Contact: Crystal M. Ricks, Pres.

52650 ■ Seneca County Chamber of Commerce
PO Box 70
Seneca Falls, NY 13148-0070
Ph:(315)568-2906
Free: 800-732-1848
Fax:(315)568-1730
Co. E-mail: info@senecachamber.org
URL: http://www.senecachamber.org
Contact: Mr. Fred Gaffney, Exec. Dir.

52651 ■ Sidney Chamber of Commerce
PO Box 2295
Sidney, NY 13838
Ph:(607)561-2642
Fax:(607)561-2644
Co. E-mail: office@sidneychamber.org
URL: http://www.sidneychamber.org
Contact: John Marano, Pres.

52652 ■ Skaneateles Area Chamber of Commerce
22 Jordan St.
PO Box 199
Skaneateles, NY 13152
Ph:(315)685-0552
Fax:(315)685-0552
Co. E-mail: info@skaneateles.com
URL: http://www.skaneateles.com
Contact: Susan Dove, Exec. Dir.

52653 ■ Sleepy Hollow Tarrytown Chamber of Commerce
54 Main St.
Tarrytown, NY 10591
Ph:(914)631-1705
Fax:(914)366-4291
Co. E-mail: info@sleepyhollowchamber.com
URL: http://www.sleepyhollowchamber.com
Contact: Katharine Swibold, Exec. Dir.

52654 ■ Sodus Town Chamber of Commerce
PO Box 187
Sodus, NY 14551-0187
Ph:(315)398-8473
Co. E-mail: chamber14551@yahoo.com
URL: http://www.sodusny.com
Contact: Mary Jane Mumby, Pres.

52655 ■ Southampton Chamber of Commerce
76 Main St.
Southampton, NY 11968
Ph:(631)283-0402
Fax:(631)283-8707
Co. E-mail: info@southamptonchamber.com
URL: http://www.southamptonchamber.com
Contact: Millie A. Fellingham, Exec. Dir.

52656 ■ Southern Ulster County Chamber of Commerce
20 Milton Ave., Ste. 3
Highland, NY 12528
Ph:(845)691-6070
Fax:(845)691-9194
Co. E-mail: info@southernulsterchamber.org
URL: http://www.southernulsterchamber.org
Contact: William J. Farrell, Pres.

52657 ■ Staten Island Chamber of Commerce
130 Bay St.
Staten Island, NY 10301-2503
Ph:(718)727-1900
Fax:(718)727-2295
Co. E-mail: info@sichamber.com
URL: http://www.sichamber.com
Contact: Ms. Linda Baran, Pres./CEO

52658 ■ Suffern Chamber of Commerce
PO Box 291
Suffern, NY 10901
Ph:(845)357-8424
Co. E-mail: suffernchamberofcommerce@yahoo.com
URL: http://www.suffernchamberofcommerce.org
Contact: Aury Licata, Pres.

52659 ■ Sullivan County Chamber of Commerce
452 Broadway, Ste. 1
Monticello, NY 12701
Ph:(845)791-4200
Fax:(845)791-4400
Co. E-mail: chamber@catskills.com
URL: http://www.catskills.com
Contact: Terri Ward, Pres./CEO

52660 ■ Swedish-American Chamber of Commerce, New York
570 Lexington Ave., 20th Fl.
New York, NY 10022
Ph:(212)838-5530
Fax:(212)755-7953
Co. E-mail: dragana.pajovic@saccny.org
Contact: Tomas K.G. Ericson, Chm.

52661 ■ Syosset Chamber of Commerce
36 Church St.
Syosset, NY 11791
Ph:(516)346-7150
URL: http://www.syossetchamber.com
Contact: Kevin Allison, Pres.

52662 ■ Ticonderoga Area Chamber of Commerce
94 Montcalm St., Ste. 1
Ticonderoga, NY 12883
Ph:(518)585-6619
Fax:(518)585-9184
Co. E-mail: chamberinfo@bluemoo.net
URL: http://www.ticonderogany.com
Contact: Joseph Conway, Exec. Dir.

52663 ■ Tioga County Chamber of Commerce
80 North Ave.
Owego, NY 13827
Ph:(607)687-2020
Fax:(607)687-9028
Co. E-mail: business@tiogachamber.com
URL: http://www.tiogachamber.com
Contact: Martha Sauerbrey, Pres./CEO

52664 ■ Tompkins County Chamber of Commerce
904 E Shore Dr.
Ithaca, NY 14850-1026
Ph:(607)273-7080
Fax:(607)272-7617
Co. E-mail: jean@tompkinschamber.org
URL: http://tompkinschamber.org
Contact: Jean McPheeters, Pres.

52665 ■ Town of Hunter Chamber of Commerce
PO Box 177
Hunter, NY 12442
Ph:(518)263-4900
Fax:(518)589-0117
Co. E-mail: chamberinfo@hunterchamber.org
URL: http://www.hunterchamber.org
Contact: Michael McCrary

52666 ■ Town of Montgomery Chamber of Commerce
2365 Albany Post Rd.
Walden, NY 12586
Ph:(845)778-0514
Fax:(845)778-6346
Contact: Florence Valk, Admin.

52667 ■ Tupper Lake Chamber of Commerce
121 Park St.
PO Box 987
Tupper Lake, NY 12986
Ph:(518)359-3328
Free: 888-887-5253
Fax:(518)359-2434
Co. E-mail: marti@tupperlakeinfo.com
URL: http://www.tupperlakeinfo.com
Contact: Marti Mozdzier, Exec. Dir.

52668 ■ Victor Chamber of Commerce
37 E Main St.
Victor, NY 14564-1301
Ph:(585)742-1476
Fax:(585)742-1501
Co. E-mail: info@victorchamber.com
URL: http://www.victorchamber.com
Contact: Mitch Donovan, Pres.

52669 ■ Waddington Area Chamber of Commerce
PO Box 291
Waddington, NY 13694-0291
Ph:(315)388-5576
Co. E-mail: waddingtonchamber@gmail.com
URL: http://www.waddingtonny.us/chamber
Contact: Alicia Murphy, Pres.

52670 ■ Warrensburg Chamber of Commerce
3847 Main St.
Warrensburg, NY 12885
Ph:(518)623-2161
Fax:(518)623-2184
Co. E-mail: info@warrensburgchamber.com
URL: http://www.warrensburgchamber.com

52671 ■ Warwick Valley Chambe ʳ ᶠ Commerce
PO Box 202
Warwick, NY 10990
Ph:(845)986-2720
Co. E-mail: info@warwickcc.org
URL: http://www.warwickcc.org
Contact: Michael Johndrow, Exec. Dir.

52672 ■ Webster Chamber of Commerce
1110 Crosspoint Ln., Ste. C
Webster, NY 14580-3280
Ph:(585)265-3960
Fax:(585)265-3702
Co. E-mail: bbernard@websterchamber.com
URL: http://www.websterchamber.com
Contact: Elizabeth Bernard, Admin.

52673 ■ Wellsville Area Chamber of Commerce
114 N Main St.
Wellsville, NY 14895
Ph:(585)593-5080
Fax:(585)593-5088
Co. E-mail: info@wellsvilleareachamber.com
URL: http://www.wellsvilleareachamber.com
Contact: Steven Havey, Exec. Dir.

52674 ■ West Seneca Chamber of Commerce
950A Union Rd., Ste. 5
West Seneca, NY 14224
Ph:(716)674-4900
Co. E-mail: cdillchamber@westseneca.org
URL: http://www.westseneca.org
Contact: Carol Dill

52675 ■ Woodstock Chamber of Commerce and Arts
PO Box 36
Woodstock, NY 12498
Ph:(845)679-6234
Co. E-mail: info@woodstockchamber.com
URL: http://woodstockchamber.com
Contact: Joyce Beymer, Pres.

52676 ■ Wyoming County Chamber of Commerce
6470 Rte. 20A, Ste. 2
Perry, NY 14530-9798
Ph:(585)237-0230
Free: 800-951-9774
Fax:(585)237-0231
Co. E-mail: info@wycochamber.org
URL: http://www.wycochamber.org
Contact: James Pierce, Pres./CEO

52677 ■ Yonkers Chamber of Commerce
55 Main St., 2nd Fl.
Yonkers, NY 10701
Ph:(914)963-0332
Fax:(914)963-0455
Co. E-mail: info@yonkerschamber.com
URL: http://www.yonkerschamber.com/home.html
Contact: Kevin T. Cacace, Pres.

MINORITY BUSINESS ASSISTANCE PROGRAMS

52678 ■ Empire State Development–Minority and Women's Business Development Division
Empire State Development
633 3rd Ave., 33rd Fl.
New York, NY 10017-6706
Ph:(212)803-2414
Free: 800-STA-TENY
Fax:(212)803-2459
Co. E-mail: esd@empire.state.ny.us
URL: http://www.nylovesmwbe.ny.gov/
Contact: Dasil Velez, Exec Dir
Description: Assists in obtaining statewide certification, financing, business development and technical assistance, permit and regulatory assistance, market and sales exposure, and employment and training.

52679 ■ Jamaica Business Resource Center–Queens, Nassau, Suffolk Minority Business Enterprise Center
90-33 160th St.
Jamaica, NY 11432
Ph:(718)206-2255
Fax:(718)206-3693
Co. E-mail: jbrc@jbrc.org
URL: http://www.queensmbec.org
Contact: Timothy Marshall, Pres & CEO

52680 ■ New York State Office of General Services–Minority and Women-Owned Business and Community Relations
Corning Tower, 41st Fl.
Empire State Plaza
Albany, NY 12242
Ph:(518)486-9284
Fax:(518)486-9285
Co. E-mail: omwbeo@ogs.state.ny.us
URL: http://www.ogs.state.ny.us/mwbe/AboutUs.html
Contact: William Clay, Asst Commissioner

52681 ■ Williamsburg (Brooklyn) Minority Business Development Center–Opportunity Development Association (ODA)
12 Heyward St.
Brooklyn, NY 11211
Ph:(718)522-5620
Fax:(718)522-5931
Co. E-mail: odacdc@idt.net
URL: http://www.odabdc.org
Contact: Zvi Kestenbaum, Pres

52682 ■ Women's Venture Fund
319 W 39th St., 5th Fl.
New York, NY 10018
Ph:(212)563-0499
Fax:(212)284-6951
Co. E-mail: info@wvf-ny.org
URL: http://www.wvf-ny.org
Description: Provides business development services for the creation or expansion of women-owned businesses in New York.

FINANCING AND LOAN PROGRAMS

52683 ■ 4C Ventures / Olivetti Holding, N.V.
21 E. 94th St., 3rd Fl.
New York, NY 10128
Ph:(212)996-3133
Fax:(212)996-1838
URL: http://www.4cventures.com
Contact: Alexandra Giurgiu, Partner
E-mail: agiurgiu@4cventures.com
Preferred Investment Size: $500,000 to $150,000,000. **Investment Types:** Early stage. **Industry Preferences:** Computer hardware, computer software and services, communications and media, semiconductors and other electronics, consumer related, Internet specific, other products, and industrial and energy. **Geographic Preferences:** U.S. and Canada. **Principal Exhibits:**

52684 ■ Alimansky Capital Group, Inc.
12 E. 44th St., Penthouse
New York, NY 10017
Ph:(212)832-7300
Co. E-mail: info@alimansky.com
URL: http://www.alimansky.com
Contact: Burt Alimansky, Managing Director
Preferred Investment Size: $2,000,000. **Investment Types:** First and second stage, mezzanine, leveraged buyout, and special situation. **Industry Preferences:** Communications and media, computer, related, semiconductors and other electronics, biotechnology, medical and health, consumer related, industrial and energy, transportation, financial services, business service, manufacturing, agriculture, forestry and fishing. **Geographic Preferences:** U.S. and Canada. **Principal Exhibits:**

52685 ■ Allegra Partners / Lawrence, Smith & Horey
320 Park Ave., 18th Fl.
New York, NY 10022
Ph:(212)277-1526
Fax:(212)277-1533
Co. E-mail: info@allegrapartners.com
URL: http://www.allegrapartners.com
Contact: Larry J. Lawrence, General Partner
E-mail: ljl@allegrapartners.com
Preferred Investment Size: $5,000,000 to $20,000,000. **Investment Types:** Early, expansion, and later stage. **Industry Preferences:** Computer software and services, communications and media, other products, Internet specific, consumer related, medical and health. **Geographic Preferences:** Eastern U.S. **Principal Exhibits:**

52686 ■ The Argentum Group
60 Madison, Ste. 701
New York, NY 10010
Ph:(212)949-6262
Fax:(212)949-8294
URL: http://www.argentumgroup.com
Contact: Walter H. Barandiaran, Managing Partner
E-mail: walter@argentumgroup.com
Preferred Investment Size: $2,000,000-$10,000,000. **Investment Types:** Second stage, mezzanine, leveraged buyout, other products, and special situation. **Industry Preferences:** Internet specific, medical and health, computer software and services, communications and media, industrial and energy, and computer hardware. **Geographic Preferences:** U.S. **Principal Exhibits:**

52687 ■ Arthur P. Gould & Co.
1 Wilshire Dr.
Lake Success, NY 11020
Ph:(914)723-2560
Fax:(914)723-1756
URL: http://www.gouldco.com
Contact: Andrew G. Gould, President
E-mail: andrew@gouldco.com
Preferred Investment Size: $5,000,000 minimum. **Investment Types:** Seed, start-up, first and second stage, research and development, mezzanine, generalist PE, and leveraged buyout. **Industry Preferences:** Communications, computer hardware and software, semiconductors and other electronics, biotechnology, medical and health, consumer related, industrial and energy, transportation, financial services, manufacturing, agriculture, forestry and fishing. **Principal Exhibits:**

52688 ■ Baker Capital
575 Madison Ave., 8th Fl.
New York, NY 10022
Ph:(212)848-2000
Fax:(212)468-0660
URL: http://www.bakercapital.com
Contact: John Baker, Principal
Investment Types: Early and later stage. **Industry Preferences:** Internet specific, communications and media, computer software and services, computer hardware, semiconductors and other electronics. **Geographic Preferences:** U.S. **Principal Exhibits:**

52689 ■ Bedford Capital Corp.
81 Main St., Ste. 515
White Plains, NY 10601
Ph:(914)948-3840

Fax:(914)285-9282
Co. E-mail: info@bedfordnyc.com
URL: http://www.bedfordnyc.com
Preferred Investment Size: $100,000 to $300,000. **Investment Types:** First and second stage, industry rollups, recapitalizations, and leveraged buyout. **Industry Preferences:** Internet specific, medical and health, consumer related, industrial and energy, financial services, and manufacturing. **Geographic Preferences:** Midwest. **Principal Exhibits:**

52690 ■ Bessemer Venture Partners (Larchmont)
1865 Palmer Ave., Ste. 104
Larchmont, NY 10538
Ph:(914)833-5300
Fax:(914)833-5499
Co. E-mail: businessplan@bvp.com
URL: http://www.bessemervp.com
Contact: Jeremy Levine, Partner
Preferred Investment Size: $1,000,000 to $10,000,000. **Investment Types:** Seed, start-up, early, first and second stage, research and development, leveraged buyout, special situation, control-block purchases, and expansion. **Industry Preferences:** Internet specific, communications and media, computer software and services, computer hardware, semiconductors and other electronics, consumer related, medical and health, industrial and energy, biotechnology, and other products. **Geographic Preferences:** U.S. **Principal Exhibits:**

52691 ■ BlueCar Partners
The Chrysler Bldg.
405 Lexington Ave., 26th Fl.
New York, NY 10174
Ph:(212)907-6444
Fax:(775)796-3875
Co. E-mail: info@bluecarpartners.com
URL: http://www.bluecarpartners.com
Contact: Granger B. Whitelaw, Managing Director
Investment Policies: Seed and early stage. **Industry Preferences:** Communications, Internet specific, biotechnology, medical and health, and transportation. **Geographic Preferences:** U.S. **Principal Exhibits:**

52692 ■ Bluefish Ventures
990 Avenue of the Americas, Ste., 17J
New York, NY 10018
Ph:(415)614-1161
Fax:(212)695-3449
URL: http://www.bluefishventures.com
Contact: Alex Miller, Partner
E-mail: alex@bluefishventures.com
Preferred Investment Size: $250,000 to $2,000,000. **Investment Policies:** Seed, start-up, early, first, and second stage. **Industry Preferences:** Communications, computer software, industrial and energy, and business service. **Geographic Preferences:** Northeast and Northwest. **Principal Exhibits:**

52693 ■ Bristol Capital
110 E. 59th St., 29th Fl.
New York, NY 10022
Ph:(212)593-3157
Fax:(212)202-5022
URL: http://www.bristolcap.com
Contact: Alan Donenfield, President
E-mail: alan@bristolcap.com
Preferred Investment Size: $1,000,000 to $10,000,000. **Investment Types:** Generalist PE, later stage, leveraged buyout, management buyouts, mezzanine, private placement, public companies, recapitalizations, second stage, and special situation. **Principal Exhibits:**

52694 ■ Carrot Capital Healthcare Ventures
802 6th Ave., Ste. 63
New York, NY 10001
Ph:(212)586-2226
Fax:(212)586-2246
Co. E-mail: sjacobson@carrotcapital.com
URL: http://www.carrotcapitalhealthcareventures.com
Contact: David Geliebter, Managing Partner
Preferred Investment Size: $50,000 to $1,000,000. **Investment Policies:** Seed, start-up, and early stage. **Industry Preferences:** Communications, computer hardware and software, semiconductors

and other electronics, biotechnology, medical and health, and industrial and energy. **Geographic Preferences:** Canada. **Principal Exhibits:**

52695 ■ CM Equity Partners, L.P.
900 Third Ave., 33rd Fl.
New York, NY 10022
Ph:(212)909-8400
Fax:(212)829-0553
URL: http://www.cmequity.com
Contact: Joel R. Jacks, Founder and Managing Partner
Preferred Investment Size: $2,000,000 minimum. **Investment Types:** Acquisition, leveraged buyout, and recapitalizations. **Industry Preferences:** Communications and media, and Internet specific. **Geographic Preferences:** U.S. and Canada. **Principal Exhibits:**

52696 ■ Cornerstone Equity Investors, LLC
281 Tresser Blvd., 12th Fl.
Stamford, CT 06901
Ph:(212)753-0901
Fax:(212)826-6798
URL: http://www.cornerstone-equity.com
Contact: Mark Rossi, Managing Director
E-mail: Mrossi@Cornerstone-equity.com
Preferred Investment Size: $15,000,000 to $250,000,000. **Investment Types:** Leveraged buyout, management buyouts, and special situation. **Industry Preferences:** Consumer related, medical and health, communications and media, semiconductors and other electronics, computer software and services, Internet specific, semiconductors and other electronics, other products, computer hardware, industrial and energy, and biotechnology. **Principal Exhibits:**

52697 ■ CW Group, Inc.
910 Harvest Dr., Ste. 105
New York, NY 10021
Ph:(212)308-5266
Fax:(212)644-0354
URL: http://www.cwventures.com
Contact: Walter Channing, General Partner
Preferred Investment Size: $500,000 to $5,000,000. **Investment Types:** Seed, start-up, first and second stage, leveraged buyout, research and development, special situation, control block purchases, and balanced. **Industry Preferences:** Medical and health, biotechnology, Internet specific, computer software and services, industrial and energy, other products, computer hardware, semiconductors and other electronics. **Geographic Preferences:** U.S. **Principal Exhibits:**

52698 ■ Dauphin Capital Partners
108 Forest Ave.
Locust Valley, NY 11560
Ph:(516)759-3339
Fax:(516)759-3322
URL: http://www.dauphincapital.com
Contact: James B. Hoover, Managing Member
E-mail: jhoover@dauphincapital.com
Preferred Investment Size: $1,000,000 to $10,000,000. **Investment Types:** First and second stage, acquisition, expansion, and management buyouts. **Industry Preferences:** Medical and health. **Geographic Preferences:** Mid Atlantic, Northeast, and Southeast. **Principal Exhibits:**

52699 ■ Dawntreader Ventures
1270 Avenue of the Americas, 5th Fl.
New York, NY 10022
Ph:(646)452-6100
Fax:(646)452-6101
Co. E-mail: businessplans@dtventures.com
URL: http://www.dtventures.com
Contact: Sang Ahn, Principal
Preferred Investment Size: $1,000,000 to $15,000,000. **Investment Policies:** Seed, early, first, and second stage. **Industry Preferences:** Internet specific, computer software and services, semiconductors and other electronics, communications and media, other products, and consumer related. **Principal Exhibits:**

52700 ■ East River Ventures, L.P.
645 Madison Ave., 22nd Fl.
New York, NY 10022
Ph:(212)644-2322
Fax:(212)644-5498
URL: http://www.eastrivervc.com
Contact: Ray Mirza, Principal
E-mail: mray@eastrivervc.com
Investment Types: First and second stage, and mezzanine. **Industry Preferences:** Internet specific, medical and health, computer software and services, computer hardware, communications and media, industrial and energy, semiconductors and other electronics, biotechnology, and other products. **Geographic Preferences:** U.S. and Canada. **Principal Exhibits:**

52701 ■ Easton Hunt Capital Partners, L.P.
767 Third Ave., 7th Fl.
New York, NY 10017
Ph:(212)702-0950
Fax:(212)702-0952
Co. E-mail: info@eastoncapital.com
URL: http://www.eastoncapital.com
Contact: John H. Friedman, Managing Director
E-mail: friedman@eastoncapital.com
Preferred Investment Size: $2,000,000 to $7,500,000. **Investment Types:** Balanced, early and later stage, management buyouts, and private placements. **Industry Preferences:** Computer software, industrial and energy, medical and healthcare devices, business service, and manufacturing. **Geographic Preferences:** U.S. **Principal Exhibits:**

52702 ■ Eastport Partners
204 E. 20th St., 3rd Fl.
New York, NY 10003
Ph:(212)674-1900
Fax:(212)674-6821
URL: http://www.eastportlp.com
Contact: J. Andrew McWethy, Partner
E-mail: amcwethy@eastportlp.com
Investment Policies: Leveraged buyout and management buyouts. **Industry Preferences:** Manufacturing. **Geographic Preferences:** U.S. **Principal Exhibits:**

52703 ■ Elk Associates Funding Corp.
747 3rd Ave., 4th Fl.
New York, NY 10017
Ph:(212)355-2449
Fax:(212)759-3338
URL: http://www.elkassociates.com
Contact: Gary C. Granoff, President
E-mail: garyatelk@aol.com
Preferred Investment Size: $100,000 to $300,000. **Investment Types:** Second stage and leveraged buyout. **Industry Preferences:** Communications and media, consumer related, and transportation. **Geographic Preferences:** Southeast and Midwest. **Principal Exhibits:**

52704 ■ EOS Partners, L.P.
320 Park Ave., 9th Fl.
New York, NY 10022
Ph:(212)832-5800
Fax:(212)832-5815
URL: http://www.eospartners.com
Contact: Matt Meehan, Managing Director
E-mail: mmeehan@eospartners.com
Preferred Investment Size: $3,000,000. **Investment Types:** Start-up, first, second, and later stage, industry rollups, acquisition, expansion, recapitalizations, leveraged buyout, mezzanine, and special situation. **Industry Preferences:** Communications and media, other products, consumer related, medical and health, semiconductors and other electronics, computer software and services, Internet specific, industrial and energy. **Geographic Preferences:** U.S. and Canada. **Principal Exhibits:**

52705 ■ Euclidsr Partners
45 Rockefeller Plz., Ste. 1910
New York, NY 10111
Ph:(212)218-6880

Fax:(212)218-6877
URL: http://www.euclidsr.com
Contact: Graham Anderson, General Partner
E-mail: graham@euclidsr.com
Investment Types: First, later and second stage.
Industry Preferences: Internet specific, computer software and services, medical and health, biotechnology, semiconductors and other electronics, computer hardware, industrial and energy, communications and media, other products, and consumer related. **Geographic Preferences:** U.S. **Principal Exhibits:**

52706 ■ Exeter Capital Partners
1 Liberty Sq., Ste. 1200
Boston, MA 02109
Ph:(617)224-0100
Fax:(617)892-4311
URL: http://www.exeterfunds.com
Contact: Keith R. Fox, Managing Partner
Preferred Investment Size: $2,000,000 to $20,000,000. **Investment Types:** Management buyouts, leveraged buyout, mezzanine, later stage, expansion, and balanced. **Industry Preferences:** Consumer related, Internet specific, medical and health, computer software and services, communications and media, computer hardware, other products. **Geographic Preferences:** U.S. **Principal Exhibits:**

52707 ■ FA Technology Ventures
100 High St., Ste. 1105
Boston, MA 02110
Ph:(617)757-3883
Fax:(617)757-3881
URL: http://www.fatechventures.com
Contact: George McNamee, Managing Partner
E-mail: George@fatechventures.com
Preferred Investment Size: $3,000,000 to $8,000,000. **Investment Policies:** Early stage and expansion. **Industry Preferences:** Communications, computer software, and industrial and energy. **Geographic Preferences:** New York. **Principal Exhibits:**

52708 ■ Flatiron Partners
1221 Avenue of the Americas, 39th Fl.
New York, NY 10020-1080
Ph:(212)899-3400
Fax:(212)899-3401
URL: http://www.flatironpartners.com
Contact: Philip Summe, Principal
Investment Types: Early stage. **Industry Preferences:** Internet specific, computer software and services, communications and media, other products, and consumer related. **Geographic Preferences:** New York and Northeast. **Principal Exhibits:**

52709 ■ Gabelli Multimedia Partners
1 Corporate Ctr.
Rye, NY 10580-1422
Ph:(914)921-5100
Fax:(914)921-5031
Co. E-mail: fsommer@gabelli.com
URL: http://www.gabelli.com
Contact: Robert Zuccaro, Chief Financial Officer
Investment Types: Seed, start-up, first and second stage. **Industry Preferences:** Communications and media. **Geographic Preferences:** Northeast. **Principal Exhibits:**

52710 ■ Genesys Partners, Inc.
126 5th Ave.
New York, NY 10011
Ph:(212)686-2828
Fax:(212)686-5155
Co. E-mail: info@genesyspartners.com
URL: http://www.genesyspartners.com
Contact: James G. Kollegger, Chief Executive Officer
Investment Types: Early stage. **Industry Preferences:** Internet specific. **Geographic Preferences:** U.S. **Principal Exhibits:**

52711 ■ GlobalNet Partners LP
521 5th Ave., Ste. 1703
New York, NY 10175
Ph:(212)292-4407

Fax:(212)292-4408
Co. E-mail: info@globalnet-advisors.com
URL: http://www.globalnet-advisors.com
Contact: Jonathan B. Adler, Managing Director
Investment Policies: Early and first stage. **Industry Preferences:** Communications and media, computer software, Internet specific, and industrial and energy. **Principal Exhibits:**

52712 ■ GMG Capital Partners, L.P.
575 Lexington Ave., 28th Fl.
New York, NY 10022
Ph:(212)832-4013
Fax:(212)980-1695
Co. E-mail: info@gmgpartners.net
URL: http://www.gmgpartners.net
Contact: Joachim Gfoeller, Managing General Partner
Investment Types: Early stage. **Industry Preferences:** Communications and media, and Internet specific. **Geographic Preferences:** U.S. **Principal Exhibits:**

52713 ■ Golub Capital
551 Madison Ave.
New York, NY 10022
Ph:(212)750-6060
Fax:(212)750-5505
URL: http://wwwgolubassoc.com
Contact: Andrew H. Steuerman, Managing Director
E-mail: asteuerman@golubcapital.com
Preferred Investment Size: $4,000,000 to $25,000,000. **Investment Types:** Later stage, mezzanine, generalist PE, recapitalizations, and private placement. **Industry Preferences:** Medical and health, consumer related, industrial and energy, transportation, business service, and manufacturing. **Geographic Preferences:** U.S. **Principal Exhibits:**

52714 ■ Harris & Harris Group, Inc.
1450 Broadway, 24th Fl.
New York, NY 10018
Ph:(212)582-0900
Fax:(212)582-9563
Co. E-mail: admin@tinytechvc.com
URL: http://www.tinytechvc.com
Contact: Douglas W. Jamison, President and Chief Operating Officer
Preferred Investment Size: $100,000 to $2,500,000. **Investment Policies:** Early stage. **Industry Preferences:** Communications, semiconductors and other electronics, biotechnology, medical and health, and industrial and energy. **Geographic Preferences:** U.S. **Principal Exhibits:**

52715 ■ Harvest Partners, LLC
280 Park Ave., 25th Fl.
New York, NY 10017
Ph:(212)559-6300
Fax:(212)812-0100
URL: http://www.harvpart.com
Contact: Thomas W. Arenz, Senior Managing Director
E-mail: tarenz@harvpart.com
Preferred Investment Size: $40,000,000 to $600,000,000. **Investment Types:** Acquisition, leveraged buyout, management buyouts, and later stage. **Industry Preferences:** Other products, industrial and energy, consumer related, communications and media, and Internet specific. **Geographic Preferences:** U.S. **Principal Exhibits:**

52716 ■ Holding Capital Group, Inc.
45 W. 45th St., 12th Fl.
New York, NY 10036
Ph:(212)486-6670
Fax:(212)486-0843
Co. E-mail: investmentdirector@holdingcapital.com
URL: http://www.holdingcapital.com
Contact: James W. Donaghy
E-mail: jdonaghy@holdingcapital.com
Preferred Investment Size: $2,000,000 to $150,000,000. **Investment Types:** Management and leveraged buyouts and acquisitions. **Geographic Preferences:** U.S. **Principal Exhibits:**

52717 ■ Hudson Venture Partners
535 5th Ave., 14th Fl.
New York, NY 10017
Ph:(212)644-9797
Fax:(212)644-7430
Co. E-mail: info@hudsonptr.com
URL: http://www.hudsonptr.com
Contact: Lawrence Howard, Senior Managing Director
Preferred Investment Size: $1,000,000 to $3,000,000. **Investment Types:** First, Early, second and later stage. **Industry Preferences:** Internet specific, computer software and services, communications and media, computer hardware, biotechnology, medical and health, other products, semiconductors and other electronics. **Geographic Preferences:** Mid Atlantic and Northeast. **Principal Exhibits:**

52718 ■ I-Hatch Ventures, LLC
584 Broadway, Ste. 1103
New York, NY 10012
Ph:(212)651-1750
Fax:(212)208-4590
Co. E-mail: info@i-hatch.com
URL: http://www.i-hatch.com
Contact: Brad Farkas, Principal
Investment Types: Seed and early stage. **Industry Preferences:** Internet specific, computer software, hardware and services, consumer related, communications and media. **Geographic Preferences:** Northeast. **Principal Exhibits:**

52719 ■ Impact Venture Partners
2705 Westlake Dr.
Austin, TX 78746
Ph:(512)827-9039
Fax:(212)214-0909
Co. E-mail: eve@impactvp.com
URL: http://www.impactvp.com
Contact: Adam Dell, Managing General Partner
Preferred Investment Size: $3,000,000 to $5,000,000. **Investment Policies:** Early stage. **Industry Preferences:** Internet specific, computer software and services, communications and media, and computer hardware. **Geographic Preferences:** Northeast and Texas. **Principal Exhibits:**

52720 ■ Insight Venture Partners / Insight Capital Partners
680 5th Ave., 8th Fl.
New York, NY 10019
Ph:(212)230-9200
Fax:(212)230-9272
URL: http://www.insightpartners.com
Contact: Deven Parekh, Managing Director
Preferred Investment Size: $5,000,000 to $30,000,000. **Investment Types:** Late stage and expansion. **Industry Preferences:** Internet specific, computer software and services, other products, consumer related, computer hardware, communications and media. **Geographic Preferences:** U.S and Canada. **Principal Exhibits:**

52721 ■ InterEquity Capital Partners, L.P.
220 5th Ave.
New York, NY 10001
Ph:(212)779-2022
Fax:(212)779-2103
URL: http://www.interequity-capital.com
Contact: Irwin Schlass, President
Preferred Investment Size: $1,000,000 to $3,000,000. **Investment Types:** First and second stage, mezzanine, leveraged buyout, and special situation. **Industry Preferences:** Internet specific, medical and health, computer software and services, consumer related, other products, industrial and energy, communications and media. **Geographic Preferences:** U.S. **Principal Exhibits:**

52722 ■ Jegi Capital, LLC
150 E. 52nd St., 18th Fl.
New York, NY 10022
Ph:(212)754-0710

Fax:(212)754-0337
URL: http://www.jegi.com
Contact: David Clark, Managing Director
Preferred Investment Size: $5,000,000 to $10,000,000. **Investment Policies:** Early, first and second stage. **Industry Preferences:** Computer hardware and software, Internet specific, and semiconductors and other electronics. **Geographic Preferences:** U.S. **Principal Exhibits:**

52723 ■ Jerusalem Venture Partners /JVP
156 5th Ave., Ste. 410
New York, NY 10010
Ph:(212)479-5100
Fax:(212)213-1776
URL: http://www.jvpvc.com
Contact: Erel N. Margalit, Founder and Managing Partner
Preferred Investment Size: $2,000,000 to $35,000,000. **Investment Types:** Early stage. **Industry Preferences:** Internet specific, semiconductors and other electronics, communications and media, computer software and services, and computer hardware. **Principal Exhibits:**

52724 ■ The Jordan Edmiston Group Inc. / JEGI Capital
150 East 52nd St., 18th Fl.
New York, NY 10022
Ph:(212)754-0710
Fax:(212)754-0337
URL: http://www.jegi.com
Contact: Richard Mead, Managing Director
Preferred Investment Size: $5,000,000 to $10,000,000. **Investment Policies:** Early, first and second stage. **Industry Preferences:** Computer hardware and software, Internet specific, and semiconductors and other electronics. **Geographic Preferences:** U.S. **Principal Exhibits:**

52725 ■ J.P. Morgan Capital Corp.
101 California St., 38th Fl.
San Francisco, CA 94111
Ph:(415)954-4704
Fax:(415)954-4737
URL: http://www.jpmorgan.com
Contact: John Mayer, Chief Executive Officer
Preferred Investment Size: $10,000,000 to $20,000,000. **Investment Types:** Balanced and early stage. **Industry Preferences:** Other products, communications and media, Internet specific, computer software and services, semiconductors and other electronics, consumer related, medical and health, computer hardware, biotechnology, industrial and energy. **Geographic Preferences:** U.S. and Canada. **Principal Exhibits:**

52726 ■ KBL Healthcare Ventures
52 East 72nd St. - PH
New York, NY 10021
Ph:(212)319-5555
Fax:(212)319-5591
Co. E-mail: inquiries@kblhealthcare.com
URL: http://www.kblhealthcare.com
Contact: Marlene Krauss, Managing Director
E-mail: mkrauss@kblhealthcare.com
Preferred Investment Size: $110,000,000 to $500,000,000. **Investment Types:** Seed, start-up, early, first, second and later stage, expansion, mezzanine, private placement, public companies, recapitalizations, research and development, and turnaround. **Industry Preferences:** Medical and health, biotechnology, Internet specific, communications and media, computer software and services. **Geographic Preferences:** U.S. **Principal Exhibits:**

52727 ■ The Lambda Funds
432 E. 84th St.
New York, NY 10028
Ph:(212)774-1812
Fax:(212)230-9886
URL: http://www.lambdafund.com
Contact: Anthony Lamport, General Partner
E-mail: alamport@lambdafund.com
Preferred Investment Size: $100,000 to $1,500,000. **Investment Policies:** First stage and management buyouts. **Industry Preferences:** Biotechnology, computer hardware, computer software and services, industrial and energy, consumer related, other

products, semiconductors and other electronics, medical and health, communications and media, Internet specific. **Geographic Preferences:** Mid Atlantic, Northeast, and West Coast. **Principal Exhibits:**

52728 ■ Lazard Technology Partners
30 Rockefeller Plz., 48th Fl.
New York, NY 10020
Ph:(212)632-6000
Fax:(212)332-8677
URL: http://www.lazardtp.com
Contact: Russell Planitzer, Managing Principal
Preferred Investment Size: $2,000,000 to $8,000,000. **Investment Types:** Early, first, second and later stage, and expansion. **Industry Preferences:** Internet specific, computer software and services, computer hardware, communications and media, semiconductors and other electronics, and consumer related. **Geographic Preferences:** District of Columbia, East Coast, and New York. **Principal Exhibits:**

52729 ■ Lepercq Capital Management, Inc. / Lepercq de Neuflize & Co., Inc.
156 W. 56th St., 18th Fl.
New York, NY 10019
Ph:(212)698-0700
Fax:(212)262-1055
Co. E-mail: elleng@lepercq.com
URL: http://www.lepercq.com
Contact: Francois Letaconnoux, President and Chief Executive Officer
Preferred Investment Size: $1,000,000 to $10,000,000. **Investment Types:** Control-block purchases, leveraged buyout, second stage, funds of funds. **Industry Preferences:** Communications, computer hardware and software, Internet specific, and consumer related. **Principal Exhibits:**

52730 ■ Loeb Partners Corp.
61 Broadway
New York, NY 10006
Ph:(212)483-7000
Fax:(212)574-2001
URL: http://www.loebpartners.com
Contact: Thomas Kempner, Chief Executive Officer
Preferred Investment Size: $100,000 minimum. **Investment Types:** Early stage, acquisition, expansion, leveraged buyout, and management buyouts. **Industry Preferences:** Internet specific, biotechnology, medical and health, Internet specific, computer software and services, semiconductors and other electronics. **Geographic Preferences:** U.S. **Principal Exhibits:**

52731 ■ McGraw-Hill Ventures /McGraw-Hill Capital Corp.
1221 Avenue of the Americas
New York, NY 10020-1095
Ph:(212)512-2000
Fax:(212)512-3840
URL: http://www.mcgraw-hill.com
Contact: Brian Casey, Vice President
Preferred Investment Size: $500,000 to $5,000,000. **Investment Types:** Early, second and later stage, and expansion. **Industry Preferences:** Communications and media, computer software, Internet specific, medical and health, industrial and energy, financial services, business service, and manufacturing. **Geographic Preferences:** U.S. **Principal Exhibits:**

52732 ■ Metropolitan Venture Partners (METVP)
590 Madison Ave., 34th Fl.
New York, NY 10022
Ph:(212)561-1219
Fax:(212)561-1201
Co. E-mail: contact@metvp.com
URL: http://www.metvp.com
Contact: Michael Levin, Managing Director
Preferred Investment Size: $500,000 to $5,000,000. **Investment Types:** Early, first, and second stage, expansion, management buyouts, recapitalizations, and special situation. **Industry Preferences:** Communications, computer software, semiconductors and other electronics, and Internet specific. **Geographic Preferences:** Northeast. **Principal Exhibits:**

52733 ■ Milestone Venture Partners
551 Madison Ave., 7th Fl.
New York, NY 10022
Ph:(212)223-7400
Fax:(212)223-0315
Co. E-mail: bplans@milestonevp.com
URL: http://www.milestonevp.com
Contact: Richard J. Dumler, General Partner
E-mail: rjd@milestonevp.com
Preferred Investment Size: $250,000 to $2,000,000. **Investment Types:** Early stage. **Industry Preferences:** Communications and media, computer software, and Internet specific. **Geographic Preferences:** Connecticut, New Jersey, New York, Eastern Pennsylvania, and to a lesser extent, the Northeast and Mid Atlantic. **Principal Exhibits:**

52734 ■ Mitsui & Co. Venture Partners (MCVP)
200 Park Ave.
New York, NY 10166-0130
Ph:(212)878-4050
Fax:(212)878-4070
URL: http://www.mitsuiventures.com
Contact: Koichi Ando, President and Chief Executive Officer
Investment Policies: Start-up, seed, early, first and second stage, and research and development. **Industry Preferences:** Communications and media, Internet specific, computer software and services, biotechnology, medical and health, computer hardware, semiconductors and other electronics, and other products. **Geographic Preferences:** U.S. and Canada. **Principal Exhibits:**

52735 ■ Murphy and Partners, L.P.
708 3rd Ave., 6th Fl.
New York, NY 10017
Ph:(212)209-3879
Fax:(212)209-7148
URL: http://www.murphy-partners.com
Contact: John J. Murphy Jr., Managing General Partner
E-mail: john@murphy-partners.com
Preferred Investment Size: $1,000,000 to $10,000,000. **Investment Types:** Seed, early, first and second stage, leveraged buyout, expansion, and control-block purchases. **Industry Preferences:** Communications, medical and health, and consumer related. **Geographic Preferences:** U.S. **Principal Exhibits:**

52736 ■ Nazem and Co.
570 Lexington Ave., 15th Fl.
New York, NY 10022
Ph:(212)371-7900
Fax:(212)371-2150
URL: http://www.nazem.com
Contact: Fred F. Nazem, Managing Partner
E-mail: fnazem@nazem.com
Preferred Investment Size: $1,000,000 minimum. **Investment Types:** Seed, start-up, first, second, and later stage, mezzanine, leveraged buyout, special situation, expansion, recapitalizations, and turnaround. **Industry Preferences:** Computer hardware, computer software and services, medical and health, communications and media, biotechnology, semiconductors and other electronics, Internet specific, industrial and energy, other products, and consumer related. **Geographic Preferences:** U.S. **Principal Exhibits:**

52737 ■ Needham Asset Management
445 Park Ave.
New York, NY 10022
Ph:(212)705-0404
Fax:(212)705-0455
Co. E-mail: jgiangrasso@needhamco.com
URL: http://www.needhamfunds.com
Contact: George Needham, Chief Executive Officer
Preferred Investment Size: $2,000,000 to $10,000,000. **Investment Types:** Later stage, leveraged buyout, management buyouts, and mezzanine. **Industry Preferences:** Semiconductors and other electronics, computer software and services, communications and media, Internet specific, medical

and health, computer hardware, other products, consumer related, industrial and energy. **Geographic Preferences:** U.S. **Principal Exhibits:**

52738 ■ Northwood Ventures
485 Underhill Blvd., Ste. 205
Syosset, NY 11791
Ph:(516)364-5544
Fax:(516)364-0879
URL: http://www.northwoodventures.com
Contact: Henry T. Wilson, Managing Director
E-mail: hwilson@northwoodventures.com
Preferred Investment Size: $1,000,000 to $15,000,000. **Investment Types:** Early, first, second, early, and later stage, acquisition, expansion, leveraged buyout, management buyouts, private placement, special situation, balanced, generalist PE, industry rollups, and recapitalizations. **Industry Preferences:** Communications and media, Internet specific, consumer related, biotechnology ind— ial and energy, semiconduct— ——— s, computer so———. **Geographic Preferences:** U.S. and Canada. **Principal Exhibits:**

52739 ■ Norwood Venture Corp.
174 Dezenzo Ln.
West Orange, NJ 107043
Ph:(917)748-5734
Fax:(212)869-5331
Co. E-mail: nvc@norven.com
URL: http://www.norven.com
Contact: Mark R. Littell, President and Director
Preferred Investment Size: $250,000 to $1,000,000. **Investment Types:** Early stage, mezzanine, leveraged buyout, balanced, turnaround, and special situation. **Industry Preferences:** Business services. **Geographic Preferences:** U.S. **Principal Exhibits:**

52740 ■ Onondaga Venture Capital Fund, Inc.
241 W. Fayette St.
Syracuse, NY 13202
Ph:(315)478-0157
Fax:(315)478-0158
Co. E-mail: info@ovcfund.com
URL: http://www.ovcfund.com
Contact: Michael Schattner, President
Preferred Investment Size: $50,000 to $300,000. **Investment Types:** Early, first, and second stage, and expansion. **Industry Preferences:** Communications, computer software, semiconductors and other electronics, biotechnology, medical and health, consumer related, and manufacturing. **Geographic Preferences:** Northeast. **Principal Exhibits:**

52741 ■ Opticality Ventures
29 Country Club Ln., S.
Briarcliff Manor, NY 10510
Ph:(914)923-0003
Fax:(413)487-2114
URL: http://www.opticality.com
Contact: Hadar Pedhazur, Founder and Principal
E-mail: hadar@opticality.com
Preferred Investment Size: $1,000,000 to $5,000,000. **Investment Policies:** Early stage. **Industry Preferences:** Computer software and Internet specific. **Principal Exhibits:**

52742 ■ Ovation Capital Partners
800 3rd Ave., 21st Fl.
New York, NY 10605
Ph:(212)209-3036
Fax:(212)209-3039
URL: http://www.ovationcapital.com
Contact: Greg Frank, Managing General Partner
Preferred Investment Size: $1,000,000 to $5,000,000. **Investment Types:** Early stage. **Industry Preferences:** Internet related. **Geographic Preferences:** Northeast. **Principal Exhibits:**

52743 ■ Pennell Venture Partners, LLC
332 Bleecker St., Ste. K-67
New York, NY 10014
Ph:(718)855-7087
Fax:(646)365-3195
Co. E-mail: plans@pennell.com
URL: http://www.pennell.com
Contact: Thomas Pennell, President
Preferred Investment Size: $300,000 to $1,500,000. **Investment Policies:** Early stage. **Industry Preferences:** Computer software and business services. **Geographic Preferences:** New York. **Principal Exhibits:**

52744 ■ Pomona Capital
780 3rd Ave.
New York, NY 10017-7076
Ph:(212)593-3639
Fax:(212)593-3987
Co. E-mail: contactus@pomonacapital.com
URL: http://www.pomonacapital.com
Contact: Mark Marusezewski, Principal
Preferred Investment Size: $1,000,000 minimum. **Investment Types:** Fund of funds, and fund of funds of second. **Industry Preferences:** Communications and media, computer hardware and software, biotechnology, medical and health, consumer related, industrial and energy, financial services, and manufacturing. **Geographic Preferences:** U.S. and Canada. **Principal Exhibits:**

52745 ■ Prospect Street Ventures / Prospect Capital Corporation
10 East 40th St., 44th Fl.
New York, NY 10016
Ph:(212)448-0702
Fax:(212)448-9652
Co. E-mail: Deals@prospectstreet.com
URL: http://www.prospectstreet.com
Contact: John Francis Barry III, Managing Director
Preferred Investment Size: $5,000,000 to $25,000,000. **Investment Types:** Seed, start-up, early, first, second, and later stage, mezzanine, recapitalization, expansion, generalist PE, joint ventures, leveraged buyout, and management buyouts. **Industry Preferences:** Internet specific, computer software and services, other products, communications and media, medical and health. **Geographic Preferences:** U.S. and Canada. **Principal Exhibits:**

52746 ■ Rand Capital Corporation
2200 Rand Bldg.
Buffalo, NY 14203
Ph:(716)853-0802
Fax:(716)854-8480
URL: http://www.randcapital.com
Contact: Allen F. Grum, President and Chief Executive Officer
E-mail: pgrum@randcorp.com
Preferred Investment Size: $500,000 to $1,500,000. **Investment Types:** Early, later and second stage, and expansion. **Industry Preferences:** Industrial and energy, other products, communications and media, computer software and services, Internet specific, medical and health, industrial and energy, consumer related, semiconductors and other electronics, computer hardware, and biotechnology. **Geographic Preferences:** Western and Upstate New York and syndicates outside these areas. York. **Principal Exhibits:**

52747 ■ Sandler Capital Management
711 Fifth Ave., 15th Fl.
New York, NY 10022
Ph:(212)754-8100
Fax:(212)826-0280
URL: http://www.sandlercap.com
Contact: Andrew Sandler, Managing Director
Preferred Investment Size: $20,000,000 minimum. **Investment Policies:** Equity. **Investment Types:** Seed, start-up, first and second stage, control-block purchases, leveraged buyout, mezzanine, research and development, and special situation. **Industry Preferences:** Internet specific, communications and media, other products, computer software and services, consumer related, medical and health, semiconductors and other electronics. **Geographic Preferences:** U.S. and Canada. **Principal Exhibits:**

52748 ■ Seed Capital Partners/ SoftBank Capital
1 HSBC Ctr., Ste. 3850
Buffalo, NY 14203
Ph:(716)845-7520
Fax:(716)845-7539
URL: http://www.seedcp.com
Contact: Jordan A. Levy, Partner
Preferred Investment Size: $250 to $2,500,000. **Investment Types:** Seed and early stage. **Industry Preferences:** Computer software and services, communications and media, Internet specific, semiconductors and other electronics, and other products. **Geographic Preferences:** Northeast U.S. and southeastern Canada. **Principal Exhibits:**

52749 ■ Siguler Guff & Company
825 3rd Ave., 10th Fl.
New York, NY 10022
Ph:(212)332-5100
Fax:(212)332-5120
Co. E-mail: info@sigulerguff.com
URL: http://www.sigulerguff.com
Contact: Drew Guff, Managing Director
Investment Types: Start-up, first and second stage, control-block purchases, mezzanine, leveraged buyout, special situations, distressed debt, fund of funds. **Industry Preferences:** Communications, computer software and hardware, Internet specific, semiconductors and other electronics, biotechnology, medical and health, consumer related, industrial and energy, transportation, financial services, business service, manufacturing, agriculture, forestry and fishing. **Geographic Preferences:** U.S. **Principal Exhibits:**

52750 ■ Silicon Alley Venture Partners LLC / SAVP
300 Park Ave.
New York, NY 10022
Ph:(212)389-1600
Fax:(212)389-1805
Co. E-mail: partners@savp.com
URL: http://www.savp.com
Contact: Steve Brotman, Managing Director
E-mail: sbrotman@greenhill.com
Preferred Investment Size: $3,000,000 to $6,000,000. **Investment Policies:** Start-up, seed, first, early and second stage. **Industry Preferences:** Computer software, Internet specific, technology, and business services. **Geographic Preferences:** Northeast. **Principal Exhibits:**

52751 ■ Spencer Trask Ventures, Inc. / Spencer Trask Securities
750 3rd Ave., 11th Fl.
New York, NY 10017
Free: 800-622-7078
Co. E-mail: inquiries@spencertrask.com
URL: http://www.spencertrask.com
Contact: William Dioguardi, President
Preferred Investment Size: $1,000,000 to $20,000,000. **Investment Types:** Start-up, first, early and second stage. **Industry Preferences:** Communications and media, computer hardware and software, Internet specific, semiconductors and other electronics, biotechnology, medical and health, consumer related, industrial and energy, financial services, and manufacturing. **Geographic Preferences:** U.S. **Principal Exhibits:**

52752 ■ Sprout Group (New York City)
11 Madison Ave., 13th Fl.
New York, NY 10010
Ph:(212)325-7587
Fax:(212)322-0530
URL: http://www.sproutgroup.com
Contact: Robert Finzi, Managing Partner
Preferred Investment Size: $5,000,000 to $50,000,000. **Investment Types:** Start-up, early and later stage, expansion, leveraged buyout, and management buyouts. **Industry Preferences:** Medical and health, Internet specific, communications and media, biotechnology, consumer related, computer software and services, semiconductors and other electronics, industrial and energy, other products, and computer hardware. **Geographic Preferences:** U.S. **Principal Exhibits:**

STATE LISTINGS

52753 ■ Stamford Financial Consulting
108 Main St.
Stamford, NY 12167
Ph:(607)652-3311
Fax:(607)652-6301
Co. E-mail: dcre@wpe.com
URL: http://www.stamfordfinancial.com
Preferred Investment Size: $2,000,000 to $5,000,000. **Investment Types:** Expansion, mezzanine, early stage, management buyouts, private placement, and turnaround. **Industry Preferences:** Communications, semiconductors and other electronics, consumer related, medical and health, industrial and energy, financial services, and business service. **Geographic Preferences:** U.S. **Principal Exhibits:**

52754 ■ Vencon Management, Inc.
65 W. 55th St.
New York, NY 10019
Ph:(212)581-8787
Fax:(208)955-5165
Co. E-mail: vencon@worldnet.att.net
URL: http://www.venconinc.com
Contact: Irvin Barash, President
Preferred Investment Size: $500,000 to $3,000,000. **Investment Types:** First and second stage, leveraged buyout, seed, special situation, and start-up. **Industry Preferences:** Communications, computer software, Internet specific, semiconductors and other electronics, biotechnology, medical and health. **Geographic Preferences:** U.S. and Canada. **Principal Exhibits:**

52755 ■ Venrock Associates
530 5th Ave., 22nd Fl.
New York, NY 10036
Ph:(212)444-4100
Fax:(212)444-4101
URL: http://www.venrock.com
Contact: Mike Brooks, General Partner
Preferred Investment Size: $5,000,000 to $15,000,000. **Investment Types:** Seed, start-up, early, first, and later stage. **Industry Preferences:** Biotechnology, Internet specific, computer software and services, communications and media, medical and health, semiconductors and other electronics, industrial and energy, computer hardware, other products, and consumer related. **Geographic Preferences:** U.S. **Principal Exhibits:**

52756 ■ Venture Capital Fund of America, Inc. / VCFA Group
509 Madison Ave.
New York, NY 10022
Ph:(212)838-5577
Fax:(212)838-7614
URL: http://www.vcfa.com
Contact: Dayton T. Carr, Managing Director
E-mail: carr@vcfa.com
Preferred Investment Size: $1,000,000 to $100,000,000. **Investment Types:** Fund of funds of second, leveraged buyout, and mezzanine. **Geographic Preferences:** U.S and Canada. **Principal Exhibits:**

52757 ■ Warburg Pincus LLC
450 Lexington Ave.
New York, NY 10017
Ph:(212)878-0600
Fax:(212)878-9351
Co. E-mail: info@warburgpincus.com
URL: http://www.warburgpincus.com
Contact: Scott Arenare, Managing Director
Preferred Investment Size: $1,000,000 minimum. **Investment Types:** Seed, start-up, first, early, second, and later stage, mezzanine, leveraged buyout, management buyouts, private placements, acquisition, expansion, generalist PE, open market, research and development, turnaround, recapitalizations, and special situation. **Industry Preferences:** Other products, communications and media, medical and health, Internet specific, computer hardware computer software and services, consumer related, industrial and energy, biotechnology, semiconductors and other electronics. **Geographic Preferences:** U.S. and Canada. **Principal Exhibits:**

52758 ■ Welsh, Carson, Anderson, & Stowe
320 Park Ave., Ste. 2500
New York, NY 10022-6815
Ph:(212)893-9500
Fax:(212)893-9575
URL: http://www.welshcarson.com
Contact: Johnathan Rather, General Partner and Chief Financial Offi
Preferred Investment Size: $100,000,000 to $500,000,000. **Investment Types:** Leveraged buyout, management buyouts, expansion, joint ventures, mezzanine, turnaround, and special situation. **Industry Preferences:** Medical and health, other products, communications and media, Internet specific, computer software and services, computer hardware, consumer related, semiconductors and other electronics. **Principal Exhibits:**

PROCUREMENT ASSISTANCE PROGRAMS

52759 ■ Empire State Development–Division for Small Business–Procurement Assistance Program (30 S)
30 S Pearl St.
Albany, NY 12245
Ph:(518)292-5250
Free: 800-STA-TENY
Fax:(518)592-5884
Co. E-mail: mylovessmbiz@empire.state.ny.us
URL: http://www.empire.state.ny.us
Contact: Arlene Germain
Description: Assists businesses in obtaining contracts and subcontracts from federal and state agencies, departments, and authorities, and from prime contractors in the private sector. Offers training, technical, management, and marketing assistance. Also assists New York state small businesses to compete for Federal research and development grants. The Procurement Assistance Unit also puts out a publication entitled *Selling to Government: Finding New Customers for New York's Businesses.*

52760 ■ New York City Department of Business Services–New York City Procurement Outreach Program
110 William St., 7th Fl.
New York, NY 10038
Ph:(212)513-6444
Fax:(212)618-8899
Co. E-mail: bizhelp@nyc.gov
URL: http://www.nyc.gov
Contact: Robert W. Walsh, Commissioner

52761 ■ New York Procurement Center
U.S. Army Corps of Engineers
26 Federal Plaza, Rm. 3100
New York, NY 10278
Ph:(212)264-1762
Fax:(202)481-4286
Co. E-mail: malinda.chen@sba.gov
URL: http://www.sba.gov
Contact: Malinda Chen, Specialist
E-mail: debra.libow@sba.gov
Description: Covers activities for GSA, Federal Supply Service (New York, NY), GSA, Public Buildings Service (New York, NY), Army Corps of Engineers (New York, NY), U.S. Military Academy (West Point, NY).

52762 ■ New York Procurement Technical Assistance Center
50 W Main St., Ste. 8100
Rochester, NY 14614
Ph:(585)753-2015
Co. E-mail: pbirch@monroecounty.gov
URL: http://www.RochesterPTCA.com
Contact: Paulette Birch, Program Dir.
E-mail: PBirch@MonroeCounty.gov
Description: Assists members in all facets of selling to the government and military.

52763 ■ New York Procurement Technical Assistance Center–Cattaraugus County
303 Court St.
Little Valley, NY 14755
Ph:(716)938-2331

Free: 800-331-0543
Fax:(716)938-2779
Co. E-mail: jjwilliams@cattco.com
URL: http://ww2.cattco.org/procurement-technical-assistance-center/government-marketing
Contact: Joseph Williams, Prgm Mgr
Description: Assist businesses in marketing goods and services to military, federal, state, and local government agencies.

52764 ■ New York Procurement Technical Assistance Center–LaGuardia Community College PTAC
31-10 Thomson Ave.
Long Island City, NY 11101
Ph:(718)482-5315
Fax:(718)609-2091
Co. E-mail: PTAC@lagcc.cuny.edu
URL: http://www.laguardia-ptac.org
Contact: Edgard Hernandez, Dir.
E-mail: benh@lagcc.cuny.edu
Description: Assists Queens and other New York City firms market their goods and services to the federal, state, and local governments.

52765 ■ New York Procurement Technical Assistance Center–Long Island Development Corporation
45 Seaman Ave.
Bethpage, NY 11714
Free: (866)433-5432
Fax:(516)433-5046
Co. E-mail: info@lidc.org
URL: http://www.lidc.org
Contact: Roslyn D. Goldmacher, Pres. & CEO
Description: Assistance to small businesses desiring to win contracts to supply the government, both federal and state

52766 ■ New York Procurement Technical Assistance Center–Rochester Business Alliance
50 W Main St., Ste. 8100
Rochester, NY 14614
Ph:(585)753-2015
Co. E-mail: pbirch@monroecounty.gov
URL: http://www.RochesterPTAC.com
Contact: Paulette Birch, Dir.
E-mail: paulette.birch@RBAlliance.com
Description: Provides free government contract consulting to diverse business concerns serving Monroe, Genesee, Livingston, Ontario, Orleans, Seneca, and Wayne counties.

52767 ■ New York Procurement Technical Assistance Center–Rockland Economic Development Corporation
Two Blue Hill Plaza
PO Box 1575, 3rd Fl.
Pearl River, NY 10965
Ph:(845)735-7040
Fax:(845)735-5736
Co. E-mail: info@redc.org
URL: http://www.redc.org
Contact: Liz Kallen, Program Mgr.
Description: Provides programs and services to make your relocation and expansion decisions easier and cost effective.

52768 ■ New York Procurement Technical Assistance Center–South Bronx Overall Economic Development Corporation
555 Bergen Ave.
Bronx, NY 10455
Ph:(718)292-3113
Fax:(718)292-3115
Co. E-mail: mjohnson@sobro.org
URL: http://www.sobro.org
Contact: Miriam Johnson
Description: Assists local businesses in securing government contracts.

52769 ■ Rochester Procurement Technical Assistance Center
50 West Main St., Ste. 8100
Rochester, NY 14614
Ph:(585)753-2015
Co. E-mail: pbirch@monroecounty.gov
URL: http://www.rochesterptac.com
Contact: Paulette Birch, Dir.
E-mail: PBirch@MonroeCounty.com
Description: Provides free government contract consulting to diverse business concerns. Rochester PTAC serves the counties of Monroe, Genesee, Livingston, Ontario, Orleans, Seneca, and Wayne.

INCUBATORS/RESEARCH AND TECHNOLOGY PARKS

52770 ■ Adirondack Regional Business Incubator
234 Glen St.
Glen Falls, NY 12801
Ph:(518)761-6007
Fax:(518)761-9053
Co. E-mail: pwohl@arbi.biz
URL: http://www.arbi.biz/
Description: A small business incubator seeking to enhance economic development in Warren County by having a state-of-the-art business center offering value-added programs advisory talent, integrated with ACC and the area business community, to unleash the leadership potential and nurture the success of innovative regional businesses.

52771 ■ Albany Center for Economic Success
255 Orange St., Ste. 101
Albany, NY 12210
Ph:(518)427-7804
URL: http://www.acesincubator.org/
Description: A private, non-profit organization focusing on building local business by providing incubator services and technical assistance programs. It provides below market rate office space and supports tenants through shared clerical staff, general office equipment, conference space, and on-going technical service.

52772 ■ Batavia Industrial Center
56 Harvester Ave.
Batavia, NY 14020
Ph:(585)343-2800
Fax:(585)343-7096
Co. E-mail: info@bic4biz.com
URL: http://www.bic4biz.com
Description: A small business incubator focused on the success of small, emerging and established businesses with a large inventory of space, knowledge and experience.

52773 ■ Broome County Industrial Development Agency
Edwin L. Crawford County Office Bldg.
60 Hawley St., 5th Fl.
PO Box 1510
Binghamton, NY 13902-0995
Ph:(607)584-9000
Free: 800-836-6740
Fax:(607)584-9009
Co. E-mail: info@bcida.com
URL: http://www.bcida.com
Contact: Richard D'Attilio, Exec. Dir.
Description: Provides comprehensive services to companies, including needs assessment, site selection, financial aide, and more.

52774 ■ The Case Center
2-212 Center for Science and Technology
Syracuse University Office of Research
Syracuse, NY 13244
Ph:(315)443-1060
Fax:(315)443-4745
Co. E-mail: case@syr.edu
URL: http://www.case.syr.edu
Contact: Pramod Varshney, Dir.
Description: An applied research center for advanced technology, Provides R&D collaboration, networking, incubation services, and more.

52775 ■ Center for Environmental Sciences and Technology Management
University at Albany
251 Fuller Rd.
CESTM B110
Albany, NY 12203
Ph:(518)437-8686
Fax:(518)437-8610
URL: http://www.albanynanotech.org
Contact: Jackie DiStefano, Director Of Operations
Description: This incubator for emerging technology firms offers abundant resources to its tenants, including the University's Nuclear Accelerator Laboratory, electron microscopes, cluster tools, and much more.

52776 ■ Ceramics Corridor Innovation Center
109 Canada Rd.
Painted Post, NY 14870
Ph:(607)962-6387
Fax:(607)962-0645
Co. E-mail: webmaster@ceramicscorridor.org
URL: http://www.ceramicscorridor.org/
Description: A not-for-profit incubation program dedicated to expansion, research and development, and job creation in the ceramics, glass, advanced materials, and materials science technologies in the Ceramics Corridor of New York State. Provides leasing space, technology resources and support, and networking opportunities.

52777 ■ City University of New York–Sponsored Research
Graduate School & University Center
365 5th Ave.
New York, NY 10016-4309
Ph:(212)817-7523
Fax:(212)817-1629
Co. E-mail: hfisher@gc.cuny.edu
URL: http://web.gc.cuny.edu/orup
Contact: Hilry Fisher, Dir.
E-mail: hfisher@gc.cuny.edu
Scope: Administers and coordinates research and project planning in speech and hearing, anthropology, art history, biology, chemistry, comparative literature, computer science, criminal justice, earth and environmental sciences, economics, physics, political science, sociology, Spanish, theatre, child development, mathematics, environmental and social-personality psychologies, education, special education, mental health, linguistics, French, classics, history, urban education, audiology, nursing, physical therapy and public health.

52778 ■ Colgate University–Research Council
13 Oak Dr.
Hamilton, NY 13346
Ph:(315)228-7629
Fax:(315)228-7883
Co. E-mail: joliver@mail.colgate.edu
URL: http://www.colgate.edu/offices/academic/
  deanoffacultyoffice/currentfaculty/fundin gopportunities
Contact: Judith Oliver, Ch.
E-mail: joliver@mail.colgate.edu
Scope: Administers the University's research funds, receiving applications from faculty members and making awards each spring for amounts between $1,000-$4,000, plus the possibility of a two-course sabbatical leave. Throughout the year, some money is reserved to support incidental expenses incurred by faculty and costs associated with hiring student assistants.

52779 ■ Columbia University–Science and Technology Ventures
80 Claremont Ave., 4th Fl., MC 9606
New York, NY 10027
Ph:(212)854-8444
Fax:(212)854-8463
Co. E-mail: orin.herskowitz@columbia.edu
URL: http://techventures.columbia.edu
Contact: Orin Herskowitz, Exec.Dir.
E-mail: orin.herskowitz@columbia.edu
Scope: Transfers technology from the University to business and industry, especially in the area of biotechnology.

52780 ■ Columbia University–Sponsored Projects Administration
Studebaker Bldg., Rm. 254, MC 8725
615 W 131st St.
New York, NY 10027-7922
Ph:(212)854-6851
Fax:(212)854-2738
Co. E-mail: la2348@columbia.edu
URL: http://spa.columbia.edu
Contact: Lynette Arias, Assoc.VP
E-mail: la2348@columbia.edu
Scope: Solicits, administers, and coordinates extramurally sponsored research conducted in various departments and special research units of the University and assists faculty members in preparation of applications for research contracts and grants-in-aid.

52781 ■ Cornell University–Cornell Business and Technology Park
Real Estate Department
15 Thornwood Dr.
Ithaca, NY 14850
Ph:(607)266-7866
Fax:(607)266-7876
Co. E-mail: tpl6@cornell.edu
URL: http://www.cornellbtp.com
Contact: Thomas P. LiVigne, Interim Dir.
E-mail: tpl6@cornell.edu
Scope: The Park serves as a conduit between Cornell University and business, especially in electronics, computer manufacturing, and biotechnology and is a home for the independent development of technologies resulting from efforts by Cornell researchers. Leases space for business incubator activities and start-up companies.

52782 ■ Cornell University–Cornell Center for Technology, Enterprise and Commercialization
395 Pine Tree Rd., Ste. 310
Ithaca, NY 14850
Ph:(607)254-4698
Fax:(607)254-5454
Co. E-mail: ap364@cornell.edu
URL: http://www.cctec.cornell.edu
Contact: Alan Paau PhD, Exec.Dir.
E-mail: ap364@cornell.edu
Scope: Patent and technology marketing arm of the University. Activities include technology transfer, evaluating legal and business contracts, and assisting with patenting and licensing. Holds title to patents and promotes technology transfer to industry. **Publications:** Selected Technology Available for Licensing (semiannually).

52783 ■ East Side Business Center
1201 E. Fayette St.
Syracuse, NY 13210
Ph:(315)475-8456
Co. E-mail: jkeller@housingvisions.org
URL: http://esbc.housingvisions.org
Description: A small business incubator offering office and light manufacturing/industrial space to new ventures, entrepreneurs and expanding businesses. Formerly the Samuel W. Williams Jr. Business Center.

52784 ■ Fordham University–Office of Research and Sponsored Programs
441 E Fordham Rd., Bldg. 540
Bronx, NY 10458
Ph:(718)817-4651
Fax:(718)817-5575
Co. E-mail: ebert@fordham.edu
URL: http://www.fordham.edu/Academics/Office_of_
  Research/index.asp
Contact: Laura Ebert
E-mail: ebert@fordham.edu
Scope: Provides coordination and administrative services for extramurally sponsored research by faculty members of the University, including studies on urban education problems, psychological processes in human creativity, problems of juvenile delinquency, drug addiction in urban areas, social tensions in urban communities, models of religious education systems, the abortion process, and basic investigations in chemistry, physics, and biology.

52785 ■ Hudson Valley Center for Innovation
Hudson Valley Technology Development Center
300 Westage Business Center
Fishkill, NY 12524
Ph:(845)943-5660
Fax:(845)336-8050
Co. E-mail: lneumann@hvcfi.com
URL: http://www.hvcfi.com/index2.aspx
Contact: Les Neumann, Dir.
Description: A not-for-profit corporation formed to foster the growth and development of emerging high value business and technology development firms, and the creation of high-value jobs throughout the Hudson Valley region of New York State through the implementation, and enhancement, of the cost-effective business incubation model.

52786 ■ Jefferson County Job Development Corporation
800 Starbuck Ave., Ste. 800
Watertown, NY 13601
Ph:(315)782-5865
Free: 800-553-4111
Fax:(315)782-7915
URL: http://www.jcjdc.net/
Description: A small business incubator offering a one-stop-shop for business development assistance, from capital financing to low-cost facility options to economic development incentives.

52787 ■ Lennox Tech Enterprise Center
High Tech Rochester
150 Lucius Gordon Dr., Ste. 100
West Henrietta, NY 14586
Ph:(585)214-2400
Co. E-mail: info@htr.org
URL: http://htr.org/incubator.asp
Description: A catalyst for innovators who plan to build high-growth businesses, offering success services for startup entrepreneurs.

52788 ■ Local Development Corporation of East New York–East Brooklyn Enterprise Center
80 Jamaica Ave., 3rd Fl.
Brooklyn, NY 11207
Ph:(718)385-6700
Fax:(718)385-7505
Co. E-mail: info@ldceny.org
URL: http://www.ldceny.org
Contact: Sherry Roberts, Exec Dir
Description: Works to improve the economic situation of East Brooklyn. Operates four divisions: industry, business development, environment, and housing.

52789 ■ Long Island Forum for Technology
510 Grumman Rd. W, Ste. 201
Bethpage, NY 11714
Ph:(631)969-3700
Fax:(631)969-2789
Co. E-mail: info@lift.org
URL: http://www.lift.org
Description: A non-profit development organization offering networking, access to technology, and other business services.

52790 ■ Long Island High Technology Incubator
25 Health Sciences Drive
Box 100
Stony Brook, NY 11790-3350
Ph:(631)444-8800
Fax:(631)444-8825
Co. E-mail: anil.chundale@stonybrook.edu
URL: http://www.lihti.org
Contact: Anil Dhundale, Exec Dir
Description: The LIHTI offers tenants a place to start up companies without the difficulties normally associated with emerging businesses. The incubator also provides numerous services through its alliances with both public and private sector organizations.

52791 ■ Mi Kitchen es su Kitchen
370 E. 76th St., Ste. A2004
New York, NY 10021-2550
Ph:(212)452-1866

Fax:(212)452-1767
Co. E-mail: mikitchen1866@aol.com
URL: http://www.mikitchenessukitchen.com/
Contact: Katherine Gregory, Dir
Description: A small business incubator offering a time-share rental facility available to up-and-coming food entrepreneurs.

52792 ■ New York University–Office of Sponsored Programs
665 Broadway, Ste. 801
New York, NY 10012-2331
Ph:(212)998-2121
Fax:(212)995-4029
Co. E-mail: richard.louth@nyu.edu
URL: http://www.nyu.edu/research/resources-and-support-offices/getting-started-withyou rresearch/office-of-sponsored-programs.html
Contact: Richard Louth, Dir.
E-mail: richard.louth@nyu.edu
Scope: Serves as central coordinating agency for sponsored activities at the University (exclusive of Medical Center), advises on matters of research policy, recommends operating guidelines for administration of sponsored programs, provides information and assistance to faculty and research staff, maintains records on sponsored research, and allocates some funds internally in support of research programs.

52793 ■ Operation Oswego County
44 W. Bridge St.
Oswego, NY 13126
Ph:(315)343-1545
Fax:(315)343-1546
Co. E-mail: ooc@oswegocounty.org
URL: http://www.oswegocounty.org/
Description: A small business incubator created to establish and implement sound economic development strategies in order to enhance the economic vitality of Oswego County's businesses, industries and citizens leading to an overall better quality of life; its mission is the creation and retention of job opportunities, diversification and strengthening of the economic base, and developing the local economy in a planned, organized and environmentally-friendly atmosphere.

52794 ■ Queens College of City University of New York–Office of Research and Sponsored Programs
65-30 Kissena Blvd.
Flushing, NY 11367
Ph:(718)997-5400
Fax:(718)997-5409
Co. E-mail: michael_prasad@qc.cuny.edu
URL: http://www.qc.edu/ORSP
Contact: Gautama M. Prasad, Dir.
E-mail: michael_prasad@qc.cuny.edu
Scope: Coordinates all research activities conducted at the College, including extramurally supported projects. **Publications:** Annual Report.

52795 ■ Rensselaer Incubation Program
110 8th St., 3210 J Bldg.
Troy, NY 12180-3590
Ph:(518)276-6658
Fax:(518)276-6380
Co. E-mail: incubator@rpi.edu
URL: http://www.incubator.com
Contact: Ronald M. Kudia, Exec Dir
Description: This program, located at Rensselaer Polytechnic Institute, seeks to nurture new technological ventures. It offers tenants affordable offices space, laboratories, and light manufacturing space as well as other services.

52796 ■ Rensselaer Polytechnic Institute–Office of Contracts and Grants
West Hall, 4th Fl.
110 8th St.
Troy, NY 12180
Ph:(518)276-6281

Fax:(518)276-4820
Co. E-mail: scammr@rpi.edu
Contact: Richard E. Scammell, Dir.
E-mail: scammr@rpi.edu
Scope: Administers research projects at the Institute conducted in such areas as bioenvironmental engineering, machines and structures, materials, electrophysics, mechanics, systems engineering, fluid, chemical, and thermal processes, architecture, economics, history and political sciences, anthropology and sociology, language and literature, philosophy, psychology, management, biology, chemistry, geology, mathematics, computer science, nuclear science, physics, and astronomy.

52797 ■ Rensselaer Polytechnic Institute–Rensselaer Technology Park
100 Defreest Dr.
Troy, NY 12180
Ph:(518)283-7102
Fax:(518)283-0695
Co. E-mail: wachom@rpi.edu
URL: http://www.rpitechpark.com
Contact: Michael Wacholder, Dir.
E-mail: wachom@rpi.edu
Scope: Serves as a conduit for joint research activities, consultancies, refresher studies, associate programs, and human interactions between Park tenants and the Institute.

52798 ■ Research Foundation of the City University of New York
230 W 41st St., 7th Fl.
New York, NY 10036
Ph:(212)417-8300
Fax:(212)417-8510
Co. E-mail: richard_rothbard@rfcuny.org
URL: http://www.rfcuny.org
Contact: Richard F. Rothbard, Pres.
E-mail: richard_rothbard@rfcuny.org
Scope: Receives, holds, and administers grants, contracts, and gifts for constituent colleges and works to maximize usage of faculty skills as a resource to the community, private industry, government, and the media. **Publications:** Research Foundation Annual Report.

52799 ■ Schenectady County Community Business Center
920 Albany St.
Schenectady, NY 12307
Ph:(518)382-3069
Fax:(518)688-2028
Co. E-mail: info@sccbc.org
URL: http://www.sccbc.org/
Description: A small business incubator offering a one-stop resource center for new, growing and challenged small businesses in Schenectady County, New York by providing whatever an entrepreneur needs to build a business.

52800 ■ Second Century Innovation and Ideas Corp
163 William St., 3rd Fl.
New York, NY 10038-2602
Ph:(212)346-1064
Fax:(212)346-1116
Co. E-mail: info@sci2
URL: http://www.sci2.org/
Description: A commercialization accelerator for early stage companies seeking funding, intellectual capital, business development expertise, and potential strategic relationships with Fortune 1000 companies that results in jobs and economic development in Westchester and in lower Manhattan.

52801 ■ State University of New York at Binghamton–Division of Research
Innovative Technologies Complex
PO Box 6000
Binghamton, NY 13902-6000
Ph:(607)777-6136

Fax:(607)777-4354
Co. E-mail: sgilje@binghamton.edu
URL: http://research.binghamton.edu
Contact: Stephen A. Gilje, Assoc.VP
E-mail: sgilje@binghamton.edu
Scope: Facilitates faculty research funding searches, helps faculty manage funded projects, helps faculty keep current on research policies and practices, enhances awareness of and appreciation for the process and products of discovery. **Publications:** Binghamton Research (biennially); Discover-E (bimonthly). **Awards:** Office of Sponsored Programs (daily), pre-award activities; Sponsored Funds Administration (daily), post award activities; Technology Transfer and Innovation Partnerships (daily), works with faculty to protect and market intellectual property and assist faculty with entrepreneurial activities.

52802 ■ State University of New York at Buffalo–Office of the Vice President for Research
516 Capen Hall
Buffalo, NY 14260
Ph:(716)645-3321
Fax:(716)645-6792
Co. E-mail: rjgenco@research.buffalo.edu
URL: http://www.research.buffalo.edu
Contact: Alexander N. Cartwright PhD, VP
E-mail: rjgenco@research.buffalo.edu
Scope: Administers and coordinates extramurally sponsored research conducted in various departments and research units of the University. **Publications:** Research report.

52803 ■ State University of New York College at Cortland–Research and Sponsored Programs Office
Miller Bldg., Rm. 402
PO Box 2000
Cortland, NY 13045
Ph:(607)753-2511
Fax:(607)753-5590
Co. E-mail: amyh@em.cortland.edu
URL: http://www2.cortland.edu/offices/rspo
Contact: Amy L. Henderson-Harr, Asst.VP
E-mail: amyh@em.cortland.edu
Scope: Serves as liaison for matters pertaining to extramurally funded research at the College, including such projects as the basidiomycetes of the Greater Antilles, especially the Luquillo LTER site; wetland-lake connections and amphibian communities of the Onondaga Lake; trail-based communication in tent caterpillars; and the thermodynamics of binding of simple cationic lipids to DNA. **Publications:** Research News. **Awards:** Faculty Development Grants (annually), through the Faculty Research Program, Research and Travel Grant Program, Research Enrichment Development Initiative.

52804 ■ State University of New York College at Fredonia–Grants Administration/Research Services Office
E230 Thompson Hall
Fredonia, NY 14063
Ph:(716)673-3528
Fax:(716)673-3802
Co. E-mail: maggie.bryan-peterson@fredonia.edu
URL: http://www.fredonia.edu/sponsoredprograms/
  grantdevelopment.asp
Contact: Maggie Bryan Peterson, Dir.
E-mail: maggie.bryan-peterson@fredonia.edu
Scope: Administers grants and contracts at the University through the processing of grant proposals, assistance in finding funding sources, services for faculty proposal and budget development, and manuscript typing for publications. **Publications:** Newsletter (quarterly). **Educational Activities:** Workshops, in community grant writing.

52805 ■ State University of New York Health Science Center at Brooklyn–Office of Research Administration
450 Clarkson Ave., Box 69
Brooklyn, NY 11203-2098
Ph:(718)270-3176

Fax:(718)270-1407
URL: http://www.downstate.edu/finance/research.
  html
Contact: Paul J. Davis, Oper.Mgr.
Scope: Administers sponsors programs, extramural funding, and contracts for research in medical and basic sciences. Also transfers technology from the University to business and industry.

52806 ■ SUNY Fredonia Technology Incubator
214 Central Ave.
338 Central Ave., Ste. 340
PO Box 26
Dunkirk, NY 14048
Ph:(716)681-6009
Fax:(715)680-6008
Co. E-mail: incubator@fredonia.edu
URL: http://incubator.fredonia.edu
Description: In incubator supporting technology-based businesses. Entrepreneurs also receive help in getting their ideas and businesses up and running, such as through development of business plans, accounting and legal services, office management, financing/venture capital strategies, and marketing plans.

52807 ■ U-Start Business Incubator
4 Nott Terrace
Schenectady, NY 12308
Ph:(518)631-0472
Fax:(518)631-0475
Co. E-mail: execdir@ustartincubator.org
URL: http://www.ustartincubator.org
Contact: William Johnson, Exec Dir
Description: A small business incubator whose mission is to support and encourage promising entrepreneurs to grow their ideas in Schenectady County.

52808 ■ UB Technology Incubator
Office of Science, Technology Transfer and
  Economic Outreach
1576 Sweet Home Rd.
Amherst, NY 14228
Ph:(716)645-5500
Fax:(716)636-5921
Co. E-mail: prv-stor@buffalo.edu
URL: http://www.research.buffalo.edu/stor/incubator/
Description: A small business incubator supporting the creation of new technology-based businesses by providing affordable business services to entrepreneurs.

52809 ■ University of Rochester–Office of Research and Project Administration
515 Hylan Bldg., RC Box 270140
Rochester, NY 14627
Ph:(585)275-4031
Fax:(585)275-9492
Co. E-mail: gunta.liders@rochester.edu
URL: http://www.rochester.edu/orpa
Contact: Gunta J. Liders, Assoc.VP, for Res.
  Administration
E-mail: gunta.liders@rochester.edu
Scope: Serves as central administrative unit for coordination of research programs and extramural sponsored activities conducted at the University in physical and life sciences, education, engineering, medicine, management, social sciences, the humanities, music, and art. Administrative activities include research administration, legislative liaison, and intellectual property management. **Publications:** Annual Report. **Educational Activities:** Administrative Workshops (periodically), for departmental administrators in sponsored research administration; Regular workshops (quarterly), for administrators and faculty in areas of sponsored program activity.

EDUCATIONAL PROGRAMS

52810 ■ Board of Cooperative Educational Services–Adult and Continuing Education
53 Gibson Rd.
Goshen, NY 10924-9777
Ph:(845)291-0100

Fax:(845)291-0498
Co. E-mail: adulted@ouboces.mhrcc.org
URL: http://www.ouboces.org/
Description: Offers a ten-session class in small business organization.

52811 ■ Bryant and Stratton Business Institute–Henrietta Campus
1225 Jefferson Rd.
Henrietta, NY 14623
Ph:(585)292-5627
Fax:(585)292-6015
URL: http://www.bryantstratton.edu
Description: Business college offering programs in business management and business operations.

52812 ■ Bryant and Stratton Business Institute–Syracuse Campus
953 James St.
Syracuse, NY 13203
Ph:(315)472-6603
Fax:(315)474-4383
URL: http://www.bryantstratton.edu
Description: Business college offering programs in business management and business operations.

52813 ■ Bryant and Stratton College–Buffalo Campus
465 Main St., Ste. 400
Buffalo, NY 14203
Ph:(716)884-9120
Fax:(716)884-0091
URL: http://www.bryantstratton.edu
Description: Business college offering programs in business management and business operations.

52814 ■ C. W Post Campus of Long Island University–Long Island University
720 Northern Blvd.
Brookville, NY 11548
Ph:(516)299-2000
Free: 800-LIU-PIAW
Fax:(516)299-3829
Co. E-mail: enroll@cwpost.liu.edu
URL: http://www.liu.edu
Description: Offers programs in small business management and entrepreneurship.

52815 ■ Erie Community College, City Campus
121 Ellicott St.
Buffalo, NY 14203
Ph:(716)842-2770
Fax:(716)851-1129
URL: http://www.ecc.edu/
Description: Two-year college offering a certificate in small business management.

52816 ■ Fiorello H. LaGuardia Community College of the City University of New York–Division of Adult and Continuing Education–Center for Corporate Education (31-10)
31-10 Thomson Ave., Rm. E-405
c/o Mr. Wilford Saunders
31-10 Thomson Ave.
Long Island City, NY 11101
Ph:(718)482-7200
Fax:(718)482-5176
Co. E-mail: lagcc@cuny.edu
URL: http://www.lagcc.cuny.edu
Contact: Timothy Rucinsky, Director
Description: Offers courses in supervisory skills and management, microcomputer applications, communication and interpersonal skills, specialized business workshops, and technical training and workshops in retailing skills for small business owners. Maintains an interest in small business by offering programs at no cost to the community through funding by the New York State Department of Education. Small business courses cover personal selling, customer service, merchandise management, accounting, time and stress management, and microcomputers.

52817 ■ Herkimer County Community College
100 Reservoir Rd.
Herkimer, NY 13350
Ph:(315)866-0300
Fax:(315)866-7253
URL: http://www.hccc.ntcnet.com
Description: Two-year college offering a small business management program.

52818 ■ SUNY Canton College
34 Cornell Dr.
Canton, NY 13617
Ph:(315)386-7011
Free: 800-388-7123
Fax:(315)393-5940
URL: http://www.canton.edu/
Description: Two-year college offering a small business management program.

LEGISLATIVE ASSISTANCE

52819 ■ New York Assembly Standing Committee on Small Business
Legislative Office Bldg., Rm. 202
Albany, NY 12248
Ph:(518)455-4218
Fax:(518)455-3976
Co. E-mail: sweeney@assembly.state.ny.us
URL: http://www.assembly.state.ny.us
Contact: Robert Sweeney

52820 ■ New York Senate Standing Committee
Legislative Office Bldg., Rm. 304
Albany, NY 12247
Ph:(518)455-2015
Fax:(518)426-6968
Co. E-mail: alesi@senate.state.ny.us
URL: http://www.senatoralesi.com
Description: Small Business

TRADE PERIODICALS

52821 ■ Proof
Pub: Direct Marketing Club of New York
Contact: Stuart Boysen
E-mail: stuboysen@earthlink.net
Released: 10/year. **Description:** Provides information concerning direct marketing to members of the Direct Marketing Club of New York. Recurring features include a calendar of events, news of members, news of educational opportunities, book reviews, and various columns on direct marketing techniques and advancements.

52822 ■ Queensborough
Pub: Queens Chamber of Commerce
Ed: Released: 5/year. **Price:** Included in membership. **Description:** Focuses on business trends in Queens County, New York.

PUBLICATIONS

52823 ■ Capital District Business Review
2 Computer Dr. W.
PO Box 15081
Albany, NY 12212-5081
Ph:(518)437-9855
Fax:(518)438-9219
Co. E-mail: cdbr@logical.net
URL: http://www.amcity.com/albany

52824 ■ Crain's New York Business
220 E. 42nd St.
New York, NY 10017-5846
Ph:(212)210-0100
Fax:(212)210-0799
URL: http://www.crainsny.com

52825 ■ How to Form Your Own New York Corporation
Nolo Press
950 Parker St.
Berkeley, CA 94710
Ph:(510)549-1976

Free: 800-992-6656
URL: http://www.nolo.com
Ed: Anthony Mancuso. **Released:** 1989. **Price:** $24.95. **Description:** Also available for use on IBM PC 3 (1/4 inch disk), IBM PC 5 (disk), and Macintosh (1/2 inch disk).

52826 ■ Hudson Valley Business Journal
P.O. Box 339
Pine Island, NY 10969
Ph:(914)258-4008
Fax:(914)258-4111
Co. E-mail: hvbsnjnl@warwick.net
URL: http://www.hubj.com

52827 ■ Long Island Business News
2150 Smithtown Ave.
Ronkonkoma, NY 11779-7358
Ph:(516)737-1700
Fax:(516)737-1890
Co. E-mail: editor@libn.com
URL: http://www.libn.com

52828 ■ Long Island Magazine
80 Hauppauge Rd.
Commack, NY 11725
Ph:(516)493-3020
Fax:(516)499-2194
URL: http://www.liassoc.com

52829 ■ Rochester Business Journal
55 St. Paul St.
Rochester, NY 14604
Ph:(716)546-8303
Fax:(716)546-3398
Co. E-mail: rbjournal@aol.com
URL: http://www.rbj.net

52830 ■ Smart Start your New York Business
PSI Research
300 N. Valley Dr.
Grants Pass, OR 97526
Ph:(503)479-9464
Free: 800-228-2275
Fax:(503)476-1479
Co. E-mail: info@psi-research.com
URL: http://www.psi-research.com
Ed: Michael D. Jenkins. **Released:** Revised edition, 1992. **Price:** $29.95 (looseleaf binder); $24.95 (paper). **Description:** Part of the Successful Business Library series.

52831 ■ Westchester County Business Journal
3 Gannett Dr.
White Plains, NY 10604
Ph:(914)694-3600
Fax:(914)694-3699

PUBLISHERS

52832 ■ Allworth Press
307 W 36th St., 11th Fl.
New York, NY 10018
Ph:(212)643-6816
Free: 800-491-2808
Fax:(212)777-8261
Co. E-mail: pub@allworth.com
URL: http://www.allworth.com
Contact: Tad Crawford, Publisher
E-mail: crawford@allworth.com
Description: Publishes practical business and self-help information for photographers, designers, artists, authors, and performing artists. Classic and contemporary critical writings on art and graphic design. Accepts unsolicited manuscripts. Reaches market through direct and special sales programs; the Internet; and Georgetown Publications. **Founded:** 1989.

52833 ■ American Booksellers Association
200 White Plains Rd., Ste. 600
Tarrytown, NY 10591
Ph:(914)591-2665
Free: 800-637-0037

Fax:(914)591-2720
Contact: Rosemary Hawkins, Director
Description: Publishes a book buyer's handbook and returns handbooks. Also offers information, interaction, education and advocacy in bookselling. **Founded:** 1900.

52834 ■ Center for Entrepreneurial Management Inc.
180 Varick St.
New York, NY 10014
Ph:(212)633-0060
Fax:(212)633-0063
Contact: Karla Mancuso, Vice President
Description: Publishes business and management information targeted for officials of small and medium businesses. Many titles available on audio and video cassettes. Also produces newsletters and magazines. Reaches market through direct mail. Does not accept unsolicited manuscripts. **Founded:** 1978.

52835 ■ Doubleday Publishing Group
1745 Broadway
New York, NY 10019-4368
Ph:(212)782-9000
Free: 800-733-3000
Fax:(212)940-7390
Co. E-mail: ddaypub@randomhouse.com
URL: http://doubleday.com
Contact: Stephen Rubin, President
E-mail: mpalgon@randomhouse.com
Description: Publishes mysteries, romances, westerns, and science fiction. Publishes nonfiction books in many areas including biographies, cookbooks, business, parenting, science, technology, parenting, child care, finance, gay and lesbian studies, money management and psychology. **Founded:** 1897.

52836 ■ Forum Publishing Co.
383 E Main St.
Centerport, NY 11721
Ph:(631)754-5000
Free: 800-635-7654
Co. E-mail: forumpublishing@aol.com
URL: http://www.forum123.com
Contact: Martin Stevens, CEO
Description: Publishes books and directories on business start-ups and expansions. Offers audio cassettes. Accepts unsolicited manuscripts. Reaches market through direct mail. **Founded:** 1981.

52837 ■ Genesis Society Inc.
102-06 Metropolitan Ave.
Forest Hills, NY 11375
Ph:(718)544-5997
Fax:(718)544-5488
Co. E-mail: info@genesissociety.com
URL: http://www.genesissociety.org
Contact: Rene David Alkalay, CEO & Pres
Description: Publishes health-related hand books. **Founded:** 1999.

52838 ■ H.W. Wilson Co.
950 University Ave.
Bronx, NY 10452-4224
Ph:(718)588-8400
Free: 800-367-6770
Fax:(718)590-1617
Co. E-mail: custserv@hwwilson.com
URL: http://www.hwwilson.com
Contact: Michael Heelan, Director
E-mail: mheelan@hwwilson.ie
Description: Publishes reference tools for libraries and book trade. Also offers videotapes, computer software, CD-ROMs and online databases. **Founded:** 1898.

52839 ■ International Trademark Association
655 3rd Ave., 10th Fl.
New York, NY 10017
Ph:(212)642-1700

Fax:(212)768-7796
Co. E-mail: info@inta.org
URL: http://www.inta.org
Contact: Tish Berard, Mgr
Description: Publishes information on the use, registration and protection of trademarks in the U. S. and abroad. Reaches market through direct mail. Does not accept unsolicited manuscripts; proposals only. **Founded:** 1878.

52840 ■ International Wealth Success Inc.
PO Box 186
Merrick, NY 11566-0186
Ph:(516)766-5850
Free: 800-323-0548
Fax:(516)766-5919
Co. E-mail: admin@iwsmoney.com
URL: http://www.iwsmoney.com
Contact: Tyler G. Hicks, President
E-mail: dhicks@iwsmoney.com
Description: Publishes on capital sources, mail order, import/export and real-estate. Accepts unsolicited manuscripts; include a self-addressed, stamped envelope. Reaches market through commission representatives, direct mail and trade sales. **Founded:** 1967.

52841 ■ JMW Group Inc.
1 West Ave.
Larchmont, NY 10538-2470
Ph:(914)769-6400
Fax:(914)769-0250
Co. E-mail: bdiedrick@att.net
URL: http://www.jmwgroup.net
Contact: Brice Diedrick, President
E-mail: bdiedrick@att.net
Description: Publishes both fiction and nonfiction books. **Founded:** 1985.

52842 ■ Macmillan Online USA
c/o Nature America Inc.
345 Park Ave. S
New York, NY 10010-1707
Ph:(212)726-9200
Free: 800-221-2123
Fax:(212)696-9006
Co. E-mail: a.thomas@nature.com
URL: http://www.macmillan.com
Contact: Sue Bale, Director
Description: Publishes scientific and medical journals. **Founded:** 1869.

52843 ■ McGraw-Hill Trade
2 Penn Plz.
New York, NY 10121-0101
Ph:(212)904-4610
Fax:(212)904-4091
Co. E-mail: customer.service@mcgraw-hill.com
URL: http://www.mcgraw-hill.com
Contact: Robert J. Bahash, Exec VP
E-mail: philip_ruppel@mcgraw-hill.com
Description: Publishes business and general reference books.

52844 ■ Passion Profit Co.
PO Box 618, Church Street Sta.
New York, NY 10008-0618
Ph:(212)831-1854
Fax:(212)658-9232
Co. E-mail: orders@passionprofit.com
URL: http://www.passionprofit.com
Contact: Walt Goodridge, President
Description: Publishes how-to books primarily. **Founded:** 1990.

52845 ■ Productivity Press (New York, New York)
270 Madison Ave.
New York, NY 10016
Ph:(212)216-7800
Free: 888-319-5852
Fax:(212)686-5411
Co. E-mail: info@productivitypress.com
URL: http://www.productivitypress.com
Contact: Maura May, Publisher
E-mail: mmay@productivitypress.com
Founded: 1983.

52846 ■ Rock Beach Press
1255 University Ave.
Rochester, NY 14607
Contact: William J. Stolze, President
Description: Publishes a book about entrepreneurship. Reaches market through direct mail, Baker & Taylor and MacLean Hunter. **Founded:** 1989.

52847 ■ SelectBooks Inc.
1 Union Sq. W, Ste. 909
New York, NY 10003
Ph:(212)206-1997
Fax:(212)206-3815
Co. E-mail: info@selectbooks.com
URL: http://www.selectbooks.com
Contact: Mark W. Hordes, Editor
Description: Publishes non-fiction in the areas of biography, politics, business administration and alternative medicine. **Founded:** 2001.

52848 ■ Standard & Poor's
55 Water St.
New York, NY 10041-0004
Ph:(212)438-2000
Free: 800-852-1641
Co. E-mail: questions@standardandpoors.com
URL: http://www.standardandpoors.com
Contact: Torsten Hinrichs
Description: Publishes on financial information. Offers more than 50 publications and services, disseminates information electronically and produces historical data on microfiche. Offers periodicals and software. Reaches market through commission representatives, direct mail and telephone sales. **Founded:** 1860.

52849 ■ Tokyo Stock Exchange Inc.
45 Broadway, Ste. 2103
New York, NY 10006
Ph:(212)363-2350
Fax:(212)363-2354
Co. E-mail: contact@tsenyrep.com
URL: http://www.tse.or.jp/english/about/oversea.html
Contact: Toshitsugu Shimizu, Director
Description: Publishes on business and statistics, stocks and shares. **Founded:** 1870.

52850 ■ Vault.com Inc.
132 W 31st St., 15th Fl.
New York, NY 10001
Ph:(212)366-4212
Free: 888-562-8285
Fax:(212)366-6117
URL: http://www.vault.com
Contact: Samer Hamadeh, Owner
E-mail: rbirgfeld@staff.vault.com
Description: Publishes insider career development books for professionals and recruiters. Accepts unsolicited manuscripts. Reaches market through commission representatives, direct mail, reviews, listing, telephone sales and CDs. **Founded:** 1996.

52851 ■ Wise Counsel Press L.L.C.
230 Park Ave., Ste. 1000
New York, NY 10169-1099
Fax:(212)481-4039
Co. E-mail: info@wisecounselpress.com
URL: http://www.wisecounselpress.com
Contact: Nina L. Kaufman, Owner
Description: Publishes legal materials aimed at assisting small businesses and entrepreneurs.

SMALL BUSINESS ASSISTANCE PROGRAMS

52852 ■ Council for Entrepreneurial Development
Alexandria Technology Center
100 Capitola Dr., Ste. 101
PO Box 13353
Durham, NC 27713
Ph:(919)549-7500
Fax:(919)549-7405
Co. E-mail: info@cednc.org
URL: http://www.cednc.org
Contact: Joan Siefert Rose, Pres
Description: Council of entrepreneurs, business and financial service providers, public policy makers, and university faculty, united to promote the enhancement of entrepreneurial development in North Carolina through monthly programs, newsletters, consultation programs, membership directories, seminars and workshops, and an annual venture capital conference.

52853 ■ East Carolina University–Center for Applied Technology
Technology Enterprise Center
Greenville, NC 27858-4353
Ph:(252)328-6708
Fax:(252)328-1545
Co. E-mail: gaulandd@mail.ecu.edu
URL: http://www.ecu.edu/rds/CAT/
Description: Provides technical and scientific assistance through contract research for industries, businesses, and municipalities.

52854 ■ Frank Hawkins Kenan Institute of Private Enterprise
Campus Box 3440
The Kenan Center
Chapel Hill, NC 27599-3440
Ph:(919)962-8201
Fax:(919)962-8202
Co. E-mail: kenan_institute@unc.edu
URL: http://www.kenan-flagler.unc.edu/KI/
Contact: John D. Kasarda, Dir.
Description: National center for private enterprise research focusing on entrepreneurial development, new venture management, and coursework development.

52855 ■ North Carolina Community College System–Small Business Center Network
Caswell Bldg.
200 W Jones St.
Raleigh, NC 27603-5003
Ph:(919)807-7100
Fax:(919)807-7164
Co. E-mail: sbcndirector@nccommunitycolleges.edu
URL: http://www.ncccs.cc.nc.us/Business_and_Industry
Contact: George Millsaps, State Dir.
Description: Offers consultations and referrals, including business planning. Operates a resource and information center containing printed and elec-

tronic resources. Sponsors business and computer expos in cooperation with business and community organizations. Offers workshops to potential and existing small businesses on business topics, including business plans, basics of business, motivation, management, financial planning, computer and software applications, customer relations, farm recordkeeping, and franchising.

52856 ■ North Carolina Department of Agriculture and Consumers Services–Marketing Division
2 W Edenton St., Rm.402
Raleigh, NC 27601
Ph:(919)733-7887
Fax:(919)733-0999
URL: http://www.ncagr.com/markets/
Contact: Tom Slade, Dir
Description: Provides small businesses with information on doing business internationally.

52857 ■ North Carolina Department of Commerce–Business/Industry Development Division
4301 Mail Service Ctr.
Raleigh, NC 27699-4301
Ph:(919)733-4151
Fax:(919)733-9265
URL: http://www.nccommerce.com/en
Contact: Roger J. Shackleford, Exec. Dir.
Description: Assists international, national, and state firms in locating new or expanded facilities in North Carolina.

52858 ■ North Carolina Rural Economic Development Center
4021 Carya Dr.
Raleigh, NC 27610
Ph:(919)250-4314
Fax:(919)250-4325
Co. E-mail: info@ncruralcenter.org
URL: http://www.ncruralcenter.org
Contact: Valerie Lee, Chairman
Description: Provides and is involved in research and demonstration efforts to identify new ideas, strategies, or programs that will generate economic development in rural North Carolina.

52859 ■ North Carolina Small Business Partnership
5003 Mail Service Ctr.
Raleigh, NC 27699-5003
Ph:(919)807-7100
Fax:(919)807-7164
Co. E-mail: dickens@ncccs.cc.nc.us
URL: http://www.nccs.cc.nc.us
Contact: Willa Dickens, Dir
Description: Consists of eleven state and state-supported organizations united to promote cooperation and collaboration in meeting economic concerns. Purposes include serving as an advocate for smaller business interests, and informing public policy makers of small business assistance resources and services.

52860 ■ North Carolina Small Business and Technology Development Center
5 W. Hargett St., Ste. 600
Raleigh, NC 27601-1348
Ph:(919)715-7272
Free: 800-621-0008
Fax:(915)715-7777
Co. E-mail: info@sbtdc.org
URL: http://www.sbtdc.org
Contact: Scott Daugherty, Exec Dir.
Description: Goals are to increase job opportunities and capital investments; to assist in the creation or retention of jobs; to expand economic opportunities; to reduce the incidence of business failure; to assist in community development efforts; and to assist in the development, growth, and expansion of commercial, industrial, and business activities.

52861 ■ North Carolina State University–Industrial Extension Service
Campus Box 7902
Raleigh, NC 27695-7902
Ph:(919)515-2358
Fax:(919)515-6159
Co. E-mail: ies_services@ncsu.edu
URL: http://www.ies.ncsu.edu
Description: Provides assistance to North Carolina industries to help them have a competitive advantage through better utilization of engineering technologies.

SCORE OFFICES

52862 ■ Coastal Carolina SCORE
c/o Joan Lamson, Chair
3615 Arendell St.
Morehead City, NC 28557
Ph:(252)222-6126
Co. E-mail: score@carteret.edu
URL: http://www.score660.com
Description: Promotes business and community development in Morehead City, NC. Conducts business education seminars and workshops to those wanting to start a business.

52863 ■ Durham SCORE
Path:

52864 ■ East Carolina SCORE
Path: www.eastcarolinascore.org

52865 ■ Outer Banks SCORE
Path: www.score497.org

52866 ■ SCORE Asheboro/Randolph
c/o Asheboro/Randolph Chamber of Commerce
317 E Dixie Dr.
Asheboro, NC 27203
Ph:(336)626-2626
Fax:(336)626-7077
Co. E-mail: chamber@asheboro.com
URL: http://www.scoreasheboro.org
Contact: Philip Brown, Chm.
Description: Provides public service to America by offering small business advice and training.

52867 ■ SCORE Asheville
Federal Bldg., Rm. 259
151 Patton Ave.
Asheville, NC 28801
Ph:(828)271-4786
Fax:(828)271-4786
Co. E-mail: info@ashevillescore.org
URL: http://www.ashevillescore.org
Contact: Mr. David Hymer, Chm.
Description: Serves as volunteer program in which working and retired business management professionals provide free business counseling to men and women who are considering starting a small business, encountering problems with their business, or expanding their business. Offers free one-on-one counseling, online counseling and low cost workshops on a variety of business topics.

52868 ■ SCORE Chapel Hill
c/o Chapel Hill/Carrboro Chamber of Commerce
104 S Estes Dr.
Chapel Hill, NC 27514
Ph:(919)968-6894
Fax:(919)967-7000
URL: http://www.scorechapelhill.org
Description: Provides in-depth, industry-specific business assistance to evaluate a business idea or plan, stimulates business growth and ensure long-term stability.

52869 ■ SCORE Charlotte
One Fairview Center
6302 Fairview Rd., Ste. 300
Charlotte, NC 28210
Ph:(704)344-6576
Co. E-mail: charlottescore47@carolina.rr.com
URL: http://www.charlottescore.org
Contact: Mr. Michael O'Hara, Chm.
Description: Serves as volunteer program in which working and retired business management professionals provide free business counseling to men and women who are considering starting a small business, encountering problems with their business, or expanding their business. Offers free one-on-one counseling, online counseling and low cost workshops on a variety of business topics.

52870 ■ SCORE Down East
PO Box 790
New Bern, NC 28563
Ph:(252)633-6688
Fax:(252)633-9608
Co. E-mail: score@esisnet.com
URL: http://www.scorenewbern.org
Description: Provides entrepreneur education for the formation, growth and success of small businesses in the area.

52871 ■ SCORE Greensboro
2007 Yanceyville St.
Box 48
Greensboro, NC 27405
Ph:(336)333-5399
Co. E-mail: info@scoregso.org
URL: http://www.scoregso.org
Description: Serves as volunteer program in which working and retired business management professionals provide free business counseling to men and women who are considering starting a small business, encountering problems with their business, or expanding their business. Offers free one-on-one counseling, online counseling and low cost workshops on a variety of business topics.

52872 ■ SCORE Hendersonville
140 4th Ave. W
Hendersonville, NC 28792
Ph:(828)693-8702
Co. E-mail: hcounselors@scorewnc.org
URL: http://www.scorewnc.org
Description: Serves as volunteer program in which working and retired business management professionals provide free business counseling to men and women who are considering starting a small business, encountering problems with their business, or expanding their business. Offers free one-on-one counseling, online counseling and low cost workshops on a variety of business topics.

52873 ■ SCORE High Point
PO Box 5025
High Point, NC 27262
Ph:(336)882-8625
Fax:(336)889-9499
Co. E-mail: contact@highpointscore.org
URL: http://www.highpointscore.org
Description: Serves as volunteer program in which working and retired business management professionals provide free business counseling to men and women who are considering starting a small business, encountering problems with their business, or expanding their business. Offers free one-on-one counseling, online counseling and low cost workshops on a variety of business topics.

52874 ■ SCORE Raleigh
PO Box 406
Raleigh, NC 27602
Ph:(919)856-4739
Fax:(919)856-4466
Co. E-mail: contactus@raleighscore.org
URL: http://www.raleighscore.org
Description: Serves as volunteer program in which working and retired business management professionals provide free business counseling to men and women who are considering starting a small business, encountering problems with their business, or expanding their business. Offers free one-on-one counseling, online counseling and low cost workshops on a variety of business topics.

52875 ■ SCORE Sandhills Area - No. 364
c/o Chamber of Commerce
10677 US 15-501 Hwy.
Southern Pines, NC 28387
Ph:(910)692-3926
Co. E-mail: contact@sandhillsscore.org
URL: http://www.sandhillsscore.org
Description: Serves as volunteer program in which working and retired business management professionals provide free business counseling to men and women who are considering starting a small business, encountering problems with their business, or expanding their business. Offers free one-on-one counseling, online counseling and low cost workshops on a variety of business topics.

52876 ■ SCORE Wilmington
4010 Oleander Dr.
Wilmington, NC 28411
Ph:(910)452-5395
Fax:(910)452-5369
Co. E-mail: counselor@wilmingtonscore.org
URL: http://www.wilmingtonscore.org
Description: Serves as volunteer program in which working and retired business management professionals provide free business counseling to men and women who are considering starting a small business, encountering problems with their business, or expanding their business. Offers free one-on-one counseling, online counseling and low cost workshops on a variety of business topics.

BETTER BUSINESS BUREAUS

52877 ■ Better Business Bureau of Asheville/ Western North Carolina
112 Executive Park
Asheville, NC 28801
Ph:(828)253-2392
Fax:(828)252-5039
URL: http://www.asheville.bbb.org
Contact: Ms. Norma Messer, Pres.

52878 ■ Better Business Bureau of Eastern North Carolina
5540 Munford Rd., Ste. 130
Raleigh, NC 27612
Ph:(919)277-4222
Free: 800-222-0950
Fax:(919)277-4221
Co. E-mail: info@raleigh.bbb.org
URL: http://easternnc.bbb.org
Contact: Beverly D. Baskin, Pres./Ed.

52879 ■ Better Business Bureau of Northwest North Carolina
500 W 5th St., Ste. 202
Winston-Salem, NC 27101-2728
Ph:(336)725-8348
Free: 800-777-8348
Fax:(336)777-3727
Co. E-mail: info@nwncbbb.com
URL: http://www.winstonsalem.bbb.org
Contact: David W. Dalrymple, Pres./CEO

52880 ■ Better Business Bureau of Southern Piedmont
13860 Ballantyne Corporate Pl., Ste. 225
Charlotte, NC 28277
Ph:(704)927-8611
Free: 877-317-7236
Fax:(704)927-8615
Co. E-mail: info@charlotte.bbb.org
URL: http://charlotte.bbb.org
Contact: Tom Bartholomy, Pres./CEO

CHAMBERS OF COMMERCE

52881 ■ Alamance County Area Chamber of Commerce
PO Box 450
Burlington, NC 27216-0450
Ph:(336)228-1338
Fax:(336)228-1330
Co. E-mail: info@alamancechamber.com
URL: http://www.alamancechamber.com
Contact: Mac Williams, Pres.

52882 ■ Alexander County Chamber of Commerce
16 W Main Ave.
Taylorsville, NC 28681
Ph:(828)632-8141
Fax:(828)632-1096
Co. E-mail: delder@alexandercountychamber.com
URL: http://www.alexandercountychamber.com
Contact: Denise Elder, Exec. Dir.

52883 ■ Alleghany County Chamber of Commerce
58 S Main St.
PO Box 1237
Sparta, NC 28675
Ph:(336)372-5473
Free: 800-372-5473
Fax:(336)372-8251
Co. E-mail: director@sparta-nc.com
URL: http://www.sparta-nc.com
Contact: Bob Bamberg, Exec. Dir.

52884 ■ Andrews Chamber of Commerce
PO Box 800
Andrews, NC 28901
Ph:(828)321-3584
Free: 877-558-0005
Co. E-mail: info@andrewschamber.com
URL: http://www.andrewschambercommerce.com
Contact: Tom Nash, Co-Dir.

52885 ■ Angier Chamber of Commerce
24 E Depot St.
PO Box 47
Angier, NC 27501
Ph:(919)639-2500
Fax:(919)639-8826
Co. E-mail: angiercc@angierchamber.org
URL: http://www.angierchamber.org
Contact: Jamie Strickland, Exec. Dir.

52886 ■ Anson County Chamber of Commerce
PO Box 305
107-A E Wade St.
Wadesboro, NC 28170
Ph:(704)694-4181
Fax:(704)694-3830
Co. E-mail: ansonchamber@windstream.net
URL: http://www.ansoncounty.org
Contact: Lynn Edwards, Exec. Dir.

52887 ■ Apex Chamber of Commerce
220 N Salem St.
Apex, NC 27502
Ph:(919)362-6456
Free: 800-345-4504
Fax:(919)362-9050
Co. E-mail: info@apexchamber.com
URL: http://www.apexchamber.com
Contact: Brenda Steen, Exec. Dir.

52888 ■ Archdale-Trinity Chamber of Commerce
213 Balfour Dr.
Archdale, NC 27263
Ph:(336)434-2073
Fax:(336)431-5845
Co. E-mail: info@archdaletrinitychamber.com
URL: http://www.archdaletrinitychamber.com
Contact: Beverly M. Nelson, Pres.

52889 ■ Ashe County Chamber of Commerce and Visitors Center
PO Box 31
303 E Second St.
West Jefferson, NC 28694
Ph:(336)846-9550
Free: 888-343-2743
Fax:(336)846-8671
Co. E-mail: info@ashechamber.com
URL: http://www.ashechamber.com
Contact: Cabot Hamilton, Exec. Dir.

52890 ■ Asheboro/Randolph Chamber of Commerce
317 E Dixie Dr.
Asheboro, NC 27203
Ph:(336)626-2626
Fax:(336)626-7077
Co. E-mail: chamber@asheboro.com
URL: http://chamber.asheboro.com
Contact: George W. Gusler, Pres.

52891 ■ Asheville Area Chamber of Commerce
PO Box 1010
Asheville, NC 28802-1010
Ph:(828)258-6101
Fax:(828)251-0926
Co. E-mail: member@ashevillechamber.org
URL: http://www.ashevillechamber.org
Contact: Richard J. Lutovsky, Pres./CEO

52892 ■ Ayden Chamber of Commerce
PO Box 31
Ayden, NC 28513
Ph:(252)746-2266
Co. E-mail: chamber@ayden.com
URL: http://www.aydenchamber.com
Contact: Jennifer Barr, Pres./Exec. Dir.

52893 ■ Beech Mountain Area Chamber of Commerce
403-A Beech Mountain Pkwy.
Beech Mountain, NC 28604
Free: 800-468-5506
Co. E-mail: chamber@beechmtn.com
URL: http://www.beechmtn.com/portal
Contact: Peggy Coscia, Exec. Dir.

52894 ■ Belhaven Community Chamber of Commerce
125 W Main St.
PO Box 147
Belhaven, NC 27810-0147
Ph:(252)943-3770
Fax:(252)943-3769
Co. E-mail: info@belhavenchamber.com
URL: http://www.belhavenchamber.com
Contact: Margie Miller, Exec. Dir.

52895 ■ Benson Area Chamber of Commerce
303 E Church St.
PO Box 246
Benson, NC 27504-0246
Ph:(919)894-3825

Fax:(919)894-1052
Co. E-mail: loretta@benson-chamber.com
URL: http://www.benson-chamber.com
Contact: Loretta Byrd, Exec. Dir.

52896 ■ Black Mountain-Swannanoa Chamber of Commerce
201 E State St.
Black Mountain, NC 28711
Ph:(828)669-2300
Free: 800-669-2301
Fax:(828)669-1407
Co. E-mail: info@blackmountain.org
URL: http://www.blackmountain.org
Contact: Bob McMurray, Exec. Dir.

52897 ■ Blowing Rock Chamber of Commerce
PO Box 406
Blowing Rock, NC 28605
Ph:(828)295-7851
Free: 800-295-7851
Fax:(828)295-4643
Co. E-mail: hardince@blowingrock.com
URL: http://www.blowingrock.com/chamber.php
Contact: Charles Hardin, Exec. Dir.

52898 ■ Boone Area Chamber of Commerce
208 Howard St.
Boone, NC 28607-4032
Ph:(828)264-2225
Free: 800-852-9506
Fax:(828)264-6644
Co. E-mail: info@boonechamber.com
URL: http://www.boonechamber.com
Contact: Daniel F. Meyer, Pres./CEO

52899 ■ Brevard - Transylvania Chamber of Commerce
175 E Main St.
Brevard, NC 28712
Ph:(828)883-3700
Fax:(828)883-8550
Co. E-mail: brevchamber@citcom.net
URL: http://www.brevardncchamber.org
Contact: Tad Fogel, Pres.

52900 ■ Brunswick County Chamber of Commerce
PO Box 1185
Shallotte, NC 28459
Ph:(910)754-6644
Free: 800-426-6644
Fax:(910)754-6539
Co. E-mail: president@brunswickcountychamber.org
URL: http://www.brunswickcountychamber.org
Contact: Cathy Altman, Pres./CEO

52901 ■ Burke County Chamber of Commerce
110 E Meeting St.
Morganton, NC 28655
Ph:(828)437-3021
Fax:(828)437-1613
Co. E-mail: info@burkecounty.org
URL: http://www.burkecounty.org
Contact: Anissa Starnes, Pres./CEO

52902 ■ Caldwell County Chamber of Commerce
1909 Hickory Blvd. SE
Lenoir, NC 28645
Ph:(828)726-0616
Fax:(828)726-0385
Co. E-mail: visitors@caldwellcochamber.org
URL: http://www.caldwellcochamber.org
Contact: Deborah Ashley, Pres./CEO

52903 ■ Carteret County Chamber of Commerce
801 Arendell St., Ste. 1
Morehead City, NC 28557
Ph:(252)726-6350
Free: 800-622-6278
Fax:(252)726-3505
Co. E-mail: cart.coc@nccoastchamber.com
URL: http://www.nccoastchamber.com
Contact: Mike Wagoner, Pres.

52904 ■ Cary Chamber of Commerce
307 N Academy St.
Cary, NC 27513
Ph:(919)467-1016
Free: 800-919-CARY
Fax:(919)469-2375
Co. E-mail: info@carychamber.com
URL: http://www.carychamber.com
Contact: Howard S. Johnson, Pres.

52905 ■ Cashiers Area Chamber of Commerce
PO Box 238
Cashiers, NC 28717-0238
Ph:(828)743-5941
Co. E-mail: cashcham@dnet.net
URL: http://www.cashiers-nc.com

52906 ■ Caswell County Chamber of Commerce
PO Box 29
Yanceyville, NC 27379
Ph:(336)694-6106
Fax:(336)694-9983
Co. E-mail: sharon@caswellchamber.com
URL: http://www.caswellnc.com
Contact: Sharon Sexton, Dir.

52907 ■ Catawba County Chamber of Commerce
PO Box 1828
Hickory, NC 28603-1828
Ph:(828)328-6111
Fax:(828)328-1175
Co. E-mail: info@catawbachamber.org
URL: http://www.catawbachamber.org
Contact: Danny Hearn, Pres./CEO

52908 ■ Chapel Hill - Carrboro Chamber of Commerce
104 S Estes Dr.
PO Box 2897
Chapel Hill, NC 27515-2897
Ph:(919)967-7075
Fax:(919)968-6874
Co. E-mail: anelson@carolinachamber.org
URL: http://www.carolinachamber.org
Contact: Aaron Nelson, Pres./CEO

52909 ■ Charlotte Chamber of Commerce
330 S Tryon St.
PO Box 32785
Charlotte, NC 28232
Ph:(704)378-1300
Co. E-mail: awilliams@charlottechamber.com
URL: http://www.charlottechamber.com
Contact: Mr. Bob Morgan, Pres.

52910 ■ Chatham County United Chamber of Commerce
1609 E 11th St.
Siler City, NC 27344-2823
Ph:(919)742-3333
Fax:(919)742-1333
Co. E-mail: info@ccucc.net
URL: http://www.ccucc.net
Contact: Gary Kibler, Pres.

52911 ■ Cherokee Chamber of Commerce
PO Box 460
Cherokee, NC 28719-0460
Free: 800-438-1601
Fax:(828)497-8196
Co. E-mail: travel@nc-cherokee.com
URL: http://www.cherokee-nc.com/index.php-?page=290
Contact: Mary Jane Ferguson, Dir.

52912 ■ Cherokee County Chamber of Commerce
805 U.S. 64 W
Murphy, NC 28906
Ph:(828)837-2242
Fax:(828)837-6012
Co. E-mail: info@cherokeecountychamber.com
URL: http://www.cherokeecountychamber.com
Contact: Marvin Raper, Pres.

52913 ■ Cherryville Chamber of Commerce EDC
220 E Main St.
PO Box 305
Cherryville, NC 28021
Ph:(704)435-3451
Fax:(704)435-4200
Co. E-mail: chamber@cityofcherryville.com
URL: http://www.cherryvillechamber.com
Contact: Mr. Richard Randall, Exec. Dir.

52914 ■ Clay County Chamber of Commerce
388 Business Hwy. 64
PO Box 88
Hayesville, NC 28904-0088
Ph:(828)389-3704
Fax:(828)389-1033
Co. E-mail: info@ncmtnchamber.com
URL: http://www.ncmtnchamber.com
Contact: Marcile Smith, Exec. Dir.

52915 ■ Clayton Chamber of Commerce
301 E Main St.
PO Box 246
Clayton, NC 27520
Ph:(919)553-6352
Fax:(919)553-1758
Co. E-mail: chamber@claytonchamber.com
URL: http://www.claytonchamber.com
Contact: Sally Schlindwein, Exec. Dir.

52916 ■ Cleveland County Chamber of Commerce
PO Box 879
Shelby, NC 28150
Ph:(704)487-8521
Fax:(704)487-7458
Co. E-mail: info@clevelandchamber.org
URL: http://www.clevelandchamber.org
Contact: Michael Chrisawn, Pres.

52917 ■ Clinton-Sampson Chamber of Commerce
PO Box 467
Clinton, NC 28329-0467
Ph:(910)592-6177
Fax:(910)592-5770
Co. E-mail: info@clintonsampsonchamber.org
URL: http://www.clintonsampsonchamber.org
Contact: Ms. Amber Cava, Exec. Dir.

52918 ■ Davie County Chamber of Commerce
135 S Salisbury St.
Mocksville, NC 27028-2331
Ph:(336)751-3304
Fax:(336)751-5697
Co. E-mail: chamber@daviecounty.com
URL: http://www.daviecounty.com
Contact: Joan Carter, Pres.

52919 ■ Dunn Area Chamber of Commerce
209 W Divine St.
PO Box 548
Dunn, NC 28335
Ph:(910)892-4113
Fax:(910)892-4071
Co. E-mail: office@dunnchamber.com
URL: http://www.dunnchamber.com
Contact: Tammy Williams, Exec. VP

52920 ■ Eden Chamber of Commerce
678 S Van Buren Rd.
Eden, NC 27288
Ph:(336)623-3336
Fax:(336)623-8800
Co. E-mail: info@edenchamber.com
URL: http://www.edenchamber.com
Contact: Cindy Adams, Pres.

52921 ■ Edenton-Chowan Chamber of Commerce
116 E King St.
Edenton, NC 27932-0245
Ph:(252)482-3400
Free: 800-775-0111

Fax:(252)482-7093
Co. E-mail: richard.bunch@ncmail.net
URL: http://www.chowancounty-nc.gov
Contact: Richard Bunch, Exec. Dir.

52922 ■ Elizabeth City Area Chamber of Commerce
PO Box 426
Elizabeth City, NC 27907-0426
Ph:(252)335-4365
Fax:(252)335-5732
Co. E-mail: info@elizabethcitychamber.org
URL: http://www.elizabethcitychamber.org
Contact: Kelly Thorsby, Membership Dir.

52923 ■ Elizabethtown-White Lake Area Chamber of Commerce
103 E Broad St.
PO Box 306
Elizabethtown, NC 28337-0306
Ph:(910)862-4368
Fax:(910)862-4368
Co. E-mail: tourism28337@embarqmail.com
URL: http://www.elizabethtownwhitelake.com
Contact: Rich Glenn, Pres.

52924 ■ Fayetteville Chamber of Commerce
201 Hay St.
PO Box 9
Fayetteville, NC 28302-0009
Ph:(910)483-8133
Fax:(910)483-0263
Co. E-mail: dpeters@fayettevillencchamber.org
URL: http://www.fayettevillencchamber.org
Contact: Douglas S. Peters, Pres./CEO

52925 ■ Franklin Area Chamber of Commerce
425 Porter St.
Franklin, NC 28734
Ph:(828)524-3161
Free: (866)372-5546
Fax:(828)369-7516
Co. E-mail: facc@franklin-chamber.com
URL: http://www.franklin-chamber.com
Contact: Linda Harbuck, Exec. Dir.

52926 ■ Franklin County Chamber of Commerce
PO Box 62
Louisburg, NC 27549
Ph:(919)496-3056
Fax:(919)496-0422
Co. E-mail: mail@franklin-chamber.com
URL: http://www.franklin-chamber.com
Contact: Laureen Jones, Chair

52927 ■ Fuquay-Varina Area Chamber of Commerce
121 N Main St.
Fuquay Varina, NC 27526
Ph:(919)552-4947
Fax:(919)552-1029
Co. E-mail: andrew@fuquay-varina.com
URL: http://www.fuquay-varina.com
Contact: Ron Tropcich, Exec. Dir.

52928 ■ Garner Chamber of Commerce
401 Circle Dr.
Garner, NC 27529
Ph:(919)772-6440
Fax:(919)772-6443
Co. E-mail: info@garnerchamber.com
URL: http://www.garnerchamber.com/garner/index.
  html
Contact: Neal Padgett, Pres.

52929 ■ Gaston Chamber of Commerce
601 W Franklin Blvd.
Gastonia, NC 28052
Ph:(704)864-2621
Free: 800-348-8461
Fax:(704)854-8723
Co. E-mail: elyse@gastonchamber.com
URL: http://www.gastonchamber.com
Contact: Elyse Hillegass, Pres./CEO

52930 ■ Granville County Chamber of Commerce
PO Box 820
Oxford, NC 27565
Ph:(919)693-6125
Fax:(919)693-6126
Co. E-mail: granvillechamber@embarqmail.com
URL: http://www.granville-chamber.com
Contact: Johnny Blamer, Pres.

52931 ■ Greater Durham Chamber of Commerce
PO Box 3829
Durham, NC 27702-3829
Ph:(919)682-2133
Fax:(919)688-8351
Co. E-mail: info@durhamchamber.org
URL: http://www.durhamchamber.org
Contact: Bob Zimmer, COO

52932 ■ Greater Hampstead Chamber of Commerce
PO Box 211
Hampstead, NC 28443
Ph:(910)270-9642
Free: 800-833-2483
Fax:(910)270-4000
Co. E-mail: hampsteadcoc1@bellsouth.net
URL: http://www.hampsteadchamber.com
Contact: Pat Funigello, Pres.

52933 ■ Greater Hendersonville Chamber of Commerce
204 Kanuga Rd.
Hendersonville, NC 28739
Ph:(828)692-1413
Fax:(828)693-8802
Co. E-mail: chamber@hendersonvillechamber.org
URL: http://www.hendersonvillechamber.org
Contact: Robert R. Williford, Pres.

52934 ■ Greater Mount Airy Chamber of Commerce
200 N Main St.
PO Box 913
Mount Airy, NC 27030-0913
Ph:(336)786-6116
Free: 800-948-0949
Fax:(336)786-1488
Co. E-mail: admin@mtairyncchamber.org
URL: http://www.mtairyncchamber.org
Contact: Yvonne Nichols, Exec. Asst.

52935 ■ Greater Raleigh Chamber of Commerce
PO Box 2978
Raleigh, NC 27602-2978
Ph:(919)664-7000
Fax:(919)664-7097
Co. E-mail: hschmitt@the-chamber.org
URL: http://www.raleighchamber.org
Contact: Harvey A. Schmitt, Pres./CEO

52936 ■ Greater Smithfield-Selma Area Chamber of Commerce
1115 Industrial Park Dr.
PO Box 467
Smithfield, NC 27577-0467
Ph:(919)934-9166
Fax:(919)934-1337
Co. E-mail: rchildrey@smithfieldselma.com
URL: http://www.smithfieldselma.com
Contact: Richard Childrey, Pres.

52937 ■ Greater Topsail Area Chamber of Commerce and Tourism
PO Box 2486
Surf City, NC 28445
Ph:(910)329-4446
Free: 800-626-2780
Fax:(910)329-4432
Co. E-mail: info@topsailcoc.com
URL: http://www.topsailcoc.com
Contact: Allan W. Libby, Pres.

52938 ■ Greater Whiteville Chamber of Commerce
601 S Madison St.
Whiteville, NC 28472
Ph:(910)642-3171
Free: 888-533-7196
Fax:(910)642-6047
Co. E-mail: chambercow@weblnk.net
URL: http://www.whitevillechamber.org
Contact: Janice Young, Exec. VP

52939 ■ Greater Wilmington Chamber of Commerce
1 Estell Lee Pl.
Wilmington, NC 28401
Ph:(910)762-2611
Fax:(910)762-9765
Co. E-mail: info@wilmingtonchamber.org
URL: http://www.wilmingtonchamber.org
Contact: Connie Majure-Rhett CCE, Pres./CEO

52940 ■ Greater Winston-Salem Chamber of Commerce
601 W 4th St.
PO Box 1408
Winston-Salem, NC 27102
Ph:(336)728-9200
Fax:(336)721-2209
Co. E-mail: anderson@winstonsalem.com
URL: http://www.winstonsalem.com
Contact: Gayle N. Anderson, Pres./CEO

52941 ■ Greensboro Area Chamber of Commerce
342 N Elm St.
Greensboro, NC 27401
Ph:(336)387-8300
Fax:(336)275-9299
Co. E-mail: info@greensboro.org
URL: http://www.greensborochamber.com
Contact: Robert H. Clapper, Pres.

52942 ■ Greenville - Pitt County Chamber of Commerce
302 S Greene St.
Greenville, NC 27834-1564
Ph:(252)752-4101
Fax:(252)752-5934
Co. E-mail: chamber@greenvillenc.org
URL: http://www.greenvillenc.org
Contact: Susanne D. Sartelle CCE, Pres.

52943 ■ Havelock Chamber of Commerce
201 Tourist Center Dr.
PO Box 21
Havelock, NC 28532
Ph:(252)447-1101
Fax:(252)447-0241
Co. E-mail: info1@havelockchamber.net
Contact: Stephanie Duncan, Exec. Dir.

52944 ■ Haywood County Chamber of Commerce
591 N Main St.
PO Box 600
Waynesville, NC 28786-0600
Ph:(828)456-3021
Free: 877-456-3073
Fax:(828)452-7265
Co. E-mail: info@haywood-nc.com
URL: http://www.haywood-nc.com
Contact: CeCe Hipps, Exec. Dir.

52945 ■ Henderson-Vance County Chamber of Commerce
414 S Garnett St.
PO Box 1302
Henderson, NC 27536
Ph:(252)438-8414
Fax:(252)492-8989
Co. E-mail: chamber@hendersonvance.org
URL: http://www.hendersonvance.org
Contact: Bill Edwards, Pres.

52946 ■ Hickory Nut Gorge Chamber of Commerce
PO Box 32
Chimney Rock, NC 28720
Ph:(828)625-2725
Free: 877-625-2725
Fax:(828)625-9601
Co. E-mail: director@hickorynut.org
URL: http://www.hickorynut.org
Contact: Judy Beeson, Exec. Dir.

52947 ■ High Point Chamber of Commerce
1634 N Main St.
High Point, NC 27262
Ph:(336)882-5000
Fax:(336)889-9499
Co. E-mail: info@highpointchamber.org
URL: http://www.highpointchamber.org
Contact: Tom Dayvault, Pres.

52948 ■ Highlands Area Chamber of Commerce
PO Box 62
Highlands, NC 28741
Ph:(828)526-5841
Fax:(828)526-5803
Co. E-mail: president@highlandschamber.org
URL: http://www.highlandschamber.org
Contact: Bob Kieltyka, Exec. Dir.

52949 ■ Hillsborough/Orange County Chamber of Commerce
102 N Church St.
Hillsborough, NC 27278
Ph:(919)732-8156
Fax:(919)732-4566
Co. E-mail: info@hillsboroughchamber.com
URL: http://www.hillsboroughchamber.com
Contact: Margaret Wood Cannell, Exec. Dir.

52950 ■ Jackson County Chamber of Commerce
773 W Main St.
Sylva, NC 28779-8211
Ph:(828)586-2155
Free: 800-962-1911
URL: http://www.mountainlovers.com
Contact: Julie H. Spiro, Dir.

52951 ■ Jacksonville - Onslow Chamber of Commerce
1099 Gum Branch Rd.
Jacksonville, NC 28540
Ph:(910)347-3141
Fax:(910)347-4705
Co. E-mail: mpadrick@jacksonvilleonline.org
URL: http://www.jacksonvilleonline.org
Contact: Mona Padrick, Pres.

52952 ■ Kernersville Chamber of Commerce
136 E Mountain St.
Kernersville, NC 27284-2939
Ph:(336)993-4521
Fax:(336)993-3756
Co. E-mail: kchamber@kernersvillenc.com
URL: http://www.kernersvillenc.com
Contact: Bruce Boyer, Pres./CEO

52953 ■ King Chamber of Commerce
PO Box 863
King, NC 27021
Ph:(336)983-9308
Fax:(336)983-9526
Co. E-mail: kingchamber@windstream.net
URL: http://www.kingnc.com
Contact: Deanne M. Moore, Exec. Dir.

52954 ■ Kings Mountain - Branch of Cleveland County Chamber of Commerce
150 W Mountain St.
Kings Mountain, NC 28086-0794
Ph:(704)739-4755
Fax:(704)739-8149
Co. E-mail: shirley@clevelandchamber.org
URL: http://www.clevelandchamber.org
Contact: Michael Chrisawn, Pres.

52955 ■ Kinston-Lenoir County Chamber of Commerce
301 N Queen St.
PO Box 157
Kinston, NC 28502-0157
Ph:(252)527-1131
Fax:(252)527-1914
Co. E-mail: info@kinstonchamber.com
URL: http://www.kinstonchamber.com
Contact: Laura Lee Sylvester, Pres.

52956 ■ Knightdale Chamber of Commerce
PO Box 601
207 Main St.
Knightdale, NC 27545-0601
Ph:(919)266-4603
Fax:(919)266-8010
Co. E-mail: knightdalechamber@knightdalechamber.com
URL: http://www.knightdalechamber.com
Contact: Jennifer Bryan, Exec. Dir.

52957 ■ Lake Gaston Chamber of Commerce
2475 Eaton Ferry Rd.
Littleton, NC 27850
Ph:(252)586-5711
Free: (866)730-5711
Fax:(252)586-3152
Co. E-mail: lgcc@earthlink.net
URL: http://www.lakegastonchamber.com
Contact: Almira Papierniak, Exec. Dir.

52958 ■ Lake Norman Chamber and Convention and Visitors Bureau
19900 W Catawba Ave., Ste. 100
Cornelius, NC 28031
Ph:(704)892-1922
Fax:(704)892-5313
Co. E-mail: chamber@lakenorman.org
URL: http://www.lakenormanchamber.org
Contact: Bill Russell, Pres.

52959 ■ Laurinburg/Scotland County Area Chamber of Commerce
606 Atkinson St.
PO Box 1025
Laurinburg, NC 28353-1025
Ph:(910)276-7420
Fax:(910)277-8785
Co. E-mail: info@laurinburgchamber.com
URL: http://www.laurinburgchamber.com
Contact: Theresa Lamson, Pres.

52960 ■ Lillington Area Chamber of Commerce
PO Box 967
Lillington, NC 27546
Ph:(910)893-3751
Co. E-mail: contact@lillingtonchamber.org
URL: http://www.lillingtonchamber.org
Contact: Aneta Brewer, Sec.

52961 ■ Lincolnton-Lincoln County Chamber of Commerce
PO Box 1617
Lincolnton, NC 28093-1617
Ph:(704)735-3096
Fax:(704)735-5449
Co. E-mail: lincolnchambernc@bellsouth.net
URL: http://www.lincolnchambernc.org
Contact: Ken Kindley, Pres.

52962 ■ Lumberton Area Chamber of Commerce
PO Box 1008
Lumberton, NC 28359-1008
Ph:(910)739-4750
Fax:(910)671-9722
Co. E-mail: lumbertonchamber@bellsouth.net
URL: http://www.lumbertonchamber.com
Contact: Ray Shaw, Chm.

52963 ■ Maggie Valley Area Chamber of Commerce and Convention and Visitors' Bureau
PO Box 279
Maggie Valley, NC 28751
Ph:(828)926-1686

Free: 800-624-4431
Fax:(828)926-9398
Co. E-mail: cmaggie@maggievalley.org
URL: http://www.maggievalley.org
Contact: Ms. Lynn Collins, Exec. Dir.

52964 ■ Martin County Chamber of Commerce
419 E Blvd.
Williamston, NC 27892
Ph:(252)792-4131
Fax:(252)792-1013
Co. E-mail: info@martincountync.com
URL: http://www.martincountync.com
Contact: Ashley Dews Smith, Exec. Dir.

52965 ■ Matthews Chamber of Commerce
PO Box 601
Matthews, NC 28106-0601
Ph:(704)847-3649
Fax:(704)847-3364
Co. E-mail: tbwhitley@matthewschamber.com
URL: http://www.matthewschamber.com
Contact: Tina Whitley, Exec. Dir.

52966 ■ McDowell Chamber of Commerce
1170 W Tate St.
Marion, NC 28752-4487
Ph:(828)652-4240
Fax:(828)659-9620
Co. E-mail: mountains@mcdowellchamber.com
URL: http://www.mcdowellchamber.com
Contact: Rod Birdsong, Exec. Dir.

52967 ■ Mitchell County Chamber of Commerce
PO Box 858
Spruce Pine, NC 28777
Ph:(828)765-9483
Free: 800-227-3912
Fax:(828)765-9034
URL: http://www.mitchell-county.com
Contact: Shirley Hise, Exec. Dir.

52968 ■ Montgomery County Chamber of Commerce
444 N Main St.
PO Box 637
Troy, NC 27371-0637
Ph:(910)572-4300
Co. E-mail: chamber@montgomery-county.com
URL: http://montgomery-county.com
Contact: Judy Stevens, Dir.

52969 ■ Moore County Chamber of Commerce
10677 Hwy. 15-501
Southern Pines, NC 28387
Ph:(910)692-3926
Fax:(910)692-0619
Co. E-mail: info@moorecountychamber.com
URL: http://www.moorecountychamber.com
Contact: Patrick J. Coughlin, Pres./CEO

52970 ■ Mooresville-South Iredell Chamber of Commerce
PO Box 628
Mooresville, NC 28115
Ph:(704)664-3898
Fax:(704)664-2549
Co. E-mail: info@mooresvillenc.org
URL: http://www.mooresvillenc.org
Contact: Scott Melius, Chm.

52971 ■ Morrisville Chamber of Commerce
260 Town Hall Dr., Ste. A
Morrisville, NC 27560
Ph:(919)463-7150
Fax:(919)380-9021
Co. E-mail: chamber@morrisvillenc.com
URL: http://www.morrisvillenc.com
Contact: Sharon Rosche, Pres.

52972 ■ Mount Olive Area Chamber of Commerce
123 N Center St.
Mount Olive, NC 28365
Ph:(919)658-3113
Co. E-mail: moacc@bellsouth.net
URL: http://www.moachamber.com

52973 ■ New Bern Area Chamber of Commerce
PO Drawer C
New Bern, NC 28563-8503
Ph:(252)637-3111
Fax:(252)637-7541
Co. E-mail: kroberts@newbernchamber.com
URL: http://www.newbernchamber.com
Contact: Kevin Roberts, Pres.

52974 ■ Outer Banks Chamber of Commerce
101 Town Hall Dr.
PO Box 1757
Kill Devil Hills, NC 27948-1757
Ph:(252)441-8144
Fax:(252)441-0338
Co. E-mail: chamber@outer-banks.com
URL: http://www.outerbankschamber.com
Contact: John Bone, Pres.

52975 ■ Perquimans County Chamber of Commerce
118 W Market St.
Hertford, NC 27944
Ph:(252)426-5657
Fax:(252)426-7542
Co. E-mail: chamber@perquimans.com
URL: http://www.visitperquimans.com

52976 ■ Pleasure Island, Carolina Beach, and Kure Beach Chamber of Commerce
1121 N Lake Park Blvd.
Carolina Beach, NC 28428
Ph:(910)458-8434
Fax:(910)458-7969
Co. E-mail: visitor@pleasureislandnc.org
URL: http://www.pleasureislandnc.org
Contact: Gail McCloskey, Exec. Dir.

52977 ■ Polk County Chamber of Commerce
2753 Lynn Rd., Ste. A
Tryon, NC 28782
Ph:(828)859-6236
Fax:(828)859-2301
Co. E-mail: info@polkchamber.org
URL: http://www.polkchamber.org
Contact: Janet Wooley, Exec. Dir.

52978 ■ Raeford - Hoke Chamber of Commerce
101 N Main St.
Raeford, NC 28376
Ph:(910)875-5929
Fax:(910)875-1010
Co. E-mail: chamberhok@aol.com
URL: http://www.raefordhokechamber.com
Contact: Tony Santangelo, Pres.

52979 ■ Randleman Chamber of Commerce
PO Box 207
Randleman, NC 27317
Ph:(336)495-1100
Fax:(336)495-1133
URL: http://www.randlemanchamber.com
Contact: David Caughron, Exec. Dir.

52980 ■ Richmond County Chamber of Commerce
101 W Broad Ave.
Rockingham, NC 28379
Ph:(910)895-9058
Free: 800-858-1688
Fax:(910)895-9056
Co. E-mail: info@richmondcountychamber.com
URL: http://www.richmondcountychamber.com
Contact: Emily Tucker, Pres.

52981 ■ Roanoke Valley Chamber of Commerce
260 Premier Blvd.
Roanoke Rapids, NC 27870
Ph:(252)537-3513
Fax:(252)535-5767
Co. E-mail: bblackburn@rvchamber.com
URL: http://www.rvchamber.com
Contact: Allan Purser, Pres./CEO

52982 ■ Rocky Mount Area Chamber of Commerce
PO Box 392
Rocky Mount, NC 27802-0392
Ph:(252)446-0323
Fax:(252)446-5103
Co. E-mail: rmacc@rockymountchamber.org
URL: http://www.rockymountchamber.org
Contact: Eddie Baysden, CEO

52983 ■ Rowan County Chamber of Commerce
204 E Innes St.
PO Box 559
Salisbury, NC 28145-0559
Ph:(704)633-4221
Fax:(704)639-1200
Co. E-mail: info@rowanchamber.com
URL: http://www.rowanchamber.com

52984 ■ Roxboro Area Chamber of Commerce
211 N Main St.
Roxboro, NC 27573
Ph:(336)599-8333
Fax:(336)599-8336
Co. E-mail: chamber@roxboronc.com
URL: http://www.roxboronc.com
Contact: Marcia O'Neil, Pres./CEO

52985 ■ Rutherford County Chamber of Commerce
162 N Main St.
Rutherfordton, NC 28139-2502
Ph:(828)287-3090
Fax:(828)287-0799
Co. E-mail: info@rutherfordcoc.com
URL: http://www.rutherfordcoc.org
Contact: William L. Hall, Exec. Dir.

52986 ■ Southport-Oak Island Chamber of Commerce
4841 Long Beach Rd. SE
Southport, NC 28461-8712
Ph:(910)457-6964
Free: 800-457-6964
Fax:(910)457-0598
Co. E-mail: info@southport-oakisland.com
URL: http://www.southport-oakisland.com
Contact: Karen Sphar, Exec. VP

52987 ■ Spring Lake Area Chamber of Commerce
PO Box 333
Spring Lake, NC 28390
Ph:(910)497-8821
Fax:(910)497-1897
Co. E-mail: sprlkchamber@faynet.com
URL: http://www.springlakenc.org
Contact: George W. Williams Sr., Pres.

52988 ■ Stanly County Chamber of Commerce
116 E North St.
Albemarle, NC 28002-4048
Ph:(704)982-8116
Fax:(704)983-5000
Co. E-mail: info@stanlychamber.org
URL: http://www.stanlychamber.org
Contact: Tom Ramseur, Pres./CEO

52989 ■ Swain County Chamber of Commerce
210 Main St.
PO Box 509
Bryson City, NC 28713
Ph:(828)488-3681
Free: 800-867-9246

Fax:(828)488-6858
Co. E-mail: chamber@greatsmokies.com
URL: http://www.greatsmokies.com
Contact: Karen Wilmot, Dir.

52990 ■ Swedish-American Chamber of Commerce of the Carolinas
PO Box 18443
Raleigh, NC 27619
Ph:(919)412-4229
Fax:(919)782-0791
Co. E-mail: admin@saccofnc.org
URL: http://www.saccofnc.org
Contact: Thomas Swanson, Pres.

52991 ■ Tarboro - Edgecombe Chamber of Commerce
PO Drawer F
Tarboro, NC 27886
Ph:(252)823-7241
Fax:(252)823-1499
Co. E-mail: jbgarris@embarqmail.com
URL: http://www.tarborochamber.com
Contact: Sally Davis, Pres.

52992 ■ Union County Chamber of Commerce
903 Skyway Dr.
Monroe, NC 28111
Ph:(704)289-4567
Fax:(704)282-0122
Co. E-mail: info@unioncountycoc.com
URL: http://www.unioncountycoc.com
Contact: Jim Carpenter CCE, Pres.

52993 ■ Wake Forest Chamber of Commerce
350 S White St.
Wake Forest, NC 27587
Ph:(919)556-1519
Fax:(919)556-8570
Co. E-mail: info@wakeforestchamber.org
URL: http://www.wakeforestchamber.org
Contact: Jodi LaFreniere, Exec. Dir.

52994 ■ Wallace Chamber of Commerce
PO Box 427
Wallace, NC 28466
Ph:(910)285-4044
Fax:(910)285-3310
Co. E-mail: lou@wallacechamber.com
URL: http://www.wallacechamberofcommerce.com
Contact: Lou N. Powell, Dir.

52995 ■ Warsaw Chamber of Commerce
PO Box 585
Warsaw, NC 28398
Ph:(910)293-7804
Fax:(910)293-6773
Co. E-mail: warsawchamber@earthlink.net
URL: http://www.townofwarsawnc.com
Contact: Linda Kitchen, Exec. Dir.

52996 ■ Washington - Beaufort County Chamber of Commerce
PO Box 665
Washington, NC 27889
Ph:(252)946-9168
Co. E-mail: info@wbcchamber.com
URL: http://www.wbcchamber.com
Contact: Anne Crumpler, Asst. Dir.

52997 ■ Wayne County Chamber of Commerce
308 N William St.
Goldsboro, NC 27530
Ph:(919)734-2241
Fax:(919)734-2247
Co. E-mail: steveh@waynecountychamber.com
URL: http://www.waynecountychamber.com
Contact: Steve Hicks, Exec. Dir.

52998 ■ Wendell Chamber of Commerce
115 N Pine St.
PO Box 562
Wendell, NC 27591-0562
Ph:(919)365-6318

Fax:(919)366-2010
Co. E-mail: wendellcc@bellsouth.net
URL: http://www.wendellchamber.com
Contact: John Welch, Chm.

52999 ■ Western Rockingham Chamber of Commerce
112 W Murphy St.
Madison, NC 27025-1924
Ph:(336)548-6248
Fax:(336)548-4466
Co. E-mail: wrcc1@embarqmail.com
URL: http://www.westernrockinghamchamber.com
Contact: Donnie Joyce, Exec. Dir.

53000 ■ Wilkes Chamber of Commerce
717 Main St.
PO Box 727
North Wilkesboro, NC 28659
Ph:(336)838-8662
Fax:(336)838-3728
Co. E-mail: info@wilkesnc.org
URL: http://www.wilkesnc.org
Contact: Linda S. Cheek, Pres.

53001 ■ Wilson Chamber of Commerce
200 W Nash St.
PO Box 1146
Wilson, NC 27894-1146
Ph:(252)237-0165
Fax:(252)243-7931
Co. E-mail: lsoprun@wilsonncchamber.com
URL: http://www.wilsonncchamber.com
Contact: Lucille Soprun, Office Mgr.

53002 ■ Windsor/Bertie County Chamber of Commerce
102 N York St.
PO Box 572
Windsor, NC 27983-0572
Ph:(252)794-4277
Fax:(252)794-5070
Co. E-mail: windsorchamber@gate811.net
URL: http://windsorbertiechamber.com
Contact: Steve Wishall, Pres.

53003 ■ Yadkin County Chamber of Commerce
PO Box 1840
Yadkinville, NC 27055-1840
Ph:(336)679-2200
Fax:(336)679-3034
Co. E-mail: btodd@yadkinchamber.org
URL: http://www.yadkinchamber.org
Contact: Robert J. Todd, Dir.

53004 ■ Yadkin Valley Chamber of Commerce
PO Box 496
116 E Market St.
Elkin, NC 28621
Ph:(336)526-1111
Fax:(336)526-1879
Co. E-mail: lauretteleagon@yadkinvalley.org
URL: http://www.yadkinvalley.org
Contact: Laurette Leagon, Pres./CEO

53005 ■ Yancey County/Burnsville Chamber of Commerce
106 W Main St.
Burnsville, NC 28714
Ph:(828)682-7413
Free: 800-948-1632
Fax:(828)682-6599
Co. E-mail: info@yanceychamber.com
URL: http://www.yanceychamber.com
Contact: Miki Pontorno, Exec. Dir.

53006 ■ Zebulon Chamber of Commerce
PO Box 546
Zebulon, NC 27597
Ph:(919)269-6320
Fax:(919)269-6350
Co. E-mail: zebcoc@bellsouth.net
URL: http://www.zebulonchamber.org
Contact: Tammy J. Russo, Exec. Dir.

MINORITY BUSINESS ASSISTANCE PROGRAMS

53007 ■ Center for Economic Empowerment & Development–Women's Business Center of Fayetteville
230 Hay St.
Fayetteville, NC 28301
Ph:(910)323-3377
Fax:(910)323-8828
Co. E-mail: ceedinfo@ncceed.org
URL: http://www.ncceed.org
Contact: S. Ray, Exec Dir
Description: Works to promote the economic empowerment of women in North Carolina. Provides a variety of business ownership services.

53008 ■ North Carolina Cherokee Satellite Office–Native American Business Development Center
70 Woodfin Pl., Ste. 305
Park Place Offices
Asheville, NC 28801
Ph:(828)252-2516
Fax:(828)497-9009
Co. E-mail: ashevillebdc@yahoo.com
URL: http://www.mbda.gov Center

53009 ■ North Carolina Institute of Minority Economic Development–NC Minority Business Enterprise Center
114 W Parrish St.
Durham, NC 27701
Ph:(919)956-8889
Fax:(919)688-7668
Co. E-mail: info@ncimed.com
URL: http://www.ncimed.com
Contact: Farad Ali, Project Dir
Description: Provides finance management, access to capital, consulting, and procurement services to minority businesses in North Carolina.

FINANCING AND LOAN PROGRAMS

53010 ■ Academy Funds / Longleaf Venture Fund LLC
PO Box 99748
Raleigh, NC 27624
Ph:(919)991-5425
Fax:(919)991-5421
Co. E-mail: info@academyfunds.com
URL: http://www.academyfunds.com
Contact: Glenn Kline, Managing Partner
Investment Policies: Seed, start-up, early and first stage, and research and development. **Industry Preferences:** Communications and media, computer software and hardware, Internet specific, semiconductors and other electronics, biotechnology, medical and health, consumer related, industrial and energy, and transportation. **Geographic Preferences:** North Carolina. **Principal Exhibits:**

53011 ■ A.M. Pappas & Associates, LLC
PO Box 110287
Research Triangle Park, NC 27709
Ph:(919)998-3300
Fax:(919)998-3301
Co. E-mail: info@pappasventures.com
URL: http://www.pappasventures.com
Contact: Arthur M. Pappas, Managing Partner
E-mail: apappas@pappasventures.com
Preferred Investment Size: $100,000 to $6,000,000.
Investment Policies: Balanced, first, early, later, and second stage, and mezzanine. **Industry Preferences:** Medical and health, biotechnology, computer software and services, and Internet specific. **Geographic Preferences:** Mid Atlantic, Northeast, Northern California, Southeast, and West Coast U.S.; Ontario and Quebec, Canada. **Principal Exhibits:**

53012 ■ Aurora Funds, Inc.
3100 Tower Blvd., Ste. 1600
Durham, NC 27707
Ph:(919)484-0400

Fax:(919)484-0444
URL: http://www.aurorafunds.com
Contact: Scott Albert, Managing General Partner
Preferred Investment Size: $50,000 to $2,500,000.
Investment Types: Seed, start-up, and early stage.
Industry Preferences: Medical and health, Internet specific, computer software and services, biotechnology, semiconductors and other electronics, communications and other media, industrial and energy.
Geographic Preferences: Mid Atlantic and Southeast. **Principal Exhibits:**

53013 ■ Frontier Capital, LLC
1111 Metropolitan Ave., Ste. 1050
Charlotte, NC 28204
Ph:(704)414-2880
Fax:(704)414-2881
URL: http://www.frontierfunds.com
Contact: Richard Maclean, Managing Partner
E-mail: richard@frontiercapital.com
Preferred Investment Size: $5,000,000 to $15,000,000. **Investment Types:** First and second stage, expansion, and balanced. **Industry Preferences:** Internet specific, Communications, computer software, medical and health, financial services, and business service. **Geographic Preferences:** Mid Atlantic, South, and Southeast. **Principal Exhibits:**

53014 ■ Intersouth Partners
406 Blackwell St., Ste. 200
Durham, NC 27701
Ph:(919)493-6640
Fax:(919)493-6649
Co. E-mail: contact@intersouth.com
URL: http://www.intersouth.com
Contact: Dennis Dougherty, Venture Partner
Preferred Investment Size: $500,000 to $6,000,000.
Investment Types: Seed and early stage. **Industry Preferences:** Medical and health, biotechnology, Internet specific, computer software and services, industrial and energy, semiconductors and other electronics, other products, computer hardware, communications and media, and consumer related. **Geographic Preferences:** Southeast. **Principal Exhibits:**

53015 ■ MCNC Ventures LLC
3021 Cornwallis Rd.
PO Box 12889
Research Triangle Park, NC 27709-2889
Ph:(919)248-1900
Fax:(919)248-1101
URL: http://www.mcnc.org
Contact: Joe Freddoso, President and Chief Executive Officer
E-mail: joe@mcnc.org
Investment Policies: Seed and early stage. **Industry Preferences:** Communications. **Geographic Preferences:** North Carolina. **Principal Exhibits:**

53016 ■ The North Carolina Enterprise Fund, L.P.
3600 Glenwood Ave., Ste. 107
Raleigh, NC 27612
Ph:(919)781-2691
Fax:(919)783-9195
Co. E-mail: info@ncef.com
URL: http://www.ncef.com
Preferred Investment Size: $2,000,000 minimum.
Investment Types: Start-up, first stage, and mezzanine. **Industry Preferences:** Medical and health, communications and media, computer software and services, biotechnology, computer hardware, other products, Internet specific, semiconductors and other electronics, and consumer related. **Geographic Preferences:** North Carolina and Southeast. **Principal Exhibits:**

53017 ■ Southern Capitol Ventures
21 Glenwood Ave., Ste. 105
Raleigh, NC 27603
Ph:(919)858-7580
Fax:(919)863-2394
Co. E-mail: info@southerncapitalventures.com
URL: http://www.southerncapitolventures.com
Contact: Benjamin Brooks, Founding Partner
Preferred Investment Size: $500,000 to $1,500,000.
Investment Types: Seed and early stage. **Industry Preferences:** Semiconductors and other electronics,

computer software and services, Internet specific, communications and media. **Geographic Preferences:** Southeast and Mid Atlantic. **Principal Exhibits:**

53018 ■ The Sustainable Jobs Fund / SJF Ventures
200 N. Mangum St., Ste. 203
Durham, NC 27701
Ph:(919)530-1177
Fax:(919)530-1178
URL: http://www.sjfund.com
Contact: David Griest, Managing Director
E-mail: dgriest@sjfund.com
Preferred Investment Size: $1,000,000 to $2,000,000. **Investment Types:** Early, first and second stage, expansion, and private placement. **Industry Preferences:** Computer software, semiconductors and other electronics, medical and health, consumer related, industrial and energy, business service, manufacturing, and utilities. **Geographic Preferences:** U.S. **Principal Exhibits:**

53019 ■ Truepilot, LLC
2505 Meridian Pky., Ste. 250
Durham, NC 27713
Ph:(919)433-3705
Fax:(919)433-3719
Co. E-mail: foundation@b-a.org
URL: http://www.b-a.org
Contact: Michael Brader-Araje, Chief Executive Officer
Preferred Investment Size: $50,000 to $500,000.
Investment Types: Early stage. **Industry Preferences:** Internet specific. **Geographic Preferences:** North Carolina. **Principal Exhibits:**

PROCUREMENT ASSISTANCE PROGRAMS

53020 ■ North Carolina Department of Administration–Purchase and Contract Division–State Purchasing Office (1305)
1305 Mail Service Center
Raleigh, NC 27699-1305
Ph:(919)807-4500
Fax:(919)807-4502
Co. E-mail: doa.pchelpdesk@ncmail.net
URL: http://www.doa.state.nc.us/PandC/
Contact: James D. Staton, Dir

53021 ■ North Carolina Small Business and Technology Development Center–SBTDC Regional Office
1612 Military Cutoff Rd., Ste. 208
Wilmington, NC 28403-5977
Ph:(910)962-3744
Co. E-mail: uncw@sbtdc.org
URL: http://www.sbtdc.org
Contact: Fran Scarlett, Regional Dir.
Description: Helps businesses obtain contracts by providing comprehensive assistance in selling products and services to local, state and federal government entities.

INCUBATORS/RESEARCH AND TECHNOLOGY PARKS

53022 ■ Babcock Demon Incubator
Wake Forest University
3455 University Pky.
Winston-Salem, NC 27106
Ph:(336)758-5422
Free: (866)925-3622
Fax:(336)758-5830
Co. E-mail: email-bdi@wfubdi.org
URL: http://www.wfubdi.org/
Description: A small business incubator whose mission is to foster entrepreneurial education at Wake Forest and an entrepreneurial spirit in the Triad by providing personalized services and relationships to growth-oriented, early stage ventures. It offers office space, Internet access, and business resources for growing companies.

53023 ■ Ben Craig Center Incubator & Accelerator
8701 Mallard Creek Rd.
Charlotte, NC 28262
Ph:(704)548-9113
Fax:(704)602-2179
Co. E-mail: contact@bencraigcenter.com
URL: http://bencraigcenter.com/site/index.cfm
Contact: Paul Wetenhall, Pres.
Description: A small business incubator providing state-of-the-art office space to the region's most promising companies in order to accelerate their growth by offering them advisory services, mentoring relationships, sales and marketing expertise and access to capital.

53024 ■ Fayetteville Business Center
2520 Murchison Rd.
Fayetteville, NC 28301
Ph:(910)222-8900
Fax:(910)222-8910
Co. E-mail: fshorter@uncfsu.edu
URL: http://www.fayettevillebusinesscenter.com/
Contact: Floyd Shorter, Dir.
Description: A small business incubator promoting economic development in the City of Fayetteville and the Murchison Road corridor by providing nurturing to entrepreneurs and business assistance in the growth and development of small business concerns and promoting a healthy entrepreneurial spirit for the growth and economic renewal of the community.

53025 ■ First Flight Venture Center
2 Davis Dr.
PO Box 13169
Research Triangle Park, NC 27709-3169
Ph:(919)990-8558
Fax:(919)558-0156
Co. E-mail: jdraper@nctda.org
URL: http://www.ffvcn.org
Contact: John Draper, Pres & CEO
Description: A technology incubator serving entrepreneurs and early-stage businesses in the Research Triangle Park area.

53026 ■ MCNC Research and Development
3021 Cornwallis Rd.
Durham, NC 27709
Ph:(919)248-1900
Fax:(919)248-1101
URL: http://www.mcnc.org
Contact: John Crites, Pres & CEO
Description: Promotes the use and development of electronic and information technologies by providing advanced research facilities in North Carolina's universities.

53027 ■ North Carolina A&T State University–Division of Research and Economic Development
1601 E Market St.
Greensboro, NC 27411
Ph:(336)334-7995
Fax:(336)334-7086
Co. E-mail: radha@ncat.edu
URL: http://research.ncat.edu
Contact: Dr. N. Radhakrishnan
E-mail: radha@ncat.edu
Scope: Administers and coordinates extramurally supported research in various departments of the University, including studies in nutrition, human resources, engineering, manpower, and urban mass transportation.

53028 ■ Nussbaum Center for Entrepreneurship
2007 Yanceyville St.
Greensboro, NC 27405
Ph:(336)379-5001
Fax:(336)379-5020
Co. E-mail: director@nussbaumcfe.com
URL: http://www.nussbaumcfe.com/
Description: A small business incubator designed to support non-retail, new or emerging businesses by providing modestly-priced office and light manufacturing space, along with shared support services such as business counseling, a receptionist, copier, fax, mail boxes, and data entry.

53029 ■ Research Triangle Foundation of North Carolina–Research Triangle Park
12 Davis Dr.
PO Box 12255
Research Triangle Park, NC 27709
Ph:(919)549-8181
Fax:(919)549-8246
Co. E-mail: parkinfo@rtp.org
URL: http://www.rtp.org
Contact: Liz Rooks, Interim CEO/Pres.
E-mail: parkinfo@rtp.org
Scope: Telecommunications, microelectronics, environmental research, materials science, biotechnology, pharmaceuticals, chemistry, nanotechnology, and software and hardware development. Facilitates interaction between industrial and governmental research and development organizations with the research communities of the three universities. **Publications:** Viewpoints (quarterly).

EDUCATIONAL PROGRAMS

53030 ■ Caldwell Community College and Technical Institute–Small Business Center
2855 Hickory Blvd.
Hudson, NC 28638
Ph:(828)726-2200
Fax:(828)726-2472
URL: http://www.cccti.edu
Description: Seminars, workshops, and management consultation are available for small business owners.

53031 ■ Sandhills Community College
3395 Airport Rd.
Pinehurst, NC 28374
Ph:(910)692-6185

Free: 800-338-3944
Fax:(910)695-1823
Co. E-mail: neelym@sandhills.edu
URL: http://www.sandhills.edu
Description: Offers many business-related and personal enrichment classes, both at the college and at various off-campus sites. A Small Business Center has been established to attract, train, counsel, and provide educational services to small business owners or individuals interested in establishing small businesses in the area.

53032 ■ South College
1567 Patton Ave.
Asheville, NC 28806
Ph:(828)252-2486
Fax:(828)252-8558
Co. E-mail: ecue@cecilscollege.com
URL: http://www.southcollegenc.com
Description: Offers a program in small business administration.

53033 ■ Wilson Technical Community College–Small Business Center
PO Box 4305
902 Herring Ave.
Wilson, NC 27893
Ph:(252)291-1195
Fax:(252)243-7148
URL: http://www.wilsontech.cc.nc.us
Description: Provides consultative services, resource information, and a variety of seminars, workshops, and courses to assist in the development of new businesses and the success of existing businesses.

PUBLICATIONS

53034 ■ *Smart Start your North Carolina Business*
PSI Research
300 N. Valley Dr.
Grants Pass, OR 97526
Ph:(503)479-9464
Free: 800-228-2275
Fax:(503)476-1479
Co. E-mail: info@psi-research.com
URL: http://www.psi-research.com
Ed: Michael D. Jenkins. **Released:** Revised edition, 1992. **Price:** $29.95 (looseleaf binder); $24.95 (paper). **Description:** Part of the Successful Business Library series.

PUBLISHERS

53035 ■ International Puzzle Features
4507 Panther Pl.
Charlotte, NC 28269
Ph:(704)921-1818
Fax:(704)597-1331
Co. E-mail: drfun@cleverpuzzles.com
URL: http://www.cleverpuzzles.com
Contact: Pat Battaglia, Publisher
E-mail: publisher@cleverpuzzles.com
Description: Publishes books of clever word games with surprising answers and amusing features for readers of all ages. Also provides a weekly variety puzzle/game column to newspapers. Accepts submissions of individual puzzles/games, not columns. Send for Writers Guidelines with SASE. Refer to web site for samples. Reaches market through reviews, listings, and distributors and wholesalers. **Founded:** 1990.

SMALL BUSINESS DEVELOPMENT CENTERS

53036 ■ North Dakota Small Business Development Center - Belcourt
Box 900
Belcourt, ND 58316
Co. E-mail: hamleyb@utma.com
URL: http://www.ndsbdc.org
Contact: Betty Hamley, Consultant

53037 ■ North Dakota Small Business Development Center - Bismarck
Bank of North Dakota Bldg.
1200 Memorial Hwy.
Bismarck, ND 58504
Co. E-mail: nancy@dakotamep.com
URL: http://www.ndsbdc.org
Contact: Nancy Krogen-Abel, Regional Dir.

53038 ■ North Dakota Small Business Development Center - Devils Lake
PO Box 651
Devils Lake, ND 58301
Fax:(701)662-8132
Co. E-mail: barbncpc@gondtc.com
URL: http://www.ndsbdc.org
Contact: Barbara Britsch, Consultant

53039 ■ North Dakota Small Business Development Center - Dickinson
Strom Center for Entrepreneurship & Innovation
1679 6th Ave. W
Dickinson, ND 58601
Co. E-mail: rayann@goinnovative.us
URL: http://www.ndsbdc.org
Contact: Ray Ann Kilen, Regional Dir.

53040 ■ North Dakota Small Business Development Center - Fargo
51 N Broadway, Ste. 505
Fargo, ND 58102
Co. E-mail: djwadholm@dakotamep.com
URL: http://www.ndsbdc.org
Contact: Donovan Wadholm, Regional Dir.

53041 ■ North Dakota Small Business Development Center - Fort Yates
1341 92nd St.
Fort Yates, ND 58538
Co. E-mail: jonathana@sbci.edu
URL: http://www.ndsbdc.org
Contact: Jonathan Anderson, Mgr.

53042 ■ North Dakota Small Business Development Center - Grand Forks
600 Demers Ave., Ste. 501
Grand Forks, ND 58201
Co. E-mail: joklug@nd.gov
URL: http://www.ndsbdc.org
Contact: Josh Klug, Consultant

53043 ■ North Dakota Small Business Development Center - Jamestown
120 2nd St. SE
Jamestown, ND 58402
Co. E-mail: scdrc@daktel.com
URL: http://www.ndsbdc.org
Contact: Deb Kantrud, Regional Dir.

53044 ■ North Dakota Small Business Development Center - Minot
1925 S Broadway, Ste. 2
Minot, ND 58703
Co. E-mail: marybethv@dakotamep.com
URL: http://www.ndsbdc.org
Contact: Mary Beth Votava, Regional Dir.

SMALL BUSINESS ASSISTANCE PROGRAMS

53045 ■ North Dakota Department of Commerce–Division of Economic Development and Finance
PO Box 2057
Bismarck, ND 58502-2057
Ph:(701)328-5300
Fax:(701)328-5320
Co. E-mail: plucy@nd.gov
URL: http://www.growingnd.com
Contact: Paul Lucy, Dir
Description: Encourages the establishment of new businesses and industries and assists new and expanding businesses with information and location decisions.

53046 ■ University of North Dakota–Center for Innovation
Ina Mae Rude Entrepreneur Center
4200 James Ray Dr.
Grand Forks, ND 58203
Ph:(701)777-3132
Fax:(701)777-2339
Co. E-mail: askme@innovators.net
URL: http://www.innovators.net
Contact: Bruce Gjovig, Dir
Description: Provides technical and business support services to entrepreneurs, inventors, and small manufacturers. Assists specifically with the product evaluation process, the patenting process, and technology transfer.

SCORE OFFICES

53047 ■ SCORE Bismarck-Mandan
PO Box 5509
Bismarck, ND 58506-5509
Ph:(701)328-5861
Fax:(701)328-5861
Co. E-mail: score365@btinet.net
Description: Provides entrepreneur education for the formation, growth and success of small businesses in the area.

53048 ■ SCORE Fargo
51 Broadway, Ste. 505
Fargo, ND 58108
Ph:(701)239-5677
Fax:(701)237-9734
Co. E-mail: info@fargoscore.org
URL: http://www.fargoscore.org
Contact: Joel Simons, Pres.
Description: Provides entrepreneur education for the formation, growth and success of small businesses in the area.

53049 ■ SCORE Minot
1925 S Broadway, Ste. 2
Minot, ND 58701
Ph:(701)852-6883
Fax:(701)852-6905
Co. E-mail: scoreminot1@srt.com
Description: Provides entrepreneur education for the formation, growth and success of small businesses in the area.

53050 ■ SCORE Upper Red River
1501 28th Ave. S
Grand Forks, ND 58201-6727
Ph:(701)746-5851
Fax:(701)746-5748
Co. E-mail: score@gra.midco.net
Description: Provides entrepreneur education for the formation, growth and success of small businesses in the area.

CHAMBERS OF COMMERCE

53051 ■ Beulah Chamber of Commerce
120 Central Ave. N
PO Box 730
Beulah, ND 58523-0730
Ph:(701)873-4585
Free: 800-441-2649
Fax:(701)873-5361
Co. E-mail: chamber@westriv.com
URL: http://www.beulahnd.org

53052 ■ Bismarck-Mandan Chamber of Commerce
PO Box 1675
Bismarck, ND 58502-1675
Ph:(701)223-5660
Fax:(701)255-6125
Co. E-mail: info@bismarckmandan.com
URL: http://www.bismarckmandan.com
Contact: Kelvin Hullet, Pres.

53053 ■ Bowman Area Chamber of Commerce
PO Box 1143
Bowman, ND 58623
Ph:(701)523-5880
Free: (866)752-2691
Fax:(701)523-3322
Co. E-mail: chamber@bowmannd.com
URL: http://www.bowmannd.com
Contact: Teran Doerr, Office Mgr.

53054 ■ Carrington Area Chamber of Commerce
871 Main St.
PO Box 439
Carrington, ND 58421
Ph:(701)652-2524
Free: 800-641-9668
Fax:(701)652-2391
Co. E-mail: cgtncham@daktel.com
URL: http://www.cgtn-nd.com
Contact: Laurie Dietz, Exec. Dir.

53055 ■ Cavalier Area Chamber of Commerce
301 Division Ave. N
PO Box 271
Cavalier, ND 58220-0271
Ph:(701)265-8188
Fax:(701)265-8720
Co. E-mail: cacc@polarcomm.com
URL: http://www.cavaliernd.com

53056 ■ Chamber of Commerce of Fargo Moorhead
PO Box 2443
Fargo, ND 58108-2443
Ph:(218)233-1100
Fax:(218)233-1200
Co. E-mail: info@fmchamber.com
URL: http://www.fmchamber.com
Contact: David K. Martin, Pres./CEO

53057 ■ Devils Lake Area Chamber of Commerce
208 Hwy. 2 W
PO Box 879
Devils Lake, ND 58301-0879
Ph:(701)662-4903
Free: 800-233-8048
Fax:(701)662-2147
Co. E-mail: chamber@gondtc.com
URL: http://www.devilslakend.com
Contact: John Campbell, Pres.

53058 ■ Dickinson Area Chamber of Commerce
314 3rd Ave. W
PO Box C
Dickinson, ND 58601
Ph:(701)225-5115
Fax:(701)225-5116
Co. E-mail: team@dickinsonchamber.org
URL: http://www.dickinsonchamber.org
Contact: Lexi Sebastian, Exec. Dir.

53059 ■ Geographical Center of North America Chamber of Commerce
224 Hwy. 2 SW
Rugby, ND 58368-2426
Ph:(701)776-5846
Fax:(701)776-6390
Co. E-mail: rugbychamber@stellarnet.com
URL: http://www.rugbynorthdakota.com
Contact: Sonia Mullally, Pres.

53060 ■ Grafton Area Chamber of Commerce
432 Hill Ave.
Grafton, ND 58237
Ph:(701)352-0781
Fax:(701)352-3043
Co. E-mail: gracha@polarcomm.com
URL: http://www.graftonchamber.com
Contact: Dan Kohler, Pres.

53061 ■ Grand Forks Chamber of Commerce
202 N 3rd St.
Grand Forks, ND 58203-3733
Ph:(701)772-7271
Fax:(701)772-9238
Co. E-mail: info@gochamber.org
URL: http://www.gfchamber.com
Contact: Rich Becker, Dir.

53062 ■ Greater Bottineau Area Chamber of Commerce
519 Main St.
Bottineau, ND 58318-1202
Ph:(701)228-3849

Free: 800-735-6932
Fax:(701)228-5130
Co. E-mail: bcc@utma.com
URL: http://bottineau.org
Contact: Clint M. Reinoehl, Exec. Dir.

53063 ■ Harvey Area Chamber of Commerce
120 W 8th St., Ste. 3
Harvey, ND 58341
Ph:(701)324-2604
Fax:(701)324-2674
Co. E-mail: chamber@harveynd.com
URL: http://www.harveynd.com
Contact: Ms. Sara Balfour, Exec. VP

53064 ■ Hazen Chamber of Commerce
PO Box 423
Hazen, ND 58545
Ph:(701)748-6848
Free: 888-464-2936
Fax:(701)748-2559
Co. E-mail: hazenchamber@westriv.com
URL: http://www.hazennd.org
Contact: Myra Axtman, Exec. Dir.

53065 ■ Hettinger Area Chamber of Commerce
PO Box 1031
Hettinger, ND 58639-1031
Ph:(701)567-2531
Fax:(701)567-2690
Co. E-mail: adamschmbr@ndsupernet.com
URL: http://www.hettingernd.com
Contact: Earleen Friez, Sec.

53066 ■ Jamestown Area Chamber of Commerce
120 2nd St. SE
PO Box 1530
Jamestown, ND 58402
Ph:(701)252-4830
Fax:(701)252-4837
Co. E-mail: info@jamestownchamber.com
URL: http://www.jamestownchamber.com
Contact: JoDee Rasmusson, Exec. Dir.

53067 ■ Kenmare Association of Commerce
PO Box 896
Kenmare, ND 58746
Ph:(701)385-4275
Fax:(701)385-4395
Co. E-mail: news@kenmarend.com
URL: http://www.kenmarend.com
Contact: Troy Hedbeg, Pres.

53068 ■ Linton Industrial Development Corporation
PO Box 433
Linton, ND 58552
Ph:(701)254-4267
Fax:(701)254-4382
Co. E-mail: lidcbek@bektel.com
URL: http://lintonnd.org
Contact: Sharon Jangula, Coor.

53069 ■ North Dakota Chamber of Commerce
PO Box 2639
Bismarck, ND 58502-2639
Ph:(701)222-0929
Free: 800-382-1405
Fax:(701)222-1611
Co. E-mail: ndchamber@ndchamber.com
URL: http://www.ndchamber.com
Contact: Dave MacIver, Pres.

53070 ■ Oakes Area Chamber of Commerce
412 Main Ave.
Oakes, ND 58474
Ph:(701)742-3508
Co. E-mail: oakesnd@drtel.net
URL: http://www.oakesnd.com/chamber.php
Contact: Ptacek Finacial, Co-Pres.

53071 ■ Valley City Area Chamber of Commerce/CVB
PO Box 724
Valley City, ND 58072-0724
Ph:(701)845-1891

Fax:(701)845-1892
Co. E-mail: chamber@hellovalley.com
URL: http://www.hellovalley.com/valleycity
Contact: Dean Ihla

53072 ■ Wahpeton Breckenridge Area Chamber of Commerce and Visitors Center
118 6th St. N
Wahpeton, ND 58075-4327
Ph:(701)642-8744
Free: 800-892-6673
Fax:(701)642-8745
Co. E-mail: info@wahpetonbreckenridgechamber.com
URL: http://www.wahpetonbreckenridgechamber.com
Contact: Jim Oliver, Exec. VP

53073 ■ Walhalla Area Chamber of Commerce
PO Box 34
Walhalla, ND 58282
Ph:(701)549-3939
Fax:(701)549-2410
Co. E-mail: walchmbr@utma.com
URL: http://walhalland.org
Contact: Melanie Thornberg, Exec. Dir.

53074 ■ Watford City Area Chamber of Commerce
PO Box 458
Watford City, ND 58854-0458
Ph:(701)444-2526
Fax:(701)444-2526
Co. E-mail: tforeman@ruggedwest.com
URL: http://www.4eyes.net/ChamberofCommerce
Contact: Mandy Foreman

53075 ■ West Fargo Chamber of Commerce
PO Box 753
West Fargo, ND 58078-0753
Ph:(701)282-4444
Fax:(701)282-3665
Co. E-mail: member5@westfargochamber.com
URL: http://www.westfargochamber.com
Contact: Chris Barton, Exec. Dir.

53076 ■ Williston Area Chamber of Commerce
10 Main St.
PO Box G
Williston, ND 58802
Ph:(701)577-6000
Fax:(701)577-8591
Co. E-mail: wchamber@willistonchamber.net
URL: http://www.willistonchamber.net/default.aspx-?AspxAutoDetectCookieSupport=1
Contact: Diane Hagen, Exec. Dir.

MINORITY BUSINESS ASSISTANCE PROGRAMS

53077 ■ North Dakota/South Dakota Native American Business Enterprise Center
3315 University Dr., Bldg. 61
Bismarck, ND 58504
Ph:(701)530-0608
Fax:(701)530-0607
Co. E-mail: bmaxon@uttc.edu
URL: http://www.ndsd-nabec.com
Contact: Brek Maxon, Project Dir
Description: Offers management and technical assistance services to Native American businesses.

PROCUREMENT ASSISTANCE PROGRAMS

53078 ■ Fargo Small Business Development Center-University of North Dakota
51 N Broadway, Ste. 505
Fargo, ND 58102
Ph:(701)235-1495
Free: 800-698-5726
Fax:(701)235-9734
Co. E-mail: djwadholm@dakotamep.com
URL: http://www.ndsbdc.org
Contact: Donovan Wadholm, Dir

53079 ■ North Dakota Economic Development and Finance Department–Procurement Division
State Capital Tower, 14th Fl.
600 E Boulevard Ave., Dept. 012
Bismarck, ND 58505-0310
Ph:(701)328-2683
Fax:(701)328-1615
Co. E-mail: infospo@nd.gov
URL: http://www.nd.gov/spo/
Contact: Nancy Abfalter, Procurement Officer
Description: Helps businesses obtain federal, state, and local government contracts.

INCUBATORS/RESEARCH AND TECHNOLOGY PARKS

53080 ■ NDSU Research & Technology Park
1854 NDSU Research Cir. N
Fargo, ND 58102
Ph:(701)499-3600
Fax:(701)499-3610
Co. E-mail: tony@ndsuresearchpark.com
URL: http://www.ndsuresearchpark.com/Pages/
default.aspx
Contact: Tony S, Grindberg, Dir.
Description: A small business incubator whose mission is to be a hub of technology entrepreneurship in Fargo-Moorhead and the region by providing proactive, value-added support to startup companies.

53081 ■ North Dakota State University–Upper Great Plains Transportation Institute–North Dakota Local Technical Assistance Program (515 1)
515 1/2 E Broadway, Ste. 101
Bismarck, ND 58501
Ph:(701)328-9855
Free: 800-726-4143
Fax:(701)328-9866
Co. E-mail: ndsu.ndltap@ndsu.edu
URL: http://www.ndltap.org/
Contact: Dr. Donald Anderson, Dir
E-mail: theusch@planis.nodak.edu
Description: Enables North Dakota businesses to use the most advanced technologies available.

53082 ■ Regional Small Business Center
417 Main Ave.
Fargo, ND 58103
Ph:(701)235-7885

Fax:(701)235-6706
Co. E-mail: don@lakeagassiz.com
URL: http://www.lakeagassiz.com/rsbc/rsbcmain.html
Contact: Don Litch, Operations Mgr.
Description: A non-profit business incubator operated by the Lake Agassiz Regional Development Corporation, Fargo, North Dakota whose purpose is to assist new and existing smaller businesses in critical areas such as management, marketing, manufacturing and finance. The Center provides attractive, cost-effective space and administrative support services to its tenants.

53083 ■ University of North Dakota–Vice President for Research
Twamley Hall, Rm. 103
264 Centennial Dr., Stop 8367
Grand Forks, ND 58202-8367
Ph:(701)777-6736
Fax:(701)777-2193
Co. E-mail: phyllis.e.johnson@research.und.edu
URL: http://und.edu/research/research-economic-
development
Contact: Phyllis E. Johnson PhD, VP for Res. and
Economic Devel.
E-mail: phyllis.e.johnson@research.und.edu
Scope: Promotes research and scholarly activity and reviews all proposals for compliance with fiscal and general University policies. Provides information on funding sources for research, fellowships, and other programs sponsored by outside agencies. Also provides assistance to the Senate Scholarly Activities Committee and to several institutional compliance committees. Administers and awards internal funds for research and scholarly achievement activities. **Publications:** Annual Report; UND Discovery (annually).

53084 ■ University of North Dakota Center for Innovation
Ina Mae Rude Entrepreneur Center
4200 James Ray Dr.
Grand Forks, ND 58203
Ph:(701)777-3132
Fax:(701)777-2339
Co. E-mail: info@innovators.net
URL: http://www.innovators.net/
Description: A small business incubator providing assistance to innovators, entrepreneurs, and researchers to launch new ventures, commercialize new technologies, and secure access to capital from private and public sources.

EDUCATIONAL PROGRAMS

53085 ■ Lake Region State College
1801 N College Dr.
Devils Lake, ND 58301

Ph:(701)662-1600
Free: 800-443-1313
Fax:(701)662-1570
URL: http://www.lrsc.nodak.edu
Description: Two-year college offering a accounting and business management.

53086 ■ University of North Dakota–Workforce Development
PO Box 7131
Grand Forks, ND 58202-7131
Ph:(701)777-2313
Fax:(701)777-2140
Co. E-mail: galen_cariveau@mail.und.nodak.edu
URL: http://www.und.nodak.edu
Contact: Galen Cariveau
Description: Offers a variety of business-related and professional enrichment courses, institutes, seminars, and workshops. The Department of Conferences and Institutes coordinates a large number of business skills and management development seminars and workshops geared for particular audiences, including small business owners/managers.

PUBLISHERS

53087 ■ Center for Innovation
University of North Dakota
Ina Mae Rude Entrepreneur Ctr., 4200 James Ray
Dr.
PO Box 8372
Grand Forks, ND 58203
Ph:(701)777-3132
Fax:(701)777-2339
Co. E-mail: bruce@innovators.net
URL: http://www.innovators.net
Contact: Yong Hou, Mgr
E-mail: yong@innovators.net
Description: Publishes on business planning, entrepreneurial history, etiquette, protocol and market planning. Does not accept unsolicited manuscripts. Reaches market through direct mail and trade sales. **Founded:** 1984.

53088 ■ Gateway Publishing Company Ltd. (Pembina, North Dakota)
276 Cavalier St.
PO Box 559
Pembina, ND 58271-0559
Free: 800-665-4878
Co. E-mail: cookbooks@gatebook.com
URL: http://www.gatebook.com
Contact: Sherry Phaneuf, Director
Description: Publishes books about child safety and also cookbooks. **Founded:** 1965.